This book belongs to:

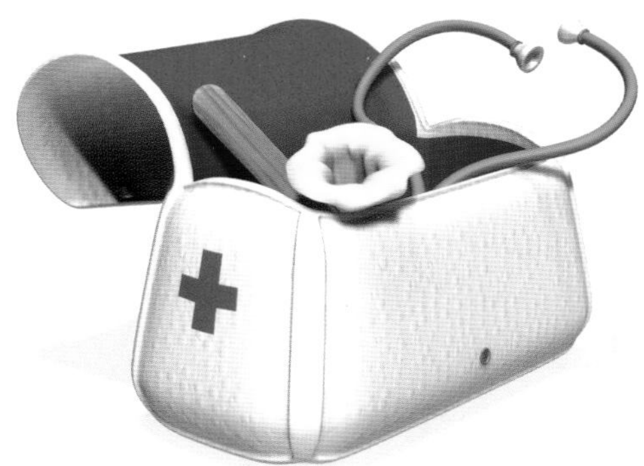

Published by Callaway & Kirk Company, a division of Callaway Arts & Entertainment.

Digital art by Callaway Animation Studios under the direction of David Kirk in collaboration with Nelvana Limited.

This book is based on the TV episode "The Bug Flu," written by Robin Stein, from the animated TV series *Miss Spider's Sunny Patch Friends* on Nick Jr., a Nelvana Limited/Absolute Pictures Limited co-production in association with Callaway Arts & Entertainment, based on the Miss Spider books by David Kirk.

Nicholas Callaway, President and Publisher
Cathy Ferrara, Managing Editor and Production Director
Toshiya Masuda, Art Director • Nelson Gómez, Director of Digital Technology
Joya Rajadhyaksha, Editor • Amy Cloud, Editor
Bill Burg, Digital Artist • Christina Pagano, Digital Artist
Raphael Shea, Senior Designer • Krupa Jhaveri, Designer

Special thanks to the Nelvana staff, including Doug Murphy, Scott Dyer, Tracy Ewing, Pam Lehn, Tonya Lindo, Mark Picard, Jane Sobol, Luis Lopez, Eric Pentz, and John Cvecich.

Library of Congress Cataloging-in-Publication Data available upon request.

Distributed in the United States by Penguin Young Readers Group.

Visit Callaway Arts & Entertainment at www.callaway.com.

ISBN 978-0-448-45021-6

10 9 8 7 6 5 4 3 2 1   08 09 10 11

First edition, September 2007

Printed in China

The Bug Flu

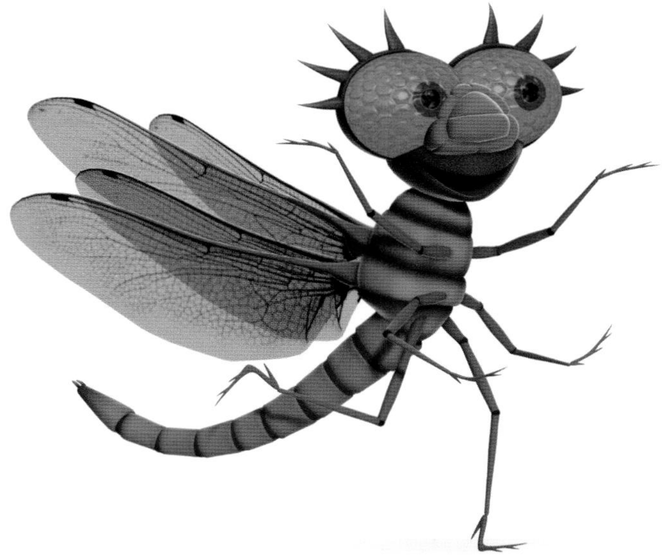

David Kirk

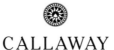

CALLAWAY
NEW YORK
2008

"Work, work, work!" Spiderus was so busy grumbling about having to pick sunflower seeds that he didn't look where he was going and tripped over a leaf!

Ha! he thought. If I pretend to be hurt, I won't have to work.

"Oh, woe! I think I injured my left third leg!" he wailed.

Shimmer, Squirt, and Dragon offered to help collect seeds so Spiderus could rest.

Soon, Miss Spider crawled by. "I'd like to invite your whole family to a tea party tomorrow to thank your kids for helping!" Spindella said.

"We'd love to come!" Miss Spider exclaimed.

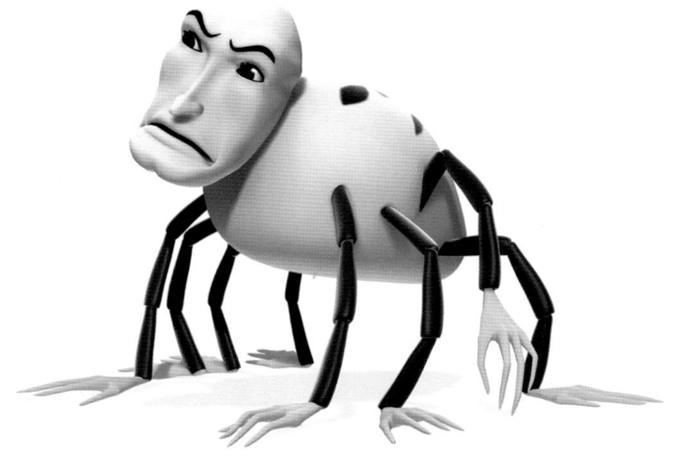

Later that afternoon, Shimmer noticed Spiderus skittering along happily by the Taddy Puddle.

"He tricked us into thinking he was hurt so we would do his work!" she cried.

"Hmm," Dragon mused, "that's a pretty cool idea."

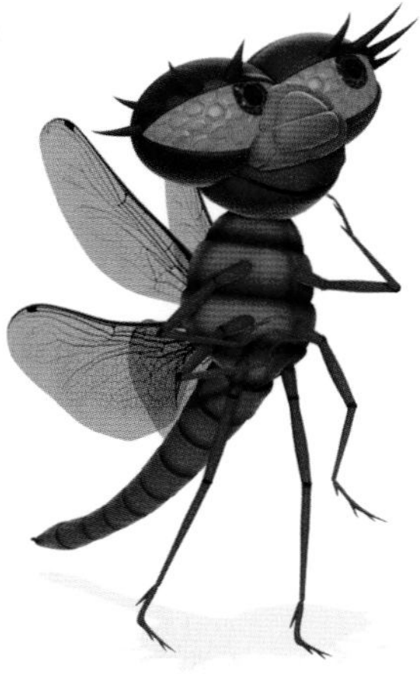

The next day, everybuggy was getting ready to go to Spindella and Spiderus's tea party.

"It's going to be boring!" Bounce whined.

Dragon began coughing. "I don't feel so well!" he wheezed.

"You must be getting the bug flu," Miss Spider said. She decided to stay home and take care of him.

Dr. Bee Better came over. She listened to Dragon's spiracles, the holes through which dragonflies breathe. She made him open up his mouth and say, "Anthill."

"I think our little patient has a case of the Fakey Flu," Dr. Bee Better told Miss Spider.

"Hmm . . . I know just the cure for pretending to be sick!" Miss Spider said with a smile.

Soon the other kids came back, stuffed with sweets and still laughing. The party had been a buggy blast!

“Spindella taught us some really cool games!” Wiggle grinned.

“Let’s play one now!” cried Dragon, leaping out of bed.

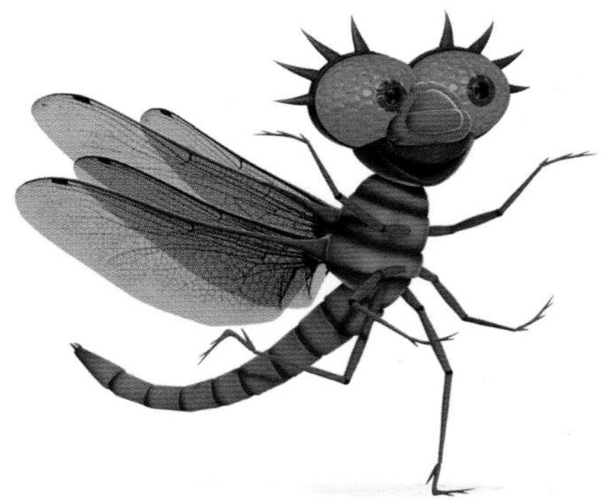

"Oh no, Dragon," Miss Spider said. "You're too sick to play."

"But I'm feeling better!" Dragon insisted.

"I don't think so," Holley said. "Back up to bed, li'l bug!"

So, Dragon lay alone and listened as his siblings laughed and played.

The next morning, Holley announced that the whole family would go berry picking.

"All right!" Dragon whooped. "Betcha I get the biggest berry!"

"Not so fast," said Holley. "You're still sick, and you need to rest."

After Holley and the kids had left, Dragon snuck out the window and flew to the blueberry bush. He watched everybuggy laughing and having fun.

"I'm sick of being sick," he decided.

Dragon flew back into the bedroom and stopped short with a gasp. There was Miss Spider, along with Spiderus and Spindella, who had brought him some get-well cookies.

"Care to explain yourself?" his mother asked.

Dragon gulped. "I only pretended to be sick," he confessed. "I'm really sorry."

"Pretending to be sick is like telling a lie," Miss Spider said sternly. "I think you owe Spindella an apology."

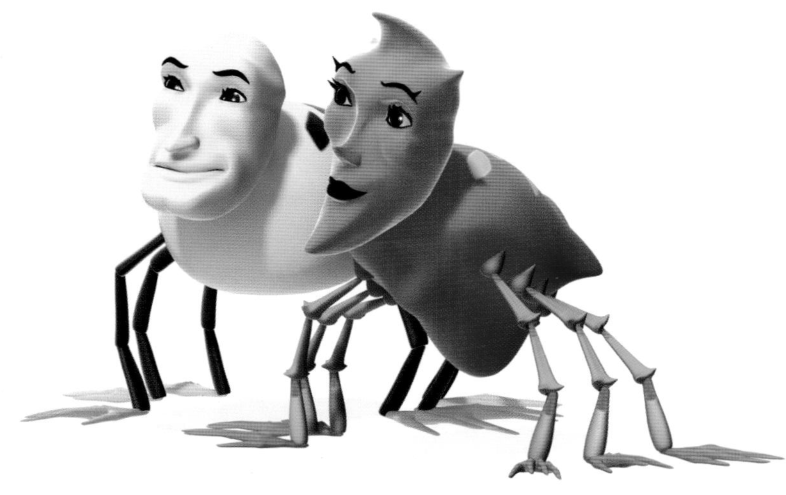

"I'm sorry if I hurt your feelings, Spindella," Dragon said sheepishly.

"That's okay," Spindella said. "I'm just glad you're healthy."

"I have an idea," said Miss Spider, "a way that you can make this up to everybuggy."

The next morning, Dragon brought a big bushel of blueberries to Spindella and Spiderus.

"I picked these myself," he said proudly. "No faking!"

RAND McNALLY WORLD ATLAS

RAND McNALLY
Chicago New York San Francisco

CONTENTS

USING THE ATLAS .... **I·3 – I·4**

WORLD PATTERNS .... **I·5 – I·16**
World Terrain .... I·6 – I·7
World Climate .... I·8 – I·9
World Vegetation .... I·10 – I·11
World Population .... I·12 – I·13
World Environments .... I·14 – I·15
World Time Zones .... I·16

REFERENCE MAPS .... **1 – 128**
Map Symbols and Index Map 1
World .... 2 – 3

Europe .... **4 – 5**
Scandinavia 6
British Isles 7
Central Europe .... 8 – 9
France and the Alps .... 10 – 11
Spain and Portugal .... 12 – 13
Italy .... 14 – 15
Southeastern Europe .... 16 – 17
Western and Central
Soviet Union .... 18 – 19
Central and Eastern
Soviet Union .... 20 – 21
Baltic and Moscow Regions .... 22 – 23

Asia .... **24 – 25**
China, Japan, and Korea .... 26 – 27
Eastern and Southeastern China .. 28 – 29
Japan .... 30 – 31
Southeastern Asia .... 32 – 33
Burma, Thailand, and Indochina .. 34 – 35
India and Pakistan 36
Southern India and Sri Lanka 37
Northern India and Pakistan .... 38 – 39
Eastern Mediterranean Lands 40

Africa **41**
Northern Africa .... 42 – 43
Southern Africa .... 44 – 45
Eastern Africa and Middle East 46

Antarctica **47**

Pacific Ocean .... **48 – 49**

Australia .... **50 – 51**
New Zealand 52

South America **53**
Northern South America .... 54 – 55
Southern South America 56
Southeastern Brazil 57
Colombia, Ecuador, Venezuela,
and Guyana .... 58 – 59

Atlantic Ocean **60**

North America **61**
Mexico .... 62 – 63
Central America
and the Caribbean .... 64 – 65

Canada .... ***66 – 67***
Alberta 68
British Columbia 69
Manitoba 70
New Brunswick, Nova Scotia,
and Prince Edward Island 71
Newfoundland 72
Ontario 73
Quebec 74
Saskatchewan 75

United States of America .... ***76 – 77***
Alabama 78
Alaska 79
Arizona 80
Arkansas 81
California 82
Colorado 83
Connecticut 84
Delaware 85
Florida 86
Georgia 87
Hawaii 88
Idaho 89
Illinois 90
Indiana 91
Iowa 92
Kansas 93
Kentucky 94
Louisiana 95
Maine 96
Maryland 97
Massachusetts 98
Michigan 99
Minnesota 100
Mississippi 101
Missouri 102
Montana 103
Nebraska 104
Nevada 105
New Hampshire 106
New Jersey 107
New Mexico 108
New York 109
North Carolina 110
North Dakota 111
Ohio 112
Oklahoma 113
Oregon 114
Pennsylvania 115
Rhode Island 116
South Carolina 117
South Dakota 118
Tennessee 119
Texas 120
Utah 121
Vermont 122
Virginia 123
Washington 124
West Virginia 125
Wisconsin 126
Wyoming 127

North Polar Regions **128**

**INDEX TO
REFERENCE MAPS** .... **129 – 192**

**WORLD GEOGRAPHICAL
TABLES** .... **193 – 215**
World Political Information ...... 193 – 196
General Information 197
Principal Mountains 198
World Oceans, Seas, Gulfs, Lakes,
Rivers, and Islands 199
World Populations .... 200 – 215

**UNITED STATES
GEOGRAPHICAL
TABLES** .... **216 – 240**
United States General Information ... 216

**United States Populations
and Zip Codes** .... **217 – 240**
Latest 1990 Census Information

Library of Congress Cataloging-in-Publication Data

Rand McNally and Company.
World Atlas.
p. cm.
Includes index.
1. Atlases. I. Title.
G1021.R21 1991 <G&M> 91-16938
912—dc20 CIP
MAP

USING THE ATLAS

Maps and Atlases

Satellite images of the world (figure 1) constantly give us views of the shape and size of the earth. It is hard, therefore, to imagine how difficult it once was to ascertain the look of our planet. Yet from early history we have evidence of humans trying to work out what the world actually looked like.

Twenty-five hundred years ago, on a tiny clay tablet the size of a hand, the Babylonians inscribed the earth as a flat disk (figure 2) with Babylon at the center. The section of the Cantino map of 1502 (figure 3) is an example of a *portolan* chart used by mariners to chart the newly discovered Americas. The maps in this atlas, show the detail and accuracy that cartographers are now able to achieve.

In 1589 Gerardus Mercator used the word *atlas* to describe a collection of maps. Atlases now bring together not only a variety of maps, but an assortment of tables and other reference material as well. They have become a unique and indispensable reference for graphically defining the world and answering the question *where*. With them routes between places can be traced, trips planned, distances measured, places imagined, and our earth visualized.

FIGURE 1

FIGURE 2

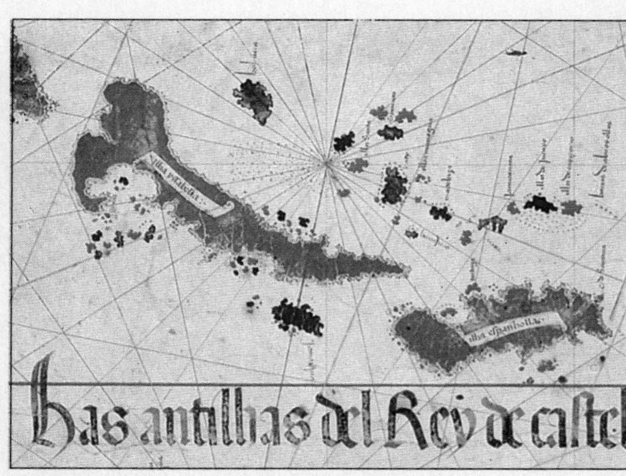

FIGURE 3

Sequence of the Maps

The world is made up of seven major landmasses: the continents of Europe, Asia, Africa, Antarctica, Australia, South America, and North America. The maps in this atlas follow this continental sequence. To allow for the inclusion of detail, each continent is broken down into a series of maps, and this grouping is arranged so that as consecutive pages are turned, a continuous successive part of the continent is shown. Larger-scale maps are used for regions of greater detail or for areas of global significance.

Getting the Information

To realize the potential of an atlas the user must be able to:

1. Find places on the maps
2. Measure distances
3. Determine directions
4. Understand map symbols

Finding Places

One of the most common and important tasks facilitated by an atlas is finding the location of a place in the world. A river's name in a book, a city mentioned in the news, or a vacation spot may prompt your need to know where the place is located. The illustrations and text below explain how to find Yangon (Rangoon), Burma.

Yancheng, China	**B9**	28
Yandoon, Burma	**F3**	34
Yangjiang, China	**G9**	26
Yangon (Rangoon), Burma	**B2**	32
Yangquan, China	**D9**	26
Yangtze see Chang, stm., China	**E10**	26
Yangzhou, China	**C8**	28

FIGURE 4

1. Look up the place-name in the index at the back of the atlas. Yangon, Burma can be found on the map on page 32, and it can be located on the map by the letter-number key *B2* (figure 4). If you know the general area in which a place is found, you may turn directly to the appropriate map and use the special marginal index.

2. Turn to the map of Southeastern Asia found on page 32. Note that the letters *A* through *H* and the numbers *1* through *11* appear in the margins of the map.

3. To find Yangon, on the map, place your left index finger on *B* and your right index finger on *2*. Move your left finger across the map and your right finger down the map. Your fingers will meet in the area in which Yangon is located (figure 5).

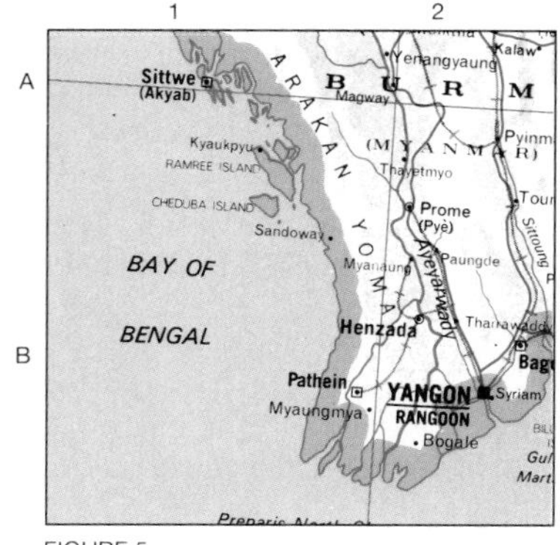

FIGURE 5

Measuring Distances

In planning trips, determining the distance between two places is essential, and an atlas can help in travel preparation. For instance, to determine the approximate distance between Paris and Rouen, France, follow these three steps:

1. Lay a slip of paper on the map on page 10 so that its edge touches the two cities. Adjust the paper so one corner touches Rouen. Mark the paper directly at the spot where Paris is located (figure 6).

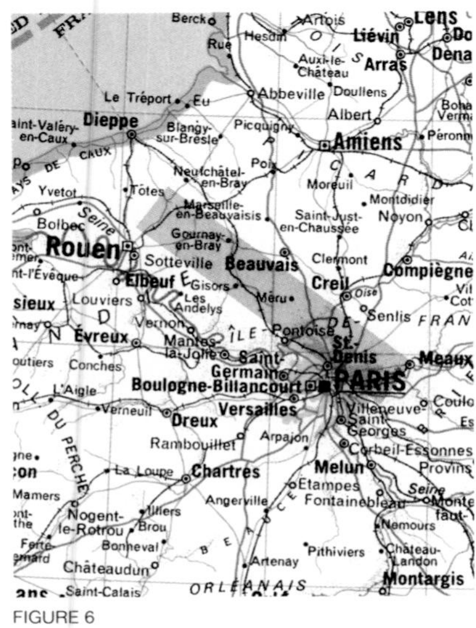

FIGURE 6

2. Place the paper along the scale of miles beneath the map. Position the corner at 0 and line up the edge of the paper along the scale. The pencil mark on the paper indicates Rouen is between 50 and 100 miles from Paris (figure 7).

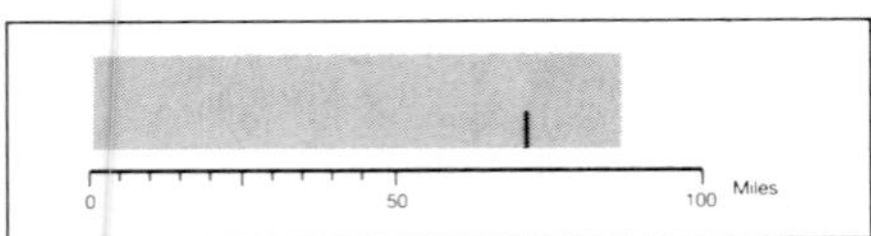

FIGURE 7

3. To find the exact distance, move the paper to the left so that the pencil mark is at 100 on the scale. The corner of the paper stands on the fourth 5-mile unit on the scale. This means that the two towns are 50 plus 20, or 70 miles apart (figure 8).

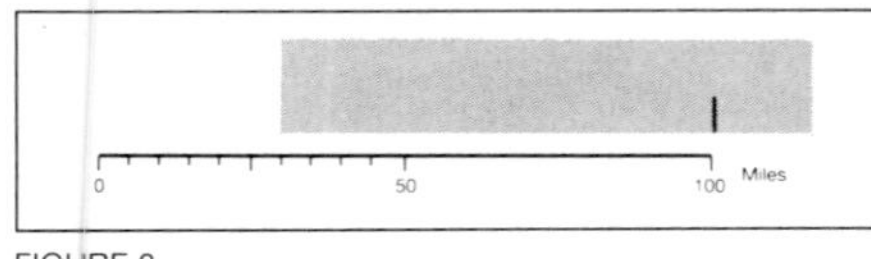

FIGURE 8

Determining Directions

Most of the maps in the atlas are drawn so that when oriented for normal reading, north is at the top of the map, south is at the bottom, west is at the left, and east is at the right. Most maps have a series of lines drawn across them–the lines of *latitude* and *longitude*. Lines of latitude, or *parallels* of latitude, are drawn east and west. Lines of longitude, or *meridians* of longitude, are drawn north and south (figure 9).

Parallels and meridians appear as either curved or straight lines. For example, in the section of the map of Europe (figure 10) the parallels of latitude appear as curved lines. The meridians of longitude are straight lines that come together toward the top of the map. Latitude and longitude lines help locate places on maps. Parallels of latitude are numbered in degrees north and south of the *Equator*. Meridians of longitude are numbered in degrees east and west of a line called the *Prime Meridian*, running through Greenwich, England, near London. Any place on earth can be located by the latitude and longitude lines running through it.

To determine directions or locations on the map, you must use the parallels and meridians. For example, suppose you want to know which is farther north, Bergen, Norway, or Stockholm, Sweden. The map (figure 10) shows that Stockholm is south of the 60° parallel of latitude and Bergen is north of it. Bergen is farther north than Stockholm. By looking at the meridians of longitude, you can determine which city is farther east. Bergen is approximately 5° east of the 0° meridian (Prime Meridian), and Stockholm is almost 20° east of it. Stockholm is farther east than Bergen.

FIGURE 9

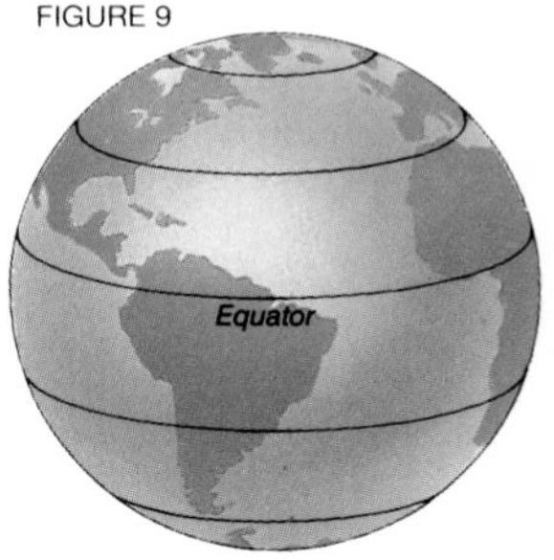

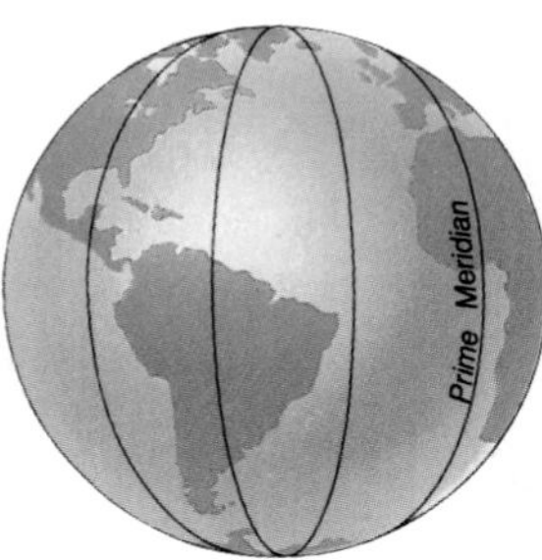

FIGURE 10

Understanding Map Symbols

In a very real sense, the whole map is a symbol, representing the world or a part of it. It is a reduced representation of the earth; each of the world's features–cities, rivers, etc.–is represented on the map by a symbol. Map symbols may take the form of points, such as dots or squares (often used for cities, capital cities, or points of interest), or lines (roads, railroads, rivers). Symbols may also occupy an area, showing extent of coverage (terrain, forests, deserts). They seldom look like the feature they represent and therefore must be identified and interpreted. For instance, the maps in this atlas define political units by a colored line depicting their boundaries. Neither the colors nor the boundary lines are actually found on the surface of the earth, but because countries and states are such important political components of the world, strong symbols are used to represent them. The Map Symbols page in this atlas identifies the symbols used on the maps.

WORLD PATTERNS

The five world maps in this section portray the distribution of major natural and human elements that describe the world's fundamental geographic character. The lines and colors show basic patterns caused by the movement and interaction of land, air, water, and human activity.

The world terrain map on pages I·6 and I·7 portrays the surface of the uppermost layer of the earth's crust. The crust, broken into six gigantic and several smaller plates, floats on denser rock. Constant movement of the plates in the geologic past helped create the terrain features we see today. Motion of the plates along with the erosive force of water, wind, and human development continues to reshape the earth's terrain.

The earth's oceans are in constant motion. Water near the surface and in the deeps flows in well established currents that are like rivers within the ocean. The earth's atmosphere is an ocean of gases with currents that span the globe. The sun drives these moving currents of water and air. The average of the widely varying weather phenomena caused by these movements establishes the patterns of global climate shown on pages I·8 and I·9.

Climate is the single most important factor determining where plants can grow. And vegetation is the major factor determining where animals–including humans–can live. The map on pages I·10 and I·11 shows the distribution of vegetation types that might exist if humans did not intervene. Notice how similar the patterns of vegetation and climate are. Tundra vegetation is associated with polar climates. The rain forests of South America, Africa, and Asia grow in hot, wet climates near the Equator. The steppes of Central Asia and the short-grass prairies of North America grow in cool climates with dry summers. The evergreen forests of northern Eurasia and North America coincide with moist climates with cold winters and cool summers.

The population density map on pages I·12 and I·13 indicates that almost all areas of the earth are inhabited by humankind, from the Poles to the Equator. Humanity's densest settlement has been in the most fertile regions of the earth. These areas combine adequate rainfall and growing season with terrain that is neither too rough nor mountainous. A comparison of the terrain and climate maps with the population map shows this relationship. Abundant mineral deposits as well as people's ability to develop natural resources also explain settlement preferences. Densely settled areas in Southwest Asia, Southeast Asia, and China are rural-agricultural populations. In western Europe, the northeastern United States, and parts of Japan, high-density regions are urban-industrial in character.

The environment map on pages I·14 and I·15 indicates how human habitation has impacted our planet. Compare this map with the vegetation map that shows what the world might be like if humankind had played a less dominant role. Millions of square miles of land that were once forests or grasslands are now plowed fields and pastures. Much of North America, Europe, and Southeast Asia has been almost completely remade by farmers. Though the urban areas occupy a small percentage of the land area in the world, their impact on the environment is extensive.

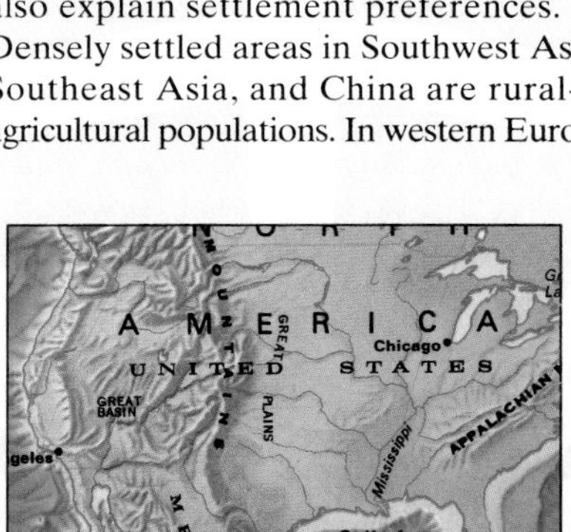

Terrain

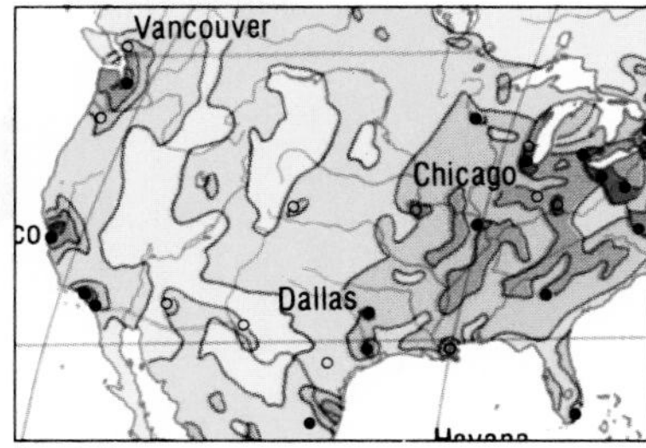

Population

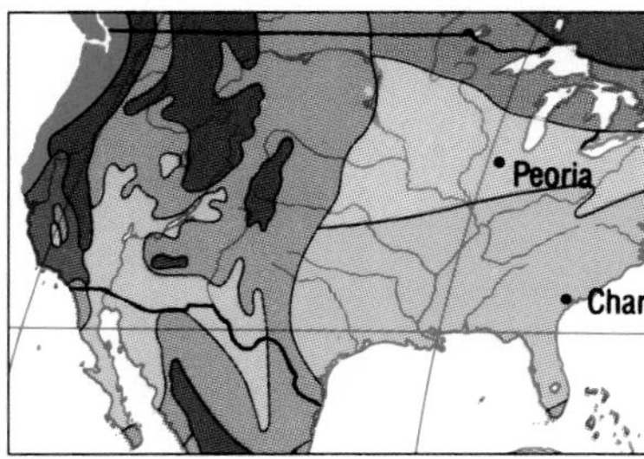

Climate

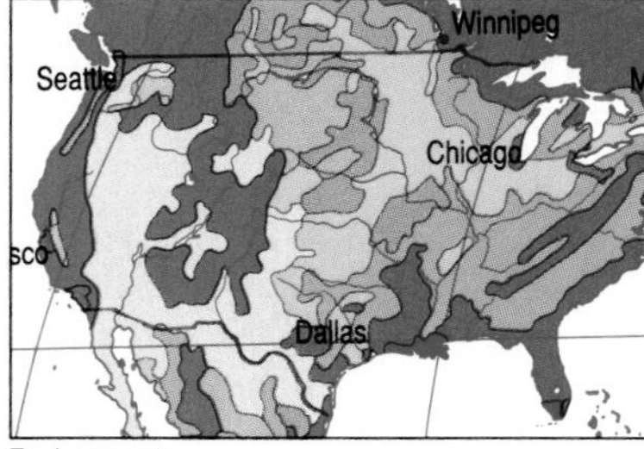

Environments

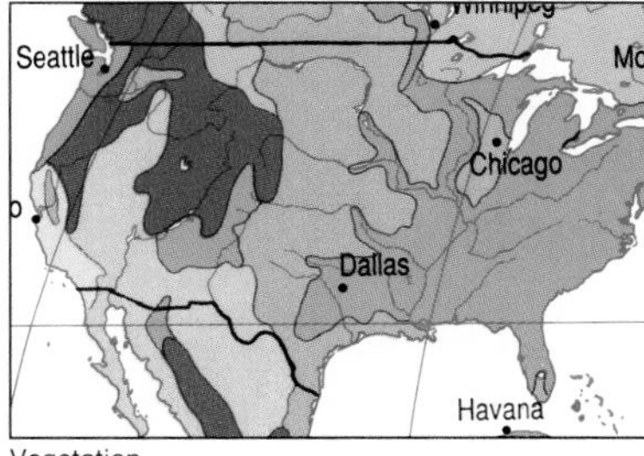

Vegetation

The distribution, relationship, and interaction of the major elements shown on the maps establish fundamental world patterns that distinguish one area from another. Upon the differences and similarities indicated by these patterns the world builds its intriguing variety of cultures and histories.

WORLD TERRAIN

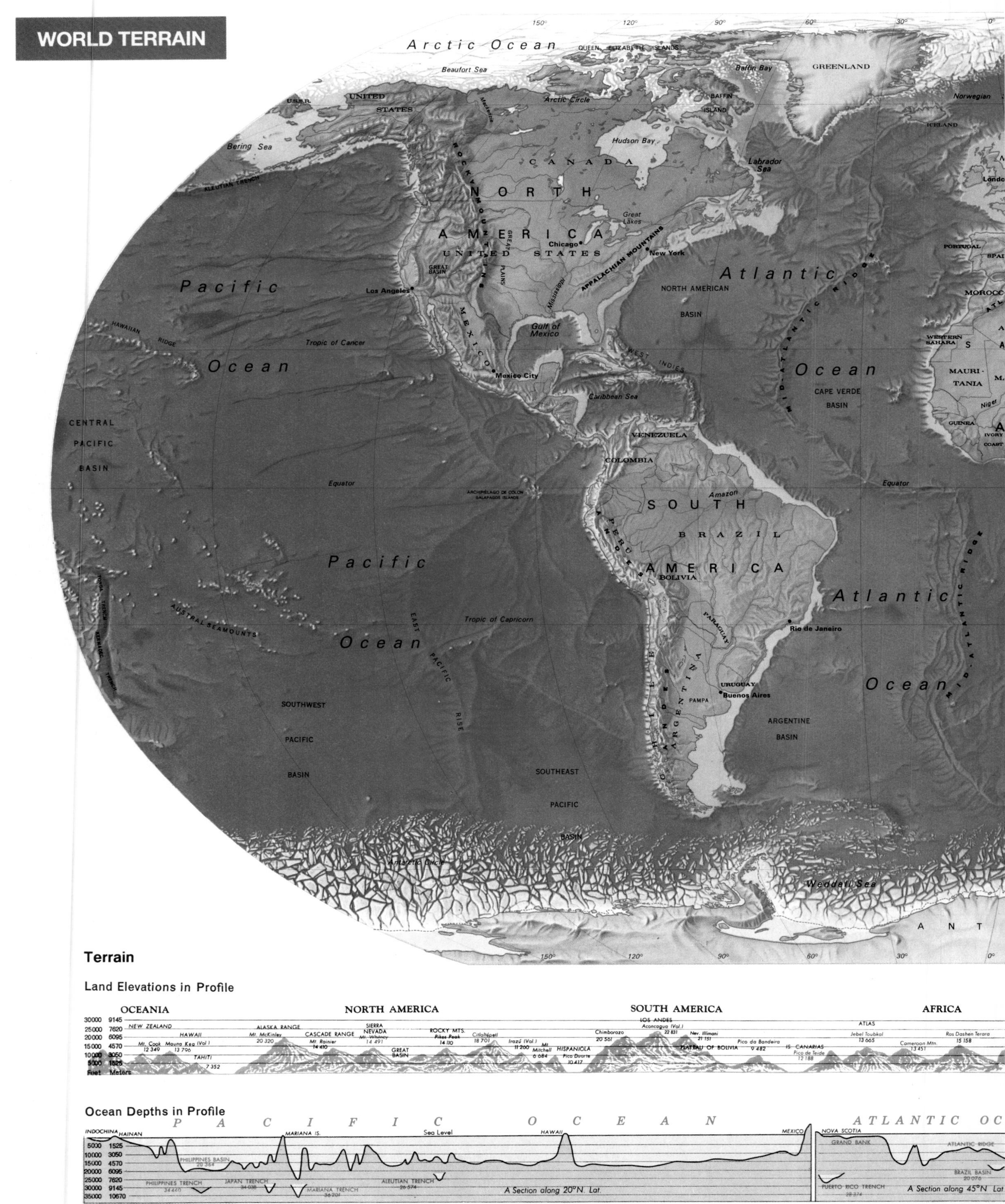

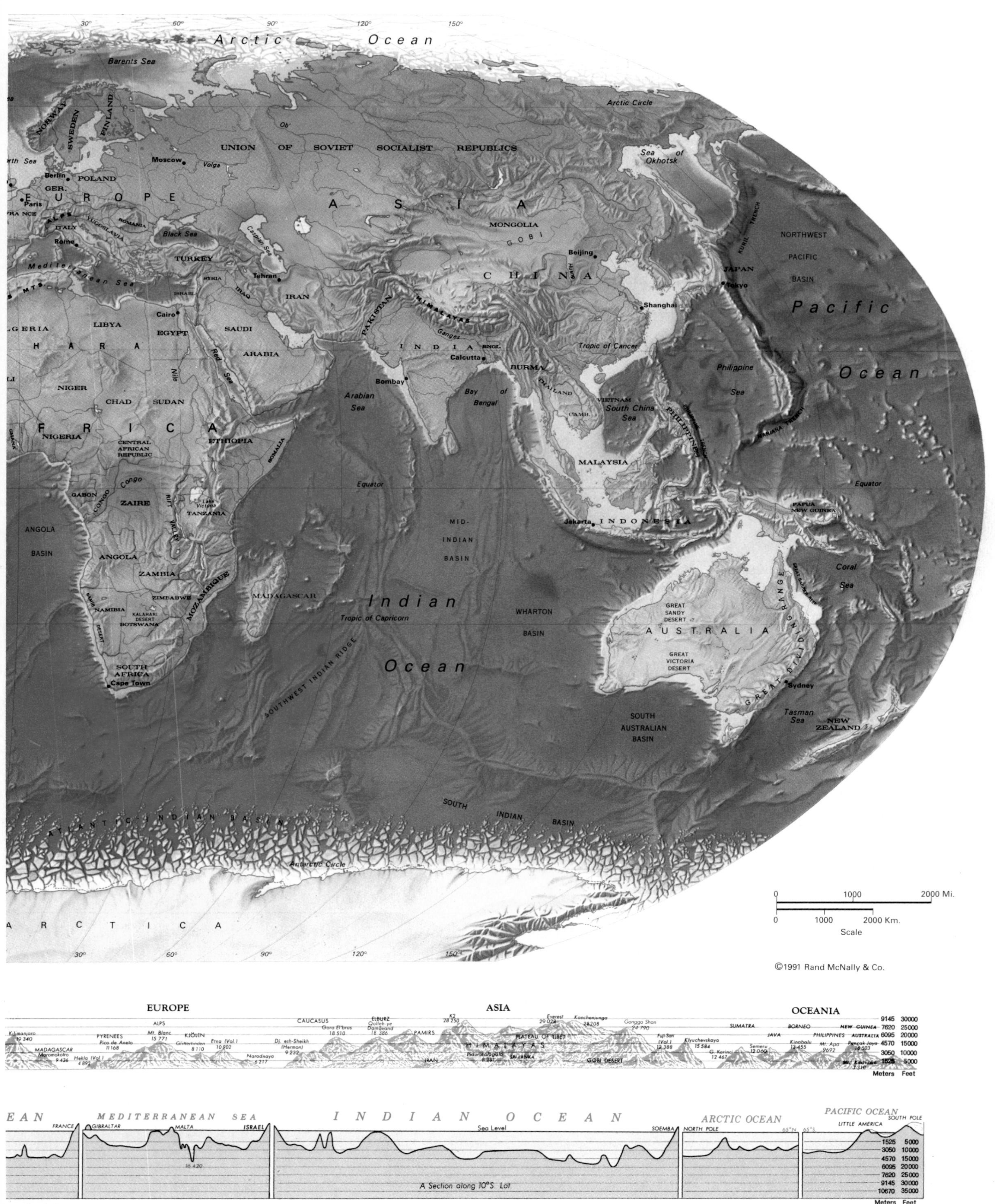

Arctic Ocean
Barents Sea
NORWAY
SWEDEN
FINLAND
UNION OF SOVIET SOCIALIST REPUBLICS
Moscow
Volga
Ob'
Berlin
POLAND
GER.
Paris
EUROPE
ALPS
ITALY
YUGOSLAVIA
ROMANIA
Rome
Black Sea
Caspian Sea
TURKEY
Mediterranean Sea
SYRIA
ISRAEL
IRAQ
Tehran
IRAN
ASIA
MONGOLIA
GOBI
Beijing
CHINA
Sea of Okhotsk
Arctic Circle
KURIL TRENCH
NORTHWEST PACIFIC BASIN
JAPAN
Tokyo
Shanghai
Pacific Ocean
PAKISTAN
HIMALAYAS
Ganges
INDIA
BNGL.
Calcutta
Tropic of Cancer
BURMA
THAILAND
Philippine Sea
LIBYA
Cairo
EGYPT
SAUDI ARABIA
Red Sea
Nile
Arabian Sea
Bombay
Bay of Bengal
VIETNAM
CAMB.
South China Sea
PHILIPPINES
MARIANA TRENCH
NIGER
CHAD
SUDAN
AFRICA
NIGERIA
CENTRAL AFRICAN REPUBLIC
ETHIOPIA
SOMALIA
MALAYSIA
Congo
GABON
CONGO
ZAIRE
RIFT VALLEY
Lake Victoria
TANZANIA
Equator
PAPUA NEW GUINEA
Jakarta
INDONESIA
ANGOLA BASIN
ANGOLA
MID-INDIAN BASIN
ZAMBIA
MOZAMBIQUE
ZIMBABWE
MADAGASCAR
NAMIBIA
KALAHARI DESERT
BOTSWANA
Indian Ocean
Tropic of Capricorn
WHARTON BASIN
GREAT SANDY DESERT
AUSTRALIA
GREAT VICTORIA DESERT
Coral Sea
GREAT BARRIER REEF
GREAT DIVIDING RANGE
Sydney
SOUTH AFRICA
Cape Town
SOUTHWEST INDIAN RIDGE
Tasman Sea
NEW ZEALAND
SOUTH AUSTRALIAN BASIN
SOUTH INDIAN BASIN
ATLANTIC-INDIAN BASIN
Antarctic Circle
ANTARCTICA
0 1000 2000 Mi.
0 1000 2000 Km.
Scale
©1991 Rand McNally & Co.
EUROPE
ASIA
OCEANIA
Kilimanjaro 19 340
MADAGASCAR
Maromokotro 9 436
Hekla (Vol.) 4 892
PYRENEES
Pico de Aneto 11 168
ALPS
Mt. Blanc 15 771
KJÖLEN
Glittertinden 8 110
Etna (Vol.) 10 902
Narodnaya 6 217
Dj. esh-Sheikh (Hermon) 9 232
CAUCASUS
Gora El'brus 18 510
ELBURZ
Qolleh ye Damavand 18 386
PAMIRS
IRAN
K2 28 250
Everest 29 028
Kanchenjunga 28 208
HIMALAYAS
PLATEAU OF TIBET
GOBI DESERT
Gongga Shan 24 790
Fuji San (Vol.) 12 388
Klyuchevskaya 15 584
G. Kerinci 12 467
SUMATRA
JAVA
Semeru 12 060
BORNEO
Kinabalu 13 455
PHILIPPINES
Mt. Apo 9692
NEW GUINEA
AUSTRALIA
Pencak Jaya 16 503
Mt. Kosciusko 7 310
Meters Feet
9145 30000
7620 25000
6095 20000
4570 15000
3050 10000
1525 5000
OCEAN
MEDITERRANEAN SEA
FRANCE
GIBRALTAR
MALTA
ISRAEL
16 420
INDIAN OCEAN
Sea Level
SOEMBA
A Section along 10°S. Lat.
ARCTIC OCEAN
NORTH POLE
65°N
65°S
PACIFIC OCEAN
LITTLE AMERICA
SOUTH POLE
1525 5000
3050 10000
4570 15000
6095 20000
7620 25000
9145 30000
10670 35000
Meters Feet
are given in feet

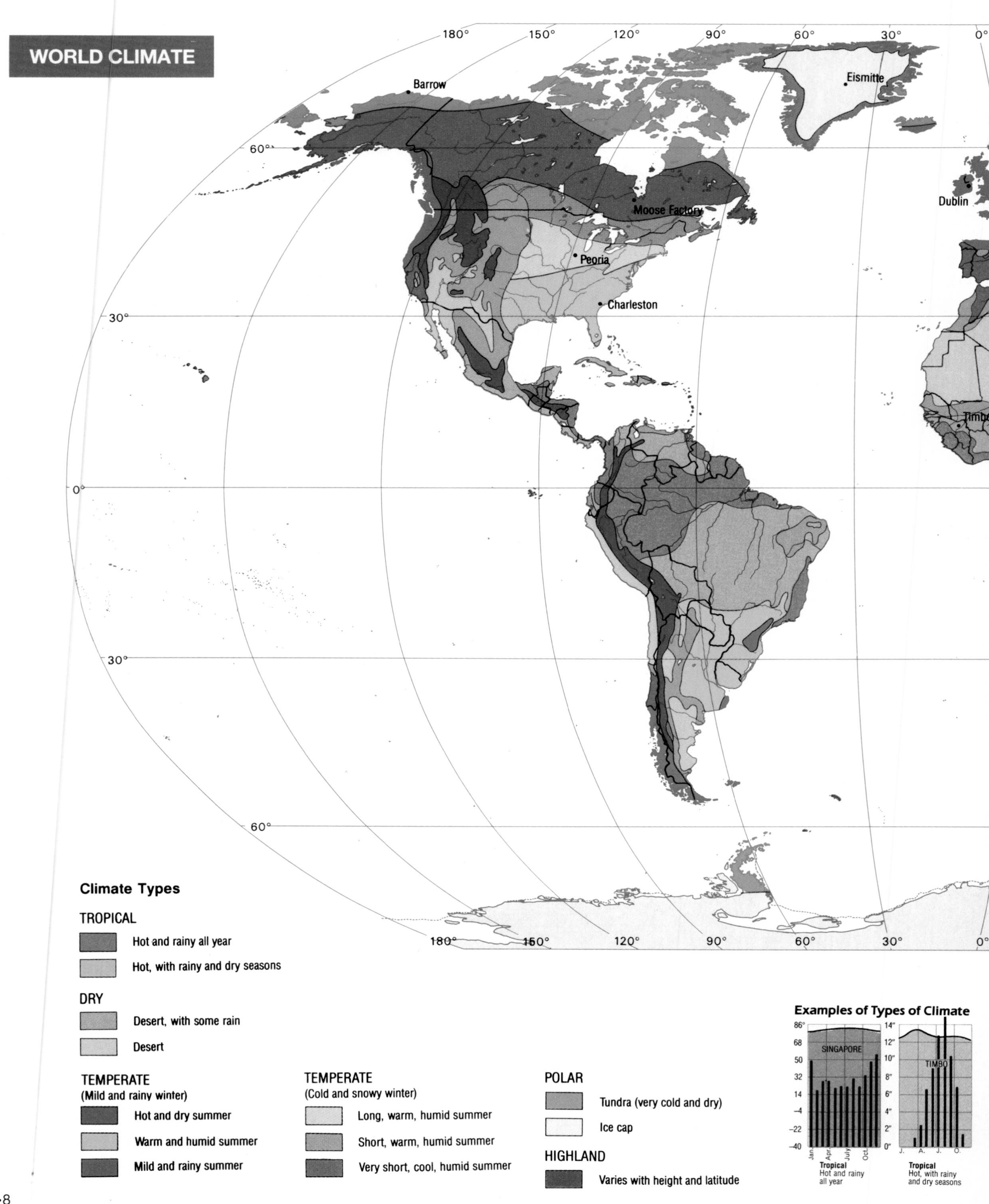
WORLD CLIMATE
180°
150°
120°
90°
60°
30°
0°
60°
30°
0°
30°
60°
Barrow
Eismitte
Dublin
Moose Factory
Peoria
Charleston
Timbo
Climate Types
TROPICAL
Hot and rainy all year
Hot, with rainy and dry seasons
DRY
Desert, with some rain
Desert
TEMPERATE
(Mild and rainy winter)
Hot and dry summer
Warm and humid summer
Mild and rainy summer
TEMPERATE
(Cold and snowy winter)
Long, warm, humid summer
Short, warm, humid summer
Very short, cool, humid summer
POLAR
Tundra (very cold and dry)
Ice cap
HIGHLAND
Varies with height and latitude
Examples of Types of Climate
86°
68
50
32
14
−4
−22
−40
14"
12"
10"
8"
6"
4"
2"
0"
SINGAPORE
Jan.
Apr.
July
Oct.
Tropical
Hot and rainy all year
TIMBO
J.
A.
J.
O.
Tropical
Hot, with rainy and dry seasons

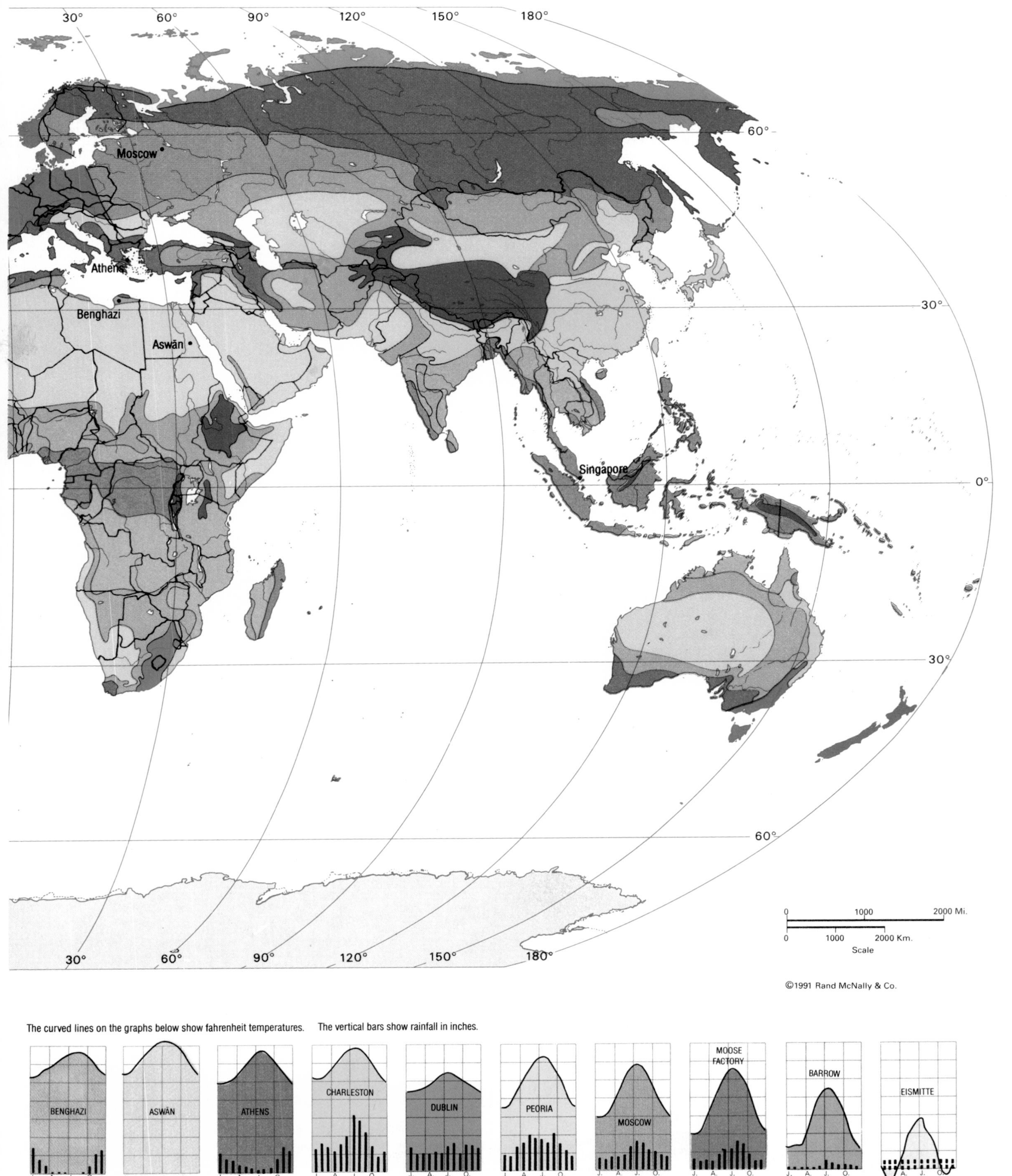

The curved lines on the graphs below show fahrenheit temperatures. The vertical bars show rainfall in inches.

WORLD VEGETATION

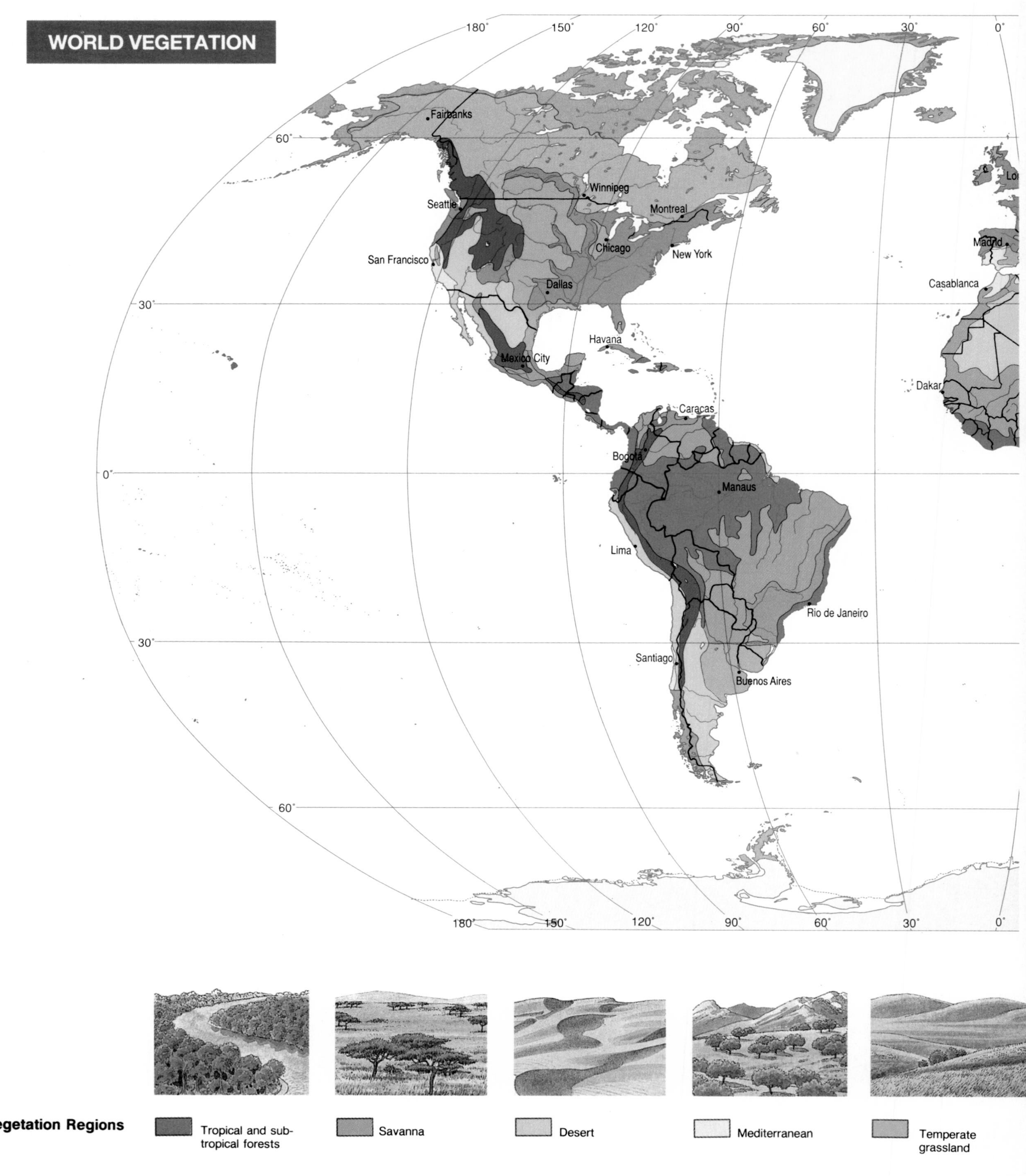

180°
150°
120°
90°
60°
30°
0°
60°
30°
0°
30°
60°
Fairbanks
Winnipeg
Seattle
Montreal
Chicago
New York
San Francisco
Dallas
Havana
Mexico City
Caracas
Bogotá
Manaus
Lima
Rio de Janeiro
Santiago
Buenos Aires
Madrid
Casablanca
Dakar
Vegetation Regions
Tropical and subtropical forests
Savanna
Desert
Mediterranean
Temperate grassland

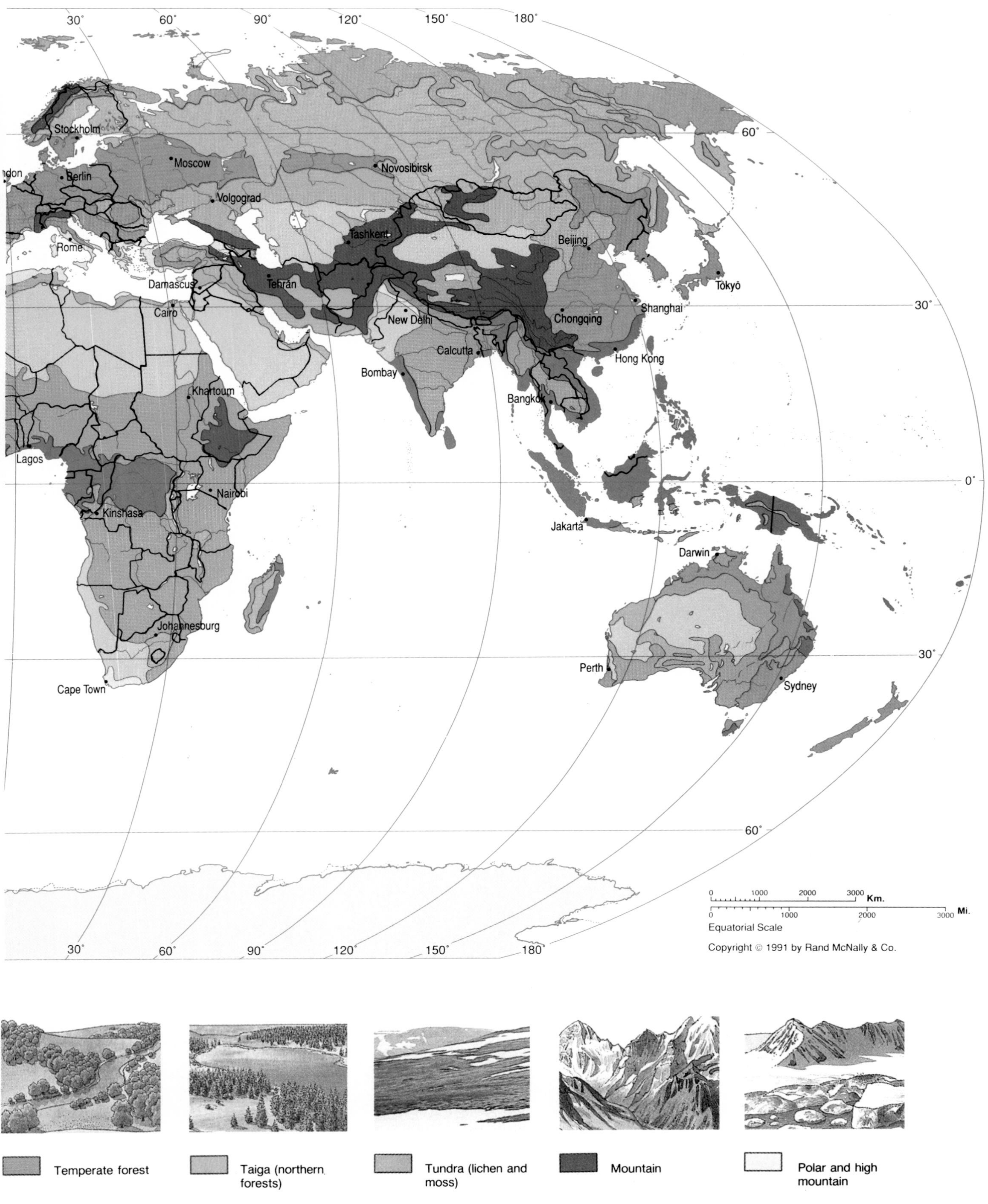
30°
60°
90°
120°
150°
180°
Stockholm
Moscow
Berlin
Novosibirsk
Volgograd
Rome
Tashkent
Beijing
Tōkyō
Damascus
Tehrān
Cairo
Shanghai
New Delhi
Chongqing
Calcutta
Hong Kong
Bombay
Khartoum
Bangkok
Lagos
Nairobi
Kinshasa
Jakarta
Darwin
Johannesburg
Perth
Sydney
Cape Town
60°
30°
0°
30°
60°
0 1000 2000 3000 Km.
0 1000 2000 3000 Mi.
Equatorial Scale
Copyright © 1991 by Rand McNally & Co.
Temperate forest
Taiga (northern forests)
Tundra (lichen and moss)
Mountain
Polar and high mountain

WORLD POPULATION

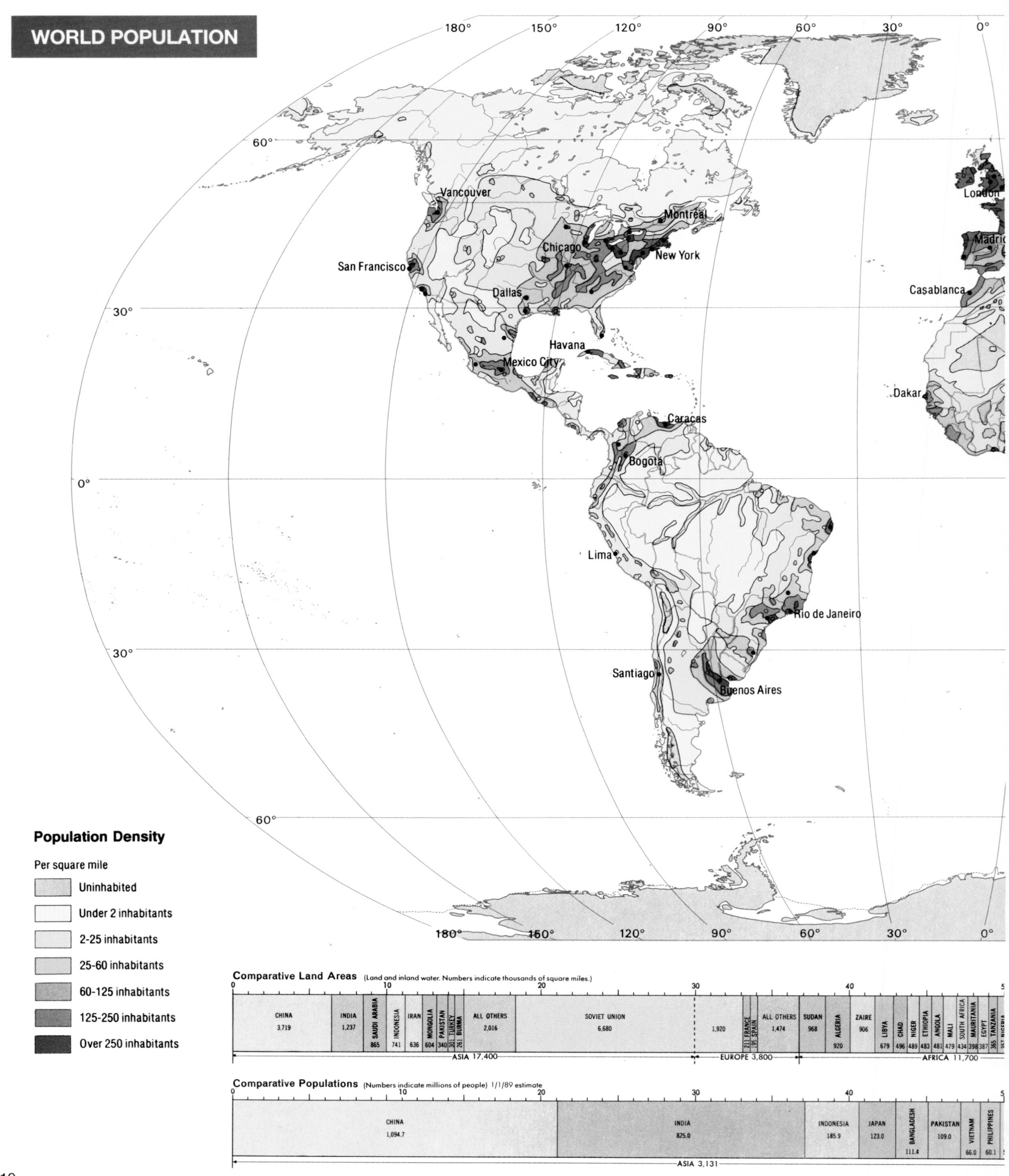
180°
150°
120°
90°
60°
30°
0°
60°
30°
0°
30°
60°
Vancouver
Montréal
London
Madrid
Chicago
New York
San Francisco
Dallas
Casablanca
Havana
Mexico City
Dakar
Caracas
Bogotá
Lima
Rio de Janeiro
Santiago
Buenos Aires
180°
150°
120°
90°
60°
30°
0°
Population Density
Per square mile
Uninhabited
Under 2 inhabitants
2-25 inhabitants
25-60 inhabitants
60-125 inhabitants
125-250 inhabitants
Over 250 inhabitants
Comparative Land Areas (Land and inland water. Numbers indicate thousands of square miles.)
0
10
20
30
40
CHINA 3,719
INDIA 1,237
SAUDI ARABIA 865
INDONESIA 741
IRAN 636
MONGOLIA 604
PAKISTAN 340
TURKEY 301
BURMA 261
ALL OTHERS 2,016
SOVIET UNION 6,680
1,920
FRANCE 211
SPAIN 195
ALL OTHERS 1,474
SUDAN 968
ALGERIA 920
ZAIRE 906
LIBYA 679
CHAD 496
NIGER 489
ETHIOPIA 483
ANGOLA 481
MALI 479
SOUTH AFRICA 434
MAURITANIA 398
EGYPT 387
TANZANIA 365
ASIA 17,400
EUROPE 3,800
AFRICA 11,700
Comparative Populations (Numbers indicate millions of people) 1/1/89 estimate
0
10
20
30
40
CHINA 1,094.7
INDIA 825.0
INDONESIA 185.9
JAPAN 123.0
BANGLADESH 111.4
PAKISTAN 109.0
VIETNAM 66.0
PHILIPPINES 60.1
ASIA 3,131

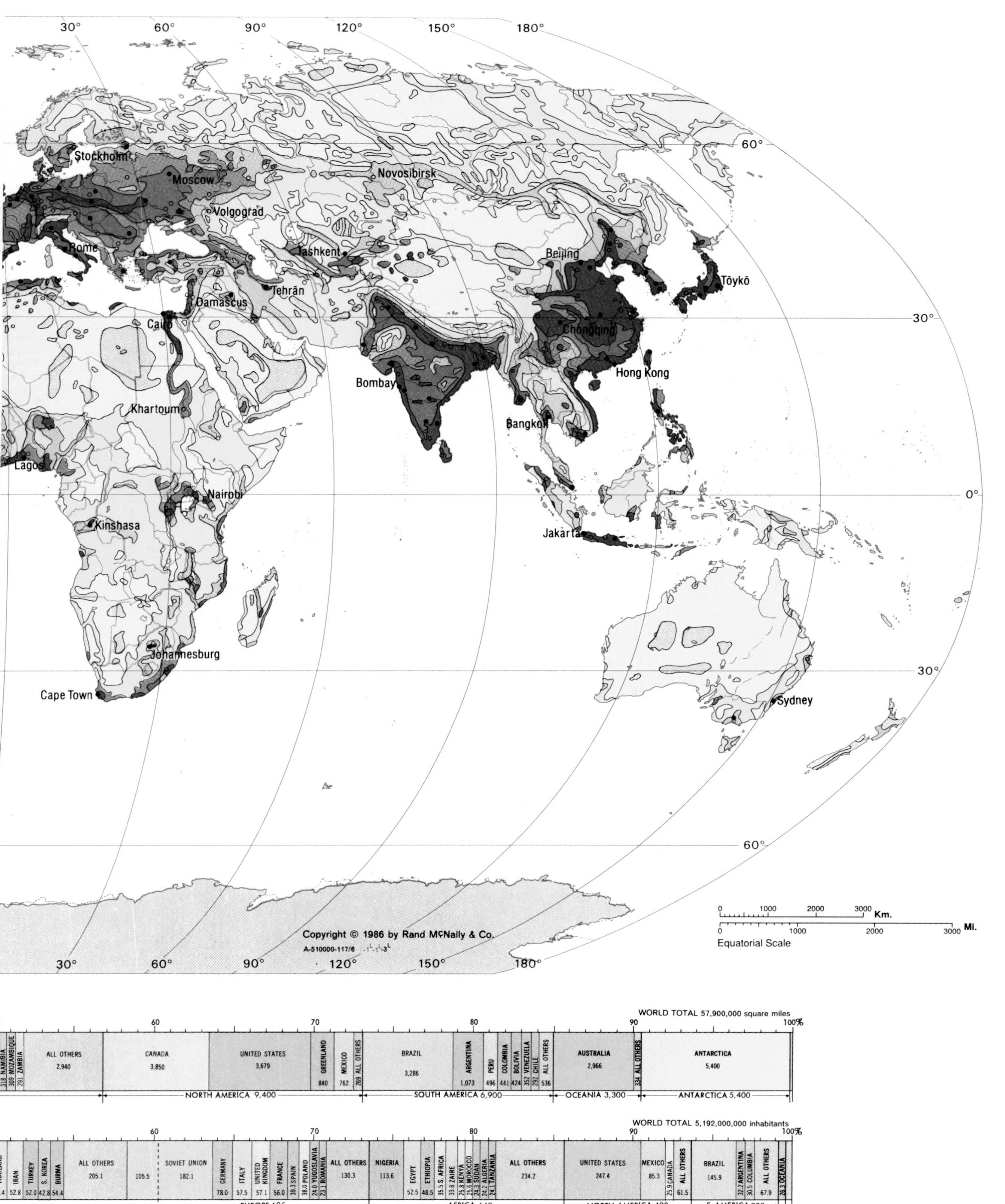

30°
60°
90°
120°
150°
180°
Stockholm
Moscow
Novosibirsk
Volgograd
Rome
Tashkent
Beijing
Tōkyō
Tehrān
Damascus
Cairo
Chongqing
Hong Kong
Bombay
Khartoum
Bangkok
Lagos
Nairobi
Kinshasa
Jakarta
Johannesburg
Cape Town
Sydney
60°
30°
0°
30°
60°
Copyright © 1986 by Rand McNally & Co.
A-510000-117/6
0 1000 2000 3000 Km.
0 1000 2000 3000 Mi.
Equatorial Scale
WORLD TOTAL 57,900,000 square miles
60
70
80
90
100%
318 NAMIBIA
309 MOZAMBIQUE
291 ZAMBIA
ALL OTHERS 2,940
CANADA 3,850
UNITED STATES 3,679
GREENLAND 840
MEXICO 762
269 ALL OTHERS
BRAZIL 3,286
ARGENTINA 1,073
PERU 496
COLOMBIA 441
BOLIVIA 424
352 VENEZUELA
292 CHILE
ALL OTHERS 536
AUSTRALIA 2,966
334 ALL OTHERS
ANTARCTICA 5,400
NORTH AMERICA 9,400
SOUTH AMERICA 6,900
OCEANIA 3,300
ANTARCTICA 5,400
WORLD TOTAL 5,192,000,000 inhabitants
60
70
80
90
100%
IRAN 52.8
TURKEY 52.0
S. KOREA 42.8
BURMA 54.4
ALL OTHERS 205.1
105.5
SOVIET UNION 182.1
GERMANY 78.0
ITALY 57.5
UNITED KINGDOM 57.1
FRANCE 56.0
39.3 SPAIN
38.0 POLAND
24.0 YUGOSLAVIA
23.1 ROMANIA
ALL OTHERS 130.3
NIGERIA 113.6
EGYPT 52.5
ETHIOPIA 48.5
35.5 S. AFRICA
33.8 ZAIRE
25.8 KENYA
25.6 MOROCCO
24.3 SUDAN
24.2 ALGERIA
24.1 TANZANIA
ALL OTHERS 234.2
UNITED STATES 247.4
MEXICO 85.3
25.9 CANADA
ALL OTHERS 61.5
BRAZIL 145.9
32.2 ARGENTINA
30.5 COLUMBIA
ALL OTHERS 67.9
26.3 OCEANIA
EUROPE 685
AFRICA 642
NORTH AMERICA 420
S. AMERICA 288

WORLD ENVIRONMENTS

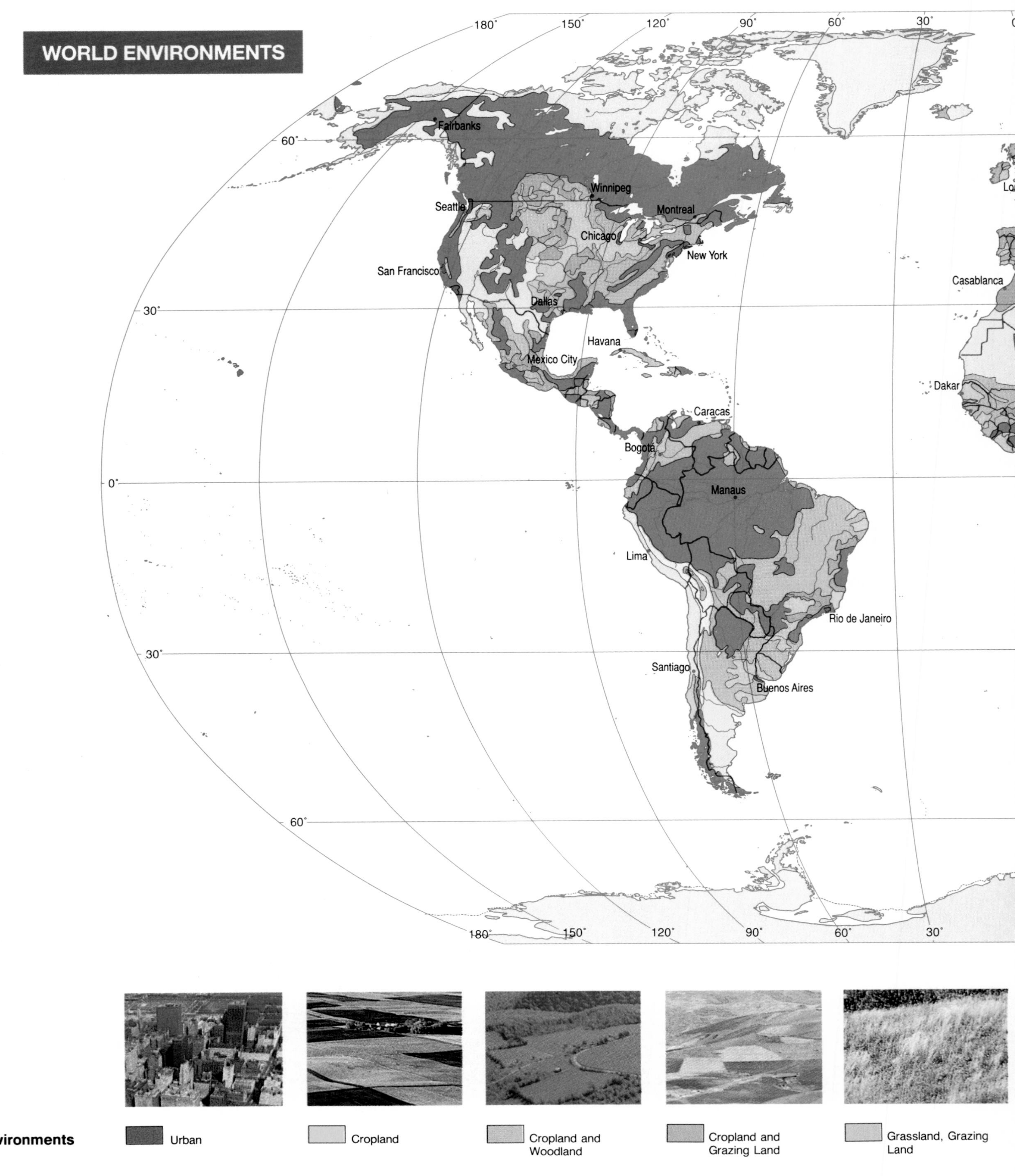

180°
150°
120°
90°
60°
30°
Fairbanks
Winnipeg
Seattle
Montreal
Chicago
New York
San Francisco
Casablanca
Dallas
Havana
Mexico City
Dakar
Caracas
Bogotá
Manaus
Lima
Rio de Janeiro
Santiago
Buenos Aires
Environments
Urban
Cropland
Cropland and Woodland
Cropland and Grazing Land
Grassland, Grazing Land

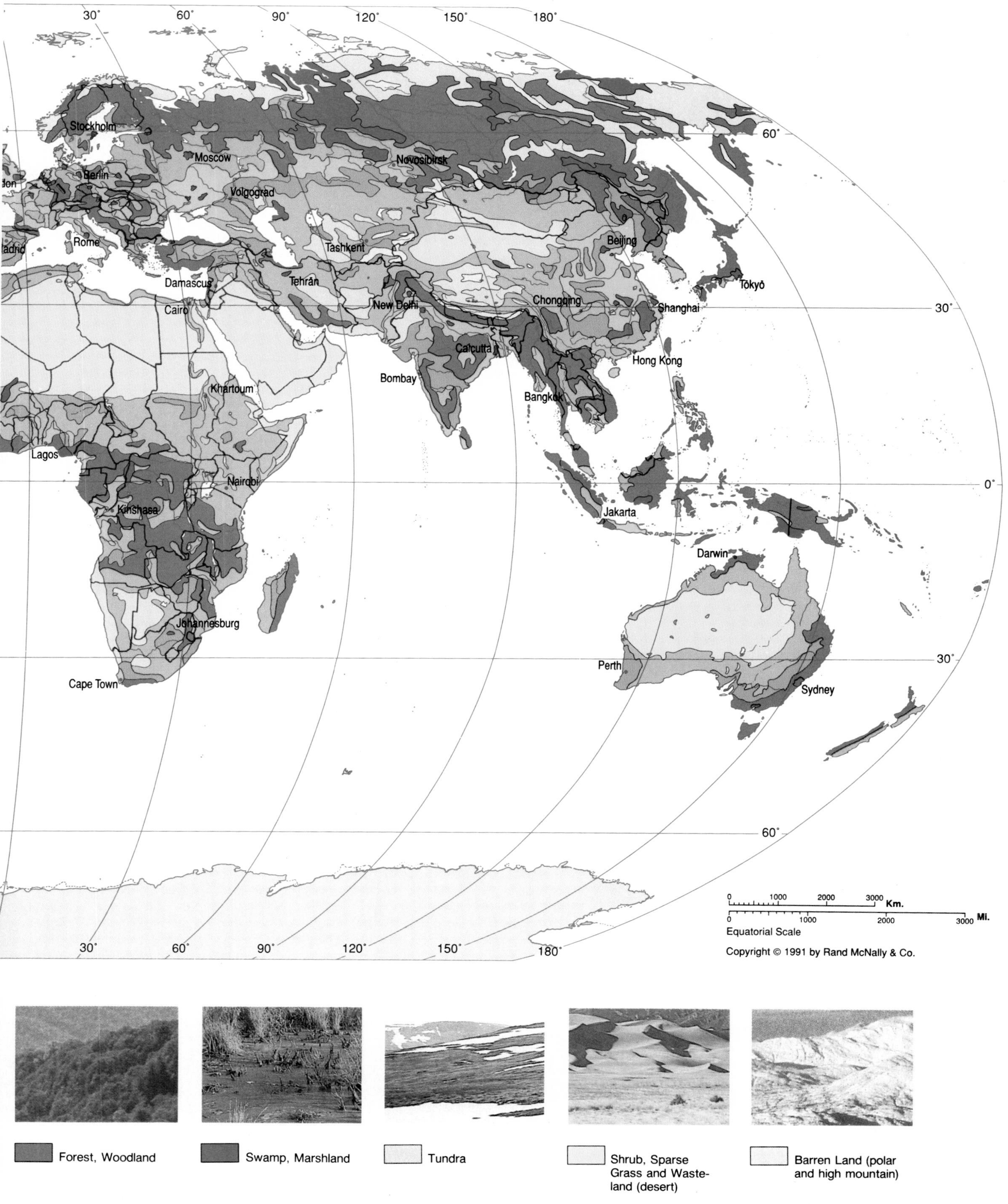

30°
60°
90°
120°
150°
180°
Stockholm
Moscow
Novosibirsk
Berlin
Volgograd
Rome
Tashkent
Beijing
Damascus
Tehrān
Tōkyō
Cairo
New Delhi
Chongqing
Shanghai
Calcutta
Hong Kong
Bombay
Khartoum
Bangkok
Lagos
Nairobi
Kinshasa
Jakarta
Darwin
Johannesburg
Perth
Sydney
Cape Town
0°
0 1000 2000 3000 Km.
0 1000 2000 3000 Mi.
Equatorial Scale
Copyright © 1991 by Rand McNally & Co.
Forest, Woodland
Swamp, Marshland
Tundra
Shrub, Sparse Grass and Wasteland (desert)
Barren Land (polar and high mountain)

WORLD TIME ZONES

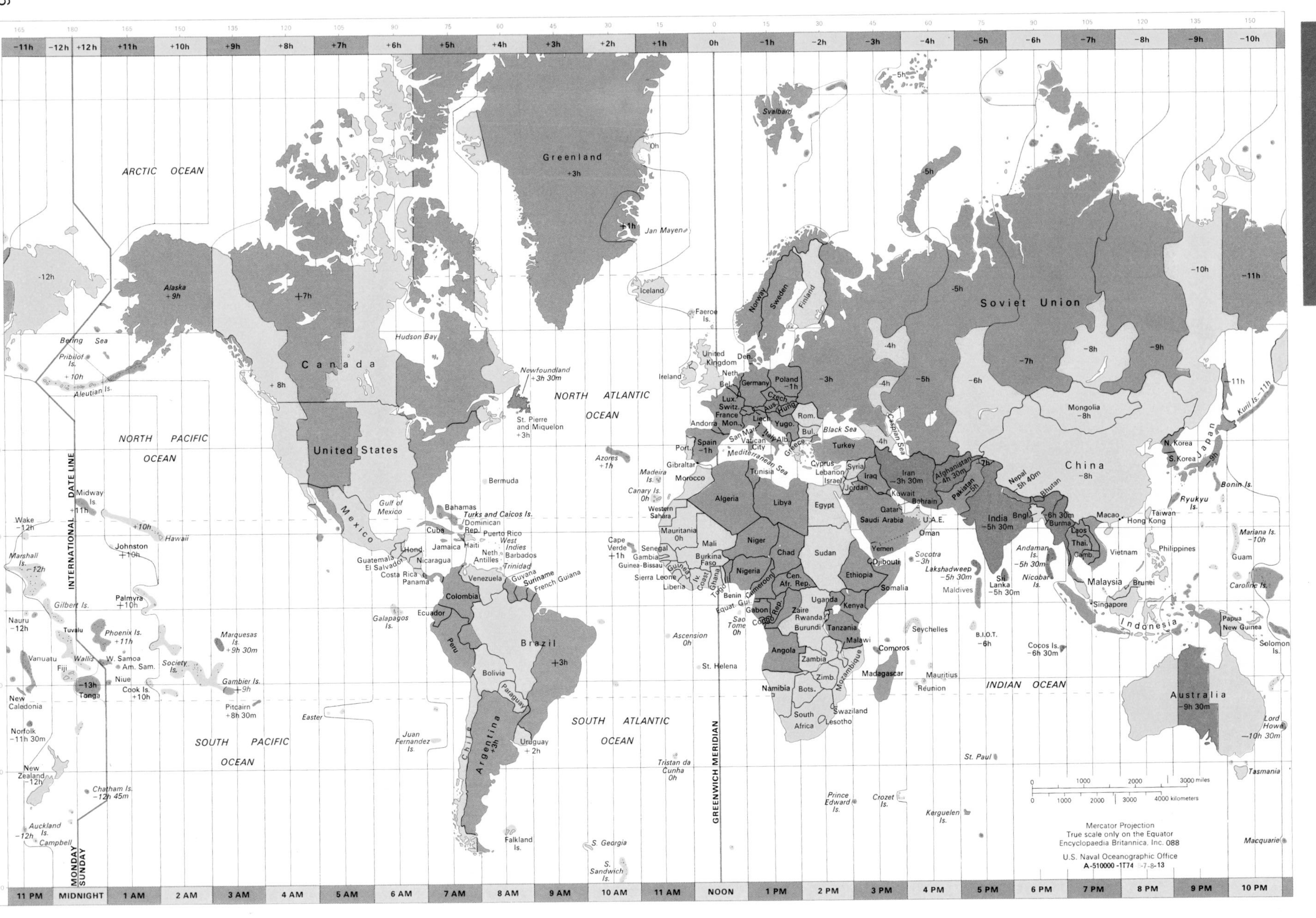

Time Zones

- Standard time zone of even-numbered hours from Greenwich time
- Standard time zone of odd-numbered hours from Greenwich time
- Time varies from the standard time zone by half an hour
- Time varies from the standard time zone by other than half an hour

h m — hours, minutes

The standard time zone system, fixed by international agreement and by law in each country, is based on a theoretical division of the globe into 24 zones of 15° longitude each. The mid-meridian of each zone fixes the hour for the entire zone. The zero time zone extends 7½° east and 7½° west of the Greenwich meridian, 0° longitude. Since the earth rotates toward the east, time zones to the west of Greenwich are earlier, to the east, later.

Plus and minus hours at the top of the map are added to or subtracted from local time to find Greenwich time. Local standard time can be determined for any area in the world by adding one hour for each time zone counted in an easterly direction from one's own, or by subtracting one hour for each zone counted in a westerly direction. To separate one day from the next, the 180th meridian has been designated as the international date line. On both sides of the line the time of day is the same, but west of the line it is one day later than it is to the east.

Countries that adhere to the international zone system adopt the zone applicable to their location. Some countries, however, establish time zones based on political boundaries, or adopt the time zone of a neighboring unit. For all or part of the year some countries also advance their time by one hour, thereby utilizing more daylight hours each day.

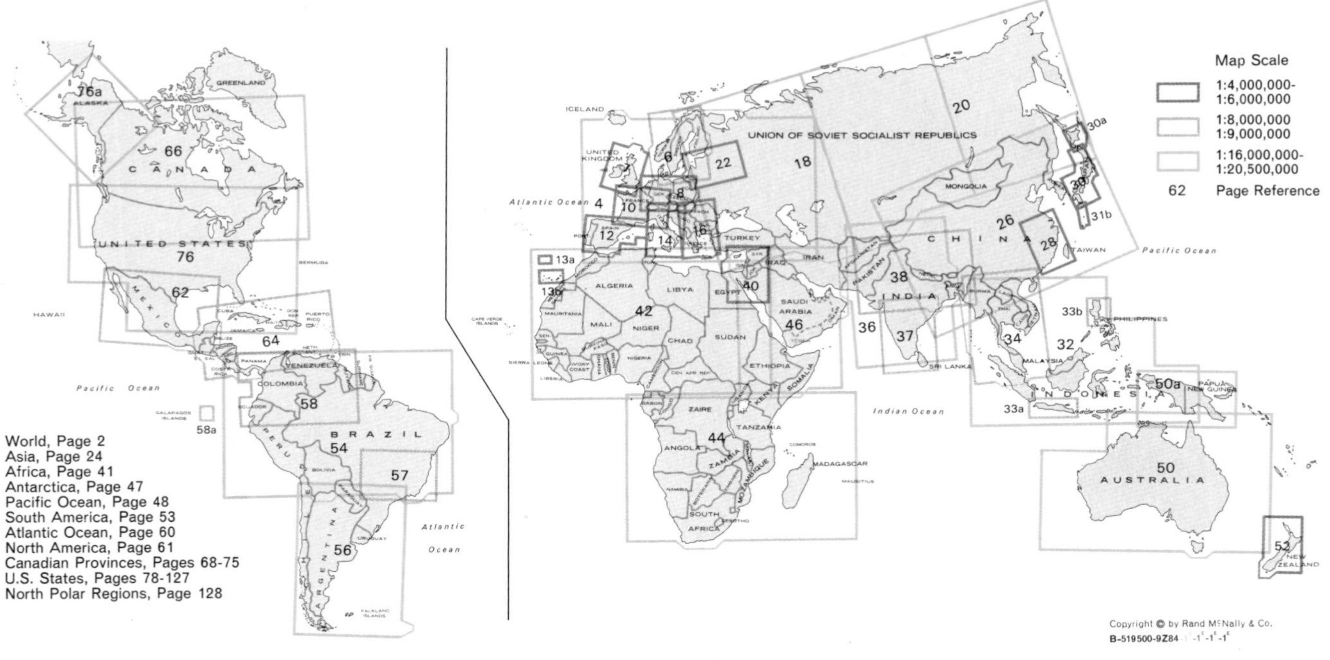

World Maps Symbols

Inhabited Localities

The size of type indicates the relative economic and political importance of the locality

Écommoy	Lisieux	Rouen
Trouville	Orléans	PARIS
Bi'r Safājah °	Oasis	

Alternate Names

MOSKVA
MOSCOW
Basel
Bâle
— English or second official language names are shown in reduced size lettering

Volgograd
(Stalingrad) — Historical or other alternates in the local language are shown in parentheses

Urban Area (Area of continuous industrial, commercial, and residential development)

Capitals of Political Units

- BUDAPEST — Independent Nation
- Cayenne — Dependency (Colony, protectorate, etc.)
- Recife — State, Province, County, Oblast, etc.

Political Boundaries

International (First-order political unit)

- Demarcated and Undemarcated
- Disputed de jure
- Indefinite or Undefined
- Demarcation Line

Internal

- State, Province, etc. (Second-order political unit)
- MURCIA — Historical Region (No boundaries indicated)
- GALAPAGOS (Ecuador) — Administering Country

Transportation

- Primary Road
- Secondary Road
- Minor Road, Trail
- Railway
- Canal du Midi — Navigable Canal
- Bridge
- Tunnel
- TO MALMÖ — Ferry

Hydrographic Features

- Shoreline
- Undefined or Fluctuating Shoreline
- Amur — River, Stream
- Intermittent Stream
- Rapids, Falls
- Irrigation or Drainage Canal
- Reef
- The Everglades — Swamp
- RIMO GLACIER — Glacier
- L. Victoria — Lake, Reservoir
- Tuz Gölü — Salt Lake
- Intermittent Lake, Reservoir
- Dry Lake Bed
- (395) — Lake Surface Elevation

Topographic Features

- Matterhorn △ 4478 — Elevation Above Sea Level
- 76 ▽ — Elevation Below Sea Level
- Mount Cook ▲ 3764 — Highest Elevation in Country
- 133 ▼ — Lowest Elevation in Country
- Khyber Pass 1067 — Mountain Pass

Elevations are given in meters.
The highest and lowest elevations in a continent are underlined

- Sand Area
- Lava
- Salt Flat

State, Province Maps Symbols

- ✪ Capital
- ∘ County Seat
- ▲ Military Installation
- △ Point of Interest
- + Mountain Peak
- International Boundary
- State, Province Boundary
- County Boundary
- Railroad
- Road
- Urban Area

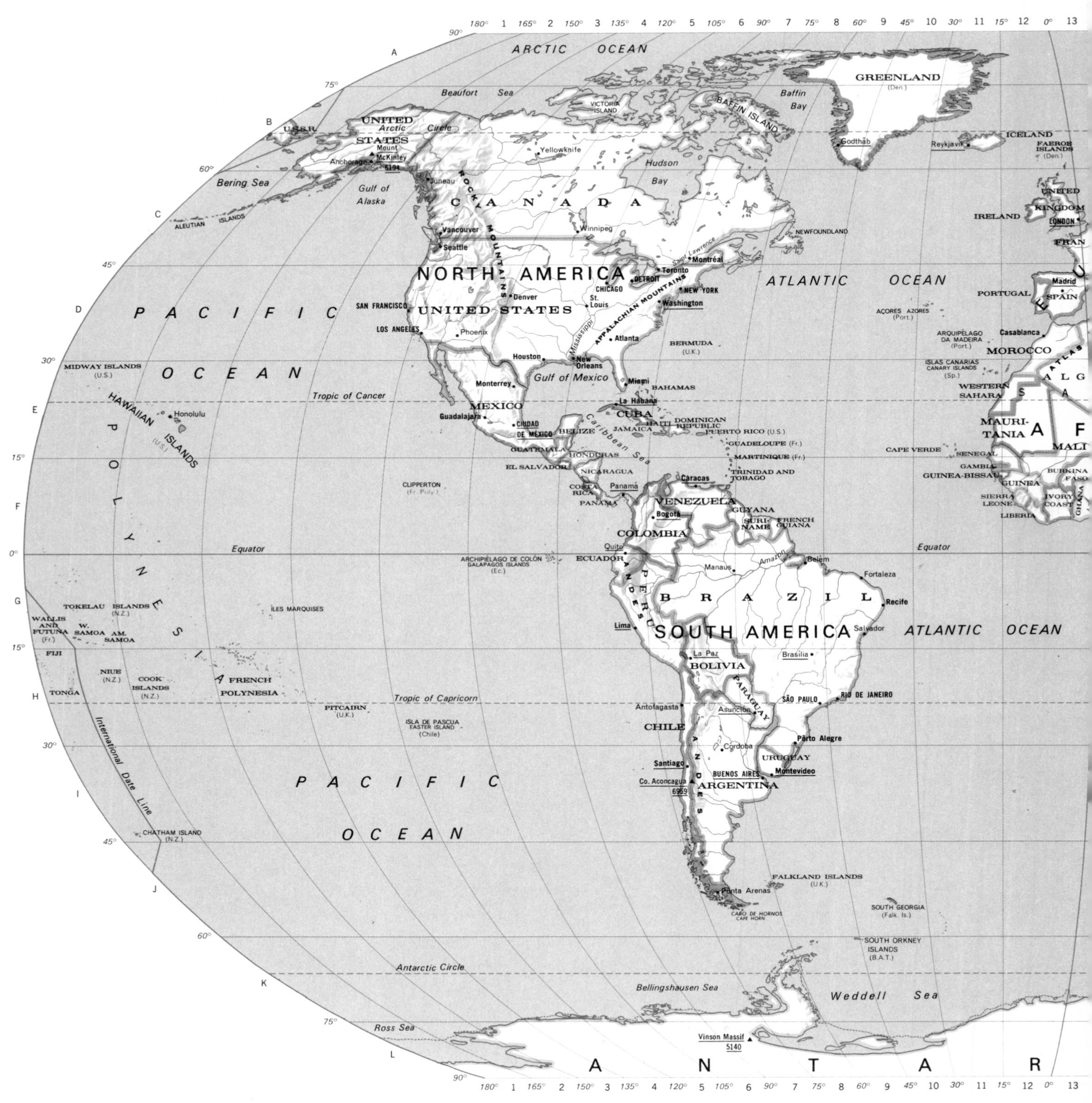
ARCTIC OCEAN
GREENLAND (Den.)
Beaufort Sea
VICTORIA ISLAND
BAFFIN ISLAND
Baffin Bay
UNITED STATES
Arctic Circle
Mount McKinley 6194
Anchorage
Yellowknife
Bering Sea
Gulf of Alaska
Hudson Bay
Juneau
ROCKY MOUNTAINS
C A N A D A
ALEUTIAN ISLANDS
Vancouver
Seattle
Winnipeg
NEWFOUNDLAND
Montréal
Toronto
NORTH AMERICA
DETROIT
CHICAGO
NEW YORK
Washington
Denver
St. Louis
SAN FRANCISCO
UNITED STATES
LOS ANGELES
Phoenix
APPALACHIAN MOUNTAINS
Mississippi
Atlanta
ATLANTIC OCEAN
PACIFIC OCEAN
MIDWAY ISLANDS (U.S.)
Houston
New Orleans
Gulf of Mexico
Miami
BAHAMAS
BERMUDA (U.K.)
Tropic of Cancer
HAWAIIAN ISLANDS (U.S.)
Honolulu
Monterrey
MEXICO
La Habana
CUBA
Guadalajara
CIUDAD DE MÉXICO
BELIZE
JAMAICA
HAITI
DOMINICAN REPUBLIC
PUERTO RICO (U.S.)
GUADELOUPE (Fr.)
MARTINIQUE (Fr.)
Caribbean Sea
GUATEMALA
HONDURAS
EL SALVADOR
NICARAGUA
TRINIDAD AND TOBAGO
Caracas
CLIPPERTON (Fr. Poly.)
COSTA RICA
Panamá
PANAMA
VENEZUELA
GUYANA
SURINAME
FRENCH GUIANA
Bogotá
COLOMBIA
Quito
ECUADOR
ARCHIPIÉLAGO DE COLÓN GALAPAGOS ISLANDS (Ec.)
Equator
Manaus
Amazon
Belém
Fortaleza
Recife
PERU
B R A Z I L
ANDES
Lima
SOUTH AMERICA
Salvador
ATLANTIC OCEAN
TOKELAU ISLANDS (N.Z.)
ÎLES MARQUISES
WALLIS AND FUTUNA (Fr.)
W. SAMOA
AM. SAMOA
FIJI
POLYNESIA
NIUE (N.Z.)
COOK ISLANDS (N.Z.)
FRENCH POLYNESIA
TONGA
La Paz
BOLIVIA
Brasília
PARAGUAY
Tropic of Capricorn
PITCAIRN (U.K.)
ISLA DE PASCUA EASTER ISLAND (Chile)
Antofagasta
Asunción
SÃO PAULO
RIO DE JANEIRO
CHILE
Córdoba
Pôrto Alegre
URUGUAY
Santiago
BUENOS AIRES
Montevideo
Co. Aconcagua 6959
ARGENTINA
International Date Line
CHATHAM ISLAND (N.Z.)
FALKLAND ISLANDS (U.K.)
Punta Arenas
CABO DE HORNOS CAPE HORN
SOUTH GEORGIA (Falk. Is.)
SOUTH ORKNEY ISLANDS (B.A.T.)
Antarctic Circle
Bellingshausen Sea
Weddell Sea
Ross Sea
Vinson Massif 5140
A N T A R
ICELAND
Reykjavík
Godthåb
FAEROE ISLANDS (Den.)
IRELAND
UNITED KINGDOM
LONDON
PORTUGAL
Madrid
SPAIN
AÇORES AZORES (Port.)
ARQUIPÉLAGO DA MADEIRA (Port.)
Casablanca
MOROCCO
ISLAS CANARIAS CANARY ISLANDS (Sp.)
WESTERN SAHARA
ATLAS
MAURITANIA
MALI
CAPE VERDE
SENEGAL
GAMBIA
GUINEA-BISSAU
GUINEA
SIERRA LEONE
LIBERIA
IVORY COAST
BURKINA FASO
GHANA
180° 1 165° 2 150° 3 135° 4 120° 5 105° 6 90° 7 75° 8 60° 9 45° 10 30° 11 15° 12 0° 13
A B C D E F G H I J K L
90° 75° 60° 45° 30° 15° 0° 15° 30° 45° 60° 75° 90°

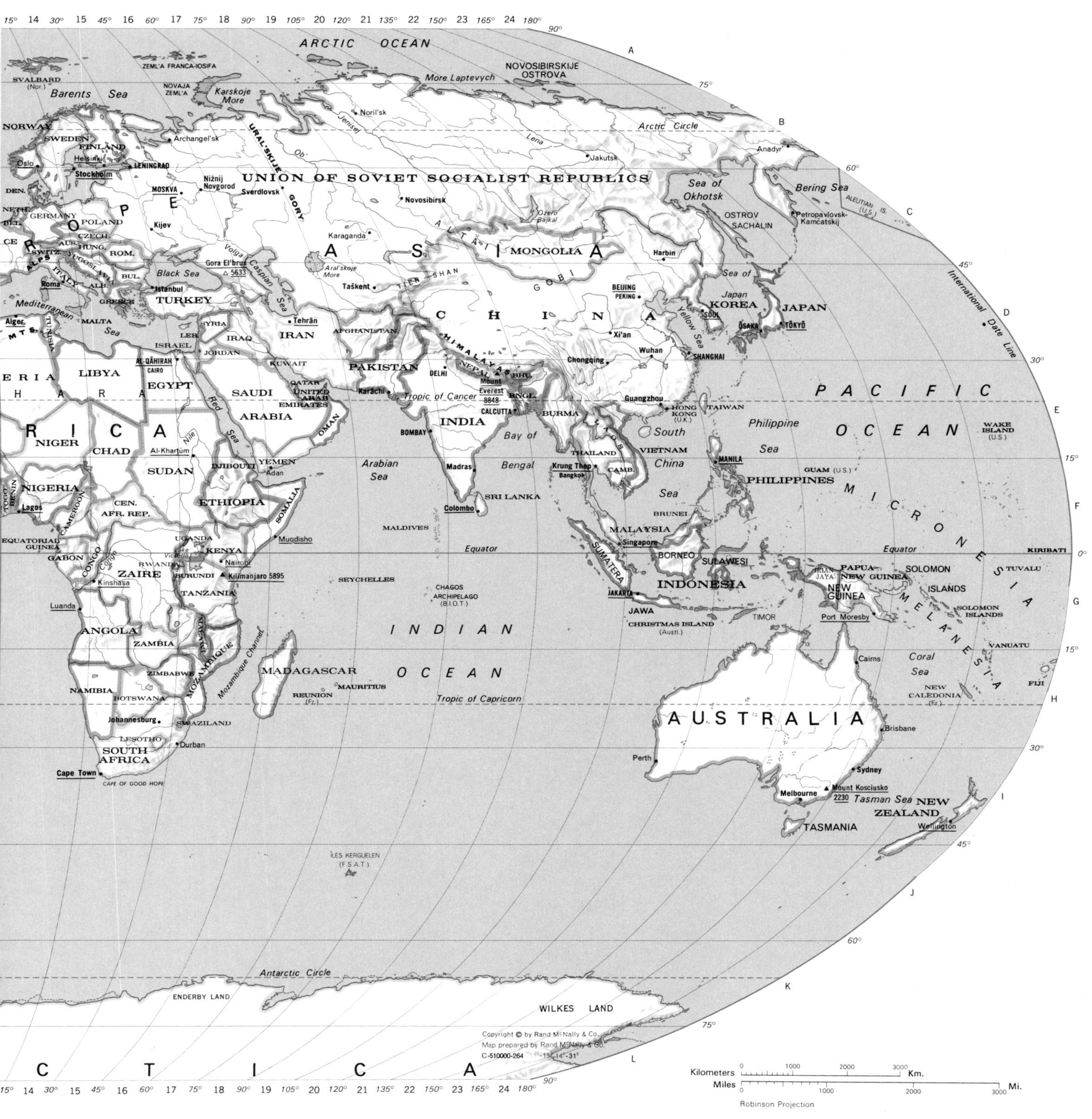
ARCTIC OCEAN
Barents Sea
Karskoje More
More Laptevych
NOVOSIBIRSKIJE OSTROVA
UNION OF SOVIET SOCIALIST REPUBLICS
ASIA
CHINA
MONGOLIA
JAPAN
KOREA
INDIA
PAKISTAN
IRAN
TURKEY
SAUDI ARABIA
EGYPT
LIBYA
SUDAN
ETHIOPIA
ZAIRE
ANGOLA
SOUTH AFRICA
MADAGASCAR
INDIAN OCEAN
PACIFIC OCEAN
AUSTRALIA
NEW ZEALAND
INDONESIA
PHILIPPINES
MICRONESIA
MELANESIA
Arctic Circle
Tropic of Cancer
Equator
Tropic of Capricorn
Antarctic Circle
International Date Line
ENDERBY LAND
WILKES LAND
Copyright © by Rand McNally & Co.
Map prepared by Rand McNally & Co.
C-510000-264
Kilometers 0 1000 2000 3000 Km.
Miles 0 1000 2000 3000 Mi.
Robinson Projection

Europe

ALBANIA.................... G11
Amsterdam, 6,965,000 ('89) (1,860,000★) .... E 8
ANDORRA.................... G 8
Antwerpen, 497,748 ('87) (1,100,000★) .... E 8
Athínai (Athens), 885,737 ('81) (3,027,331★) ... H12
AUSTRIA.................... F10
Barcelona, 1,714,355 ('88) (4,040,000★) .... G 8
Belfast, 303,800 ('87) (685,000★) .... E 6
BELGIUM.................... E 8
Beograd (Belgrade), 1,130,000 ('87) (1,400,000★) G12
Berlin, 3,352,848 ('89) (3,825,000★) E10
Bern, 134,393 ('90) (298,800★) .... F 9
Birmingham, 1,013,995 ('81) (2,675,000★) .... E 7
Bonn, 282,190 ('89) (570,000★) .... E 9
Bremen, 535,058 ('89) (800,000★) .... E 9
Bruxelles, 136,920 ('87) (2,385,000★) .... E 8
București, 1,989,823 ('86) (2,275,000★) G13
Budapest, 2,016,132 ('90) (2,565,000★) F11
BULGARIA.................. G12
Cardiff, 262,313 ('81) (625,000★) .... E 7
Char'kov (Kharkov), 1,611,000 ('89) (1,940,000★) F15
Cork, 133,271 ('86) (173,694★) .... E 6
CZECHOSLOVAKIA.... F11
DENMARK.................. D 9
Dnepropetrovsk, 1,179,000 ('89) (1,600,000★) F14
Doneck, 1,110,000 ('89) (2,200,000★) F15
Dresden, 518,057 ('89) (670,000★) E10
Dublin, 502,749 ('86) (1,140,000★) .... E 6
Düsseldorf, 569,641 ('89) (1,190,000★) .... E 9
Edinburgh, 433,200 ('89) (630,000★) .... D 7
Essen, 620,594 ('89) (4,950,000★) .... E 9
FAEROE ISLANDS...... C 6
FINLAND.................... C13
Firenze, 425,835 ('87) (640,000★) G10
FRANCE..................... F 8
Frankfurt, 625,258 ('89) (1,855,000★) .... E 9
Gdańsk, 461,500 ('89) (909,000★) E11
Genève (Geneva), 165,404 ('90) (460,000★) .... F 9
Genova, 727,427 ('87) (805,000★) .... G 9
GERMANY.................. E10
Gibraltar, 30,077 ('88). H 6
Glasgow, 695,630 ('89) (1,800,000★) .... D 7
Göteborg, 431,840 ('90) (710,894★) D10
GREECE.................... H12
GUERNSEY................ F 7
Hamburg, 1,603,070 ('89) (2,225,000★) .... E 9
Helsinki, 490,034 ('88) (1,040,000★) C12
HUNGARY.................. F11
ICELAND.................... B 4
Innsbruck, 117,287 ('81) (185,000★) F10
IRELAND.................... E 6
ISLE OF MAN............. E 7
İstanbul, 6,748,435 ('90) (7,000,000★) G13
ITALY........................ G10
JERSEY...................... F 7
Katowice, 365,800 ('89) (2,778,000★) E11
Kazan', 1,094,000 ('89) (1,140,000★) D17
Kijev (Kiev), 2,587,000 ('89) (2,900,000★) ... E14
København, 466,723 ('90) (1,685,000★) D10
Köln, 937,482 ('89) (1,760,000★) .... E 9
Kraków, 743,700 ('89) (828,000★) E11
Leipzig, 545,307 ('89) (700,000★) E10
Leningrad, 4,456,000 ('89) (5,825,000★) D14
LIECHTENSTEIN......... F 9
Liège, 200,891 ('87) (750,000★) .... E 9
Lille, 168,424 ('82) (1,020,000★) .... E 8

★ Population of metropolitan area, including suburbs.

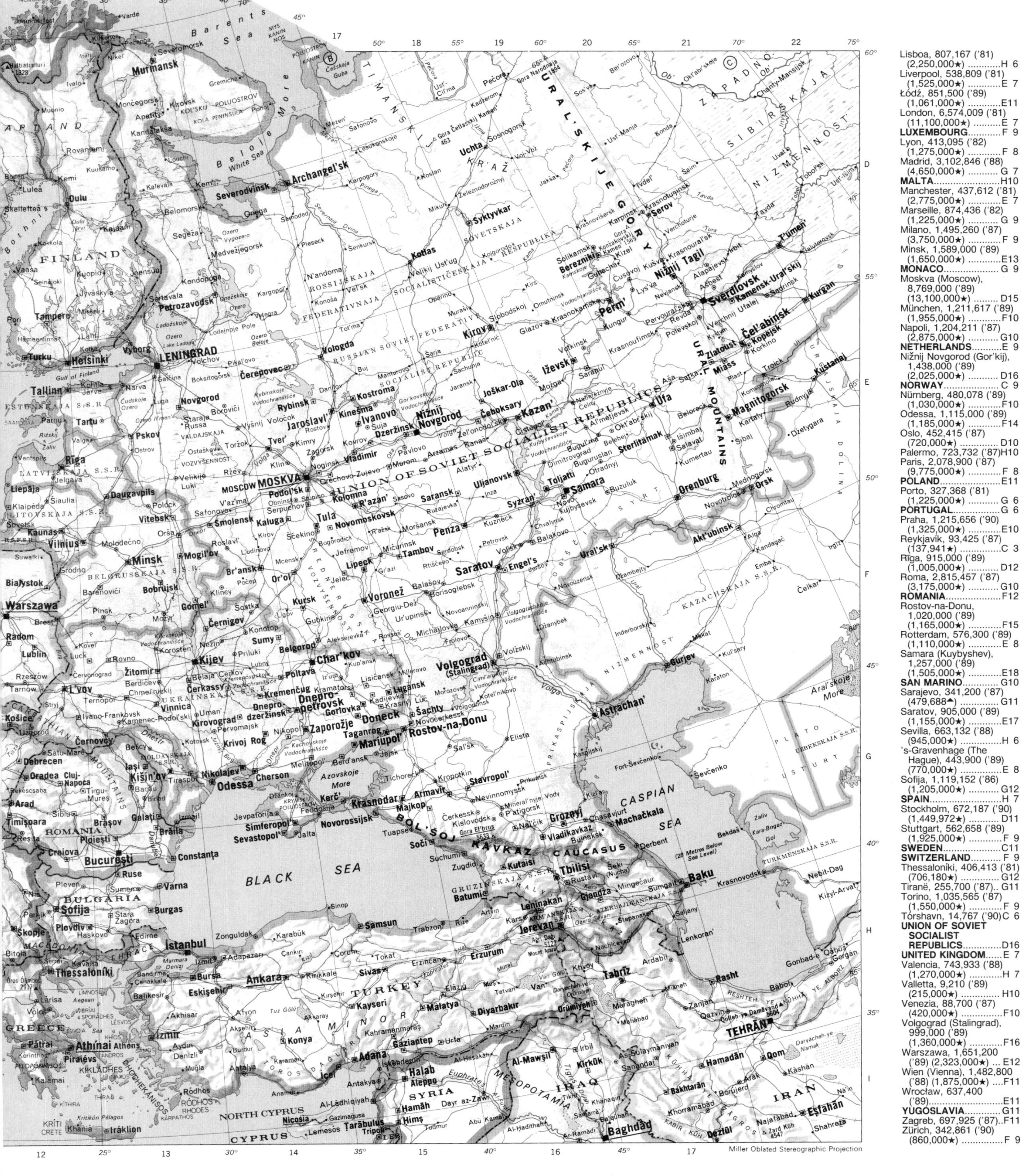

Lisboa, 807,167 ('81) (2,250,000★) ....H 6
Liverpool, 538,809 ('81) (1,525,000★) ....E 7
Łódź, 851,500 ('89) (1,061,000★) E11
London, 6,574,009 ('81) (11,100,000★) ....E 7
LUXEMBOURG...........F 9
Lyon, 413,095 ('82) (1,275,000★) ....F 8
Madrid, 3,102,846 ('88) (4,650,000★) .... G 7
MALTA.......................H10
Manchester, 437,612 ('81) (2,775,000★) ....E 7
Marseille, 874,436 ('82) (1,225,000★) .... G 9
Milano, 1,495,260 ('87) (3,750,000★) ....F 9
Minsk, 1,589,000 ('89) (1,650,000★) E13
MONACO...................G 9
Moskva (Moscow), 8,769,000 ('89) (13,100,000★) D15
München, 1,211,617 ('89) (1,955,000★) F10
Napoli, 1,204,211 ('87) (2,875,000★) G10
NETHERLANDS..........E 9
Nižnij Novgorod (Gor'kij), 1,438,000 ('89) (2,025,000★) D16
NORWAY..................C 9
Nürnberg, 480,078 ('89) (1,030,000★) F10
Odessa, 1,115,000 ('89) (1,185,000★) F14
Oslo, 452,415 ('87) (720,000★) D10
Palermo, 723,732 ('87)H10
Paris, 2,078,900 ('87) (9,775,000★) ....F 8
POLAND......................E11
Porto, 327,368 ('81) (1,225,000★) .... G 6
PORTUGAL................G 6
Praha, 1,215,656 ('90) (1,325,000★) E10
Reykjavík, 93,425 ('87) (137,941★) ....C 3
Riga, 915,000 ('89) (1,005,000★) D12
Roma, 2,815,457 ('87) (3,175,000★) G10
ROMANIA......................F12
Rostov-na-Donu, 1,020,000 ('89) (1,165,000★) F15
Rotterdam, 576,300 ('89) (1,110,000★) ....E 8
Samara (Kuybyshev), 1,257,000 ('89) (1,505,000★) E18
SAN MARINO............ G10
Sarajevo, 341,200 ('87) (479,688▲) G11
Saratov, 905,000 ('89) (1,155,000★) E17
Sevilla, 663,132 ('88) (945,000★) ....H 6
's-Gravenhage (The Hague), 443,900 ('89) (770,000★) ....E 8
Sofija, 1,119,152 ('86) (1,205,000★) G12
SPAIN........................H 7
Stockholm, 672,187 ('90) (1,449,972★) D11
Stuttgart, 562,658 ('89) (1,925,000★) ....F 9
SWEDEN......................C11
SWITZERLAND..........F 9
Thessaloníki, 406,413 ('81) (706,180★) G12
Tiranë, 255,700 ('87).. G11
Torino, 1,035,565 ('87) (1,550,000★) ....F 9
Tórshavn, 14,767 ('90)C 6
UNION OF SOVIET SOCIALIST REPUBLICS.............D16
UNITED KINGDOM......E 7
Valencia, 743,933 ('88) (1,270,000★) ....H 7
Valletta, 9,210 ('89) (215,000★) H10
Venezia, 88,700 ('87) (420,000★) F10
Volgograd (Stalingrad), 999,000 ('89) (1,360,000★) F16
Warszawa, 1,651,200 ('89) (2,323,000★) ... E12
Wien (Vienna), 1,482,800 ('88) (1,875,000★) F11
Wrocław, 637,400 ('89)...........................E11
YUGOSLAVIA............G11
Zagreb, 697,925 ('87)..F11
Zürich, 342,861 ('90) (860,000★) ....F 9

Scandinavia

Denmark

1990 ESTIMATE

Ålborg, 114,000 (155,019▲) . . . . H 7
Århus, 202,300 (261,437▲) . . . . H 8
Copenhagen *see* København . . . . I 9
København (Copenhagen), 466,723 (1,685,000★) . . . . . . I 9
Odense, 140,100 (176,133▲) . . . . I 8

Finland

1988 ESTIMATE

Helsinki (Helsingfors), 490,034 (1,040,000★) F15
Lahti, 74,300 (108,000★) F15
Oulu, 98,582 (121,000★) D15
Tampere, 170,533 (241,000★) F14
Turku (Åbo), 160,456 (228,000★) F14

Norway

1987 ESTIMATE

Bergen, 209,320 (239,000★) . . . . F 5
Hammerfest, 7,208('83) A14
Oslo, 452,415 (720,000★) . . . . . . G 8
Stavanger, 94,200 (132,000★)('85) . . . . G 5
Trondheim, 135,010 . . E 8

Sweden

1990 ESTIMATE

Göteborg (Gothenburg), 431,840 (710,894★) H 8
Helsingborg, 108,359 H 9
Jönköping, 110,860 . . H10
Linköping, 120,562 . . G10
Malmö, 232,908 (445,000★) . . . . I 9
Norrköping, 119,921 G11
Örebro, 120,353 . . . . G10
Stockholm, 672,187 (1,449,972★) G12
Uppsala, 164,754 . . . . G11
Västerås, 118,386 . . G11

★ Population of metropolitan area, including suburbs.
▲ Population of entire district, including rural area.

Ireland

1986 CENSUS

Cork, 133,271 (173,694★) . . . . . J 4
Dublin (Baile Átha Cliath), 502,749 (1,140,000★) . . . . H 6
Galway, 47,104 . . . . H 3
Limerick, 56,279 (76,557★) . . . . I 4
Waterford, 39,529 (41,054★) . . . . I 5

Isle of Man

1986 CENSUS

Douglas, 20,368 (28,500★) . . . . . . G 8

United Kingdom

England

1981 CENSUS

Birmingham, 1,013,995 (2,675,000★) I11
Blackpool, 146,297 (280,000★) . . . . . . H 9
Bournemouth, 142,829 (315,000★) K11
Bradford, 293,336 . . H11
Brighton, 134,581 (420,000★) K12
Bristol, 413,861 (630,000★) J10
Coventry, 318,718 (645,000★) I11
Derby, 218,026 (275,000★) I11
Kingston upon Hull, 322,144 (350,000★) H12
Leeds, 445,242 (1,540,000★) H11
Leicester, 324,394 (495,000★) I11
Liverpool, 538,809 (1,525,000★) H10
London, 6,574,009 (11,100,000★) J12
Manchester, 437,612 (2,775,000★) H10
Newcastle upon Tyne, 199,064 (1,300,000★) G11
Nottingham, 273,300 (655,000★) I11
Oxford, 113,847 (230,000★) J11
Plymouth, 238,583 (290,000★) . . . . . . K 8
Portsmouth, 174,218 (485,000★) K11
Preston, 166,675 (250,000★) H10
Reading, 194,727 (200,000★) J12
Sheffield, 470,685 (710,000★) H11
Southampton, 211,321 (415,000★) K11
Southend-on-Sea, 155,720 . . . . J13
Stoke-on-Trent, 272,446 (440,000★) H10
Sunderland, 195,064 G11
Teesside, 158,516 (580,000★) G11
Wolverhampton, 263,501 . . . . I10

Northern Ireland

1987 ESTIMATE

Bangor, 70,700 . . . . G 7
Belfast, 303,800 (685,000★) . . . . . . G 7
Londonderry, 97,500 (97,200★) . . . . . . G 5
Newtownabbey, 72,300 . . . . G 7

Scotland

1989 ESTIMATE

Aberdeen, 210,700 . . D10
Dundee, 172,540 . . . . E 9
Edinburgh, 433,200 (630,000★) . . . . . . F 9
Glasgow, 695,630 (1,800,000★) . . . . F 8
Greenock, 58,436 (101,000★)('81) . . F 8
Inverness, 38,204('81) D 8
Paisley, 84,330('81) . . F 8

Wales

1981 CENSUS

Cardiff, 262,313 (625,000★) . . . . . . J 9
Newport, 115,896 (310,000★) . . . . . . J 9
Swansea, 172,433 (275,000★) . . . . . . J 9

★ Population of metropolitan area, including suburbs.

Central Europe

Austria

1981 CENSUS

Graz, 243,166 (325,000★)........H15
Innsbruck, 117,287 (185,000★)........H11
Linz, 199,910 (335,000★) G14
Salzburg, 139,426 (220,000★)........H13
Vienna *see* Wien G16
Villach, 52,692 (65,000★) I13
Wien (Vienna), 1,482,800 (1,875,000★)('88) .. G16

Belgium

1987 ESTIMATE

Antwerpen (Antwerp), 479,748 (1,100,000★)...... D 4
Brugge, 117,755 (223,000★)........D 3
Bruxelles (Brussel), 136,920 (2,385,000★)...... E 4
Charleroi, 209,395 (480,000★)........E 4
Gent (Gand), 233,856 (465,000★)........D 3
Hasselt, 65,563 (290,000★)........E 5
Liège, 200,891 (750,000★)........E 5
Mons, 89,697 (242,000★)........E 3

Czechoslovakia

1990 ESTIMATE

Bratislava, 442,999 .. G17
Brno, 392,285 (450,000★)........F16
Hradec Králové, 101,302 (113,000★)........E15
Košice, 237,099 .... G21
Liberec, 104,256 (175,000★)........E15
Olomouc, 107,044 (126,000★)........F17
Ostrava, 331,557 (760,000★)........F18
Plzeň, 175,038 (210,000★)........F13
Praha (Prague), 1,215,656 (1,325,000★)........E14
Ústí nad Labem, 106,499 (115,000★)........E14

Germany

1989 ESTIMATE

Aachen, 233,255 (535,000★)........E 6
Augsburg, 247,731 (405,000★) G10
Berlin, 3,352,848 (3,825,000★)......C13
Bielefeld, 311,946 (515,000★)........C 8
Bochum, 389,087 ....D 7
Bonn, 282,190 (570,000★)........E 7
Braunschweig, 253,794 (330,000★)........C10
Bremen, 535,058 (800,000★)........B 8
Bremerhaven, 126,934 (190,000★)........B 8
Chemnitz, 311,765 (450,000★)........E12
Cologne *see* Köln .... E 6
Dortmund, 587,328 .. D 7
Dresden, 518,057 (670,000★)........D13
Duisburg, 527,447 .. D 6
Düsseldorf, 569,641 (1,190,000★)........D 6
Erfurt, 220,016 ...... E11
Essen, 620,594 (4,950,000★)...... D 7
Frankfurt am Main, 625,258 (1,855,000★)...... E 8
Gelsenkirchen, 287,255..........D 7
Hagen, 210,640 .... D 7
Halle, 236,044 (475,000★)........D11
Hamburg, 1,603,070 (2,225,000★)........B 9
Hannover, 498,495 (1,000,000★)...... C 9
Karlsruhe, 265,100 (485,000★)........F 8
Kiel, 240,675 (335,000★)........A10
Köln (Cologne), 937,482 (1,760,000★)...... E 6
Leipzig, 545,307 (700,000★)........D12
Lübeck, 210,681 (260,000★)........B10

★ Population of metropolitan area, including suburbs.

Magdeburg, 290,579 (400,000★) C11
Mannheim, 300,468 (1,400,000★) . . . . . . F 8
Mönchengladbach, 252,910 (410,000★) D 6
München (Munich), 1,211,617 (1,955,000★) G11
Münster, 248,919 . . . . D 7
Nürnberg, 480,078 (1,030,000★) F11
Potsdam, 142,862 . . C13
Rostock, 253,990 . . . . A12
Saarbrücken, 188,467 (385,000★) . . . . F 6
Stuttgart, 562,658 (1,925,000★) . . . . . . G 9
Wiesbaden, 254,209 (795,000★) . . . . E 8
Wuppertal, 371,283 (830,000★) . . . . D 7

Hungary
1990 ESTIMATE

Budapest, 2,016,132 (2,565,000★) H19
Debrecen, 212,247 . . H21
Győr, 129,356 . . . . . . H 7
Miskolc, 196,449 . . . . G20
Pécs, 170,119 . . . . . . I18
Szeged, 175,338 . . . . I20
Szombathely, 85,418 H16

Liechtenstein
1990 ESTIMATE

Vaduz, 4,874 . . . . . . H 9

Luxembourg
1985 ESTIMATE

Luxembourg, 76,130 (136,000★) . . . . F 6

Netherlands
1989 ESTIMATE

Amsterdam, 6,965,000 (1,860,000★) . . . . . . C 4
Eindhoven, 190,700 (379,377★) . . . . D 5
Groningen, 167,800 (206,781★) . . . . B 6
Nijmegen, 145,400 (240,085★) . . . . D 5
Rotterdam, 576,300 (1,110,000★) . . . . . . D 4
's-Gravenhage (The Hague), 443,900 (770,000★) . . . . C 4
Tilburg, 155,100 (224,934★) . . . . D 5
Utrecht, 230,700 (518,779★) . . . . C 5

Poland
1989 ESTIMATE

Białystok, 263,900 . . B23
Bydgoszcz, 377,900 B18
Częstochowa, 254,600 . . . . E19
Gdańsk (Danzig), 461,500 (909,000★) A18
Gdynia, 250,200 . . . . A18
Katowice, 365,800 (2,778,000★) E19
Kielce, 211,100 . . . . . . E20
Kraków, 743,700 (828,000★) E19
łódź, 851,500 (1,061,000★) D19
Lublin, 339,500 (389,000★) D22
Poznań, 586,500 (672,000★) C16
Radom, 223,600 . . . . D21
Szczecin (Stettin), 409,500 (449,000★) B14
Toruń, 199,600 . . . . . . B18
Wałbrzych (Waldenburg), 141,400 (207,000★) E16
Warszawa (Warsaw), 1,651,200 (2,323,000★) C21
Wrocław (Breslau), 637,400 . . . . D17

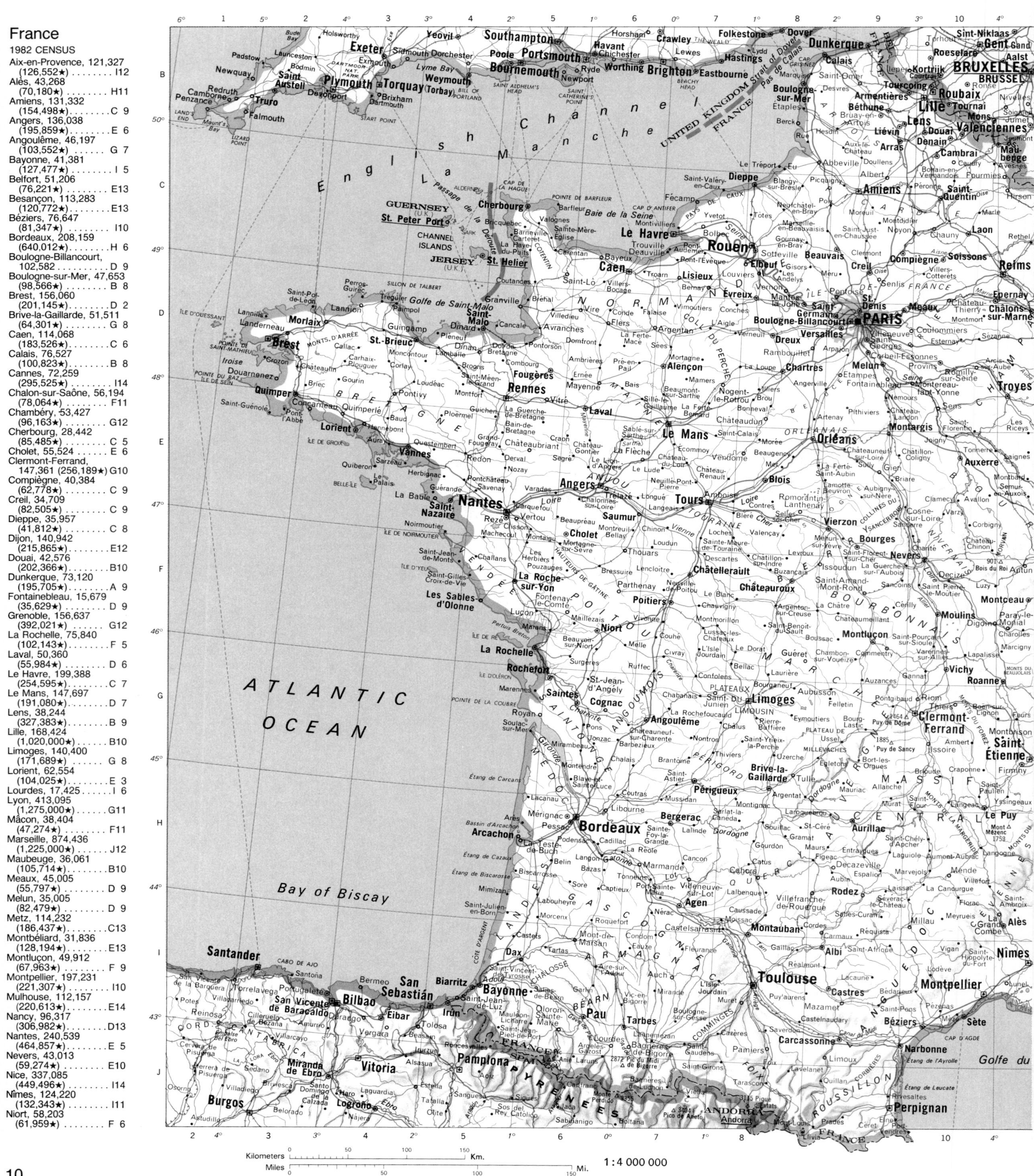

France

1982 CENSUS

Aix-en-Provence, 121,327 (126,552★) I12
Alès, 43,268 (70,180★) H11
Amiens, 131,332 (154,498★) . . . . C 9
Angers, 136,038 (195,859★) . . . . E 6
Angoulême, 46,197 (103,552★) . . . . . . G 7
Bayonne, 41,381 (127,477★) . . . . I 5
Belfort, 51,206 (76,221★) E13
Besançon, 113,283 (120,772★) E13
Béziers, 76,647 (81,347★) I10
Bordeaux, 208,159 (640,012★) . . . . H 6
Boulogne-Billancourt, 102,582 . . . . D 9
Boulogne-sur-Mer, 47,653 (98,566★) . . . . B 8
Brest, 156,060 (201,145★) . . . . D 2
Brive-la-Gaillarde, 51,511 (64,301★) . . . . G 8
Caen, 114,068 (183,526★) . . . . C 6
Calais, 76,527 (100,823★) . . . . B 8
Cannes, 72,259 (295,525★) I14
Chalon-sur-Saône, 56,194 (78,064★) F11
Chambéry, 53,427 (96,163★) G12
Cherbourg, 28,442 (85,485★) . . . . C 5
Cholet, 55,524 . . . . . . E 6
Clermont-Ferrand, 147,361 (256,189★) G10
Compiègne, 40,384 (62,778★) . . . . C 9
Creil, 34,709 (82,505★) . . . . C 9
Dieppe, 35,957 (41,812★) . . . . C 8
Dijon, 140,942 (215,865★) E12
Douai, 42,576 (202,366★) B10
Dunkerque, 73,120 (195,705★) . . . . A 9
Fontainebleau, 15,679 (35,629★) . . . . D 9
Grenoble, 156,637 (392,021★) G12
La Rochelle, 75,840 (102,143★) . . . . F 5
Laval, 50,360 (55,984★) . . . . D 6
Le Havre, 199,388 (254,595★) . . . . C 7
Le Mans, 147,697 (191,080★) . . . . D 7
Lens, 38,244 (327,383★) . . . . B 9
Lille, 168,424 (1,020,000★) B10
Limoges, 140,400 (171,689★) . . . . . . G 8
Lorient, 62,554 (104,025★) . . . . E 3
Lourdes, 17,425 . . . . . . I 6
Lyon, 413,095 (1,275,000★) G11
Mâcon, 38,404 (47,274★) F11
Marseille, 874,436 (1,225,000★) J12
Maubeuge, 36,061 (105,714★) B10
Meaux, 45,005 (55,797★) . . . . D 9
Melun, 35,005 (82,479★) . . . . D 9
Metz, 114,232 (186,437★) C13
Montbéliard, 31,836 (128,194★) E13
Montluçon, 49,912 (67,963★) . . . . F 9
Montpellier, 197,231 (221,307★) I10
Mulhouse, 112,157 (220,613★) E14
Nancy, 96,317 (306,982★) D13
Nantes, 240,539 (464,857★) . . . . E 5
Nevers, 43,013 (59,274★) E10
Nice, 337,085 (449,496★) I14
Nîmes, 124,220 (132,343★) I11
Niort, 58,203 (61,959★) . . . . F 6

Orléans, 102,710 (220,478★) . . . . E 8
Paris, 2,078,900 (9,775,000★)('87) . . D 9
Pau, 83,790 (131,265★) . . . . I 6
Perpignan, 111,669 (137,915★) . . . . J 9
Poitiers, 79,350 (103,204★) . . . . F 7
Quimper, 56,907 . . . . D 2
Reims, 194,656 (199,388★) C11
Rennes, 117,234 (234,418★) . . . . D 5
Roanne, 48,705 (81,786★) F11
Roubaix, 101,602 . . . . B10
Rouen, 101,945 (379,879★) . . . . C 8
Saint-Brieuc, 48,563 (83,900★) . . . . D 4
Saint-Denis, 90,829 . . D 9
Saint-Étienne, 204,955 (317,228★) G11
Saint-Germain, 38,499 D 9
Saint-Malo, 46,347 . . D 4
Saint-Nazaire, 68,348 (130,271★) . . . . E 4
Saint-Quentin, 63,567 (71,887★) C10
Saint-Tropez, 4,961 (6,213▲) I13
Sedan, 23,477 (30,871★) C11
Strasbourg, 248,712 (400,000★) D14
Toulon, 179,423 (410,393★) I12
Toulouse, 347,995 (541,271★) . . . . I 8
Tourcoing, 96,908 . . B10
Tours, 132,209 (262,786★) . . . . E 7
Troyes, 63,581 (125,240★) D11
Valence, 66,356 (106,041★) H11
Valenciennes, 40,275 (349,505★) B10
Verdun, 21,516 (26,944★) C12
Versailles, 91,494 . . . . D 9
Vichy, 30,527 (63,501★) F10
Villeurbanne, 115,960 G11

Guernsey

1986 CENSUS

Saint Peter Port, 16,085 (36,000★) . . . . C 4

Jersey

1986 CENSUS

Saint Helier, 27,083 (46,500★) . . . . C 4

Liechtenstein

1990 ESTIMATE

Vaduz, 4,874 . . . . E16

Luxembourg

1985 ESTIMATE

Luxembourg, 76,130 (136,000★) C13

Monaco

1982 CENSUS

Monaco, 27,063 (87,000★) I14

Switzerland

1990 ESTIMATE

Basel (Bâle), 169,587 (575,000★) E14
Bern (Berne), 134,393 (298,800★) F14
Fribourg (Freiburg), 33,962 (56,800★) F14
Genève, 165,404 (460,000★) F13
Lausanne, 122,600 (259,900★) F13
Luzern, 59,115 (159,500★) E15
Neuchâtel, 32,509 (65,900★) F13
Sankt Gallen, 73,191 (125,000★) E16
Sankt Moritz, 5,335('87) F16
Schaffhausen, 33,956 (53,000★) E15
Thun, 37,707 (77,200★) F14
Winterthur, 85,174 (107,400★) E15
Zürich, 342,861 (860,000★) E15

★ Population of metropolitan area, including suburbs.
▲ Population of entire district, including rural area.

Spain and Portugal

Andorra

1986 CENSUS

Andorra, 18,463 .... C13

Gibraltar

1988 ESTIMATE

Gibraltar, 30,077 .... I 6

Portugal

1981 CENSUS

Almada, 42,607 .... G 2
Barreiro, 50,863 .... G 2
Beja, 19,643 .... G 4
Braga, 63,033 .... D 3
Coimbra, 74,616 .... E 3
Covilhã, 21,807 ...... E 4
Évora, 34,851 ...... G 4
Faro, 27,974 .... H 4
Funchal, 44,111 .... m21
Guimarães, 21,947 .. D 3
Lisboa (Lisbon), 807,167 (2,250,000★) ...... G 2
Montijo, 23,017 ...... G 3
Porto, 327,368 (1,225,000★) ...... D 3
Póvoa de Varzim, 23,729 .... D 3
Santarém, 19,761 .... F 3
Setúbal, 77,885 .... G 3
Vila do Conde, 20,613 D 3
Vila Nova de Gaia, 62,469 .... D 3

Spain

1988 ESTIMATE

Albacete, 125,997 .. G10
Alcalá de Guadaira, 50,935 .... H 6
Alcalá de Henares, 150,021 .... E 8
Alcantarilla, 28,279 .. H10
Alcázar de San Juan, 26,258 .... F 8
Alcira, 40,575 ...... F11
Alcoy, 66,074 ...... G11
Algeciras, 99,528 .... I 6
Alicante, 261,051 .... G11
Almendralejo, 25,352 G 5
Almería, 157,644 .... I 9
Andújar, 32,300 (37,020▲) .... G 7
Antequera, 32,200 (41,284▲) .... H 7
Aranjuez, 37,694 .... E 8
Arcos de la Frontera, 19,600 (27,311▲) .. I 6
Arrecife, 36,297 ...... p27
Ávila, 45,092 .... E 7
Avilés, 87,811 (131,000★) .... B 6
Badajoz, 106,400 (122,407▲) ...... G 5
Badalona, 225,229 .. D14
Barcelona, 1,714,355 (4,040,000★) D14
Baza, 20,910 ...... H 9
Bilbao, 384,733 (985,000★) .... B 9
Burgos, 160,561 .... C 8
Burjasot, 35,011 .... F11
Cáceres, 71,598 .... F 5
Cádiz, 156,591 (240,000★) .... I 5
Cartagena, 70,000 (172,710▲) H11
Castellón de la Plana, 131,809 .... F11
Chiclana de la Frontera, 43,157 .... I 5
Ciudad Real, 56,300 G 8
Córdoba, 302,301 .. H 7
Coria del Río, 21,844 H 5
Cuenca, 42,222 ...... E 9
Don Benito, 24,500 (29,324▲) .... G 6
Durango, 27,425 .... B 9
Écija, 30,900 (35,836▲) .... H 6
Éibar, 34,355 ...... B 9
Elche, 158,300 (180,256▲) G11
Elda, 56,756 .... G11
El Ferrol del Caudillo, 86,503 (129,000★) B 3
El Puerto de Santa María, 49,900 (62,285▲) .. I 5
Gandía, 46,100 (52,646▲) G11
Gavá, 34,613 ...... D14
Gerona, 30,900 (68,902▲) D14
Getafe, 135,367 .... E 8
Gijón, 262,156 .... B 6
Granada, 263,334 .... H 8
Granollers, 49,045 .. D14
Guadalajara, 61,309 .. E 8
Hospitalet, 278,449 .. D14
Huelva, 137,826 .... H 5
Huesca, 41,841 .... C11
Irún, 54,886 .... B10
Jaén, 106,435 ...... H 8

★ Population of metropolitan area, including suburbs.
▲ Population of entire district, including rural area.

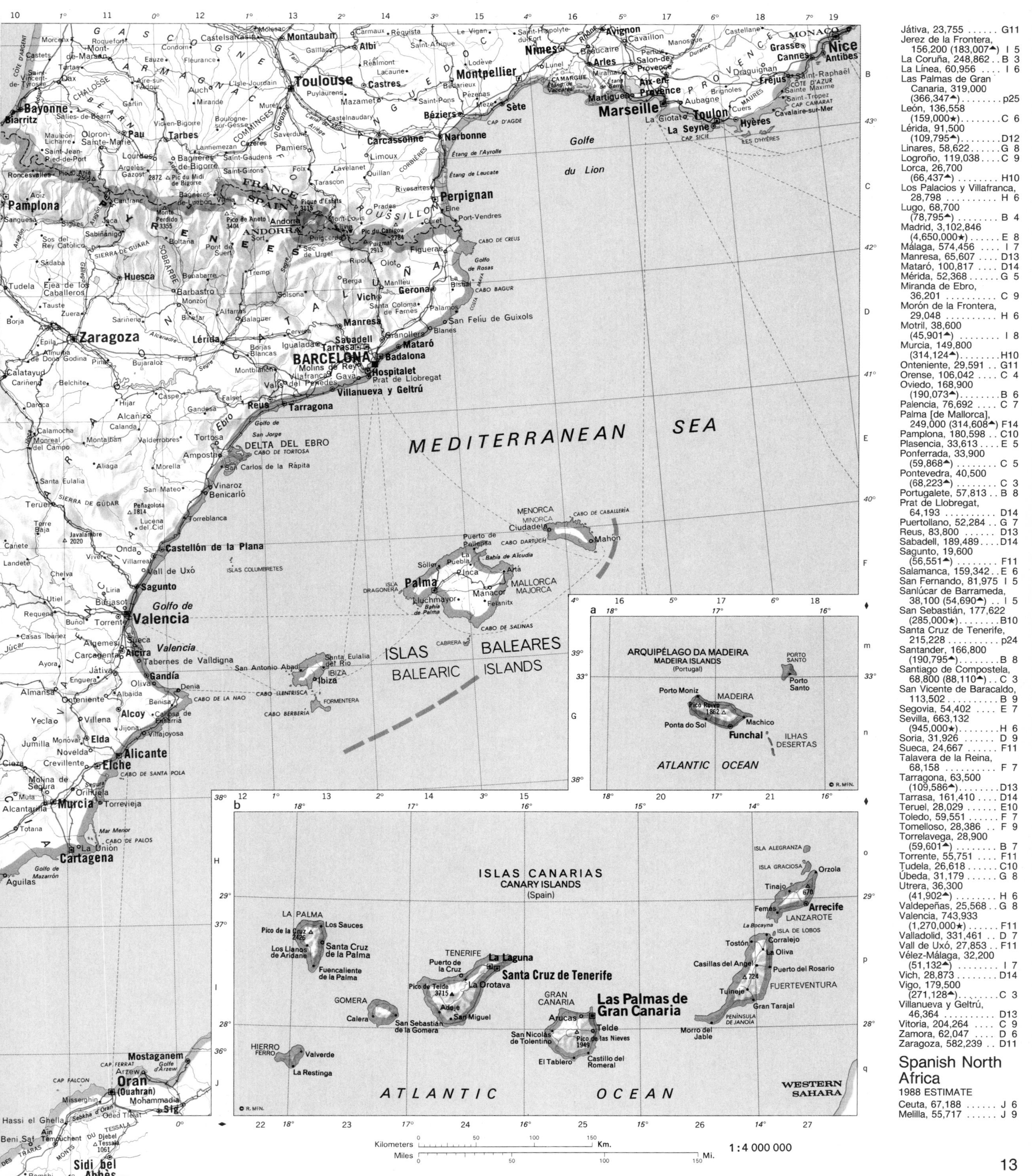

Játiva, 23,755 ...... G11
Jerez de la Frontera, 156,200 (183,007▲) I 5
La Coruña, 248,862 .. B 3
La Línea, 60,956 .... I 6
Las Palmas de Gran Canaria, 319,000 (366,347▲) p25
León, 136,558 (159,000★)........C 6
Lérida, 91,500 (109,795▲)........D12
Linares, 58,622......G 8
Logroño, 119,038....C 9
Lorca, 26,700 (66,437▲) H10
Los Palacios y Villafranca, 28,798 .... H 6
Lugo, 68,700 (78,795▲) .... B 4
Madrid, 3,102,846 (4,650,000★) ...... E 8
Málaga, 574,456 .... I 7
Manresa, 65,607 .... D13
Mataró, 100,817 .... D14
Mérida, 52,368 ...... G 5
Miranda de Ebro, 36,201 .... C 9
Morón de la Frontera, 29,048 .... H 6
Motril, 38,600 (45,901▲) .... I 8
Murcia, 149,800 (314,124▲)........H10
Onteniente, 29,591 .. G11
Orense, 106,042 .... C 4
Oviedo, 168,900 (190,073▲)........B 6
Palencia, 76,692 .... C 7
Palma [de Mallorca], 249,000 (314,608▲) F14
Pamplona, 180,598 .. C10
Plasencia, 33,613 .... E 5
Ponferrada, 33,900 (59,868▲) .... C 5
Pontevedra, 40,500 (68,223▲) .... C 3
Portugalete, 57,813 .. B 8
Prat de Llobregat, 64,193 .... D14
Puertollano, 52,284 .. G 7
Reus, 83,800 ...... D13
Sabadell, 189,489....D14
Sagunto, 19,600 (56,551▲) F11
Salamanca, 159,342 .. E 6
San Fernando, 81,975 I 5
Sanlúcar de Barrameda, 38,100 (54,690▲) .. I 5
San Sebastián, 177,622 (285,000★)........B10
Santa Cruz de Tenerife, 215,228 .... p24
Santander, 166,800 (190,795▲)........B 8
Santiago de Compostela, 68,800 (88,110▲) .. C 3
San Vicente de Baracaldo, 113,502 .... B 9
Segovia, 54,402 .... E 7
Sevilla, 663,132 (945,000★)........H 6
Soria, 31,926 ...... D 9
Sueca, 24,667 ...... F11
Talavera de la Reina, 68,158 .... F 7
Tarragona, 63,500 (109,586▲)........D13
Tarrasa, 161,410 .... D14
Teruel, 28,029 ...... E10
Toledo, 59,551 ...... F 7
Tomelloso, 28,386 ... F 9
Torrelavega, 28,900 (59,601▲) .... B 7
Torrente, 55,751 .... F11
Tudela, 26,618 ...... C10
Úbeda, 31,179 ...... G 8
Utrera, 36,300 (41,902▲) .... H 6
Valdepeñas, 25,568 .. G 8
Valencia, 743,933 (1,270,000★) F11
Valladolid, 331,461 .. D 7
Vall de Uxó, 27,853 .. F11
Vélez-Málaga, 32,200 (51,132▲) .... I 7
Vich, 28,873 .... D14
Vigo, 179,500 (271,128▲)..........C 3
Villanueva y Geltrú, 46,364 .... D13
Vitoria, 204,264 .... C 9
Zamora, 62,047 .... D 6
Zaragoza, 582,239 .. D11

Spanish North Africa

1988 ESTIMATE

Ceuta, 67,188 ...... J 6
Melilla, 55,717 ...... J 9

Italy

1987 ESTIMATE

Acireale, 46,997 ...... L10
Agrigento, 41,200 (54,600▲) .... L 8
Alcamo, 43,072 ...... L 7
Alessandria, 76,100 (96,014▲) .... E 3
Altamura, 54,784 ...... I11
Ancona, 104,409 ...... F 8
Andria, 88,348 .... H11
Anzio, 30,806 .... H 7
Aosta, 36,856 .... D 2
Arezzo, 74,200 (91,681▲) .... F 6
Ascoli Piceno, 43,600 (53,281▲) .... G 8
Asti, 63,600 (75,459▲) E 3
Avellino, 56,407 .... I 9
Bagheria, 43,725 ...... K 8
Bari, 362,524 (475,000★) H11
Barletta, 86,954 ...... H11
Benevento, 54,400 (65,661▲) .... H 9
Bergamo, 118,959 (345,000★) .... D 4
Bisceglie, 47,771 ...... H11
Bologna, 432,406 (525,000★) .... E 6
Bolzano (Bozen), 101,515 .... C 6
Brescia, 199,286 ...... D 5
Brindisi, 92,280 ...... I12
Busto Arsizio, 78,056 .. D 3
Cagliari, 220,574 (305,000★) .... J 4
Caltanissetta, 62,352 .. L 9
Carrara, 69,229 ...... E 5
Caserta, 65,974 ...... H 9
Castellammare [di Stabia], 68,491 .... I 9
Catania, 372,486 (550,000★) L10
Catanzaro, 102,558 .... K11
Cerignola, 53,463 .... H10
Cesena, 72,600 (90,012▲) .... E 7
Civitavecchia, 50,806 .. G 6
Como, 91,738 (165,000★) .... D 4
Cosenza, 106,026 (150,000★) J11
Cremona, 76,979 ...... D 5
Ferrara, 113,300 (143,950▲) .... E 6
Firenze (Florence), 425,835 (640,000★) .... F 6
Foggia, 155,051 ...... H10
Forlì, 91,200 (110,482▲) E 7
Gela, 79,378 .... L 9
Genova (Genoa), 727,427 (805,000★) .... E 3
Grosseto, 56,400 (70,592▲) .... G 6
Iesi, 40,855 .... F 8
Imola, 48,200 (61,587▲) E 6
Imperia, 41,481 ...... F 3
La Spezia, 108,937 (185,000★) .... E 4
Latina, 67,800 (98,479▲) .... H 7
Lecce, 100,981 .... I13
Lecco, 48,844 .... D 4
Livorno (Leghorn), 174,065 .... F 5
Lodi, 42,460 .... D 4
Lucca, 88,024 .... F 5
Macerata, 34,400 (43,719▲) .... F 8
Manfredonia, 57,707 .. H10
Marsala, 80,468 ...... L 7
Massa, 66,872 (145,000★) .... E 5
Messina, 268,896 .... K10
Mestre, 189,700 ...... D 7
Milano (Milan), 1,495,260 (3,750,000★) .... D 4
Modena, 176,880 .... E 5
Molfetta, 64,519 ...... H11
Monza, 122,064 ...... D 4
Napoli (Naples), 1,204,211 (2,875,000★) .... I 9
Novara, 102,742 ...... D 3

★ Population of metropolitan area, including suburbs. ▲ Population of entire district, including rural area.

- Padova, 225,769 (270,000★) . . . . D 6
- Palermo, 723,732 . . . . K 8
- Parma, 175,842 . . . . . E 5
- Pavia, 82,065 . . . . D 4
- Perugia, 106,700 (146,713▲) . . . . F 7
- Pesaro, 78,700 (90,336▲) . . . . F 7
- Pescara, 131,027 . . . . G 9
- Piacenza, 105,626 . . . . D 4
- Pisa, 104,384 . . . . F 5
- Pistoia, 76,800 (90,689▲) . . . . F 5
- Pozzuoli, 65,000 . . . . . . I 9
- Prato, 164,595 (215,000★) . . . . F 6
- Ragusa, 67,748 . . . . . . M 9
- Ravenna, 86,500 (136,016▲) . . . . E 7
- Reggio di Calabria, 178,821 . . . . K10
- Reggio nell'emilia, 107,300 (130,086▲) . . . . E 5
- Rimini, 114,600 (130,698▲) . . . . E 7
- Roma (Rome), 2,815,457 (3,175,000★) . . . . . . H 7
- Salerno, 154,848 (250,000★). . . . . I 9
- San Remo, 60,797 . . . . F 2
- Sassari, 120,152 . . . . . . I 3
- Savona, 62,300 (112,000★) . . . . E 3
- Siracusa, 122,857 . . . . L10
- Taranto, 244,997 . . . . . . I12
- Terni, 94,500 (111,157▲) . . . . G 7
- Torino (Turin), 1,035,565 (1,550,000★) . . . . . . D 2
- Trapani, 63,000 (73,083▲). . . . . K 7
- Trento, 81,500 (100,202▲) . . . . C 6
- Treviso, 85,083 . . . . . . D 7
- Trieste, 239,031 . . . . . . D 8
- Udine, 100,211 (126,000★) . . . . C 8
- Varese, 88,353 . . . . . . D 3
- Venezia (Venice), 88,700 (420,000★) . . . . D 7
- Verona, 259,151 . . . . . . D 6
- Vicenza, 110,449. . . . . . D 6
- Vigevano, 62,671 . . . . D 3
- Viterbo, 47,900 (59,267▲). . . . . G 7

Malta
1989 ESTIMATE

- Valletta, 9,210 (215,000★) . . . . N 9

San Marino
1988 ESTIMATE

- San Marino, 2,777 . . . . F 7

Vatican City
1988 ESTIMATE

- Vatican City, 766. . . . . .H 7

Yugoslavia
1987 ESTIMATE

- Banja Luka, 130,900 (193,890▲) E12
- Ljubljana, 233,200 (316,607▲) . . . . C 9
- Maribor, 107,400 (187,651▲) C10
- Mostar, 47,606('71). . . . F12
- Osijek, 106,800 (162,490▲) D13
- Rijeka, 166,400 (199,282▲) . . . . D 9
- Sarajevo, 341,200 (479,688▲) F13
- Sisak, 38,421('71) D11
- Split, 191,074 . . . . F11
- Tuzla, 67,300 (129,967▲) E13
- Zadar, 43,187('71) E10
- Zagreb, 697,925 . . . . . . D10
- Zenica, 67,500 (144,869▲) E12

Albania
1987 ESTIMATE

Berat, 40,500 . . . . I 3
Durrës, 78,700 . . . . . . H 3
Elbasan, 78,300 . . . . . . H 4
Fier, 40,300 . . . . I 3
Korçë, 61,500 . . . . I 4
Shkodër, 76,300 . . . . G 3
Tiranë, 255,700 . . . . . . H 3
Vlorë, 67,700 . . . . I 3

Bulgaria
1986 ESTIMATE

Asenovgrad, 47,143('85) . . . . . . G 8
Burgas, 186,369 . . . . G11
Dimitrovgrad, 54,898 . . G 9
Gabrovo, 81,688 . . . . G 9
Haskovo, 89,273 . . . . H 9
Jambol, 92,321 . . . . . . G10
Kărdžali, 56,906 . . . . . H 9
Kazanlăk, 61,780 . . . . G 9
Kjustendil, 54,773 . . . . G 6
Lom, 32,121 . . . . F 7
Loveč, 48,862('85) . . . . F 8
Mihajlovgrad, 53,529 . . F 7
Pazardžik, 79,198 . . . . G 8
Pernik, 96,277 . . . . . . G 7
Pleven, 132,206 . . . . . . F 8
Plovdiv, 349,148 . . . . G 8
Razgrad, 51,277 . . . . . F10
Ruse, 186,428 . . . . . . F 9
Silistra, 54,627 . . . . . . E11
Sliven, 104,345 . . . . . . G10
Sofija (Sofia), 1,119,152 (1,205,000★) . . . . . . G 7
Stanke Dimitrov, 42,153('85) . . . . . . G 7
Stara Zagora, 153,538 G 9
Šumen, 102,886 . . . . . . F10
Târgovište, 46,522('85) F10
Tolbuhin, 110,471 . . . . F11
Varna, 303,071 . . . . . . F11
Veliko Târnovo, 70,610 F 9
Vidin, 63,813 . . . . F 6
Vraca, 77,934 . . . . . . F 7

Greece
1981 CENSUS

Agrínion, 35,774 (45,087★) . . . . K 5
Athínai (Athens), 885,737 (3,027,331★) . . . . . . L 7
Ioánnina, 44,829 . . . . . . J 4
Iráklion, 102,398 (110,958★) . . . . N 9
Kalámai, 42,075 (43,235★) . . . . L 6
Kavála, 56,375 . . . . . . I 8
Kérkira (Corfu), 33,561 . . . . J 3
Khalkís, 44,867 . . . . . . K 7
Khaniá, 47,451 (61,976★) . . . . N 8
Kórinthos (Corinth), 22,658 . . . . L 6
Lamía, 41,667 . . . . . . K 6
Lárisa, 102,048 . . . . . . J 6
Pátrai, 142,163 (154,596★) . . . . K 5
Piraiévs (Piraeus), 196,389 . . . . L 7
Ródhos (Rhodes), 40,392 . . . . M12
Sérrai, 45,213 . . . . . . H 7
Thessaloníki (Salonika), 406,413 (706,180★) . . . . I 6
Tríkala, 40,857 . . . . . . J 5
Véroia, 37,087 . . . . I 6
Vólos, 71,378 (107,407★) . . . . J 6

Romania
1986 ESTIMATE

Arad, 187,744 . . . . . . C 5
Bacău, 179,877 . . . . . . C10
Baia-Mare, 139,704 . . B 7
Brăila, 235,620 . . . . . . D11
Brașov, 351,493 . . . . D 9
București (Bucharest), 1,989,823 (2,275,000★) E10
Buzău, 136,080 . . . . . . D10

★ Population of metropolitan area, including suburbs. ▲ Population of entire district, including rural area.

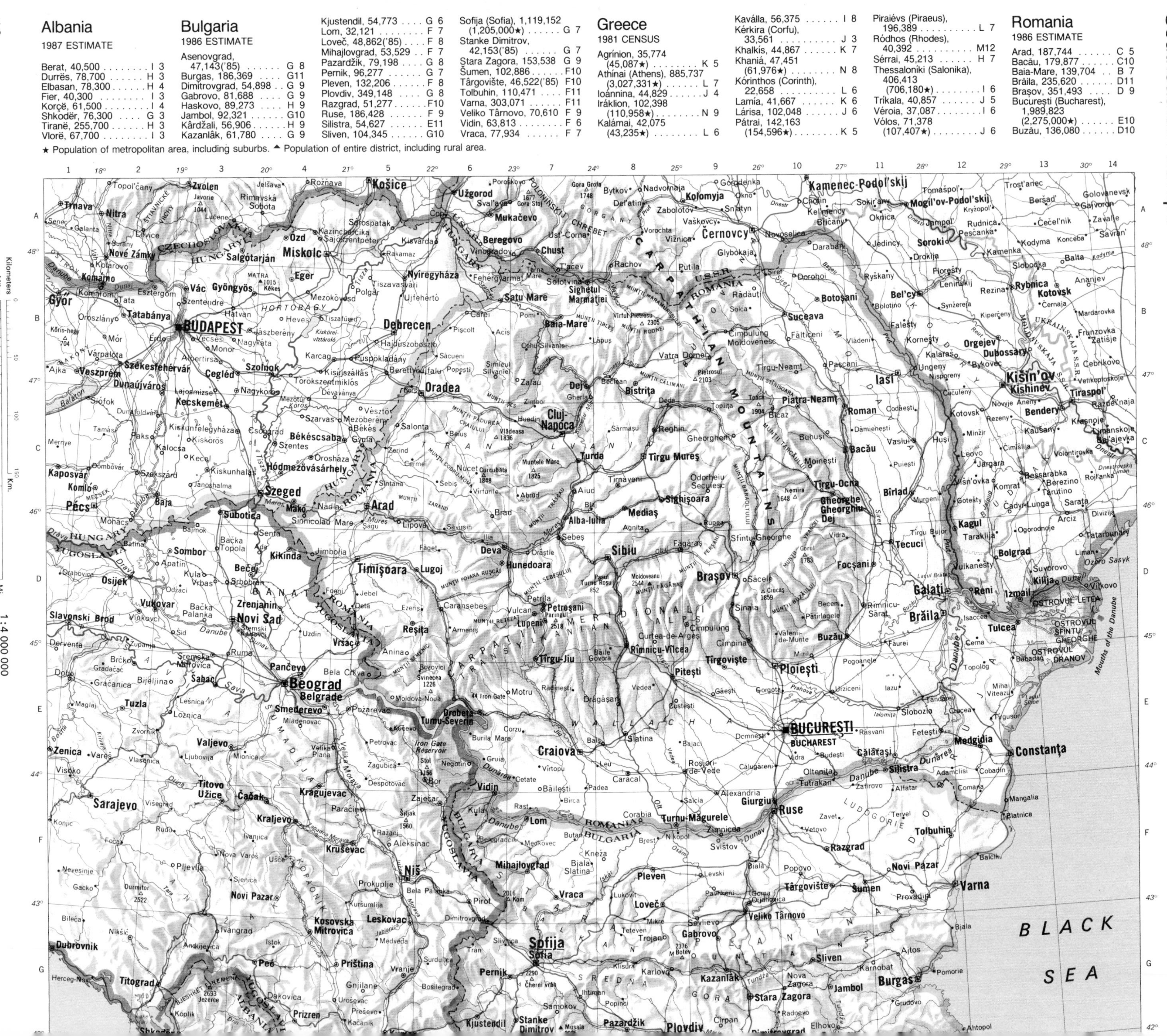

Cluj-Napoca, 310,017 . . C 7
Constanța, 327,676 . . E12
Craiova, 281,044 . . . . E 7
Galați, 295,372 . . . . . . D12
Iași, 313,060 . . . . B11
Oradea, 213,846 . . . . B 5
Ploiești, 234,886
(310,000★) E10
Satu Mare, 130,082 . . B 6
Sibiu, 177,511 . . . . . . D 8
Timișoara, 325,272 . . . D 5
Tîrgu Mureș, 158,998 . . C 8

Turkey

1990 CENSUS

Bursa, 838,323 . . . . . . I13
Denizli, 203,130 . . . . . . L13
İstanbul, 6,748,435
(7,000,000★) H12
İzmir, 2,553,209
(1,620,000★) K11
Manisa, 158,283 . . . . K11
Ödemiș, 511,110 . . . . K11
Uşak, 104,980 . . . . . . K13

Yugoslavia

1987 ESTIMATE

Beograd (Belgrade),
1,130,000
(1,400,000★) . . . . . . E 4
Niš, 168,400 (240,219▲) F 5
Novi Sad, 176,000
(266,772▲) . . . . D 3
Pančevo, 62,700 . . . . E 4
Priština, 125,400
(244,830▲) . . . . G 5
Sarajevo, 341,200
(479,688▲) . . . . F 2
Skopje, 444,900
(547,214▲) . . . . H 5
Subotica, 100,500
(153,306▲) . . . . C 3
Titograd, 82,500
(145,163▲) . . . . G 3
Zenica, 67,500
(144,869▲) . . . . E 1
Zrenjanin, 65,400
(140,009▲) . . . . D 4

Western and Central Soviet Union

Union of Soviet Socialist Republics

1989 CENSUS

Akt'ubinsk, 253,000 . . G 9
Alma-Ata, 1,128,000 (1,190,000★) I13
Andižan, 293,000 . . . . I12
Angarsk, 266,000 . . . . G18
Archangel'sk, 416,000 E 6
Aščhabad, 398,000 . . J 9
Astrachan', 509,000 . . H 7
Baku, 1,150,000 (2,020,000★) . . . . . . I 7
Barnaul, 602,000 (665,000★) G14
Belgorod, 300,000 . . G 5
Berezniki, 201,000 . . F 9
Bijsk, 233,000 . . . . . . G15
Bobrujsk, 223,000 . . G 3
Br'ansk, 452,000 . . . . G 4
Bratsk, 255,000 . . . . F18
Brest, 258,000 . . . . . . G 2
Buchara, 224,000 . . . . J10
Čeboksary, 420,000 . . F 7
Čel'abinsk, 1,143,000 (1,325,000★) F10
Čelinograd, 277,000 . . G12
Čeremchovo, 73,000('87) G18
Čerepovec, 310,000 . . F 5
Čerkassy, 290,000 . . H 4
Černigov, 296,000 . . G 4
Černovcy, 257,000 . . H 3
Char'kov, 1,611,000 (1,940,000★) . . . . . . G 5
Cherson, 355,000 . . . . H 4
Čimkent, 393,000 . . . . I11
Čita, 366,000 . . . . . . G20
Dneprodzeržinsk, 282,000 . . . . H 4
Dnepropetrovsk, 1,179,000 (1,600,000★) . . . . . . H 4
Doneck, 1,110,000 (2,200,000★) . . . . . . H 5
Dušanbe, 595,000 . . . . J11
Džambul, 307,000 . . . . I12
Dzeržinsk, 285,000 . . F 6
Fergana, 200,000 . . . . I12
Frunze, 616,000 . . . . . . I12
Gjandža, 278,000 . . . . I 7
Gomel', 500,000 . . . . G 4
Gor'kij *see* Nižnij Novgorod . . . . F 6
Gorlovka, 337,000 (710,000★) . . . . H 5
Grodno, 270,000 . . . . G 2
Groznyj, 401,000 . . . . I 7
Irkutsk, 626,000 . . . . G18
Ivano-Frankovsk, 214,000 . . . . H 2
Ivanovo, 481,000 . . . . F 6
Iževsk, 635,000 . . . . . . F 8
Jalta, 89,000('87) . . . . I 4
Jaroslavl', 633,000 . . F 5
Jerevan, 1,199,000 (1,315,000★) . . . . . . I 6
Joškar-Ola, 242,000 . . F 7
Kaliningrad, 401,000 G 2
Kaluga, 312,000 . . . . G 5
Kamensk-Ural'skij, 209,000 . . . . F10
Karaganda, 614,000 . . H12
Kaunas, 423,000 . . . . G 2
Kazan', 1,094,000 (1,140,000★) . . . . . . F 7
Kemerovo, 520,000 . . F15
Kijev (Kiev), 2,587,000 (2,900,000★) . . . . . . G 4
Kirov, 441,000 . . . . . . F 7
Kirovograd, 269,000 . . H 4
Kišin'ov, 665,000 . . . . H 3
Klaipėda, 204,000 . . . . F 2
Kostroma, 278,000 . . F 6
Krasnodar, 620,000 . . H 5
Krasnojarsk, 912,000 F16
Kremenčug, 236,000 H 4
Krivoj Rog, 713,000 . . H 4
Kurgan, 356,000 . . . . F11
Kursk, 424,000 . . . . . . G 5
Kustanaj, 224,000 . . G10
Kutaisi, 235,000 . . . . . . I 6
Leningrad, 4,456,000 (5,825,000★) . . . . . . F 4
Leninsk-Kuzneckij, 165,000 . . . . G15
Lipeck, 450,000 . . . . G 5
Luck, 198,000 . . . . . . G 3
Lugansk, 497,000 . . . . H 5
L'vov, 790,000 . . . . . . H 2
Machačkala, 315,000 . . I 7
Magnitogorsk, 440,000 . . . . G 9
Mariupol' (Ždanov), 517,000 . . . . H 5
Minsk, 1,589,000 (1,650,000★) . . . . . . G 3
Mogil'ov, 356,000 . . . . G 4
Moskva (Moscow), 8,769,000 (13,100,000★) . . . . F 5

★ Population of metropolitan area, including suburbs.

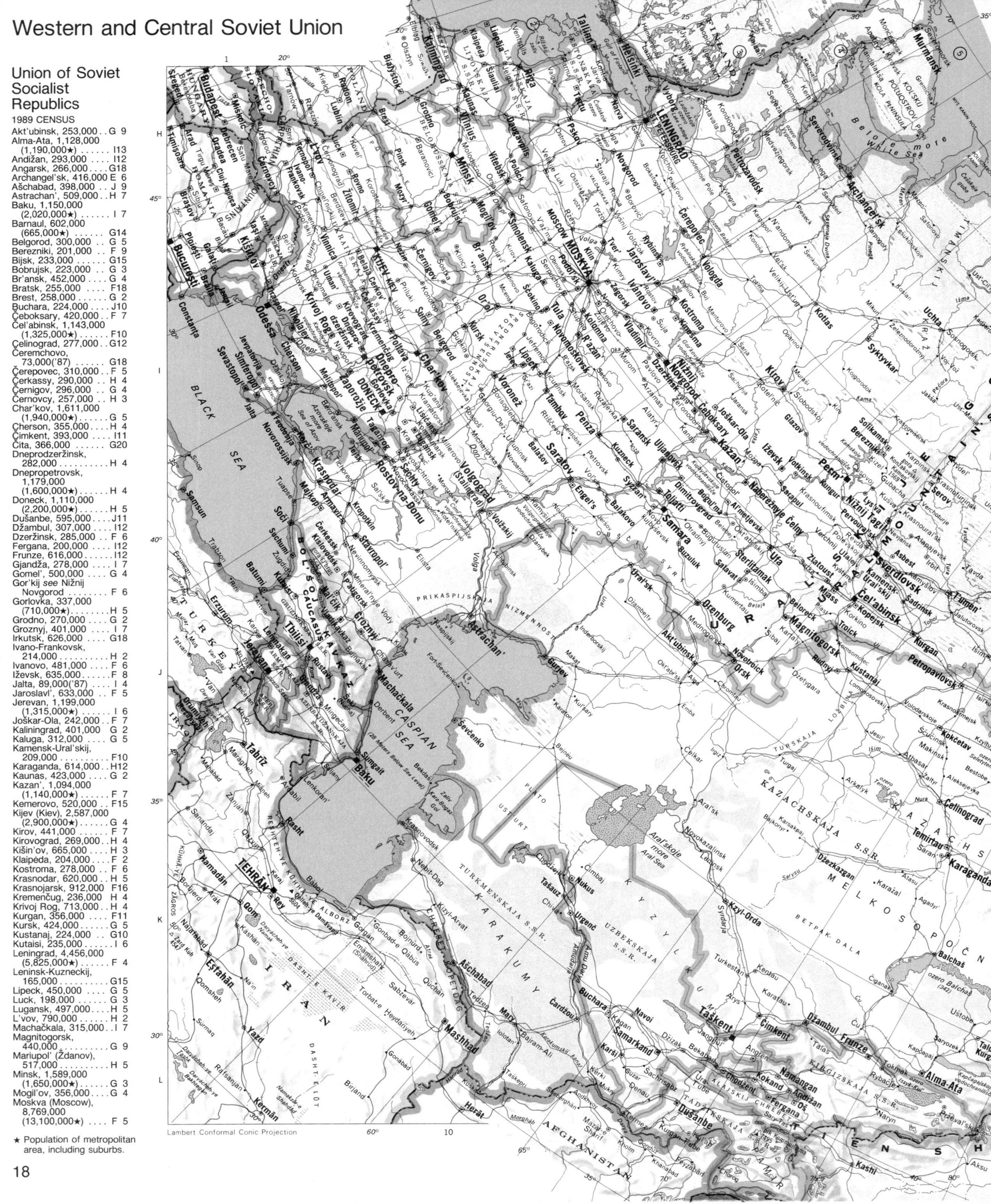

Murmansk, 468,000 . . D 4
Naberežnyje Čelny, 501,000 . . . . F 8
Nal'čik, 235,000 . . . . . . I 6
Namangan, 308,000 . . I12
Nikolajev, 503,000 . . H 4
Nižnij Novgorod (Gor'kij), 1,438,000 (2,025,000★) . . . . . . F 6
Nižnij Tagil, 440,000 . . F 9
Novgorod, 229,000 . . F 4
Novokuzneck, 600,000 . . . . G15
Novomoskovsk, 146,000 (365,000★) . . . . . . G 5
Novorossijsk, 186,000 I 5
Novosibirsk, 1,436,000 (1,600,000★) F14
Odessa, 1,115,000 (1,185,000★) . . . . . . H 4
Omsk, 1,148,000 (1,175,000★) F12
Orenburg, 547,000 . . G 9
Or'ol, 337,000 . . . . . . G 5
Orsk, 271,000 . . . . . . G 9
Oš, 213,000 . . . . I12
Pavlodar, 331,000 . . G13
Penza, 543,000 . . . . G 7
Perm', 1,091,000 (1,160,000★) . . . . . . F 9
Petropavlovsk, 241,000 . . . . G11
Petrozavodsk, 270,000 . . . . E 4
Podol'sk, 210,000 . . . . F 5
Poltava, 315,000 . . . . H 4
Prokopjevsk, 274,000 (410,000★) G15
Pskov, 204,000 . . . . . . F 3
R'azan', 515,000 . . . . G 5
Rīga, 915,000 (1,005,000★) . . . . . . F 2
Rostov-na-Donu, 1,020,000 (1,165,000★) . . . . . . H 5
Rovno, 228,000 . . . . G 3
Rubcovsk, 172,000 . . G14
Rybinsk, 252,000 . . . . F 5
Šachty, 224,000 . . . . H 6
Samara, 1,257,000 (1,505,000★) . . . . . . G 8
Samarkand, 366,000 . . J11
Saransk, 312,000 . . . . G 7
Saratov, 905,000 (1,155,000★) . . . . . . G 7
Semipalatinsk, 334,000 . . . . G14
Sevastopol', 356,000 . . I 4
Severodvinsk, 249,000 E 5
Simferopol', 344,000 . . I 4
Smolensk, 341,000 . . G 4
Soči, 337,000 . . . . I 5
Stalingrad *see* Volgograd . . . . H 6
Stavropol', 318,000 . . H 6
Sterlitamak, 248,000 G 9
Sumgait, 231,000 . . . . I 7
Sumy, 291,000 . . . . . . G 4
Surgut, 248,000 . . . . E12
Sverdlovsk, 1,367,000 (1,620,000★) F10
Syktyvkar, 233,000 . . E 8
Syzran', 174,000 . . . . G 7
Taganrog, 291,000 . . H 5
Tallinn, 482,000 . . . . . . F 2
Tambov, 305,000 . . . . G 6
Taškent, 2,073,000 (2,325,000★) I11
Tbilisi, 1,260,000 (1,460,000★) . . . . . . I 6
Temirtau, 212,000 . . G12
Ternopol', 205,000 . . H 3
Tiraspol', 182,000 . . . . H 3
Toljatti, 630,000 . . . . G 7
Tomsk, 502,000 . . . . F14
Tula, 540,000 (640,000★) . . . . . . G 5
T'umen', 477,000 . . . . F11
Tver' (Kalinin), 451,000 F 5
Ufa, 1,083,000 (1,100,000★) . . . . . . G 9
Ulan-Ude, 353,000 . . G19
Uljanovsk, 625,000 . . G 7
Ural'sk, 200,000 . . . . G 8
Usolje-Sibirskoje, 107,000 . . . . G18
Ust'-Kamenogorsk, 324,000 . . . . H14
Vilnius, 582,000 . . . . . . F 3
Vinnica, 374,000 . . . . H 3
Vitebsk, 350,000 . . . . F 4
Vladikavkaz, 300,000 . . I 6
Vladimir, 350,000 . . . . F 6
Volgograd (Stalingrad), 999,000 (1,360,000★) . . . . . . H 6
Vologda, 283,000 . . . . F 5
Volžskij, 269,000 . . . . H 6
Voronež, 887,000 . . . . G 5
Yalta *see* Jalta . . . . . . I 4
Zaporožje, 884,000 . . H 5
Žitomir, 292,000 . . . . G 3
Zlatoust, 208,000 . . . . F 9

Kilometers 0 200 400 600 Km.
Miles 0 200 400 600 Mi.
1:16 000 000

Central and Eastern Soviet Union

Union of Soviet Socialist Republics

1989 CENSUS

Abakan, 154,000 .... G12
Ačinsk, 122,000 .... F12
Ajaguz, 40,091('79) .. H10
Alapajevsk, 51,000('87) ...... F 6
Aldan, 20,000('74) .. F19
Alejsk, 31,390('79) .. G10
Aleksandrovsk-Sachalinskij, 20,000('74) G22
Alma-Ata, 1,128,000 (1,190,000★) ...... I 9
Angarsk, 266,000 .... G14
Anžero-Sudžensk, 108,000 .... F11
Arsenjev, 67,000('87) .. I20
Art'om, 73,000('87) .. I20
Asbest, 83,000('87) .. F 6
Asino, 31,329('79) ... F11
Atbasar, 35,787('79) G 7
Balchaš, 84,000('87) H 8
Barabinsk, 35,035('79) F 9
Barnaul, 602,000 (665,000★) G10
Belogorsk, 71,000('87) G19
Belovo, 118,000('87) G11
Berdsk, 77,000('87) .. G10
Berezniki, 201,000 .. F 5
Bijsk, 233,000 ...... G11
Birobidžan, 82,000('87) H20
Blagoveščensk, 206,000 .... G19
Bratsk, 255,000 .... F14
Čel'abinsk, 1,143,000 (1,325,000★) ...... F 6
Čelinograd, 277,000 .. G 8
Čeremchovo, 73,000('87) G14
Černogorsk, 80,000('87) G12
Chabarovsk, 601,000 H21
Chanty-Mansijsk, 27,961('79) ...... E 7
Čita, 366,000 ...... G16
Čusovoj, 59,000('87) F 5
Dudinka, 23,000('74) D11
Ekibastuz, 135,000 .. G 9
Gorno-Altajsk, 39,917('79) G11
Gubacha, 32,461('79) F 5
Igarka, 16,918('79) .. D11
Inta, 58,000('87) .... D 6
Irbit, 53,000('87) .... F 6
Irkutsk, 626,000 .... G14
Iskitim, 69,000('87) .. G10
Jakutsk, 187,000 .... E19
Jenisejsk, 22,000('79) F12
Jurga, 92,000('87) .. F10
Južno-Sachalinsk, 157,000 .... H22
Kamen'-na-Obi, 40,684('79) G10
Kamensk-Ural'skij, 209,000 .... F 6
Kansk, 110,000 ...... F13
Karaganda, 614,000 .. H 8
Karpinsk, 36,569('79) F 6
Kemerovo, 520,000 .. F11
Kirensk, 16,000('74) .. F15
Kisel'ovsk, 128,000 .. G11
Kizel, 40,157('79) .... F 5
Kokčetav, 137,000 .. G 7
Komsomol'sk-na-Amure, 315,000 .... G21
Kopejsk, 99,000('87) F 6
Korkino, 63,000('81) G 6
Korsakov, 43,348('79) H22
Krasnojarsk, 912,000 F12

★ Population of metropolitan area, including suburbs.

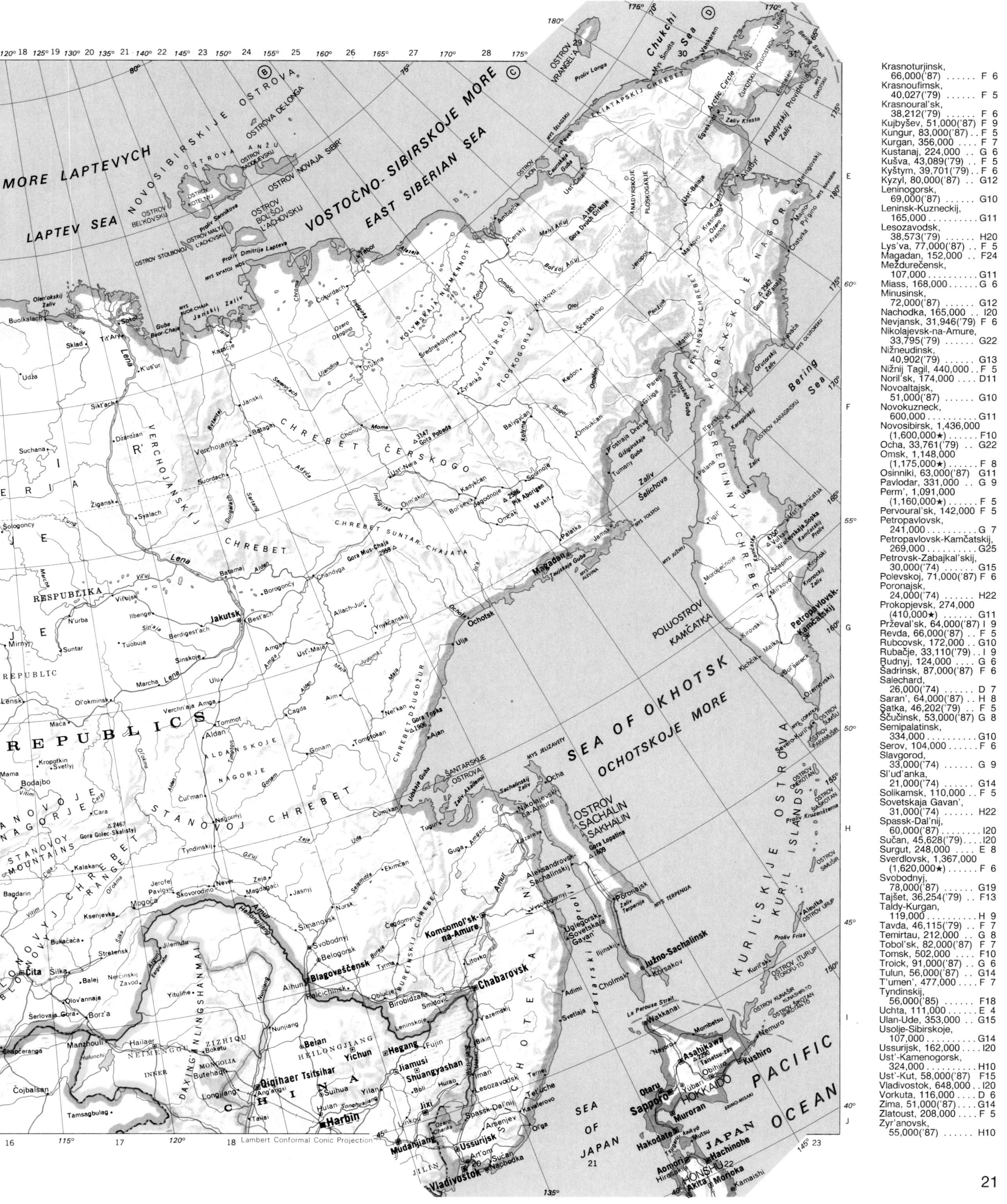

MORE LAPTEVYCH
LAPTEV SEA
NOVOSIBIRSKIJE OSTROVA
VOSTOČNO-SIBIRSKOJE MORE
EAST SIBERIAN SEA
Chukchi Sea
OSTROV VRANGEL'A
Arctic Circle
Bering Strait
Bering Sea
POLUOSTROV KAMČATKA
SEA OF OKHOTSK
OCHOTSKOJE MORE
OSTROV SACHALIN
SAKHALIN
KURIL'SKIJE OSTROVA
KURIL ISLANDS
SEA OF JAPAN
PACIFIC OCEAN
HOKKAIDO
HONSHU
JAPAN
CHINA
Magadan
Jakutsk
Chabarovsk
Komsomol'sk-na-Amure
Petropavlovsk-Kamčatskij
Vladivostok
Harbin
Blagoveščensk
Lambert Conformal Conic Projection

Krasnoturjinsk, 66,000('87) ...... F 6
Krasnoufimsk, 40,027('79) ...... F 5
Krasnoural'sk, 38,212('79) ...... F 6
Kujbyšev, 51,000('87) F 9
Kungur, 83,000('87) .. F 5
Kurgan, 356,000 .... F 7
Kustanaj, 224,000 .. G 6
Kušva, 43,089('79) .. F 5
Kyštym, 39,701('79) .. F 6
Kyzyl, 80,000('87) .. G12
Leninogorsk, 69,000('87) G10
Leninsk-Kuzneckij, 165,000 .... G11
Lesozavodsk, 38,573('79) H20
Lys'va, 77,000('87) .. F 5
Magadan, 152,000 .. F24
Meždurečensk, 107,000 .... G11
Miass, 168,000 ...... G 6
Minusinsk, 72,000('87) G12
Nachodka, 165,000 .. I20
Nevjansk, 31,946('79) F 6
Nikolajevsk-na-Amure, 33,795('79) G22
Nižneudinsk, 40,902('79) G13
Nižnij Tagil, 440,000 .. F 5
Noril'sk, 174,000 .... D11
Novoaltajsk, 51,000('87) G10
Novokuzneck, 600,000 .... G11
Novosibirsk, 1,436,000 (1,600,000★) F10
Ocha, 33,761('79) .. G22
Omsk, 1,148,000 (1,175,000★) ...... F 8
Osinniki, 63,000('87) G11
Pavlodar, 331,000 .. G 9
Perm', 1,091,000 (1,160,000★) ...... F 5
Pervoural'sk, 142,000 F 5
Petropavlovsk, 241,000 .... G 7
Petropavlovsk-Kamčatskij, 269,000 .... G25
Petrovsk-Zabajkal'skij, 30,000('74) G15
Polevskoj, 71,000('87) F 6
Poronajsk, 24,000('74) H22
Prokopjevsk, 274,000 (410,000★) G11
Prževal'sk, 64,000('87) I 9
Revda, 66,000('87) .. F 5
Rubcovsk, 172,000 .. G10
Rubačje, 33,110('79) .. I 9
Rudnyj, 124,000 .... G 6
Šadrinsk, 87,000('87) F 6
Salechard, 26,000('74) ...... D 7
Saran', 64,000('87) .. H 8
Şatka, 46,202('79) .. F 5
Ščučinsk, 53,000('87) G 8
Semipalatinsk, 334,000 .... G10
Serov, 104,000 ...... F 6
Slavgorod, 33,000('74) ...... G 9
Sl'ud'anka, 21,000('74) G14
Solikamsk, 110,000 .. F 5
Sovetskaja Gavan', 31,000('74) H22
Spassk-Dal'nij, 60,000('87) I20
Sučan, 45,628('79) I20
Surgut, 248,000 .... E 8
Sverdlovsk, 1,367,000 (1,620,000★) ...... F 6
Svobodnyj, 78,000('87) G19
Tajšet, 36,254('79) .. F13
Taldy-Kurgan, 119,000 .... H 9
Tavda, 46,115('79) .. F 7
Temirtau, 212,000 .. G 8
Tobol'sk, 82,000('87) F 7
Tomsk, 502,000 .... F10
Troick, 91,000('87) .. G 6
Tulun, 56,000('87) .. G14
T'umen', 477,000 .... F 7
Tyndinskij, 56,000('85) F18
Uchta, 111,000 ...... E 4
Ulan-Ude, 353,000 .. G15
Usolje-Sibirskoje, 107,000 .... G14
Ussurijsk, 162,000 .... I20
Ust'-Kamenogorsk, 324,000 .... H10
Ust'-Kut, 58,000('87) F15
Vladivostok, 648,000 .. I20
Vorkuta, 116,000 .... D 6
Zima, 51,000('87) G14
Zlatoust, 208,000 .... F 5
Zyr'anovsk, 55,000('87) H10

Baltic and Moscow Regions

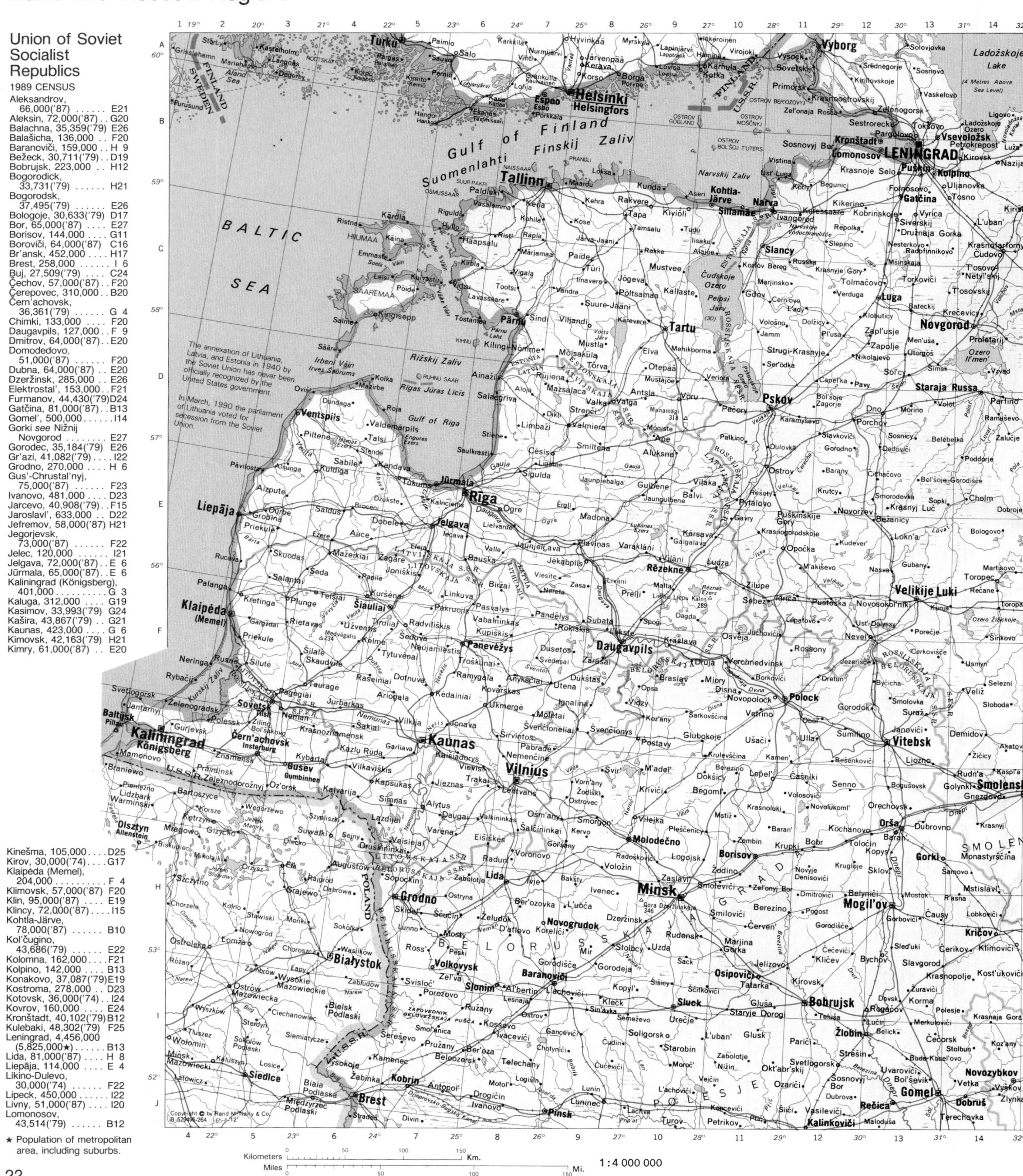

Union of Soviet Socialist Republics

1989 CENSUS

Aleksandrov, 66,000('87) E21
Aleksin, 72,000('87) .. G20
Balachna, 35,359('79) E26
Balašicha, 136,000 .. F20
Baranoviči, 159,000 .. H 9
Bežeck, 30,711('79) .. D19
Bobrujsk, 223,000 .. H12
Bogorodick, 33,731('79) H21
Bogorodsk, 37,495('79) E26
Bologoje, 30,633('79) D17
Bor, 65,000('87) E27
Borisov, 144,000 .... G11
Boroviči, 64,000('87) C16
Br'ansk, 452,000 .... H17
Brest, 258,000 ...... I 6
Buj, 27,509('79) C24
Čechov, 57,000('87) .. F20
Čerepovec, 310,000 .. B20
Čern'achovsk, 36,361('79) ...... G 4
Chimki, 133,000 .... F20
Daugavpils, 127,000 .. F 9
Dmitrov, 64,000('87) .. E20
Domodedovo, 51,000('87) F20
Dubna, 64,000('87) .. E20
Dzeržinsk, 285,000 .. E26
Elektrostal', 153,000 .. F21
Furmanov, 44,430('79) D24
Gatčina, 81,000('87) .. B13
Gomel', 500,000 ...... I14
Gorki *see* Nižnij Novgorod E27
Gorodec, 35,184('79) E26
Gr'azi, 41,082('79) I22
Grodno, 270,000 .... H 6
Gus'-Chrustal'nyj, 75,000('87) F23
Ivanovo, 481,000 .... D23
Jarcevo, 40,908('79) .. F15
Jaroslavl', 633,000 .. D22
Jefremov, 58,000('87) H21
Jegorjevsk, 73,000('87) F22
Jelec, 120,000 ...... I21
Jelgava, 72,000('87) .. E 6
Jūrmala, 65,000('87) .. E 6
Kaliningrad (Königsberg), 401,000 .... G 3
Kaluga, 312,000 .... G19
Kasimov, 33,993('79) G24
Kašira, 43,867('79) .. G21
Kaunas, 423,000 .... G 6
Kimovsk, 42,163('79) H21
Kimry, 61,000('87) .. E20
Kinešma, 105,000 .... D25
Kirov, 30,000('74) G17
Klaipėda (Memel), 204,000 .... F 4
Klimovsk, 57,000('87) F20
Klin, 95,000('87) E19
Klincy, 72,000('87) I15
Kohtla-Järve, 78,000('87) B10
Kol'čugino, 43,686('79) E22
Kolomna, 162,000 .... F21
Kolpino, 142,000 .... B13
Konakovo, 37,087('79) E19
Kostroma, 278,000 .. D23
Kotovsk, 36,000('74) .. I24
Kovrov, 160,000 .... E24
Kronštadt, 40,102('79) B12
Kulebaki, 48,302('79) F25
Leningrad, 4,456,000 (5,825,000★) B13
Lida, 81,000('87) .... H 8
Liepāja, 114,000 .... E 4
Likino-Dulevo, 30,000('74) F22
Lipeck, 450,000 ...... I22
Livny, 51,000('87) I20
Lomonosov, 43,514('79) B12

★ Population of metropolitan area, including suburbs.

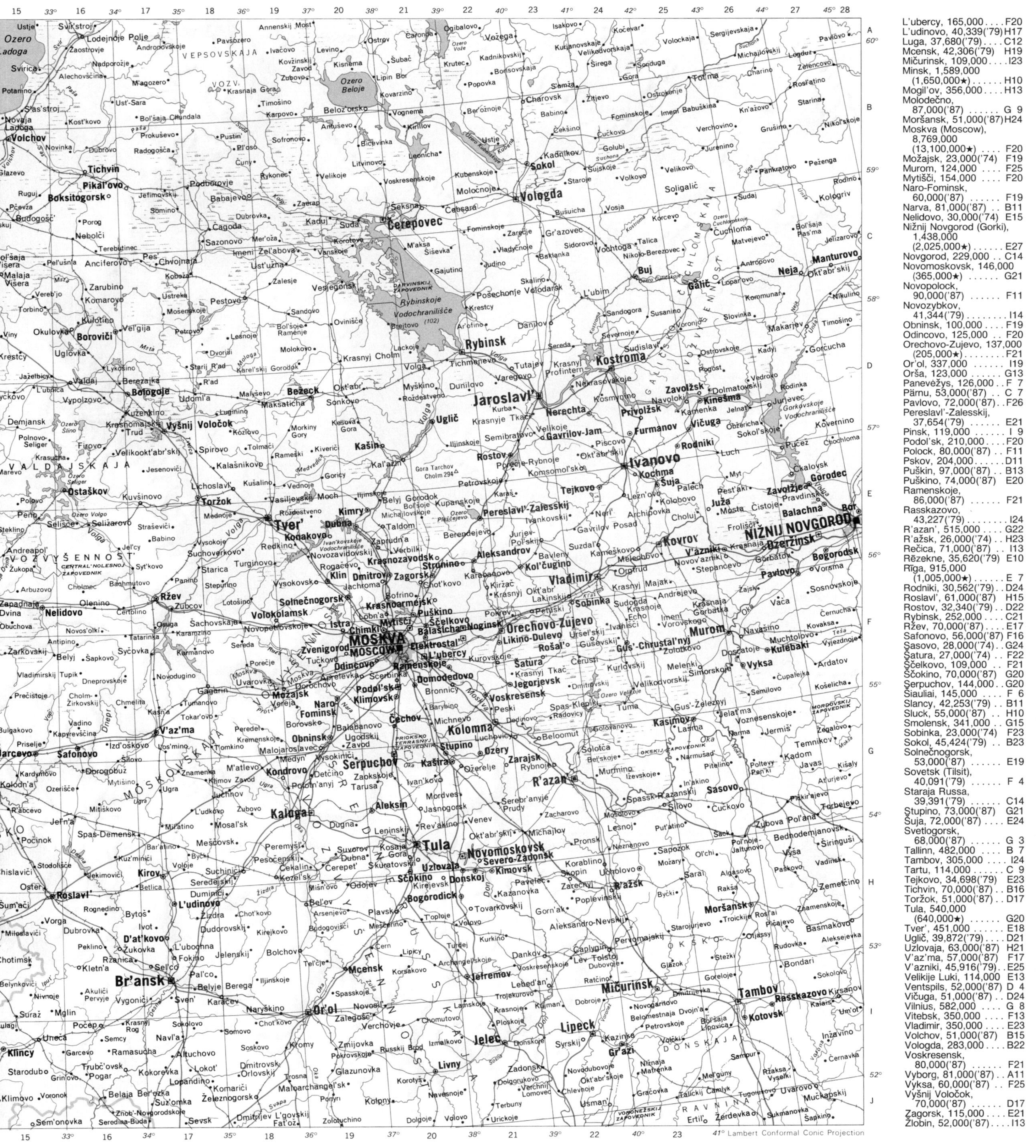

L'ubercy, 165,000 .... F20
L'udinovo, 40,339('79) H17
Luga, 37,680('79) C12
Mcensk, 42,306('79) H19
Mičurinsk, 109,000 .... I23
Minsk, 1,589,000 (1,650,000★) H10
Mogil'ov, 356,000 .... H13
Molodečno, 87,000('87) ...... G 9
Moršansk, 51,000('87) H24
Moskva (Moscow), 8,769,000 (13,100,000★) F20
Možajsk, 23,000('74) F19
Murom, 124,000 .... F25
Mytišči, 154,000 .... F20
Naro-Fominsk, 60,000('87) F19
Narva, 81,000('87) .. B11
Nelidovo, 30,000('74) E15
Nižnij Novgorod (Gorki), 1,438,000 (2,025,000★) E27
Novgorod, 229,000 .. C14
Novomoskovsk, 146,000 (365,000★) G21
Novopolock, 90,000('87) F11
Novozybkov, 41,344('79) I14
Obninsk, 100,000 .... F19
Odincovo, 125,000 .. F20
Orechovo-Zujevo, 137,000 (205,000★) F21
Or'ol, 337,000 ...... I19
Orša, 123,000 ...... G13
Panevėžys, 126,000 .. F 7
Pärnu, 53,000('87) .. C 7
Pavlovo, 72,000('87) .. F26
Pereslavl'-Zalesskij, 37,654('79) E21
Pinsk, 119,000 ...... I 9
Podol'sk, 210,000 .... F20
Polock, 80,000('87) .. F11
Pskov, 204,000 ...... D11
Puškin, 97,000('87) .. B13
Puškino, 74,000('87) E20
Ramenskoje, 86,000('87) F21
Rasskazovo, 43,227('79) I24
R'azan', 515,000 .... G22
R'ažsk, 26,000('74) .. H23
Rečica, 71,000('87) .. I13
Rēzekne, 35,620('79) E10
Rīga, 915,000 (1,005,000★) ...... E 7
Rodniki, 30,562('79) .. D24
Roslavl', 61,000('87) H15
Rostov, 32,340('79) .. D22
Rybinsk, 252,000 .... C21
Ržev, 70,000('87) E17
Safonovo, 56,000('87) F16
Şasovo, 28,000('74) .. G24
Şatura, 27,000('74) .. F22
Ščelkovo, 109,000 .. F21
Ščokino, 70,000('87) G20
Şerpuchov, 144,000 .. G20
Šiauliai, 145,000 .... F 6
Slancy, 42,253('79) .. B11
Sluck, 55,000('87) .. H10
Smolensk, 341,000 .. G15
Sobinka, 23,000('74) F23
Sokol, 45,424('79) .. B23
Solnečnogorsk, 53,000('87) E19
Sovetsk (Tilsit), 40,091('79) ...... F 4
Staraja Russa, 39,391('79) C14
Ştupino, 73,000('87) G21
Šuja, 72,000('87) E24
Svetlogorsk, 68,000('87) ...... G 3
Tallinn, 482,000 .... B 7
Tambov, 305,000 .... I24
Tartu, 114,000 ...... C 9
Tejkovo, 34,698('79) E23
Tichvin, 70,000('87) .. B16
Toržok, 51,000('87) .. D17
Tula, 540,000 (640,000★) G20
Tver', 451,000 ...... E18
Uglič, 39,872('79) D21
Uzlovaja, 63,000('87) H21
V'az'ma, 57,000('87) F17
V'azniki, 45,916('79) .. E25
Velikije Luki, 114,000 E13
Ventspils, 52,000('87) D 4
Vičuga, 51,000('87) .. D24
Vilnius, 582,000 .... G 8
Vitebsk, 350,000 .... F13
Vladimir, 350,000 .... E23
Volchov, 51,000('87) B15
Vologda, 283,000 .... B22
Voskresensk, 80,000('87) F21
Vyborg, 81,000('87) .. A11
Vyksa, 60,000('87) .. F25
Vyšnij Voločok, 70,000('87) D17
Zagorsk, 115,000 .... E21
Žlobin, 52,000('87) I13

Asia

'Adan, 176,100 ('84) (318,000★) ....H 7
AFGHANISTAN............F 9
Ahmadābād, 2,059,725 ('81) (2,400,000★) .. G10
Al Başrah, 616,700 ('85).........................F 7
Al-Kuwayt, 44,335 ('85) (1,375,000★) ....G 7
Alma-Ata, 1,128,000 ('89) (1,190,000★) E10
Al-Madīnah, 290,000 ('80)......................... G 6
'Ammān, 936,300 ('89) (1,450,000★) .... F 6
Ankara, 2,553,209 ('90) (2,670,000★) .... F 6
Ar-Riyāḍ, 1,250,000 ('80)......................... G 7
Aščhabad, 398,000 ('89).........................F 8
Baghdād, 3,841,268 ('87).........................F 7
Bangalore, 2,476,355 ('81) (2,950,000★) H10
Bangkok see Krung Thep........................ H13
BANGLADESH............G12
Bayrūt, 509,000 ('82) (1,675,000★) .... F 6
Beijing (Peking), 6,710,000 ('88) (6,450,000★) F14
BHUTAN.....................G12
Bombay, 8,243,405 ('81) (9,950,000★) H10
BRUNEI........................I14
BURMA.......................G12
Calcutta, 3,305,006 ('81) (11,100,000★) H11
CAMBODIA.................H13
Canton see Guangzhou.............. G14
Chabarovsk, 601,000 ('89)........................E16
Changchun, 1,822,000 ('88) (2,000,000▲) ...E15
Changsha, 1,230,000 ('88)......................... G14
Chengdu, 1,884,000 ('88) (2,960,000▲) F13
CHINA..........................F12
Chongqing (Chungking), 2,502,000 ('88) (2,890,000▲) G13
Čita, 366,000 ('89)...... D14
Colombo, 683,000 ('86) (2,050,000★) I10
CYPRUS...................... F 6
CYPRUS, NORTH........F 6
Dacca see Dhaka........G12
Dalian, 2,280,000 ('88).........F15
Damascus see Dimashq.................. F 6
Da Nang, 318,653 ('79)......................... H13
Delhi, 4,884,234 ('81) (7,200,000★) G10
Dhaka (Dacca), 2,365,695 ('81) (3,430,312★) G12
Dimashq (Damascus), 1,326,000 ('88) (1,950,000★) .... F 6
Dušanbe, 595,000 ('89)..........................F 9
Eşfahān, 986,753 ('86) (1,175,000★) .... F 8
Fukuoka, 1,160,440 ('85) (1,750,000★) F16
Fuzhou, 910,000 ('88) (1,240,000▲) G14
George Town, 248,241 ('80) (495,000★) I13
Guangzhou (Canton), 3,100,000 ('88) (3,420,000▲) G14
Ha Noi, 1,089,000 ('89) (1,500,000★) G13
Harbin, 2,710,000 ('88).........................E15
Hiroshima, 1,044,118 ('85) (1,575,000★) F16
HONG KONG.............. G14
Hyderābād, 2,187,262 ('81) (2,750,000★) .. H10
INDIA.......................... G10
INDONESIA.................. I13
IRAN............................ F 8
IRAQ............................F 7
Irkutsk, 626,000 ('89)..D13
Islāmābād, 204,364 ('81).........................F10
ISRAEL.......................F 6
izmir, 2,553,209 ('90) (1,620,000★) .... F 5
Jakutsk, 187,000 ('89)........... C15
JAPAN.........................F16
Jerusalem see Yerushalayim............F 6
Jiddah, 1,300,000 ('80)......................... G 6
Jinan, 1,546,000 ('88) (2,140,000▲) F14
JORDAN.....................F 6
Kābol (Kabul), 1,424,400 ('88)..........................F 9
Kānpur, 1,481,789 ('81) (1,875,000★) G11
Karāchi, 4,901,627 ('81) (5,300,000★) ....G 9
Kashi, 146,300 ('86) (194,500▲) F10
Kaṭhmāṇḍāū, 235,160 ('81) (320,000★) G11
Kermān, 257,284 ('86).F 8
Konsomol'sk-na-Amure, 315,000 ('89)........... D16
KOREA, NORTH..........E15
KOREA, SOUTH.........F15
Krasnojarsk, 912,000 ('89)......................... D12
Krung Thep (Bangkok), 5,716,779 ('88) (6,450,000★) H13
Kuala Lumpur, 919,610 ('80) (1,475,000★) I13
Kuching, 72,555 ('80)... I14
Kunming, 1,310,000 ('88) (1,550,000▲) G13

Miles 0 200 400 600 800 1000 Mi.
Kilometers 0 400 800 1200 1600 Km.
1:40 000 000

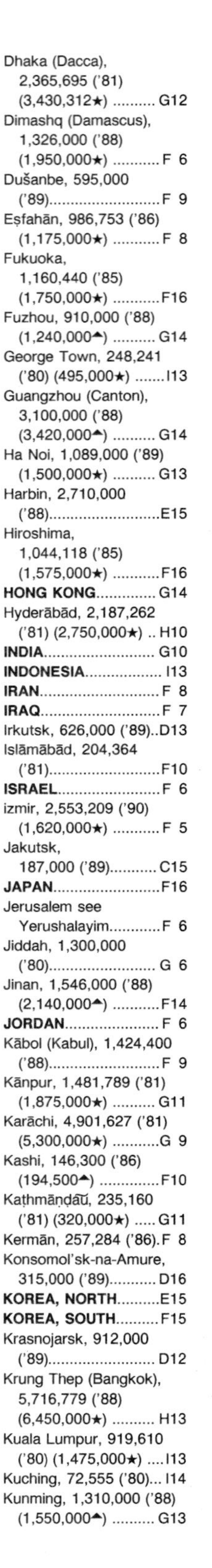

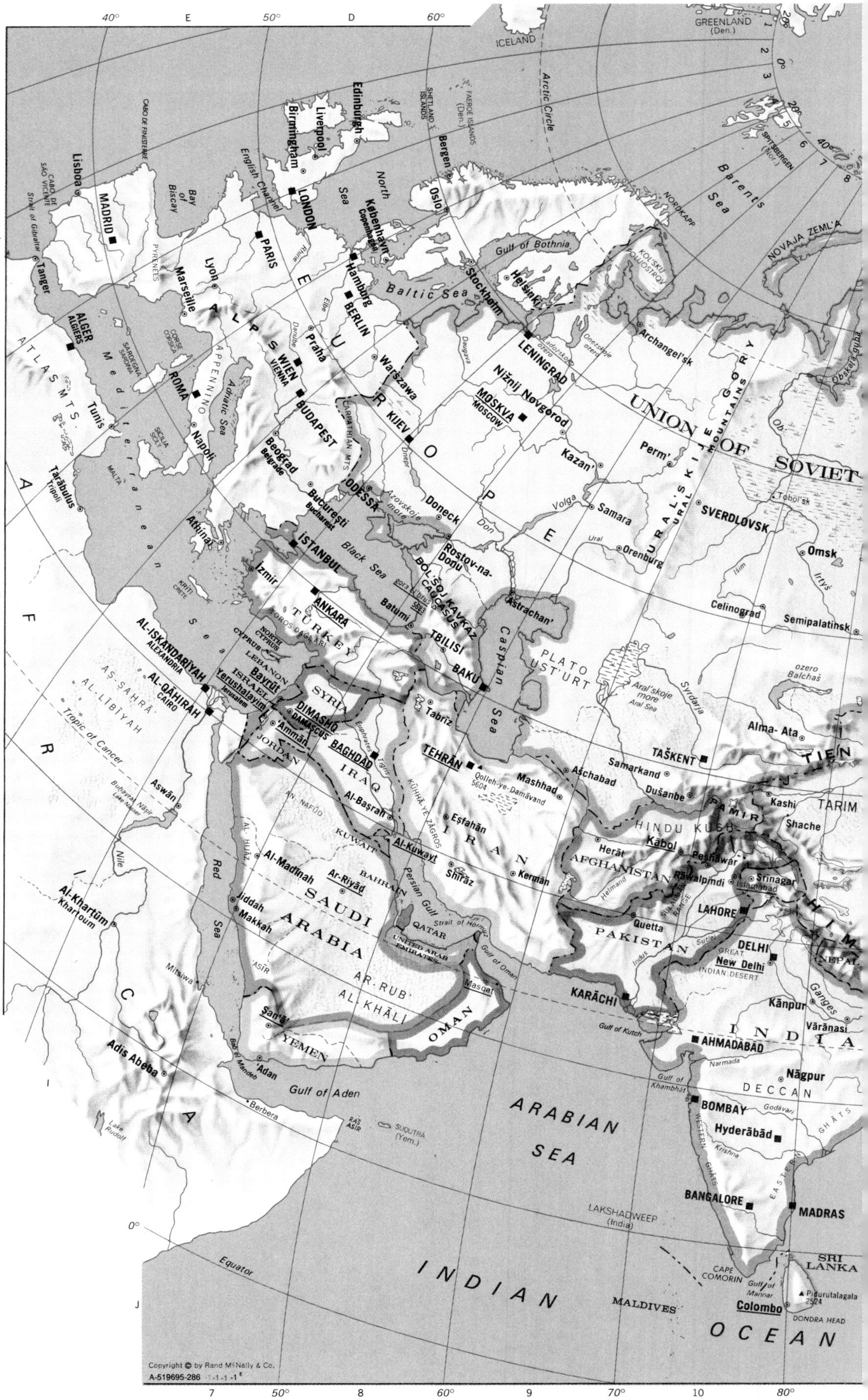

KUWAIT..................G 7
Kyōto,
1,479,218 ('85).........F16
Kyzyl, 80,000 ('87)......D12
Lahore, 2,707,215 ('81)
(3,025,000★) F10
Lanzhou, 1,297,000 ('88)
(1,420,000▲) F13
LAOS........................H13
LEBANON...................F 6
Lhasa, 84,400 ('86)
(107,700▲) G12
MACAU......................G14
Madras, 3,276,622 ('81)
(4,475,000★) H11
Makkah,
550,000 ('80).......... G 6
MALAYSIA.................. I13
MALDIVES...................I10
Mandalay, 532,949
('83)........................ G12
Manila, 1,587,000 ('90)
(6,800,000★) H15
Mashhad, 1,463,508
('86)........................F 8
Masqaţ, 50,000 ('81)...G 8
Mawlamyine, 219,961
('83)........................ H12
MONGOLIA................ E13
Nāgpur, 1,219,461 ('81)
(1,302,066★) G10
Nanjing, 2,390,000
('88)........................F14
NEPAL.......................G11
New Delhi, 273,036
('81)........................ G10
Novosibirsk,
1,436,000 ('89)
(1,600,000★) D11
OMAN........................ G 8
Omsk, 1,148,000 ('89)
(1,175,000★) D10
Ōsaka, 2,636,249 ('85)
(1,645,000★) F16
PAKISTAN..................G 9
Patna, 776,371 ('81)
(1,025,000★) G11
Peking see Beijing.......F14
Peshāwar, 506,896 ('81)
(566,248★) F10
Petropavlovsk-
Kamčatskij, 269,000
('89)........................ D18
PHILIPPINES..............H15
Phnum Penh, 700,000
('86)........................ H13
Pyŏngyang, 1,283,000
('81) (1,600,000★) ...F15
QATAR.......................G 8
Qingdao (Tsingtao),
1,300,000 ('88).........F15
Quetta, 244,842 ('81)
(285,719★) .... F 9
Quezon City, 1,632,000
('90)........................ H15
Rangoon see Yangon. H12
Rāwalpindi,
457,091 ('81)
(1,040,000★) F10
Saigon see Thanh Pho Ho
Chi Minh................. H13
Samarkand, 366,000
('89)........................F 9
Şan'ā', 427,150 ('86)...H 7
SAUDI ARABIA...........G 7

Semipalatinsk, 334,000
('89)........................ D11
Sendai, 700,254 ('85)
(1,175,000★) F17
Shanghai,
7,220,000 ('88)
(9,300,000★) F15
Shenyang (Mukden),
3,910,000 ('88)
(4,370,000▲) E15
Shīrāz, 848,289 ('86)...G 8
SINGAPORE.................I13
Sŏul, 10,522,000 ('89)
(15,850,000★) F15
SRI LANKA..................I11
Srīnagar, 594,775 ('81)
(606,002★) F10
SYRIA.........................F 6
Tabrīz, 971,482 ('86)... F 7
T'aipei, 2,637,100 ('88)
(6,130,000★) G15
TAIWAN......................G15
Taiyuan, 1,700,000 ('88)
(1,980,000▲) F14
Taškent, 2,073,000 ('89)
(2,325,000★) ....E 9
Tehrān, 6,042,584 ('86)
(7,500,000★) ....F 8
THAILAND.................. H13
Thanh Pho Ho Chi Minh
(Saigon), 3,169,000 ('89)
(3,100,000★) H13
Tianjin (Tientsin),
4,950,000 ('88)
(5,540,000▲) F14
Tobol'sk,
82,000 ('87)............. D 9
Tōkyō, 8,354,615 ('85)
(27,700,000★) F16
Tomsk, 502,000 ('89)..D11
TURKEY......................F 6
Ulaanbaatar, 548,400
('89)........................E13
UNION OF SOVIET SOCIALIST REPUBLICS.............C11
UNITED ARAB EMIRATES............. G 8
Ürümqi, 1,060,000
('88)........................E11
Vārānasi, 708,647 ('81)
(925,000★) G11
Viangchan, 377,409
('85)........................ H13
VIETNAM................... H13
Vladivostok, 648,000
('89)........................E16
Wuhan, 3,570,000
('88)........................F14
Xiamen, 343,700 ('86)
(546,400▲) G14
Xi'an, 2,210,000 ('88)
(2,580,000▲) F13
Yangon (Rangoon),
2,705,039 ('83)
(2,800,000★) H12
YEMEN.......................H 7
Yerushalayim
(Jerusalem), 493,500
('89) (530,000★) ......F 6
Yokohama, 2,992,926
('85)........................F16
Zhangjiakou,
500,000 ('88)
(640,000▲) E14

★ Population of metropolitan area, including suburbs.
▲ Population of entire district, including rural area.

China, Japan, and Korea

Bhutan

1982 ESTIMATE

Thimphu, 12,000 .... F 4

China

1988 ESTIMATE

Andong, 579,800('86) C11
Anshan, 1,330,000 .. C11
Bangbu, 403,900 (612,600▲)('86) E10
Baoding, 423,200 (535,100▲)('86) D10
Baotou, 1,130,000 .. C 8
Beijing (Peking), 6,710,000 (6,450,000★) D10
Benxi, 860,000 ...... C11
Canton *see* Guangzhou ...... G 9
Changchun, 1,822,000 (2,000,000▲) C12
Changsha, 1,230,000 F 9
Changzhou, 522,700('86) E10
Chengdu, 1,884,000 (2,960,000▲) ...... E 7
Chongqing, 2,502,000 (2,890,000▲) ...... F 8
Dalian, 2,280,000 .... D11
Datong, 810,000 (1,040,000▲) ...... C 9
Fushun, 1,290,000 .. C11
Fuzhou, 910,000 (1,240,000▲) F10
Guangzhou (Canton), 3,100,000 (3,420,000▲) ...... G 9
Guiyang, 1,030,000 (1,430,000▲) ...... F 8
Handan, 870,000 (1,030,000▲) ...... D 9
Hanzhou, 1,290,000 E 11
Harbin, 2,710,000 .... B12
Hefei, 740,000 (930,000▲) E10
Hegang, 588,300('86) B13
Hengyang, 419,200 (601,300▲)('86) .... F 9
Hohhot, 670,000 (830,000▲) .... C 9
Huainan, 700,000 (1,110,000▲) E10
Huangshi, 451,900('86) E10
Jilin, 1,200,000 ...... C12
Jinan (Tsinan), 1,546,000 (2,140,000▲) D10
Jinzhou, 710,000 (810,000▲) C11
Jixi, 700,000 (820,000▲) B13
Kaifeng, 458,800 (629,100▲)('86) .... E 9
Kunming, 1,310,000 (1,550,000▲) ...... F 7
Lanzhou, 1,297,000 (1,420,000▲) ...... D 7
Lasa (Lhasa), 84,400 (107,700▲)('86) .... F 5
Liuzhou, 680,000 .... G 8
Luoyang, 760,000 (1,090,000▲) ...... E 9
Mudanjiang, 650,000 C12
Nanchang, 1,090,000 (1,260,000▲) F10
Nanjing, 2,390,000 .. E10
Nanning, 720,000 (1,000,000▲) ...... G 8
Ningbo, 570,000 (1,050,000▲) F11
Peking *see* Beijing .. D10
Qingdao (Tsingtao), 1,300,000 .... D11
Shanghai, 7,220,000 (9,300,000★) E11
Shantou (Swatow), 560,000 (790,000▲) G10
Shenyang (Mukden), 3,910,000 (4,370,000▲) C11
Shijiazhuang, 1,220,000 .... D 9
Suzhou, 740,000 .... E11
Taiyuan, 1,700,000 (1,980,000▲) ...... D 9
Tangshan, 1,080,000 (1,440,000▲) D10
Tianjin (Tientsin), 4,950,000 (5,540,000▲) D10
Ürümqi, 1,060,000 .. C 4
Wenzhou, 372,200 (530,600▲)('86) F11
Wuhan, 3,570,000 .. E 9
Wuhu, 396,000 (502,200▲)('86) E10
Wuxi, 880,000 ...... E11
Xi'an (Sian), 2,210,000 (2,580,000▲) ...... E 8
Xining, 620,000 ...... D 7
Xuzhou, 860,000 .... E10
Zhangjiakou (Kalgan), 500,000 (640,000▲) C 9

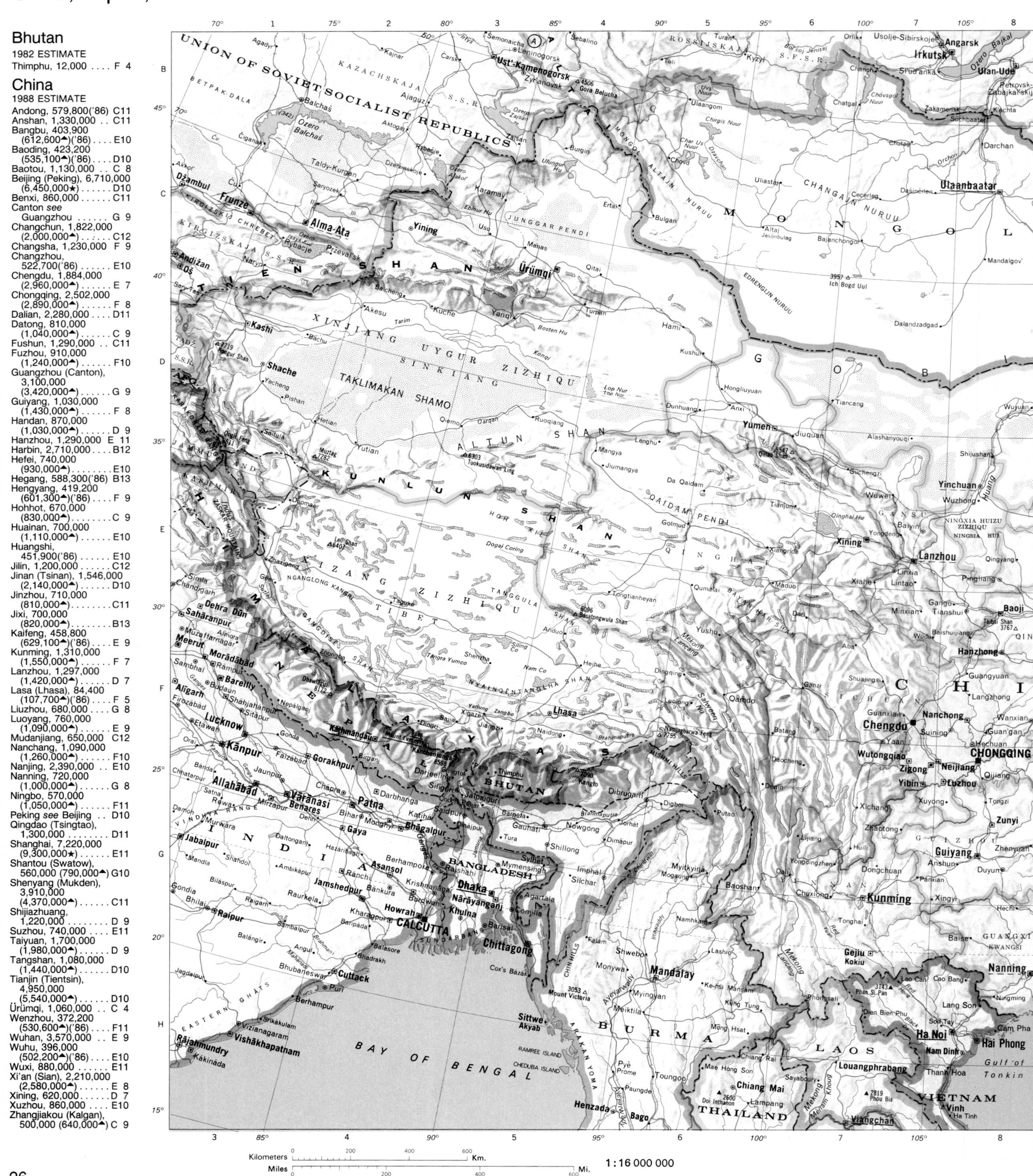

Zhengzhou, 1,150,000 (1,580,000▲) . . . . . . E 9
Zibo, 840,000 (2,370,000▲) D10

Hong Kong
1986 CENSUS

Kowloon (Jiulong), 774,781 . . . . G 9
Victoria (Xianggang), 1,175,860 (4,770,000★) . . . . . . G 9

Japan
1985 CENSUS

Asahikawa, 363,631 . . C15
Chiba, 788,930 . . . . . . D15
Fukuoka, 1,160,440 (1,750,000★) E13
Hakodate, 319,194 . . C15
Hamamatsu, 514,118 E14
Himeji, 452,917 (660,000★) E13
Hiroshima, 1,044,118 (1,575,000★) E13
Kagoshima, 530,502 . . E13
Kanazawa, 430,481 . . D14
Kitakyūshū, 1,056,402 (1,525,000★) E13
Kōbe, 1,410,834 . . . . E14
Kumamoto, 555,719 . . E13
Kurashiki, 413,632 . . E13
Kyōto, 1,479,218 . . . . D14
Matsuyama, 426,658 E13
Nagasaki, 449,382 . . E12
Nagoya, 2,116,381 (4,800,000★) D14
Niigata, 475,630 . . . . D14
Okayama, 572,479 . . E13
Ōsaka, 2,636,249 (16,450,000★) E14
Sapporo, 1,542,979 (1,900,000★) C15
Sendai, 700,254 (1,175,000★) D15
Shizuoka, 468,362 (975,000★) E14
Tōkyō, 8,354,615 (27,700,000★) D14
Utsunomiya, 405,375 D14
Yokohama, 2,992,926 D14

Korea, North
1981 ESTIMATE

Ch'ŏngjin, 490,000 . . C12
Kaesŏng, 259,000 . . D12
Namp'o, 241,000 . . . . D12
P'yŏngyang, 1,283,000 (1,600,000★) D12
Sinŭiju, 305,000 . . . . C11
Wŏnsan, 398,000 . . . . D12

Korea, South
1989 ESTIMATE

Chŏnju, 426,473('85) D12
Inch'ŏn, 1,628,000 . . D12
Kwangju, 1,165,000 . . D12
Masan, 448,746 (625,000★)('85) D12
Pusan, 3,773,000 (3,800,000★) D12
Sŏul (Seoul), 10,522,000 (15,850,000★) D12
Taegu, 2,207,000 . . . . D12
Taejŏn, 1,041,000 . . D12

Macau
1987 ESTIMATE

Macau (Aomen), 429,000 . . . . G 9

Mongolia
1989 ESTIMATE

Ulaanbaatar (Ulan Bator), 548,400 . . . . B 8

Nepal
1981 CENSUS

Kāthmāṇḍau (Kathmandu), 235,160 (320,000★) . . . . F 4

Taiwan
1988 ESTIMATE

Kaohsiung, 1,342,797 (1,845,000★) G11
T'aichung, 715,107 . . G11
T'ainan, 656,927 . . . . G11
T'aipei, 2,637,100 (6,130,000★) F11

★ Population of metropolitan area, including suburbs.
▲ Population of entire district, including rural area.

Eastern and Southeastern China

China

1986 ESTIMATE

Anlu, 35,199('85) . . . . . D 2
Anqing, 213,200 (433,900▲) . . . . E 6
Baoying, 50,479('85) . . B 8
Bengbu, 403,900 (612,600▲) . . . . C 6
Binhai (Dongkan), 37,565('85) . . . . A 8
Boxian, 63,222('85) . . . . B 4
Canton *see* Guangzhou L 2
Changsha, 1,230,000('88) . . . . . . G 1
Changshu, 281,300 (998,000▲) . . . . D 9
Changzhou (Changchow), 522,700 . . . . D 8
Chaoan, 265,400 (1,214,500▲) . . . . L 5
Chaoxian, 116,800 (739,500▲) . . . . D 6
Chezhou, 143,500 (191,900▲) . . . . J 1
Chuxian, 113,300 (365,000▲) . . . . C 7
Dinghai, 50,161('85) . . E11
Dingshan, 46,373('85) . . D 8
Dongguan, 254,900 (1,208,500▲) . . . . L 2
Echeng, 217,400 (938,000▲) . . . . E 3
Foshan, 243,500 (312,700▲) . . . . L 2
Fuyang, 143,400 (195,200▲) . . . . C 4
Fuzhou, 106,700 (171,800▲) . . . . G 5
Fuzhou (Foochow), 910,000 (1,240,000▲)('88) . . . . I 8
Ganzhou, 191,600 (346,000▲) . . . . J 3
Gaoyou, 57,844('85) . . C 8
Guangzhou (Canton), 3,100,000 (3,420,000▲)('88) . . . L 2
Hangzhou (Hangchow), 1,290,000('88) . . . . . . E 9
Hefei, 740,000 (930,000▲)('88) . . . . D 6
Huainan, 700,000 (1,110,000▲)('88) . . . . C 6
Huaiyin, 201,700 (382,500▲) . . . . B 8
Huanggang, 65,961('82) E 3
Huangshi, 451,900 . . . . E 4
Huiyang (Huizhou), 117,000 (182,100▲) . . . . L 3
Huzhou, 208,500 (964,400▲) . . . . E 9
Jian, 132,200 (184,300▲) . . . . H 3
Jiangmen, 168,800 (231,700▲) . . . . M 2
Jiangyin, 66,476('85) . . D 9
Jiaxing, 210,200 (686,500▲) . . . . E 9
Jieyang, 98,531('85) . . L 5
Jingdezhen (Kingtechen), 304,000 (569,700▲) . . F 6
Jinhua, 147,800 (799,900▲) . . . . F 8
Jiujiang, 248,500 (382,300▲) . . . . F 4
Lanxi, 70,500 (606,800▲) . . . . F 8
Lechang, 56,913 . . . . . . J 2
Liling, 107,100 (856,300▲) . . . . H 2
Linhai, 52,653('85) G10
Liuan, 122,600 (163,400▲) . . . . D 5
Longyan, 114,500 (378,500▲) . . . . J 6
Luohe, 102,300 (159,100▲) . . . . B 3
Maanshan, 258,900 (367,000▲) . . . . D 7
Meixian, 169,100 (740,600▲) . . . . K 5
Nanchang, 1,090,000 (1,260,000)('88) . . . . G 4
Nanjing (Nanking), 2,390,000('88) . . . . . . C 7

★ Population of metropolitan area, including suburbs. ▲ Population of entire district, including rural area.

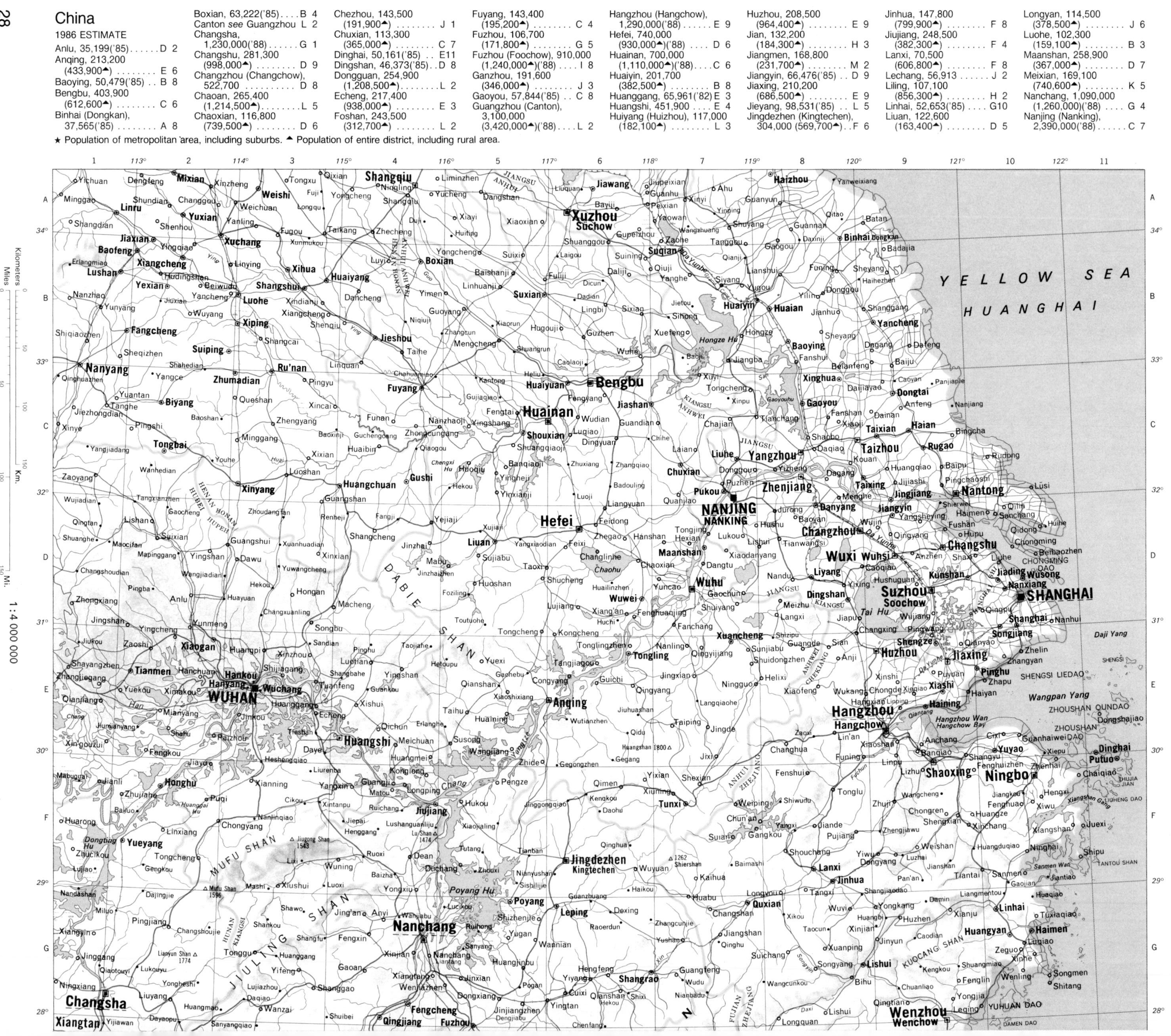

Nanping, 157,100 (420,800▲) . . . . I 7
Nantong, 308,800 (411,000▲) . . . . C 9
Nanyang, 199,400 (294,800▲) . . . . B 1
Ningbo, 570,000 (1,050,000▲)('88) F10
Pingxiang, 368,700 (1,286,700▲) . . . . . . H 2
Quanzhou, 157,000 (436,000▲) . . . . K 7
Shanghai, 7,220,000 (9,300,000★)('88) D10
Shantou (Swatow), 560,000 (790,000▲)('88) . . . . L 5
Shaoguan, 363,100 (344,892▲) . . . . K 2
Shaoxing, 167,100 (250,900▲) . . . . E 9
Suixian, 187,700 (1,281,600▲) . . . . . . D 2
Suzhou (Soochow), 740,000('88) . . . . D 9
Tongling, 182,900 (216,400▲) . . . . E 6
Wenzhou, 372,200 (530,600▲) . . . . G 9
Wuhan, 3,570,000('88) E 3
Wuhu, 396,000 (502,200▲) . . . . D 7
Wusong, 64,017('82) . . D10
Wuxi (Wuhsi), 880,000('88) . . . . D 9
Xiamen (Amoy), 343,700 (546,400▲) . . . . K 7
Xiangcheng, 363,200 (819,900▲) . . . . B 2
Xiangtan, 389,500 (511,100▲) . . . . H 1
Xinyang, 169,100 (234,200▲) . . . . C 3
Xuchang, 167,800 (247,200▲) . . . . A 2
Xuzhou (Süchow), 860,000('88) . . . . A 6
Yancheng, 258,400 (1,251,400▲) . . . . . . B 9
Yangzhou, 321,500 (417,300▲) . . . . C 8
Yanling, 52,679('82) . . C 8
Yueyang, 239,500 (411,300▲) . . . . F 2
Yuyao, 169,700 (772,700▲) E10
Zhangzhou (Longxi), 159,400 (310,400▲) K 6
Zhenjiang, 412,400 . . . . C 8
Zhongshan, 238,700 (1,059,700▲) . . . . . . M 2
Zhuzhou, 344,800 (499,600▲) . . . . H 2

Hong Kong
1986 CENSUS

Kowloon (Jiulong), 774,781 . . . . M 3
Victoria (Xianggang), 1,175,860 (4,770,000★) . . . . . . M 3

Macau
1987 ESTIMATE

Macau (Aomen), 429,000 . . . . M 2

Taiwan
1988 ESTIMATE

Changhua, 158,400 (206,603▲) . . . . K 9
Chiai, 254,875 . . . . L 9
Chilung, 348,541 . . . . . . J10
Hsinchu, 309,899 . . . . K 9
Kaohsiung, 1,342,797 (1,845,000★) . . . . . . M 9
Kaohsiunghsien, 276,259 . . . . M 9
P'ingtung, 167,600 (204,990▲) . . . . M 9
T'ainan, 656,927 . . . . . . L 9
T'aipei, 2,637,100 (6,130,000★) J10
T'aipeihsien, 506,220 . . J10

Japan

1985 CENSUS

Aizu-wakamatsu, 118,140 . . . . E12
Akashi, 263,363 . . . . . . H 7
Akita, 296,400 . . . . C13
Amagasaki, 509,115 . . H 8
Aomori, 294,045 . . . . . . B13
Asahikawa, 363,631 . . p20
Ashikaga, 167,656 . . . . F12
Beppu, 134,775 . . . . . . I 4
Chiba, 788,930 . . . . . . G13
Chigasaki, 185,030 . . . . G12
Chōshi, 87,883 . . . . . . G13
Fuji, 214,448 (370,000★) G11
Fujinomiya, 112,642 . . G11
Fujisawa, 328,387 . . . . G12
Fukui, 250,261 . . . . F 9
Fukuoka, 1,160,440 (1,750,000★) . . . . I 3
Fukushima, 270,762 . . E13
Fukuyama, 360,261 . . H 6
Funabashi, 506,966 . . G13
Gifu, 411,743 . . . . G 9
Hachinohe, 241,430 . . B14
Hachiōji, 426,654 . . . . G12
Hakodate, 319,194 . . . . r18
Hamamatsu, 514,118 . . H10
Handa, 92,883 . . . . H 9
Higashiōsaka, 522,805 H 8
Hikone, 94,204 . . . . . . G 9
Himeji, 452,917 (660,000★) . . . . H 7
Hiratsuka, 229,990 . . . . G12
Hirosaki, 134,800 (176,082▲) B13
Hiroshima, 1,044,118 (1,575,000★) . . . . . . H 5
Hitachi, 206,074 . . . . . . F13
Hōfu, 118,067 . . . . H 4
Ichinomiya, 257,388 . . G 9
Iizuka, 81,868 (110,000★) . . . . I 3
Imabari, 125,115 . . . . . . H 6
Ise, 105,455 . . . . H 9
Isesaki, 112,459 . . . . . . F12
Ishinomaki, 122,674 . . D14
Iwaki (Taira), 350,569 . . E13
Iwakuni, 111,833 . . . . . . H 5
Kagoshima, 530,502 . . K 3
Kakogawa, 227,311 . . H 7
Kamaishi, 60,007 . . . . . . C14
Kamakura, 175,495 . . . G12
Kanazawa, 430,481 . . . . F 9
Kariya, 112,403 . . . . . . H 9
Kashiwa, 273,128 . . . . G12
Kasugai, 256,990 . . . . G 9
Kawagoe, 285,437 . . . . G12
Kawaguchi, 403,015 . . G12
Kawasaki, 1,088,624 . . G12
Kiryū, 131,267 . . . . F12
Kishiwada, 185,731 . . . . H 8
Kitakyūshū, 1,056,402 (1,525,000★) . . . . I 3
Kitami, 107,281 . . . . . . p21
Kōbe, 1,410,834 . . . . . . H 8
Kōchi, 312,241 . . . . I 6
Kōfu, 202,405 . . . . G11
Komatsu, 106,041 . . . . F 9
Kōriyama, 301,673 . . . . E13
Kumagaya, 143,496 . . F12
Kumamoto, 555,719 . . J 3
Kurashiki, 413,632 . . . . H 6
Kure, 226,488 . . . . H 5
Kurume, 222,847 . . . . . . I 3
Kushiro, 214,541 . . . . . . q22
Kyōto, 1,479,218 . . . . . . G 8
Maebashi, 277,319 . . . . F12
Maizuru, 98,775 . . . . . . G 8
Matsudo, 427,473 . . . . G12
Matsue, 140,005 . . . . . . G 6
Matsumoto, 197,340 . . F10
Matsusaka, 116,886 . . H 9
Matsuyama, 426,658 . . I 5
Mito, 228,985 . . . . F13
Miyazaki, 279,114 . . . . K 4
Morioka, 235,469 . . . . C14
Muroran, 136,208 (195,000★) q18
Nagahama, 55,531 . . . . G 9
Nagano, 336,973 . . . . . . F11
Nagaoka, 183,756 . . . . E11
Nagasaki, 449,382 . . . . J 2

★ Population of metropolitan area, including suburbs. ▲ Population of entire district, including rural area.

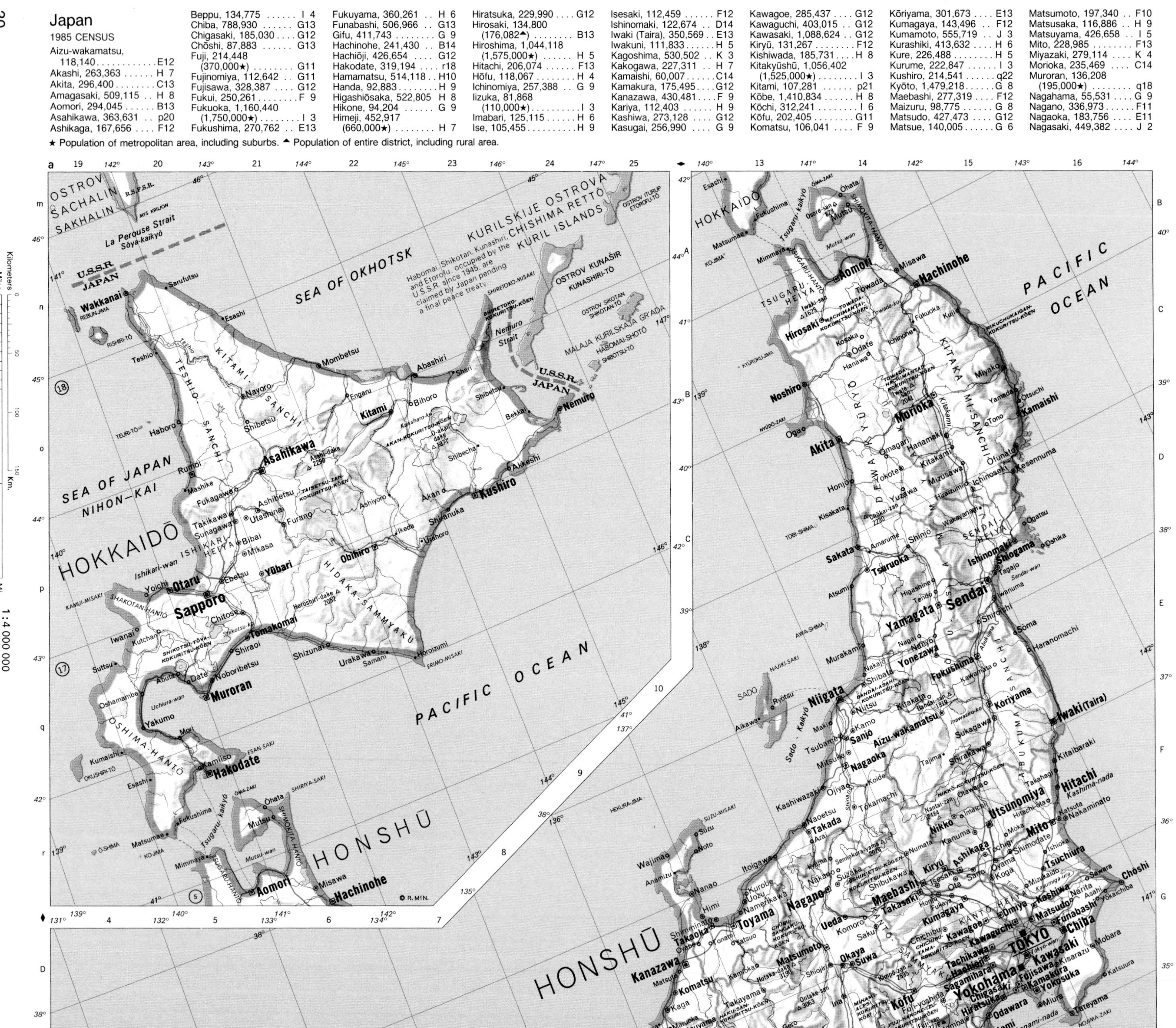

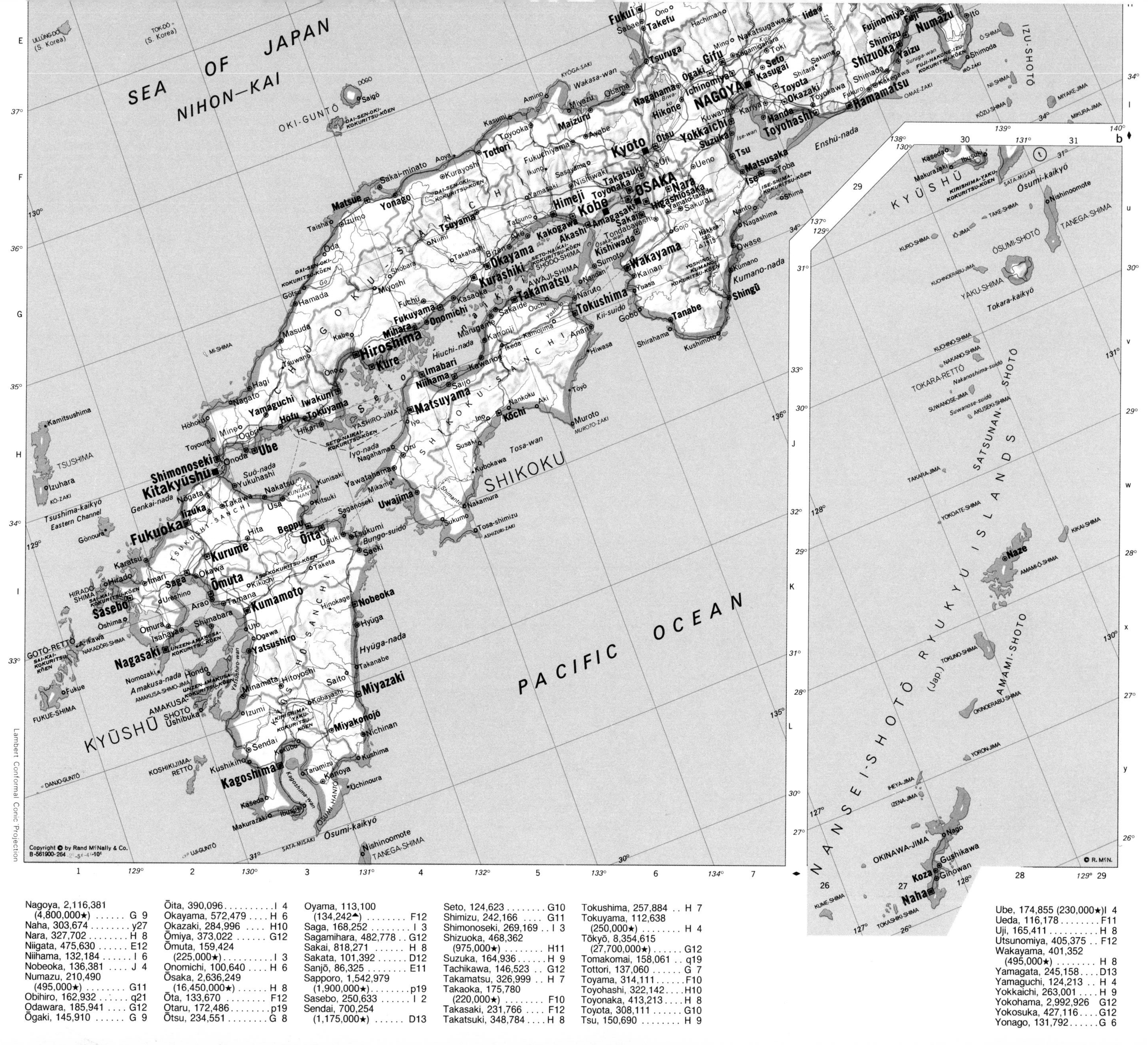

Nagoya, 2,116,381 (4,800,000★) ...... G 9
Naha, 303,674 .... y27
Nara, 327,702 .... H 8
Niigata, 475,630 ...... E12
Niihama, 132,184 ...... I 6
Nobeoka, 136,381 .... J 4
Numazu, 210,490 (495,000★) G11
Obihiro, 162,932 ...... q21
Odawara, 185,941 .... G12
Ōgaki, 145,910 ...... G 9
Ōita, 390,096 .... I 4
Okayama, 572,479 .... H 6
Okazaki, 284,996 .... H10
Ōmiya, 373,022 ...... G12
Ōmuta, 159,424 (225,000★) .... I 3
Onomichi, 100,640 .... H 6
Ōsaka, 2,636,249 (16,450,000★) ...... H 8
Ōta, 133,670 .... F12
Otaru, 172,486 .... p19
Ōtsu, 234,551 .... G 8
Oyama, 113,100 (134,242▲) F12
Saga, 168,252 .... I 3
Sagamihara, 482,778 .. G12
Sakai, 818,271 ...... H 8
Sakata, 101,392 ...... D12
Sanjō, 86,325 .... E11
Sapporo, 1,542,979 (1,900,000★) p19
Sasebo, 250,633 ...... I 2
Sendai, 700,254 (1,175,000★) D13
Seto, 124,623 .... G10
Shimizu, 242,166 .... G11
Shimonoseki, 269,169 .. I 3
Shizuoka, 468,362 (975,000★) H11
Suzuka, 164,936 ...... H 9
Tachikawa, 146,523 .. G12
Takamatsu, 326,999 .. H 7
Takaoka, 175,780 (220,000★) F10
Takasaki, 231,766 .... F12
Takatsuki, 348,784 .... H 8
Tokushima, 257,884 .. H 7
Tokuyama, 112,638 (250,000★) .... H 4
Tōkyō, 8,354,615 (27,700,000★) G12
Tomakomai, 158,061 .. q19
Tottori, 137,060 ...... G 7
Toyama, 314,111 ...... F10
Toyohashi, 322,142 .... H10
Toyonaka, 413,213 .... H 8
Toyota, 308,111 ...... G10
Tsu, 150,690 .... H 9
Ube, 174,855 (230,000★) I 4
Ueda, 116,178 .... F11
Uji, 165,411 .... H 8
Utsunomiya, 405,375 .. F12
Wakayama, 401,352 (495,000★) .... H 8
Yamagata, 245,158 .... D13
Yamaguchi, 124,213 .. H 4
Yokkaichi, 263,001 .... H 9
Yokohama, 2,992,926 G12
Yokosuka, 427,116 .... G12
Yonago, 131,792 ...... G 6

Southeastern Asia

Brunei
1981 CENSUS
Bandar Seri Begawan, 22,777 (64,000★) . . E 5

Burma
1983 CENSUS
Bago, 150,528 . . . . . . B 2
Henzada, 82,005 . . . . B 2
Mandalay, 532,949 . . A 2
Mawlamyine, 219,961 B 2
Monywa, 106,843 . . . . A 2
Pathein, 144,096 . . . . B 1
Pyè (Prome), 83,332 . . B 2
Sittwe (Akyab), 107,621 . . . . A 1
Yangon (Rangoon), 2,705,039 (2,800,000★) . . . . . . B 2

Cambodia
1986 ESTIMATE
Phnum Pénh, 700,000 C 3

Indonesia
1980 CENSUS
Ambon, 111,914 (207,702▲) . . . . F 8
Balikpapan, 208,040 (279,852▲) . . . . F 6
Bandung, 1,633,000 (1,800,000★)('85) . . m13
Banjarmasin, 424,000('83) . . . . . . F 5
Banjuwangi, 90,378 . . n17
Blitar, 78,503 (100,000★) n16
Bogor, 246,946 (560,000★) m13
Cilacap, 127,017 . . . . m14
Cirebon, 223,504 (275,000★) m14
Denpasar, 159,233 . . G 6
Dili, 6,890 (67,039▲) G 8
Garut, 145,624 . . . . . . m13
Jakarta, 9,200,000 (10,000,000★)('89) m13
Jambi, 155,761 (230,046▲) . . . . F 3
Jember, 171,284 . . . . n16
Kediri, 176,261 (221,830▲) m16
Kudus, 154,478 . . . . m15
Kupang, 84,587 . . . . H 7
Madiun, 150,562 (180,000★) m15
Magelang, 123,358 (160,000★) m15
Malang, 547,000('83) m16
Manado, 217,091 . . . . E 7
Medan, 2,110,000('85) E 2
Padang, 405,600 (657,000▲)('83) . . . . F 3
Pakanbaru, 186,199 . . E 3
Palembang, 874,000('83) . . . . . . F 3
Pangkalpinang, 90,078 F 4
Pasuruan, 95,864 (125,000★) m16
Pekalongan, 132,413 (260,000★) m14
Pemalang, 72,663 . . m14
Pematangsiantar, 150,296 (175,000★) . . . . E 2
Pontianak, 343,000('83) . . . . . . F 4
Probolinggo, 100,296 m16
Purwokerto, 143,787 m14
Salatiga, 85,740 . . . . m15
Samarinda, 182,473 (264,012▲) . . . . F 6
Semarang, 1,206,000('83) m15
Sukabumi, 109,898 (225,000★) m13
Surabaya, 2,345,000('85) m16
Surakarta, 491,000 (575,000★)('83) m15
Tanjungkarang-Telukbetung, 284,167 (375,000★) k12
Tasikmalaya, 192,267 m14
Tegal, 131,440 (340,000★) m14
Tual, 7,833 . . . . G 9
Tulungagung, 91,585 n15
Ujungpandang, 841,000('83) . . . . . . G 6
Yogyakarta, 421,000 (510,000★)('83) m15

Laos
1975 ESTIMATE
Louangphrabang, 46,000 . . . . B 3
Paksé, 47,000 . . . . . . B 4
Savannakhet, 53,000 B 3
Viangchan, 377,409('85) . . . . . . B 3

Ma

1980 C

Alor Seta
George T
248,241
Ipoh, 293,84
Johor Baharu,
246,395 ....
Kelang, 192,080
Kota Baharu, 167,
Kuala Lumpur, 919,
(1,475,000★) .....
Kuala Terengganu,
180,296 L
Kuantan, 131,547 .... E
Kuching, 72,555 .... E 5
Melaka, 87,494 ...... E 3
Sandakan, 70,420 .. D 6
Seremban, 132,911 .. E 3
Sibu, 85,231 .... E 5

Philippines

1990 CENSUS

Angeles, 236,000 .... q19
Bacolod, 364,000 .... C 7
Baguio, 183,000 .... p19
Batangas, 31,600 (184,000▲) r19
Cabanatuan, 75,700 (173,000▲) q19
Cavite, 92,000 (175,000★) q19
Cebu, 610,000 (720,000★) .... C 7
Cotabato, 127,000 .. D 7
Dagupan, 122,000 .. p19
Davao, 569,300 (850,000▲) .... D 8
Dumaguete, 80,000 .. D 7
Iloilo, 311,000 ...... C 7
Legaspi, 63,000 (121,000▲) r20
Lipa, 30,000 (160,000▲) r19
Lucena, 151,000 .... r19
Malolos, 95,699('80) .. q19
Manila, 1,587,000 (6,800,000★) q19
Naga, 115,000 ...... r20
Pasig, 318,853('84) .. q19
Puerto Princesa, 52,000 (92,000▲) .... D 6
Quezon City, 1,632,000 .... q19
San Fernando, 110,891('80) q19
San Pablo, 83,900 (161,000▲) q19
Tarlac, 38,205 (175,691▲)('80) q19
Zamboanga, 107,000 (444,000▲) .... D 7

Singapore

1989 ESTIMATE

Singapore, 2,685,400 (3,025,000★) ...... E 3

Thailand

1988 ESTIMATE

Bangkok *see* Krung Thep .... C 3
Chiang Mai, 164,030 B 2
Hat Yai, 138,046 .... D 3
Khon Kaen, 131,340 B 3
Krung Thep (Bangkok), 5,716,779 (6,450,000★) .... C 3
Nakhon Ratchasima, 204,982 .... C 3
Nakhon Sawan, 105,220 .... B 3
Nakhon Si Thammarat, 72,407 .... D 2
Phitsanulok, 77,675 .. B 3
Songkhla, 84,433 .... D 3
Ubon Ratchathani, 100,374 .... B 3
Udon Thani, 81,202 .. B 3

Vietnam

1979 CENSUS

Can Tho, 182,856 .. C 4
Da Nang, 318,653 .. B 4
Hai Phong, 456,000 (1,279,067▲)('89) .. A 4
Ha Noi, 1,089,000 (1,500,000★)('89) .. A 4
Hue, 165,710 ...... B 4
My Tho, 101,493 .... C 4
Nam Dinh, 160,179 .. A 4
Nha Trang, 172,663 .. C 4
Phan Thiet, 75,241 .. C 4
Qui Nhon, 127,211 .. C 4
Rach Gia, 81,075 .... C 4
Saigon *see* Thanh Pho Ho Chi Minh .... C 4
Thanh Pho Ho Chi Minh (Saigon), 3,169,000 (3,300,000★)('89) .. C 4
Vinh, 159,753 ...... B 4

★ Population of metropolitan area, including suburbs.
▲ Population of entire district, including rural area.

...na, Thailand, and Indochina

Burma
1983 CENSUS

Bago, 150,528 . . . . F 4
Chauk, 51,437 . . . . D 3
Dawei, 69,882 . . . . G 5
Henzada, 82,005 . . . . . . F 3
Mandalay, 532,949 . . . . C 4
Mawlamyine (Moulmein), 219,961 . . . . F 4
Maymyo, 63,782 . . . . . . C 4
Meiktila, 96,496 . . . . . . D 3
Mergui (Myeik), 88,600 H 5
Monywa, 106,843 . . . . C 3
Myingyan, 77,060 . . . . D 3
Myitkyinā, 56,427 . . . . B 4
Pakokku, 71,860 . . . . . . D 3
Pathein, 144,096 . . . . . . F 3
Pyè (Prome), 83,332 . . E 3
Rangoon *see* Yangon . . F 4
Sittwe (Akyab), 107,621 D 2
Thaton, 61,790 . . . . F 4
Toungoo, 65,861 . . . . . . E 4
Yangon (Rangoon), 2,705,039 (2,800,000★) . . . . F 4
Yenangyaung, 62,582 . . D 3

Cambodia
1986 ESTIMATE

Bătdâmbâng, 38,780('62) . . . . H 7
Kâmpóng Cham, 35,000('71) . . . . H 8
Kâmpóng Saôm, 53,000('81) . . . . I 7
Phnum Pénh (Phnom Penh), 700,000 . . . . I 8

Indonesia
1980 CENSUS

Banda Aceh, 71,868 . . L 3
Binjai, 71,444 . . . . M 5
Bukittinggi, 55,577 (70,691▲) . . . . O 6
Medan, 2,110,000('85) M 5
Padang, 405,600 (657,000▲)('83) . . . . O 6
Padangsidempuan, 56,984 . . . . N 5
Payakumbuh, 24,567 (78,789▲) . . . . O 6
Pekanbaru, 186,199 . . N 6
Pematangsiantar, 150,296 (175,000★) . . . . M 5
Rantauprapat, 25,043 M 5
Sibolga, 59,466 . . . . . . N 5
Singkawang, 58,693 . . N10
Tanjungpinang, 36,999 N 8
Tarutung, 5,522 . . . . . . M 5
Tebingtinggi, 69,569 (92,068▲) . . . . M 5

Laos
1975 ESTIMATE

Louangphrabang, 46,000 . . . . E 7
Pakxé, 47,000 . . . . G 8
Savannakhet, 53,000 . . F 8
Viangchan, 377,409('85) F 7

Malaysia
1980 CENSUS

Batu Pahat, 64,727 . . . . N 7
Butterworth, 77,982 . . L 6
George Town (Pinang), 248,241 (495,000★) . . L 6
Ipoh, 293,849 . . . . L 6
Johor Baharu, 246,395 N 7
Kelang, [illegible]
Kota Baharu, [illegible]
Kuala Lumpur, 919,610 (1,475,000★) . . . . . . M 6
Kuala Terengganu, 180,296 . . . . L 7
Kuantan, 131,547 . . . . M 7
Kuching, 72,555 . . . . . . N11
Melaka, 87,494 . . . . . . M 7
Muar, 65,151 . . . . M 7
Seremban, 132,911 . . M 6
Taiping, 146,000 . . . . . . L 6

★ Population of metropolitan area, including suburbs. ▲ Population of entire district, including rural area.

Lambert Conformal Conic Projection

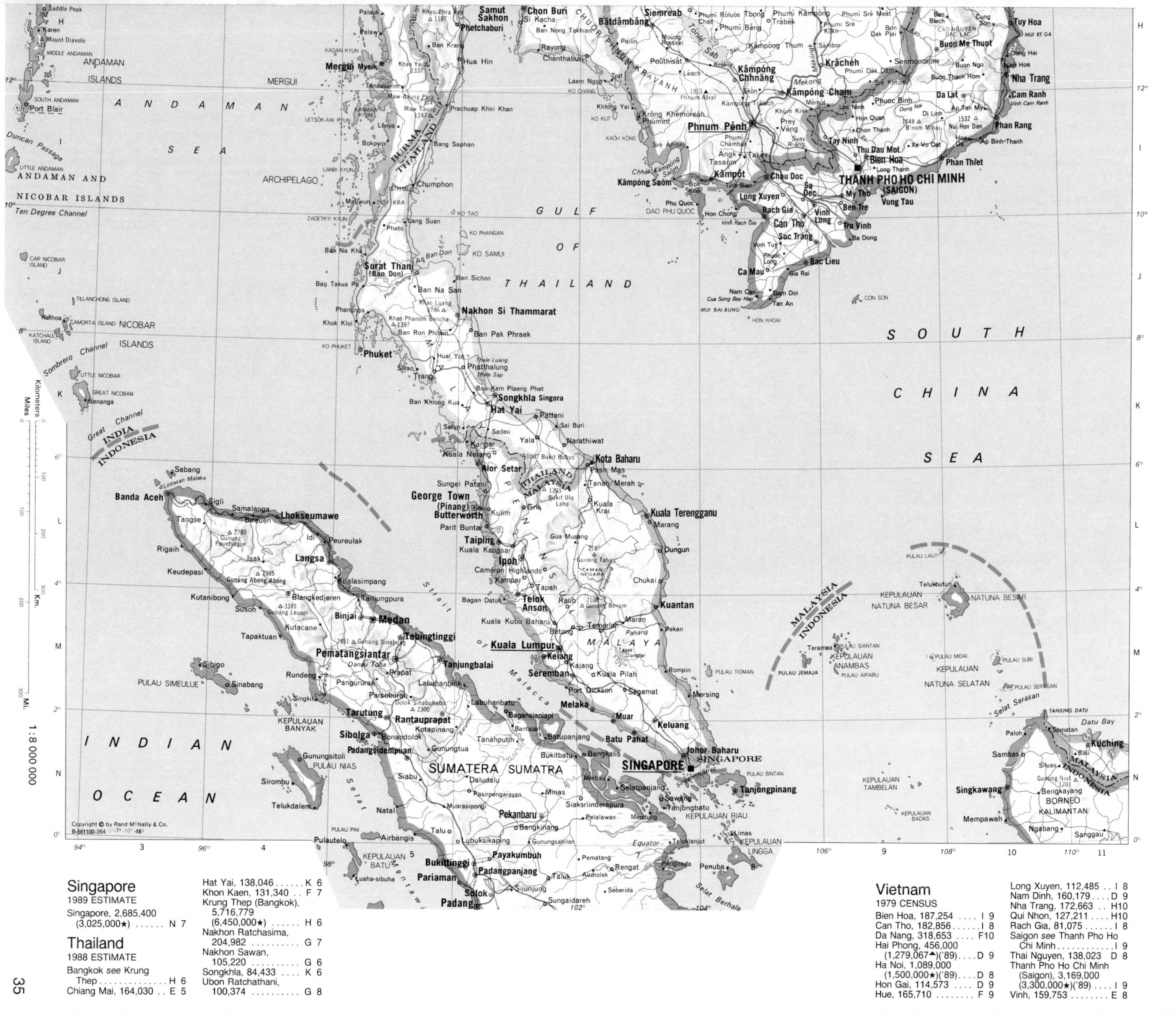

Singapore
1989 ESTIMATE

Singapore, 2,685,400 (3,025,000★) ...... N 7

Thailand
1988 ESTIMATE

Bangkok *see* Krung Thep .... H 6
Chiang Mai, 164,030 .. E 5
Hat Yai, 138,046 ...... K 6
Khon Kaen, 131,340 .. F 7
Krung Thep (Bangkok), 5,716,779 (6,450,000★) ...... H 6
Nakhon Ratchasima, 204,982 .... G 7
Nakhon Sawan, 105,220 .... G 6
Songkhla, 84,433 .... K 6
Ubon Ratchathani, 100,374 .... G 8

Vietnam
1979 CENSUS

Bien Hoa, 187,254 .... I 9
Can Tho, 182,856 ...... I 8
Da Nang, 318,653 .... F10
Hai Phong, 456,000 (1,279,067▲)('89) .... D 9
Ha Noi, 1,089,000 (1,500,000★)('89) .... D 8
Hon Gai, 114,573 .... D 9
Hue, 165,710 .... F 9
Long Xuyen, 112,485 .. I 8
Nam Dinh, 160,179 .... D 9
Nha Trang, 172,663 .. H10
Qui Nhon, 127,211 .... H10
Rach Gia, 81,075 ...... I 8
Saigon *see* Thanh Pho Ho Chi Minh .... I 9
Thai Nguyen, 138,023 D 8
Thanh Pho Ho Chi Minh (Saigon), 3,169,000 (3,300,000★)('89) .... I 9
Vinh, 159,753 .... E 8

India and Pakistan

Afghanistan
1988 ESTIMATE
Herāt, 177,300 . . . . . . C 1
Kābul, 1,424,400 . . . . C 2

Bangladesh
1981 CENSUS
Chittagong, 980,000
(1,391,877★) . . . . . . E 7
Dhaka, 2,365,695
(3,430,312★) . . . . . . E 7
Nārāyanganj, 405,562 E 7

Bhutan
1982 ESTIMATE
Thimphu, 12,000 . . . . D 6

India
1981 CENSUS
Ahmadābād, 2,059,725
(2,400,000★) . . . . . . E 3
Bangalore, 2,476,355
(2,950,000★) . . . . . . G 4
Bombay, 8,243,405
(9,950,000★) . . . . . . F 3
Calcutta, 3,305,006
(11,100,000★) . . . . E 6
Delhi, 4,884,234
(7,200,000★) . . . . . . D 4
Hyderābād, 2,187,262
(2,750,000★) . . . . . . F 4
Kānpur, 1,481,789
(1,875,000★) . . . . . . D 5
Madras, 3,276,622
(4,475,000★) . . . . . . G 5
Nāgpur, 1,219,461
(1,302,066★) . . . . . . E 4
New Delhi, 273,036 . . D 4

Nepal
1981 CENSUS
Kāṭhmāṇḍau, 235,160
(320,000★) . . . . D 6

Pakistan
1981 CENSUS
Islāmābād, 204,364 . . C 3
Karāchi, 4,901,627
(5,300,000★) . . . . . . E 2
Lahore, 2,707,215
(3,025,000★) . . . . . . C 3

Sri Lanka
1986 ESTIMATE
Colombo, 683,000
(2,050,000★) . . . . . . H 4

★ Population of metropolitan area, including suburbs.

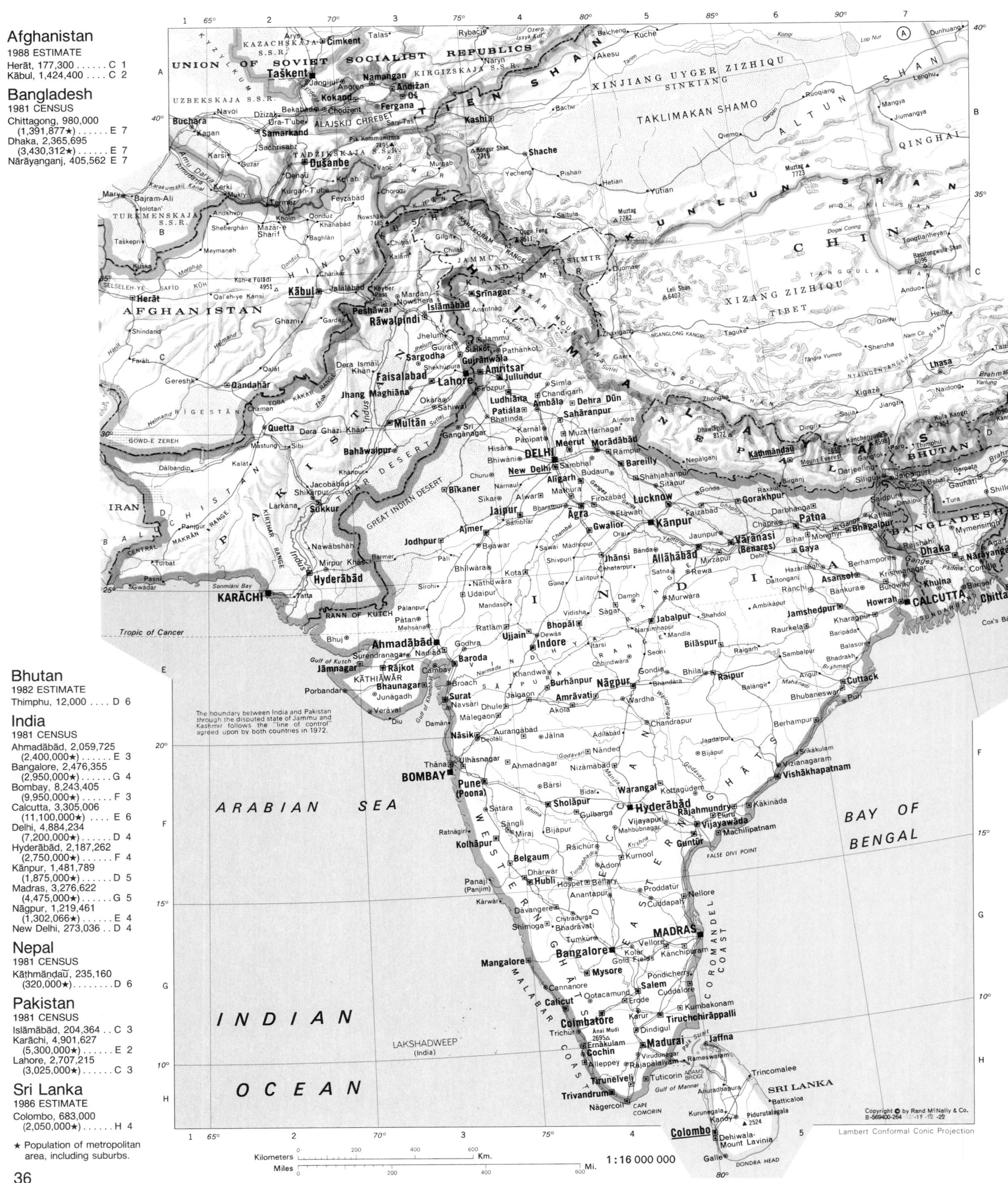

India

1981 CENSUS

Akola, 225,412 . . . . . . B 4
Amrāvati, 261,404 . . B 4
Aurangābād, 284,607 (316,421★) . . . . C 3
Bangalore, 2,476,355 (2,950,000★) . . . . . . F 4
Baroda, 734,473 (744,881★) . . . . A 2
Belgaum, 274,430 (300,372★) . . . . E 3
Bhāvnagar, 307,121 (308,642★) . . . . B 2
Bhilai, 290,090 (490,214★) . . . . B 6
Bhubaneswar, 219,211 . . . . B 8
Bombay, 8,243,405 (9,950,000★) . . . . . . C 2
Calicut, 394,447 (546,058★) . . . . . . G 3
Cochin, 513,249 (685,836★) . . . . H 4
Coimbatore, 704,514 (965,000★) . . . . . . G 4
Cuttack, 269,950 (327,412★) . . . . B 8
Dhule, 210,759 . . . . . . B 3
Gulbarga, 221,325 . . D 4
Guntūr, 367,699 . . . . D 6
Hubli, 527,108 . . . . . . E 3
Hyderābād, 2,187,262 (2,750,000★) . . . . . . D 5
Indore, 829,327 (850,000★) . . . . A 3
Kolhāpur, 340,625 (351,392★) . . . . D 3
Madras, 3,276,622 (4,475,000★) . . . . . . F 6
Madurai, 820,891 (960,000★) . . . . H 5
Mālegaon, 245,883 . . B 3
Mysore, 441,754 (479,081★) . . . . F 4
Nāgpur, 1,219,461 (1,302,066★) . . . . . . B 5
Nāsik, 262,428 (429,034★) . . . . C 2
Nellore, 237,065 . . . . E 5
Pondicherry, 162,636 (251,420★) . . . . . . G 5
Pune (Poona), 1,203,351 (1,775,000★) . . . . . . C 2
Raipur, 338,245 . . . . B 6
Salem, 361,394 (518,615★) . . . . . . G 5
Sholāpur, 511,103 (514,860★) . . . . D 3
Surat, 776,583 (913,806★) . . . . B 2
Thāna, 309,897 . . . . C 2
Tiruchchirāppalli, 362,045 (609,548★) . . . . . . G 5
Trivandrum, 483,086 (520,125★) . . . . H 4
Ulhāsnagar, 273,668 C 2
Vijayawāda, 454,577 (543,008★) . . . . D 6
Vishākhapatnam, 565,321 (603,630★) . . . . D 7
Warangal, 335,150 . . C 5

Sri Lanka

1986 ESTIMATE

Colombo, 683,000 (2,050,000★) . . . . . . I 5
Dehiwala-Mount Lavinia, 191,000 . . . . I 5
Kandy, 130,000 . . . . . . I 6
Kotte, 104,000 . . . . . . I 5

★ Population of metropolitan area, including suburbs.

Northern India and Pakistan

Afghanistan

1981 ESTIMATE

Baghlān, 41,000('82) B 3
Ghaznī, 31,196 . . . . . . D 3
Jalālābād, 58,000('82) C 4
Kābul, 1,424,400('88) C 3
Khānābād, 27,482 . . B 3
Kholm, 28,788 . . . . . . B 2
Mazār-e Sharīf, 130,600('88) . . . . . . B 2
Meymaneh, 39,218 . . C 1
Qandahār, 225,500('88) . . . . . . E 1
Sheberghān, 19,475 . . B 1

Bangladesh

1981 CENSUS

Barisāl, 172,905 . . . . . . I14
Brāhmanbāria, 87,570 I14
Chittagong, 980,000 (1,391,877★) I14
Comilla, 184,132 . . . . I14
Dhaka, 2,365,695 (3,430,312★) I14
Jessore, 148,927 . . . . I13
Khulna, 648,359 . . . . . . I13
Mymensingh, 190,991 H14
Nārāyanganj, 405,562 I14
Pābna, 109,065 . . . . H13
Rājshāhi, 253,740 . . . . H13
Rangpur, 153,174 . . . . H13
Saidpur, 126,608 . . . . H13
Sirājganj, 106,774 . . . . H13
Sylhet, 168,371 . . . . H14

Bhutan

1982 ESTIMATE

Thimphu, 12,000 . . . . G13

India

1981 CENSUS

Āgra, 694,191 (747,318★) . . . . . . G 8
Ahmadābād, 2,059,725 (2,400,000★) . . . . . . I 5
Ajmer, 375,593 . . . . . . G 6
Alīgarh, 320,861 . . . . G 8
Allāhābād, 616,051 (650,070★) . . . . H 9
Alwar, 145,795 . . . . . . G 7
Amritsar, 594,844 . . . . E 6
Asansol, 183,375 (1,050,000★) I12
Bareilly, 386,734 (449,425★) . . . . F 8
Baroda, 734,473 (744,881★) . . . . I 5
Bhāgalpur, 225,062 . . H12
Bhātpāra, 260,761 . . . . I13
Bhāvnagar, 307,121 (308,642★) . . . . J 5
Bhilai, 290,090 (490,214★) . . . . J 9
Bhopāl, 671,018 . . . . . . I 7
Bhubaneswar, 219,211 J11
Bīkaner, 253,174 (287,712★) . . . . F 5
Calcutta, 3,305,006 (11,100,000★) I13
Chandīgarh, 373,789 (422,841★) . . . . E 7
Cuttack, 269,950 (327,412★) J11
Dehra Dūn, 211,416 (293,010★) . . . . E 8
Delhi, 4,884,234 (7,200,000★) . . . . . . F 7
Durgāpur, 311,798 . . . . I12
Gaya, 247,075 . . . . . . H11
Ghāziābād, 271,730 (287,170★) . . . . F 7
Gorakhpur, 290,814 (307,501★) G10
Gwalior, 539,015 (555,862★) . . . . . . G 8
Howrah, 744,429 . . . . I13
Indore, 829,327 (850,000★) . . . . I 6
Jabalpur, 614,162 (757,303★) . . . . I 8
Jaipur, 977,165 (1,025,000★) . . . . . . G 6
Jammu, 206,135 (223,361★) . . . . D 6
Jāmnagar, 277,615 (317,362★) . . . . I 4
Jamshedpur, 438,385 (669,580★) I12
Jhānsi, 246,172 (284,141★) . . . . H 8
Jodhpur, 506,345 . . . . G 5
Jullundur, 408,186 (441,552★) . . . . E 6
Kānpur, 1,481,789 (1,875,000★) . . . . . . G 9
Kota, 358,241 . . . . . . H 6
Lucknow, 895,721 (1,060,000★) . . . . . . G 9
Ludhiāna, 607,052 . . E 6
Mathura, 147,493 (160,995★) . . . . . . G 7

★ Population of metropolitan area, including suburbs.

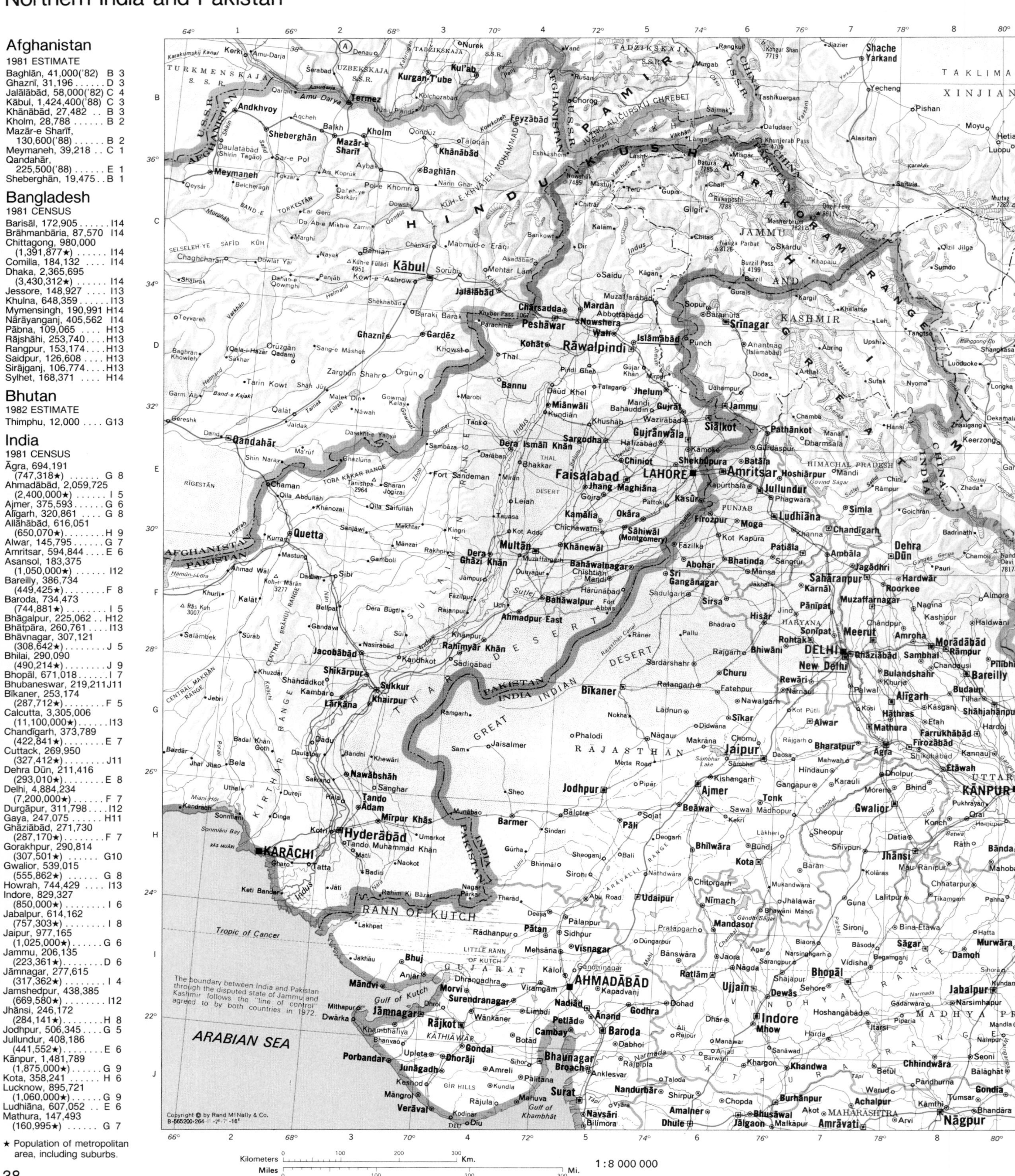

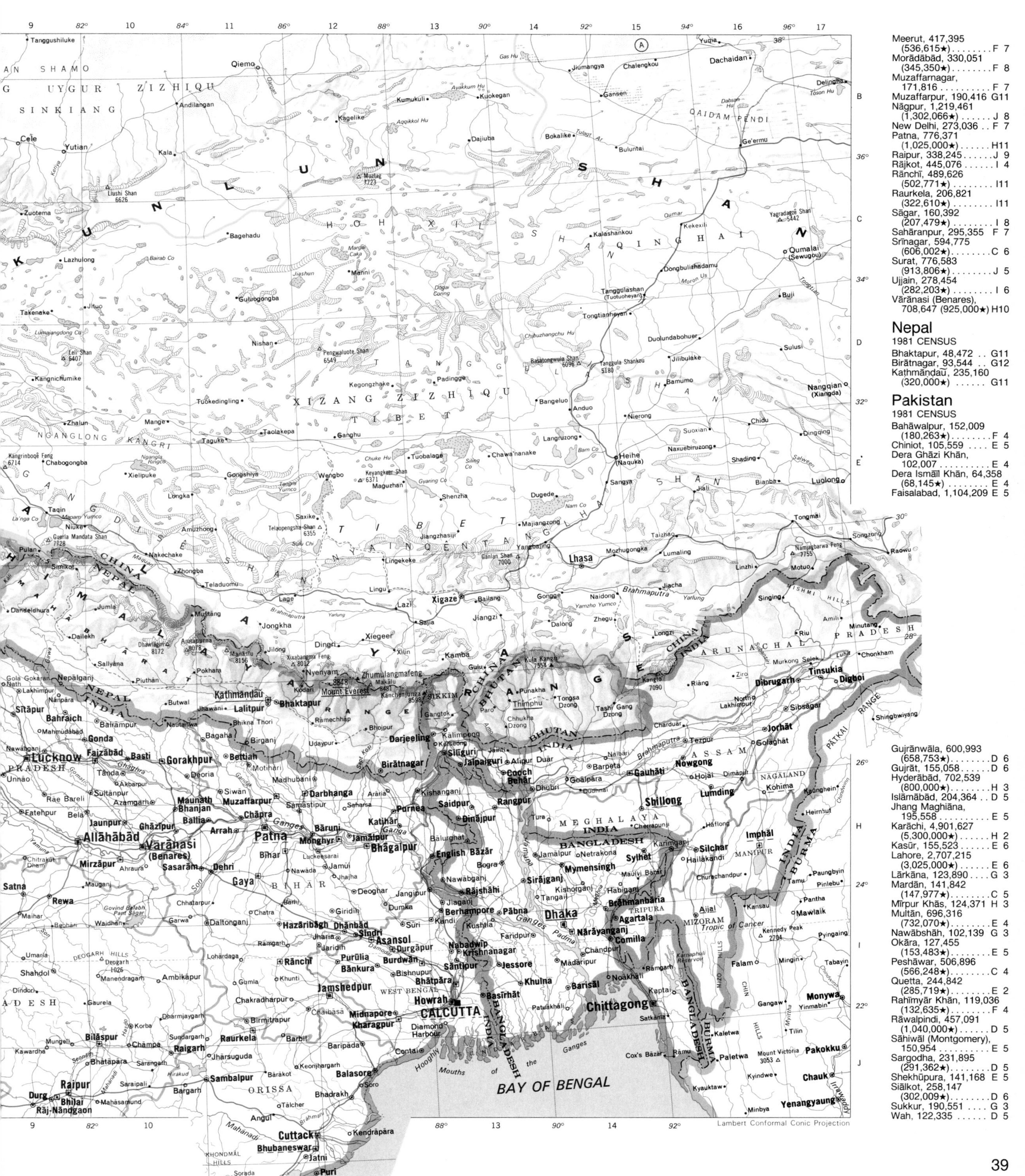

Meerut, 417,395 (536,615★) .... F 7
Morādābād, 330,051 (345,350★) .... F 8
Muzaffarnagar, 171,816 .... F 7
Muzaffarpur, 190,416 G11
Nāgpur, 1,219,461 (1,302,066★) ...... J 8
New Delhi, 273,036 .. F 7
Patna, 776,371 (1,025,000★) H11
Raipur, 338,245 ...... J 9
Rājkot, 445,076 ...... I 4
Rānchī, 489,626 (502,771★) I11
Raurkela, 206,821 (322,610★) I11
Sāgar, 160,392 (207,479★) .... I 8
Sahāranpur, 295,355 F 7
Srīnagar, 594,775 (606,002★) .... C 6
Surat, 776,583 (913,806★) .... J 5
Ujjain, 278,454 (282,203★) .... I 6
Vārānasi (Benares), 708,647 (925,000★) H10

Nepal

1981 CENSUS

Bhaktapur, 48,472 .. G11
Birātnagar, 93,544 .. G12
Kathmāndau, 235,160 (320,000★) G11

Pakistan

1981 CENSUS

Bahāwalpur, 152,009 (180,263★) .... F 4
Chiniot, 105,559 .... E 5
Dera Ghāzi Khān, 102,007 .... E 4
Dera Ismāīl Khān, 64,358 (68,145★) .... E 4
Faisalabad, 1,104,209 E 5
Gujrānwāla, 600,993 (658,753★) .... D 6
Gujrāt, 155,058 ...... D 6
Hyderābād, 702,539 (800,000★) .... H 3
Islāmābād, 204,364 .. D 5
Jhang Maghiāna, 195,558 .... E 5
Karāchi, 4,901,627 (5,300,000★) ...... H 2
Kasūr, 155,523 ...... E 6
Lahore, 2,707,215 (3,025,000★) ...... E 6
Lārkāna, 123,890 .... G 3
Mardān, 141,842 (147,977★) .... C 5
Mīrpur Khās, 124,371 H 3
Multān, 696,316 (732,070★) .... E 4
Nawābshāh, 102,139 G 3
Okāra, 127,455 (153,483★) .... E 5
Peshāwar, 506,896 (566,248★) .... C 4
Quetta, 244,842 (285,719★) .... E 2
Rahīmyār Khān, 119,036 (132,635★) .... F 4
Rāwalpindi, 457,091 (1,040,000★) ...... D 5
Sāhiwāl (Montgomery), 150,954 .... E 5
Sargodha, 231,895 (291,362★) .... D 5
Shekhūpura, 141,168 E 5
Siālkot, 258,147 (302,009★) .... D 6
Sukkur, 190,551 .... G 3
Wah, 122,335 ...... D 5

Eastern Mediterranean Lands

Cyprus
1982 CENSUS
Lemesós (Limassol), 74,782 (107,161★) B 3
Nicosia, 48,221 (185,000★) . . . . . . B 3

Cyprus, North
1985 ESTIMATE
Nicosia, 37,400 . . . . B 3

Egypt
1986 CENSUS
Al-Iskandarīyah (Alexandria), 2,917,327 (3,350,000★) . . . . D 1
Al-Ismā'īlīyah (Ismailia), 212,567 (235,000★) D 3
Al-Jīzah (Giza), 1,870,508 . . . . . . D 2
Al-Qāhirah (Cairo), 6,052,836 (9,300,000★) . . . . D 2
As-Suways (Suez), 326,820 . . . . E 3
Asyūt, 273,191 . . . . F 2
Būr Sa'īd (Port Said), 399,793 . . . . D 3
Cairo *see* Al-Qāhirah D 2
Ṭanṭā, 334,505 . . . . D 2

Israel
1989 ESTIMATE
Be'er Sheva', 113,200 D 4
Ḥefa (Haifa), 222,600 (435,000★) . . . . . . C 4

Jerusalem *see* Yerushalayim . . . . D 4
Tel Aviv-Yafo, 317,800 (1,735,000★) . . . . C 4
Yerushalayim (Jerusalem), 493,500 (530,000★) D 4

Israeli Occupied Territories
1971 ESTIMATE
Ghazzah (Gaza), 118,272('67) . . . . D 4
Nābulus, 64,000 . . . . C 4

Jordan
1989 ESTIMATE
'Ammān, 936,300 (1,450,000★) . . . . D 4
Az-Zarqā', 318,055 . . C 5
Irbid, 167,785 . . . . . . C 4

Lebanon
1982 ESTIMATE
Bayrūt (Beirut), 509,000 (1,675,000★) . . . . C 4
Ṭarābulus (Tripoli), 198,000 . . . . B 4

Saudi Arabia
1980 ESTIMATE
Al-Madīnah (Medina), 290,000 . . . . G 6

Syria
1988 ESTIMATE
Al-Lādhiqīyah (Latakia), 249,000 . . . . B 4
Al-Qāmishlī, 126,236 A 7
Dayr az-Zawr, 112,000 . . . . B 7
Dimashq (Damascus), 1,326,000 (1,950,000★) . . . . C 5
Ḥalab (Aleppo), 1,261,000 (1,275,000★) . . . . A 5
Ḥamāh, 222,000 . . . . B 5
Ḥimṣ (Homs), 447,000 B 5

★ Population of metropolitan area, including suburbs.

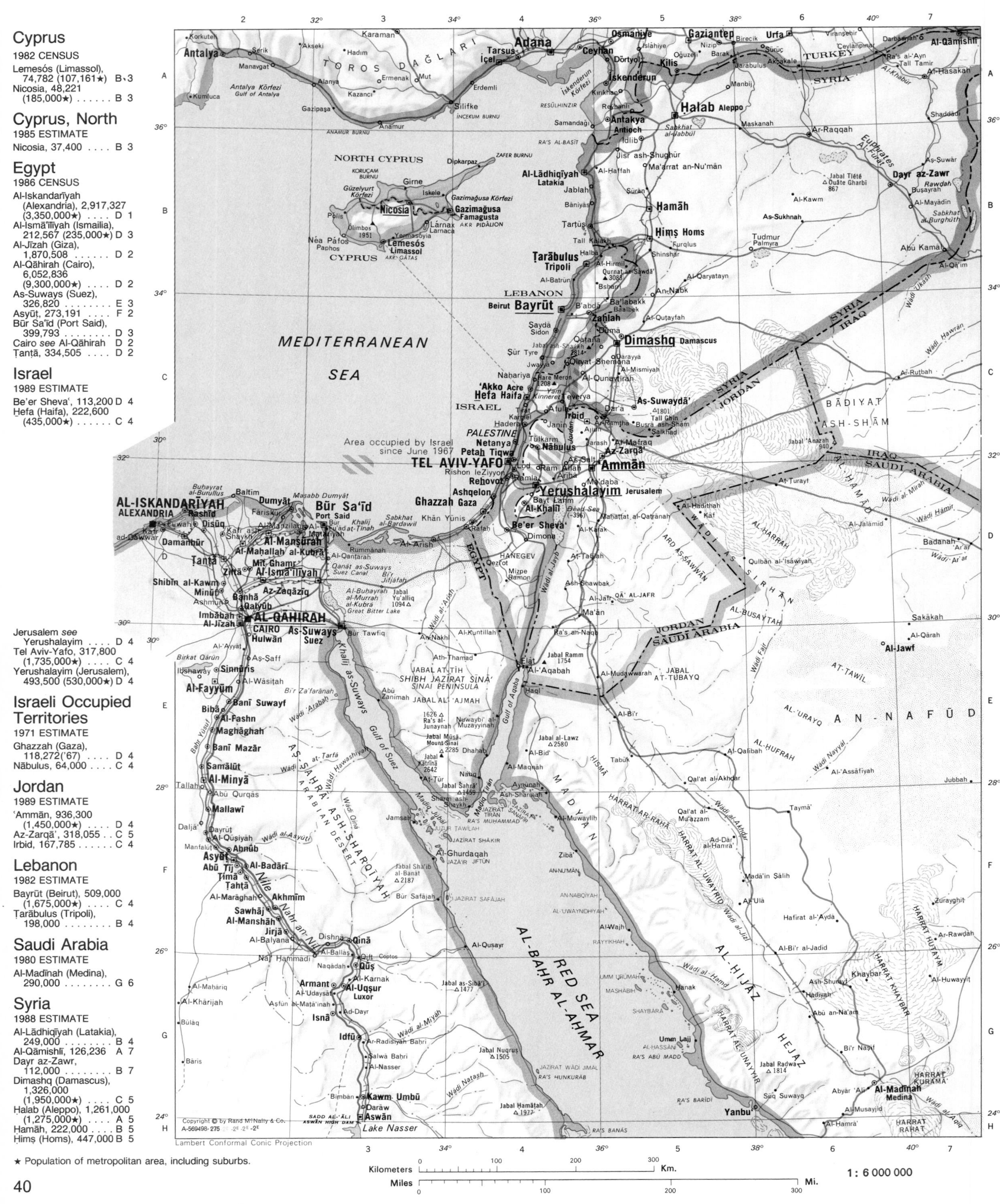

Abidjan, 1,950,000 ('83)........E 3
Accra, 859,640 ('84) (1,250,000★)..........E 3
Adis Abeba (Addis Ababa), 1,686,300 ('88) (1,500,000★)..........E 7
Alger (Algiers), 1,507,241 ('87) (2,547,983★)...B 4
ALGERIA..................C 4
Al-Iskandarīyah (Alexandria), 2,917,327 ('86) (3,350,000★)..........B 6
Al-Kharṭūm (Khartoum), 476,218 ('83) (1,450,000★)..........D 7
Al-Qāhirah (Cairo), 6,052,836 ('86) (9,300,000★)..........B 7
ANGOLA..................G 5
BENIN..................E 4
BOTSWANA..................H 6
Brazzaville, 585,812 ('84)..................F 5
BURKINA FASO..........D 3
BURUNDI..................F 6
Cairo see Al-Qāhirah...B 7
CAMEROON..................E 5
Cape Town, 776,617 ('85) (1,790,000★)..........I 5
Casablanca, 2,139,204 ('82) (2,475,000★)...B 3
CENTRAL AFRICAN REPUBLIC..................E 5
CHAD..................D 5
COMOROS..................G 8
CONGO..................F 5
Dakar, 1,447,642 ('88) D 2
Dar es Salaam, 1,300,000 ('84)..................F 7
DJIBOUTI..................D 8
EGYPT..................C 6
EQUATORIAL GUINEA..................E 4
ETHIOPIA..................E 7
GABON..................F 5
GAMBIA..................D 2
GHANA..................E 3
GUINEA..................D 2
GUINEA-BISSAU..........D 2
IVORY COAST..........E 3
Johannesburg, 632,369 ('85) (3,650,000★)..........H 6
Kampala, 1,008,707 ('90)..................E 7
KENYA..................E 7
Kinshasa (Léopoldville), 3,000,000 ('86)..........F 5
Lagos, 1,213,000 ('87) (3,800,000★)..........E 4
LESOTHO..................H 6
LIBERIA..................E 3
LIBYA..................C 5
MADAGASCAR..........G 8
MALAWI..................G 7
MALI..................D 3
Maputo (Lourenço Marques), 1,069,727 ('89)..................H 7
MAURITANIA..........D 2
MOROCCO..................B 3
MOZAMBIQUE..........G 7
Nairobi, 1,505,000 ('90)..................F 7
NAMIBIA..................H 5
NIGER..................D 4
NIGERIA..................E 4
RWANDA..................F 6
SAO TOME AND PRINCIPE..................E 4
SENEGAL..................D 2
SIERRA LEONE..........E 2
SOMALIA..................E 8
SOUTH AFRICA..........I 6
SUDAN..................D 6
SWAZILAND..........H 7
TANZANIA..................F 7
Tarābulus (Tripoli), 990,697 ('84)..........B 5
TOGO..................E 4
Tunis, 596,654 ('84) (1,225,000★)..........B 5
TUNISIA..................B 4
UGANDA..................E 7
WESTERN SAHARA...C 2
ZAIRE..................F 6
ZAMBIA..................G 6
ZIMBABWE..................G 6

★ Population of metropolitan area, including suburbs.

Northern Africa

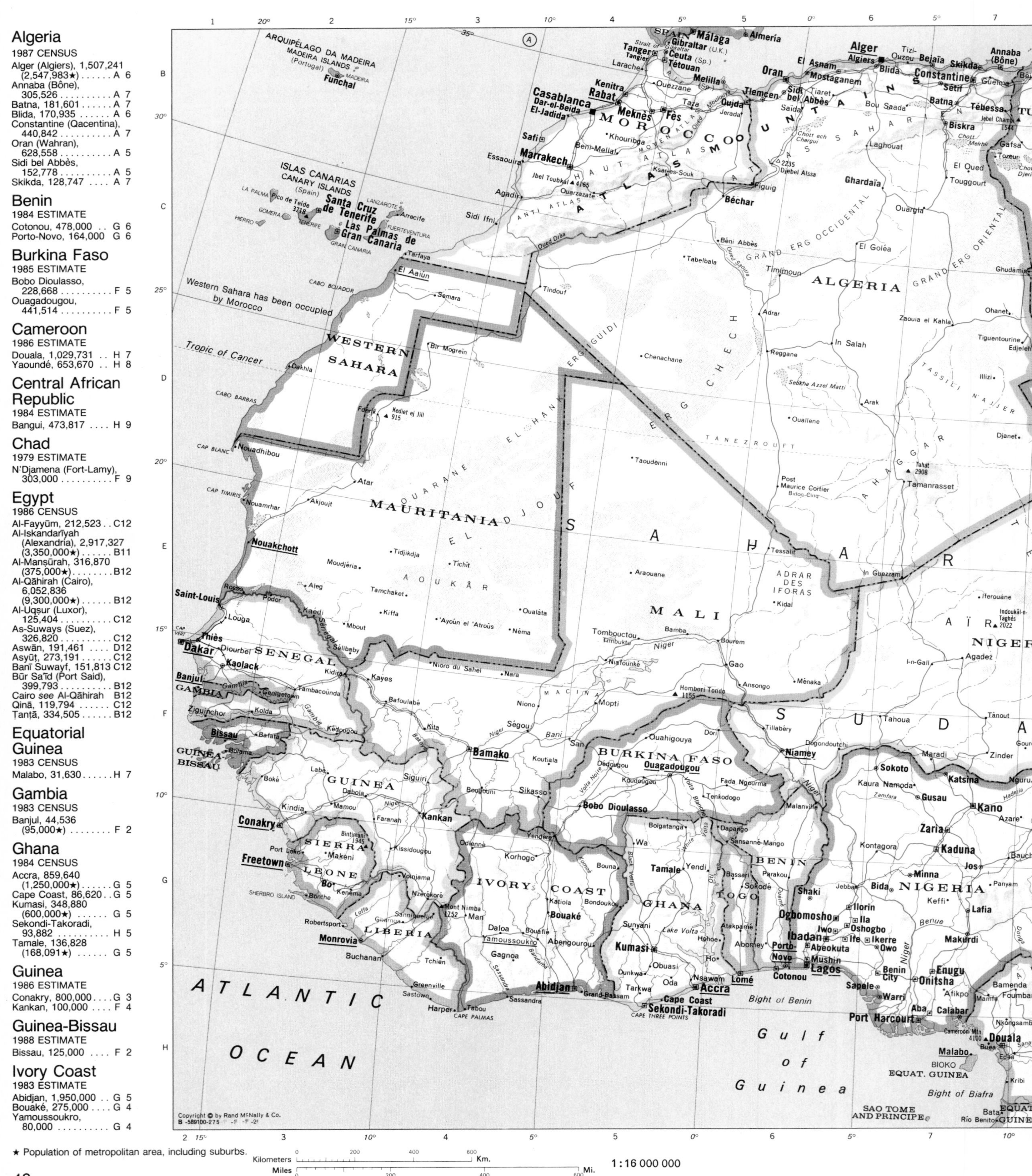

Algeria
1987 CENSUS
Alger (Algiers), 1,507,241 (2,547,983★) . . . . . A 6
Annaba (Bône), 305,526 . . . . A 7
Batna, 181,601 . . . . . A 7
Blida, 170,935 . . . . . . A 6
Constantine (Qacentina), 440,842 . . . . A 7
Oran (Wahran), 628,558 . . . . A 5
Sidi bel Abbès, 152,778 . . . . A 5
Skikda, 128,747 . . . . A 7

Benin
1984 ESTIMATE
Cotonou, 478,000 . . G 6
Porto-Novo, 164,000 G 6

Burkina Faso
1985 ESTIMATE
Bobo Dioulasso, 228,668 . . . . F 5
Ouagadougou, 441,514 . . . . F 5

Cameroon
1986 ESTIMATE
Douala, 1,029,731 . . H 7
Yaoundé, 653,670 . . H 8

Central African Republic
1984 ESTIMATE
Bangui, 473,817 . . . . H 9

Chad
1979 ESTIMATE
N'Djamena (Fort-Lamy), 303,000 . . . . F 9

Egypt
1986 CENSUS
Al-Fayyūm, 212,523 . . C12
Al-Iskandarīyah (Alexandria), 2,917,327 (3,350,000★) B11
Al-Manṣūrah, 316,870 (375,000★) B12
Al-Qāhirah (Cairo), 6,052,836 (9,300,000★) B12
Al-Uqṣur (Luxor), 125,404 . . . . C12
As-Suways (Suez), 326,820 . . . . C12
Aswān, 191,461 . . . . D12
Asyūṭ, 273,191 . . . . . . C12
Banī Suwayf, 151,813 C12
Būr Sa'īd (Port Said), 399,793 . . . . B12
Cairo *see* Al-Qāhirah B12
Qinā, 119,794 . . . . . . C12
Ṭanṭā, 334,505 . . . . . . B12

Equatorial Guinea
1983 CENSUS
Malabo, 31,630 . . . . . . H 7

Gambia
1983 CENSUS
Banjul, 44,536 (95,000★) . . . . F 2

Ghana
1984 CENSUS
Accra, 859,640 (1,250,000★) . . . . G 5
Cape Coast, 86,620 . . G 5
Kumasi, 348,880 (600,000★) . . . . . . G 5
Sekondi-Takoradi, 93,882 . . . . H 5
Tamale, 136,828 (168,091★) . . . . . . G 5

Guinea
1986 ESTIMATE
Conakry, 800,000 . . . . G 3
Kankan, 100,000 . . . . F 4

Guinea-Bissau
1988 ESTIMATE
Bissau, 125,000 . . . . F 2

Ivory Coast
1983 ESTIMATE
Abidjan, 1,950,000 . . G 5
Bouaké, 275,000 . . . . G 4
Yamoussoukro, 80,000 . . . . G 4

★ Population of metropolitan area, including suburbs.

Kilometers 0 200 400 600 Km.
Miles 0 200 400 600 Mi.

1:16 000 000

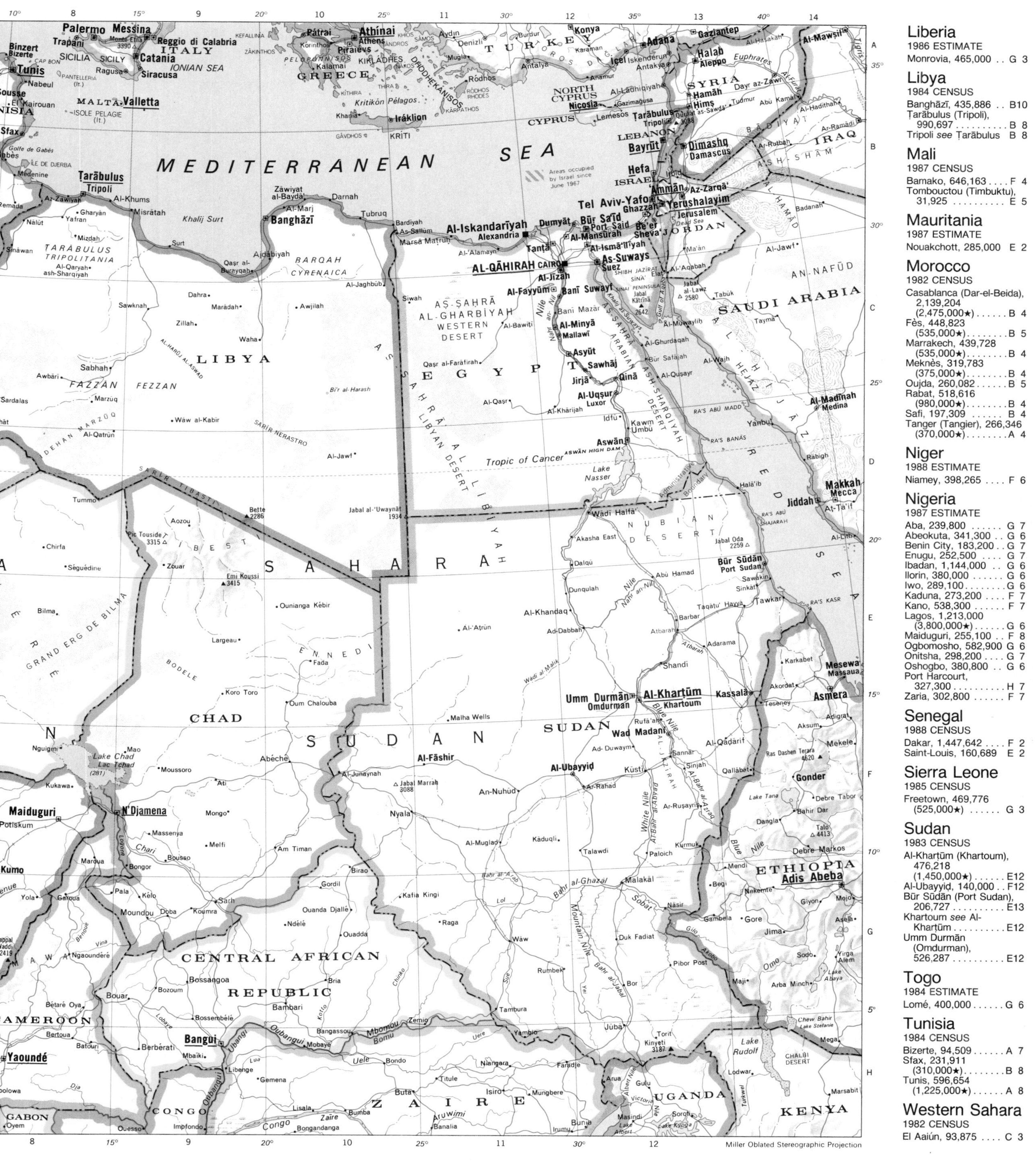

Liberia
1986 ESTIMATE
Monrovia, 465,000 . . G 3

Libya
1984 CENSUS
Banghāzī, 435,886 . . B10
Ṭarābulus (Tripoli), 990,697 . . . . B 8
Tripoli *see* Ṭarābulus B 8

Mali
1987 CENSUS
Bamako, 646,163 . . . . F 4
Tombouctou (Timbuktu), 31,925 . . . . E 5

Mauritania
1987 ESTIMATE
Nouakchott, 285,000 E 2

Morocco
1982 CENSUS
Casablanca (Dar-el-Beida), 2,139,204 (2,475,000★) . . . . . . B 4
Fès, 448,823 (535,000★) . . . . B 5
Marrakech, 439,728 (535,000★) . . . . B 4
Meknès, 319,783 (375,000★) . . . . B 4
Oujda, 260,082 . . . . . . B 5
Rabat, 518,616 (980,000★) . . . . B 4
Safi, 197,309 . . . . . . B 4
Tanger (Tangier), 266,346 (370,000★) . . . . A 4

Niger
1988 ESTIMATE
Niamey, 398,265 . . . . F 6

Nigeria
1987 ESTIMATE
Aba, 239,800 . . . . . . G 7
Abeokuta, 341,300 . . G 6
Benin City, 183,200 . . G 7
Enugu, 252,500 . . . . G 7
Ibadan, 1,144,000 . . G 6
Ilorin, 380,000 . . . . . . G 6
Iwo, 289,100 . . . . G 6
Kaduna, 273,200 . . . . F 7
Kano, 538,300 . . . . . . F 7
Lagos, 1,213,000 (3,800,000★) . . . . . . G 6
Maiduguri, 255,100 . . F 8
Ogbomosho, 582,900 G 6
Onitsha, 298,200 . . . . G 7
Oshogbo, 380,800 . . G 6
Port Harcourt, 327,300 . . . . H 7
Zaria, 302,800 . . . . . . F 7

Senegal
1988 CENSUS
Dakar, 1,447,642 . . . . F 2
Saint-Louis, 160,689 E 2

Sierra Leone
1985 CENSUS
Freetown, 469,776 (525,000★) . . . . . . G 3

Sudan
1983 CENSUS
Al-Kharṭūm (Khartoum), 476,218 (1,450,000★) E12
Al-Ubayyiḍ, 140,000 . . F12
Būr Sūdān (Port Sudan), 206,727 . . . . E13
Khartoum *see* Al-Kharṭūm E12
Umm Durmān (Omdurman), 526,287 . . . . E12

Togo
1984 ESTIMATE
Lomé, 400,000 . . . . . . G 6

Tunisia
1984 CENSUS
Bizerte, 94,509 . . . . . . A 7
Sfax, 231,911 (310,000★) . . . . B 8
Tunis, 596,654 (1,225,000★) . . . . . . A 8

Western Sahara
1982 CENSUS
El Aaiún, 93,875 . . . . C 3

Southern Africa

Angola
1983 ESTIMATE
Benguela, 155,000 . . D 2
Huambo, 203,000 . . D 3
Lobito, 150,000 . . . . D 2
Luanda, 1,459,900('89) . . . . C 2
Namibe, 100,000('81) E 2

Botswana
1987 ESTIMATE
Gaborone, 107,677 . . F 5

Burundi
1986 ESTIMATE
Bujumbura, 273,000 B 5

Comoros
1990 ESTIMATE
Moroni, 23,432 . . . . D 8

Congo
1984 CENSUS
Brazzaville, 585,812 B 3
Pointe-Noire, 294,203 B 2

Gabon
1985 ESTIMATE
Libreville, 235,700 . . A 1
Port-Gentil, 124,400 . . B 1

Kenya
1990 ESTIMATE
Mombasa, 537,000 . . B 7
Nairobi, 1,505,000 . . B 7
Nakuru, 101,700('84) B 7

Lesotho
1986 CENSUS
Maseru, 109,382 . . . . G 5

Madagascar
1984 ESTIMATE
Antananarivo, 663,000('85) . . . . E 9
Antsiranana, 100,000 D 9
Fianarantsoa, 130,000 F 9
Mahajanga, 85,000 . . E 9
Toamasina, 100,000 E 9

Malawi
1987 CENSUS
Blantyre, 331,588 . . E 7
Lilongwe, 233,973 . . D 6
Zomba, 42,878 . . . . E 7

Mauritius
1987 ESTIMATE
Port Louis, 139,730 (420,000★) F11

Mayotte
1985 ESTIMATE
Dzaoudzi, 5,865 (6,979★) . . . . D 9

Mozambique
1989 ESTIMATE
Beira, 291,604 . . . . . . E 6
Maputo (Lourenço Marques), 1,069,727 . . . . . . G 6
Xai-Xai, 51,620('86) . . G 6

Namibia
1988 ESTIMATE
Windhoek, 114,500 . . F 3

Reunion
1982 CENSUS
Saint-Denis, 84,400 (109,072▲) F11

Rwanda
1983 ESTIMATE
Kigali, 181,600 . . . . B 6

Sao Tome and Principe
1970 CENSUS
São Tomé, 17,380 . . A 1

Seychelles
1984 ESTIMATE
Victoria, 23,000 . . . . B11

Miller Oblated Stereographic Projection

★ Population of metropolitan area, including suburbs.
▲ Population of entire district, including rural area.

Somalia
1984 ESTIMATE
Kismayu, 70,000 . . . . B 8

South Africa
1985 CENSUS
Bloemfontein, 104,381 (235,000★) . . . . . . G 5
Cape Town (Kaapstad), 776,617 (1,790,000★) . . . . H 3
Durban, 634,301 (1,550,000★) . . . . G 6
East London (Oos-Londen), 85,699 (320,000★) . . . . . . H 5
Germiston, 116,718 . . G 5
Johannesburg, 632,369 (3,650,000★) . . . . G 5
Kimberley, 74,061 (145,000★) . . . . . . G 4
King William's Town, 16,123 (48,300★) . . H 5
Klerksdorp, 48,947 (205,000★) . . . . . . G 5
Ladysmith, 25,102 (31,670★) . . . . . . G 5
Pietermaritzburg, 133,809 (230,000★) . . . . . . G 6
Port Elizabeth, 272,844 (690,000★) . . . . . . H 5
Potchefstroom, 43,766 (78,865★) . . . . . . G 5
Pretoria, 443,059 (960,000★) . . . . . . G 5
Springs, 68,235 . . . . G 5
Uitenhage, 54,987 . . H 5
Vereeniging, 60,584 (525,000★) . . . . . . G 5
Walvisbaai (Walvis Bay), 9,687 (16,607★) . . F 2
Welkom, 54,488 (215,000★) . . . . . . G 5

Swaziland
1986 CENSUS
Mbabane, 38,290 . . G 6

Tanzania
1984 ESTIMATE
Arusha, 69,000 . . . . B 7
Dar es Salaam, 1,300,000 . . . . . C 7
Mwanza, 110,611('78) B 6
Tanga, 121,000 . . . . C 7
Zanzibar, 133,000('85) C 7

Uganda
1990 ESTIMATE
Kampala, 1,008,707 . . A 6

Zaire
1984 CENSUS
Boma, 88,556 . . . . . . C 2
Bukavu, 171,064 . . . . B 5
Kalemie (Albertville), 70,694 . . . . C 5
Kananga (Luluabourg), 290,898 . . . . C 4
Kikwit, 146,784 . . . . C 3
Kinshasa (Léopoldville), 3,000,000('86) . . . . B 3
Kisangani (Stanleyville), 282,650 . . . . A 5
Kolwezi, 201,382 . . . . D 5
Likasi (Jadotville), 194,465 . . . . D 5
Lubumbashi (Élisabethville), 543,268 . . . . D 5
Matadi, 144,742 . . . . C 2
Mbandaka (Coquilhatville), 125,263 . . . . A 3
Mbuji-Mayi (Bakwanga), 423,363 . . . . C 4

Zambia
1980 CENSUS
Chingola, 130,872 . . D 5
Kabwe (Broken Hill), 127,420 . . . . D 5
Kitwe, 207,500 (283,962★) . . . . . . D 5
Livingstone, 61,296 . . E 5
Luanshya, 61,600 (113,422★) . . . . . . D 5
Lusaka, 535,830 . . . . E 5
Mufulira, 77,100 (138,824★) . . . . . . D 5
Ndola, 250,490 . . . . D 5

Zimbabwe
1983 ESTIMATE
Bulawayo, 429,000 . . F 5
Harare, 681,000 (890,000★) . . . . . . E 6

Eastern Africa and Middle East

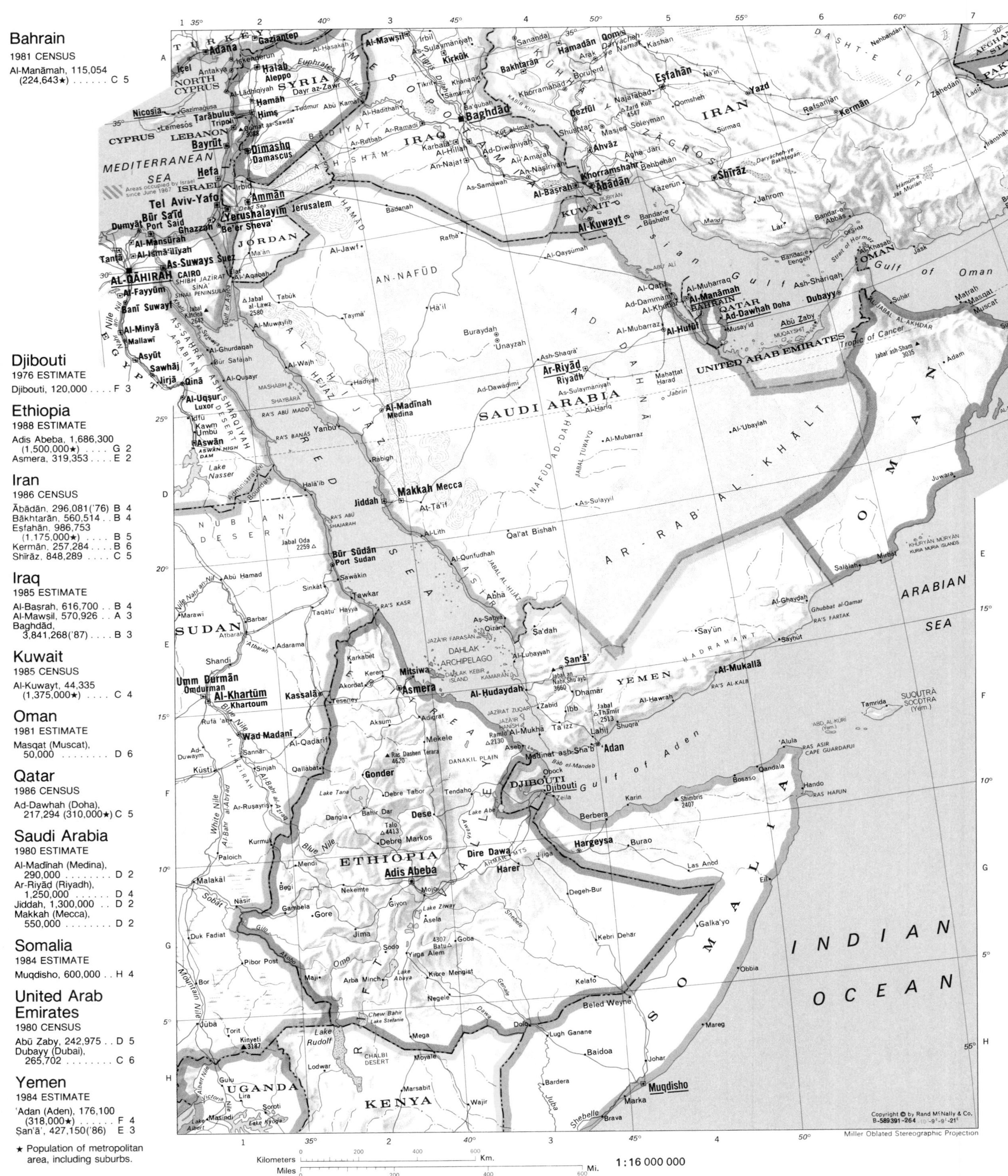

Bahrain
1981 CENSUS

Al-Manāmah, 115,054 (224,643★) . . . . . . C 5

Djibouti
1976 ESTIMATE

Djibouti, 120,000 . . . F 3

Ethiopia
1988 ESTIMATE

Adis Abeba, 1,686,300 (1,500,000★) . . . . G 2

Asmera, 319,353 . . . . E 2

Iran
1986 CENSUS

Ābādān, 296,081('76) B 4

Bākhtarān, 560,514 . . B 4

Eṣfahān, 986,753 (1,175,000★) . . . . B 5

Kermān, 257,284 . . . . B 6

Shīrāz, 848,289 . . . . C 5

Iraq
1985 ESTIMATE

Al-Baṣrah, 616,700 . . B 4

Al-Mawṣil, 570,926 . . A 3

Baghdād, 3,841,268('87) . . . . B 3

Kuwait
1985 CENSUS

Al-Kuwayt, 44,335 (1,375,000★) . . . . C 4

Oman
1981 ESTIMATE

Masqaṭ (Muscat), 50,000 . . . . D 6

Qatar
1986 CENSUS

Ad-Dawhah (Doha), 217,294 (310,000★) C 5

Saudi Arabia
1980 ESTIMATE

Al-Madīnah (Medina), 290,000 . . . . D 2

Ar-Riyāḍ (Riyadh), 1,250,000 . . . . . . D 4

Jiddah, 1,300,000 . . D 2

Makkah (Mecca), 550,000 . . . . D 2

Somalia
1984 ESTIMATE

Muqdisho, 600,000 . . H 4

United Arab Emirates
1980 CENSUS

Abū Ẓaby, 242,975 . . D 5

Dubayy (Dubai), 265,702 . . . . C 6

Yemen
1984 ESTIMATE

'Adan (Aden), 176,100 (318,000★) . . . . . . F 4

Ṣan'ā', 427,150('86) E 3

★ Population of metropolitan area, including suburbs.

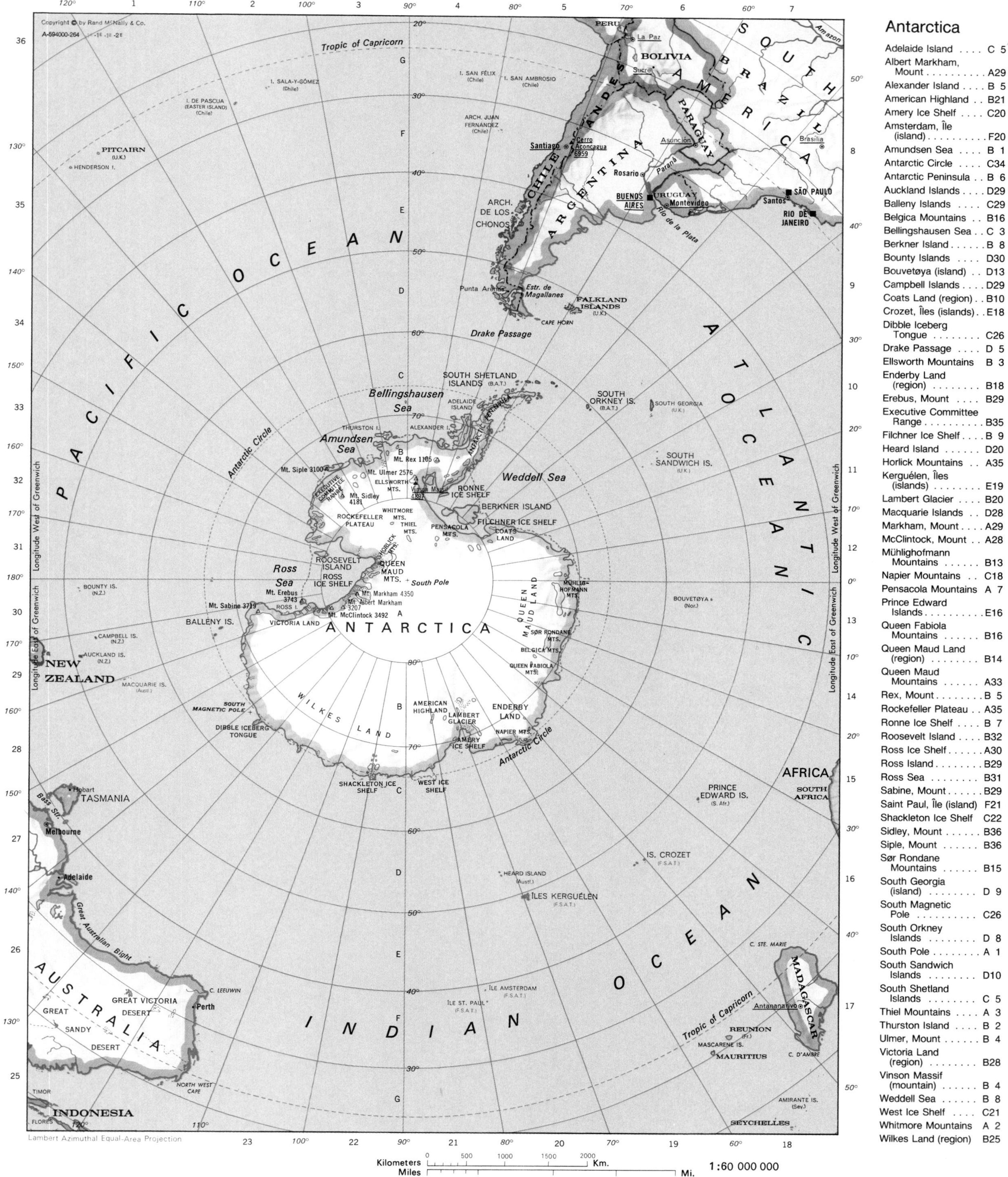

Antarctica

Place	Grid
Adelaide Island	C 5
Albert Markham, Mount	A29
Alexander Island	B 5
American Highland	B21
Amery Ice Shelf	C20
Amsterdam, Île (island)	F20
Amundsen Sea	B 1
Antarctic Circle	C34
Antarctic Peninsula	B 6
Auckland Islands	D29
Balleny Islands	C29
Belgica Mountains	B16
Bellingshausen Sea	C 3
Berkner Island	B 8
Bounty Islands	D30
Bouvetøya (island)	D13
Campbell Islands	D29
Coats Land (region)	B10
Crozet, Îles (islands)	E18
Dibble Iceberg Tongue	C26
Drake Passage	D 5
Ellsworth Mountains	B 3
Enderby Land (region)	B18
Erebus, Mount	B29
Executive Committee Range	B35
Filchner Ice Shelf	B 9
Heard Island	D20
Horlick Mountains	A35
Kerguélen, Îles (islands)	E19
Lambert Glacier	B20
Macquarie Islands	D28
Markham, Mount	A29
McClintock, Mount	A28
Mühlighofmann Mountains	B13
Napier Mountains	C18
Pensacola Mountains	A 7
Prince Edward Islands	E16
Queen Fabiola Mountains	B16
Queen Maud Land (region)	B14
Queen Maud Mountains	A33
Rex, Mount	B 5
Rockefeller Plateau	A35
Ronne Ice Shelf	B 7
Roosevelt Island	B32
Ross Ice Shelf	A30
Ross Island	B29
Ross Sea	B31
Sabine, Mount	B29
Saint Paul, Île (island)	F21
Shackleton Ice Shelf	C22
Sidley, Mount	B36
Siple, Mount	B36
Sør Rondane Mountains	B15
South Georgia (island)	D 9
South Magnetic Pole	C26
South Orkney Islands	D 8
South Pole	A 1
South Sandwich Islands	D10
South Shetland Islands	C 5
Thiel Mountains	A 3
Thurston Island	B 2
Ulmer, Mount	B 4
Victoria Land (region)	B28
Vinson Massif (mountain)	B 4
Weddell Sea	B 8
West Ice Shelf	C21
Whitmore Mountains	A 2
Wilkes Land (region)	B25

Pacific Ocean

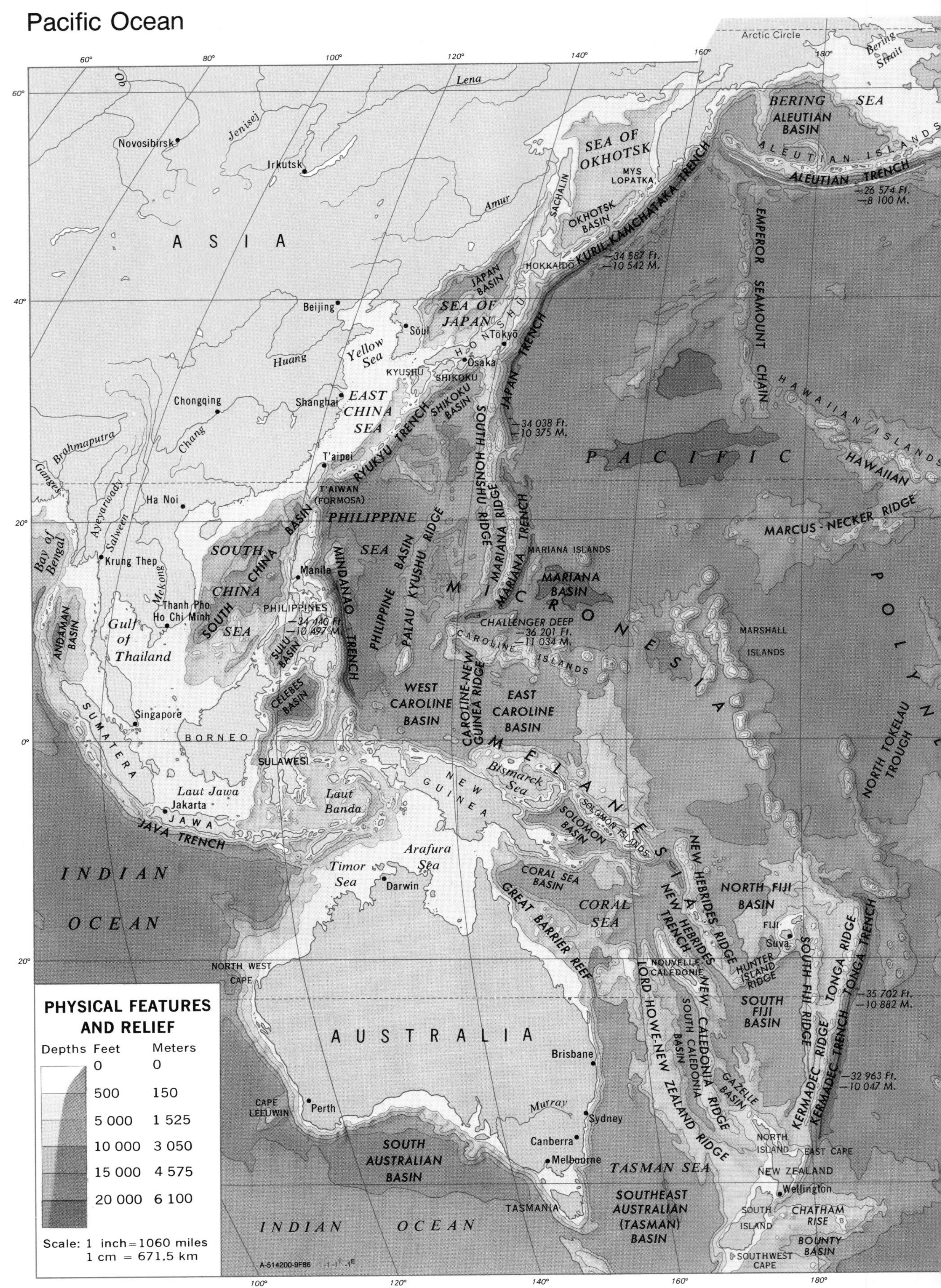

PHYSICAL FEATURES AND RELIEF
Depths Feet Meters
0 0
500 150
5 000 1 525
10 000 3 050
15 000 4 575
20 000 6 100
Scale: 1 inch=1060 miles
1 cm = 671.5 km
A S I A
P A C I F I C
A U S T R A L I A
I N D I A N O C E A N
INDIAN OCEAN
Arctic Circle
Bering Strait
BERING SEA
ALEUTIAN BASIN
ALEUTIAN ISLANDS
ALEUTIAN TRENCH
−26 574 Ft.
−8 100 M.
SEA OF OKHOTSK
MYS LOPATKA
OKHOTSK BASIN
SACHALIN
KURIL-KAMCHATAKA TRENCH
−34 587 Ft.
−10 542 M.
HOKKAIDO
EMPEROR SEAMOUNT CHAIN
HAWAIIAN ISLANDS
HAWAIIAN
JAPAN BASIN
SEA OF JAPAN
HONSHU
Tōkyō
Ōsaka
JAPAN TRENCH
−34 038 Ft.
−10 375 M.
KYUSHU
SHIKOKU
SHIKOKU BASIN
SOUTH HONSHU RIDGE
MARIANA RIDGE
MARIANA TRENCH
MARIANA ISLANDS
MARIANA BASIN
MARCUS-NECKER RIDGE
Ob
Lena
Jenisej
Novosibirsk
Irkutsk
Amur
Beijing
Sŏul
Yellow Sea
Huang
Chongqing
Chang
Shanghai
EAST CHINA SEA
RYUKYU TRENCH
T'aipei
T'AIWAN (FORMOSA)
Brahmaputra
Ganges
Ayeyarwady
Salween
Ha Noi
Bay of Bengal
Krung Thep
Mekong
Thanh Pho Ho Chi Minh
Gulf of Thailand
ANDAMAN BASIN
SOUTH CHINA SEA
SOUTH CHINA BASIN
PHILIPPINE SEA
PHILIPPINE BASIN
Manila
PHILIPPINES
−34 440 Ft.
−10 497 M.
MINDANAO TRENCH
PHILIPPINE TRENCH
KYUSHU-PALAU RIDGE
PALAU BASIN
SULU BASIN
CELEBES BASIN
M I C R O N E S I A
CHALLENGER DEEP
−36 201 Ft.
−11 034 M.
CAROLINE ISLANDS
MARSHALL ISLANDS
P O L Y N E
WEST CAROLINE BASIN
EAST CAROLINE BASIN
CAROLINE-NEW GUINEA RIDGE
NORTH TOKELAU TROUGH
Singapore
SUMATERA
BORNEO
SULAWESI
Laut Jawa
Jakarta
JAWA
JAVA TRENCH
Laut Banda
NEW GUINEA
Bismarck Sea
M E L A N E S I A
SOLOMON ISLANDS
SOLOMON BASIN
Arafura Sea
Timor Sea
Darwin
CORAL SEA BASIN
CORAL SEA
GREAT BARRIER REEF
NEW HEBRIDES RIDGE
NEW HEBRIDES TRENCH
NORTH FIJI BASIN
FIJI
Suva
HUNTER ISLAND RIDGE
SOUTH FIJI RIDGE
SOUTH FIJI BASIN
TONGA RIDGE
TONGA TRENCH
−35 702 Ft.
−10 882 M.
NOUVELLE CALEDONIE
NEW CALEDONIA RIDGE
SOUTH CALEDONIA BASIN
LORD HOWE-NEW ZEALAND RIDGE
GAZELLE BASIN
KERMADEC RIDGE
KERMADEC TRENCH
−32 963 Ft.
−10 047 M.
NORTH WEST CAPE
Brisbane
CAPE LEEUWIN
Perth
Murray
Sydney
Canberra
Melbourne
TASMAN SEA
SOUTH AUSTRALIAN BASIN
TASMANIA
SOUTHEAST AUSTRALIAN (TASMAN) BASIN
NORTH ISLAND
EAST CAPE
NEW ZEALAND
Wellington
SOUTH ISLAND
CHATHAM RISE
BOUNTY BASIN
SOUTHWEST CAPE
A-514200-9F86

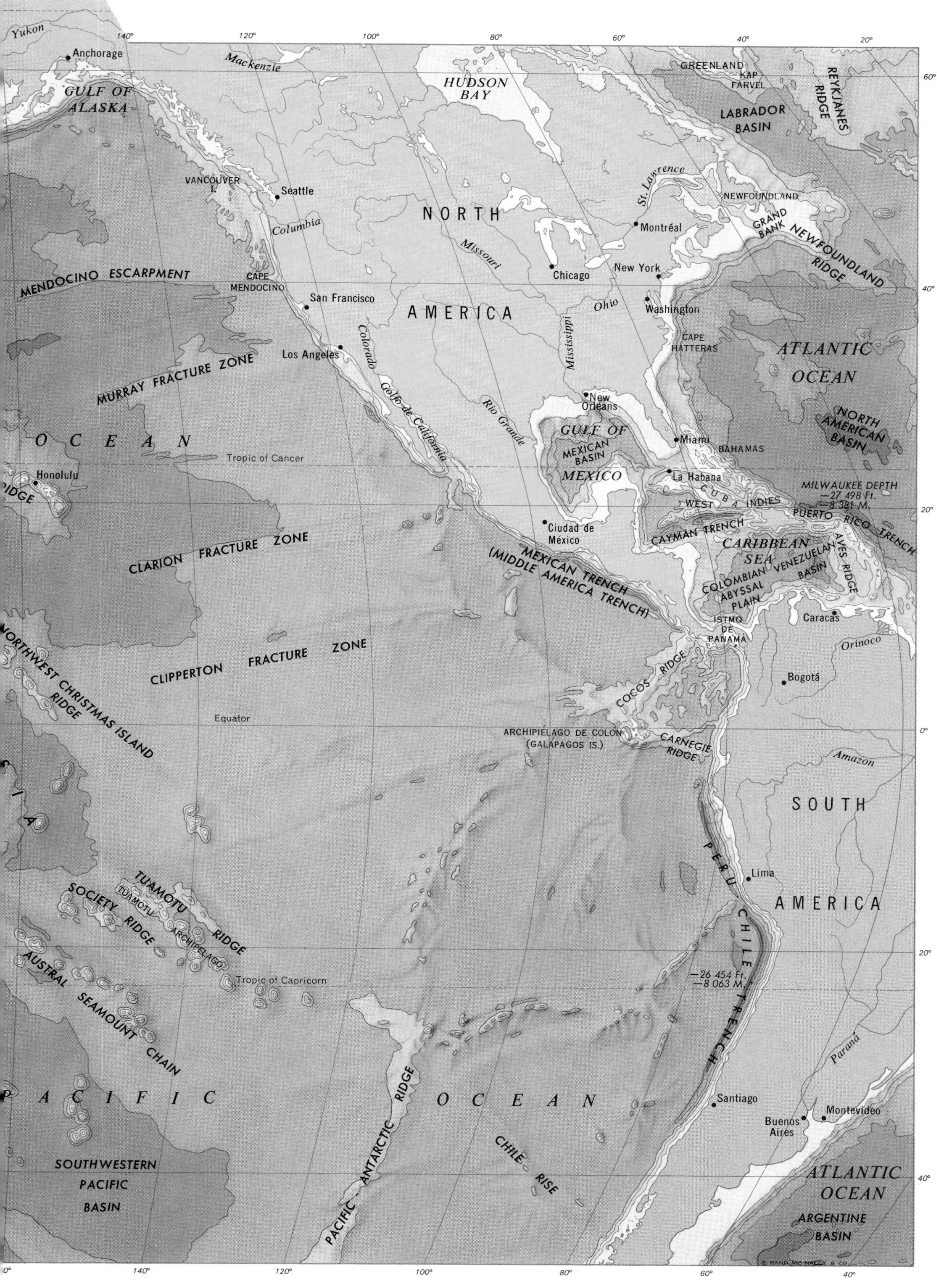

Yukon
Anchorage
Mackenzie
GULF OF ALASKA
HUDSON BAY
GREENLAND
KAP FARVEL
REYKJANES RIDGE
LABRADOR BASIN
St. Lawrence
NEWFOUNDLAND
GRAND BANK
NEWFOUNDLAND RIDGE
VANCOUVER I.
Seattle
Columbia
NORTH AMERICA
Missouri
Montréal
Chicago
New York
Washington
Ohio
MENDOCINO ESCARPMENT
CAPE MENDOCINO
San Francisco
Colorado
Mississippi
CAPE HATTERAS
ATLANTIC OCEAN
Los Angeles
MURRAY FRACTURE ZONE
Golfo de California
Rio Grande
New Orleans
NORTH AMERICAN BASIN
GULF OF MEXICO
MEXICAN BASIN
Miami
BAHAMAS
OCEAN
Tropic of Cancer
Honolulu
La Habana
CUBA
WEST INDIES
MILWAUKEE DEPTH
−27 498 Ft.
−8 381 M.
PUERTO RICO TRENCH
Ciudad de México
CAYMAN TRENCH
CARIBBEAN SEA
CLARION FRACTURE ZONE
MEXICAN TRENCH (MIDDLE AMERICA TRENCH)
COLOMBIAN ABYSSAL PLAIN
VENEZUELAN BASIN
AVES RIDGE
ISTMO DE PANAMA
Caracas
Orinoco
CLIPPERTON FRACTURE ZONE
NORTHWEST CHRISTMAS ISLAND RIDGE
COCOS RIDGE
Bogotá
Equator
ARCHIPIÉLAGO DE COLON (GALAPAGOS IS.)
CARNEGIE RIDGE
Amazon
SOUTH AMERICA
PERU CHILE TRENCH
Lima
TUAMOTU RIDGE
SOCIETY RIDGE
TUAMOTU ARCHIPELAGO
AUSTRAL SEAMOUNT CHAIN
Tropic of Capricorn
−26 454 Ft.
−8 063 M.
Paraná
PACIFIC OCEAN
PACIFIC-ANTARCTIC RIDGE
CHILE RISE
Santiago
Buenos Aires
Montevideo
SOUTHWESTERN PACIFIC BASIN
ATLANTIC OCEAN
ARGENTINE BASIN
© RAND McNALLY & CO.
140° 120° 100° 80° 60° 40° 20°
60° 40° 20° 0° 20° 40°

Australia

Australia

1989 ESTIMATE

Adelaide, 12,340 (1,036,747★) . . . . . F 7
Albany, 14,958 . . . . . G 3
Albury, 40,730 (66,530★) . . . . G 9
Alice Springs, 23,600 . . . . D 6
Ararat, 8,015('86) . . . . G 8
Armidale, 21,600 . . . . F10
Augusta, 933('86) . . . . F 3
Ballarat, 36,680 (80,090★) . . . . G 8
Barcaldine, 1,427('86) . . . . D 9
Bendigo, 32,050 (67,920★) . . . . G 8
Blackall, 1,497('86) . . D 9
Bombala, 1,458('86) . . G 9
Bordertown, 2,318('86) . . . . G 8
Bourke, 3,018('86) . . F 9
Bowen, 7,705('86) . . C 9
Brisbane, 744,828 (1,273,511★) E10
Broken Hill, 22,550 . . F 8
Broome, 5,778('86) . . C 4
Bunbury, 26,398 . . . . F 3
Bundaberg, 33,024 (45,161★) D10
Burketown, 232('86) . . . . C 7
Burnie, 20,665('86) . . H 9
Busselton, 7,784('86) . . . . F 3
Cairns, 42,839 (80,875★) . . . . C 9
Camooweal, 315('86) . . . . C 7
Canberra, 247,194 (271,362★)('86) . . . . G 9
Carnarvon, 6,847('86) . . . . D 2
Ceduna, 2,877('86) . . F 6
Cessnock, 43,870 . . . . F10
Charleville, 3,588('86) . . . . E 9
Charters Towers, 7,208('86) . . . . D 9
Cloncurry, 2,297('86) . . . . D 8
Coffs Harbour, 47,890 . . . . F10
Cooktown, 964('86) . . C 9
Coolgardie, 989('86) . . F 4
Cooma, 7,406('86) . . G 9
Croydon, 229('86) . . C 8
Cunnamulla, 1,697('86) . . . . E 9
Dampier, 2,201('86) . . D 3
Darwin, 63,900 (72,937★) . . . . B 6
Derby, 3,258('86) . . . . C 4
Devonport, 25,370 . . H 9
Dongara, 1,496('86) . . E 2
Dubbo, 32,230 . . . . . . F 9
Elizabeth, 29,998 . . . . F 7
Emerald, 5,982('86) . . D 9
Esperance, 6,440('86) . . . . F 4
Geelong, 13,190 (148,980★) . . . . . . G 8
Geraldton, 20,968 . . . . E 2
Gladstone, 22,033('86) D10
Glen Innes, 5,971('86) E10
Goondiwindi, 4,103('86) E10
Goulburn, 21,580 . . . . F 9
Grafton, 15,890 . . . . . . E10
Griffith, 13,630('86) . . F 9
Gympie, 10,772('86) . . E10
Halls Creek, 1,182('86) . . . . C 5
Hay, 2,961('86) . . . . . . F 8
Hobart, 47,280 (181,210★) . . . . H 9
Home Hill, 3,286('86) . . . . C 9
Horsham, 12,850 . . . . G 8
Hughenden, 1,791('86) . . . . D 8
Ingham, 5,202('86) . . C 9
Inverell, 9,693('86) . . E10
Ipswich, 75,283 . . . . . . E10
Kalgoorlie, 26,813 . . . . F 4
Kingaroy, 6,362('86) . . E10
Launceston, 32,150 (92,350★) . . . . H 9
Leonora, 1,004('86) . . E 4
Lismore, 39,450 . . . . E10
Longreach, 3,159('86) . . . . D 8
Mackay, 22,583 (50,885★) . . . . D 9
Maitland, 47,280 . . . . F10
Marble Bar, 332('86) D 3
Mareeba, 6,614('86) . . C 9
Marree, 300('76) . . . . E 7
Meekatharra, 1,018('86) . . . . E 3

★ Population of metropolitan area, including suburbs.

Melbourne, 55,300 (3,039,100★) . . . . . . G 8
Mildura, 20,512('86) . . F 8
Mitchell, 1,212('86) . . E 9
Moora, 1,469('86) . . . . F 3
Moree, 10,215('86) . . E 9
Morwell, 16,880 . . . . G 9
Mount Gambier, 22,194 (27,228★) . . . . G 8
Mount Isa, 24,023 . . D 7
Mount Magnet, 1,000('86) . . . . E 3
Mullewa, 758('86) . . . . E 3
Murwillumbah, 7,678('86) E10
Nambour, 9,579('86) E10
Naracoorte, 4,636('86) . . . . G 8
Newcastle, 130,940 (425,610★) F10
New Norfolk, 6,152('86) . . . . H 9
Normanton, 1,109('86) . . . . C 8
Norseman, 1,775('86) . . . . F 4
Northam, 6,377('86) . . F 3
Nyngan, 2,502('86) . . F 9
Onslow, 750('86) . . . . D 3
Oodnadatta, 200('76) E 7
Orange, 32,980 . . . . . . F 9
Pemberton, 802('86) . . F 3
Perth, 82,413 (1,158,387★) . . . . . . F 3
Peterborough, 2,239('86) . . . . F 7
Port Augusta, 15,752 . . . . F 7
Port Hedland, 13,069('86) . . . . . . D 3
Port Lincoln, 12,941 . . F 7
Port Macquarie, 22,884('86) F10
Port Pirie, 15,210 . . . . F 7
Quilpie, 780('86) . . . . E 8
Ravensthorpe, 299('86) . . . . F 3
Richmond, 704('86) . . D 8
Rockhampton, 58,890 (61,694★) D10
Roebourne, 1,269('86) . . . . D 3
Roma, 6,069('86) . . . . E 9
Saint George, 2,323('86) . . . . E 9
Sale, 13,800 . . . . G 9
Shepparton, 26,420 (39,700★) . . . . G 9
Smithton, 3,414('86) . . H 9
Southern Cross, 898('86) . . . . F 3
Swan Hill, 8,831('86) . . . . G 8
Sydney, 9,800 (3,623,550★) F10
Tamworth, 34,430 . . F10
Taree, 38,760 . . . . . . F10
Tennant Creek, 3,503('86) . . . . C 6
Tenterfield, 3,370('86) E10
Theodore, 576('86) . . D10
Toowoomba, 81,071 . . . . E10
Townsville, 83,339 (111,972★) . . . . C 9
Wagga Wagga, 52,180 . . . . G 9
Walgett, 2,151('86) . . E 9
Wangaratta, 16,320 . . G 9
Warrnambool, 24,480 . . . . G 8
Weipa, 2,406('86) . . . . B 8
Whyalla, 26,706 . . . . . F 7
Wilcannia, 1,048('86) F 8
Wiluna, 279('86) . . . . E 4
Winton, 1,281('86) . . D 8
Wollongong, 174,770 (236,690★) F10
Woomera, 1,805('86) . . . . F 7
Wyndham, 1,329('86) . . . . C 5

Indonesia

1980 CENSUS

Jayapura, 60,641 . . . . k15
Kupang, 84,587 . . . . B 4
Sorong, 52,041 . . . . . . k13

Papua New Guinea

1987 ESTIMATE

Lae, 79,600 . . . . m16
Madang, 24,700 . . . . m16
Port Moresby, 152,100 . . . . m16
Rabaul, 14,954('80) . . k17
Wewak, 23,200 . . . . . . k15

New Zealand

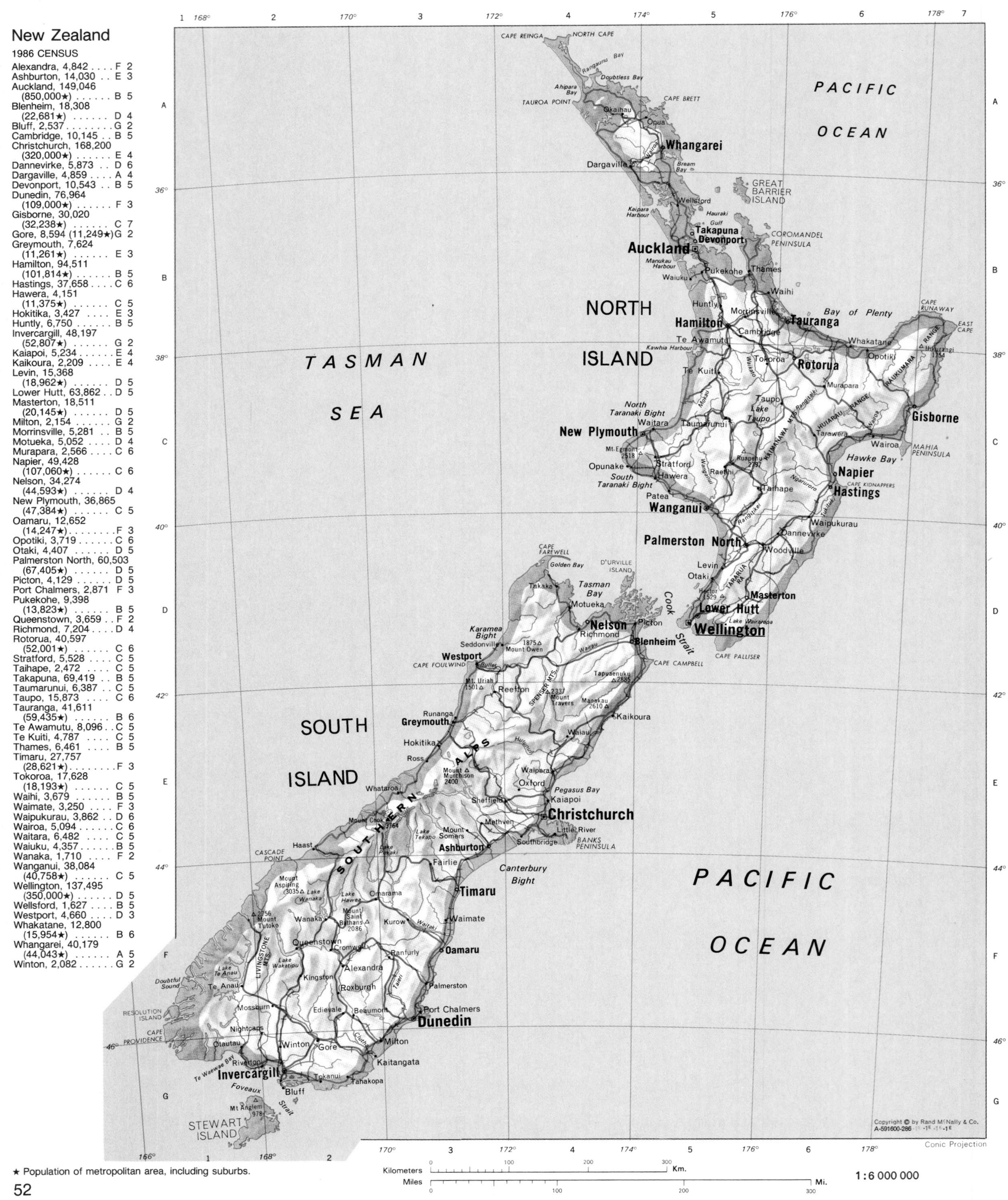

New Zealand

1986 CENSUS

Alexandra, 4,842 . . . . F 2
Ashburton, 14,030 . . E 3
Auckland, 149,046 (850,000★) . . . . . . B 5
Blenheim, 18,308 (22,681★) . . . . . . D 4
Bluff, 2,537 . . . . G 2
Cambridge, 10,145 . . B 5
Christchurch, 168,200 (320,000★) . . . . . . E 4
Dannevirke, 5,873 . . D 6
Dargaville, 4,859 . . . . A 4
Devonport, 10,543 . . B 5
Dunedin, 76,964 (109,000★) . . . . . . F 3
Gisborne, 30,020 (32,238★) . . . . . . C 7
Gore, 8,594 (11,249★) G 2
Greymouth, 7,624 (11,261★) . . . . . . E 3
Hamilton, 94,511 (101,814★) . . . . . . B 5
Hastings, 37,658 . . . . C 6
Hawera, 4,151 (11,375★) . . . . . . C 5
Hokitika, 3,427 . . . . E 3
Huntly, 6,750 . . . . . . B 5
Invercargill, 48,197 (52,807★) . . . . . . G 2
Kaiapoi, 5,234 . . . . . . E 4
Kaikoura, 2,209 . . . . E 4
Levin, 15,368 (18,962★) . . . . . . D 5
Lower Hutt, 63,862 . . D 5
Masterton, 18,511 (20,145★) . . . . . . D 5
Milton, 2,154 . . . . . . G 2
Morrinsville, 5,281 . . B 5
Motueka, 5,052 . . . . D 4
Murapara, 2,566 . . . . C 6
Napier, 49,428 (107,060★) . . . . . . C 6
Nelson, 34,274 (44,593★) . . . . . . D 4
New Plymouth, 36,865 (47,384★) . . . . . . C 5
Oamaru, 12,652 (14,247★) . . . . F 3
Opotiki, 3,719 . . . . . . C 6
Otaki, 4,407 . . . . . . D 5
Palmerston North, 60,503 (67,405★) . . . . . . D 5
Picton, 4,129 . . . . . . D 5
Port Chalmers, 2,871 F 3
Pukekohe, 9,398 (13,823★) . . . . . . B 5
Queenstown, 3,659 . . F 2
Richmond, 7,204 . . . . D 4
Rotorua, 40,597 (52,001★) . . . . . . C 6
Stratford, 5,528 . . . . C 5
Taihape, 2,472 . . . . C 5
Takapuna, 69,419 . . B 5
Taumarunui, 6,387 . . C 5
Taupo, 15,873 . . . . C 6
Tauranga, 41,611 (59,435★) . . . . . . B 6
Te Awamutu, 8,096 . . C 5
Te Kuiti, 4,787 . . . . C 5
Thames, 6,461 . . . . B 5
Timaru, 27,757 (28,621★) . . . . F 3
Tokoroa, 17,628 (18,193★) . . . . . . C 5
Waihi, 3,679 . . . . . . B 5
Waimate, 3,250 . . . . F 3
Waipukurau, 3,862 . . D 6
Wairoa, 5,094 . . . . . . C 6
Waitara, 6,482 . . . . C 5
Waiuku, 4,357 . . . . . . B 5
Wanaka, 1,710 . . . . F 2
Wanganui, 38,084 (40,758★) . . . . . . C 5
Wellington, 137,495 (350,000★) . . . . . . D 5
Wellsford, 1,627 . . . . B 5
Westport, 4,660 . . . . D 3
Whakatane, 12,800 (15,954★) . . . . . . B 6
Whangarei, 40,179 (44,043★) . . . . . . A 5
Winton, 2,082 . . . . . . G 2

★ Population of metropolitan area, including suburbs.

Antofagasta, 185,486 ('82)..........F 3
Arequipa, 108,023 ('81) (446,942★) ....E 3
ARGENTINA..........G 4
Asunción, 477,100 ('85) (700,000★) ....F 5
Bahía Blanca, 223,818 ('80)..........G 4
Barranquilla, 899,781 ('85) (1,140,000★) ....B 3
Belém, 1,116,578 ('85) (1,200,000★) ....D 6
Belo Horizonte, 2,114,429 ('85) (2,950,000★) ...E 6
Bogotá, 3,982,941 ('85) (4,260,000★) ....C 3
BOLIVIA..........E 4
Brasília, 1,567,709 ('85)..........E 6
BRAZIL..........E 5
Buenos Aires, 2,922,829 ('80) (10,750,000★) G 5
Caracas, 1,816,901 ('81) (3,600,000★) ....B 4
Cartagena, 531,426 ('85)..........B 3
Cayenne, 38,091 ('82).C 5
Chiclayo, 213,095 ('81) (279,527★) ....D 3
CHILE..........G 3
Ciudad Bolívar, 182,941 ('81)..........C 4
COLOMBIA..........C 3
Concepción, 267,891 ('82) (675,000★) ....G 3
Cuzco, 89,563 ('81) (184,550★) ....E 3
ECUADOR..........D 3
FALKLAND ISLANDS... I 5
Fortaleza, 1,582,414 ('85) (1,825,000★) ....D 7
FRENCH GUIANA.......C 5
Georgetown, 78,500 ('83) (188,000★) ....C 5
Guayaquil, 1,572,615 ('87) (1,580,000★) ....D 3
GUYANA..........C 5
Iquitos, 178,738 ('81).. D 3
João Pessoa, 348,500 ('85) (550,000★) ..... D 7
La Paz, 992,592 ('85).. E 4
La Plata, 477,175 ('80)..........G 5
Lima, 371,122 ('81) (4,608,010★) ....E 3
Maceió, 482,195 ('85). D 7
Manaus, 809,914 ('85) D 5
Maracaibo, 890,643 ('81)..........B 3
Medellín, 1,468,089 ('85) (2,095,000★) ....C 3
Mendoza, 119,088 ('80) (650,000★) ....G 4
Montevideo, 1,251,647 ('85) (1,550,000★) .. G 5
Natal, 510,106 ('85).....D 7
PARAGUAY..........F 5
Paramaribo, 241,000 ('88) (296,000★) ....C 5
PERU..........E 3
Porto Alegre, 1,272,121 ('85) (2,600,000★) .. G 5
Potosí, 113,380 ('85)...E 4
Punta Arenas, 95,332 ('82).......... I 3
Quito, 1,137,705 ('87) (1,300,000★) ....D 3
Recife, 1,287,623 ('85) (2,625,000★) ....D 7
Rio Branco, 109,800 ('85) (145,486▲) ....D 4
Rio de Janeiro, 5,603,388 ('85) (10,150,000★) . F 6
Rosario, 938,120 ('80) (1,045,000★) ....G 4
Salta, 260,744 ('80).....F 4
Salvador, 1,804,438 ('85) (2,050,000★) ....E 7
San Miguel de Tucumán, 392,888 ('80) (525,000★) ....F 4
Santa Fe, 292,165 ('80)..........G 4
Santiago, 232,667 ('82) (4,100,000★) ....G 3
Santos, 460,100 ('85) (1,065,000★) ....F 6
São Luís, 227,900 ('85) (600,000★) ....D 6
São Paulo, 10,063,110 ('85) (15,175,000★) . F 6
Stanley, 1,200 ('86).......I 5
Sucre, 86,609 ('85)......E 4
SURINAME..........C 5
Teresina, 425,300 ('85) (525,000★) ....D 6
Trujillo, 202,469 ('81) (354,301★) ....D 3
URUGUAY..........G 5
Valparaíso, 265,355 ('82) (675,000★) ....G 3
VENEZUELA..........C 4
Vitória, 201,500 ('85) (735,000★) ....F 6

★ Population of metropolitan area, including suburbs.
▲ Population of entire district, including rural area.

Miles 0 200 400 600 800 1000 Mi.
Kilometers 0 400 800 1200 1600 Km.

1:40 000 000

Northern South America

Bolivia

1985 ESTIMATE

Cochabamba, 317,251 G 5
La Paz, 992,592 .... G 5
Oruro, 178,393 ...... G 5
Potosí, 113,380 .... G 5
Santa Cruz, 441,717 G 6
Sucre, 86,609 ...... G 5

Brazil

1985 ESTIMATE

Anápolis, 225,840 .. G 9
Aracaju, 360,013 .... F11
Araçatuba, 129,304 .. H 8
Bauru, 220,105 ...... H 9
Belém, 1,116,578 (1,200,000★) ...... D 9
Belo Horizonte, 2,114,429 (2,950,000★) G10
Brasília, 1,567,709 .. G 9
Campina Grande, 279,929 .... E11
Campinas, 841,016 (1,125,000★) ...... H 9
Campo Grande, 384,398 .... H 8
Campos, 187,900 (366,716▲) H10
Caruaru, 152,100 (190,794▲) E11
Cuiabá, 220,400 (279,651▲) ...... G 7
Feira de Santana, 278,600 (355,201▲) F11
Fortaleza, 1,582,414 (1,825,000★) D11
Goiânia, 923,333 (990,000★) ...... G 9
Governador Valadares, 192,300 (216,957▲) G10
João Pessoa, 348,500 (550,000★) E12
Juàzeiro do Norte, 159,806 .... E11
Juiz de Fora, 349,720 H10
Jundiaí, 268,900 (313,652▲) .... H 9
Maceió, 482,195 .... E11
Manaus, 809,914 .... D 6
Montes Claros, 183,500 (214,472▲) G10
Natal, 510,106 ...... E11
Niterói, 441,684 .... H10
Petrolina, 92,100 (225,000★) E10
Petrópolis, 170,300 .. H10
Piracicaba, 211,000 (252,079▲) .... H 9
Porto Velho, 152,700 (202,011▲) .... E 6
Presidente Prudente, 155,883 .... H 8
Recife, 1,287,623 (2,625,000★) E12
Ribeirão Prêto, 383,125 .... H 9
Rio de Janeiro, 5,603,388 (10,150,000★) H10
Salvador, 1,804,438 (2,050,000★) F11
Santarém, 120,800 (226,618▲) .... D 8
Santos, 460,100 (1,065,000★) ...... H 9
São Carlos, 140,383 H 9
São José do Rio Prêto, 229,221 .... H 9
São Luís, 227,900 (600,000★) D10
São Paulo, 10,063,110 (15,175,000★) .... H 9
Sorocaba, 327,468 .. H 9
Teresina, 425,300 (525,000★) E10
Uberaba, 244,875 .... G 9
Uberlândia, 312,024 .. G 9
Vitória, 201,500 (735,000★) H10
Vitória da Conquista, 145,800 (198,150▲) F10
Volta Redonda, 219,267 (375,000★) H10

Colombia

1985 CENSUS

Armenia, 187,130 .... C 3
Barrancabermeja, 137,406 .... B 4
Barranquilla, 899,781 (1,140,000★) ...... A 4
Bogotá, 3,982,941 (4,260,000★) ...... C 4
Bucaramanga, 352,326 (550,000★) .... B 4
Buenaventura, 160,342 .... C 3
Buga, 82,992 ...... C 3
Cali, 1,350,565 (1,400,000★) ...... C 3
Cartagena, 531,426 .. A 3
Cúcuta, 379,478 (445,000★) .... B 4

Ibagué, 292,965 .... C 3
Manizales, 299,352 (330,000★) .... B 3
Medellín, 1,468,089 (2,095,000★) ...... B 3
Montería, 157,466 .. B 3
Neiva, 194,556 ...... C 3
Palmira, 175,186 .... C 3
Pasto, 197,407 ...... C 3
Pereira, 233,271 (390,000★) .... C 3
Popayán, 141,964 .. C 3
Santa Marta, 177,922 A 4
Tuluá, 99,721 ...... C 3
Tunja, 93,792 ...... B 4
Valledupar, 142,771 .. A 4
Villavicencio, 178,685 C 4

Ecuador
1987 ESTIMATE

Ambato, 126,067 .... D 3
Cuenca, 201,490 .... D 3
Guayaquil, 1,572,615 (1,580,000★) ...... D 3
Machala, 144,396 .... D 3
Manta, 135,990 .... D 2
Portoviejo, 141,568 .. D 2
Quito, 1,137,705 (1,300,000★) ...... D 3
Riobamba, 75,455('82) ...... D 3

French Guiana
1982 CENSUS

Cayenne, 38,091 .... C 8

Guyana
1983 ESTIMATE

Georgetown, 78,500 (188,000★) .... B 7

Peru
1981 CENSUS

Arequipa, 108,023 (446,942★) ...... G 4
Ayacucho, 57,432 (69,533★) .... F 4
Cajamarca, 62,259 .. E 3
Callao, 264,133 ...... F 3
Cerro de Pasco, 55,597 (66,373★) .... F 3
Chiclayo, 213,095 (279,527★) .... E 3
Chimbote, 223,341 .. E 3
Cuzco, 89,563 (184,550★) .... F 4
Huancayo, 84,845 (164,954★) .... F 3
Huánuco, 61,812 .... E 3
Ica, 114,786 .... F 3
Iquitos, 178,738 .... D 4
Lima, 371,122 (4,608,010★) ...... F 3
Piura, 144,609 (207,934★) .... E 2
Sullana, 89,037 ...... D 2
Tacna, 97,173 ...... G 4
Trujillo, 202,469 (354,301★) .... E 3
Tumbes, 47,936 .... D 2
Vitarte, 145,504 .... F 3

Suriname
1988 ESTIMATE

Paramaribo, 241,000 (296,000★) .... B 7

Venezuela
1981 CENSUS

Acarigua, 91,662 .... B 5
Barinas, 110,462 .... B 4
Barquisimeto, 497,635 A 5
Cabimas, 140,435 .. A 4
Calabozo, 61,995 .... B 5
Caracas, 1,816,901 (3,600,000★) ...... A 5
Ciudad Bolívar, 182,941 .... B 6
Ciudad Guayana, 314,497 .... B 6
Ciudad Ojeda, 83,565 A 4
Cumaná, 179,814 .... A 6
El Tigre, 73,595 .... B 6
Maracaibo, 890,643 .. A 4
Maracay, 322,560 .... A 5
Maturín, 154,976 .... B 6
Mérida, 143,209 .... B 4
Puerto Cabello, 71,759 .... A 5
Punto Fijo, 71,114 .. A 4
San Cristóbal, 198,793 .... B 4
Valencia, 616,224 .... A 5
Valera, 102,068 .... B 4

★ Population of metropolitan area, including suburbs.
▲ Population of entire district, including rural area.

Southern South America

Argentina

1980 CENSUS

Avellaneda, 334,145 . . C 5
Bahía Blanca, 223,818 D 4
Buenos Aires, 2,922,829 (10,750,000★) . . . . C 5
Catamarca, 78,799 (90,000★) . . . . B 3
Comodoro Rivadavia, 96,817 . . . . F 3
Concordia, 94,222 . . C 5
Córdoba, 993,055 (1,070,000★) . . . . . . C 4
Corrientes, 180,612 . . B 5
La Plata, 477,175 . . . . C 5
Mar del Plata, 414,696 . . . . D 5
Mendoza, 119,088 (650,000★) . . . . C 3
Paraná, 161,638 . . . . C 4
Posadas, 143,889 . . . . B 5
Río Cuarto, 110,254 . . C 4
Rosario, 938,120 (1,045,000★) . . . . . . C 4
Salta, 260,744 . . . . . . A 3
San Isidro, 289,170 . . C 5
San Juan, 118,046 (300,000★) . . . . C 3
San Miguel de Tucumán, 392,888 (525,000★) B 3
Santa Fe, 292,165 . . C 4
Santiago del Estero, 148,758 (200,000★) B 4

Brazil

1985 ESTIMATE

Bauru, 220,105 . . . . . . A 7
Blumenau, 192,074 . . B 7
Campinas, 841,016 (1,125,000★) . . . . . . A 7
Caxias do Sul, 266,809 . . . . B 6
Curitiba, 1,279,205 (1,700,000★) . . . . . . B 7
Florianópolis, 178,400 (365,000★) . . . . B 7
Joinvile, 302,877 . . . . B 7
Jundiaí, 268,900 (313,652▲) . . . . A 7
Londrina, 296,400 (346,676▲) . . . . A 6
Maringá, 196,871 . . . . A 6
Pelotas, 210,300 (277,730▲) . . . . C 6
Piracicaba, 211,000 (252,079▲) . . . . A 7
Ponta Grossa, 223,154 . . . . B 6
Porto Alegre, 1,272,121 (2,600,000★) . . . . . . C 6
Presidente Prudente, 155,883 . . . . A 6
Ribeirão Prêto, 383,125 . . . . A 7
Rio Grande, 164,221 C 6
Santa Maria, 163,900 (196,827▲) . . . . B 6
Santos, 460,100 (1,065,000★) . . . . . . A 7
São Carlos, 140,383 A 7
São Paulo, 10,063,110 (15,175,000★) . . . . A 7
Sorocaba, 327,468 . . A 7

Chile

1982 CENSUS

Antofagasta, 185,486 A 2
Chillán, 118,163 . . . . D 2
Concepción, 267,891 (675,000★) . . . . D 2
Osorno, 95,286 . . . . . . E 2
Punta Arenas, 95,332 G 2
Rancagua, 139,925 . . C 2
Santiago, 232,667 (4,100,000★) . . . . . . C 2
Talca, 128,544 . . . . . . D 2
Talcahuano, 202,368 D 2
Temuco, 157,297 . . . . D 2
Valdivia, 100,046 . . . . D 2
Valparaíso, 265,355 (675,000★) . . . . C 2
Viña del Mar, 244,899 C 2

Falkland Islands

1986 ESTIMATE

Stanley, 1,200 . . . . . . G 5

Paraguay

1985 ESTIMATE

Asunción, 477,100 (700,000★) . . . . B 5

Uruguay

1985 CENSUS

Montevideo, 1,251,647 (1,550,000★) . . . . . . C 5
Paysandú, 76,191 . . . . C 5
Salto, 80,823 . . . . . . C 5

★ Population of metropolitan area, including suburbs.
▲ Population of entire district, including rural area.

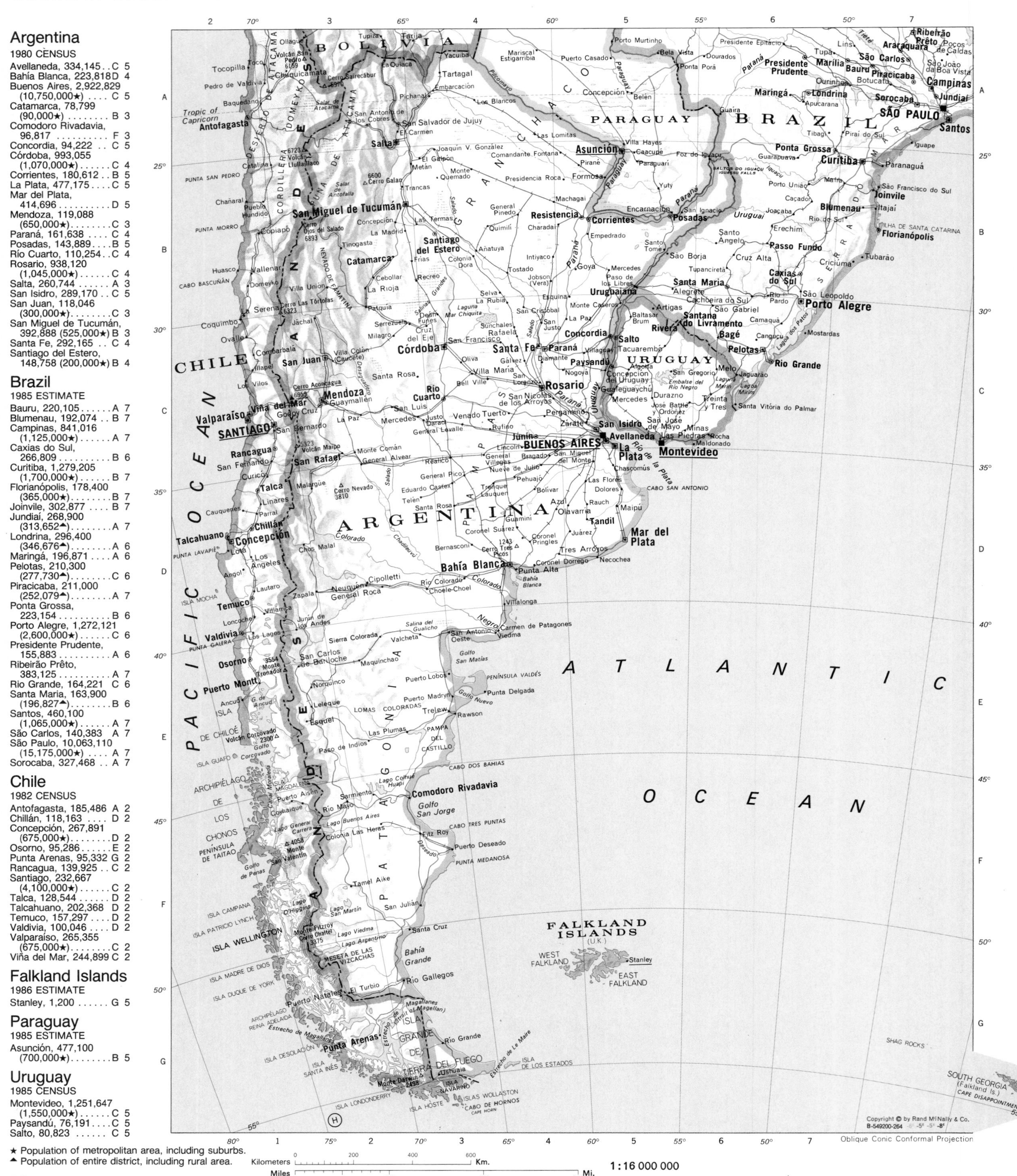

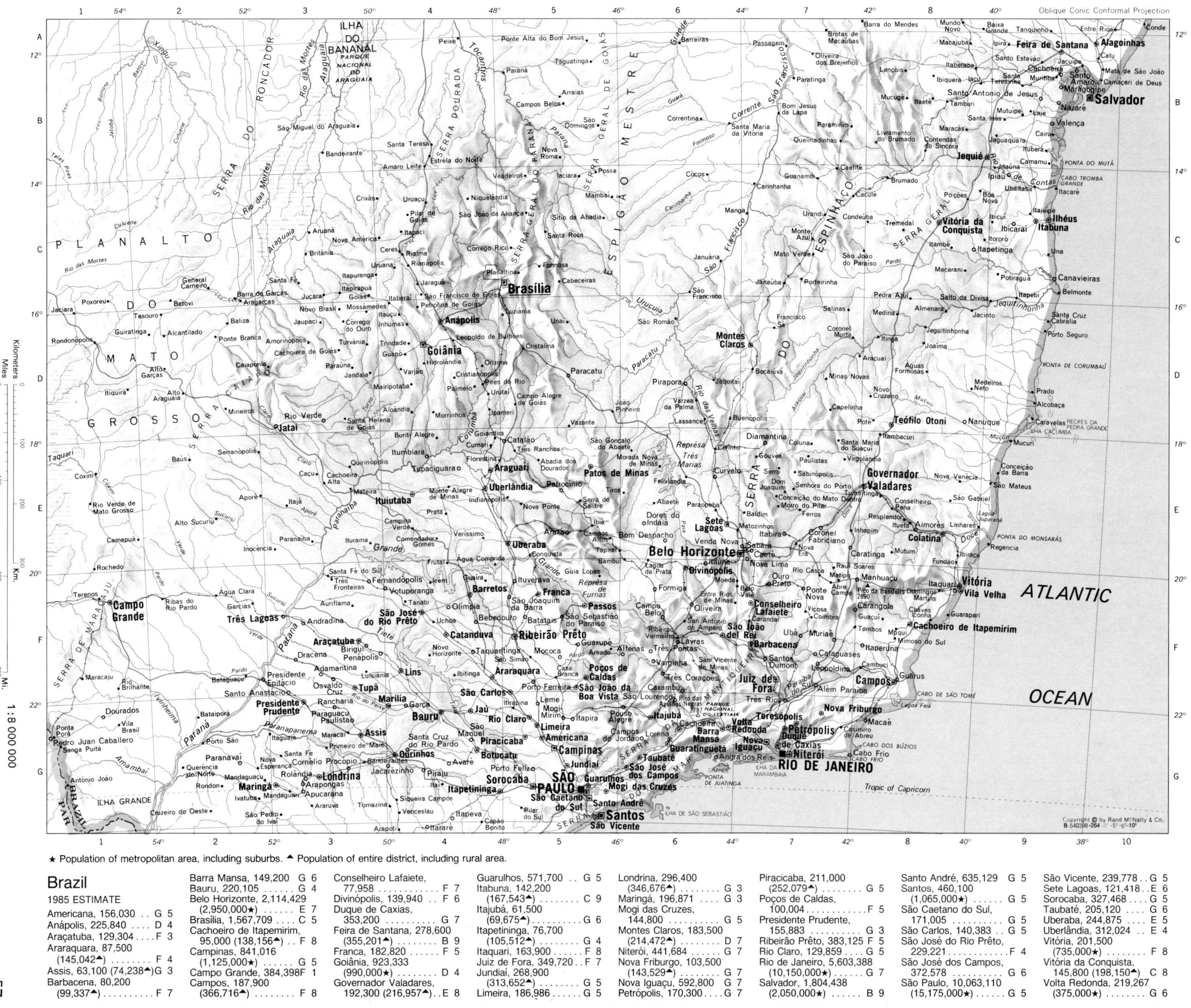

★ Population of metropolitan area, including suburbs. ▲ Population of entire district, including rural area.

Brazil

1985 ESTIMATE

Americana, 156,030 .. G 5
Anápolis, 225,840 .... D 4
Araçatuba, 129,304 .... F 3
Araraquara, 87,500 (145,042▲) .... F 4
Assis, 63,100 (74,238▲)G 3
Barbacena, 80,200 (99,337▲) .... F 7
Barra Mansa, 149,200 G 6
Bauru, 220,105 ...... G 4
Belo Horizonte, 2,114,429 (2,950,000★) ...... E 7
Brasília, 1,567,709 .... C 5
Cachoeiro de Itapemirim, 95,000 (138,156▲) .. F 8
Campinas, 841,016 (1,125,000★) ...... G 5
Campo Grande, 384,398F 1
Campos, 187,900 (366,716▲) .... F 8
Conselheiro Lafaiete, 77,958 .... F 7
Divinópolis, 139,940 .. F 6
Duque de Caxias, 353,200 .... G 7
Feira de Santana, 278,600 (355,201▲) .... B 9
Franca, 182,820 ...... F 5
Goiânia, 923,333 (990,000★) .... D 4
Governador Valadares, 192,300 (216,957▲) .. E 8
Guarulhos, 571,700 .. G 5
Itabuna, 142,200 (167,543▲) .... C 9
Itajubá, 61,500 (69,675▲) .... G 6
Itapetininga, 76,700 (105,512▲) .... G 4
Itaquari, 163,900 ...... F 8
Juiz de Fora, 349,720 .. F 7
Jundiaí, 268,900 (313,652▲) .... G 5
Limeira, 186,986 ...... G 5
Londrina, 296,400 (346,676▲) .... G 3
Maringá, 196,871 .... G 3
Mogi das Cruzes, 144,800 .... G 5
Montes Claros, 183,500 (214,472▲) .... D 7
Niterói, 441,684 .... G 7
Nova Friburgo, 103,500 (143,529▲) .... G 7
Nova Iguaçu, 592,800 G 7
Petrópolis, 170,300 .... G 7
Piracicaba, 211,000 (252,079▲) .... G 5
Poços de Caldas, 100,004 .... F 5
Presidente Prudente, 155,883 .... G 3
Ribeirão Prêto, 383,125 F 5
Rio Claro, 129,859 .... G 5
Rio de Janeiro, 5,603,388 (10,150,000★) ...... G 7
Salvador, 1,804,438 (2,050,000★) ...... B 9
Santo André, 635,129 G 5
Santos, 460,100 (1,065,000★) ...... G 5
São Caetano do Sul, 171,005 .... G 5
São Carlos, 140,383 .. G 5
São José do Rio Prêto, 229,221 .... F 4
São José dos Campos, 372,578 .... G 6
São Paulo, 10,063,110 (15,175,000★) ...... G 5
São Vicente, 239,778 .. G 5
Sete Lagoas, 121,418 .. E 6
Sorocaba, 327,468 .... G 5
Taubaté, 205,120 .... G 6
Uberaba, 244,875 .... E 5
Uberlândia, 312,024 .. E 4
Vitória, 201,500 (735,000★) .... F 8
Vitória da Conquista, 145,800 (198,150▲) C 8
Volta Redonda, 219,267 (375,000★) .... G 6

Colombia, Ecuador, Venezuela, and Guyana

Aruba
1987 ESTIMATE
Oranjestad, 19,800 . . A 7

Colombia
1985 CENSUS
Armenia, 187,130 . . . . E 5
Barrancabermeja, 137,406 . . . . D 6
Barranquilla, 899,781 (1,140,000★) . . . . . B 5
Bello, 212,861 . . . . . . D 5
Bogotá, 3,982,941 (4,260,000★) . . . . . E 5
Bucaramanga, 352,326 (550,000★) . . . . D 6
Buenaventura, 160,342 . . . . F 4
Buga, 82,992 . . . . F 4
Cali, 1,350,565 (1,400,000★) . . . . . F 4
Cartagena, 531,426 . . B 5
Cartago, 97,791 . . . . E 5
Ciénaga, 56,860 . . . . B 5
Cúcuta, 379,478 (445,000★) . . . . D 6
Duitama, 56,390 . . . . E 6
Envigado, 91,391 . . . . D 5
Espinal, 37,563 . . . . . E 5
Facatativá, 44,331 . . E 5
Florencia, 66,430 . . . . G 5
Florida, 30,040 . . . . . F 4
Floridablanca, 143,824 . . . . D 6
Girardot, 70,078 . . . . E 5
Ibagué, 292,965 . . . . E 5
Ipiales, 45,419 . . . . . G 4
Itagüí, 137,623 . . . . . . D 5
La Dorada, 48,572 . . E 5
Magangué, 49,160 . . C 5
Manizales, 299,352 (330,000★) . . . . E 5
Medellín, 1,468,089 (2,095,000★) . . . . . D 5
Montería, 157,466 . . C 5
Neiva, 194,556 . . . . . F 5
Ocaña, 51,443 . . . . . C 6
Palmira, 175,186 . . . . F 4
Pamplona, 34,213 . . D 6
Pasto, 197,407 . . . . . G 4
Pereira, 233,271 (390,000★) . . . . E 5
Planeta Rica, 24,238 C 5
Popayán, 141,964 . . . F 4
Puerto Berrío, 21,414 D 5
Quibdó, 47,950 . . . . . E 4
Ríohacha, 46,667 . . . B 6
Santa Marta, 177,922 . . . . B 5
Santa Rosa de Cabal, 37,112 . . . . E 5
Sincelejo, 120,537 . . C 5
Sogamoso, 64,437 . . E 6
Soledad, 165,791 . . . B 5
Tuluá, 99,721 . . . . . . E 4
Tumaco, 45,456 . . . . G 3
Tunja, 93,792 . . . . . . E 6
Valledupar, 142,771 . . B 6
Villavicencio, 178,685 E 6
Zipaquirá, 45,676 . . . . E 5

Ecuador
1987 ESTIMATE
Alfaro, 51,023('82) . . . . I 3
Ambato, 126,067 . . . . H 3
Azogues, 14,548('82) I 3
Babahoyo, 42,266('82) . . . . . . H 3
Chone, 33,839('82) . . H 2
Cuenca, 201,490 . . . . I 3
Esmeraldas, 120,387 G 3
Guaranda, 13,685('82) . . . . . . H 3
Guayaquil, 1,572,615 (1,580,000★) . . . . . . I 3
Ibarra, 53,428('82) . . G 3
Jipijapa, 27,146('82) . . H 2
Latacunga, 28,764('82) . . . . . . H 3
Loja, 71,652('82) . . . . J 3
Machala, 144,396 . . . . I 3
Manta, 135,990 . . . . H 2
Milagro, 102,884 . . . . I 3
Portoviejo, 141,568 . . H 2
Quevedo, 67,023('82) . . . . . . H 3
Quito, 1,137,705 (1,300,000★) . . . . . . H 3
Riobamba, 75,455('82) . . . . . . H 3
Santo Domingo de los Colorados, 104,059 H 3
Tulcán, 30,985('82) . . G 4

Guyana
1983 ESTIMATE
Georgetown, 78,500 (188,000★) D13
New Amsterdam, 20,000('82) D14

★ Population of metropolitan area, including suburbs.

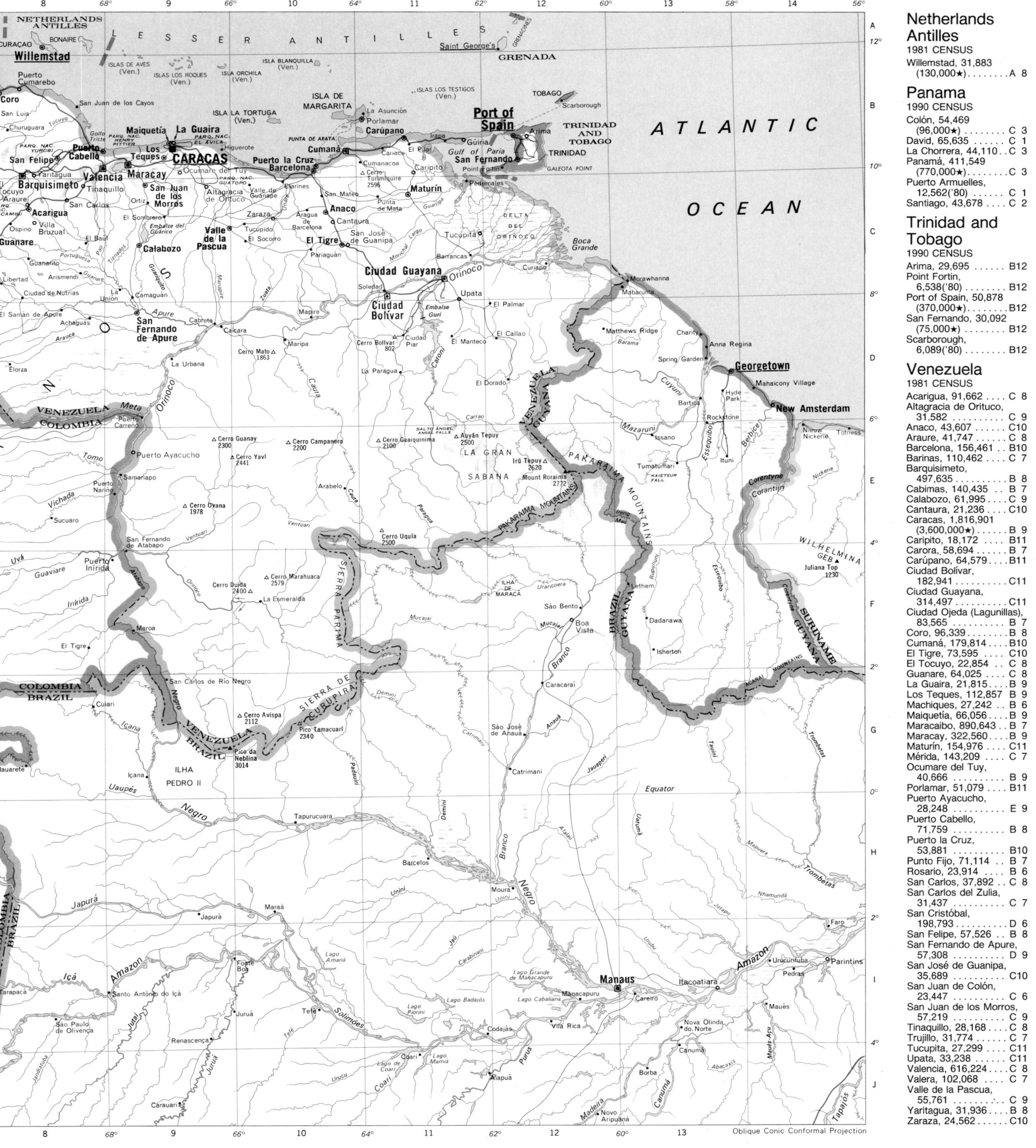

Netherlands Antilles

1981 CENSUS

Willemstad, 31,883 (130,000★) . . . . A 8

Panama

1990 CENSUS

Colón, 54,469 (96,000★) . . . . C 3
David, 65,635 . . . . . . C 1
La Chorrera, 44,110 . . C 3
Panamá, 411,549 (770,000★) . . . . C 3
Puerto Armuelles, 12,562('80) . . . . . . C 1
Santiago, 43,678 . . . . C 2

Trinidad and Tobago

1990 CENSUS

Arima, 29,695 . . . . . . B12
Point Fortin, 6,538('80) B12
Port of Spain, 50,878 (370,000★) B12
San Fernando, 30,092 (75,000★) B12
Scarborough, 6,089('80) B12

Venezuela

1981 CENSUS

Acarigua, 91,662 . . . . C 8
Altagracia de Orituco, 31,582 . . . . C 9
Anaco, 43,607 . . . . . . C10
Araure, 41,747 . . . . . . C 8
Barcelona, 156,461 . . B10
Barinas, 110,462 . . . . C 7
Barquisimeto, 497,635 . . . . B 8
Cabimas, 140,435 . . B 7
Calabozo, 61,995 . . . . C 9
Cantaura, 21,236 . . . . C10
Caracas, 1,816,901 (3,600,000★) . . . . . . B 9
Caripito, 18,172 . . . . B11
Carora, 58,694 . . . . . . B 7
Carúpano, 64,579 . . . . B11
Ciudad Bolívar, 182,941 . . . . C11
Ciudad Guayana, 314,497 . . . . C11
Ciudad Ojeda (Lagunillas), 83,565 . . . . B 7
Coro, 96,339 . . . . B 8
Cumaná, 179,814 . . . . B10
El Tigre, 73,595 . . . . C10
El Tocuyo, 22,854 . . C 8
Guanare, 64,025 . . . . C 8
La Guaira, 21,815 . . . . B 9
Los Teques, 112,857 B 9
Machiques, 27,242 . . B 6
Maiquetía, 66,056 . . . . B 9
Maracaibo, 890,643 . . B 7
Maracay, 322,560 . . . . B 9
Maturín, 154,976 . . . . C11
Mérida, 143,209 . . . . C 7
Ocumare del Tuy, 40,666 . . . . B 9
Porlamar, 51,079 . . . . B11
Puerto Ayacucho, 28,248 . . . . E 9
Puerto Cabello, 71,759 . . . . B 8
Puerto la Cruz, 53,881 . . . . B10
Punto Fijo, 71,114 . . B 7
Rosario, 23,914 . . . . B 6
San Carlos, 37,892 . . C 8
San Carlos del Zulia, 31,437 . . . . C 7
San Cristóbal, 198,793 . . . . D 6
San Felipe, 57,526 . . B 8
San Fernando de Apure, 57,308 . . . . D 9
San José de Guanipa, 35,689 . . . . C10
San Juan de Colón, 23,447 . . . . C 6
San Juan de los Morros, 57,219 . . . . C 9
Tinaquillo, 28,168 . . . . C 8
Trujillo, 31,774 . . . . . . C 7
Tucupita, 27,299 . . . . C11
Upata, 33,238 . . . . . . C11
Valencia, 616,224 . . . . C 8
Valera, 102,068 . . . . C 7
Valle de la Pascua, 55,761 . . . . C 9
Yaritagua, 31,936 . . . . B 8
Zaraza, 24,562 . . . . . . C10

Atlantic Ocean

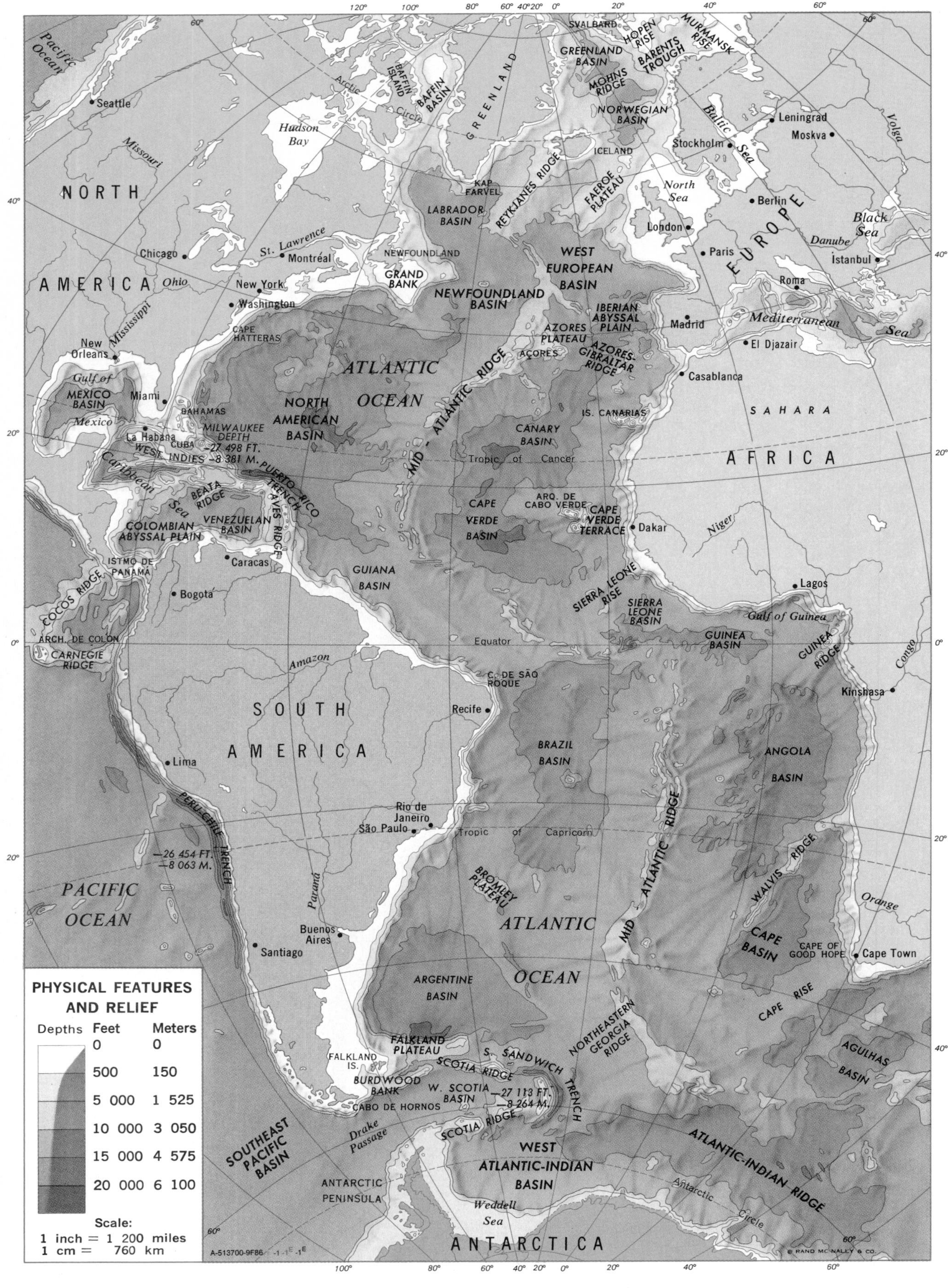

Atlanta, 394,017 ('90)..F12
BAHAMAS.................. G13
Baltimore, 736,014 ('90)........................F13
BARBADOS................ H14
BELIZE.........................H12
Boston, 574,283 ('90). E13
Calgary, 636,104 ('86) (671,326★) ....D 9
CANADA...................... D11
Chicago, 2,783,726 ('90)..........................E12
Ciudad de México (Mexico City), 8,831,079 ('80) (14,100,000★) H11
COSTA RICA.............. H12
CUBA........................... G13
Dallas, 1,006,877 ('90) F11
Denver, 467,610 ('90)..F10
Detroit, 1,027,974 ('90)........................E12
DOMINICAN REPUBLIC............... H13
EL SALVADOR........... H12
GREENLAND............. B16
Guadalajara, 1,626,152 ('80) (2,325,000★) .. H10
GUATEMALA............... H11
HAITI............................H13
HONDURAS............... H12
Houston, 1,630,553 ('90)......................... G11
JAMAICA...................... H13
Kansas City, 435,146 ('90).........................F11
La Habana (Havana), 2,036,800 ('87) (2,125,000★) G12
Los Angeles, 3,485,398 ('90)........................F 9
Memphis, 610,337 ('90)..........................F11
MEXICO...................... G10
Miami, 358,548 ('90)... G12
Milwaukee, 628,088 ('90)..........................E12
Minneapolis, 368,383 ('90)..........................E11
Montréal, 1,015,420 ('86) (2,921,357★) E13
New Orleans, 496,938 ('90).......................... G11
New York, 7,322,564 ('90)..........................E13
NICARAGUA............... H12
Ottawa, 300,763 ('86) (819,263★) E13
PANAMA....................... I13
Philadelphia, 1,585,577 ('90)..........................F13
Phoenix, 900,013 ('90) F 9
PUERTO RICO............H14
San Antonio, 935,933 ('90)......................... G11
San Francisco, 723,959 ('90)..........................F 8
Santo Domingo, 1,313,172 ('81)........................ H13
Seattle, 516,259 ('90)..E 8
Toronto, 612,289 ('86) (3,427,168★) E13
TRINIDAD AND TOBAGO................. H14
UNITED STATES.........F11
Washington, 606,900 ('90)..........................F13

★ Population of metropolitan area, including suburbs.

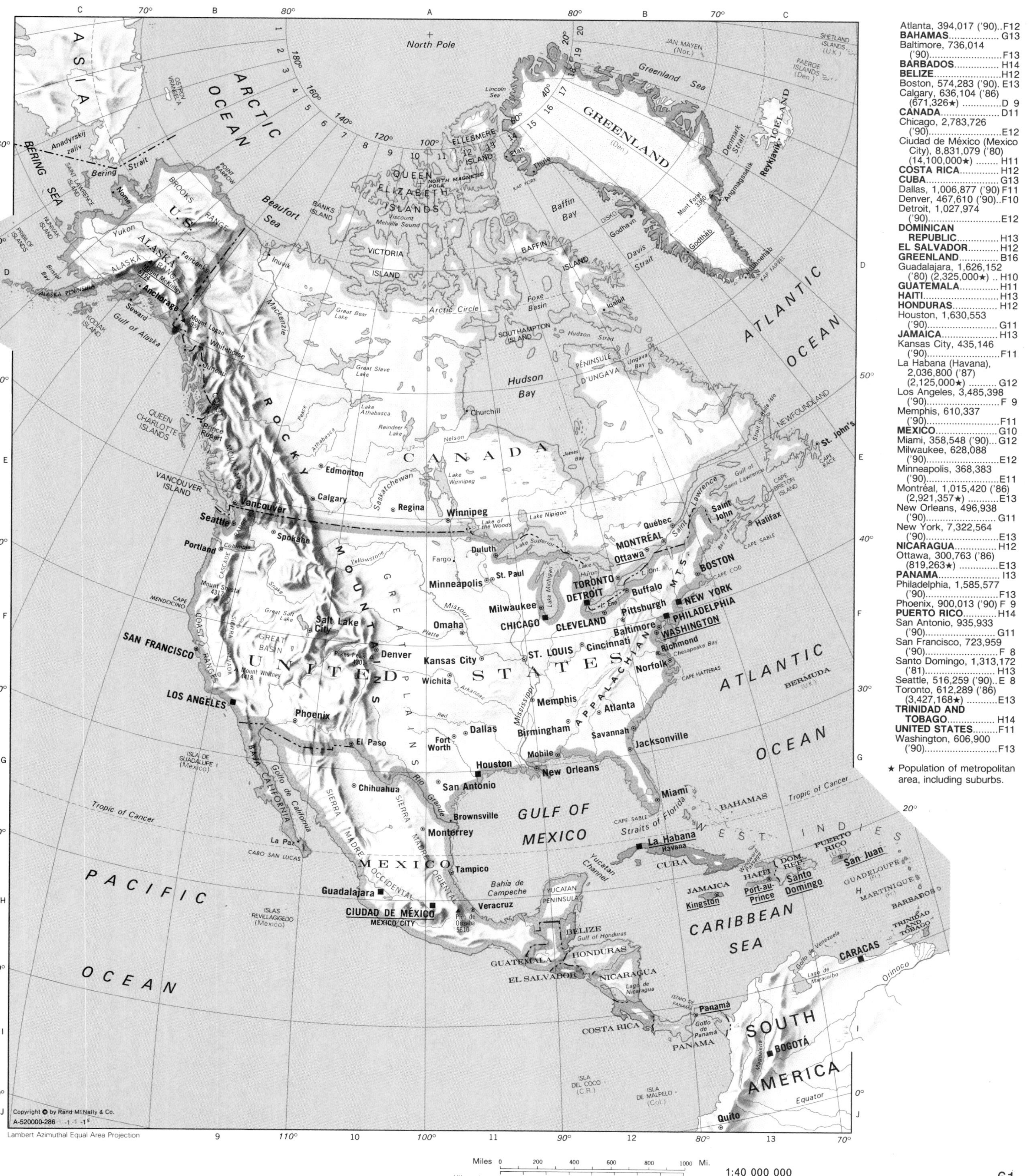

Mexico

Mexico

1980 CENSUS

Acámbaro, 38,224 . . G 9
Acapulco [de Juárez], 301,902 . . . . I10
Aguascalientes, 293,152 . . . . G 8
Ameca, 25,946 . . . . G 7
Apatzingán [de la Constitución], 55,522 . . . . H 8
Apizaco, 30,498 . . . . H10
Caborca, 33,696 . . . . B 3
Campeche, 128,434 H14
Celaya, 141,675 . . . . G 9
Chihuahua, 385,603 C 6
Chilpancingo [de los Bravos], 67,498 . . . . I10
Ciudad Acuña, 38,898 C 9
Ciudad Chetumal, 56,709 . . . . H15
Ciudad del Carmen, 72,489 . . . . H14
Ciudad de México (Mexico City), 8,831,079 (14,100,000★) H10
Ciudad de Valles, 65,609 . . . . G10
Ciudad Guzmán, 60,938 . . . . H 8
Ciudad Hidalgo, 32,311 . . . . H 9
Ciudad Juárez, 544,496 . . . . B 6
Ciudad Madero, 132,444 . . . . F11
Ciudad Mante, 70,647 F10
Ciudad Obregón, 165,572 . . . . D 5
Ciudad Victoria, 140,161 . . . . F10
Coatzacoalcos, 127,170 . . . . H12
Colima, 86,044 . . . . H 8
Córdoba, 99,972 . . . . H11
Cuernavaca, 192,770 H10
Culiacán, 304,826 . . E 6
Delicias, 65,504 . . . . C 7
Durango, 257,915 . . E 7
Empalme, 31,555 . . D 4
Ensenada, 120,483 . . B 1
Fresnillo, 56,066 . . . . F 8
Gómez Palacio, 116,967 . . . . E 8
Guadalajara, 1,626,152 (2,325,000★) . . . . G 8
Guadalupe, 370,524 . . E 9
Guanajuato, 48,981 . . G 9
Guaymas, 54,826 . . D 4
Hermosillo, 297,175 . . C 4
Hidalgo del Parral, 75,590 . . . . D 7
Iguala, 66,005 . . . . . . H10
Irapuato, 170,138 . . G 9
Jalapa Enríquez, 204,594 . . . . H11
Juchitán [de Zaragoza], 38,801 . . . . I12
La Barca, 20,889 . . G 8
Lagos de Moreno, 44,223 . . . . G 9
La Paz, 91,453 . . . . E 4
La Piedad [Cavadas], 47,441 . . . . G 8
León [de los Aldamas], 593,002 . . . . G 9
Los Mochis, 122,531 E 5
Manzanillo, 39,088 . . H 7
Matamoros, 188,745 E11
Matehuala, 41,550 . . F 9
Mazatlán, 199,830 . . F 6
Mérida, 400,142 . . . . G15
Mexicali, 341,559 (365,000★) . . . . . . A 2
Mexico City *see* Ciudad de México H10
Minatitlán, 106,765 . . I12
Monclova, 115,786 . . D 9
Montemorelos, 28,342 E10
Monterrey, 1,090,009 (2,015,000★) . . . . E 9
Morelia, 297,544 . . . . H 9
Navojoa, 62,901 . . . . D 5
Nogales, 65,603 . . . . B 4
Nueva Casas Grandes, 28,514 . . . . B 6
Nueva Rosita, 33,121 D 9
Nuevo Laredo, 201,731 . . . . D10
Oaxaca [de Juárez], 154,223 . . . . I11
Ocotlán, 48,931 . . . . G 8
Orizaba, 114,848 (215,000★) H11
Pachuca [de Soto], 110,351 . . . . G10
Papantla [de Olarte], 43,935 . . . . G11
Pátzcuaro, 32,902 . . H 9
Piedras Negras, 67,455 . . . . C 9
Poza Rica de Hidalgo, 166,799 . . . . G11

★ Population of metropolitan area, including suburbs.

GULF
OF
MEXICO
Bahía de Campeche
Golfo de Tehuantepec
Tropic of Cancer
Lambert Conformal Conic Projection
TEXAS
LOUISIANA
MISSISSIPPI
ALABAMA
UNITED STATES
MEXICO
BELIZE
GUATEMALA
HONDURAS
YUCATAN PENINSULA
SIERRA MADRE ORIENTAL
SIERRA MADRE DEL SUR
EDWARDS PLATEAU
Fort Worth
Dallas
Arlington
Abilene
Big Spring
Midland
San Angelo
Waco
Killeen
Temple
Bryan
College Station
Austin
San Antonio
Houston
Baytown
Galveston
Texas City
Beaumont
Port Arthur
Orange
Lake Charles
Lafayette
Baton Rouge
New Orleans
Shreveport
Monroe
Alexandria
Vicksburg
Jackson
Meridian
Hattiesburg
Laurel
Mobile
Biloxi
Gulfport
Pascagoula
Tyler
Longview
Corpus Christi
Kingsville
Laredo
Nuevo Laredo
McAllen
Harlingen
Brownsville
Reynosa
Matamoros
Monterrey
Saltillo
Monclova
Piedras Negras
Del Rio
Nueva Rosita
Guadalupe
Ciudad Victoria
Ciudad Madero
Tampico
San Luis Potosí
Aguascalientes
León
Guanajuato
Irapuato
Salamanca
Querétaro
Celaya
Acámbaro
Zamora de Hidalgo
Morelia
Uruapan
CIUDAD DE MÉXICO
MEXICO CITY
Toluca
Pachuca
Tulancingo
Puebla
Cuernavaca
Iguala
Veracruz
Jalapa Enríquez
Orizaba
Córdoba
Tehuacán
Oaxaca
Acapulco
Coatzacoalcos
Minatitlán
Villahermosa
Tuxtla Gutiérrez
Campeche
Mérida
Progreso
Cancún
Belize City
Belmopan
Guatemala
Quezaltenango
Tapachula
San Pedro Sula
63

Progreso, 24,257 .. G15
Puebla [de Zaragoza], 835,759 (1,055,000★) H10
Puerto Vallarta, 38,645 .... G 7
Querétaro, 215,976 .. G 9
Reynosa, 194,693 .. D10
Sabinas, 27,413 .... D 9
Sabinas Hidalgo, 23,187 .... D 9
Sahuayo, 43,258 .... G 8
Salamanca, 96,703 .. G 9
Salina Cruz, 40,010 .. I12
Saltillo, 284,937 .... E 9
Salvatierra, 28,878 .. G 9
San Andrés Tuxtla, 40,412 .... H12
San Cristóbal las Casas, 42,026 .... I13
San Francisco del Rincón, 40,943 .... G 9
San Luis Potosí, 362,371 (470,000★) ...... F 9
San Luis Río Colorado, 76,684 ....A 2
San Pedro de las Colonias, 35,879 .. E 8
Santa Bárbara, 14,894D 7
Tampico, 267,957 (435,000★) F11
Tapachula, 85,766 .. J13
Tecomán, 46,371 .. H 8
Tehuacán, 79,547 .. H11
Tehuantepec, 22,019 I12
Teocaltiche, 16,559 .. G 8
Tepatitlán [de Morelos], 41,813 .... G 8
Tepic, 145,741 .... G 7
Ticul, 18,255 ...... G15
Tierra Blanca, 31,653 H11
Tijuana, 429,500 .... A 1
Tizimín, 26,305 .... G15
Toluca [de Lerdo], 199,778 .... H10
Torreón, 328,086 (575,000★) ...... E 8
Tulancingo, 53,400 .. G10
Tuxpan de Rodríguez Cano, 56,037 .... G11
Tuxtla Gutiérrez, 131,096 .... I13
Uruapan [del Progreso], 122,828 .... H 8
Valle de Santiago, 37,645 .... G 9
Valle Hermoso, 27,966E11
Veracruz [Llave], 284,822 (385,000★) H11
Villa Frontera, 32,568 D 9
Villahermosa, 158,216 I13
Zacapu, 39,570 .... H 9
Zacatecas, 80,088 .. F 8
Zamora de Hidalgo, 86,998 .... H 8
Zitácuaro, 47,520 .. H 9

Central America and the Caribbean

Antigua and Barbuda
1977 ESTIMATE
Saint Johns, 24,359 . . F17

Bahamas
1982 ESTIMATE
Nassau, 135,000 . . . . B 9

Barbados
1980 CENSUS
Bridgetown, 7,466
(115,000★) H18

Belize
1985 ESTIMATE
Belize City, 47,000 . . F 3
Belmopan, 4,500 . . . . F 3

Cayman Islands
1988 ESTIMATE
Georgetown, 13,700 E 7

Costa Rica
1988 ESTIMATE
Limón, 40,400
(62,600▲) . . . . I 6
San José, 278,600
(670,000★) . . . . . . J 5

Cuba
1987 ESTIMATE
Camagüey, 265,588 D 9
Guantánamo, 179,091 D10
Havana *see* La
Habana . . . . C 6
Holguín, 199,861 . . . . D 9
La Habana (Havana),
2,036,800
(2,125,000★) . . . . C 6
Santa Clara, 182,349 C 8
Santiago de Cuba,
364,554 . . . . D10

Dominican Republic
1981 CENSUS
Santiago, 278,638 . . E 12
Santo Domingo,
1,313,172 . . . . . . E 13

El Salvador
1985 ESTIMATE
San Salvador, 462,652
(920,000★) . . . . . . H 3
Santa Ana, 137,879 . . H 3

Guadeloupe
1982 CENSUS
Basse-Terre, 13,656
(26,600★) F17

Guatemala
1989 ESTIMATE
Guatemala, 1,057,210
(1,400,000★) . . . . G 2

★ Population of metropolitan area, including suburbs.

Haiti
1987 ESTIMATE
Port-au-Prince, 797,000 (880,000★) E11

Honduras
1988 CENSUS
San Pedro Sula, 279,356 . . . . G 4
Tegucigalpa, 551,606 G 4

Jamaica
1987 ESTIMATE
Kingston, 646,400 (770,000★) . . . . . . E 9
Montego Bay, 70,265('82) . . . . . . E 9

Martinique
1982 CENSUS
Fort-de-France, 99,844 (116,017★) G17

Netherlands Antilles
1981 CENSUS
Willemstad, 31,883 (130,000★). . . . . .H 13

Nicaragua
1985 ESTIMATE
León, 101,000 . . . . . H 4
Managua, 682,000 . . H 4

Panama
1990 CENSUS
Colón, 54,469 (96,000★). . . . . J 8
Panamá, 411,549 (770,000★) . . . . . . J 8

Puerto Rico
1980 CENSUS
Ponce, 161,739 (232,551★) E14
San Juan, 424,600 (1,775,260★) E14

Saint Lucia
1987 ESTIMATE
Castries, 53,933 . . . . G17

Saint Vincent and the Grenadines
1987 ESTIMATE
Kingstown, 19,028 (28,936★) H17

Trinidad and Tobago
1988 ESTIMATE
Port of Spain, 59,200 (370,000★) I17

ALBERTA.................... F10
Alma, 25,923 ('86) (29,977★) G18
Baie-Comeau, 26,244 ('86) (33,047★) G19
Banff, 4,208 ('81)......... F 9
Barrie, 48,287 ('86) (67,703★) H17
Bathurst, 14,683 ('86) (34,895★) G19
Belleville, 36,041 ('86) (87,530★) H17
Brandon, 38,708 ('86). G13
BRITISH COLUMBIA... F 8
Brockville, 20,880 ('86) (37,115★) H17
Calgary, 636,104 ('86) (671,326★) F10
Cambridge, 79,920 ('86)........................... H16
Campbell River, 15,370 ('81)............................ F 7
Campbellton, 9,077 ('86) (17,418★) G19
CANADA..................... D13
Charlottetown, 15,776 ('86) (53,868★) G20
Chatham, 42,211 ('86) H16
Chicoutimi, 61,083 ('86) (158,468★) G18
Chilliwack, 41,337 ('86) (50,288★) .... G 8
Churchill, 1,186 ('81)... E14
Corner Brook, 22,719 ('86) (33,730★) G21
Cornwall, 46,425 ('86) (51,719★) G18
Dartmouth, 65,243 ('86)........................... H20
Dawson Creek, 10,544 ('86)............................ E 8
Dolbeau, 8,554 ('86) (15,288★) G18
Drummondville, 36,020 ('86) (56,283★) G18
Edmonton, 573,982 ('86) (785,465★) F10
Edmundston, 11,497 ('86) (22,614★) G19
Eskimo Point, 1,189 ('86)........................... D14
Flin Flon, 7,591 ('86) (9,211★) F12
Fort McMurray, 34,949 ('86) (48,497★) E10
Fort Saint John, 13,355 ('86)............................ E 8
Fredericton, 44,352 ('86) (65,768★) G19
Gander, 10,207 ('86) (10,899★) G22
Gaspé, 17,350 ('86).... G20
Granby, 38,508 ('86) (51,176★) G18
Grande-Prairie, 26,471 ('86)............................ E 9
Grand Falls, 9,121 ('86) (25,612★) G21
Guelph, 78,235 ('86) (85,962★) H16
Halifax, 113,577 ('86) (295,990★) H20
Hamilton, 306,728 ('86) (557,029★) H17
Happy Valley-Goose Bay, 7,248 ('86)................ F20
Hull, 58,722 ('86)........ G17
Inuvik, 3,389 ('86)........ C 6
Jasper, 3,269 ('81)....... F 9
Joliette, 16,845 ('86) (34,897★) G18
Jonquière, 58,467 ('86)........................... G18
Kamloops, 61,773 ('86)............................ F 8
Kelowna, 61,213 ('86) (89,730★) .... G 9
Kenora, 9,621 ('86) (15,456★) G14
Kirkland Lake, 11,604 ('86)........................... G16
Kitchener, 150,604 ('86) (311,195★) H16
Kitimat, 11,196 ('86).... F 7
Labrador City, 8,664 ('86) (11,301★) F19
La Tuque, 10,723 ('86) (13,468★) G18
Laval, 284,164 ('86).... G18
Lethbridge, 58,841 ('86)........................... G10
Lloydminster, 17,356 ('86)............................ F11
London, 269,140 ('86) (342,302★) H16
MANITOBA.................. F13
Matane, 13,243 ('86) (15,361★) G19
Medicine Hat, 41,804 ('86) (50,734★) F10
Midland, 12,092 ('86) (35,003★) H17
Moncton, 55,468 ('86) (102,084★) G20

★ Population of metropolitan area, including suburbs.

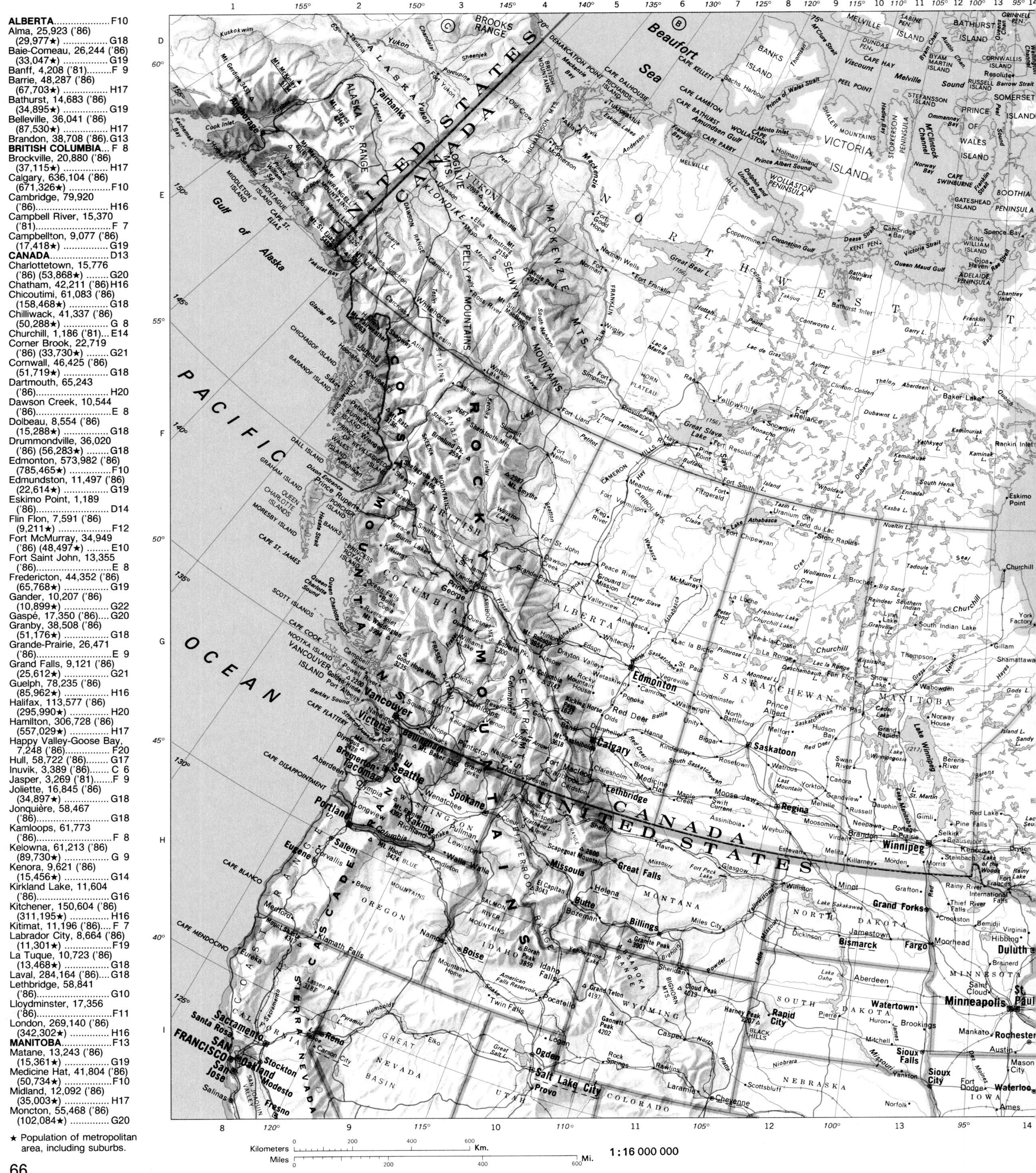

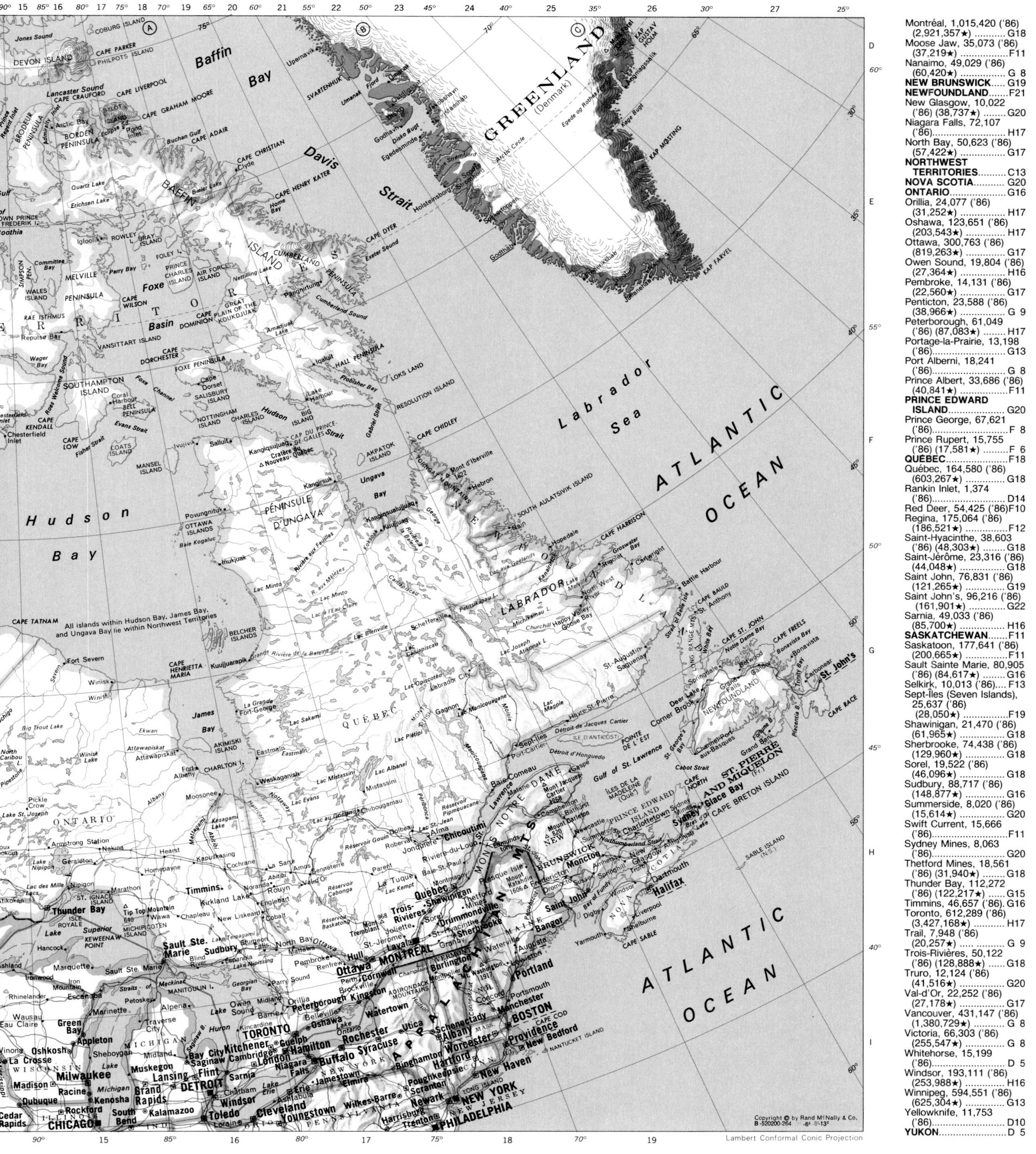

Montréal, 1,015,420 ('86) (2,921,357★) G18
Moose Jaw, 35,073 ('86) (37,219★) F11
Nanaimo, 49,029 ('86) (60,420★) .... G 8
NEW BRUNSWICK..... G19
NEWFOUNDLAND....... F21
New Glasgow, 10,022 ('86) (38,737★) G20
Niagara Falls, 72,107 ('86)......................... H17
North Bay, 50,623 ('86) (57,422★) G17
NORTHWEST TERRITORIES......... C13
NOVA SCOTIA........... G20
ONTARIO.................... G16
Orillia, 24,077 ('86) (31,252★) H17
Oshawa, 123,651 ('86) (203,543★) H17
Ottawa, 300,763 ('86) (819,263★) G17
Owen Sound, 19,804 ('86) (27,364★) H16
Pembroke, 14,131 ('86) (22,560★) G17
Penticton, 23,588 ('86) (38,966★) .... G 9
Peterborough, 61,049 ('86) (87,083★) H17
Portage-la-Prairie, 13,198 ('86)......................... G13
Port Alberni, 18,241 ('86)......................... G 8
Prince Albert, 33,686 ('86) (40,841★) F11
PRINCE EDWARD ISLAND.................. G20
Prince George, 67,621 ('86)......................... F 8
Prince Rupert, 15,755 ('86) (17,581★) .... F 6
QUÉBEC.................... F18
Québec, 164,580 ('86) (603,267★) G18
Rankin Inlet, 1,374 ('86)......................... D14
Red Deer, 54,425 ('86)F10
Regina, 175,064 ('86) (186,521★) F12
Saint-Hyacinthe, 38,603 ('86) (48,303★) G18
Saint-Jérôme, 23,316 ('86) (44,048★) G18
Saint John, 76,831 ('86) (121,265★) G19
Saint John's, 96,216 ('86) (161,901★) G22
Sarnia, 49,033 ('86) (85,700★) H16
SASKATCHEWAN....... F11
Saskatoon, 177,641 ('86) (200,665★) F11
Sault Sainte Marie, 80,905 ('86) (84,617★) G16
Selkirk, 10,013 ('86).... F13
Sept-Îles (Seven Islands), 25,637 ('86) (28,050★) F19
Shawinigan, 21,470 ('86) (61,965★) G18
Sherbrooke, 74,438 ('86) (129,960★) G18
Sorel, 19,522 ('86) (46,096★) G18
Sudbury, 88,717 ('86) (148,877★) G16
Summerside, 8,020 ('86) (15,614★) G20
Swift Current, 15,666 ('86)......................... F11
Sydney Mines, 8,063 ('86)......................... G20
Thetford Mines, 18,561 ('86) (31,940★) G18
Thunder Bay, 112,272 ('86) (122,217★) G15
Timmins, 46,657 ('86). G16
Toronto, 612,289 ('86) (3,427,168★) H17
Trail, 7,948 ('86) (20,257★) .... G 9
Trois-Rivières, 50,122 ('86) (128,888★) G18
Truro, 12,124 ('86) (41,516★) G20
Val-d'Or, 22,252 ('86) (27,178★) G17
Vancouver, 431,147 ('86) (1,380,729★) .... G 8
Victoria, 66,303 ('86) (255,547★) .... G 8
Whitehorse, 15,199 ('86)......................... D 5
Windsor, 193,111 ('86) (253,988★) H16
Winnipeg, 594,551 ('86) (625,304★) G13
Yellowknife, 11,753 ('86)......................... D10
YUKON........................ D 5

Alberta

1986 CENSUS

Airdrie, 10,390 . . . . . . D 3
Athabasca, 1,970 . . . . B 4
Banff . . . . D 3
Barrhead, 3,991 . . . . B 3
Beaumont, 3,944 . . . . C 4
Beaverlodge, 1,808 . . B 1
Blackfalds, 1,688 . . . . C 4
Bonnyville, 5,470 . . . . B 5
Bow Island, 1,650 . . E 5
Brooks, 9,464 . . . . . . D 5
Calgary, 636,104
(671,326★) . . . . . . D 3
Camrose, 12,968 . . . . C 4
Canmore, 4,182 . . . . D 3
Cardston, 3,497 . . . . E 4
Carstairs, 1,629 . . . . D 3
Claresholm, 3,382 . . D 4
Coaldale, 4,796 . . . . E 4
Cochrane, 4,190 . . . . D 3
Cold Lake, 3,195 . . . . B 5
Coronation, 1,310 . . C 5
Crowsnest Pass,
6,912 . . . . E 3
Devon, 3,691 . . . . . . C 4
Didsbury, 3,184 . . . . D 3
Drayton Valley, 5,290 C 3
Drumheller, 6,366 . . D 4
Edmonton, 573,982
(785,465★) . . . . . . C 4
Edson, 7,323 . . . . . . C 2
Fairview, 2,998 . . . . A 1
Fort Chipewyan, 922 f 8
Fort Macleod, 3,123 E 4
Fort McMurray, 34,949
(48,497★) . . . . A 5
Fort Saskatchewan,
11,983 . . . . C 4
Fox Creek, 2,068 . . . . B 2
Gibbons, 2,335 . . . . C 4
Grand Centre, 3,655 B 5
Grande Cache, 3,646 C 1
Grande Prairie,
26,471 . . . . B 1
Grimshaw, 2,579 . . . . A 2
Hanna, 3,017 . . . . . . D 5
High Level, 3,004 . . . . F 7
High Prairie, 2,817 . . B 2
High River, 5,096 . . . . D 4
Hinton, 8,629 . . . . . . C 2
Innisfail, 5,535 . . . . . . C 4
Jasper . . . . C 1
Lac La Biche, 2,553 B 5
Lacombe, 6,080 . . . . . C 4
La Crete, 689 . . . . . . f 7
Lake Louise, 688 . . . . D 2
Lamont, 1,576 . . . . . . C 4
Leduc, 13,126 . . . . . . C 4
Lethbridge, 58,841 . . E 4
Lloydminster, 17,354 C 5
Magrath, 1,637 . . . . . . E 4
Medicine Hat, 41,804
(50,734★) . . . . D 5
Morinville, 5,364 . . . . C 4
Nordegg, 53 . . . . C 2
Okotoks, 5,214 . . . . . D 4
Olds, 4,871 . . . . D 3
Peace River, 6,288 . . A 2
Penhold, 1,580 . . . . . . C 4
Picture Butte, 1,576 . . E 4
Pincher Creek, 3,800 E 4
Ponoka, 5,473 . . . . . . C 4
Provost, 1,725 . . . . . . C 5
Raymond, 2,957 . . . . E 4
Redcliff, 3,834 . . . . . . D 5
Red Deer, 54,425 . . C 4
Redwater, 1,982 . . . . C 4
Rimbey, 1,786 . . . . . . C 3
Rocky Mountain House,
5,182 . . . . C 3
Saint Albert, 36,710 . . C 4
Saint Paul, 5,030 . . . . B 5
Sherwood Park . . . . C 4
Slave Lake, 5,429 . . B 3
Smith, 251 . . . . B 3
Spruce Grove, 11,918 C 4
Stettler, 5,147 . . . . . . C 4
Stony Plain, 5,802 . . C 3
Strathmore, 3,544 . . D 4
Sundre, 1,712 . . . . . . D 3
Swan Hills, 2,403 . . . B 3
Sylvan Lake, 3,937 . . C 3
Taber, 6,382 . . . . E 4
Three Hills, 2,528 . . . D 4
Valleyview, 1,987 . . . . B 2
Vegreville, 5,276 . . . . C 4
Vermilion, 3,879 . . . . C 5
Vulcan, 1,420 . . . . . . D 4
Wainwright, 4,665 . . C 5
Westlock, 4,532 . . . . B 4
Wetaskiwin, 10,071 . . C 4
Whitecourt, 5,737 . . B 3

★ Population of metropolitan area, including suburbs.

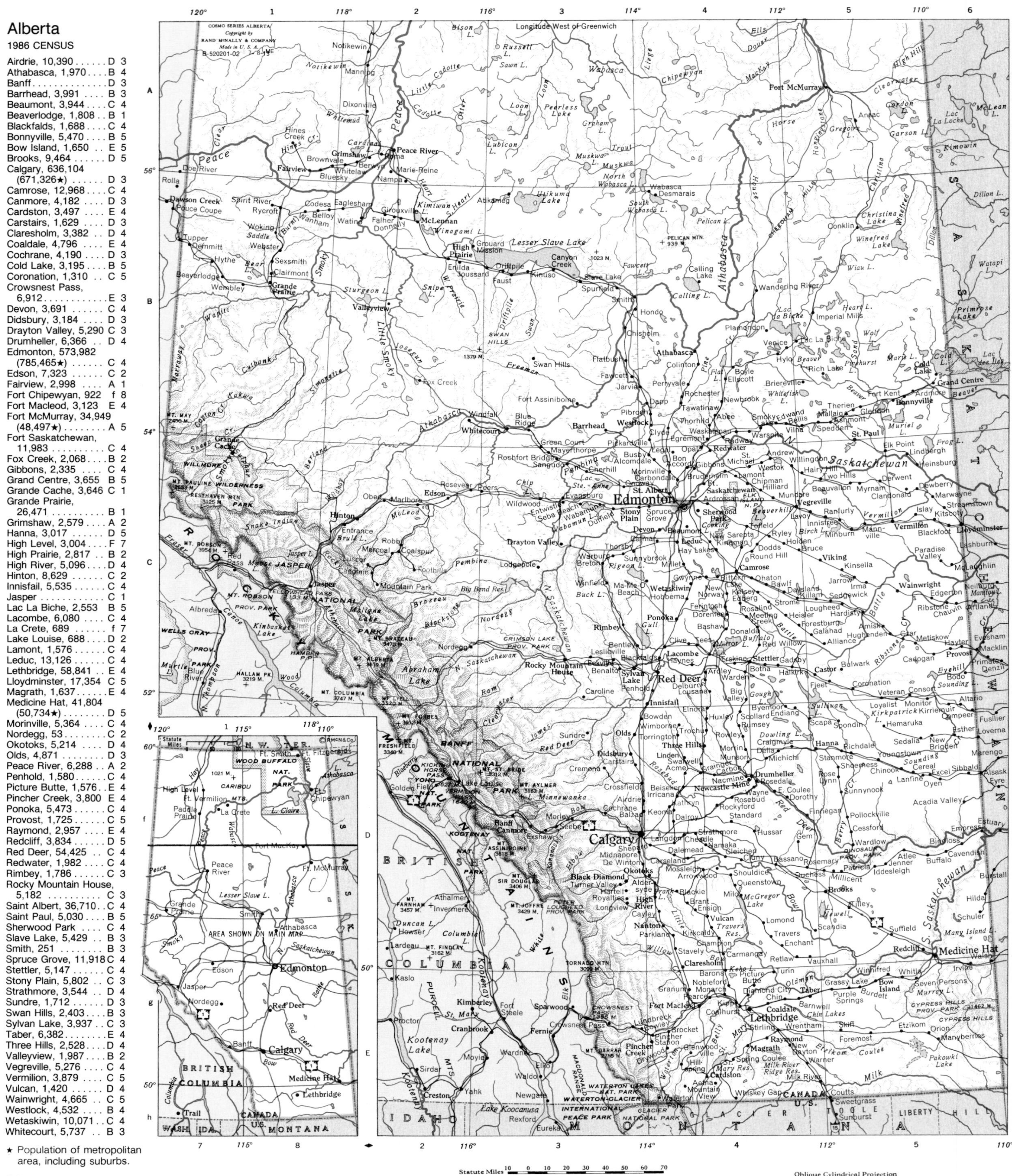

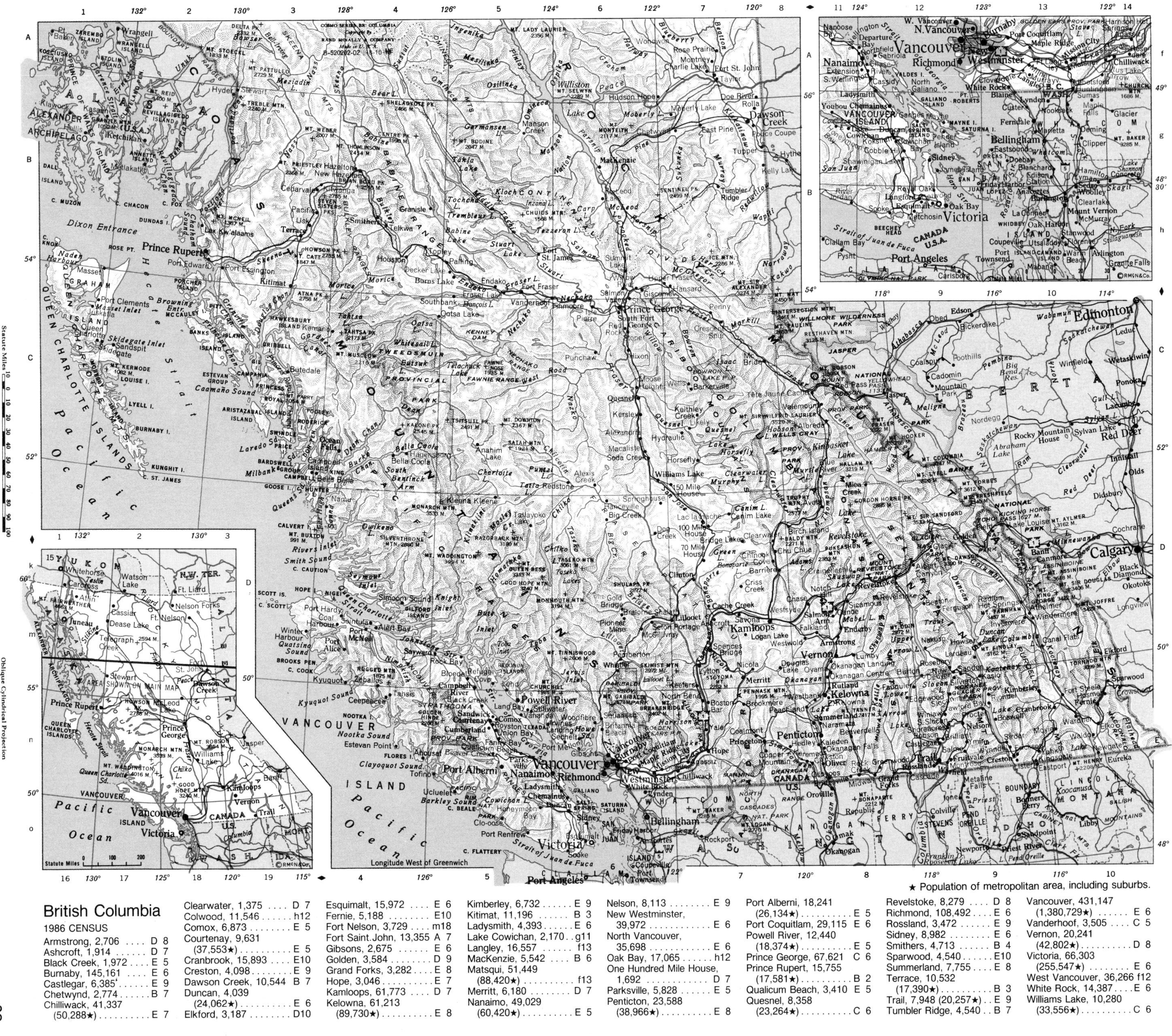

Oblique Cylindrical Projection

British Columbia

1986 CENSUS

Armstrong, 2,706 .... D 8
Ashcroft, 1,914 ...... D 7
Black Creek, 1,972 .... E 5
Burnaby, 145,161 .... E 6
Castlegar, 6,385 ...... E 9
Chetwynd, 2,774 ...... B 7
Chilliwack, 41,337 (50,288★) .... E 7
Clearwater, 1,375 .... D 7
Colwood, 11,546 ...... h12
Comox, 6,873 .... E 5
Courtenay, 9,631 (37,553★) .... E 5
Cranbrook, 15,893 .... E10
Creston, 4,098 .... E 9
Dawson Creek, 10,544 B 7
Duncan, 4,039 (24,062★) .... E 6
Elkford, 3,187 .... D10
Esquimalt, 15,972 .... E 6
Fernie, 5,188 .... E10
Fort Nelson, 3,729 .... m18
Fort Saint John, 13,355 A 7
Gibsons, 2,675 ...... E 6
Golden, 3,584 .... D 9
Grand Forks, 3,282 .... E 8
Hope, 3,046 .... E 7
Kamloops, 61,773 .... D 7
Kelowna, 61,213 (89,730★) .... E 8
Kimberley, 6,732 ...... E 9
Kitimat, 11,196 ...... B 3
Ladysmith, 4,393 ...... E 6
Lake Cowichan, 2,170 .. g11
Langley, 16,557 ...... f13
MacKenzie, 5,542 .... B 6
Matsqui, 51,449 (88,420★) f13
Merritt, 6,180 .... D 7
Nanaimo, 49,029 (60,420★) .... E 5
Nelson, 8,113 .... E 9
New Westminster, 39,972 .... E 6
North Vancouver, 35,698 .... E 6
Oak Bay, 17,065 ...... h12
One Hundred Mile House, 1,692 .... D 7
Parksville, 5,828 ...... E 5
Penticton, 23,588 (38,966★) .... E 8
Port Alberni, 18,241 (26,134★) .... E 5
Port Coquitlam, 29,115 E 6
Powell River, 12,440 (18,374★) .... E 5
Prince George, 67,621 C 6
Prince Rupert, 15,755 (17,581★) .... B 2
Qualicum Beach, 3,410 E 5
Quesnel, 8,358 (23,264★) .... C 6
Revelstoke, 8,279 .... D 8
Richmond, 108,492 .... E 6
Rossland, 3,472 ...... E 9
Sidney, 8,982 .... E 6
Smithers, 4,713 ...... B 4
Sparwood, 4,540 ...... E10
Summerland, 7,755 .... E 8
Terrace, 10,532 (17,390★) .... B 3
Trail, 7,948 (20,257★) .. E 9
Tumbler Ridge, 4,540 .. B 7
Vancouver, 431,147 (1,380,729★) ...... E 6
Vanderhoof, 3,505 .... C 5
Vernon, 20,241 (42,802★) .... D 8
Victoria, 66,303 (255,547★) .... E 6
West Vancouver, 36,266 f12
White Rock, 14,387 .... E 6
Williams Lake, 10,280 (33,556★) .... C 6

★ Population of metropolitan area, including suburbs.

Manitoba

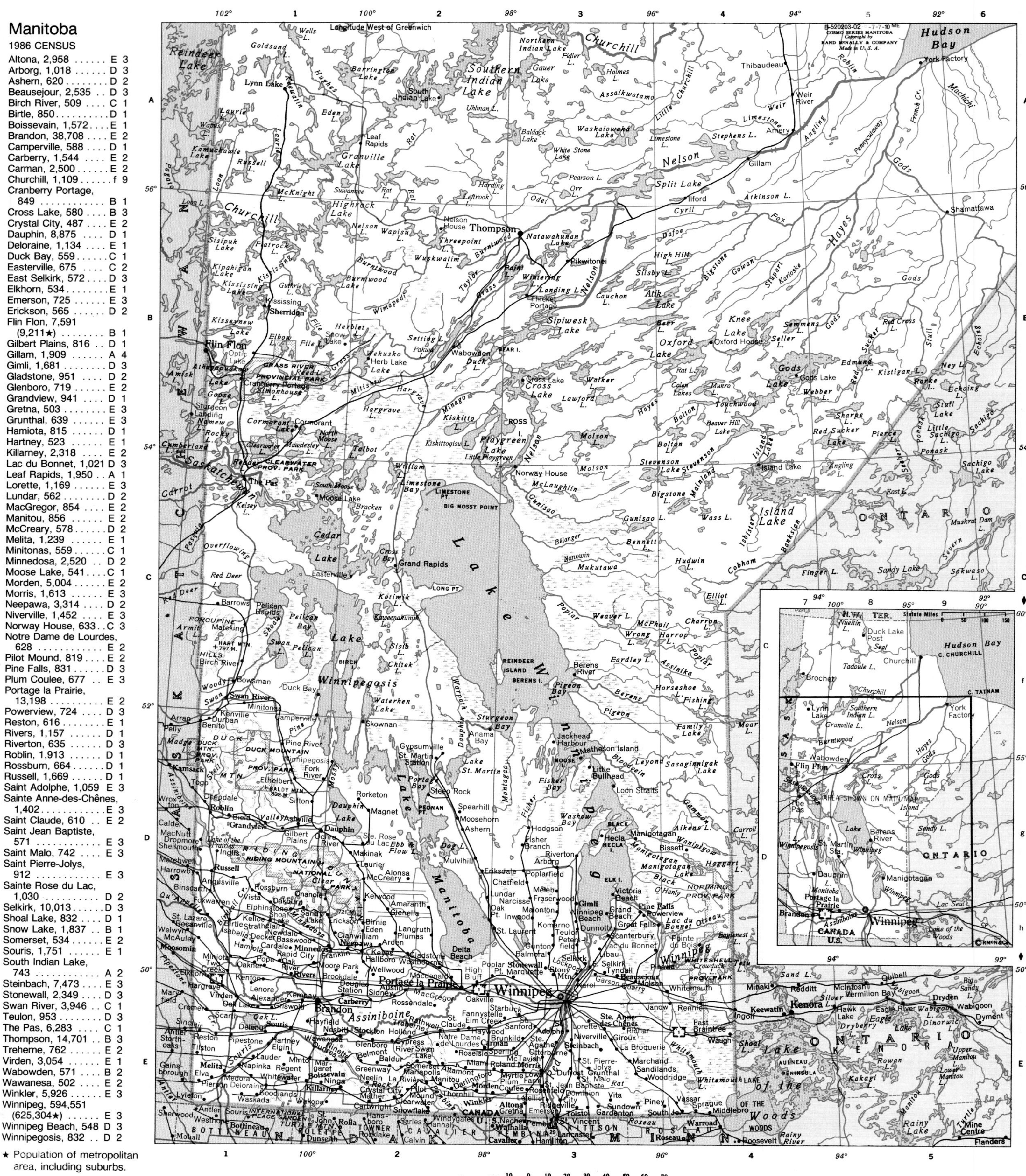

Manitoba

1986 CENSUS

Altona, 2,958 ...... E 3
Arborg, 1,018 ...... D 3
Ashern, 620 .... D 2
Beausejour, 2,535 .. D 3
Birch River, 509 .... C 1
Birtle, 850.......... D 1
Boissevain, 1,572.... E 1
Brandon, 38,708 .... E 2
Camperville, 588 .... D 1
Carberry, 1,544 .... E 2
Carman, 2,500 ...... E 2
Churchill, 1,109...... f 9
Cranberry Portage, 849 .... B 1
Cross Lake, 580 .... B 3
Crystal City, 487 .... E 2
Dauphin, 8,875 ...... D 1
Deloraine, 1,134 .... E 1
Duck Bay, 559....... C 1
Easterville, 675 ..... C 2
East Selkirk, 572.... D 3
Elkhorn, 534......... E 1
Emerson, 725 .... E 3
Erickson, 565 .... D 2
Flin Flon, 7,591 (9,211★) .... B 1
Gilbert Plains, 816 .. D 1
Gillam, 1,909 .... A 4
Gimli, 1,681 .... D 3
Gladstone, 951 ..... D 2
Glenboro, 719 .... E 2
Grandview, 941 ..... D 1
Gretna, 503 .... E 3
Grunthal, 639 .... E 3
Hamiota, 815 .... D 1
Hartney, 523 .... E 1
Killarney, 2,318 .... E 2
Lac du Bonnet, 1,021 D 3
Leaf Rapids, 1,950 .. A 1
Lorette, 1,169 .... E 3
Lundar, 562 .... D 2
MacGregor, 854 ..... E 2
Manitou, 856 .... E 2
McCreary, 578....... D 2
Melita, 1,239 .... E 1
Minitonas, 559....... C 1
Minnedosa, 2,520 .. D 2
Moose Lake, 541.... C 1
Morden, 5,004 ...... E 2
Morris, 1,613 .... E 3
Neepawa, 3,314 .... D 2
Niverville, 1,452 .... E 3
Norway House, 633.. C 3
Notre Dame de Lourdes, 628 .... E 2
Pilot Mound, 819.... E 2
Pine Falls, 831 ...... D 3
Plum Coulee, 677 .. E 3
Portage la Prairie, 13,198 .... E 2
Powerview, 724 .... D 3
Reston, 616 .... E 1
Rivers, 1,157 .... D 1
Riverton, 635 .... D 3
Roblin, 1,913 .... D 1
Rossburn, 664 .... D 1
Russell, 1,669 .... D 1
Saint Adolphe, 1,059 E 3
Sainte Anne-des-Chênes, 1,402............ E 3
Saint Claude, 610 .. E 2
Saint Jean Baptiste, 571 .... E 3
Saint Malo, 742 .... E 3
Saint Pierre-Jolys, 912 .... E 3
Sainte Rose du Lac, 1,030 .... D 2
Selkirk, 10,013.......D 3
Shoal Lake, 832 .... D 1
Snow Lake, 1,837 .. B 1
Somerset, 534 .... E 2
Souris, 1,751 .... E 1
South Indian Lake, 743 .... A 2
Steinbach, 7,473 .... E 3
Stonewall, 2,349 .... D 3
Swan River, 3,946 .. C 1
Teulon, 953 .... D 3
The Pas, 6,283 ...... C 1
Thompson, 14,701 .. B 3
Treherne, 762 .... E 2
Virden, 3,054 .... E 1
Wabowden, 571 .... B 2
Wawanesa, 502 ..... E 2
Winkler, 5,926 ...... E 3
Winnipeg, 594,551 (625,304★) ...... E 3
Winnipeg Beach, 548 D 3
Winnipegosis, 832 .. D 2

★ Population of metropolitan area, including suburbs.

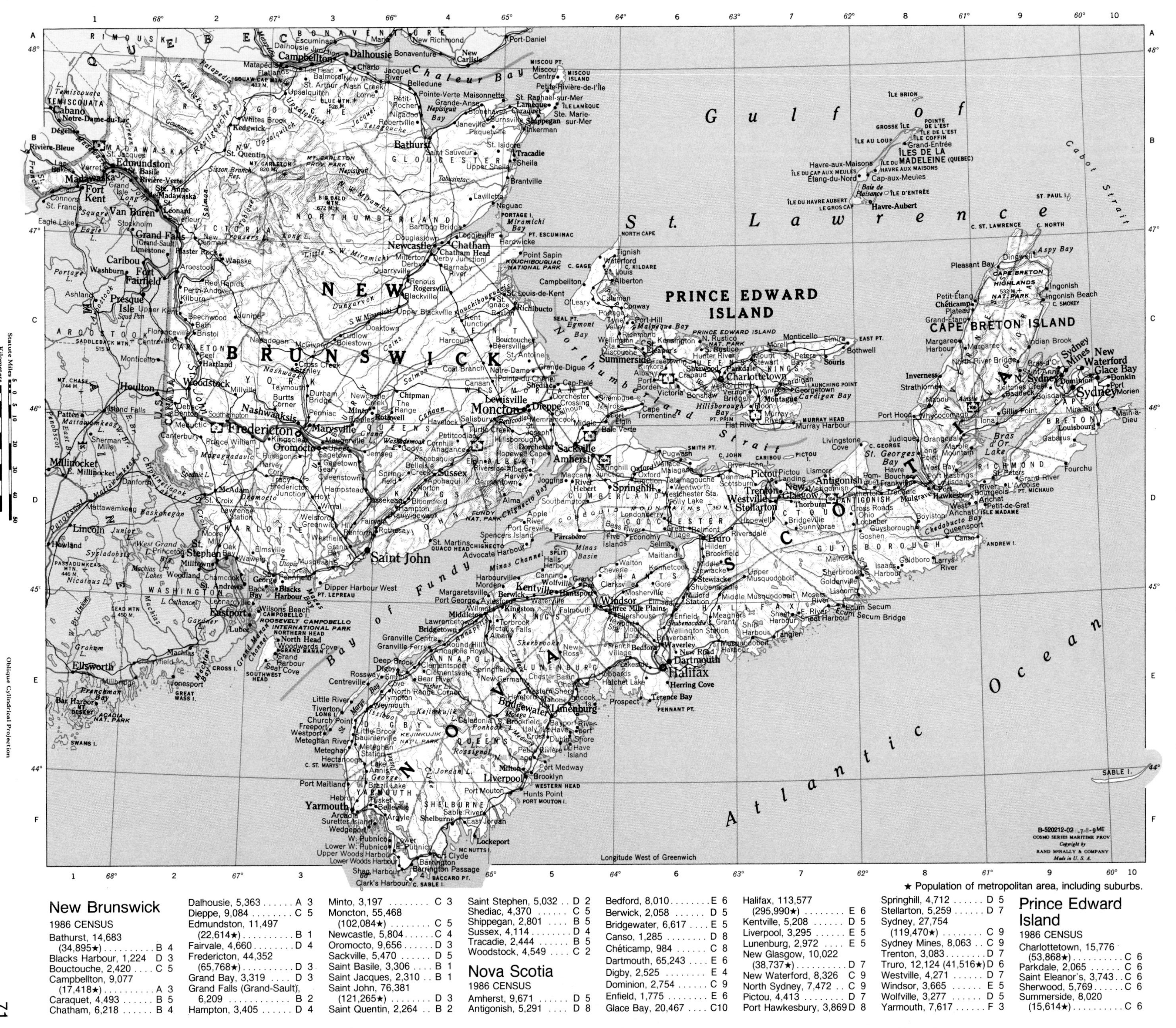

★ Population of metropolitan area, including suburbs.

New Brunswick

1986 CENSUS

Bathurst, 14,683 (34,895★)	B 4
Blacks Harbour, 1,224	D 3
Bouctouche, 2,420	C 5
Campbellton, 9,077 (17,418★)	A 3
Caraquet, 4,493	B 5
Chatham, 6,218	B 4
Dalhousie, 5,363	A 3
Dieppe, 9,084	C 5
Edmundston, 11,497 (22,614★)	B 1
Fairvale, 4,660	D 4
Fredericton, 44,352 (65,768★)	D 3
Grand Bay, 3,319	D 3
Grand Falls (Grand-Sault), 6,209	B 2
Hampton, 3,405	D 4
Minto, 3,197	C 3
Moncton, 55,468 (102,084★)	C 5
Newcastle, 5,804	C 4
Oromocto, 9,656	D 3
Sackville, 5,470	D 5
Saint Basile, 3,306	B 1
Saint Jacques, 2,310	B 1
Saint John, 76,381 (121,265★)	D 3
Saint Quentin, 2,264	B 2
Saint Stephen, 5,032	D 2
Shediac, 4,370	C 5
Shippegan, 2,801	B 5
Sussex, 4,114	D 4
Tracadie, 2,444	B 5
Woodstock, 4,549	C 2

Nova Scotia

1986 CENSUS

Amherst, 9,671	D 5
Antigonish, 5,291	D 8
Bedford, 8,010	E 6
Berwick, 2,058	D 5
Bridgewater, 6,617	E 5
Canso, 1,285	D 8
Chéticamp, 984	C 8
Dartmouth, 65,243	E 6
Digby, 2,525	E 4
Dominion, 2,754	C 9
Enfield, 1,775	E 6
Glace Bay, 20,467	C10
Halifax, 113,577 (295,990★)	E 6
Kentville, 5,208	D 5
Liverpool, 3,295	E 5
Lunenburg, 2,972	E 5
New Glasgow, 10,022 (38,737★)	D 7
New Waterford, 8,326	C 9
North Sydney, 7,472	C 9
Pictou, 4,413	D 7
Port Hawkesbury, 3,869	D 8
Springhill, 4,712	D 5
Stellarton, 5,259	D 7
Sydney, 27,754 (119,470★)	C 9
Sydney Mines, 8,063	C 9
Trenton, 3,083	D 7
Truro, 12,124 (41,516★)	D 6
Westville, 4,271	D 7
Windsor, 3,665	E 5
Wolfville, 3,277	D 5
Yarmouth, 7,617	F 3

Prince Edward Island

1986 CENSUS

Charlottetown, 15,776 (53,868★)	C 6
Parkdale, 2,065	C 6
Saint Eleanor's, 3,743	C 6
Sherwood, 5,769	C 6
Summerside, 8,020 (15,614★)	C 6

Newfoundland

Newfoundland and Labrador

1986 CENSUS

Arnold's Cove, 1,117 E 4
Badger, 1,151 . . . . . . D 3
Baie Verte, 2,049 . . . . D 3
Bay Bulls, 1,114 . . . . E 5
Bay Roberts, 4,446 . . E 5
Bishop's Falls, 4,213 D 4
Bonavista, 4,605 . . . . D 5
Botwood, 3,916 . . . . D 4
Buchans, 1,281 . . . . D 3
Burgeo, 2,582 . . . . . . E 3
Burin, 2,892 . . . . E 4
Burnt Islands, 1,042 E 2
Carbonear, 5,337 (13,082★) . . . . E 5
Carmanville, 987 . . . D 4
Cartwright, 674 . . . . B 3
Catalina, 1,211 . . . . . . D 5
Channel-Port-aux-Basques, 5,901 . . E 2
Clarenville, 2,967 . . . . D 4
Conception Bay South, 15,531 . . . . E 5
Corner Brook, 22,719 (33,730★) . . . . D 3
Cox's Cove, 999 . . . D 2
Deer Lake, 4,233 . . . D 3
Dunville, 1,833 . . . . . . E 5
Durrell, 1,060 . . . . . . D 4
Englee, 1,012 . . . . C 3
Fogo, 1,153 . . . . D 4
Fortune, 2,370 . . . . . . E 4
Gambo, 2,723 . . . . . . D 4
Gander, 10,207 . . . . D 4
Glenwood, 1,038 . . . . D 4
Glovertown, 2,184 . . D 4
Grand Bank, 3,732 . . E 4
Grand Falls, 9,121 (25,612★) . . . . D 4
Hampden, 875 . . . . . . D 3
Happy Valley-Goose Bay, 7,248 . . . . B 1
Harbour Breton, 2,432 . . . . E 4
Harbour Grace, 3,053 E 5
Hare Bay, 1,436 . . . D 4
Hermitage, 831 . . . . E 4
Isle-aux-Morts, 1,203 E 2
Joe Batt's Arm [-Barr'd Islands-Shoal Bay], 1,232 . . . . D 4
King's Point, 923 . . . . D 3
Labrador City, 8,664 (11,301★) . . . . h 8
Lark Harbour, 829 . . D 2
La Scie, 1,429 . . . . . . D 4
Lawn, 1,015 . . . . E 4
Lewisporte, 3,978 . . D 4
Lourdes, 937 . . . . . . D 2
Marystown, 6,660 . . E 4
Milltown [-Head of Bay d'Espoir], 1,276 . . E 4
Mount Pearl, 20,293 E 5
Musgrave Harbour, 1,527 . . . . D 5
Nain, 1,018 . . . . g 9
New Harbour, 957 . . E 5
Norris Arm, 1,127 . . D 4
Norris Point, 1,010 . . D 3
Pasadena, 3,268 . . . . D 3
Placentia, 2,016 . . . . E 5
Point Leamington, 850 . . . . D 4
Port au Port [West-Aguathuna-Felix Cove], 842 . . . . D 2
Pouch Cove, 1,576 . . E 5
Ramea, 1,380 . . . . . . E 3
Robert's Arm, 1,111 D 4
Rocky Harbour, 1,268 D 3
Roddickton, 1,223 . . C 3
Rose-Blanche [-Harbour le Cou], 967 . . . . E 2
Saint Alban's, 1,780 E 4
Saint Anthony, 3,182 C 4
Saint George's, 1,852 D 2
Saint John's, 96,216 (161,901★) . . . . . . E 5
Saint Lawrence, 1,841 . . . . E 4
Shoal Harbour, 1,049 D 4
Spaniard's Bay, 2,190 E 5
Springdale, 3,555 . . . . D 3
Stephenville, 7,994 . . D 2
Stephenville Crossing, 2,252 . . . . D 2
Summerford, 1,169 . . D 4
Torbay, 3,730 . . . . . . E 5
Trepassey, 1,460 . . . . E 5
Twillingate, 1,506 . . . . D 4
Upper Island Cove, 2,055 . . . . E 5
Victoria, 1,895 . . . . . . E 5
Wabana (Bell Island), 4,057 . . . . E 5
Wabush, 2,637 . . . . h 8
Wesleyville, 1,208 . . D 5
Whitbourne, 1,151 . . E 5
Windsor, 5,545 . . . . D 4
Witless Bay, 1,022 . . E 5

★ Population of metropolitan area, including suburbs.

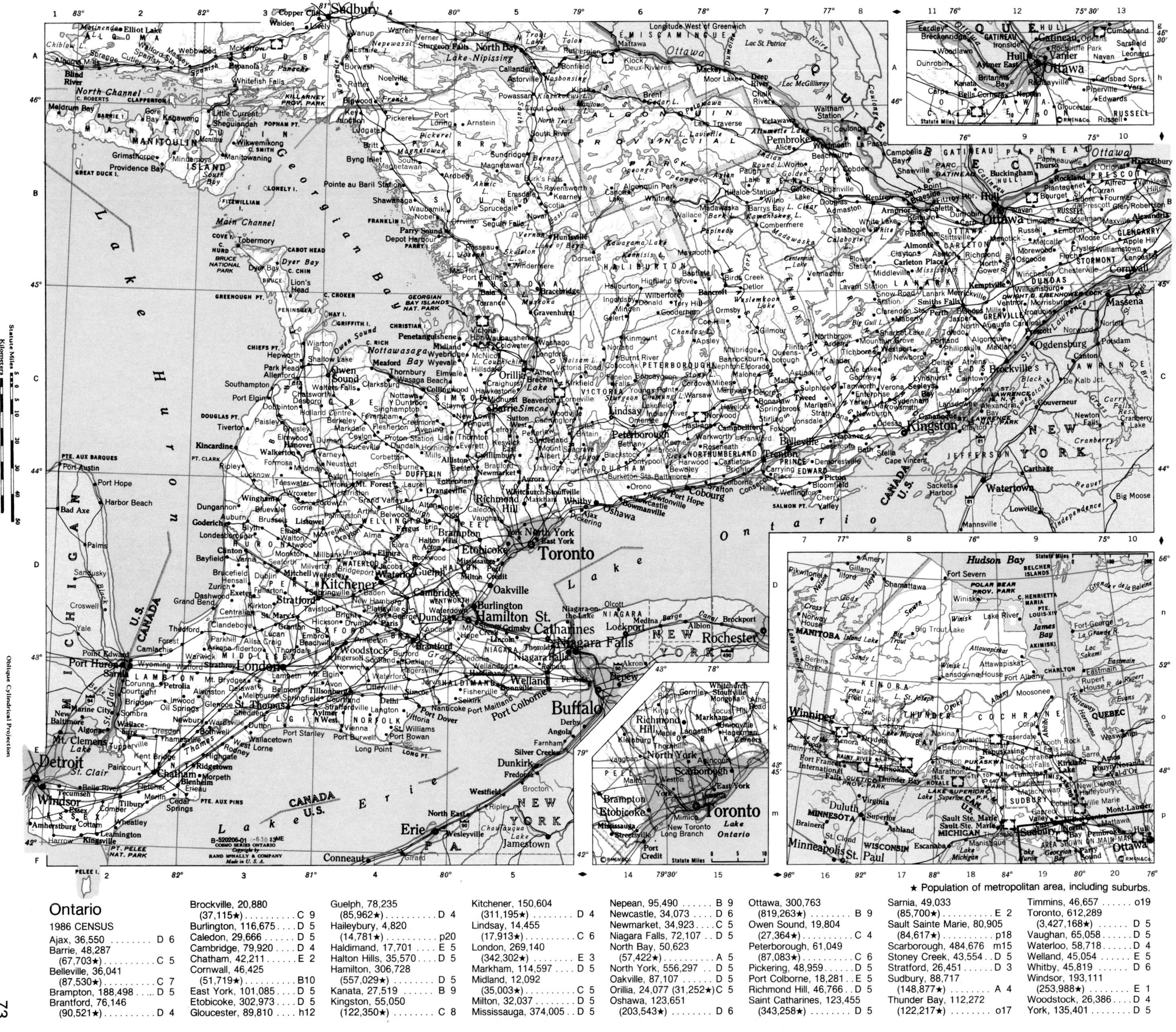

Ontario

1986 CENSUS

Ajax, 36,550 . . . . D 6
Barrie, 48,287
(67,703★) . . . . .C 5
Belleville, 36,041
(87,530★) . . . . .C 7
Brampton, 188,498 . . . . D 5
Brantford, 76,146
(90,521★) . . . . .D 4
Brockville, 20,880
(37,115★) . . . . .C 9
Burlington, 116,675 . . . . D 5
Caledon, 29,666 . . . . . . D 5
Cambridge, 79,920 . . . . D 4
Chatham, 42,211 . . . . . . E 2
Cornwall, 46,425
(51,719★) B10
East York, 101,085 . . . . D 5
Etobicoke, 302,973 . . . . D 5
Gloucester, 89,810 . . . . h12
Guelph, 78,235
(85,962★) . . . . .D 4
Haileybury, 4,820
(14,781★) p20
Haldimand, 17,701 . . . . E 5
Halton Hills, 35,570 . . . . D 5
Hamilton, 306,728
(557,029★) . . . . D 5
Kanata, 27,519 . . . . . . B 9
Kingston, 55,050
(122,350★) . . . . C 8
Kitchener, 150,604
(311,195★) . . . . D 4
Lindsay, 14,455
(17,913★) . . . . .C 6
London, 269,140
(342,302★) . . . . E 3
Markham, 114,597 . . . . D 5
Midland, 12,092
(35,003★) . . . . C 5
Milton, 32,037 . . . . D 5
Mississauga, 374,005 . . D 5
Nepean, 95,490 . . . . . . B 9
Newcastle, 34,073 . . . . . D 6
Newmarket, 34,923 . . . . C 5
Niagara Falls, 72,107 . . D 5
North Bay, 50,623
(57,422★) . . . . .A 5
North York, 556,297 . . D 5
Oakville, 87,107 . . . . . . D 5
Orillia, 24,077 (31,252★)C 5
Oshawa, 123,651
(203,543★) . . . . D 6
Ottawa, 300,763
(819,263★) . . . . B 9
Owen Sound, 19,804
(27,364★) . . . . .C 4
Peterborough, 61,049
(87,083★) . . . . .C 6
Pickering, 48,959 . . . . . D 5
Port Colborne, 18,281 . . E 5
Richmond Hill, 46,766 . . D 5
Saint Catharines, 123,455
(343,258★) . . . . D 5
Sarnia, 49,033
(85,700★) . . . . .E 2
Sault Sainte Marie, 80,905
(84,617★) p18
Scarborough, 484,676 m15
Stoney Creek, 43,554 . . D 5
Stratford, 26,451 . . . . . . D 3
Sudbury, 88,717
(148,877★) . . . . A 4
Thunder Bay, 112,272
(122,217★) o17
Timmins, 46,657 . . . . . . o19
Toronto, 612,289
(3,427,168★) . . . . . . D 5
Vaughan, 65,058 . . . . . . D 5
Waterloo, 58,718 . . . . . . D 4
Welland, 45,054 . . . . . . E 5
Whitby, 45,819 . . . . D 6
Windsor, 193,111
(253,988★) . . . . E 1
Woodstock, 26,386 . . . . D 4
York, 135,401 . . . . D 5

★ Population of metropolitan area, including suburbs.

Quebec

1986 CENSUS

Alma, 25,923 (29,977★) A 6
Ancienne-Lorette, 13,747 C 6
Anjou, 36,916 p19
Aylmer East, 28,976 D 2
Baie-Comeau, 26,244 (33,047★) k13
Beaconsfield, 19,301 q19
Beauport, 62,869 n17
Boucherville, 31,116 D 4
Brossard, 57,441 q20
Cap-de-la-Madeleine, 32,800 C 5
Charlesbourg, 68,996 n17
Châteauguay, 37,865 D 4
Chicoutimi, 61,083 (158,468★) A 6
Drummondville, 36,020 (56,283★) D 5
Gaspé, 17,350 k14
Gatineau, 81,244 D 2
Granby, 38,508 (51,176★) D 5
Grand-Mère, 14,582 C 5
Hull, 58,722 D 2
Joliette, 16,845 (34,897★) C 4
Jonquière, 58,467 A 6
Lachine, 34,906 D 4
Lachute, 11,586 D 3
LaSalle, 75,621 q19
La Tuque, 10,723 (13,468★) B 5
Laval, 284,164 D 4
Lévis, 18,310 C 6
Longueuil, 125,441 D 4
Magog, 13,530 (18,738★) D 5
Mascouche, 21,285 D 4
Matane, 13,243 (15,361★) k13
Montréal, 1,015,420 (2,921,357★) D 4
Montréal-Nord, 90,303 p19
Outremont, 23,080 p19
Pierrefonds, 39,605 q19
Pointe-Claire, 26,026 D 4
Québec, 164,580 (603,267★) C 6
Repentigny, 40,778 D 4
Rimouski, 29,672 (46,210★) A 9
Rivière-du-Loup, 13,321 (22,471★) B 8
Rouyn, 17,319 (36,495★) k11
Saint-Eustache, 32,226 D 4
Sainte-Foy, 69,615 n17
Saint-Hubert, 66,218 q20
Saint-Hyacinthe, 38,603 (48,303★) D 5
Saint-Jean-sur-Richelieu, 34,745 (59,958★) D 4
Saint-Jérôme, 23,316 (44,048★) D 3
Saint-Laurent, 67,002 p19
Salaberry-de-Valleyfield, 27,942 (38,797★) D 3
Sept-Îles (Seven Islands), 25,637 (28,050★) h13
Shawinigan, 21,412 (61,965★) C 5
Sherbrooke, 74,438 (129,960★) D 6
Sorel, 19,522 (46,096★) C 4
Terrebonne, 31,310 D 4
Thetford Mines, 18,561 (31,940★) C 6
Trois-Rivières, 50,122 (128,888★) C 5
Verdun, 60,246 q19
Victoriaville, 21,587 (38,003★) C 6
Ville Saint-Georges, 11,723 (21,022★) C 7

★ Population of metropolitan area, including suburbs.

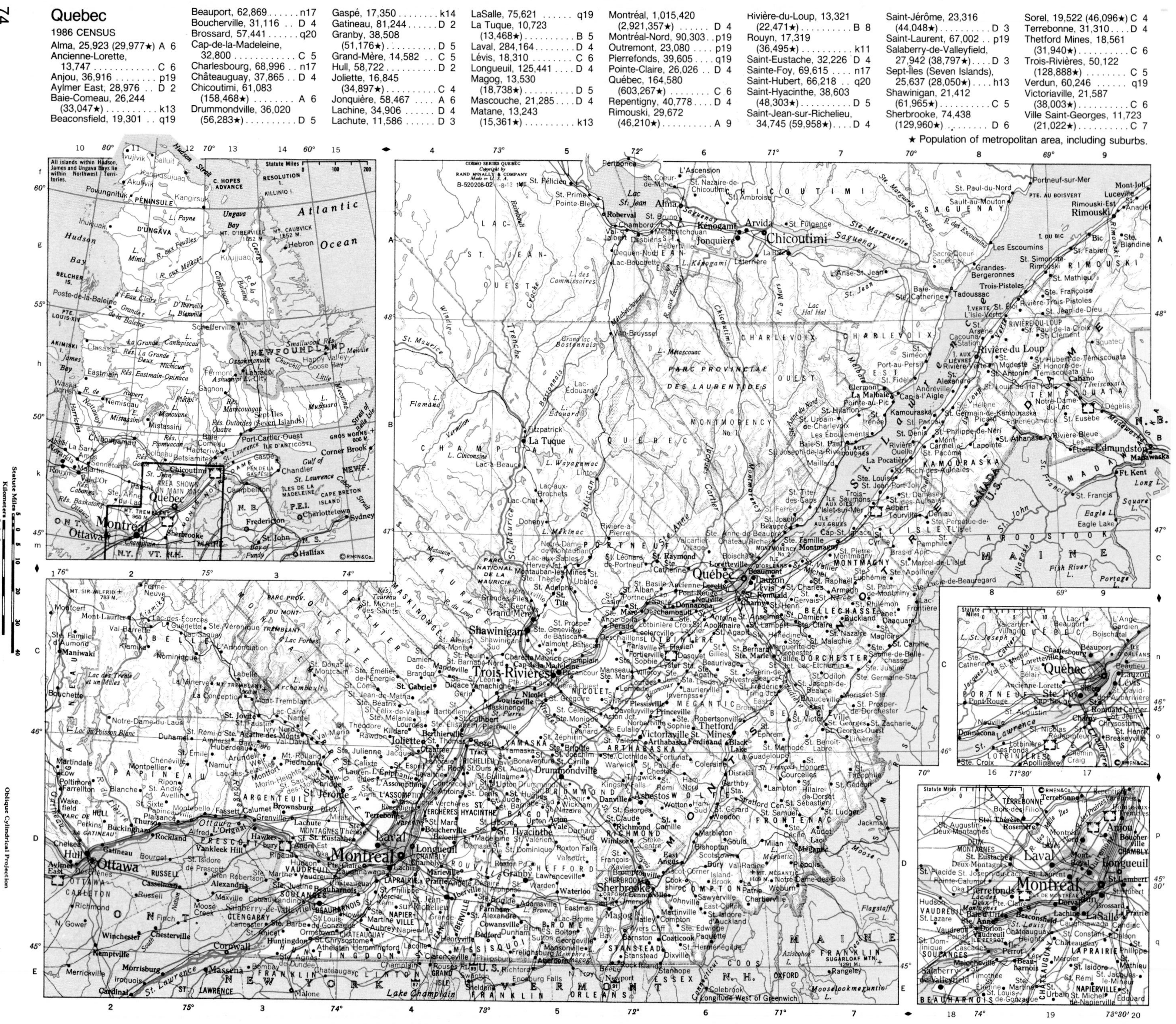

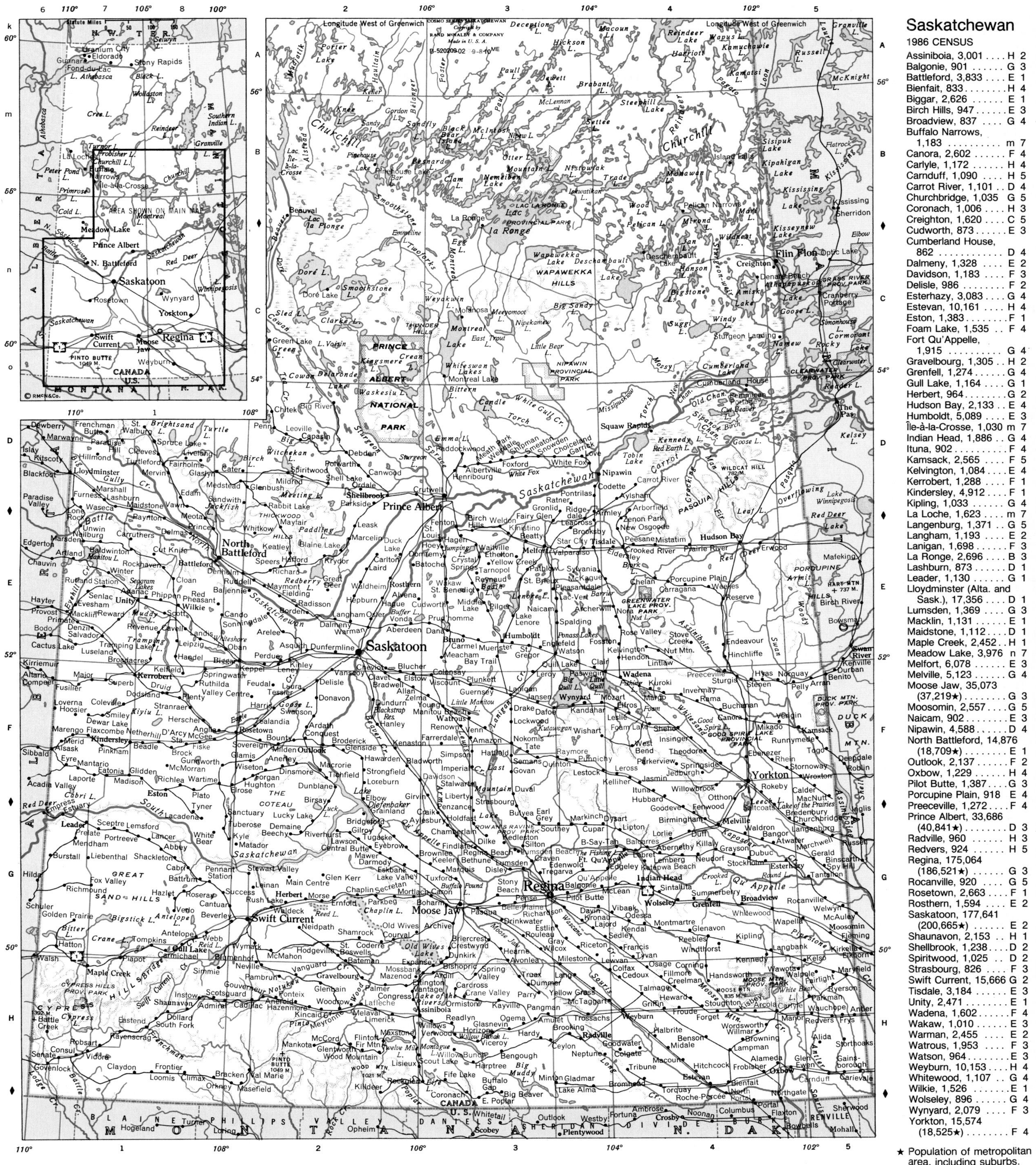

Statute Miles 10 0 10 20 30 40 50 60

Kilometers 10 0 10 20 40 60 80

Oblique Cylindrical Projection

Saskatchewan

1986 CENSUS

Assiniboia, 3,001 . . . . H 2
Balgonie, 901 . . . . . . G 3
Battleford, 3,833 . . . . E 1
Bienfait, 833 . . . . H 4
Biggar, 2,626 . . . . . . E 1
Birch Hills, 947 . . . . . E 3
Broadview, 837 . . . . G 4
Buffalo Narrows, 1,183 . . . . m 7
Canora, 2,602 . . . . . . F 4
Carlyle, 1,172 . . . . . . H 4
Carnduff, 1,090 . . . . . H 5
Carrot River, 1,101 . . D 4
Churchbridge, 1,035 G 5
Coronach, 1,006 . . . . H 3
Creighton, 1,620 . . . . C 5
Cudworth, 873 . . . . . . E 3
Cumberland House, 862 . . . . D 4
Dalmeny, 1,328 . . . . E 2
Davidson, 1,183 . . . . F 3
Delisle, 986 . . . . F 2
Esterhazy, 3,083 . . . . G 4
Estevan, 10,161 . . . . H 4
Eston, 1,383 . . . . F 1
Foam Lake, 1,535 . . F 4
Fort Qu'Appelle, 1,915 . . . . G 4
Gravelbourg, 1,305 . . H 2
Grenfell, 1,274 . . . . . . G 4
Gull Lake, 1,164 . . . . . G 1
Herbert, 964 . . . . G 2
Hudson Bay, 2,133 . . E 4
Humboldt, 5,089 . . . . E 3
Île-à-la-Crosse, 1,030 m 7
Indian Head, 1,886 . . G 4
Ituna, 902 . . . . F 4
Kamsack, 2,565 . . . . . F 5
Kelvington, 1,084 . . . . E 4
Kerrobert, 1,288 . . . . F 1
Kindersley, 4,912 . . . . F 1
Kipling, 1,033 . . . . . . G 4
La Loche, 1,623 . . . . m 7
Langenburg, 1,371 . . G 5
Langham, 1,193 . . . . E 2
Lanigan, 1,698 . . . . . . F 3
La Ronge, 2,696 . . . . . B 3
Lashburn, 873 . . . . . . D 1
Leader, 1,130 . . . . G 1
Lloydminster (Alta. and Sask.), 17,356 . . . . D 1
Lumsden, 1,369 . . . . . G 3
Macklin, 1,131 . . . . . . E 1
Maidstone, 1,112 . . . . D 1
Maple Creek, 2,452 . . H 1
Meadow Lake, 3,976 n 7
Melfort, 6,078 . . . . . . E 3
Melville, 5,123 . . . . . . G 4
Moose Jaw, 35,073 (37,219★) . . . . G 3
Moosomin, 2,557 . . . . G 5
Naicam, 902 . . . . E 3
Nipawin, 4,588 . . . . . . D 4
North Battleford, 14,876 (18,709★) . . . . E 1
Outlook, 2,137 . . . . . . F 2
Oxbow, 1,229 . . . . H 4
Pilot Butte, 1,387 . . . . G 3
Porcupine Plain, 918 E 4
Preeceville, 1,272 . . . . F 4
Prince Albert, 33,686 (40,841★) . . . . D 3
Radville, 960 . . . . H 3
Redvers, 924 . . . . H 5
Regina, 175,064 (186,521★) . . . . G 3
Rocanville, 920 . . . . . G 5
Rosetown, 2,663 . . . . . F 1
Rosthern, 1,594 . . . . . E 2
Saskatoon, 177,641 (200,665★) . . . . E 2
Shaunavon, 2,153 . . . . H 1
Shellbrook, 1,238 . . . . D 2
Spiritwood, 1,025 . . . . D 2
Strasbourg, 826 . . . . . F 3
Swift Current, 15,666 G 2
Tisdale, 3,184 . . . . E 3
Unity, 2,471 . . . . E 1
Wadena, 1,602 . . . . F 4
Wakaw, 1,010 . . . . E 3
Warman, 2,455 . . . . . . E 2
Watrous, 1,953 . . . . . . F 3
Watson, 964 . . . . E 3
Weyburn, 10,153 . . . . H 4
Whitewood, 1,107 . . . . G 4
Wilkie, 1,526 . . . . E 1
Wolseley, 896 . . . . G 4
Wynyard, 2,079 . . . . . . F 3
Yorkton, 15,574 (18,525★) . . . . F 4

★ Population of metropolitan area, including suburbs.

United States of America

Akron, 223,019 ('90)...C10
ALABAMA...................E 9
ALASKA....................M19
Albany, 101,082 ('90)..C12
Albuquerque, 384,736 ('90)......................... D 5
Amarillo, 157,615 ('90) D 6
Anchorage, 226,338 ('90)..........................M20
Annapolis, 33,187 ('90)......................... D11
ARIZONA....................E 4
ARKANSAS................E 8
Atlanta, 394,017 ('90)..E10
Augusta, 21,325 ('90). C13
Austin, 465,622 ('90)... E 7
Baltimore, 736,014 ('90)......................... D11
Baton Rouge, 219,531 ('90)..........................E 8
Billings, 81,151 ('90)....B 5
Birmingham, 265,968 ('90)..........................E 9
Bismarck, 49,256 ('90) B 6
Boise, 125,738 ('90)....C 3
Boston, 574,283 ('90). C12
Buffalo, 328,123 ('90). C11
CALIFORNIA..............D 2
Carson City, 40,443 ('90)......................... D 3
Charleston, 57,287 ('90)......................... D10
Charleston, 80,414 ('90)..........................E11
Charlotte, 395,934 ('90)......................... D10
Chattanooga, 152,466 ('90)......................... D 9
Cheyenne, 50,008 ('90)......................... C 6
Chicago, 2,783,726 ('90)......................... C 9
Cincinnati, 364,040 ('90)......................... D10
Cleveland, 505,616 ('90)......................... C10
COLORADO............... D 5
Colorado Springs, 281,140 ('90)......................... D 6
Columbia, 98,052 ('90) E10
Columbus, 178,681 ('90)..........................E10
Columbus, 632,910 ('90)......................... D10
Concord, 36,006 ('90). C12
CONNECTICUT...........C12
Dallas, 1,006,877 ('90) E 7
DELAWARE............... D11
Denver, 467,610 ('90). D 6
Des Moines, 193,187 ('90)......................... C 8
Detroit, 1,027,974 ('90)......................... C10
Dover, 27,630 ('90)..... D11
El Paso, 515,342 ('90). E 5
FLORIDA..................... F10
Fort Wayne, 173,072 ('90)......................... C 9
Fort Worth, 447,619 ('90)..........................E 7
Frankfort, 25,968 ('90) D10
Fresno, 354,202 ('90)..D 3
GEORGIA...................E10
Grand Rapids, 189,126 ('90)......................... C 9
Harrisburg, 52,376 ('90)......................... C11
Hartford, 139,739 ('90)......................... C12
Helena, 24,569 ('90)....B 4
Houston, 1,630,553 ('90)..........................F 7
IDAHO.........................C 4
ILLINOIS......................C 9
INDIANA.....................C 9
Indianapolis, 731,327 ('90)......................... D 9
IOWA..........................C 8
Jackson, 196,637 ('90) E 8
Jacksonville, 635,230 ('90)..........................E10
Jefferson City, 35,481 ('90)......................... D 8
Juneau, 26,751 ('90)... N21
KANSAS.....................D 7
Kansas City, 435,146 ('90)......................... D 8
KENTUCKY................ D 9
Knoxville, 165,121 ('90)......................... D10
Las Vegas, 258,295 ('90)......................... D 3
Lincoln, 191,972 ('90)..C 7
Little Rock, 175,795 ('90)..........................E 8
Los Angeles, 3,485,398 ('90)..........................E 3
LOUISIANA.................E 8
Louisville, 269,063 ('90)......................... D 9
Madison, 191,262 ('90)......................... C 9
MAINE........................B13
MARYLAND............... D11

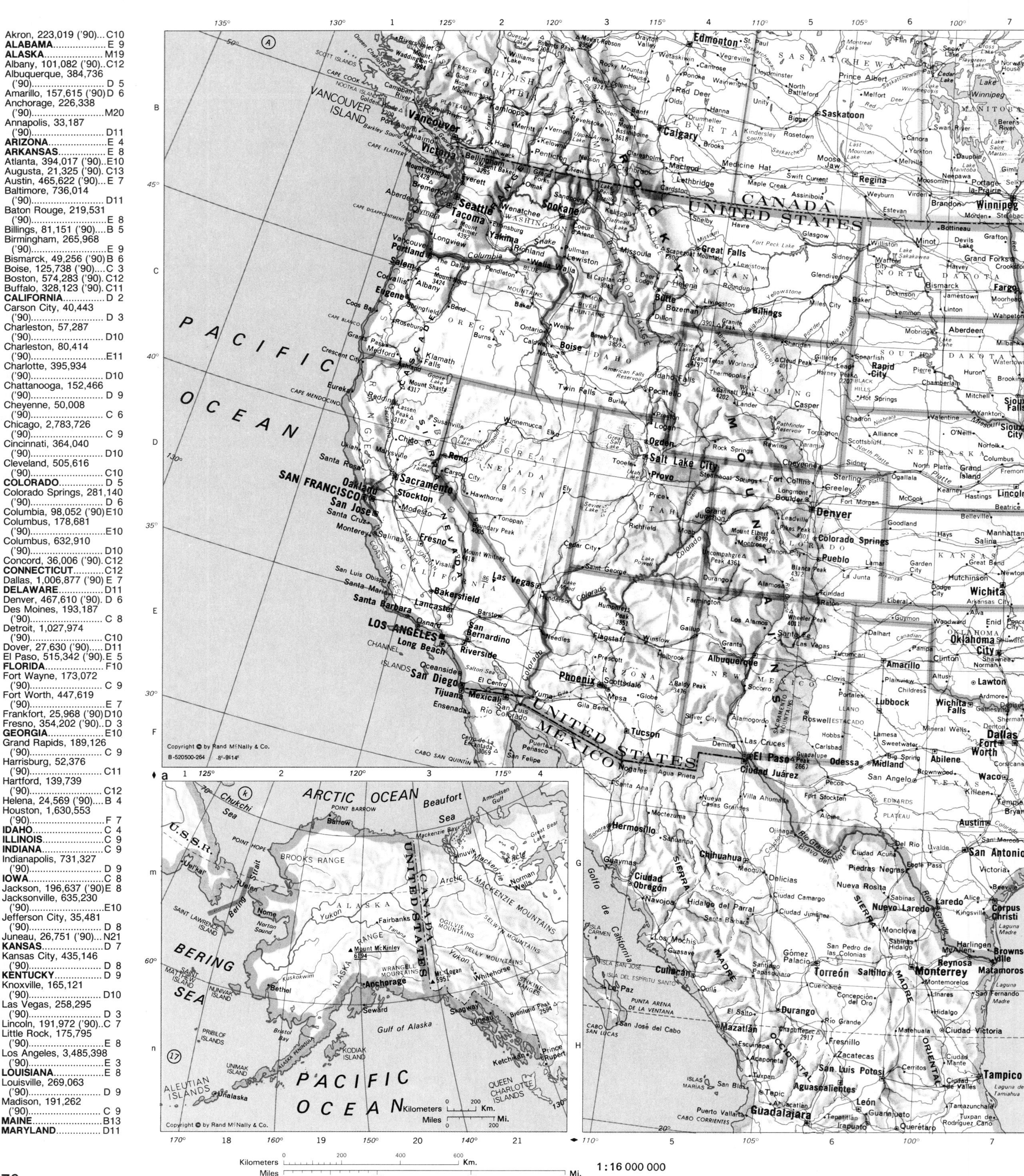

MASSACHUSETTS.....C12
Memphis, 610,337 ('90).........................D 8
Miami, 358,548 ('90)....F10
MICHIGAN.................C10
Milwaukee, 628,088 ('90)........................C 9
Minneapolis, 368,383 ('90)........................C 8
MINNESOTA..............B 8
MISSISSIPPI...............E 9
MISSOURI..................D 8
Mobile, 196,278 ('90)...E 9
MONTANA..................B 5
Montgomery, 187,106 ('90)..........................E 9
Montpelier, 8,247 ('90)C12
Nashville, 487,969 ('90)..........................D 9
NEBRASKA..................C 7
NEVADA....................D 3
Newark, 275,221 ('90) C12
NEW HAMPSHIRE......C12
NEW JERSEY............C12
NEW MEXICO............E 5
New Orleans, 496,938 ('90)..........................F 8
NEW YORK................C11
New York, 7,322,564 ('90).........................C12
Norfolk, 261,229 ('90).D11
NORTH CAROLINA.....D11
NORTH DAKOTA........B 6
Oakland, 372,242 ('90)D 2
OHIO..........................C10
OKLAHOMA.................D 7
Oklahoma City, 444,719 ('90)..........................D 7
Olympia, 33,840 ('90)..B 2
Omaha, 335,795 ('90). C 7
OREGON......................C 2
PENNSYLVANIA........C11
Philadelphia, 1,585,577 ('90)........................D11
Phoenix, 900,013 ('90) E 4
Pierre, 12,906 ('90)..... C 6
Pittsburgh, 369,879 ('90)..........................C11
Portland, 64,358 ('90). C12
Providence, 160,728 ('90).........................C12
Raleigh, 207,951 ('90).D11
Rapid City, 54,523 ('90)..........................C 6
Reno, 133,850 ('90).... D 3
RHODE ISLAND..........C12
Richmond, 203,056 ('90)..........................D11
Rochester, 231,636 ('90)..........................C11
Sacramento, 369,365 ('90)..........................D 2
Saint Louis, 396,685 ('90)..........................D 8
Saint Paul, 272,235 ('90)..........................C 8
Saint Petersburg, 238,629 ('90)..........................F10
Salem, 107,786 ('90)....C 2
Salt Lake City, 159,936 ('90)..........................C 4
San Antonio, 935,933 ('90)..........................F 7
San Diego, 1,110,549 ('90)..........................E 3
San Francisco, 723,959 ('90)..........................D 2
San Jose, 782,248 ('90)..........................D 2
Santa Fe, 55,859 ('90) D 5
Savannah, 137,560 ('90)..........................E10
Seattle, 516,259 ('90)..B 2
Shreveport, 198,525 ('90)..........................E 8
SOUTH CAROLINA.....E10
SOUTH DAKOTA........C 7
Spokane, 177,196 ('90)..........................B 3
Springfield, 105,227 ('90)..........................D 9
Syracuse, 163,860 ('90)..........................C11
Tacoma, 176,664 ('90)B 2
Tallahassee, 124,773 ('90)..........................E10
Tampa, 280,015 ('90)..F10
TENNESSEE..............D 9
TEXAS........................E 7
Toledo, 332,943 ('90)..C10
Topeka, 119,883 ('90).D 7
Trenton, 88,675 ('90).. C12
Tulsa, 367,302 ('90)..... D 7
UNITED STATES........ D 7
UTAH...........................D 4
VERMONT..................C12
VIRGINIA....................D11
WASHINGTON............ B 2
Washington, 606,900 ('90)..........................D11
WEST VIRGINIA.........D10
Wichita, 304,011 ('90). D 7
WISCONSIN................C 9
WYOMING..................C 5

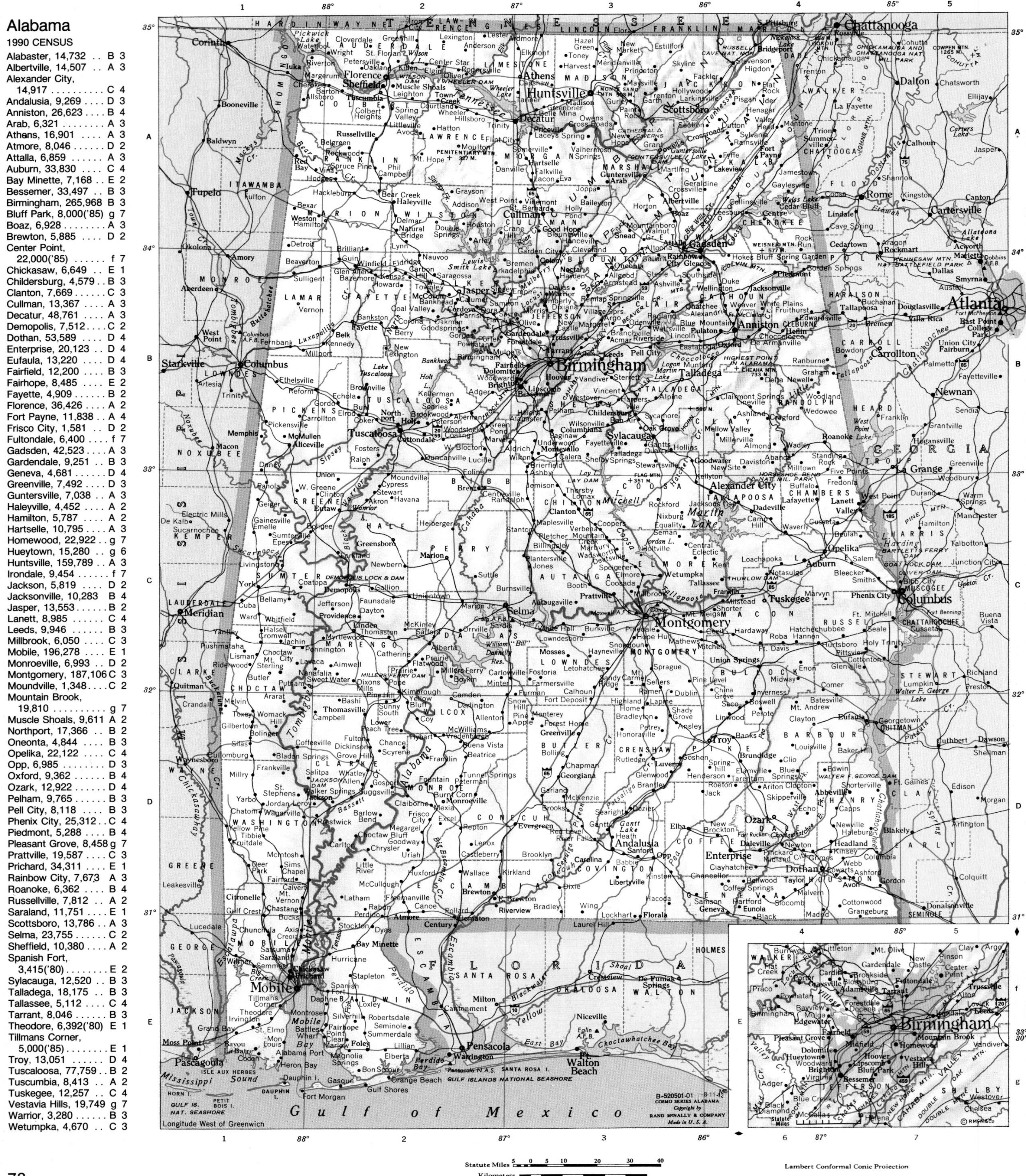

Alabama

1990 CENSUS

- Alabaster, 14,732 .. B 3
- Albertville, 14,507 .. A 3
- Alexander City, 14,917 .... C 4
- Andalusia, 9,269 .... D 3
- Anniston, 26,623 .... B 4
- Arab, 6,321 .... A 3
- Athens, 16,901 .... A 3
- Atmore, 8,046 ...... D 2
- Attalla, 6,859 ...... A 3
- Auburn, 33,830 .... C 4
- Bay Minette, 7,168 .. E 2
- Bessemer, 33,497 .. B 3
- Birmingham, 265,968 B 3
- Bluff Park, 8,000('85) g 7
- Boaz, 6,928 .... A 3
- Brewton, 5,885 .... D 2
- Center Point, 22,000('85) ...... f 7
- Chickasaw, 6,649 .. E 1
- Childersburg, 4,579 .. B 3
- Clanton, 7,669 ...... C 3
- Cullman, 13,367 .... A 3
- Decatur, 48,761 .... A 3
- Demopolis, 7,512.... C 2
- Dothan, 53,589 .... D 4
- Enterprise, 20,123 .. D 4
- Eufaula, 13,220 .... D 4
- Fairfield, 12,200 .... B 3
- Fairhope, 8,485 .... E 2
- Fayette, 4,909 ...... B 2
- Florence, 36,426 .... A 2
- Fort Payne, 11,838 .. A 4
- Frisco City, 1,581 .. D 2
- Fultondale, 6,400 .... f 7
- Gadsden, 42,523 .... A 3
- Gardendale, 9,251 .. B 3
- Geneva, 4,681 ...... D 4
- Greenville, 7,492 .... D 3
- Guntersville, 7,038 .. A 3
- Haleyville, 4,452 .... A 2
- Hamilton, 5,787 .... A 2
- Hartselle, 10,795 .... A 3
- Homewood, 22,922 .. g 7
- Hueytown, 15,280 .. g 6
- Huntsville, 159,789 .. A 3
- Irondale, 9,454 ...... f 7
- Jackson, 5,819 .... D 2
- Jacksonville, 10,283 B 4
- Jasper, 13,553...... B 2
- Lanett, 8,985 ...... C 4
- Leeds, 9,946 ...... B 3
- Millbrook, 6,050 .... C 3
- Mobile, 196,278 .... E 1
- Monroeville, 6,993 .. D 2
- Montgomery, 187,106 C 3
- Moundville, 1,348.... C 2
- Mountain Brook, 19,810 .... g 7
- Muscle Shoals, 9,611 A 2
- Northport, 17,366 .. B 2
- Oneonta, 4,844 .... B 3
- Opelika, 22,122 .... C 4
- Opp, 6,985 .... D 3
- Oxford, 9,362 ...... B 4
- Ozark, 12,922 ...... D 4
- Pelham, 9,765 ...... B 3
- Pell City, 8,118 .... B 3
- Phenix City, 25,312.. C 4
- Piedmont, 5,288 .... B 4
- Pleasant Grove, 8,458 g 7
- Prattville, 19,587 .... C 3
- Prichard, 34,311 .... E 1
- Rainbow City, 7,673 A 3
- Roanoke, 6,362 .... B 4
- Russellville, 7,812 .. A 2
- Saraland, 11,751 .... E 1
- Scottsboro, 13,786 .. A 3
- Selma, 23,755 ...... C 2
- Sheffield, 10,380 .... A 2
- Spanish Fort, 3,415('80) .... E 2
- Sylacauga, 12,520 .. B 3
- Talladega, 18,175 .. B 3
- Tallassee, 5,112 .... C 4
- Tarrant, 8,046 ...... B 3
- Theodore, 6,392('80) E 1
- Tillmans Corner, 5,000('85) .... E 1
- Troy, 13,051 ...... D 4
- Tuscaloosa, 77,759 .. B 2
- Tuscumbia, 8,413 .. A 2
- Tuskegee, 12,257 .... C 4
- Vestavia Hills, 19,749 g 7
- Warrior, 3,280 ...... B 3
- Wetumpka, 4,670 .. C 3

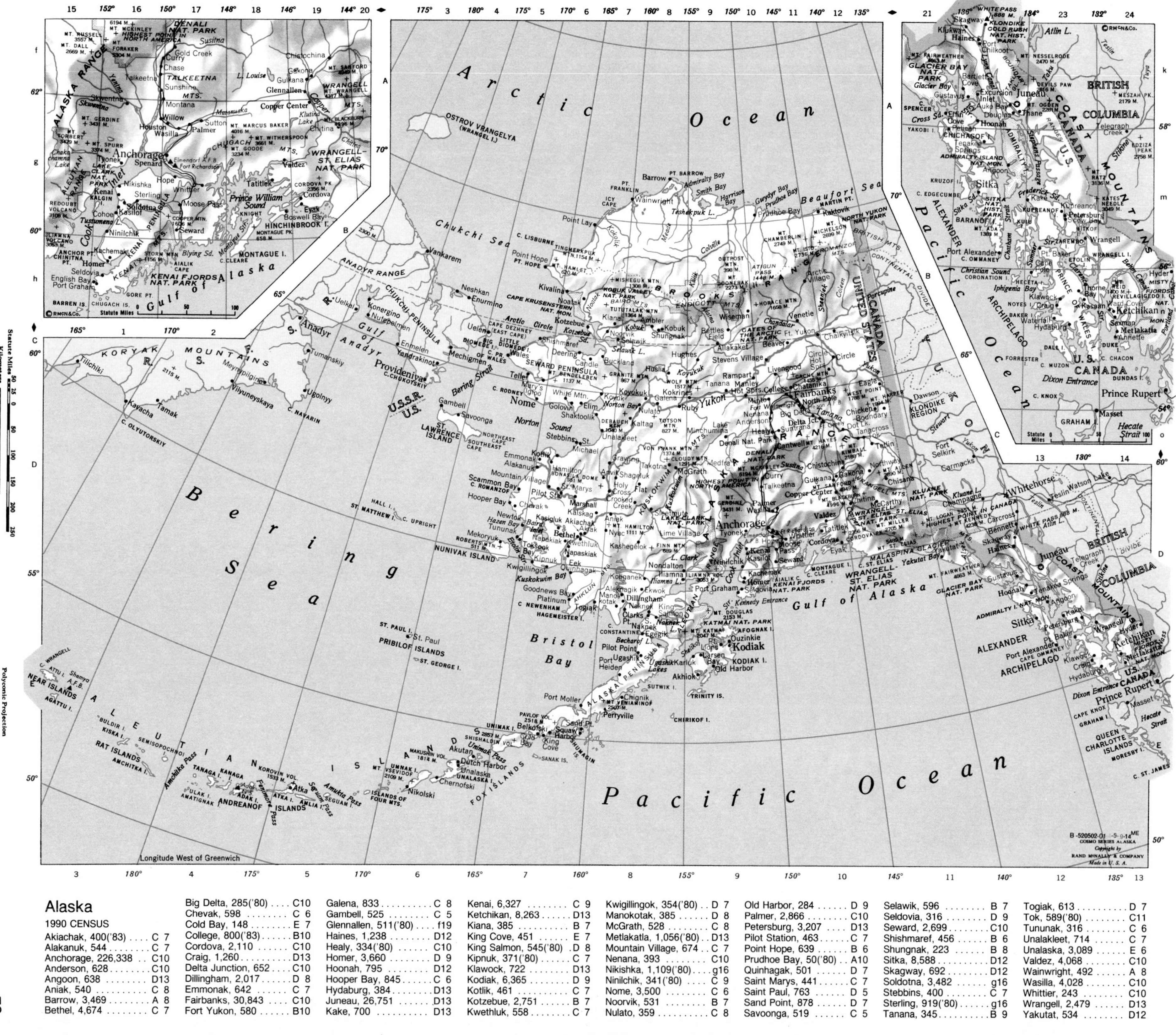

Alaska

1990 CENSUS

Akiachak, 400('83) .... C 7
Alakanuk, 544 .... C 7
Anchorage, 226,338 .. C10
Anderson, 628 .... C10
Angoon, 638 .... D13
Aniak, 540 .... C 8
Barrow, 3,469 .... A 8
Bethel, 4,674 .... C 7
Big Delta, 285('80) C10
Chevak, 598 .... C 6
Cold Bay, 148 .... E 7
College, 800('83) B10
Cordova, 2,110 ...... C10
Craig, 1,260 .... D13
Delta Junction, 652 .... C10
Dillingham, 2,017 ...... D 8
Emmonak, 642 .... C 7
Fairbanks, 30,843 .... C10
Fort Yukon, 580 ...... B10
Galena, 833 .... C 8
Gambell, 525 .... C 5
Glennallen, 511('80) f19
Haines, 1,238 .... D12
Healy, 334('80) C10
Homer, 3,660 .... D 9
Hoonah, 795 .... D12
Hooper Bay, 845 ...... C 6
Hydaburg, 384 .... D13
Juneau, 26,751 ...... D13
Kake, 700 .... D13
Kenai, 6,327 .... C 9
Ketchikan, 8,263 ...... D13
Kiana, 385 .... B 7
King Cove, 451 ...... E 7
King Salmon, 545('80) .D 8
Kipnuk, 371('80) ...... C 7
Klawock, 722 .... D13
Kodiak, 6,365 .... D 9
Kotlik, 461 .... C 7
Kotzebue, 2,751 ...... B 7
Kwethluk, 558 .... C 7
Kwigillingok, 354('80) .. D 7
Manokotak, 385 ...... D 8
McGrath, 528 .... C 8
Metlakatla, 1,056('80) .. D13
Mountain Village, 674 .. C 7
Nenana, 393 .... C10
Nikishka, 1,109('80) g16
Ninilchik, 341('80) .... C 9
Nome, 3,500 .... C 6
Noorvik, 531 .... B 7
Nulato, 359 .... C 8
Old Harbor, 284 ...... D 9
Palmer, 2,866 .... C10
Petersburg, 3,207 .... D13
Pilot Station, 463 ...... C 7
Point Hope, 639 ...... B 6
Prudhoe Bay, 50('80) .. A10
Quinhagak, 501 ...... D 7
Saint Marys, 441 ...... C 7
Saint Paul, 763 ...... D 5
Sand Point, 878 ...... D 7
Savoonga, 519 ...... C 5
Selawik, 596 .... B 7
Seldovia, 316 .... D 9
Seward, 2,699 .... C10
Shishmaref, 456 ...... B 6
Shungnak, 223 ...... B 8
Sitka, 8,588 .... D12
Skagway, 692 .... D12
Soldotna, 3,482 ...... g16
Stebbins, 400 .... C 7
Sterling, 919('80) g16
Tanana, 345 .... B 9
Togiak, 613 .... D 7
Tok, 589('80) C11
Tununak, 316 .... C 6
Unalakleet, 714 ...... C 7
Unalaska, 3,089 ...... E 6
Valdez, 4,068 .... C10
Wainwright, 492 ...... A 8
Wasilla, 4,028 .... C10
Whittier, 243 .... C10
Wrangell, 2,479 ...... D13
Yakutat, 534 .... D12

Arizona

1990 CENSUS

Ajo, 5,189('80) . . . . . E 3
Apache Junction, 18,100 . . . . m 9
Avondale, 16,169 . . . . D 3
Bagdad, 2,331('80) . . C 2
Benson, 3,824 . . . . . . F 5
Bisbee, 6,288 . . . . . . F 6
Black Canyon City, 850('86) . . . . C 3
Buckeye, 5,038 . . . . D 3
Bullhead City, 21,951 B 1
Camp Verde, 6,243 . . C 4
Casa Grande, 19,082 E 4
Casas Adobes, 12,155('86) . . . . . . E 5
Cashion, 3,014('80) . . m 8
Cave Creek, 2,925 . . D 4
Chandler, 90,533 . . . D 4
Chinle, 2,815('80) . . . A 6
Chino Valley, 4,837 . . C 3
Claypool, 2,362('80) D 5
Clifton, 2,840 . . . . . . D 6
Coolidge, 6,927 . . . . E 4
Cottonwood, 5,918 . . C 3
Crane, 2,650('86) . . . E 1
Douglas, 12,822 . . . . F 6
Eagar, 4,025 . . . . . . C 6
El Mirage, 5,001 . . . . k 8
Eloy, 7,211 . . . . E 4
Flagstaff, 45,857 . . . B 4
Florence, 7,510 . . . . D 4
Fort Defiance, 3,431('80) . . . . B 6
Ganado, 3,400('86) . . B 6
Gila Bend, 1,747 . . . E 3
Gilbert, 29,188 . . . . . D 4
Glendale, 148,134 . . D 3
Globe, 6,062 . . . . . . D 5
Goodyear, 6,258 . . . . D 3
Grand Canyon, 1,348('80) . . . . A 3
Green Valley, 7,999('80) . . . . F 5
Guadalupe, 5,458 . . . m 9
Holbrook, 4,686 . . . . C 5
Huachuca City, 1,782 F 5
Kayenta, 3,343('80) . . A 5
Kearny, 2,262 . . . . . . D 5
Kingman, 12,722 . . . . B 1
Lake Havasu City, 24,363 . . . . C 1
Lakeside-Pinetop, 2,422 . . . . C 6
Litchfield Park, 3,303 m 8
Mammoth, 1,845 . . . . E 5
Mesa, 288,091 . . . . . D 4
Miami, 2,018 . . . . . . D 5
Nogales, 19,489 . . . . F 5
Oracle, 2,484('80) . . E 5
Page, 6,598 . . . . A 4
Paradise Valley, 11,671 . . . . k 9
Parker, 2,897 . . . . . . C 1
Payson, 8,377 . . . . . . C 4
Peoria, 50,618 . . . . . . D 3
Phoenix, 900,013 . . . . D 3
Prescott, 26,455 . . . . C 3
Sacaton, 1,951('80) . . D 4
Safford, 7,359 . . . . . . E 6
Saint Johns, 3,294 . . C 6
San Carlos, 2,668('80) . . . . D 5
San Luis, 70('86) . . . . E 3
San Manuel, 5,443('80) . . . . E 5
Scottsdale, 130,069 D 4
Sedona, 7,720 . . . . . . C 4
Sells, 1,864('80) . . . . F 4
Show Low, 5,019 . . C 5
Sierra Vista, 32,983 . . F 5
Snowflake, 3,679 . . . . C 5
Somerton, 5,282 . . . . E 1
South Tucson, 5,093 E 5
Sun City, 57,000 . . . . k 8
Superior, 3,468 . . . . D 4
Surprise, 7,122 . . . . . k 8
Taylor, 2,418 . . . . . . C 5
Tempe, 141,865 . . . . D 4
Thatcher, 3,763 . . . . E 6
Tolleson, 4,434 . . . . m 8
Tombstone, 1,220 . . F 5
Tuba City, 5,045('80) A 4
Tucson, 405,390 . . . . E 5
Twin Knolls, 5,210('86) . . . . m 9
Wickenburg, 4,515 . . D 3
Willcox, 3,122 . . . . . . E 6
Williams, 2,532 . . . . . B 3
Window Rock, 2,230('80) . . . . B 6
Winslow, 8,190 . . . . C 5
Youngtown, 2,542 . . k 8
Yuma, 54,923 . . . . . E 1

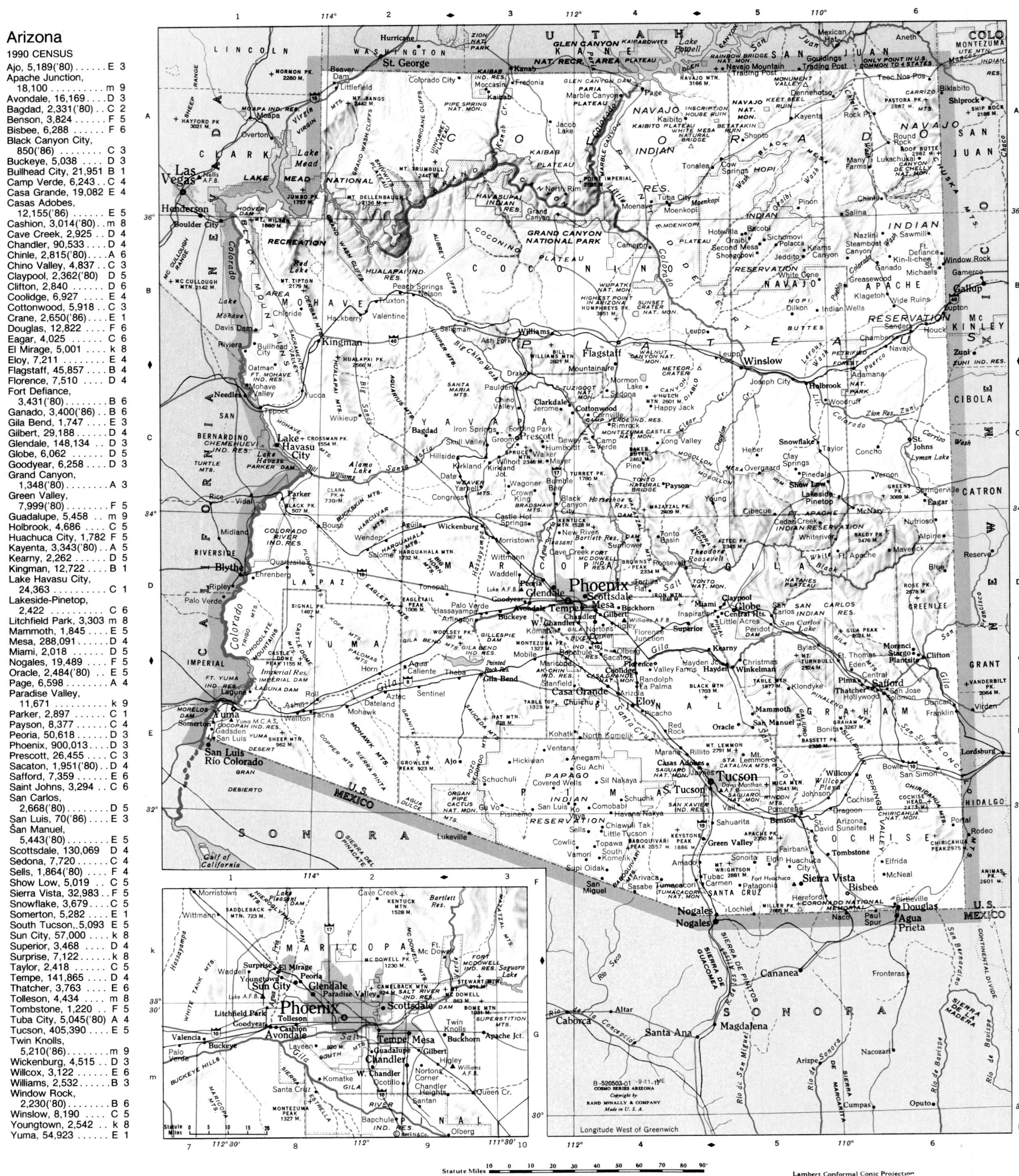

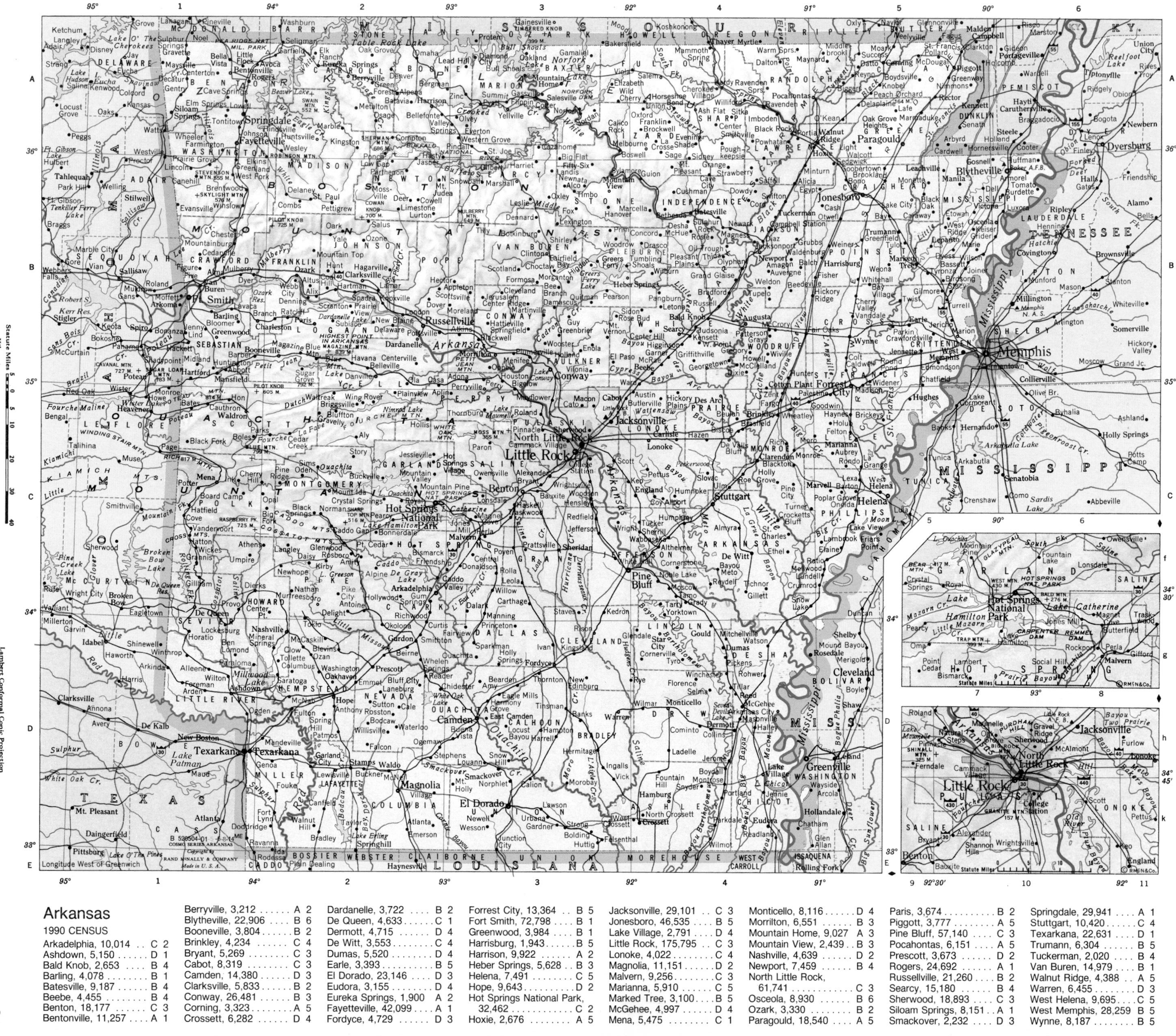

Arkansas

1990 CENSUS

Arkadelphia, 10,014 .. C 2
Ashdown, 5,150 ...... D 1
Bald Knob, 2,653 .... B 4
Barling, 4,078 .... B 1
Batesville, 9,187 ..... B 4
Beebe, 4,455 .... B 4
Benton, 18,177 .... C 3
Bentonville, 11,257 .... A 1
Berryville, 3,212 ...... A 2
Blytheville, 22,906 .... B 6
Booneville, 3,804 ...... B 2
Brinkley, 4,234 .... C 4
Bryant, 5,269 .... C 3
Cabot, 8,319 .... C 3
Camden, 14,380 ...... D 3
Clarksville, 5,833 ..... B 2
Conway, 26,481 ...... B 3
Corning, 3,323 .... A 5
Crossett, 6,282 .... D 4
Dardanelle, 3,722 .... B 2
De Queen, 4,633 ...... C 1
Dermott, 4,715 .... D 4
De Witt, 3,553 .... C 4
Dumas, 5,520 .... D 4
Earle, 3,393 .... B 5
El Dorado, 23,146 .... D 3
Eudora, 3,155 .... D 4
Eureka Springs, 1,900 . A 2
Fayetteville, 42,099 ... A 1
Fordyce, 4,729 .... D 3
Forrest City, 13,364 .. B 5
Fort Smith, 72,798 .... B 1
Greenwood, 3,984 .... B 1
Harrisburg, 1,943 ...... B 5
Harrison, 9,922 .... A 2
Heber Springs, 5,628 .. B 3
Helena, 7,491 .... C 5
Hope, 9,643 .... D 2
Hot Springs National Park, 32,462 .... C 2
Hoxie, 2,676 .... A 5
Jacksonville, 29,101 .. C 3
Jonesboro, 46,535 .... B 5
Lake Village, 2,791 .... D 4
Little Rock, 175,795 .. C 3
Lonoke, 4,022 .... C 4
Magnolia, 11,151 ...... D 2
Malvern, 9,256 .... C 3
Marianna, 5,910 .... C 5
Marked Tree, 3,100 .... B 5
McGehee, 4,997 ...... D 4
Mena, 5,475 .... C 1
Monticello, 8,116 ...... D 4
Morrilton, 6,551 .... B 3
Mountain Home, 9,027 A 3
Mountain View, 2,439 .. B 3
Nashville, 4,639 .... D 2
Newport, 7,459 .... B 4
North Little Rock, 61,741 .... C 3
Osceola, 8,930 .... B 6
Ozark, 3,330 .... B 2
Paragould, 18,540 .... A 5
Paris, 3,674 .... B 2
Piggott, 3,777 .... A 5
Pine Bluff, 57,140 ..... C 3
Pocahontas, 6,151 .... A 5
Prescott, 3,673 .... D 2
Rogers, 24,692 .... A 1
Russellville, 21,260 .... B 2
Searcy, 15,180 .... B 4
Sherwood, 18,893 ..... C 3
Siloam Springs, 8,151 .. A 1
Smackover, 2,232 .... D 3
Springdale, 29,941 .... A 1
Stuttgart, 10,420 ...... C 4
Texarkana, 22,631 ..... D 1
Trumann, 6,304 .... B 5
Tuckerman, 2,020 .... B 4
Van Buren, 14,979 .... B 1
Walnut Ridge, 4,388 .. A 5
Warren, 6,455 .... D 3
West Helena, 9,695 .... C 5
West Memphis, 28,259 B 5
Wynne, 8,187 .... B 5

California

1990 CENSUS

Alameda, 76,459 .... h 8
Alhambra, 82,106 .. m12
Anaheim, 266,406 .. F 5
Antioch, 62,195 .... h 9
Bakersfield, 174,820 E 4
Berkeley, 102,724 .. D 2
Beverly Hills, 31,971 m12
Burbank, 93,643 .... E 4
Calexico, 18,633 .... F 6
Chico, 40,079 ...... C 3
Chula Vista, 135,163 F 5
Compton, 90,454 .... n12
Concord, 111,348 .. h 8
Costa Mesa, 96,357 .. n13
Daly City, 92,311 .... h 8
Davis, 46,209 ...... C 3
Downey, 91,444 .... n12
East Los Angeles, 126,379 .... m12
El Cajon, 88,693 .... F 5
El Centro, 31,384 .... F 6
Escondido, 108,635 .. F 5
Eureka, 27,025 .... B 1
Fairfield, 77,211 .... C 2
Fremont, 173,339 .. D 2
Fresno, 354,202 .... D 4
Fullerton, 114,144 .. n13
Garden Grove, 143,050 .... n13
Glendale, 180,038 .. m12
Hayward, 111,498 .. h 8
Huntington Beach, 181,519 .... F 4
Indio, 36,793 ...... F 5
Inglewood, 109,602 .. n12
Irvine, 110,330 ...... n13
Lancaster, 97,291 .. E 4
Lompoc, 37,649 .... E 3
Long Beach, 429,433 F 4
Los Angeles, 3,485,398 .... E 4
Marysville, 12,324 .. C 3
Menlo Park, 28,040 .. k 8
Merced, 56,216 .... D 3
Modesto, 164,730 .. D 3
Monterey, 31,954 .. D 3
Napa, 61,842 ...... C 2
Newport Beach, 66,643 .... n13
Norwalk, 94,279 .... n12
Oakland, 372,242 .. D 2
Oceanside, 128,398 .. F 5
Ontario, 133,179 .... E 5
Orange, 110,658 .... n13
Oxnard, 142,21[illegible] .... E 4
Palm Springs, 40,181 F 5
Palo Alto, 55,900 .... D 2
Pasadena, 131,591 .. E 4
Pomona, 131,723 .... E 5
Redding, 66,462 .... B 2
Redwood City, 66,072 .... D 2
Richmond, 87,425 .. D 2
Riverside, 226,505 .. F 5
Sacramento, 369,365 C 3
Salinas, 108,777 .... D 3
San Bernardino, 164,164 .... E 5
San Clemente, 41,100 F 5
San Diego, 1,110,549 F 5
San Francisco, 723,959 .... D 2
San Jose, 782,248 .. D 3
San Juan Capistrano, 26,183 .... F 5
San Luis Obispo, 41,958 .... E 3
San Mateo, 85,486 .. D 2
Santa Ana, 293,742 .. F 5
Santa Barbara, 85,571 .... E 4
Santa Clara, 93,613 D 2
Santa Cruz, 49,040 .. D 2
Santa Maria, 61,284 E 3
Santa Monica, 86,905 m12
Santa Rosa, 113,313 C 2
Simi Valley, 100,217 E 4
South Gate, 86,284 .. n12
South Lake Tahoe, 21,586 .... C 4
Stockton, 210,943 .. D 3
Sunnyvale, 117,229 .. k 8
Torrance, 133,107 .. n12
Tulare, 33,249 ...... D 4
Turlock, 42,198 .... D 3
Vallejo, 109,199 .... C 2
Ventura (San Buenaventura), 92,575 .... E 4
Visalia, 75,636 ...... D 4
West Covina, 96,086 m13
Westminster, 78,118 n12
Whittier, 77,671 .... F 4
Yuba City, 27,437 .. C 3

B-520505-01-9-12-18 ME
COSMO SERIES CALIFORNIA

Statute Miles 10 0 10 20 30 40 50 60 70 80 90
Kilometers 10 0 10 20 40 60 80 100 120

Lambert Conformal Conic Projection

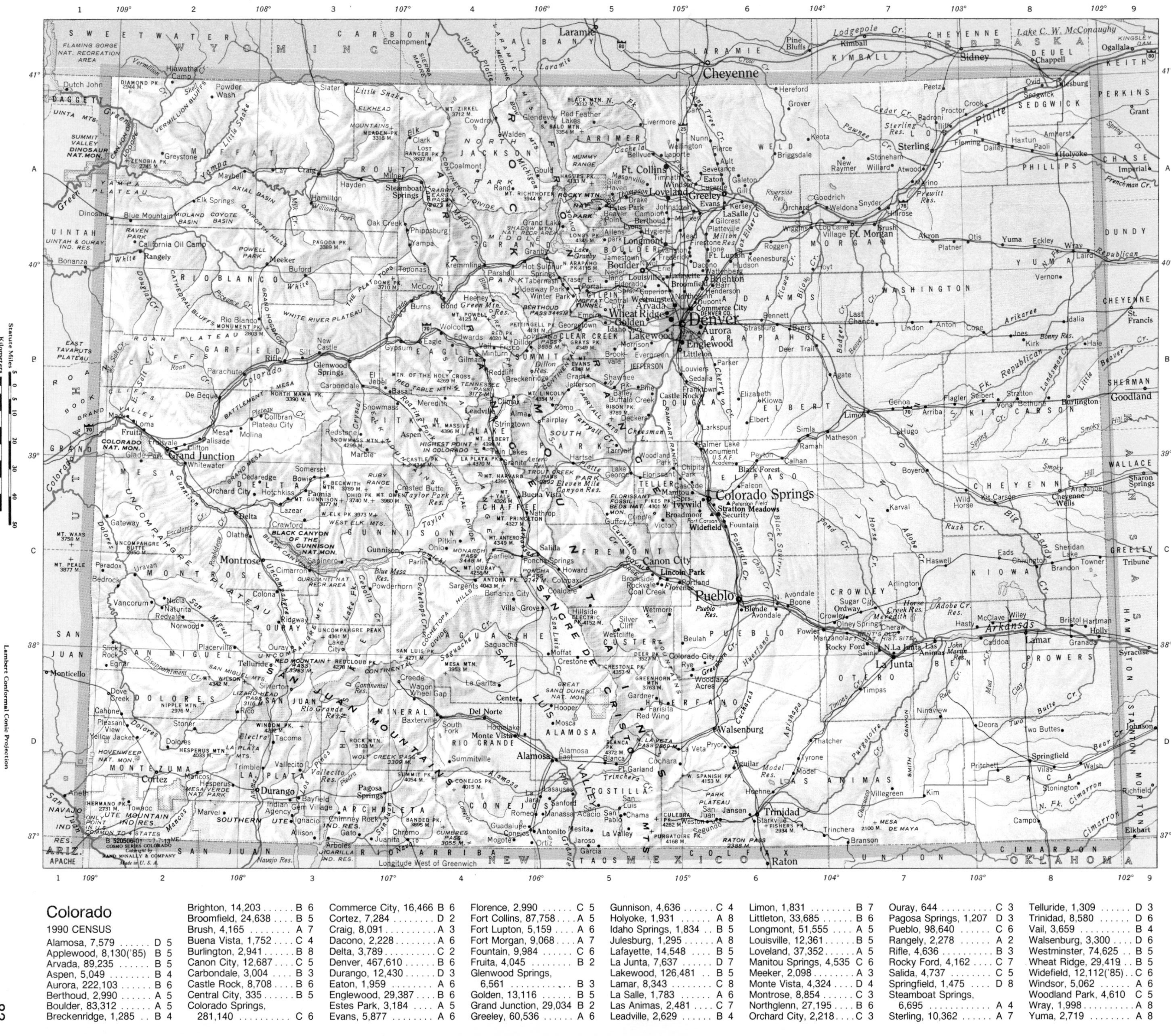

Colorado

1990 CENSUS

Alamosa, 7,579 . . . . . . D 5
Applewood, 8,130('85) B 5
Arvada, 89,235 . . . . . . B 5
Aspen, 5,049 . . . . B 4
Aurora, 222,103 . . . . . B 6
Berthoud, 2,990 . . . . . . A 5
Boulder, 83,312 . . . . . . A 5
Breckenridge, 1,285 . . B 4
Brighton, 14,203 . . . . . . B 6
Broomfield, 24,638 . . . . B 5
Brush, 4,165 . . . . A 7
Buena Vista, 1,752 . . . . C 4
Burlington, 2,941 . . . . . . B 8
Canon City, 12,687 . . . . C 5
Carbondale, 3,004 . . . . . B 3
Castle Rock, 8,708 . . . . B 6
Central City, 335 . . . . . . B 5
Colorado Springs, 281,140 . . . . C 6
Commerce City, 16,466 B 6
Cortez, 7,284 . . . . D 2
Craig, 8,091 . . . . A 3
Dacono, 2,228 . . . . A 6
Delta, 3,789 . . . . C 2
Denver, 467,610 . . . . B 6
Durango, 12,430 . . . . . . D 3
Eaton, 1,959 . . . . A 6
Englewood, 29,387 . . . . B 6
Estes Park, 3,184 . . . . A 5
Evans, 5,877 . . . . A 6
Florence, 2,990 . . . . . . C 5
Fort Collins, 87,758 . . . . A 5
Fort Lupton, 5,159 . . . . A 6
Fort Morgan, 9,068 . . . . A 7
Fountain, 9,984 . . . . . . C 6
Fruita, 4,045 . . . . B 2
Glenwood Springs, 6,561 . . . . B 3
Golden, 13,116 . . . . . . B 5
Grand Junction, 29,034 B 2
Greeley, 60,536 . . . . . . A 6
Gunnison, 4,636 . . . . . . C 4
Holyoke, 1,931 . . . . . . A 8
Idaho Springs, 1,834 . . B 5
Julesburg, 1,295 . . . . . . A 8
Lafayette, 14,548 . . . . . B 5
La Junta, 7,637 . . . . D 7
Lakewood, 126,481 . . B 5
Lamar, 8,343 . . . . C 8
La Salle, 1,783 . . . . . . A 6
Las Animas, 2,481 . . . . C 7
Leadville, 2,629 . . . . . . B 4
Limon, 1,831 . . . . B 7
Littleton, 33,685 . . . . . . B 6
Longmont, 51,555 . . . . A 5
Louisville, 12,361 . . . . . B 5
Loveland, 37,352 . . . . . . A 5
Manitou Springs, 4,535 C 6
Meeker, 2,098 . . . . A 3
Monte Vista, 4,324 . . . . D 4
Montrose, 8,854 . . . . . . C 3
Northglenn, 27,195 . . . . B 6
Orchard City, 2,218 . . . . C 3
Ouray, 644 . . . . C 3
Pagosa Springs, 1,207 D 3
Pueblo, 98,640 . . . . C 6
Rangely, 2,278 . . . . A 2
Rifle, 4,636 . . . . B 3
Rocky Ford, 4,162 . . . . C 7
Salida, 4,737 . . . . C 5
Springfield, 1,475 . . . . . D 8
Steamboat Springs, 6,695 . . . . A 4
Sterling, 10,362 . . . . . . A 7
Telluride, 1,309 . . . . . . D 3
Trinidad, 8,580 . . . . D 6
Vail, 3,659 . . . . B 4
Walsenburg, 3,300 . . . . D 6
Westminster, 74,625 . . B 5
Wheat Ridge, 29,419 . . B 5
Widefield, 12,112('85) . . C 6
Windsor, 5,062 . . . . A 6
Woodland Park, 4,610 C 5
Wray, 1,998 . . . . A 8
Yuma, 2,719 . . . . A 8

Connecticut

1990 CENSUS

Ansonia, 18,403 . . . . . . D 3
Bethel, 8,755 (17,541▲) D 2
Bloomfield, 7,120 (19,483▲) . . . . B 5
Branford, 5,438 (27,603▲) . . . . D 4
Bridgeport, 141,686 . . E 3
Bristol, 60,640 . . . . C 4
Cheshire, 5,722 (25,684▲) . . . . D 4
Clinton, 11,195('87) . . . D 5
Coventry, 3,769 (10,063▲) . . . . B 6
Danbury, 65,585 . . . . . . D 2
Danielson, 4,441 . . . . . B 8
Derby, 12,199 . . . . D 3
East Hartford, 50,452 . . B 5
East Haven, 26,144 . . . D 4
Enfield, 8,454 (45,532▲) B 5
Fairfield, 52,400 . . . . . . E 2
Glastonbury, 7,049 (27,901▲) . . . . C 5
Greenwich, 58,000 . . . . E 1
Groton, 9,837 . . . . D 7
Hamden, 53,100 . . . . . . D 4
Hartford, 139,739 . . . . . B 5
Harwinton, 3,293 (5,228▲) . . . . B 3
Jewett City, 3,349 . . . . C 8
Manchester, 51,000 . . B 5
Meriden, 59,479 . . . . . . C 4
Middlebury, 4,140 (6,145▲) . . . . C 3
Middletown, 42,762 . . . . C 5
Milford, 48,168 . . . . . . E 3
Mystic, 2,333('80) . . . . D 8
Naugatuck, 30,625 . . . . D 3
New Britain, 75,491 . . C 4
New Fairfield, 4,600 (12,911▲) . . . . D 2
New Haven, 130,474 . . D 4
Newington, 29,800 . . . . C 5
New London, 28,540 . . D 7
New Milford, 5,186 (23,629▲) . . . . C 2
North Branford, 6,600 (12,996▲) . . . . D 4
North Haven, 22,700 . . D 4
Norwalk, 78,331 . . . . . . E 2
Norwich, 37,391 . . . . . . C 7
Orange, 13,300 . . . . . . D 3
Putnam, 6,850 (9,031▲) B 8
Ridgefield, 6,066 (20,919▲) . . . . D 2
Shelton, 35,418 . . . . . . D 3
Simsbury, 5,488 (22,023▲) . . . . B 4
Southington, 40,700 . . C 4
South Windsor, 10,800 (22,090▲) . . . . B 5
Stafford Springs, 4,100 B 6
Stamford, 108,056 . . . . E 1
Stratford, 50,400 . . . . . . E 3
Thomaston, 3,590 (6,947▲) . . . . C 3
Torrington, 33,687 . . . . B 3
Trumbull, 33,200 . . . . . . E 3
Wallingford, 41,400 . . . . D 4
Waterbury, 108,961 . . C 3
Watertown, 5,920 (20,456▲) . . . . C 3
West Hartford, 59,100 B 4
West Haven, 54,021 . . D 4
Westport, 25,300 . . . . . . E 2
Wethersfield, 26,500 . . C 5
Willimantic, 14,600('87) C 7
Wilton, 7,200 (15,989▲) E 2
Windsor, 17,517 (27,817▲) . . . . B 5
Windsor Locks, 12,190('80) . . . . B 5
Wolcott, 6,070 (13,700▲) . . . . C 4
Woodbridge, 7,700 (7,924▲) . . . . D 3

▲ Population of entire town (township), including rural area.

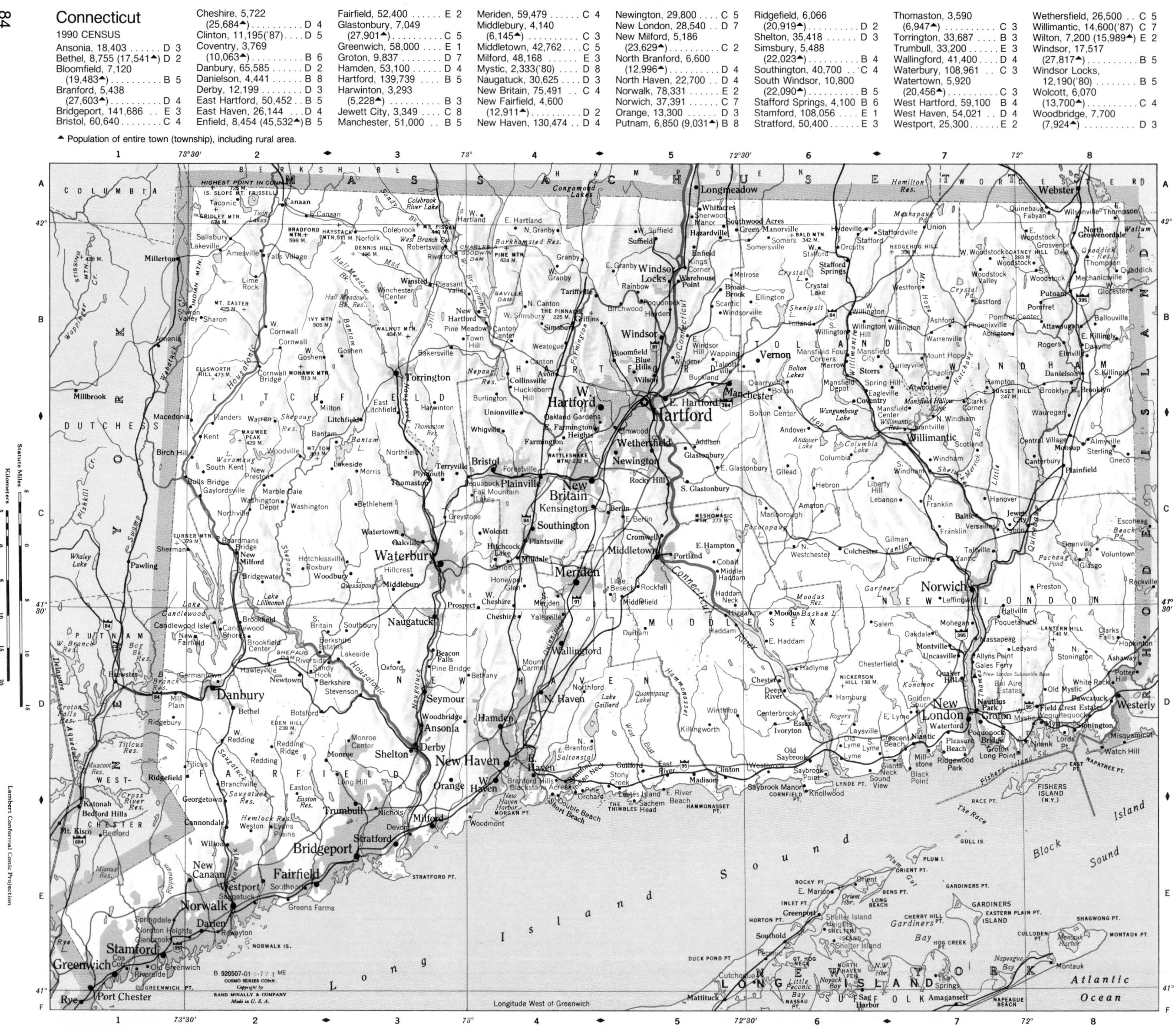

Delaware

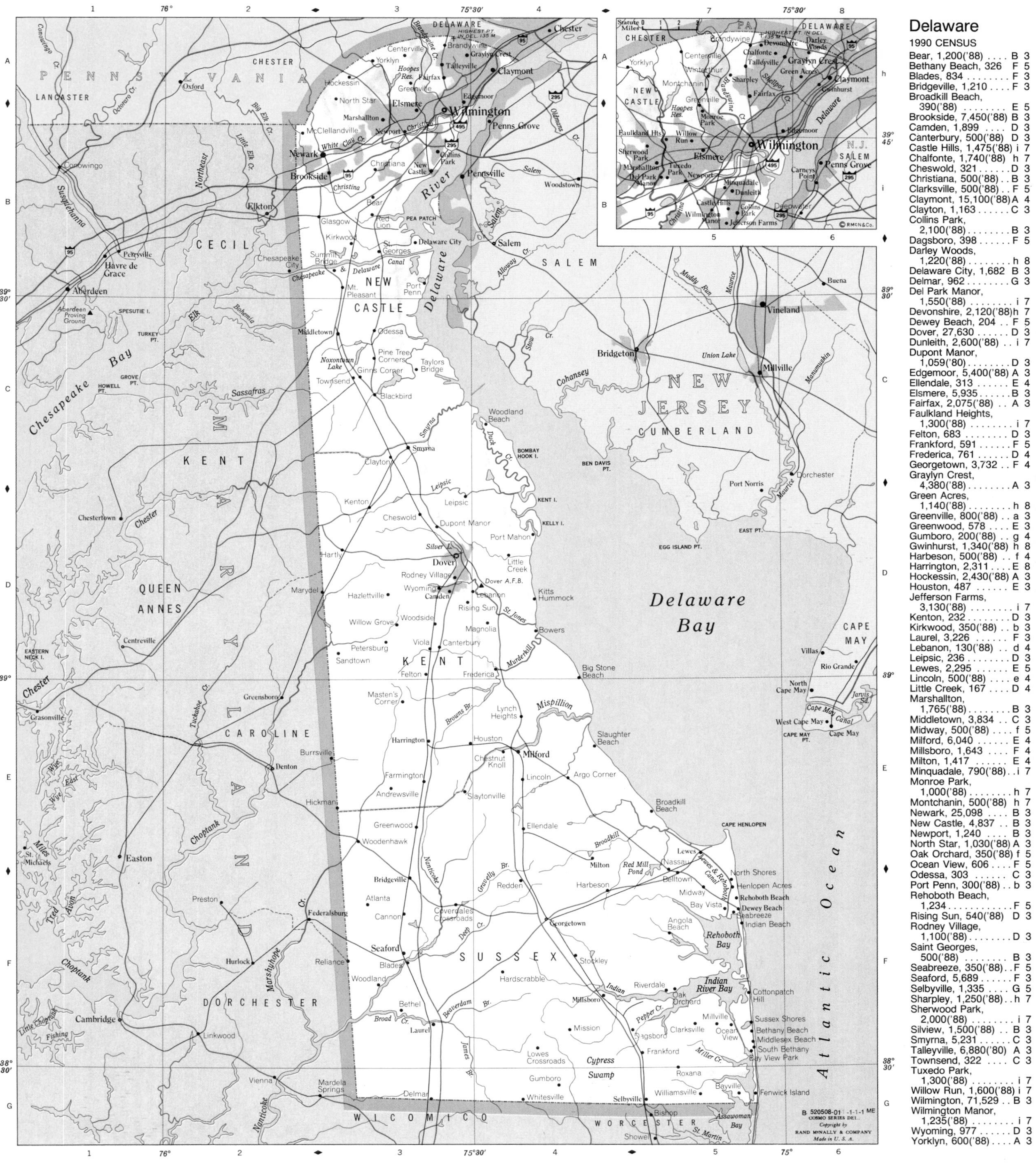

Delaware

1990 CENSUS

Bear, 1,200('88) . . . . B 3
Bethany Beach, 326 F 5
Blades, 834 . . . . F 3
Bridgeville, 1,210 . . . . F 3
Broadkill Beach, 390('88) . . . . E 5
Brookside, 7,450('88) B 3
Camden, 1,899 . . . . D 3
Canterbury, 500('88) D 3
Castle Hills, 1,475('88) i 7
Chalfonte, 1,740('88) h 7
Cheswold, 321 . . . . . . D 3
Christiana, 500('88) . . B 3
Clarksville, 500('88) . . F 5
Claymont, 15,100('88) A 4
Clayton, 1,163 . . . . . . C 3
Collins Park, 2,100('88) . . . . B 3
Dagsboro, 398 . . . . . . F 5
Darley Woods, 1,220('88) . . . . h 8
Delaware City, 1,682 B 3
Delmar, 962 . . . . G 3
Del Park Manor, 1,550('88) . . . . i 7
Devonshire, 2,120('88) h 7
Dewey Beach, 204 . . D 5
Dover, 27,630 . . . . . . D 3
Dunleith, 2,600('88) . . i 7
Dupont Manor, 1,059('80) . . . . D 3
Edgemoor, 5,400('88) A 3
Ellendale, 313 . . . . . . E 4
Elsmere, 5,935 . . . . . . B 3
Fairfax, 2,075('88) . . A 3
Faulkland Heights, 1,300('88) . . . . i 7
Felton, 683 . . . . D 3
Frankford, 591 . . . . . . F 5
Frederica, 761 . . . . . . D 4
Georgetown, 3,732 . . F 4
Graylyn Crest, 4,380('88) . . . . A 3
Green Acres, 1,140('88) . . . . h 8
Greenville, 800('88) . . a 3
Greenwood, 578 . . . . E 3
Gumboro, 200('88) . . g 4
Gwinhurst, 1,340('88) h 8
Harbeson, 500('88) . . f 4
Harrington, 2,311 . . . . E 8
Hockessin, 2,430('88) A 3
Houston, 487 . . . . . . E 3
Jefferson Farms, 3,130('88) . . . . i 7
Kenton, 232 . . . . D 3
Kirkwood, 350('88) . . b 3
Laurel, 3,226 . . . . . . F 3
Lebanon, 130('88) . . d 4
Leipsic, 236 . . . . D 3
Lewes, 2,295 . . . . . . E 5
Lincoln, 500('88) . . . . e 4
Little Creek, 167 . . . . D 4
Marshallton, 1,765('88) . . . . B 3
Middletown, 3,834 . . C 3
Midway, 500('88) . . . . f 5
Milford, 6,040 . . . . . . E 4
Millsboro, 1,643 . . . . F 4
Milton, 1,417 . . . . . . E 4
Minquadale, 790('88). . i 7
Monroe Park, 1,000('88) . . . . h 7
Montchanin, 500('88) h 7
Newark, 25,098 . . . . B 3
New Castle, 4,837 . . B 3
Newport, 1,240 . . . . B 3
North Star, 1,030('88) A 3
Oak Orchard, 350('88) f 5
Ocean View, 606 . . . . F 5
Odessa, 303 . . . . . . C 3
Port Penn, 300('88) . . b 3
Rehoboth Beach, 1,234 . . . . F 5
Rising Sun, 540('88) D 3
Rodney Village, 1,100('88) . . . . D 3
Saint Georges, 500('88) . . . . B 3
Seabreeze, 350('88). . F 5
Seaford, 5,689 . . . . . . F 3
Selbyville, 1,335 . . . . G 5
Sharpley, 1,250('88). . h 7
Sherwood Park, 2,000('88) . . . . i 7
Silview, 1,500('88) . . B 3
Smyrna, 5,231 . . . . . . C 3
Talleyville, 6,880('80) A 3
Townsend, 322 . . . . . . C 3
Tuxedo Park, 1,300('88) . . . . i 7
Willow Run, 1,600('88) i 7
Wilmington, 71,529 . . B 3
Wilmington Manor, 1,235('88) . . . . i 7
Wyoming, 977 . . . . . . D 3
Yorklyn, 600('88) . . . . A 3

Florida

1990 CENSUS

Altamonte Springs, 34,879 .... D 5
Bartow, 14,716 .... E 5
Belle Glade, 16,177 .. F 6
Boca Raton, 61,492 .. F 6
Boynton Beach, 46,194 .... F 6
Bradenton, 43,779 .. E 4
Brandon, 36,300 .... E 4
Brownsville, 18,058('80) s13
Cape Canaveral, 8,014 .... D 6
Cape Coral, 74,991 .. F 5
Carol City, 52,800 .. s13
Clearwater, 98,784 .. E 4
Cocoa, 17,722 ...... D 6
Coral Gables, 40,091 G 6
Cutler Ridge, 20,886('80) s13
Davie, 47,217 ...... F 6
Daytona Beach, 61,921 .... C 5
Deerfield Beach, 46,325 .... F 6
De Land, 16,491 ..... C 5
Delray Beach, 47,181 F 6
Dunedin, 34,012 .... D 4
Fort Lauderdale, 149,377 .... F 6
Fort Myers, 45,206 .. F 5
Fort Pierce, 36,830 .. E 6
Fort Walton Beach, 21,471 .... u15
Gainesville, 84,770 .. C 4
Hallandale, 30,996 .. G 6
Hialeah, 188,004 .... G 6
Hollywood, 121,697 .. F 6
Homestead, 26,866 .. G 6
Jacksonville, 635,230 B 5
Kendall, 53,100 ...... s13
Key Largo, 7,447('80) G 6
Key West, 24,832 ... H 5
Kissimmee, 30,050 .. D 5
Lake City, 10,005 .. B 4
Lakeland, 70,576 .... D 5
Lake Worth, 28,564 .. F 6
Largo, 65,674 ...... E 4
Lauderdale Lakes, 27,341 .... r13
Lealman, 19,873('80) p10
Leesburg, 14,903 .... D 5
Leisure City, 17,905('80) s13
Margate, 42,985 .... F 6
Melbourne, 59,646 .. D 6
Merritt Island, 44,300 D 6
Miami, 358,548 ..... G 6
Miami Beach, 92,639 G 6
Miramar, 40,663 .... s13
Naples, 19,505 ...... F 5
New Smyrna Beach, 16,543 .... C 6
North Fort Myers, 17,200('83) ...... F 5
North Miami, 49,998 G 6
North Miami Beach, 35,359 .... s13
Oakland Park, 26,326 r13
Ocala, 42,045 ...... C 4
Orlando, 164,693 .... D 5
Ormond Beach, 29,721 .... C 5
Palm Bay, 62,632 .. D 6
Panama City, 34,378 u16
Pembroke Pines, 65,452 .... r13
Pensacola, 58,165 ... u14
Pine Hills, 35,600 ... D 5
Pinellas Park, 43,426 E 4
Plantation, 66,692 .... r13
Plant City, 22,754 ... D 4
Pompano Beach, 72,411 .... F 6
Port Charlotte, 43,300 F 4
Port Orange, 35,317 C 6
Riviera Beach, 27,639 F 6
Saint Augustine, 11,692 .... C 5
Saint Petersburg, 238,629 .... E 4
Sanford, 32,387 ..... D 5
Sarasota, 50,961 .... E 4
Sebring, 8,900 ...... E 5
South Miami Heights, 18,000('83) s13
Sweetwater Creek, 18,000('83) p10
Tallahassee, 124,773 B 2
Tampa, 280,015 ..... E 4
Tarpon Springs, 17,906 .... D 4
Titusville, 39,394 .... D 6
Venice, 16,922 ...... E 4
Vero Beach, 17,350 .. E 6
West Palm Beach, 67,643 .... F 6
West Pensacola, 30,200 .... u14
Winter Haven, 24,725 D 5
Winter Park, 22,242 D 5

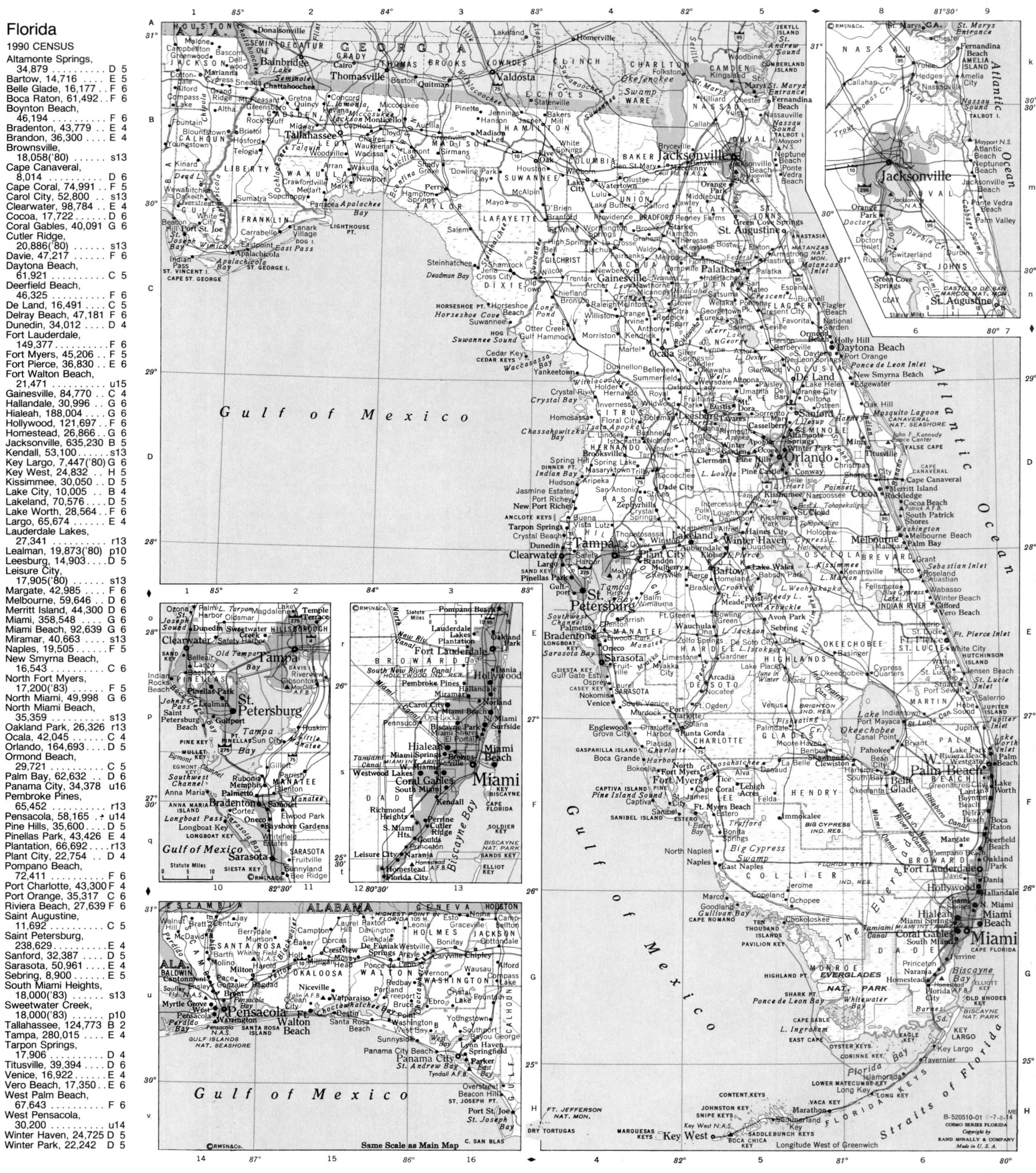

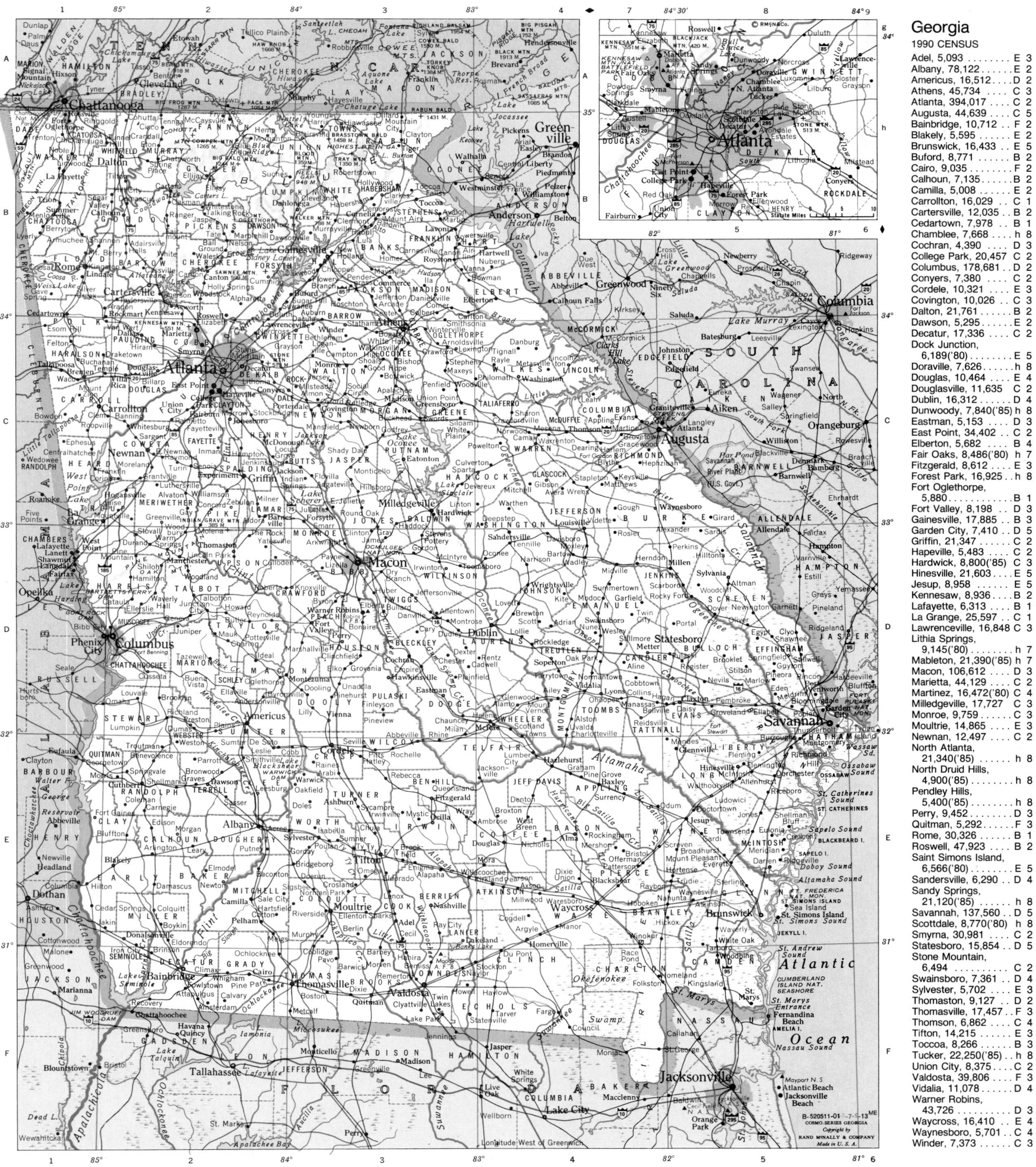

Georgia

1990 CENSUS

Adel, 5,093 . . . . E 3
Albany, 78,122 . . . . . . E 2
Americus, 16,512 . . . . D 2
Athens, 45,734 . . . . C 3
Atlanta, 394,017 . . . . C 2
Augusta, 44,639 . . . . C 5
Bainbridge, 10,712 . . F 2
Blakely, 5,595 . . . . . . E 2
Brunswick, 16,433 . . E 5
Buford, 8,771 . . . . . . B 2
Cairo, 9,035 . . . . F 2
Calhoun, 7,135 . . . . . . B 2
Camilla, 5,008 . . . . . E 2
Carrollton, 16,029 . . C 1
Cartersville, 12,035 . . B 2
Cedartown, 7,978 . . B 1
Chamblee, 7,668 . . . . h 8
Cochran, 4,390 . . . . D 3
College Park, 20,457 C 2
Columbus, 178,681 . . D 2
Conyers, 7,380 . . . . C 2
Cordele, 10,321 . . . . E 3
Covington, 10,026 . . C 3
Dalton, 21,761 . . . . . B 2
Dawson, 5,295 . . . . . . E 2
Decatur, 17,336 . . . . C 2
Dock Junction,
6,189('80) . . . . E 5
Doraville, 7,626 . . . . . . h 8
Douglas, 10,464 . . . . E 4
Douglasville, 11,635 C 2
Dublin, 16,312 . . . . . . D 4
Dunwoody, 7,840('85) h 8
Eastman, 5,153 . . . . D 3
East Point, 34,402 . . C 2
Elberton, 5,682 . . . . B 4
Fair Oaks, 8,486('80) h 7
Fitzgerald, 8,612 . . . . E 3
Forest Park, 16,925 . . h 8
Fort Oglethorpe,
5,880 . . . . B 1
Fort Valley, 8,198 . . D 3
Gainesville, 17,885 . . B 3
Garden City, 7,410 . . D 5
Griffin, 21,347 . . . . . . C 2
Hapeville, 5,483 . . . . C 2
Hardwick, 8,800('85) C 3
Hinesville, 21,603 . . . . E 5
Jesup, 8,958 . . . . . . E 5
Kennesaw, 8,936 . . . . B 2
Lafayette, 6,313 . . . . B 1
La Grange, 25,597 . . . C 1
Lawrenceville, 16,848 C 3
Lithia Springs,
9,145('80) . . . . h 7
Mableton, 21,390('85) h 7
Macon, 106,612 . . . . D 3
Marietta, 44,129 . . . . . C 2
Martinez, 16,472('80) C 4
Milledgeville, 17,727 C 3
Monroe, 9,759 . . . . . . C 3
Moultrie, 14,865 . . . . E 3
Newnan, 12,497 . . . . C 2
North Atlanta,
21,340('85) . . . . . . h 8
North Druid Hills,
4,900('85) . . . . h 8
Pendley Hills,
5,400('85) . . . . h 8
Perry, 9,452 . . . . D 3
Quitman, 5,292 . . . . . F 3
Rome, 30,326 . . . . B 1
Roswell, 47,923 . . . . . B 2
Saint Simons Island,
6,566('80) . . . . E 5
Sandersville, 6,290 . . D 4
Sandy Springs,
21,120('85) . . . . . . h 8
Savannah, 137,560 . . D 5
Scottdale, 8,770('80) h 8
Smyrna, 30,981 . . . . C 2
Statesboro, 15,854 . . D 5
Stone Mountain,
6,494 . . . . C 2
Swainsboro, 7,361 . . . D 4
Sylvester, 5,702 . . . . . E 3
Thomaston, 9,127 . . . D 2
Thomasville, 17,457 . . F 3
Thomson, 6,862 . . . . . C 4
Tifton, 14,215 . . . . . . E 3
Toccoa, 8,266 . . . . . . B 3
Tucker, 22,250('85) . . h 8
Union City, 8,375 . . . . C 2
Valdosta, 39,806 . . . . F 3
Vidalia, 11,078 . . . . . . D 4
Warner Robins,
43,726 . . . . D 3
Waycross, 16,410 . . . . E 4
Waynesboro, 5,701 . . C 4
Winder, 7,373 . . . . . . C 3

Hawaii

1990 CENSUS

Aiea, 8,906 . . . . B 4
Anahola, 1,181 . . . . . . A 2
Captain Cook, 2,595 . . D 6
Ewa, 3,780 . . . . B 3
Ewa Beach, 14,315 . . . B 3
Halawa Heights, 7,000('83) g10
Haleiwa, 2,442 . . . . B 3
Haliimaile, 841 . . . . C 5
Hana, 683 . . . . C 6
Hanamaulu, 3,611 . . . . B 2
Hanapepe, 1,395 . . . . . . B 2
Hauula, 3,479 . . . . B 4
Hawi, 924 . . . . C 6
Hilo, 37,808 . . . . D 6
Holualoa, 3,834 . . . . . . D 6
Honokaa, 2,186 . . . . . . C 6
Honolulu, 365,272 . . . . B 4
Honomu, 532 . . . . D 6
Kaaawa, 1,138 . . . . f10
Kahaluu, 3,068 . . . . g10
Kahuku, 2,063 . . . . B 4
Kahului, 16,889 . . . . . . C 5
Kailua, 36,818 . . . . B 4
Kailua Kona, 9,126 . . . . D 6
Kalaheo, 3,592 . . . . . . B 2
Kamuela (Waimea), 5,972 . . . . C 6
Kaneohe, 35,448 . . . . . . B 4
Kapaa, 8,149 . . . . A 2
Kapaau, 1,083 . . . . C 6
Kaumakani, 803 . . . . . . B 2
Kaunakakai, 2,658 . . . . B 4
Keaau, 1,584 . . . . D 6
Kealakekua, 1,453 . . . . D 6
Kealia, 700('83) . . . . . . A 2
Kekaha, 3,506 . . . . B 2
Keokea, 900('83) . . . . . . C 5
Kihei, 11,107 . . . . C 5
Kilauea, 1,685 . . . . A 2
Koloa, 1,791 . . . . B 2
Kula, 1,300('83) . . . . . . C 5
Kurtistown, 910 . . . . . . D 6
Lahaina, 9,073 . . . . C 5
Laie, 5,577 . . . . B 4
Lanai City, 2,400 . . . . . . C 5
Lawai, 1,787 . . . . B 2
Lihue, 5,536 . . . . B 2
Lower Paia, 1,500('80) C 5
Maili, 6,059 . . . . g 9
Makaha, 7,990 . . . . g 9
Makakilo City, 9,828 . . g 9
Makawao, 5,405 . . . . . . C 5
Makaweli, 565 . . . . B 2
Maunaloa, 405 . . . . B 4
Maunawili, 4,847 . . . . . . g10
Mililani Town, 29,359 . . g 9
Naalehu, 1,027 . . . . D 6
Nanakuli, 9,575 . . . . . . B 3
Paauilo, 620 . . . . C 6
Pacific Palisades, 10,000('83) g10
Pahala, 1,520 . . . . D 6
Pahoa, 1,027 . . . . D 7
Paia, 2,091 . . . . C 5
Papaikou, 1,634 . . . . . . D 6
Pearl City, 30,993 . . . . . B 4
Pepeekeo, 1,813 . . . . . . D 6
Poipu, 975 . . . . B 2
Puhi, 1,210 . . . . B 2
Pukalani, 5,879 . . . . . . C 5
Sunset Beach, 800('83) f 9
Volcano, 1,516 . . . . . . D 6
Wahiawa, 17,386 . . . . . . B 3
Waialua, 3,943 . . . . B 3
Waianae, 8,758 . . . . B 3
Waikapu, 729 . . . . C 5
Wailua, 2,018 . . . . A 2
Wailuku, 10,688 . . . . . . C 5
Waimanalo, 3,508 . . . . B 4
Waimea, 600('83) . . . . . . f 9
Waimea, 1,840 . . . . . . B 2
Waipahu, 31,435 . . . . . . B 3
Waipio Acres, 5,304 . . g 9
Whitmore Village, 3,373 f 9

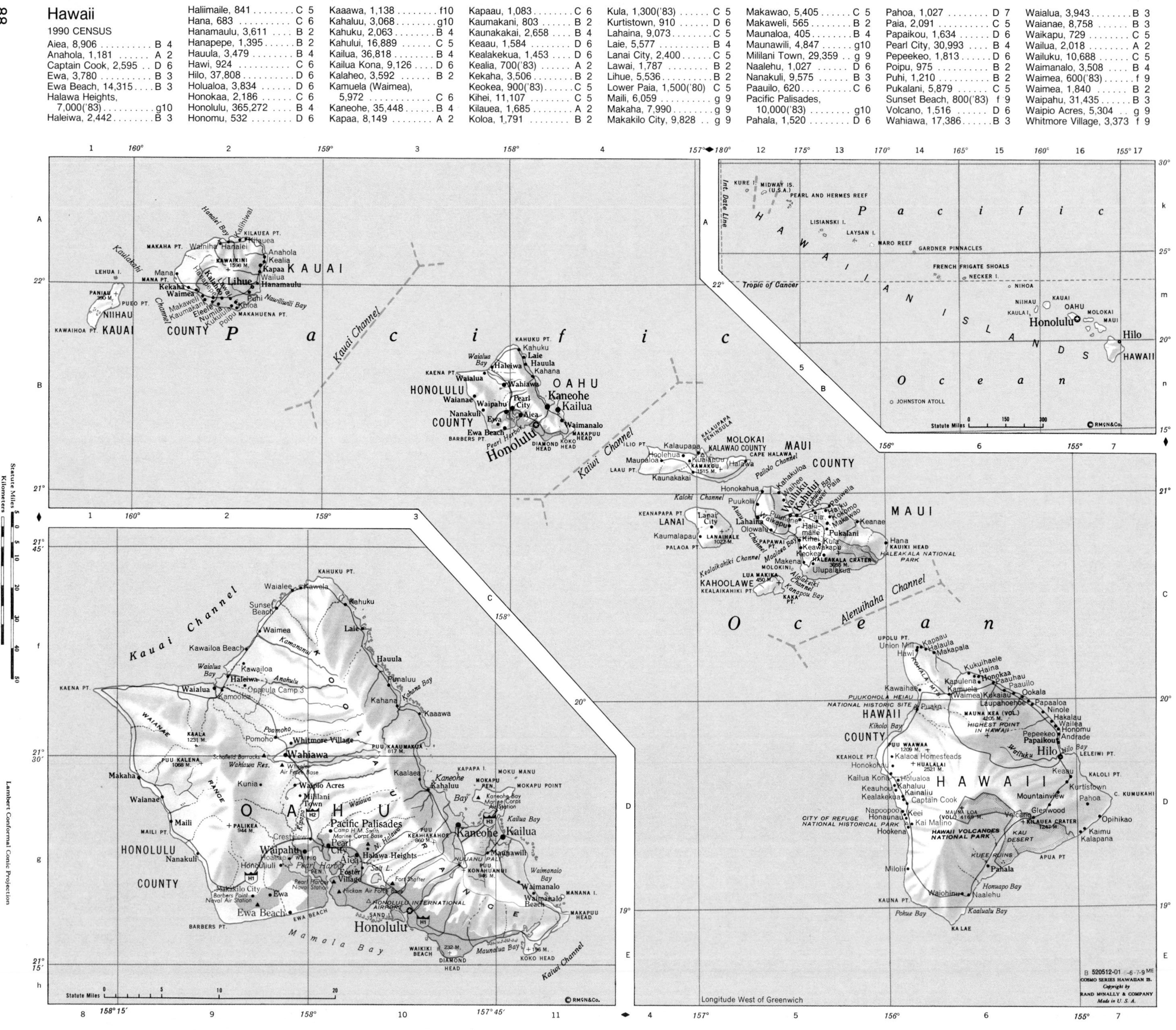

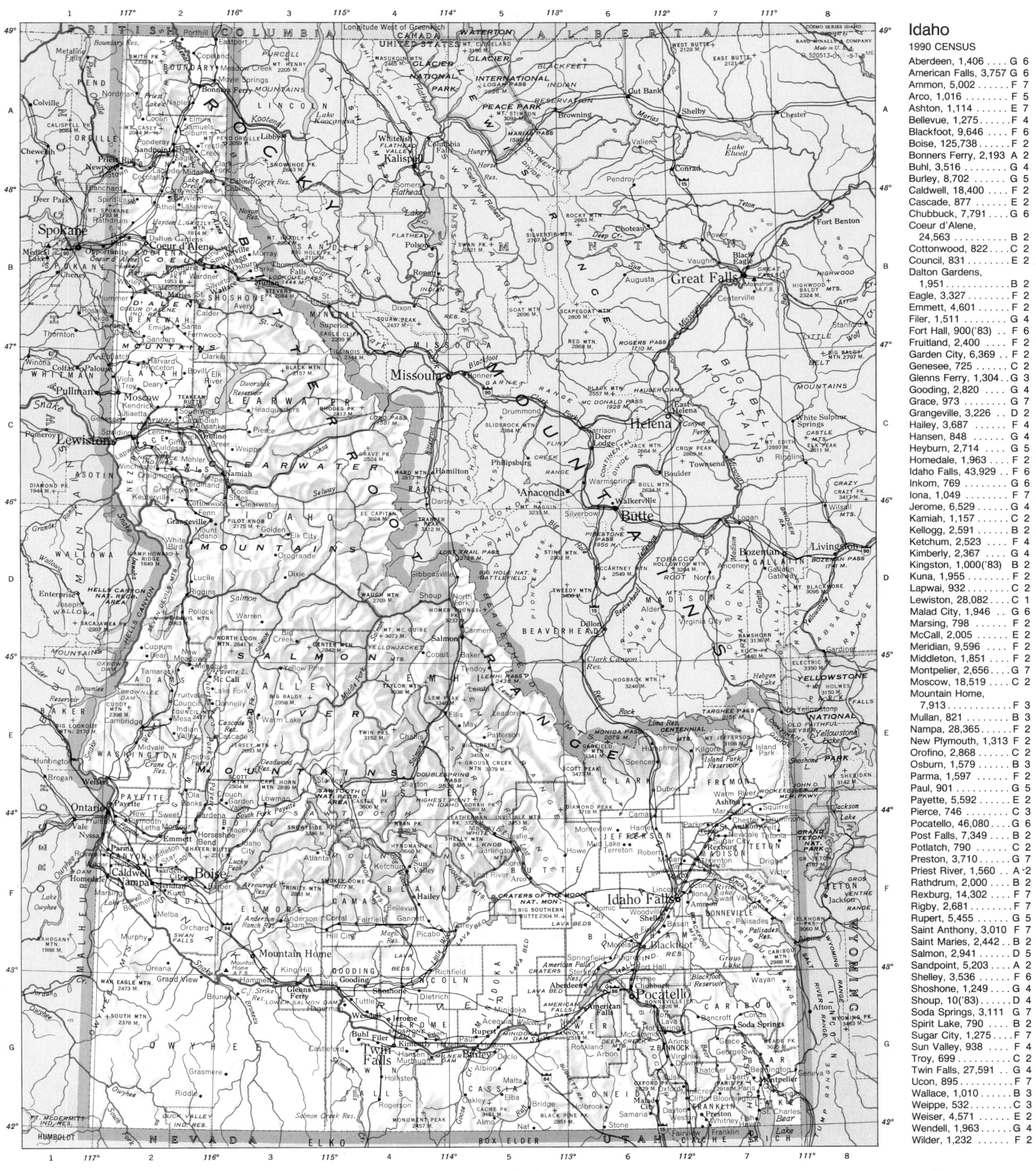

Idaho

1990 CENSUS

Aberdeen, 1,406 .... G 6
American Falls, 3,757 G 6
Ammon, 5,002 ...... F 7
Arco, 1,016 .... F 5
Ashton, 1,114 ...... E 7
Bellevue, 1,275...... F 4
Blackfoot, 9,646 .... F 6
Boise, 125,738...... F 2
Bonners Ferry, 2,193 A 2
Buhl, 3,516 .... G 4
Burley, 8,702 ...... G 5
Caldwell, 18,400 .... F 2
Cascade, 877 ...... E 2
Chubbuck, 7,791 .... G 6
Coeur d'Alene,
24,563 .... B 2
Cottonwood, 822.... C 2
Council, 831 .... E 2
Dalton Gardens,
1,951............ B 2
Eagle, 3,327 .... F 2
Emmett, 4,601 ...... F 2
Filer, 1,511 .... G 4
Fort Hall, 900('83) .. F 6
Fruitland, 2,400 .... F 2
Garden City, 6,369 .. F 2
Genesee, 725 ...... C 2
Glenns Ferry, 1,304.. G 3
Gooding, 2,820 .... G 4
Grace, 973 .... G 7
Grangeville, 3,226 .. D 2
Hailey, 3,687 ...... F 4
Hansen, 848 ...... G 4
Heyburn, 2,714 .... G 5
Homedale, 1,963 .... F 2
Idaho Falls, 43,929 .. F 6
Inkom, 769 .... G 6
Iona, 1,049 .... F 7
Jerome, 6,529 ...... G 4
Kamiah, 1,157 ...... C 2
Kellogg, 2,591 ...... B 2
Ketchum, 2,523 .... F 4
Kimberly, 2,367 .... G 4
Kingston, 1,000('83) B 2
Kuna, 1,955 .... F 2
Lapwai, 932........ C 2
Lewiston, 28,082.... C 1
Malad City, 1,946 .. G 6
Marsing, 798 ...... F 2
McCall, 2,005 ...... E 2
Meridian, 9,596 .... F 2
Middleton, 1,851 .... F 2
Montpelier, 2,656.... G 7
Moscow, 18,519 .... C 2
Mountain Home,
7,913............ F 3
Mullan, 821 .... B 3
Nampa, 28,365...... F 2
New Plymouth, 1,313 F 2
Orofino, 2,868 ...... C 2
Osburn, 1,579 ...... B 3
Parma, 1,597 ...... F 2
Paul, 901 .... G 5
Payette, 5,592 ...... E 2
Pierce, 746 .... C 3
Pocatello, 46,080.... G 6
Post Falls, 7,349 .... B 2
Potlatch, 790 ...... C 2
Preston, 3,710...... G 7
Priest River, 1,560 .. A 2
Rathdrum, 2,000 .... B 2
Rexburg, 14,302 .... F 7
Rigby, 2,681........ F 7
Rupert, 5,455 ...... G 5
Saint Anthony, 3,010 F 7
Saint Maries, 2,442 .. B 2
Salmon, 2,941 ...... D 5
Sandpoint, 5,203 .... A 2
Shelley, 3,536 ...... F 6
Shoshone, 1,249 .... G 4
Shoup, 10('83)...... D 4
Soda Springs, 3,111 G 7
Spirit Lake, 790 .... B 2
Sugar City, 1,275.... F 7
Sun Valley, 938 .... F 4
Troy, 699.......... C 2
Twin Falls, 27,591 .. G 4
Ucon, 895.......... F 7
Wallace, 1,010...... B 3
Weippe, 532........ C 3
Weiser, 4,571 ...... E 2
Wendell, 1,963...... G 4
Wilder, 1,232 ...... F 2

Illinois

1990 CENSUS

Addison, 32,058 . . . . k 8
Alton, 32,905 . . . . . . E 3
Arlington Heights,
75,460 . . . . A 5
Aurora, 99,581 . . . . . . B 5
Belleville, 42,785 . . . . E 4
Berwyn, 45,426 . . . . k 9
Bloomington, 51,972 C 4
Bolingbrook, 40,843 . . k 8
Bourbonnais, 13,934 B 6
Brookfield, 18,876 . . k 9
Burbank, 27,600 . . . . k 9
Cahokia, 17,550 . . . . E 3
Cairo, 4,846 . . . . F 4
Calumet City, 37,840 B 6
Canton, 13,922 . . . . C 3
Carbondale, 27,033 . . F 4
Centralia, 14,274 . . . . E 4
Champaign, 63,502 . . C 5
Charleston, 20,398 . . D 5
Chicago, 2,783,726 . . B 6
Chicago Heights,
33,072 . . . . B 6
Cicero, 67,436 . . . . . . B 6
Danville, 33,828 . . . . C 6
Decatur, 83,885 . . . . D 5
De Kalb, 34,925 . . . . B 5
Des Plaines, 53,223 . . A 6
Dixon, 15,144 . . . . . . B 4
Downers Grove,
46,858 . . . . B 5
East Saint Louis,
40,944 . . . . E 3
Elgin, 77,010 . . . . . . A 5
Elk Grove Village,
33,429 . . . . h 9
Elmhurst, 42,029 . . . . B 6
Evanston, 73,233 . . . . A 6
Freeport, 25,840 . . . . A 4
Galena, 3,647 . . . . . . A 3
Galesburg, 33,530 . . . C 3
Glenview, 37,093 . . . . h 9
Granite City, 32,862 . . E 3
Gurnee, 13,701 . . . . h 9
Hanover Park, 32,895 k 8
Harvey, 29,771 . . . . B 6
Highland Park, 30,575 A 6
Hoffman Estates,
46,561 . . . . h 8
Jacksonville, 19,324 D 3
Joliet, 76,836 . . . . . . B 5
Kankakee, 27,575 . . B 6
Kewanee, 12,969 . . . . B 4
Lake Forest, 17,836 A 6
Lansing, 28,086 . . . . B 6
La Salle, 9,717 . . . . . B 4
Lincoln, 15,418 . . . . C 4
Lombard, 39,408 . . . . k 8
Macomb, 19,952 . . . . C 3
Marion, 14,545 . . . . . F 5
Mattoon, 18,441 . . . . D 5
Moline, 43,202 . . . . . B 3
Monmouth, 9,489 . . C 3
Mount Prospect,
53,170 . . . . A 6
Mount Vernon, 16,988 E 5
Naperville, 85,351 . . B 5
Nauvoo, 1,108 . . . . . . C 2
Niles, 28,284 . . . . h 9
Normal, 40,023 . . . . C 5
Northbrook, 32,308 . . h 9
North Chicago,
34,978 . . . . A 6
Oak Lawn, 56,182 . . B 6
Oak Park, 53,648 . . B 6
Ottawa, 17,451 . . . . B 5
Palatine, 39,253 . . . . A 5
Park Ridge, 36,175 . . B 6
Pekin, 32,254 . . . . . . C 4
Peoria, 113,504 . . . . C 4
Peru, 9,302 . . . . B 4
Pontiac, 11,428 . . . . C 5
Quincy, 39,681 . . . . . D 2
Rockford, 139,426 . . A 4
Rock Island, 40,552 . . B 3
Salem, 7,470 . . . . . . E 5
Schaumburg, 68,586 h 8
Skokie, 59,432 . . . . . A 6
Springfield, 105,227 . . D 4
Sterling, 15,132 . . . . B 4
Streator, 14,121 . . . . B 5
Taylorville, 11,133 . . D 4
Tinley Park, 37,121 . . k 9
Urbana, 36,344 . . . . C 5
Vandalia, 6,114 . . . . E 4
Waukegan, 69,392 . . A 6
Wheaton, 51,464 . . . . B 5
Zion, 19,775 . . . . A 6

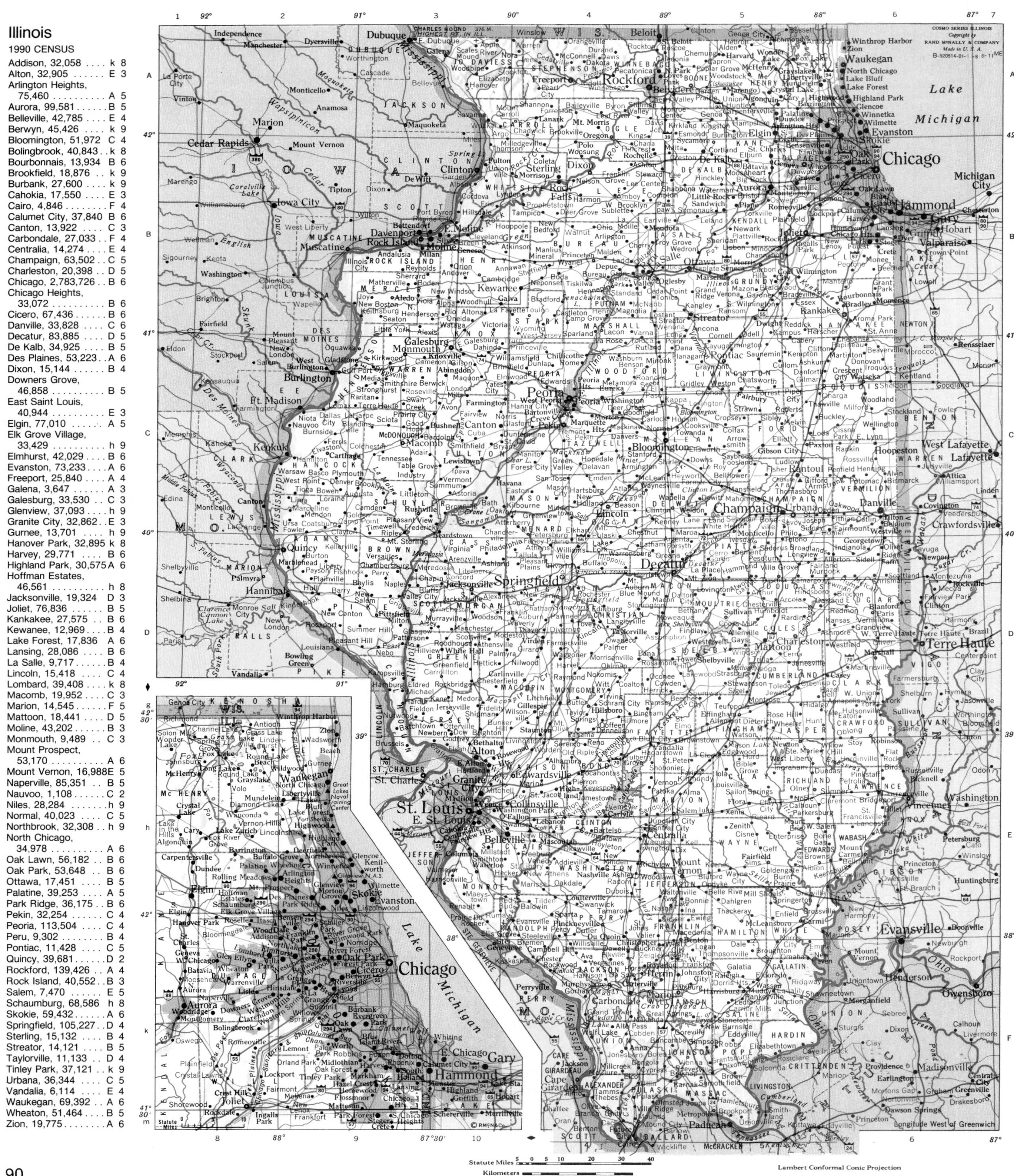

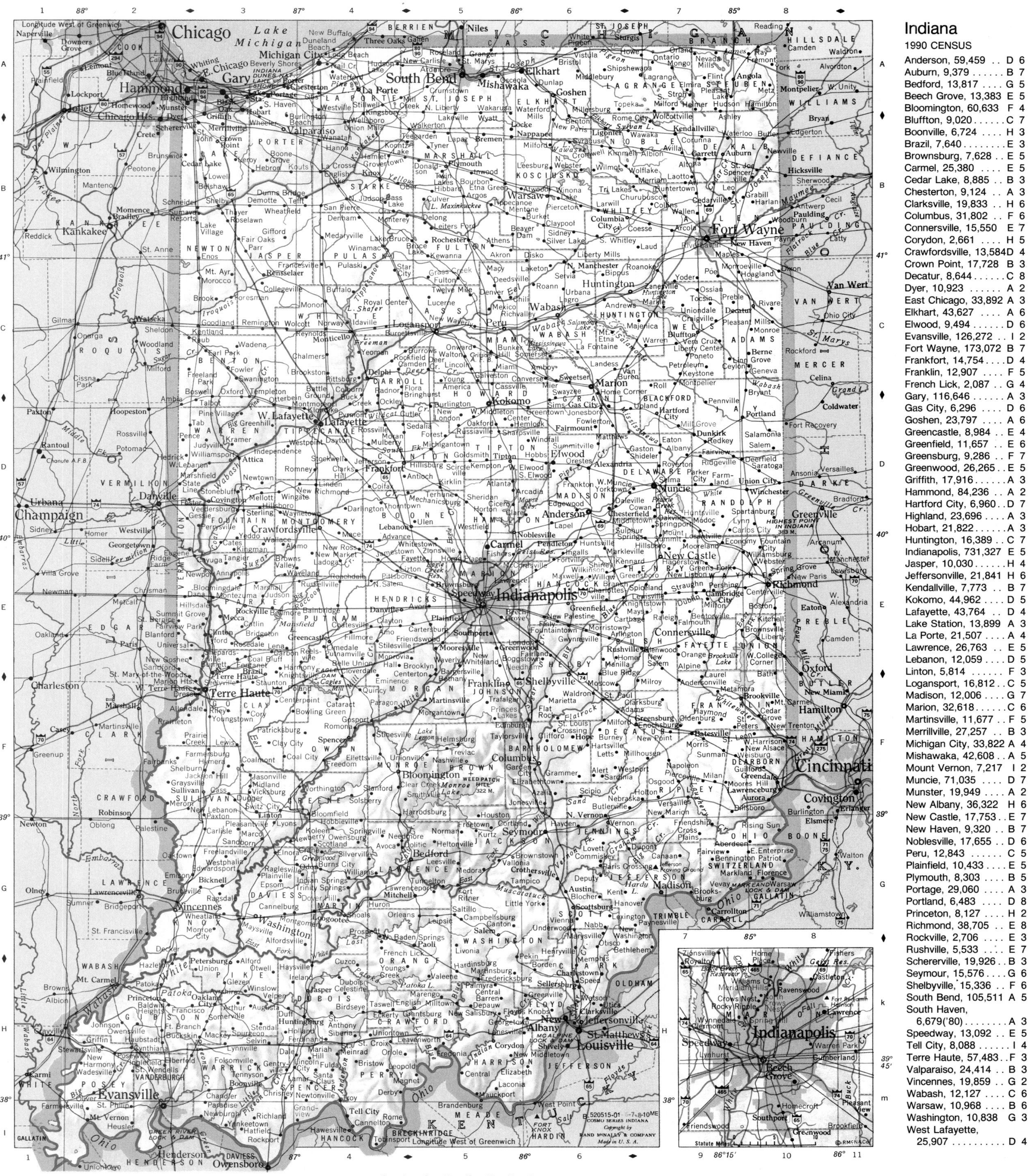

Indiana

1990 CENSUS

City, population	Grid
Anderson, 59,459	D 6
Auburn, 9,379	B 7
Bedford, 13,817	G 5
Beech Grove, 13,383	E 5
Bloomington, 60,633	F 4
Bluffton, 9,020	C 7
Boonville, 6,724	H 3
Brazil, 7,640	E 3
Brownsburg, 7,628	E 5
Carmel, 25,380	E 5
Cedar Lake, 8,885	B 3
Chesterton, 9,124	A 3
Clarksville, 19,833	H 6
Columbus, 31,802	F 6
Connersville, 15,550	E 7
Corydon, 2,661	H 5
Crawfordsville, 13,584	D 4
Crown Point, 17,728	B 3
Decatur, 8,644	C 8
Dyer, 10,923	A 2
East Chicago, 33,892	A 3
Elkhart, 43,627	A 6
Elwood, 9,494	D 6
Evansville, 126,272	I 2
Fort Wayne, 173,072	B 7
Frankfort, 14,754	D 4
Franklin, 12,907	F 5
French Lick, 2,087	G 4
Gary, 116,646	A 3
Gas City, 6,296	D 6
Goshen, 23,797	A 6
Greencastle, 8,984	E 4
Greenfield, 11,657	E 6
Greensburg, 9,286	F 7
Greenwood, 26,265	E 5
Griffith, 17,916	A 3
Hammond, 84,236	A 2
Hartford City, 6,960	D 7
Highland, 23,696	A 3
Hobart, 21,822	A 3
Huntington, 16,389	C 7
Indianapolis, 731,327	E 5
Jasper, 10,030	H 4
Jeffersonville, 21,841	H 6
Kendallville, 7,773	B 7
Kokomo, 44,962	D 5
Lafayette, 43,764	D 4
Lake Station, 13,899	A 3
La Porte, 21,507	A 4
Lawrence, 26,763	E 5
Lebanon, 12,059	D 5
Linton, 5,814	F 3
Logansport, 16,812	C 5
Madison, 12,006	G 7
Marion, 32,618	C 6
Martinsville, 11,677	F 5
Merrillville, 27,257	B 3
Michigan City, 33,822	A 4
Mishawaka, 42,608	A 5
Mount Vernon, 7,217	I 2
Muncie, 71,035	D 7
Munster, 19,949	A 2
New Albany, 36,322	H 6
New Castle, 17,753	E 7
New Haven, 9,320	B 7
Noblesville, 17,655	D 6
Peru, 12,843	C 5
Plainfield, 10,433	E 5
Plymouth, 8,303	B 5
Portage, 29,060	A 3
Portland, 6,483	D 8
Princeton, 8,127	H 2
Richmond, 38,705	E 8
Rockville, 2,706	E 3
Rushville, 5,533	E 7
Schererville, 19,926	B 3
Seymour, 15,576	G 6
Shelbyville, 15,336	F 6
South Bend, 105,511	A 5
South Haven, 6,679('80)	A 3
Speedway, 13,092	E 5
Tell City, 8,088	I 4
Terre Haute, 57,483	F 3
Valparaiso, 24,414	B 3
Vincennes, 19,859	G 2
Wabash, 12,127	C 6
Warsaw, 10,968	B 6
Washington, 10,838	G 3
West Lafayette, 25,907	D 4

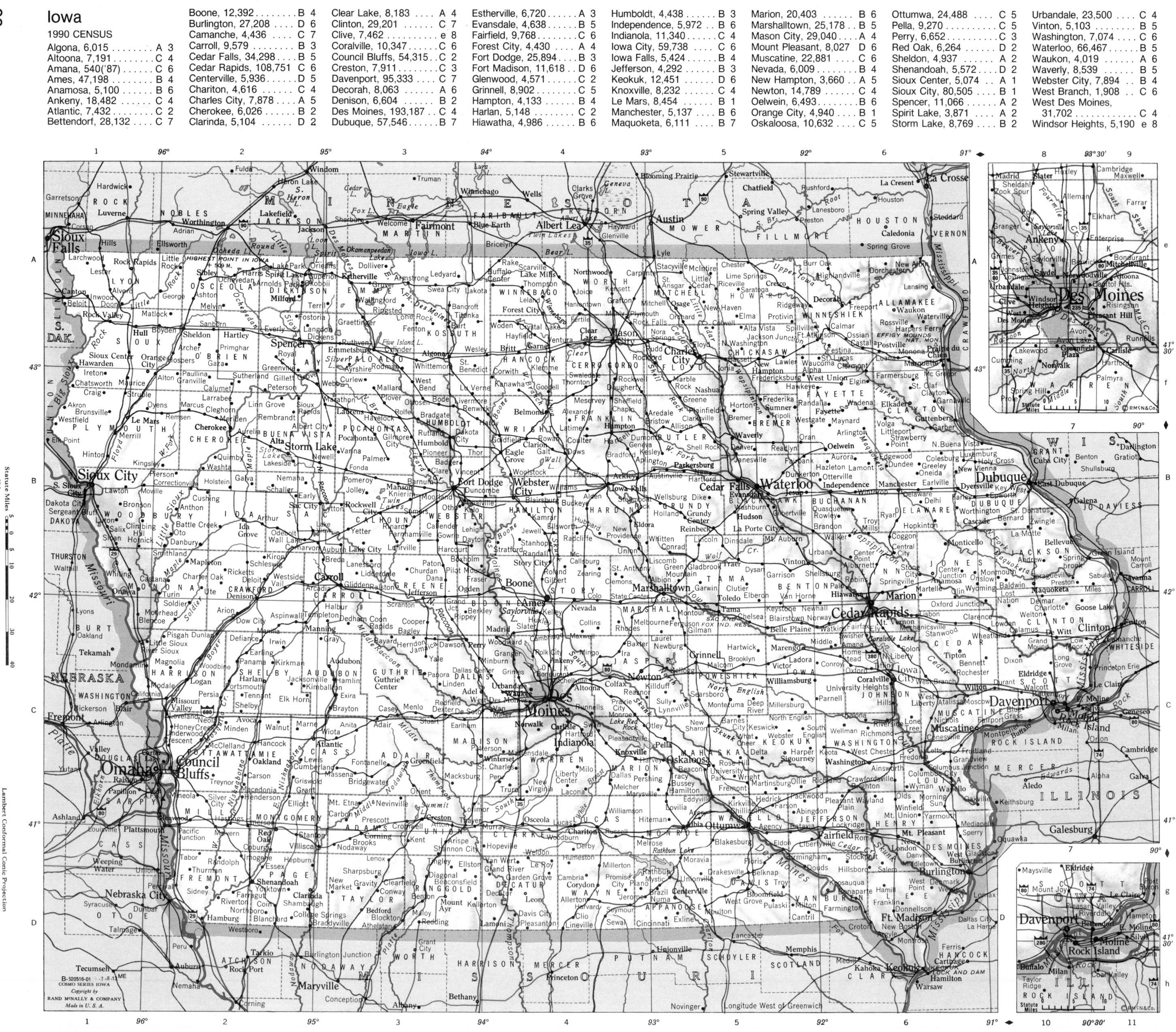

Iowa

1990 CENSUS

Place	Key
Algona, 6,015	A 3
Altoona, 7,191	C 4
Amana, 540('87)	C 6
Ames, 47,198	B 4
Anamosa, 5,100	B 6
Ankeny, 18,482	C 4
Atlantic, 7,432	C 2
Bettendorf, 28,132	C 7
Boone, 12,392	B 4
Burlington, 27,208	D 6
Camanche, 4,436	C 7
Carroll, 9,579	B 3
Cedar Falls, 34,298	B 5
Cedar Rapids, 108,751	C 6
Centerville, 5,936	D 5
Chariton, 4,616	C 4
Charles City, 7,878	A 5
Cherokee, 6,026	B 2
Clarinda, 5,104	D 2
Clear Lake, 8,183	A 4
Clinton, 29,201	C 7
Clive, 7,462	e 8
Coralville, 10,347	C 6
Council Bluffs, 54,315	C 2
Creston, 7,911	C 3
Davenport, 95,333	C 7
Decorah, 8,063	A 6
Denison, 6,604	B 2
Des Moines, 193,187	C 4
Dubuque, 57,546	B 7
Estherville, 6,720	A 3
Evansdale, 4,638	B 5
Fairfield, 9,768	C 6
Forest City, 4,430	A 4
Fort Dodge, 25,894	B 3
Fort Madison, 11,618	D 6
Glenwood, 4,571	C 2
Grinnell, 8,902	C 5
Hampton, 4,133	B 4
Harlan, 5,148	C 2
Hiawatha, 4,986	B 6
Humboldt, 4,438	B 3
Independence, 5,972	B 6
Indianola, 11,340	C 4
Iowa City, 59,738	C 6
Iowa Falls, 5,424	B 4
Jefferson, 4,292	B 3
Keokuk, 12,451	D 6
Knoxville, 8,232	C 4
Le Mars, 8,454	B 1
Manchester, 5,137	B 6
Maquoketa, 6,111	B 7
Marion, 20,403	B 6
Marshalltown, 25,178	B 5
Mason City, 29,040	A 4
Mount Pleasant, 8,027	D 6
Muscatine, 22,881	C 6
Nevada, 6,009	B 4
New Hampton, 3,660	A 5
Newton, 14,789	C 4
Oelwein, 6,493	B 6
Orange City, 4,940	B 1
Oskaloosa, 10,632	C 5
Ottumwa, 24,488	C 5
Pella, 9,270	C 5
Perry, 6,652	C 3
Red Oak, 6,264	D 2
Sheldon, 4,937	A 2
Shenandoah, 5,572	D 2
Sioux Center, 5,074	A 1
Sioux City, 80,505	B 1
Spencer, 11,066	A 2
Spirit Lake, 3,871	A 2
Storm Lake, 8,769	B 2
Urbandale, 23,500	C 4
Vinton, 5,103	B 5
Washington, 7,074	C 6
Waterloo, 66,467	B 5
Waukon, 4,019	A 6
Waverly, 8,539	B 5
Webster City, 7,894	B 4
West Branch, 1,908	C 6
West Des Moines, 31,702	C 4
Windsor Heights, 5,190	e 8

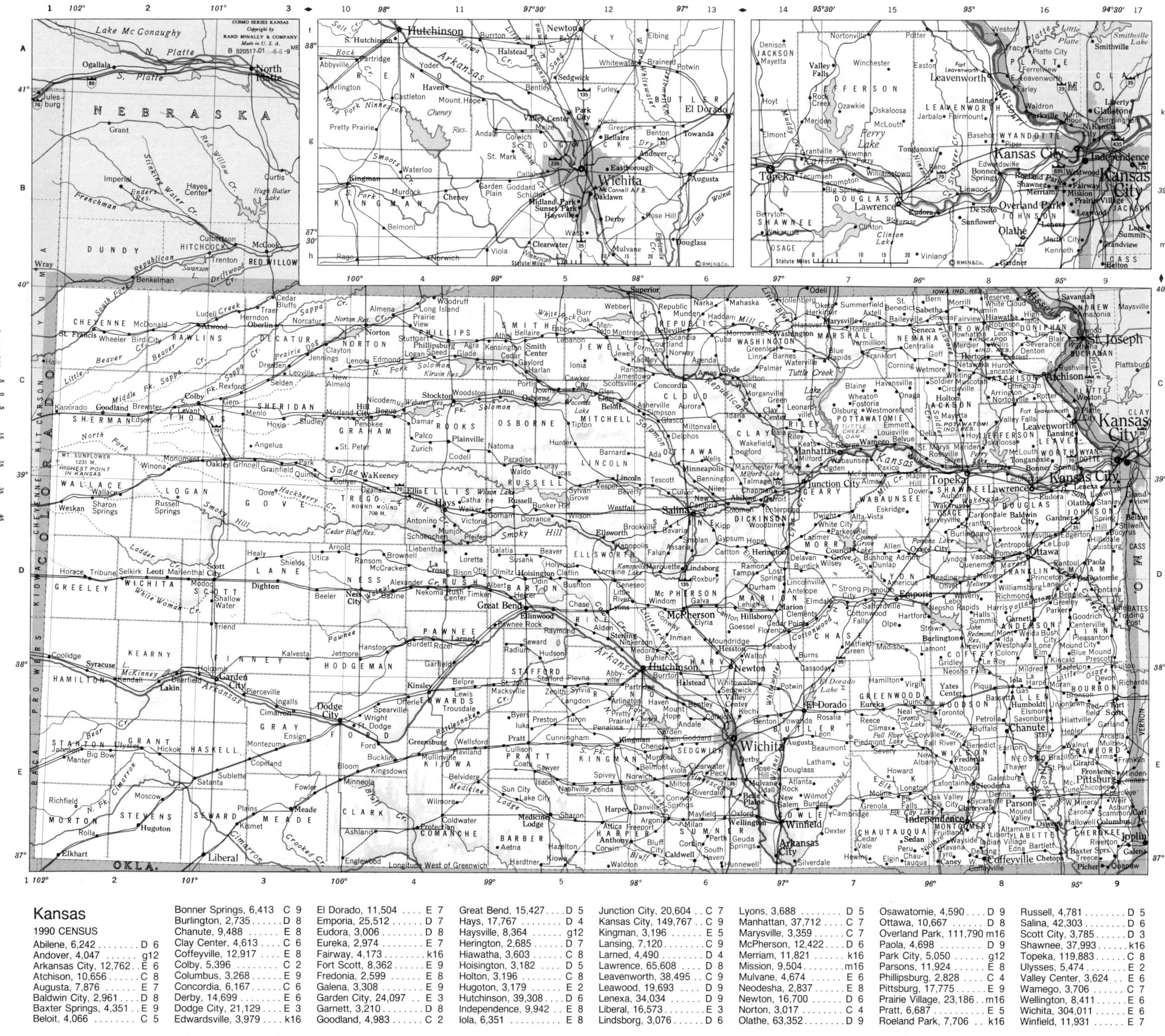

Kansas

1990 CENSUS

Abilene, 6,242 . . . . D 6
Andover, 4,047 . . . . g12
Arkansas City, 12,762 . . E 6
Atchison, 10,656 . . . . . . C 8
Augusta, 7,876 . . . . E 7
Baldwin City, 2,961 . . . . D 8
Baxter Springs, 4,351 . . E 9
Beloit, 4,066 . . . . C 5
Bonner Springs, 6,413 C 9
Burlington, 2,735 . . . . . . D 7
Chanute, 9,488 . . . . E 8
Clay Center, 4,613 . . . . C 6
Coffeyville, 12,917 . . . . E 8
Colby, 5,396 . . . . C 2
Columbus, 3,268 . . . . . . E 9
Concordia, 6,167 . . . . . . C 6
Derby, 14,699 . . . . E 6
Dodge City, 21,129 . . . . E 3
Edwardsville, 3,979 . . . . k16
El Dorado, 11,504 . . . . E 7
Emporia, 25,512 . . . . . . D 7
Eudora, 3,006 . . . . D 8
Eureka, 2,974 . . . . E 7
Fairway, 4,173 . . . . k16
Fort Scott, 8,362 . . . . . . E 9
Fredonia, 2,599 . . . . . . E 8
Galena, 3,308 . . . . E 9
Garden City, 24,097 . . . E 3
Garnett, 3,210 . . . . D 8
Goodland, 4,983 . . . . . . C 2
Great Bend, 15,427 . . . D 5
Hays, 17,767 . . . . D 4
Haysville, 8,364 . . . . . . g12
Herington, 2,685 . . . . . . D 7
Hiawatha, 3,603 . . . . . . C 8
Hoisington, 3,182 . . . . D 5
Holton, 3,196 . . . . C 8
Hugoton, 3,179 . . . . E 2
Hutchinson, 39,308 . . . . D 6
Independence, 9,942 . . E 8
Iola, 6,351 . . . . E 8
Junction City, 20,604 . . C 7
Kansas City, 149,767 . . C 9
Kingman, 3,196 . . . . E 5
Lansing, 7,120 . . . . C 9
Larned, 4,490 . . . . D 4
Lawrence, 65,608 . . . . D 8
Leavenworth, 38,495 . . C 9
Leawood, 19,693 . . . . D 9
Lenexa, 34,034 . . . . . . D 9
Liberal, 16,573 . . . . E 3
Lindsborg, 3,076 . . . . . . D 6
Lyons, 3,688 . . . . D 5
Manhattan, 37,712 . . . . C 7
Marysville, 3,359 . . . . . . C 7
McPherson, 12,422 . . . . D 6
Merriam, 11,821 . . . . . . k16
Mission, 9,504 . . . . m16
Mulvane, 4,674 . . . . E 6
Neodesha, 2,837 . . . . . . E 8
Newton, 16,700 . . . . D 6
Norton, 3,017 . . . . C 4
Olathe, 63,352 . . . . D 9
Osawatomie, 4,590 . . . . D 9
Ottawa, 10,667 . . . . D 8
Overland Park, 111,790 m16
Paola, 4,698 . . . . D 9
Park City, 5,050 . . . . . . g12
Parsons, 11,924 . . . . . . E 8
Phillipsburg, 2,828 . . . . C 4
Pittsburg, 17,775 . . . . . E 9
Prairie Village, 23,186 . . m16
Pratt, 6,687 . . . . E 5
Roeland Park, 7,706 . . k16
Russell, 4,781 . . . . D 5
Salina, 42,303 . . . . D 6
Scott City, 3,785 . . . . . . D 3
Shawnee, 37,993 . . . . . . k16
Topeka, 119,883 . . . . . . C 8
Ulysses, 5,474 . . . . E 2
Valley Center, 3,624 . . . E 6
Wamego, 3,706 . . . . C 7
Wellington, 8,411 . . . . . . E 6
Wichita, 304,011 . . . . . . E 6
Winfield, 11,931 . . . . E 7

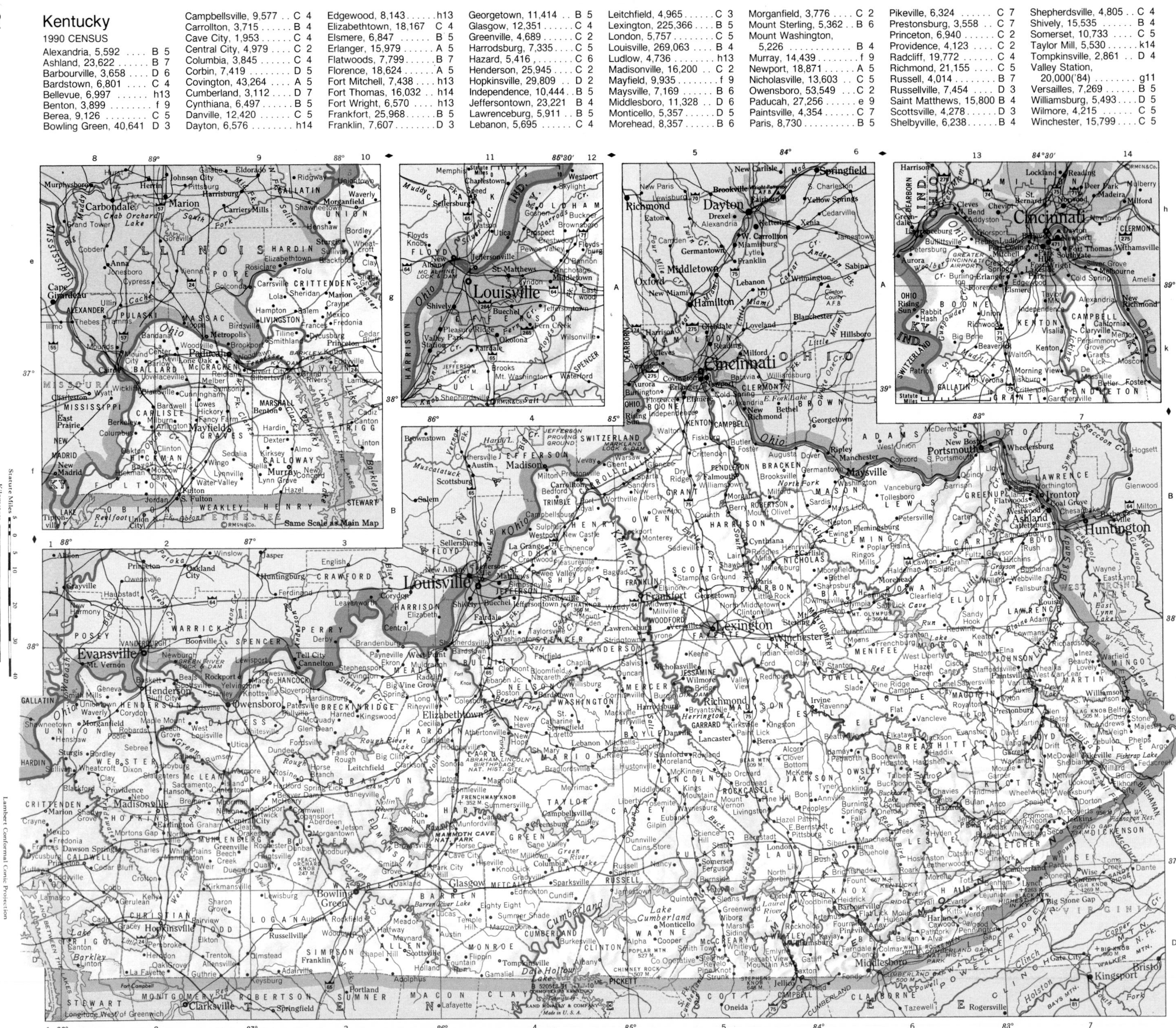

Kentucky

1990 CENSUS

Alexandria, 5,592 . . . . B 5
Ashland, 23,622 . . . . . . B 7
Barbourville, 3,658 . . . . D 6
Bardstown, 6,801 . . . . C 4
Bellevue, 6,997 . . . . . . h13
Benton, 3,899 . . . . f 9
Berea, 9,126 . . . . C 5
Bowling Green, 40,641 D 3
Campbellsville, 9,577 . . C 4
Carrollton, 3,715 . . . . . B 4
Cave City, 1,953 . . . . . . C 4
Central City, 4,979 . . . . C 2
Columbia, 3,845 . . . . . . C 4
Corbin, 7,419 . . . . D 5
Covington, 43,264 . . . . A 5
Cumberland, 3,112 . . . . D 7
Cynthiana, 6,497 . . . . . B 5
Danville, 12,420 . . . . . . C 5
Dayton, 6,576 . . . . h14
Edgewood, 8,143 . . . . . . h13
Elizabethtown, 18,167 C 4
Elsmere, 6,847 . . . . . . B 5
Erlanger, 15,979 . . . . . . A 5
Flatwoods, 7,799 . . . . . B 7
Florence, 18,624 . . . . . . A 5
Fort Mitchell, 7,438 . . . . h13
Fort Thomas, 16,032 . . h14
Fort Wright, 6,570 . . . . h13
Frankfort, 25,968 . . . . . . B 5
Franklin, 7,607 . . . . D 3
Georgetown, 11,414 . . B 5
Glasgow, 12,351 . . . . . . C 4
Greenville, 4,689 . . . . . . C 2
Harrodsburg, 7,335 . . . . C 5
Hazard, 5,416 . . . . C 6
Henderson, 25,945 . . . . C 2
Hopkinsville, 29,809 . . . D 2
Independence, 10,444 . . B 5
Jeffersontown, 23,221 B 4
Lawrenceburg, 5,911 . . B 5
Lebanon, 5,695 . . . . . . C 4
Leitchfield, 4,965 . . . . . . C 3
Lexington, 225,366 . . . . B 5
London, 5,757 . . . . C 5
Louisville, 269,063 . . . . B 4
Ludlow, 4,736 . . . . h13
Madisonville, 16,200 . . C 2
Mayfield, 9,935 . . . . f 9
Maysville, 7,169 . . . . . . B 6
Middlesboro, 11,328 . . D 6
Monticello, 5,357 . . . . . D 5
Morehead, 8,357 . . . . . B 6
Morganfield, 3,776 . . . . C 2
Mount Sterling, 5,362 . . B 6
Mount Washington, 5,226 . . . . B 4
Murray, 14,439 . . . . f 9
Newport, 18,871 . . . . A 5
Nicholasville, 13,603 . . . C 5
Owensboro, 53,549 . . . C 2
Paducah, 27,256 . . . . . . e 9
Paintsville, 4,354 . . . . . . C 7
Paris, 8,730 . . . . B 5
Pikeville, 6,324 . . . . . . C 7
Prestonsburg, 3,558 . . C 7
Princeton, 6,940 . . . . . . C 2
Providence, 4,123 . . . . C 2
Radcliff, 19,772 . . . . . . C 4
Richmond, 21,155 . . . . C 5
Russell, 4,014 . . . . B 7
Russellville, 7,454 . . . . D 3
Saint Matthews, 15,800 B 4
Scottsville, 4,278 . . . . . D 3
Shelbyville, 6,238 . . . . . B 4
Shepherdsville, 4,805 . . C 4
Shively, 15,535 . . . . B 4
Somerset, 10,733 . . . . C 5
Taylor Mill, 5,530 . . . . . k14
Tompkinsville, 2,861 . . D 4
Valley Station, 20,000('84) g11
Versailles, 7,269 . . . . . . B 5
Williamsburg, 5,493 . . . D 5
Wilmore, 4,215 . . . . . . C 5
Winchester, 15,799 . . . . C 5

Louisiana

1990 CENSUS

Abbeville, 11,187 . . . . . . E 3
Alexandria, 49,188 . . . . . C 3
Arabi, 10,248('80) k11
Baker, 13,233 . . . . D 4
Bastrop, 13,916 . . . . B 4
Baton Rouge, 219,531 D 4
Berwick, 4,375 . . . . E 4
Bogalusa, 14,280 . . . . D 6
Bossier City, 52,721 . . B 2
Breaux Bridge, 6,515 . . D 4
Bunkie, 5,044 . . . . D 3
Chalmette, 31,860 . . . . E 6
Church Point, 4,677 . . . D 3
Covington, 7,691 . . . . . . D 5
Crowley, 13,983 . . . . . . D 3
Cut Off, 5,049('80) . . . . E 5
Denham Springs, 8,381 D 5
De Ridder, 9,868 . . . . . . D 2
Donaldsonville, 7,949 . . D 4
Eunice, 11,162 . . . . D 3
Ferriday, 4,111 . . . . . . C 4
Franklin, 9,004 . . . . E 4
Gonzales, 7,003 . . . . . . D 5
Grambling, 5,484 . . . . . . B 3
Gretna, 17,208 . . . . E 5
Hammond, 15,871 . . . . D 5
Harahan, 9,927 . . . . . . k11
Harvey, 15,000 . . . . . . E 5
Houma, 96,982 . . . . . . E 5
Jeanerette, 6,205 . . . . . . E 4
Jefferson, 15,550('80) . . k11
Jena, 2,626 . . . . C 3
Jennings, 11,305 . . . . . . D 3
Jonesboro, 4,305 . . . . B 3
Kaplan, 4,535 . . . . D 3
Kenner, 72,033 . . . . . . E 5
Lafayette, 94,440 . . . . D 3
Lake Charles, 70,580 . . D 2
Lake Providence, 5,380 B 4
La Place, 16,112('80) . . h11
Leesville, 7,638 . . . . . . C 2
Lutcher, 3,907 . . . . D 5
Mandeville, 7,083 . . . . D 5
Mansfield, 5,389 . . . . . . B 2
Marksville, 5,526 . . . . . . C 3
Marrero, 36,671 . . . . . . E 5
Metairie, 149,428 . . . . . . k11
Minden, 13,661 . . . . . . B 2
Monroe, 54,909 . . . . . . B 3
Morgan City, 14,531 . . E 4
Moss Bluff, 7,004('80) D 2
Natchitoches, 16,609 . . C 2
New Iberia, 31,828 . . . . D 4
New Orleans, 496,938 E 5
Oakdale, 6,832 . . . . . . D 3
Opelousas, 18,151 . . . . D 3
Patterson, 4,736 . . . . . . E 4
Pineville, 12,251 . . . . . . C 3
Plaquemine, 7,186 . . . . D 4
Ponchatoula, 5,425 . . . . D 5
Port Allen, 6,277 . . . . . . D 4
Raceland, 6,302('80) . . E 5
Rayne, 8,502 . . . . D 3
Rayville, 4,411 . . . . B 4
Reserve, 7,288('80) h10
River Ridge, 17,146('80) k11
Ruston, 20,027 . . . . . . B 3
Saint Martinville, 7,137 D 4
Scotlandville, 15,113('80) . . . . D 4
Shreveport, 198,525 . . B 2
Slidell, 24,124 . . . . D 6
Springhill, 5,668 . . . . . . A 2
Sulphur, 20,125 . . . . . . D 2
Tallulah, 8,526 . . . . B 4
Thibodaux, 14,035 . . . . E 5
Vidalia, 4,953 . . . . C 4
Ville Platte, 9,037 . . . . D 3
Violet, 6,000 . . . . k12
Westlake, 5,007 . . . . . . D 2
West Monroe, 14,096 . . B 3
Westwego, 11,218 . . . . k11
Winnfield, 6,138 . . . . . . C 3
Winnsboro, 5,755 . . . . B 4
Zachary, 9,036 . . . . D 4

Maine

1990 CENSUS

Auburn, 24,309 .... D 2
Augusta, 21,325 .... D 3
Bangor, 33,181 .... D 4
Bar Harbor, 2,685
(4,443▲) .... D 4
Bath, 9,799 .... E 3
Belfast, 6,355 ...... D 3
Berwick, 2,378
(5,995▲) .... E 2
Biddeford, 20,710 .. E 2
Brewer, 9,021 ...... D 4
Bridgton, 1,639
(4,307▲) .... D 2
Brunswick, 10,990
(20,906▲) .... E 3
Bucksport, 2,853
(4,825▲) .... D 4
Calais, 3,963 ...... C 5
Camden, 3,743
(5,060▲) .... D 3
Caribou, 9,415 ...... B 5
Dexter, 3,118
(4,419▲) .... C 3
Dixfield, 1,725
(2,574▲) .... D 2
Dover-Foxcroft, 2,974
(4,657▲) .... C 3
Eastport, 1,965 ...... D 6
Ellsworth, 5,975 .... D 4
Fairfield, 3,169
(6,718▲) .... D 3
Farmingdale, 2,014
(2,918▲) .... D 3
Farmington, 3,583
(7,436▲) .... D 2
Fort Fairfield, 2,282
(3,998▲) .... B 5
Fort Kent, 2,375
(4,268▲) .... A 4
Fryeburg, 1,644
(2,968▲) .... D 2
Gardiner, 6,746 .... D 3
Gorham, 4,052
(11,856▲) .... E 2
Hallowell, 2,534 .... D 3
Hampden, 2,300
(5,974▲) .... D 4
Houlton, 5,730
(6,613▲) .... B 5
Kennebunk, 3,294
(8,004▲) .... E 2
Kennebunkport, 1,685
(3,356▲) .... E 2
Kittery, 5,465
(9,372▲) .... E 2
Lewiston, 39,757 .... D 2
Lincoln, 3,524
(5,587▲) .... C 4
Livermore Falls, 2,441
(3,455▲) .... D 2
Madawaska, 4,165
(4,803▲) .... A 4
Madison, 2,788
(4,725▲) .... D 3
Mexico, 3,207
(3,344▲) .... D 2
Milford, 1,688
(2,884▲) .... D 4
Milo, 2,255 (2,600▲) C 4
Newport, 1,748
(3,036▲) .... D 3
Norway, 2,653
(4,754▲) .... D 2
Oakland, 3,387
(5,595▲) .... D 3
Old Town, 8,317 .... D 4
Pittsfield, 3,117
(4,190▲) .... D 3
Portland, 64,358 .... E 2
Presque Isle, 10,550 B 5
Richmond, 1,578
(3,072▲) .... D 3
Rockland, 7,972 .... D 3
Rumford, 6,256
(7,078▲) .... D 2
Saco, 15,181 .... E 2
Sanford, 10,268
(20,463▲) .... E 2
Scarborough, 2,280
(12,518▲) .... E 2
Skowhegan, 6,517
(8,725▲) .... D 3
South Berwick, 2,120
(5,877▲) .... E 2
South Portland,
23,163 .... E 2
Thomaston, 2,348
(3,306▲) .... D 3
Topsham, 4,657
(8,746▲) .... E 3
Waterville, 17,173 .. D 3
Westbrook, 16,121 .. E 2
Wilton, 2,262
(4,242▲) .... D 2
Winslow, 5,903
(7,997▲) .... D 3
Winthrop, 3,264
(5,968▲) .... D 3
Yarmouth, 2,981
(7,862▲) .... E 2
York, 3,130 (9,818▲) E 2

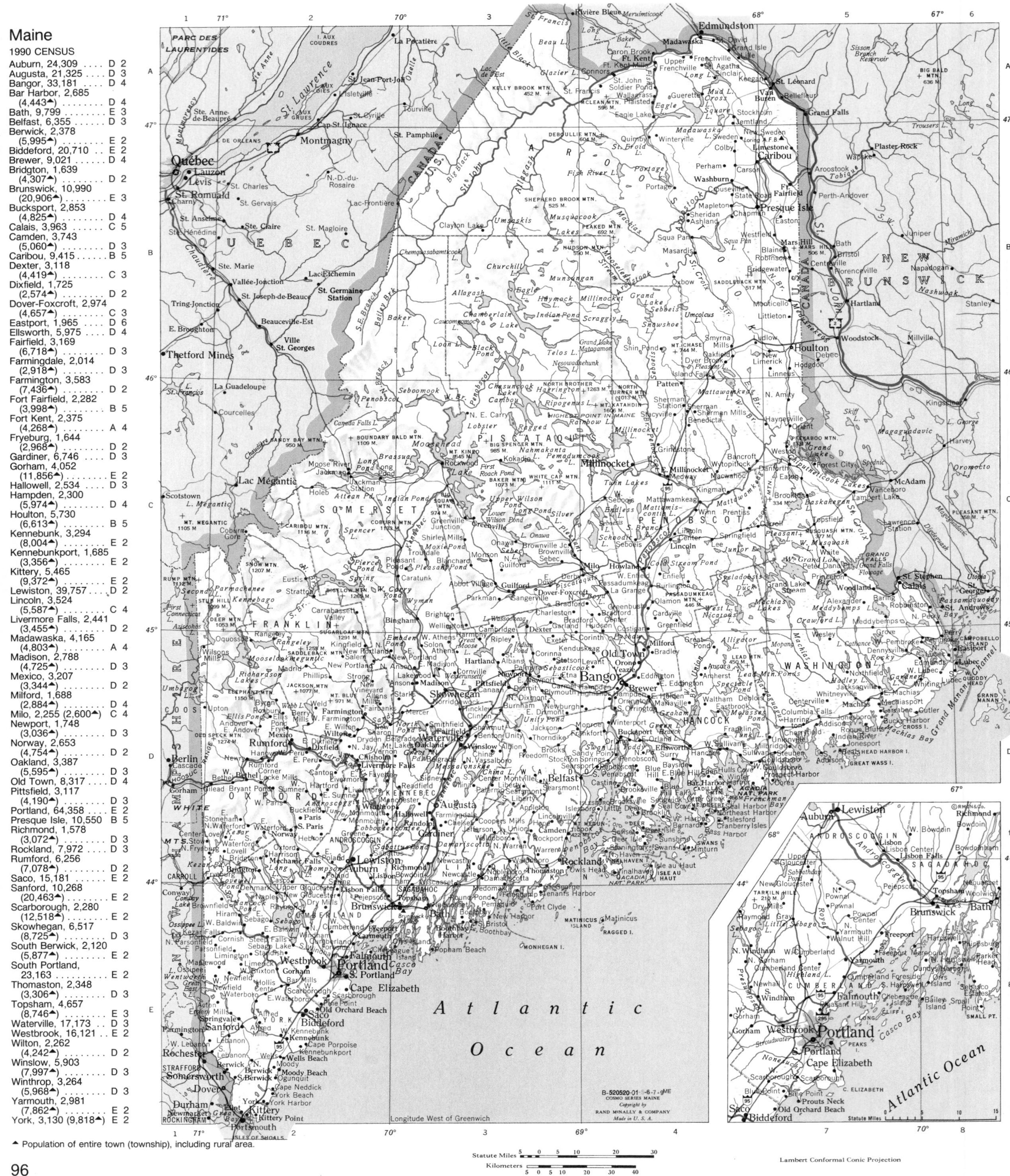

▲ Population of entire town (township), including rural area.

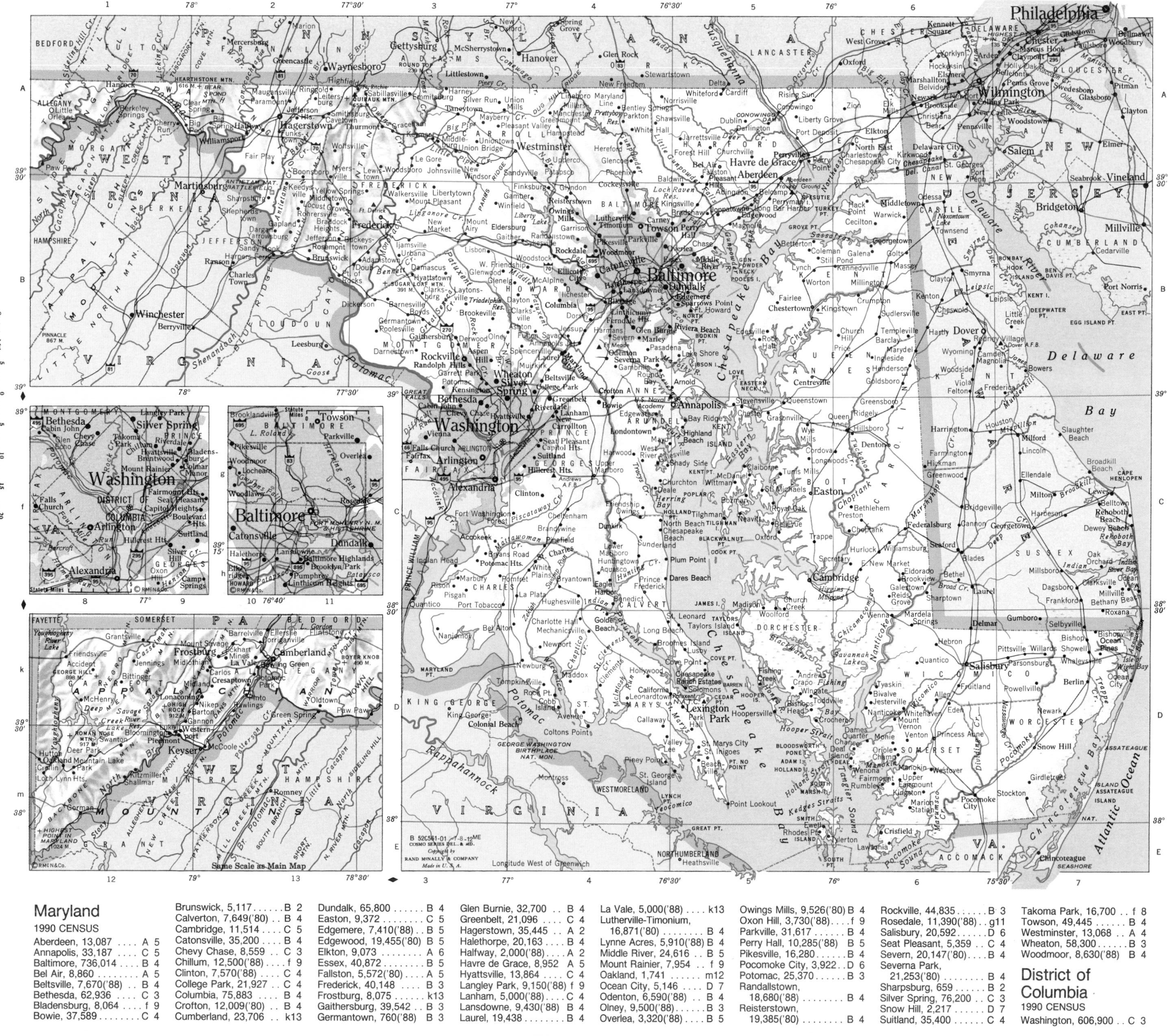

Maryland
1990 CENSUS

Aberdeen, 13,087 .... A 5
Annapolis, 33,187 .... C 5
Baltimore, 736,014 .... B 4
Bel Air, 8,860 .... A 5
Beltsville, 7,670('88) .. B 4
Bethesda, 62,936 .... C 3
Bladensburg, 8,064 .... f 9
Bowie, 37,589 .... C 4
Brunswick, 5,117 ...... B 2
Calverton, 7,649('80) .. B 4
Cambridge, 11,514 .... C 5
Catonsville, 35,200 .... B 4
Chevy Chase, 8,559 .. C 4
Chillum, 12,500('88) .... f 9
Clinton, 7,570('88) .... C 4
College Park, 21,927 .. C 4
Columbia, 75,883 .... B 4
Crofton, 12,009('80) .. B 4
Cumberland, 23,706 .. k13
Dundalk, 65,800 ...... B 4
Easton, 9,372 .... C 5
Edgemere, 7,410('88) .. B 5
Edgewood, 19,455('80) B 5
Elkton, 9,073 .... A 6
Essex, 40,872 .... B 5
Fallston, 5,572('80) .... A 5
Frederick, 40,148 .... B 3
Frostburg, 8,075 ...... k13
Gaithersburg, 39,542 .. B 3
Germantown, 760('88) B 3
Glen Burnie, 32,700 .. B 4
Greenbelt, 21,096 .... C 4
Hagerstown, 35,445 .. A 2
Halethorpe, 20,163 .... B 4
Halfway, 2,000('88) .... A 2
Havre de Grace, 8,952 A 5
Hyattsville, 13,864 .... C 4
Langley Park, 9,150('88) f 9
Lanham, 5,000('88) .... C 4
Lansdowne, 9,430('88) B 4
Laurel, 19,438 .... B 4
La Vale, 5,000('88) k13
Lutherville-Timonium, 16,871('80) .... B 4
Lynne Acres, 5,910('88) B 4
Middle River, 24,616 .. B 5
Mount Rainier, 7,954 .. f 9
Oakland, 1,741 ...... m12
Ocean City, 5,146 .... D 7
Odenton, 6,590('88) .. B 4
Olney, 9,500('88) ...... B 3
Overlea, 3,320('88) .... B 5
Owings Mills, 9,526('80) B 4
Oxon Hill, 3,730('88) .... f 9
Parkville, 31,617 ...... B 4
Perry Hall, 10,285('88) B 5
Pikesville, 16,280 ...... B 4
Pocomoke City, 3,922 . D 6
Potomac, 25,370 ...... B 3
Randallstown, 18,680('88) .... B 4
Reisterstown, 19,385('80) .... B 4
Rockville, 44,835 ...... B 3
Rosedale, 11,390('88) .. g11
Salisbury, 20,592 ...... D 6
Seat Pleasant, 5,359 .. C 4
Severn, 20,147('80) .... B 4
Severna Park, 21,253('80) .... B 4
Sharpsburg, 659 ...... B 2
Silver Spring, 76,200 .. C 3
Snow Hill, 2,217 ...... D 7
Suitland, 35,400 ...... C 4
Takoma Park, 16,700 .. f 8
Towson, 49,445 .... B 4
Westminster, 13,068 .. A 4
Wheaton, 58,300 ...... B 3
Woodmoor, 8,630('88) B 4

District of Columbia
1990 CENSUS

Washington, 606,900 .. C 3

Massachusetts

1990 CENSUS

Amherst, 17,773 (35,228▲) . . . . . B 2
Arlington, 44,630 . . . . . B 5
Attleboro, 38,383 . . . . C 5
Belmont, 24,720 . . . . . g11
Beverly, 38,195 . . . . . A 6
Boston, 574,283 . . . . . B 5
Braintree, 33,836 . . . . . B 5
Brockton, 92,788 . . . . . B 5
Brookline, 54,718 . . . . B 5
Burlington, 23,302 . . . . f11
Cambridge, 95,802 . . . . B 5
Chelmsford, 32,383 . . . . A 5
Chelsea, 28,710 . . . . . B 5
Chicopee, 56,632 . . . . B 2
Concord, 4,680 (17,076▲) . . . . . B 5
Danvers, 24,174 . . . . . A 6
Dedham, 23,782 . . . . . B 5
Everett, 35,701 . . . . . g11
Fall River, 92,703 . . . . C 5
Fitchburg, 41,194 . . . . A 4
Framingham, 64,989 . . . B 5
Gardner, 20,125 . . . . . A 4
Gloucester, 28,716 . . . . A 6
Greenfield, 14,198 (18,666▲) . . . . . A 2
Haverhill, 51,418 . . . . . A 5
Holyoke, 43,704 . . . . . B 2
Hyannis, 9,900 . . . . . C 7
Lawrence, 70,207 . . . . A 5
Leominster, 38,145 . . . . A 4
Lexington, 28,974 . . . . B 5
Lowell, 103,439 . . . . . A 5
Lynn, 81,245 . . . . . B 6
Malden, 53,884 . . . . . B 5
Marblehead, 20,126('80) B 6
Marlborough, 31,813 . . B 4
Medford, 57,407 . . . . . B 5
Melrose, 28,150 . . . . . B 5
Methuen, 40,300 . . . . . A 5
Milford, 25,200 . . . . . B 4
Milton, 25,725 . . . . . B 5
Nantucket, 3,229 (6,012▲) . . . . . D 7
Natick, 30,100 . . . . . B 5
Needham, 27,557 . . . . g11
New Bedford, 99,922 . . C 6
Newburyport, 16,317 . . A 6
Newton, 82,585 . . . . . B 5
North Adams, 16,797 . . A 1
Northampton, 29,289 . . B 2
North Andover, 20,129('87) . . . . . A 5
North Attleboro, 24,200 C 5
Norwood, 28,700 . . . . . B 5
Peabody, 47,039 . . . . . A 6
Pittsfield, 48,622 . . . . . B 1
Plymouth, 7,232 (45,608▲) . . . . . C 6
Quincy, 84,985 . . . . . B 5
Randolph, 30,093 . . . . B 5
Reading, 22,539 . . . . . A 5
Revere, 42,786 . . . . . g11
Salem, 38,091 . . . . . A 6
Saugus, 25,549 . . . . . g11
Shrewsbury, 23,400 . . B 4
Somerville, 76,210 . . . . B 5
Springfield, 156,983 . . B 2
Stoneham, 22,203 . . . . g11
Stoughton, 27,800 . . . . B 5
Taunton, 49,832 . . . . . C 5
Vineyard Haven, 1,704('80) . . . . . D 6
Wakefield, 24,825 . . . . B 5
Waltham, 57,878 . . . . . B 5
Watertown, 33,284 . . . . g11
Wellesley, 26,615 . . . . B 5
Westfield, 38,372 . . . . B 2
West Springfield, 27,537 B 2
Weymouth, 54,063 . . . . B 6
Winchester, 20,701('80) g11
Winthrop, 19,294('80) . . B 6
Woburn, 35,943 . . . . . B 5
Worcester, 169,759 . . . B 4

▲ Population of entire town (township), including rural area.

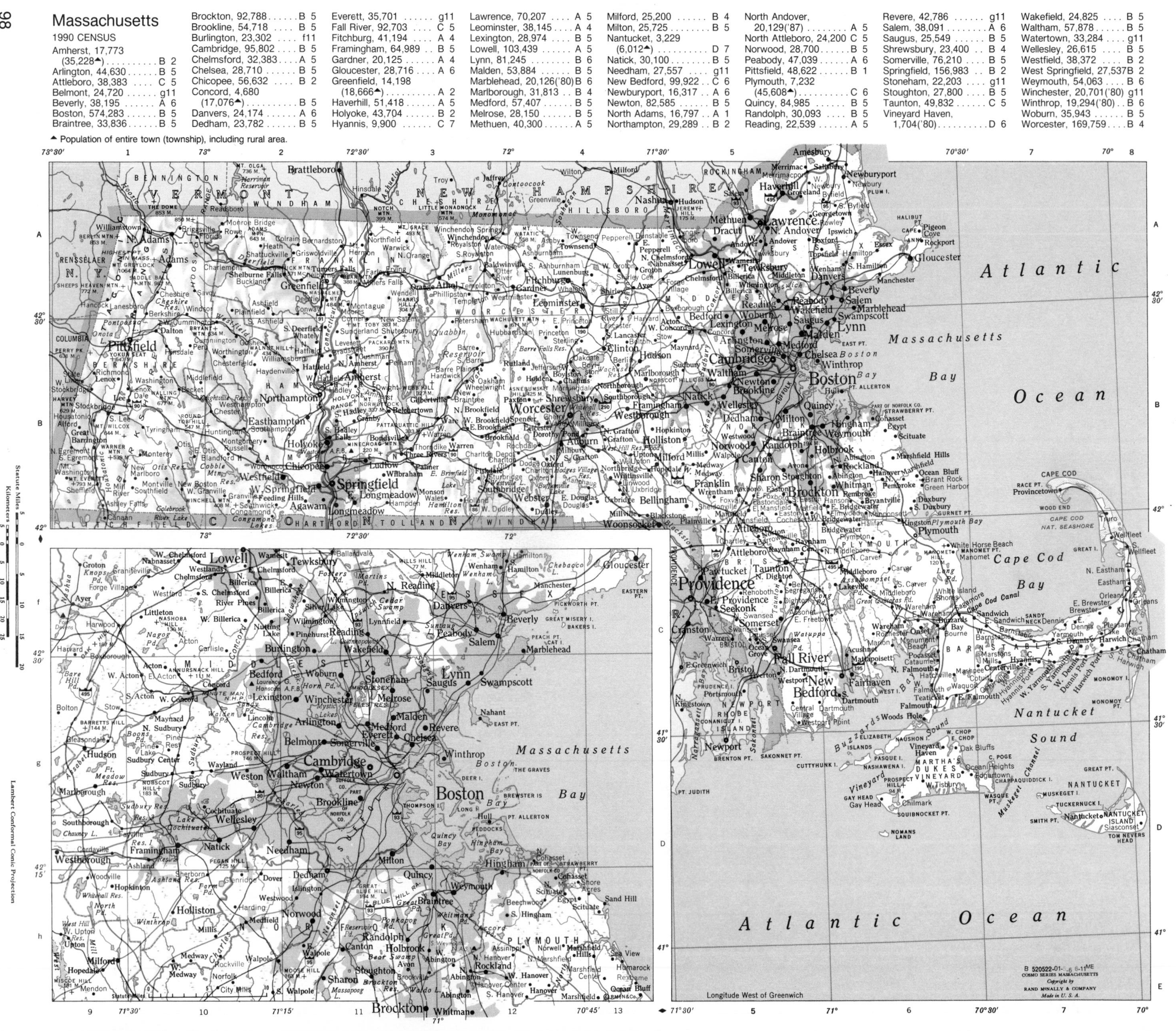

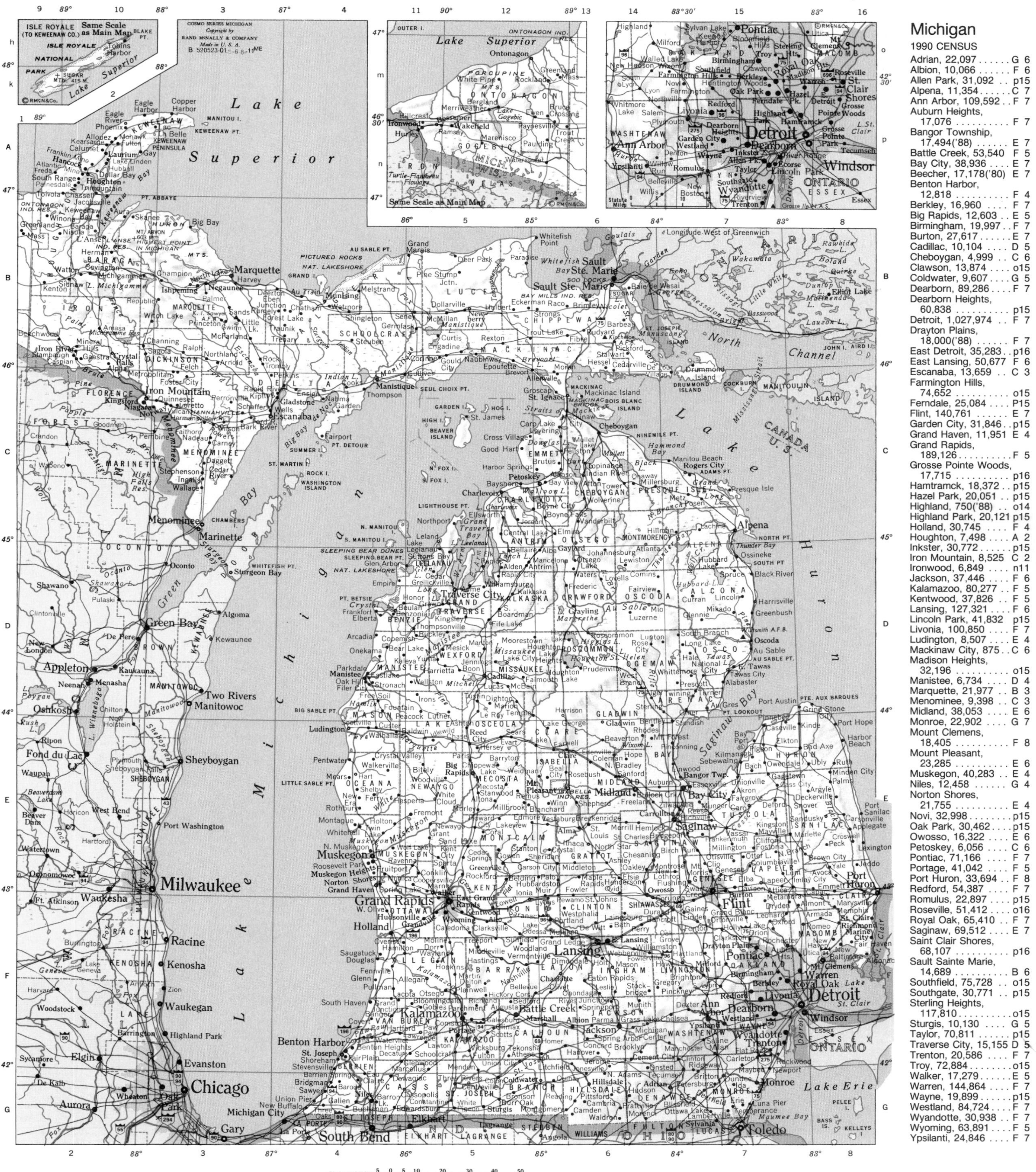

Michigan

1990 CENSUS

Adrian, 22,097 . . . . . G 6
Albion, 10,066 . . . . . F 6
Allen Park, 31,092 . . p15
Alpena, 11,354 . . . . . C 7
Ann Arbor, 109,592 . . F 7
Auburn Heights, 17,076 . . . . F 7
Bangor Township, 17,494('88) . . . . . . E 7
Battle Creek, 53,540 F 5
Bay City, 38,936 . . . . E 7
Beecher, 17,178('80) E 7
Benton Harbor, 12,818 . . . . F 4
Berkley, 16,960 . . . . F 7
Big Rapids, 12,603 . . E 5
Birmingham, 19,997 . . F 7
Burton, 27,617 . . . . . E 7
Cadillac, 10,104 . . . . D 5
Cheboygan, 4,999 . . C 6
Clawson, 13,874 . . . . o15
Coldwater, 9,607 . . . . G 5
Dearborn, 89,286 . . . . F 7
Dearborn Heights, 60,838 . . . . p15
Detroit, 1,027,974 . . F 7
Drayton Plains, 18,000('88) . . . . F 7
East Detroit, 35,283 . . p16
East Lansing, 50,677 F 6
Escanaba, 13,659 . . C 3
Farmington Hills, 74,652 . . . . o15
Ferndale, 25,084 . . . . P15
Flint, 140,761 . . . . . . E 7
Garden City, 31,846 . . p15
Grand Haven, 11,951 E 4
Grand Rapids, 189,126 . . . . F 5
Grosse Pointe Woods, 17,715 . . . . p16
Hamtramck, 18,372 . . p15
Hazel Park, 20,051 . . p15
Highland, 750('88) . . o14
Highland Park, 20,121 p15
Holland, 30,745 . . . . F 4
Houghton, 7,498 . . . . A 2
Inkster, 30,772 . . . . . p15
Iron Mountain, 8,525 C 2
Ironwood, 6,849 . . . . n11
Jackson, 37,446 . . . . F 6
Kalamazoo, 80,277 . . F 5
Kentwood, 37,826 . . . F 5
Lansing, 127,321 . . . . F 6
Lincoln Park, 41,832 p15
Livonia, 100,850 . . . . F 7
Ludington, 8,507 . . . . E 4
Mackinaw City, 875 . . C 6
Madison Heights, 32,196 . . . . o15
Manistee, 6,734 . . . . D 4
Marquette, 21,977 . . B 3
Menominee, 9,398 . . . C 3
Midland, 38,053 . . . . E 6
Monroe, 22,902 . . . . G 7
Mount Clemens, 18,405 . . . . F 8
Mount Pleasant, 23,285 . . . . E 6
Muskegon, 40,283 . . E 4
Niles, 12,458 . . . . . . G 4
Norton Shores, 21,755 . . . . E 4
Novi, 32,998 . . . . p15
Oak Park, 30,462 . . . . p15
Owosso, 16,322 . . . . E 6
Petoskey, 6,056 . . . . C 6
Pontiac, 71,166 . . . . F 7
Portage, 41,042 . . . . F 5
Port Huron, 33,694 . . F 8
Redford, 54,387 . . . . F 7
Romulus, 22,897 . . . . p15
Roseville, 51,412 . . . . o16
Royal Oak, 65,410 . . . F 7
Saginaw, 69,512 . . . . E 7
Saint Clair Shores, 68,107 . . . . p16
Sault Sainte Marie, 14,689 . . . . B 6
Southfield, 75,728 . . o15
Southgate, 30,771 . . p15
Sterling Heights, 117,810 . . . . o15
Sturgis, 10,130 . . . . G 5
Taylor, 70,811 . . . . . . p15
Traverse City, 15,155 D 5
Trenton, 20,586 . . . . F 7
Troy, 72,884 . . . . o15
Walker, 17,279 . . . . . E 5
Warren, 144,864 . . . . F 7
Wayne, 19,899 . . . . p15
Westland, 84,724 . . . . F 7
Wyandotte, 30,938 . . F 7
Wyoming, 63,891 . . . . F 5
Ypsilanti, 24,846 . . . . F 7

Minnesota

1990 CENSUS

Albert Lea, 18,310 .. G 5
Alexandria, 7,838 .... E 3
Andover, 15,216 ..... m12
Anoka, 17,192 ...... E 5
Apple Valley, 34,598 n12
Austin, 21,907 ...... G 6
Bemidji, 11,245 .... C 4
Blaine, 38,975 ...... m12
Bloomington, 86,335 F 5
Brainerd, 12,353 .... D 4
Brooklyn Center, 28,887 .... E 5
Brooklyn Park, 56,381 .... m12
Burnsville, 51,288 .... F 5
Champlin, 16,849 .. m12
Chisholm, 5,290 ..... C 6
Cloquet, 10,885 .... D 6
Columbia Heights, 18,910 .... m12
Coon Rapids, 52,978 E 5
Cottage Grove, 22,935 .... n13
Crookston, 8,119 .... C 2
Crystal, 23,788 .... m12
Detroit Lakes, 6,635 D 3
Duluth, 85,493 ...... D 6
Eagan, 47,409 ...... n12
East Bethel, 8,050 .. E 5
East Grand Forks, 8,658 .... C 2
Eden Prairie, 39,311 .. n12
Edina, 46,070 ...... F 5
Ely, 3,968 .... C 7
Fairmont, 11,265 .... G 4
Faribault, 17,085 .... F 5
Fergus Falls, 12,362 D 2
Fridley, 28,335 ...... m12
Golden Valley, 20,971 n12
Grand Marais, 1,171 k 9
Grand Rapids, 7,976 C 5
Hastings, 15,445 .... F 6
Hibbing, 18,046 ..... C 6
Hopkins, 16,534 .... n12
Hutchinson, 11,523 .. F 4
International Falls, 8,325 .... B 5
Inver Grove Heights, 22,477 .... n12
Lakeville, 24,854 .... F 5
Litchfield, 6,041 .... E 4
Little Falls, 7,232 .... E 4
Mankato, 31,477 .... F 5
Maple Grove, 38,736 m12
Maplewood, 30,954 .. n12
Marshall, 12,023 .... F 3
Minneapolis, 368,383 F 5
Minnetonka, 48,370 .. n12
Montevideo, 5,499 .. F 3
Moorhead, 32,295 .. D 2
Morris, 5,613 ...... E 3
Mound, 9,634 ...... n11
Mounds View, 12,541 m12
New Brighton, 22,207 m12
New Hope, 21,853 .. m12
New Ulm, 13,132 .... F 4
Northfield, 14,684 ... F 5
North Mankato, 10,164 .... F 4
North St. Paul, 12,376 .... m13
Owatonna, 19,386 .. F 5
Pipestone, 4,554 .... G 2
Plymouth, 50,889 .. m12
Prior Lake, 11,482 .. F 5
Ramsey, 12,408 ..... E 5
Red Wing, 15,134 .. F 6
Redwood Falls, 4,859 F 3
Richfield, 35,710 .... F 5
Robbinsdale, 14,396 m12
Rochester, 70,745 .. F 6
Roseville, 33,485 .... m12
Saint Cloud, 48,812 .. E 4
Saint Louis Park, 43,787 .... n12
Saint Paul, 272,235 .. F 5
Saint Peter, 9,421 .. F 5
Shakopee, 11,739 .. F 5
Shoreview, 24,587 .. m12
South St. Paul, 20,197 .... n12
Stillwater, 13,882 .... E 6
Thief River Falls, 8,010 .... B 2
Virginia, 9,410 ...... C 6
Waseca, 8,385 ...... F 5
West Saint Paul, 19,248 .... n12
White Bear Lake, 24,704 .... E 5
Willmar, 17,531 .... E 3
Winona, 25,399 .... F 7
Woodbury, 20,075 .. F 6
Worthington, 9,977 .. G 3

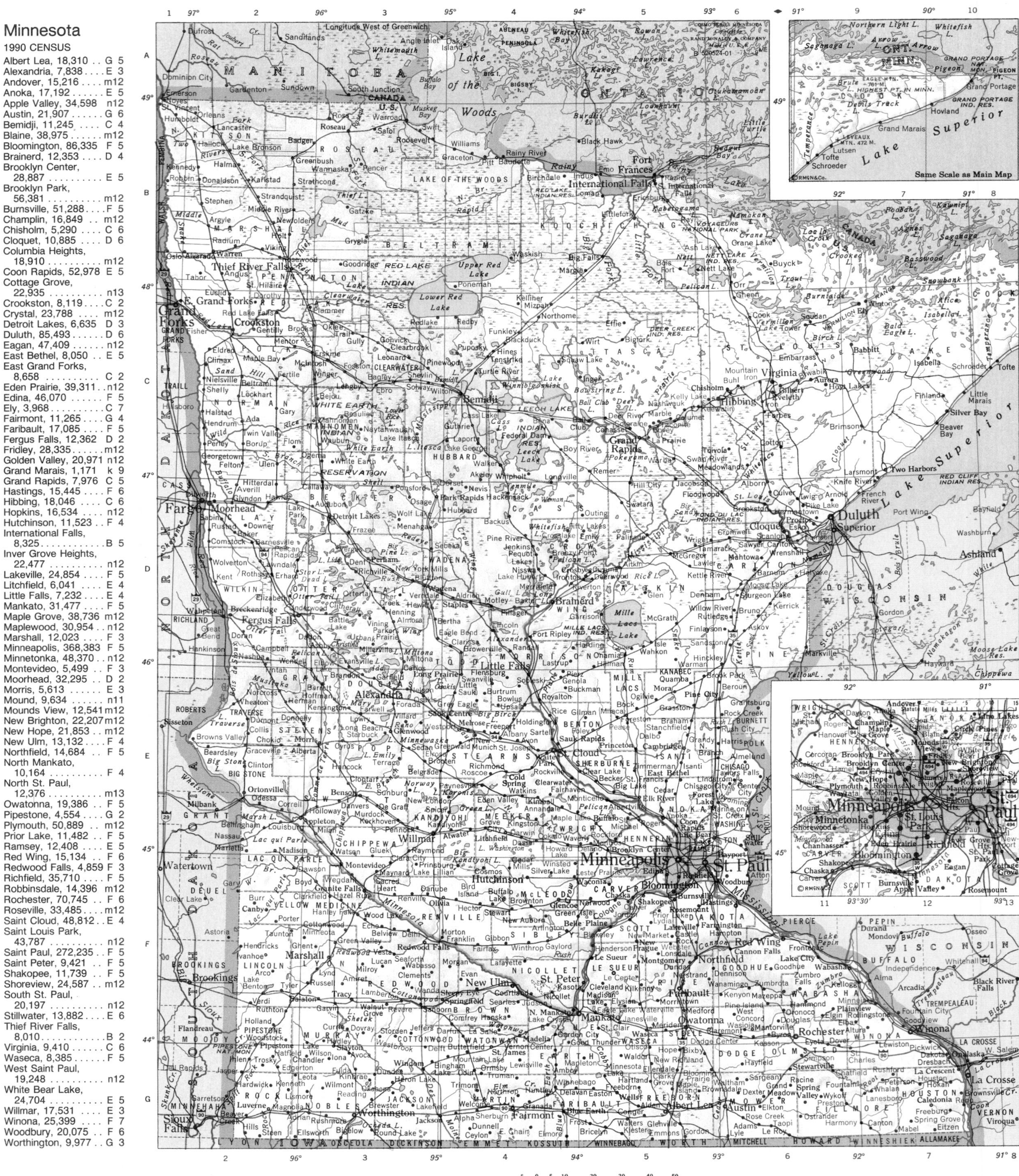

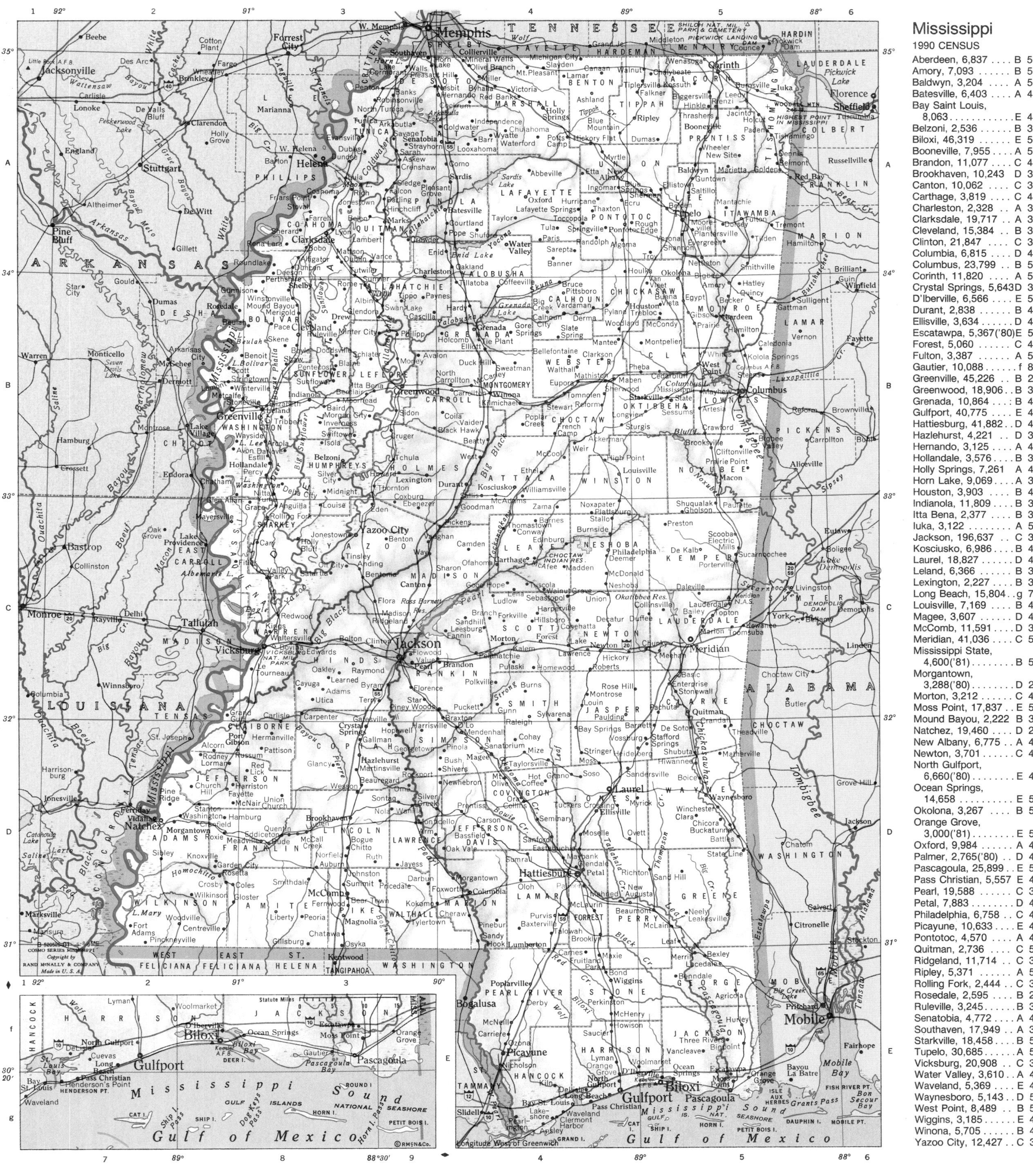

Mississippi

1990 CENSUS

Aberdeen, 6,837 . . . . B 5
Amory, 7,093 . . . . . . B 5
Baldwyn, 3,204 . . . . . A 5
Batesville, 6,403 . . . . A 4
Bay Saint Louis, 8,063 . . . . E 4
Belzoni, 2,536 . . . . B 3
Biloxi, 46,319 . . . . . . E 5
Booneville, 7,955 . . . . A 5
Brandon, 11,077 . . . . C 4
Brookhaven, 10,243 D 3
Canton, 10,062 . . . . . C 3
Carthage, 3,819 . . . . C 4
Charleston, 2,328 . . A 3
Clarksdale, 19,717 . . A 3
Cleveland, 15,384 . . B 3
Clinton, 21,847 . . . . C 3
Columbia, 6,815 . . . . D 4
Columbus, 23,799 . . B 5
Corinth, 11,820 . . . . A 5
Crystal Springs, 5,643 D 3
D'Iberville, 6,566 . . . . E 5
Durant, 2,838 . . . . . . B 4
Ellisville, 3,634 . . . . . D 4
Escatawpa, 5,367('80) E 5
Forest, 5,060 . . . . . . C 4
Fulton, 3,387 . . . . . . A 5
Gautier, 10,088 . . . . . . f 8
Greenville, 45,226 . . B 2
Greenwood, 18,906 . . B 3
Grenada, 10,864 . . . B 4
Gulfport, 40,775 . . . . E 4
Hattiesburg, 41,882 . . D 4
Hazlehurst, 4,221 . . D 3
Hernando, 3,125 . . . . A 4
Hollandale, 3,576 . . . . B 3
Holly Springs, 7,261 A 4
Horn Lake, 9,069 . . . . A 3
Houston, 3,903 . . . . B 4
Indianola, 11,809 . . . . B 3
Itta Bena, 2,377 . . . . B 3
Iuka, 3,122 . . . . A 5
Jackson, 196,637 . . . C 3
Kosciusko, 6,986 . . . . B 4
Laurel, 18,827 . . . . . . D 4
Leland, 6,366 . . . . . . B 3
Lexington, 2,227 . . . . B 3
Long Beach, 15,804 . . g 7
Louisville, 7,169 . . . . B 4
Magee, 3,607 . . . . . . D 4
McComb, 11,591 . . . . D 3
Meridian, 41,036 . . . . C 5
Mississippi State, 4,600('81) . . . . B 5
Morgantown, 3,288('80) . . . . D 2
Morton, 3,212 . . . . . . C 4
Moss Point, 17,837 . . E 5
Mound Bayou, 2,222 B 3
Natchez, 19,460 . . . . D 2
New Albany, 6,775 . . A 4
Newton, 3,701 . . . . . . C 4
North Gulfport, 6,660('80) . . . . E 4
Ocean Springs, 14,658 . . . . E 5
Okolona, 3,267 . . . . B 5
Orange Grove, 3,000('81) . . . . E 5
Oxford, 9,984 . . . . . . A 4
Palmer, 2,765('80) . . D 4
Pascagoula, 25,899 . . E 5
Pass Christian, 5,557 E 4
Pearl, 19,588 . . . . . . C 3
Petal, 7,883 . . . . D 4
Philadelphia, 6,758 . . C 4
Picayune, 10,633 . . . . E 4
Pontotoc, 4,570 . . . . A 4
Quitman, 2,736 . . . . . C 5
Ridgeland, 11,714 . . C 3
Ripley, 5,371 . . . . . . A 5
Rolling Fork, 2,444 . . C 3
Rosedale, 2,595 . . . . B 2
Ruleville, 3,245 . . . . . B 3
Senatobia, 4,772 . . . . A 4
Southaven, 17,949 . . A 3
Starkville, 18,458 . . . . B 5
Tupelo, 30,685 . . . . . . A 5
Vicksburg, 20,908 . . . C 3
Water Valley, 3,610 . . A 4
Waveland, 5,369 . . . . E 4
Waynesboro, 5,143 . . D 5
West Point, 8,489 . . . B 5
Wiggins, 3,185 . . . . . . E 4
Winona, 5,705 . . . . . . B 4
Yazoo City, 12,427 . . C 3

Missouri

1990 CENSUS

Arnold, 18,828 . . . . C 7
Aurora, 6,459 . . . . E 4
Ballwin, 21,816 . . . . f12
Belton, 18,150 . . . . C 3
Berkeley, 12,450 . . . . . f13
Blue Springs, 40,153 . . h11
Bolivar, 6,845 . . . . D 4
Boonville, 7,095 . . . . . C 5
Brentwood, 8,150 . . . . . . f13
Bridgeton, 17,779 . . . . C 7
Brookfield, 4,888 . . . . . B 4
Cape Girardeau, 34,438 D 8
Carthage, 10,747 . . . . . D 3
Caruthersville, 7,389 . . E 8
Charleston, 5,085 . . . . E 8
Chillicothe, 8,804 . . . . . B 4
Clayton, 13,874 . . . . . . C 7
Clinton, 8,703 . . . . C 4
Columbia, 69,101 . . . . C 5
De Soto, 5,993 . . . . . . C 7
Des Peres, 8,395 . . . . . . f13
Dexter, 7,559 . . . . E 8
Ellisville, 7,545 . . . . f12
Eureka, 4,683 . . . . f12
Excelsior Springs, 10,354 . . . . B 3
Farmington, 11,598 . . . D 7
Ferguson, 22,286 . . . . C 7
Festus, 8,105 . . . . C 7
Florissant, 51,206 . . . . . f13
Fulton, 10,033 . . . . C 6
Gladstone, 26,243 . . . . h10
Grandview, 24,967 . . . . C 3
Hannibal, 18,004 . . . . . B 6
Harrisonville, 7,683 . . . . C 3
Independence, 112,301 B 3
Jackson, 9,256 . . . . D 8
Jefferson City, 35,481 C 5
Jennings, 15,905 . . . . . . f13
Joplin, 40,961 . . . . D 3
Kansas City, 435,146 . . B 3
Kennett, 10,941 . . . . . . E 7
Kirksville, 17,152 . . . . . A 5
Kirkwood, 27,291 . . . . . . f13
Lebanon, 9,983 . . . . . . D 5
Lees Summit, 46,418 . . C 3
Liberty, 20,459 . . . . . . B 3
Macon, 5,571 . . . . B 5
Malden, 5,123 . . . . E 8
Manchester, 6,542 . . . . f12
Maplewood, 9,962 . . . . f13
Marshall, 12,711 . . . . . . B 4
Maryland Heights, 25,407 . . . . f13
Maryville, 10,663 . . . . . . A 3
Mexico, 11,290 . . . . . . B 6
Moberly, 12,839 . . . . . . B 5
Monett, 6,529 . . . . E 4
Neosho, 9,254 . . . . E 3
Nevada, 8,597 . . . . D 3
O'Fallon, 18,698 . . . . . . f12
Overland, 17,987 . . . . . . f13
Perryville, 6,933 . . . . . . D 8
Pine Lawn, 5,092 . . . . . . f13
Poplar Bluff, 16,996 . . E 7
Raytown, 30,601 . . . . . . h11
Richmond Heights, 10,448 . . . . f13
Rolla, 14,090 . . . . D 6
Saint Charles, 54,555 . . C 7
Sainte Genevieve, 4,411 D 7
Saint Joseph, 71,852 . . B 3
Saint Louis, 396,685 . . C 7
Saint Peters, 45,779 . . C 7
Sedalia, 19,800 . . . . . . C 4
Sikeston, 17,641 . . . . . E 8
Springfield, 140,494 . . D 4
Sullivan, 5,661 . . . . C 6
Trenton, 6,129 . . . . A 4
University City, 40,087 C 7
Warrensburg, 15,244 . . C 4
Washington, 10,704 . . C 6
Webb City, 7,449 . . . . D 3
Webster Groves, 22,987 f13
West Plains, 8,913 . . . . E 6

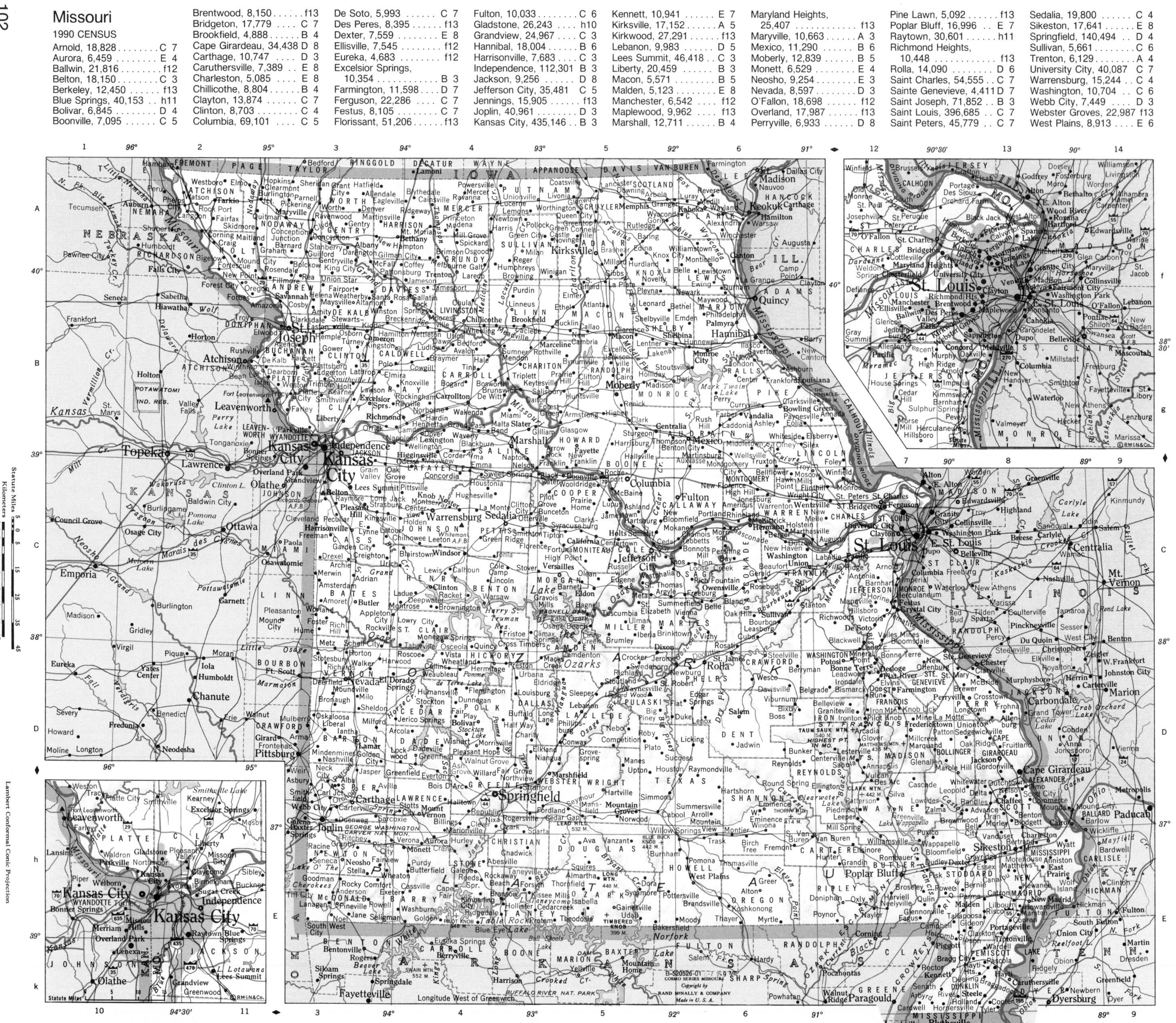

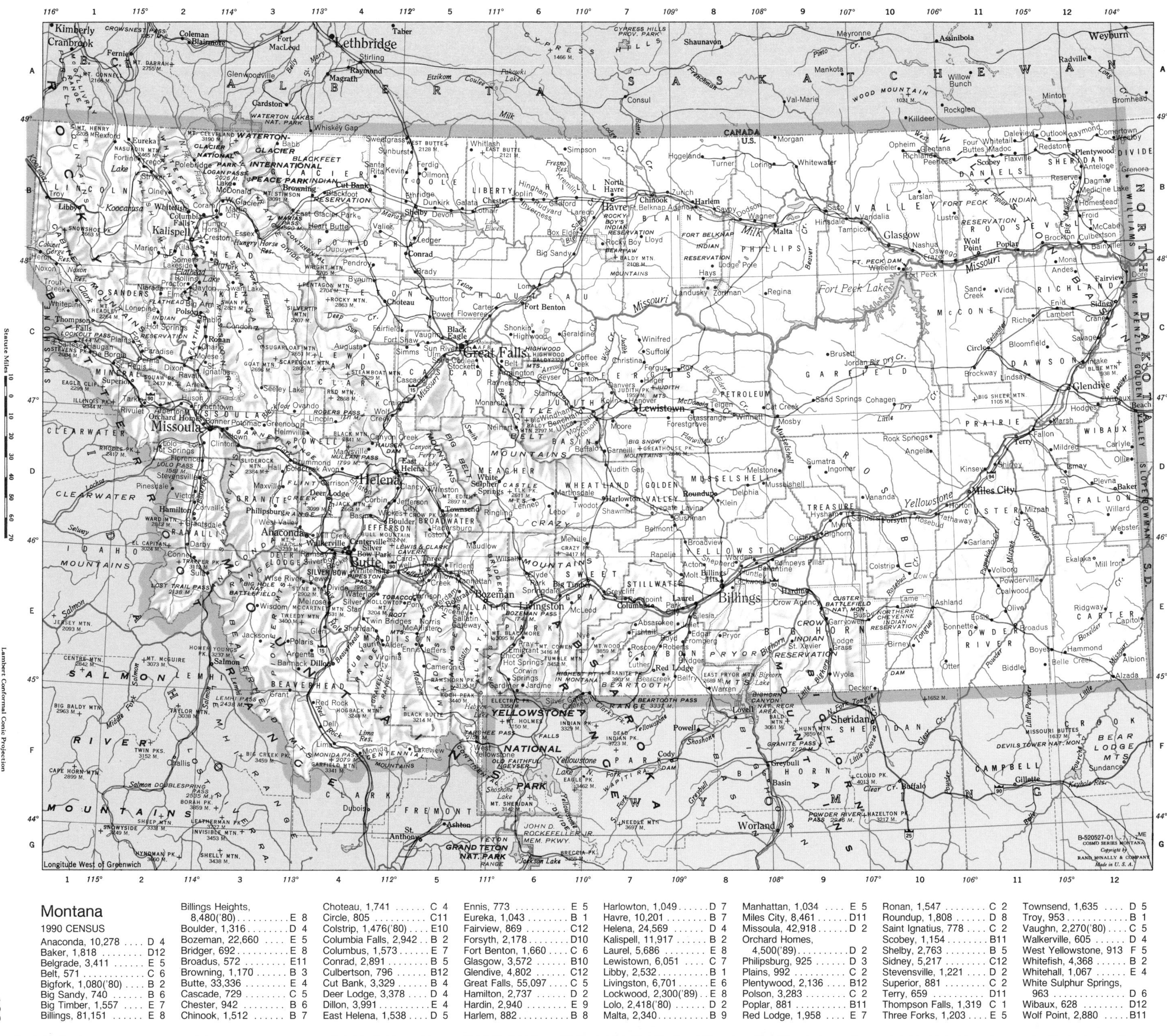

Montana

1990 CENSUS

Anaconda, 10,278 .... D 4
Baker, 1,818 .... D12
Belgrade, 3,411 ...... E 5
Belt, 571 .... C 6
Bigfork, 1,080('80) .... B 2
Big Sandy, 740 ...... B 6
Big Timber, 1,557 .... E 7
Billings, 81,151 ...... E 8
Billings Heights, 8,480('80) .... E 8
Boulder, 1,316 .... D 4
Bozeman, 22,660 .... E 5
Bridger, 692 .... E 8
Broadus, 572 .... E11
Browning, 1,170 ...... B 3
Butte, 33,336 .... E 4
Cascade, 729 .... C 5
Chester, 942 .... B 6
Chinook, 1,512 .... B 7
Choteau, 1,741 ...... C 4
Circle, 805 .... C11
Colstrip, 1,476('80) E10
Columbia Falls, 2,942 . B 2
Columbus, 1,573 ...... E 7
Conrad, 2,891 .... B 5
Culbertson, 796 ...... B12
Cut Bank, 3,329 ...... B 4
Deer Lodge, 3,378 .... D 4
Dillon, 3,991 .... E 4
East Helena, 1,538 .... D 5
Ennis, 773 .... E 5
Eureka, 1,043 .... B 1
Fairview, 869 .... C12
Forsyth, 2,178 .... D10
Fort Benton, 1,660 .... C 6
Glasgow, 3,572 ...... B10
Glendive, 4,802 ...... C12
Great Falls, 55,097 .... C 5
Hamilton, 2,737 ...... D 2
Hardin, 2,940 .... E 9
Harlem, 882 .... B 8
Harlowton, 1,049 ...... D 7
Havre, 10,201 .... B 7
Helena, 24,569 ...... D 4
Kalispell, 11,917 ...... B 2
Laurel, 5,686 .... E 8
Lewistown, 6,051 .... C 7
Libby, 2,532 .... B 1
Livingston, 6,701 ...... E 6
Lockwood, 2,300('89) .. E 8
Lolo, 2,418('80) ...... D 2
Malta, 2,340 .... B 9
Manhattan, 1,034 .... E 5
Miles City, 8,461 ...... D11
Missoula, 42,918 ...... D 2
Orchard Homes, 4,500('89) .... D 2
Philipsburg, 925 ...... D 3
Plains, 992 .... C 2
Plentywood, 2,136 .... B12
Polson, 3,283 .... C 2
Poplar, 881 .... B11
Red Lodge, 1,958 .... E 7
Ronan, 1,547 .... C 2
Roundup, 1,808 ...... D 8
Saint Ignatius, 778 .... C 2
Scobey, 1,154 .... B11
Shelby, 2,763 .... B 5
Sidney, 5,217 .... C12
Stevensville, 1,221 .... D 2
Superior, 881 .... C 2
Terry, 659 .... D11
Thompson Falls, 1,319 C 1
Three Forks, 1,203 .... E 5
Townsend, 1,635 .... D 5
Troy, 953 .... B 1
Vaughn, 2,270('80) .... C 5
Walkerville, 605 ...... D 4
West Yellowstone, 913 F 5
Whitefish, 4,368 ...... B 2
Whitehall, 1,067 ...... E 4
White Sulphur Springs, 963 .... D 6
Wibaux, 628 .... D12
Wolf Point, 2,880 ..... B11

Nebraska

1990 CENSUS

Ainsworth, 1,870 . . . . . B 6
Albion, 1,916 . . . . C 7
Alliance, 9,765 . . . . B 3
Alma, 1,226 . . . . D 6
Ashland, 2,136 . . . . . . C 9
Atkinson, 1,380 . . . . . . B 7
Auburn, 3,443 . . . . D10
Aurora, 3,810 . . . . D 7
Bayard, 1,196 . . . . C 2
Beatrice, 12,354 . . . . . . D 9
Bellevue, 30,982 . . . . . . C10
Blair, 6,860 . . . . C 9
Bridgeport, 1,581 . . . . C 2
Broken Bow, 3,778 . . . . C 6
Central City, 2,868 . . . . C 7
Chadron, 5,588 . . . . . . B 3
Columbus, 19,480 . . . . C 8
Cozad, 3,823 . . . . D 6
Creighton, 1,223 . . . . . . B 8
Crete, 4,841 . . . . D 9
Dakota City, 1,470 . . . . B 9
David City, 2,522 . . . . . . C 8
Elkhorn, 1,398 . . . . g12
Fairbury, 4,335 . . . . . . D 8
Falls City, 4,769 . . . . . . D10
Fremont, 23,680 . . . . . . C 9
Fullerton, 1,452 . . . . . . C 8
Geneva, 2,310 . . . . D 8
Gering, 7,946 . . . . C 2
Gibbon, 1,525 . . . . D 7
Gordon, 1,803 . . . . B 3
Gothenburg, 3,232 . . . . D 5
Grand Island, 39,386 . . D 7
Gretna, 2,249 . . . . C 9
Hartington, 1,583 . . . . . . B 8
Hastings, 22,837 . . . . . . D 7
Hebron, 1,765 . . . . D 8
Holdrege, 5,671 . . . . . . D 6
Imperial, 2,007 . . . . D 4
Kearney, 24,396 . . . . . . D 6
Kimball, 2,574 . . . . C 2
La Vista, 9,840 . . . . . . g12
Lexington, 6,601 . . . . . . D 6
Lincoln, 191,972 . . . . . . D 9
Loup City, 1,104 . . . . . . C 7
Madison, 2,135 . . . . . . C 8
McCook, 8,112 . . . . D 5
Milford, 1,886 . . . . D 8
Minden, 2,749 . . . . D 7
Mitchell, 1,743 . . . . C 2
Nebraska City, 6,547 . . D10
Neligh, 1,742 . . . . B 7
Norfolk, 21,476 . . . . . . B 8
North Bend, 1,249 . . . . C 9
North Platte, 22,605 . . C 5
Ogallala, 5,095 . . . . C 4
Omaha, 335,795 . . . . . . C10
O'Neill, 3,852 . . . . B 7
Ord, 2,481 . . . . C 7
Papillion, 10,372 . . . . . . C 9
Pierce, 1,615 . . . . B 8
Plainview, 1,333 . . . . . . B 8
Plattsmouth, 6,412 . . . . D10
Ralston, 6,236 . . . . g12
Saint Paul, 2,009 . . . . . . C 7
Schuyler, 4,052 . . . . C 8
Scottsbluff, 13,711 . . . . C 2
Seward, 5,634 . . . . D 8
Sidney, 5,959 . . . . C 3
South Sioux City, 9,677 B 9
Stanton, 1,549 . . . . C 8
Superior, 2,397 . . . . D 7
Sutton, 1,353 . . . . D 8
Syracuse, 1,646 . . . . . . D 9
Tecumseh, 1,702 . . . . . D 9
Tekamah, 1,852 . . . . C 9
Valentine, 2,826 . . . . . . B 5
Valley, 1,775 . . . . C 9
Wahoo, 3,681 . . . . C 9
Waverly, 1,869 . . . . D 9
Wayne, 5,142 . . . . B 8
West Point, 3,250 . . . . C 9
Wilber, 1,527 . . . . D 9
Wymore, 1,611 . . . . D 9
York, 7,884 . . . . D 8

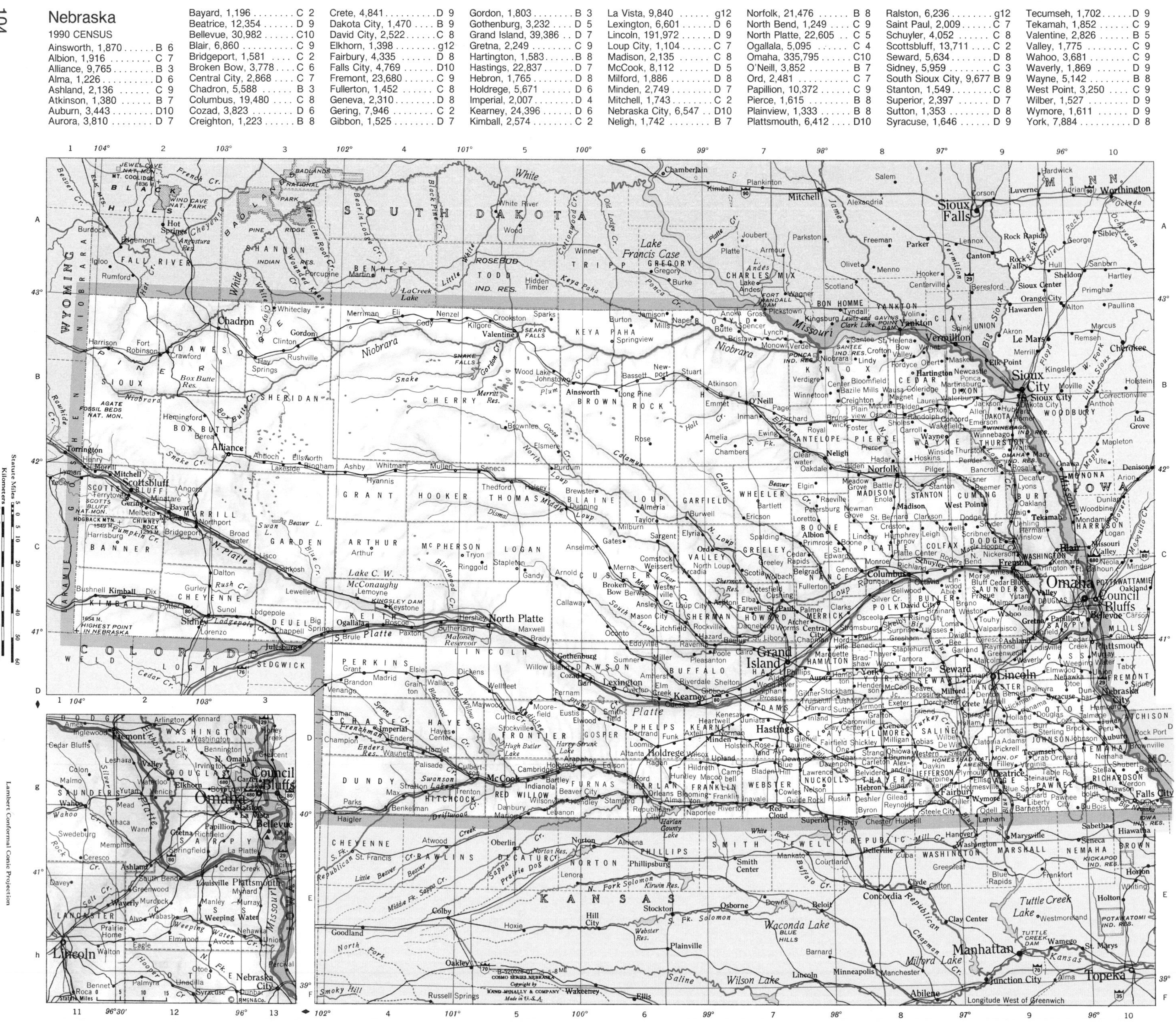

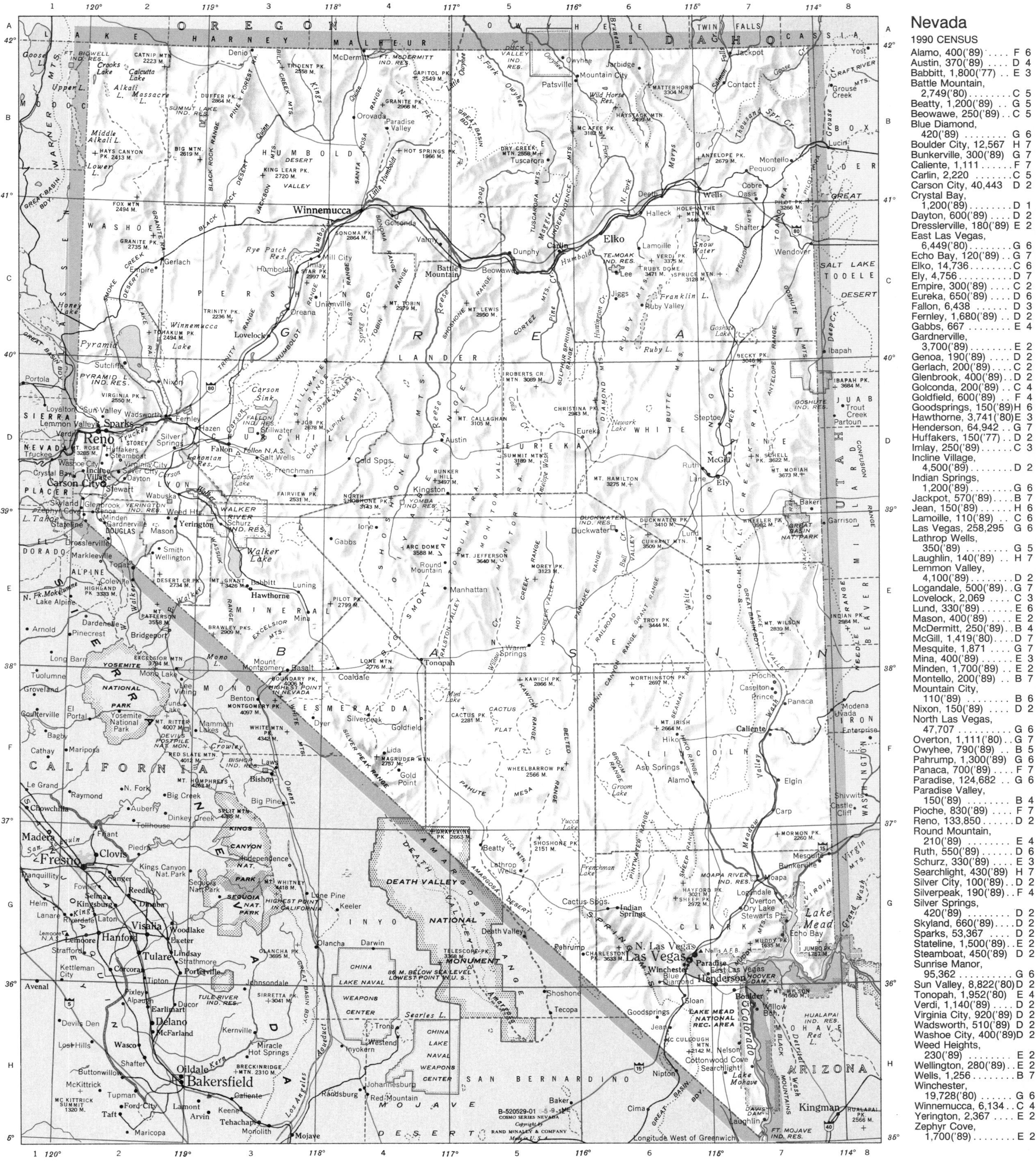

Nevada

1990 CENSUS

Alamo, 400('89) . . . . F 6
Austin, 370('89) . . . . D 4
Babbitt, 1,800('77) . . E 3
Battle Mountain, 2,749('80) . . . . C 5
Beatty, 1,200('89) . . G 5
Beowawe, 250('89) . . C 5
Blue Diamond, 420('89) . . . . G 6
Boulder City, 12,567 H 7
Bunkerville, 300('89) G 7
Caliente, 1,111 . . . . . F 7
Carlin, 2,220 . . . . . . C 5
Carson City, 40,443 D 2
Crystal Bay, 1,200('89) . . . . D 1
Dayton, 600('89) . . . . D 2
Dresslerville, 180('89) E 2
East Las Vegas, 6,449('80) . . . . G 6
Echo Bay, 120('89) . . G 7
Elko, 14,736 . . . . C 6
Ely, 4,756 . . . . D 7
Empire, 300('89) . . . . C 2
Eureka, 650('89) . . . . D 6
Fallon, 6,438 . . . . . . D 3
Fernley, 1,680('89) . . D 2
Gabbs, 667 . . . . E 4
Gardnerville, 3,700('89) . . . . E 2
Genoa, 190('89) . . . . D 2
Gerlach, 200('89) . . . . C 2
Glenbrook, 400('89) . . D 2
Golconda, 200('89) . . C 4
Goldfield, 600('89) . . . F 4
Goodsprings, 150('89)H 6
Hawthorne, 3,741('80)E 3
Henderson, 64,942 . . G 7
Huffakers, 150('77) . . D 2
Imlay, 250('89) . . . . . . C 3
Incline Village, 4,500('89) . . . . D 2
Indian Springs, 1,200('89) . . . . G 6
Jackpot, 570('89) . . . . B 7
Jean, 150('89) . . . . . H 6
Lamoille, 110('89) . . C 6
Las Vegas, 258,295 G 6
Lathrop Wells, 350('89) . . . . G 5
Laughlin, 140('89) . . H 7
Lemmon Valley, 4,100('89) . . . . D 2
Logandale, 500('89). . G 7
Lovelock, 2,069 . . . . C 3
Lund, 330('89) . . . . . . E 6
Mason, 400('89) . . . . . E 2
McDermitt, 250('89). . B 4
McGill, 1,419('80). . . . D 7
Mesquite, 1,871 . . . . G 7
Mina, 400('89) . . . . . E 3
Minden, 1,700('89) . . E 2
Montello, 200('89) . . B 7
Mountain City, 110('89) . . . . B 6
Nixon, 150('89) . . . . D 2
North Las Vegas, 47,707 . . . . G 6
Overton, 1,111('80). . G 7
Owyhee, 790('89) . . B 5
Pahrump, 1,300('89) G 6
Panaca, 700('89) . . . F 7
Paradise, 124,682 . . G 6
Paradise Valley, 150('89) . . . . B 4
Pioche, 830('89) . . . . F 7
Reno, 133,850 . . . . . . D 2
Round Mountain, 210('89) . . . . E 4
Ruth, 550('89) . . . . . . D 6
Schurz, 330('89) . . . . E 3
Searchlight, 430('89) H 7
Silver City, 100('89). . D 2
Silverpeak, 190('89). . F 4
Silver Springs, 420('89) . . . . D 2
Skyland, 660('89) . . . D 2
Sparks, 53,367 . . . . D 2
Stateline, 1,500('89). . E 2
Steamboat, 450('89) D 2
Sunrise Manor, 95,362 . . . . G 6
Sun Valley, 8,822('80)D 2
Tonopah, 1,952('80) E 4
Verdi, 1,140('89) . . . . D 2
Virginia City, 920('89) D 2
Wadsworth, 510('89) D 2
Washoe City, 400('89)D 2
Weed Heights, 230('89) . . . . E 2
Wellington, 280('89). . E 2
Wells, 1,256 . . . . B 7
Winchester, 19,728('80) . . . . . . G 6
Winnemucca, 6,134. . C 4
Yerington, 2,367 . . . . E 2
Zephyr Cove, 1,700('89) . . . . E 2

New Hampshire

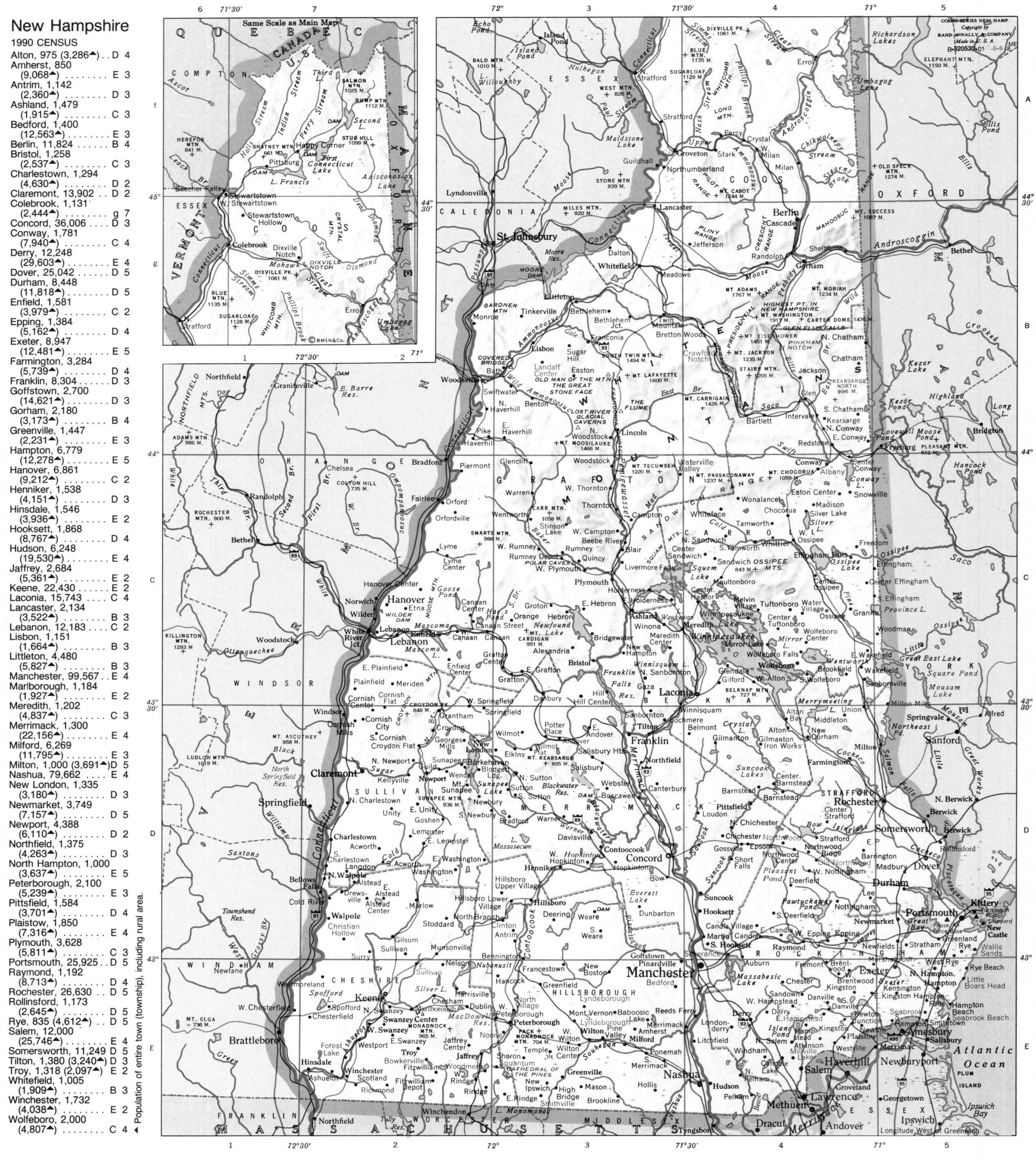

New Hampshire

1990 CENSUS

Alton, 975 (3,286▲) . . D 4
Amherst, 850 (9,068▲) . . . . E 3
Antrim, 1,142 (2,360▲) . . . . D 3
Ashland, 1,479 (1,915▲) . . . . C 3
Bedford, 1,400 (12,563▲) . . . . E 3
Berlin, 11,824 . . . . . . B 4
Bristol, 1,258 (2,537▲) . . . . C 3
Charlestown, 1,294 (4,630▲) . . . . D 2
Claremont, 13,902 . . D 2
Colebrook, 1,131 (2,444▲) . . . . g 7
Concord, 36,006 . . . . D 3
Conway, 1,781 (7,940▲) . . . . C 4
Derry, 12,248 (29,603▲) . . . . E 4
Dover, 25,042 . . . . . . D 5
Durham, 8,448 (11,818▲) . . . . D 5
Enfield, 1,581 (3,979▲) . . . . C 2
Epping, 1,384 (5,162▲) . . . . D 4
Exeter, 8,947 (12,481▲) . . . . E 5
Farmington, 3,284 (5,739▲) . . . . D 4
Franklin, 8,304 . . . . . . D 3
Goffstown, 2,700 (14,621▲) . . . . D 3
Gorham, 2,180 (3,173▲) . . . . B 4
Greenville, 1,447 (2,231▲) . . . . E 3
Hampton, 6,779 (12,278▲) . . . . E 5
Hanover, 6,861 (9,212▲) . . . . C 2
Henniker, 1,538 (4,151▲) . . . . D 3
Hinsdale, 1,546 (3,936▲) . . . . E 2
Hooksett, 1,868 (8,767▲) . . . . D 4
Hudson, 6,248 (19,530▲) . . . . E 4
Jaffrey, 2,684 (5,361▲) . . . . E 2
Keene, 22,430 . . . . . . E 2
Laconia, 15,743 . . . . C 4
Lancaster, 2,134 (3,522▲) . . . . B 3
Lebanon, 12,183 . . . . C 2
Lisbon, 1,151 (1,664▲) . . . . B 3
Littleton, 4,480 (5,827▲) . . . . B 3
Manchester, 99,567 . . E 4
Marlborough, 1,184 (1,927▲) . . . . E 2
Meredith, 1,202 (4,837▲) . . . . C 3
Merrimack, 1,300 (22,156▲) . . . . E 4
Milford, 6,269 (11,795▲) . . . . E 3
Milton, 1,000 (3,691▲) D 5
Nashua, 79,662 . . . . . E 4
New London, 1,335 (3,180▲) . . . . D 3
Newmarket, 3,749 (7,157▲) . . . . D 5
Newport, 4,388 (6,110▲) . . . . D 2
Northfield, 1,375 (4,263▲) . . . . D 3
North Hampton, 1,000 (3,637▲) . . . . E 5
Peterborough, 2,100 (5,239▲) . . . . E 3
Pittsfield, 1,584 (3,701▲) . . . . D 4
Plaistow, 1,850 (7,316▲) . . . . E 4
Plymouth, 3,628 (5,811▲) . . . . C 3
Portsmouth, 25,925 . . D 5
Raymond, 1,192 (8,713▲) . . . . D 4
Rochester, 26,630 . . D 5
Rollinsford, 1,173 (2,645▲) . . . . D 5
Rye, 835 (4,612▲) . . D 5
Salem, 12,000 (25,746▲) . . . . E 4
Somersworth, 11,249 D 5
Tilton, 1,380 (3,240▲) D 3
Troy, 1,318 (2,097▲) E 2
Whitefield, 1,005 (1,909▲) . . . . B 3
Winchester, 1,732 (4,038▲) . . . . E 2
Wolfeboro, 2,000 (4,807▲) . . . . C 4

▲ Population of entire town (township), including rural area.

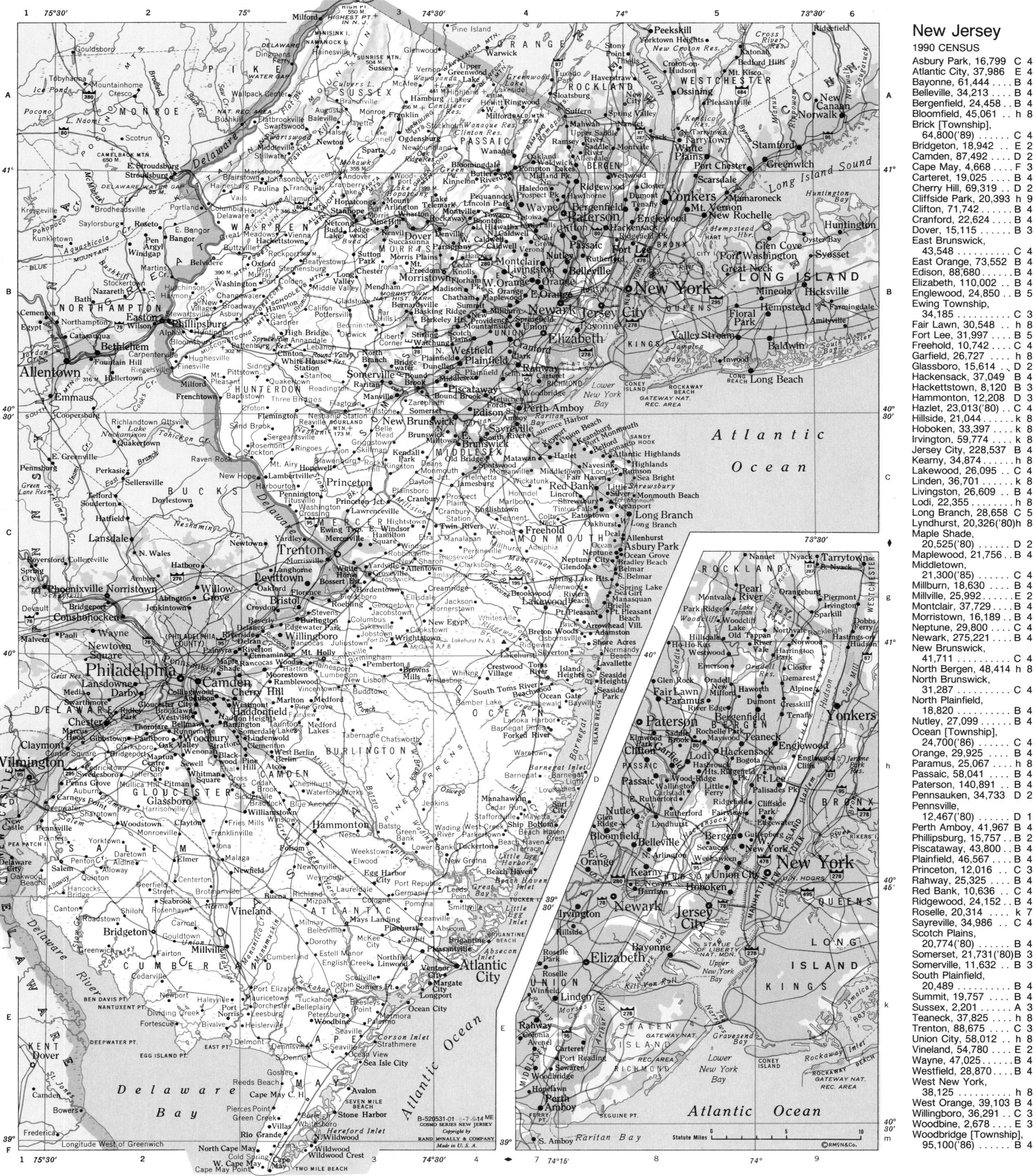

New Jersey

1990 CENSUS

Asbury Park, 16,799 C 4
Atlantic City, 37,986 E 4
Bayonne, 61,444 . . . . B 4
Belleville, 34,213 . . . . B 4
Bergenfield, 24,458 . . B 4
Bloomfield, 45,061 . . h 8
Brick [Township], 64,800('89) . . . . . . C 4
Bridgeton, 18,942 . . E 2
Camden, 87,492 . . . . D 2
Cape May, 4,668 . . . . F 3
Carteret, 19,025 . . . . B 4
Cherry Hill, 69,319 . . D 2
Cliffside Park, 20,393 h 9
Clifton, 71,742 . . . . . . B 4
Cranford, 22,624 . . . . B 4
Dover, 15,115 . . . . . . B 3
East Brunswick, 43,548 . . . . C 4
East Orange, 73,552 B 4
Edison, 88,680 . . . . . . B 4
Elizabeth, 110,002 . . B 4
Englewood, 24,850 . . B 5
Ewing Township, 34,185 . . . . C 3
Fair Lawn, 30,548 . . h 8
Fort Lee, 31,997 . . . . B 5
Freehold, 10,742 . . . . C 4
Garfield, 26,727 . . . . h 8
Glassboro, 15,614 . . D 2
Hackensack, 37,049 B 4
Hackettstown, 8,120 B 3
Hammonton, 12,208 D 3
Hazlet, 23,013('80) . . C 4
Hillside, 21,044 . . . . . . k 8
Hoboken, 33,397 . . . . k 8
Irvington, 59,774 . . . . k 8
Jersey City, 228,537 B 4
Kearny, 34,874 . . . . . . h 8
Lakewood, 26,095 . . C 4
Linden, 36,701 . . . . . . k 8
Livingston, 26,609 . . B 4
Lodi, 22,355 . . . . h 8
Long Branch, 28,658 C 5
Lyndhurst, 20,326('80)h 8
Maple Shade, 20,525('80) . . . . . . D 2
Maplewood, 21,756 . . B 4
Middletown, 21,300('85) . . . . . . C 4
Millburn, 18,630 . . . . . B 4
Millville, 25,992 . . . . . . E 2
Montclair, 37,729 . . . . B 4
Morristown, 16,189 . . B 4
Neptune, 29,800 . . . . C 4
Newark, 275,221 . . . . B 4
New Brunswick, 41,711 . . . . C 4
North Bergen, 48,414 h 8
North Brunswick, 31,287 . . . . C 4
North Plainfield, 18,820 . . . . B 4
Nutley, 27,099 . . . . . . B 4
Ocean [Township], 24,700('86) . . . . . . C 4
Orange, 29,925 . . . . B 4
Paramus, 25,067 . . . . h 8
Passaic, 58,041 . . . . . B 4
Paterson, 140,891 . . B 4
Pennsauken, 34,733 D 2
Pennsville, 12,467('80) . . . . . . D 1
Perth Amboy, 41,967 B 4
Phillipsburg, 15,757 . . B 2
Piscataway, 43,800 . . B 4
Plainfield, 46,567 . . . . B 4
Princeton, 12,016 . . . . C 3
Rahway, 25,325 . . . . . . B 4
Red Bank, 10,636 . . C 4
Ridgewood, 24,152 . . B 4
Roselle, 20,314 . . . . k 7
Sayreville, 34,986 . . C 4
Scotch Plains, 20,774('80) . . . . . . B 4
Somerset, 21,731('80)B 3
Somerville, 11,632 . . B 3
South Plainfield, 20,489 . . . . B 4
Summit, 19,757 . . . . B 4
Sussex, 2,201 . . . . A 3
Teaneck, 37,825 . . . . h 8
Trenton, 88,675 . . . . C 3
Union City, 58,012 . . h 8
Vineland, 54,780 . . . . E 2
Wayne, 47,025 . . . . . . B 4
Westfield, 28,870 . . . . B 4
West New York, 38,125 . . . . h 8
West Orange, 39,103 B 4
Willingboro, 36,291 . . C 3
Woodbine, 2,678 . . . . E 3
Woodbridge [Township], 95,100('86) . . . . . . B 4

New Mexico

New Mexico

1990 CENSUS

Alameda, 5,900('87) B 3
Alamogordo, 27,596 E 4
Albuquerque, 384,736 B 3
Anthony, 3,285('80) . . F 3
Armijo, 14,600('87) . . k 7
Artesia, 10,610 . . . . . . E 5
Aztec, 5,479 . . . . A 2
Bayard, 2,598 . . . . . . E 1
Belen, 6,547 . . . . C 3
Bernalillo, 5,960 . . . . B 3
Bloomfield, 5,214 . . . . A 2
Carlsbad, 24,952 . . . . E 5
Carrizozo, 1,075 . . . . D 4
Cedar Crest, 1,200('87) . . . . k 8
Central, 1,835 . . . . . . E 1
Chama, 1,048 . . . . . . A 3
Chimayo, 1,993('80) A 4
Clayton, 2,484 . . . . . . A 6
Clovis, 30,954 . . . . . . C 6
Crownpoint, 1,134('80) . . . . B 1
Deming, 10,970 . . . . . E 2
Dona Ana, 950('87) . . E 3
Dulce, 1,648('80) . . . A 2
Espanola, 8,389 . . . . B 3
Eunice, 2,676 . . . . . . E 6
Farmington, 33,997 . . A 1
Five Points, 4,200('87) . . . . B 3
Fort Sumner, 1,269 . . C 5
Fort Wingate, 950('87) . . . . B 1
Gallup, 19,154 . . . . . . B 1
Grants, 8,626 . . . . . . B 2
Hagerman, 961 . . . . D 5
Hatch, 1,136 . . . . E 2
Hobbs, 29,115 . . . . . . E 6
Hurley, 1,534 . . . . . . E 1
Isleta, 1,246('80) . . . C 3
Jal, 2,156 . . . . E 6
Jemez Pueblo, 1,503('80) . . . . B 3
Kirtland, 2,358('80) . . A 1
La Luz, 1,194('80) . . D 4
La Mesa, 900('87) . . E 3
Las Cruces, 62,126 . . E 3
Las Vegas, 14,753 . . B 4
Lordsburg, 2,951 . . . . E 1
Los Alamos, 11,039('80) . . . . B 3
Los Lunas, 6,013 . . . C 3
Los Ranchos de Albuquerque, 3,955 B 3
Loving, 1,243 . . . . . . E 5
Lovington, 9,322 . . . . E 6
Magdalena, 861 . . . . C 2
Mescalero, 1,259('80) D 4
Mesilla, 1,975 . . . . . . E 3
Milan, 1,911 . . . . B 2
Moriarty, 1,399 . . . . C 3
Mountainair, 926 . . . . C 3
Mountain View, 2,300('87) . . . . C 3
Paradise Hills, 5,096('80) . . . . B 3
Portales, 10,690 . . . . C 6
Questa, 1,707 . . . . . . A 4
Ranchos de Taos, 1,411('80) . . . . A 4
Raton, 7,372 . . . . A 5
Rio Rancho, 32,505 . . B 3
Roswell, 44,654 . . . . D 5
Ruidoso, 4,600 . . . . . D 4
Ruidoso Downs, 920 D 4
San Felipe Pueblo, 1,465('80) . . . . B 3
Santa Cruz, 975('87) B 3
Santa Fe, 55,859 . . . . B 4
Santa Rosa, 2,263 . . C 5
Santo Domingo Pueblo, 2,082('80) . . . . B 3
Shiprock, 7,237('80) A 1
Silver City, 10,683 . . E 1
Socorro, 8,159 . . . . . . C 3
Springer, 1,262 . . . . A 5
Sunland Park, 8,179 F 3
Taos, 4,065 . . . . A 4
Taos Pueblo, 1,030('87) . . . . A 4
Tesuque, 1,014('80) B 4
Texico, 966 . . . . C 6
Thoreau, 1,099('80) . . B 1
Tierra Amarilla, 900('87) . . . . A 3
Tohatchi, 1,011('80) . . B 1
Truth or Consequences (Hot Springs), 6,221 D 2
Tucumcari, 6,831 . . . . B 6
Tularosa, 2,615 . . . . . D 3
Tyrone, 950('87) . . . . E 1
University Park, 4,353('80) . . . . E 3
Zuni, 5,551('80) . . . . B 1

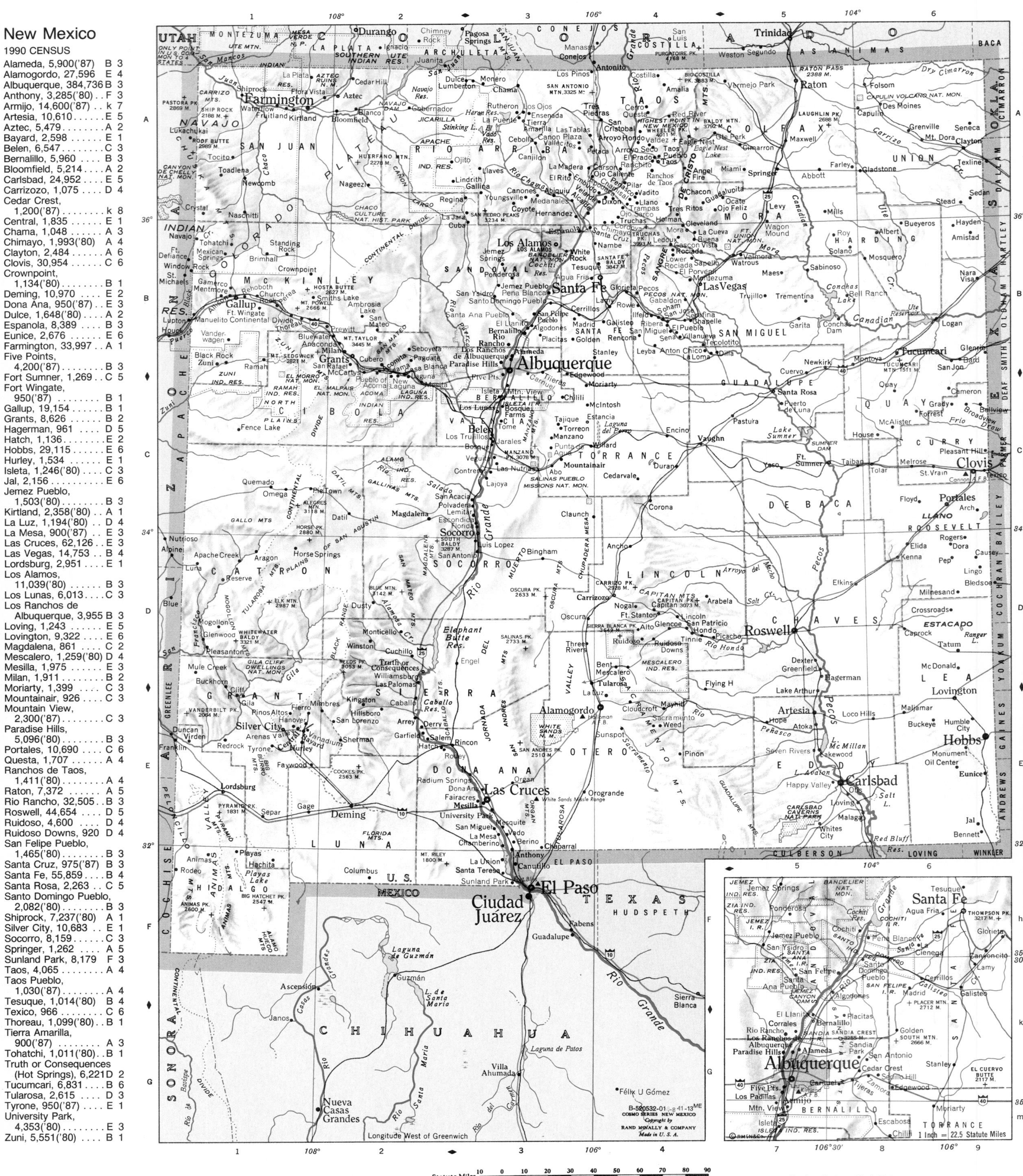

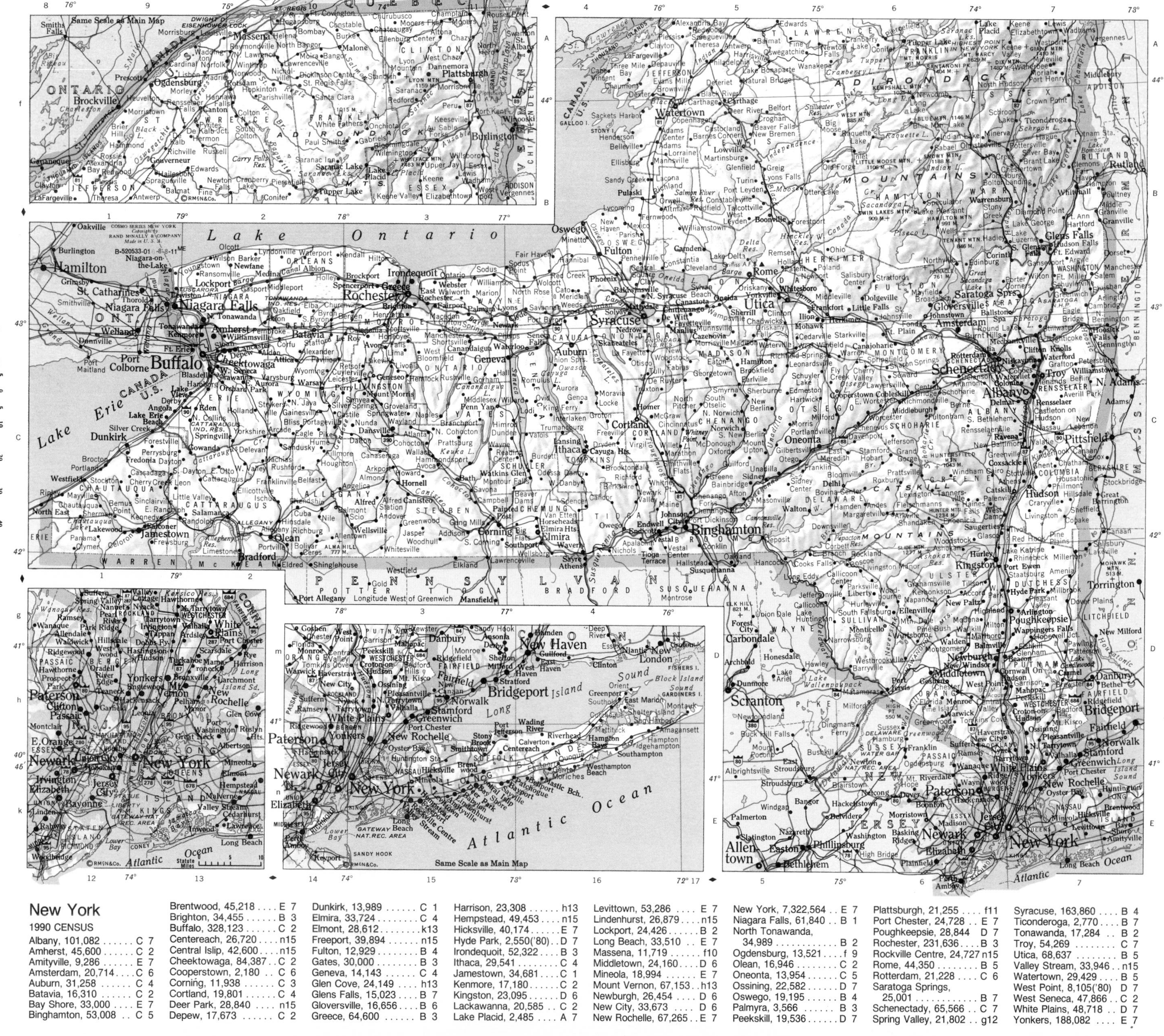

New York

1990 CENSUS

Albany, 101,082 . . . . . . C 7
Amherst, 45,600 . . . . . . C 2
Amityville, 9,286 . . . . . . E 7
Amsterdam, 20,714 . . . . C 6
Auburn, 31,258 . . . . C 4
Batavia, 16,310 . . . . . . C 2
Bay Shore, 33,000 . . . . E 7
Binghamton, 53,008 . . C 5
Brentwood, 45,218 . . . . E 7
Brighton, 34,455 . . . . . . B 3
Buffalo, 328,123 . . . . . . C 2
Centereach, 26,720 . . . . n15
Central Islip, 42,600 . . . . n15
Cheektowaga, 84,387 . . C 2
Cooperstown, 2,180 . . C 6
Corning, 11,938 . . . . . . C 3
Cortland, 19,801 . . . . . . C 4
Deer Park, 28,840 . . . . n15
Depew, 17,673 . . . . . . C 2
Dunkirk, 13,989 . . . . . . C 1
Elmira, 33,724 . . . . C 4
Elmont, 28,612 . . . . k13
Freeport, 39,894 . . . . . . n15
Fulton, 12,929 . . . . B 4
Gates, 30,000 . . . . B 3
Geneva, 14,143 . . . . C 4
Glen Cove, 24,149 . . . . h13
Glens Falls, 15,023 . . . . B 7
Gloversville, 16,656 . . . . B 6
Greece, 64,600 . . . . B 3
Harrison, 23,308 . . . . . . h13
Hempstead, 49,453 . . . . n15
Hicksville, 40,174 . . . . . . E 7
Hyde Park, 2,550('80) . . D 7
Irondequoit, 52,322 . . . . . B 3
Ithaca, 29,541 . . . . C 4
Jamestown, 34,681 . . . . . C 1
Kenmore, 17,180 . . . . C 2
Kingston, 23,095 . . . . D 6
Lackawanna, 20,585 . . . C 2
Lake Placid, 2,485 . . . . A 7
Levittown, 53,286 . . . . E 7
Lindenhurst, 26,879 . . . . n15
Lockport, 24,426 . . . . . . B 2
Long Beach, 33,510 . . . E 7
Massena, 11,719 . . . . . . f10
Middletown, 24,160 . . . . D 6
Mineola, 18,994 . . . . . . E 7
Mount Vernon, 67,153 . . h13
Newburgh, 26,454 . . . . . D 6
New City, 33,673 . . . . D 6
New Rochelle, 67,265 . . E 7
New York, 7,322,564 . . E 7
Niagara Falls, 61,840 . . B 1
North Tonawanda,
34,989 . . . . B 2
Ogdensburg, 13,521 . . . . f 9
Olean, 16,946 . . . . C 2
Oneonta, 13,954 . . . . . . C 5
Ossining, 22,582 . . . . . . D 7
Oswego, 19,195 . . . . . . B 4
Palmyra, 3,566 . . . . B 3
Peekskill, 19,536 . . . . . . D 7
Plattsburgh, 21,255 . . . . f11
Port Chester, 24,728 . . E 7
Poughkeepsie, 28,844 D 7
Rochester, 231,636 . . . B 3
Rockville Centre, 24,727 n15
Rome, 44,350 . . . . B 5
Rotterdam, 21,228 . . . . C 6
Saratoga Springs,
25,001 . . . . B 7
Schenectady, 65,566 . . C 7
Spring Valley, 21,802 . . g12
Syracuse, 163,860 . . . . B 4
Ticonderoga, 2,770 . . . . B 7
Tonawanda, 17,284 . . B 2
Troy, 54,269 . . . . C 7
Utica, 68,637 . . . . B 5
Valley Stream, 33,946 . . n15
Watertown, 29,429 . . . . B 5
West Point, 8,105('80) D 7
West Seneca, 47,866 . . C 2
White Plains, 48,718 . . D 7
Yonkers, 188,082 . . . . E 7

North Carolina

1990 CENSUS

Ahoskie, 4,391 . . . . A 6
Albemarle, 14,939 . . . . B 2
Archdale, 6,913 . . . . . . B 3
Asheboro, 16,362 . . . . . B 3
Asheville, 61,607 . . . . . . f10
Bessemer City, 4,698 . . B 1
Boone, 12,915 . . . . A 1
Brevard, 5,388 . . . . f10
Burlington, 39,498 . . . . A 3
Carrboro, 11,553 . . . . . . B 3
Cary, 43,858 . . . . B 4
Chapel Hill, 38,719 . . . . B 3
Charlotte, 395,934 . . . . B 2
Cherryville, 4,756 . . . . . B 1
Clemmons, 6,020 . . . . . . A 2
Clinton, 8,204 . . . . C 4
Concord, 27,347 . . . . . . B 2
Dunn, 8,336 . . . . B 4
Durham, 136,611 . . . . . . B 4
Eden, 15,238 . . . . A 3
Edenton, 5,268 . . . . A 6
Elizabeth City, 14,292 . . A 6
Farmville, 4,392 . . . . B 5
Fayetteville, 75,695 . . . . B 4
Forest City, 7,475 . . . . . B 1
Garner, 14,967 . . . . B 4
Gastonia, 54,732 . . . . . . B 1
Goldsboro, 40,709 . . . . . B 5
Graham, 10,426 . . . . A 3
Greensboro, 183,521 . . A 3
Greenville, 44,972 . . . . B 5
Hamlet, 6,196 . . . . C 3
Havelock, 20,268 . . . . . C 6
Henderson, 15,655 . . . . A 4
Hendersonville, 7,284 . . . f10
Hickory, 28,301 . . . . B 1
High Point, 69,496 . . . . B 2
Hope Mills, 8,184 . . . . . C 4
Jacksonville, 30,013 . . . C 5
Kannapolis, 29,696 . . . . B 2
Kernersville, 10,836 . . . . A 2
Kings Mountain, 8,763 B 1
Kinston, 25,295 . . . . . . B 5
Laurinburg, 11,643 . . . . C 3
Lenoir, 14,192 . . . . B 1
Lexington, 16,581 . . . . . B 2
Lincolnton, 6,847 . . . . . . B 1
Lumberton, 18,601 . . . . . C 3
Matthews, 13,651 . . . . . B 2
Mint Hill, 11,567 . . . . B 2
Monroe, 16,127 . . . . C 2
Mooresville, 9,317 . . . . . B 2
Morehead City, 6,046 . . C 6
Morganton, 15,085 . . . . . B 1
Mount Airy, 7,156 . . . . . A 2
Mount Olive, 4,582 . . . . B 4
Nags Head, 1,838 . . . . . B 7
New Bern, 17,363 . . . . . B 5
Newton, 9,304 . . . . B 1
Oxford, 7,913 . . . . A 4
Plymouth, 4,328 . . . . B 6
Raleigh, 207,951 . . . . . . B 4
Reidsville, 12,183 . . . . . A 3
Roanoke Rapids, 15,722 . . . . A 5
Rockingham, 9,399 . . . . C 3
Rocky Mount, 48,997 . . B 5
Roxboro, 7,332 . . . . A 4
Salisbury, 23,087 . . . . . . B 2
Sanford, 14,475 . . . . . . B 3
Selma, 4,600 . . . . B 4
Shelby, 14,669 . . . . B 1
Smithfield, 7,540 . . . . . . B 4
Southern Pines, 9,129 . . B 3
Spring Lake, 7,524 . . . . B 4
Statesville, 17,567 . . . . . B 2
Tarboro, 11,037 . . . . B 5
Thomasville, 15,915 . . . B 2
Washington, 9,075 . . . . B 5
Waynesville, 6,758 . . . . f10
Whiteville, 5,078 . . . . . . C 4
Williamston, 5,503 . . . . . B 5
Wilmington, 55,530 . . . . C 5
Wilson, 36,930 . . . . B 5
Winston-Salem, 143,485 A 2

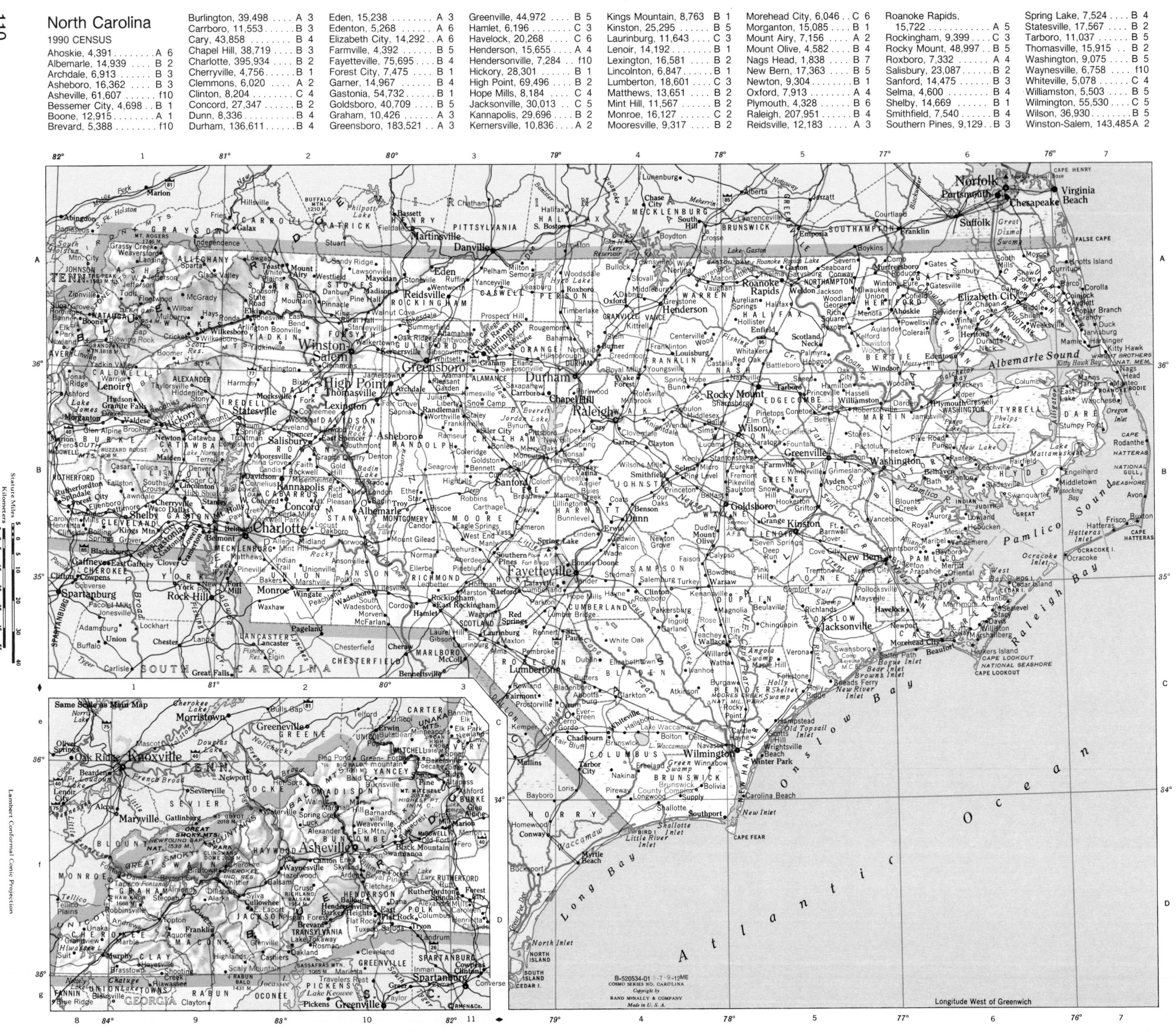

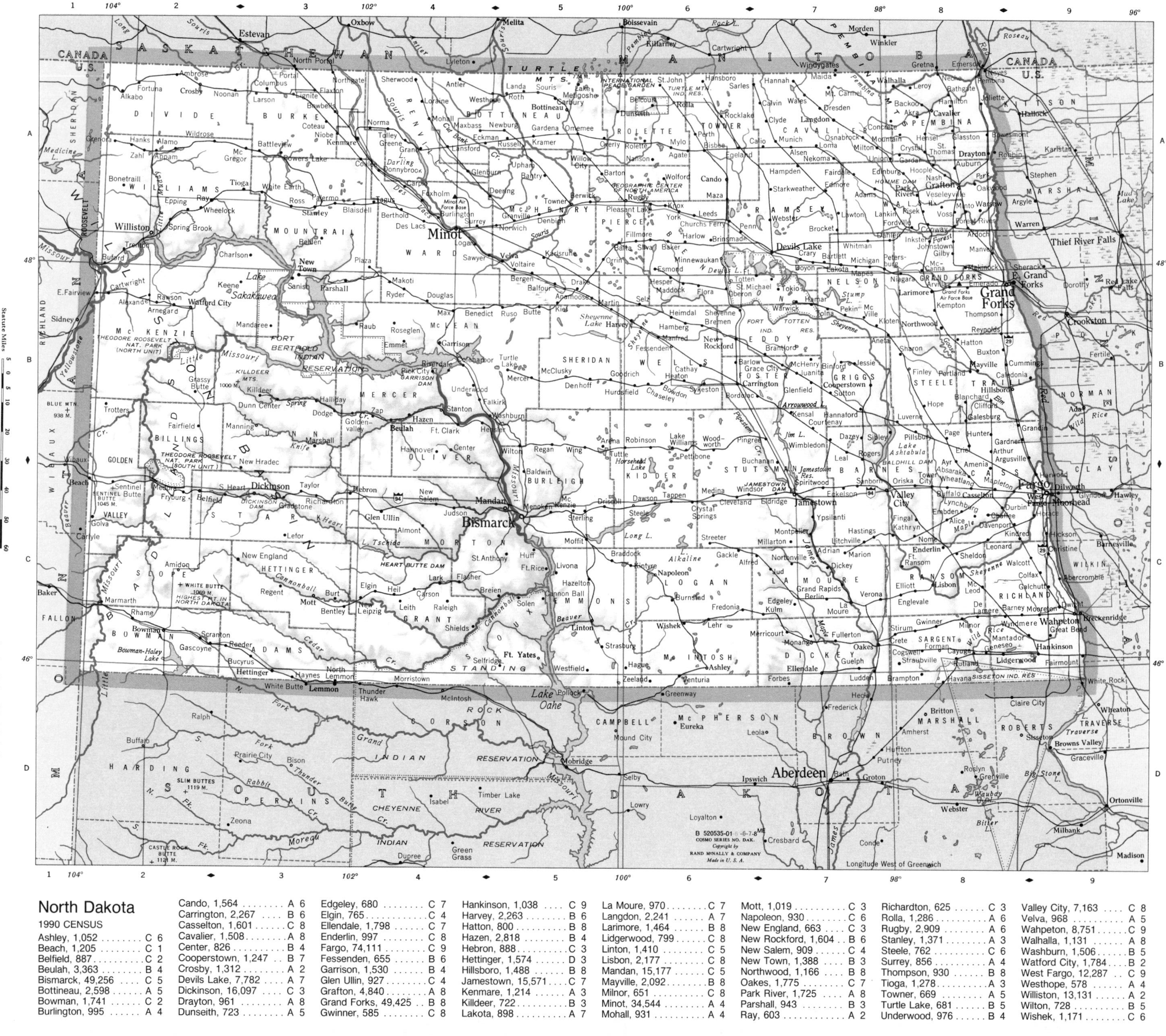

North Dakota

1990 CENSUS

Place	Key
Ashley, 1,052	C 6
Beach, 1,205	C 1
Belfield, 887	C 2
Beulah, 3,363	B 4
Bismarck, 49,256	C 5
Bottineau, 2,598	A 5
Bowman, 1,741	C 2
Burlington, 995	A 4
Cando, 1,564	A 6
Carrington, 2,267	B 6
Casselton, 1,601	C 8
Cavalier, 1,508	A 8
Center, 826	B 4
Cooperstown, 1,247	B 7
Crosby, 1,312	A 2
Devils Lake, 7,782	A 7
Dickinson, 16,097	C 3
Drayton, 961	A 8
Dunseith, 723	A 5
Edgeley, 680	C 7
Elgin, 765	C 4
Ellendale, 1,798	C 7
Enderlin, 997	C 8
Fargo, 74,111	C 9
Fessenden, 655	B 6
Garrison, 1,530	B 4
Glen Ullin, 927	C 4
Grafton, 4,840	A 8
Grand Forks, 49,425	B 8
Gwinner, 585	C 8
Hankinson, 1,038	C 9
Harvey, 2,263	B 6
Hatton, 800	B 8
Hazen, 2,818	B 4
Hebron, 888	C 3
Hettinger, 1,574	D 3
Hillsboro, 1,488	B 8
Jamestown, 15,571	C 7
Kenmare, 1,214	A 3
Killdeer, 722	B 3
Lakota, 898	A 7
La Moure, 970	C 7
Langdon, 2,241	A 7
Larimore, 1,464	B 8
Lidgerwood, 799	C 8
Linton, 1,410	C 5
Lisbon, 2,177	C 8
Mandan, 15,177	C 5
Mayville, 2,092	B 8
Milnor, 651	C 8
Minot, 34,544	A 4
Mohall, 931	A 4
Mott, 1,019	C 3
Napoleon, 930	C 6
New England, 663	C 3
New Rockford, 1,604	B 6
New Salem, 909	C 4
New Town, 1,388	B 3
Northwood, 1,166	B 8
Oakes, 1,775	C 7
Park River, 1,725	A 8
Parshall, 943	B 3
Ray, 603	A 2
Richardton, 625	C 3
Rolla, 1,286	A 6
Rugby, 2,909	A 6
Stanley, 1,371	A 3
Steele, 762	C 6
Surrey, 856	A 4
Thompson, 930	B 8
Tioga, 1,278	A 3
Towner, 669	A 5
Turtle Lake, 681	B 5
Underwood, 976	B 4
Valley City, 7,163	C 8
Velva, 968	A 5
Wahpeton, 8,751	C 9
Walhalla, 1,131	A 8
Washburn, 1,506	B 5
Watford City, 1,784	B 2
West Fargo, 12,287	C 9
Westhope, 578	A 4
Williston, 13,131	A 2
Wilton, 728	B 5
Wishek, 1,171	C 6

Ohio

1990 CENSUS

- Akron, 223,019 . . . . . . A 4
- Alliance, 23,376 . . . . . . B 4
- Ashland, 20,079 . . . . . . B 3
- Ashtabula, 21,633 . . . . . A 5
- Athens, 21,265 . . . . . . C 3
- Austintown, 23,300 . . . . A 5
- Barberton, 27,623 . . . . . A 4
- Beavercreek, 33,626 . . C 1
- Bellefontaine, 12,142 . . B 2
- Boardman, 38,596 . . . . A 5
- Bowling Green, 28,176 A 2
- Brook Park, 22,865 . . . . h 9
- Brunswick, 28,230 . . . . A 4
- Canton, 84,161 . . . . . . B 4
- Chillicothe, 21,923 . . . . C 3
- Cincinnati, 364,040 . . . . C 1
- Cleveland, 505,616 . . . . A 4
- Cleveland Heights, 54,052 . . . . A 4
- Columbus, 632,910 . . . . C 2
- Cuyahoga Falls, 48,950 A 4
- Dayton, 182,044 . . . . . . C 1
- Defiance, 16,768 . . . . . . A 1
- Delaware, 20,030 . . . . B 2
- East Cleveland, 33,096 g 9
- Eastlake, 21,161 . . . . . . A 4
- East Liverpool, 13,654 B 5
- Elyria, 56,746 . . . . A 3
- Euclid, 54,875 . . . . A 4
- Fairborn, 31,300 . . . . . C 1
- Fairfield, 39,729 . . . . . . n12
- Findlay, 35,703 . . . . . A 2
- Fostoria, 14,983 . . . . . . A 2
- Fremont, 17,648 . . . . . . A 2
- Garfield Heights, 31,739 h 9
- Greenville, 12,863 . . . . B 1
- Hamilton, 61,368 . . . . . . C 1
- Ironton, 12,751 . . . . . . D 3
- Kent, 28,835 . . . . A 4
- Kettering, 60,569 . . . . . C 1
- Lakewood, 59,718 . . . . A 4
- Lancaster, 34,507 . . . . C 3
- Lima, 45,549 . . . . B 1
- Lorain, 71,245 . . . . A 3
- Mansfield, 50,627 . . . . . B 3
- Maple Heights, 27,089 . . h 9
- Marietta, 15,026 . . . . . . C 4
- Marion, 34,075 . . . . B 2
- Massillon, 31,007 . . . . B 4
- Medina, 19,231 . . . . . . A 4
- Mentor, 47,358 . . . . . . A 4
- Middletown, 46,022 . . . . C 1
- Mount Vernon, 14,550 B 3
- Newark, 44,389 . . . . . . B 3
- New Philadelphia, 15,698 . . . . B 4
- Niles, 21,128 . . . . A 5
- North Olmsted, 34,204 h 9
- Norwalk, 14,731 . . . . . . A 3
- Norwood, 23,674 . . . . . . o13
- Oxford, 18,937 . . . . . . C 1
- Parma, 87,876 . . . . A 4
- Parma Heights, 21,448 h 9
- Piqua, 20,612 . . . . B 1
- Portsmouth, 22,676 . . D 3
- Reynoldsburg, 25,748 . . C 3
- Salem, 12,233 . . . . B 5
- Sandusky, 29,764 . . . . A 3
- Shaker Heights, 30,831 A 4
- South Euclid, 23,866 . . g 9
- Springfield, 70,487 . . . C 2
- Steubenville, 22,125 . . B 5
- Stow, 27,702 . . . . A 4
- Strongsville, 35,308 . . . A 4
- Tiffin, 18,604 . . . . A 2
- Toledo, 332,943 . . . . . . A 2
- Upper Arlington, 34,128 B 2
- Urbana, 11,353 . . . . . . B 2
- Warren, 50,793 . . . . . . A 5
- Westerville, 30,269 . . . . B 3
- Whitehall, 20,572 . . . . . m11
- Wooster, 22,191 . . . . . . B 4
- Xenia, 24,664 . . . . C 2
- Youngstown, 95,732 . . . A 5
- Zanesville, 26,778 . . . . C 4

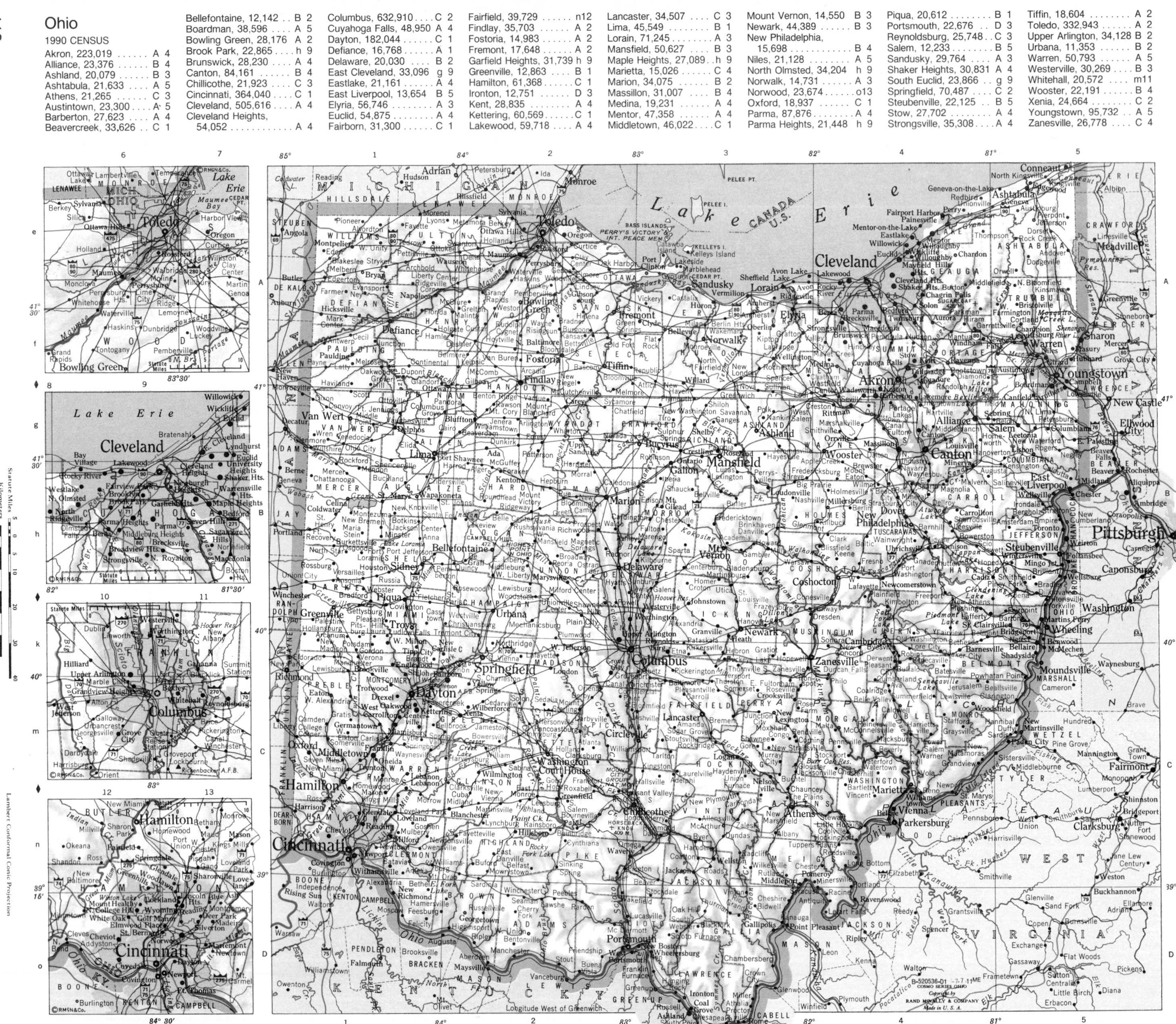

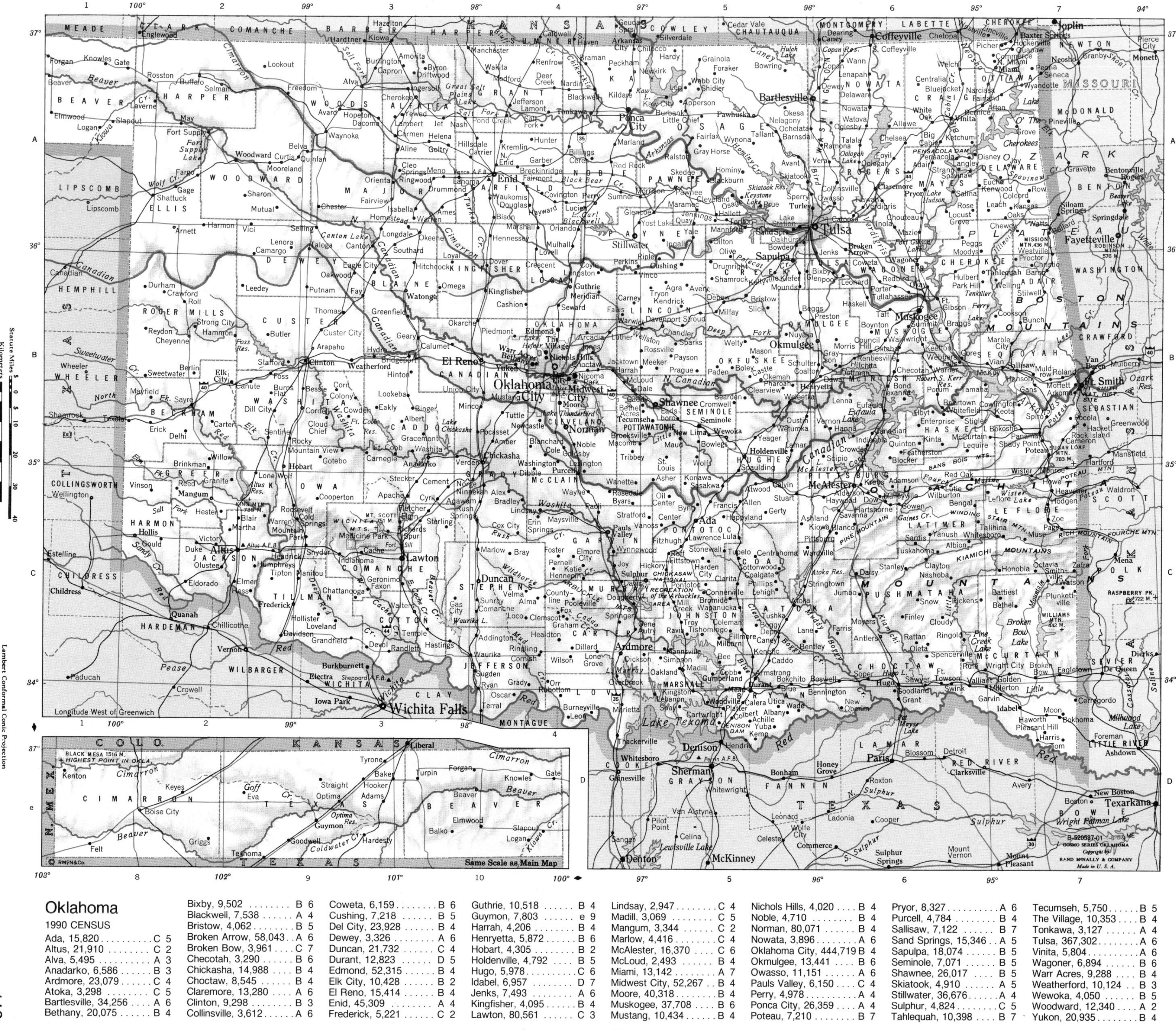

Statute Miles 5 0 5 10 20 30 40
Kilometers 5 0 5 15 25 35 45 55

Lambert Conformal Conic Projection

Oklahoma

1990 CENSUS

Ada, 15,820 .... C 5
Altus, 21,910 .... C 2
Alva, 5,495 .... A 3
Anadarko, 6,586 ...... B 3
Ardmore, 23,079 ...... C 4
Atoka, 3,298 .... C 5
Bartlesville, 34,256 .... A 6
Bethany, 20,075 ...... B 4
Bixby, 9,502 .... B 6
Blackwell, 7,538 ...... A 4
Bristow, 4,062 .... B 5
Broken Arrow, 58,043 . A 6
Broken Bow, 3,961 .... C 7
Checotah, 3,290 ...... B 6
Chickasha, 14,988 .... B 4
Choctaw, 8,545 .... B 4
Claremore, 13,280 .... A 6
Clinton, 9,298 .... B 3
Collinsville, 3,612 ..... A 6
Coweta, 6,159 .... B 6
Cushing, 7,218 ...... B 5
Del City, 23,928 ...... B 4
Dewey, 3,326 .... A 6
Duncan, 21,732 ...... C 4
Durant, 12,823 .... D 5
Edmond, 52,315 ...... B 4
Elk City, 10,428 ...... B 2
El Reno, 15,414 ...... B 4
Enid, 45,309 .... A 4
Frederick, 5,221 ...... C 2
Guthrie, 10,518 ...... B 4
Guymon, 7,803 ...... e 9
Harrah, 4,206 .... B 4
Henryetta, 5,872 ...... B 6
Hobart, 4,305 .... B 2
Holdenville, 4,792 .... B 5
Hugo, 5,978 .... C 6
Idabel, 6,957 .... D 7
Jenks, 7,493 .... A 6
Kingfisher, 4,095 ..... B 4
Lawton, 80,561 .... C 3
Lindsay, 2,947 .... C 4
Madill, 3,069 .... C 5
Mangum, 3,344 .... C 2
Marlow, 4,416 .... C 4
McAlester, 16,370 ..... C 6
McLoud, 2,493 .... B 4
Miami, 13,142 .... A 7
Midwest City, 52,267 .. B 4
Moore, 40,318 .... B 4
Muskogee, 37,708 .... B 6
Mustang, 10,434 ...... B 4
Nichols Hills, 4,020 .... B 4
Noble, 4,710 .... B 4
Norman, 80,071 .... B 4
Nowata, 3,896 .... A 6
Oklahoma City, 444,719 B 4
Okmulgee, 13,441 .... B 6
Owasso, 11,151 ...... A 6
Pauls Valley, 6,150 .... C 4
Perry, 4,978 .... A 4
Ponca City, 26,359 .... A 4
Poteau, 7,210 .... B 7
Pryor, 8,327 .... A 6
Purcell, 4,784 .... B 4
Sallisaw, 7,122 .... B 7
Sand Springs, 15,346 .. A 5
Sapulpa, 18,074 ...... B 5
Seminole, 7,071 ...... B 5
Shawnee, 26,017 .... B 5
Skiatook, 4,910 ...... A 5
Stillwater, 36,676 ...... A 4
Sulphur, 4,824 .... C 5
Tahlequah, 10,398 .... B 7
Tecumseh, 5,750 ..... B 5
The Village, 10,353 .... B 4
Tonkawa, 3,127 ...... A 4
Tulsa, 367,302 .... A 6
Vinita, 5,804 .... A 6
Wagoner, 6,894 ...... B 6
Warr Acres, 9,288 .... B 4
Weatherford, 10,124 .. B 3
Wewoka, 4,050 .... B 5
Woodward, 12,340 .... A 2
Yukon, 20,935 .... B 4

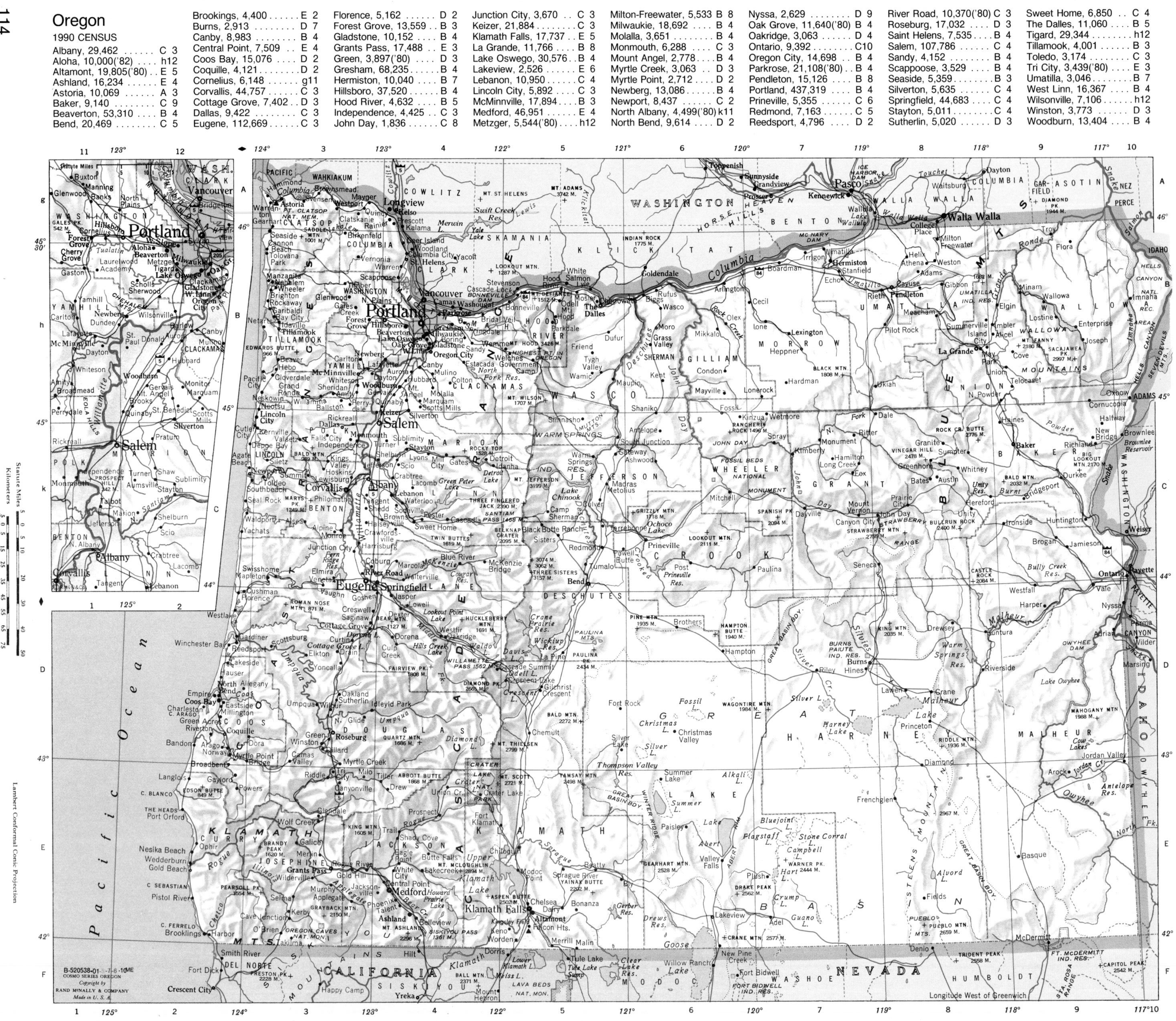
Oregon
1990 CENSUS
Albany, 29,462 . . . . . . C 3
Aloha, 10,000('82) h12
Altamont, 19,805('80) . . E 5
Ashland, 16,234 . . . . . . E 4
Astoria, 10,069 . . . . . . A 3
Baker, 9,140 . . . . C 9
Beaverton, 53,310 . . . . B 4
Bend, 20,469 . . . . C 5
Brookings, 4,400 . . . . . . E 2
Burns, 2,913 . . . . D 7
Canby, 8,983 . . . . B 4
Central Point, 7,509 . . . E 4
Coos Bay, 15,076 . . . . . D 2
Coquille, 4,121 . . . . D 2
Cornelius, 6,148 . . . . . . g11
Corvallis, 44,757 . . . . . . C 3
Cottage Grove, 7,402 . . D 3
Dallas, 9,422 . . . . C 3
Eugene, 112,669 . . . . . . C 3
Florence, 5,162 . . . . . . D 2
Forest Grove, 13,559 . . B 3
Gladstone, 10,152 . . . . B 4
Grants Pass, 17,488 . . . E 3
Green, 3,897('80) . . . . . D 3
Gresham, 68,235 . . . . . . B 4
Hermiston, 10,040 . . . . . B 7
Hillsboro, 37,520 . . . . . . B 4
Hood River, 4,632 . . . . . B 5
Independence, 4,425 . . . C 3
John Day, 1,836 . . . . . . C 8
Junction City, 3,670 . . C 3
Keizer, 21,884 . . . . C 3
Klamath Falls, 17,737 . . E 5
La Grande, 11,766 . . . . B 8
Lake Oswego, 30,576 . . B 4
Lakeview, 2,526 . . . . . . E 6
Lebanon, 10,950 . . . . . . C 4
Lincoln City, 5,892 . . . . C 3
McMinnville, 17,894 . . . . B 3
Medford, 46,951 . . . . . . E 4
Metzger, 5,544('80) h12
Milton-Freewater, 5,533 B 8
Milwaukie, 18,692 . . . . . B 4
Molalla, 3,651 . . . . B 4
Monmouth, 6,288 . . . . . C 3
Mount Angel, 2,778 . . . B 4
Myrtle Creek, 3,063 . . D 3
Myrtle Point, 2,712 . . . . D 2
Newberg, 13,086 . . . . . . B 4
Newport, 8,437 . . . . C 2
North Albany, 4,499('80) k11
North Bend, 9,614 . . . . D 2
Nyssa, 2,629 . . . . D 9
Oak Grove, 11,640('80) B 4
Oakridge, 3,063 . . . . . . D 4
Ontario, 9,392 . . . . C10
Oregon City, 14,698 . . . B 4
Parkrose, 21,108('80) . . B 4
Pendleton, 15,126 . . . . . B 8
Portland, 437,319 . . . . B 4
Prineville, 5,355 . . . . . . C 6
Redmond, 7,163 . . . . . . C 5
Reedsport, 4,796 . . . . . D 2
River Road, 10,370('80) C 3
Roseburg, 17,032 . . . . . D 3
Saint Helens, 7,535 . . . . B 4
Salem, 107,786 . . . . . . C 4
Sandy, 4,152 . . . . B 4
Scappoose, 3,529 . . . . . B 4
Seaside, 5,359 . . . . B 3
Silverton, 5,635 . . . . . . C 4
Springfield, 44,683 . . . . C 4
Stayton, 5,011 . . . . C 4
Sutherlin, 5,020 . . . . . . D 3
Sweet Home, 6,850 . . . C 4
The Dalles, 11,060 . . . . B 5
Tigard, 29,344 . . . . h12
Tillamook, 4,001 . . . . . . B 3
Toledo, 3,174 . . . . C 3
Tri City, 3,439('80) . . . . E 3
Umatilla, 3,046 . . . . B 7
West Linn, 16,367 . . . . B 4
Wilsonville, 7,106 . . . . . . h12
Winston, 3,773 . . . . D 3
Woodburn, 13,404 . . . . . B 4
Pacific Ocean
WASHINGTON
IDAHO
NEVADA
CALIFORNIA
Longitude West of Greenwich
Statute Miles
Kilometers
Lambert Conformal Conic Projection
B-520538-01-1-1-6-10ME
COSMO SERIES OREGON
Copyright by RAND McNALLY & COMPANY
Made in U. S. A.

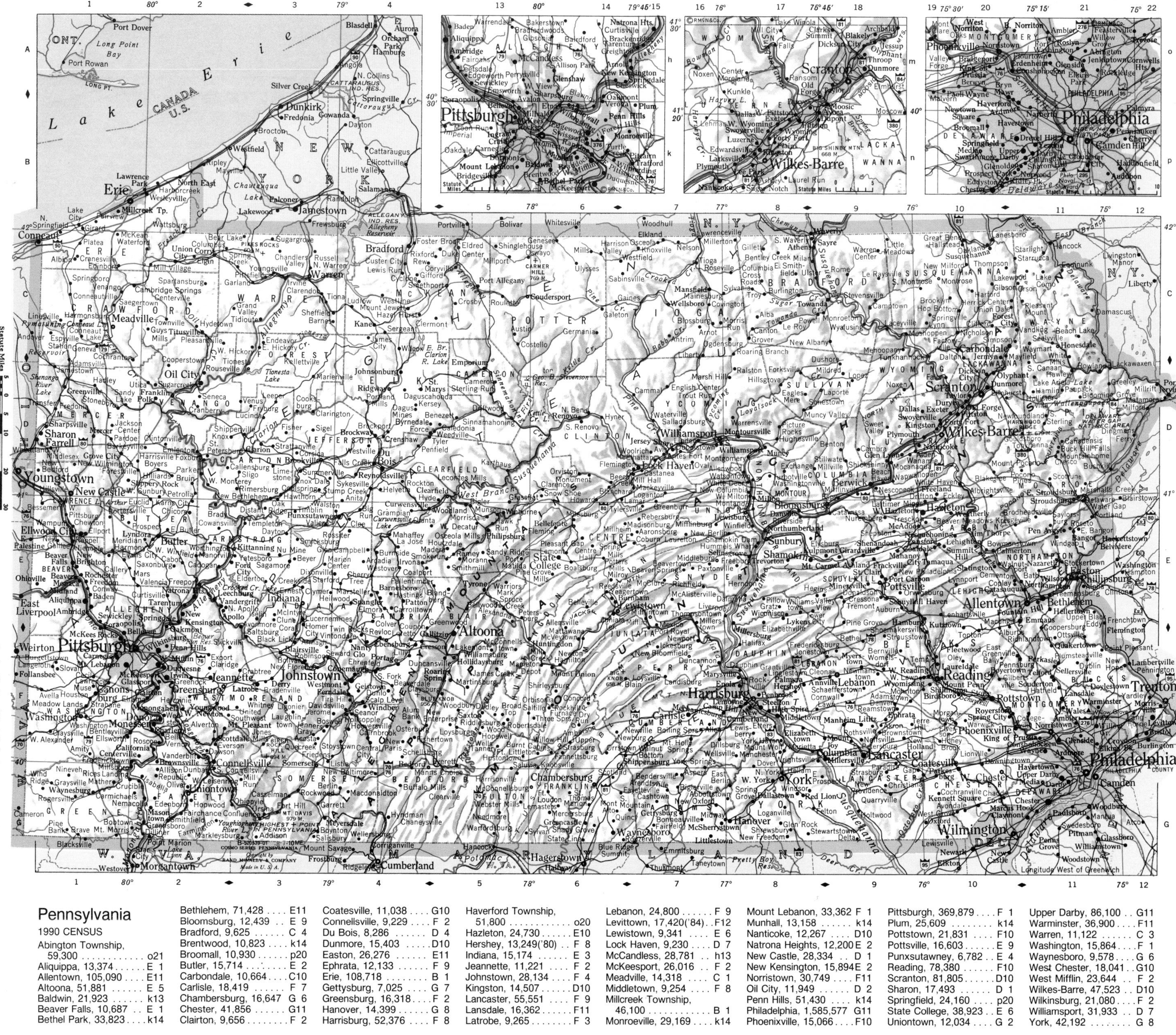

Pennsylvania

1990 CENSUS

Abington Township, 59,300 . . . . o21
Aliquippa, 13,374 . . . . . . E 1
Allentown, 105,090 . . . . E11
Altoona, 51,881 . . . . E 5
Baldwin, 21,923 . . . . . . k13
Beaver Falls, 10,687 . . E 1
Bethel Park, 33,823 . . . . k14
Bethlehem, 71,428 . . . . E11
Bloomsburg, 12,439 . . E 9
Bradford, 9,625 . . . . . . C 4
Brentwood, 10,823 . . . . k14
Broomall, 10,930 . . . . . . p20
Butler, 15,714 . . . . E 2
Carbondale, 10,664 . . . . C10
Carlisle, 18,419 . . . . F 7
Chambersburg, 16,647 G 6
Chester, 41,856 . . . . . . G11
Clairton, 9,656 . . . . F 2
Coatesville, 11,038 . . . . G10
Connellsville, 9,229 . . . . F 2
Du Bois, 8,286 . . . . D 4
Dunmore, 15,403 . . . . . D10
Easton, 26,276 . . . . E11
Ephrata, 12,133 . . . . . . F 9
Erie, 108,718 . . . . B 1
Gettysburg, 7,025 . . . . . G 7
Greensburg, 16,318 . . . . F 2
Hanover, 14,399 . . . . . . G 8
Harrisburg, 52,376 . . . . F 8
Haverford Township, 51,800 . . . . o20
Hazleton, 24,730 . . . . E10
Hershey, 13,249('80) . . F 8
Indiana, 15,174 . . . . . . E 3
Jeannette, 11,221 . . . . . F 2
Johnstown, 28,134 . . . . F 4
Kingston, 14,507 . . . . . . D10
Lancaster, 55,551 . . . . . F 9
Lansdale, 16,362 . . . . . . F11
Latrobe, 9,265 . . . . F 3
Lebanon, 24,800 . . . . . . F 9
Levittown, 17,420('84) . . F12
Lewistown, 9,341 . . . . . E 6
Lock Haven, 9,230 . . . . D 7
McCandless, 28,781 . . . h13
McKeesport, 26,016 . . . F 2
Meadville, 14,318 . . . . C 1
Middletown, 9,254 . . . . . F 8
Millcreek Township, 46,100 . . . . B 1
Monroeville, 29,169 . . . . k14
Mount Lebanon, 33,362 F 1
Munhall, 13,158 . . . . k14
Nanticoke, 12,267 . . . . . D10
Natrona Heights, 12,200 E 2
New Castle, 28,334 . . . D 1
New Kensington, 15,894 E 2
Norristown, 30,749 . . . . F11
Oil City, 11,949 . . . . D 2
Penn Hills, 51,430 . . . . . k14
Philadelphia, 1,585,577 G11
Phoenixville, 15,066 . . . . F10
Pittsburgh, 369,879 . . . . F 1
Plum, 25,609 . . . . k14
Pottstown, 21,831 . . . . F10
Pottsville, 16,603 . . . . . . E 9
Punxsutawney, 6,782 . . E 4
Reading, 78,380 . . . . F10
Scranton, 81,805 . . . . . . D10
Sharon, 17,493 . . . . D 1
Springfield, 24,160 . . . . p20
State College, 38,923 . . E 6
Uniontown, 12,034 . . . . G 2
Upper Darby, 86,100 . . G11
Warminster, 36,900 . . . F11
Warren, 11,122 . . . . C 3
Washington, 15,864 . . . . F 1
Waynesboro, 9,578 . . . . G 6
West Chester, 18,041 . . G10
West Mifflin, 23,644 . . F 2
Wilkes-Barre, 47,523 . . D10
Wilkinsburg, 21,080 . . . F 2
Williamsport, 31,933 . . D 7
York, 42,192 . . . . G 8

Rhode Island

1990 CENSUS

Abbott Run Valley, 1,050('87) . . . . B 4
Adamsville, 600('87) E 6
Albion, 1,600('87) . . B 4
Allenton, 600('87) . . . . E 4
Anthony, 2,980('87) . . D 3
Arnold Mills, 600('87) B 4
Ashton, 820('87) . . . . B 4
Barrington, 16,174('80) . . . . . . D 5
Berkeley, 830('87) . . B 4
Block Island, 620('87) h 7
Branch Village, 400('87) . . . . B 3
Bristol, 20,128('80) . . D 5
Burdickville, 500('87) F 2
Carolina, 650('87) . . . . F 2
Central Falls, 17,637 B 4
Charlestown, 1,500 (6,478▲) . . . . F 2
Chepachet, 900('87) B 2
Common Fence Point, 860('87) . . . . D 6
Coventry, 6,980 (31,083▲) . . . . D 3
Cranston, 76,060 . . . . C 4
Davisville, 500('87) . . E 4
Diamond Hill, 810('87) B 4
East Greenwich, 10,211('87) . . . . . . D 4
East Matunuck, 500('87) . . . . F 3
East Providence, 50,380 . . . . C 4
Esmond, 4,320('87) . . B 4
Forestdale, 530('87) B 3
Glendale, 700('87) . . B 2
Greenville, 7,576('80) C 3
Harmony, 820('87) . . B 3
Harris, 1,050('87) . . . . D 3
Hope, 270('87) . . . . . D 3
Hopkinton, 550 (6,873▲) . . . . F 1
Island Park, 1,240('87) . . . . E 6
Jamestown, 4,040('87) . . . . F 5
Johnston, 26,800 . . . . C 4
Kenyon, 400('87) . . . . F 2
Kingston, 5,479('80) . . F 3
La Fayette, 640('87) E 4
Little Compton, 500 (3,339▲) . . . . E 6
Lonsdale, 3,850('87) B 4
Manville, 3,030('87) . . B 4
Mapleville, 1,300('87) B 2
Matunuck, 550('87) . . G 3
Middletown, 3,350 (19,460▲) . . . . E 5
Mount View, 610('87) D 4
Narragansett, 3,342 (14,985▲) . . . . F 4
Newport, 28,227 . . . . F 5
North Kingstown, 2,750 (23,786▲) . . . . E 4
North Providence, 32,090 . . . . C 4
Oakland, 600('87) . . B 2
Pascoag, 3,807('80) B 2
Pawtucket, 72,644 . . C 4
Peace Dale, 3,100('87) . . . . F 3
Plum Beach, 400('87) E 4
Portsmouth, 3,540 (16,857▲) . . . . E 6
Primrose, 500('87) . . B 3
Providence, 160,728 C 4
Quidnessett, 3,300('87) . . . . E 4
Quidnick, 2,300('87) D 3
Quonochontaug, 1,500('87) . . . . G 2
Saunderstown, 400('87) . . . . E 4
Saylesville, 3,510('87) B 4
Shannock, 950('87) . . F 2
Shores Acres, 410('87) . . . . E 4
Slatersville, 2,330('87) A 3
South Hopkinton, 900('87) . . . . F 1
Tiverton, 7,653 (14,312▲) . . . . D 6
Union Village, 2,150('87) . . . . B 3
Usquepaug, 400('87) F 3
Valley Falls, 10,892('80) . . . . . . B 4
Wakefield, 3,450('87) F 3
Warren, 10,640('87) . . D 5
Warwick, 85,427 . . . . D 4
Westerly, 16,477 (21,605▲) . . . . F 1
West Kingston, 1,150('87) . . . . F 3
West Warwick, 29,268 . . . . D 3
Woonsocket, 43,877 A 3
Yorktown Manor, 2,520('87) . . . . C 3

▲ Population of entire town (township), including rural area.

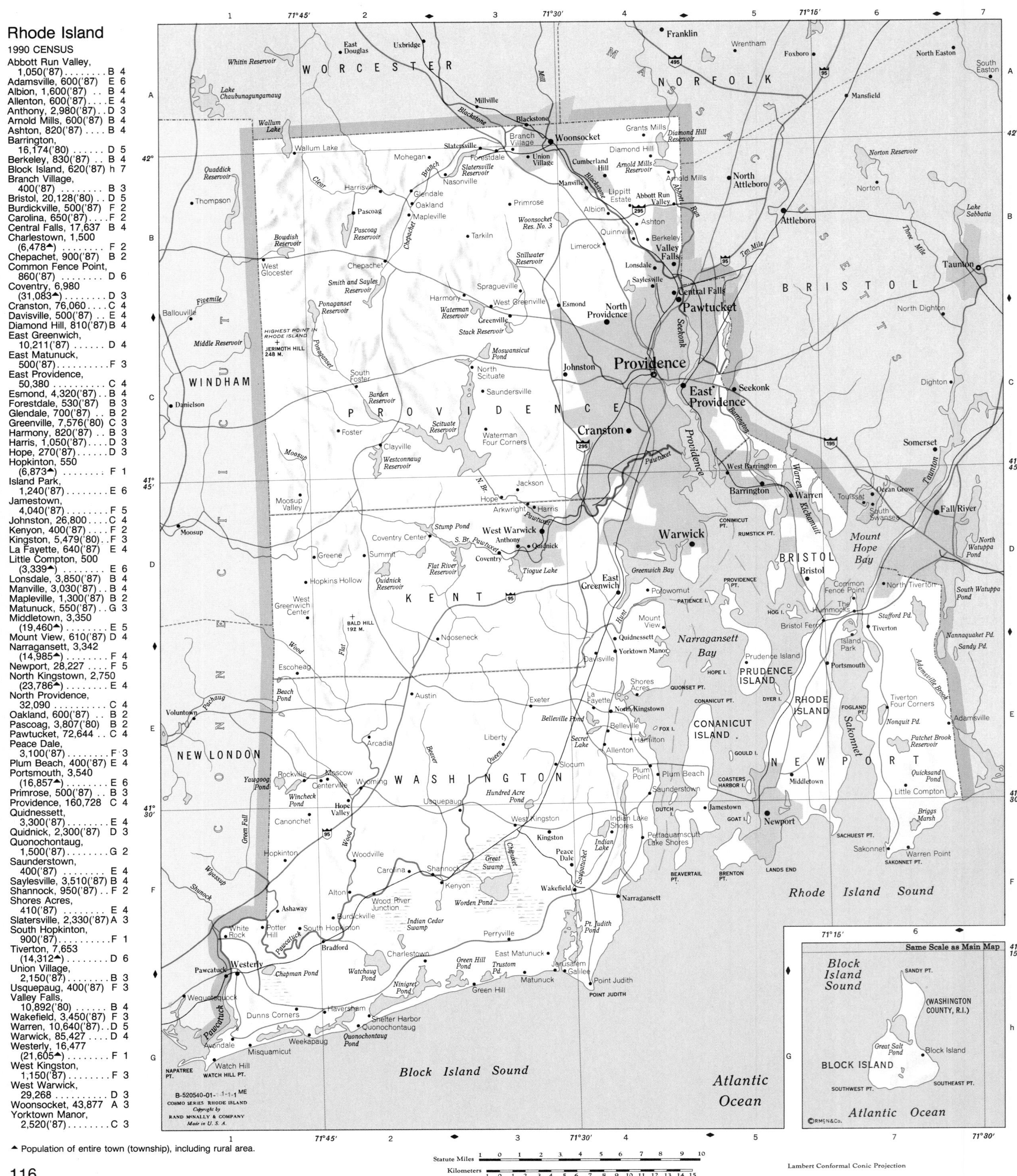

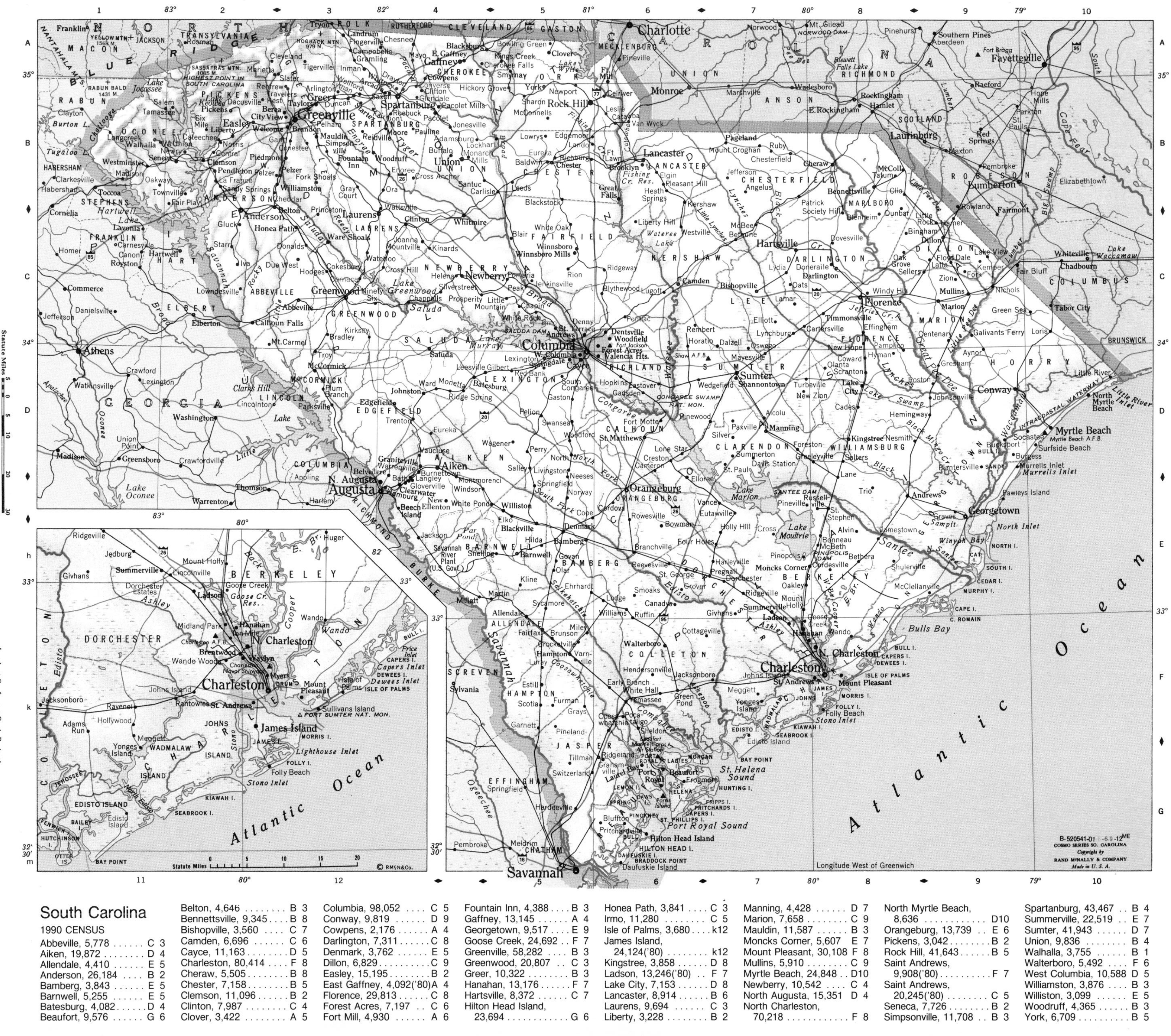

South Carolina

1990 CENSUS

Abbeville, 5,778 ...... C 3
Aiken, 19,872 .... D 4
Allendale, 4,410 ...... E 5
Anderson, 26,184 .... B 2
Bamberg, 3,843 ...... E 5
Barnwell, 5,255 ...... E 5
Batesburg, 4,082 ...... D 4
Beaufort, 9,576 ...... G 6
Belton, 4,646 .... B 3
Bennettsville, 9,345 .... B 8
Bishopville, 3,560 .... C 7
Camden, 6,696 ...... C 6
Cayce, 11,163 .... D 5
Charleston, 80,414 .... F 8
Cheraw, 5,505 .... B 8
Chester, 7,158 .... B 5
Clemson, 11,096 ...... B 2
Clinton, 7,987 .... C 4
Clover, 3,422 .... A 5
Columbia, 98,052 .... C 5
Conway, 9,819 ...... D 9
Cowpens, 2,176 ...... A 4
Darlington, 7,311 ...... C 8
Denmark, 3,762 ...... E 5
Dillon, 6,829 .... C 9
Easley, 15,195 .... B 2
East Gaffney, 4,092('80) A 4
Florence, 29,813 ...... C 8
Forest Acres, 7,197 .. C 6
Fort Mill, 4,930 ...... A 6
Fountain Inn, 4,388 .... B 3
Gaffney, 13,145 ...... A 4
Georgetown, 9,517 .... E 9
Goose Creek, 24,692 .. F 7
Greenville, 58,282 .... B 3
Greenwood, 20,807 .. C 3
Greer, 10,322 .... B 3
Hanahan, 13,176 ...... F 7
Hartsville, 8,372 ...... C 7
Hilton Head Island, 23,694 .... G 6
Honea Path, 3,841 .... C 3
Irmo, 11,280 .... C 5
Isle of Palms, 3,680 .... k12
James Island, 24,124('80) k12
Kingstree, 3,858 ...... D 8
Ladson, 13,246('80) .. F 7
Lake City, 7,153 .... D 8
Lancaster, 8,914 ...... B 6
Laurens, 9,694 ...... C 3
Liberty, 3,228 .... B 2
Manning, 4,428 ...... D 7
Marion, 7,658 .... C 9
Mauldin, 11,587 ...... B 3
Moncks Corner, 5,607 E 7
Mount Pleasant, 30,108 F 8
Mullins, 5,910 .... C 9
Myrtle Beach, 24,848 .. D10
Newberry, 10,542 .... C 4
North Augusta, 15,351 D 4
North Charleston, 70,218 .... F 8
North Myrtle Beach, 8,636 .... D10
Orangeburg, 13,739 .. E 6
Pickens, 3,042 .... B 2
Rock Hill, 41,643 ...... B 5
Saint Andrews, 9,908('80) .... F 7
Saint Andrews, 20,245('80) .... C 5
Seneca, 7,726 .... B 2
Simpsonville, 11,708 .. B 3
Spartanburg, 43,467 .. B 4
Summerville, 22,519 .. E 7
Sumter, 41,943 .... D 7
Union, 9,836 .... B 4
Walhalla, 3,755 ...... B 1
Walterboro, 5,492 ...... F 6
West Columbia, 10,588 D 5
Williamston, 3,876 .... B 3
Williston, 3,099 ...... E 5
Woodruff, 4,365 ...... B 3
York, 6,709 .... B 5

South Dakota

1990 CENSUS

Aberdeen, 24,927 . . . . B 7
Alcester, 843 . . . . D 9
Arlington, 908 . . . . C 8
Armour, 854 . . . . D 7
Belle Fourche, 4,335 . . C 2
Beresford, 1,849 . . . . . . D 9
Box Elder, 2,680 . . . . . . C 2
Brandon, 3,543 . . . . . . D 9
Britton, 1,394 . . . . B 8
Brookings, 16,270 . . . . C 9
Burke, 756 . . . . D 6
Canton, 2,787 . . . . D 9
Centerville, 887 . . . . . . D 9
Chamberlain, 2,347 . . . . D 6
Clark, 1,292 . . . . C 8
Clear Lake, 1,247 . . . . C 9
Custer, 1,741 . . . . D 2
Deadwood, 1,830 . . . . . C 2
Dell Rapids, 2,484 . . . . D 9
De Smet, 1,172 . . . . . . C 8
Edgemont, 906 . . . . . . D 2
Elk Point, 1,423 . . . . . . E 9
Eureka, 1,197 . . . . B 6
Faulkton, 809 . . . . B 6
Flandreau, 2,311 . . . . . . C 9
Fort Pierre, 1,854 . . . . C 5
Freeman, 1,293 . . . . . . D 8
Garretson, 924 . . . . D 9
Gettysburg, 1,510 . . . . C 6
Gregory, 1,384 . . . . D 6
Groton, 1,196 . . . . B 7
Hartford, 1,262 . . . . . . D 9
Highmore, 835 . . . . C 6
Hot Springs, 4,325 . . . . D 2
Howard, 1,156 . . . . C 8
Huron, 12,448 . . . . C 7
Ipswich, 965 . . . . B 6
Kadoka, 736 . . . . D 4
Lake Andes, 846 . . . . . . D 7
Lake Preston, 663 . . . . C 8
Lead, 3,632 . . . . C 2
Lemmon, 1,614 . . . . . . B 3
Lennox, 1,767 . . . . D 9
Madison, 6,257 . . . . . . C 8
Marion, 831 . . . . D 8
Martin, 1,151 . . . . D 4
McLaughlin, 780 . . . . . . B 5
Menno, 768 . . . . D 8
Milbank, 3,879 . . . . B 9
Miller, 1,678 . . . . C 7
Mitchell, 13,798 . . . . . . D 7
Mobridge, 3,768 . . . . . . B 5
North Sioux City, 2,019 E 9
Onida, 761 . . . . C 5
Parker, 984 . . . . D 8
Parkston, 1,572 . . . . . . D 8
Philip, 1,077 . . . . C 4
Pierre, 12,906 . . . . C 5
Platte, 1,311 . . . . D 7
Presho, 654 . . . . D 5
Rapid City, 54,523 . . . . C 2
Redfield, 2,770 . . . . . . C 7
Saint Francis, 815 . . . . D 5
Salem, 1,289 . . . . D 8
Scotland, 968 . . . . D 8
Selby, 707 . . . . B 5
Sioux Falls, 100,814 . . D 9
Sisseton, 2,181 . . . . . . B 8
Spearfish, 6,966 . . . . . . C 2
Springfield, 834 . . . . . . E 8
Sturgis, 5,330 . . . . C 2
Tyndall, 1,201 . . . . E 8
Valley Springs, 739 . . . . D 9
Vermillion, 10,034 . . . . E 9
Volga, 1,263 . . . . C 9
Wagner, 1,462 . . . . D 7
Wall, 834 . . . . D 3
Watertown, 17,592 . . . . C 8
Webster, 2,017 . . . . . . B 8
Wessington Springs, 1,083 . . . . C 7
Whitewood, 891 . . . . . . C 2
Winner, 3,354 . . . . D 6
Woonsocket, 766 . . . . . . C 7
Yankton, 12,703 . . . . . . E 8

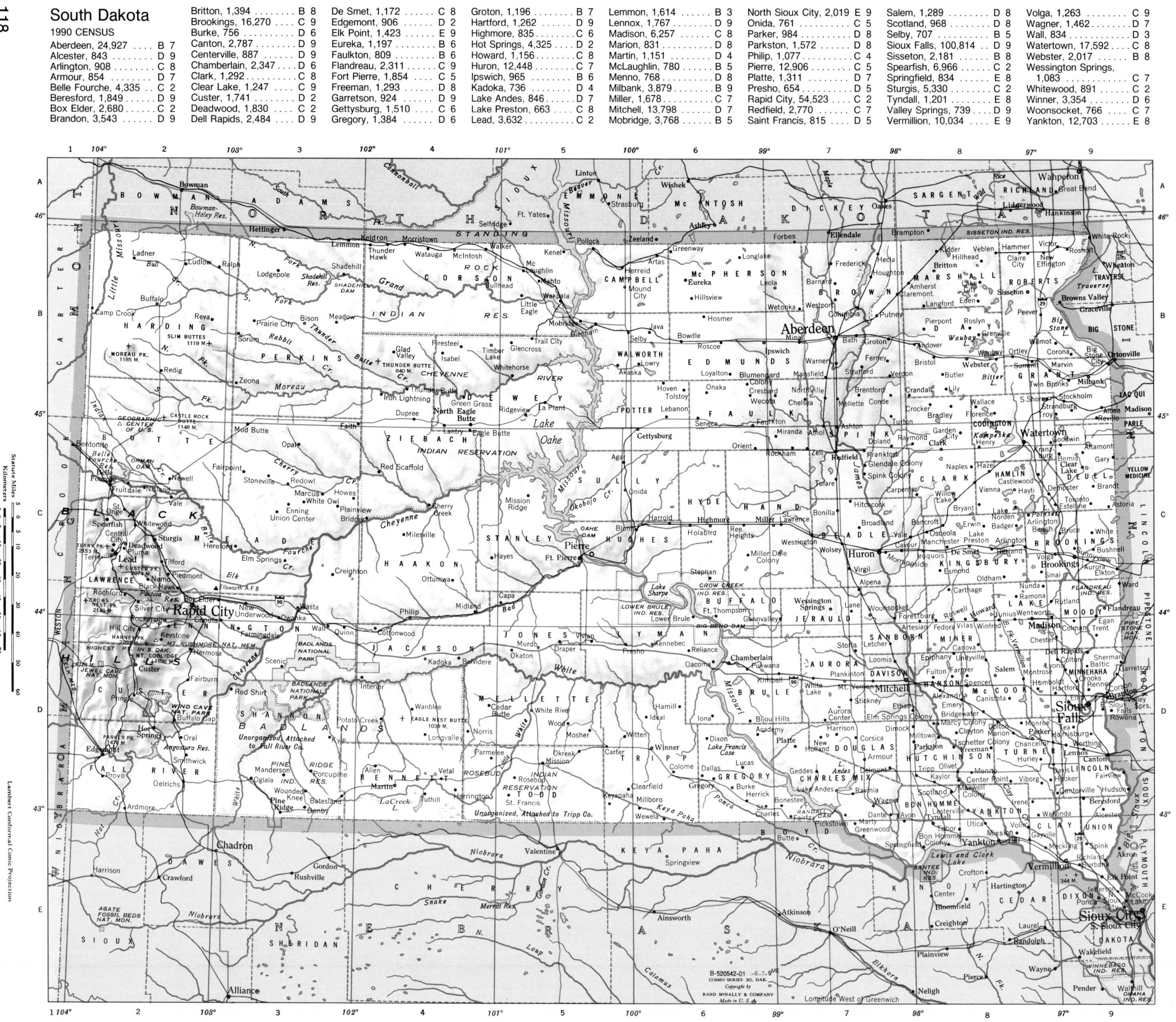

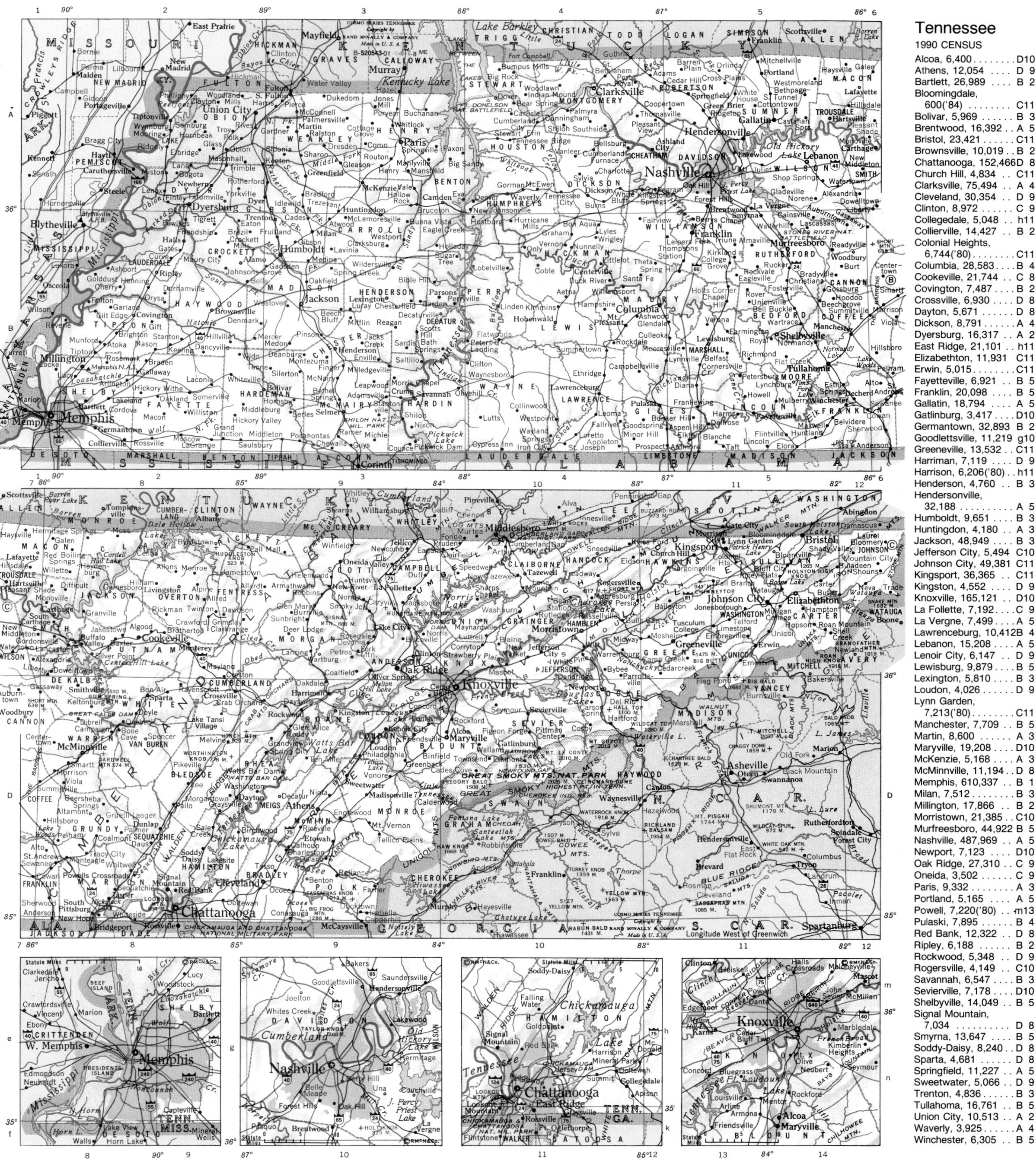

Tennessee

1990 CENSUS

Alcoa, 6,400 . . . . D10
Athens, 12,054 . . . . D 9
Bartlett, 26,989 . . . . B 2
Bloomingdale, 600('84) C11
Bolivar, 5,969 . . . . . . B 3
Brentwood, 16,392 . . A 5
Bristol, 23,421 . . . . . . C11
Brownsville, 10,019 . . B 2
Chattanooga, 152,466 D 8
Church Hill, 4,834 . . C11
Clarksville, 75,494 . . A 4
Cleveland, 30,354 . . D 9
Clinton, 8,972 . . . . . . C 9
Collegedale, 5,048 . . h11
Collierville, 14,427 . . B 2
Colonial Heights, 6,744('80) C11
Columbia, 28,583 . . . . B 4
Cookeville, 21,744 . . C 8
Covington, 7,487 . . . . B 2
Crossville, 6,930 . . . . D 8
Dayton, 5,671 . . . . . . D 8
Dickson, 8,791 . . . . . . A 4
Dyersburg, 16,317 . . A 2
East Ridge, 21,101 . . h11
Elizabethton, 11,931 C11
Erwin, 5,015 . . . . C11
Fayetteville, 6,921 . . B 5
Franklin, 20,098 . . . . B 5
Gallatin, 18,794 . . . . A 5
Gatlinburg, 3,417 . . . . D10
Germantown, 32,893 B 2
Goodlettsville, 11,219 g10
Greeneville, 13,532 . . C11
Harriman, 7,119 . . . . D 9
Harrison, 6,206('80) . . h11
Henderson, 4,760 . . B 3
Hendersonville, 32,188 . . . . A 5
Humboldt, 9,651 . . . . B 3
Huntingdon, 4,180 . . A 3
Jackson, 48,949 . . . . B 3
Jefferson City, 5,494 C10
Johnson City, 49,381 C11
Kingsport, 36,365 . . C11
Kingston, 4,552 . . . . D 9
Knoxville, 165,121 . . D10
La Follette, 7,192 . . . . C 9
La Vergne, 7,499 . . . . A 5
Lawrenceburg, 10,412 B 4
Lebanon, 15,208 . . . . A 5
Lenoir City, 6,147 . . D 9
Lewisburg, 9,879 . . . . B 5
Lexington, 5,810 . . . . B 3
Loudon, 4,026 . . . . . . D 9
Lynn Garden, 7,213('80) C11
Manchester, 7,709 . . B 5
Martin, 8,600 . . . . . . A 3
Maryville, 19,208 . . . . D10
McKenzie, 5,168 . . . . A 3
McMinnville, 11,194 . . D 8
Memphis, 610,337 . . B 1
Milan, 7,512 . . . . B 3
Millington, 17,866 . . B 2
Morristown, 21,385 . . C10
Murfreesboro, 44,922 B 5
Nashville, 487,969 . . A 5
Newport, 7,123 . . . . D10
Oak Ridge, 27,310 . . C 9
Oneida, 3,502 . . . . . . C 9
Paris, 9,332 . . . . A 3
Portland, 5,165 . . . . A 5
Powell, 7,220('80) . . m13
Pulaski, 7,895 . . . . . . B 4
Red Bank, 12,322 . . D 8
Ripley, 6,188 . . . . . . B 2
Rockwood, 5,348 . . D 9
Rogersville, 4,149 . . C10
Savannah, 6,547 . . . . B 3
Sevierville, 7,178 . . . . D10
Shelbyville, 14,049 . . B 5
Signal Mountain, 7,034 . . . . D 8
Smyrna, 13,647 . . . . B 5
Soddy-Daisy, 8,240 . . D 8
Sparta, 4,681 . . . . . . D 8
Springfield, 11,227 . . A 5
Sweetwater, 5,066 . . D 9
Trenton, 4,836 . . . . . . B 3
Tullahoma, 16,761 . . B 5
Union City, 10,513 . . A 2
Waverly, 3,925 . . . . . . A 4
Winchester, 6,305 . . B 5

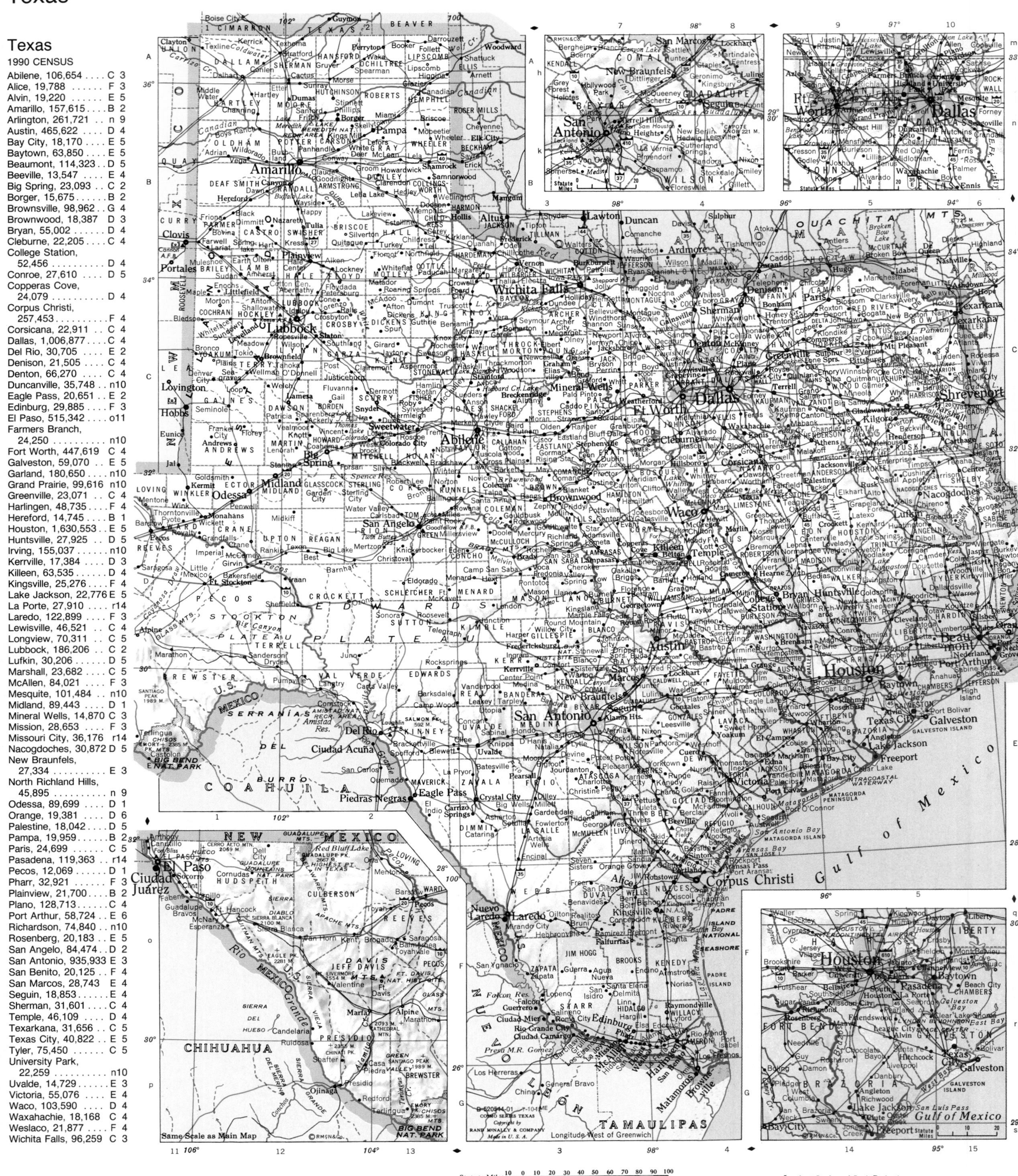
Texas
1990 CENSUS
Abilene, 106,654 .... C 3
Alice, 19,788 ...... F 3
Alvin, 19,220 ...... E 5
Amarillo, 157,615... B 2
Arlington, 261,721 .. n 9
Austin, 465,622 .... D 4
Bay City, 18,170 .... E 5
Baytown, 63,850 .... E 5
Beaumont, 114,323.. D 5
Beeville, 13,547 .... E 4
Big Spring, 23,093 .. C 2
Borger, 15,675...... B 2
Brownsville, 98,962.. G 4
Brownwood, 18,387 D 3
Bryan, 55,002 ...... D 4
Cleburne, 22,205 .... C 4
College Station, 52,456 .... D 4
Conroe, 27,610 .... D 5
Copperas Cove, 24,079 .... D 4
Corpus Christi, 257,453.......... F 4
Corsicana, 22,911 .. C 4
Dallas, 1,006,877 .... C 4
Del Rio, 30,705 .... E 2
Denison, 21,505 .... C 4
Denton, 66,270 .... C 4
Duncanville, 35,748.. n10
Eagle Pass, 20,651.. E 2
Edinburg, 29,885 .... F 3
El Paso, 515,342 .... o11
Farmers Branch, 24,250 .... n10
Fort Worth, 447,619 C 4
Galveston, 59,070 .. E 5
Garland, 180,650.... n10
Grand Prairie, 99,616 n10
Greenville, 23,071 .. C 4
Harlingen, 48,735.... F 4
Hereford, 14,745.... B 1
Houston, 1,630,553.. E 5
Huntsville, 27,925 .. D 5
Irving, 155,037 ...... n10
Kerrville, 17,384 .... D 3
Killeen, 63,535...... D 4
Kingsville, 25,276.... F 4
Lake Jackson, 22,776 E 5
La Porte, 27,910 ...... r14
Laredo, 122,899 .... F 3
Lewisville, 46,521 .. C 4
Longview, 70,311 .. C 5
Lubbock, 186,206 .. C 2
Lufkin, 30,206 ...... D 5
Marshall, 23,682 .... C 5
McAllen, 84,021 .... F 3
Mesquite, 101,484 .. n10
Midland, 89,443 .... D 1
Mineral Wells, 14,870 C 3
Mission, 28,653 .... F 3
Missouri City, 36,176 r14
Nacogdoches, 30,872 D 5
New Braunfels, 27,334 .... E 3
North Richland Hills, 45,895 .... n 9
Odessa, 89,699 .... D 1
Orange, 19,381 .... D 6
Palestine, 18,042.... D 5
Pampa, 19,959...... B 2
Paris, 24,699 ...... C 5
Pasadena, 119,363 .. r14
Pecos, 12,069 ...... D 1
Pharr, 32,921 ...... F 3
Plainview, 21,700.... B 2
Plano, 128,713...... C 4
Port Arthur, 58,724 .. E 6
Richardson, 74,840 .. n10
Rosenberg, 20,183 .. E 5
San Angelo, 84,474 .. D 2
San Antonio, 935,933 E 3
San Benito, 20,125 .. F 4
San Marcos, 28,743 E 4
Seguin, 18,853...... E 4
Sherman, 31,601.... C 4
Temple, 46,109 .... D 4
Texarkana, 31,656 .. C 5
Texas City, 40,822 .. E 5
Tyler, 75,450 ...... C 5
University Park, 22,259 .... n10
Uvalde, 14,729...... E 3
Victoria, 55,076 .... E 4
Waco, 103,590 .... D 4
Waxahachie, 18,168 C 4
Weslaco, 21,877 .... F 4
Wichita Falls, 96,259 C 3
Gulf of Mexico
COAHUILA
CHIHUAHUA
TAMAULIPAS
NUEVO LEON
MEXICO
Same Scale as Main Map
Longitude West of Greenwich
RAND McNALLY & COMPANY
Made in U. S. A.
Statute Miles
Kilometers
Lambert Conformal Conic Projection

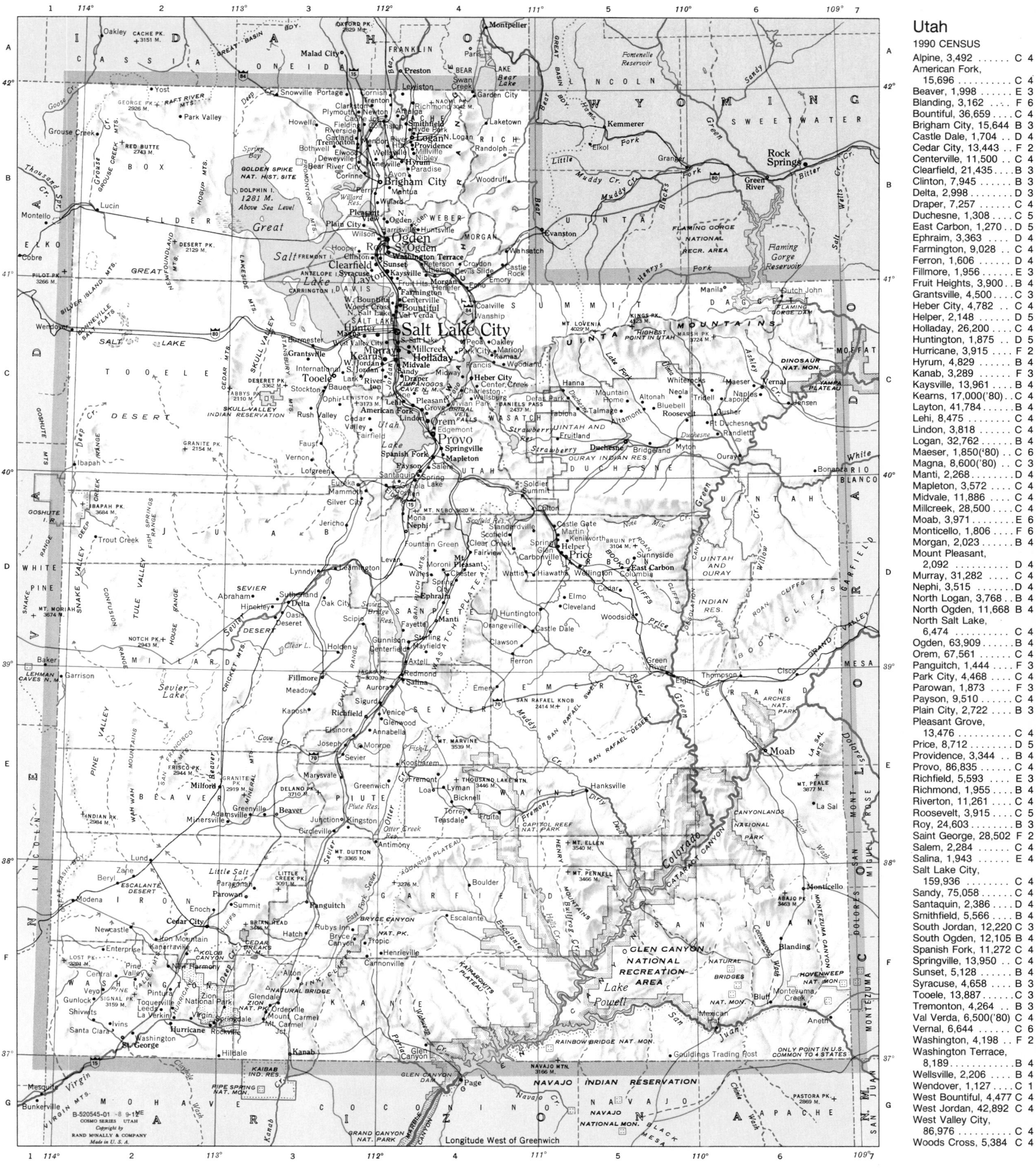

Utah

1990 CENSUS

Alpine, 3,492 . . . . . . C 4
American Fork, 15,696 . . . . C 4
Beaver, 1,998 . . . . E 3
Blanding, 3,162 . . . . F 6
Bountiful, 36,659 . . . . C 4
Brigham City, 15,644 B 3
Castle Dale, 1,704 . . D 4
Cedar City, 13,443 . . F 2
Centerville, 11,500 . . C 4
Clearfield, 21,435 . . . B 3
Clinton, 7,945 . . . . . . B 3
Delta, 2,998 . . . . D 3
Draper, 7,257 . . . . . . C 4
Duchesne, 1,308 . . . . C 5
East Carbon, 1,270 . . D 5
Ephraim, 3,363 . . . . D 4
Farmington, 9,028 . . C 4
Ferron, 1,606 . . . . . . D 4
Fillmore, 1,956 . . . . . . E 3
Fruit Heights, 3,900 . . B 4
Grantsville, 4,500 . . . . C 3
Heber City, 4,782 . . C 4
Helper, 2,148 . . . . . . D 5
Holladay, 26,200 . . . . C 4
Huntington, 1,875 . . . D 5
Hurricane, 3,915 . . . . F 2
Hyrum, 4,829 . . . . . . B 4
Kanab, 3,289 . . . . . . F 3
Kaysville, 13,961 . . . . B 4
Kearns, 17,000('80) . . C 4
Layton, 41,784 . . . . . . B 4
Lehi, 8,475 . . . . C 4
Lindon, 3,818 . . . . . . C 4
Logan, 32,762 . . . . . . B 4
Maeser, 1,850('80) . . C 6
Magna, 8,600('80) . . C 3
Manti, 2,268 . . . . D 4
Mapleton, 3,572 . . . . C 4
Midvale, 11,886 . . . . C 4
Millcreek, 28,500 . . . . C 4
Moab, 3,971 . . . . E 6
Monticello, 1,806 . . . F 6
Morgan, 2,023 . . . . . . B 4
Mount Pleasant, 2,092 . . . . D 4
Murray, 31,282 . . . . C 4
Nephi, 3,515 . . . . . . D 4
North Logan, 3,768 . . B 4
North Ogden, 11,668 B 4
North Salt Lake, 6,474 . . . . C 4
Ogden, 63,909 . . . . . . B 4
Orem, 67,561 . . . . . . C 4
Panguitch, 1,444 . . . . F 3
Park City, 4,468 . . . . C 4
Parowan, 1,873 . . . . . F 3
Payson, 9,510 . . . . . . C 4
Plain City, 2,722 . . . . B 3
Pleasant Grove, 13,476 . . . . C 4
Price, 8,712 . . . . D 5
Providence, 3,344 . . B 4
Provo, 86,835 . . . . . . C 4
Richfield, 5,593 . . . . E 3
Richmond, 1,955 . . . . B 4
Riverton, 11,261 . . . . C 4
Roosevelt, 3,915 . . . . C 5
Roy, 24,603 . . . . B 3
Saint George, 28,502 F 2
Salem, 2,284 . . . . . . C 4
Salina, 1,943 . . . . . . E 4
Salt Lake City, 159,936 . . . . C 4
Sandy, 75,058 . . . . . . C 4
Santaquin, 2,386 . . . . D 4
Smithfield, 5,566 . . . . B 4
South Jordan, 12,220 C 3
South Ogden, 12,105 B 4
Spanish Fork, 11,272 C 4
Springville, 13,950 . . C 4
Sunset, 5,128 . . . . . . B 4
Syracuse, 4,658 . . . . B 3
Tooele, 13,887 . . . . . . C 3
Tremonton, 4,264 . . B 3
Val Verda, 6,500('80) C 4
Vernal, 6,644 . . . . . . C 6
Washington, 4,198 . . F 2
Washington Terrace, 8,189 . . . . B 4
Wellsville, 2,206 . . . . B 4
Wendover, 1,127 . . . . C 1
West Bountiful, 4,477 C 4
West Jordan, 42,892 C 4
West Valley City, 86,976 . . . . C 4
Woods Cross, 5,384 C 4

Vermont

1990 CENSUS

Arlington, 700 (2,299▲) . . . . E 2
Barre, 9,482 . . . . C 4
Barton, 908 . . . . B 4
Bellows Falls, 3,313 . . E 4
Bennington, 9,349 (16,451▲) . . . . F 2
Bethel, 1,016 (1,866▲) . . . . D 3
Bradford, 672 . . . . . . D 4
Brandon, 1,925 (4,223▲) . . . . D 2
Brattleboro, 8,596 (12,241▲) . . . . F 3
Bristol, 1,801 . . . . . . C 2
Burlington, 39,127 . . C 2
Castleton, 600 (4,278▲) . . . . D 2
Chester, 550 (2,832▲) E 3
Chester Depot, 500 . . E 3
Derby Line, 855 . . . . A 4
Dorset, 550 (1,918▲) E 2
East Arlington, 600 . . E 2
East Barre, 700 . . . . C 4
East Middlebury, 500 D 2
East Montpelier, 600 (2,239▲) . . . . C 4
Enosburg Falls, 1,350 B 3
Essex, 800 (16,498▲) B 2
Essex Junction, 8,396 C 2
Fair Haven, 2,887 . . D 2
Forest Dale, 350 . . . . D 2
Gilman, 500 . . . . C 5
Graniteville, 500 . . . . C 4
Hardwick, 1,400 (2,964▲) . . . . B 4
Hartford, 500 (9,404▲) . . . . D 4
Hydeville, 450 . . . . . . D 2
Jericho, 1,300 (4,302▲) . . . . B 3
Johnson, 1,470 . . . . . B 3
Ludlow, 1,123 . . . . . . E 3
Lyndonville, 1,255 . . B 4
Manchester, 561 . . . . E 2
Middlebury, 5,591 (8,034▲) . . . . C 2
Milton, 1,578 . . . . . . B 2
Montpelier, 8,247 . . . . C 3
Morrisville, 1,984 . . . . B 3
Newport, 4,434 . . . . . . B 4
North Bennington, 1,520 . . . . F 2
North Clarendon, 500 D 3
Northfield, 1,889 . . . . C 3
Northfield Falls, 600 C 3
North Springfield, 750 E 3
North Troy, 723 . . . . B 4
Norwich, 1,000 (3,093▲) . . . . D 4
Orleans, 806 . . . . . . B 4
Pittsford, 650 (2,919▲) . . . . D 2
Plainfield, 600 (1,302▲) . . . . C 4
Poultney, 1,731 . . . . D 2
Proctor, 1,979 . . . . . . D 2
Proctorsville, 480 . . . . E 3
Putney, 1,100 (2,352▲) . . . . F 3
Quechee, 550 . . . . . . D 4
Randolph, 2,200 (4,764▲) . . . . D 3
Richford, 1,425 . . . . . B 3
Richmond, 650 (3,729▲) . . . . C 3
Riverton, 150 . . . . . . C 3
Rochester, 500 (1,181▲) . . . . D 3
Rutland, 18,230 . . . . D 3
Saint Albans, 7,339 . . B 2
Saint Johnsbury, 7,150 (7,608▲) . . . . C 4
Saxtons River, 541 . . E 3
Shaftsbury, 700 (3,368▲) . . . . E 2
South Burlington, 12,809 . . . . C 2
South Royalton, 700 D 3
Springfield, 5,603 (9,579▲) . . . . E 4
Stamford, 400 (773▲) F 2
Stowe, 450 . . . . C 3
Swanton, 2,360 . . . . . B 2
Vergennes, 2,578 . . C 2
Wallingford, 1,141 (2,184▲) . . . . E 3
Warren, 350 (1,172▲) C 3
Waterbury, 1,702 . . . . C 3
Waterbury Center, 500 . . . . C 3
Websterville, 600 . . . . C 4
West Pawlet, 350 . . E 2
West Rutland, 2,448 D 2
Williamstown, 650 (2,839▲) . . . . C 3
Wilmington, 550 (1,968▲) . . . . F 3
Windsor, 3,714 . . . . . E 4
Winooski, 6,649 . . . . C 2
Woodstock, 1,037 . . D 3

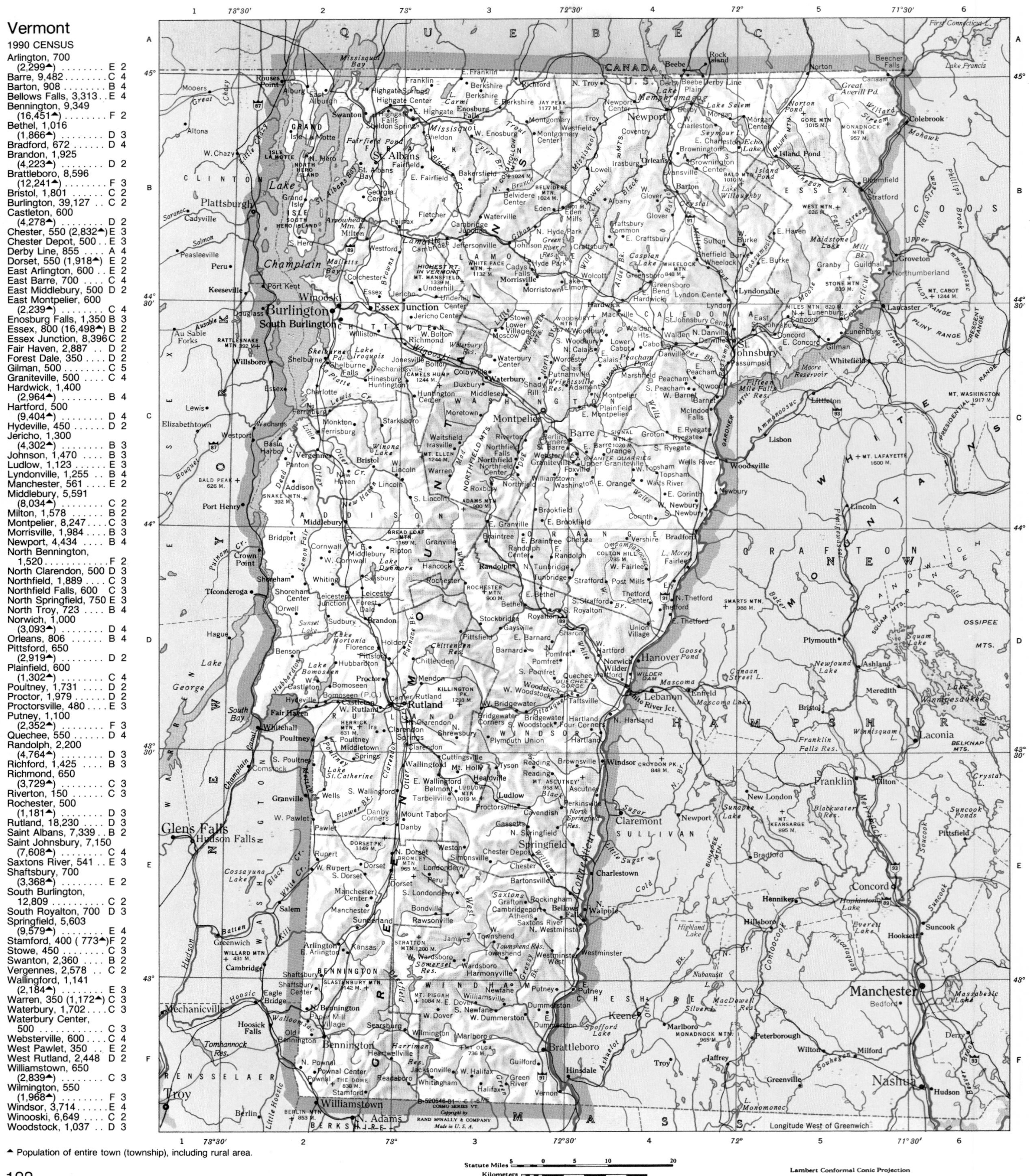

▲ Population of entire town (township), including rural area.

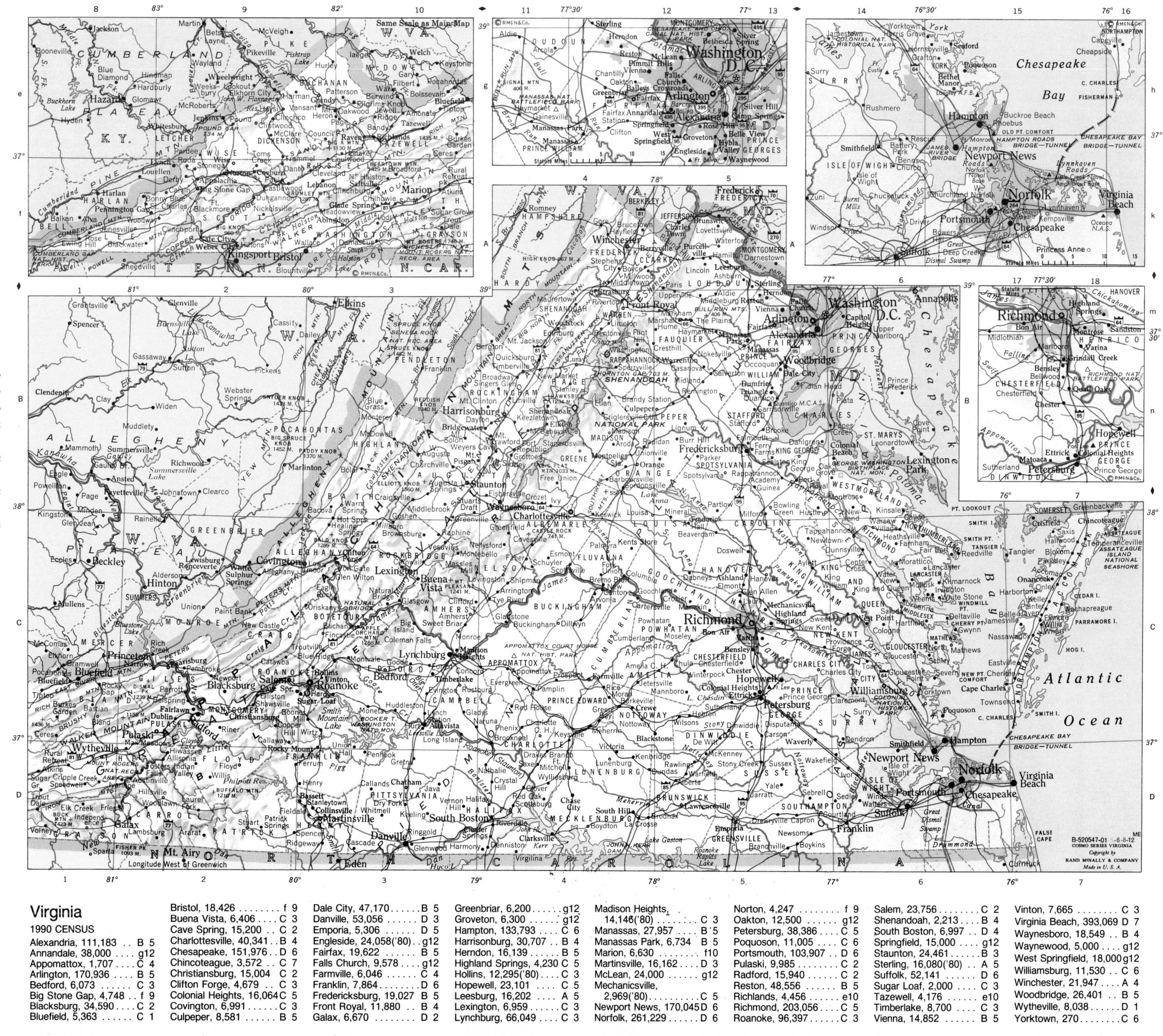

Virginia

1990 CENSUS

Alexandria, 111,183 .. B 5
Annandale, 38,000 ..... g12
Appomattox, 1,707 ..... C 4
Arlington, 170,936 .... B 5
Bedford, 6,073 .... C 3
Big Stone Gap, 4,748 .. f 9
Blacksburg, 34,590 .... C 2
Bluefield, 5,363 ...... C 1
Bristol, 18,426 .... f 9
Buena Vista, 6,406 .... C 3
Cave Spring, 15,200 ... C 2
Charlottesville, 40,341 .. B 4
Chesapeake, 151,976 .. D 6
Chincoteague, 3,572 .. C 7
Christiansburg, 15,004 C 2
Clifton Forge, 4,679 .. C 3
Colonial Heights, 16,064 C 5
Covington, 6,991 ...... C 3
Culpeper, 8,581 ...... B 5
Dale City, 47,170 ..... B 5
Danville, 53,056 ...... D 3
Emporia, 5,306 .... D 5
Engleside, 24,058('80) .. g12
Fairfax, 19,622 .... B 5
Falls Church, 9,578 .... g12
Farmville, 6,046 ...... C 4
Franklin, 7,864 .... D 6
Fredericksburg, 19,027 B 5
Front Royal, 11,880 .. B 4
Galax, 6,670 .... D 2
Greenbriar, 6,200 ..... g12
Groveton, 6,300 ...... g12
Hampton, 133,793 .... C 6
Harrisonburg, 30,707 .. B 4
Herndon, 16,139 ...... B 5
Highland Springs, 4,230 C 5
Hollins, 12,295('80) .... C 3
Hopewell, 23,101 ..... C 5
Leesburg, 16,202 ..... A 5
Lexington, 6,959 ...... C 3
Lynchburg, 66,049 .... C 3
Madison Heights, 14,146('80) .... C 3
Manassas, 27,957 .... B 5
Manassas Park, 6,734 B 5
Marion, 6,630 .... f10
Martinsville, 16,162 ... D 3
McLean, 24,000 ...... g12
Mechanicsville, 2,969('80) .... C 5
Newport News, 170,045 D 6
Norfolk, 261,229 ...... D 6
Norton, 4,247 .... f 9
Oakton, 12,500 ...... g12
Petersburg, 38,386 .... C 5
Poquoson, 11,005 .... C 6
Portsmouth, 103,907 .. D 6
Pulaski, 9,985 .... C 2
Radford, 15,940 .... C 2
Reston, 48,556 .... B 5
Richlands, 4,456 ...... e10
Richmond, 203,056 .... C 5
Roanoke, 96,397 ...... C 3
Salem, 23,756 .... C 2
Shenandoah, 2,213 ... B 4
South Boston, 6,997 .. D 4
Springfield, 15,000 ..... g12
Staunton, 24,461 ...... B 3
Sterling, 16,080('80) ... A 5
Suffolk, 52,141 .... D 6
Sugar Loaf, 2,000 .... C 3
Tazewell, 4,176 ...... e10
Timberlake, 8,700 .... C 3
Vienna, 14,852 .... B 5
Vinton, 7,665 .... C 3
Virginia Beach, 393,069 D 7
Waynesboro, 18,549 .. B 4
Waynewood, 5,000 .... g12
West Springfield, 18,000 g12
Williamsburg, 11,530 .. C 6
Winchester, 21,947 .... A 4
Woodbridge, 26,401 .. B 5
Wytheville, 8,038 ...... D 1
Yorktown, 270 .... C 6

Washington

1990 CENSUS

Aberdeen, 16,565 .... C 2
Anacortes, 11,451 .... A 3
Auburn, 33,102 ...... B 3
Bellevue, 86,874 .... e11
Bellingham, 52,179 .... A 3
Bonney Lake, 7,494 .. B 3
Bothell, 12,345 ...... B 3
Bremerton, 38,142 .... B 3
Camas, 6,442 .... D 3
Centralia, 12,101 ..... C 3
Chehalis, 6,527 ...... C 3
Cheney, 7,723 .... B 8
Clarkston, 6,753 ..... C 8
College Place, 6,308 .. C 7
Colville, 4,360 .... A 8
Coulee Dam, 1,087 ... B 7
Des Moines, 17,283 .. B 3
Edmonds, 30,744 .... B 3
Ellensburg, 12,361 .... C 5
Enumclaw, 7,227 ..... B 4
Ephrata, 5,349 .... B 6
Everett, 69,961 .... B 3
Ferndale, 5,398 ...... A 3
Fircrest, 5,258 .... f10
Goldendale, 3,319 .... D 5
Grandview, 7,169 .... C 6
Hoquiam, 8,972 ...... C 2
Issaquah, 7,786 ...... B 3
Kelso, 11,820 .... C 3
Kennewick, 42,155 .... C 6
Kent, 37,960 .... B 3
Kirkland, 40,052 ...... B 3
Lacey, 19,279 .... B 3
Lakewood Center,
 62,000 .... B 3
Longview, 31,499 .... C 3
Lynden, 5,709 .... A 3
Lynnwood, 28,695 .... B 3
Marysville, 10,328 .... A 3
Medical Lake, 3,664 .. B 8
Mercer Island, 20,816 . B 3
Montesano, 3,064 .... C 2
Moses Lake, 11,235 .. B 6
Mount Vernon, 17,647 A 3
Oak Harbor, 17,176 .. A 3
Olympia, 33,840 ...... B 3
Omak, 4,117 .... A 6
Othello, 4,638 .... C 6
Parkland, 27,300 ...... f11
Parkwater, 4,300('91) .. g14
Pasco, 20,337 .... C 6
Port Angeles, 17,710 .. A 2
Port Orchard, 4,984 .. B 3
Port Townsend, 7,001 A 3
Prosser, 4,476 .... C 6
Pullman, 23,478 ...... C 8
Puyallup, 23,875 ...... B 3
Quincy, 3,738 .... B 6
Redmond, 35,800 .... e11
Renton, 41,688 ...... B 3
Richland, 32,315 ...... C 6
Richmond Beach,
 6,700('91) .... B 3
Richmond Highlands,
 27,900 .... B 3
Riverton Heights, 14,182 f11
Seattle, 516,259 ...... B 3
Sedro Woolley, 6,031 . A 3
Selah, 5,113 .... C 5
Shelton, 7,241 .... B 2
Snohomish, 6,499 .... B 3
Spokane, 177,196 .... B 8
Steilacoom, 5,728 ...... f10
Sumner, 6,281 .... B 3
Sunnyside, 11,238 .... C 5
Tacoma, 176,664 .... B 3
Toppenish, 7,419 .... C 5
Tukwila, 11,874 .... f11
Tumwater, 9,976 ...... B 3
Vancouver, 46,380 .... D 3
Walla Walla, 26,478 .. C 7
Wenatchee, 21,756 ... B 5
White Center,
 18,000('91) e11
Yakima, 54,827 ...... C 5

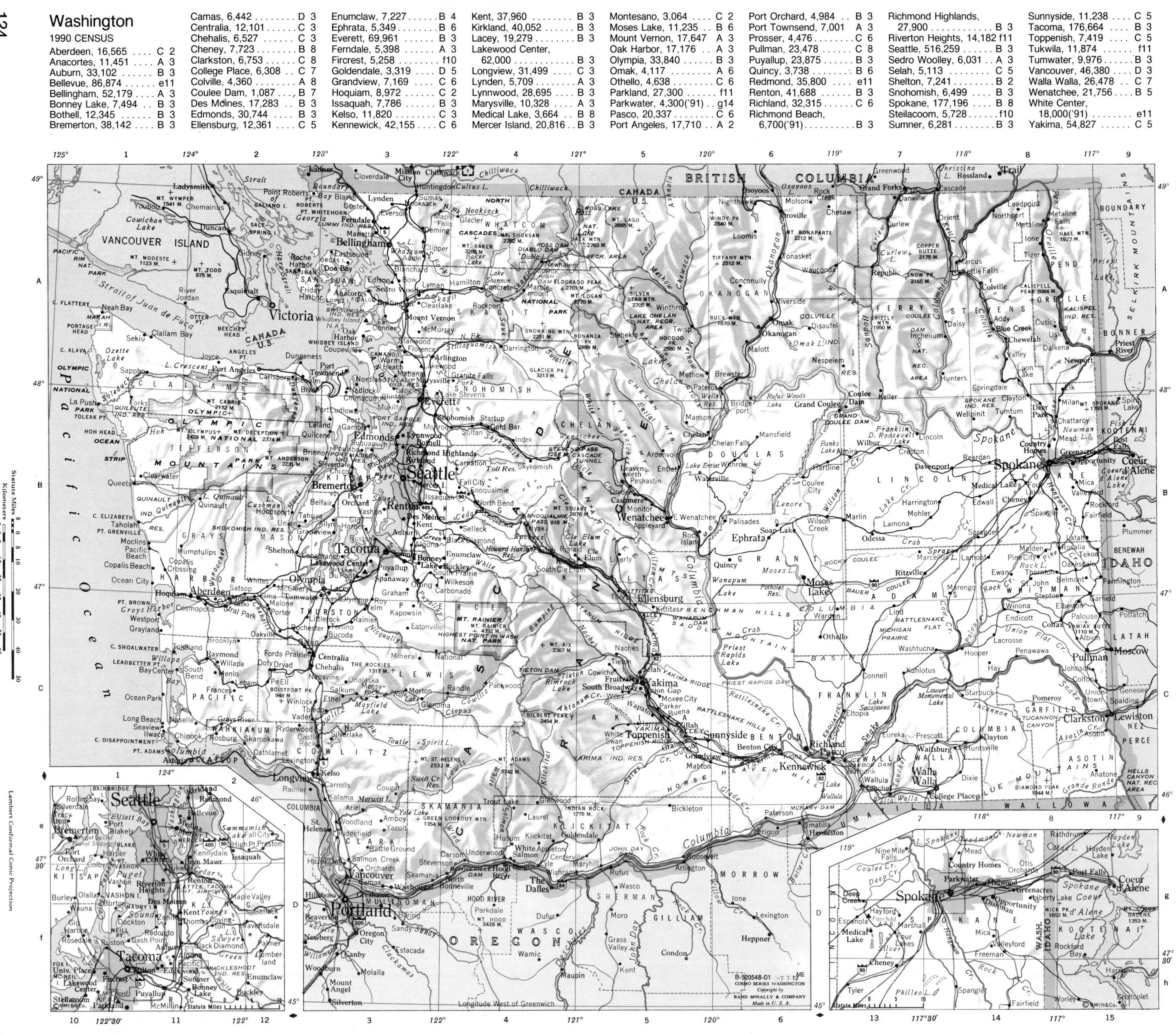

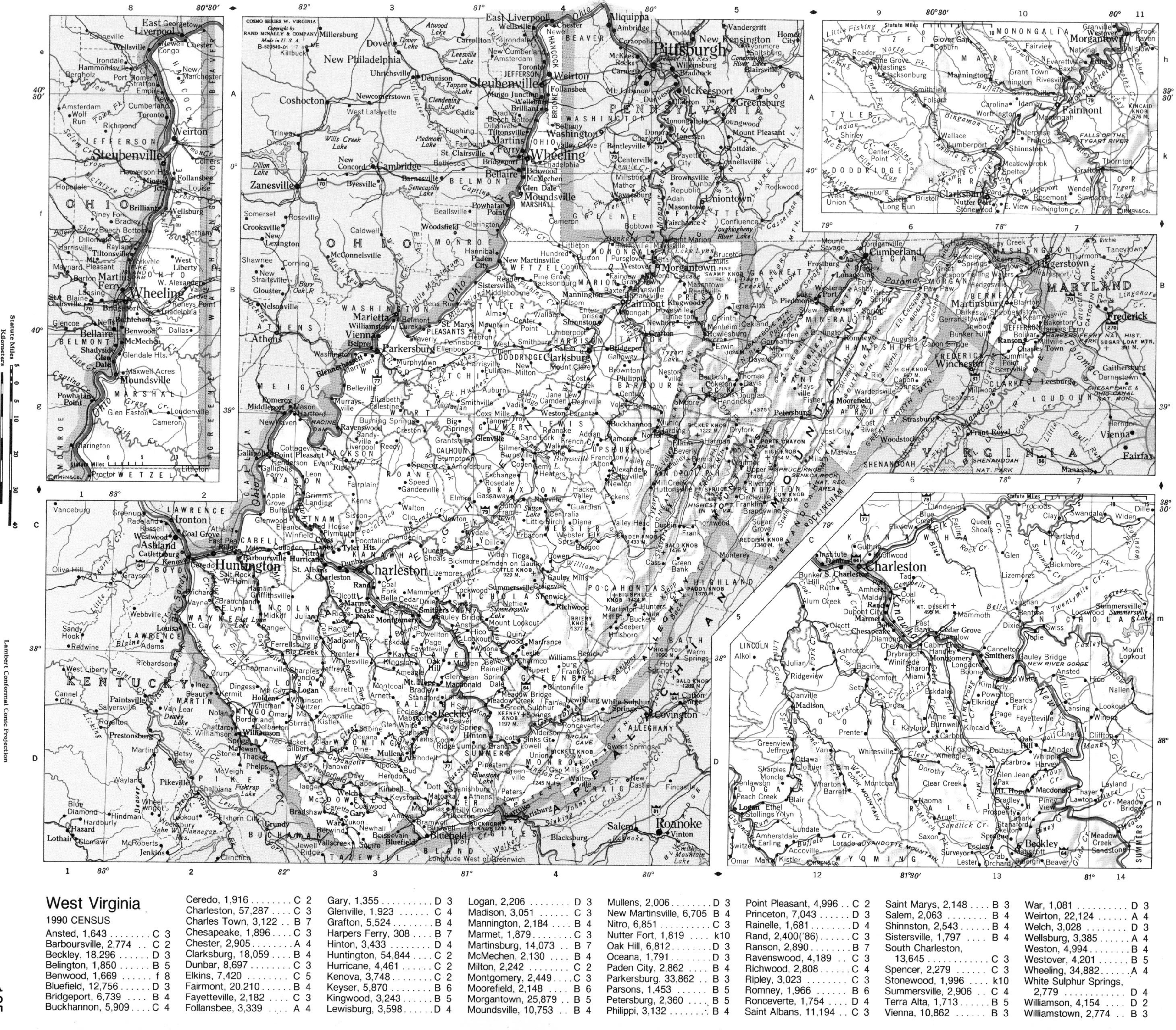

West Virginia

1990 CENSUS

Ansted, 1,643 . . . . C 3
Barboursville, 2,774 . . C 2
Beckley, 18,296 . . . . . D 3
Belington, 1,850 . . . . . . B 5
Benwood, 1,669 . . . . f 8
Bluefield, 12,756 . . . . . . D 3
Bridgeport, 6,739 . . . . B 4
Buckhannon, 5,909 . . . . C 4
Ceredo, 1,916 . . . . C 2
Charleston, 57,287 . . . . C 3
Charles Town, 3,122 . . . B 7
Chesapeake, 1,896 . . . . C 3
Chester, 2,905 . . . . A 4
Clarksburg, 18,059 . . . . B 4
Dunbar, 8,697 . . . . C 3
Elkins, 7,420 . . . . C 5
Fairmont, 20,210 . . . . . . B 4
Fayetteville, 2,182 . . . . . C 3
Follansbee, 3,339 . . . . . A 4
Gary, 1,355 . . . . D 3
Glenville, 1,923 . . . . C 4
Grafton, 5,524 . . . . B 4
Harpers Ferry, 308 . . . . B 7
Hinton, 3,433 . . . . D 4
Huntington, 54,844 . . . . C 2
Hurricane, 4,461 . . . . . . C 2
Kenova, 3,748 . . . . C 2
Keyser, 5,870 . . . . B 6
Kingwood, 3,243 . . . . . . B 5
Lewisburg, 3,598 . . . . . . D 4
Logan, 2,206 . . . . D 3
Madison, 3,051 . . . . . . C 3
Mannington, 2,184 . . . . B 4
Marmet, 1,879 . . . . C 3
Martinsburg, 14,073 . . . B 7
McMechen, 2,130 . . . . . B 4
Milton, 2,242 . . . . C 2
Montgomery, 2,449 . . . . C 3
Moorefield, 2,148 . . . . . B 6
Morgantown, 25,879 . . B 5
Moundsville, 10,753 . . . B 4
Mullens, 2,006 . . . . D 3
New Martinsville, 6,705 B 4
Nitro, 6,851 . . . . C 3
Nutter Fort, 1,819 . . . . . k10
Oak Hill, 6,812 . . . . D 3
Oceana, 1,791 . . . . D 3
Paden City, 2,862 . . . . . B 4
Parkersburg, 33,862 . . . B 3
Parsons, 1,453 . . . . B 5
Petersburg, 2,360 . . . . . B 5
Philippi, 3,132 . . . . B 4
Point Pleasant, 4,996 . . C 2
Princeton, 7,043 . . . . . . D 3
Rainelle, 1,681 . . . . D 4
Rand, 2,400('86) . . . . . . C 3
Ranson, 2,890 . . . . B 7
Ravenswood, 4,189 . . . C 3
Richwood, 2,808 . . . . . . C 4
Ripley, 3,023 . . . . C 3
Romney, 1,966 . . . . B 6
Ronceverte, 1,754 . . . . D 4
Saint Albans, 11,194 . . C 3
Saint Marys, 2,148 . . . . B 3
Salem, 2,063 . . . . B 4
Shinnston, 2,543 . . . . . B 4
Sistersville, 1,797 . . . . B 4
South Charleston,
13,645 . . . . C 3
Spencer, 2,279 . . . . C 3
Stonewood, 1,996 . . . . . k10
Summersville, 2,906 . . . C 4
Terra Alta, 1,713 . . . . . . B 5
Vienna, 10,862 . . . . B 3
War, 1,081 . . . . D 3
Weirton, 22,124 . . . . A 4
Welch, 3,028 . . . . D 3
Wellsburg, 3,385 . . . . . . A 4
Weston, 4,994 . . . . B 4
Westover, 4,201 . . . . B 5
Wheeling, 34,882 . . . . . . A 4
White Sulphur Springs,
2,779 . . . . D 4
Williamson, 4,154 . . . . D 2
Williamstown, 2,774 . . B 3

Wisconsin

1990 CENSUS

Allouez, 14,431 .... h 9
Antigo, 8,276 ...... C 4
Appleton, 65,695 .... D 5
Ashland, 8,695 ...... B 3
Ashwaubenon, 16,376 D 5
Baraboo, 9,203 .... E 4
Beaver Dam, 14,196 E 5
Beloit, 35,573 ...... F 4
Brookfield, 35,184 .. m11
Brown Deer, 12,236 m12
Burlington, 8,855 .... F 5
Cedarburg, 9,895 .... E 6
Chippewa Falls, 12,727 .... D 2
Cudahy, 18,659 ..... F 6
De Pere, 16,569 ..... D 5
Eau Claire, 56,856 .. D 2
Fond du Lac, 37,757 E 5
Fort Atkinson, 10,227 F 5
Franklin, 21,855 ..... n11
Germantown, 13,658 E 5
Glendale, 14,088 .... m12
Grafton, 9,340 ...... E 6
Green Bay, 96,466 .. D 6
Greendale, 15,128 .. F 6
Greenfield, 33,403 .. n11
Hayward, 1,897 .... B 2
Howard, 9,874 ...... D 5
Hudson, 6,378 ...... D 1
Janesville, 52,133 ... F 4
Kaukauna, 11,982 .. D 5
Kenosha, 80,352 ..... F 6
La Crosse, 51,003 .. E 2
Lake Geneva, 5,979 .. F 5
Little Chute, 9,207 .. D 5
Madison, 191,262 .. E 4
Manitowoc, 32,520 .. D 6
Marinette, 11,843 .. C 6
Marshfield, 19,291 .. D 3
Menasha, 14,711 .... D 5
Menomonee Falls, 26,840 .... E 5
Menomonie, 13,547 .. D 2
Mequon, 18,885 .... E 6
Merrill, 9,860 ...... C 4
Middleton, 13,289 .. E 4
Milwaukee, 628,088 .. E 6
Monona, 8,637 ...... E 4
Monroe, 10,241 ..... F 4
Muskego, 16,813 .... F 5
Neenah, 23,219 .... D 5
New Berlin, 33,592 .. n11
New London, 6,658 .. D 5
Oak Creek, 19,513 .. n12
Oconomowoc, 10,993 E 5
Oconto, 4,474 ...... D 6
Onalaska, 11,284 .... E 2
Oshkosh, 55,006 .... D 5
Park Falls, 3,104 .... C 3
Platteville, 9,708 .... F 3
Portage, 8,640 ...... E 4
Port Washington, 9,338 .... E 6
Prairie du Chien, 5,659 .... E 2
Racine, 84,298 ...... F 6
Reedsburg, 5,834 .. E 3
Rhinelander, 7,427 .. C 4
Rice Lake, 7,998 .... C 2
River Falls, 10,610 .. D 1
Saint Francis, 9,245 .. n12
Shawano, 7,598 .... D 5
Sheboygan, 49,676 .. E 6
Shorewood, 14,116 .. E 6
South Milwaukee, 20,958 .... F 6
Stevens Point, 23,006 D 4
Stoughton, 8,786 .... F 4
Sturgeon Bay, 9,176 D 6
Sun Prairie, 15,333 .. E 4
Superior, 27,134 .... B 1
Tomah, 7,570 ...... E 3
Two Rivers, 13,030 .. D 6
Watertown, 19,142 .. E 5
Waukesha, 56,958 .. F 5
Waupun, 8,207 ...... E 5
Wausau, 37,060 .... D 4
Wauwatosa, 49,366 m12
West Allis, 63,221 .. m11
West Bend, 23,916 .. E 5
Weston, 8,775('80) .. D 4
Whitefish Bay, 14,272 m12
Whitewater, 12,636 .. F 5
Wisconsin Dells, 2,393 .... E 4
Wisconsin Rapids, 18,245 .... D 4

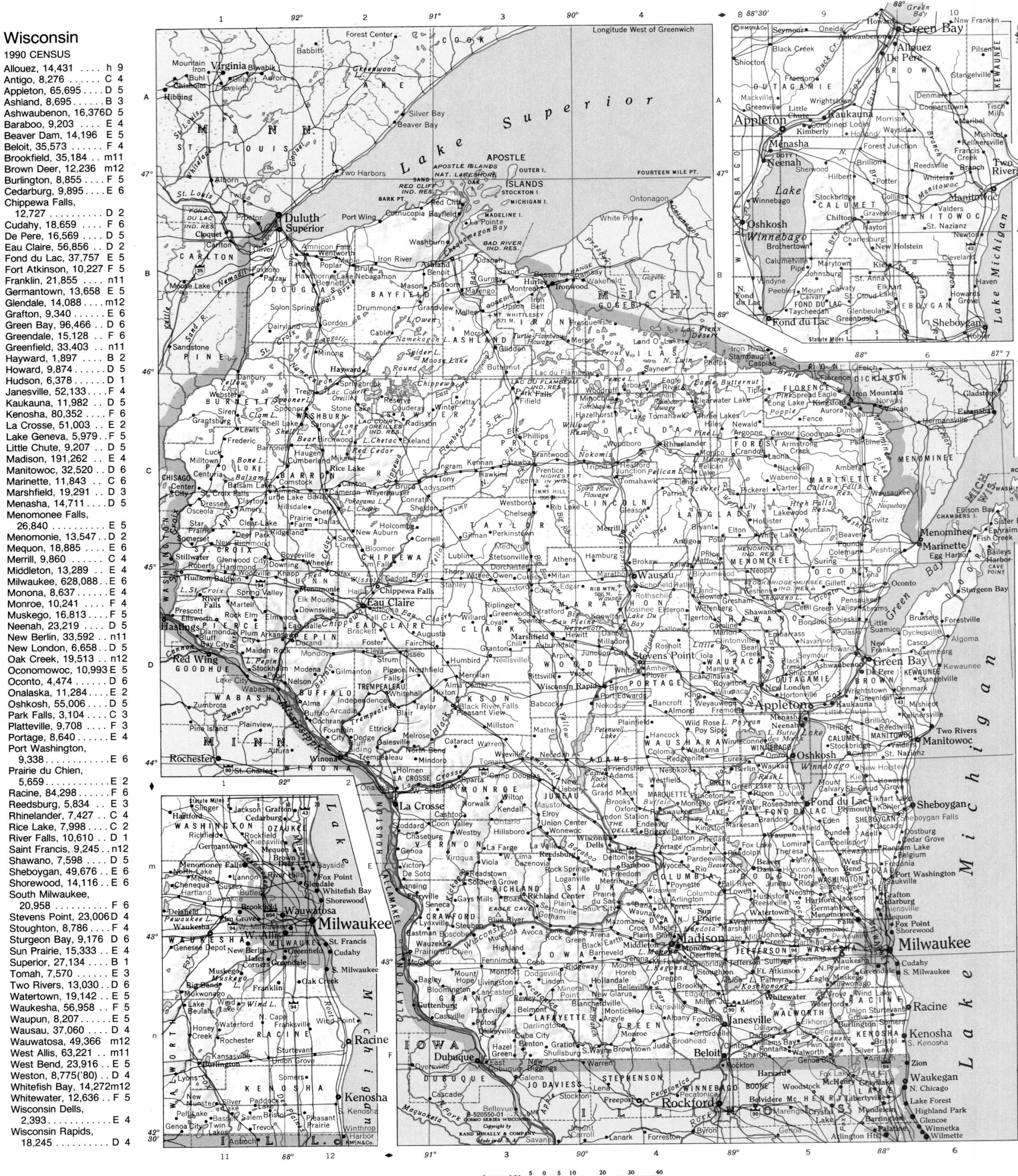

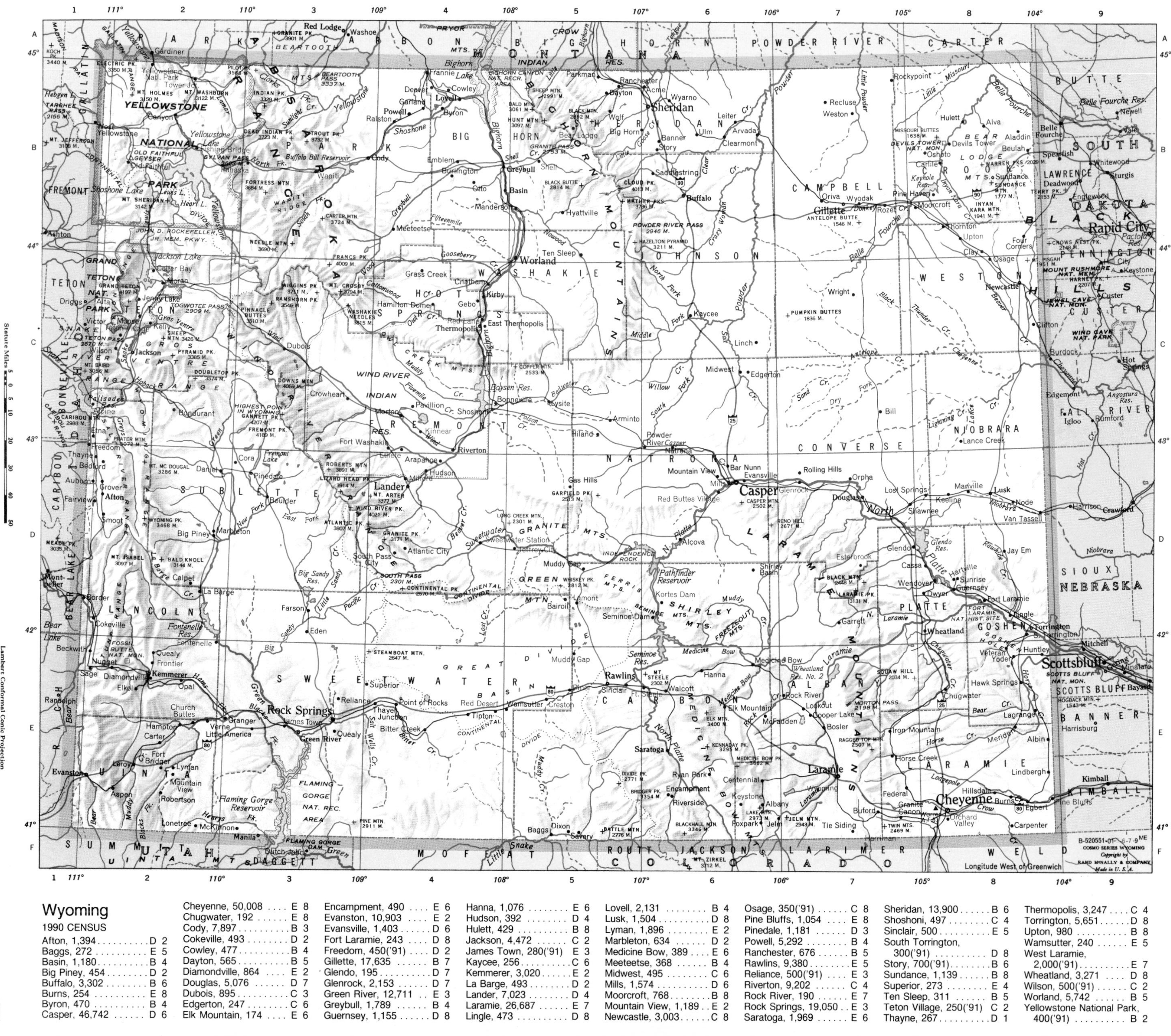

Wyoming

1990 CENSUS

Afton, 1,394 . . . . . D 2
Baggs, 272 . . . . . E 5
Basin, 1,180 . . . . . B 4
Big Piney, 454 . . . . . D 2
Buffalo, 3,302 . . . . . B 6
Burns, 254 . . . . . E 8
Byron, 470 . . . . . B 4
Casper, 46,742 . . . . . D 6
Cheyenne, 50,008 . . . . E 8
Chugwater, 192 . . . . . E 8
Cody, 7,897 . . . . . B 3
Cokeville, 493 . . . . . D 2
Cowley, 477 . . . . . B 4
Dayton, 565 . . . . . B 5
Diamondville, 864 . . . . E 2
Douglas, 5,076 . . . . . D 7
Dubois, 895 . . . . . C 3
Edgerton, 247 . . . . . C 6
Elk Mountain, 174 . . . . E 6
Encampment, 490 . . . . E 6
Evanston, 10,903 . . . . E 2
Evansville, 1,403 . . . . D 6
Fort Laramie, 243 . . . . D 8
Freedom, 450('91) . . . . D 2
Gillette, 17,635 . . . . . B 7
Glendo, 195 . . . . . D 7
Glenrock, 2,153 . . . . . D 7
Green River, 12,711 . . E 3
Greybull, 1,789 . . . . . B 4
Guernsey, 1,155 . . . . . D 8
Hanna, 1,076 . . . . . E 6
Hudson, 392 . . . . . D 4
Hulett, 429 . . . . . B 8
Jackson, 4,472 . . . . . C 2
James Town, 280('91) . . E 3
Kaycee, 256 . . . . . C 6
Kemmerer, 3,020 . . . . E 2
La Barge, 493 . . . . . D 2
Lander, 7,023 . . . . . D 4
Laramie, 26,687 . . . . . E 7
Lingle, 473 . . . . . D 8
Lovell, 2,131 . . . . . B 4
Lusk, 1,504 . . . . . D 8
Lyman, 1,896 . . . . . E 2
Marbleton, 634 . . . . . D 2
Medicine Bow, 389 . . . . E 6
Meeteetse, 368 . . . . . B 4
Midwest, 495 . . . . . C 6
Mills, 1,574 . . . . . D 6
Moorcroft, 768 . . . . . B 8
Mountain View, 1,189 . . E 2
Newcastle, 3,003 . . . . C 8
Osage, 350('91) . . . . . C 8
Pine Bluffs, 1,054 . . . . E 8
Pinedale, 1,181 . . . . . D 3
Powell, 5,292 . . . . . B 4
Ranchester, 676 . . . . . B 5
Rawlins, 9,380 . . . . . E 5
Reliance, 500('91) . . . . E 3
Riverton, 9,202 . . . . . C 4
Rock River, 190 . . . . . E 7
Rock Springs, 19,050 . . E 3
Saratoga, 1,969 . . . . . E 6
Sheridan, 13,900 . . . . . B 6
Shoshoni, 497 . . . . . C 4
Sinclair, 500 . . . . . E 5
South Torrington, 300('91) . . . . . D 8
Story, 700('91) . . . . . B 6
Sundance, 1,139 . . . . . B 8
Superior, 273 . . . . . E 4
Ten Sleep, 311 . . . . . B 5
Teton Village, 250('91) C 2
Thayne, 267 . . . . . D 1
Thermopolis, 3,247 . . . . C 4
Torrington, 5,651 . . . . . D 8
Upton, 980 . . . . . B 8
Wamsutter, 240 . . . . . E 5
West Laramie, 2,000('91) . . . . . E 7
Wheatland, 3,271 . . . . D 8
Wilson, 500('91) . . . . . C 2
Worland, 5,742 . . . . . B 5
Yellowstone National Park, 400('91) . . . . . B 2

North Polar Regions

Anchorage, 226,338 ('90)........................ C27
Archangel'sk, 416,000 ('89)........................C 8
Beijing (Peking), 6,710,000 ('88) (6,450,000★) ...F 1
BELGIUM...................D12
Berlin, 3,352,848 ('89) (3,825,000★) D11
CANADA....................D22
Chicago, 2,783,726 ('90)........................E21
CHINA.........................F 2
Churchill, 1,186 ('81)...D22
CZECHOSLOVAKIA....E11
DENMARK.................D11
Dublin, 502,749 ('86) (1,140,000★) D13
Dutch Harbor, 20 ('81)D29
Edmonton, 573,982 ('86) (785,465★) D24
FAEROE ISLANDS.....C13
Fairbanks, 30,843 ('90)........................C27
FINLAND....................C10
FRANCE......................E12
Gander, 10,207 ('86) (10,899★) E18
GERMANY..................D11
Godthåb, 12,217 ('90).C18
GREENLAND.............B17
Hammerfest, 7,208 ('83)........................B10
Happy Valley-Goose Bay, 7,248 ('86)..............D19
Harbin, 2,710,000 ('88)........................E36
Helsinki, 490,034 ('88) (1,040,000★) C10
ICELAND.....................C14
Igarka, 16,918 ('79).....C 4
IRELAND....................D13
JAPAN........................F35
Juneau, 26,751 ('90)...D26
Kijev (Kiev), 2,587,000 ('89) (2,900,000★) .. D 9
KOREA, NORTH.........E36
KOREA, SOUTH.........F36
Leningrad, 4,456,000 ('89) (5,825,000★) ....D 9
LUXEMBOURG...........E12
Magadan, 152,000 ('89)........................D33
MONGOLIA..................E 2
Moskva (Moscow), 8,769,000 ('89) (13,100,000★) ....D 9
Murmansk, 468,000 ('89)........................C 9
NETHERLANDS..........D12
New York, 7,322,564 ('90)........................E20
Nižnij Novgorod (Gorky), 1,438,000 ('89) (2,025,000★)..........D 8
Nome, 3,500 ('90).........C29
Noril'sk, 174,000 ('89).C 4
NORWAY...................C12
Novosibirsk, 1,436,000 ('89) (1,600,000★) .. D 4
Ōsaka, 2,636,249 ('85) (16,450,000★) F35
Oslo, 452,415 ('87) (720,000★) D11
Ottawa, 300,763 ('86) (819,263★) E20
Paris, 2,078,900 ('87) (9,775,000★) E12
POLAND......................D11
Québec, 164,580 ('86) (603,267★) E20
Reykjavík, 93,425 ('87) (137,941★) C15
Saint John's, 96,216 ('86) (161,901★) E18
Seattle, 516,259 ('90)..E25
Shenyang (Mukden), 3,910,000 ('88) (4,370,000▲) E36
Sŏul (Seoul), 10,522,000 ('89) (15,850,000★) .F36
Stockholm, 672,187 ('90) (1,449,972★) D11
Sverdlovsk, 1,367,000 ('89) (1,620,000★) .. D 6
SWEDEN....................C11
Thule, 551 ('90)...........B19
Tōkyō, 8,354,615 ('85) (27,700,000★) F35
Ulaanbaatar (Ulan Bator), 548,400 ('89)............E 2
UNION OF SOVIET SOCIALIST REPUBLICS.............C 4
UNITED KINGDOM..... D13
UNITED STATES........F22
Vancouver, 431,147 ('86) (1,380,729★) E25
Vladivostok, 648,000 ('89)........................E35
Vorkuta, 116,000 ('89)C 6
Warszawa, 1,651,200 ('89) (2,323,000★) .. D10
Winnipeg, 594,551 ('86) (625,304★) E22

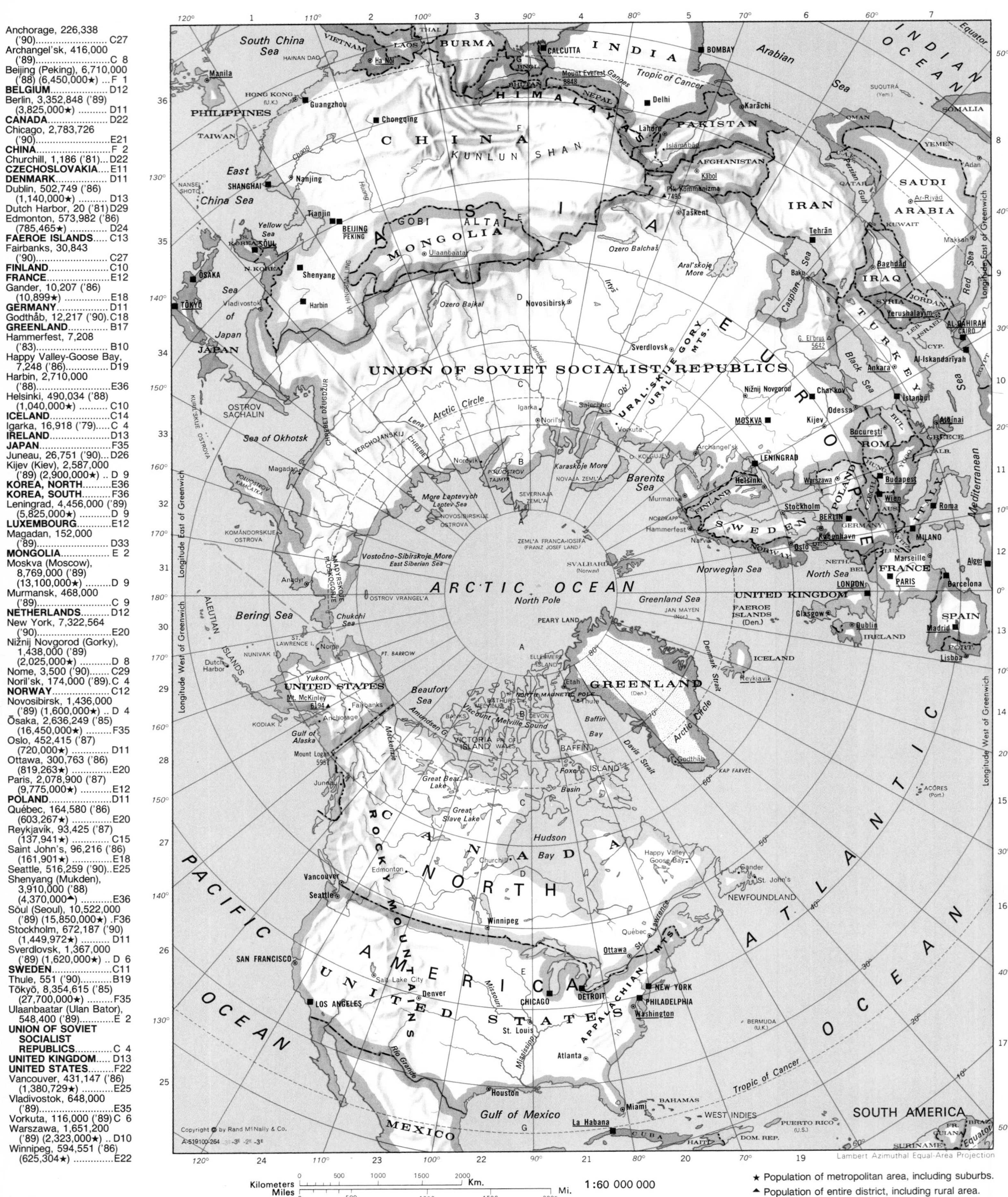

★ Population of metropolitan area, including suburbs.
▲ Population of entire district, including rural area.

Index to World Reference Maps

Introduction to the Index

This universal index includes in a single alphabetical list approximately 38,000 names of features that appear on the reference maps. Each name is followed by the name of the country or continent in which it is located, a map-reference key and a page reference.

Names The names of cities appear in the index in regular type. The names of all other features appear in *italics*, followed by descriptive terms (hill, mtn., state) to indicate their nature.

Names that appear in shortened versions on the maps due to space limitations are spelled out in full in the index. The portions of these names omitted from the maps are enclosed in brackets — for example, Acapulco [de Juárez].

Abbreviations of names on the maps have been standardized as much as possible. Names that are abbreviated on the maps are generally spelled out in full in the index.

Country names and names of features that extend beyond the boundaries of one country are followed by the name of the continent in which each is located. Country designations follow the names of all other places in the index. The locations of places in the United States, Canada, and the United Kingdom are further defined by abbreviations that indicate the state, province, or political division in which each is located.

All abbreviations used in the index are defined in the List of Abbreviations below.

Alphabetization Names are alphabetized in the order of the letters of the English alphabet. Spanish *ll* and *ch*, for example, are not treated as distinct letters. Furthermore, diacritical marks are disregarded in alphabetization — German or Scandinavian *ä* or *ö* are treated as *a* or *o*.

The names of physical features may appear inverted, since they are always alphabetized under the proper, not the generic, part of the name, thus: 'Gibraltar, Strait of'. Otherwise every entry, whether consisting of one word or more, is alphabetized as a single continuous entity. 'Lakeland', for example, appears after 'La Crosse' and before 'La Salle'. Names beginning with articles (Le Havre, Den Helder, Al Manṣūrah) are not inverted. Names beginning 'St.', 'Ste.' and 'Sainte' are alphabetized as though spelled 'Saint'.

In the case of identical names, towns are listed first, then political divisions, then physical features. Entries that are completely identical are listed alphabetically by country name.

Map-Reference Keys and Page References The map-reference keys and page references are found in the last two columns of each entry.

Each map-reference key consists of a letter and number. The letters appear along the sides of the maps. Lowercase letters indicate reference to inset maps. Numbers appear across the tops and bottoms of the maps.

Map reference keys for point features, such as cities and mountain peaks, indicate the locations of the symbols. For extensive areal features, such as countries or mountain ranges, locations are given for the approximate centers of the features. Those for linear features, such as canals and rivers, are given for the locations of the names.

Names of some important places or features that are omitted from the maps due to space limitations are included in the index. Each of these places is identified by an asterisk (*) preceding the map-reference key.

The page number generally refers to the main map for the country in which the feature is located. Page references to two-page maps always refer to the left-hand page.

List of Abbreviations

Afg.	Afghanistan
Afr.	Africa
Ak., U.S.	Alaska, U.S.
Al., U.S.	Alabama, U.S.
Alb.	Albania
Alg.	Algeria
Alta., Can.	Alberta, Can.
Am. Sam.	American Samoa
anch.	anchorage
And.	Andorra
Ang.	Angola
Ant.	Antarctica
Antig.	Antigua and Barbuda
Ar., U.S.	Arkansas, U.S.
Arg.	Argentina
Aus.	Austria
Austl.	Australia
Az., U.S.	Arizona, U.S.
b.	bay, gulf, inlet, lagoon
Bah.	Bahamas
Bahr.	Bahrain
Barb.	Barbados
B.A.T.	British Antarctic Territory
B.C., Can.	British Columbia, Can.
Bdi.	Burundi
Bel.	Belgium
Ber.	Bermuda
Bhu.	Bhutan
B.I.O.T.	British Indian Ocean Territory
Bngl.	Bangladesh
Bol.	Bolivia
Boph.	Bophuthatswana
Bots.	Botswana
Braz.	Brazil
Bru.	Brunei
Br. Vir. Is.	British Virgin Islands
Bul.	Bulgaria
Burkina	Burkina Faso
c.	cape, point
Ca., U.S.	California, U.S.
Cam.	Cameroon
Camb.	Cambodia
Can.	Canada
Cay. Is.	Cayman Islands
Cen. Afr. Rep.	Central African Republic
Christ. I.	Christmas Island
clf.	cliff, escarpment
co.	county, parish
Co., U.S.	Colorado, U.S.
Col.	Colombia
Com.	Comoros
cont.	continent
C.R.	Costa Rica
crat.	crater
Ct., U.S.	Connecticut, U.S.
ctry.	country
C.V.	Cape Verde
Cyp.	Cyprus
Czech.	Czechoslovakia
D.C., U.S.	District of Columbia, U.S.
De., U.S.	Delaware, U.S.
Den.	Denmark
dep.	dependency, colony
depr.	depression
dept.	department, district
des.	desert
Dji.	Djibouti
Dom.	Dominica
Dom. Rep.	Dominican Republic
Ec.	Ecuador
El Sal.	El Salvador
Eng., U.K.	England, U.K.
Eq. Gui.	Equatorial Guinea
est.	estuary
Eth.	Ethiopia
Eur.	Europe
Faer. Is.	Faeroe Islands
Falk. Is.	Falkland Islands
Fin.	Finland
Fl., U.S.	Florida, U.S.
for.	forest, moor
Fr.	France
Fr. Gu.	French Guiana
Fr. Poly.	French Polynesia
F.S.A.T.	French Southern and Antarctic Territory
Ga., U.S.	Georgia, U.S.
Gam.	Gambia
Ger.	Germany
Gib.	Gibraltar
Grc.	Greece
Gren.	Grenada
Grnld.	Greenland
Guad.	Guadeloupe
Guat.	Guatemala
Gui.	Guinea
Gui.-B.	Guinea-Bissau
Guy.	Guyana
Hi., U.S.	Hawaii, U.S.
hist.	historic site, ruins
hist. reg.	historic region
H.K.	Hong Kong
Hond.	Honduras
Hung.	Hungary
i.	island
Ia., U.S.	Iowa, U.S.
I.C.	Ivory Coast
Ice.	Iceland
ice	ice feature, glacier
Id., U.S.	Idaho, U.S.
Il., U.S.	Illinois, U.S.
In., U.S.	Indiana, U.S.
Indon.	Indonesia
I. of Man	Isle of Man
Ire.	Ireland
is.	islands
Isr.	Israel
Isr. Occ.	Israeli Occupied Territories
Jam.	Jamaica
Jord.	Jordan
Kir.	Kiribati
Ks., U.S.	Kansas, U.S.
Kuw.	Kuwait
Ky., U.S.	Kentucky, U.S.
l.	lake, pond
La., U.S.	Louisiana, U.S.
Leb.	Lebanon
Leso.	Lesotho
Lib.	Liberia
Liech.	Liechtenstein
Lux.	Luxembourg
Ma., U.S.	Massachusetts, U.S.
Madag.	Madagascar
Malay.	Malaysia
Mald.	Maldives
Man., Can.	Manitoba, Can.
Marsh. Is.	Marshall Islands
Mart.	Martinique
Maur.	Mauritania
May.	Mayotte
Md., U.S.	Maryland, U.S.
Me., U.S.	Maine, U.S.
Mex.	Mexico
Mi., U.S.	Michigan, U.S.
Micron.	Federated States of Micronesia
Mid. Is.	Midway Islands
mil.	military installation
Mn., U.S.	Minnesota, U.S.
Mo., U.S.	Missouri, U.S.
Mon.	Monaco
Mong.	Mongolia
Monts.	Montserrat
Mor.	Morocco
Moz.	Mozambique
Mrts.	Mauritius
Ms., U.S.	Mississippi, U.S.
Mt., U.S.	Montana, U.S.
mth.	river mouth or channel
mtn.	mountain
mts.	mountains
Mwi.	Malawi
N.A.	North America
N.B., Can.	New Brunswick, Can.
N.C., U.S.	North Carolina, U.S.
N. Cal.	New Caledonia
N. Cyp.	North Cyprus
N.D., U.S.	North Dakota, U.S.
Ne., U.S.	Nebraska, U.S.
Neth.	Netherlands
Neth. Ant.	Netherlands Antilles
Newf., Can.	Newfoundland, Can.
N.H., U.S.	New Hampshire, U.S.
Nic.	Nicaragua
Nig.	Nigeria
N. Ire., U.K.	Northern Ireland, U.K.
N.J., U.S.	New Jersey, U.S.
N. Kor.	North Korea
N.M., U.S.	New Mexico, U.S.
N. Mar. Is.	Northern Mariana Islands
Nmb.	Namibia
Nor.	Norway
Norf. I.	Norfolk Island
N.S., Can.	Nova Scotia, Can.
Nv., U.S.	Nevada, U.S.
N.W. Ter., Can.	Northwest Territories, Can.
N.Y., U.S.	New York, U.S.
N.Z.	New Zealand
Oc.	Oceania
Oh., U.S.	Ohio, U.S.
Ok., U.S.	Oklahoma, U.S.
Ont., Can.	Ontario, Can.
Or., U.S.	Oregon, U.S.
Pa., U.S.	Pennsylvania, U.S.
Pak.	Pakistan
Pan.	Panama
Pap. N. Gui.	Papua New Guinea
Para.	Paraguay
P.E.I., Can.	Prince Edward Island, Can.
pen.	peninsula
Phil.	Philippines
Pit.	Pitcairn
pl.	plain, flat
plat.	plateau, highland
Pol.	Poland
Port.	Portugal
P.R.	Puerto Rico
prov.	province, region
Que., Can.	Quebec, Can.
reg.	physical region
res.	reservoir
Reu.	Reunion
rf.	reef, shoal
R.I., U.S.	Rhode Island, U.S.
Rom.	Romania
Rw.	Rwanda
S.A.	South America
S. Afr.	South Africa
Sask., Can.	Saskatchewan, Can.
Sau. Ar.	Saudi Arabia
S.C., U.S.	South Carolina, U.S.
sci.	scientific station
Scot., U.K.	Scotland, U.K.
S.D., U.S.	South Dakota, U.S.
Sen.	Senegal
Sey.	Seychelles
Sing.	Singapore
S. Kor.	South Korea
S.L.	Sierra Leone
S. Mar.	San Marino
Sol. Is.	Solomon Islands
Som.	Somalia
Sp. N. Afr.	Spanish North Africa
Sri L.	Sri Lanka
state	state, republic, canton
St. Hel.	St. Helena
St. K./N	St. Kitts and Nevis
St. Luc.	St. Lucia
stm.	stream (river, creek)
S. Tom./P.	Sao Tome and Principe
St. P./M.	St. Pierre and Miquelon
strt.	strait, channel, sound
St. Vin.	St. Vincent and the Grenadines
Sud.	Sudan
Sur.	Suriname
sw.	swamp, marsh
Swaz.	Swaziland
Swe.	Sweden
Switz.	Switzerland
Tai.	Taiwan
Tan.	Tanzania
T./C. Is.	Turks and Caicos Islands
ter.	territory
Thai.	Thailand
Tn., U.S.	Tennessee, U.S.
Tok.	Tokelau
Trin.	Trinidad and Tobago
T.T.P.I.	Trust Territory of the Pacific Islands
Tun.	Tunisia
Tur.	Turkey
Tx., U.S.	Texas, U.S.
U.A.E.	United Arab Emirates
Ug.	Uganda
U.K.	United Kingdom
Ur.	Uruguay
U.S.S.R.	Union of Soviet Socialist Republics
U.S.	United States
Ut., U.S.	Utah, U.S.
Va., U.S.	Virginia, U.S.
val.	valley, watercourse
Vat.	Vatican City
Ven.	Venezuela
Viet.	Vietnam
V.I.U.S.	Virgin Islands (U.S.)
vol.	volcano
Vt., U.S.	Vermont, U.S.
Wa., U.S.	Washington, U.S.
Wal./F.	Wallis and Futuna
Wi., U.S.	Wisconsin, U.S.
W. Sah.	Western Sahara
W. Sam.	Western Samoa
wtfl.	waterfall
W.V., U.S.	West Virginia, U.S.
Wy., U.S.	Wyoming, U.S.
Yugo.	Yugoslavia
Yukon, Can.	Yukon Territory, Can.
Zam.	Zambia
Zimb.	Zimbabwe

Index

A

Name | Map Ref | Page

Aachen, Ger. E6 8
Aalen, Ger. G10 8
Aalst, Bel. E4 8
Äänekoski, Fin. E15 6
Aarau, Switz. E15 10
Aarschot, Bel. E4 8
Aba, China E7 26
Aba, Nig. G7 42
Ābādān, Iran B4 46
Abaeté, Braz. E6 57
Abajo Peak, mtn., Ut., U.S. F6 121
Abakan, U.S.S.R. G12 20
Abancay, Peru F4 54
Abashiri, Japan o22 30a
Abasolo, Mex. E7 62
Abaya, Lake, l., Eth. G2 46
Abaza, U.S.S.R. G12 20
Abbadia San Salvatore, Italy G6 14
Abbaye, Point, c., Mi., U.S. B2 99
Abbeville, Fr. B8 10
Abbeville, Al., U.S. D4 78
Abbeville, Ga., U.S. E3 87
Abbeville, La., U.S. E3 95
Abbeville, S.C., U.S. C3 117
Abbeville, co., S.C., U.S. C2 117
Abbotsford, Wi., U.S. D3 126
Abbottābād, Pak. C5 38
Abbott Butte, mtn., Or., U.S. E4 114
Abbott Run, stm., U.S. B4 116
Abbott Run Valley, R.I., U.S. B4 116
'Abd al-Kūrī, i., Yemen F5 46
Abe, Lake, l., Afr. F3 46
Abéché, Chad F10 42
Abéjar, Spain D9 12
Abengourou, I.C. G5 42
Abeokuta, Nig. G6 42
Aberayron, Wales, U.K. I8 7
Aberdeen, Scot., U.K. D10 7
Aberdeen, Id., U.S. G6 89
Aberdeen, Md., U.S. A5 97
Aberdeen, Ms., U.S. B5 101
Aberdeen, N.C., U.S. B3 110
Aberdeen, Oh., U.S. D2 112
Aberdeen, S.D., U.S. B7 118
Aberdeen, Wa., U.S. C2 124
Aberdeen Lake, l., N.W. Ter., Can. D13 66
Aberdeen Proving Ground, mil., Md., U.S. A5 97
Abernathy, Tx., U.S. C2 120
Abert, Lake, l., Or., U.S. E6 114
Abert Rim, clf, Or., U.S. E6 114
Aberystwyth, Wales, U.K. I8 7
Abhā, Sau. Ar. E3 46
Abidjan, I.C. G5 42
Abilene, Ks., U.S. D6 93
Abilene, Tx., U.S. C3 120
Abingdon, Il., U.S. C3 90
Abingdon, Md., U.S. B5 97
Abingdon, Va., U.S. f10 123
Abington, Ma., U.S. B6 98
Abington [Township], Pa., U.S. o21 115
Abisko, Swe. B12 6
Abita Springs, La., U.S. D5 95
Abitibi, stm., Ont., Can. o19 73
Abitibi, Lake, l., Can. G17 66
Abohar, India E6 38
Abomey, Benin G6 42
Aborigen, Pik, mtn., U.S.S.R. E23 20
Abraham Lake, res., Alta., Can. C2 68
Abraham Lincoln Birthplace National Historic Site, hist., Ky., U.S. C4 94
Abrantes, Port. F3 12
Absaroka Range, mts., U.S. F7 127
Absarokee, Mt., U.S. E7 103
Absecon, N.J., U.S. E4 107
Absecon Inlet, b., N.J., U.S. E4 107
Abū 'Alī, i., Sau. Ar. C4 46
Abu Dhabi see Abū Ẓaby, U.A.E. D5 46
Abū Ḥamad, Sudan E12 42
Abū Kamāl, Syria B7 40
Abukuma-sanchi, mts., Japan E13 30
Abū Madd, Ra's, c., Sau. Ar. D2 46
Abunã, Braz. E5 54
Abū Shajarah, Ra's, c., Sudan D13 42
Abū Ẓaby, U.A.E. D5 46
Academia, Oh., U.S. B3 112
Acadia, co., La., U.S. D3 95
Acadia National Park, Me., U.S. D4 96
Acajutla, El Sal. H3 64
Acámbaro, Mex. G9 62
Acaponeta, Mex. F7 62
Acapulco [de Juárez], Mex. I10 62
Acaraí Mountains, mts., S.A. C7 54
Acaraú, Braz. D10 54
Acarigua, Ven. C8 58
Acatlán [de Osorio], Mex. H10 62
Acayucan, Mex. I12 62
Accomack, co., Va., U.S. C7 123
Accoville, W.V., U.S. D3 125
Accra, Ghana G5 42
Acerra, Italy I9 14
Achaguas, Ven. D8 58
Achalpur, India B4 37
Acheng, China B12 26
Achí, Col. C5 58
Achill Island, i., Ire. H2 7
Achtubinsk, U.S.S.R. H7 18
Ačinsk, U.S.S.R. F12 20
Acireale, Italy L10 14
Ackerman, Ms., U.S. B4 101
Ackley, Ia., U.S. B4 92
Acklins Island, i., Bah. C10 64
Acoma Indian Reservation, N.M., U.S. C2 108
Aconcagua, Cerro, mtn., Arg. C2 56
Açores (Azores), is., Port. D11 2
Acquapendente, Italy G6 14
Acqui Terme, Italy E3 14
Acre, stm., S.A. E5 54
Acri, Italy J11 14
Acton, Ma., U.S. B5 98
Acton Vale, Que., Can. D5 74
Acushnet, Ma., U.S. C6 98
Acworth, Ga., U.S. B2 87
Ada, Mn., U.S. C2 100
Ada, Oh., U.S. B2 112
Ada, Ok., U.S. C5 113
Ada, co., Id., U.S. F2 89
Ada, Mount, mtn., Ak., U.S. m22 79
Adair, Ia., U.S. C3 92
Adair, Ok., U.S. A6 113
Adair, co., Ia., U.S. C3 92
Adair, co., Ky., U.S. C4 94
Adair, co., Mo., U.S. A5 102
Adair, co., Ok., U.S. B7 113
Adair, Cape, c., N.W. Ter., Can. B18 66
Adairsville, Ga., U.S. B2 87
Adairville, Ky., U.S. D3 94
Adak Island, i., Ak., U.S. E4 79
Adak Naval Station, mil., Ak., U.S. E4 79
Ādam, Oman D6 46
Adamantina, Braz. F3 57
Adamawa, mts., Afr. G8 42
Adam Island, i., Md., U.S. D5 97
Adams, Ma., U.S. A1 98
Adams, Mn., U.S. G6 100
Adams, N.Y., U.S. B4 109
Adams, Wi., U.S. E4 126
Adams, co., Co., U.S. B6 83
Adams, co., Id., U.S. E2 89
Adams, co., Il., U.S. D2 90
Adams, co., In., U.S. C8 91
Adams, co., Ia., U.S. C3 92
Adams, co., Ms., U.S. D2 101
Adams, co., Ne., U.S. D7 104
Adams, co., N.D., U.S. C3 111
Adams, co., Oh., U.S. D2 112
Adams, co., Pa., U.S. G7 115
Adams, co., Wa., U.S. B7 124
Adams, co., Wi., U.S. D4 126
Adams, Mount, mtn., N.H., U.S. B4 106
Adams, Mount, mtn., Wa., U.S. C4 124
Adams Bridge, rf., Asia H5 37
Adams Point, c., Mi., U.S. C7 99
Adams Run, S.C., U.S. k11 117
Adamstown, Pa., U.S. F9 115
Adamsville, Al., U.S. f7 78
Adamsville, R.I., U.S. E6 116
Adamsville, Tn., U.S. B3 119
Adamsville Brook, stm., R.I., U.S. E6 116
'Adan (Aden), Yemen F4 46
Adana, Tur. H15 4
Adapazarı, Tur. G14 4
Adarama, Sudan E12 42
Ad-Dabbah, Sudan E12 42
Ad-Dahnā, des., Sau. Ar. D4 46
Ad-Dammām, Sau. Ar. C5 46
Ad-Dawādimī, Sau. Ar. D3 46
Ad-Dawḥah (Doha), Qatar C5 46
Addis, La., U.S. D4 95
Addis Ababa see Adis Abeba, Eth. G2 46
Addison, Al., U.S. A2 78
Addison, Ct., U.S. C5 84
Addison, Il., U.S. k8 90
Addison, N.Y., U.S. C3 109
Addison, co., Vt., U.S. C2 122
Ad-Dīwānīyah, Iraq B3 46
Ad-Duwaym, Sudan F12 42
Addyston, Oh., U.S. o12 112
Adel, Ga., U.S. E3 87
Adel, Ia., U.S. C3 92
Adelaide, Austl. F7 50
Adelaide Peninsula, pen., N.W. Ter., Can. C13 66
Adelanto, Ca., U.S. E5 82
Aden, Gulf of, b. F4 46
Aden see 'Adan, Yemen F4 46
Adieu, Cape, c., Austl. F6 50
Adige, stm., Italy D7 14
Adigrat, Eth. F2 46
Ādilābād, India C5 37
Adimi, U.S.S.R. H21 20
Adirondack Mountains, mts., N.Y., U.S. A6 109
Adis Abeba, Eth. G2 46
Admiralty Bay, b., Ak., U.S. A9 79
Admiralty Inlet, b., N.W. Ter., Can. B15 66
Admiralty Island, i., Ak., U.S. m22 79
Admiralty Islands, is., Pap. N. Gui. k16 50a
Adobe Acres, N.M., U.S. B3 108
Adobe Creek Reservoir, res., Co., U.S. C7 83
Adolfo López Mateos, Presa, res., Mex. E6 62
Ādoni, India E4 37
Adour, stm., Fr. I7 10
Adra, Spain I8 12
Adrano, Italy L9 14
Adrar, Alg. C5 42
Adria, Italy D7 14
Adrian, Ga., U.S. D4 87
Adrian, Mi., U.S. G6 99
Adrian, Mn., U.S. G3 100
Adrian, Mo., U.S. C3 102
Adriatic Sea, Eur. G11 4
Advance, Mo., U.S. D8 102
Adyča, stm., U.S.S.R. D21 20
Aegean Sea J8 16
Afars and Issas see Djibouti, ctry., Afr. F3 46
Afghanistan, ctry., Asia C1 36
Afikpo, Nig. G7 42
Åfjord, Nor. E8 6
Afmadu, Som. A8 44
Afognak Island, i., Ak., U.S. D9 79
Africa D6 41
Afton, Ia., U.S. C3 92
Afton, Mn., U.S. F6 100
Afton, Ok., U.S. A7 113
Afton, Wy., U.S. D2 127
'Afula, Isr. C4 40
Afyon, Tur. H14 4
Agadez, Niger E7 42
Agadir, Mor. B4 42
Agalega Islands, is., Mrts. D11 44
Agalta, Cordillera de, mts., Hond. G5 64
Agapa, U.S.S.R. C11 20
Agartala, India I14 38
Agate Fossil Beds National Monument, Ne., U.S. B2 104
Agattu Island, i., Ak., U.S. E2 79
Agawam, Ma., U.S. B2 98
Agen, Fr. H7 10
Agency, Ia., U.S. D5 92
Agency, Mo., U.S. B3 102
Āghā Jārī, Iran B4 46
Agira, Italy L9 14
Agnone, Italy H9 14
Agoura Hills, Ca., U.S. m11 82
Āgra, India G8 38
Ágreda, Spain D10 12
Ağrı Dağı (Mount Ararat), mtn., Tur. H16 4
Agrigento, Italy L8 14
Agrínion, Grc. K5 16
Agropoli, Italy I9 14
Agua Caliente, Mex. F7 62
Agua Caliente Grande, Mex. D5 62
Aguachica, Col. C6 58
Água Clara, Braz. F2 57
Agua Fria, N.M., U.S. B3 108
Agua Fria, stm., Az., U.S. D3 80
Agua Prieta, Mex. B5 62
Aguascalientes, Mex. G8 62
Águas Formosas, Braz. D8 57
Águeda, Port. E3 12
Aguila, Az., U.S. D2 80
Aguilar, Spain H7 12
Águilas, Spain H10 12
Agulhas, Cape, c., S. Afr. H3 44
Agustín Codazzi, Col. B6 58
Agustín Codazzi, Col. I11 64
Ahaggar, mts., Alg. D7 42
Ahipara Bay, b., N.Z. A4 52
Ahklun Mountains, mts., Ak., U.S. D7 79
Ahlen, Ger. D7 8
Ahmadābād, India I5 38
Ahmadnagar, India C3 37
Ahmadpur East, Pak. F4 38
Ahmar Mountains, mts., Eth. G3 46
Ahoskie, N.C., U.S. A6 110
Ahtanum Creek, stm., Wa., U.S. C5 124
Ahu, China A7 28
Ahuacatlán, Mex. G7 62
Ahvāz, Iran B4 46
Ahvenanmaa (Åland), is., Fin. F12 6
Aialik, Cape, c., Ak., U.S. D10 79
Aichach, Ger. G11 8
Aiea, Hi., U.S. B4 88
Aihun, China A12 26
Aijal, India I15 38
Aiken, S.C., U.S. D4 117
Aiken, co., S.C., U.S. D4 117
Ailsa Craig, Ont., Can. D3 73
Aim, U.S.S.R. F20 20
Aimorés, Braz. E8 57
Ainslie Lake, l., N.S., Can. C8 71
Ainsworth, Ne., U.S. B6 104
Aipe, Col. F5 58
Aïr, mts., Niger E7 42
Airdrie, Alta., Can. D3 68
Aire-sur-l'Adour, Fr. I6 10
Air Force Island, i., N.W. Ter., Can. C18 66
Air Park West, Ne., U.S. D9 104
Aisne, stm., Fr. C10 10
Aïssa, Djebel, mtn., Alg. B5 42
Aitape, Pap. N. Gui. k15 50a
Aitkin, Mn., U.S. D5 100
Aitkin, co., Mn., U.S. D5 100
Aix, Mount, mtn., Wa., U.S. C4 124
Aix-en-Provence, Fr. I12 10
Aix-la-Chapelle see Aachen, Ger. E6 8
Aix-les-Bains, Fr. G12 10
Aizu-wakamatsu, Japan E12 30
Ajaguz, U.S.S.R. H10 20
Ajan, U.S.S.R. F21 20
Ajan, stm., U.S.S.R. C13 20
Ajax, Ont., Can. D6 73
Ajdābiyā, Libya B10 42
Ajjer, Tassili n', plat., Alg. C7 42
'Ajlūn, Jord. C4 40
Ajmer, India G6 38
Ajo, Az., U.S. E3 80
Ajo, Cabo de, c., Spain B8 12
Ajon, Ostrov, i., U.S.S.R. D27 20
Ajtos, Bul. G11 16
Akademii, Zaliv, b., U.S.S.R. G21 20
Akaltara, India A7 37
Akan, Japan p22 30a
'Akasha East, Sudan D12 42
Akashi, Japan H7 30
Akçakale, Tur. A6 40
Ak-Chin Indian Reservation, Az., U.S. E3 80
Akesu, China C3 26
Akharnaí, Grc. K7 16
Akhisar, Tur. H13 4
Akiachak, Ak., U.S. C7 79
Akimiski Island, i., N.W. Ter., Can. F16 66
Akita, Japan C13 30
Akjoujt, Maur. E3 42
'Akko (Acre), Isr. C4 40
Aklavik, N.W. Ter., Can. C6 66
Akō, Japan H7 30
Akobo, stm., Afr. G12 42
Akola, India B4 37
Akordat, Eth. E2 46
Akot, India B4 37
Akpatok Island, i., N.W. Ter., Can. D19 66
Akron, Co., U.S. A7 83
Akron, In., U.S. B5 91
Akron, Ia., U.S. B1 92
Akron, N.Y., U.S. B2 109
Akron, Oh., U.S. A4 112
Akron, Pa., U.S. F9 115
Aksaray, Tur. H14 4
Akşehir, Tur. H14 4
Aksum, Eth. F2 46
Akt'ubinsk, U.S.S.R. G9 18
Akureyri, Ice. B4 4
Ål, Nor. F7 6
Alabama, state, U.S. C3 78
Alabama, stm., Al., U.S. D2 78
Alabaster, Al., U.S. B3 78
Alachua, Fl., U.S. C4 86
Alachua, co., Fl., U.S. C4 86
Alagoinhas, Braz. B9 57
Alagón, Spain D10 12
Alajuela, C.R. I5 64
Alakanuk, Ak., U.S. C7 79
Alalakeiki Channel, strt., Hi., U.S. C5 88
Al-'Alamayn, Egypt B11 42
Alamance, co., N.C., U.S. B3 110
Al-'Amārah, Iraq B4 46
Alameda, Ca., U.S. h8 82
Alameda, N.M., U.S. B3 108
Alameda, co., Ca., U.S. D3 82
Alameda Naval Air Station, mil., Ca., U.S. h8 82
Alamito Creek, stm., Tx., U.S. p12 120
Alamo, Ga., U.S. D4 87
Alamo, Nv., U.S. F6 105
Alamo, Tn., U.S. B2 119
Alamo, Tx., U.S. F3 120
Alamogordo, N.M., U.S. E4 108
Alamo Heights, Tx., U.S. E3 120
Alamo Hueco Mountains, mts., N.M., U.S. F1 108
Alamo Indian Reservation, N.M., U.S. C2 108
Alamo Lake, res., Az., U.S. C2 80
Alamosa, Co., U.S. D5 83
Alamosa, co., Co., U.S. D5 83
Alamosa, stm., Co., U.S. D4 83
Alamosa Creek, stm., N.M., U.S. D2 108
Alamosa East, Co., U.S. D5 83
Alanäs, Swe. D10 6
Alanya, Tur. A3 40
Alapaha, Ga., U.S. E3 87
Alapaha, stm., U.S. E3 87
Al-'Aqabah, Jord. E4 40
Alaşehir, Tur. K12 16
Alashanyouqi, China C7 26
Alaska, state, U.S. C9 79
Alaska, Gulf of, b., Ak., U.S. D10 79
Alaska Peninsula, pen., Ak., U.S. D8 79
Alaska Range, mts., Ak., U.S. C9 79
Alassio, Italy E3 14
Alatna, stm., Ak., U.S. B9 79
Al-'Aṭrūn, Sudan E11 42
Alava, Cape, c., Wa., U.S. A1 124
Alazeja, stm., U.S.S.R. C24 20
Alba, Italy E3 14
Albacete, Spain G10 12
Alba de Tormes, Spain E6 12
Albaida, Spain G11 12
Albanel, Lac, l., Que., Can. F18 66
Albania, ctry., Eur. G11 4
Albano Laziale, Italy H7 14
Albany, Austl. G3 50
Albany, Ga., U.S. E2 87
Albany, Il., U.S. B3 90
Albany, In., U.S. D7 91
Albany, Ky., U.S. D4 94
Albany, La., U.S. g10 95
Albany, Mn., U.S. E4 100
Albany, Mo., U.S. A3 102
Albany, N.Y., U.S. C7 109
Albany, Or., U.S. C3 114
Albany, Tx., U.S. C3 120
Albany, Wi., U.S. F4 126
Albany, co., N.Y., U.S. C6 109
Albany, co., Wy., U.S. E7 127
Albany, stm., Ont., Can. o18 73
Al-Baṣrah, Iraq B4 46
Albatross Bay, b., Austl. B8 50
Al-Batrūn, Leb. B4 40
Al-Bawīṭī, Egypt C11 42
Albemarle, N.C., U.S. B2 110
Albemarle, co., Va., U.S. C4 123
Albemarle Lake, l., Ms., U.S. C2 101
Albemarle Sound, strt., N.C., U.S. A6 110
Albenga, Italy E3 14
Albergaria-a-Velha, Port. E3 12
Albert, Fr. B9 10
Albert, Lake, l., Afr. A6 44
Alberta, prov., Can. C4 68
Alberta, Mount, mtn., Alta., Can. C2 68
Albert City, Ia., U.S. B3 92
Albert Lea, Mn., U.S. G5 100
Albert Nile, stm., Ug. H12 42
Alberton, P.E.I., Can. C5 71
Albertson, N.Y., U.S. k13 109
Albertville, Fr. G13 10
Albertville, Al., U.S. A3 78
Albertville, Mn., U.S. E5 100
Albertville see Kalemie, Zaire C5 44
Albi, Fr. I9 10
Albia, Ia., U.S. C5 92
Albino, Italy D4 14
Albion, Il., U.S. E5 90
Albion, In., U.S. B7 91
Albion, Mi., U.S. F6 99
Albion, Ne., U.S. C7 104
Albion, N.Y., U.S. B2 109
Albion, Pa., U.S. C1 115
Albion, R.I., U.S. B4 116
Albion, Wa., U.S. C8 124
Alborán, Isla de, i., Spain J8 12
Ålborg, Den. H7 6
Alborz, Reshteh-ye Kūhhā-ye, mts., Iran J8 18
Albufeira, Port. H3 12
Albuñol, Spain I8 12
Albuquerque, N.M., U.S. B3 108
Alburquerque, Spain F4 12
Alburtis, Pa., U.S. F10 115
Albury, Austl. G9 50
Alcácer do Sal, Port. G3 12
Alcalá de Guadaira, Spain H6 12
Alcalá de Henares, Spain E8 12
Alcalá la Real, Spain H8 12
Alcalde, N.M., U.S. A3 108
Alcamo, Italy L7 14
Alcañices, Spain D5 12
Alcañiz, Spain D11 12
Alcântara, Braz. D10 54
Alcántara, Spain F5 12
Alcantarilla, Spain H10 12
Alcaraz, Spain G9 12
Alcázar de San Juan, Spain F8 12
Alcester, S.D., U.S. D9 118
Alcira, Spain F11 12
Alcoa, Tn., U.S. D10 119
Alcobaça, Braz. D9 57
Alcobaça, Port. F3 12
Alcolu, S.C., U.S. D7 117
Alcona, co., Mi., U.S. D7 99
Alconchel, Spain G4 12
Alcorn, co., Ms., U.S. A5 101
Alcoy, Spain G11 12
Aldabra Islands, atoll, Sey. C9 44
Aldan, U.S.S.R. F19 20
Aldan, stm., U.S.S.R. E20 20
Aldanskoje Nagorje, plat., U.S.S.R. F19 20
Alden, Ia., U.S. B4 92
Alden, Mn., U.S. G5 100
Alden, N.Y., U.S. C2 109
Alder Brook, stm., Vt., U.S. B4 122
Aldershot, Eng., U.K. J12 7
Alderson, W.V., U.S. D4 125
Aldrich, Al., U.S. B3 78
Aledo, Il., U.S. B3 90
Aleg, Maur. E3 42
Alegres Mountain, mtn., N.M., U.S. C2 108
Alegrete, Braz. B5 56
Alejsk, U.S.S.R. G10 20
Aleksandrov, U.S.S.R. E21 22
Aleksandrovsk-Sachalinskij, U.S.S.R. G22 20
Aleksejevsk, U.S.S.R. F15 20
Aleksin, U.S.S.R. G20 22
Além Paraíba, Braz. F7 57
Alençon, Fr. D7 10
Alenuihaha Channel, strt., Hi., U.S. C5 88
Aleppo see Halab, Syria A5 40
Alert Bay, B.C., Can. D4 69
Alès, Fr. H11 10
Alessandria, Italy E3 14
Alessano, Italy J13 14
Ålesund, Nor. E6 6
Aleutian Islands, is., Ak., U.S. E3 79
Aleutian Range, mts., Ak., U.S. D9 79
Aleutka, U.S.S.R. H24 20
Alevina, Mys, c., U.S.S.R. F24 20
Alex, Ok., U.S. C4 113
Alexander, co., Il., U.S. F4 90
Alexander, co., N.C., U.S. B1 110
Alexander, Lake, l., Mn., U.S. D4 100
Alexander Archipelago, is., Ak., U.S. D12 79
Alexander Bay, S. Afr. G3 44
Alexander City, Al., U.S. C4 78
Alexander Island, i., Ant. B6 47
Alexandra, N.Z. F2 52
Alexandretta, Gulf of, see İskenderun Körfezi, b., Tur. A4 40
Alexandria, Ont., Can. B10 73
Alexandria, In., U.S. D6 91
Alexandria, Ky., U.S. B5 94
Alexandria, La., U.S. C3 95
Alexandria, Mn., U.S. E3 100
Alexandria, Tn., U.S. A5 119
Alexandria, Va., U.S. B5 123
Alexandria see Al-Iskandarīyah, Egypt B11 42
Alexandroúpolis, Grc. I9 16
Alexis, Il., U.S. B3 90
Alfalfa, co., Ok., U.S. A3 113
Alfaro, Ec. I3 58
Alfaro, Spain C10 12
Alfarrás, Spain D12 12
Al-Fāshir, Sudan F11 42
Al-Fayyūm, Egypt C12 42
Alfeld, Ger. D9 8
Alfenas, Braz. F6 57
Alfred, Ont., Can. B10 73
Alfred, N.Y., U.S. C3 109
Algarve, hist. reg., Port. H3 12
Algeciras, Spain I6 12
Algemesí, Spain F11 12
Alger, Alg. A6 42
Alger, Oh., U.S. B2 112
Alger, co., Mi., U.S. B4 99
Algeria, ctry., Afr. C6 42
Al-Ghaydah, Yemen E5 46
Alghero, Italy I3 14
Al-Ghurdaqah, Egypt C12 42
Algiers see Alger, Alg. A6 42
Algoma, Wi., U.S. D6 126
Algona, Ia., U.S. A3 92
Algona, Wa., U.S. B3 124
Algonac, Mi., U.S. F8 99
Algonquin, Il., U.S. A5 90
Algonquin Provincial Park, Ont., Can. B6 73
Algood, Tn., U.S. C8 119
Algorta, Ur. C5 56
Al-Ḥadīthah, Iraq B3 46
Al-Ḥaffah, Syria B5 40
Al-Ḥamād, pl., Sau. Ar. B2 46
Alhama de Granada, Spain H8 12
Alhambra, Ca., U.S. m12 82
Al-Ḥarīq, Sau. Ar. D4 46
Al-Ḥarūj al-Aswad, hills, Libya C9 42
Al-Ḥasakah, Syria A7 40
Alhaurín el Grande, Spain I7 12
Al-Ḥawrah, Yemen F4 46
Al-Ḥijāz (Hejaz), reg., Sau. Ar. C2 46
Al-Ḥillah, Iraq B3 46
Al-Hirmil, Leb. B5 40
Al-Ḥudaydah, Yemen F3 46
Al-Hufūf, Sau. Ar. C4 46
Aliaga, Spain E11 12
Alicante, Spain G11 12
Alice, Tx., U.S. F3 120
Alice Lake, l., Mn., U.S. C7 100
Alice Springs, Austl. D6 50
Aliceville, Al., U.S. B1 78
Alīgarh, India G8 38
Alijos, Escollos, Mex. E2 62
Alingsås, Swe. H9 6
Alīpur Duār, India G13 38
Aliquippa, Pa., U.S. E1 115
Al-Iskandarīyah (Alexandria), Egypt B11 42
Al-Ismā'īlīyah, Egypt B12 42
Aliwal North, S. Afr. H5 44
Alix, Alta., Can. C4 68
Al-Jabal al-Akhḍar, mts., Oman D6 46
Al-Jafr, Jord. D5 40
Al-Jaghbūb, Libya C10 42
Al-Jawf, Libya D10 42
Al-Jawf, Sau. Ar. C2 46

Al-Jazīrah, reg., Sudan F12 42
Aljezur, Port. H3 12
Al-Jīzah, Egypt B12 42
Al-Junaynah, Sudan F10 42
Aljustrel, Port. H3 12
Alkali Lake, l., Nv., U.S. B2 105
Alkali Lake, l., Or., U.S. E6 114
Alkaline Lake, l., N.D., U.S. C6 111
Al-Karak, Jord. D4 40
Al-Kawm, Syria B6 40
Al-Khābūr, stm., Syria A7 40
Al-Khalīl, Isr. Occ. D4 40
Al-Khandaq, Sudan E12 42
Al-Khārijah, Egypt C12 42
Al-Kharṭūm (Khartoum), Sudan E12 42
Al-Khaṣab, Oman C6 46
Al-Khubar, Sau. Ar. C5 46
Al-Khums, Libya B8 42
Alkmaar, Neth. C4 8
Al-Kuwayt, Kuw. C4 46
Allach-Jun', U.S.S.R. E21 20
Al-Lādhiqīyah (Latakia), Syria B4 40
Allagash, stm., Me., U.S. B3 96
Allagash Lake, l., Me., U.S. B3 96
Allāhābād, India H9 38
Allamakee, co., Ia., U.S. A6 92
Allan, Sask., Can. F2 75
Allanche, Fr. G9 10
Allanmyo, Burma E3 34
Allardt, Tn., U.S. C9 119
Allatoona Lake, res., Ga., U.S. B2 87
Allegan, Mi., U.S. F5 99
Allegan, co., Mi., U.S. F5 99
Allegany, N.Y., U.S. C2 109
Allegany, co., Md., U.S. k13 97
Allegany, co., N.Y., U.S. C2 109
Allegany Indian Reservation, N.Y., U.S. C2 109
Alleghany, co., N.C., U.S. A1 110
Alleghany, co., Va., U.S. C2 123
Allegheny, co., Pa., U.S. E2 115
Allegheny, stm., U.S. E2 115
Allegheny Reservoir, res., U.S. B4 115
Allemands, Lac Des, l., La., U.S. E5 95
Allen, Ok., U.S. C5 113
Allen, co., In., U.S. B7 91
Allen, co., Ks., U.S. E8 93
Allen, co., Ky., U.S. D3 94
Allen, co., La., U.S. D3 95
Allen, co., Oh., U.S. B1 112
Allen, Mount, mtn., Ak., U.S. C11 79
Allendale, N.J., U.S. A4 107
Allendale, S.C., U.S. E5 117
Allendale, co., S.C., U.S. F5 117
Allen Park, Mi., U.S. p15 99
Allenton, R.I., U.S. E4 116
Allenton, Wi., U.S. E5 126
Allentown, Pa., U.S. E11 115
Allentsteig, Aus. G15 8
Alleppey, India H4 37
Aller, stm., Ger. C9 8
Allerton, Point, c., Ma., U.S. B6 98
Allgäuer Alpen, mts., Eur. H10 8
Alliance, Ne., U.S. B3 104
Alliance, Oh., U.S. B4 112
Alligator, stm., N.C., U.S. B6 110
Alligator Lake, l., Me., U.S. D4 96
Allison, Ia., U.S. B5 92
Allison, Pa., U.S. G2 115
Allison Park, Pa., U.S. h14 115
Alliston, Ont., Can. C5 73
Al-Līth, Sau. Ar. D3 46
Allouez, Wi., U.S. h9 126
Alloway Creek, stm., N.J., U.S. D2 107
Al-Luḥayyah, Yemen E3 46
Allumette Lake, l., Can. B7 73
Allyn, Wa., U.S. B3 124
Alma, Que., Can. A6 74
Alma, Ar., U.S. B1 81
Alma, Ga., U.S. E4 87
Alma, Ks., U.S. C7 93
Alma, Mi., U.S. E6 99
Alma, Ne., U.S. D6 104
Alma, Wi., U.S. D2 126
Alma-Ata, U.S.S.R. I9 20
Almada, Port. G2 12
Al-Madīnah (Medina), Sau. Ar. D2 46
Al-Mafraq, Jord. C5 40
Almagro, Spain G8 12
Al-Manāmah, Bahr. C5 46
Almanor, Lake, l., Ca., U.S. B3 82
Almansa, Spain G10 12
Al-Manṣūrah, Egypt B12 42
Al-Marj, Libya B10 42
Almas, Pico das, mtn., Braz. F10 54
Al-Maṣīrah, i., Oman D6 46
Al-Mawṣil, Iraq A3 46
Al-Mayādīn, Syria B7 40
Almazán, Spain D9 12
Almelo, Neth. C6 8
Almenara, Braz. D8 57
Almendralejo, Spain G5 12
Almería, Spain I9 12
Al'metjevsk, U.S.S.R. G8 18
Al-Minyā, Egypt C12 42
Almirante, Pan. J6 64
Al-Mismīyah, Syria C5 40
Almodôvar, Port. H3 12
Almodóvar del Campo, Spain G7 12
Almont, Mi., U.S. F7 99
Almonte, Ont., Can. B8 73
Almonte, Spain H5 12
Almora, India F8 38
Al-Mubarraz, Sau. Ar. C4 46
Al-Mubarraz, Sau. Ar. D4 46
Al-Muglad, Sudan F11 42
Al-Muḥarraq, Bahr. C5 46
Al-Mukallā, Yemen F4 46
Al-Mukhā, Yemen F3 46
Al-Muwayliḥ, Sau. Ar. C2 46
Alnwick, Eng., U.K. F11 7
Aloândia, Braz. D4 57
Aloha, Or., U.S. h12 114
Alor, Pulau, i., Indon. G7 32
Álora, Spain I7 12
Alor Setar, Malay. K6 34
Aloysius, Mount, mtn., Austl. E5 50
Alpena, Mi., U.S. C7 99
Alpena, co., Mi., U.S. D7 99
Alpharetta, Ga., U.S. B2 87
Alphonse Island, i., Sey. C10 44
Alpiarça, Port. F3 12
Alpine, Az., U.S. D6 80
Alpine, Tx., U.S. D1 120
Alpine, Ut., U.S. C4 121
Alpine, co., Ca., U.S. C4 82
Alps, mts., Eur. F9 4
Al-Qaḍārif, Sudan F13 42
Al-Qāhirah (Cairo), Egypt B12 42
Al-Qāmishlī, Syria A7 40
Al-Qaryah ash-Sharqīyah, Libya B8 42
Al-Qaryatayn, Syria B5 40
Al-Qaṣr, Egypt C11 42
Al-Qaṭīf, Sau. Ar. C4 46
Al-Qaṭrūn, Libya D8 42
Al-Qayṣūmah, Sau. Ar. C4 46
Al-Qunayṭirah, Syria C4 40
Al-Qunfudhah, Sau. Ar. E3 46
Al-Quṣayr, Egypt C12 42
Al-Quṭayfah, Syria C5 40
Alsace, hist. reg., Fr. E14 10
Alsasua, Spain C9 12
Alsfeld, Ger. E9 8
Alta, Nor. B14 6
Alta, Ia., U.S. B2 92
Altadena, Ca., U.S. m12 82
Altagracia, Ven. B7 58
Altagracia de Orituco, Ven. C9 58
Altai, mts., Asia B4 26
Altaj (Jesönbulag), Mong. B6 26
Altamaha, stm., Ga., U.S. E4 87
Altamira, Braz. D8 54
Altamont, Il., U.S. D5 90
Altamont, Ks., U.S. E8 93
Altamont, Or., U.S. E5 114
Altamont, Tn., U.S. D8 119
Altamonte Springs, Fl., U.S. D5 86
Altamura, Italy I11 14
Altar, Mex. B4 62
Altar, Desierto de, des., Mex. B3 62
Altata, Mex. E6 62
Altavista, Va., U.S. C3 123
Altdorf, Switz. F15 10
Altenburg, Ger. E12 8
Altheimer, Ar., U.S. C4 81
Altiplano, plat., S.A. G5 54
Alto, Ga., U.S. B3 87
Alto, N.M., U.S. D4 108
Alto Araguaia, Braz. D2 57
Alton, Il., U.S. E3 90
Alton, Ia., U.S. B2 92
Alton, Mo., U.S. E6 102
Alton, N.H., U.S. D4 106
Altona, Man., Can. E3 70
Alton Bay, N.H., U.S. D4 106
Altoona, Al., U.S. A3 78
Altoona, Fl., U.S. D5 86
Altoona, Ia., U.S. C4 92
Altoona, Pa., U.S. E5 115
Altoona, Wi., U.S. D2 126
Alto Parnaíba, Braz. E9 54
Altötting, Ger. G12 8
Altun Shan, mts., China D4 26
Alturas, Ca., U.S. B3 82
Altus, Ok., U.S. C2 113
Altus Air Force Base, mil., Ok., U.S. C2 113
Altus Reservoir, res., Ok., U.S. C2 113
Al-'Ubaylah, Sau. Ar. D5 46
Al-Ubayyiḍ, Sudan F12 42
'Alula, Som. F5 46
Alum Bank, Pa., U.S. F4 115
Alum Creek, stm., Oh., U.S. k11 112
Al-Uqṣur (Luxor), Egypt C12 42
Alva, Fl., U.S. F5 86
Alva, Ok., U.S. A3 113
Alvarado, Mex. H12 62
Alvarado, Tx., U.S. C4 120
Álvaro Obregón, Presa, res., Mex. D5 62
Älvdalen, Swe. F10 6
Alvin, Tx., U.S. E5 120
Alvinston, Ont., Can. E3 73
Älvkarleby, Swe. F11 6
Alvord Lake, l., Or., U.S. E8 114
Älvsbyn, Swe. D13 6
Al-Wajh, Sau. Ar. C2 46
Alwar, India G7 38
Alzamaj, U.S.S.R. F13 20
Ama, La., U.S. k11 95
Amadeus, Lake, l., Austl. D6 50
Amadjuak Lake, l., N.W. Ter., Can. C18 66
Amador, co., Ca., U.S. C3 82
Amagansett, N.Y., U.S. n16 109
Amagasaki, Japan H8 30
Amakusa-nada, Japan J2 30
Amakusa-shotō, is., Japan J3 30
Åmål, Swe. G9 6
Amalāpuram, India D7 37
Amalfi, Italy I9 14
Amalner, India J6 38
Amambaí, stm., Braz. G1 57
Amambaí, Serra de, mts., S.A. H7 54
Amami-Ō-shima, i., Japan w29 31b
Amami-shotō, is., Japan x29 31b
Amana, Ia., U.S. C6 92
Amantea, Italy J11 14
Amares, Port. D3 12
Amargosa, stm., U.S. D5 82
Amargosa Desert, des., U.S. G5 105
Amargosa Range, mts., U.S. G5 105
Amarillo, Tx., U.S. B2 120
Amatignak Island, i., Ak., U.S. E4 79
Amazon (Solimões) (Amazonas), stm., S.A. D7 54
Ambāla, India E7 38
Ambarčik, U.S.S.R. D26 20
Ambāsamudram, India H4 37
Ambato, Ec. H3 58
Ambatolampy, Madag. E9 44
Ambatondrazaka, Madag. E9 44
Amberg, Ger. F11 8
Ambérieu-en-Bugey, Fr. G1 10
Ambert, Fr. G10 10
Ambikāpur, India I10 38
Ambilobe, Madag. D9 44
Amble, Eng., U.K. F11 7
Ambler, Pa., U.S. F11 115
Amboise, Fr. E7 10
Ambon, Indon. F8 32
Ambositra, Madag. F9 44
Ambovombe, Madag. G9 44
Amboy, Il., U.S. B4 90
Ambre, Cap d', c., Madag. D9 44
Ambridge, Pa., U.S. E1 115
Ambrières, Fr. D6 10
Ambriz, Ang. C2 44
Āmbūr, India F5 37
Amchitka Island, i., Ak., U.S. E3 79
Amchitka Pass, strt., Ak., U.S. E4 79
Ameca, Mex. G7 62
Amecameca [de Juárez], Mex. H10 62
Amelia, La., U.S. E4 95
Amelia, Oh., U.S. C1 112
Amelia, co., Va., U.S. C4 123
Amelia Court House, Va., U.S. C5 123
Amelia Island, i., Fl., U.S. k9 86
American, stm., Ca., U.S. C3 82
Americana, Braz. G5 57
American Falls, Id., U.S. G6 89
American Falls Dam, Id., U.S. G6 89
American Falls Reservoir, res., Id., U.S. F5 89
American Fork, Ut., U.S. C4 121
American Highland, plat., Ant. B20 47
American Samoa, dep., Oc. G1 2
Americus, Ga., U.S. D2 87
Americus, Ks., U.S. D7 93
Amersfoort, Neth. C5 8
Amery, Wi., U.S. C1 126
Ames, Ia., U.S. B4 92
Amesbury, Ma., U.S. A6 98
Amfilokhía, Grc. K5 16
Ámfissa, Grc. K6 16
Amga, U.S.S.R. E20 20
Amga, stm., U.S.S.R. E20 20
Amgun', stm., U.S.S.R. G21 20
Amherst, Ma., U.S. B2 98
Amherst, N.H., U.S. E3 106
Amherst, N.Y., U.S. C2 109
Amherst, Oh., U.S. A3 112
Amherst, Va., U.S. C3 123
Amherst, Wi., U.S. D4 126
Amherst, co., Va., U.S. C3 123
Amherstburg, Ont., Can. E1 73
Amherstdale, W.V., U.S. n12 125
Amiens, Fr. C9 10
Amīndīvi Islands, is., India G2 37
Amirante Islands, is., Sey. C10 44
Amisk Lake, l., Sask., Can. C4 75
Amistad National Recreation Area, Tx., U.S. E2 120
Amistad Reservoir, res., N.A. C9 62
Amite, La., U.S. D5 95
Amite, co., Ms., U.S. D3 101
Amite, stm., La., U.S. D5 95
Amity, Or., U.S. B3 114
Amityville, N.Y., U.S. E7 109
Amlia Island, i., Ak., U.S. E5 79
'Ammān, Jord. D4 40
Ämmänsaari, Fin. D17 6
Ammon, Id., U.S. F7 89
Ammonoosuc, stm., N.H., U.S. B3 106
Amo, stm., Asia G13 38
Amory, Ms., U.S. B5 101
Amos, Que., Can. k11 74
Åmot, Nor. G6 6
Amoy see Xiamen, China K7 28
Amposta, Spain E12 12
Amrāvati, India B4 37
Amreli, India J4 38
Amritsar, India E6 38
Amroha, India F8 38
Amsterdam, Neth. C4 8
Amsterdam, N.Y., U.S. C6 109
Amstetten, Aus. G14 8
Am Timan, Chad F10 42
Amu Darya (Amudarja), stm., Asia I10 38
Amukta Pass, strt., Ak., U.S. E5 79
Amundsen Gulf, b., N.W. Ter., Can. B8 66
Amundsen Sea, Ant. B1 47
Amuntai, Indon. F6 32
Amur (Heilongjiang), stm., Asia G21 20
An, Burma E3 34
Anabar, stm., U.S.S.R. C16 20
Anaco, Ven. C10 58
Anacoco, La., U.S. C2 95
Anaconda, Mt., U.S. D4 103
Anaconda Range, mts., Mt., U.S. E3 103
Anacortes, Wa., U.S. A3 124
Anacostia, stm., U.S. C4 97
Anacostia, Northwest Branch, stm., Md., U.S. B3 97
Anadarko, Ok., U.S. B3 113
Anadyr', U.S.S.R. E29 20
Anadyr', stm., U.S.S.R. E29 20
Anadyrskij Zaliv, b., U.S.S.R. E30 20
Anadyrskoje Ploskogorje, plat., U.S.S.R. D28 20
Anagni, Italy H8 14
Anaheim, Ca., U.S. F5 82
Anahola, Hi., U.S. A2 88
Anahuac, Tx., U.S. E5 120
Ānai Mudi, mtn., India G4 37
Anakāpalle, India D7 37
Analalava, Madag. D9 44
Ana María, Golfo de, b., Cuba D8 64
Anambas, Kepulauan, is., Indon. M9 34
Anamosa, Ia., U.S. B6 92
Anamur, Tur. H14 4
Anamur Burnu, c., Tur. A3 40
Anan, Japan I7 30
Ānand, India I5 38
Anantapur, India E4 37
Anantnāg (Islāmābād), India D6 38
Anápolis, Braz. D4 57
Anastasia Island, i., Fl., U.S. C5 86
Añatuya, Arg. B4 56
'Anazah, Jabal, mtn., Asia C6 40
Ancaster, Ont., Can. D4 73
Ancha, Sierra, mts., Az., U.S. D4 80
Anchang, China E9 28
Anchorage, Ak., U.S. C10 79
Anchorage, Ky., U.S. g11 94
Anchor Point, Ak., U.S. D9 79
Anchor Point, c., Ak., U.S. h15 79
Ancienne-Lorette, Que., Can. C6 74
Anclote Keys, is., Fl., U.S. D4 86
Ancona, Italy F8 14
Ancud, Chile E2 56
Ancud, Golfo de, b., Chile E2 56
Andalucía, hist. reg., Spain H7 12
Andalusia, Al., U.S. D3 78
Andalusia, Il., U.S. B3 90
Andaman Islands, is., India H2 34
Andaman Sea, Asia I3 34
Andermatt, Switz. F15 10
Andernach, Ger. E7 8
Anderson, Ak., U.S. C10 79
Anderson, Ca., U.S. B2 82
Anderson, In., U.S. D6 91
Anderson, Mo., U.S. E3 102
Anderson, S.C., U.S. B2 117
Anderson, co., Ks., U.S. D8 93
Anderson, co., Ky., U.S. C4 94
Anderson, co., S.C., U.S. B2 117
Anderson, co., Tn., U.S. C9 119
Anderson, co., Tx., U.S. D5 120
Anderson, stm., N.W. Ter., Can. C7 66
Anderson, stm., In., U.S. H4 91
Anderson, Mount, mtn., Wa., U.S. B2 124
Anderson Ranch Reservoir, res., Id., U.S. F3 89
Andes, mts., S.A. F4 53
Andes, Lake, l., S.D., U.S. D7 118
Andhra Pradesh, state, India D5 37
Andižan, U.S.S.R. I12 18
Andkhvoy, Afg. B1 38
Andong, China C11 26
Andong, S. Kor. D12 26
Andorra, And. C13 12
Andorra, ctry., Eur. G8 4
Andover, Ks., U.S. g12 93
Andover, Ma., U.S. A5 98
Andover, Mn., U.S. m12 100
Andover, Oh., U.S. A5 112
Andover Lake, res., Ct., U.S. C6 84
Andradina, Braz. F3 57
Andreanof Islands, is., Ak., U.S. E4 79
Andrew, co., Mo., U.S. B3 102
Andrew Island, i., N.S., Can. D9 71
Andrews, In., U.S. C6 91
Andrews, N.C., U.S. f9 110
Andrews, S.C., U.S. E8 117
Andrews, Tx., U.S. C1 120
Andrews, co., Tx., U.S. C1 120
Andrews Air Force Base, mil., Md., U.S. C4 97
Andria, Italy H11 14
Androka, Madag. G8 44
Ándros, i., Grc. L8 16
Androscoggin, co., Me., U.S. D2 96
Androscoggin, stm., Me., U.S. D2 96
Androscoggin Lake, l., Me., U.S. D2 96
Andros Island, i., Bah. B8 64
Andros Town, Bah. B9 64
Andújar, Spain G7 12
Anduo, China D14 38
Anegada Passage, strt., N.A. E16 64
Anfeng, China C9 28
Anfu, China H3 28
Ang'angxi, China B11 26
Angara, stm., U.S.S.R. F13 20
Angarsk, U.S.S.R. G14 20
Ånge, Swe. E10 6
Ángel, Salto (Angel Falls), wtfl, Ven. E11 58
Ángel de la Guarda, Isla, i., Mex. C3 62
Angeles, Phil. q19 32
Angeles Point, c., Wa., U.S. A2 124
Angel Falls see Ángel, Salto, wtfl, Ven. E11 58
Ängelholm, Swe. H9 6
Angelina, co., Tx., U.S. D5 120
Angels Camp, Ca., U.S. C3 82
Angermünde, Ger. B13 8
Angers, Fr. E6 10
Angerville, Fr. D8 10
Angicos, Braz. E11 54
Angier, N.C., U.S. B4 110
Ângk Tasaôm, Camb. I8 34
Angleton, Tx., U.S. E5 120
Angmagssalik, Grnld. C25 66
Angol, Chile D2 56
Angola, In., U.S. A8 91
Angola, N.Y., U.S. C1 109
Angola, ctry., Afr. D3 44
Angola Swamp, sw., N.C., U.S. C5 110
Angoon, Ak., U.S. D13 79
Angostura Reservoir, res., S.D., U.S. D2 118
Angoulême, Fr. G7 10
Angra dos Reis, Braz. G6 57
Anguilla, Ms., U.S. C3 101
Anguilla, dep., N.A. E16 64
Anguille, Cape, c., Newf., Can. E2 72
Angul, India J11 38
Anhai, China K7 28
Anhui, prov., China E10 26
Aniak, Ak., U.S. C8 79
Animas, stm., U.S. D3 83
Animas Mountains, mts., N.M., U.S. F1 108
Animas Peak, mtn., N.M., U.S. F2 108
Animas Valley, val., N.M., U.S. F1 108
Anita, Ia., U.S. C3 92
Anjār, India I4 38
Anji, China E8 28
Anjiang, China F9 26
Anjou, Que., Can. p19 74
Anjouan, i., Com. D8 44
Ankang, China E8 26
Ankara, Tur. H14 4
Ankavandra, Madag. E9 44
Ankazoabo, Madag. F8 44
Ankazobe, Madag. E9 44
Ankeny, Ia., U.S. C4 92
Anklesvar, India B2 37
Anlong, China B8 34
Anlu, China D2 28
Ann, Cape, c., Ma., U.S. A6 98
Anna, Il., U.S. F4 90
Anna, Oh., U.S. B1 112
Anna, Lake, res., Va., U.S. B5 123
Annaba (Bône), Alg. A7 42
Annaberg-Buchholz, Ger. E12 8
An-Nabk, Syria B5 40
An-Nafūd, des., Sau. Ar. C3 46
An-Najaf, Iraq B3 46
Anna Maria, Fl., U.S. p10 86
Anna Maria Island, i., Fl., U.S. q10 86
Annandale, Mn., U.S. E4 100
Annandale, Va., U.S. g12 123
Annapolis, Md., U.S. C5 97
Annapolis, stm., N.S., Can. E4 71
Annapolis Junction, Md., U.S. B4 97
Annapolis Royal, N.S., Can. E4 71
Annapurna, mtn., Nepal F10 38
Ann Arbor, Mi., U.S. F7 99
Anna Regina, Guy. D13 58
An-Nāṣirīyah, Iraq B4 46
Annawan, Il., U.S. B4 90
Anne Arundel, co., Md., U.S. B4 97
Annecy, Fr. G13 10
Annemasse, Fr. F13 10
Annette, Ak., U.S. n24 79
Anniston, Al., U.S. B4 78
Annobón, i., Eq. Gui. B1 44
Annonay, Fr. G11 10
An-Nuhūd, Sudan F11 42
Annville, Pa., U.S. F8 115
Anoka, Mn., U.S. E5 100
Anoka, co., Mn., U.S. E5 100
Anqing, China E6 28
Anren, China I2 28
Ansbach, Ger. F10 8
Anshan, China C11 26
Anshun, China A8 34
Anson, Me., U.S. D3 96
Anson, Tx., U.S. C3 120
Anson, co., N.C., U.S. B2 110
Ansonia, Ct., U.S. D3 84
Ansonia, Oh., U.S. B1 112
Ansted, W.V., U.S. C3 125
Antakya, Tur. H15 4
Antalaha, Madag. D10 44
Antalya, Tur. H14 4
Antalya, Gulf of see Antalya Körfezi, b., Tur. A2 40
Antalya Körfezi, b., Tur. A2 40
Antananarivo, Madag. E9 44
Antarctica A18 47
Antarctic Peninsula, pen., Ant. C6 47
Antelope, co., Ne., U.S. B7 104
Antelope Creek, stm., Wy., U.S. C7 127
Antelope Island, i., Ut., U.S. B3 121
Antelope Peak, mtn., Nv., U.S. B7 105
Antelope Range, mts., Nv., U.S. D7 105
Antelope Reservoir, res., Or., U.S. E9 114
Antelope Wash, val., Nv., U.S. D5 105
Antequera, Spain H7 12
Antero, Mount, mtn., Co., U.S. C4 83
Antero Reservoir, res., Co., U.S. C5 83
Anthon, Ia., U.S. B2 92
Anthony, Fl., U.S. C4 86
Anthony, Ks., U.S. E5 93
Anthony, N.M., U.S. F3 108
Anthony, R.I., U.S. D3 116
Anthony, Tx., U.S. o11 120
Anthony Creek, stm., W.V., U.S. D4 125
Anti Atlas, mts., Mor. B4 42
Antibes, Fr. I14 10
Anticosti, Île d', i., Que., Can. k14 74
Antietam National Battlefield, hist., Md., U.S. B2 97
Antigo, Wi., U.S. C4 126
Antigua and Barbuda, ctry., N.A. F17 64
Antioch, Ca., U.S. h9 82
Antioch, Il., U.S. A5 90
Antioch see Antakya, Tur. H15 4
Antisana, vol., Ec. H3 58
Antlers, Ok., U.S. C6 113
Antofagasta, Chile A2 56
Antofalla, Salar de, pl., Arg. B3 56
Anton, Tx., U.S. C1 120
Antongila, Helodrano, b., Madag. E9 44
António Enes, Moz. E7 44
Antônio João, Braz. G1 57
Antonito, Co., U.S. D5 83
Antora Peak, mtn., Co., U.S. C4 83
Antrim, N.H., U.S. D3 106
Antrim, co., Mi., U.S. C5 99
Antrodoco, Italy G8 14
Antsirabe, Madag. E9 44
Antsiranana, Madag. D9 44
Antwerp, Oh., U.S. A1 112
Antwerp see Antwerpen, Bel. D4 8
Antwerpen (Antwerp), Bel. D4 8
Anuradhapura, Sri L. H6 37
Anxi, China C6 26
Anxi, China J7 28
Anyang, China D9 26
Anyi, China G4 28
Anyuan, China H2 28
Anyuan, China J4 28
Anžero-Sudžensk, U.S.S.R. F11 20
Anzio, Italy H7 14
Anžu, Ostrova, is., U.S.S.R. B23 20
Aoíz, Spain C10 12
Aomori, Japan B13 30
Aóös (Vijosë), stm., Eur. J4 16
Aôral, Phnum, mtn., Camb. H8 34
Aosta, Italy D2 14
Aoukâr, reg., Maur. E4 42
Aozou, Chad D9 42
Apache, Ok., U.S. C3 113
Apache, co., Az., U.S. B6 80
Apache Junction, Az., U.S. m9 80
Apache Peak, mtn., Az., U.S. F5 80
Apalachee Bay, b., Fl., U.S. B2 86
Apalachicola, Fl., U.S. C2 86
Apalachicola, stm., Fl., U.S. B1 86
Apalachicola Bay, b., Fl., U.S. C2 86
Apaporis, stm., S.A. H7 58
Aparri, Phil. B7 32
Apatzingán [de la Constitución], Mex. H8 62
Apeldoorn, Neth. C5 8

Name — Map Ref — Page

Apennines see Appennino, mts., Italy F7 14
Apex, N.C., U.S. B4 110
Apishapa, stm., Co., U.S. D6 83
Apizaco, Mex. H10 62
Aplington, Ia., U.S. B5 92
Apo, Mount, mtn., Phil. D8 32
Apolda, Ger. D11 8
Apollo, Pa., U.S. E2 115
Apopka, Fl., U.S. D5 86
Apopka, Lake, l., Fl., U.S. D5 86
Aporé, Braz. E2 57
Apostle Islands, is., Wi., U.S. A3 126
Apostle Islands National Lakeshore, Wi., U.S. A3 126
Appalachia, Va., U.S. f9 123
Appalachian Mountains, mts., N.A. D10 76
Appanoose, co., Ia., U.S. D5 92
Appennino (Apennines), mts., Italy F7 14
Appiano, Italy C6 14
Apple, stm., Wi., U.S. C1 126
Apple Creek, Oh., U.S. B4 112
Applegate, Or., U.S. E3 114
Applegate, stm., Or., U.S. E3 114
Appleton, Mn., U.S. E2 100
Appleton, Wi., U.S. D5 126
Appleton City, Mo., U.S. C3 102
Apple Valley, Ca., U.S. E5 82
Apple Valley, Mn., U.S. n12 100
Applewood, Co., U.S. B5 83
Appleyard, Wa., U.S. B5 124
Appling, co., Ga., U.S. E4 87
Appomattox, Va., U.S. C4 123
Appomattox, co., Va., U.S. C4 123
Appomattox, stm., Va., U.S. C4 123
Appomattox Court House National Historical Park, Va., U.S. C4 123
Apua Point, c., Hi., U.S. D6 88
Apucarana, Braz. G3 57
Apure, stm., Ven. D9 58
Apurímac, stm., Peru F4 54
Aqaba, Gulf of, b. E4 40
Āqcheh, Afg. B2 38
Āq Koprūk, Afg. B2 38
Aquarius Mountains, mts., Az., U.S. C2 80
Aquidauana, Braz. H7 54
Arab, Al., U.S. A3 78
'Arab, Baḥr al-, stm., Sudan G11 42
Arabelo, Ven. E10 58
Arabi, La., U.S. k11 95
Arabian Desert see Sharqīyah, Aṣ-Ṣaḥrā' al-, des., Egypt C12 42
Arabian Sea E17 2
Aracaju, Braz. F11 54
Aracati, Braz. D11 54
Araçatuba, Braz. F3 57
Aracena, Spain H5 12
Araçuaí, Braz. D7 57
Arad, Rom. C5 16
Arafura Sea G9 32
Arago, Cape, c., Or., U.S. D2 114
Aragon, Ga., U.S. B1 87
Aragón, hist. reg., Spain D11 12
Araguacema, Braz. E9 54
Aragua de Barcelona, Ven. C10 58
Araguari, Braz. E4 57
Arak, Alg. C6 42
Arāk, Iran B4 46
Arakan Yoma, mts., Burma E3 34
Aral Sea see Aral'skoje more, U.S.S.R. H10 18
Aral'skoje more (Aral Sea), U.S.S.R. H10 18
Arambaza, Col. I6 58
Aranda de Duero, Spain D8 12
Arandas, Mex. G8 62
Ārani, India F5 37
Aran Island, i., Ire. G4 7
Aran Islands, is., Ire. H3 7
Aranjuez, Spain E8 12
Aransas, co., Tx., U.S. E4 120
Aransas Bay, b., Tx., U.S. E4 120
Aransas Pass, Tx., U.S. F4 120
Aranyaprathet, Thai. H7 34
Arao, Japan I3 30
Arapaho, Ok., U.S. B3 113
Arapahoe, Ne., U.S. D6 104
Arapahoe, co., Co., U.S. B6 83
Arapiraca, Braz. E11 54
Arapongas, Braz. G3 57
Araraquara, Braz. F4 57
Ararat, Austl. G8 50
Ararat, Mount see Ağrı Dağı, mtn., Tur. H16 4
Arauca, Col. D7 58
Araure, Ven. C8 58
Arāvalli Range, mts., India H5 38
Araxá, Braz. E5 57
Araya, Punta de, c., Ven. B10 58
Arba Minch, Eth. G2 46
Arbois, Fr. F12 10
Arbon, Switz. E16 10
Arborg, Man., Can. D3 70
Arbroath, Scot., U.K. E10 7
Arbuckle, Lake, l., Fl., U.S. E5 86
Arbuckle Mountains, mts., Ok., U.S. C4 113
Arbuckles, Lake of the, res., Ok., U.S. C5 113
Arcachon, Fr. H5 10
Arcade, Ca., U.S. c3 82
Arcade, Ga., U.S. B3 87
Arcade, N.Y., U.S. C2 109
Arcadia, Ca., U.S. m12 82
Arcadia, Fl., U.S. E5 86
Arcadia, In., U.S. D5 91
Arcadia, La., U.S. B3 95
Arcadia, Mo., U.S. D7 102
Arcadia, S.C., U.S. B4 117
Arcadia, Wi., U.S. D2 126
Arcanum, Oh., U.S. C1 112
Arcata, Ca., U.S. B1 82
Arc Dome, mtn., Nv., U.S. E4 105
Archangel'sk, U.S.S.R. E6 18
Archbald, Pa., U.S. m18 115
Archbold, Oh., U.S. A1 112
Archdale, N.C., U.S. B3 110
Archer, Fl., U.S. C4 86
Archer, co., Tx., U.S. C3 120
Archer City, Tx., U.S. C3 120
Arches National Park, Ut., U.S. E6 121
Archidona, Spain H7 12
Archie, Mo., U.S. C3 102
Archuleta, co., Co., U.S. D3 83
Arcis-sur-Aube, Fr. D11 10
Arco, Id., U.S. F5 89
Arco de Baúlhe, Port. D4 12
Arcola, Il., U.S. D5 90
Arcos de la Frontera, Spain I6 12
Arctic Bay, N.W. Ter., Can. B15 66
Arctic Ocean A32 128
Arda, stm., Eur. H9 16
Ardabīl, Iran J7 18
Årdalstangen, Nor. F6 6
Ardennes, reg., Eur. E5 8
Ardlussa, Scot., U.K. E7 7
Ardmore, Al., U.S. A3 78
Ardmore, In., U.S. A5 91
Ardmore, Ok., U.S. C4 113
Ardmore, Tn., U.S. B5 119
Ardsley, N.Y., U.S. g13 109
Åre, Swe. E9 6
Arecibo, P.R. E14 64
Arena, Point, c., Ca., U.S. C2 82
Arena, Punta, c., Mex. F5 62
Arenac, co., Mi., U.S. D7 99
Arenas de San Pedro, Spain E6 12
Arendal, Nor. G7 6
Arequipa, Peru G4 54
Arès, Fr. H5 10
Arévalo, Spain D7 12
Arezzo, Italy F6 14
Arganda, Spain E8 12
Arga-Sala, stm., U.S.S.R. D15 20
Argelès-Gazost, Fr. I7 10
Argenta, Italy E6 14
Argenta, Il., U.S. D5 90
Argentan, Fr. D6 10
Argentat, Fr. G8 10
Argentera, mtn., Italy E2 14
Argentina, ctry., S.A. C4 56
Argentino, Lago, l., Arg. G2 56
Argenton-sur-Creuse, Fr. F8 10
Argonne, reg., Fr. C12 10
Árgos, Grc. L6 16
Argos, In., U.S. B5 91
Argostólion, Grc. K4 16
Argun' (Ergun), stm., Asia A11 26
Argyle, Mn., U.S. B2 100
Argyle, Wi., U.S. F4 126
Århus, Den. H8 6
Ariano Irpino, Italy H10 14
Arica, Chile G4 54
Arica, Col. I7 58
Arichat, N.S., Can. D8 71
Arid, Cape, c., Austl. F4 50
Arīḥā (Jericho), Jord. D4 40
Arikaree, stm., U.S. B8 83
Arima, Trin. I17 64
Arinos, stm., Braz. F7 54
Aripuanã, stm., Braz. E7 54
Ariquemes, Braz. E6 54
Arismendi, Ven. C8 58
Aristazabal Island, i., B.C., Can. C3 69
Ariton, Al., U.S. D4 78
Arizona, state, U.S. C4 80
Arizona Sunsites, Az., U.S. F6 80
Arizpe, Mex. B4 62
Arjay, Ky., U.S. D6 94
Arjeplog, Swe. C11 6
Arjona, Col. B5 58
Arkabutla Lake, res., Ms., U.S. A4 101
Arkadelphia, Ar., U.S. C2 81
Arkansas, co., Ar., U.S. C4 81
Arkansas, state, U.S. C3 81
Arkansas, stm., U.S. D8 76
Arkansas City, Ks., U.S. E6 93
Arklow, Ire. I6 7
Arkoma, Ok., U.S. B7 113
Arkonam, India F5 37
Arktičeskogo Instituta, Ostrova, is., U.S.S.R. B10 20
Arles, Fr. I11 10
Arlington, Ga., U.S. E2 87
Arlington, Ma., U.S. B5 98
Arlington, Mn., U.S. F4 100
Arlington, Ne., U.S. C9 104
Arlington, N.Y., U.S. D7 109
Arlington, N.C., U.S. A2 110
Arlington, Oh., U.S. B2 112
Arlington, S.C., U.S. B3 117
Arlington, S.D., U.S. C8 118
Arlington, Tn., U.S. B2 119
Arlington, Tx., U.S. n9 120
Arlington, Vt., U.S. E2 122
Arlington, Va., U.S. B5 123
Arlington, Wa., U.S. A3 124
Arlington, co., Va., U.S. g12 123
Arlington, Lake, res., Tx., U.S. n9 120
Arlington Heights, Il., U.S. A5 90
Arma, Ks., U.S. E9 93
Armada, Mi., U.S. F8 99
Armagh, Que., Can. C7 74
Arm'anskaja Sovetskaja Socialističeskaja Respublika, state, U.S.S.R. I6 18
Armavir, U.S.S.R. H6 18
Armenia, Col. E5 58
Armenia see Arm'anskaja Sovetskaja Socialističeskaja Respublika, state, U.S.S.R. I6 18
Armentières, Fr. B9 10
Armidale, Austl. F10 50
Armijo, N.M., U.S. k7 108
Armour, S.D., U.S. D7 118
Armstrong, B.C., Can. D8 69
Armstrong, Ia., U.S. A3 92
Armstrong, co., Pa., U.S. E2 115
Armstrong, co., Tx., U.S. B2 120
Armstrong, Mount, mtn., Yukon, Can. D6 66
Armstrong Creek, stm., W.V., U.S. m13 125
Arnaudville, La., U.S. D4 95
Arnedo, Spain C9 12
Arnett, W.V., U.S. D3 125
Arnhem, Neth. D5 8
Arnhem, Cape, c., Austl. B7 50
Arnhem Land, reg., Austl. B6 50
Árnissa, Grc. I5 16
Arno, stm., Italy F5 14
Arnold, Mn., U.S. D6 100
Arnold, Mo., U.S. C7 102
Arnold, Ne., U.S. C5 104
Arnold, Pa., U.S. h14 115
Arnold Mills, R.I., U.S. B4 116
Arnold Mills Reservoir, res., R.I., U.S. B4 116
Arnold's Cove, Newf., Can. E4 72
Arnolds Park, Ia., U.S. A2 92
Arnprior, Ont., Can. B8 73
Arnsberg, Ger. D8 8
Arnstadt, Ger. E10 8
Arona, Italy D3 14
Aroostook, co., Me., U.S. B4 96
Arpajon, Fr. D9 10
Ar-Rab' al-Khālī, des., Asia D5 46
Arrah, India H11 38
Ar-Rahad, Sudan F12 42
Ar-Ramadi, Iraq B3 46
Ar-Ramthā, Jord. C4 40
Arran, Island of, i., Scot., U.K. F7 7
Ar-Raqqah, Syria B6 40
Arras, Fr. B9 10
Arrecife, Spain C3 42
Arriaga, Mex. I13 62
Ar-Riyāḍ (Riyadh), Sau. Ar. D4 46
Arronches, Port. F4 12
Arrowhead Mountain Lake, res., Vt., U.S. B2 122
Arrowrock Reservoir, res., Id., U.S. F3 89
Arrowwood Lake, res., N.D., U.S. B7 111
Arroyo de la Luz, Spain F5 12
Arroyo Grande, Ca., U.S. E3 82
Ar-Ruṣayriṣ, Sudan F12 42
Ar-Ruṭbah, Iraq C7 40
Arsenjev, U.S.S.R. I20 20
Árta, Grc. J4 16
Artá, Spain F15 12
Artemisa, Cuba C6 64
Artemus, Ky., U.S. D6 94
Artenay, Fr. D8 10
Arter, Mount, mtn., Wy., U.S. D4 127
Artesia, N.M., U.S. E5 108
Arthabaska, Que., Can. C6 74
Arthur, Ont., Can. D4 73
Arthur, Il., U.S. D5 90
Arthur, co., Ne., U.S. C4 104
Arthur, Lake, l., La., U.S. D3 95
Arthur, Lake, res., Pa., U.S. E1 115
Arthur Kill, stm., N.J., U.S. k8 107
Arthurs Town, Bah. B10 64
Artigas, Ur. C5 56
Art'om, U.S.S.R. I20 20
Art'omovsk, U.S.S.R. G12 20
Artvin, Tur. G16 4
Aru, Kepulauan, is., Indon. G9 32
Arua, Ug. H12 42
Aruanã, Braz. C3 57
Aruba, dep., N.A. H13 64
Arunachal Pradesh, ter., India F16 38
Aruppukkottai, India H5 37
Arusha, Tan. B7 44
Aruwimi, stm., Zaire A5 44
Arvada, Co., U.S. B5 83
Arvi, India B5 37
Arvidsjaur, Swe. D12 6
Arvika, Swe. G9 6
Arvin, Ca., U.S. E4 82
Arvon, Mount, mtn., Mi., U.S. B2 99
Arvonia, Va., U.S. C4 123
Arzachena, Italy H4 14
Arzignano, Italy D6 14
Arzúa, Spain C3 12
Asadābād, Afg. C4 38
Asahi-dake, mtn., Japan p20 30a
Asahikawa, Japan p20 30a
Asansol, India I12 38
Asbestos, Que., Can. D6 74
Asbury Park, N.J., U.S. C4 107
Ascensión, Mex. E10 62
Ascension, co., La., U.S. D5 95
Ascensión, Bahía de la, b., Mex. H16 62
Ašchabad, U.S.S.R. J9 18
Aschaffenburg, Ger. F9 8
Aschersleben, Ger. D11 8
Asciano, Italy F6 14
Ascoli Piceno, Italy G8 14
Ascoli Satriano, Italy H10 14
Aseb, Eth. F3 46
Asela, Eth. G2 46
Åsele, Swe. D11 6
Åsen, Nor. E8 6
Asenovgrad, Bul. G8 16
Ashaway, R.I., U.S. F1 116
Ashburn, Ga., U.S. E3 87
Ashburton, N.Z. E3 52
Ashcroft, B.C., Can. D7 69
Ashdown, Ar., U.S. D1 81
Ashe, co., N.C., U.S. A1 110
Asheboro, N.C., U.S. B3 110
Ashepoo, stm., S.C., U.S. F6 117
Ashern, Man., Can. D2 70
Asherton, Tx., U.S. E3 120
Asheville, N.C., U.S. f10 110
Ash Flat, Ar., U.S. A4 81
Ashford, Eng., U.K. J13 7
Ashford, Al., U.S. D4 78
Ashford, W.V., U.S. m12 125
Ash Grove, Mo., U.S. D4 102
Ashibetsu, Japan p20 30a
Ashikaga, Japan F12 30
Ashizuri-zaki, c., Japan J6 30
Ashkhabad see Ašchabad, U.S.S.R. J9 18
Ashland, Al., U.S. B4 78
Ashland, Il., U.S. D3 90
Ashland, Ks., U.S. E4 93
Ashland, Ky., U.S. B7 94
Ashland, Me., U.S. B4 96
Ashland, Ma., U.S. g10 98
Ashland, Mo., U.S. C5 102
Ashland, Ne., U.S. C9 104
Ashland, N.H., U.S. C3 106
Ashland, Oh., U.S. B3 112
Ashland, Or., U.S. E4 114
Ashland, Pa., U.S. E9 115
Ashland, Va., U.S. C5 123
Ashland, Wi., U.S. B3 126
Ashland, co., Oh., U.S. B3 112
Ashland, co., Wi., U.S. B3 126
Ashland, Mount, mtn., Or., U.S. E4 114
Ashland City, Tn., U.S. A4 119
Ashland Reservoir, res., Ma., U.S. h10 98
Ashley, In., U.S. A7 91
Ashley, N.D., U.S. C6 111
Ashley, Oh., U.S. B3 112
Ashley, Pa., U.S. n17 115
Ashley, co., Ar., U.S. D4 81
Ashley, stm., S.C., U.S. F7 117
Ashley Creek, stm., Ut., U.S. C6 121
Ashmore, Il., U.S. D5 90
Ashokan Reservoir, res., N.Y., U.S. D6 109
Ashqelon, Isr. D4 40
Ash-Shaqrā', Sau. Ar. C4 46
Ash-Shāriqah, U.A.E. C6 46
Ash-Shawbak, Jord. D4 40
Ashtabula, Oh., U.S. A5 112
Ashtabula, co., Oh., U.S. A5 112
Ashtabula, Lake, res., N.D., U.S. B8 111
Ashton, Id., U.S. E7 89
Ashton, Il., U.S. B4 90
Ashton, Md., U.S. B3 97
Ashton, R.I., U.S. B4 116
Ashuanipi Lake, l., Newf., Can. h8 72
Ashuelot, stm., N.H., U.S. E2 106
Ashville, Al., U.S. B3 78
Ashville, Oh., U.S. C3 112
Ashwaubenon, Wi., U.S. D5 126
Asia D12 84
Asia, Kepulauan, is., Indon. E9 32
Asia Minor, reg., Tur. H14 4
Asino, U.S.S.R. F11 20
'Asīr, reg., Sau. Ar. E3 46
Asir, Ras, c., Som. F5 46
Askham, S. Afr. G4 44
Askvoll, Nor. F5 6
Asmara see Asmera, Eth. E2 46
Asmera, Eth. E2 46
Asotin, Wa., U.S. C8 124
Asotin, co., Wa., U.S. C8 124
Asotin Creek, stm., Wa., U.S. C8 124
Aspang Markt, Aus. H16 8
Aspen, Co., U.S. B4 83
Aspen Butte, mtn., Or., U.S. E4 114
Aspermont, Tx., U.S. C2 120
Aspinwall, Pa., U.S. k14 115
Aspiring, Mount, mtn., N.Z. F2 52
Aspres-sur-Buëch, Fr. H12 10
Aspy Bay, b., N.S., Can. C9 71
Assabet, stm., Ma., U.S. g9 98
Aṣ-Ṣabyā, Sau. Ar. E3 46
As-Sallūm, Egypt B11 42
As-Salṭ, Jord. C4 40
Assam, state, India G15 38
As-Samāwah, Iraq B4 46
Assateague Island, i., U.S. D7 97
Assateague Island National Seashore, U.S. D7 97
Assawoman Bay, b., Md., U.S. D7 97
Assen, Neth. C6 8
Assiniboine, stm., Can. E2 70
Assiniboine, Mount, mtn., Can. D3 68
Assis, Braz. G3 57
Assisi, Italy F7 14
As-Sulaymānīyah, Iraq A4 46
As-Sulaymānīyah, Sau. Ar. D4 46
As-Sulayyil, Sau. Ar. D4 46
Assumption, Il., U.S. D4 90
Assumption, co., La., U.S. E4 95
Assumption Island, i., Sey. C9 44
Aṣ-Ṣuwār, Syria B7 40
As-Suwaydā', Syria C5 40
As-Suways (Suez), Egypt C12 42
Asti, Italy E3 14
Astorga, Spain C5 12
Astoria, Il., U.S. C3 90
Astoria, Or., U.S. A3 114
Astove Island, i., Sey. D9 44
Astrachan', U.S.S.R. H7 18
Astrakhan see Astrachan', U.S.S.R. H7 18
Astudillo, Spain C7 12
Asunción, Para. B5 56
Aswān, Egypt D12 42
Aswān High Dam, Egypt D12 42
Asyūṭ, Egypt C12 42
Atacama, Desierto de, des., Chile A3 56
Atacama, Puna de, plat., S.A. A3 56
Atacama, Salar de, pl., Chile A3 56
Ataco, Col. F5 58
Atakpamé, Togo G6 42
Atami, Japan G12 30
Atar, Maur. D3 42
Atascadero, Ca., U.S. E3 82
Atascosa, co., Tx., U.S. E3 120
'Aṭbarah, Sudan E12 42
'Aṭbarah (Atbara), stm., Afr. E12 42
Atchafalaya, stm., La., U.S. D4 95
Atchafalaya Bay, b., La., U.S. E4 95
Atchison, Ks., U.S. C8 93
Atchison, co., Ks., U.S. C8 93
Atchison, co., Mo., U.S. A2 102
Ateca, Spain D10 12
Athabasca, Alta., Can. B4 68
Athabasca, stm., Alta., Can. f8 68
Athabasca, Lake, l., Can. m7 75
Athena, Or., U.S. B8 114
Athenry, Ire. H4 7
Athens, Ont., Can. C9 73
Athens, Al., U.S. A3 78
Athens, Ga., U.S. C3 87
Athens, Il., U.S. D4 90
Athens, Mi., U.S. F5 99
Athens, N.Y., U.S. C7 109
Athens, Oh., U.S. C3 112
Athens, Pa., U.S. C8 115
Athens, Tn., U.S. D9 119
Athens, Tx., U.S. C5 120
Athens, W.V., U.S. D3 125
Athens, Wi., U.S. C3 126
Athens, co., Oh., U.S. C3 112
Athens see Athínai, Grc. L7 16
Athínai (Athens), Grc. L7 16
Athlone, Ire. H5 7
Athol, Ma., U.S. A3 98
Ati, Chad F9 42
Atienza, Spain D9 12
Atik Lake, l., Man., Can. B4 70
Atikonak Lake, l., Newf., Can. h8 72
Atka Island, i., Ak., U.S. E5 79
Atkins, Ar., U.S. B3 81
Atkins, Va., U.S. D1 123
Atkinson, Il., U.S. B3 90
Atkinson, Ne., U.S. B7 104
Atkinson, N.H., U.S. E4 106
Atkinson, co., Ga., U.S. E4 87
Atlanta, Ga., U.S. C2 87
Atlanta, Il., U.S. C4 90
Atlanta, In., U.S. D5 91
Atlanta, Mi., U.S. C6 99
Atlanta, Tx., U.S. C5 120
Atlantic, Ia., U.S. C2 92
Atlantic, N.C., U.S. C6 110
Atlantic, co., N.J., U.S. E3 107
Atlantic Beach, Fl., U.S. m9 86
Atlantic City, N.J., U.S. E4 107
Atlantic Highlands, N.J., U.S. C4 107
Atlantic Ocean F10 2
Atlantic Peak, mtn., Wy., U.S. D3 127
Atlas Mountains, mts., Afr. B5 42
Atlas Saharien, mts., Alg. B6 42
Atmore, Al., U.S. D2 78
Atna Peak, mtn., B.C., Can. C3 69
Atoka, Ok., U.S. C5 113
Atoka, Tn., U.S. B2 119
Atoka, co., Ok., U.S. C5 113
Atoka Reservoir, res., Ok., U.S. C5 113
Atotonilco el Alto, Mex. G8 62
Atrato, stm., Col. D4 58
Aṭ-Ṭafīlah, Jord. D4 40
Aṭ-Ṭā'if, Sau. Ar. D3 46
Attala, co., Ms., U.S. B4 101
Attalla, Al., U.S. A3 78
Attawapiskat, stm., Ont., Can. n18 73
Attica, In., U.S. D3 91
Attica, Ks., U.S. E5 93
Attica, N.Y., U.S. C2 109
Attica, Oh., U.S. A3 112
Attleboro, Ma., U.S. C5 98
Attopeu, Laos G9 34
Attow, Ben, mtn., Scot., U.K. D7 7
Attu Island, i., Ak., U.S. E2 79
Āttūr, India G5 37
Atwater, Ca., U.S. D3 82
Atwater, Mn., U.S. E4 100
Atwood, Ont., Can. D3 73
Atwood, Il., U.S. D5 90
Atwood, Ks., U.S. C2 93
Atwood, Tn., U.S. B3 119
Atwood Lake, res., Oh., U.S. B4 112
Auau Channel, strt., Hi., U.S. C5 88
Aubagne, Fr. I12 10
Aube, stm., Fr. D11 10
Auberry, Ca., U.S. D4 82
Aubigny-sur-Nère, Fr. E9 10
Aubin, Fr. H9 10
Auburn, Al., U.S. C4 78
Auburn, Ca., U.S. C3 82
Auburn, Ga., U.S. B3 87
Auburn, Il., U.S. D4 90
Auburn, In., U.S. B7 91
Auburn, Ks., U.S. D8 93
Auburn, Ky., U.S. D3 94
Auburn, Me., U.S. D2 96
Auburn, Ma., U.S. B4 98
Auburn, Mi., U.S. E6 99
Auburn, Ne., U.S. D10 104
Auburn, N.Y., U.S. C4 109
Auburn, Wa., U.S. B3 124
Auburndale, Fl., U.S. D5 86
Auburn Heights, Mi., U.S. F7 99
Aubusson, Fr. G9 10
Auch, Fr. I7 10
Aucilla, stm., Fl., U.S. B3 86
Auckland, N.Z. B5 52
Audincourt, Fr. E13 10
Audrain, co., Mo., U.S. B6 102
Audubon, Ia., U.S. C3 92
Audubon, N.J., U.S. D2 107
Audubon, co., Ia., U.S. C2 92
Aue, Ger. E12 8
Auglaize, co., Oh., U.S. B1 112
Auglaize, stm., Oh., U.S. A1 112
Au Gres, Mi., U.S. D7 99
Augsburg, Ger. G10 8
Augusta, Italy L10 14
Augusta, Ar., U.S. B4 81
Augusta, Ga., U.S. C5 87
Augusta, Ks., U.S. E7 93
Augusta, Ky., U.S. B6 94
Augusta, Me., U.S. D3 96
Augusta, Mi., U.S. F5 99
Augusta, Wi., U.S. D2 126
Augusta, co., Va., U.S. B3 123
Augustus, Mount, mtn., Austl. D3 50
Aulander, N.C., U.S. A5 110
Auld, Lake, l., Austl. D4 50
Aulneau Peninsula, pen., Ont., Can. E4 70
Ault, Co., U.S. A6 83
Aumont-Aubrac, Fr. H10 10
Aumsville, Or., U.S. k12 114
Aurangābād, India C3 37
Auray, Fr. E4 10
Aurelia, Ia., U.S. B2 92
Aurich, Ger. B7 8

Auriflama, Braz. F3 57
Aurillac, Fr. H9 10
Aurora, Ont., Can. C5 73
Aurora, Co., U.S. B6 83
Aurora, Il., U.S. B5 90
Aurora, In., U.S. F8 91
Aurora, Mn., U.S. C6 100
Aurora, Mo., U.S. E4 102
Aurora, Ne., U.S. D7 104
Aurora, Oh., U.S. A4 112
Aurora, S.D., U.S. C9 118
Aurora, Ut., U.S. E4 121
Aurora, co., S.D., U.S. D7 118
Aus, Nmb. G3 44
Au Sable, Mi., U.S. D7 99
Au Sable, stm., Mi., U.S. D6 99
Ausable, stm., N.Y., U.S. f11 109
Au Sable Forks, N.Y., U.S. f11 109
Au Sable Point, c., Mi., U.S. B4 99
Au Sable Point, c., Mi., U.S. D7 99
Auschwitz see Oświęcim, Pol. E19 8
Austell, Ga., U.S. h7 87
Austin, In., U.S. G6 91
Austin, Mn., U.S. G6 100
Austin, Nv., U.S. D4 105
Austin, Tx., U.S. D4 120
Austin, co., Tx., U.S. E4 120
Austin, Lake, l., Austl. E3 50
Austin Channel, strt., N.W. Ter., Can. A12 66
Austintown, Oh., U.S. A5 112
Austinville, Va., U.S. D2 123
Australia, ctry., Oc. D6 50
Australian Capital Territory, ter., Austl. G9 50
Austria, ctry., Eur. F10 4
Autauga, co., Al., U.S. C3 78
Autaugaville, Al., U.S. C3 78
Autlán de Navarro, Mex. H7 62
Autun, Fr. F11 10
Auxerre, Fr. E10 10
Auxier, Ky., U.S. C7 94
Auxi-le-Château, Fr. B9 10
Auxonne, Fr. E12 10
Auxvasse, Mo., U.S. B6 102
Auyán Tepuy, mtn., Ven. E11 58
Auzances, Fr. F9 10
Ava, Mo., U.S. E5 102
Avallon, Fr. E10 10
Avalon, Ca., U.S. F4 82
Avalon, Pa., U.S. h13 115
Avalon, Lake, res., N.M., U.S. E5 108
Avalon Peninsula, pen., Newf., Can. E5 72
Avaré, Braz. G4 57
Aveiro, Port. E3 12
Avella, Pa., U.S. F1 115
Avellaneda, Arg. C5 56
Avellino, Italy I9 14
Avenal, Ca., U.S. E3 82
Avery, co., N.C., U.S. e11 110
Aves, Islas de, is., Ven. A9 58
Avesnes, Fr. B10 10
Avesta, Swe. F11 6
Avezzano, Italy G8 14
Aviemore, Scot., U.K. D9 7
Avignon, Fr. I11 10
Ávila, Spain E7 12
Avilés, Spain B6 12
Avilla, In., U.S. B7 91
Avis, Pa., U.S. D7 115
Avispa, Cerro, mtn., Ven. G10 58
Aviston, Il., U.S. E4 90
Aviz, Port. F4 12
Avoca, Ia., U.S. C2 92
Avoca, Pa., U.S. m18 115
Avola, Italy M10 14
Avon, Ct., U.S. B4 84
Avon, Il., U.S. C3 90
Avon, Ma., U.S. B5 98
Avon, Mn., U.S. E4 100
Avon, N.Y., U.S. C3 109
Avon, Oh., U.S. A3 112
Avondale, Az., U.S. D3 80
Avondale, Co., U.S. C6 83
Avondale, Pa., U.S. G10 115
Avondale Estates, Ga., U.S. h8 87
Avon Lake, Ia., U.S. e8 92
Avon Lake, Oh., U.S. A3 112
Avonmore, Pa., U.S. E3 115
Avon Park, Fl., U.S. E5 86
Avoyelles, co., La., U.S. C3 95
Avranches, Fr. D5 10
Awaji-shima, i., Japan H7 30
Awash, stm., Eth. F3 46
Awbārī, Libya C8 42
Awe, Loch, l., Scot., U.K. E7 7
Awjilah, Libya C10 42
Axiós (Vardar), stm., Eur. I6 16
Axis, Al., U.S. E1 78
Axtell, Ne., U.S. D6 104
Ayabe, Japan G8 30
Ayacucho, Peru F4 54
Ayamonte, Spain H4 12
Ayapel, Col. C5 58
Ayaviri, Peru F4 54
Āybak, Afg. B3 38
Ayden, N.C., U.S. B5 110
Aydın, Tur. H13 4
Ayer, Ma., U.S. A4 98
Ayers Cliff, Que., Can. D5 74
Ayeyarwady (Irrawaddy), stm., Burma G3 34
Áyion Óros, pen., Grc. I8 16
Áyios Nikólaos, Grc. N9 16
Aylesbury, Eng., U.K. J12 7
Aylesford, N.S., Can. D5 71
Aylmer, Mount, mtn., Alta., Can. D3 68
Aylmer East, Que., Can. D2 74
Aylmer Lake, l., N.W. Ter., Can. D11 66
Aylmer West, Ont., Can. E4 73
Ayora, Spain F10 12
'Ayoûn el 'Atroûs, Maur. E4 42
Ayr, Scot., U.K. F8 7
Ayre, Point of, c., I. of Man G8 7
Ayu, Kepulauan, is., Indon. E9 32
Ayvalık, Tur. J10 16
Azambuja, Port. F3 12
Azamgarh, India G10 38
Azare, Nig. F8 42
Azerbaijan see Azerbajdžanskaja Sovetskaja Socialističeskaja Respublika, state, U.S.S.R. I7 18
Azerbajdžanskaja Sovetskaja Socialističeskaja Respublika, state, U.S.S.R. I7 18
Aziscohos Lake, l., Me., U.S. C1 96
Azle, Tx., U.S. n9 120
Azogues, Ec. I3 58
Azores see Açores, is., Port. D11 2
Azov, Sea of see Azovskoje more, U.S.S.R. H5 18
Azovskoje more (Sea of Azov), U.S.S.R. H5 18
Aztec, N.M., U.S. A2 108
Aztec Peak, mtn., Az., U.S. D5 80
Aztec Ruins National Monument, N.M., U.S. A1 108
Azua, Dom. Rep. E12 64
Azuaga, Spain G6 12
Azuero, Península de, pen., Pan. K7 64
Azul, Arg. D5 56
Azur, Côte d', Fr. I14 10
Azusa, Ca., U.S. m13 82
Az-Zaqāzīq, Egypt D2 40
Az-Zarqā', Jord. C5 40
Az-Zāwiyah, Libya B8 42
Azzel Matti, Sebkha, pl., Alg. C6 42

B

Ba, stm., Viet. H10 34
Babaeski, Tur. H11 16
Babahoyo, Ec. H3 58
Babar, Kepulauan, is., Indon. G8 32
Babb Creek, stm., Pa., U.S. C7 115
Babbitt, Mn., U.S. C7 100
Babbitt, Nv., U.S. E3 105
B'abdā, Leb. C4 40
Bāb el-Mandeb see Mandeb, Bāb el-, strt. F3 46
Babine, stm., B.C., Can. B4 69
Babine Lake, l., B.C., Can. B5 69
Babine Range, mts., B.C., Can. B4 69
Bābol, Iran J8 18
Baboquivari Mountains, mts., Az., U.S. F4 80
Baboquivari Peak, mtn., Az., U.S. F4 80
Babuyan Islands, is., Phil. B7 32
Babylon, N.Y., U.S. n15 109
Baca, co., Co., U.S. D8 83
Bacabal, Braz. D10 54
Bacan, Pulau, i., Indon. F8 32
Bacău, Rom. C10 16
Bac Can, Viet. C8 34
Bacerac, Mex. B5 62
Bachaquero, Ven. C7 58
Bachta, U.S.S.R. E11 20
Bachu, China D2 26
Back, stm., N.W. Ter., Can. C13 66
Back, stm., S.C., U.S. h12 117
Backbone Mountain, mtn., U.S. m12 97
Backnang, Ger. G9 8
Bac Lieu, Viet. J8 34
Bac Ninh, Viet. D9 34
Bacolod, Phil. C7 32
Bacon, co., Ga., U.S. E4 87
Baconton, Ga., U.S. E2 87
Bacoor, Phil. q19 33b
Bad, stm., S.D., U.S. C5 118
Bad, stm., Wi., U.S. B3 126
Badagara, India G3 37
Badajia, China B9 28
Badajoz, Spain G5 12
Badalona, Spain D14 12
Badanah, Sau. Ar. B3 46
Bad Aussee, Aus. H13 8
Bad Axe, Mi., U.S. E8 99
Baddeck, N.S., Can. C9 71
Bad Doberan, Ger. A11 8
Bad Ems, Ger. E7 8
Baden, Aus. G16 8
Baden, Ont., Can. D4 73
Baden, Switz. E15 10
Baden, Pa., U.S. E1 115
Baden-Baden, Ger. G8 8
Badgastein, Aus. H13 8
Badger, Newf., Can. D3 72
Bad Hersfeld, Ger. E9 8
Bad Homburg [vor der Höhe], Ger. E8 8
Bad Honnef, Ger. E7 8
Badin, N.C., U.S. B2 110
Badin Lake, res., N.C., U.S. B2 110
Bad Ischl, Aus. H13 8
Bad Kissingen, Ger. E10 8
Bad Kreuznach, Ger. F7 8
Badlands, hills, S.D., U.S. D3 118
Badlands, reg., U.S. C2 111
Badlands National Park, S.D., U.S. D3 118
Bad Lauterberg, Ger. D10 8
Bad Nauheim, Ger. E8 8
Bad Neustadt an der Saale, Ger. E10 8
Bad Oldesloe, Ger. B10 8
Bad Reichenhall, Ger. H12 8
Bad River Indian Reservation, Wi., U.S. B3 126
Bad Salzungen, Ger. E10 8
Bad Schwartau, Ger. B10 8
Bad Segeberg, Ger. B10 8
Bad Tölz, Ger. H11 8
Badulla, Sri L. I6 37
Badwater Creek, stm., Wy., U.S. C5 127
Bad Wildungen, Ger. D9 8
Bad Wörishofen, Ger. G10 8
Baena, Spain H7 12
Baeza, Spain H8 12
Bafatá, Gui.-B. F3 42
Baffin Bay, b., N.A. B14 61
Baffin Bay, b., Tx., U.S. E4 120
Baffin Island, i., N.W. Ter., Can. C18 66
Bafwasende, Zaire A5 44
Bagaha, India G11 38
Bāgalkot, India D3 37
Bagansiapiapi, Indon. M6 34
Bağarası, Tur. L11 16
Bagdad, Az., U.S. C2 80
Bagdad, Fl., U.S. u14 86
Bagdad see Baghdād, Iraq B3 46
Bagdarin, U.S.S.R. G16 20
Bagé, Braz. C6 56
Baggs, Wy., U.S. E5 127
Baghdād, Iraq B3 46
Bagheria, Italy K8 14
Baghlān, Afg. B3 38
Baghrān Khowleh, Afg. D1 38
Bagley, Mn., U.S. C3 100
Bagnères-de-Bigorre, Fr. I7 10
Bagnères-de-Luchon, Fr. J7 10
Bagnols-sur-Cèze, Fr. H11 10
Bago, Burma F4 34
Baguio, Phil. p19 32
Bahamas, ctry., N.A. B9 64
Bahāwalnagar, Pak. F5 38
Bahāwalpur, Pak. F4 38
Bahía, Islas de la, is., Hond. F4 64
Bahía Blanca, Arg. D4 56
Bahía de Caráquez, Ec. H2 58
Bahía Kino, Mex. C4 62
Bahir Dar, Eth. F2 46
Bahraich, India G9 38
Bahrain, ctry., Asia C5 46
Baia-Mare, Rom. B7 16
Bai Bung, Muy, c., Viet. J8 34
Baicheng, China B11 26
Baicheng, China C3 26
Baidoa, Som. H3 46
Baie-Comeau, Que., Can. k13 74
Baie-d'Urfé, Que., Can. q19 74
Baie-Saint-Paul, Que., Can. B7 74
Baie Verte, Newf., Can. D3 72
Baigneux-les-Juifs, Fr. E11 10
Baiju, China B9 28
Baikal, Lake see Bajkal, Ozero, l., U.S.S.R. G15 20
Bailén, Spain G8 12
Bailey, co., Tx., U.S. B1 120
Bailey Island, Me., U.S. g8 96
Bailey Island, i., S.C., U.S. k11 117
Baileys Crossroads, Va., U.S. g12 123
Bainbridge, Ga., U.S. F2 87
Bainbridge, In., U.S. E4 91
Bainbridge, Oh., U.S. C2 112
Bainbridge Island, i., Wa., U.S. e10 124
Bain-de-Bretagne, Fr. E5 10
Baing, Indon. H7 32
Baird, Tx., U.S. C3 120
Bairdford, Pa., U.S. h14 115
Baird Inlet, b., Ak., U.S. C7 79
Baird Mountains, mts., Ak., U.S. B7 79
Bais, Fr. D6 10
Baise, China C9 34
Baishuijiang, China E8 26
Baiyin, China D7 26
Baiyunebo, China C9 26
Baja, Hung. I18 8
Baja, Punta, c., Mex. C4 62
Baja California, pen., Mex. D3 62
Bajanchongor, Mong. B7 26
Bajkal, Ozero (Lake Baykal), l., U.S.S.R. G15 20
Bajkal'skoje, U.S.S.R. F15 20
Bajkit, U.S.S.R. E13 20
Bajkonyr, U.S.S.R. H11 18
Bajo Baudó, Col. E4 58
Baker, La., U.S. D4 95
Baker, Mt., U.S. D12 103
Baker, Or., U.S. C9 114
Baker, co., Fl., U.S. B4 86
Baker, co., Ga., U.S. E2 87
Baker, co., Or., U.S. C9 114
Baker, stm., N.H., U.S. C3 106
Baker, Mount, mtn., Wa., U.S. A4 124
Baker Air Force Base, mil., Ar., U.S. B6 81
Baker Butte, mtn., Az., U.S. C4 80
Baker Island, i., Ak., U.S. n22 79
Baker Lake, N.W. Ter., Can. D13 66
Baker Lake, l., Me., U.S. B3 96
Baker Lake, res., Wa., U.S. A4 124
Bakersfield, Ca., U.S. E4 82
Bakers Island, i., Ma., U.S. f12 98
Bakerstown, Pa., U.S. h14 115
Bakhtarān, Iran B4 46
Bakhtegān, Daryācheh-ye, l., Iran C5 46
Bakır, stm., Tur. J11 16
Bakoye, stm., Afr. F4 42
Baku, U.S.S.R. I7 18
Balabac Island, i., Phil. D6 32
Balabac Strait, strt., Asia D6 32
Ba'labakk (Baalbek), Leb. B5 40
Balachna, U.S.S.R. E26 22
Bālāghāt, India J9 38
Bālāghāt Range, mts., India C4 37
Balaguer, Spain D12 12
Balakovo, U.S.S.R. G7 18
Balallan, Scot., U.K. C6 7
Balāngīr, India B7 37
Balašicha, U.S.S.R. F20 22
Balasore, India J12 38
Balašov, U.S.S.R. G6 18
Balaton, Mn., U.S. F3 100
Balaton, l., Hung. I17 8
Balbriggan, Ire. H6 7
Balcarres, Sask., Can. G4 75
Balchaš, Ozero, l., U.S.S.R. H9 20
Bald Eagle Lake, l., Mn., U.S. m12 100
Bald Eagle Lake, l., Mn., U.S. C7 100
Baldhill Dam, N.D., U.S. B7 111
Bald Knob, Ar., U.S. B4 81
Bald Knoll, mtn., Wy., U.S. D2 127
Bald Mountain, mtn., Or., U.S. D5 114
Bald Mountain, mtn., Or., U.S. C9 114
Bald Mountain, mtn., Wy., U.S. B5 127
Bald Mountains, mts., N.C., U.S. f10 110
Baldwin, Fl., U.S. B5 86
Baldwin, Ga., U.S. B3 87
Baldwin, La., U.S. E4 95
Baldwin, Mi., U.S. E5 99
Baldwin, Pa., U.S. k13 115
Baldwin, S.C., U.S. B5 117
Baldwin, Wi., U.S. D1 126
Baldwin, co., Al., U.S. E2 78
Baldwin, co., Ga., U.S. C3 87
Baldwin City, Ks., U.S. D8 93
Baldwinsville, N.Y., U.S. B4 109
Baldwinville, Ma., U.S. A3 98
Baldwyn, Ms., U.S. A5 101
Baldy Mountain, mtn., B.C., Can. D7 69
Baldy Mountain, mtn., Man., Can. D1 70
Baldy Mountain, mtn., Mt., U.S. B7 103
Baldy Mountain, mtn., N.M., U.S. A4 108
Baldy Peak, mtn., Az., U.S. D6 80
Baleares, Islas (Balearic Islands), is., Spain F14 12
Balearic Islands see Baleares, Islas, is., Spain E15 12
Baleine, Rivière à la, stm., Que., Can. g13 74
Balej, U.S.S.R. G17 20
Balfate, Hond. G4 64
Balfour, N.C., U.S. f10 110
Bali, i., Indon. G5 32
Bali, Laut (Bali Sea), Indon. G6 32
Balıkesir, Tur. H13 4
Balikpapan, Indon. F6 32
Balimo, Pap. N. Gui. G11 32
Balingen, Ger. G8 8
Balintang Channel, strt., Phil. B7 32
Baliza, Braz. D2 57
Balkan Mountains see Stara Planina, mts., Eur. G8 16
Balkh, Afg. B2 38
Balkhash, Lake see Balchaš, Ozero, l., U.S.S.R. H9 20
Ball, La., U.S. C3 95
Ballachulish, Scot., U.K. E7 7
Ballālpur, India C5 37
Ballarat, Austl. G8 50
Ballard, co., Ky., U.S. e8 94
Ball Club Lake, l., Mn., U.S. C5 100
Ballenas, Canal de, strt., Mex. C3 62
Ball Ground, Ga., U.S. B2 87
Ballia, India H11 38
Ballina, Ire. G3 7
Ballinger, Tx., U.S. D3 120
Ballinrobe, Ire. H3 7
Ball Mountain Lake, res., Vt., U.S. E3 122
Ballston Spa, N.Y., U.S. B7 109
Ballwin, Mo., U.S. f12 102
Bally, Pa., U.S. F10 115
Ballycastle, N. Ire., U.K. F6 7
Ballymena, N. Ire., U.K. G6 7
Ballyshannon, Ire. G4 7
Balmoral, N.B., Can. B3 71
Balmoral, Scot., U.K. D9 7
Balmville, N.Y., U.S. D6 109
Balovale, Zam. D4 44
Balrāmpur, India G10 38
Balsam Lake, Wi., U.S. C1 126
Balsam Lake, l., Wi., U.S. C1 126
Balsas, Braz. E9 54
Baltasar Brum, Ur. C5 56
Baltic, Ct., U.S. C7 84
Baltic, S.D., U.S. D9 118
Baltic Sea, Eur. H12 6
Baltijsk, U.S.S.R. G2 22
Baltijskaja Kosa, spit, Eur. A19 8
Baltimore, Ire. J3 7
Baltimore, Md., U.S. B4 97
Baltimore, Oh., U.S. C3 112
Baltimore, co., Md., U.S. B4 97
Baltimore Highlands, Md., U.S. h11 97
Baluchistan, hist. reg., Asia D1 36
Bālurghāt, India H13 38
Balygyčan, U.S.S.R. E24 20
Balzar, Ec. H3 58
Bamako, Mali F4 42
Bambana, stm., Nic. H6 64
Bambari, Cen. Afr. Rep. G10 42
Bamberg, Ger. F10 8
Bamberg, S.C., U.S. E5 117
Bamberg, co., S.C., U.S. E5 117
Bamenda, Cam. G8 42
Bāmīān, Afg. C2 38
Banalia, Zaire A5 44
Banana, Zaire C2 44
Bananal, Ilha do, i., Braz. F8 54
Banana River, b., Fl., U.S. D6 86
Banās, Ra's, c., Egypt D13 42
Banbridge, N. Ire., U.K. G6 7
Banbury, Eng., U.K. I11 7
Bancroft, Ont., Can. B7 73
Bancroft, Ia., U.S. A3 92
Bānda, India H9 38
Banda, Kepulauan, is., Indon. F8 32
Banda, Laut (Banda Sea), Indon. G8 32
Banda Aceh, Indon. D2 32
Bandama, stm., I.C. G4 42
Bandar Beheshtī, Iran C7 46
Bandar-e 'Abbās, Iran C6 46
Bandar-e Būshehr, Iran C5 46
Bandar-e Lengeh, Iran C5 46
Bandar Seri Begawan, Bru. E5 32
Banded Peak, mtn., Co., U.S. D4 83
Bandeira, Pico da, mtn., Braz. F8 57
Bandelier National Monument, N.M., U.S. B3 108
Bandera, co., Tx., U.S. E3 120
Banderas, Bahía de, b., Mex. G7 62
Bandırma, Tur. G13 4
Bandon, Ire. J4 7
Bandon, Or., U.S. D2 114
Bandundu, Zaire B3 44
Bandung, Indon. m13 32
Banes, Cuba D10 64
Banff, Scot., U.K. D10 7
Banff National Park, Alta., Can. D2 68
Bangalore, India F4 37
Bangassou, Cen. Afr. Rep. H10 42
Banggai, Kepulauan, is., Indon. F7 32
Banggi, Pulau, i., Malay. D6 32
Banghāzī, Libya B10 42
Bangil, Indon. m16 33a
Bangka, i., Indon. F4 32
Bangkalan, Indon. m16 33a
Bangkinang, Indon. N6 34
Bangkok see Krung Thep, Thai. H6 34
Bangladesh, ctry., Asia E6 36
Bangor, N. Ire., U.K. G7 7
Bangor, Wales, U.K. H8 7
Bangor, Me., U.S. D4 96
Bangor, Mi., U.S. F4 99
Bangor, Pa., U.S. E11 115
Bangor, Wi., U.S. E3 126
Bangor Township, Mi., U.S. E7 99
Bangs, Tx., U.S. D3 120
Bangs, Mount, mtn., Az., U.S. A2 80
Bangui, Cen. Afr. Rep. H9 42
Bangweulu, Lake, l., Zam. D5 44
Baní, Dom. Rep. E12 64
Banī Mazār, Egypt C12 42
Banister, stm., Va., U.S. D4 123
Banī Suwayf, Egypt C12 42
Bāniyās, Syria B4 40
Banja Luka, Yugo. E12 14
Banjarmasin, Indon. F5 32
Banjul, Gam. F2 42
Bankhead Lake, res., Al., U.S. B2 78
Banks, co., Ga., U.S. B3 87
Banks Island, i., B.C., Can. C2 69
Banks Island, i., N.W. Ter., Can. B8 66
Banks Lake, res., Wa., U.S. B6 124
Banks Strait, strt., Austl. H9 50
Bānkura, India I12 38
Bann, stm., N. Ire., U.K. G6 7
Banner, co., Ne., U.S. C2 104
Banner Elk, N.C., U.S. A1 110
Banning, Ca., U.S. F5 82
Bannock, co., Id., U.S. G6 89
Bannock Peak, mtn., Id., U.S. F6 89
Bannock Range, mts., Id., U.S. G6 89
Bannu, Pak. D4 38
Baños de Cerrato, Spain D7 12
Ban Pak Phraek, Thai. J6 34
Ban Pak Phang, Thai. F6 34
Ban Pong, Thai. H5 34
Banská Bystrica, Czech. G19 8
Bānswāra, India I6 38
Bantam, stm., Ct., U.S. B3 84
Bantam Lake, l., Ct., U.S. C3 84
Bantry, Ire. J3 7
Banyak, Kepulauan, is., Indon. M4 34
Banyuwangi, Indon. n17 33a
Baoding, China D10 26
Baofeng, China B2 28
Bao Ha, Viet. C8 34
Baoji, China E8 26
Baoshan, China B5 34
Baotou, China C8 26
Baoying, China B8 28
Ba'qūbah, Iraq B3 46
Baquedano, Chile A3 56
Baraboo, Wi., U.S. E4 126
Baraboo, stm., Wi., U.S. E3 126
Baracoa, Cuba D10 64
Baraga, Mi., U.S. B2 99
Baraga, co., Mi., U.S. B2 99
Barakī Barak, Afg. D3 38
Baram, stm., Malay. E5 32
Bārāmati, India C3 37
Bārāmūla, India C6 38
Bārān, India H7 38
Baranagar, India I13 38
Baranoa, Col. B5 58
Baranof Island, i., Ak., U.S. m22 79
Baranoviči, U.S.S.R. H9 22
Barataria, La., U.S. E5 95
Barataria Bay, b., La., U.S. E6 95
Barat Daya, Kepulauan, is., Indon. G8 32
Barbacena, Braz. F7 57
Barbados, ctry., N.A. H18 64
Barbar, Sudan E12 42
Barbas, Cabo, c., W. Sah. D2 42
Barbastro, Spain C12 12
Barbate de Franco, Spain I6 12
Barber, co., Ks., U.S. E5 93
Barbers Point, c., Hi., U.S. B3 88
Barbers Point Naval Air Station, mil., Hi., U.S. g9 88
Barberton, Oh., U.S. A4 112
Barbezieux, Fr. G6 10
Barbosa, Col. E6 58
Barbour, co., Al., U.S. D4 78
Barbour, co., W.V., U.S. B4 125
Barboursville, W.V., U.S. C2 125
Barbourville, Ky., U.S. D6 94
Barbuda, i., Antig. F17 64
Barcaldine, Austl. D9 50
Barcellona Pozzo di Gotto, Italy K10 14
Barcelona, Spain D14 12
Barcelona, Ven. B10 58
Barcelos, Braz. D6 54
Barcelos, Port. D3 12
Barcroft, Lake, res., Va., U.S. g12 123
Barden Reservoir, res., R.I., U.S. C2 116
Bardera, Som. H3 46
Bardīyah, Libya B11 42
Bardstown, Ky., U.S. C4 94
Bardufoss, Nor. B12 6
Bardwell, Ky., U.S. f9 94
Bardwell Lake, res., Tx., U.S. C4 120
Bareilly, India F8 38
Barents Sea, Eur. B8 128
Barfleur, Fr. C5 10
Bargersville, In., U.S. E5 91
Bar Harbor, Me., U.S. D4 96
Bari, Italy H11 14
Barīkowṭ, Afg. C4 38
Barillas, Guat. G2 64
Barinas, Ven. C7 58
Barinitas, Ven. C7 58
Baripāda, India J12 38
Barisāl, Bngl. I14 38
Barisan, Pegunungan, mts., Indon. F3 32
Barito, stm., Indon. F5 32
Barker Heights, N.C., U.S. f10 110
Barkhamsted Reservoir, res., Ct., U.S. B3 84
Barkley, Lake, res., U.S. f10 94
Barkley Sound, strt., B.C., Can. E5 69
Barkly Tableland, plat., Austl. C7 50
Bark Point, c., Wi., U.S. B2 126
Barksdale Air Force Base, mil., La., U.S. B2 95
Bar-le-Duc, Fr. D12 10
Barlee, Lake, l., Austl. E3 50

Name	Map Ref	Page
Barletta, Italy	H11	14
Barling, Ar., U.S.	B1	81
Barlow, Ky., U.S.	e8	94
Barmer, India	H4	38
Barmouth, Wales, U.K.	I8	7
Barnaul, U.S.S.R.	G10	20
Barnegat Bay, b., N.J., U.S.	D4	107
Barnegat Inlet, b., N.J., U.S.	D4	107
Barnes, co., N.D., U.S.	B7	111
Barnesboro, Pa., U.S.	E4	115
Barnes Sound, strt., Fl., U.S.	G6	86
Barnesville, Ga., U.S.	C2	87
Barnesville, Mn., U.S.	D2	100
Barnesville, Oh., U.S.	C4	112
Barneville-Carteret, Fr.	C5	10
Barnhart, Mo., U.S.	C7	102
Barnsdall, Ok., U.S.	A5	113
Barnsley, Eng., U.K.	H11	7
Barnstable, Ma., U.S.	C7	98
Barnstable, co., Ma., U.S.	C7	98
Barnstaple, Eng., U.K.	J8	7
Barnwell, S.C., U.S.	E5	117
Barnwell, co., S.C., U.S.	E5	117
Baroda, India	I5	38
Barpeta, India	G14	38
Barqah (Cyrenaica), reg., Libya	B10	42
Barques, Pointe aux, c., Mi., U.S.	D8	99
Barquisimeto, Ven.	B8	58
Barra, Braz.	F10	54
Barra, Ponta da, c., Moz.	F7	44
Barrackville, W.V., U.S.	B4	125
Barra do Corda, Braz.	E9	54
Barra Falsa, Ponta da, c., Moz.	F7	44
Barra Mansa, Braz.	G6	57
Barrancabermeja, Col.	D6	58
Barranca del Cobre, Parque Nacional, Mex.	D6	62
Barrancas, Ven.	C11	58
Barrancos, Port.	G5	12
Barranquilla, Col.	B5	58
Barras, Braz.	D10	54
Barrax, Spain	F9	12
Barre, Vt., U.S.	C4	122
Barre, Lake, l., La., U.S.	E5	95
Barre Falls Reservoir, res., Ma., U.S.	B4	98
Barreiras, Braz.	B6	57
Barreiro, Port.	G2	12
Barreiros, Braz.	E11	54
Barrême, Fr.	I13	10
Barren, co., Ky., U.S.	D4	94
Barren, stm., Ky., U.S.	C3	94
Barren Island, i., Md., U.S.	D5	97
Barren Islands, is., Ak., U.S.	h15	79
Barren River Lake, res., Ky., U.S.	D3	94
Barretos, Braz.	F4	57
Barrett, W.V., U.S.	D3	125
Barrhead, Alta., Can.	B3	68
Barrie, Ont., Can.	C5	73
Barrie Island, i., Ont., Can.	B2	73
Barrière, B.C., Can.	D7	69
Barrington, Il., U.S.	A5	90
Barrington, N.J., U.S.	D2	107
Barrington, R.I., U.S.	D5	116
Barrington, stm., R.I., U.S.	C5	116
Barron, Wi., U.S.	C2	126
Barron, co., Wi., U.S.	C2	126
Barron Lake, Mi., U.S.	G4	99
Barrow, Ak., U.S.	A8	79
Barrow, co., Ga., U.S.	B3	87
Barrow, Point, c., Ak., U.S.	A8	79
Barrow Creek, Austl.	D6	50
Barrow-in-Furness, Eng., U.K.	G9	7
Barrow Island, i., Austl.	D3	50
Barrow Strait, strt., N.W. Ter., Can.	B14	66
Barry, Il., U.S.	D2	90
Barry, co., Mi., U.S.	F5	99
Barry, co., Mo., U.S.	E4	102
Barrys Bay, Ont., Can.	B7	73
Bārsi, India	C3	37
Barstow, Ca., U.S.	E5	82
Bar-sur-Aube, Fr.	D11	10
Barth, Ger.	A12	8
Bartholomew, co., In., U.S.	F6	91
Bartholomew, Bayou, stm., U.S.	D4	81
Bartica, Guy.	D13	58
Bartlesville, Ok., U.S.	A6	113
Bartlett, N.H., U.S.	B4	106
Bartlett, Tn., U.S.	B2	119
Bartlett, Tx., U.S.	D4	120
Bartlett Reservoir, res., Az., U.S.	D4	80
Bartletts Ferry Dam, U.S.	C4	78
Barton, Oh., U.S.	B5	112
Barton, Vt., U.S.	B4	122
Barton, co., Ks., U.S.	D5	93
Barton, co., Mo., U.S.	D3	102
Barton, stm., Vt., U.S.	B4	122
Bartonville, Il., U.S.	C4	90
Bartow, Fl., U.S.	E5	86
Bartow, co., Ga., U.S.	B2	87
Barú, Volcán, vol., Pan.	J6	64
Bāruni, India	H11	38
Barun-Šibertuj, Gora, mtn., U.S.S.R.	H15	20
Baruun Urt, Mong.	B9	26
Barvas, Scot., U.K.	C6	7
Basalt, Co., U.S.	B3	83
Basankusu, Zaire	A3	44
Basatongwula Shan, mtn., China	D14	38
Bascuñán, Cabo, c., Chile	B2	56
Basehor, Ks., U.S.	k16	93
Basel (Bâle), Switz.	E14	10
Bashan Lake, l., Ct., U.S.	D6	84
Bashaw, Alta., Can.	C4	68
Bashi Channel, strt., Asia	G11	26
Basilan Island, i., Phil.	D7	32
Basildon, Eng., U.K.	J13	7
Basile, La., U.S.	D3	95
Basin, Wy., U.S.	B4	127
Basingstoke, Eng., U.K.	J11	7
Basīrhāt, India	I13	38
Basīt, Ra's al-, c., Syria	B4	40
Baskahegan Lake, l., Me., U.S.	C5	96
Baskatong, Réservoir, res., Que., Can.	G17	66
Basking Ridge, N.J., U.S.	B3	107
Basoko, Zaire	A4	44
Basra see Al-Baṣrah, Iraq	B4	46
Bassano, Alta., Can.	D4	68
Bassano del Grappa, Italy	D6	14
Bassari, Togo	G6	42
Bassas da India, rf., Reu.	F7	44
Basse-Terre, Guad.	F17	64
Basseterre, St. K./N.	F16	64
Basse-Terre, i., Guad.	F17	64
Bassett, Ne., U.S.	B6	104
Bassett, Va., U.S.	D3	123
Bassett Peak, mtn., Az., U.S.	E5	80
Bass Islands, is., Oh., U.S.	A3	112
Bass Lake, In., U.S.	B4	91
Bass Strait, strt., Austl.	G9	50
Basswood Lake, l., Mn., U.S.	B7	100
Basti, India	G10	38
Bastogne, Bel.	E5	8
Bastrop, La., U.S.	B4	95
Bastrop, Tx., U.S.	D4	120
Bastrop, co., Tx., U.S.	D4	120
Bastuträsk, Swe.	D13	6
Bata, Eq. Gui.	H7	42
Bataan Peninsula, pen., Phil.	q19	33b
Batabanó, Golfo de, b., Cuba	C6	64
Batagaj, U.S.S.R.	D20	20
Bataguaçu, Braz.	F2	57
Bataiporã, Braz.	G2	57
Batāla, India	E6	38
Batalha, Port.	F3	12
Batamaj, U.S.S.R.	E19	20
Batang, China	E6	26
Batangas, Phil.	r19	33b
Batan Islands, is., Phil.	A7	32
Batanta, Pulau, i., Indon.	F9	32
Batatais, Braz.	F5	57
Batavia, Il., U.S.	B5	90
Batavia, N.Y., U.S.	C2	109
Batavia, Oh., U.S.	C1	112
Batchelor Bay, b., N.C., U.S.	B6	110
Bătdâmbâng, Camb.	H7	34
Batepito, Mex.	B5	62
Bates, co., Mo., U.S.	C3	102
Batesburg, S.C., U.S.	D4	117
Batesville, Ar., U.S.	B4	81
Batesville, In., U.S.	F7	91
Batesville, Ms., U.S.	A4	101
Bath, N.B., Can.	C2	71
Bath, Ont., Can.	C8	73
Bath, Eng., U.K.	J10	7
Bath, Me., U.S.	E3	96
Bath, N.Y., U.S.	C3	109
Bath, Pa., U.S.	E11	115
Bath, S.C., U.S.	D4	117
Bath, co., Ky., U.S.	B6	94
Bath, co., Va., U.S.	B3	123
Bathurst, N.B., Can.	B4	71
Bathurst, Cape, c., N.W. Ter., Can.	B7	66
Bathurst Inlet, N.W. Ter., Can.	C11	66
Bathurst Inlet, b., N.W. Ter., Can.	C11	66
Bathurst Island, i., Austl.	B6	50
Bathurst Island, i., N.W. Ter., Can.	A12	66
Batiscan, stm., Que., Can.	B5	74
Batna, Alg.	A7	42
Baton Rouge, La., U.S.	D4	95
Batouri, Cam.	H8	42
Batsto, stm., N.J., U.S.	D3	107
Batten Kill, stm., U.S.	E2	122
Batticaloa, Sri L.	I6	37
Battle, stm., Can.	F10	66
Battle Creek, Ia., U.S.	B2	92
Battle Creek, Mi., U.S.	F5	99
Battle Creek, Ne., U.S.	C8	104
Battle Ground, In., U.S.	C4	91
Battle Ground, Wa., U.S.	D3	124
Battle Lake, Mn., U.S.	D3	100
Battle Mountain, Nv., U.S.	C5	105
Battle Mountain, mtn., Wy., U.S.	E5	127
Batu, mtn., Eth.	G2	46
Batu, Kepulauan, is., Indon.	O5	34
Batumi, U.S.S.R.	I6	18
Batu Pahat, Malay.	N7	34
Baturité, Braz.	D11	54
Baubau, Indon.	G7	32
Bauchi, Nig.	F7	42
Baud, Fr.	E3	10
Baudette, Mn., U.S.	B4	100
Bauld, Cape, c., Newf., Can.	C4	72
Baume-les-Dames, Fr.	E13	10
Baunei, Italy	I4	14
Bauru, Braz.	G4	57
Baús, Braz.	E2	57
Bautzen, Ger.	D14	8
Bawean, Pulau, i., Indon.	G5	32
Baxley, Ga., U.S.	E4	87
Baxter, Ia., U.S.	C4	92
Baxter, Mn., U.S.	D4	100
Baxter, Tn., U.S.	C8	119
Baxter, co., Ar., U.S.	A3	81
Baxter Springs, Ks., U.S.	E9	93
Bay, Ar., U.S.	B5	81
Bay, co., Fl., U.S.	u16	86
Bay, co., Mi., U.S.	E6	99
Bay, Laguna de, l., Phil.	q19	33b
Bayamo, Cuba	D9	64
Bayan Har Shan, mts., China	E6	26
Bayard, Ne., U.S.	C2	104
Bayard, N.M., U.S.	E1	108
Bayberry, N.Y., U.S.	B4	109
Bayboro, N.C., U.S.	B6	110
Bay Bulls, Newf., Can.	E5	72
Bay City, Mi., U.S.	E7	99
Bay City, Or., U.S.	B3	114
Bay City, Tx., U.S.	E5	120
Bay de Verde, Newf., Can.	D5	72
Bayerische Alpen, mts., Eur.	H11	8
Bayeux, Fr.	C6	10
Bayfield, Ont., Can.	D3	73
Bayfield, Co., U.S.	D3	83
Bayfield, Wi., U.S.	B3	126
Bayfield, co., Wi., U.S.	B2	126
Bayındır, Tur.	K11	16
Baykonur see Bajkonyr, U.S.S.R.	H11	18
Baylor, co., Tx., U.S.	C3	120
Bay Mills Indian Reservation, Mi., U.S.	B6	99
Bay Minette, Al., U.S.	E2	78
Bayo, Spain	B3	12
Bayona, Spain	C3	12
Bayonne, Fr.	I5	10
Bayonne, N.J., U.S.	B4	107
Bayou Bodcau Reservoir, res., La., U.S.	B2	95
Bayou D'Arbonne Lake, res., La., U.S.	B3	95
Bayou George, Fl., U.S.	u16	86
Bayou Goula, La., U.S.	D4	95
Bayou La Batre, Al., U.S.	E1	78
Bay Point, c., S.C., U.S.	G7	117
Bayport, Mn., U.S.	E6	100
Bayport, N.Y., U.S.	n15	109
Bayramıç, Tur.	J10	16
Bayreuth, Ger.	F11	8
Bay Ridge, Md., U.S.	C5	97
Bay Roberts, Newf., Can.	E5	72
Bayrūt (Beirut), Leb.	C4	40
Bays, Lake of, l., Ont., Can.	B5	73
Bay Saint Louis, Ms., U.S.	E4	101
Bay Shore, N.Y., U.S.	E7	109
Bayshore Gardens, Fl., U.S.	q10	86
Bayside, Wi., U.S.	m12	126
Bay Springs, Ms., U.S.	D4	101
Bayt Laḥm, Isr. Occ.	D4	40
Baytown, Tx., U.S.	E5	120
Bayview, Al., U.S.	f7	78
Bay Village, Oh., U.S.	h9	112
Baza, Spain	H9	12
Bazaruto, Ilha do, i., Moz.	F7	44
Bazas, Fr.	H6	10
Be, Nosy, i., Madag.	D9	44
Beach, Il., U.S.	h9	90
Beach, N.D., U.S.	C1	111
Beachburg, Ont., Can.	B8	73
Beach City, Oh., U.S.	B4	112
Beach Haven Inlet, b., N.J., U.S.	D4	107
Beach Pond, res., U.S.	C8	84
Beachville, Ont., Can.	D4	73
Beachwood, N.J., U.S.	D4	107
Beachy Head, c., Eng., U.K.	K13	7
Beacon, N.Y., U.S.	D7	109
Beacon Falls, Ct., U.S.	D3	84
Beaconsfield, Que., Can.	q19	74
Beadle, co., S.D., U.S.	C7	118
Beagle Gulf, b., Austl.	B6	50
Bealanana, Madag.	D9	44
Beale, Cape, c., B.C., Can.	E5	69
Beale Air Force Base, mil., Ca., U.S.	C3	82
Bear, De., U.S.	B3	85
Bear, stm., U.S.	B3	121
Bear Creek, Al., U.S.	A2	78
Bear Creek, stm., U.S.	E2	93
Bear Creek, stm., Or., U.S.	E4	114
Bear Creek, stm., Wy., U.S.	E8	127
Bearden, Ar., U.S.	D3	81
Beardstown, Il., U.S.	C3	90
Bear Inlet, b., N.C., U.S.	C5	110
Bear Lake, co., Id., U.S.	G7	89
Bear Lake, l., U.S.	A4	121
Bear Lake, l., Wi., U.S.	C2	126
Bear Lodge Mountains, mts., Wy., U.S.	B8	127
Bear Mountain, mtn., Or., U.S.	D4	114
Bearpaw Mountains, mts., Mt., U.S.	B7	103
Bear River, N.S., Can.	E4	71
Bear River City, Ut., U.S.	B3	121
Beartooth Pass, Wy., U.S.	B3	127
Beartooth Range, mts., U.S.	E7	103
Bear Town, Ms., U.S.	D3	101
Beasain, Spain	B9	12
Beas de Segura, Spain	G9	12
Beata, Isla, i., Dom. Rep.	F12	64
Beatrice, Ne., U.S.	D9	104
Beatton, stm., B.C., Can.	E8	66
Beatty, Nv., U.S.	G5	105
Beattyville, Ky., U.S.	C6	94
Beaucaire, Fr.	I11	10
Beaufort, N.C., U.S.	C6	110
Beaufort, S.C., U.S.	G6	117
Beaufort, co., N.C., U.S.	B5	110
Beaufort, co., S.C., U.S.	G6	117
Beaufort Marine Corps Air Station, mil., S.C., U.S.	F6	117
Beaufort Sea, N.A.	B7	61
Beaufort West, S. Afr.	H4	44
Beaugency, Fr.	E8	10
Beauharnois, Que., Can.	D4	74
Beau Lake, l., Me., U.S.	A4	96
Beauly, Scot., U.K.	D8	7
Beaumont, Alta., Can.	C4	68
Beaumont, Ms., U.S.	D5	101
Beaumont, Tx., U.S.	D5	120
Beaumont-sur-Sarthe, Fr.	D7	10
Beaune, Fr.	E11	10
Beauport, Que., Can.	n17	74
Beaupré, Que., Can.	B7	74
Beaupréau, Fr.	E5	10
Beauregard, co., La., U.S.	D2	95
Beausejour, Man., Can.	D3	70
Beauvais, Fr.	C9	10
Beauval, Sask., Can.	B2	75
Beauvoir-sur-Niort, Fr.	F6	10
Beaver, Ok., U.S.	A1	113
Beaver, Pa., U.S.	E1	115
Beaver, Ut., U.S.	E3	121
Beaver, W.V., U.S.	D3	125
Beaver, co., Ok., U.S.	e10	113
Beaver, co., Pa., U.S.	E1	115
Beaver, co., Ut., U.S.	E2	121
Beaver, stm., Can.	D7	66
Beaver, stm., Can.	B2	75
Beaver, stm., U.S.	A2	113
Beaver, stm., N.Y., U.S.	B6	109
Beaver, stm., R.I., U.S.	E2	116
Beaver, stm., Ut., U.S.	E2	121
Beaverbank, N.S., Can.	E6	71
Beaver Brook, stm., U.S.	E4	106
Beaver City, Ne., U.S.	D6	104
Beavercreek, Oh., U.S.	C1	112
Beaver Creek, stm., U.S.	E4	104
Beaver Creek, stm., U.S.	C8	127
Beaver Creek, stm., N.D., U.S.	C1	111
Beaver Creek, stm., N.D., U.S.	C5	111
Beaver Creek, stm., Ok., U.S.	C3	113
Beaver Creek, stm., Tn., U.S.	m13	119
Beaver Creek, stm., Wy., U.S.	D4	127
Beaverdale, Pa., U.S.	F4	115
Beaver Dam, Ky., U.S.	C3	94
Beaver Dam, Wi., U.S.	E5	126
Beaverdam Branch, stm., De., U.S.	F3	85
Beaverdam Lake, res., Wi., U.S.	E5	126
Beaver Falls, Pa., U.S.	E1	115
Beaverhead, co., Mt., U.S.	E3	103
Beaverhead, stm., Mt., U.S.	E4	103
Beaverhead Mountains, mts., U.S.	D5	89
Beaverhill Lake, l., Alta., Can.	C4	68
Beaver Island, i., Mi., U.S.	C5	99
Beaver Lake, res., Ar., U.S.	A2	81
Beaverlodge, Alta., Can.	B1	68
Beaver Meadows, Pa., U.S.	E10	115
Beaver Run Reservoir, res., Pa., U.S.	F2	115
Beavertail Point, c., R.I., U.S.	F4	116
Beaverton, Mi., U.S.	E6	99
Beaverton, Or., U.S.	B4	114
Beāwar, India	G6	38
Bebedouro, Braz.	F4	57
Bécancour, Que., Can.	C5	74
Bečej, Yugo.	D4	16
Becerreá, Spain	C4	12
Béchar, Alg.	B5	42
Becharof Lake, l., Ak., U.S.	D8	79
Beckemeyer, Il., U.S.	E4	90
Becker, Mn., U.S.	E5	100
Becker, co., Mn., U.S.	D3	100
Beckham, co., Ok., U.S.	B2	113
Beckley, W.V., U.S.	D3	125
Beckum, Ger.	D8	8
Becky Peak, mtn., Nv., U.S.	D7	105
Bédarieux, Fr.	I10	10
Bedford, Que., Can.	D5	74
Bedford, Eng., U.K.	I12	7
Bedford, In., U.S.	G5	91
Bedford, Ia., U.S.	D3	92
Bedford, Ky., U.S.	B4	94
Bedford, Ma., U.S.	B5	98
Bedford, N.H., U.S.	E3	106
Bedford, Oh., U.S.	A4	112
Bedford, Pa., U.S.	F4	115
Bedford, Va., U.S.	C3	123
Bedford, co., Pa., U.S.	G4	115
Bedford, co., Tn., U.S.	B5	119
Bedford, co., Va., U.S.	C3	123
Bedford Hills, N.Y., U.S.	D7	109
Bee, co., Tx., U.S.	E4	120
Beebe, Que., Can.	D5	74
Beebe, Ar., U.S.	B4	81
Beecher, Il., U.S.	B6	90
Beecher, Mi., U.S.	E7	99
Beech Fork, stm., Ky., U.S.	C4	94
Beech Grove, In., U.S.	E5	91
Beech Island, S.C., U.S.	E4	117
Beemer, Ne., U.S.	C9	104
Bee Ridge, Fl., U.S.	q11	86
Beersheba see Be'er Sheva', Isr.	D4	40
Be'er Sheva', Isr.	D4	40
Beeton, Ont., Can.	C5	73
Beeville, Tx., U.S.	E4	120
Befale, Zaire	A4	44
Befandriana, Madag.	E9	44
Beggs, Ok., U.S.	B5	113
Begi, Eth.	G1	46
Behbehān, Iran	B5	46
Behm Canal, strt., Ak., U.S.	n24	79
Bei, stm., China	G9	26
Bei'an, China	B12	26
Beihai, China	D10	34
Beijing (Peking), China	D10	26
Beijing Shih, China	C10	26
Beipiao, China	C11	26
Beira, Moz.	E6	44
Beirut see Bayrūt, Leb.	C4	40
Beja, Port.	G4	12
Béja, Tun.	M4	14
Bejaïa, Alg.	A7	42
Béjar, Spain	E6	12
Békéscsaba, Hung.	I21	8
Bekily, Madag.	F9	44
Bela, India	H9	38
Bel Air, Md., U.S.	A5	97
Bel Aire, Ks., U.S.	g12	93
Belaja Cerkov', U.S.S.R.	H4	18
Belalcázar, Spain	G6	12
Bel Alton, Md., U.S.	D4	97
Belampalli, India	C5	37
Bela Vista, Braz.	A5	56
Belaya Tserkov' see Belaja Cerkov', U.S.S.R.	H4	18
Belcamp, Md., U.S.	B5	97
Belcherāgh, Afg.	C1	38
Belcher Islands, is., N.W. Ter., Can.	E17	66
Belchertown, Ma., U.S.	B3	98
Belchite, Spain	D11	12
Belcourt, N.D., U.S.	A6	111
Belden, Ms., U.S.	A5	101
Belding, Mi., U.S.	E5	99
Beled Weyne, Som.	H4	46
Belém, Braz.	D9	54
Belén, Para.	A5	56
Belen, N.M., U.S.	C3	108
Belfair, Wa., U.S.	B3	124
Belfast, N. Ire., U.K.	G7	7
Belfast, Me., U.S.	D3	96
Belfield, N.D., U.S.	C2	111
Belford, N.J., U.S.	C4	107
Belfort, Fr.	E13	10
Belfry, Ky., U.S.	C7	94
Belgaum, India	E3	37
Belgium, Wi., U.S.	E6	126
Belgium, ctry., Eur.	E8	4
Belgorod, U.S.S.R.	G5	18
Belgrade, Mn., U.S.	E3	100
Belgrade, Mt., U.S.	E5	103
Belgrade see Beograd, Yugo.	E4	16
Belhaven, N.C., U.S.	B6	110
Belin, Fr.	H6	10
Belington, W.V., U.S.	B5	125
Belitung, i., Indon.	F4	32
Belize, ctry., N.A.	F3	64
Belize City, Belize	F3	64
Belknap, co., N.H., U.S.	C3	106
Belknap Crater, crat., Or., U.S.	C5	114
Bel'kovskij, Ostrov, i., U.S.S.R.	B21	20
Bell, co., Ky., U.S.	D6	94
Bell, co., Tx., U.S.	D4	120
Bellac, Fr.	F8	10
Bella Coola, stm., B.C., Can.	C4	69
Bellaire, Mi., U.S.	D5	99
Bellaire, Oh., U.S.	B5	112
Bellaire, Tx., U.S.	r14	120
Bellamy, Al., U.S.	C1	78
Bellary, India	E4	37
Bellavista, Peru	E3	54
Bella Vista, Ar., U.S.	A1	81
Bellbrook, Oh., U.S.	C1	112
Belle, Mo., U.S.	C6	102
Belle, W.V., U.S.	C3	125
Belle, stm., La., U.S.	k9	95
Belleair, Fl., U.S.	p10	86
Belle Bay, b., Newf., Can.	E4	72
Belle Chasse, La., U.S.	E5	95
Bellefontaine, Oh., U.S.	B2	112
Bellefonte, Pa., U.S.	E6	115
Belle Fourche, S.D., U.S.	C2	118
Belle Fourche, stm., U.S.	C3	118
Belle Fourche Reservoir, res., S.D., U.S.	C2	118
Bellegarde, Fr.	F12	10
Belle Glade, Fl., U.S.	F6	86
Belle Isle, Fl., U.S.	D5	86
Belle Isle, i., Newf., Can.	C4	72
Belle Isle, Strait of, strt., Newf., Can.	C3	72
Belle Meade, Tn., U.S.	g10	119
Belle Plaine, Ia., U.S.	C5	92
Belle Plaine, Ks., U.S.	E6	93
Belle Plaine, Mn., U.S.	F5	100
Belle River, Ont., Can.	E2	73
Belle Rose, La., U.S.	D4	95
Belle Vernon, Pa., U.S.	F2	115
Belleview, Fl., U.S.	C4	86
Belle View, Va., U.S.	g12	123
Belleville, Ont., Can.	C7	73
Belleville, Il., U.S.	E4	90
Belleville, Ks., U.S.	C6	93
Belleville, Mi., U.S.	p15	99
Belleville, N.J., U.S.	B4	107
Belleville, Pa., U.S.	E6	115
Belleville, Wi., U.S.	F4	126
Belleville Pond, l., R.I., U.S.	E4	116
Bellevue, Id., U.S.	F4	89
Bellevue, Ia., U.S.	B7	92
Bellevue, Ky., U.S.	h13	94
Bellevue, Mi., U.S.	F5	99
Bellevue, Ne., U.S.	C10	104
Bellevue, Oh., U.S.	A3	112
Bellevue, Pa., U.S.	F1	115
Bellevue, Wa., U.S.	e11	124
Belley, Fr.	G12	10
Bellflower, Ca., U.S.	n12	82
Bellingham, Ma., U.S.	B5	98
Bellingham, Wa., U.S.	A3	124
Bellingshausen Sea, Ant.	B4	47
Bellinzona, Switz.	F16	10
Bell Island, i., Newf., Can.	C4	72
Bellmawr, N.J., U.S.	D2	107
Bello, Col.	D5	58
Bellows Falls, Vt., U.S.	E4	122
Bell Peninsula, pen., N.W. Ter., Can.	D16	66
Bellport, N.Y., U.S.	n16	109
Bells, Tn., U.S.	B2	119
Bells Creek, stm., W.V., U.S.	m13	125
Belluno, Italy	C7	14
Bell Ville, Arg.	C4	56
Bellville, Oh., U.S.	B3	112
Bellville, Tx., U.S.	E4	120
Bellwood, Il., U.S.	k9	90
Bellwood, Pa., U.S.	E5	115
Bellwood, Va., U.S.	n18	123
Belmar, N.J., U.S.	C4	107
Belmond, Ia., U.S.	B4	92
Belmont, Ont., Can.	E3	73
Belmont, Ca., U.S.	h8	82
Belmont, Ma., U.S.	g11	98
Belmont, Ms., U.S.	A5	101
Belmont, N.H., U.S.	D4	106
Belmont, N.C., U.S.	B1	110
Belmont, W.V., U.S.	B3	125
Belmont, Wi., U.S.	F3	126
Belmont, co., Oh., U.S.	C4	112
Belmonte, Braz.	C9	57
Belmonte, Port.	E4	12
Belmonte, Spain	B5	12
Belmonte, Spain	F9	12
Belmopan, Belize	F3	64
Belmullet, Ire.	G2	7
Bel-Nor, Mo., U.S.	f13	102
Belo, Madag.	E8	44
Beloeil, Que., Can.	D4	74
Belogorsk, U.S.S.R.	G19	20
Belo Horizonte, Braz.	E7	57
Beloit, Ks., U.S.	C5	93
Beloit, Oh., U.S.	B5	112
Beloit, Wi., U.S.	F4	126
Beloit North, Wi., U.S.	F4	126
Beloje, Ozero, l., U.S.S.R.	A20	22
Beloje more (White Sea), U.S.S.R.	D5	18
Belorado, Spain	C8	12
Beloreck, U.S.S.R.	G9	18
Belorussia see Belorusskaja Sovetskaja Socialističeskaja Respublika, state, U.S.S.R.	G3	18
Belorusskaja Sovetskaja Socialističeskaja Respublika, state, U.S.S.R.	G3	18
Belovo, U.S.S.R.	G11	20
Belpre, Oh., U.S.	C4	112

Name	Map Ref	Page
Belt, Mt., U.S.	C6	103
Belted Range, mts., Nv., U.S.	F5	105
Belton, Mo., U.S.	C3	102
Belton, S.C., U.S.	B3	117
Belton, Tx., U.S.	D4	120
Belton Lake, res., Tx., U.S.	D4	120
Beltrami, co., Mn., U.S.	B3	100
Beltsville, Md., U.S.	B4	97
Belucha, Gora, mtn., U.S.S.R.	H11	20
Belvedere, S.C., U.S.	D4	117
Belvedere Marittimo, Italy	J10	14
Belvidere, Il., U.S.	A5	90
Belvidere, N.J., U.S.	B2	107
Belyj, Ostrov, i., U.S.S.R.	C8	20
Belyj Jar, U.S.S.R.	F11	20
Belzoni, Ms., U.S.	B3	101
Bement, Il., U.S.	D5	90
Bemidji, Mn., U.S.	C4	100
Bemidji, Lake, l., Mn., U.S.	C4	100
Benabarre, Spain	C12	12
Bena-Dibele, Zaire	B4	44
Benavente, Port.	G3	12
Benavente, Spain	C6	12
Benavides, Tx., U.S.	F3	120
Benbrook Lake, res., Tx., U.S.	n9	120
Bend, Or., U.S.	C5	114
Ben Davis Point, c., N.J., U.S.	E2	107
Bendeleben, Mount, mtn., Ak., U.S.	B7	79
Bendigo, Austl.	G8	50
Benedict, Md., U.S.	C4	97
Benedito Leite, Braz.	E10	54
Benevento, Italy	H9	14
Benewah, co., Id., U.S.	B2	89
Bengal, Bay of, b., Asia	F6	36
Bengbu, China	C6	28
Benghazi see Banghāzī, Libya	B10	42
Bengkalis, Indon.	N7	34
Bengkulu, Indon.	F3	32
Benguela, Ang.	D2	44
Benham, Ky., U.S.	D7	94
Ben Hill, co., Ga., U.S.	E3	87
Beni, stm., Bol.	F5	54
Béni Abbès, Alg.	B5	42
Benicarló, Spain	E12	12
Benicia, Ca., U.S.	C2	82
Beni-Mellal, Mor.	B4	42
Benin, ctry., Afr.	G6	42
Benin, Bight of, Afr.	G6	42
Benin City, Nig.	G7	42
Benisa, Spain	G12	12
Benito Juárez, Presa, res., Mex.	I12	62
Benjamin Constant, Braz.	D4	54
Benjamín Hill, Mex.	B4	62
Benkelman, Ne., U.S.	D4	104
Benld, Il., U.S.	D4	90
Bennett, Co., U.S.	B6	83
Bennett, co., S.D., U.S.	D4	118
Bennettsville, S.C., U.S.	B8	117
Bennington, Ne., U.S.	g12	104
Bennington, N.H., U.S.	D3	106
Bennington, Vt., U.S.	F2	122
Bennington, co., Vt., U.S.	E2	122
Benoit, Ms., U.S.	B2	101
Bénoué (Benue), stm., Afr.	G8	42
Bensenville, Il., U.S.	B6	90
Bensheim, Ger.	F8	8
Bensley, Va., U.S.	C5	123
Benson, Az., U.S.	F5	80
Benson, Mn., U.S.	E3	100
Benson, N.C., U.S.	B4	110
Benson, co., N.D., U.S.	A6	111
Bent, co., Co., U.S.	D7	83
Bentley, Alta., Can.	C3	68
Bentleyville, Pa., U.S.	F1	115
Benton, Ar., U.S.	C3	81
Benton, Il., U.S.	E5	90
Benton, Ks., U.S.	E6	93
Benton, Ky., U.S.	f9	94
Benton, La., U.S.	B2	95
Benton, Pa., U.S.	D9	115
Benton, Tn., U.S.	B7	119
Benton, Wi., U.S.	F3	126
Benton, co., Ar., U.S.	A1	81
Benton, co., In., U.S.	C3	91
Benton, co., Ia., U.S.	B5	92
Benton, co., Mn., U.S.	E4	100
Benton, co., Ms., U.S.	A4	101
Benton, co., Mo., U.S.	C4	102
Benton, co., Or., U.S.	C3	114
Benton, co., Tn., U.S.	A3	119
Benton, co., Wa., U.S.	C6	124
Benton City, Wa., U.S.	C6	124
Benton Harbor, Mi., U.S.	F4	99
Benton Heights, Mi., U.S.	F4	99
Bentonville, Ar., U.S.	A1	81
Ben Treang, Viet.	I9	34
Bent's Old Fort National Historic Site, hist., Co., U.S.	C7	83
Benue (Bénoué), stm., Afr.	G7	42
Benwood, W.V., U.S.	f8	125
Benxi, China	C11	26
Benzie, co., Mi., U.S.	D4	99
Beograd (Belgrade), Yugo.	E4	16
Beowawe, Nv., U.S.	C5	105
Beppu, Japan	I4	30
Berau, Teluk, b., Indon.	F9	32
Berbera, Som.	F4	46
Berbérati, Cen. Afr. Rep.	H9	42
Berchtesgaden, Ger.	H13	8
Berck, Fr.	B8	10
Berdigest'ach, U.S.S.R.	E19	20
Berdsk, U.S.S.R.	G10	20
Berea, Ky., U.S.	C5	94
Berea, Oh., U.S.	A4	112
Berea, S.C., U.S.	B3	117
Berens, stm., Can.	F13	66
Berens, stm., Can.	C3	70
Beresford, S.D., U.S.	D9	118
Berg, Nor.	B11	6
Berga, Spain	C13	12
Bergama, Tur.	J11	16
Bergamo, Italy	D4	14
Bergen, Nor.	F5	6
Bergen, co., N.J., U.S.	A4	107
Bergen [auf Rügen], Ger.	A13	8
Bergenfield, N.J., U.S.	B4	107
Bergen op Zoom, Neth.	D4	8
Bergerac, Fr.	H7	10
Bergland, Mi., U.S.	m12	99
Bergstrom Air Force Base, mil., Tx., U.S.	D4	120
Berhampore, India	H13	38
Berhampur, India	C8	37
Beringovskij, U.S.S.R.	E29	20
Bering Sea	D30	128
Bering Strait, strt.	m18	76a
Berja, Spain	I9	12
Berkåk, Nor.	E7	6
Berkeley, Ca., U.S.	D2	82
Berkeley, Mo., U.S.	f13	102
Berkeley, R.I., U.S.	B4	116
Berkeley, co., S.C., U.S.	E8	117
Berkeley, co., W.V., U.S.	B6	125
Berkeley Heights, N.J., U.S.	B4	107
Berkeley Springs, W.V., U.S.	B6	125
Berkley, Mi., U.S.	F7	99
Berkner Island, i., Ant.	B8	47
Berks, co., Pa., U.S.	F9	115
Berkshire, co., Ma., U.S.	B1	98
Berkshire Hills, hills, Ma., U.S.	B1	98
Berlin, Ger.	C13	8
Berlin, Ct., U.S.	C5	84
Berlin, Md., U.S.	D7	97
Berlin, N.H., U.S.	B4	106
Berlin, N.J., U.S.	D3	107
Berlin, Pa., U.S.	G4	115
Berlin, Wi., U.S.	E5	126
Berlin Lake, res., Oh., U.S.	A4	112
Bermeo, Spain	B9	12
Bermuda, dep., N.A.	E14	76
Bern (Berne), Switz.	F14	10
Bernalillo, N.M., U.S.	B3	108
Bernalillo, co., N.M., U.S.	C3	108
Bernardsville, N.J., U.S.	B3	107
Bernasconi, Arg.	D4	56
Bernau bei Berlin, Ger.	C13	8
Bernay, Fr.	C7	10
Bernburg, Ger.	D11	8
Berne, In., U.S.	C8	91
Bernice, La., U.S.	B3	95
Bernie, Mo., U.S.	E8	102
Bernier Island, i., Austl.	D2	50
Bernina, Piz, mtn., Eur.	F16	10
Beroroha, Madag.	F9	44
Berre, Étang de, b., Fr.	I12	10
Berrien, co., Ga., U.S.	E3	87
Berrien, co., Mi., U.S.	F4	99
Berrien Springs, Mi., U.S.	G4	99
Berry, Al., U.S.	B2	78
Berryessa, Lake, res., Ca., U.S.	C2	82
Berry Hill, Tn., U.S.	g10	119
Berry Islands, is., Bah.	B9	64
Berryville, Ar., U.S.	A2	81
Berryville, Va., U.S.	A5	123
Berthierville, Que., Can.	C4	74
Berthoud, Co., U.S.	A5	83
Berthoud Pass, Co., U.S.	B5	83
Bertie, co., N.C., U.S.	A5	110
Bertoua, Cam.	H8	42
Bertrand, Mo., U.S.	E8	102
Bertrand, Ne., U.S.	D6	104
Berwick, Ia., U.S.	e8	92
Berwick, La., U.S.	E4	95
Berwick, Me., U.S.	E2	96
Berwick, Pa., U.S.	D9	115
Berwick-upon-Tweed, Eng., U.K.	F10	7
Berwyn, Alta., Can.	A2	68
Berwyn, Il., U.S.	k9	90
Berwyn, Pa., U.S.	o20	115
Besalampy, Madag.	E8	44
Besançon, Fr.	E13	10
Beskid Mountains, mts., Eur.	F19	8
Bessemer, Al., U.S.	B3	78
Bessemer, Mi., U.S.	n11	99
Bessemer, Pa., U.S.	E1	115
Bessemer City, N.C., U.S.	B1	110
Best'ach, U.S.S.R.	E19	20
Betanzos, Spain	B3	12
Bétaré Oya, Cam.	G8	42
Betatakin Ruin, hist., Az., U.S.	A5	80
Bethalto, Il., U.S.	E3	90
Bethany, Ct., U.S.	D4	84
Bethany, Il., U.S.	D5	90
Bethany, Mo., U.S.	A3	102
Bethany, Ok., U.S.	B4	113
Bethany, W.V., U.S.	A4	125
Bethany Beach, De., U.S.	F5	85
Bethel, Ak., U.S.	C7	79
Bethel, Ct., U.S.	D2	84
Bethel, Me., U.S.	D2	96
Bethel, N.C., U.S.	B5	110
Bethel, Oh., U.S.	D1	112
Bethel, Vt., U.S.	D3	122
Bethel Park, Pa., U.S.	k14	115
Bethel Springs, Tn., U.S.	B3	119
Bethesda, Md., U.S.	C3	97
Bethesda, Oh., U.S.	B4	112
Bethlehem, S. Afr.	G5	44
Bethlehem, Ct., U.S.	C3	84
Bethlehem, N.H., U.S.	B3	106
Bethlehem, Pa., U.S.	E11	115
Bethlehem see Bayt Laḥm, Jord.	D4	40
Béthune, Fr.	B9	10
Beticos, Sistemas, mts., Spain	H9	12
Betioky, Madag.	F8	44
Betong, Malay.	M6	34
Betroka, Madag.	F9	44
Betsiboka, stm., Madag.	E9	44
Betsie, Point, c., Mi., U.S.	D4	99
Betsy Layne, Ky., U.S.	C7	94
Bette, mtn., Libya	D9	42
Bettendorf, Ia., U.S.	C7	92
Bettiah, India	G11	38
Betūl, India	B4	37
Betzdorf, Ger.	E7	8
Beulah, Co., U.S.	C6	83
Beulah, N.D., U.S.	B4	111
Beulah, Lake, l., Ms., U.S.	B3	101
Beulaville, N.C., U.S.	C5	110
B. Everett Jordan Lake, res., N.C., U.S.	B3	110
Beverley, Austl.	F3	50
Beverley, Eng., U.K.	H12	7
Beverley Head, c., Newf., Can.	D2	72
Beverly, Ma., U.S.	A6	98
Beverly, N.J., U.S.	C3	107
Beverly, Oh., U.S.	C4	112
Beverly, W.V., U.S.	C5	125
Beverly Hills, Ca., U.S.	m12	82
Beverly Shores, In., U.S.	A4	91
Bexar, co., Tx., U.S.	E3	120
Bexley, Oh., U.S.	m11	112
Beypore, India	G3	37
Bežeck, U.S.S.R.	D19	22
Béziers, Fr.	I10	10
Bhadrakh, India	J12	38
Bhadrāvati, India	F3	37
Bhāgalpur, India	H12	38
Bhakkar, Pak.	E4	38
Bhaktapur, Nepal	G11	38
Bhandāra, India	B5	37
Bharatpur, India	G7	38
Bhatinda, India	E6	38
Bhātpāra, India	I13	38
Bhāvnagar, India	J5	38
Bhilai, India	B6	37
Bhīlwāra, India	H6	38
Bhīma, stm., India	D4	37
Bhīmavaram, India	D6	37
Bhind, India	G8	38
Bhiwandi, India	C2	37
Bhiwāni, India	F7	38
Bhopāl, India	I7	38
Bhubaneswar, India	J11	38
Bhuj, India	I3	38
Bhusāwal, India	B3	37
Bhutan, ctry., Asia	D7	36
Bia, Phou, mtn., Laos	E7	34
Biafra, Bight of, Afr.	H7	42
Biak, i., Indon.	F10	32
Biała Podlaska, Pol.	C23	8
Białystok, Pol.	B23	8
Biarritz, Fr.	I5	10
Biasca, Switz.	F15	10
Bibai, Japan	p19	30a
Bibb, co., Al., U.S.	C2	78
Bibb, co., Ga., U.S.	D3	87
Biberach an der Riss, Ger.	G9	8
Bic, Que., Can.	A9	74
Bic, Île du, i., Que., Can.	A9	74
Biche, Lac la, l., Alta., Can.	B4	68
Bicknell, In., U.S.	G3	91
Bida, Nig.	G7	42
Bīdar, India	D4	37
Biddeford, Me., U.S.	E2	96
Bideford, Eng., U.K.	J8	7
Bidwell, Mount, mtn., Ca., U.S.	B3	82
Biel [Bienne], Switz.	E14	10
Bielefeld, Ger.	C8	8
Bieler Lake, l., N.W. Ter., Can.	B18	66
Bielersee, l., Switz.	E14	10
Biella, Italy	D3	14
Bielsko-Biała, Pol.	F19	8
Bien Hoa, Viet.	I9	34
Bienville, co., La., U.S.	B2	95
Bienville, Lac, l., Que., Can.	g12	74
Big, stm., Mo., U.S.	c7	102
Biga, Tur.	I11	16
Bigadiç, Tur.	J12	16
Big Bald, mtn., Ga., U.S.	B2	87
Big Bald Mountain, mtn., N.B., Can.	B3	71
Big Baldy, mtn., Id., U.S.	E3	89
Big Baldy Mountain, mtn., Mt., U.S.	D6	103
Big Bay De Noc, b., Mi., U.S.	C4	99
Big Bear City, Ca., U.S.	E5	82
Big Belt Mountains, mts., Mt., U.S.	D5	103
Big Bend, Wi., U.S.	n11	126
Big Bend Dam, S.D., U.S.	C6	118
Big Bend National Park, Tx., U.S.	E1	120
Big Birch Lake, l., Mn., U.S.	E4	100
Big Black, stm., Me., U.S.	B3	96
Big Black, stm., Ms., U.S.	C3	101
Big Blue, stm., In., U.S.	E6	91
Big Burro Mountains, mts., N.M., U.S.	E1	108
Big Cabin Creek, stm., Ok., U.S.	A6	113
Big Coal, stm., W.V., U.S.	C3	125
Big Costilla Peak, mtn., N.M., U.S.	A4	108
Big Creek, stm., Tn., U.S.	e8	119
Big Creek Lake, res., Al., U.S.	E1	78
Big Creek Peak, mtn., Id., U.S.	E5	89
Big Cypress Indian Reservation, Fl., U.S.	F5	86
Big Cypress Swamp, sw., Fl., U.S.	F5	86
Big Darby Creek, stm., Oh., U.S.	C2	112
Big Delta, Ak., U.S.	C10	79
Big Duke Dam, N.C., U.S.	B2	110
Big Eau Pleine, stm., Wi., U.S.	D3	126
Big Eau Pleine Reservoir, res., Wi., U.S.	D4	126
Big Escambia Creek, stm., U.S.	D2	78
Big Flats, N.Y., U.S.	C4	109
Bigfork, Mt., U.S.	B2	103
Big Fork, stm., Mn., U.S.	B5	100
Biggs, Ca., U.S.	C3	82
Big Hatchet Peak, mtn., N.M., U.S.	F1	108
Big Hole, stm., Mt., U.S.	E4	103
Big Hole National Battlefield, hist., Mt., U.S.	E3	103
Big Horn, co., Mt., U.S.	E9	103
Big Horn, co., Wy., U.S.	B4	127
Bighorn Canyon National Recreation Area, U.S.	F8	103
Bighorn Lake, res., U.S.	E8	103
Bighorn Mountains, mts., U.S.	B5	127
Big Horn Mountains, mts., Az., U.S.	D2	80
Big Kandiyohi Lake, l., Mn., U.S.	F4	100
Big Lake, Mn., U.S.	E5	100
Big Lake, Tx., U.S.	D2	120
Big Lake, l., Me., U.S.	C5	96
Biglerville, Pa., U.S.	G7	115
Big Lookout Mountain, mtn., Or., U.S.	C9	114
Big Lost, stm., Id., U.S.	F5	89
Big Mossy Point, c., Man., Can.	C2	70
Big Mountain, mtn., Nv., U.S.	B2	105
Big Muddy, stm., Il., U.S.	F4	90
Big Nemaha, stm., Ne., U.S.	D10	104
Big Otter, stm., Va., U.S.	C3	123
Big Pine Lake, l., Mn., U.S.	D3	100
Big Pine Mountain, mtn., Ca., U.S.	E4	82
Big Piney, Wy., U.S.	D2	127
Big Piney, stm., Mo., U.S.	D5	102
Bigpoint, Ms., U.S.	E5	101
Big Rapids, Mi., U.S.	E5	99
Big Rib, stm., Wi., U.S.	C3	126
Big River, Sask., Can.	D2	75
Big Sable Point, c., Mi., U.S.	D4	99
Big Sandy, Mt., U.S.	B6	103
Big Sandy, Tx., U.S.	C5	120
Big Sandy, stm., U.S.	C2	125
Big Sandy, stm., Az., U.S.	C2	80
Big Sandy, stm., Tn., U.S.	B3	119
Big Sandy, stm., Wy., U.S.	D3	127
Big Sandy Creek, stm., W.V., U.S.	C3	125
Big Sandy Lake, l., Mn., U.S.	D5	100
Big Sandy Reservoir, res., Wy., U.S.	D3	127
Big Sheep Mountain, mtn., Mt., U.S.	C11	103
Big Sioux, stm., U.S.	E9	118
Big Smoky Valley, val., Nv., U.S.	E4	105
Big Snowy Mountains, mts., Mt., U.S.	D7	103
Big Southern Butte, mtn., Id., U.S.	F5	89
Big South Fork, stm., Ky., U.S.	k13	94
Big Spring, Tx., U.S.	C2	120
Big Stone, co., Mn., U.S.	E2	100
Big Stone City, S.D., U.S.	B9	118
Big Stone Gap, Va., U.S.	f9	123
Big Stone Lake, l., U.S.	E2	100
Big Sunflower, stm., Ms., U.S.	B3	101
Big Thompson, stm., Co., U.S.	A5	83
Big Timber, Mt., U.S.	E7	103
Big Trout Lake, l., Ont., Can.	n17	73
Big Walnut Creek, stm., Oh., U.S.	m11	112
Big Wood, stm., Id., U.S.	F4	89
Bihać, Yugo.	E10	14
Bihār, India	H11	38
Bihār, state, India	H11	38
Biharamulo, Tan.	B6	44
Bihoro, Japan	p22	30a
Bija, stm., U.S.S.R.	G11	20
Bijāpur, India	C6	37
Bijāpur, India	D3	37
Bijsk, U.S.S.R.	G11	20
Bikaner, India	F5	38
Bikin, U.S.S.R.	H20	20
Bikoro, Zaire	B3	44
Bilāspur, India	I10	38
Bilauktaung Range, mts., Asia	G5	34
Bilbao, Spain	B9	12
Bilimora, India	B2	37
Bilk Creek Mountains, mts., Nv., U.S.	B3	105
Billerica, Ma., U.S.	A5	98
Billings, Mo., U.S.	D4	102
Billings, Mt., U.S.	E8	103
Billings, co., N.D., U.S.	B2	111
Billings Heights, Mt., U.S.	E8	103
Bill Williams, stm., Az., U.S.	C1	80
Bill Williams Mountain, mtn., Az., U.S.	B3	80
Bilma, Niger	E8	42
Biloxi, Ms., U.S.	E5	101
Biloxi, stm., Ms., U.S.	E4	101
Biloxi Bay, b., Ms., U.S.	f8	101
Biltmore Forest, N.C., U.S.	f10	110
Bimini Islands, is., Bah.	B8	64
Bīna-Etāwa, India	H8	38
Bindura, Zimb.	E6	44
Binéfar, Spain	D12	12
Binga, Monte, mtn., Afr.	E6	44
Bingamon Creek, stm., W.V., U.S.	k10	125
Bingen, Ger.	F7	8
Bingen, Wa., U.S.	D4	124
Binger, Ok., U.S.	B3	113
Bingham, Me., U.S.	C3	96
Bingham, co., Id., U.S.	F6	89
Binghamton, N.Y., U.S.	C5	109
Binhai (Dongkan), China	A8	28
Binjai, Indon.	M5	34
Bintimani, mtn., S.L.	G3	42
Biograd, Yugo.	F10	14
Bioko, i., Eq. Gui.	H7	42
Bīr, India	C3	37
Birao, Cen. Afr. Rep.	F10	42
Birātnagar, Nepal	G12	38
Birch, stm., W.V., U.S.	C4	125
Birch Island, i., Man., Can.	C2	70
Birch Lake, l., Mn., U.S.	C7	100
Birch River, Man., Can.	C1	70
Birch Run, Mi., U.S.	E7	99
Birchwood City, Md., U.S.	f9	97
Birchy Bay, Newf., Can.	D4	72
Bird Creek, stm., Ok., U.S.	A6	113
Bird Island, Mn., U.S.	F4	100
Bird Island, i., N.C., U.S.	D4	110
Birdsboro, Pa., U.S.	F10	115
Birdum, Austl.	C6	50
Birecik, Tur.	A5	40
Bīrganj, Nepal	G11	38
Birigui, Braz.	F3	57
Biril'ussy, U.S.S.R.	F12	20
Bīrjand, Iran	K9	18
Birkenfeld, Ger.	F7	8
Birkenhead, Eng., U.K.	H9	7
Bîrlad, Rom.	C11	16
Birmingham, Eng., U.K.	I11	7
Birmingham, Al., U.S.	B3	78
Birmingham, Mi., U.S.	F7	99
Birmitrapur, India	I11	38
Bir Mogreïn, Maur.	C3	42
Birobidžan, U.S.S.R.	H20	20
Biron, Wi., U.S.	D4	126
Birr, Ire.	H5	7
Bi'r Safājah, Egypt	C12	42
Birtle, Man., Can.	D1	70
Bir'usa, stm., U.S.S.R.	F13	20
Bisbee, Az., U.S.	F6	80
Biscarrosse, Fr.	H5	10
Biscay, Bay of, b., Eur.	G7	4
Biscayne, Key, i., Fl., U.S.	s13	86
Biscayne Bay, b., Fl., U.S.	G6	86
Biscayne National Monument, Fl., U.S.	G6	86
Biscayne Park, Fl., U.S.	s13	86
Bisceglie, Italy	H11	14
Bischofshofen, Aus.	H13	8
Biscoe, N.C., U.S.	B3	110
Bishnupur, India	I12	38
Bishop, Ca., U.S.	D4	82
Bishop, Tx., U.S.	F4	120
Bishop Auckland, Eng., U.K.	G11	7
Bishop's Falls, Newf., Can.	D4	72
Bishopville, S.C., U.S.	C7	117
Biskra, Alg.	B7	42
Bismarck, Il., U.S.	C6	90
Bismarck, Mo., U.S.	D7	102
Bismarck, N.D., U.S.	C5	111
Bismarck Archipelago, is., Pap. N. Gui.	m16	50a
Bismarck Range, mts., Pap. N. Gui.	m15	50a
Bison Peak, mtn., Co., U.S.	B5	83
Bissau, Gui.-B.	F2	42
Bistineau, Lake, res., La., U.S.	B2	95
Bistrița, Rom.	B8	16
Bitola, Yugo.	H5	16
Bitonto, Italy	H11	14
Bitter Creek, stm., Wy., U.S.	E4	127
Bitterfeld, Ger.	D12	8
Bitterfontein, S. Afr.	H3	44
Bitter Lake, l., S.D., U.S.	B8	118
Bitterroot, stm., Mt., U.S.	D2	103
Bitterroot Range, mts., U.S.	B3	89
Bitti, Italy	I4	14
Biwabik, Mn., U.S.	C6	100
Biwa-ko, l., Japan	G9	30
Bixby, Ok., U.S.	B6	113
Biyang, China	C2	28
Bizen, Japan	H7	30
Bizerte, Tun.	L4	14
Bjelovar, Yugo.	D11	14
Black (Lixian) (Da), stm., Asia	D8	34
Black, stm., Az., U.S.	D5	80
Black, stm., Ar., U.S.	B4	81
Black, stm., La., U.S.	C4	95
Black, stm., Mi., U.S.	E8	99
Black, stm., N.Y., U.S.	B4	109
Black, stm., N.C., U.S.	C4	110
Black, stm., S.C., U.S.	D8	117
Black, stm., Vt., U.S.	B4	122
Black, stm., Vt., U.S.	E3	122
Black, stm., Wi., U.S.	D3	126
Blackall, Austl.	D9	50
Black Bear Creek, stm., Ok., U.S.	A4	113
Blackbeard Island, i., Ga., U.S.	E5	87
Blackburn, Eng., U.K.	H10	7
Blackburn, Mount, mtn., Ak., U.S.	C11	79
Black Butte, mtn., Mt., U.S.	F5	103
Black Butte Lake, res., Ca., U.S.	C2	82
Black Canyon, val., Co., U.S.	C3	83
Black Canyon City, Az., U.S.	C3	80
Black Canyon of the Gunnison National Monument, Co., U.S.	C3	83
Black Creek, B.C., Can.	E5	69
Black Creek, Wi., U.S.	D5	126
Black Creek, stm., U.S.	B1	108
Black Creek, stm., S.C., U.S.	B7	117
Black Diamond, Alta., Can.	D3	68
Black Diamond, Wa., U.S.	B4	124
Blackduck, Mn., U.S.	C4	100
Black Eagle, Mt., U.S.	C5	103
Black Earth, Wi., U.S.	E4	126
Blackfalds, Alta., Can.	C4	68
Blackfeet Indian Reservation, Mt., U.S.	B4	103
Blackfoot, Id., U.S.	F6	89
Blackfoot, stm., Mt., U.S.	C3	103
Blackfoot Mountains, mts., Id., U.S.	F7	89
Blackfoot Reservoir, res., Id., U.S.	G7	89
Blackford, co., In., U.S.	D7	91
Black Forest, Co., U.S.	C6	83
Black Forest see Schwarzwald, mts., Ger.	G8	8
Blackhall Mountain, mtn., Wy., U.S.	E6	127
Black Hawk, S.D., U.S.	C2	118
Black Hawk, co., Ia., U.S.	B5	92
Black Hills, mts., U.S.	C2	118
Blackjack Mountain, mtn., Ga., U.S.	h8	87
Black Lake, Que., Can.	C6	74
Black Lake, l., Mi., U.S.	C6	99
Black Lake, l., N.Y., U.S.	f9	109
Black Lick, Pa., U.S.	F3	115
Blacklick Estates, Oh., U.S.	m11	112
Black Mesa, mtn., Ok., U.S.	e8	113
Black Mingo Creek, stm., S.C., U.S.	D9	117
Blackmore, Mount, mtn., Mt., U.S.	E6	103
Black Mountain, N.C., U.S.	f10	110
Black Mountain, mtn., U.S.	D7	94
Black Mountain, mtn., Az., U.S.	E4	80
Black Mountain, mtn., Co., U.S.	A5	83
Black Mountain, mtn., Id., U.S.	C3	89
Black Mountain, mtn., Mt., U.S.	D4	103
Black Mountain, mtn., Or., U.S.	B7	114
Black Mountain, mtn., Wy., U.S.	B5	127
Black Mountain, mtn., Wy., U.S.	D7	127
Black Mountains, mts., Az., U.S.	B1	80
Black Peak, mtn., Az., U.S.	C1	80
Black Pine Peak, mtn., Id., U.S.	G5	89
Blackpool, Eng., U.K.	H9	7
Black Range, mts., N.M., U.S.	D2	108
Black River Falls, Wi., U.S.	D3	126
Black Rock, Ar., U.S.	A4	81
Black Rock, N.M., U.S.	B1	108
Black Rock Desert, des., Nv., U.S.	B3	105
Black Rock Range, mts., Nv., U.S.	B3	105
Blacksburg, S.C., U.S.	A4	117
Blacksburg, Va., U.S.	C2	123
Black Sea	G14	4
Blacks Fork, stm., U.S.	E3	127
Blacks Harbour, N.B., Can.	D3	71
Blackshear, Ga., U.S.	E4	87
Blackstone, Ma., U.S.	B4	98

Name	Map Ref	Page
Blackstone, Va., U.S.	C5	123
Blackstone, stm., R.I., U.S.	B4	116
Black Thunder Creek, stm., Wy., U.S.	C8	127
Blackville, N.B., Can.	C4	71
Blackville, S.C., U.S.	E5	117
Black Volta (Volta Noire), stm., Afr.	G5	42
Blackwalnut Point, c., Md., U.S.	C5	97
Black Warrior, stm., Al., U.S.	C2	78
Blackwater, stm., Fl., U.S.	u15	86
Blackwater, stm., Md., U.S.	D5	97
Blackwater, stm., N.H., U.S.	D3	106
Blackwater, stm., Va., U.S.	D6	123
Blackwater Reservoir, res., N.H., U.S.	D3	106
Blackwell, Ok., U.S.	A4	113
Blackwood, N.J., U.S.	D2	107
Bladen, co., N.C., U.S.	C4	110
Bladenboro, N.C., U.S.	C4	110
Bladensburg, Md., U.S.	f9	97
Blades, De., U.S.	F3	85
Blagoevgrad, Bul.	G7	16
Blagoveščensk, U.S.S.R.	G19	20
Blaine, Me., U.S.	B5	96
Blaine, Mn., U.S.	m12	100
Blaine, Tn., U.S.	C10	119
Blaine, Wa., U.S.	A3	124
Blaine, co., Id., U.S.	F4	89
Blaine, co., Mt., U.S.	B7	103
Blaine, co., Ne., U.S.	C6	104
Blaine, co., Ok., U.S.	B3	113
Blaine Lake, Sask., Can.	E2	75
Blair, Ne., U.S.	C9	104
Blair, Ok., U.S.	C2	113
Blair, W.V., U.S.	n12	125
Blair, Wi., U.S.	D2	126
Blair, co., Pa., U.S.	E5	115
Blair Athol, Austl.	D9	50
Blairstown, Ia., U.S.	C5	92
Blairsville, Pa., U.S.	F3	115
Blake Island, i., Wa., U.S.	e11	124
Blakely, Ga., U.S.	E2	87
Blakely, Pa., U.S.	m18	115
Blake Point, c., Mi., U.S.	h10	99
Blanc, Cap, c., Afr.	D2	42
Blanc, Mont (Monte Bianco), mtn., Eur.	G13	10
Blanca Peak, mtn., Co., U.S.	D5	83
Blanchard, La., U.S.	B2	95
Blanchard, Ok., U.S.	B4	113
Blanchard, stm., Oh., U.S.	A1	112
Blanchardville, Wi., U.S.	F4	126
Blanchester, Oh., U.S.	C2	112
Blanco, Tx., U.S.	D3	120
Blanco, co., Tx., U.S.	D3	120
Blanco, Cape, c., Or., U.S.	E2	114
Bland, Mo., U.S.	C6	102
Bland, co., Va., U.S.	C1	123
Blanding, Ut., U.S.	F6	121
Blandinsville, Il., U.S.	C3	90
Blanes, Spain	D14	12
Blangkedjeren, Indon.	M4	34
Blangy-sur-Bresle, Fr.	C8	10
Blanquilla, Isla, i., Ven.	B10	58
Blantyre, Mwi.	E7	44
Blasdell, N.Y., U.S.	C2	109
Blawnox, Pa., U.S.	k14	115
Blaye-et-Sainte-Luce, Fr.	G6	10
Bleckley, co., Ga., U.S.	D3	87
Bled, Yugo.	C9	14
Bledsoe, co., Tn., U.S.	D8	119
Blende, Co., U.S.	C6	83
Blenheim, Ont., Can.	E3	73
Blenheim, N.Z.	D4	52
Blennerhassett, W.V., U.S.	B3	125
Bléré, Fr.	E7	10
Blida, Alg.	A6	42
Blind, stm., La., U.S.	h10	95
Blind River, Ont., Can.	A2	73
Blissfield, Mi., U.S.	G7	99
Blitar, Indon.	n16	32
Block Island, R.I., U.S.	h7	116
Block Island, i., R.I., U.S.	h7	116
Block Island Sound, strt., U.S.	G2	116
Bloemfontein, S. Afr.	G5	44
Bloemhof, S. Afr.	G5	44
Blois, Fr.	E8	10
Blood Mountain, mtn., Ga., U.S.	B3	87
Bloodsworth Island, i., Md., U.S.	D5	97
Bloodvein, stm., Can.	D3	70
Bloody Foreland, c., Ire.	F4	7
Bloomer, Wi., U.S.	C2	126
Bloomfield, Ont., Can.	D7	73
Bloomfield, Ct., U.S.	B5	84
Bloomfield, In., U.S.	F4	91
Bloomfield, Ia., U.S.	D5	92
Bloomfield, Ky., U.S.	C4	94
Bloomfield, Mo., U.S.	E8	102
Bloomfield, Ne., U.S.	B8	104
Bloomfield, N.J., U.S.	h8	107
Bloomfield, N.M., U.S.	A2	108
Bloomfield Hills, Mi., U.S.	o15	99
Bloomingdale, Ga., U.S.	D5	87
Bloomingdale, Il., U.S.	k8	90
Bloomingdale, N.J., U.S.	A4	107
Bloomingdale, Tn., U.S.	C11	119
Blooming Prairie, Mn., U.S.	G5	100
Bloomington, Il., U.S.	C4	90
Bloomington, In., U.S.	F4	91
Bloomington, Mn., U.S.	F5	100
Bloomington, Tx., U.S.	E4	120
Bloomington, Wi., U.S.	F3	126
Bloomington, Lake, res., Il., U.S.	C5	90
Bloomsburg, Pa., U.S.	E9	115
Bloomville, Oh., U.S.	A2	112
Blora, Indon.	m15	33a
Blossburg, Pa., U.S.	C7	115
Blossom, Tx., U.S.	C5	120
Blount, co., Al., U.S.	B3	78
Blount, co., Tn., U.S.	D10	119
Blountstown, Fl., U.S.	B1	86
Blountsville, Al., U.S.	A3	78
Blountville, Tn., U.S.	C11	119
Blowing Rock, N.C., U.S.	A1	110
Bludenz, Aus.	H9	8
Blue, stm., Co., U.S.	B4	83
Blue, stm., In., U.S.	H5	91
Blue, stm., Mo., U.S.	k10	102
Blue, stm., Ok., U.S.	C5	113
Blue Ash, Oh., U.S.	o13	112
Blue Buck Point, c., La., U.S.	E2	95
Blue Creek, W.V., U.S.	m13	125
Blue Creek, stm., W.V., U.S.	m13	125
Blue Cypress Lake, l., Fl., U.S.	E6	86
Blue Diamond, Nv., U.S.	G6	105
Blue Earth, Mn., U.S.	G4	100
Blue Earth, co., Mn., U.S.	G4	100
Blue Earth, stm., Mn., U.S.	G4	100
Bluefield, Va., U.S.	C1	123
Bluefield, W.V., U.S.	D3	125
Bluefields, Nic.	H6	64
Blue Grass, Ia., U.S.	C7	92
Blue Hill, Me., U.S.	D4	96
Blue Hill, Ne., U.S.	D7	104
Blue Hill Range, hills, Ma., U.S.	h11	98
Blue Hills, Ct., U.S.	B5	84
Blue Island, Il., U.S.	B6	90
Bluejoint Lake, l., Or., U.S.	E7	114
Blue Lake, Ca., U.S.	B2	82
Blue Mesa Reservoir, res., Co., U.S.	C3	83
Blue Mound, Il., U.S.	D4	90
Blue Mountain, Ms., U.S.	A4	101
Blue Mountain, mtn., Mt., U.S.	C12	103
Blue Mountain, mtn., N.M., U.S.	D2	108
Blue Mountain, mtn., Pa., U.S.	F6	115
Blue Mountain Lake, res., Ar., U.S.	B2	81
Blue Mountain Peak, mtn., Jam.	E9	64
Blue Nile (Al-Bahr al-Azraq), stm., Afr.	F12	42
Blue Point, Me., U.S.	g7	96
Blue Rapids, Ks., U.S.	C7	93
Blue Ridge, Ga., U.S.	B2	87
Blue Ridge, Va., U.S.	C3	123
Blue Ridge, mts., U.S.	E10	76
Blue Ridge Summit, Pa., U.S.	G7	115
Blue Springs, Mo., U.S.	h11	102
Bluestone, stm., W.V., U.S.	D3	125
Bluestone Lake, res., U.S.	D4	125
Bluewell, W.V., U.S.	D3	125
Bluff City, Tn., U.S.	C11	119
Bluff Creek, stm., Ok., U.S.	A4	113
Bluff Lake, res., Ms., U.S.	B5	101
Bluff Park, Al., U.S.	g7	78
Bluffs, Il., U.S.	D3	90
Bluffton, In., U.S.	C7	91
Bluffton, Oh., U.S.	B2	112
Bluffton, S.C., U.S.	G6	117
Blumenau, Braz.	B7	56
Bly, Or., U.S.	E5	114
Blying Sound, strt., Ak., U.S.	h17	79
Blyth, Ont., Can.	D3	73
Blyth, Eng., U.K.	F11	7
Blythe, Ca., U.S.	F6	82
Blytheville, Ar., U.S.	B6	81
Bø, Nor.	B10	6
Bø, Nor.	G7	6
Bo, S.L.	G3	42
Boaco, Nic.	H5	64
Boalsburg, Pa., U.S.	E6	115
Boa Nova, Braz.	C8	57
Boardman, Oh., U.S.	A5	112
Boardman, Or., U.S.	B7	114
Boa Vista, Braz.	C6	54
Boavita, Col.	D6	58
Boaz, Al., U.S.	A3	78
Bobbili, India	C7	37
Bobbio, Italy	E4	14
Bobcaygeon, Ont., Can.	C6	73
Böblingen, Ger.	G9	8
Bobo Dioulasso, Burkina	F5	42
Bobrujsk, U.S.S.R.	H12	22
Bobtown, Pa., U.S.	G2	115
Bobures, Ven.	C7	58
Boby, Pic, mtn., Madag.	F9	44
Boca Chica Key, i., Fl., U.S.	H5	86
Boca Ciega Bay, b., Fl., U.S.	p10	86
Bôca do Acre, Braz.	E5	54
Boca Grande, Fl., U.S.	F4	86
Boca Raton, Fl., U.S.	F6	86
Bocas del Toro, Pan.	J6	64
Bocholt, Ger.	D6	8
Bochum, Ger.	D7	8
Bodajbo, U.S.S.R.	F16	20
Bodega Head, c., Ca., U.S.	C2	82
Bodele, reg., Chad	E9	42
Boden, Swe.	D13	6
Bodensee, l., Eur.	H9	8
Bodhan, India	C4	37
Bodie Island, i., N.C., U.S.	B7	110
Bodināyakkanūr, India	G4	37
Bodkin Point, c., Md., U.S.	B5	97
Bodø, Nor.	C10	6
Boende, Zaire	B4	44
Boën-sur-Lignon, Fr.	G10	10
Boerne, Tx., U.S.	E3	120
Boeuf, stm., La., U.S.	C4	95
Boeuf, Lake, l., La., U.S.	k10	95
Bogale, Burma	F3	34
Bogalusa, La., U.S.	D6	95
Bogart, Ga., U.S.	C3	87
Bogata, Tx., U.S.	C5	120
Bogenfels, Nmb.	G3	44
Boger City, N.C., U.S.	B1	110
Bognes, Nor.	B10	6
Bogor, Indon.	m13	32
Bogorodick, U.S.S.R.	H21	22
Bogorodsk, U.S.S.R.	E26	22
Bogotá, Col.	E5	58
Bogota, N.J., U.S.	h8	107
Bogotol, U.S.S.R.	F11	20
Bogra, Bngl.	H13	38
Bogučany, U.S.S.R.	F13	20
Bogue Chitto, Ms., U.S.	D3	101
Bogue Chitto, stm., U.S.	D5	95
Bogue Inlet, b., N.C., U.S.	C5	110
Bogue Phalia, stm., Ms., U.S.	B3	101
Bo Hai, b., China	D10	26
Bohain-en-Vermandois, Fr.	C10	10
Bohemia see Čechy, hist. reg., Czech.	F14	8
Bohemian Forest, mts., Eur.	F12	8
Bohol, i., Phil.	D7	32
Boiano, Italy	H9	14
Boigu, i., Austl.	A8	50
Boiling Springs, N.C., U.S.	B1	110
Boiling Springs, Pa., U.S.	F7	115
Bois Blanc Island, i., Mi., U.S.	C6	99
Bois Brule, stm., Wi., U.S.	B2	126
Boischâtel, Que., Can.	C6	74
Bois-des-Filion, Que., Can.	p19	74
Bois de Sioux, stm., Mn., U.S.	E2	100
Boise, Id., U.S.	F2	89
Boise, co., Id., U.S.	F3	89
Boise City, Ok., U.S.	e8	113
Boissevain, Man., Can.	E1	70
Boissevain, Va., U.S.	e10	123
Boistfort Peak, mtn., Wa., U.S.	C2	124
Boizenburg, Ger.	B10	8
Bojador, Cabo, c., W. Sah.	C3	42
Bojeador, Cape, c., Phil.	B7	32
Bojnūrd, Iran	J9	18
Bojonegoro, Indon.	m15	33a
Boké, Gui.	F3	42
Boketu, China	B11	26
Boknafjorden, Nor.	G5	6
Boksitogorsk, U.S.S.R.	B16	22
Bokungu, Zaire	B4	44
Bolama, Gui.-B.	F2	42
Bolbec, Fr.	C7	10
Bolesławiec, Pol.	D15	8
Boley, Ok., U.S.	B5	113
Bolgatanga, Ghana	F5	42
Boli, China	B13	26
Bolingbrook, Il., U.S.	k8	90
Bolívar, Arg.	D4	56
Bolivar, Mo., U.S.	D4	102
Bolivar, Oh., U.S.	B4	112
Bolivar, Tn., U.S.	B3	119
Bolivar, W.V., U.S.	B7	125
Bolivar, co., Ms., U.S.	B3	101
Bolívar, Cerro, mtn., Ven.	D11	58
Bolivar, Lake, l., Ms., U.S.	B3	101
Bolívar, Pico, mtn., Ven.	C7	58
Bolivia, ctry., S.A.	G5	54
Bollène, Fr.	H11	10
Bollinger, co., Mo., U.S.	D7	102
Bollnäs, Swe.	F11	6
Bollullos par del Condado, Spain	H5	12
Bolobo, Zaire	B3	44
Bologna, Italy	E6	14
Bologoje, U.S.S.R.	D17	22
Bolotnoje, U.S.S.R.	F10	20
Bolsena, Italy	G6	14
Bol'šereck, U.S.S.R.	G25	20
Bol'ševik, U.S.S.R.	E23	20
Bol'ševik, Ostrov, i., U.S.S.R.	B14	20
Bol'šoj An'uj, stm., U.S.S.R.	D26	20
Bol'šoj Begičev, Ostrov, i., U.S.S.R.	C16	20
Bol'šoj Kavkaz (Caucasus), mts., U.S.S.R.	I6	18
Bol'šoj L'achovskij, Ostrov, i., U.S.S.R.	C22	20
Bolton, Eng., U.K.	H10	7
Bolton, Ms., U.S.	C3	101
Bolton Lakes, l., Ct., U.S.	B6	84
Bolton Landing, N.Y., U.S.	B7	109
Bolzano (Bozen), Italy	C6	14
Boma, Zaire	C2	44
Bombala, Austl.	G9	50
Bombarral, Port.	F2	12
Bombay, India	C2	37
Bombay Hook Island, i., De., U.S.	C4	85
Bom Despacho, Braz.	E6	57
Bom Jesus da Lapa, Braz.	B7	57
Bomoseen, Lake, l., Vt., U.S.	D2	122
Bomu (Mbomou), stm., Afr.	H10	42
Bon, Cap, c., Tun.	A8	42
Bon Accord, Alta., Can.	C4	68
Bon Air, Va., U.S.	C5	123
Bonaire, Ga., U.S.	D3	87
Bonaire, i., Neth. Ant.	H13	64
Bonanza Peak, mtn., Wa., U.S.	A5	124
Bonao, Dom. Rep.	E12	64
Bonaparte, Mount, mtn., Wa., U.S.	A6	124
Bonaparte Archipelago, is., Austl.	B5	50
Bonarbridge, Scot., U.K.	D8	7
Bonasila Dome, mtn., Ak., U.S.	C7	79
Bonaventure, Que., Can.	A4	71
Bonavista, Newf., Can.	D5	72
Bonavista, Cape, c., Newf., Can.	D5	72
Bonavista Bay, b., Newf., Can.	G22	66
Bonavista Bay, b., Newf., Can.	D5	72
Bond, co., Il., U.S.	E4	90
Bondeno, Italy	E6	14
Bondo, Zaire	H10	42
Bondoukou, I.C.	G5	42
Bondowoso, Indon.	m16	33a
Bondsville, Ma., U.S.	B3	98
Bonduel, Wi., U.S.	D5	126
Bondurant, Ia., U.S.	C4	92
Bone, Teluk, b., Indon.	F7	32
Bone Lake, l., Wi., U.S.	C1	126
Bongandanga, Zaire	A4	44
Bongor, Chad	F9	42
Bonham, Tx., U.S.	C4	120
Bon Homme, co., S.D., U.S.	D8	118
Bonifati, Capo, c., Italy	J10	14
Bonifay, Fl., U.S.	u16	86
Bonita Springs, Fl., U.S.	F5	86
Bonn, Ger.	E7	8
Bonneauville, Pa., U.S.	G7	115
Bonne Bay, b., Newf., Can.	D3	72
Bonner, co., Id., U.S.	A2	89
Bonners Ferry, Id., U.S.	A2	89
Bonner Springs, Ks., U.S.	C9	93
Bonnet Carre Floodway, La., U.S.	h11	95
Bonne Terre, Mo., U.S.	D7	102
Bonneval, Fr.	D8	10
Bonneville, Fr.	F13	10
Bonneville, co., Id., U.S.	F7	89
Bonneville Dam, U.S.	B4	114
Bonneville Peak, mtn., Id., U.S.	F6	89
Bonneville Salt Flats, pl., Ut., U.S.	C2	121
Bonney Lake, Wa., U.S.	B3	124
Bonnie Doone, N.C., U.S.	B4	110
Bonny Reservoir, res., Co., U.S.	B8	83
Bonnyville, Alta., Can.	B5	68
Bono, Ar., U.S.	B5	81
Bonorva, Italy	I3	14
Bon Secour, Al., U.S.	E2	78
Bonthe, S.L.	G3	42
Booker, Tx., U.S.	A2	120
Booker T. Washington National Monument, Va., U.S.	C3	123
Boomer, W.V., U.S.	C3	125
Boone, Ia., U.S.	B4	92
Boone, N.C., U.S.	A1	110
Boone, co., Ar., U.S.	A2	81
Boone, co., Il., U.S.	A5	90
Boone, co., In., U.S.	D4	91
Boone, co., Ia., U.S.	B3	92
Boone, co., Ky., U.S.	B5	94
Boone, co., Mo., U.S.	B5	102
Boone, co., Ne., U.S.	C7	104
Boone, co., W.V., U.S.	C3	125
Boone, stm., Ia., U.S.	B4	92
Boone Lake, res., Tn., U.S.	C11	119
Booneville, Ar., U.S.	B2	81
Booneville, Ms., U.S.	A5	101
Boonsboro, Md., U.S.	A2	97
Boonton, N.J., U.S.	B4	107
Boonville, In., U.S.	H3	91
Boonville, Mo., U.S.	C5	102
Boonville, N.Y., U.S.	B5	109
Boonville, N.C., U.S.	A2	110
Boothbay Harbor, Me., U.S.	E3	96
Boothia, Gulf of, b., N.W. Ter., Can.	B14	66
Boothia Peninsula, pen., N.W. Ter., Can.	B14	66
Booths Creek, stm., W.V., U.S.	h11	125
Boothville, La., U.S.	E6	95
Booué, Gabon	B2	44
Boquete, Pan.	J6	64
Boquillas del Carmen, Mex.	C8	62
Bor, Sudan	G12	42
Bor, U.S.S.R.	E27	22
Boraha, Nosy, i., Madag.	E9	44
Borah Peak, mtn., Id., U.S.	E5	89
Borås, Swe.	H9	6
Bordeaux, Fr.	H6	10
Borden, co., Tx., U.S.	C2	120
Borden Peninsula, pen., N.W. Ter., Can.	B16	66
Bordentown, N.J., U.S.	C3	107
Bordertown, Austl.	G8	50
Borgå (Porvoo), Fin.	F15	6
Borgarnes, Ice.	C3	4
Borger, Tx., U.S.	B2	120
Borgne, Lake, b., La., U.S.	D6	95
Borgo, Italy	C6	14
Borgo San Dalmazzo, Italy	E2	14
Borgosesia, Italy	D3	14
Borgo Val di Taro, Italy	E4	14
Borisov, U.S.S.R.	G11	22
Borja, Spain	D10	12
Borjas Blancas, Spain	D12	12
Borken, Ger.	D6	8
Borlänge, Swe.	F10	6
Borlu, Tur.	K12	16
Borneo (Kalimantan), i., Asia	E5	32
Bornholm, i., Den.	I10	6
Bornova, Tur.	K11	16
Borogoncy, U.S.S.R.	E20	20
Boron, Ca., U.S.	E5	82
Boronga Islands, is., Burma	E2	34
Boroviči, U.S.S.R.	C16	22
Borrego Springs, Ca., U.S.	F5	82
Bort-les-Orgues, Fr.	G9	10
Borūjerd, Iran	B4	46
Borz'a, U.S.S.R.	G17	20
Bosa, Italy	I3	14
Bosanska Gradiška, Yugo.	D12	14
Bosanska Krupa, Yugo.	E11	14
Bosanski Novi, Yugo.	D11	14
Bosanski Petrovac, Yugo.	E11	14
Bosaso, Som.	F4	46
Boscobel, Wi., U.S.	E3	126
Boshan, China	D10	26
Bosporus see İstanbul Boğazı, strt., Tur.	H13	16
Bosque, co., Tx., U.S.	D4	120
Bossangoa, Cen. Afr. Rep.	G9	42
Bossembélé, Cen. Afr. Rep.	G9	42
Bossier, co., La., U.S.	B2	95
Bossier City, La., U.S.	B2	95
Bosten Hu, l., China	C4	26
Boston, Eng., U.K.	I12	7
Boston, Ga., U.S.	F3	87
Boston, Ma., U.S.	B5	98
Boston Bay, b., Ma., U.S.	B6	98
Boston Mountains, mts., Ar., U.S.	B2	81
Boswell, In., U.S.	C3	91
Boswell, Ok., U.S.	C6	113
Boswell, Pa., U.S.	F3	115
Botād, India	I4	38
Boteti, stm., Bots.	F4	44
Botetourt, co., Va., U.S.	C3	123
Bothell, Wa., U.S.	B3	124
Bothnia, Gulf of, b., Eur.	E12	6
Bothwell, Ont., Can.	E3	73
Botkins, Oh., U.S.	B1	112
Botoșani, Rom.	B10	16
Botswana, ctry., Afr.	F4	44
Bottenhavet (Selkämeri), b., Eur.	F12	6
Bottenviken (Perämeri), b., Eur.	D14	6
Bottineau, N.D., U.S.	A5	111
Bottineau, co., N.D., U.S.	A4	111
Botucatu, Braz.	G4	57
Botwood, Newf., Can.	D4	72
Bouaflé, I.C.	G4	42
Bouaké, I.C.	G4	42
Bouar, Cen. Afr. Rep.	G9	42
Bou Arada, Tun.	M4	14
Boucherville, Que., Can.	D4	74
Bouctouche, N.B., Can.	C5	71
Boudreaux, Lake, l., La., U.S.	E5	95
Bou Ficha, Tun.	M5	14
Bougainville Reef, rf., Austl.	C9	50
Bougouni, Mali	F4	42
Bouillon, Bel.	F5	8
Boulder, Co., U.S.	A5	83
Boulder, Mt., U.S.	D4	103
Boulder, co., Co., U.S.	A5	83
Boulder City, Nv., U.S.	H7	105
Boulevard Heights, Md., U.S.	f9	97
Boulogne-Billancourt, Fr.	D9	10
Boulogne-sur-Gesse, Fr.	I7	10
Boulogne-sur-Mer, Fr.	B8	10
Bouna, I.C.	G5	42
Boundary, co., Id., U.S.	A2	89
Boundary Bay, b., Wa., U.S.	A3	124
Boundary Peak, mtn., Nv., U.S.	F3	105
Bound Brook, N.J., U.S.	B3	107
Bountiful, Ut., U.S.	C4	121
Bourbeuse, stm., Mo., U.S.	C6	102
Bourbon, In., U.S.	B5	91
Bourbon, Mo., U.S.	C6	102
Bourbon, co., Ks., U.S.	E9	93
Bourbon, co., Ky., U.S.	B5	94
Bourbonnais, Il., U.S.	B6	90
Bourbonnais, hist. reg., Fr.	F9	10
Bourbonne-les-Bains, Fr.	E12	10
Bourem, Mali	E5	42
Bourg, La., U.S.	E5	95
Bourganeuf, Fr.	G8	10
Bourg-en-Bresse, Fr.	F12	10
Bourges, Fr.	E9	10
Bourg-Lastic, Fr.	G9	10
Bourgogne, hist. reg., Fr.	E11	10
Bourgoin, Fr.	G12	10
Bourg-Saint-Andéol, Fr.	H11	10
Bourg-Saint-Maurice, Fr.	G13	10
Bourke, Austl.	F9	50
Bournemouth, Eng., U.K.	K11	7
Bou Saâda, Alg.	A6	42
Bouse, Az., U.S.	D2	80
Boussac, Fr.	F9	10
Bousso, Chad	F9	42
Boutte, La., U.S.	k11	95
Bøvågen, Nor.	F5	6
Bovalino Marina, Italy	K11	14
Bovec, Yugo.	C8	14
Bøverdal, Nor.	F7	6
Bovey, Mn., U.S.	C5	100
Bovina, Tx., U.S.	B1	120
Bow, N.H., U.S.	D3	106
Bow, stm., Alta., Can.	D4	68
Bowden, Alta., Can.	D4	68
Bowdish Reservoir, res., R.I., U.S.	B1	116
Bowdon, Ga., U.S.	C1	87
Bowen, Austl.	C9	50
Bowie, Az., U.S.	E6	80
Bowie, Md., U.S.	C4	97
Bowie, Tx., U.S.	C4	120
Bowie, co., Tx., U.S.	C5	120
Bow Island, Alta., Can.	E5	68
Bow Lake, l., N.H., U.S.	D4	106
Bowling Green, Fl., U.S.	E5	86
Bowling Green, Ky., U.S.	D3	94
Bowling Green, Mo., U.S.	B6	102
Bowling Green, Oh., U.S.	A2	112
Bowling Green, S.C., U.S.	A5	117
Bowling Green, Va., U.S.	B5	123
Bowman, Ga., U.S.	B3	87
Bowman, N.D., U.S.	C2	111
Bowman, S.C., U.S.	E6	117
Bowman, co., N.D., U.S.	C2	111
Bowman Creek, stm., Pa., U.S.	m16	115
Bowman-Haley Lake, res., N.D., U.S.	C2	111
Bowron, stm., B.C., Can.	C7	69
Bowstring Lake, l., Mn., U.S.	C5	100
Box Butte, co., Ne., U.S.	B2	104
Box Butte Reservoir, res., Ne., U.S.	B2	104
Box Elder, S.D., U.S.	C2	118
Box Elder, co., Ut., U.S.	B2	121
Boxford, Ma., U.S.	A6	98
Boxian, China	B4	28
Boyce, La., U.S.	C3	95
Boyceville, Wi., U.S.	C1	126
Boyd, Tx., U.S.	C4	120
Boyd, co., Ky., U.S.	B7	94
Boyd, co., Ne., U.S.	B7	104
Boyden, Ia., U.S.	A2	92
Boyd Lake, l., Me., U.S.	C4	96
Boyer, stm., Ia., U.S.	C2	92
Boyertown, Pa., U.S.	F10	115
Boykins, Va., U.S.	D5	123
Boyle, Alta., Can.	B4	68
Boyle, Ire.	H4	7
Boyle, Ms., U.S.	B3	101
Boyle, co., Ky., U.S.	C5	94
Boyne City, Mi., U.S.	C6	99
Boynton Beach, Fl., U.S.	F6	86
Boysen Reservoir, res., Wy., U.S.	C4	127
Boys Town, Ne., U.S.	g12	104
Bozburun, Tur.	M12	16
Boz Dağ, mtn., Tur.	L13	16
Bozeman, Mt., U.S.	E5	103
Bozeman Pass, Mt., U.S.	E6	103
Bozoum, Cen. Afr. Rep.	G9	42
Bra, Italy	E2	14
Bracciano, Italy	G7	14
Bracebridge, Ont., Can.	B5	73
Bräcke, Swe.	E10	6
Bracken, co., Ky., U.S.	B5	94
Brackenridge, Pa., U.S.	h15	115
Brackettville, Tx., U.S.	E2	120
Braddock, Pa., U.S.	k14	115
Braddock Heights, Md., U.S.	B2	97
Braddock Point, c., S.C., U.S.	G6	117
Bradenton, Fl., U.S.	E4	86
Bradenville, Pa., U.S.	F3	115
Bradford, Ont., Can.	C5	73
Bradford, Eng., U.K.	H11	7
Bradford, Ar., U.S.	B4	81
Bradford, Oh., U.S.	B1	112
Bradford, Pa., U.S.	C4	115
Bradford, R.I., U.S.	F2	116
Bradford, Tn., U.S.	A3	119
Bradford, Vt., U.S.	D4	122
Bradford, co., Fl., U.S.	C4	86

Bradford, co., Pa., U.S. C8 115
Bradfordwoods, Pa., U.S. h13 115
Bradley, Il., U.S. B6 90
Bradley, Me., U.S. D4 96
Bradley, W.V., U.S. D3 125
Bradley, co., Ar., U.S. D3 81
Bradley, co., Tn., U.S. D9 119
Bradley Beach, N.J., U.S. C4 107
Bradner, Oh., U.S. A2 112
Bradshaw, Md., U.S. B5 97
Bradshaw Mountains, mts., Az., U.S. C3 80
Brady, Tx., U.S. D3 120
Braga, Port. D3 12
Bragado, Arg. D4 56
Bragança, Port. D5 12
Braham, Mn., U.S. E5 100
Brāhmanbāria, Bngl. I14 38
Brāhmani, stm., India J11 38
Brahmaputra (Yarlung), stm., Asia G15 38
Braich y Pwll, c., Wales, U.K. I8 7
Braidwood, Il., U.S. B5 90
Brăila, Rom. D11 16
Brainerd, Mn., U.S. D4 100
Braintree, Ma., U.S. B5 98
Brake, Ger. B8 8
Brampton, Ont., Can. D5 73
Bramsche, Ger. C7 8
Bramwell, W.V., U.S. D3 125
Branch, co., Mi., U.S. G5 99
Branch, stm., R.I., U.S. B3 116
Branch, stm., Wi., U.S. h10 126
Branch Lake, l., Me., U.S. D4 96
Branch Village, R.I., U.S. B3 116
Branchville, S.C., U.S. E6 117
Branco, stm., Braz. C6 54
Brandberg, mtn., Nmb. F2 44
Brandbu, Nor. F8 6
Brandenburg, Ger. C12 8
Brandenburg, Ky., U.S. C3 94
Brandon, Man., Can. E2 70
Brandon, Fl., U.S. E4 86
Brandon, Ms., U.S. C4 101
Brandon, S.C., U.S. B3 117
Brandon, S.D., U.S. D9 118
Brandon, Vt., U.S. D2 122
Brandon, Wi., U.S. E5 126
Brandvlei, S. Afr. H4 44
Brandy Peak, mtn., Or., U.S. E3 114
Brandywine, Md., U.S. C4 97
Brandywine Creek, stm., U.S. A3 85
Branford, Ct., U.S. D4 84
Branford Hills, Ct., U.S. D4 84
Br'ansk, U.S.S.R. H17 22
Branson, Mo., U.S. E4 102
Brantford, Ont., Can. D4 73
Brantley, Al., U.S. D3 78
Brantley, co., Ga., U.S. E4 87
Brantôme, Fr. G7 10
Brant Rock, Ma., U.S. B6 98
Brantville, N.B., Can. B5 71
Bras d'Or Lake, l., N.S., Can. D9 71
Brasília, Braz. C5 57
Braşov, Rom. D9 16
Brasstown Bald, mtn., Ga., U.S. B3 87
Brassua Lake, res., Me., U.S. C3 96
Bratenahl, Oh., U.S. g9 112
Bratislava, Czech. G17 8
Bratsk, U.S.S.R. F14 20
Bratskoje Vodochranilišče, res., U.S.S.R. F14 20
Brattleboro, Vt., U.S. F3 122
Braunau [am Inn], Aus. G13 8
Braunschweig, Ger. C10 8
Brava, Som. H3 46
Brava, Costa, Spain D15 12
Bravo del Norte (Río Grande), stm., N.A. F6 76
Brawley, Ca., U.S. F6 82
Brawley Peaks, mts., Nv., U.S. E3 105
Braxton, co., W.V., U.S. C4 125
Bray, Ire. H6 7
Bray, Ok., U.S. C4 113
Bray Island, i., N.W. Ter., Can. C17 66
Braymer, Mo., U.S. B4 102
Brazeau, stm., Alta., Can. C2 68
Brazil, In., U.S. E3 91
Brazil, ctry., S.A. E7 54
Brazoria, Tx., U.S. r14 120
Brazoria, co., Tx., U.S. E5 120
Brazos, co., Tx., U.S. D4 120
Brazos, stm., Tx., U.S. D4 120
Brazzaville, Congo B3 44
Brčko, Yugo. E2 16
Brea, Ca., U.S. n13 82
Breakenridge, Mount, mtn., B.C., Can. E7 69
Breathitt, co., Ky., U.S. C6 94
Breaux Bridge, La., U.S. D4 95
Brebes, Indon. m14 33a
Breckenridge, Co., U.S. B4 83
Breckenridge, Mi., U.S. E6 99
Breckenridge, Mn., U.S. D2 100
Breckenridge, Tx., U.S. C3 120
Breckinridge, co., Ky., U.S. C3 94
Brecksville, Oh., U.S. A4 112
Brecon Beacons National Park, Wales, U.K. J9 7
Breda, Neth. D4 8
Bredstedt, Ger. A8 8
Breese, Il., U.S. E4 90
Bréhal, Fr. D5 10
Brekstad, Nor. E7 6
Bremen, Ger. B8 8
Bremen, Ga., U.S. C1 87
Bremen, In., U.S. B5 91
Bremen, Oh., U.S. C3 112
Bremer, co., Ia., U.S. B5 92
Bremerhaven, Ger. B8 8
Bremerton, Wa., U.S. B3 124
Bremond, Tx., U.S. D4 120
Brenham, Tx., U.S. D4 120
Brenner Pass, Eur. B6 14
Breno, Italy D5 14
Brent, Al., U.S. C2 78
Brent, Fl., U.S. u14 86
Brenton Point, c., R.I., U.S. F5 116
Brentwood, Ca., U.S. h9 82
Brentwood, Md., U.S. f9 97
Brentwood, Mo., U.S. f13 102
Brentwood, N.Y., U.S. E7 109
Brentwood, Pa., U.S. k14 115
Brentwood, S.C., U.S. k11 117
Brentwood, Tn., U.S. A5 119
Brescia, Italy D5 14
Breslau see Wrocław, Pol. D17 8
Bressanone, Italy C6 14
Bressuire, Fr. F6 10
Brest, Fr. D2 10
Brest, U.S.S.R. I6 22
Bretagne, hist. reg., Fr. D3 10
Breton Islands, is., La., U.S. E6 95
Breton Sound, strt., La., U.S. E6 95
Brevard, N.C., U.S. f10 110
Brevard, co., Fl., U.S. E6 86
Brevoort Lake, l., Mi., U.S. B6 99
Brewer, Me., U.S. D4 96
Brewster, Ma., U.S. C7 98
Brewster, N.Y., U.S. D7 109
Brewster, Oh., U.S. B4 112
Brewster, Wa., U.S. A6 124
Brewster, co., Tx., U.S. E1 120
Brewster Islands, is., Ma., U.S. g12 98
Brewton, Al., U.S. D2 78
Brežice, Yugo. D10 14
Bria, Cen. Afr. Rep. G10 42
Brian Boru Peak, mtn., B.C., Can. B4 69
Briançon, Fr. H13 10
Brian Head, mtn., Ut., U.S. F3 121
Briare, Fr. E9 10
Briceville, Tn., U.S. C9 119
Brick [Township], N.J., U.S. C4 107
Bricquebec, Fr. C5 10
Bridal Veil Falls, wtfl, Ut., U.S. C4 121
Bridgehampton, N.Y., U.S. n16 109
Bridgeport, Al., U.S. A4 78
Bridgeport, Ct., U.S. E3 84
Bridgeport, Il., U.S. E6 90
Bridgeport, Mi., U.S. E7 99
Bridgeport, Ne., U.S. C2 104
Bridgeport, Oh., U.S. B5 112
Bridgeport, Pa., U.S. o20 115
Bridgeport, Tx., U.S. C4 120
Bridgeport, Wa., U.S. B6 124
Bridgeport, W.V., U.S. B4 125
Bridger, Mt., U.S. E8 103
Bridger Peak, mtn., Wy., U.S. E5 127
Bridger Range, mts., Mt., U.S. E6 103
Bridgeton, Mo., U.S. C7 102
Bridgeton, N.J., U.S. E2 107
Bridgetown, Barb. H18 64
Bridgetown, N.S., Can. E4 71
Bridgeville, De., U.S. F3 85
Bridgeville, Pa., U.S. k13 115
Bridgewater, Ma., U.S. C6 98
Bridgewater, N.J., U.S. B3 107
Bridgewater, Va., U.S. B4 123
Bridgman, Mi., U.S. G4 99
Bridgton, Me., U.S. D2 96
Bridgwater, Eng., U.K. J9 7
Bridlington, Eng., U.K. G12 7
Briec, Fr. D2 10
Brielle, N.J., U.S. C4 107
Brienne-le-Château, Fr. D11 10
Brienz, Switz. F15 10
Brig, Switz. F14 10
Brigantine, N.J., U.S. E4 107
Brigantine Beach, N.J., U.S. E4 107
Brigden, Ont., Can. E2 73
Briggs Marsh, sw., R.I., U.S. F6 116
Brigham City, Ut., U.S. B3 121
Brighton, Ont., Can. C7 73
Brighton, Eng., U.K. K12 7
Brighton, Al., U.S. B3 78
Brighton, Co., U.S. B6 83
Brighton, Il., U.S. D3 90
Brighton, Ia., U.S. C6 92
Brighton, Mi., U.S. F7 99
Brighton, N.Y., U.S. B3 109
Brighton, Tn., U.S. B2 119
Brighton Indian Reservation, Fl., U.S. E5 86
Brihuega, Spain E9 12
Brilliant, Al., U.S. A2 78
Brilliant, Oh., U.S. B5 112
Brillion, Wi., U.S. D5 126
Brilon, Ger. D8 8
Brimfield, Il., U.S. C4 90
Brindisi, Italy I12 14
Brinkley, Ar., U.S. C4 81
Brinnon, Wa., U.S. B3 124
Brioude, Fr. G10 10
Brisbane, Austl. E10 50
Briscoe, co., Tx., U.S. B2 120
Bristol, N.B., Can. C2 71
Bristol, Eng., U.K. J10 7
Bristol, Ct., U.S. C4 84
Bristol, In., U.S. A6 91
Bristol, N.H., U.S. C3 106
Bristol, R.I., U.S. D5 116
Bristol, Tn., U.S. C11 119
Bristol, Vt., U.S. C2 122
Bristol, Va., U.S. f9 123
Bristol, co., Ma., U.S. C5 98
Bristol, co., R.I., U.S. D5 116
Bristol Bay, b., Ak., U.S. D7 79
Bristol Channel, strt., U.K. J8 7
Bristol [Township], Pa., U.S. F12 115
Bristow, Ok., U.S. B5 113
British Columbia, prov., Can. C6 69
British Honduras see Belize, ctry., N.A. F3 64
British Indian Ocean Territory, dep., Afr. G17 2
British Mountains, mts., N.A. C5 66
British Solomon Islands see Solomon Islands, ctry., Oc. G23 2
Britstown, S. Afr. H4 44
Britt, Ia., U.S. A4 92
Brittany see Bretagne, hist. reg., Fr. D3 10
Britton, S.D., U.S. B8 118
Brive-la-Gaillarde, Fr. G8 10
Briviesca, Spain C8 12
Brno, Czech. F16 8
Broach, India B2 37
Broad, stm., S.C., U.S. C5 117
Broad Brook, Ct., U.S. B5 84
Broadford, Scot., U.K. D7 7
Broadkill, stm., De., U.S. E4 85
Broadkill Beach, De., U.S. E5 85
Broad Law, mtn., Scot., U.K. F9 7
Broad Run, stm., Va., U.S. g11 123
Broadus, Mt., U.S. E11 103
Broadview Heights, Oh., U.S. h9 112
Broadview Park, Fl., U.S. F6 86
Broadwater, co., Mt., U.S. D5 103
Broadway, N.C., U.S. B3 110
Broadway, Va., U.S. B4 123
Brockport, N.Y., U.S. B3 109
Brockton, Ma., U.S. B5 98
Brockton Reservoir, res., Ma., U.S. h11 98
Brockville, Ont., Can. C9 73
Brockway, Pa., U.S. D4 115
Brodeur Peninsula, pen., N.W. Ter., Can. B15 66
Brodhead, Ky., U.S. C5 94
Brodhead, Wi., U.S. F4 126
Brodheadsville, Pa., U.S. E11 115
Broken Arrow, Ok., U.S. A6 113
Broken Bow, Ne., U.S. C6 104
Broken Bow, Ok., U.S. C7 113
Broken Bow Lake, res., Ok., U.S. C7 113
Broken Hill, Austl. F8 50
Brokopondo, Sur. B8 54
Brome, Lac, l., Que., Can. D5 74
Bromptonville, Que., Can. D6 74
Bromsgrove, Eng., U.K. I10 7
Bronlund Peak, mtn., B.C., Can. E7 66
Brønnøysund, Nor. D9 6
Bronson, Mi., U.S. G5 99
Bronte, Italy L9 14
Bronx, co., N.Y., U.S. E7 109
Bronxville, N.Y., U.S. h13 109
Brook, In., U.S. C3 91
Brooke, co., W.V., U.S. A4 125
Brookfield, N.S., Can. D6 71
Brookfield, Ct., U.S. D2 84
Brookfield, Il., U.S. k9 90
Brookfield, Mo., U.S. B4 102
Brookfield, Va., U.S. B5 123
Brookfield, Wi., U.S. m11 126
Brookfield Center, Ct., U.S. D2 84
Brookhaven, Ms., U.S. D3 101
Brookhaven, W.V., U.S. h11 125
Brookings, Or., U.S. E2 114
Brookings, S.D., U.S. C9 118
Brookings, co., S.D., U.S. C9 118
Brookland, Ar., U.S. B5 81
Brooklandville, Md., U.S. g10 97
Brooklet, Ga., U.S. D5 87
Brookline, Ma., U.S. B5 98
Brooklyn, N.S., Can. E5 71
Brooklyn, Ct., U.S. B8 84
Brooklyn, In., U.S. E5 91
Brooklyn, Ia., U.S. C5 92
Brooklyn, Mi., U.S. F6 99
Brooklyn, Ms., U.S. D4 101
Brooklyn, Oh., U.S. h9 112
Brooklyn, S.C., U.S. B6 117
Brooklyn, Wi., U.S. F4 126
Brooklyn Center, Mn., U.S. E5 100
Brooklyn Park, Md., U.S. h11 97
Brooklyn Park, Mn., U.S. m12 100
Brookneal, Va., U.S. C4 123
Brook Park, Oh., U.S. h9 112
Brookport, Il., U.S. F5 90
Brooks, Alta., Can. D5 68
Brooks, Ky., U.S. g11 94
Brooks, co., Ga., U.S. F3 87
Brooks, co., Tx., U.S. F3 120
Brooks Air Force Base, mil., Tx., U.S. k7 120
Brookshire, Tx., U.S. E5 120
Brookside, Al., U.S. f7 78
Brookside, De., U.S. B3 85
Brooks Range, mts., Ak., U.S. B9 79
Brookston, In., U.S. C4 91
Brooksville, Fl., U.S. D4 86
Brooksville, Ky., U.S. B5 94
Brooksville, Ms., U.S. B5 101
Brookville, In., U.S. F8 91
Brookville, Oh., U.S. C1 112
Brookville, Pa., U.S. D3 115
Brookville Lake, res., In., U.S. E7 91
Brookwood, Al., U.S. B2 78
Brookwood, N.J., U.S. C4 107
Broomall, Pa., U.S. p20 115
Broome, Austl. C4 50
Broome, co., N.Y., U.S. C5 109
Broomfield, Co., U.S. B5 83
Broons, Fr. D4 10
Brossard, Que., Can. q20 74
Brou, Fr. D8 10
Broussard, La., U.S. D4 95
Broward, co., Fl., U.S. F6 86
Browardale, Fl., U.S. r13 86
Browerville, Mn., U.S. D4 100
Brown, co., Il., U.S. D3 90
Brown, co., In., U.S. F5 91
Brown, co., Ks., U.S. C8 93
Brown, co., Mn., U.S. F4 100
Brown, co., Ne., U.S. B6 104
Brown, co., Oh., U.S. D2 112
Brown, co., S.D., U.S. B7 118
Brown, co., Tx., U.S. D3 120
Brown, co., Wi., U.S. D6 126
Brown, Point, c., Wa., U.S. C1 124
Brown City, Mi., U.S. E8 99
Brown Deer, Wi., U.S. m12 126
Brownfield, Tx., U.S. C1 120
Browning, Mt., U.S. B3 103
Brownlee Dam, U.S. E2 89
Brownlee Reservoir, res., U.S. C10 114
Browns, stm., Vt., U.S. B2 122
Browns Branch, stm., De., U.S. E3 85
Brownsburg, Que., Can. D3 74
Brownsburg, In., U.S. E5 91
Brownsdale, Mn., U.S. G6 100
Browns Inlet, b., N.C., U.S. C5 110
Browns Mills, N.J., U.S. D3 107
Browns Peak, mtn., Az., U.S. D4 80
Brownstown, In., U.S. G5 91
Browns Valley, Mn., U.S. E2 100
Brownsville, Fl., U.S. s13 86
Brownsville, Ky., U.S. C3 94
Brownsville, Or., U.S. C4 114
Brownsville, Pa., U.S. F2 115
Brownsville, Tn., U.S. B2 119
Brownsville, Tx., U.S. G4 120
Brownton, Mn., U.S. F4 100
Brownville Junction, Me., U.S. C3 96
Brownwood, Tx., U.S. D3 120
Brownwood, Lake, res., Tx., U.S. D3 120
Broxton, Ga., U.S. E4 87
Bruay-en-Artois, Fr. B9 10
Bruce, Ms., U.S. B4 101
Bruce, Wi., U.S. C2 126
Bruce, Mount, mtn., Austl. D3 50
Bruce National Park, Ont., Can. B3 73
Bruce Peninsula, pen., Ont., Can. B3 73
Bruceton, Tn., U.S. A3 119
Bruchsal, Ger. F8 8
Bruck an der Leitha, Aus. H16 8
Bruck an der Mur, Aus. H15 8
Bruderheim, Alta., Can. C4 68
Brugge, Bel. D3 8
Bruin Point, mtn., Ut., U.S. D5 121
Brule, co., S.D., U.S. D6 118
Brule, stm., U.S. C5 126
Brule Lake, l., Mn., U.S. k9 100
Brundidge, Al., U.S. D4 78
Bruneau, stm., U.S. G3 89
Brunei, ctry., Asia E5 32
Brunico, Italy C6 14
Brunkeberg, Nor. G7 6
Bruno, Sask., Can. E3 75
Brunsbüttel, Ger. B9 8
Brunswick, Ga., U.S. E5 87
Brunswick, Me., U.S. E3 96
Brunswick, Md., U.S. B2 97
Brunswick, Mo., U.S. B4 102
Brunswick, Oh., U.S. A4 112
Brunswick, co., N.C., U.S. C4 110
Brunswick, co., Va., U.S. D5 123
Brunswick Naval Air Station, mil., Me., U.S. E3 96
Brush, Co., U.S. A7 83
Brushy Mountains, mts., N.C., U.S. B1 110
Brus Laguna, Hond. G5 64
Brusly, La., U.S. D4 95
Brussels, Ont., Can. D3 73
Brussels see Bruxelles, Bel. E4 8
Bruxelles (Brussel), Bel. E4 8
Bryan, Oh., U.S. A1 112
Bryan, Tx., U.S. D4 120
Bryan, co., Ga., U.S. D5 87
Bryan, co., Ok., U.S. D5 113
Bryans Road, Md., U.S. C3 97
Bryant, Ar., U.S. C3 81
Bryantville, Ma., U.S. B6 98
Bryce Canyon National Park, Ut., U.S. F3 121
Bryn Mawr, Wa., U.S. e11 124
Bryson City, N.C., U.S. f9 110
Brzeg, Pol. E17 8
Bsharrī, Leb. B5 40
Būbiyān, i., Kuw. C4 46
Bucaramanga, Col. D6 58
Buccaneer Archipelago, is., Austl. C4 50
Buchanan, Lib. G3 42
Buchanan, Ga., U.S. C1 87
Buchanan, Mi., U.S. G4 99
Buchanan, Va., U.S. C3 123
Buchanan, co., Ia., U.S. B6 92
Buchanan, co., Mo., U.S. B3 102
Buchanan, co., Va., U.S. e9 123
Buchan Gulf, b., N.W. Ter., Can. B18 66
Buchans, Newf., Can. D3 72
Buchara, U.S.S.R. J10 18
Bucharest see Bucureşti, Rom. E10 16
Buchholz, Ger. B9 8
Buckatunna, Ms., U.S. D5 101
Bückeburg, Ger. C9 8
Buckeye, Az., U.S. D3 80
Buckeye Lake, Oh., U.S. C3 112
Buckhannon, W.V., U.S. C4 125
Buck Hill Falls, Pa., U.S. D11 115
Buckhorn Lake, res., Ky., U.S. C6 94
Buckingham, Que., Can. D2 74
Buckingham, co., Va., U.S. C4 123
Buckley, Wa., U.S. B3 124
Bucklin, Ks., U.S. E4 93
Bucklin, Mo., U.S. B5 102
Buck Mountain, mtn., Wa., U.S. A6 124
Buckner, Mo., U.S. h11 102
Bucks, co., Pa., U.S. F11 115
Buckskin Mountains, mts., Az., U.S. C2 80
Bucksport, Me., U.S. D4 96
Bucksport, S.C., U.S. D9 117
Bucureşti (Bucharest), Rom. E10 16
Bucyrus, Oh., U.S. B3 112
Buda, Tx., U.S. D4 120
Budapest, Hung. H19 8
Budaun, India F8 38
Budd Lake, l., N.J., U.S. B3 107
Buddusò, Italy I4 14
Bude, Eng., U.K. K8 7
Bude, Ms., U.S. D3 101
Buea, Cam. H7 42
Buechel, Ky., U.S. B4 94
Buena, N.J., U.S. D3 107
Buena, Wa., U.S. C5 124
Buena Park, Ca., U.S. n12 82
Buena Vista, Bol. G6 54
Buena Vista, Co., U.S. C4 83
Buena Vista, Fl., U.S. D4 86
Buena Vista, Ga., U.S. D2 87
Buena Vista, Va., U.S. C3 123
Buena Vista, co., Ia., U.S. B2 92
Buenópolis, Braz. D6 57
Buenos Aires, Arg. C5 56
Buffalo, Ia., U.S. C7 92
Buffalo, Mn., U.S. E5 100
Buffalo, Mo., U.S. D4 102
Buffalo, N.Y., U.S. C2 109
Buffalo, Ok., U.S. A2 113
Buffalo, S.C., U.S. B4 117
Buffalo, Tx., U.S. D5 120
Buffalo, W.V., U.S. C3 125
Buffalo, Wi., U.S. D2 126
Buffalo, Wy., U.S. B6 127
Buffalo, co., Ne., U.S. D6 104
Buffalo, co., S.D., U.S. C6 118
Buffalo, co., Wi., U.S. D2 126
Buffalo, stm., Ar., U.S. B3 81
Buffalo, stm., Mn., U.S. D2 100
Buffalo, stm., Tn., U.S. B4 119
Buffalo, stm., Wi., U.S. D2 126
Buffalo Bill Reservoir, res., Wy., U.S. B3 127
Buffalo Center, Ia., U.S. A4 92
Buffalo Creek, stm., U.S. f8 125
Buffalo Creek, stm., W.V., U.S. h10 125
Buffalo Creek, stm., W.V., U.S. n12 125
Buffalo Grove, Il., U.S. h9 90
Buffalo Lake, Mn., U.S. F4 100
Buffalo Lake, l., Alta., Can. C4 68
Buffalo Lake, l., N.W. Ter., Can. D9 66
Buffalo Lake, res., Tx., U.S. B1 120
Buffalo Lake, res., Wi., U.S. E4 126
Buffumville Lake, res., Ma., U.S. B4 98
Buford, Ga., U.S. B2 87
Bug, stm., Eur. E12 4
Buga, Col. F4 58
Bugøynes, Nor. B17 6
Bugsuk Island, i., Phil. D6 32
Bugul'ma, U.S.S.R. G8 18
Buhl, Id., U.S. G4 89
Buhl, Mn., U.S. C6 100
Buhler, Ks., U.S. D6 93
Buies Creek, N.C., U.S. B4 110
Buj, U.S.S.R. C24 22
Bujalance, Spain H7 12
Bujaraloz, Spain D11 12
Bujumbura, Bdi. B5 44
Bukačača, U.S.S.R. G17 20
Bukama, Zaire C5 44
Bukavu, Zaire B5 44
Bukittinggi, Indon. F3 32
Bukoba, Tan. B6 44
Bukovina, hist. reg., Eur. B9 16
Bula, Indon. F9 32
Bulan, Ky., U.S. C6 94
Bulandshahr, India F7 38
Bulawayo, Zimb. F5 44
Buldan, Tur. K12 16
Buldāna, India B4 37
Bulgan, Mong. B5 26
Bulgaria, ctry., Eur. G12 4
Bulkley, stm., B.C., Can. B4 69
Bull Creek, stm., S.D., U.S. B2 118
Bulle, Switz. F14 10
Bullfinch, Austl. F3 50
Bullfrog Creek, stm., Ut., U.S. F5 121
Bullhead City, Az., U.S. B1 80
Bull Island, i., S.C., U.S. F8 117
Bull Island, i., S.C., U.S. D9 117
Bull Island, i., S.C., U.S. G6 117
Bullitt, co., Ky., U.S. C4 94
Bull Mountain, mtn., Mt., U.S. D4 103
Bulloch, co., Ga., U.S. D5 87
Bullock, co., Al., U.S. C4 78
Bullock Creek, Mi., U.S. E6 99
Bull Run, stm., Va., U.S. g11 123
Bullrun Rock, mtn., Or., U.S. C8 114
Bulls Bay, b., S.C., U.S. F8 117
Bulls Gap, Tn., U.S. C10 119
Bull Shoals, Ar., U.S. A3 81
Bull Shoals Lake, res., U.S. A3 81
Bully Creek Reservoir, res., Or., U.S. C9 114
Bulsār, India B2 37
Bulukumba, Indon. G7 32
Bumba, Zaire A4 44
Bumping, stm., Wa., U.S. C4 124
Buna, Tx., U.S. D6 120
Bunbury, Austl. F3 50
Buncombe, co., N.C., U.S. f10 110
Buncrana, Ire. F5 7
Bundaberg, Austl. D10 50
Būndi, India H6 38
Bundoran, Ire. G4 7
Bungo-suidō, strt., Japan I5 30
Bunia, Zaire A6 44
Bunker Hill, Il., U.S. D4 90
Bunker Hill, In., U.S. C5 91
Bunker Hill, W.V., U.S. B6 125
Bunker Hill, W.V., U.S. m12 125
Bunker Hill, mtn., Nv., U.S. D4 105
Bunkerville, Nv., U.S. G7 105
Bunkie, La., U.S. D3 95
Bunnell, Fl., U.S. C5 86
Buñol, Spain F11 12
Buntok, Indon. F5 32
Buolkalach, U.S.S.R. C17 20
Buon Me Thuot, Viet. H10 34
Buor-Chaja, Guba, b., U.S.S.R. C20 20
Buor-Chaja, Mys, c., U.S.S.R. C20 20
Bura, Kenya B7 44
Burao, Som. G4 46
Buras, La., U.S. E6 95
Buraydah, Sau. Ar. C3 46
Burbank, Ca., U.S. E4 82
Burbank, Il., U.S. k9 90
Burbank, Wa., U.S. C7 124
Burdickville, R.I., U.S. F2 116
Burdur, Tur. H14 4
Burdwān, India I12 38
Bureau, co., Il., U.S. B4 90
Bureinskij Chrebet, mts., U.S.S.R. G20 20
Bureja, stm., U.S.S.R. G20 20
Burfjord, Nor. B13 6
Burgas, Bul. G11 16
Bur Gavo, Som. B8 44
Burgaw, N.C., U.S. C5 110
Burg [bei Magdeburg], Ger. C11 8
Burgdorf, Switz. E14 10
Burgeo, Newf., Can. E3 72
Burgettstown, Pa., U.S. F1 115
Burghausen, Ger. G12 8
Burghūth, Sabkhat al-, l., Syria B7 40
Burgin, China B4 26
Burgin, Ky., U.S. C5 94
Burglengenfeld, Ger. F12 8
Burgos, Spain C8 12
Burgsteinfurt, Ger. C7 8

Name	Map Ref	Page
Burgundy see Bourgogne, hist. reg., Fr.	E11	10
Burhaniye, Tur.	J10	16
Burhānpur, India	B4	37
Burica, Punta, c., N.A.	J6	64
Burin, Newf., Can.	E4	72
Burin Peninsula, pen., Newf., Can.	E4	72
Buriram, Thai.	G7	34
Burjasot, Spain	F11	12
Burkburnett, Tx., U.S.	B3	120
Burke, S.D., U.S.	D6	118
Burke, co., Ga., U.S.	C4	87
Burke, co., N.C., U.S.	B1	110
Burke, co., N.D., U.S.	A3	111
Burke Channel, strt., B.C., Can.	C4	69
Burkesville, Ky., U.S.	D4	94
Burketown, Austl.	C7	50
Burkina Faso, ctry., Afr.	F5	42
Burk's Falls, Ont., Can.	B5	73
Burleigh, co., N.D., U.S.	C5	111
Burleson, Tx., U.S.	n9	120
Burleson, co., Tx., U.S.	D4	120
Burley, Id., U.S.	G5	89
Burlingame, Ca., U.S.	h8	82
Burlingame, Ks., U.S.	D8	93
Burlington, Ont., Can.	D5	73
Burlington, Co., U.S.	B8	83
Burlington, Ia., U.S.	D6	92
Burlington, Ks., U.S.	D8	93
Burlington, Ky., U.S.	A5	94
Burlington, Ma., U.S.	f11	98
Burlington, N.J., U.S.	C3	107
Burlington, N.C., U.S.	A3	110
Burlington, N.D., U.S.	A4	111
Burlington, Vt., U.S.	C2	122
Burlington, Wa., U.S.	A3	124
Burlington, Wi., U.S.	F5	126
Burlington, co., N.J., U.S.	D3	107
Burlington Beach, In., U.S.	B3	91
Burlington Junction, Mo., U.S.	A2	102
Burma, ctry., Asia	A2	32
Burnaby, B.C., Can.	E6	69
Burnet, Tx., U.S.	D3	120
Burnet, co., Tx., U.S.	D3	120
Burnett, co., Wi., U.S.	C1	126
Burney, Ca., U.S.	B3	82
Burnham, Pa., U.S.	E6	115
Burnie, Austl.	H9	50
Burns, Or., U.S.	D7	114
Burns, Tn., U.S.	A4	119
Burns, Wy., U.S.	E8	127
Burns Flat, Ok., U.S.	B2	113
Burnside, Ky., U.S.	D5	94
Burns Lake, B.C., Can.	B5	69
Burns Paiute Indian Reservation, Or., U.S.	D7	114
Burnsville, Mn., U.S.	F5	100
Burnsville, Ms., U.S.	A5	101
Burnsville, N.C., U.S.	f10	110
Burnsville Lake, res., W.V., U.S.	C4	125
Burnt Islands, Newf., Can.	E2	72
Burnt Mills, Lake, l., Va., U.S.	k14	123
Burntside Lake, l., Mn., U.S.	C6	100
Burntwood, stm., Man., Can.	B2	70
Burravoe, Scot., U.K.	A11	7
Burr Oak, Mi., U.S.	G5	99
Burr Oak Reservoir, res., Oh., U.S.	C3	112
Burrton, Ks., U.S.	D6	93
Bursa, Tur.	G13	4
Būr Sa'īd (Port Said), Egypt	B12	42
Būr Sūdān (Port Sudan), Sudan	E13	42
Burt, co., Ne., U.S.	C9	104
Burt Lake, l., Mi., U.S.	C6	99
Burton, Mi., U.S.	E7	99
Burton, Oh., U.S.	A4	112
Burton upon Trent, Eng., U.K.	I11	7
Burtts Corner, N.B., Can.	C3	71
Buru, i., Indon.	F8	32
Burundi, ctry., Afr.	B5	44
Burwell, Ne., U.S.	C6	104
Burwick, Scot., U.K.	C10	7
Bury Saint Edmunds, Eng., U.K.	I13	7
Busalla, Italy	E3	14
Buşayrah, Syria	B7	40
Bushnell, Fl., U.S.	D4	86
Bushnell, Il., U.S.	C3	90
Bush River, b., Md., U.S.	B5	97
Buşrá ash-Shām, Syria	C5	40
Busselton, Austl.	F3	50
Busto Arsizio, Italy	D3	14
Busuanga Island, i., Phil.	C7	32
Buta, Zaire	H10	42
Butare, Rw.	B5	44
Butehaqi, China	B11	26
Bute Inlet, b., B.C., Can.	D5	69
Butler, Al., U.S.	C1	78
Butler, Ga., U.S.	D2	87
Butler, In., U.S.	B8	91
Butler, Ky., U.S.	B5	94
Butler, Mo., U.S.	C3	102
Butler, N.J., U.S.	B4	107
Butler, Oh., U.S.	B3	112
Butler, Pa., U.S.	E2	115
Butler, Wi., U.S.	m11	126
Butler, co., Al., U.S.	D3	78
Butler, co., Ia., U.S.	B5	92
Butler, co., Ks., U.S.	E7	93
Butler, co., Ky., U.S.	C3	94
Butler, co., Mo., U.S.	E7	102
Butler, co., Ne., U.S.	C8	104
Butler, co., Oh., U.S.	C1	112
Butler, co., Pa., U.S.	E2	115
Butner, N.C., U.S.	A4	110
Buttahatchee, stm., U.S.	B5	101
Butte, Mt., U.S.	E4	103
Butte, co., Ca., U.S.	C3	82
Butte, co., Id., U.S.	F5	89
Butte, co., S.D., U.S.	C2	118
Butte des Morts, Lake, l., Wi., U.S.	D5	126
Butte Mountains, mts., Nv., U.S.	D6	105
Butternut Lake, l., Wi., U.S.	C5	126
Butterworth, Malay.	L6	34
Butt of Lewis, c., Scot., U.K.	C6	7
Buttonwillow, Ca., U.S.	E4	82
Butts, co., Ga., U.S.	C3	87
Butuan, Phil.	D8	32
Butung, Pulau, i., Indon.	F7	32
Bützow, Ger.	B11	8
Buxtehude, Ger.	B9	8
Buxton, N.C., U.S.	B7	110
Büyükmenderes, stm., Tur.	L11	16
Buzançais, Fr.	F8	10
Buzău, Rom.	D10	16
Búzi, stm., Moz.	F6	44
Buzuluk, U.S.S.R.	G8	18
Buzzards Bay, Ma., U.S.	C6	98
Buzzards Bay, b., Ma., U.S.	C6	98
Byam Channel, strt., N.W. Ter., Can.	A11	66
Byam Martin Island, i., N.W. Ter., Can.	A12	66
Bydgoszcz, Pol.	B18	8
Byelorussia see Belorusskaja Sovetskaja Socialističeskaja Respublika, state, U.S.S.R.	G3	18
Byers, Co., U.S.	B6	83
Byesville, Oh., U.S.	C4	112
Byhalia, Ms., U.S.	A4	101
Bylas, Az., U.S.	D5	80
Bylot Island, i., N.W. Ter., Can.	B17	66
Byng, Ok., U.S.	C5	113
Byrdstown, Tn., U.S.	C8	119
Byron, Ga., U.S.	D3	87
Byron, Il., U.S.	A4	90
Byron, Mn., U.S.	F6	100
Byron, Wy., U.S.	B4	127
Byrranga, Gory, mts., U.S.S.R.	B14	20
Bytantaj, stm., U.S.S.R.	D20	20
Bytom (Beuthen), Pol.	E18	8
Byxelkrok, Swe.	H11	6
C		
Caacupé, Para.	B5	56
Cabaiguán, Cuba	C8	64
Caballo Mountains, mts., N.M., U.S.	E2	108
Caballo Reservoir, res., N.M., U.S.	E2	108
Cabanatuan, Phil.	q19	32
Cabano, Que., Can.	B9	74
Cabarrus, co., N.C., U.S.	B2	110
Cabbage Swamp, sw., Fl., U.S.	m9	86
Cabell, co., W.V., U.S.	C2	125
Cabeza del Buey, Spain	G6	12
Cabimas, Ven.	B7	58
Cabin Creek, W.V., U.S.	m13	125
Cabin Creek, stm., W.V., U.S.	m13	125
Cabinda, Ang.	C2	44
Cabinda, dept., Ang.	C2	44
Cabinet Gorge Reservoir, res., U.S.	B1	103
Cabinet Mountains, mts., Mt., U.S.	B1	103
Cabin John, Md., U.S.	C3	97
Cabo Frio, Braz.	G7	57
Cabonga, Réservoir, res., Que., Can.	k11	74
Cabool, Mo., U.S.	D5	102
Caborca, Mex.	B3	62
Cabot, Ar., U.S.	C3	81
Cabot, Mount, mtn., N.H., U.S.	A4	106
Cabot Head, c., Ont., Can.	B3	73
Cabot Strait, strt., Can.	G21	66
Cabra, Spain	H7	12
Cabri, Sask., Can.	G1	75
Cabrillo National Monument, Ca., U.S.	o15	82
Cabrobó, Braz.	E11	54
Cabruta, Ven.	D9	58
Caçador, Braz.	B6	56
Čačak, Yugo.	F4	16
Cacapon, stm., W.V., U.S.	B6	125
Cáceres, Braz.	G7	54
Cáceres, Col.	D5	58
Cáceres, Spain	F5	12
Cache, Ok., U.S.	C3	113
Cache, co., Ut., U.S.	B4	121
Cache, stm., Ar., U.S.	C4	81
Cache, stm., Il., U.S.	F4	90
Cache Bay, Ont., Can.	A5	73
Cache Creek, B.C., Can.	D7	69
Cache la Poudre, stm., Co., U.S.	A5	83
Cache Mountain, mtn., Ak., U.S.	B10	79
Cache Peak, mtn., Id., U.S.	G5	89
Cachimbo, Serra do, mts., Braz.	E7	54
Cachoeira, Braz.	B9	57
Cachoeira do Sul, Braz.	C6	56
Cachoeiro de Itapemirim, Braz.	F8	57
Cacólo, Ang.	D3	44
Caconda, Ang.	D3	44
Cactus Flat, pl., Nv., U.S.	F5	105
Cactus Peak, mtn., Nv., U.S.	F5	105
Caddo, Ok., U.S.	C5	113
Caddo, co., La., U.S.	B2	95
Caddo, co., Ok., U.S.	B3	113
Caddo, stm., Ar., U.S.	C2	81
Caddo Creek, stm., Ok., U.S.	C4	113
Caddo Lake, res., U.S.	B2	95
Cader Idris, mtn., Wales, U.K.	I9	7
Cadillac, Fr.	H6	10
Cadillac, Mi., U.S.	D5	99
Cadillac Mountain, mtn., Me., U.S.	D4	96
Cádiz, Spain	I5	12
Cadiz, Ky., U.S.	D2	94
Cadiz, Oh., U.S.	B4	112
Cádiz, Golfo de, b., Eur.	I4	12
Cadott, Wi., U.S.	D2	126
Caen, Fr.	C6	10
Caernarvon, Wales, U.K.	H8	7
Caesar Creek Lake, res., Oh., U.S.	C2	112
Caeté, Braz.	E7	57
Cagayan de Oro, Phil.	D7	32
Cagayan Islands, is., Phil.	D7	32
Čagda, U.S.S.R.	F20	20
Cagles Mill Lake, res., In., U.S.	F4	91
Cagli, Italy	F7	14
Cagliari, Italy	J4	14
Caguas, P.R.	E14	64
Cahaba, stm., Al., U.S.	C2	78
Caha Mountains, mts., Ire.	J3	7
Cahirciveen, Ire.	J2	7
Cahokia, Il., U.S.	E3	90
Cahore Point, c., Ire.	I6	7
Cahors, Fr.	H8	10
Caiapó, Serra, mts., Braz.	D2	57
Caibarién, Cuba	C8	64
Caicara, Ven.	D9	58
Caicos Islands, is., T./C. Is.	D12	64
Caicos Passage, strt., N.A.	C11	64
Caillou Bay, b., La., U.S.	E5	95
Caillou Lake, l., La., U.S.	E5	95
Cairnbrook, Pa., U.S.	F4	115
Cairngorm Mountains, mts., Scot., U.K.	D9	7
Cairns, Austl.	C9	50
Cairo, Ga., U.S.	F2	87
Cairo, Il., U.S.	F4	90
Cairo, Ne., U.S.	D7	104
Cairo see Al-Qāhirah, Egypt	B12	42
Caiundo, Ang.	E3	44
Cajamarca, Peru	E3	54
Cajàzeiras, Braz.	E11	54
Čakovec, Yugo.	C11	14
Calabar, Nig.	H7	42
Calabozo, Ven.	C9	58
Calahorra, Spain	C10	12
Calais, Fr.	B8	10
Calais, Me., U.S.	C5	96
Calais, Pas de (Strait of Dover), strt., Eur.	K14	7
Calamar, Col.	B5	58
Calamian Group, is., Phil.	C6	32
Calamocha, Spain	E10	12
Calamus, stm., Ne., U.S.	B6	104
Calanda, Spain	E11	12
Calapan, Phil.	r19	33b
Călăraşi, Rom.	E11	16
Calatayud, Spain	D10	12
Calaveras, co., Ca., U.S.	C3	82
Calcasieu, co., La., U.S.	D2	95
Calcasieu, stm., La., U.S.	D2	95
Calcasieu Lake, l., La., U.S.	E2	95
Calcasieu Pass, strt., La., U.S.	E2	95
Calçoene, Braz.	C8	54
Calcutta, India	I13	38
Calcutta, Oh., U.S.	B5	112
Calcutta Lake, l., Nv., U.S.	B2	105
Caldas da Rainha, Port.	F2	12
Calderwood, Tn., U.S.	D10	119
Caldron Falls Reservoir, res., Wi., U.S.	C5	126
Caldwell, Id., U.S.	F2	89
Caldwell, Ks., U.S.	E6	93
Caldwell, N.J., U.S.	B4	107
Caldwell, Oh., U.S.	C4	112
Caldwell, Tx., U.S.	D4	120
Caldwell, co., Ky., U.S.	C2	94
Caldwell, co., La., U.S.	B3	95
Caldwell, co., Mo., U.S.	B3	102
Caldwell, co., N.C., U.S.	B1	110
Caldwell, co., Tx., U.S.	E4	120
Caledon, Ont., Can.	D5	73
Caledonia, Mi., U.S.	F5	99
Caledonia, Mn., U.S.	G7	100
Caledonia, Ms., U.S.	B5	101
Caledonia, N.Y., U.S.	C3	109
Caledonia, co., Vt., U.S.	C4	122
Calera, Al., U.S.	B3	78
Calera, Ok., U.S.	D5	113
Calexico, Ca., U.S.	F6	82
Calgary, Alta., Can.	D3	68
Calhoun, Ga., U.S.	B2	87
Calhoun, Ky., U.S.	C2	94
Calhoun, co., Al., U.S.	B4	78
Calhoun, co., Ar., U.S.	D3	81
Calhoun, co., Fl., U.S.	B1	86
Calhoun, co., Ga., U.S.	E2	87
Calhoun, co., Il., U.S.	D3	90
Calhoun, co., Ia., U.S.	B3	92
Calhoun, co., Mi., U.S.	F5	99
Calhoun, co., Ms., U.S.	B4	101
Calhoun, co., S.C., U.S.	D6	117
Calhoun, co., Tx., U.S.	E4	120
Calhoun, co., W.V., U.S.	C3	125
Calhoun City, Ms., U.S.	B4	101
Calhoun Falls, S.C., U.S.	C2	117
Cali, Col.	F4	58
Calico Rock, Ar., U.S.	A3	81
Calicut, India	G3	37
Caliente, Nv., U.S.	F7	105
California, Mo., U.S.	C5	102
California, Pa., U.S.	F2	115
California, state, U.S.	D4	82
California, Golfo de, b., Mex.	D4	62
California Aqueduct, Ca., U.S.	E4	82
Calimere, Point, c., India	G5	37
Calipatria, Ca., U.S.	F6	82
Calispell Peak, mtn., Wa., U.S.	A8	124
Calistoga, Ca., U.S.	C2	82
Calitri, Italy	I10	14
Callac, Fr.	D3	10
Callaghan, Mount, mtn., Nv., U.S.	D5	105
Callahan, co., Tx., U.S.	C3	120
Callao, Peru	F3	54
Callaway, co., Mo., U.S.	C6	102
Calling Lake, l., Alta., Can.	B4	68
Callosa de Ensarriá, Spain	G11	12
Calloway, co., Ky., U.S.	f9	94
Calmar, Alta., Can.	C4	68
Calmar, Ia., U.S.	A6	92
Caloosahatchee, stm., Fl., U.S.	F5	86
Caltagirone, Italy	L9	14
Caltanissetta, Italy	L9	14
Calumet, Que., Can.	D3	74
Calumet, Mi., U.S.	A2	99
Calumet, co., Wi., U.S.	D5	126
Calumet, Lake, l., Il., U.S.	k9	90
Calumet City, Il., U.S.	B6	90
Calunda, Ang.	D4	44
Calvert, Tx., U.S.	D4	120
Calvert, co., Md., U.S.	C4	97
Calvert City, Ky., U.S.	e9	94
Calverton, Md., U.S.	B4	97
Calverton Park, Mo., U.S.	f13	102
Calvinia, S. Afr.	H3	44
Camacho, Mex.	E8	62
Camacupa, Ang.	D3	44
Camaguán, Ven.	C9	58
Camagüey, Cuba	D9	64
Camaná, Peru	G4	54
Camanche, Ia., U.S.	C7	92
Camano Island, i., Wa., U.S.	A3	124
Camapuã, Braz.	E1	57
Camaquã, Braz.	C6	56
Camas, Spain	H5	12
Camas, Wa., U.S.	D3	124
Camas, co., Id., U.S.	F4	89
Ca Mau, Viet.	J8	34
Cambados, Spain	C3	12
Cambay, India	I5	38
Cambodia (Kampuchea), ctry., Asia	C3	32
Cambrai, Fr.	B10	10
Cambria, Ca., U.S.	E3	82
Cambria, Wi., U.S.	E4	126
Cambria, co., Pa., U.S.	E4	115
Cambrian Mountains, mts., Wales, U.K.	I9	7
Cambridge, Ont., Can.	D4	73
Cambridge, Eng., U.K.	I13	7
Cambridge, Il., U.S.	B3	90
Cambridge, Ia., U.S.	C4	92
Cambridge, Md., U.S.	C5	97
Cambridge, Ma., U.S.	B5	98
Cambridge, Mn., U.S.	E5	100
Cambridge, Ne., U.S.	D5	104
Cambridge, N.Y., U.S.	B7	109
Cambridge, Oh., U.S.	B4	112
Cambridge, Wi., U.S.	E4	126
Cambridge Bay, N.W. Ter., Can.	C11	66
Cambridge City, In., U.S.	E7	91
Cambridge Reservoir, res., Ma., U.S.	g10	98
Cambridge Springs, Pa., U.S.	C1	115
Cambuci, Braz.	F8	57
Camden, Al., U.S.	D2	78
Camden, Ar., U.S.	D3	81
Camden, De., U.S.	D3	85
Camden, In., U.S.	C4	91
Camden, Me., U.S.	D3	96
Camden, N.J., U.S.	D2	107
Camden, N.Y., U.S.	B5	109
Camden, Oh., U.S.	C1	112
Camden, S.C., U.S.	C6	117
Camden, Tn., U.S.	A3	119
Camden, co., Ga., U.S.	F5	87
Camden, co., Mo., U.S.	C5	102
Camden, co., N.J., U.S.	D3	107
Camden, co., N.C., U.S.	A6	110
Camdenton, Mo., U.S.	D5	102
Camelback Mountain, mtn., Az., U.S.	k9	80
Cameron, Az., U.S.	B4	80
Cameron, La., U.S.	E2	95
Cameron, Mo., U.S.	B3	102
Cameron, Tx., U.S.	D4	120
Cameron, W.V., U.S.	B4	125
Cameron, Wi., U.S.	C2	126
Cameron, co., La., U.S.	E2	95
Cameron, co., Pa., U.S.	D5	115
Cameron, co., Tx., U.S.	F4	120
Cameron Highlands, Malay.	L6	34
Cameron Hills, hills, Can.	E9	66
Cameroon, ctry., Afr.	G8	42
Cameroon Mountain, mtn., Cam.	H7	42
Cametá, Braz.	D9	54
Camilla, Ga., U.S.	E2	87
Camino, Ca., U.S.	C3	82
Camiranga, Braz.	D9	54
Camissombo, Ang.	C4	44
Cam Lo, Viet.	F9	34
Cammack Village, Ar., U.S.	C3	81
Camooweal, Austl.	C7	50
Camorta Island, i., India	J2	34
Camp, co., Tx., U.S.	C5	120
Campana, Isla, i., Chile	F1	56
Campanero, Cerro, mtn., Ven.	E10	58
Campbell, Ca., U.S.	k8	82
Campbell, Fl., U.S.	D5	86
Campbell, Mo., U.S.	E7	102
Campbell, Oh., U.S.	A5	112
Campbell, co., Ky., U.S.	B5	94
Campbell, co., S.D., U.S.	B5	118
Campbell, co., Tn., U.S.	C9	119
Campbell, co., Va., U.S.	C3	123
Campbell, co., Wy., U.S.	B7	127
Campbellford, Ont., Can.	C7	73
Campbell Hill, hill, Oh., U.S.	B2	112
Campbell Lake, l., Or., U.S.	E7	114
Campbellsburg, In., U.S.	G5	91
Campbellsburg, Ky., U.S.	B4	94
Campbells Creek, stm., W.V., U.S.	m13	125
Campbellsport, Wi., U.S.	E5	126
Campbellsville, Ky., U.S.	C4	94
Campbellton, N.B., Can.	A3	71
Campbellton, Newf., Can.	D4	72
Campbeltown, Scot., U.K.	F7	7
Campeche, Mex.	H14	62
Campeche, Bahía de, b., Mex.	H13	62
Camperville, Man., Can.	D1	70
Camp Hill, Al., U.S.	C4	78
Camp Hill, Pa., U.S.	F8	115
Camp H. M. Smith Marine Corps Base, mil., Hi., U.S.	g10	88
Camp Howard Ridge, mtn., Id., U.S.	D2	89
Campina Grande, Braz.	E11	54
Campinas, Braz.	G5	57
Camp Lejeune Marine Corps Base, mil., N.C., U.S.	C5	110
Campoalegre, Col.	F5	58
Campo Alegre de Goiás, Braz.	D5	57
Campobasso, Italy	H9	14
Campobello Island, i., N.B., Can.	E3	71
Campo Belo, Braz.	F6	57
Campo de Criptana, Spain	F8	12
Campo de la Cruz, Col.	B5	58
Campo Grande, Braz.	F1	57
Campo Maior, Braz.	D10	54
Campos, Braz.	F8	57
Campos do Jordão, Braz.	G6	57
Camp Pendleton Marine Corps Base, mil., Ca., U.S.	F5	82
Camp Point, Il., U.S.	C2	90
Camp Springs, Md., U.S.	f9	97
Campti, La., U.S.	C2	95
Campton, N.H., U.S.	C3	106
Camp Verde, Az., U.S.	C4	80
Camp Verde Indian Reservation, Az., U.S.	C4	80
Cam Ranh, Viet.	I10	34
Camrose, Alta., Can.	C4	68
Canaan, Ct., U.S.	A2	84
Canaan, N.H., U.S.	C2	106
Canaan, stm., N.B., Can.	C4	71
Canada, ctry., N.A.	D14	66
Canada Bay, b., Newf., Can.	C3	72
Canada Falls Lake, res., Me., U.S.	C2	96
Canadensis, Pa., U.S.	D11	115
Canadian, Tx., U.S.	B2	120
Canadian, co., Ok., U.S.	B3	113
Canadian, stm., U.S.	D6	76
Canajoharie, N.Y., U.S.	C6	109
Çanakkale, Tur.	G13	4
Çanakkale Boğazı (Dardanelles), strt., Tur.	I10	16
Canal Flats, B.C., Can.	D10	69
Canal Fulton, Oh., U.S.	B4	112
Canal Winchester, Oh., U.S.	C3	112
Canandaigua, N.Y., U.S.	C3	109
Canandaigua Lake, l., N.Y., U.S.	C3	109
Cananea, Mex.	B4	62
Cañar, Ec.	I3	58
Canarias, Islas (Canary Islands), is., Spain	C2	42
Canary Islands see Canarias, Islas, is., Spain	C2	42
Cañas, C.R.	I5	64
Canastota, N.Y., U.S.	B5	109
Canaveral, Cape, c., Fl., U.S.	D6	86
Canaveral National Seashore, Fl., U.S.	D6	86
Canavieiras, Braz.	C9	57
Canberra, Austl.	G9	50
Canby, Mn., U.S.	F2	100
Canby, Or., U.S.	B4	114
Cancale, Fr.	D5	10
Cancon, Fr.	H7	10
Cancún, Mex.	G16	62
Candeleda, Spain	E6	12
Candiac, Que., Can.	q19	74
Candle Lake, l., Sask., Can.	D3	75
Candler, co., Ga., U.S.	D4	87
Candlewood, Lake, l., Ct., U.S.	D1	84
Candlewood Isle, Ct., U.S.	D2	84
Candlewood Shores, Ct., U.S.	D2	84
Cando, N.D., U.S.	A6	111
Candor, N.C., U.S.	B3	110
Cane, stm., La., U.S.	C2	95
Cañete, Spain	E10	12
Caney, Ks., U.S.	E8	93
Caney, stm., Ok., U.S.	A5	113
Caney Creek, stm., Tx., U.S.	r14	120
Caney Fork, stm., Tn., U.S.	C8	119
Canfield, Oh., U.S.	A5	112
Canfranc, Spain	C11	12
Cangas de Onís, Spain	B6	12
Cangombe, Ang.	D3	44
Canguçu, Braz.	C6	56
Cangzhou, China	D10	26
Caniapiscau, stm., Que., Can.	g13	74
Caniapiscau, Lac, l., Que., Can.	F19	66
Canicattì, Italy	L8	14
Canistear Reservoir, res., N.J., U.S.	A4	107
Canisteo, N.Y., U.S.	C3	109
Canisteo, stm., N.Y., U.S.	C3	109
Canistota, S.D., U.S.	D8	118
Cañitas, Mex.	F8	62
Çankırı, Tur.	G14	4
Canmore, Alta., Can.	D3	68
Cannanore, India	G3	37
Cannelton, In., U.S.	I4	91
Cannes, Fr.	I14	10
Canning, N.S., Can.	D5	71
Cannon, co., Tn., U.S.	B5	119
Cannon, stm., Mn., U.S.	F5	100
Cannon Air Force Base, mil., N.M., U.S.	C6	108
Cannonball, stm., N.D., U.S.	C5	111
Cannon Beach, Or., U.S.	B3	114
Cannondale, Ct., U.S.	E2	84
Cannon Falls, Mn., U.S.	F6	100
Cannonsburg, Ky., U.S.	B7	94
Cannonsville Reservoir, res., N.Y., U.S.	C5	109
Canon, Ga., U.S.	B3	87
Canon City, Co., U.S.	C5	83
Canonsburg, Pa., U.S.	F1	115
Canosa [di Puglia], Italy	H11	14
Cantábrica, Cordillera, mts., Spain	B7	12
Cantalejo, Spain	D8	12
Cantanhede, Port.	E3	12
Cantaura, Ven.	C10	58
Canterbury, Eng., U.K.	J14	7
Canterbury, De., U.S.	D3	85
Canterbury Bight, N.Z.	F3	52
Can Tho, Viet.	I8	34
Canton, Ct., U.S.	B4	84
Canton, Ga., U.S.	B2	87
Canton, Il., U.S.	C3	90
Canton, Ks., U.S.	D6	93
Canton, Ma., U.S.	B5	98
Canton, Ms., U.S.	C3	101
Canton, Mo., U.S.	A6	102
Canton, N.Y., U.S.	f9	109
Canton, N.C., U.S.	f10	110
Canton, Oh., U.S.	B4	112
Canton, Ok., U.S.	A3	113
Canton, Pa., U.S.	C8	115
Canton, S.D., U.S.	D9	118
Canton, Tx., U.S.	C5	120
Canton see Guangzhou, China	L2	28
Canton Lake, res., Ok., U.S.	A3	113

Name — Map Ref — Page

Cantonment, Fl., U.S. u14 86
Cantù, Italy D4 14
Canutillo, Tx., U.S. o11 120
Canyon, Tx., U.S. B2 120
Canyon, co., Id., U.S. F2 89
Canyon City, Or., U.S. C8 114
Canyon de Chelly National Monument, Az., U.S. A6 80
Canyon Ferry Lake, res., Mt., U.S. D5 103
Canyon Lake, Tx., U.S. E3 120
Canyon Lake, res., Tx., U.S. E3 120
Canyonlands National Park, Ut., U.S. E6 121
Canyonville, Or., U.S. E3 114
Cao Bang, Viet. C9 34
Capac, Mi., U.S. F8 99
Cap-à-l'Aigle, Que., Can. B7 74
Cap-aux-Meules, Que., Can. B8 71
Cap-de-la-Madeleine, Que., Can. C5 74
Cape Breton Highlands National Park, N.S., Can. C9 71
Cape Breton Island, i., N.S., Can. C9 71
Cape Broyle, Newf., Can. E5 72
Cape Canaveral, Fl., U.S. D6 86
Cape Charles, Va., U.S. C6 123
Cape Coast, Ghana G5 42
Cape Cod Bay, b., Ma., U.S. C7 98
Cape Cod Canal, Ma., U.S. C6 98
Cape Cod National Seashore, Ma., U.S. C7 98
Cape Coral, Fl., U.S. F5 86
Cape Dorset, N.W. Ter., Can. D17 66
Cape Elizabeth, Me., U.S. E2 96
Cape Fear, stm., N.C., U.S. C4 110
Cape Girardeau, Mo., U.S. D8 102
Cape Girardeau, co., Mo., U.S. D8 102
Cape Hatteras National Seashore, N.C., U.S. B7 110
Cape Horn Mountain, mtn., Id., U.S. E3 89
Cape Island, i., S.C., U.S. E9 117
Cape Lookout National Seashore, N.C., U.S. C6 110
Cape May, N.J., U.S. F3 107
Cape May, co., N.J., U.S. E3 107
Cape May Court House, N.J., U.S. E3 107
Capers Inlet, b., S.C., U.S. k12 117
Capers Island, i., S.C., U.S. F8 117
Capers Island, i., S.C., U.S. G6 117
Cape Sable Island, i., N.S., Can. F4 71
Cape Town (Kaapstad), S. Afr. H3 44
Cape Verde, ctry., Afr. E11 2
Cape York Peninsula, pen., Austl. B8 50
Cap-Haïtien, Haiti E11 64
Capim, stm., Braz. D9 54
Capitan, N.M., U.S. D4 108
Capitan Mountains, mts., N.M., U.S. D4 108
Capitan Peak, mtn., N.M., U.S. D4 108
Capitol Heights, Ia., U.S. e8 92
Capitol Heights, Md., U.S. C4 97
Capitol Peak, mtn., Nv., U.S. B4 105
Capitol Reef National Park, Ut., U.S. E4 121
Čapljina, Yugo. F12 14
Cap-Pelé, N.B., Can. C5 71
Capreol, Ont., Can. p19 73
Capri, Italy I9 14
Caprivi Strip, hist. reg., Nmb. E4 44
Cap-Rouge, Que., Can. n17 74
Cap-Saint-Ignace, Que., Can. B7 74
Captain Cook, Hi., U.S. D6 88
Captieux, Fr. H6 10
Captiva, Fl., U.S. F4 86
Captiva Island, i., Fl., U.S. F4 86
Capua, Italy H9 14
Capulin Volcano National Monument, N.M., U.S. A6 108
Caquetá (Japurá), stm., S.A. D5 54
Čara, U.S.S.R. F17 20
Čara, stm., U.S.S.R. F17 20
Caracaraí, Braz. C6 54
Caracas, Ven. B9 58
Carajás, Serra dos, mts., Braz. E8 54
Carangola, Braz. F7 57
Caraquet, N.B., Can. B5 71
Caratasca, Laguna de, b., Hond. G6 64
Caratinga, Braz. E7 57
Carauari, Braz. D5 54
Caravaca, Spain G10 12
Caravelas, Braz. D9 57
Caraway, Ar., U.S. B5 81
Carballo, Spain B3 12
Carberry, Man., Can. E2 70
Carbon, co., Mt., U.S. E7 103
Carbon, co., Pa., U.S. E10 115
Carbon, co., Ut., U.S. D5 121
Carbon, co., Wy., U.S. E5 127
Carbondale, Co., U.S. B3 83
Carbondale, Il., U.S. F4 90
Carbondale, Ks., U.S. D8 93
Carbondale, Pa., U.S. C10 115
Carbonear, Newf., Can. E5 72
Carboneras de Guadazaon, Spain F10 12
Carbon Hill, Al., U.S. B2 78
Carbonia, Italy J3 14
Carcagente, Spain F11 12
Carcassonne, Fr. I9 10
Carcross, Yukon, Can. D6 66
Cárdenas, Cuba C7 64
Cárdenas, Mex. F10 62
Cardiff, Wales, U.K. J9 7
Cardigan, Wales, U.K. I8 7
Cardigan Bay, b., P.E.I., Can. C7 71
Cardigan Bay, b., Wales, U.K. I8 7
Cardinal, Ont., Can. C9 73
Cardington, Oh., U.S. B3 112
Cardston, Alta., Can. E4 68
Cardwell, Mo., U.S. E7 102
Čardžou, U.S.S.R. J10 18
Carencro, La., U.S. D3 95
Carentan, Fr. C5 10
Caretta, W.V., U.S. D3 125
Carey, Id., U.S. F5 89
Carey, Oh., U.S. B2 112
Carey, Lake, l., Austl. E4 50
Caribbean Sea G10 64
Cariboo Mountains, mts., B.C., Can. C7 69
Caribou, Me., U.S. B5 96
Caribou, co., Id., U.S. G7 89
Caribou Island, i., N.S., Can. D7 71
Caribou Lake, l., Me., U.S. C3 96
Caribou Mountain, mtn., Id., U.S. F7 89
Caribou Mountains, mts., Alta., Can. f7 68
Caribou Range, mts., Id., U.S. F7 89
Carignan, Fr. C12 10
Cariñena, Spain D10 12
Carinhanha, Braz. C7 57
Carini, Italy K8 14
Caripito, Ven. B11 58
Carl Blackwell, Lake, res., Ok., U.S. A4 113
Carleton, Mi., U.S. F7 99
Carleton, Mount, mtn., N.B., Can. B3 71
Carleton Place, Ont., Can. B8 73
Carlin, Nv., U.S. C5 105
Carlinville, Il., U.S. D4 90
Carlisle, Eng., U.K. G10 7
Carlisle, Ar., U.S. C4 81
Carlisle, In., U.S. G3 91
Carlisle, Ia., U.S. C4 92
Carlisle, Ky., U.S. B5 94
Carlisle, Oh., U.S. C1 112
Carlisle, Pa., U.S. F7 115
Carlisle, co., Ky., U.S. f8 94
Carl Junction, Mo., U.S. D3 102
Carlow, Ire. I6 7
Carlsbad, Ca., U.S. F5 82
Carlsbad, N.M., U.S. E5 108
Carlsbad Caverns National Park, N.M., U.S. E5 108
Carlstadt, N.J., U.S. h8 107
Carlton, Mn., U.S. D6 100
Carlton, Or., U.S. B3 114
Carlton, co., Mn., U.S. D6 100
Carlyle, Il., U.S. E4 90
Carlyle Lake, res., Il., U.S. E4 90
Carmacks, Yukon, Can. D5 66
Carmagnola, Italy E2 14
Carman, Man., Can. E2 70
Carmanville, Newf., Can. D4 72
Carmarthen, Wales, U.K. J8 7
Carmaux, Fr. H9 10
Carmel, Ca., U.S. D3 82
Carmel, In., U.S. E5 91
Carmel, N.Y., U.S. D7 109
Carmel Head, c., Wales, U.K. H8 7
Carmen, Isla, i., Mex. E4 62
Carmen, Isla del, i., Mex. H14 62
Carmen de Patagones, Arg. E4 56
Carmi, Il., U.S. E5 90
Carmi, Lake, l., Vt., U.S. B3 122
Carmona, Spain H6 12
Carnarvon, Austl. D2 50
Carnarvon, S. Afr. H4 44
Carnation, Wa., U.S. B4 124
Carndonagh, Ire. F5 7
Carnegie, Ok., U.S. B3 113
Carnegie, Pa., U.S. F1 115
Carnegie, Lake, l., Austl. E4 50
Carneys Point, N.J., U.S. D2 107
Carniche, Alpi, mts., Eur. C8 14
Car Nicobar Island, i., India J2 34
Carnsore Point, c., Ire. I6 7
Caro, Mi., U.S. E7 99
Carol City, Fl., U.S. s13 86
Caroleen, N.C., U.S. B1 110
Carolina, Braz. E9 54
Carolina, Col. D5 58
Carolina, R.I., U.S. F2 116
Carolina, W.V., U.S. k10 125
Carolina Beach, N.C., U.S. C5 110
Caroline, co., Md., U.S. C6 97
Caroline, co., Va., U.S. C5 123
Caroní, stm., Ven. D11 58
Carora, Ven. B7 58
Carpathian Mountains, mts., Eur. F12 4
Carpații Meridionali, mts., Rom. D8 16
Carpentaria, Gulf of, b., Austl. B7 50
Carpenter Dam, Ar., U.S. g7 81
Carpentersville, Il., U.S. A5 90
Carpentras, Fr. H12 10
Carpi, Italy E5 14
Carpinteria, Ca., U.S. E4 82
Carquefou, Fr. E5 10
Carrabelle, Fl., U.S. C2 86
Carrara, Italy E5 14
Carrauntoohill, mtn., Ire. I3 7
Carrboro, N.C., U.S. B3 110
Carreta, Punta, c., Peru F3 54
Carrickfergus, N. Ire., U.K. G7 7
Carrickmacross, Ire. H6 7
Carrie, Mount, mtn., Wa., U.S. B2 124
Carriere, Ms., U.S. E4 101
Carrier Mills, Il., U.S. F5 90
Carrillo, Mex. D8 62
Carrington, N.D., U.S. B6 111
Carrington Island, i., Ut., U.S. C3 121
Carrión de los Condes, Spain C7 12
Carrizo Creek, stm., U.S. A1 120
Carrizo Mountain, mtn., N.M., U.S. D4 108
Carrizo Mountains, mts., U.S. A6 80
Carrizo Springs, Tx., U.S. E3 120
Carrizozo, N.M., U.S. D4 108
Carroll, Ia., U.S. B3 92
Carroll, co., Ar., U.S. A2 81
Carroll, co., Ga., U.S. C1 87
Carroll, co., Il., U.S. A4 90
Carroll, co., In., U.S. C4 91
Carroll, co., Ia., U.S. B3 92
Carroll, co., Ky., U.S. B4 94
Carroll, co., Md., U.S. A3 97
Carroll, co., Ms., U.S. B4 101
Carroll, co., Mo., U.S. B4 102
Carroll, co., N.H., U.S. C4 106
Carroll, co., Oh., U.S. B4 112
Carroll, co., Tn., U.S. B3 119
Carroll, co., Va., U.S. D2 123
Carrollton, Al., U.S. B1 78
Carrollton, Ga., U.S. C1 87
Carrollton, Il., U.S. D3 90
Carrollton, Ky., U.S. B4 94
Carrollton, Mi., U.S. E7 99
Carrollton, Mo., U.S. B4 102
Carrollton, Oh., U.S. B4 112
Carrolltown, Pa., U.S. E4 115
Carrot, stm., Can. D4 75
Carry Falls Reservoir, res., N.Y., U.S. f10 109
Čarsk, U.S.S.R. H10 20
Carson, Ia., U.S. C2 92
Carson, Wa., U.S. D4 124
Carson, co., Tx., U.S. B2 120
Carson, stm., Nv., U.S. D2 105
Carson City, Mi., U.S. E6 99
Carson City, Nv., U.S. D2 105
Carson Lake, l., Nv., U.S. D3 105
Carson Sink, l., Nv., U.S. D3 105
Carson Spring, Tn., U.S. D10 119
Carstairs, Alta., Can. D3 68
Carswell Air Force Base, mil., Tx., U.S. n9 120
Cartagena, Col. B5 58
Cartagena, Spain H11 12
Cartago, Col. E5 58
Cartago, C.R. J6 64
Carter, co., Ky., U.S. B6 94
Carter, co., Mo., U.S. E7 102
Carter, co., Mt., U.S. E12 103
Carter, co., Ok., U.S. C4 113
Carter, co., Tn., U.S. C11 119
Carteret, N.J., U.S. B4 107
Carteret, co., N.C., U.S. C6 110
Carter Lake, Ia., U.S. C2 92
Carter Mountain, mtn., Wy., U.S. B3 127
Carters Lake, res., Ga., U.S. B2 87
Cartersville, Ga., U.S. B2 87
Carterville, Il., U.S. F4 90
Carterville, Mo., U.S. D3 102
Carthage, Il., U.S. C2 90
Carthage, In., U.S. E6 91
Carthage, Ms., U.S. C4 101
Carthage, Mo., U.S. D3 102
Carthage, N.Y., U.S. B5 109
Carthage, N.C., U.S. B3 110
Carthage, Tn., U.S. C8 119
Carthage, Tx., U.S. C5 120
Cartier Island, i., Austl. B4 50
Cartwright, Newf., Can. B3 72
Cartwright, Ok., U.S. D5 113
Caruaru, Braz. E11 54
Carúpano, Ven. B11 58
Caruthersville, Mo., U.S. E8 102
Carver, Ma., U.S. C6 98
Carver, Mn., U.S. F5 100
Carver, co., Mn., U.S. F5 100
Carville, La., U.S. h9 95
Cary, Il., U.S. A5 90
Cary, N.C., U.S. B4 110
Caryville, Tn., U.S. C9 119
Casablanca (Dar-el-Beida), Mor. B4 42
Casacalenda, Italy H9 14
Casa Grande, Az., U.S. E4 80
Casa Grande National Monument, Az., U.S. E4 80
Casale Monferrato, Italy D3 14
Casarano, Italy I13 14
Casas Adobes, Az., U.S. E5 80
Casas Ibáñez, Spain F10 12
Cascade, Co., U.S. C6 83
Cascade, Id., U.S. E2 89
Cascade, Ia., U.S. B6 92
Cascade, Mt., U.S. C5 103
Cascade, co., Mt., U.S. C5 103
Cascade Locks, Or., U.S. B5 114
Cascade Range, mts., N.A. C2 76
Cascade Reservoir, res., Id., U.S. E3 89
Cascade Tunnel, Wa., U.S. B4 124
Cascais, Port. G2 12
Cascina, Italy F5 14
Casco Bay, b., Me., U.S. E3 96
Caserta, Italy H9 14
Caseville, Mi., U.S. E7 99
Casey, Il., U.S. D6 90
Casey, co., Ky., U.S. C5 94
Casey, Mount, mtn., Id., U.S. A2 89
Casey Key, i., Fl., U.S. E4 86
Cashion, Az., U.S. m8 80
Cashmere, Wa., U.S. B5 124
Cashton, Wi., U.S. E3 126
Casigua, Ven. C6 58
Caspe, Spain D11 12
Casper, Wy., U.S. D6 127
Casper Mountain, mtn., Wy., U.S. D6 127
Caspian, Mi., U.S. B2 99
Caspian Lake, l., Vt., U.S. B4 122
Caspian Sea G17 4
Cass, co., Il., U.S. D3 90
Cass, co., In., U.S. C5 91
Cass, co., Ia., U.S. C3 92
Cass, co., Mi., U.S. G4 99
Cass, co., Mn., U.S. D4 100
Cass, co., Mo., U.S. C3 102
Cass, co., Ne., U.S. D9 104
Cass, co., N.D., U.S. C8 111
Cass, co., Tx., U.S. C5 120
Cass, stm., Mi., U.S. E7 99
Cassai (Kasai), stm., Afr. C4 44
Cassano allo Ionio, Italy J11 14
Cass City, Mi., U.S. E7 99
Casselberry, Fl., U.S. D5 86
Casselman, Ont., Can. B9 73
Casselman, stm., U.S. k12 97
Casselton, N.D., U.S. C8 111
Cassia, co., Id., U.S. G5 89
Cassiar, B.C., Can. m17 69
Cassinga, Ang. E3 44
Cassino, Italy H8 14
Cass Lake, Mn., U.S. C4 100
Cass Lake, l., Mn., U.S. C4 100
Cassopolis, Mi., U.S. G4 99
Cassville, Ga., U.S. B2 87
Cassville, Mo., U.S. E4 102
Cassville, Wi., U.S. F3 126
Castalia, Oh., U.S. A3 112
Castanea, Pa., U.S. D7 115
Castanheira de Pêra, Port. E3 12
Castel del Piano, Italy G6 14
Castelfranco Veneto, Italy D6 14
Castellamare del Golfo, Italy K7 14
Castellammare [di Stabia], Italy I9 14
Castellane, Fr. I13 10
Castellón de la Plana, Spain F11 12
Castelnaudary, Fr. I8 10
Castelo Branco, Port. F4 12
Castelsarrasin, Fr. H8 10
Castelvetrano, Italy L7 14
Castets, Fr. I5 10
Castiglione del Lago, Italy F7 14
Castilla, Peru E2 54
Castilla la Nueva, hist. reg., Spain F8 12
Castillo de San Marcos National Monument, Fl., U.S. n9 86
Castine, Me., U.S. D4 96
Castle Air Force Base, mil., Ca., U.S. D3 82
Castlebar, Ire. H3 7
Castleberry, Al., U.S. D2 78
Castle Dale, Ut., U.S. D4 121
Castle Dome Mountains, mts., Az., U.S. D1 80
Castle Dome Peak, mtn., Az., U.S. D1 80
Castlegar, B.C., Can. E9 69
Castle Hayne, N.C., U.S. C5 110
Castle Hills, De., U.S. i7 85
Castle Mountain, mtn., Yukon, Can. D5 66
Castle Mountains, mts., Mt., U.S. D6 103
Castle Peak, mtn., Co., U.S. B4 83
Castle Peak, mtn., Id., U.S. E4 89
Castle Point, Mo., U.S. f13 102
Castle Rock, Co., U.S. B6 83
Castle Rock, Wa., U.S. C3 124
Castle Rock, mtn., Or., U.S. C8 114
Castle Rock Lake, res., Wi., U.S. E4 126
Castleton, Vt., U.S. D2 122
Castletown, I. of Man G8 7
Castletown Berehaven, Ire. J3 7
Castlewood, Va., U.S. f9 123
Castor, Alta., Can. C5 68
Castor, stm., Mo., U.S. D7 102
Castres, Fr. I9 10
Castries, St. Luc. G17 64
Castro, co., Tx., U.S. B1 120
Castro Daire, Port. E4 12
Castro del Río, Spain H7 12
Castropol, Spain B4 12
Castro Valley, Ca., U.S. h8 82
Castrovillari, Italy J11 14
Castroville, Tx., U.S. E3 120
Castuera, Spain G6 12
Caswell, co., N.C., U.S. A3 110
Catacamas, Hond. G5 64
Cataguases, Braz. F7 57
Catahoula, co., La., U.S. C4 95
Catahoula Lake, l., La., U.S. C3 95
Catalão, Braz. E5 57
Catalina, Newf., Can. D5 72
Catalina, Chile B3 56
Catamarca, Arg. B3 56
Catamayo, Ec. I3 58
Catanduanes Island, i., Phil. C7 32
Catanduva, Braz. F4 57
Catania, Italy L10 14
Catanzaro, Italy K11 14
Cataouatche, Lake, l., La., U.S. k11 95
Catarman, Phil. C7 32
Catasauqua, Pa., U.S. E11 115
Catastrophe, Cape, c., Austl. F7 50
Cataumet, Ma., U.S. C6 98
Catawba, co., N.C., U.S. B1 110
Catawba, stm., S.C., U.S. B6 117
Catawba, South Fork, stm., N.C., U.S. B1 110
Catawissa, Pa., U.S. E9 115
Catete, Ang. C2 44
Cathance, Lake, l., Me., U.S. D5 96
Cathcart, S. Afr. H5 44
Cathedral City, Ca., U.S. F5 82
Cathedral of the Pines, N.H., U.S. E3 106
Catherine, Lake, res., Ar., U.S. C3 81
Cat Island, i., Bah. B10 64
Cat Island, i., Ma., U.S. f12 98
Cat Island, i., Ms., U.S. E4 101
Cat Island, i., S.C., U.S. E9 117
Catlettsburg, Ky., U.S. B7 94
Catlin, Il., U.S. C6 90
Catnip Mountain, mtn., Nv., U.S. B2 105
Catoche, Cabo, c., Mex. G16 62
Cato Island, i., Austl. D11 50
Catonsville, Md., U.S. B4 97
Catoosa, Ok., U.S. A6 113
Catoosa, co., Ga., U.S. B1 87
Catorce, Mex. F9 62
Catron, co., N.M., U.S. D1 108
Catskill, N.Y., U.S. C7 109
Catskill Mountains, mts., N.Y., U.S. C6 109
Catt, Mount, mtn., B.C., Can. B3 69
Cattaraugus, co., N.Y., U.S. C2 109
Cattaraugus Creek, stm., N.Y., U.S. C2 109
Cattaraugus Indian Reservation, N.Y., U.S. C2 109
Cattolica, Italy F7 14
Catus, Fr. H8 10
Caubvick, Mount (Mont d'Iberville), mtn., Can. f9 72
Cauca, stm., Col. D5 58
Caucasia, Col. C5 58
Caucasus see Bol'šoj Kavkaz, mts., U.S.S.R. I6 18
Caucomgomoc Lake, l., Me., U.S. B3 96
Caudry, Fr. B10 10
Caulonia, Italy K11 14
Caúngula, Ang. C3 44
Čaunskaja Guba, b., U.S.S.R. D27 20
Cauquenes, Chile D2 56
Caura, stm., Ven. D10 58
Caussade, Fr. H8 10
Cauvery, stm., India G5 37
Cavalaire-sur-Mer, Fr. I13 10
Cavalier, N.D., U.S. A8 111
Cavalier, co., N.D., U.S. A7 111
Cavan, Ire. G5 7
Cave City, Ar., U.S. B4 81
Cave City, Ky., U.S. C4 94
Cave Creek, Az., U.S. D4 80
Cave Junction, Or., U.S. E3 114
Cave Point, c., Wi., U.S. D6 126
Cave Run Lake, res., Ky., U.S. B6 94
Cave Spring, Ga., U.S. B1 87
Cave Spring, Va., U.S. C2 123
Cavetown, Md., U.S. A2 97
Caviana, Ilha, i., Braz. C8 54
Cavite, Phil. q19 33b
Cawood, Ky., U.S. D6 94
Cawston, B.C., Can. E8 69
Caxambu, Braz. F6 57
Caxias, Braz. D10 54
Caxias do Sul, Braz. B6 56
Caxito, Ang. C2 44
Cayambe, Ec. G3 58
Cayambe, vol., Ec. H4 58
Cayce, S.C., U.S. D5 117
Cayenne, Fr. Gu. C8 54
Cayman Brac, i., Cay. Is. E8 64
Cayman Islands, dep., N.A. E7 64
Cayuga, In., U.S. E3 91
Cayuga, co., N.Y., U.S. C4 109
Cayuga Heights, N.Y., U.S. C4 109
Cayuga Lake, l., N.Y., U.S. C4 109
Cazenovia, N.Y., U.S. C5 109
Cazères, Fr. I8 10
Cazin, Yugo. E10 14
Cazorla, Spain H8 12
Čeboksary, U.S.S.R. F7 18
Cebollar, Arg. B3 56
Cebreros, Spain E7 12
Cebu, Phil. C7 32
Cebu, i., Phil. C7 32
Cecerleg, Mong. B7 26
Čechov, U.S.S.R. F20 22
Čechy, hist. reg., Czech. F14 8
Cecil, co., Md., U.S. A6 97
Cecil Field Naval Air Station, mil., Fl., U.S. B5 86
Cecilia, Ky., U.S. C4 94
Cecina, Italy F5 14
Cedar, co., Ia., U.S. C6 92
Cedar, co., Mo., U.S. D4 102
Cedar, co., Ne., U.S. B8 104
Cedar, stm., U.S. C6 92
Cedar, stm., Ne., U.S. B7 104
Cedar, stm., Wa., U.S. B4 124
Cedar Bluff, Al., U.S. A4 78
Cedar Bluff Reservoir, res., Ks., U.S. D4 93
Cedar Bluff Two, Tn., U.S. D9 119
Cedar Breaks National Monument, Ut., U.S. F3 121
Cedarburg, Wi., U.S. E6 126
Cedar City, Ut., U.S. F2 121
Cedar Creek, stm., N.J., U.S. D4 107
Cedar Creek, stm., N.D., U.S. C3 111
Cedar Creek, stm., Oh., U.S. e7 112
Cedar Creek Lake, res., Tx., U.S. C4 120
Cedar Crest, N.M., U.S. k8 108
Cedaredge, Co., U.S. C3 83
Cedar Falls, Ia., U.S. B5 92
Cedar Grove, N.J., U.S. B4 107
Cedar Grove, W.V., U.S. C3 125
Cedar Grove, Wi., U.S. E6 126
Cedar Hill, Mo., U.S. g12 102
Cedar Hill, Tx., U.S. n10 120
Cedarhurst, N.Y., U.S. k13 109
Cedar Island, i., N.C., U.S. C6 110
Cedar Island, i., S.C., U.S. E9 117
Cedar Island, i., Va., U.S. C7 123
Cedar Key, Fl., U.S. C3 86
Cedar Keys, is., Fl., U.S. C3 86
Cedar Lake, In., U.S. B3 91
Cedar Lake, res., Man., Can. C1 70
Cedar Lake, res., Il., U.S. F4 90
Cedar Mountain, mtn., Ca., U.S. B3 82
Cedar Point, c., Md., U.S. D5 97
Cedar Point, c., Oh., U.S. A3 112
Cedar Point, c., Oh., U.S. e7 112
Cedar Rapids, Ia., U.S. C6 92
Cedar Springs, Mi., U.S. E5 99
Cedartown, Ga., U.S. B1 87
Cedar Vale, Ks., U.S. E7 93
Cedarville, Oh., U.S. C2 112
Cedros, Isla, i., Mex. C2 62
Ceduna, Austl. F6 50
Cefalù, Italy K9 14
Čegdomyn, U.S.S.R. G20 20
Cegléd, Hung. H19 8
Cehegín, Spain G10 12
Cela, Ang. D3 44
Čel'abinsk, U.S.S.R. F10 18
Celano, Italy G8 14
Celanova, Spain C4 12
Celaya, Mex. G9 62
Cele, China B9 38
Celebes Sea, Asia E7 32
Celebes see Sulawesi, i., Indon. F7 32
Celina, Oh., U.S. B1 112
Celina, Tn., U.S. C8 119
Celina, Tx., U.S. C4 120
Celinograd, U.S.S.R. G8 20
Celje, Yugo. C10 14
Celle, Ger. C10 8
Cement, Ok., U.S. C3 113
Cementon, Pa., U.S. E10 115
Centennial Mountains, mts., Id., U.S. E7 89
Center, Co., U.S. D4 83
Center, N.D., U.S. B4 111
Center, Tx., U.S. D5 120
Centerbrook, Ct., U.S. D6 84
Centerburg, Oh., U.S. B3 112
Centereach, N.Y., U.S. n15 109
Centerfield, Ut., U.S. D4 121
Center Hill Lake, res., Tn., U.S. C8 119
Center Moriches, N.Y., U.S. n16 109
Center Mountain, mtn., Id., U.S. D3 89
Center Point, Al., U.S. f7 78
Center Point, Ia., U.S. B6 92
Centerville, In., U.S. E8 91
Centerville, Ia., U.S. D5 92
Centerville, La., U.S. E4 95
Centerville, Ma., U.S. C7 98
Centerville, Oh., U.S. C1 112
Centerville, Pa., U.S. F2 115

Name	Map Ref	Page
Centerville, S.D., U.S.	D9	118
Centerville, Tn., U.S.	B4	119
Centerville, Ut., U.S.	C4	121
Cento, Italy	E6	14
Central, N.M., U.S.	E1	108
Central, S.C., U.S.	B2	117
Central, Cordillera, mts., Bol.	G6	54
Central, Cordillera, mts., Col.	E5	58
Central, Cordillera, mts., Peru	E3	54
Central, Massif, mts., Fr.	G10	10
Central, Planalto, plat., Braz.	G9	54
Central, Sistema, mts., Spain	E6	12
Central African Republic, ctry., Afr.	G10	42
Central City, Co., U.S.	B5	83
Central City, Il., U.S.	E4	90
Central City, Ia., U.S.	B6	92
Central City, Ky., U.S.	C2	94
Central City, Ne., U.S.	C7	104
Central City, Pa., U.S.	F4	115
Central Falls, R.I., U.S.	B4	116
Central Heights, Az., U.S.	D5	80
Centralia, Il., U.S.	E4	90
Centralia, Mo., U.S.	B5	102
Centralia, Wa., U.S.	C3	124
Central Islip, N.Y., U.S.	n15	109
Central Lake, Mi., U.S.	C5	99
Central Makrān Range, mts., Pak.	D1	36
Central Park, Wa., U.S.	C2	124
Central Point, Or., U.S.	E4	114
Central Square, N.Y., U.S.	B4	109
Central Valley, Ca., U.S.	B2	82
Central Valley, N.Y., U.S.	D6	109
Central Village, Ct., U.S.	C8	84
Centre, Al., U.S.	A4	78
Centre, co., Pa., U.S.	E6	115
Centre Hall, Pa., U.S.	E6	115
Centreville, Al., U.S.	C2	78
Centreville, Il., U.S.	E3	90
Centreville, Md., U.S.	B5	97
Centreville, Mi., U.S.	G5	99
Centreville, Ms., U.S.	D2	101
Centuria, Wi., U.S.	C1	126
Century, Fl., U.S.	u14	86
Cepu, Indon.	m15	33a
Ceram Sea see Seram, Laut, Indon.	F8	32
Cerbat Mountains, mts., Az., U.S.	B1	80
Ceredo, W.V., U.S.	C2	125
Čeremchovo, U.S.S.R.	G14	20
Čerepovec, U.S.S.R.	B20	22
Ceres, Ca., U.S.	D3	82
Ceresco, Ne., U.S.	C9	104
Céret, Fr.	J9	10
Cereté, Col.	C5	58
Cerf Island, i., Sey.	C10	44
Cerignola, Italy	H10	14
Cérilly, Fr.	F9	10
Čerkassy, U.S.S.R.	H4	18
Čerkessk, U.S.S.R.	I6	18
Čern'achovsk, U.S.S.R.	G4	22
Černigov, U.S.S.R.	G4	18
Černobyl' (Chernobyl), U.S.S.R.	G4	18
Černogorsk, U.S.S.R.	G12	20
Černovcy, U.S.S.R.	H3	18
Černyševskij, U.S.S.R.	E16	20
Cerralvo, Isla, i., Mex.	E5	62
Cerritos, Mex.	F9	62
Cerro de Pasco, Peru	F3	54
Cerro Gordo, Il., U.S.	D5	90
Cerro Gordo, co., Ia., U.S.	A4	92
Čerskij, U.S.S.R.	D26	20
Čerskogo, Chrebet, mts., U.S.S.R.	E23	20
Cervera del Río Alhama, Spain	C10	12
Cervera de Pisuerga, Spain	C7	12
Cervia, Italy	E7	14
Cesena, Italy	E7	14
Cesenatico, Italy	E7	14
České Budějovice, Czech.	G14	8
Cessnock, Austl.	F10	50
Ceuta, Sp. N. Afr.	A4	42
Ceyhan, Tur.	A4	40
Ceylânpınar, Tur.	A7	40
Ceylon see Sri Lanka, ctry., Asia	H5	36
Chabanais, Fr.	G7	10
Chabarovsk, U.S.S.R.	H21	20
Chachoengsao, Thai.	H6	34
Chaco, stm., N.M., U.S.	A1	108
Chaco Culture National Historic Park, N.M., U.S.	A2	108
Chacon, Cape, c., Ak., U.S.	n24	79
Chad, ctry., Afr.	E9	42
Chad, Lake (Lac Tchad), l., Afr.	F8	42
Chadbourn, N.C., U.S.	C4	110
Chadds Ford, Pa., U.S.	G10	115
Chadileuvú, stm., Arg.	D3	56
Chadron, Ne., U.S.	B3	104
Chadwicks, N.Y., U.S.	B5	109
Chaffee, Mo., U.S.	D8	102
Chaffee, co., Co., U.S.	C4	83
Chaffin, Ma., U.S.	B4	98
Chaghcharān, Afg.	C1	38
Chagny, Fr.	F11	10
Chagos Archipelago, is., B.I.O.T.	G17	2
Chagrin Falls, Oh., U.S.	A4	112
Chāībāsā, India	I11	38
Chaîne Annamitique, mts., Asia	F9	34
Chakachamna Lake, l., Ak., U.S.	g15	79
Chake Chake, Tan.	C7	44
Chalais, Fr.	G7	10
Chalbi Desert, des., Kenya	H2	46
Chalcuapa, El Sal.	H3	64
Chaleur Bay, b., Can.	B4	71
Chalfonte, De., U.S.	h7	85
Chālisgaon, India	B3	37
Chalk River, Ont., Can.	A7	73
Challans, Fr.	F5	10
Challis, Id., U.S.	E4	89
Chalmette, La., U.S.	E6	95
Chalonnes-sur-Loire, Fr.	E6	10
Châlons-sur-Marne, Fr.	D11	10
Chalon-sur-Saône, Fr.	F11	10
Châlus, Fr.	G7	10
Cham, Ger.	F12	8
Chama, N.M., U.S.	A3	108
Chama, Rio, stm., N.M., U.S.	A3	108
Chaman, Pak.	E2	38
Chambal, stm., India	G7	38
Chamberlain, S.D., U.S.	D6	118
Chamberlain Lake, l., Me., U.S.	B3	96
Chamberlin, Mount, mtn., Ak., U.S.	B10	79
Chambers, co., Al., U.S.	C4	78
Chambers, co., Tx., U.S.	E5	120
Chambersburg, Pa., U.S.	G6	115
Chambers Island, i., Wi., U.S.	C6	126
Chambéry, Fr.	G12	10
Chambi, Jebel, mtn., Tun.	A7	42
Chamblee, Ga., U.S.	h8	87
Chambly, Que., Can.	D4	74
Chambon-sur-Voueize, Fr.	F9	10
Chamisal, N.M., U.S.	A4	108
Chamonix-Mont-Blanc, Fr.	G13	10
Champagne, hist. reg., Fr.	D11	10
Champagnole, Fr.	F12	10
Champaign, Il., U.S.	C5	90
Champaign, co., Il., U.S.	C5	90
Champaign, co., Oh., U.S.	B2	112
Champassak, Laos	G8	34
Champion, Oh., U.S.	A5	112
Champlain, Lake, l., N.A.	C12	76
Champlin, Mn., U.S.	m12	100
Chāmrājnagar Rāmasamudram, India	G4	37
Chañaral, Chile	B2	56
Chance, Md., U.S.	D6	97
Chanch, Mong.	A7	26
Chanchelulla Peak, mtn., Ca., U.S.	B2	82
Chandalar, stm., Ak., U.S.	B10	79
Chandausi, India	F8	38
Chandeleur Islands, is., La., U.S.	E7	95
Chandeleur Sound, strt., La., U.S.	E6	95
Chandīgarh, India	E7	38
Chandler, Que., Can.	k14	74
Chandler, Az., U.S.	D4	80
Chandler, In., U.S.	H3	91
Chandler, Ok., U.S.	B5	113
Chandler, Tx., U.S.	C5	120
Chandler Heights, Az., U.S.	m9	80
Chāndpur, Bngl.	I14	38
Chāndpur, India	F8	38
Chandrapur, India	C5	37
Chandyga, U.S.S.R.	E21	20
Chang (Yangtze), stm., China	E10	26
Changajn Nuruu, mts., Mong.	B6	26
Changchun, China	C12	26
Changde, China	F9	26
Changhua, Tai.	K9	28
Changjiang, China	J5	28
Changli, China	D10	26
Changsha, China	G1	28
Changshu, China	D9	28
Changzhi, China	D9	26
Changzhou (Changchow), China	D8	28
Chanhassen, Mn., U.S.	n11	100
Chanka, Ozero (Xingkathu), l., Asia	I20	20
Channahon, Il., U.S.	B5	90
Channapatna, India	F4	37
Channel Islands, is., Eur.	C4	10
Channel Islands National Park, Ca., U.S.	F4	82
Channel Lake, Il., U.S.	H8	90
Channel-Port-aux-Basques, Newf., Can.	E2	72
Channelview, Tx., U.S.	r14	120
Chantada, Spain	C4	12
Chantajskoje, Ozero, l., U.S.S.R.	D12	20
Chanthaburi, Thai.	H7	34
Chantilly, Va., U.S.	g12	123
Chantrey Inlet, b., N.W. Ter., Can.	C13	66
Chanute, Ks., U.S.	E8	93
Chanute Air Force Base, mil., Il., U.S.	C5	90
Chaoan, China	L5	28
Chao Phraya, stm., Thai.	G6	34
Chapala, Lago de, l., Mex.	G8	62
Chaparral, Col.	F5	58
Chapčeranga, U.S.S.R.	H16	20
Chapel Hill, N.C., U.S.	B3	110
Chapel Hill, Tn., U.S.	B5	119
Chaplin, stm., Ky., U.S.	C4	94
Chaplin Lake, l., Sask., Can.	G2	75
Chapman, Ks., U.S.	D6	93
Chapman Pond, l., R.I., U.S.	F1	116
Chapmanville, W.V., U.S.	D2	125
Chappaquiddick Island, i., Ma., U.S.	D7	98
Chappell, Ne., U.S.	C3	104
Chāpra, India	H11	38
Chapultepec, mtn., Mex.	F8	62
Charadai, Arg.	B5	56
Charcas, Mex.	F9	62
Chardon, Oh., U.S.	A4	112
Chardzhou see Čardžou, U.S.S.R.	J10	18
Charenton, La., U.S.	E4	95
Chari, stm., Afr.	F9	42
Chārīkār, Afg.	C3	38
Chariton, Ia., U.S.	C4	92
Chariton, co., Mo., U.S.	B4	102
Chariton, stm., U.S.	A5	102
Charity, Guy.	D13	58
Char'kov, U.S.S.R.	G5	18
Charleroi, Bel.	E4	8
Charleroi, Pa., U.S.	F2	115
Charles, co., Md., U.S.	C3	97
Charles, stm., Ma., U.S.	B5	98
Charles, Cape, c., Va., U.S.	C6	123
Charles A. Goodwin Dam, Ct., U.S.	B3	84
Charlesbourg, Que., Can.	n17	74
Charles City, Ia., U.S.	A5	92
Charles City, co., Va., U.S.	C5	123
Charles Island, i., N.W. Ter., Can.	D18	66
Charles Mill Lake, res., Oh., U.S.	B3	112
Charles Mix, co., S.D., U.S.	D7	118
Charles Mound, hill, Il., U.S.	A3	90
Charleston, Ar., U.S.	B1	81
Charleston, Il., U.S.	D5	90
Charleston, Ms., U.S.	A3	101
Charleston, Mo., U.S.	E8	102
Charleston, Or., U.S.	D2	114
Charleston, S.C., U.S.	F8	117
Charleston, Tn., U.S.	D9	119
Charleston, W.V., U.S.	C3	125
Charleston, co., S.C., U.S.	F8	117
Charleston Air Force Base, mil., S.C., U.S.	k11	117
Charleston Naval Shipyard, mil., S.C., U.S.	k12	117
Charleston Peak, mtn., Nv., U.S.	G6	105
Charlestown, In., U.S.	H6	91
Charlestown, N.H., U.S.	D2	106
Charlestown, R.I., U.S.	F2	116
Charles Town, W.V., U.S.	B7	125
Charleville, Austl.	E9	50
Charleville-Mézières, Fr.	C11	10
Charlevoix, Mi., U.S.	C5	99
Charlevoix, co., Mi., U.S.	C5	99
Charlevoix, Lake, l., Mi., U.S.	C5	99
Charlo, N.B., Can.	B3	71
Charlotte, Mi., U.S.	F6	99
Charlotte, N.C., U.S.	B2	110
Charlotte, Tn., U.S.	A4	119
Charlotte, Tx., U.S.	E3	120
Charlotte, co., Fl., U.S.	F5	86
Charlotte, co., Va., U.S.	C4	123
Charlotte Amalie, V.I.U.S.	E15	64
Charlotte Hall, Md., U.S.	D4	97
Charlotte Harbor, Fl., U.S.	F4	86
Charlotte Harbor, b., Fl., U.S.	F4	86
Charlottenberg, Swe.	G9	6
Charlottesville, Va., U.S.	B4	123
Charlottetown, P.E.I., Can.	C6	71
Charlton, co., Ga., U.S.	F4	87
Charmco, W.V., U.S.	C4	125
Charmes, Fr.	D13	10
Charny, Que., Can.	C6	74
Charolles, Fr.	F11	10
Chārsadda, Pak.	C4	38
Charters Towers, Austl.	D9	50
Chartres, Fr.	D8	10
Char Us Nuur, l., Mong.	B5	26
Chascomús, Arg.	D5	56
Chase, B.C., Can.	D8	69
Chase, Md., U.S.	B5	97
Chase, co., Ks., U.S.	D7	93
Chase, co., Ne., U.S.	D4	104
Chase City, Va., U.S.	D4	123
Chase Field Naval Air Station, mil., Tx., U.S.	E4	120
Chaska, Mn., U.S.	F5	100
Chassahowitzka Bay, b., Fl., U.S.	D4	86
Chassell, Mi., U.S.	A2	99
Chatanbulag, Mong.	C8	26
Chatanga, U.S.S.R.	C14	20
Chatanga, stm., U.S.S.R.	C14	20
Chatangskij Zaliv, b., U.S.S.R.	C15	20
Châteaubriant, Fr.	E5	10
Château-du-Loir, Fr.	E7	10
Châteaudun, Fr.	D8	10
Château-Gontier, Fr.	E6	10
Châteauguay, Que., Can.	D4	74
Château-Landon, Fr.	D9	10
Châteaulin, Fr.	D2	10
Châteaumeillant, Fr.	F9	10
Châteauneuf-sur-Charente, Fr.	G6	10
Châteauneuf-sur-Loire, Fr.	E9	10
Château-Renault, Fr.	E7	10
Château-Richer, Que., Can.	C6	74
Châteauroux, Fr.	F8	10
Château-Thierry, Fr.	C10	10
Châtellerault, Fr.	F7	10
Chatfield, Mn., U.S.	G6	100
Chatgal, Mong.	A7	26
Chatham, N.B., Can.	B4	71
Chatham, Ont., Can.	E2	73
Chatham, Eng., U.K.	J13	7
Chatham, Il., U.S.	D4	90
Chatham, La., U.S.	B3	95
Chatham, Ma., U.S.	C8	98
Chatham, N.J., U.S.	B4	107
Chatham, N.Y., U.S.	C7	109
Chatham, Va., U.S.	D3	123
Chatham, co., Ga., U.S.	E5	87
Chatham, co., N.C., U.S.	B3	110
Chatham Strait, strt., Ak., U.S.	m22	79
Châtillon, Italy	D2	14
Châtillon-Coligny, Fr.	E9	10
Châtillon-sur-Indre, Fr.	F8	10
Châtillon-sur-Seine, Fr.	E11	10
Chatom, Al., U.S.	D1	78
Chatsworth, Ga., U.S.	B2	87
Chatsworth, Il., U.S.	C5	90
Chatsworth Reservoir, res., Ca., U.S.	m11	82
Chattahoochee, Fl., U.S.	B2	86
Chattahoochee, co., Ga., U.S.	D2	87
Chattahoochee, stm., U.S.	E1	87
Chattanooga, Tn., U.S.	D8	119
Chattaroy, W.V., U.S.	D2	125
Chattooga, co., Ga., U.S.	B1	87
Chattooga, stm., U.S.	B1	117
Chatuge Lake, res., U.S.	g9	110
Chatyrka, U.S.S.R.	E29	20
Chaudière, stm., Que., Can.	C7	74
Chau Doc, Viet.	I8	34
Chauk, Burma	D3	34
Chaumont, Fr.	D12	10
Chauncey, Oh., U.S.	C3	112
Chauny, Fr.	C10	10
Chautauqua, co., Ks., U.S.	E7	93
Chautauqua, co., N.Y., U.S.	C1	109
Chautauqua Lake, l., N.Y., U.S.	C1	109
Chauvigny, Fr.	F7	10
Chauvin, La., U.S.	E5	95
Chavakkad, India	G4	37
Chaves, Port.	D4	12
Chaves, co., N.M., U.S.	D5	108
Cháviva, Col.	E6	58
Chbukha Dzong, Bhu.	G13	38
Cheaha Mountain, mtn., Al., U.S.	B4	78
Cheat, Shavers Fork, stm., W.V., U.S.	B5	125
Cheatham, co., Tn., U.S.	A4	119
Chebanse, Il., U.S.	C6	90
Cheboygan, Mi., U.S.	C6	99
Cheboygan, co., Mi., U.S.	C6	99
Chech, Erg, des., Afr.	C5	42
Checotah, Ok., U.S.	B6	113
Chedabucto Bay, b., N.S., Can.	D8	71
Cheduba Island, i., Burma	E2	34
Cheektowaga, N.Y., U.S.	C2	109
Cheeseman Lake, res., Co., U.S.	B5	83
Chehalem Mountains, mts., Or., U.S.	h12	114
Chehalis, Wa., U.S.	C3	124
Chehalis, stm., Wa., U.S.	C2	124
Cheju-do, i., S. Kor.	E12	26
Chelan, Wa., U.S.	B5	124
Chelan, co., Wa., U.S.	B4	124
Chelan, Lake, l., Wa., U.S.	A5	124
Chelan Mountains, mts., Wa., U.S.	A5	124
Chełm, Pol.	D23	8
Chełmno, Pol.	B18	8
Chelmsford, Eng., U.K.	J13	7
Chelmsford, Ma., U.S.	A5	98
Chelsea, Que., Can.	D2	74
Chelsea, Al., U.S.	g7	78
Chelsea, Ma., U.S.	B5	98
Chelsea, Mi., U.S.	F6	99
Chelsea, Ok., U.S.	A6	113
Cheltenham, Eng., U.K.	J10	7
Cheltenham, Md., U.S.	C4	97
Chelva, Spain	F11	12
Chelyabinsk see Čel'abinsk, U.S.S.R.	F10	18
Chelyan, W.V., U.S.	C3	125
Chemehuevi Indian Reservation, Ca., U.S.	E6	82
Chemnitz, Ger.	E12	8
Chemquasabamticook Lake (Ross Lake), l., Me., U.S.	B3	96
Chemung, co., N.Y., U.S.	C4	109
Chemung, stm., Pa., U.S.	C8	115
Chemung Lake, l., Ont., Can.	C6	73
Chenāb, stm., Asia	E5	38
Chenachane, Alg.	C6	42
Chenango, co., N.Y., U.S.	C5	109
Chenango, stm., N.Y., U.S.	C5	109
Chenango Bridge, N.Y., U.S.	C5	109
Chenes, River Aux, b., La., U.S.	k12	95
Chénéville, Que., Can.	D2	74
Cheney, Ks., U.S.	E6	93
Cheney, Wa., U.S.	B8	124
Cheney Reservoir, res., Ks., U.S.	E6	93
Cheneyville, La., U.S.	C3	95
Chengde, China	C10	26
Chengdu, China	E7	26
Chengutu, Zimb.	E6	44
Chenoa, Il., U.S.	C5	90
Chenoweth, Or., U.S.	B5	114
Chepachet, R.I., U.S.	B2	116
Chepachet, stm., R.I., U.S.	B2	116
Chepo, Pan.	J8	64
Chequamegon Bay, b., Wi., U.S.	B3	126
Cheraw, S.C., U.S.	B8	117
Cherbourg, Fr.	C5	10
Chergui, Chott ech, l., Alg.	B6	42
Cherkassy see Čerkassy, U.S.S.R.	H4	18
Chernigov see Černigov, U.S.S.R.	G4	18
Chernobyl see Černobyl', U.S.S.R.	G4	18
Cherokee, Al., U.S.	A2	78
Cherokee, Ia., U.S.	B2	92
Cherokee, Ks., U.S.	E9	93
Cherokee, Ok., U.S.	A3	113
Cherokee, co., Al., U.S.	A4	78
Cherokee, co., Ga., U.S.	B2	87
Cherokee, co., Ia., U.S.	B2	92
Cherokee, co., Ks., U.S.	E9	93
Cherokee, co., N.C., U.S.	f8	110
Cherokee, co., Ok., U.S.	B6	113
Cherokee, co., S.C., U.S.	A4	117
Cherokee, co., Tx., U.S.	D5	120
Cherokee Indian Reservation, N.C., U.S.	f9	110
Cherokee Lake, res., Tn., U.S.	C10	119
Cherokees, Lake O' The, res., Ok., U.S.	A7	113
Cherokee Village, Ar., U.S.	A4	81
Cherry, co., Ne., U.S.	B4	104
Cherry Creek, stm., S.D., U.S.	C3	118
Cherry Hill, N.J., U.S.	D2	107
Cherry Point, c., Va., U.S.	C6	123
Cherry Point Marine Corps Air Station, mil., N.C., U.S.	C6	110
Cherryvale, Ks., U.S.	E8	93
Cherry Valley, Ar., U.S.	B5	81
Cherry Valley, Il., U.S.	A5	90
Cherryville, N.C., U.S.	B1	110
Cherson, U.S.S.R.	H4	18
Chesaning, Mi., U.S.	E6	99
Chesapeake, Oh., U.S.	D3	112
Chesapeake, Va., U.S.	D6	123
Chesapeake, W.V., U.S.	C3	125
Chesapeake and Delaware Canal, U.S.	B3	85
Chesapeake Bay, b., U.S.	D11	76
Chesapeake Bay Bridge-Tunnel, Va., U.S.	D7	123
Chesapeake Beach, Md., U.S.	C4	97
Chesapeake City, Md., U.S.	A6	97
Chesdin, Lake, res., Va., U.S.	C5	123
Cheshire, Ct., U.S.	D4	84
Cheshire, co., N.H., U.S.	E2	106
Cheshire Reservoir, res., Ma., U.S.	A1	98
Chesley, Ont., Can.	C3	73
Chesnee, S.C., U.S.	A4	117
Chester, Eng., U.K.	H10	7
Chester, Ca., U.S.	B3	82
Chester, Ct., U.S.	D6	84
Chester, Ga., U.S.	D3	87
Chester, Il., U.S.	F4	90
Chester, Md., U.S.	C5	97
Chester, Mt., U.S.	B6	103
Chester, N.H., U.S.	E4	106
Chester, N.Y., U.S.	D6	109
Chester, Pa., U.S.	G11	115
Chester, S.C., U.S.	B5	117
Chester, Vt., U.S.	E3	122
Chester, Va., U.S.	C5	123
Chester, W.V., U.S.	A4	125
Chester, co., Pa., U.S.	G10	115
Chester, co., S.C., U.S.	B5	117
Chester, co., Tn., U.S.	B3	119
Chester, stm., Md., U.S.	B5	97
Chester Basin, N.S., Can.	E5	71
Chester Depot, Vt., U.S.	E3	122
Chesterfield, In., U.S.	D6	91
Chesterfield, S.C., U.S.	B7	117
Chesterfield, co., S.C., U.S.	B7	117
Chesterfield, co., Va., U.S.	C5	123
Chesterfield, Îles, is., N. Cal.	C11	50
Chesterfield Inlet, N.W. Ter., Can.	D14	66
Chesterfield Inlet, b., N.W. Ter., Can.	D14	66
Chesterton, In., U.S.	A3	91
Chestertown, Md., U.S.	B5	97
Chesterville, Ont., Can.	B9	73
Chesuncook Lake, l., Me., U.S.	C3	96
Cheswick, Pa., U.S.	h14	115
Cheswold, De., U.S.	D3	85
Cheta, stm., U.S.S.R.	C13	20
Chetac, Lake, l., Wi., U.S.	C2	126
Chetco, stm., Or., U.S.	E2	114
Chetek, Wi., U.S.	C2	126
Chetek, Lake, l., Wi., U.S.	C2	126
Chetopa, Ks., U.S.	E8	93
Chetumal Bay, b., N.A.	H15	62
Chetwynd, B.C., Can.	B7	69
Chevak, Ak., U.S.	C6	79
Cheval Blanc, Pointe du, c., Haiti	E11	64
Cheviot, Oh., U.S.	C1	112
Chevreuil, Point, c., La., U.S.	E4	95
Chevy Chase, Md., U.S.	C3	97
Chewack, stm., Wa., U.S.	A5	124
Chew Bahir (Lake Stefanie), l., Afr.	H2	46
Chewelah, Wa., U.S.	A8	124
Cheyenne, Ok., U.S.	B2	113
Cheyenne, Wy., U.S.	E8	127
Cheyenne, co., Co., U.S.	C8	83
Cheyenne, co., Ks., U.S.	C2	93
Cheyenne, co., Ne., U.S.	C2	104
Cheyenne, stm., U.S.	C4	118
Cheyenne, Dry Fork, stm., Wy., U.S.	C7	127
Cheyenne River Indian Reservation, S.D., U.S.	B4	118
Cheyenne Wells, Co., U.S.	C8	83
Chezhou, China	J1	28
Chhatarpur, India	H8	38
Chhindwāra, India	I8	38
Chi, stm., Thai.	G8	34
Chiai, Tai.	L9	28
Chiali, Tai.	L9	28
Chiang Khan, Thai.	F6	34
Chiang Mai, Thai.	E5	34
Chiang Rai, Thai.	E5	34
Chiari, Italy	D4	14
Chiavari, Italy	E4	14
Chiavenna, Italy	C4	14
Chiba, Japan	G13	30
Chiblow Lake, l., Ont., Can.	A1	73
Chibougamau, Que., Can.	k12	74
Chibuto, Moz.	F6	44
Chicago, Il., U.S.	B6	90
Chicago Heights, Il., U.S.	B6	90
Chicago Sanitary and Ship Canal, Il., U.S.	k8	90
Chicamacomico, stm., Md., U.S.	D6	97
Chicapa, stm., Afr.	C4	44
Chichagof Island, i., Ak., U.S.	m22	79
Chīchāwatni, Pak.	E5	38
Chichén Itzá, Mex.	G15	62
Chichibu, Japan	G12	30
Chickahominy, stm., Va., U.S.	C5	123
Chickamauga, Ga., U.S.	B1	87
Chickamauga and Chattanooga National Military Park, U.S.	k11	119
Chickamauga Dam, Tn., U.S.	h11	119
Chickamauga Lake, res., Tn., U.S.	D8	119
Chickasaw, Al., U.S.	E1	78
Chickasaw, co., Ia., U.S.	A5	92
Chickasaw, co., Ms., U.S.	B5	101
Chickasawhay, stm., Ms., U.S.	D5	101
Chickasaw National Recreation Area, Ok., U.S.	C5	113
Chickasha, Ok., U.S.	B4	113
Chickasha, Lake, res., Ok., U.S.	B3	113
Chickwolnepy Stream, stm., N.H., U.S.	A4	106
Chiclana de la Frontera, Spain	I5	12
Chiclayo, Peru	E3	54
Chico, Ca., U.S.	C3	82
Chicoa, Moz.	E6	44
Chicopee, Ga., U.S.	B3	87
Chicopee, Ma., U.S.	B2	98
Chicora, Pa., U.S.	E2	115
Chicot, Lake, l., Ar., U.S.	D4	81
Chicot Island, i., La., U.S.	E6	95
Chicoutimi, Que., Can.	A6	74
Chicoutimi, stm., Que., Can.	A6	74
Chidambaram, India	G5	37
Chidley, Cape, c., Can.	D20	66
Chiefland, Fl., U.S.	C4	86
Chieri, Italy	D2	14
Chieti, Italy	G9	14
Chifeng, China	C10	26
Chigasaki, Japan	G12	30
Chignecto, Cape, c., N.S., Can.	D5	71
Chignecto Bay, b., Can.	D5	71
Ch'i-hu, Tai.	L9	28
Chihuahua, Mex.	C6	62
Chikaskia, stm., U.S.	A4	113
Chik Ballāpur, India	F4	37
Chikmagalūr, India	F3	37
Chilakalūrupet, India	D6	37
Chilapa de Alvarez, Mex.	I10	62
Chilās, Pak.	C6	38
Childersburg, Al., U.S.	B3	78
Childress, Tx., U.S.	B2	120
Childress, co., Tx., U.S.	B2	120
Chile, ctry., S.A.	C2	56
Chilete, Peru	E3	54
Chilhowie, Va., U.S.	f10	123

Name — Map Ref — Page

Chililabombwe (Bancroft), Zam. **D5** 44
Chilka Lake, l., India **C8** 37
Chilko, stm., B.C., Can. **D6** 69
Chilko Lake, l., B.C., Can. **D5** 69
Chillán, Chile **D2** 56
Chillicothe, Il., U.S. **C4** 90
Chillicothe, Mo., U.S. **B4** 102
Chillicothe, Oh., U.S. **C3** 112
Chilliwack, B.C., Can. **E7** 69
Chillum, Md., U.S. **f9** 97
Chiloé, Isla de, i., Chile **E2** 56
Chilok, U.S.S.R. **G16** 20
Chiloquin, Or., U.S. **E5** 114
Chilpancingo [de los Bravos], Mex. **I10** 62
Chilton, Wi., U.S. **D5** 126
Chilton, co., Al., U.S. **C3** 78
Chilung, Tai. **J10** 28
Chilwa, Lake, l., Afr. **E7** 44
Chimacum, Wa., U.S. **A3** 124
Chimayo, N.M., U.S. **A4** 108
Chimborazo, vol., Ec. **H3** 58
Chimbote, Peru **E3** 54
Chimkent see Čimkent, U.S.S.R. **I11** 18
Chimki, U.S.S.R. **F20** 22
Chimney Rock, mtn., Ne., U.S. **C2** 104
China, ctry., Asia **D7** 26
China Grove, N.C., U.S. **B2** 110
China Lake, l., Me., U.S. **D3** 96
Chinandega, Nic. **H4** 64
Chincha Alta, Peru **F3** 54
Chincilla de Monte Aragón, Spain **G10** 12
Chincoteague, Va., U.S. **C7** 123
Chincoteague Bay, b., U.S. **D7** 97
Chinde, Moz. **E7** 44
Chindwinn, stm., Burma **C3** 34
Chingleput, India **F5** 37
Chingola, Zam. **D5** 44
Ch'ingshui, Tai. **K9** 28
Chin Hills, hills, Burma **D2** 34
Chinhoyi, Zimb. **E6** 44
Chiniot, Pak. **E5** 38
Chinitna Point, c., Ak., U.S. **h15** 79
Chinju, S. Kor. **D12** 26
Chinko, stm., Cen. Afr. Rep. **G10** 42
Chinkuashih, Tai. **J10** 28
Chinle, Az., U.S. **A6** 80
Chinmen Tao, i., Tai. **K7** 28
Chino, Ca., U.S. **F5** 82
Chinon, Fr. **E7** 10
Chinook, Mt., U.S. **B7** 103
Chinook, Wa., U.S. **C2** 124
Chinook, Lake, res., Or., U.S. **C5** 114
Chino Valley, Az., U.S. **C3** 80
Chinshan, Tai. **J10** 28
Chioggia, Italy **D7** 14
Chipata, Zam. **D6** 44
Chipita Park, Co., U.S. **C6** 83
Chipley, Fl., U.S. **u16** 86
Chipman, N.B., Can. **C4** 71
Chipola, stm., Fl., U.S. **B1** 86
Chippewa, co., Mi., U.S. **B6** 99
Chippewa, co., Mn., U.S. **E3** 100
Chippewa, co., Wi., U.S. **C2** 126
Chippewa, stm., Mn., U.S. **E3** 100
Chippewa, stm., Wi., U.S. **D2** 126
Chippewa, Lake, l., Wi., U.S. **C2** 126
Chippewa Falls, Wi., U.S. **D2** 126
Chipuxet, stm., R.I., U.S. **F3** 116
Chiquimula, Guat. **G3** 64
Chiquinquirá, Col. **E6** 58
Chīrāla, India **E6** 37
Chirfa, Niger **D8** 42
Chirgis Nuur, l., Mong. **B5** 26
Chiricahua Mountains, mts., Az., U.S. **E6** 80
Chiricahua National Monument, Az., U.S. **F6** 80
Chiricahua Peak, mtn., Az., U.S. **F6** 80
Chiriguaná, Col. **C6** 58
Chirikof Island, i., Ak., U.S. **D8** 79
Chiriquí, Golfo, b., Pan. **K6** 64
Chiriquí, Laguna de, b., Pan. **J7** 64
Chirripó, Cerro, mtn., C.R. **J6** 64
Chisago, co., Mn., U.S. **E6** 100
Chisago City, Mn., U.S. **E6** 100
Chisholm, Me., U.S. **D2** 96
Chisholm, Mn., U.S. **C6** 100
Chishtiān Mandi, Pak. **F5** 38
Chisos Mountains, mts., Tx., U.S. **E1** 120
Chitato, Ang. **C4** 44
Chitembo, Ang. **D3** 44
Chitina, stm., Ak., U.S. **g19** 79
Chitipa, Mwi. **C6** 44
Chitorgarh, India **H6** 38
Chitose, Japan **q19** 30a
Chitradurga, India **E4** 37
Chitrāl, Pak. **C4** 38
Chitré, Pan. **K7** 64
Chittagong, Bngl. **I14** 38
Chittenango, N.Y., U.S. **B5** 109
Chittenden, co., Vt., U.S. **C2** 122
Chittenden Reservoir, res., Vt., U.S. **D3** 122
Chittoor, India **F5** 37
Chiusi, Italy **F6** 14
Chivasso, Italy **D2** 14
Choapan, Mex. **I12** 62
Chocolate Mountains, mts., U.S. **F6** 82
Chocontá, Col. **E6** 58
Choctaw, Ok., U.S. **B4** 113
Choctaw, co., Al., U.S. **C1** 78
Choctaw, co., Ms., U.S. **B4** 101
Choctaw, co., Ok., U.S. **C6** 113
Choctawhatchee Bay, b., Fl., U.S. **u15** 86
Choctaw Indian Reservation, Ms., U.S. **C4** 101
Choele-Choel, Arg. **D3** 56
Cholet, Fr. **E6** 10
Cholmsk, U.S.S.R. **H22** 20
Choluteca, Hond. **H4** 64
Choma, Zam. **E5** 44
Chomutov, Czech. **E13** 8
Chon Buri, Thai. **H6** 34
Chone, Ec. **H2** 58
Ch'ŏngjin, N. Kor. **C12** 26
Ch'ŏngju, S. Kor. **D12** 26
Chongmingdao, i., China **D10** 28
Chongqing, China **F8** 26
Chŏnju, S. Kor. **D12** 26
Chonos, Archipiélago de los, is., Chile **F2** 56
Chonuu, U.S.S.R. **D22** 20
Choptank, stm., Md., U.S. **C6** 97
Chōshi, Japan **G13** 30
Chos Malal, Arg. **D2** 56
Choteau, Mt., U.S. **C4** 103
Chouteau, Ok., U.S. **A6** 113
Chouteau, co., Mt., U.S. **C6** 103
Chovd, Mong. **B5** 26
Chövsgöl Nuur, l., Mong. **A7** 26
Chowan, co., N.C., U.S. **A6** 110
Chowan, stm., N.C., U.S. **A6** 110
Chowchilla, Ca., U.S. **D3** 82
Chrisman, Il., U.S. **D6** 90
Christianshåb, Grnld. **C22** 66
Christchurch, N.Z. **E4** 52
Christian, co., Il., U.S. **D4** 90
Christian, co., Ky., U.S. **D2** 94
Christian, co., Mo., U.S. **E4** 102
Christian, Cape, c., N.W. Ter., Can. **B19** 66
Christiana, De., U.S. **B3** 85
Christiana, Pa., U.S. **G9** 115
Christiansburg, Va., U.S. **C2** 123
Christian Sound, strt., Ak., U.S. **n22** 79
Christiansted, V.I.U.S. **F15** 64
Christina, stm., Alta., Can. **A5** 68
Christina, stm., De., U.S. **B3** 85
Christina, Lake, l., Mn., U.S. **D3** 100
Christina Peak, mtn., Nv., U.S. **D6** 105
Christmas, Fl., U.S. **D5** 86
Christmas Island, dep., Oc. **H4** 32
Christmas Lake, l., Or., U.S. **D6** 114
Christopher, Il., U.S. **F4** 90
Chroma, stm., U.S.S.R. **C22** 20
Chrzanów, Pol. **E19** 8
Chubbuck, Id., U.S. **G6** 89
Chugach Islands, is., Ak., U.S. **h16** 79
Chugach Mountains, mts., Ak., U.S. **g18** 79
Chūgoku-sanchi, mts., Japan **H5** 30
Chugwater, Wy., U.S. **E8** 127
Chugwater Creek, stm., Wy., U.S. **E8** 127
Chukai, Malay. **L7** 34
Chukchi Sea **C30** 128
Chula Vista, Ca., U.S. **F5** 82
Chulucanas, Peru **E2** 54
Chumphon, Thai. **I5** 34
Chum Saeng, Thai. **G6** 34
Chunchi, Ec. **I3** 58
Ch'unch'ŏn, S. Kor. **D12** 26
Chunchula, Al., U.S. **E1** 78
Ch'ungju, S. Kor. **D12** 26
Chungking see Chongqing, China **F8** 26
Chungli, Tai. **K10** 28
Chungyang Shanmo, mts., Tai. **L10** 28
Chuŏr Phnum Krâvanh, mts., Asia **H7** 34
Chupadera Mesa, mtn., N.M., U.S. **D3** 108
Chupaderos, Mex. **F8** 62
Chuquicamata, Chile **A3** 56
Chur, Switz. **F16** 10
Church Hill, Tn., U.S. **C11** 119
Churchill, Man., Can. **f9** 70
Churchill, co., Nv., U.S. **D3** 105
Churchill, stm., Can. **E13** 66
Churchill, stm., Newf., Can. **h9** 72
Churchill, Cape, c., Man., Can. **f9** 70
Churchill, Mount, mtn., B.C., Can. **E6** 69
Churchill Falls, wtfl, Newf., Can. **h8** 72
Churchill Lake, l., Sask., Can. **m7** 75
Churchill Lake, l., Me., U.S. **B3** 96
Church Point, La., U.S. **D3** 95
Church Rock, N.M., U.S. **B1** 108
Churchton, Md., U.S. **C4** 97
Churchville, N.Y., U.S. **B3** 109
Churu, India **F6** 38
Churubusco, In., U.S. **B7** 91
Churuguara, Ven. **B8** 58
Chuska Mountains, mts., Az., U.S. **A6** 80
Chutag, Mong. **B7** 26
Chuxian, China **C7** 28
Chuxiong, China **B6** 34
Chužir, U.S.S.R. **G15** 20
Cianjur, Indon. **G4** 32
Cibecue, Az., U.S. **C5** 80
Cibinong, Indon. **m13** 33a
Cibola, co., N.M., U.S. **C1** 108
Cibolo Creek, stm., Tx., U.S. **h7** 120
Cicero, Il., U.S. **B6** 90
Cicero, In., U.S. **D5** 91
Ciechanów, Pol. **C20** 8
Ciego de Avila, Cuba **D8** 64
Ciempozuelos, Spain **E8** 12
Ciénaga, Col. **B5** 58
Cienfuegos, Cuba **C7** 64
Cieszyn, Pol. **F18** 8
Cieza, Spain **G10** 12
Cifuentes, Spain **E9** 12
Cikampek, Indon. **m13** 33a
Cilacap, Indon. **m14** 33a
Cilleruelo de Bezana, Spain **C8** 12
Cimarron, Ks., U.S. **E3** 93
Cimarron, N.M., U.S. **A5** 108
Cimarron, co., Ok., U.S. **e8** 113
Čimkent, U.S.S.R. **I11** 18
Çınarcık, Tur. **I13** 16
Cincinnati, Oh., U.S. **C1** 112
Çine, Tur. **L12** 16
Ciney, Bel. **E5** 8
Cinnaminson, N.J., U.S. **D3** 107
Cipa, stm., U.S.S.R. **F17** 20
Cipolletti, Arg. **D3** 56
Circle, Ak., U.S. **B11** 79
Circle, Mt., U.S. **C11** 103
Circle Pines, Mn., U.S. **m12** 100
Circleville, Oh., U.S. **C3** 112
Cirebon, Indon. **m14** 32
Cirencester, Eng., U.K. **J11** 7
Ciriè, Italy **D2** 14
Cirò Marina, Italy **J12** 14
Cisco, Tx., U.S. **C3** 120
Cispus, stm., Wa., U.S. **C4** 124
Cissna Park, Il., U.S. **C6** 90
Cistierna, Spain **C6** 12
Čita, U.S.S.R. **G16** 20
Citra, Fl., U.S. **C4** 86
Citronelle, Al., U.S. **D1** 78
Citrus, co., Fl., U.S. **D4** 86
Città di Castello, Italy **F7** 14
City of Refuge National Historical Park, Hi., U.S. **D5** 88
City View, S.C., U.S. **B3** 117
Ciudad, Mex. **F7** 62
Ciudad Acuña, Mex. **C9** 62
Ciudad Altamirano, Mex. **H9** 62
Ciudad Bolívar, Ven. **C11** 58
Ciudad Bolivia, Ven. **C7** 58
Ciudad Camargo, Mex. **D7** 62
Ciudad Chetumal, Mex. **H15** 62
Ciudad del Carmen, Mex. **H14** 62
Ciudad del Maíz, Mex. **F10** 62
Ciudad de México (Mexico City), Mex. **H10** 62
Ciudad de Nutrias, Ven. **C8** 58
Ciudad de Valles, Mex. **G10** 62
Ciudadela, Spain **E15** 12
Ciudad Guayana, Ven. **C11** 58
Ciudad Guzmán, Mex. **H8** 62
Ciudad Hidalgo, Mex. **H9** 62
Ciudad Ixtepec, Mex. **I12** 62
Ciudad Jiménez, Mex. **D7** 62
Ciudad Juárez, Mex. **B6** 62
Ciudad Madero, Mex. **F11** 62
Ciudad Mante, Mex. **F10** 62
Ciudad Melchor Múzquiz, Mex. **D9** 62
Ciudad Obregón, Mex. **D5** 62
Ciudad Ojeda (Lagunillas), Ven. **B7** 58
Ciudad Piar, Ven. **D11** 58
Ciudad Real, Spain **G8** 12
Ciudad Rodrigo, Spain **E5** 12
Ciudad Victoria, Mex. **F10** 62
Civita Castellana, Italy **G7** 14
Civitanova Marche, Italy **F8** 14
Civitavecchia, Italy **G6** 14
Civray, Fr. **F7** 10
C.J. Strike Reservoir, res., Id., U.S. **G3** 89
Clackamas, Or., U.S. **h12** 114
Clackamas, co., Or., U.S. **B4** 114
Clacton-on-Sea, Eng., U.K. **J14** 7
Claflin, Ks., U.S. **D5** 93
Claiborne, co., La., U.S. **B2** 95
Claiborne, co., Ms., U.S. **D3** 101
Claiborne, co., Tn., U.S. **C10** 119
Claiborne, Lake, res., La., U.S. **B3** 95
Clair, N.B., Can. **B1** 71
Claire, Lake, l., Alta., Can. **f8** 68
Clair Engle Lake, res., Ca., U.S. **B2** 82
Clairton, Pa., U.S. **F2** 115
Clallam, co., Wa., U.S. **B1** 124
Clallam Bay, Wa., U.S. **A1** 124
Clamecy, Fr. **E10** 10
Clam Lake, l., Wi., U.S. **C1** 126
Clan Alpine Mountains, mts., Nv., U.S. **D4** 105
Clanton, Al., U.S. **C3** 78
Clanwilliam, S. Afr. **H3** 44
Clara City, Mn., U.S. **F3** 100
Clara Peak, mtn., Az., U.S. **C2** 80
Clare, Mi., U.S. **E6** 99
Clare, co., Mi., U.S. **E6** 99
Claremont, Ca., U.S. **m13** 82
Claremont, N.H., U.S. **D2** 106
Claremont, N.C., U.S. **B1** 110
Claremont, mtn., Ca., U.S. **C3** 82
Claremore, Ok., U.S. **A6** 113
Claremorris, Ire. **H3** 7
Clarence, Ia., U.S. **C6** 92
Clarence, Mo., U.S. **B5** 102
Clarence Strait, strt., Ak., U.S. **n23** 79
Clarendon, Ar., U.S. **C4** 81
Clarendon, Tx., U.S. **B2** 120
Clarendon, co., S.C., U.S. **D7** 117
Clarendon, stm., Vt., U.S. **E2** 122
Clarendon Hills, Il., U.S. **k9** 90
Clarenville, Newf., Can. **D4** 72
Claresholm, Alta., Can. **D4** 68
Claridge, Pa., U.S. **F2** 115
Clarinda, Ia., U.S. **D2** 92
Clarines, Ven. **C10** 58
Clarion, Ia., U.S. **B4** 92
Clarion, Pa., U.S. **D3** 115
Clarion, co., Pa., U.S. **D3** 115
Clarion, stm., Pa., U.S. **D3** 115
Clarión, Isla, i., Mex. **H2** 62
Clarissa, Mn., U.S. **D4** 100
Clark, N.J., U.S. **B4** 107
Clark, S.D., U.S. **C8** 118
Clark, co., Ar., U.S. **C2** 81
Clark, co., Id., U.S. **E6** 89
Clark, co., Il., U.S. **D6** 90
Clark, co., In., U.S. **H6** 91
Clark, co., Ks., U.S. **E4** 93
Clark, co., Ky., U.S. **C5** 94
Clark, co., Mo., U.S. **A6** 102
Clark, co., Nv., U.S. **G6** 105
Clark, co., Oh., U.S. **C2** 112
Clark, co., S.D., U.S. **C8** 118
Clark, co., Wa., U.S. **D3** 124
Clark, co., Wi., U.S. **D3** 126
Clark, Lake, l., Ak., U.S. **C9** 79
Clark, Point, c., Ont., Can. **C3** 73
Clarkdale, Az., U.S. **C3** 80
Clarkdale, Ga., U.S. **h7** 87
Clarke, co., Al., U.S. **D2** 78
Clarke, co., Ga., U.S. **C3** 87
Clarke, co., Ia., U.S. **D4** 92
Clarke, co., Ms., U.S. **C5** 101
Clarke, co., Va., U.S. **A4** 123
Clarkesville, Ga., U.S. **B3** 87
Clarkfield, Mn., U.S. **F3** 100
Clark Fork, stm., U.S. **C1** 103
Clarks, La., U.S. **B3** 95
Clarks, stm., Ky., U.S. **f9** 94
Clarksburg, Md., U.S. **B3** 97
Clarksburg, W.V., U.S. **B4** 125
Clarksdale, Ms., U.S. **A3** 101
Clarks Grove, Mn., U.S. **G5** 100
Clark's Harbour, N.S., Can. **F4** 71
Clarks Hill, In., U.S. **D4** 91
Clarkson, Ky., U.S. **C3** 94
Clarkson, Ne., U.S. **C8** 104
Clarks Summit, Pa., U.S. **m18** 115
Clarkston, Ga., U.S. **h8** 87
Clarkston, Mi., U.S. **F7** 99
Clarkston, Ut., U.S. **B3** 121
Clarkston, Wa., U.S. **C8** 124
Clarksville, Ar., U.S. **B2** 81
Clarksville, De., U.S. **F5** 85
Clarksville, In., U.S. **H6** 91
Clarksville, Ia., U.S. **B5** 92
Clarksville, Tn., U.S. **A4** 119
Clarksville, Tx., U.S. **C5** 120
Clarksville, Va., U.S. **D4** 123
Clarkton, Mo., U.S. **E8** 102
Clarkton, N.C., U.S. **C4** 110
Clatskanie, Or., U.S. **A3** 114
Clatsop, co., Or., U.S. **A3** 114
Claude, Tx., U.S. **B2** 120
Clausthal-Zellerfeld, Ger. **D10** 8
Clawson, Mi., U.S. **o15** 99
Claxton, Ga., U.S. **D5** 87
Clay, Ky., U.S. **C2** 94
Clay, co., Al., U.S. **B4** 78
Clay, co., Ar., U.S. **A5** 81
Clay, co., Fl., U.S. **B5** 86
Clay, co., Ga., U.S. **E2** 87
Clay, co., Il., U.S. **E5** 90
Clay, co., In., U.S. **F3** 91
Clay, co., Ia., U.S. **A2** 92
Clay, co., Ks., U.S. **C6** 93
Clay, co., Ky., U.S. **C6** 94
Clay, co., Mn., U.S. **D2** 100
Clay, co., Ms., U.S. **B5** 101
Clay, co., Mo., U.S. **B3** 102
Clay, co., Ne., U.S. **D7** 104
Clay, co., N.C., U.S. **f9** 110
Clay, co., S.D., U.S. **E8** 118
Clay, co., Tn., U.S. **C8** 119
Clay, co., Tx., U.S. **C3** 120
Clay, co., W.V., U.S. **C3** 125
Clay Center, Ks., U.S. **C6** 93
Clay Center, Ne., U.S. **D7** 104
Clay City, Il., U.S. **E5** 90
Clay City, In., U.S. **F3** 91
Clay City, Ky., U.S. **C6** 94
Clay Creek, stm., S.D., U.S. **D8** 118
Claymont, De., U.S. **A4** 85
Clayoquot Sound, strt., B.C., Can. **E4** 69
Claypool, Az., U.S. **D5** 80
Claysburg, Pa., U.S. **F5** 115
Claysville, Pa., U.S. **F1** 115
Clayton, Al., U.S. **D4** 78
Clayton, De., U.S. **C3** 85
Clayton, Ga., U.S. **B3** 87
Clayton, In., U.S. **E4** 91
Clayton, La., U.S. **C4** 95
Clayton, Mo., U.S. **C7** 102
Clayton, N.J., U.S. **D2** 107
Clayton, N.M., U.S. **A6** 108
Clayton, N.Y., U.S. **A4** 109
Clayton, N.C., U.S. **B4** 110
Clayton, Ok., U.S. **C6** 113
Clayton, co., Ga., U.S. **C2** 87
Clayton, co., Ia., U.S. **B6** 92
Claytor Lake, res., Va., U.S. **C2** 123
Clear, stm., R.I., U.S. **B2** 116
Clear Boggy Creek, stm., Ok., U.S. **C5** 113
Clear Creek, co., Co., U.S. **B5** 83
Clear Creek, stm., Tn., U.S. **C9** 119
Clear Creek, stm., Wy., U.S. **B6** 127
Cleare, Cape, c., Ak., U.S. **D10** 79
Clearfield, Ky., U.S. **B6** 94
Clearfield, Pa., U.S. **D5** 115
Clearfield, Ut., U.S. **B3** 121
Clearfield, co., Pa., U.S. **D5** 115
Clear Fork, stm., W.V., U.S. **D3** 125
Clear Fork, stm., W.V., U.S. **n13** 125
Clearlake, Ca., U.S. **C2** 82
Clear Lake, Ia., U.S. **A4** 92
Clear Lake, S.D., U.S. **C9** 118
Clearlake, Wa., U.S. **A3** 124
Clear Lake, Wi., U.S. **C1** 126
Clear Lake, l., Ia., U.S. **A4** 92
Clear Lake, l., Ut., U.S. **D3** 121
Clear Lake, res., Ca., U.S. **C2** 82
Clear Lake Reservoir, res., Ca., U.S. **B3** 82
Clear Lake Shores, Tx., U.S. **r15** 120
Clear Stream, stm., N.H., U.S. **g7** 106
Clearwater, B.C., Can. **D7** 69
Clearwater, Fl., U.S. **E4** 86
Clearwater, Ks., U.S. **E6** 93
Clearwater, S.C., U.S. **E4** 117
Clearwater, co., Id., U.S. **C3** 89
Clearwater, co., Mn., U.S. **C3** 100
Clearwater, stm., Can. **A5** 68
Clearwater, stm., Id., U.S. **C2** 89
Clearwater, stm., Mn., U.S. **C3** 100
Clearwater Lake, res., Mo., U.S. **D7** 102
Clearwater Mountains, mts., Id., U.S. **C2** 89
Cleburne, Tx., U.S. **C4** 120
Cleburne, co., Al., U.S. **B4** 78
Cleburne, co., Ar., U.S. **B3** 81
Cle Elum, Wa., U.S. **B5** 124
Cle Elum, stm., Wa., U.S. **B4** 124
Cle Elum Lake, res., Wa., U.S. **B4** 124
Clementon, N.J., U.S. **D3** 107
Clemmons, N.C., U.S. **A2** 110
Clemson, S.C., U.S. **B2** 117
Clendenin, W.V., U.S. **C3** 125
Clendening Lake, res., Oh., U.S. **B4** 112
Cleona, Pa., U.S. **F9** 115
Clermont, Que., Can. **B7** 74
Clermont, Fr. **C9** 10
Clermont, Fl., U.S. **D5** 86
Clermont, co., Oh., U.S. **C1** 112
Clermont-Ferrand, Fr. **G10** 10
Cles, Italy **C6** 14
Cleveland, Al., U.S. **A3** 78
Cleveland, Ga., U.S. **B3** 87
Cleveland, Mn., U.S. **F5** 100
Cleveland, Ms., U.S. **B3** 101
Cleveland, N.C., U.S. **B2** 110
Cleveland, Oh., U.S. **A4** 112
Cleveland, Ok., U.S. **A5** 113
Cleveland, Tn., U.S. **D9** 119
Cleveland, Tx., U.S. **D5** 120
Cleveland, Wi., U.S. **k10** 126
Cleveland, co., Ar., U.S. **D3** 81
Cleveland, co., N.C., U.S. **B1** 110
Cleveland, co., Ok., U.S. **B4** 113
Cleveland, Mount, mtn., Mt., U.S. **B3** 103
Cleveland Heights, Oh., U.S. **A4** 112
Cleves, Oh., U.S. **o12** 112
Clewiston, Fl., U.S. **F6** 86
Clifden, Ire. **H2** 7
Cliff Island, i., Me., U.S. **g7** 96
Clifford, Ont., Can. **D4** 73
Cliffside, N.C., U.S. **B1** 110
Cliffside Park, N.J., U.S. **h9** 107
Clifton, Az., U.S. **D6** 80
Clifton, Co., U.S. **B2** 83
Clifton, Il., U.S. **C6** 90
Clifton, N.J., U.S. **B4** 107
Clifton, S.C., U.S. **B4** 117
Clifton, Tn., U.S. **B4** 119
Clifton, Tx., U.S. **D4** 120
Clifton Forge, Va., U.S. **C3** 123
Clifton Knolls, N.Y., U.S. **C7** 109
Clifton Springs, N.Y., U.S. **C3** 109
Clinch, co., Ga., U.S. **F4** 87
Clinch, stm., U.S. **D9** 119
Clinchco, Va., U.S. **e9** 123
Clinch Mountain, mtn., U.S. **C10** 119
Clingmans Dome, mtn., U.S. **D10** 119
Clinton, B.C., Can. **D7** 69
Clinton, Ont., Can. **D3** 73
Clinton, Ar., U.S. **B3** 81
Clinton, Ct., U.S. **D5** 84
Clinton, Il., U.S. **C5** 90
Clinton, In., U.S. **E3** 91
Clinton, Ia., U.S. **C7** 92
Clinton, Ky., U.S. **f9** 94
Clinton, La., U.S. **D4** 95
Clinton, Me., U.S. **D3** 96
Clinton, Md., U.S. **C4** 97
Clinton, Ma., U.S. **B4** 98
Clinton, Mi., U.S. **F7** 99
Clinton, Ms., U.S. **C3** 101
Clinton, Mo., U.S. **C4** 102
Clinton, N.Y., U.S. **B5** 109
Clinton, N.C., U.S. **C4** 110
Clinton, Ok., U.S. **B3** 113
Clinton, S.C., U.S. **C4** 117
Clinton, Tn., U.S. **C9** 119
Clinton, Ut., U.S. **B3** 121
Clinton, Wa., U.S. **B3** 124
Clinton, Wi., U.S. **F5** 126
Clinton, co., Il., U.S. **E4** 90
Clinton, co., In., U.S. **D4** 91
Clinton, co., Ia., U.S. **C7** 92
Clinton, co., Ky., U.S. **D4** 94
Clinton, co., Mi., U.S. **F6** 99
Clinton, co., Mo., U.S. **B3** 102
Clinton, co., N.Y., U.S. **f11** 109
Clinton, co., Oh., U.S. **C2** 112
Clinton, co., Pa., U.S. **D6** 115
Clinton, Lake, res., Il., U.S. **C5** 90
Clinton-Colden Lake, l., N.W. Ter., Can. **D11** 66
Clinton Lake, res., Ks., U.S. **m15** 93
Clinton Reservoir, res., N.J., U.S. **A4** 107
Clintonville, Wi., U.S. **D5** 126
Clintwood, Va., U.S. **e9** 123
Clio, Al., U.S. **D4** 78
Clio, Mi., U.S. **E7** 99
Clio, S.C., U.S. **B8** 117
Clive, Ia., U.S. **e8** 92
Clogher Head, c., Ire. **H6** 7
Cloncurry, Austl. **D8** 50
Clonmel, Ire. **I5** 7
Cloppenburg, Ger. **C8** 8
Cloquet, Mn., U.S. **D6** 100
Cloquet, stm., Mn., U.S. **C6** 100
Closter, N.J., U.S. **B5** 107
Clothier, W.V., U.S. **n12** 125
Cloud, co., Ks., U.S. **C6** 93
Cloudcroft, N.M., U.S. **E4** 108
Cloud Peak, mtn., Wy., U.S. **B5** 127
Clover, S.C., U.S. **A5** 117
Cloverdale, Al., U.S. **A2** 78
Cloverdale, Ca., U.S. **C2** 82
Cloverdale, In., U.S. **E4** 91
Cloverport, Ky., U.S. **C3** 94
Clovis, Ca., U.S. **D4** 82
Clovis, N.M., U.S. **C6** 108
Cluj-Napoca, Rom. **C7** 16
Cluny, Fr. **F11** 10
Cluses, Fr. **F13** 10
Clusone, Italy **D4** 14
Clute, Tx., U.S. **r14** 120
Clutha, stm., N.Z. **G2** 52
Clyde, N.W. Ter., Can. **B19** 66
Clyde, Ks., U.S. **C6** 93
Clyde, N.Y., U.S. **B4** 109
Clyde, N.C., U.S. **f10** 110
Clyde, Oh., U.S. **A3** 112
Clyde, Tx., U.S. **C3** 120
Clyde, stm., Scot., U.K. **F9** 7
Clyde, Firth of, est., Scot., U.K. **F7** 7
Clymer, Pa., U.S. **E3** 115
Coachella, Ca., U.S. **F5** 82
Coachella Canal, Ca., U.S. **F6** 82
Coacoyole, Mex. **E6** 62
Coahoma, Tx., U.S. **C2** 120
Coahoma, co., Ms., U.S. **A3** 101
Coal, co., Ok., U.S. **C5** 113
Coal, stm., W.V., U.S. **C3** 125
Coal Branch, N.B., Can. **C4** 71
Coal City, Il., U.S. **B5** 90
Coalcomán de Matamoros, Mex. **H8** 62
Coal Creek, stm., Ok., U.S. **B6** 113
Coaldale, Alta., Can. **E4** 68
Coal Fork, W.V., U.S. **C3** 125
Coal Fork, stm., W.V., U.S. **m13** 125
Coalgate, Ok., U.S. **C5** 113
Coal Grove, Oh., U.S. **D3** 112
Coal Hill, Ar., U.S. **B2** 81
Coalhurst, Alta., Can. **E4** 68
Coalinga, Ca., U.S. **D3** 82
Coalmont, Tn., U.S. **D8** 119
Coalville, Ut., U.S. **C4** 121
Coalwood, W.V., U.S. **D3** 125
Coari, Braz. **D6** 54

Name | Map Ref | Page

Coasters Harbor Island, i., R.I., U.S. E5 116
Coast Mountains, mts., N.A. E6 66
Coast Ranges, mts., U.S. C2 76
Coatepeque, Guat. G2 64
Coatesville, Pa., U.S. G10 115
Coaticook, Que., Can. D6 74
Coats, N.C., U.S. B4 110
Coats Island, i., N.W. Ter., Can. D16 66
Coats Land, reg., Ant. B10 47
Coatzacoalcos, Mex. H12 62
Cobalt, Ont., Can. p19 73
Cobb, co., Ga., U.S. C2 87
Cobb, stm., Mn., U.S. G5 100
Cobble Mountain Reservoir, res., Ma., U.S. B2 98
Cobbosseecontee Lake, l., Me., U.S. D3 96
Cobden, Ont., Can. B8 73
Cobden, Il., U.S. F4 90
Cobequid Mountains, mts., N.S., Can. D5 71
Cobham, stm., Can. C4 70
Cobija, Bol. F5 54
Cobleskill, N.Y., U.S. C6 109
Cobourg, Ont., Can. D6 73
Cóbuè, Moz. D6 44
Cobun Creek, stm., W.V., U.S. h11 125
Coburg, Ger. E10 8
Coburg, Or., U.S. C3 114
Coburg Island, i., N.W. Ter., Can. A17 66
Cochabamba, Bol. G5 54
Cocheco, stm., N.H., U.S. D5 106
Cochin, India H4 37
Cochise, co., Az., U.S. F5 80
Cochise Head, mtn., Az., U.S. E6 80
Cochiti Indian Reservation, N.M., U.S. h8 108
Cochiti Reservoir, res., N.M., U.S. B3 108
Cochituate, Ma., U.S. g10 98
Cochituate, Lake, l., Ma., U.S. g10 98
Cochran, Ga., U.S. D3 87
Cochran, co., Tx., U.S. C1 120
Cochrane, Alta., Can. D3 68
Cochrane, Ont., Can. o19 73
Cochranton, Pa., U.S. C1 115
Cocke, co., Tn., U.S. D10 119
Cockeysville, Md., U.S. B4 97
Cockrell Hill, Tx., U.S. n10 120
Coco, stm., N.A. G6 64
Coco, Isla del, i., C.R. B1 54
Cocoa, Fl., U.S. D6 86
Cocoa Beach, Fl., U.S. D6 86
Coco Channel, strt., Asia H2 34
Coco Islands, is., Burma G2 34
Coconino, co., Az., U.S. B3 80
Cocopah Indian Reservation, Az., U.S. E1 80
Côcos, Braz. C6 57
Cocula, Mex. G8 62
Cod, Cape, c., Ma., U.S. C7 98
Codajás, Braz. D6 54
Coden, Al., U.S. E1 78
Codigoro, Italy E7 14
Codington, co., S.D., U.S. C8 118
Codogno, Italy D4 14
Codroipo, Italy D7 14
Cody, Wy., U.S. B3 127
Coeburn, Va., U.S. f9 123
Coen, Austl. B8 50
Coetivy Island, i., Sey. C11 44
Coeur d'Alene, Id., U.S. B2 89
Coeur d'Alene, stm., Id., U.S. B2 89
Coeur d'Alene Indian Reservation, Id., U.S. B2 89
Coeur d'Alene Lake, res., Id., U.S. B2 89
Coeur d'Alene Mountains, mts., Id., U.S. B2 89
Coffee, co., Al., U.S. D3 78
Coffee, co., Ga., U.S. E4 87
Coffee, co., Tn., U.S. B5 119
Coffeeville, Ms., U.S. B4 101
Coffey, co., Ks., U.S. D8 93
Coffeyville, Ks., U.S. E8 93
Coffs Harbour, Austl. F10 50
Coggon, Ia., U.S. B6 92
Cognac, Fr. G6 10
Cohansey, stm., N.J., U.S. E2 107
Cohasset, Ma., U.S. B6 98
Cohasset, Mn., U.S. C5 100
Cohocton, stm., N.Y., U.S. C3 109
Cohoes, N.Y., U.S. C7 109
Cohoon, Lake, res., Va., U.S. k14 123
Cohutta Mountain, mtn., Ga., U.S. B2 87
Coiba, Isla de, i., Pan. K7 64
Coimbatore, India G4 37
Coimbra, Braz. F7 57
Coimbra, Port. E3 12
Coín, Spain I7 12
Cojbalsan, Mong. B9 26
Cokato, Mn., U.S. E4 100
Coke, co., Tx., U.S. D2 120
Cokeville, Wy., U.S. D2 127
Čokurdach, U.S.S.R. C23 20
Colatina, Braz. E8 57
Colbert, Ok., U.S. D5 113
Colbert, co., Al., U.S. A2 78
Colborne, Ont., Can. C7 73
Colby, Ks., U.S. C2 93
Colby, Wi., U.S. D3 126
Colchester, Eng., U.K. J13 7
Colchester, Ct., U.S. C6 84
Colchester, Il., U.S. C3 90
Colcord, Ok., U.S. A7 113
Cold, stm., N.H., U.S. C4 106
Cold, stm., N.H., U.S. D2 106
Cold Bay, Ak., U.S. E7 79
Cold Lake, Alta., Can. B5 68
Cold Spring, Ky., U.S. A5 94
Cold Spring, Mn., U.S. E4 100
Coldwater, Ont., Can. C5 73
Coldwater, Ks., U.S. E4 93
Coldwater, Mi., U.S. G5 99
Coldwater, Ms., U.S. A4 101
Coldwater, Oh., U.S. B1 112
Coldwater, stm., Ms., U.S. A3 101
Coldwater Creek, stm., U.S. e9 113
Cole, co., Mo., U.S. C5 102
Colebrook, N.H., U.S. g7 106
Colebrook River Lake, res., Ct., U.S. A3 84
Cole Camp, Mo., U.S. C4 102
Coleen, stm., Ak., U.S. B11 79
Coleman, Mi., U.S. E6 99
Coleman, Tx., U.S. D3 120
Coleman, Wi., U.S. C5 126
Coleman, co., Tx., U.S. D3 120
Coleraine, N. Ire., U.K. F6 7
Coleraine, Mn., U.S. C5 100
Coles, co., Il., U.S. D5 90
Colesberg, S. Afr. H5 44
Colfax, Ca., U.S. C3 82
Colfax, Il., U.S. C5 90
Colfax, In., U.S. D4 91
Colfax, Ia., U.S. C4 92
Colfax, La., U.S. C3 95
Colfax, Wa., U.S. C8 124
Colfax, Wi., U.S. D2 126
Colfax, co., Ne., U.S. C8 104
Colfax, co., N.M., U.S. A5 108
Colhué Huapi, Lago, l., Arg. F3 56
Colima, Mex. H8 62
Colima, Nevado de, mtn., Mex. H8 62
Colinas, Braz. E10 54
Coll, i., Scot., U.K. E6 7
College, Ak., U.S. B10 79
Collegedale, Tn., U.S. h11 119
College Park, Ga., U.S. C2 87
College Park, Md., U.S. C4 97
College Place, Wa., U.S. C7 124
College Station, Ar., U.S. C3 81
College Station, Tx., U.S. D4 120
Collegeville, In., U.S. C3 91
Collegeville, Pa., U.S. F11 115
Colleton, co., S.C., U.S. F6 117
Collier, co., Fl., U.S. F5 86
Collier Bay, b., Austl. C4 50
Colliers, W.V., U.S. f8 125
Collierville, Tn., U.S. B2 119
Collin, co., Tx., U.S. C4 120
Collingdale, Pa., U.S. p20 115
Collingswood, N.J., U.S. D2 107
Collingsworth, co., Tx., U.S. B2 120
Collingwood, Ont., Can. C4 73
Collins, Ms., U.S. D4 101
Collins Park, De., U.S. B3 85
Collinsville, Al., U.S. A4 78
Collinsville, Ct., U.S. B4 84
Collinsville, Il., U.S. E4 90
Collinsville, Ms., U.S. C5 101
Collinsville, Ok., U.S. A6 113
Collinsville, Va., U.S. D3 123
Collinwood, Tn., U.S. B4 119
Collooney, Ire. G4 7
Colmar, Fr. D14 10
Colmar Manor, Md., U.S. f9 97
Colmenar, Spain I7 12
Colmenar de Oreja, Spain E8 12
Colmenar Viejo, Spain E8 12
Colo, Ia., U.S. B4 92
Cologne see Köln, Ger. E6 8
Coloma, Mi., U.S. F4 99
Colomb-Béchar see Béchar, Alg. B5 42
Colombia, ctry., S.A. C4 54
Colombo, Sri L. I5 37
Colón, Cuba C7 64
Colón, Pan. J8 64
Colon, Mi., U.S. G5 99
Colon, Archipiélago de (Galapagos Islands), is., Ec. m15 58a
Colonia Dora, Arg. B4 56
Colonia Las Heras, Arg. F3 56
Colonial Beach, Va., U.S. B6 123
Colonial Heights, Tn., U.S. C11 119
Colonial Heights, Va., U.S. C5 123
Colonial National Historical Park, Va., U.S. C6 123
Colonia Vicente Guerrero, Mex. B1 62
Colonie, N.Y., U.S. C7 109
Coloradas, Lomas, hills, Arg. E3 56
Colorado, co., Tx., U.S. E4 120
Colorado, state, U.S. B5 83
Colorado, stm., Arg. D4 56
Colorado, stm., N.A. E4 76
Colorado, stm., Tx., U.S. D3 120
Colorado City, Az., U.S. A3 80
Colorado City, Co., U.S. D6 83
Colorado City, Tx., U.S. C2 120
Colorado City, Lake, res., Tx., U.S. C2 120
Colorado National Monument, Co., U.S. B2 83
Colorado River Aqueduct, Ca., U.S. F6 82
Colorado River Indian Reservation, U.S. D1 80
Colorado Springs, Co., U.S. C6 83
Colotlán, Mex. F8 62
Colquitt, Ga., U.S. E2 87
Colquitt, co., Ga., U.S. E3 87
Colstrip, Mt., U.S. E10 103
Colton, S.D., U.S. D9 118
Coltons Point, Md., U.S. D4 97
Columbia, Al., U.S. D4 78
Columbia, Il., U.S. E3 90
Columbia, Ky., U.S. C4 94
Columbia, Md., U.S. B4 97
Columbia, Ms., U.S. D4 101
Columbia, Mo., U.S. C5 102
Columbia, N.C., U.S. B6 110
Columbia, Pa., U.S. F9 115
Columbia, S.C., U.S. C5 117
Columbia, Tn., U.S. B4 119
Columbia, co., Ar., U.S. D2 81
Columbia, co., Fl., U.S. B4 86
Columbia, co., Ga., U.S. C4 87
Columbia, co., N.Y., U.S. C7 109
Columbia, co., Or., U.S. B3 114
Columbia, co., Pa., U.S. D9 115
Columbia, co., Wa., U.S. C7 124
Columbia, co., Wi., U.S. E4 126
Columbia, stm., N.A. G8 66
Columbia, Mount, mtn., Can. C2 68
Columbia City, In., U.S. B7 91
Columbia City, Or., U.S. B4 114
Columbia Falls, Mt., U.S. B2 103
Columbia Heights, Mn., U.S. m12 100
Columbia Lake, res., Ct., U.S. C6 84
Columbia Mountains, mts., B.C., Can. C7 69
Columbiana, Al., U.S. B3 78
Columbiana, Oh., U.S. B5 112
Columbiana, co., Oh., U.S. B5 112
Columbiaville, Mi., U.S. E7 99
Columbus, Ga., U.S. D2 87
Columbus, In., U.S. F6 91
Columbus, Ks., U.S. E9 93
Columbus, Ms., U.S. B5 101
Columbus, Mt., U.S. E7 103
Columbus, Ne., U.S. C8 104
Columbus, N.M., U.S. F2 108
Columbus, N.C., U.S. f10 110
Columbus, Oh., U.S. C2 112
Columbus, Tx., U.S. E4 120
Columbus, Wi., U.S. E4 126
Columbus, co., N.C., U.S. C4 110
Columbus Air Force Base, mil., Ms., U.S. B5 101
Columbus Grove, Oh., U.S. B1 112
Columbus Junction, Ia., U.S. C6 92
Columbus Lake, res., Ms., U.S. B5 101
Colusa, Ca., U.S. C2 82
Colusa, co., Ca., U.S. C2 82
Colver, Pa., U.S. E4 115
Colville, Wa., U.S. A8 124
Colville, stm., Ak., U.S. B9 79
Colville, stm., Wa., U.S. A8 124
Colville Indian Reservation, Wa., U.S. A6 124
Colvos Passage, strt., Wa., U.S. f10 124
Colwich, Ks., U.S. E6 93
Colwood, B.C., Can. h12 69
Comacchio, Italy E7 14
Comal, co., Tx., U.S. E3 120
Comanche, Ok., U.S. C4 113
Comanche, Tx., U.S. D3 120
Comanche, co., Ks., U.S. E4 93
Comanche, co., Ok., U.S. C3 113
Comanche, co., Tx., U.S. D3 120
Comandante Fontana, Arg. B5 56
Comayagua, Hond. G4 64
Combahee, stm., S.C., U.S. F6 117
Combarbalá, Chile C2 56
Combeaufontaine, Fr. E12 10
Comber, Ont., Can. E2 73
Combermere Bay, b., Burma E2 34
Combined Locks, Wi., U.S. h9 126
Combourg, Fr. D5 10
Combs, Ky., U.S. C6 94
Comer, Ga., U.S. B3 87
Comfort, Tx., U.S. E3 120
Comilla, Bngl. I14 38
Comitán [de Domínguez], Mex. I13 62
Comite, stm., La., U.S. D4 95
Commentry, Fr. F9 10
Commerce, Ga., U.S. B3 87
Commerce, Ok., U.S. A7 113
Commerce, Tx., U.S. C5 120
Commerce City, Co., U.S. B6 83
Committee Bay, b., N.W. Ter., Can. C15 66
Common Fence Point, R.I., U.S. D6 116
Como, Italy D4 14
Como, Ms., U.S. A4 101
Como, Lago di, l., Italy C4 14
Comodoro Rivadavia, Arg. F3 56
Comorin, Cape, c., India H4 37
Comoros, ctry., Afr. D8 44
Comox, B.C., Can. E5 69
Compiègne, Fr. C9 10
Compton, Que., Can. D6 74
Compton, Ca., U.S. n12 82
Comstock, Mi., U.S. F5 99
Con, stm., Viet. E8 34
Čona, stm., U.S.S.R. E16 20
Conakry, Gui. G3 42
Conanicut Island, i., R.I., U.S. E5 116
Conanicut Point, c., R.I., U.S. E5 116
Concarneau, Fr. E3 10
Conceição do Araguaia, Braz. E9 54
Concepción, Arg. B3 56
Concepción, Bol. G6 54
Concepción, Chile D2 56
Concepción, Para. A5 56
Concepción, Laguna, l., Bol. G6 54
Concepción, Volcán, vol., Nic. I5 64
Concepcion del Oro, Mex. E9 62
Concepción del Uruguay, Arg. C5 56
Conception, Point, c., Ca., U.S. E3 82
Conception Bay, b., Newf., Can. E5 72
Conception Bay South, Newf., Can. E5 72
Conchas Lake, res., N.M., U.S. B5 108
Conches, Fr. D7 10
Concho, co., Tx., U.S. D3 120
Concho, stm., Tx., U.S. D2 120
Conchos, stm., Mex. C7 62
Concord, Ca., U.S. h8 82
Concord, Ma., U.S. B5 98
Concord, Mi., U.S. F6 99
Concord, Mo., U.S. g13 102
Concord, N.H., U.S. D3 106
Concord, N.C., U.S. B2 110
Concord, stm., Ma., U.S. A5 98
Concordia, Arg. C5 56
Concordia, Mex. F6 62
Concordia, Ks., U.S. C6 93
Concordia, Mo., U.S. C4 102
Concordia, co., La., U.S. C4 95
Concrete, Wa., U.S. A4 124
Condé, Fr. D6 10
Condom, Fr. I7 10
Condon, Or., U.S. B6 114
Condoto, Col. E4 58
Conecuh, co., Al., U.S. D2 78
Conecuh, stm., U.S. D3 78
Conegliano, Italy D7 14
Conejos, co., Co., U.S. D4 83
Conejos, stm., Co., U.S. D4 83
Conejos Peak, mtn., Co., U.S. D4 83
Conemaugh, Pa., U.S. F4 115
Conemaugh River Lake, res., Pa., U.S. F3 115
Confolens, Fr. F7 10
Congamond Lakes, l., U.S. A4 84
Congaree, stm., S.C., U.S. D6 117
Congaree Swamp National Monument, S.C., U.S. D6 117
Congo, ctry., Afr. B2 44
Congo (Zaire), stm., Afr. C2 44
Congress, Az., U.S. C3 80
Conimicut Point, c., R.I., U.S. D5 116
Conitaca, Mex. E6 62
Conklin, N.Y., U.S. C5 109
Conn, Lough, l., Ire. G3 7
Connaught, hist. reg., Ire. H3 7
Conneaut, Oh., U.S. A5 112
Conneaut Creek, stm., Oh., U.S. A5 112
Conneaut Lake, l., Pa., U.S. C1 115
Connecticut, state, U.S. C5 84
Connecticut, stm., U.S. C12 76
Connell, Wa., U.S. C7 124
Connellsville, Pa., U.S. F2 115
Connemara, reg., Ire. H3 7
Connersville, In., U.S. E7 91
Conover, N.C., U.S. B1 110
Conowingo, Md., U.S. A5 97
Conrad, Ia., U.S. B5 92
Conrad, Mt., U.S. B5 103
Conroe, Tx., U.S. D5 120
Conselheiro Lafaiete, Braz. F7 57
Conshohocken, Pa., U.S. F11 115
Con Son, is., Viet. J9 34
Consort, Alta., Can. C5 68
Constance, Lake see Bodensee, l., Eur. H9 8
Constanța, Rom. E12 16
Constantina, Spain H6 12
Constantine, Alg. A7 42
Constantine, Mi., U.S. G5 99
Constantine, Cape, c., Ak., U.S. D8 79
Consuegra, Spain F8 12
Contai, India J12 38
Contas, Rio de, stm., Braz. C9 57
Content Keys, is., Fl., U.S. H5 86
Continental, Oh., U.S. A1 112
Continental Peak, mtn., Wy., U.S. D4 127
Continental Reservoir, res., Co., U.S. D3 83
Contoocook, N.H., U.S. D3 106
Contoocook, stm., N.H., U.S. D3 106
Contra Costa, co., Ca., U.S. D3 82
Contrecoeur, Que., Can. D4 74
Contres, Fr. E8 10
Contwoyto Lake, l., N.W. Ter., Can. C10 66
Convención, Col. C6 58
Conversano, Italy I12 14
Converse, In., U.S. C6 91
Converse, S.C., U.S. B4 117
Converse, co., Wy., U.S. C7 127
Convoy, Oh., U.S. B1 112
Conway, Ar., U.S. B3 81
Conway, Fl., U.S. D5 86
Conway, Mo., U.S. D5 102
Conway, N.H., U.S. C4 106
Conway, N.C., U.S. A5 110
Conway, Pa., U.S. E1 115
Conway, S.C., U.S. D9 117
Conway, co., Ar., U.S. B3 81
Conway Lake, res., Ar., U.S. B3 81
Conway Lake, l., N.H., U.S. C4 106
Conway Springs, Ks., U.S. E6 93
Conyers, Ga., U.S. C2 87
Cooch Behār, India G13 38
Cook, Mn., U.S. C6 100
Cook, co., Ga., U.S. E3 87
Cook, co., Il., U.S. B6 90
Cook, co., Mn., U.S. k9 100
Cook, Cape, c., B.C., Can. D4 69
Cook, Mount, mtn., N.Z. E3 52
Cooke, co., Tx., U.S. C4 120
Cookes Peak, mtn., N.M., U.S. E2 108
Cookeville, Tn., U.S. C8 119
Cook Inlet, b., Ak., U.S. D9 79
Cook Islands, dep., Oc. H2 2
Cook Point, c., Md., U.S. C5 97
Cookshire, Que., Can. D6 74
Cookson, Ok., U.S. B7 113
Cookstown, N. Ire., U.K. G6 7
Cook Strait, strt., N.Z. D5 52
Cooktown, Austl. C9 50
Cooleemee, N.C., U.S. B2 110
Coolgardie, Austl. F4 50
Coolidge, Az., U.S. E4 80
Coolidge, Ga., U.S. E3 87
Cooma, Austl. G9 50
Coonoor, India G4 37
Coon Rapids, Ia., U.S. C3 92
Coon Rapids, Mn., U.S. E5 100
Coon Valley, Wi., U.S. E2 126
Cooper, Tx., U.S. C5 120
Cooper, co., Mo., U.S. C5 102
Cooper, stm., S.C., U.S. F8 117
Cooper Mountain, mtn., Ak., U.S. g17 79
Coopersburg, Pa., U.S. F11 115
Cooperstown, N.Y., U.S. C6 109
Cooperstown, N.D., U.S. B7 111
Coopersville, Mi., U.S. E5 99
Coos, co., N.H., U.S. A4 106
Coos, co., Or., U.S. D2 114
Coos, stm., Or., U.S. D2 114
Coosa, co., Al., U.S. C3 78
Coosa, stm., U.S. C3 78
Coosada, Al., U.S. C3 78
Coosawhatchie, stm., S.C., U.S. F5 117
Coos Bay, Or., U.S. D2 114
Copalis Beach, Wa., U.S. B1 124
Copan, Ok., U.S. A6 113
Copan Reservoir, res., Ok., U.S. A6 113
Copenhagen see København, Den. I9 6
Copiah, co., Ms., U.S. D3 101
Copiapó, Chile B2 56
Coplay, Pa., U.S. E10 115
Copparo, Italy E6 14
Copper, stm., Ak., U.S. C11 79
Copperas Cove, Tx., U.S. D4 120
Copper Butte, mtn., Wa., U.S. A7 124
Coppermine, N.W. Ter., Can. C9 66
Coppermine, stm., N.W. Ter., Can. C10 66
Copper Mountain, mtn., Wy., U.S. C5 127
Copper Mountains, mts., Az., U.S. E2 80
Coquille, Or., U.S. D2 114
Coquimbo, Chile B2 56
Coral Gables, Fl., U.S. G6 86
Coral Harbour, N.W. Ter., Can. D16 66
Coral Sea, Oc. B10 50
Coralville, Ia., U.S. C6 92
Coralville Lake, res., Ia., U.S. C5 92
Corantijn (Corentyne), stm., S.A. E14 58
Coraopolis, Pa., U.S. E1 115
Corato, Italy H11 14
Corbeil-Essonnes, Fr. D9 10
Corbigny, Fr. E10 10
Corbin, Ky., U.S. D5 94
Corcoran, Ca., U.S. D4 82
Corcoran, Mn., U.S. m11 100
Corcovado, Golfo, b., Chile E2 56
Corcovado, Volcán, vol., Chile E2 56
Corcubión, Spain C2 12
Cordele, Ga., U.S. E3 87
Cordell, Ok., U.S. B3 113
Cordell Hull Lake, res., Tn., U.S. C8 119
Cordes, Fr. H8 10
Córdoba, Arg. C4 56
Córdoba, Mex. H11 62
Córdoba, Spain H7 12
Cordova, Al., U.S. B2 78
Cordova, Ak., U.S. C10 79
Cordova, N.M., U.S. A4 108
Cordova, N.C., U.S. C3 110
Cordova Peak, mtn., Ak., U.S. C10 79
Corentyne (Corantijn), stm., S.A. E14 58
Corfu see Kérkira, Grc. J3 16
Coria, Spain F5 12
Coria del Río, Spain H5 12
Corigliano Calabro, Italy J11 14
Coringa Islets, is., Austl. C9 50
Corinna, Me., U.S. D3 96
Corinne, Ut., U.S. B3 121
Corinne Key, i., Fl., U.S. G6 86
Corinth, Ms., U.S. A5 101
Corinth, N.Y., U.S. B7 109
Corinth see Kórinthos, Grc. L6 16
Corinto, Braz. E6 57
Cork, Ire. J4 7
Corlay, Fr. D3 10
Corleone, Italy L8 14
Corleto Perticara, Italy I11 14
Çorlu, Tur. H11 16
Cormorant Lake, l., Man., Can. B1 70
Cornelia, Ga., U.S. B3 87
Cornélio Procópio, Braz. G3 57
Cornelius, N.C., U.S. B2 110
Cornelius, Or., U.S. g11 114
Cornell, Wi., U.S. C2 126
Corner Brook, Newf., Can. D3 72
Cornersville, Tn., U.S. B5 119
Cornfield Point, c., Ct., U.S. D6 84
Cornie Bayou, stm., U.S. D3 81
Corning, Ar., U.S. A5 81
Corning, Ca., U.S. C2 82
Corning, Ia., U.S. D3 92
Corning, N.Y., U.S. C3 109
Cornish, Me., U.S. E2 96
Corn Islands, is., Nic. H6 64
Corno Grande, mtn., Italy G8 14
Cornville, Az., U.S. C4 80
Cornwall, Ont., Can. B10 73
Cornwall, Pa., U.S. F9 115
Cornwallis Island, i., N.W. Ter., Can. A14 66
Cornwall on Hudson, N.Y., U.S. D6 109
Coro, Ven. B8 58
Corocoro, Bol. G5 54
Coroico, Bol. G5 54
Coromandel Coast, India F6 37
Coromandel Peninsula, pen., N.Z. B5 52
Corona, Ca., U.S. F5 82
Coronado, Ca., U.S. F5 82
Coronado National Memorial, Az., U.S. F5 80
Coronation, Alta., Can. C5 68
Coronation Gulf, b., N.W. Ter., Can. C10 66
Coronation Island, i., Ak., U.S. n22 79
Coronel Dorrego, Arg. D4 56
Coronel Fabriciano, Braz. E7 57
Coronel Pringles, Arg. D4 56
Coronel Suárez, Arg. D4 56
Coropuna, Nevado, mtn., Peru G4 54
Corpus Christi, Tx., U.S. F4 120
Corpus Christi Naval Air Station, mil., Tx., U.S. F4 120
Corral de Almaguer, Spain F8 12
Correctionville, Ia., U.S. B2 92
Correggio, Italy E5 14
Corrente, stm., Braz. B7 57
Corrib, Lough, l., Ire. H3 7
Corrientes, Arg. B5 56
Corrientes, Cabo, c., Col. E4 58
Corrientes, Cabo, c., Cuba D5 64
Corrientes, Cabo, c., Mex. G7 62
Corrigan, Tx., U.S. D5 120
Corriganville, Md., U.S. k13 97
Corry, Pa., U.S. C2 115
Corse (Corsica), i., Fr. m19 11a
Corsica, S.D., U.S. D7 118
Corsica see Corse, i., Fr. m19 11a
Corsicana, Tx., U.S. C4 120
Corson, co., S.D., U.S. B4 118
Corson Inlet, b., N.J., U.S. E3 107
Cortemilia, Italy E3 14
Cortez, Co., U.S. D2 83
Cortez, Fl., U.S. q10 86
Cortez Mountains, mts., Nv., U.S. C5 105
Cortina d'Ampezzo, Italy C7 14
Cortland, Il., U.S. B5 90

Name | Map Ref | Page

Cortland, N.Y., U.S. C4 109
Cortland, Oh., U.S. A5 112
Cortland, co., N.Y., U.S. C4 109
Çorum, Tur. G14 4
Corumbá, Braz. G7 54
Corumbá, stm., Braz. E4 57
Corunna, Mi., U.S. F6 99
Corvallis, Or., U.S. C3 114
Corydon, In., U.S. H5 91
Corydon, Ia., U.S. D4 92
Corydon, Ky., U.S. C2 94
Coryell, co., Tx., U.S. D4 120
Cosamaloapan [de Carpio], Mex. H12 62
Cosenza, Italy J11 14
Coshocton, Oh., U.S. B4 112
Coshocton, co., Oh., U.S. B4 112
Cosmoledo Group, is., Sey. C9 44
Cosmopolis, Wa., U.S. C2 124
Cosmos, Mn., U.S. F4 100
Cosne-sur-Loire, Fr. E9 10
Cossatot, stm., Ar., U.S. C1 81
Costa Mesa, Ca., U.S. n13 82
Costa Rica, Mex. C4 62
Costa Rica, ctry., N.A. I5 64
Costilla, co., Co., U.S. D5 83
Cotabato, Phil. D7 32
Coteau-Landing, Que., Can. D3 74
Cotentin, pen., Fr. C5 10
Cotonou, Benin G6 42
Cotopaxi, vol., Ec. H3 58
Cottage Grove, Mn., U.S. n13 100
Cottage Grove, Or., U.S. D3 114
Cottage Grove Reservoir, res., Or., U.S. D3 114
Cottam, Ont., Can. E2 73
Cottbus, Ger. D14 8
Cotter, Ar., U.S. A3 81
Cottiennes, Alpes (Alpi Cozie), mts., Eur. H13 10
Cottle, co., Tx., U.S. B2 120
Cottleville, Mo., U.S. f12 102
Cotton, co., Ok., U.S. C3 113
Cottondale, Al., U.S. B2 78
Cotton Plant, Ar., U.S. B4 81
Cottonport, La., U.S. C3 95
Cotton Valley, La., U.S. B2 95
Cottonwood, Al., U.S. D4 78
Cottonwood, Az., U.S. C3 80
Cottonwood, Ca., U.S. B2 82
Cottonwood, Id., U.S. C2 89
Cottonwood, Mn., U.S. F3 100
Cottonwood, co., Mn., U.S. F3 100
Cottonwood, stm., Ks., U.S. D7 93
Cottonwood, stm., Mn., U.S. F3 100
Cottonwood Creek, stm., Wy., U.S. C4 127
Cottonwood Falls, Ks., U.S. D7 93
Cotuit, Ma., U.S. C7 98
Cotulla, Tx., U.S. E3 120
Coudersport, Pa., U.S. C5 115
Cougar Reservoir, res., Or., U.S. C4 114
Couhé, Fr. F7 10
Coulee Creek, stm., Wa., U.S. g13 124
Coulee Dam, Wa., U.S. B7 124
Coulee Dam National Recreation Area, Wa., U.S. A7 124
Coulommiers, Fr. D10 10
Coulterville, Il., U.S. E4 90
Counce, Tn., U.S. B3 119
Council, Id., U.S. E2 89
Council Bluffs, Ia., U.S. C2 92
Council Grove, Ks., U.S. D7 93
Council Grove Lake, res., Ks., U.S. D7 93
Council Mountain, mtn., Id., U.S. E2 89
Country Homes, Wa., U.S. B8 124
Coupeville, Wa., U.S. A3 124
Courtenay, B.C., Can. E5 69
Courte Oreilles, Lac, l., Wi., U.S. C2 126
Courtland, Ont., Can. E4 73
Courtland, Al., U.S. A2 78
Courtland, Va., U.S. D5 123
Coushatta, La., U.S. B2 95
Coutances, Fr. C5 10
Coutras, Fr. G6 10
Cove Creek, stm., Ut., U.S. E3 121
Covedale, Oh., U.S. o12 112
Coventry, Eng., U.K. I11 7
Coventry, Ct., U.S. B6 84
Coventry, R.I., U.S. D3 116
Cove Point, c., Md., U.S. D5 97
Covilhã, Port. E4 12
Covina, Ca., U.S. m13 82
Covington, Ga., U.S. C3 87
Covington, In., U.S. D3 91
Covington, Ky., U.S. A5 94
Covington, La., U.S. D5 95
Covington, Oh., U.S. B1 112
Covington, Tn., U.S. B2 119
Covington, Va., U.S. C3 123
Covington, co., Al., U.S. D3 78
Covington, co., Ms., U.S. D4 101
Cowan, Tn., U.S. B5 119
Cowan, Lake, l., Austl. F4 50
Cowansville, Que., Can. D5 74
Cowarts, Al., U.S. D4 78
Cow Creek, stm., Wa., U.S. C7 124
Cowee Mountains, mts., N.C., U.S. f9 110
Cowen, Mount, mtn., Mt., U.S. E6 103
Coweta, Ok., U.S. B6 113
Coweta, co., Ga., U.S. C2 87
Cow Head, Newf., Can. D3 72
Cowichan Bay, B.C., Can. g12 69
Cow Lakes, l., Or., U.S. D9 114
Cowley, Wy., U.S. B4 127
Cowley, co., Ks., U.S. E7 93
Cowlington, Ok., U.S. B7 113
Cowlitz, co., Wa., U.S. C2 124
Cowlitz, stm., Wa., U.S. C3 124
Cowpasture, stm., Va., U.S. B3 123
Cowpen Mountain, mtn., Ga., U.S. B2 87
Cowpens, S.C., U.S. A4 117
Coxim, Braz. E1 57
Coxsackie, N.Y., U.S. C7 109
Cox's Bāzār, Bngl. J14 38
Cox's Cove, Newf., Can. D2 72
Coyhaique, Chile F2 56
Cozad, Ne., U.S. D6 104
Cozumel, Isla de, i., Mex. G16 62
Crab Creek, stm., Wa., U.S. C6 124
Crab Creek, stm., Wa., U.S. B7 124
Crab Orchard, Ky., U.S. C5 94
Crab Orchard, Tn., U.S. D9 119
Crab Orchard, W.V., U.S. n13 125
Crab Orchard Lake, res., Il., U.S. F4 90
Crabtree, Pa., U.S. F3 115
Crabtree Mills, Que., Can. D4 74
Cradock, S. Afr. H5 44
Crafton, Pa., U.S. k13 115
Craig, Ak., U.S. D13 79
Craig, Co., U.S. A3 83
Craig, co., Ok., U.S. A6 113
Craig, co., Va., U.S. C2 123
Craig Air Force Base, mil., Al., U.S. C3 78
Craig Creek, stm., Va., U.S. C2 123
Craighead, co., Ar., U.S. B5 81
Craigsville, Va., U.S. B3 123
Craigsville, W.V., U.S. C4 125
Crailsheim, Ger. F10 8
Craiova, Rom. E7 16
Cramerton, N.C., U.S. B1 110
Cranberry Lake, l., N.Y., U.S. A6 109
Cranberry Portage, Man., Can. B1 70
Cranbrook, B.C., Can. E10 69
Crandall, Tx., U.S. n10 120
Crandon, Wi., U.S. C5 126
Crane, Az., U.S. E1 80
Crane, Mo., U.S. E4 102
Crane, Tx., U.S. D1 120
Crane, co., Tx., U.S. D1 120
Crane Creek, stm., Oh., U.S. e7 112
Crane Creek Reservoir, res., Id., U.S. E2 89
Crane Lake, l., Il., U.S. C3 90
Crane Lake, l., Mn., U.S. B6 100
Crane Mountain, mtn., Or., U.S. E6 114
Crane Prairie Reservoir, res., Or., U.S. D5 114
Cranford, N.J., U.S. B4 107
Cranston, R.I., U.S. C4 116
Craon, Fr. E6 10
Craponne, Fr. G10 10
Crater Lake, l., Or., U.S. E4 114
Crater Lake National Park, Or., U.S. E4 114
Craters of the Moon National Monument, Id., U.S. F5 89
Cratéus, Braz. E10 54
Crato, Braz. E11 54
Crauford, Cape, c., N.W. Ter., Can. B16 66
Craven, co., N.C., U.S. B5 110
Crawford, Ga., U.S. C3 87
Crawford, Ms., U.S. B5 101
Crawford, Ne., U.S. B2 104
Crawford, co., Ar., U.S. B1 81
Crawford, co., Ga., U.S. D3 87
Crawford, co., Il., U.S. D6 90
Crawford, co., In., U.S. H4 91
Crawford, co., Ia., U.S. B2 92
Crawford, co., Ks., U.S. E9 93
Crawford, co., Mi., U.S. D6 99
Crawford, co., Mo., U.S. D6 102
Crawford, co., Oh., U.S. B3 112
Crawford, co., Pa., U.S. C1 115
Crawford, co., Wi., U.S. E3 126
Crawford Lake, l., Me., U.S. C5 96
Crawford Notch State Park, N.H., U.S. B4 106
Crawfordsville, Ar., U.S. B5 81
Crawfordsville, In., U.S. D4 91
Crawfordville, Fl., U.S. B2 86
Crazy Mountains, mts., Mt., U.S. D6 103
Crazy Peak, mtn., Mt., U.S. D6 103
Crazy Woman Creek, stm., Wy., U.S. B6 127
Creal Springs, Il., U.S. F5 90
Cree, stm., Sask., Can. E11 66
Creedmoor, N.C., U.S. A4 110
Creek, co., Ok., U.S. B5 113
Cree Lake, l., Sask., Can. m7 75
Creemore, Ont., Can. C4 73
Creighton, Ne., U.S. B8 104
Creighton, Pa., U.S. h14 115
Creil, Fr. C9 10
Crema, Italy D4 14
Cremona, Italy D5 14
Crenshaw, Ms., U.S. A3 101
Crenshaw, co., Al., U.S. D3 78
Creola, Al., U.S. E1 78
Cres, Yugo. E9 14
Cresaptown, Md., U.S. k13 97
Crescent, Ok., U.S. B4 113
Crescent, Or., U.S. D5 114
Crescent, Lake, l., Wa., U.S. A2 124
Crescent City, Ca., U.S. B1 82
Crescent City, Fl., U.S. C5 86
Crescent Lake, l., Fl., U.S. C5 86
Crescent Lake, l., Or., U.S. D5 114
Crescent Springs, Ky., U.S. h13 94
Cresco, Ia., U.S. A5 92
Cresskill, N.J., U.S. h9 107
Cresson, Pa., U.S. F4 115
Cressona, Pa., U.S. E9 115
Crest, Fr. H12 10
Crested Butte, Co., U.S. C4 83
Crest Hill, Il., U.S. k8 90
Crestline, Oh., U.S. B3 112
Creston, B.C., Can. E9 69
Creston, Ia., U.S. C3 92
Creston, Oh., U.S. B4 112
Crestone Peak, mtn., Co., U.S. D5 83
Crestview, Fl., U.S. u15 86
Crestview, Hi., U.S. g10 88
Crestwood, Ky., U.S. B4 94
Crestwood Village, N.J., U.S. D4 107
Creswell, Or., U.S. D3 114
Crete, Il., U.S. B6 90
Crete, Ne., U.S. D9 104
Crete see Kríti, i., Grc. N8 16
Creve Coeur, Il., U.S. C4 90
Crevillente, Spain G11 12
Crewe, Eng., U.K. H10 7
Crewe, Va., U.S. C4 123
Criciúma, Braz. B7 56
Cricket, N.C., U.S. A1 110
Cridersville, Oh., U.S. B1 112
Crikvenica, Yugo. D9 14
Crimea see Krymskij poluostrov, pen., U.S.S.R. H4 18
Crimmitschau, Ger. E12 8
Crisfield, Md., U.S. E6 97
Crisp, co., Ga., U.S. E3 87
Cristalândia, Braz. F9 54
Cristalina, Braz. D5 57
Cristianópolis, Braz. D4 57
Cristóbal Colón, Pico, mtn., Col. B6 58
Crittenden, Ky., U.S. B5 94
Crittenden, co., Ar., U.S. B5 81
Crittenden, co., Ky., U.S. e9 94
Çrivitz, Wi., U.S. C6 126
Črnomelj, Yugo. D10 14
Crocker, Mo., U.S. D5 102
Crockett, Ca., U.S. g8 82
Crockett, Tx., U.S. D5 120
Crockett, co., Tn., U.S. B2 119
Crockett, co., Tx., U.S. D2 120
Crofton, Ky., U.S. C2 94
Crofton, Md., U.S. B4 97
Crofton, Ne., U.S. B8 104
Croix, Lac la, l., Mn., U.S. B6 100
Croker, Cape, c., Ont., Can. C4 73
Croker Island, i., Austl. B6 50
Cromarty, Scot., U.K. D8 7
Cromona, Ky., U.S. C7 94
Cromwell, Ct., U.S. C5 84
Crook, co., Or., U.S. C6 114
Crook, co., Wy., U.S. B8 127
Crooked, stm., Or., U.S. C6 114
Crooked Creek, stm., U.S. E3 93
Crooked Creek, stm., Pa., U.S. C7 115
Crooked Creek Lake, res., Pa., U.S. E3 115
Crooked Island, i., Bah. C10 64
Crooked Island Passage, strt., Bah. C10 64
Crooked Lake, l., Fl., U.S. E5 86
Crooked Lake, l., Mn., U.S. B7 100
Crooks, S.D., U.S. D9 118
Crooks Lake, l., Nv., U.S. B2 105
Crookston, Mn., U.S. C2 100
Crooksville, Oh., U.S. C3 112
Crosby, Mn., U.S. D5 100
Crosby, N.D., U.S. A2 111
Crosby, Tx., U.S. r14 120
Crosby, co., Tx., U.S. C2 120
Crosby, Mount, mtn., Wy., U.S. C3 127
Crosbyton, Tx., U.S. C2 120
Cross, co., Ar., U.S. B5 81
Cross Bay, b., Man., Can. C2 70
Cross City, Fl., U.S. C3 86
Cross Creek, stm., W.V., U.S. f8 125
Crossett, Ar., U.S. D4 81
Crossfield, Alta., Can. D3 68
Cross Island, i., Me., U.S. D5 96
Cross Lake, Man., Can. B3 70
Crosslake, Mn., U.S. D4 100
Cross Lake, l., Me., U.S. A4 96
Cross Lake, res., La., U.S. B2 95
Cross Lanes, W.V., U.S. C3 125
Crossman Peak, mtn., Az., U.S. C1 80
Cross Plains, Tn., U.S. A5 119
Cross Plains, Tx., U.S. C3 120
Cross Plains, Wi., U.S. E4 126
Cross Sound, strt., Ak., U.S. k21 79
Crossville, Al., U.S. A4 78
Crossville, Il., U.S. E5 90
Crossville, Tn., U.S. D8 119
Croswell, Mi., U.S. E8 99
Crothersville, In., U.S. G6 91
Crotone, Italy J12 14
Croton-on-Hudson, N.Y., U.S. D7 109
Crouse, N.C., U.S. B1 110
Crow, stm., Mn., U.S. F4 100
Crow Agency, Mt., U.S. E9 103
Crow Creek, stm., U.S. A6 83
Crow Creek Indian Reservation, S.D., U.S. C6 118
Crowder, Ms., U.S. A3 101
Crowell, Tx., U.S. C3 120
Crow Indian Reservation, Mt., U.S. E9 103
Crowley, La., U.S. D3 95
Crowley, Tx., U.S. n9 120
Crowley, co., Co., U.S. C7 83
Crowley, Lake, res., Ca., U.S. D4 82
Crowleys Ridge, mtn., U.S. B5 81
Crown Point, In., U.S. B3 91
Crown Point, La., U.S. k11 95
Crownpoint, N.M., U.S. B1 108
Crown Prince Frederick Island, i., N.W. Ter., Can. B15 66
Crow Peak, mtn., Mt., U.S. D5 103
Crowsnest Pass, Alta., Can. E3 68
Crowsnest Pass, Can. E3 68
Crow Wing, co., Mn., U.S. D4 100
Crow Wing, stm., Mn., U.S. D4 100
Croydon, Austl. C8 50
Crozet, Va., U.S. B4 123
Crozon, Fr. D2 10
Cruces, Cuba C7 64
Crump Lake, l., Or., U.S. E7 114
Cruz Alta, Braz. B6 56
Cruz del Eje, Arg. C4 56
Cruzeiro do Sul, Braz. E4 54
Crystal, Mn., U.S. m12 100
Crystal, stm., Co., U.S. B3 83
Crystal Bay, Nv., U.S. D1 105
Crystal Bay, b., Fl., U.S. D4 86
Crystal Beach, Fl., U.S. D4 86
Crystal City, Man., Can. E2 70
Crystal City, Mo., U.S. C7 102
Crystal City, Tx., U.S. E3 120
Crystal Falls, Mi., U.S. B2 99
Crystal Lake, Ct., U.S. B6 84
Crystal Lake, Fl., U.S. u16 86
Crystal Lake, Il., U.S. A5 90
Crystal Lake, l., Ct., U.S. B6 84
Crystal Lake, l., Mi., U.S. D4 99
Crystal Lake, l., N.H., U.S. D4 106
Crystal Lake, l., Vt., U.S. B4 122
Crystal Lawns, Il., U.S. k8 90
Crystal Pond, res., Ct., U.S. B7 84
Crystal River, Fl., U.S. D4 86
Crystal Springs, Ms., U.S. D3 101
Cuando (Kwando), stm., Afr. E4 44
Cuangar, Ang. E3 44
Cuango, Ang. C3 44
Cuango (Kwango), stm., Afr. C3 44
Cuanza, stm., Ang. C3 44
Cuauhtémoc, Mex. C6 62
Cuautla, Mex. H10 62
Cuba, Port. G4 12
Cuba, Il., U.S. C3 90
Cuba, Mo., U.S. C6 102
Cuba, N.M., U.S. A3 108
Cuba, N.Y., U.S. C2 109
Cuba, ctry., N.A. D8 64
Cuba City, Wi., U.S. F3 126
Cubango (Okavango), stm., Afr. E3 44
Cubero, N.M., U.S. B2 108
Cucharas, Mex. F7 62
Cucharas, stm., Co., U.S. D6 83
Cudahy, Wi., U.S. F6 126
Cuddalore, India G5 37
Cuddapah, India E5 37
Çuddy Mountain, mtn., Id., U.S. E2 89
Čudskoje Ozero (Peipsi Järv), l., U.S.S.R. C10 22
Cuéllar, Spain D7 12
Cuenca, Ec. I3 58
Cuenca, Spain E9 12
Cuencamé [de Ceniceros], Mex. E8 62
Cuernavaca, Mex. H10 62
Cuero, Tx., U.S. E4 120
Cuers, Fr. I13 10
Cuervos, Mex. A2 62
Cuevas del Almanzora, Spain H10 12
Cuglieri, Italy I3 14
Cuiabá, Braz. G7 54
Cuiseaux, Fr. F12 10
Cuito, stm., Ang. E3 44
Cuito-Cuanavale, Ang. E3 44
Cuivre, West Fork, stm., Mo., U.S. B6 102
Čukotskij, Mys, c., U.S.S.R. E31 20
Čukotskij Poluostrov, pen., U.S.S.R. D30 20
Culberson, co., Tx., U.S. o12 120
Culbertson, Mt., U.S. B12 103
Culbertson, Ne., U.S. D5 104
Culebra Peak, mtn., Co., U.S. D5 83
Culiacán, Mex. E6 62
Cullen, La., U.S. B2 95
Cullman, Al., U.S. A3 78
Cullman, co., Al., U.S. A3 78
Culloden, W.V., U.S. C2 125
Çullowhee, N.C., U.S. f9 110
Čul'man, U.S.S.R. F18 20
Culpeper, Va., U.S. B5 123
Culpeper, co., Va., U.S. B5 123
Culver, In., U.S. B5 91
Culver City, Ca., U.S. m12 82
Çulvers Lake, l., N.J., U.S. A3 107
Čulym, U.S.S.R. F10 20
Cumalı, Tur. M11 16
Cumaná, Ven. B10 58
Cumanacoa, Ven. B11 58
Cumbal, Nevado de, mtn., Col. G4 58
Cumberland, B.C., Can. E5 69
Cumberland, Ky., U.S. D7 94
Cumberland, Md., U.S. k13 97
Cumberland, Wi., U.S. C1 126
Cumberland, co., Il., U.S. D5 90
Cumberland, co., Ky., U.S. D4 94
Cumberland, co., Me., U.S. E2 96
Cumberland, co., N.J., U.S. E2 107
Cumberland, co., N.C., U.S. B4 110
Cumberland, co., Pa., U.S. F7 115
Cumberland, co., Tn., U.S. D8 119
Cumberland, co., Va., U.S. C4 123
Cumberland, stm., U.S. D4 94
Cumberland, Lake, res., Ky., U.S. D5 94
Cumberland Center, Me., U.S. g7 96
Cumberland Foreside, Me., U.S. E2 96
Cumberland Gap, U.S. D6 94
Cumberland Gap National Historical Park, U.S. D6 94
Cumberland Hill, R.I., U.S. B4 116
Cumberland Island National Seashore, Ga., U.S. F5 87
Cumberland Islands, is., Austl. D9 50
Cumberland Lake, l., Sask., Can. C4 75
Cumberland Peninsula, pen., N.W. Ter., Can. C19 66
Cumberland Sound, strt., N.W. Ter., Can. C19 66
Çumbres Pass, Co., U.S. D4 83
Čumikan, U.S.S.R. G21 20
Cuming, co., Ne., U.S. C9 104
Cumming, Ga., U.S. B2 87
Çumnock, Scot., U.K. F8 7
Çuna, stm., U.S.S.R. F13 20
Čun'a, stm., U.S.S.R. E13 20
Cunani, Braz. C8 54
Cunene, stm., Afr. E2 44
Cuneo, Italy E2 14
Cunnamulla, Austl. E9 50
Cunningham, Ky., U.S. f9 94
Cupar, Sask., Can. G3 75
Curaçao, i., Neth. Ant. H13 64
Curecanti National Recreation Area, Co., U.S. C3 83
Curepipe, Mrts. F11 44
Curiapo, Ven. C12 58
Curicó, Chile C2 56
Curitiba, Braz. B7 56
Curlew Creek, stm., Wa., U.S. A7 124
Curlew Lake, l., Wa., U.S. A7 124
Curralinho, Braz. D9 54
Currant Mountain, mtn., Nv., U.S. E6 105
Current, stm., U.S. A5 81
Currituck, co., N.C., U.S. A6 110
Curry, co., N.M., U.S. C6 108
Curry, co., Or., U.S. E2 114
Curtis, Ne., U.S. D5 104
Curtisville, Pa., U.S. E2 115
Curvelo, Braz. E6 57
Curwensville, Pa., U.S. E4 115
Curwensville Lake, res., Pa., U.S. E4 115
Curwood, Mount, mtn., Mi., U.S. B2 99
Cushing, Ok., U.S. B5 113
Cushman, Lake, res., Wa., U.S. B2 124
Cusseta, Ga., U.S. D2 87
Custer, S.D., U.S. D2 118
Custer, co., Co., U.S. C5 83
Custer, co., Id., U.S. E4 89
Custer, co., Mt., U.S. D11 103
Custer, co., Ne., U.S. C6 104
Custer, co., Ok., U.S. B2 113
Custer, co., S.D., U.S. D2 118
Custer Battlefield National Monument, Mt., U.S. E9 103
Cut Bank, Mt., U.S. B4 103
Cut Bank Creek, stm., N.D., U.S. A4 111
Cutchogue, N.Y., U.S. m16 109
Cuthbert, Ga., U.S. E2 87
Cutler Ridge, Fl., U.S. s13 86
Cut Off, La., U.S. E5 95
Cutro, Italy J11 14
Cuttack, India J11 38
Cuttyhunk Island, i., Ma., U.S. D6 98
Cuxhaven, Ger. B8 8
Cuyahoga, co., Oh., U.S. A4 112
Cuyahoga, stm., Oh., U.S. A4 112
Cuyahoga Falls, Oh., U.S. A4 112
Cuyama, stm., Ca., U.S. E4 82
Cuyamaca Peak, mtn., Ca., U.S. F5 82
Cuyo Islands, is., Phil. C7 32
Cuyuni, stm., S.A. D13 58
Cuzco, Peru F4 54
C.W. McConaughy, Lake, res., Ne., U.S. C4 104
Cyclades see Kikládhes, is., Grc. L8 16
Cynthiana, In., U.S. H2 91
Cynthiana, Ky., U.S. B5 94
Cypress Creek, stm., Tx., U.S. r14 120
Cypress Hills Provincial Park, Sask., Can. H1 75
Cypress Lake, l., Fl., U.S. D5 86
Cypress Quarters, Fl., U.S. E6 86
Cypress Swamp, sw., U.S. F4 85
Cyprus, ctry., Asia B3 40
Cyril, Ok., U.S. C3 113
Czechoslovakia, ctry., Eur. F11 4
Częstochowa, Pol. E19 8

D

Dabeiba, Col. D4 58
Dabhoi, India I5 38
Dabie Shan, mts., China D4 28
Dabola, Gui. F3 42
Dacca see Dhaka, Bngl. I14 38
Dachaidan, China B16 38
Dachau, Ger. G11 8
Dacono, Co., U.S. A6 83
Dacula, Ga., U.S. C3 87
Dadanawa, Guy. F13 58
Dade, co., Fl., U.S. G6 86
Dade, co., Ga., U.S. B1 87
Dade, co., Mo., U.S. D4 102
Dade City, Fl., U.S. D4 86
Dadeville, Al., U.S. C4 78
Dādra and Nagar Haveli, ter., India B2 37
Dādu, Pak. G2 38
Daet, Phil. q20 33b
Daggett, co., Ut., U.S. C6 121
Dagsboro, De., U.S. F5 85
Dagupan, Phil. p19 33b
Dahan-e Qowmghī, Afg. C2 38
Da Hinggan Ling, mts., China C11 26
Dahlak Archipelago, is., Eth. E3 46
Dahlak Kebir Island, i., Eth. E3 46
Dahlonega, Ga., U.S. B3 87
Dahomey see Benin, ctry., Afr. G6 42
Dahra, Libya C9 42
Dahy, Nafūd ad-, des., Sau. Ar. D4 46
Daimiel, Spain F8 12
Daingerfield, Tx., U.S. C5 120
Dairen see Dalian, China D11 26
Dakar, Sen. F2 42
Dakhla, W. Sah. D2 42
Dakota, co., Mn., U.S. F5 100
Dakota, co., Ne., U.S. B9 104
Dakota City, Ia., U.S. B3 92
Dakota City, Ne., U.S. B9 104
Dalandzadgad, Mong. C7 26
Da Lat, Viet. I10 34
Dālbandin, Pak. D1 36
Dalby, Austl. E10 50
Dale, In., U.S. H4 91
Dale, co., Al., U.S. D4 78
Dale City, Va., U.S. B5 123
Dale Hollow Lake, res., U.S. C8 119
Daleville, Al., U.S. D4 78
Daleville, In., U.S. D6 91
Dalhart, Tx., U.S. A1 120
Dalhousie, N.B., Can. A3 71
Dalhousie, Cape, c., N.W. Ter., Can. B7 66
Dali, China B6 34
Dalian, China D11 26
Dall, Mount, mtn., Ak., U.S. f15 79
Dallam, co., Tx., U.S. A1 120
Dallas, Ga., U.S. C2 87
Dallas (part of Melcher), Ia., U.S. C4 92
Dallas, N.C., U.S. B1 110
Dallas, Or., U.S. C3 114
Dallas, Pa., U.S. D10 115
Dallas, Tx., U.S. C4 120
Dallas, co., Al., U.S. C2 78
Dallas, co., Ar., U.S. D3 81
Dallas, co., Ia., U.S. C3 92
Dallas, co., Mo., U.S. D4 102
Dallas, co., Tx., U.S. C4 120
Dallas Center, Ia., U.S. C4 92
Dallas City, Il., U.S. C2 90
Dallas Naval Air Station, mil., Tx., U.S. n9 120
Dallastown, Pa., U.S. G8 115
Dall Island, i., Ak., U.S. n23 79
Dalmacija, hist. reg., Yugo. F11 14
Dalmatia see Dalmacija, hist. reg., Yugo. F11 14

Name Map Ref Page

Daloa, I.C. G4 42
Dalqū, Sudan D12 42
Dalton, Ga., U.S. B2 87
Dalton, Ma., U.S. B1 98
Dalton, Oh., U.S. B4 112
Dalton, Pa., U.S. C10 115
Daltonganj, India H11 38
Dalton Gardens, Id., U.S. B2 89
Dalwallinu, Austl. F3 50
Daly City, Ca., U.S. h8 82
Damān, India B2 37
Damān, ter., India B2 37
Damar, Pulau, i., Indon. G8 32
Damariscotta, Me., U.S. D3 96
Damariscotta Lake, l., Me., U.S. D3 96
Damascus, Md., U.S. B3 97
Damascus, Va., U.S. f10 123
Damascus see Dimashq, Syria C5 40
Damāvand, Qolleh-ye, mtn., Iran J8 18
Damba, Ang. C3 44
Damoh, India I8 38
Dampar, Tasek, l., Malay. M7 34
Dampier, Austl. D3 50
Dampier, Selat, strt., Indon. F9 32
Dampier Archipelago, is., Austl. D3 50
Dan, stm., U.S. D3 123
Dana, In., U.S. E3 91
Danakil Plain, pl., Eth. F3 46
Da Nang, Viet. F10 34
Danbury, Ct., U.S. D2 84
Danbury, Tx., U.S. r14 120
Dand, Afg. E1 38
Dandridge, Tn., U.S. C10 119
Dane, co., Wi., U.S. E4 126
Dangla, Eth. F2 46
Dania, Fl., U.S. F6 86
Daniels, co., Mt., U.S. B11 103
Danielson, Ct., U.S. B8 84
Daniels Pass, Ut., U.S. C4 121
Danilov, U.S.S.R. C23 22
Danlí, Hond. G4 64
Dannemora, N.Y., U.S. f11 109
Dansville, N.Y., U.S. C3 109
Dante, Va., U.S. f9 123
Danube, stm., Eur. G13 4
Danube, Mouths of the, mth., Eur. D13 16
Danvers, Il., U.S. C4 90
Danvers, Ma., U.S. A6 98
Danville, Que., Can. D5 74
Danville, Ar., U.S. B2 81
Danville, Ca., U.S. h9 82
Danville, Il., U.S. C6 90
Danville, In., U.S. E4 91
Danville, Ia., U.S. D6 92
Danville, Ky., U.S. C5 94
Danville, Oh., U.S. B3 112
Danville, Pa., U.S. E8 115
Danville, Va., U.S. D3 123
Danyang, China C8 28
Danzig, Gulf of, b., Eur. A19 8
Danzig see Gdańsk, Pol. A18 8
Daocheng, China F7 26
Dapango, Togo F6 42
Daphne, Al., U.S. E2 78
Dar'ā, Syria C5 40
Darakht-e Yahyá, Afg. E3 38
Dārayyā, Syria C5 40
Darbāsīyah, Syria A7 40
Darbhanga, India G11 38
Darby, Mt., U.S. D2 103
Darby, Pa., U.S. G11 115
Darchan, Mong. B8 26
Dardanelle, Ar., U.S. B2 81
Dardanelle Lake, res., Ar., U.S. B2 81
Dardanelles see Çanakkale Boğazı, strt., Tur. I10 16
Dare, co., N.C., U.S. B7 110
Dar es Salaam, Tan. C7 44
Dargaville, N.Z. A4 52
Dari, China E6 26
Darien, Ct., U.S. E2 84
Darien, Ga., U.S. E5 87
Darien, Wi., U.S. F5 126
Dariganga, Mong. B9 26
Darjeeling, India G13 38
Darke, co., Oh., U.S. B1 112
Darley Woods, De., U.S. h8 85
Darling, stm., Austl. F9 50
Darling, Lake, res., N.D., U.S. A4 111
Darling Range, mts., Austl. F3 50
Darlington, Eng., U.K. G11 7
Darlington, In., U.S. D4 91
Darlington, Md., U.S. A5 97
Darlington, S.C., U.S. C8 117
Darlington, Wi., U.S. F3 126
Darlington, co., S.C., U.S. C8 117
Darmstadt, Ger. F8 8
Darnah, Libya B10 42
Daroca, Spain D10 12
Darrah, Mount, mtn., Can. E3 68
Darrington, Wa., U.S. A4 124
Dartmoor National Park, Eng., U.K. K9 7
Dartmouth, Eng., U.K. K9 7
Daru, Pap. N. Gui. G11 32
Darwin, Austl. B6 50
Dašinčilen, Mong. B7 26
Dassel, Mn., U.S. E4 100
Datia, India H8 38
Datil Mountains, mts., N.M., U.S. C2 108
D'at'kovo, U.S.S.R. H17 22
Datong, China C9 26
Datu, Tanjung, c., Asia M10 34
Dāūd Khel, Pak. D4 38
Daufuskie Island, i., S.C., U.S. G6 117
Daugavpils, U.S.S.R. F9 22
Daulatābād (Shirin Tagāo), Afg. B1 38
Daule, Ec. G2 58
Dauphin, Man., Can. D1 70
Dauphin, co., Pa., U.S. F8 115
Dauphin, stm., Man., Can. D2 70
Dauphin Island, Al., U.S. E1 78
Dauphin Island, i., Al., U.S. E1 78
Dauphin Lake, l., Man., Can. D2 70
Dāvangere, India E3 37
Davao, Phil. D8 32
Davao Gulf, b., Phil. D8 32
Daveluyville, Que., Can. C5 74
Davenport, Fl., U.S. D5 86
Davenport, Ia., U.S. C7 92
Davenport, Ok., U.S. B5 113
Davenport, Wa., U.S. B7 124
David, Pan. J6 64
David City, Ne., U.S. C8 104
Davidson, N.C., U.S. B2 110
Davidson, co., N.C., U.S. B2 110
Davidson, co., Tn., U.S. A5 119
Davidsville, Pa., U.S. F4 115
Davie, Fl., U.S. F6 86
Davie, co., N.C., U.S. B2 110
Daviess, co., In., U.S. G3 91
Daviess, co., Ky., U.S. C2 94
Daviess, co., Mo., U.S. B3 102
Davis, Ca., U.S. C3 82
Davis, Ok., U.S. C4 113
Davis, W.V., U.S. B5 125
Davis, co., Ia., U.S. D5 92
Davis, co., Ut., U.S. C3 121
Davis, Mount, mtn., Pa., U.S. G3 115
Davis Creek, stm., W.V., U.S. m12 125
Davis Dam, U.S. H7 105
Davis Islands, is., Fl., U.S. p11 86
Davis Lake, l., Or., U.S. E5 114
Davis-Monthan Air Force Base, mil., Az., U.S. E5 80
Davison, Mi., U.S. E7 99
Davison, co., S.D., U.S. D7 118
Davis Strait, strt., N.A. C21 66
Davisville, R.I., U.S. E4 116
Davos, Switz. F16 10
Dawa (Daua), stm., Afr. H3 46
Dawei, Burma G5 34
Dawes, co., Ne., U.S. B2 104
Daws Island, i., S.C., U.S. G6 117
Dawson, Ga., U.S. E2 87
Dawson, Mn., U.S. F2 100
Dawson, co., Ga., U.S. B2 87
Dawson, co., Mt., U.S. C11 103
Dawson, co., Ne., U.S. D6 104
Dawson, co., Tx., U.S. C1 120
Dawson, Mount, mtn., B.C., Can. D9 69
Dawson Creek, B.C., Can. B7 69
Dawson Springs, Ky., U.S. C2 94
Dax, Fr. I5 10
Day, co., S.D., U.S. B8 118
Dayr az-Zawr, Syria B7 40
Daysland, Alta., Can. C4 68
Dayton, In., U.S. D4 91
Dayton, Ia., U.S. B3 92
Dayton, Ky., U.S. h14 94
Dayton, Md., U.S. B4 97
Dayton, Mn., U.S. m12 100
Dayton, Nv., U.S. D2 105
Dayton, Oh., U.S. C1 112
Dayton, Or., U.S. B3 114
Dayton, Tn., U.S. D8 119
Dayton, Tx., U.S. D5 120
Dayton, Va., U.S. B4 123
Dayton, Wa., U.S. C8 124
Dayton, Wy., U.S. B5 127
Daytona Beach, Fl., U.S. C5 86
Da Yunhe, China E10 26
Dayville, Ct., U.S. B8 84
De Aar, S. Afr. H4 44
Dead, North Branch, stm., Me., U.S. C2 96
Dead, South Branch, stm., Me., U.S. C2 96
Dead Creek, stm., Vt., U.S. C2 122
Dead Diamond, stm., N.H., U.S. g7 106
Dead Indian Peak, mtn., Wy., U.S. B3 127
Dead Lake, l., Mn., U.S. D3 100
Dead Lakes, l., Fl., U.S. B1 86
Deadman Bay, b., Fl., U.S. C3 86
Deadman Creek, stm., Wa., U.S. g14 124
Deadmans Cay, Bah. C10 64
Dead Sea, l., Asia D4 40
Deadwood, S.D., U.S. C2 118
Deadwood Reservoir, res., Id., U.S. E3 89
Deaf Smith, co., Tx., U.S. B1 120
Deale, Md., U.S. C4 97
Deal Island, Md., U.S. D6 97
Deal Island, i., Md., U.S. D6 97
Dean, stm., B.C., Can. C4 69
Dean Channel, strt., B.C., Can. C4 69
Deán Funes, Arg. C4 56
Dearborn, Mi., U.S. F7 99
Dearborn, co., In., U.S. F7 91
Dearborn Heights, Mi., U.S. p15 99
Dearg, Beinn, mtn., Scot., U.K. D8 7
Dease Strait, strt., N.W. Ter., Can. C11 66
Death Valley, val., Ca., U.S. D5 82
Death Valley National Monument, U.S. D5 82
Deauville, Fr. C7 10
De Baca, co., N.M., U.S. C5 108
De Bary, Fl., U.S. D5 86
Debauch Mountain, mtn., Ak., U.S. C8 79
Dębica, Pol. E21 8
Debrecen, Hung. H21 8
Debre Markos, Eth. F2 46
Debre Tabor, Eth. F2 46
De Cade, Lake, l., La., U.S. E5 95
Decatur, Al., U.S. A3 78
Decatur, Ar., U.S. A1 81
Decatur, Ga., U.S. C2 87
Decatur, Il., U.S. D5 90
Decatur, In., U.S. C8 91
Decatur, Mi., U.S. F5 99
Decatur, Ms., U.S. C4 101
Decatur, Ne., U.S. B9 104
Decatur, Tn., U.S. D9 119
Decatur, Tx., U.S. C4 120
Decatur, co., Ga., U.S. F2 87
Decatur, co., In., U.S. F6 91
Decatur, co., Ia., U.S. D4 92
Decatur, co., Ks., U.S. C3 93
Decatur, co., Tn., U.S. B3 119
Decatur, Lake, res., Il., U.S. D5 90
Decaturville, Tn., U.S. B3 119
Decazeville, Fr. H9 10
Deccan, plat., India E4 37
Deception, Mount, mtn., Wa., U.S. B2 124
Decherd, Tn., U.S. B5 119
Děčín, Czech. E14 8
Decize, Fr. F10 10
Deckerville, Mi., U.S. E8 99
Decorah, Ia., U.S. A6 92
Dedham, Ma., U.S. B5 98
Dédougou, Burkina F5 42
Dedovsk, U.S.S.R. F20 22
Deep, stm., N.C., U.S. B3 110
Deep Creek, stm., Ut., U.S. C2 121
Deep Creek, stm., Ut., U.S. B3 121
Deep Creek, stm., Ut., U.S. F3 121
Deep Creek, stm., Wa., U.S. g13 124
Deep Creek Lake, res., Md., U.S. K12 97
Deep Creek Mountains, mts., Id., U.S. G6 89
Deep Fork, stm., Ok., U.S. B5 113
Deep Inlet, b., Newf., Can. g10 72
Deep Red Creek, stm., Ok., U.S. C3 113
Deep River, Ont., Can. A7 73
Deep River, Ct., U.S. D6 84
Deer Creek, stm., Oh., U.S. C2 112
Deer Creek Indian Reservation, Mn., U.S. C5 100
Deerfield, Il., U.S. h9 90
Deerfield, Ks., U.S. E2 93
Deerfield, Ma., U.S. A2 98
Deerfield, Mi., U.S. G7 99
Deerfield, Wi., U.S. E4 126
Deerfield, stm., U.S. A2 98
Deerfield Beach, Fl., U.S. F6 86
Deer Island, pen., Ma., U.S. g12 98
Deer Island, i., Ms., U.S. f8 101
Deer Isle, i., Me., U.S. D4 96
Deer Lake, Newf., Can. D3 72
Deer Lake, l., Newf., Can. D3 72
Deer Lake, l., Mn., U.S. C5 100
Deer Lodge, Mt., U.S. D4 103
Deer Lodge, co., Mt., U.S. E3 103
Deer Park, N.Y., U.S. n15 109
Deer Park, Oh., U.S. o13 112
Deer Park, Wa., U.S. B8 124
Deer Peak, mtn., Co., U.S. C5 83
Deer River, Mn., U.S. C5 100
Deesa, India H5 38
Defiance, Oh., U.S. A1 112
Defiance, co., Oh., U.S. A1 112
Defiance, Mount, mtn., Or., U.S. B5 114
De Forest, Wi., U.S. E4 126
De Funiak Springs, Fl., U.S. u15 86
Degeh-Bur, Eth. G3 46
Dégelis, Que., Can. B9 74
Deggendorf, Ger. G12 8
De Graff, Oh., U.S. B2 112
De Gray Lake, res., Ar., U.S. C2 81
Dehiwala-Mount Lavinia, Sri L. I5 37
Dehra Dūn, India E8 38
Dehri, India H11 38
Dehu, India C2 37
Dehui, China C12 26
Dej, Rom. B7 16
Deje, Swe. G9 6
De Kalb, Il., U.S. B5 90
De Kalb, Ms., U.S. C5 101
De Kalb, Tx., U.S. C5 120
De Kalb, co., Al., U.S. A4 78
De Kalb, co., Ga., U.S. C2 87
De Kalb, co., Il., U.S. B5 90
De Kalb, co., In., U.S. B7 91
De Kalb, co., Mo., U.S. B3 102
De Kalb, co., Tn., U.S. D8 119
Dekese, Zaire B4 44
Delafield, Wi., U.S. m11 126
Delanco, N.J., U.S. C3 107
De Land, Fl., U.S. C5 86
Delano, Ca., U.S. E4 82
Delano, Mn., U.S. E5 100
Delano Peak, mtn., Ut., U.S. E3 121
Delaronde Lake, l., Sask., Can. C2 75
Delavan, Il., U.S. C4 90
Delavan, Wi., U.S. F5 126
Delaware, Oh., U.S. B2 112
Delaware, co., In., U.S. D7 91
Delaware, co., Ia., U.S. B6 92
Delaware, co., N.Y., U.S. C5 109
Delaware, co., Oh., U.S. B2 112
Delaware, co., Ok., U.S. A7 113
Delaware, co., Pa., U.S. G11 115
Delaware, state, U.S. D3 85
Delaware, stm., U.S. G11 115
Delaware, stm., Ks., U.S. C8 93
Delaware, East Branch, stm., N.Y., U.S. C5 109
Delaware Bay, b., U.S. D11 76
Delaware City, De., U.S. B3 85
Delaware Lake, res., Oh., U.S. B3 112
Delaware Water Gap, N.J., U.S. B2 107
Delaware Water Gap National Recreation Area, U.S. B2 107
Delbarton, W.V., U.S. D2 125
Delcambre, La., U.S. E4 95
Del City, Ok., U.S. B4 113
Delémont, Switz. E14 10
De Leon, Tx., U.S. C3 120
De Leon Springs, Fl., U.S. C5 86
Delft, Neth. C4 8
Delfzijl, Neth. B6 8
Delgado, Cabo, c., Moz. D8 44
Delhi, India F7 38
Delhi, La., U.S. B4 95
Delhi, N.Y., U.S. C6 109
Delicias, Mex. C7 62
De Lisle, Ms., U.S. E4 101
Delitzsch, Ger. D12 8
Dellenbaugh, Mount, mtn., Az., U.S. A2 80
Dell Rapids, S.D., U.S. D9 118
Del Mar, Ca., U.S. o15 82
Delmar, De., U.S. G3 85
Delmar, Md., U.S. D6 97
Delmar, N.Y., U.S. C7 109
Delmenhorst, Ger. B8 8
Delnice, Yugo. D9 14
Del Norte, Co., U.S. D4 83
Del Norte, co., Ca., U.S. B2 82
De-Longa, Ostrova, is., U.S.S.R. B23 20
Deloraine, Man., Can. E1 70
Del Park Manor, De., U.S. i7 85
Delphi, In., U.S. C4 91
Delphos, Oh., U.S. B1 112
Delran, N.J., U.S. C3 107
Delray Beach, Fl., U.S. F6 86
Del Rio, Tx., U.S. E2 120
Delson, Que., Can. q19 74
Delta, Co., U.S. C2 83
Delta, Oh., U.S. A1 112
Delta, Ut., U.S. D3 121
Delta, co., Co., U.S. C3 83
Delta, co., Mi., U.S. C3 99
Delta, co., Tx., U.S. C5 120
Delta, reg., Ms., U.S. B3 101
Delta Junction, Ak., U.S. C10 79
Delta Peak, mtn., B.C., Can. A3 69
Delta Reservoir, res., N.Y., U.S. B5 109
Deltaville, Va., U.S. C6 123
Deltona, Fl., U.S. D5 86
Demarest, N.J., U.S. h9 107
Deming, N.M., U.S. E2 108
Demirci, Tur. J12 16
Demirköy, Tur. H11 16
Demmin, Ger. B13 8
Demopolis, Al., U.S. C2 78
Demorest, Ga., U.S. B3 87
Demotte, In., U.S. B3 91
Denain, Fr. B10 10
Denali National Park, Ak., U.S. C9 79
Denare Beach, Sask., Can. C4 75
Denham Springs, La., U.S. D5 95
Den Helder, Neth. C4 8
Denia, Spain G12 12
Denison, Ia., U.S. B2 92
Denison, Tx., U.S. C4 120
Denison Dam, U.S. D5 113
Denizli, Tur. H13 4
Denmark, S.C., U.S. E5 117
Denmark, Wi., U.S. D6 126
Denmark, ctry., Eur. D9 4
Denmark Strait, strt. C15 128
Dennehotso, Az., U.S. A6 80
Dennis, Ma., U.S. C7 98
Dennison, Oh., U.S. B4 112
Dennis Port, Ma., U.S. C7 98
Denny Terrace, S.C., U.S. C5 117
Denpasar, Indon. G6 32
Dent, co., Mo., U.S. D6 102
Denton, Md., U.S. C6 97
Denton, N.C., U.S. B2 110
Denton, Tx., U.S. C4 120
Denton, co., Tx., U.S. C4 120
D'Entrecasteaux Islands, is., Pap. N. Gui. m17 50a
Dentsville, S.C., U.S. C6 117
Denver, Co., U.S. B6 83
Denver, Ia., U.S. B5 92
Denver, Pa., U.S. F9 115
Denver, co., Co., U.S. B6 83
Denver City, Tx., U.S. C1 120
Denville, N.J., U.S. B4 107
Deoghar, India H12 38
Deolāli, India C2 37
Deoria, India G10 38
De Pere, Wi., U.S. D5 126
Depew, N.Y., U.S. C2 109
Depoe Bay, Or., U.S. C2 114
Depok, Indon. m13 33a
Deposit, N.Y., U.S. C5 109
Depue, Il., U.S. B4 90
Deqin, China F6 26
De Queen, Ar., U.S. C1 81
De Queen Reservoir, res., Ar., U.S. C1 81
De Quincy, La., U.S. D2 95
Dera Ghāzi Khān, Pak. E4 38
Dera Ismāīl Khān, Pak. E4 38
Derby, Austl. C4 50
Derby, Eng., U.K. I11 7
Derby, Ct., U.S. D3 84
Derby, Ks., U.S. E6 93
Derby, Vt., U.S. B4 122
Derby Line, Vt., U.S. A4 122
Derg, Lough, l., Ire. I4 7
De Ridder, La., U.S. D2 95
Derma, Ms., U.S. B4 101
Dermott, Ar., U.S. D4 81
Dernieres, Isles, is., La., U.S. E5 95
Derry, N.H., U.S. E4 106
Derry, Pa., U.S. F3 115
Derval, Fr. E5 10
Derventa, Yugo. E12 14
Derwood, Md., U.S. B3 97
Desaguadero, stm., Arg. C3 56
Des Allemands, La., U.S. E5 95
Des Arc, Ar., U.S. C4 81
Desbiens, Que., Can. A6 74
Descartes, Fr. F7 10
Deschaillons [-sur-Saint-Laurent], Que., Can. C5 74
Deschambault, Que., Can. C6 74
Deschambault Lake, l., Sask., Can. C4 75
Deschutes, co., Or., U.S. D5 114
Deschutes, stm., Or., U.S. B6 114
Dese, Eth. F2 46
Deseado, stm., Arg. F3 56
Deseret Peak, mtn., Ut., U.S. C3 121
Deseronto, Ont., Can. C7 73
Desert Creek Peak, mtn., Nv., U.S. E2 105
Desert Hot Springs, Ca., U.S. F5 82
Desert Peak, mtn., Ut., U.S. B2 121
Desert Valley, val., Nv., U.S. B3 105
Desha, Ar., U.S. B4 81
Desha, co., Ar., U.S. D4 81
Deshler, Ne., U.S. D8 104
Deshler, Oh., U.S. A2 112
Des Lacs, stm., N.D., U.S. A4 111
Desloge, Mo., U.S. D7 102
De Smet, S.D., U.S. C8 118
Des Moines, Ia., U.S. C4 92
Des Moines, Wa., U.S. B3 124
Des Moines, co., Ia., U.S. D6 92
Des Moines, stm., U.S. D5 92
Desolación, Isla, i., Chile G2 56
De Soto, Il., U.S. F4 90
De Soto, Ia., U.S. C3 92
De Soto, Ks., U.S. D9 93
De Soto, Mo., U.S. C7 102
De Soto, co., Fl., U.S. E5 86
De Soto, co., La., U.S. B2 95
De Soto, co., Ms., U.S. A3 101
Despard, W.V., U.S. k10 125
Des Peres, Mo., U.S. f13 102
Des Plaines, Il., U.S. A6 90
Des Plaines, stm., U.S. k8 90
Desroches, Île, i., Sey. C10 44
Dessau, Ger. D12 8
Destin, Fl., U.S. u15 86
Destrehan, La., U.S. E5 95
Desvres, Fr. B8 10
Detmold, Ger. D8 8
Detour, Point, c., Mi., U.S. C4 99
Detroit, Mi., U.S. F7 99
Detroit Lake, res., Or., U.S. C4 114
Detroit Lakes, Mn., U.S. D3 100
Deuel, co., Ne., U.S. C3 104
Deuel, co., S.D., U.S. C9 118
Deutsche Bucht, b., Ger. A7 8
Deutschlandsberg, Aus. I15 8
Deux-Montagnes, Que., Can. p19 74
Deux Montagnes, Lac des, l., Que., Can. q19 74
Deva, Rom. D6 16
Devakottai, India H5 37
De Valls Bluff, Ar., U.S. C4 81
Deventer, Neth. C6 8
DeView, Bayou, stm., Ar., U.S. B4 81
Devil's Island see Diable, Île du, i., Fr. Gu. B8 54
Devils Lake, N.D., U.S. A7 111
Devils Lake, l., N.D., U.S. A6 111
Devils Paw, mtn., Ak., U.S. k23 79
Devils Postpile National Monument, Ca., U.S. D4 82
Devils Tower National Monument, Wy., U.S. B8 127
Devil Track Lake, l., Mn., U.S. k9 100
Devine, Tx., U.S. E3 120
Devola, Oh., U.S. C4 112
Devon, Alta., Can. C4 68
Devon Island, i., N.W. Ter., Can. A15 66
Devonport, Austl. H9 50
Devonport, N.Z. B5 52
Devonshire, De., U.S. h7 85
Dewa-kyūryō, hills, Japan C13 30
Dewar, Ok., U.S. B6 113
Dewās, India I7 38
Dewees Inlet, b., S.C., U.S. k12 117
Dewees Island, i., S.C., U.S. F8 117
Dewey, Az., U.S. C3 80
Dewey, Ok., U.S. A6 113
Dewey, co., Ok., U.S. B2 113
Dewey, co., S.D., U.S. B4 118
Dewey Beach, De., U.S. F5 85
Dewey Lake, res., Ky., U.S. C7 94
Deweyville, Tx., U.S. D6 120
De Witt, Ar., U.S. C4 81
De Witt, Ia., U.S. C7 92
De Witt, Mi., U.S. F6 99
De Witt, N.Y., U.S. B4 109
De Witt, co., Il., U.S. C4 90
De Witt, co., Tx., U.S. E4 120
Dexter, Ia., U.S. C3 92
Dexter, Me., U.S. C3 96
Dexter, Mi., U.S. F7 99
Dexter, Mo., U.S. E8 102
Dexter, N.M., U.S. D5 108
Dexter, Lake, l., Fl., U.S. C5 86
Dezfūl, Iran B4 46
Dezhou, China D10 26
Dhaka, Bngl. I14 38
Dhamār, Yemen F3 46
Dhamtari, India B6 37
Dhānbād, India I12 38
Dhār, India I6 38
Dharmapuri, India F5 37
Dharmavaram, India E4 37
Dhārwār, India E3 37
Dhawlāgiri, mtn., Nepal F10 38
Dhodhekánisos (Dodecanese), is., Grc. M10 16
Dholpur, India G7 38
Dhorāji, India J4 38
Dhrol, India I4 38
Dhubri, India G13 38
Dhule, India B3 37
Diable, Île du, i., Fr. Gu. B8 54
Diablo, Canyon, val., Az., U.S. C4 80
Diablo, Mount, mtn., Ca., U.S. h9 82
Diablo Dam, Wa., U.S. A4 124
Diablo Lake, res., Wa., U.S. A4 124
Diablo Range, mts., Ca., U.S. D3 82
Diamante, Arg. C4 56
Diamantina, Braz. E7 57
Diamantino, Braz. F7 54
Diamond Head, crat., Hi., U.S. B4 88
Diamond Hill, R.I., U.S. B4 116
Diamond Hill Reservoir, res., R.I., U.S. A4 116
Diamond Lake, Il., U.S. h9 90
Diamond Lake, l., Or., U.S. D4 114
Diamond Mountains, mts., Nv., U.S. D6 105
Diamond Peak, mtn., Co., U.S. A2 83
Diamond Peak, mtn., Id., U.S. E5 89
Diamond Peak, mtn., Or., U.S. D4 114
Diamond Peak, mtn., Wa., U.S. C8 124
Diamondville, Wy., U.S. E2 127
Diaz, Ar., U.S. B4 81
Dibaya, Zaire C4 44
D'Iberville, Ms., U.S. E5 101
Diboll, Tx., U.S. D5 120
Dibrugarh, India G16 38
Dickens, co., Tx., U.S. C2 120
Dickenson, co., Va., U.S. e9 123

Name Map Ref Page

Dickerson, Md., U.S. B3 97
Dickey, co., N.D., U.S. C7 111
Dickeyville, Wi., U.S. F3 126
Dickinson, N.D., U.S. C3 111
Dickinson, co., Ia., U.S. A2 92
Dickinson, co., Ks., U.S. D6 93
Dickinson, co., Mi., U.S. B3 99
Dickinson Dam, N.D., U.S. C3 111
Dickson, Ok., U.S. C5 113
Dickson, Tn., U.S. A4 119
Dickson, co., Tn., U.S. A4 119
Dickson City, Pa., U.S. D10 115
Didsbury, Alta., Can. D3 68
Die, Fr. H12 10
Dieburg, Ger. F8 8
Dieciocho de Marzo, Mex. E11 62
Diefenbaker, Lake, res., Sask., Can. F2 75
Diégo-Suarez see Antsiranana, Madag. D9 44
Dien Bien Phu, Viet. D7 34
Diepholz, Ger. C8 8
Dieppe, N.B., Can. C5 71
Dieppe, Fr. C8 10
Dierks, Ar., U.S. C1 81
Dieuze, Fr. D13 10
Digboi, India G16 38
Dighton, Ks., U.S. D3 93
Digne, Fr. H13 10
Digoin, Fr. F10 10
Dijon, Fr. E12 10
Dike, Ia., U.S. B5 92
Dikson, U.S.S.R. C10 20
Dili, Indon. G8 32
Dillard, Or., U.S. D3 114
Dill City, Ok., U.S. B2 113
Dilley, Tx., U.S. E3 120
Dillingen [an der Donau], Ger. G10 8
Dillingham, Ak., U.S. D8 79
Dillon, Mt., U.S. E4 103
Dillon, S.C., U.S. C9 117
Dillon, co., S.C., U.S. C9 117
Dillon Lake, res., Oh., U.S. B3 112
Dillon Reservoir, res., Co., U.S. B4 83
Dillonvale, Oh., U.S. B5 112
Dillsboro, In., U.S. F7 91
Dillsburg, Pa., U.S. F7 115
Dilolo, Zaire D4 44
Dilworth, Mn., U.S. D2 100
Dimāpur, India H15 38
Dimashq (Damascus), Syria C5 40
Dimitrovgrad, Bul. G9 16
Dimitrovgrad, U.S.S.R. G7 18
Dimmit, co., Tx., U.S. E3 120
Dimmitt, Tx., U.S. B1 120
Dimona, Isr. D4 40
Dimondale, Mi., U.S. F6 99
Dinagat Island, i., Phil. C8 32
Dinājpur, Bngl. H13 38
Dinan, Fr. D4 10
Dinant, Bel. E4 8
Dinara, mts., Yugo. F11 14
Dinard, Fr. D4 10
Dinaric Alps see Dinara, mts., Yugo. F11 14
Dindigul, India G4 37
Dinghai, China E11 28
Dingle, Ire. I2 7
Dingmans Ferry, Pa., U.S. D12 115
Dingolfing, Ger. G12 8
Dingqing, China E16 38
Dingri, China F12 38
Dingshan, China D8 28
Dingwall, Scot., U.K. D8 7
Dinh Lap, Viet. D9 34
Dinner Point, c., Fl., U.S. D4 86
Dinosaur National Monument, U.S. C6 121
Dinuba, Ca., U.S. D4 82
Dinwiddie, co., Va., U.S. C5 123
Diourbel, Sen. F2 42
Dipkarpaz, N. Cyp. B4 40
Dipolog, Phil. D7 32
Dire Dawa, Eth. G3 46
Diriamba, Nic. I4 64
Dirico, Ang. E4 44
Dirk Hartog Island, i., Austl. E2 50
Dirty Devil, stm., Ut., U.S. E5 121
Disappointment, Cape, c., Falk. Is. G9 56
Disappointment, Cape, c., Wa., U.S. C1 124
Disappointment, Lake, l., Austl. D4 50
Disentis, Switz. F15 10
Dishman, Wa., U.S. g14 124
Disko, i., Grnld. C22 66
Disko Bugt, b., Grnld. C22 66
Dismal, stm., Ne., U.S. C5 104
Disraëli, Que., Can. D6 74
District of Columbia, dist., U.S. f8 97
Diu, India J4 38
Diu, ter., India J4 38
Divernon, Il., U.S. D4 90
Divide, co., N.D., U.S. A2 111
Divide Peak, mtn., Wy., U.S. E5 127
Divinópolis, Braz. F6 57
Divisor, Serra do, plat., S.A. E4 54
Dix, stm., Ky., U.S. C5 94
Dixfield, Me., U.S. D2 96
Dixie, co., Fl., U.S. C3 86
Dixie Valley, val., Nv., U.S. D4 105
Dixon, Ca., U.S. C3 82
Dixon, Il., U.S. B4 90
Dixon, Mo., U.S. D5 102
Dixon, N.M., U.S. A4 108
Dixon, co., Ne., U.S. B9 104
Dixon Entrance, strt., N.A. F6 66
Dixonville, Pa., U.S. E3 115
Diyarbakır, Tur. H16 4
Dja, stm., Afr. H8 42
Djakarta see Jakarta, Indon. m13 32
Djambala, Congo B2 44
Djanet, Alg. D7 42
Djebel Abiod, Tun. M4 14
Djebibina, Tun. M5 14
Djemmal, Tun. N5 14
Djerba, Île de, i., Tun. B8 42
Djerid, Chott, sw., Tun. B7 42
Djibouti, Dji. F3 46
Djibouti, ctry., Afr. F3 46
Dmitrija Lapteva, Proliv, strt., U.S.S.R. C22 20
Dmitrov, U.S.S.R. E20 22
Dnepr, stm., U.S.S.R. H4 18
Dneprodzeržinsk, U.S.S.R. H4 18
Dnepropetrovsk, U.S.S.R. H4 18
Dnestr, stm., U.S.S.R. H3 18
Dnieper see Dnepr, stm., U.S.S.R. H4 18
Dniester see Dnestr, stm., U.S.S.R. H3 18
Dno, U.S.S.R. D12 22
Do āb-e Mīkh-e Zarrīn, Afg. C2 38
Doaktown, N.B., Can. C3 71
Doany, Madag. D9 44
Doba, Chad E9 42
Dobbiaco, Italy C7 14
Dobbs Ferry, N.Y., U.S. g13 109
Döbeln, Ger. D13 8
Doberai, Jazirah, pen., Indon. F9 32
Dobo, Indon. G9 32
Doboj, Yugo. E2 16
Dobruš, U.S.S.R. I14 22
Dobson, N.C., U.S. A2 110
Doce, stm., Braz. E8 57
Docena, Al., U.S. f7 78
Dock Junction, Ga., U.S. E5 87
Doctors Lake, l., Fl., U.S. m8 86
Doddridge, co., W.V., U.S. B4 125
Dodecanese see Dhodhekánisos, is., Grc. M10 16
Dodge, Ne., U.S. C9 104
Dodge, co., Ga., U.S. D3 87
Dodge, co., Mn., U.S. G6 100
Dodge, co., Ne., U.S. C9 104
Dodge, co., Wi., U.S. E5 126
Dodge Center, Mn., U.S. F6 100
Dodge City, Ks., U.S. E3 93
Dodgeville, Wi., U.S. F3 126
Dodoma, Tan. C7 44
Doerun, Ga., U.S. E3 87
Doe Run, Mo., U.S. D7 102
Doetinchem, Neth. D6 8
Dog, stm., Vt., U.S. C3 122
Dogai Coring, l., China C13 38
Dog Island, i., Fl., U.S. C2 86
Dog Keys Pass, strt., Ms., U.S. g8 101
Dog Lake, l., Man., Can. D2 70
Dogondoutchi, Niger F6 42
Doha see Ad-Dawhah, Qatar C5 46
Dohad, India I6 38
Doiran, Lake, l., Eur. H6 16
Dokka, Nor. F8 6
Dokkum, Neth. B5 8
Dolak, Pulau, i., Indon. G10 32
Dolbeau, Que., Can. k12 74
Dol-de-Bretagne, Fr. D5 10
Dolgeville, N.Y., U.S. B6 109
Dolianova, Italy J4 14
Dolisie, Congo B2 44
Dollar Bay, Mi., U.S. A2 99
Dolo, Som. H3 46
Dolomite, Al., U.S. B3 78
Dolomites see Dolomiti, mts., Italy C6 14
Dolomiti, mts., Italy C6 14
Dolores, Arg. D5 56
Dolores, Col. F5 58
Dolores, Co., U.S. D2 83
Dolores, co., Co., U.S. D2 83
Dolores, stm., U.S. E7 121
Dolores Hidalgo, Mex. G9 62
Dolphin and Union Strait, strt., N.W. Ter., Can. C9 66
Dolphin Island, i., Ut., U.S. B3 121
Dolton, Il., U.S. k9 90
Dombås, Nor. E7 6
Dome Mountain, mtn., Az., U.S. k9 80
Dome Peak, mtn., Co., U.S. B3 83
Domeyko, Chile B2 56
Domeyko, Cordillera, mts., Chile A3 56
Domfront, Fr. D6 10
Dominica, ctry., N.A. G17 64
Dominica Channel, strt., N.A. G17 64
Dominican Republic, ctry., N.A. E12 64
Dominion, Cape, c., N.W. Ter., Can. C18 66
Domodedovo, U.S.S.R. F20 22
Domodossola, Italy C3 14
Domžale, Yugo. C9 14
Don, stm., U.S.S.R. H6 18
Dona Ana, N.M., U.S. E3 108
Dona Ana, co., N.M., U.S. E2 108
Donaldsonville, La., U.S. D4 95
Donalsonville, Ga., U.S. E2 87
Donaueschingen, Ger. H8 8
Donauwörth, Ger. G10 8
Don Benito, Spain G6 12
Doncaster, Eng., U.K. H11 7
Dondo, Ang. C2 44
Dondra Head, c., Sri L. J6 37
Doneck, U.S.S.R. H5 18
Donegal Bay, b., Ire. G4 7
Doneraile, S.C., U.S. C8 117
Donetsk see Doneck, U.S.S.R. H5 18
Donga, stm., Nig. G8 42
Dongara, Austl. E2 50
Dongchuan, China A7 34
Dongfang, China H8 26
Dongfang (Basuo), China E10 34
Dongguan, China L2 28
Donghai Dao, i., China D11 34
Dong Hoi, Viet. F9 34
Dongshan, China L6 28
Dongtai, China C9 28
Dongting Hu, l., China F1 28
Doniphan, Mo., U.S. E7 102
Doniphan, Ne., U.S. D7 104
Doniphan, co., Ks., U.S. C8 93
Donkey Creek, stm., Wy., U.S. B7 127
Donkin, N.S., Can. C10 71
Donley, co., Tx., U.S. B2 120
Donna, Tx., U.S. F3 120
Donnacona, Que., Can. C6 74
Donnellson, Ia., U.S. D6 92
Donner Pass, Ca., U.S. C3 82
Donora, Pa., U.S. F2 115
Donskoj, U.S.S.R. H21 22
Dooly, co., Ga., U.S. D3 87
Doonerak, Mount, mtn., Ak., U.S. B9 79
Door, co., Wi., U.S. D6 126
Dora, Al., U.S. B2 78
Doraville, Ga., U.S. h8 87
Dorcheat, Bayou, stm., U.S. B2 95
Dorchester, N.B., Can. D5 71
Dorchester, Eng., U.K. K10 7
Dorchester, Ne., U.S. D8 104
Dorchester, co., Md., U.S. D5 97
Dorchester, co., S.C., U.S. E7 117
Dorchester, Cape, c., N.W. Ter., Can. C17 66
Dordogne, stm., Fr. H8 10
Dordrecht, Neth. D4 8
Doré Lake, l., Sask., Can. C2 75
Dorena Lake, res., Or., U.S. D3 114
Dores do Indaiá, Braz. E6 57
Dorgali, Italy I4 14
Dori, Burkina F5 42
Dorion-Vaudreuil, Que., Can. q18 74
Dormont, Pa., U.S. k13 115
Dornbirn, Aus. H9 8
Dorothy Pond, Ma., U.S. B4 98
Dorr, Mi., U.S. F5 99
Dorset, Vt., U.S. E2 122
Dorsey, Md., U.S. B4 97
Dortmund, Ger. D7 8
Dorton, Ky., U.S. C7 94
Dorval, Que., Can. q19 74
Dos Bahías, Cabo, c., Arg. E3 56
Dothan, Al., U.S. D4 78
Douai, Fr. B10 10
Douala, Cam. H7 42
Douarnenez, Fr. D2 10
Double Beach, Ct., U.S. D4 84
Doublespring Pass, Id., U.S. E5 89
Double Springs, Al., U.S. A2 78
Doubletop Peak, mtn., Wy., U.S. C2 127
Doubs, stm., Eur. E12 10
Dougherty, co., Ga., U.S. E2 87
Douglas, I. of Man G8 7
Douglas, Az., U.S. F6 80
Douglas, Ga., U.S. E4 87
Douglas, Mi., U.S. F4 99
Douglas, Wy., U.S. D7 127
Douglas, co., Co., U.S. B6 83
Douglas, co., Ga., U.S. C2 87
Douglas, co., Il., U.S. D5 90
Douglas, co., Ks., U.S. D8 93
Douglas, co., Mn., U.S. E3 100
Douglas, co., Mo., U.S. E5 102
Douglas, co., Ne., U.S. C9 104
Douglas, co., Nv., U.S. E2 105
Douglas, co., Or., U.S. D3 114
Douglas, co., S.D., U.S. D7 118
Douglas, co., Wa., U.S. B6 124
Douglas, co., Wi., U.S. B2 126
Douglas, Mount, mtn., Ak., U.S. D9 79
Douglas Channel, strt., B.C., Can. C3 69
Douglas Lake, l., Mi., U.S. C6 99
Douglas Lake, res., Tn., U.S. D10 119
Douglass, Ks., U.S. E7 93
Douglastown, N.B., Can. B4 71
Douglasville, Ga., U.S. C2 87
Dourada, Serra, plat., Braz. B4 57
Dourados, Braz. G1 57
Douro (Duero), stm., Eur. D4 12
Dousman, Wi., U.S. E5 126
Dove Creek, Co., U.S. D2 83
Dover, Eng., U.K. J14 7
Dover, Ar., U.S. B2 81
Dover, De., U.S. D3 85
Dover, Fl., U.S. D4 86
Dover, Ma., U.S. h10 98
Dover, N.H., U.S. D5 106
Dover, N.J., U.S. B3 107
Dover, Oh., U.S. B4 112
Dover, Pa., U.S. F8 115
Dover, Tn., U.S. A4 119
Dover, Strait of (Pas de Calais), strt., Eur. J14 7
Dover Air Force Base, mil., De., U.S. D4 85
Dover-Foxcroft, Me., U.S. C3 96
Dover Plains, N.Y., U.S. D7 109
Dowagiac, Mi., U.S. G4 99
Dowlat Yār, Afg. C1 38
Downers Grove, Il., U.S. B5 90
Downey, Ca., U.S. n12 82
Downey, Id., U.S. G6 89
Downingtown, Pa., U.S. F10 115
Downpatrick, N. Ire., U.K. G7 7
Downpatrick Head, c., Ire. G3 7
Downs, Ks., U.S. C5 93
Downs Mountain, mtn., Wy., U.S. C3 127
Downton, Mount, mtn., B.C., Can. C5 69
Dows, Ia., U.S. B4 92
Dowshī, Afg. C3 38
Doylestown, Oh., U.S. B4 112
Doylestown, Pa., U.S. F11 115
Doyline, La., U.S. B2 95
Drâa, Oued, val., Afr. C4 42
Dracena, Braz. F3 57
Drachten, Neth. B6 8
Dracut, Ma., U.S. A5 98
Draguignan, Fr. I13 10
Drain, Or., U.S. D3 114
Drake Passage, strt. D6 47
Drake Peak, mtn., Or., U.S. E6 114
Dráma, Grc. H8 16
Drammen, Nor. G8 6
Draper, Ut., U.S. C4 121
Drau (Drava), stm., Eur. C8 14
Drava (Drau), stm., Eur. D13 14
Drayton, Ont., Can. D4 73
Drayton, N.D., U.S. A8 111
Drayton, S.C., U.S. B4 117
Drayton Plains, Mi., U.S. F7 99
Drayton Valley, Alta., Can. C3 68
Dresden, Ont., Can. E2 73
Dresden, Ger. D13 8
Dresden, Oh., U.S. B3 112
Dresden, Tn., U.S. A3 119
Dresslerville, Nv., U.S. E2 105
Dreux, Fr. D8 10
Drew, Ms., U.S. B3 101
Drew, co., Ar., U.S. D4 81
Drews Reservoir, res., Or., U.S. E6 114
Drexel, Mo., U.S. C3 102
Drexel, N.C., U.S. B1 110
Drexel, Oh., U.S. C1 112
Drift, Ky., U.S. C7 94
Driggs, Id., U.S. F7 89
Driskill Mountain, hill, La., U.S. B3 95
Drogheda, Ire. H6 7
Drumheller, Alta., Can. D4 68
Drum Island, i., S.C., U.S. k12 117
Drummond, Lake, l., Va., U.S. D6 123
Drummond Island, i., Mi., U.S. C7 99
Drummondville, Que., Can. D5 74
Drumright, Ok., U.S. B5 113
Družina, U.S.S.R. D23 20
Drybranch, W.V., U.S. m13 125
Dry Cimarron, stm., U.S. A6 108
Dry Creek Mountain, mtn., Nv., U.S. B5 105
Dryden, Ont., Can. o16 73
Dryden, N.Y., U.S. C4 109
Dry Fork, stm., Mo., U.S. D6 102
Dry Fork, stm., W.V., U.S. D3 125
Dry Fork, stm., W.V., U.S. B5 125
Dry Ridge, Ky., U.S. B5 94
Dry Tortugas, is., Fl., U.S. H5 86
Duarte, Pico, mtn., Dom. Rep. E12 64
Dubach, La., U.S. B3 95
Dubai see Dubayy, U.A.E. C6 46
Dubawnt, stm., N.W. Ter., Can. D12 66
Dubawnt Lake, l., N.W. Ter., Can. D12 66
Du Bay, Lake, res., Wi., U.S. D4 126
Dubayy (Dubai), U.A.E. C6 46
Dubbo, Austl. F9 50
Dublin (Baile Átha Cliath), Ire. H6 7
Dublin, Ga., U.S. D4 87
Dublin, In., U.S. E7 91
Dublin, N.H., U.S. E2 106
Dublin, Oh., U.S. k10 112
Dublin, Pa., U.S. F11 115
Dublin, Tx., U.S. C3 120
Dublin, Va., U.S. C2 123
Dubna, U.S.S.R. E20 22
Dubois, In., U.S. H4 91
Du Bois, Pa., U.S. D4 115
Dubois, Wy., U.S. C3 127
Dubois, co., In., U.S. H4 91
Duboistown, Pa., U.S. D7 115
Dubrovnik, Yugo. G13 14
Dubuque, Ia., U.S. B7 92
Dubuque, co., Ia., U.S. B7 92
Duchesne, Ut., U.S. C5 121
Duchesne, co., Ut., U.S. C5 121
Duchesne, stm., Ut., U.S. C5 121
Duchess, Austl. D7 50
Duck, stm., Tn., U.S. B4 119
Duck Bay, Man., Can. C1 70
Duck Creek, stm., Oh., U.S. C4 112
Duck Creek, stm., Wi., U.S. h9 126
Duck Lake, Sask., Can. E2 75
Duck Lake, l., Me., U.S. C4 96
Duck Mountain Provincial Park, Sask., Can. F5 75
Duck Valley Indian Reservation, U.S. B5 105
Duckwater Indian Reservation, Nv., U.S. E6 105
Duckwater Peak, mtn., Nv., U.S. E6 105
Dudelange, Lux. F6 8
Dudinka, U.S.S.R. D11 20
Dudley, Ma., U.S. B4 98
Duenweg, Mo., U.S. D3 102
Duero (Douro), stm., Eur. D5 12
Due West, S.C., U.S. C3 117
Duffer Peak, mtn., Nv., U.S. B3 105
Dufour Spitze, mtn., Eur. G14 10
Duga Resa, Yugo. D10 14
Dugdemona, stm., La., U.S. B3 95
Dugger, In., U.S. F3 91
Duida, Cerro, mtn., Ven. F10 58
Duifken Point, c., Austl. B8 50
Duisburg, Ger. D6 8
Duke Island, i., Ak., U.S. n24 79
Dukes, co., Ma., U.S. D6 98
Duk Fadiat, Sudan G12 42
Dulce, N.M., U.S. A2 108
Dulgalach, stm., U.S.S.R. D20 20
Duluth, Ga., U.S. B2 87
Duluth, Mn., U.S. D6 100
Dūmā, Syria C5 40
Dumaguete, Phil. D7 32
Dumaran Island, i., Phil. C6 32
Dumaring, Indon. E6 32
Dumas, Ar., U.S. D4 81
Dumas, Tx., U.S. B2 120
Dumbarton, Scot., U.K. F8 7
Dumfries, Scot., U.K. F9 7
Dumfries, Va., U.S. B5 123
Dumont, Ia., U.S. B5 92
Dumont, N.J., U.S. B5 107
Dumyāṭ, Egypt B12 42
Dunaújváros, Hung. I18 8
Dunbar, Pa., U.S. G2 115
Dunbar, W.V., U.S. C3 125
Duncan, B.C., Can. E6 69
Duncan, Az., U.S. E6 80
Duncan, Ok., U.S. C4 113
Duncan, S.C., U.S. B3 117
Duncan Falls, Oh., U.S. C4 112
Duncan Lake, res., B.C., Can. D9 69
Duncannon, Pa., U.S. F7 115
Duncansville, Pa., U.S. F5 115
Duncanville, Tx., U.S. n10 120
Dundalk, Ont., Can. C4 73
Dundalk, Ire. G6 7
Dundalk, Md., U.S. B4 97
Dundas, Ont., Can. D5 73
Dundas Peninsula, pen., N.W. Ter., Can. B10 66
Dundee, S. Afr. G6 44
Dundee, Scot., U.K. E9 7
Dundee, Fl., U.S. D5 86
Dundee, Il., U.S. A5 90
Dundee, Mi., U.S. G7 99
Dundee, N.Y., U.S. C4 109
Dundee, Or., U.S. h11 114
Dundy, co., Ne., U.S. D4 104
Dunedin, N.Z. F3 52
Dunedin, Fl., U.S. D4 86
Dunellen, N.J., U.S. B4 107
Dunfermline, Scot., U.K. E9 7
Dungarvan, Ire. I5 7
Dungeness, stm., Wa., U.S. A2 124
Dungun, Malay. L7 34
Dunham, Que., Can. D5 74
Dunhua, China C12 26
Dunhuang, China C5 26
Dunkard Creek, stm., U.S. B4 125
Dunkerque, Fr. A9 10
Dunkerton, Ia., U.S. B5 92
Dunkirk, In., U.S. D7 91
Dunkirk, N.Y., U.S. C1 109
Dunkirk, Oh., U.S. B2 112
Dunklin, co., Mo., U.S. E7 102
Dunkwa, Ghana G5 42
Dún Laoghaire, Ire. H6 7
Dunlap, Il., U.S. C4 90
Dunlap, In., U.S. A6 91
Dunlap, Ia., U.S. C2 92
Dunlap, Tn., U.S. D8 119
Dunleith, De., U.S. i7 85
Dunloup Creek, stm., W.V., U.S. n13 125
Dunmore, Pa., U.S. D10 115
Dunmore, Lake, l., Vt., U.S. D2 122
Dunn, N.C., U.S. B4 110
Dunn, co., N.D., U.S. B3 111
Dunn, co., Wi., U.S. D2 126
Dunnellon, Fl., U.S. C4 86
Dunnville, Ont., Can. E5 73
Dunqulah, Sudan E12 42
Duns, Scot., U.K. F10 7
Dunseith, N.D., U.S. A5 111
Dunsmuir, Ca., U.S. B2 82
Duntou, China F8 28
Dunville, Newf., Can. E5 72
Dunwoody, Ga., U.S. h8 87
Duomaer, China E2 26
Du Page, co., Il., U.S. B5 90
Du Page, stm., Il., U.S. k8 90
Duplin, co., N.C., U.S. C5 110
Dupont, Co., U.S. B6 83
Dupont, Pa., U.S. n18 115
Dupont City, W.V., U.S. m12 125
Dupont Manor, De., U.S. D3 85
Duque de Caxias, Braz. G7 57
Duque de York, Isla, i., Chile G1 56
Duquesne, Pa., U.S. F2 115
Du Quoin, Il., U.S. E4 90
Durand, Il., U.S. A4 90
Durand, Mi., U.S. F6 99
Durand, Wi., U.S. D2 126
Durango, Mex. E7 62
Durango, Spain B9 12
Durango, Co., U.S. D3 83
Durant, Ia., U.S. C7 92
Durant, Ms., U.S. B4 101
Durant, Ok., U.S. D5 113
Durazno, Ur. C5 56
Durban, S. Afr. G6 44
Đurđevac, Yugo. C12 14
Düren, Ger. E6 8
Durg, India B6 37
Durgāpur, India I12 38
Durham, Ont., Can. C4 73
Durham, Eng., U.K. G11 7
Durham, Ca., U.S. C3 82
Durham, Ct., U.S. D5 84
Durham, N.H., U.S. D5 106
Durham, N.C., U.S. B4 110
Durham, co., N.C., U.S. A4 110
Durness, Scot., U.K. C8 7
Durrell, Newf., Can. D4 72
Durrës, Alb. H3 16
Dursunbey, Tur. J12 16
D'Urville, Tanjung, c., Indon. F10 32
Duryea, Pa., U.S. D10 115
Dušanbe, U.S.S.R. J11 18
Dušekan, U.S.S.R. E15 20
Dushan, China B9 34
Dushanbe see Dušanbe, U.S.S.R. J11 18
Duson, La., U.S. D3 95
Düsseldorf, Ger. D6 8
Dutchess, co., N.Y., U.S. D7 109
Dutch Island, i., R.I., U.S. F4 116
Dutton, Ont., Can. E3 73
Dutton, Mount, mtn., Ut., U.S. E3 121
Duval, co., Fl., U.S. B5 86
Duval, co., Tx., U.S. F3 120
Duxbury, Ma., U.S. B6 98
Duyun, China A9 34
Dvuch Cirkoje, Gora, mtn., U.S.S.R. D27 20
Dwight, Il., U.S. B5 90
Dwight D. Eisenhower Lock, N.Y., U.S. f9 109
Dworshak Reservoir, res., Id., U.S. C3 89
Dyer, In., U.S. A2 91
Dyer, Tn., U.S. A3 119
Dyer, co., Tn., U.S. A2 119
Dyer, Cape, c., N.W. Ter., Can. C20 66
Dyer Island, i., R.I., U.S. E5 116
Dyersburg, Tn., U.S. A2 119
Dyersville, Ia., U.S. B6 92
Dyess Air Force Base, mil., Tx., U.S. C3 120
Dysart, Ia., U.S. B5 92
Džalinda, U.S.S.R. G18 20
Džambul, U.S.S.R. I12 18
Dzaoudzi, May. D9 44
Džardžan, U.S.S.R. D18 20
Dzavchan, stm., Mong. B5 26
Dzeržinsk, U.S.S.R. E26 22
Dzeržinskoje, U.S.S.R. H10 20
Džezkazgan, U.S.S.R. H11 18
Dzhambul see Džambul, U.S.S.R. I12 18
Dzierżoniów (Reichenbach), Pol. E16 8
Džugdžur, Chrebet, mts., U.S.S.R. F21 20

E

Eads, Co., U.S. C8 83
Eagan, Mn., U.S. n12 100
Eagar, Az., U.S. C6 80

Name	Map Ref	Page
Eagle, Co., U.S.	B4	83
Eagle, Id., U.S.	F2	89
Eagle, Ne., U.S.	h12	104
Eagle, Wi., U.S.	F5	126
Eagle, co., Co., U.S.	B4	83
Eagle, stm., Newf., Can.	B2	72
Eagle Creek Reservoir, res., In., U.S.	E5	91
Eagle Grove, Ia., U.S.	B4	92
Eagle Key, i., Fl., U.S.	G6	86
Eagle Lake, Me., U.S.	A4	96
Eagle Lake, Mn., U.S.	F5	100
Eagle Lake, Tx., U.S.	E4	120
Eagle Lake, l., Ca., U.S.	B3	82
Eagle Lake, l., Me., U.S.	A4	96
Eagle Lake, l., Me., U.S.	B3	96
Eagle Lake, l., Ms., U.S.	C3	101
Eagle Lake, l., Wi., U.S.	C4	126
Eagle Mountain, mtn., Mn., U.S.	k9	100
Eagle Mountain Lake, res., Tx., U.S.	m9	120
Eagle Nest Lake, l., N.M., U.S.	A4	108
Eagle Pass, Tx., U.S.	E2	120
Eagle Peak, mtn., Ca., U.S.	B3	82
Eagle Point, Or., U.S.	E4	114
Eagle River, Wi., U.S.	C4	126
Eagletail Mountains, mts., Az., U.S.	D2	80
Eagletail Peak, mtn., Az., U.S.	D2	80
Eagletown, Ok., U.S.	C7	113
Earle, Ar., U.S.	B5	81
Earlham, Ia., U.S.	C3	92
Earlimart, Ca., U.S.	E4	82
Earlington, Ky., U.S.	C2	94
Earlville, Il., U.S.	B5	90
Earlville, Ia., U.S.	B6	92
Early, Ia., U.S.	B2	92
Early, co., Ga., U.S.	E2	87
Earth, Tx., U.S.	B1	120
Easley, S.C., U.S.	B2	117
East, stm., Ct., U.S.	D5	84
East, stm., N.Y., U.S.	k13	109
East, stm., Wi., U.S.	h9	126
East Alton, Il., U.S.	E3	90
East Angus, Que., Can.	D6	74
East Arlington, Vt., U.S.	E2	122
East Aurora, N.Y., U.S.	C2	109
East Bangor, Pa., U.S.	E11	115
East Bank, W.V., U.S.	m13	125
East Barre, Vt., U.S.	C4	122
East Baton Rouge, co., La., U.S.	D4	95
East Bay, b., Fl., U.S.	u16	86
East Bay, b., Tx., U.S.	R15	120
East Beckwith Mountain, mtn., Co., U.S.	C3	83
East Berlin, Ct., U.S.	C5	84
East Berlin, Pa., U.S.	G8	115
East Bernard, Tx., U.S.	E4	120
East Bernstadt, Ky., U.S.	C5	94
East Bethel, Mn., U.S.	E5	100
East Billerica, Ma., U.S.	f11	98
Eastborough, Ks., U.S.	g12	93
Eastbourne, Eng., U.K.	K13	7
East Brady, Pa., U.S.	E2	115
East Branch Clarion River Lake, res., Pa., U.S.	C4	115
East Brewton, Al., U.S.	D2	78
East Bridgewater, Ma., U.S.	B6	98
East Brimfield Lake, res., Ma., U.S.	B3	98
East Brooklyn, Ct., U.S.	B8	84
East Broughton, Que., Can.	C6	74
East Brunswick, N.J., U.S.	C4	107
East Butte, mtn., Mt., U.S.	B5	103
East Cache Creek, stm., Ok., U.S.	C3	113
East Cape, c., Fl., U.S.	G5	86
East Carbon, Ut., U.S.	D5	121
East Carroll, co., La., U.S.	B4	95
East Chicago, In., U.S.	A3	91
East China Sea, Asia	E12	26
East Chop, c., Ma., U.S.	D6	98
East Cleveland, Oh., U.S.	g9	112
East Cote Blanche Bay, b., La., U.S.	E4	95
East Dennis, Ma., U.S.	C7	98
East Derry, N.H., U.S.	E4	106
East Detroit, Mi., U.S.	p16	99
East Douglas, Ma., U.S.	B4	98
East Dubuque, Il., U.S.	A3	90
Eastend, Sask., Can.	H1	75
Easter Island see Pascua, Isla de, i., Chile	H5	2
Eastern Bay, b., Md., U.S.	C5	97
Eastern Channel see Tsushima-kaikyō, strt., Japan	I2	30
Eastern Ghāts, mts., India	F5	37
Eastern Neck Island, i., Md., U.S.	B5	97
Eastern Point, c., Ma., U.S.	f13	98
Easterville, Man., Can.	C2	70
East Falkland, i., Falk. Is.	G5	56
East Falmouth, Ma., U.S.	C6	98
East Feliciana, co., La., U.S.	D4	95
East Flat Rock, N.C., U.S.	f10	110
East Fork, stm., Wy., U.S.	D3	127
East Fork Lake, res., Oh., U.S.	C1	112
East Gaffney, S.C., U.S.	A4	117
East Galesburg, Il., U.S.	C3	90
East Granby, Ct., U.S.	B5	84
East Grand Forks, Mn., U.S.	C2	100
East Grand Rapids, Mi., U.S.	F5	99
East Greenville, Pa., U.S.	F10	115
East Greenwich, R.I., U.S.	D4	116
East Gwillimbury, Ont., Can.	C5	73
East Hampstead, N.H., U.S.	E4	106
East Hampton, Ct., U.S.	C5	84
Easthampton, Ma., U.S.	B2	98
East Hanover, N.J., U.S.	B4	107
East Hartford, Ct., U.S.	B5	84
East Hartland, Ct., U.S.	B4	84
East Haven, Ct., U.S.	D4	84
East Helena, Mt., U.S.	D5	103
East Jordan, Mi., U.S.	C5	99
Eastlake, Oh., U.S.	A4	112
East Lake Tohopekaliga, l., Fl., U.S.	D5	86
Eastland, Tx., U.S.	C3	120
Eastland, co., Tx., U.S.	C3	120
East Lansing, Mi., U.S.	F6	99
East Las Vegas, Nv., U.S.	G6	105
East Liverpool, Oh., U.S.	B5	112
East London (Oos-Londen), S. Afr.	H5	44
East Longmeadow, Ma., U.S.	B2	98
East Los Angeles, Ca., U.S.	m12	82
East Lyme, Ct., U.S.	D7	84
East Lynn Lake, res., W.V., U.S.	C2	125
Eastmain, stm., Que., Can.	F17	66
Eastmain-Opinaca, Réservoir, res., Que., Can.	h11	74
Eastman, Que., Can.	D5	74
Eastman, Ga., U.S.	D3	87
East Matunuck, R.I., U.S.	F3	116
East Middlebury, Vt., U.S.	D2	122
East Millinocket, Me., U.S.	C4	96
East Moline, Il., U.S.	B3	90
East Montpelier, Vt., U.S.	C4	122
East Naples, Fl., U.S.	F5	86
East Newnan, Ga., U.S.	C2	87
East Nishnabotna, stm., Ia., U.S.	C2	92
East Norriton, Pa., U.S.	o20	115
East Olympia, Wa., U.S.	C3	124
Easton, Md., U.S.	C5	97
Easton, Pa., U.S.	E11	115
Easton Reservoir, res., Ct., U.S.	E2	84
East Orange, N.J., U.S.	B4	107
East Orleans, Ma., U.S.	C8	98
Eastover, S.C., U.S.	D6	117
East Palatka, Fl., U.S.	C5	86
East Palestine, Oh., U.S.	B5	112
East Pass, strt., Fl., U.S.	C2	86
East Pea Ridge, W.V., U.S.	C2	125
East Peoria, Il., U.S.	C4	90
East Pepperell, Ma., U.S.	A4	98
East Petersburg, Pa., U.S.	F9	115
East Pittsburgh, Pa., U.S.	k14	115
Eastpoint, Fl., U.S.	C2	86
East Point, Ga., U.S.	C2	87
East Point, c., P.E.I., Can.	C8	71
East Point, c., Ma., U.S.	B6	98
East Point, c., N.J., U.S.	E2	107
Eastport, Newf., Can.	D5	72
Eastport, Me., U.S.	D6	96
East Prairie, Mo., U.S.	E8	102
East Providence, R.I., U.S.	C4	116
East Pryor Mountain, mtn., Mt., U.S.	E8	103
East Quogue, N.Y., U.S.	n16	109
East Range, mts., Nv., U.S.	C4	105
East Ridge, Tn., U.S.	h11	119
East River, Ct., U.S.	D5	84
East Rochester, N.Y., U.S.	B3	109
East Rockingham, N.C., U.S.	C3	110
East Rutherford, N.J., U.S.	h8	107
East Saint Louis, Il., U.S.	E3	90
East Selkirk, Man., Can.	D3	70
Eastsound, Wa., U.S.	A3	124
East Spencer, N.C., U.S.	B2	110
East Stroudsburg, Pa., U.S.	D11	115
East Tawas, Mi., U.S.	D7	99
East Troy, Wi., U.S.	F5	126
East Vestal, N.Y., U.S.	C5	109
East View, W.V., U.S.	k10	125
East Walker, stm., U.S.	E2	105
East Walpole, Ma., U.S.	h11	98
East Wareham, Ma., U.S.	C6	98
East Washington, Pa., U.S.	F1	115
East Wenatchee, Wa., U.S.	B5	124
East Windsor, N.J., U.S.	C3	107
East York, Ont., Can.	D5	73
Eaton, Co., U.S.	A6	83
Eaton, In., U.S.	D7	91
Eaton, Oh., U.S.	C1	112
Eaton, co., Mi., U.S.	F6	99
Eaton Rapids, Mi., U.S.	F6	99
Eatonton, Ga., U.S.	C3	87
Eatontown, N.J., U.S.	C4	107
Eatonville, Wa., U.S.	C3	124
Eau Claire, Wi., U.S.	D2	126
Eau Claire, co., Wi., U.S.	D2	126
Eau Claire, stm., Wi., U.S.	D2	126
Eau Claire, Lac à l', l., Que., Can.	g11	74
Eauze, Fr.	I7	10
Ebano, Mex.	F10	62
Ebba Ksour, Tun.	N3	14
Ebbw Vale, Wales, U.K.	J9	7
Ebensburg, Pa., U.S.	F4	115
Eberndorf, Aus.	I14	8
Eberswalde, Ger.	C13	8
Ebetsu, Japan	p19	30a
Ebingen, Ger.	G9	8
Ebinur Hu, l., China	B3	26
Eboli, Italy	I10	14
Ebolowa, Cam.	H8	42
Ebro, stm., Spain	E12	12
Ebro, Delta del, Spain	E12	12
Eccles, W.V., U.S.	n13	125
Echo Bay, Nv., U.S.	G7	105
Echo Lake, l., Me., U.S.	D3	96
Echo Lake, l., Vt., U.S.	B5	122
Echols, co., Ga., U.S.	F4	87
Écija, Spain	H6	12
Eckernförde, Ger.	A9	8
Eckhart Mines, Md., U.S.	k13	97
Eckville, Alta., Can.	C3	68
Eclectic, Al., U.S.	C3	78
Eclipse Sound, strt., N.W. Ter., Can.	B17	66
Écommoy, Fr.	E7	10
Econfina, stm., Fl., U.S.	B3	86
Economy, Pa., U.S.	h13	115
Écorces, Rivière aux, stm., Que., Can.	A6	74
Ecorse, Mi., U.S.	p15	99
Ecru, Ms., U.S.	A4	101
Ector, co., Tx., U.S.	D1	120
Ecuador, ctry., S.A.	D3	54
Ed, Swe.	G8	6
Edcouch, Tx., U.S.	F4	120
Eddy, co., N.M., U.S.	E5	108
Eddy, co., N.D., U.S.	B7	111
Eddystone, Pa., U.S.	p20	115
Eddyville, Ia., U.S.	C5	92
Eddyville, Ky., U.S.	e9	94
Ede, Neth.	C5	8
Edéa, Cam.	H8	42
Eden, Ga., U.S.	D5	87
Eden, Md., U.S.	D6	97
Eden, N.Y., U.S.	C2	109
Eden, N.C., U.S.	A3	110
Eden, Tx., U.S.	D3	120
Edenderry, Ire.	H5	7
Eden Prairie, Mn., U.S.	n12	100
Edenton, N.C., U.S.	A6	110
Eden Valley, Mn., U.S.	E4	100
Edgar, Ne., U.S.	D8	104
Edgar, Wi., U.S.	D4	126
Edgar, co., Il., U.S.	D6	90
Edgard, La., U.S.	D5	95
Edgartown, Ma., U.S.	D6	98
Edgecombe, co., N.C., U.S.	B5	110
Edgecumbe, Cape, c., Ak., U.S.	m21	79
Edgefield, S.C., U.S.	D4	117
Edgefield, co., S.C., U.S.	D4	117
Edgeley, N.D., U.S.	C7	111
Edgemere, Md., U.S.	B5	97
Edgemont, S.D., U.S.	D2	118
Edgemoor, De., U.S.	A3	85
Edgerton, Ks., U.S.	D8	93
Edgerton, Mn., U.S.	G2	100
Edgerton, Oh., U.S.	A1	112
Edgerton, Wi., U.S.	F4	126
Edgerton, Wy., U.S.	C6	127
Edgewater, Al., U.S.	f7	78
Edgewater, Fl., U.S.	D6	86
Edgewater, Md., U.S.	C4	97
Edgewater, N.J., U.S.	h9	107
Edgewater Park, N.J., U.S.	C3	107
Edgewood, In., U.S.	D6	91
Edgewood, Ia., U.S.	B6	92
Edgewood, Ky., U.S.	h13	94
Edgewood, Md., U.S.	B5	97
Edgewood, Md., U.S.	B5	97
Edgewood, N.M., U.S.	B3	108
Edgewood, Oh., U.S.	A5	112
Edgewood, Pa., U.S.	k14	115
Edgewood, Wa., U.S.	f11	124
Edgeworth, Pa., U.S.	h13	115
Edina, Mn., U.S.	F5	100
Edina, Mo., U.S.	A5	102
Edinboro, Pa., U.S.	C1	115
Edinburg, Il., U.S.	D4	90
Edinburg, Tx., U.S.	F3	120
Edinburg, Va., U.S.	B4	123
Edinburgh, Scot., U.K.	F9	7
Edinburgh, In., U.S.	F6	91
Edirne, Tur.	G13	4
Edison, Ga., U.S.	E2	87
Edison, N.J., U.S.	B4	107
Edisto, stm., S.C., U.S.	E6	117
Edisto Island, i., S.C., U.S.	F7	117
Edith, Mount, mtn., Mt., U.S.	D5	103
Edjeleh, Alg.	C7	42
Edmond, Ok., U.S.	B4	113
Edmonds, Wa., U.S.	B3	124
Edmondson Heights, Md., U.S.	g10	97
Edmonson, co., Ky., U.S.	C3	94
Edmonton, Alta., Can.	C4	68
Edmonton, Ky., U.S.	D4	94
Edmore, Mi., U.S.	E5	99
Edmunds, co., S.D., U.S.	B6	118
Edmundston, N.B., Can.	B1	71
Edna, Tx., U.S.	E4	120
Edon, Oh., U.S.	A1	112
Édouard, Lac, l., Que., Can.	B5	74
Edremit, Tur.	J11	16
Edrengijn Nuruu, mts., Mong.	C6	26
Edsbyn, Swe.	F10	6
Edson, Alta., Can.	C2	68
Edson Butte, mtn., Or., U.S.	E2	114
Eduardo Castex, Arg.	D4	56
Edward, Lake, l., Afr.	B5	44
Edwards, Ms., U.S.	C3	101
Edwards, co., Il., U.S.	E5	90
Edwards, co., Ks., U.S.	E4	93
Edwards, co., Tx., U.S.	E2	120
Edwards Air Force Base, mil., Ca., U.S.	E5	82
Edwardsburg, Mi., U.S.	G4	99
Edwards Butte, mtn., Or., U.S.	B3	114
Edwardsville, Il., U.S.	E4	90
Edwardsville, Ks., U.S.	k16	93
Edwardsville, Pa., U.S.	n17	115
Eel, stm., Ca., U.S.	B2	82
Eel, stm., In., U.S.	C6	91
Eel, stm., In., U.S.	F3	91
Effigy Mounds National Monument, Ia., U.S.	A6	92
Effingham, Il., U.S.	D5	90
Effingham, co., Ga., U.S.	D5	87
Effingham, co., Il., U.S.	D5	90
Efland, N.C., U.S.	A3	110
Egan Range, mts., Nv., U.S.	E7	105
Eganville, Ont., Can.	B7	73
Egede og Rothes Fjord, Grnld.	C25	66
Egedesminde, Grnld.	C22	66
Eger, Hung.	H20	8
Egersund, Nor.	G5	6
Eggenfelden, Ger.	G12	8
Egg Harbor City, N.J., U.S.	D3	107
Egg Island Point, c., N.J., U.S.	E2	107
Égletons, Fr.	G9	10
Eglin Air Force Base, mil., Fl., U.S.	u15	86
Egmont, Mount, mtn., N.Z.	C5	52
Egmont Bay, b., P.E.I., Can.	C5	71
Egmont Channel, strt., Fl., U.S.	p10	86
Egmont Key, i., Fl., U.S.	p10	86
Egvekinot, U.S.S.R.	D29	20
Egypt, ctry., Afr.	C11	42
Egypt, Lake of, res., Il., U.S.	F5	90
Ehingen, Ger.	G9	8
Ehrenberg, Az., U.S.	D1	80
Éibar, Spain	B9	12
Eichstätt, Ger.	G11	8
Eidsvoll, Nor.	F8	6
Eielson Air Force Base, mil., Ak., U.S.	C10	79
Eifel, mts., Ger.	E6	8
Eighty Mile Beach, Austl.	C4	50
Eil, Som.	G4	46
Eilenburg, Ger.	D12	8
Eindhoven, Neth.	D5	8
Einsiedeln, Switz.	E15	10
Eirunepé, Braz.	E5	54
Eisenach, Ger.	E10	8
Eisenberg, Ger.	E11	8
Eisenerz, Aus.	H14	8
Eisenhower, Mount, mtn., N.H., U.S.	B4	106
Eisenhüttenstadt, Ger.	C14	8
Eisenstadt, Aus.	H16	8
Eisleben, Ger.	D11	8
Ejea de los Caballeros, Spain	C10	12
Ekiatapskij Chrebet, mts., U.S.S.R.	D29	20
Ekimčan, U.S.S.R.	G20	20
Ekwan, stm., Ont., Can.	F16	66
El Aaiún, W. Sah.	C3	42
Elaine, Ar., U.S.	C5	81
El Asnam, Alg.	A6	42
Elat, Isr.	E4	40
El Avión, Mex.	E6	62
Elâzığ, Tur.	H15	4
Elba, Al., U.S.	D3	78
Elba, Isola d', i., Italy	G5	14
El Banco, Col.	C6	58
El Barco de Valdeorras, Spain	C5	12
Elbasan, Alb.	H4	16
El Baúl, Ven.	C8	58
Elbe (Labe), stm., Eur.	B9	8
Elberfeld, In., U.S.	H3	91
Elbert, co., Co., U.S.	B6	83
Elbert, co., Ga., U.S.	B4	87
Elbert, Mount, mtn., Co., U.S.	B4	83
Elberta, Ga., U.S.	D3	87
Elberton, Ga., U.S.	B4	87
Elbeuf, Fr.	C8	10
Elbląg (Elbing), Pol.	A19	8
El Bonillo, Spain	G9	12
El Bordo, Col.	F4	58
Elbow, stm., Alta., Can.	D3	68
Elbow Lake, Mn., U.S.	E3	100
El'brus, gora, mtn., Sov. Un.	I6	18
El Burgo de Osma, Spain	D8	12
Elburn, Il., U.S.	B5	90
Elburz Mountains see Alborz, Reshteh-ye Kūhhā-ye, mts., Iran	J8	18
El Cajon, Ca., U.S.	F5	82
El Callao, Ven.	D12	58
El Campo, Tx., U.S.	E4	120
El Capitan, mtn., Mt., U.S.	D2	103
El Capitan Reservoir, res., Ca., U.S.	o16	82
El Carmen, Arg.	A3	56
El Carmen de Bolívar, Col.	C5	58
El Centro, Ca., U.S.	F6	82
El Cerrito, Col.	F4	58
El Cerrito, Ca., U.S.	h8	82
Elche, Spain	G11	12
Elche de la Sierra, Spain	G9	12
El Cozón, Mex.	B3	62
El Cuervo Butte, mtn., N.M., U.S.	k9	108
Elda, Spain	G11	12
El Desemboque, Mex.	C3	62
El Diviso, Col.	G3	58
El Djouf, des., Afr.	D4	42
Eldon, Ia., U.S.	D5	92
Eldon, Mo., U.S.	C5	102
Eldora, Ia., U.S.	B4	92
Eldorado, Mex.	E6	62
El Dorado, Ar., U.S.	D3	81
Eldorado, Il., U.S.	F5	90
El Dorado, Ks., U.S.	E7	93
Eldorado, Tx., U.S.	D2	120
El Dorado, co., Ca., U.S.	C3	82
Eldorado Peak, mtn., Wa., U.S.	A4	124
Eldorado Springs, Co., U.S.	B5	83
El Dorado Springs, Mo., U.S.	D3	102
Eldoret, Kenya	A7	44
Eldridge, Ia., U.S.	C7	92
Eleanor, W.V., U.S.	C3	125
Electra, Tx., U.S.	B3	120
Electra Lake, res., Co., U.S.	D3	83
Electric Peak, mtn., Co., U.S.	C5	83
Electric Peak, mtn., Mt., U.S.	E6	103
Elektrostal', U.S.S.R.	F21	22
El Encanto, Col.	H6	58
Elephant Butte Reservoir, res., N.M., U.S.	D2	108
El Estor, Guat.	G3	64
Eleuthera, i., Bah.	B9	64
Eleven Mile Canyon Reservoir, res., Co., U.S.	C5	83
Eleven Point, stm., U.S.	A4	81
Elevsís, Grc.	K7	16
El Fahs, Tun.	M4	14
El Ferrol del Caudillo, Spain	B3	12
El Galpón, Arg.	B4	56
Elgin, Scot., U.K.	D9	7
Elgin, Il., U.S.	A5	90
Elgin, Ia., U.S.	B6	92
Elgin, Mn., U.S.	F6	100
Elgin, Ne., U.S.	C7	104
Elgin, N.D., U.S.	C4	111
Elgin, Ok., U.S.	C3	113
Elgin, Or., U.S.	B9	114
Elgin, S.C., U.S.	B6	117
Elgin, Tx., U.S.	D4	120
El Goléa, Alg.	B6	42
El Golfo de Santa Clara, Mex.	B2	62
Elgon, Mount, mtn., Afr.	A6	44
El Hank, clf, Afr.	D4	42
El Haouaria, Tun.	L6	14
Elida, Oh., U.S.	B1	112
Élisabethville see Lubumbashi, Zaire	D5	44
Elizabeth, Austl.	F7	50
Elizabeth, Co., U.S.	B6	83
Elizabeth, N.J., U.S.	B4	107
Elizabeth, W.V., U.S.	B3	125
Elizabeth, Cape, c., Wa., U.S.	B1	124
Elizabeth City, N.C., U.S.	A6	110
Elizabeth Islands, is., Ma., U.S.	D6	98
Elizabeth Reef, atoll, Austl.	E11	50
Elizabethton, Tn., U.S.	C11	119
Elizabethtown, Ky., U.S.	C4	94
Elizabethtown, N.C., U.S.	C4	110
Elizabethtown, Pa., U.S.	F8	115
Elizabethville, Pa., U.S.	E8	115
El-Jadida, Mor.	B4	42
El Jebel, Co., U.S.	B3	83
Ełk, Pol.	B22	8
Elk, co., Ks., U.S.	E7	93
Elk, co., Pa., U.S.	D4	115
Elk, stm., U.S.	A2	78
Elk, stm., Co., U.S.	A4	83
Elk, stm., Ks., U.S.	E7	93
Elk, stm., W.V., U.S.	C3	125
Elk, stm., Wi., U.S.	C3	126
Elkader, Ia., U.S.	B6	92
El Kairouan, Tun.	N5	14
Elk City, Id., U.S.	D3	89
Elk City, Ok., U.S.	B2	113
Elk City Lake, res., Ks., U.S.	E7	93
Elk Creek, stm., Ok., U.S.	B2	113
Elk Creek, stm., S.D., U.S.	C3	118
El Kef, Tun.	M3	14
Elkford, B.C., Can.	D10	69
Elk Grove, Ca., U.S.	C3	82
Elk Grove Village, Il., U.S.	h9	90
Elkhart, In., U.S.	A6	91
Elkhart, Ks., U.S.	E2	93
Elkhart, Tx., U.S.	D5	120
Elkhart, co., In., U.S.	A6	91
Elkhart, stm., In., U.S.	B6	91
Elkhart Lake, Wi., U.S.	E5	126
Elkhead Mountains, mts., Co., U.S.	A3	83
Elkhorn, Man., Can.	E1	70
Elk Horn, Ia., U.S.	C2	92
Elkhorn, Ne., U.S.	g12	104
Elkhorn, Wi., U.S.	F5	126
Elkhorn, stm., Ne., U.S.	B7	104
Elkhorn City, Ky., U.S.	C7	94
Elkhorn Peaks, mts., Id., U.S.	F7	89
Elkin, N.C., U.S.	A2	110
Elkins, Ar., U.S.	A1	81
Elkins, W.V., U.S.	C5	125
Elkland, Pa., U.S.	C7	115
Elk Mills, Md., U.S.	A6	97
Elk Mound, Wi., U.S.	D2	126
Elk Mountain, Wy., U.S.	E6	127
Elk Mountain, mtn., N.M., U.S.	D1	108
Elk Mountain, mtn., Wy., U.S.	E6	127
Elk Mountains, mts., U.S.	D1	118
Elk Mountains, mts., Co., U.S.	B3	83
Elko, Nv., U.S.	C6	105
Elko, co., Nv., U.S.	B6	105
Elk Peak, mtn., Mt., U.S.	D6	103
Elk Point, Alta., Can.	C5	68
Elk Point, S.D., U.S.	E9	118
Elk Rapids, Mi., U.S.	D5	99
El Krib, Tun.	M4	14
Elkridge, Md., U.S.	B4	97
Elk River, Mn., U.S.	E5	100
Elkton, Ky., U.S.	D2	94
Elkton, Md., U.S.	A6	97
Elkton, Mi., U.S.	E7	99
Elkton, S.D., U.S.	C9	118
Elkton, Va., U.S.	B4	123
Elkview, W.V., U.S.	m13	125
Elkville, Il., U.S.	F4	90
Ellaville, Ga., U.S.	D2	87
Ellen, Mount, mtn., Ut., U.S.	E5	121
Ellendale, De., U.S.	E4	85
Ellendale, N.D., U.S.	C7	111
Ellensburg, Wa., U.S.	C5	124
Ellenton, Fl., U.S.	E4	86
Ellenville, N.Y., U.S.	D6	109
Ellerbe, N.C., U.S.	B3	110
Ellerslie, Md., U.S.	k13	97
Ellesmere Island, i., N.W. Ter., Can.	A21	128
Ellettsville, In., U.S.	F4	91
Ellice Islands see Tuvalu, ctry., Oc.	G24	2
Ellicott City, Md., U.S.	B4	97
Ellijay, Ga., U.S.	B2	87
Ellington, Ct., U.S.	B6	84
Ellington, Mo., U.S.	D7	102
Ellinwood, Ks., U.S.	D5	93
Elliot Lake, Ont., Can.	A2	73
Elliott, Ms., U.S.	B4	101
Elliott, co., Ky., U.S.	B6	94
Elliott Bay, b., Wa., U.S.	e11	124
Elliott Key, i., Fl., U.S.	G6	86
Ellis, Ks., U.S.	D4	93
Ellis, co., Ks., U.S.	D4	93
Ellis, co., Ok., U.S.	A2	113
Ellis, co., Tx., U.S.	C4	120
Ellis, stm., N.H., U.S.	B4	106
Elliston, Va., U.S.	C2	123
Ellisville, Ms., U.S.	D4	101
Ellisville, Mo., U.S.	f12	102
Ellon, Scot., U.K.	D10	7
Elloree, S.C., U.S.	D6	117
Ellport, Pa., U.S.	E1	115
Ellsworth, Ks., U.S.	D5	93
Ellsworth, Me., U.S.	D4	96
Ellsworth, Pa., U.S.	F1	115
Ellsworth, Wi., U.S.	D1	126
Ellsworth, co., Ks., U.S.	D5	93
Ellsworth Air Force Base, mil., S.D., U.S.	C2	118
Ellwangen, Ger.	G10	8
Ellwood City, Pa., U.S.	E1	115
Elm, stm., N.D., U.S.	B8	111
Elma, Ia., U.S.	A5	92
Elma, Wa., U.S.	C2	124
El Mahdia, Tun.	N6	14
El Manteco, Ven.	D11	58
Elm City, N.C., U.S.	B5	110
Elm Creek, Ne., U.S.	D6	104
El Médano, Mex.	E4	62
Elmendorf Air Force Base, mil., Ak., U.S.	C10	79
Elm Grove, Wi., U.S.	m11	126
Elmhurst, Il., U.S.	B6	90
Elmhurst, Pa., U.S.	D10	115
Elmira, N.Y., U.S.	C4	109

Name | Map Ref | Page

El Mirage, Az., U.S. k8 80
Elmira Heights, N.Y., U.S. C4 109
El Moknine, Tun. N5 14
Elmont, N.Y., U.S. k13 109
Elmora, Pa., U.S. E4 115
Elmore, Mn., U.S. G4 100
Elmore, Oh., U.S. A2 112
Elmore, co., Al., U.S. C3 78
Elmore, co., Id., U.S. F3 89
El Morro National Monument, N.M., U.S. B1 108
Elmsdale, N.S., Can. E6 71
Elmshorn, Ger. B9 8
Elm Springs, Ar., U.S. A1 81
Elmvale, Ont., Can. C5 73
Elmwood, Il., U.S. C3 90
Elmwood, Wi., U.S. D1 126
Elmwood Park, Il., U.S. k9 90
Elmwood Park, N.J., U.S. h8 107
Elmwood Place, Oh., U.S. o13 112
Elne, Fr. J9 10
Elnora, In., U.S. G3 91
Eloise, Fl., U.S. E5 86
Elon College, N.C., U.S. A3 110
Elora, Ont., Can. D4 73
Elorza, Ven. D8 58
El Oued, Alg. B7 42
Eloy, Az., U.S. E4 80
El Palmar, Ven. D12 58
El Paso, Il., U.S. C4 90
El Paso, Tx., U.S. o11 120
El Paso, co., Co., U.S. C6 83
El Paso, co., Tx., U.S. o11 120
El Pilar, Ven. B11 58
El Pital, Cerro, mtn., N.A. G3 64
El Portal, Fl., U.S. s13 86
El Prado, N.M., U.S. A4 108
El Progreso, Hond. G4 64
El Puente del Arzobispo, Spain F6 12
El Puerto de Santa María, Spain I5 12
El Quelite, Mex. F6 62
El Reno, Ok., U.S. B4 113
Elrose, Sask., Can. F1 75
Elroy, Wi., U.S. E3 126
Elsa, Yukon, Can. D5 66
Elsa, Tx., U.S. F4 120
Elsah, Il., U.S. E3 90
El Salto, Mex. F7 62
El Salvador, ctry., N.A. H3 64
El Sauce, Nic. H4 64
El Sauzal, Mex. B1 62
Elsberry, Mo., U.S. B7 102
Elsie, Mi., U.S. E6 99
Elsinore, Ut., U.S. E3 121
Elsmere, De., U.S. B3 85
Elsmere, Ky., U.S. B5 94
El Socorro, Ven. C10 58
El Sombrero, Ven. C9 58
Elspe, Ger. D8 8
Elsterwerda, Ger. D13 8
El Tigre, Col. F8 58
El Tigre, Ven. C10 58
El Tocuyo, Ven. C8 58
Elton, La., U.S. D3 95
El Toro Marine Corps Air Station, mil., Ca., U.S. n13 82
El Trapiche, Col. F4 58
El Triunfo, Mex. F4 62
El Turbio, Arg. G2 56
Elūru, India D6 37
El Vado Reservoir, res., N.M., U.S. A3 108
Elvas, Port. G4 12
Elverum, Nor. F8 6
El Vigía, Ven. C7 58
Elvins, Mo., U.S. D7 102
Elwell, Lake, res., Mt., U.S. B5 103
Elwha, stm., Wa., U.S. A2 124
Elwood, In., U.S. D6 91
Elwood, Ks., U.S. C9 93
Elwood, Ne., U.S. D6 104
Ely, Eng., U.K. I13 7
Ely, Mn., U.S. C7 100
Ely, Nv., U.S. D7 105
Elyria, Oh., U.S. A3 112
Elysburg, Pa., U.S. E8 115
Emanuel, co., Ga., U.S. D4 87
Embarcación, Arg. A4 56
Embarras, stm., Il., U.S. E6 90
Embarrass, stm., Wi., U.S. D5 126
Embro, Ont., Can. D4 73
Embrun, Fr. H13 10
Emden, Ger. B7 8
Emerald, Austl. D9 50
Emerson, Man., Can. E3 70
Emerson, Ga., U.S. B2 87
Emerson, Ne., U.S. B9 104
Emerson, N.J., U.S. h8 107
Emery, co., Ut., U.S. E5 121
Emet, Tur. J13 16
Emily, Mn., U.S. D5 100
Emily, Lake, l., Mn., U.S. E3 100
Eminence, Ky., U.S. B4 94
Emmaus, Pa., U.S. E11 115
Emmen, Neth. C6 8
Emmendingen, Ger. G7 8
Emmet, co., Ia., U.S. A3 92
Emmet, co., Mi., U.S. C6 99
Emmetsburg, Ia., U.S. A3 92
Emmett, Id., U.S. F2 89
Emmiganūru, India E4 37
Emmitsburg, Md., U.S. A3 97
Emmonak, Ak., U.S. C7 79
Emmons, co., N.D., U.S. C5 111
Emory Peak, mtn., Tx., U.S. E1 120
Empalme, Mex. D4 62
Empangeni, S. Afr. G6 44
Empedrado, Arg. B5 56
Empire, La., U.S. E6 95
Empire, Nv., U.S. C2 105
Empoli, Italy F5 14
Emporia, Ks., U.S. D7 93
Emporia, Va., U.S. D5 123
Emporium, Pa., U.S. D5 115
Empty Quarter see Ar-Rab' al-Khālī, des., Asia D5 46
Emsdetten, Ger. C7 8
Emsworth, Pa., U.S. h13 115
Encampment, Wy., U.S. E6 127
Encarnación, Para. B5 56
Encinitas, Ca., U.S. F5 82
Encontrados, Ven. C6 58
Ende, Indon. G7 32
Enderby, B.C., Can. D8 69
Enderby Land, reg., Ant. C18 47
Enderlin, N.D., U.S. C8 111
Enders Reservoir, res., Ne., U.S. D4 104
Endicott, N.Y., U.S. C4 109
Endicott Mountains, mts., Ak., U.S. B9 79
Endless Lake, l., Me., U.S. C4 96
Endwell, N.Y., U.S. C4 109
Enfida, Tun. M5 14
Enfield, Ct., U.S. B5 84
Enfield, N.H., U.S. C2 106
Enfield, N.C., U.S. A5 110
Engel's, U.S.S.R. G7 18
Enggano, Pulau, i., Indon. G3 32
England, Ar., U.S. C4 81
England, ter., U.K. I11 7
England Air Force Base, mil., La., U.S. C3 95
Englee, Newf., Can. C3 72
Engleside, Va., U.S. g12 123
Englewood, Co., U.S. B6 83
Englewood, Fl., U.S. F4 86
Englewood, N.J., U.S. B5 107
Englewood, Oh., U.S. C1 112
Englewood, Tn., U.S. D9 119
Englewood Cliffs, N.J., U.S. h9 107
English, In., U.S. H5 91
English Bāzār, India H13 38
English Channel (La Manche), strt., Eur. B5 10
Enguera, Spain G11 12
Enid, Ok., U.S. A4 113
Enid Lake, res., Ms., U.S. A4 101
Enigma, Ga., U.S. E3 87
Enka, N.C., U.S. f10 110
Enkhuizen, Neth. C5 8
Enköping, Swe. G11 6
Enmelen, U.S.S.R. D30 20
Enna, Italy L9 14
Ennadai Lake, l., N.W. Ter., Can. D12 66
Ennedi, plat., Chad E10 42
Ennis, Ire. I4 7
Ennis, Mt., U.S. E5 103
Ennis, Tx., U.S. C4 120
Enniskillen, N. Ire., U.K. G5 7
Enoch, Ut., U.S. F3 121
Enola, Pa., U.S. F8 115
Enon, Oh., U.S. C2 112
Enoree, S.C., U.S. B4 117
Enoree, stm., S.C., U.S. B3 117
Enosburg Falls, Vt., U.S. B3 122
Enriquillo, Dom. Rep. F12 64
Enschede, Neth. C6 8
Ensenada, Mex. B1 62
Enshi, China E8 26
Enshū-nada, Japan H10 30
Ensley, Fl., U.S. u14 86
Entebbe, Ug. A6 44
Enterprise, Al., U.S. D4 78
Enterprise, Ks., U.S. D6 93
Enterprise, Or., U.S. B9 114
Enterprise, Ut., U.S. F2 121
Enterprise, W.V., U.S. B4 125
Entiat, stm., Wa., U.S. B5 124
Entiat, Lake, l., Wa., U.S. B5 124
Entiat Mountains, mts., Wa., U.S. B5 124
Entraygues, Fr. H9 10
Entre-Rios, Moz. D7 44
Enugu, Nig. G7 42
Enumclaw, Wa., U.S. B4 124
Envigado, Col. D5 58
Eola Hills, hills, Or., U.S. h11 114
Épernay, Fr. C10 10
Ephraim, Ut., U.S. D4 121
Ephrata, Pa., U.S. F9 115
Ephrata, Wa., U.S. B6 124
Épila, Spain D10 12
Épinal, Fr. D13 10
Epping, N.H., U.S. D4 106
Epworth, Ia., U.S. B7 92
Equatorial Guinea, ctry., Afr. H7 42
Eraclea, Italy D7 14
Erath, La., U.S. E3 95
Erath, co., Tx., U.S. C3 120
Erdek, Tur. I11 16
Erdemli, Tur. A4 40
Erebus, Mount, mtn., Ant. B29 47
Erechim, Braz. B6 56
Erfurt, Ger. E11 8
Erichsen Lake, l., N.W. Ter., Can. B16 66
Erick, Ok., U.S. B2 113
Erickson, Man., Can. D2 70
Erie, Co., U.S. A5 83
Erie, Il., U.S. B3 90
Erie, Ks., U.S. E8 93
Erie, Mi., U.S. G7 99
Erie, Pa., U.S. B1 115
Erie, co., N.Y., U.S. C2 109
Erie, co., Oh., U.S. A3 112
Erie, co., Pa., U.S. C1 115
Erie, Lake, l., N.A. C10 76
Erie Canal, N.Y., U.S. B5 109
Erimo-misaki, c., Japan r21 30a
Erin, Ont., Can. D4 73
Erin, Tn., U.S. A4 119
Eritrea, hist. reg., Eth. E2 46
Erlangen, Ger. F11 8
Erlanger, Ky., U.S. A5 94
Erlian, China C9 26
Erling, Lake, res., Ar., U.S. D2 81
Ermelo, S. Afr. G5 44
Ermenak, Tur. A3 40
Ernākulam, India H4 37
Erne, Lower Lough, l., N. Ire., U.K. G5 7
Ernée, Fr. D6 10
Erode, India G4 37
Errigal, mtn., Ire. F4 7
Ertai, China B5 26
Erwin, N.C., U.S. B4 110
Erwin, Tn., U.S. C11 119
Erzgebirge (Krušné hory), mts., Eur. E12 8
Erzincan, Tur. H15 4
Erzurum, Tur. H16 4
Esashi, Japan A13 30
Esbjerg, Den. I7 6
Escalante, Ut., U.S. F4 121
Escalante, stm., Ut., U.S. F4 121
Escalón, Mex. D7 62
Escalon, Ca., U.S. D3 82
Escambia, co., Al., U.S. D2 78
Escambia, co., Fl., U.S. u14 86
Escambia, stm., Fl., U.S. u14 86
Escanaba, Mi., U.S. C3 99
Escanaba, stm., Mi., U.S. B3 99
Escarpada Point, c., Phil. B7 32
Escatawpa, Ms., U.S. E5 101
Escatawpa, stm., U.S. D5 101
Esch-sur-Alzette, Lux. F5 8
Eschwege, Ger. D10 8
Escondido, Ca., U.S. F5 82
Escoumins, Rivière des, stm., Que., Can. A8 74
Escuinapa [de Hidalgo], Mex. F7 62
Escuintla, Guat. G2 64
Escuintla, Mex. J13 62
Escuminac, Point, c., N.B., Can. B5 71
Eşfahān, Iran B5 46
Eshkāshem, Afg. B4 38
Eskilstuna, Swe. G11 6
Eskimo Lakes, l., N.W. Ter., Can. C6 66
Eskimo Point, N.W. Ter., Can. D14 66
Eskişehir, Tur. H14 4
Eşme, Tur. K12 16
Esmeralda, co., Nv., U.S. F4 105
Esmeraldas, Ec. G3 58
Esmond, R.I., U.S. B4 116
Espalion, Fr. H9 10
Espanola, Ont., Can. A3 73
Espanola, N.M., U.S. B3 108
Esparto, Ca., U.S. C2 82
Espelkamp, Ger. C8 8
Esperance, Austl. F4 50
Espinal, Col. E5 58
Espinhaço, Serra do, mts., Braz. C7 57
Espinho, Port. D3 12
Espíritu Santo, Bahía del, b., Mex. H16 62
Espíritu Santo, Isla del, i., Mex. E4 62
Espoo (Esbo), Fin. F15 6
Espy, Pa., U.S. D9 115
Esquel, Arg. E2 56
Esquimalt, B.C., Can. E6 69
Esquina, Arg. B5 56
Essaouira, Mor. B4 42
Essen, Ger. D7 8
Essendon, Mount, mtn., Austl. D4 50
Essequibo, stm., Guy. E13 58
Es Sers, Tun. M4 14
Essex, Ont., Can. E2 73
Essex, Ct., U.S. D6 84
Essex, Ia., U.S. D2 92
Essex, Md., U.S. B5 97
Essex, Ma., U.S. A6 98
Essex, Vt., U.S. B2 122
Essex, co., Ma., U.S. A5 98
Essex, co., N.J., U.S. B4 107
Essex, co., N.Y., U.S. B7 109
Essex, co., Vt., U.S. B5 122
Essex, co., Va., U.S. C6 123
Essex Junction, Vt., U.S. C2 122
Essexville, Mi., U.S. E7 99
Esslingen, Ger. G9 8
Es Smala es Souassi, Tun. N5 14
Est, Cap, c., Madag. E10 44
Est, Pointe de l', c., Que., Can. G20 66
Estacada, Or., U.S. B4 114
Estaca de Bares, Punta de la, c., Spain B4 12
Estacado, Llano, pl., U.S. C1 120
Estados, Isla de los, i., Arg. G4 56
Estancia, N.M., U.S. C3 108
Estcourt, S. Afr. G5 44
Este, Italy D6 14
Estelí, Nic. H4 64
Estella, Spain C9 12
Estelline, S.D., U.S. C9 118
Estepona, Spain I6 12
Esternay, Fr. D10 10
Estero Bay, b., Ca., U.S. E3 82
Estero Bay, b., Fl., U.S. F5 86
Estero Island, i., Fl., U.S. F5 86
Estes Park, Co., U.S. A5 83
Estherville, Ia., U.S. A3 92
Estherwood, La., U.S. D3 95
Estill, S.C., U.S. F5 117
Estill, co., Ky., U.S. C6 94
Estill Springs, Tn., U.S. B5 119
Estonia see Estonskaja Sovetskaja Socialističeskaja Respublika, state, U.S.S.R. F3 18
Estonskaja Sovetskaja Socialističeskaja Respublika, state, U.S.S.R. F3 18
Estremoz, Port. G4 12
Esztergom, Hung. H18 8
Etah, Grnld. B20 128
Etah, India G8 38
Étampes, Fr. D9 10
Étang-du-Nord, Que., Can. B8 71
Étaples, Fr. B8 10
Etāwah, India G8 38
Ethel, W.V., U.S. n12 125
Ethiopia, ctry., Afr. G2 46
Etna, Pa., U.S. k14 115
Etna, Monte, vol., Italy L9 14
Etobicoke, Ont., Can. D5 73
Etolin Island, i., Ak., U.S. m23 79
Etolin Strait, strt., Ak., U.S. C6 79
Etoshapan, pl., Nmb. E3 44
Etowah, Tn., U.S. D9 119
Etowah, co., Al., U.S. A3 78
Etowah, stm., Ga., U.S. B2 87
Ettelbruck, Lux. F6 8
Ettlingen, Ger. G8 8
Ettrick, Va., U.S. C5 123
Eu, Fr. B8 10
Eucla, Austl. F5 50
Euclid, Oh., U.S. A4 112
Eudora, Ar., U.S. D4 81
Eudora, Ks., U.S. D8 93
Eufaula, Al., U.S. D4 78
Eufaula, Ok., U.S. B6 113
Eufaula Lake, res., Ok., U.S. B6 113
Eugene, Or., U.S. C3 114
Eugenia, Punta, c., Mex. D2 62
Eunice, La., U.S. D3 95
Eunice, N.M., U.S. E6 108
Euphrates (Al-Furāt), stm., Asia A2 46
Eupora, Ms., U.S. B4 101
Eureka, Ca., U.S. B1 82
Eureka, Il., U.S. C4 90
Eureka, Ks., U.S. E7 93
Eureka, Mo., U.S. f12 102
Eureka, Mt., U.S. B1 103
Eureka, Nv., U.S. D6 105
Eureka, S.C., U.S. B5 117
Eureka, S.D., U.S. B6 118
Eureka, co., Nv., U.S. D5 105
Eureka Springs, Ar., U.S. A2 81
Europa, Île, i., Reu. F8 44
Europa Point, c., Gib. I6 12
Europe E11 4
Euskirchen, Ger. E6 8
Eustis, Fl., U.S. D5 86
Eutaw, Al., U.S. C2 78
Eutin, Ger. A10 8
Eutsuk Lake, l., B.C., Can. C4 69
Evangeline, co., La., U.S. D3 95
Evans, Co., U.S. A6 83
Evans, Ga., U.S. C4 87
Evans, W.V., U.S. C3 125
Evans, co., Ga., U.S. D5 87
Evans, Lac, l., Que., Can. F17 66
Evans, Mount, mtn., Co., U.S. B5 83
Evansburg, Alta., Can. C3 68
Evans City, Pa., U.S. E1 115
Evansdale, Ia., U.S. B5 92
Evans Strait, strt., N.W. Ter., Can. D16 66
Evanston, Il., U.S. A6 90
Evanston, Wy., U.S. E2 127
Evansville, Il., U.S. E4 90
Evansville, In., U.S. I2 91
Evansville, Wi., U.S. F4 126
Evansville, Wy., U.S. D6 127
Evart, Mi., U.S. E5 99
Evarts, Ky., U.S. D6 94
Eveleth, Mn., U.S. C6 100
Everard, Lake, l., Austl. F7 50
Everest, Mount, mtn., Asia G12 38
Everett, Ma., U.S. g11 98
Everett, Pa., U.S. F5 115
Everett, Wa., U.S. B3 124
Everett Lake, res., N.H., U.S. D3 106
Everglades National Park, Fl., U.S. G5 86
Evergreen, Al., U.S. D3 78
Evergreen, Co., U.S. B5 83
Evergreen Park, Il., U.S. k9 90
Everly, Ia., U.S. A2 92
Everson, Wa., U.S. A3 124
Evesham, Eng., U.K. I11 7
Evje, Nor. G6 6
Évora, Port. G4 12
Évreux, Fr. C8 10
Évros (Marica) (Meriç), stm., Eur. H10 16
E.V. Spence Reservoir, res., Tx., U.S. D2 120
Évvoia, i., Grc. K7 16
Ewa, Hi., U.S. B3 88
Ewa Beach, Hi., U.S. B3 88
Ewa Beach, Hi., U.S. g9 88
Ewing Township, N.J., U.S. C3 107
Ewo, Congo B2 44
Excelsior Mountain, mtn., Ca., U.S. C4 82
Excelsior Mountains, mts., Nv., U.S. E3 105
Excelsior Springs, Mo., U.S. B3 102
Executive Committee Range, mts., Ant. B36 47
Exeter, Ont., Can. D3 73
Exeter, Eng., U.K. K9 7
Exeter, Ca., U.S. D4 82
Exeter, Ne., U.S. D8 104
Exeter, N.H., U.S. E5 106
Exeter, Pa., U.S. D10 115
Exeter, stm., N.H., U.S. E5 106
Exeter Sound, strt., N.W. Ter., Can. C20 66
Exira, Ia., U.S. C3 92
Exmore, Va., U.S. C7 123
Exmouth, Eng., U.K. K9 7
Exmouth Gulf, b., Austl. D2 50
Experiment, Ga., U.S. C2 87
Exploits, stm., Newf., Can. D3 72
Exploits, Bay of, b., Newf., Can. D4 72
Export, Pa., U.S. F2 115
Exuma Sound, strt., Bah. B9 64
Eyasi, Lake, l., Tan. B6 44
Eylar Mountain, mtn., Ca., U.S. D3 82
Eymoutiers, Fr. G8 10
Eyota, Mn., U.S. G6 100
Eyre (North), Lake, l., Austl. E7 50
Eyre (South), Lake, l., Austl. E7 50
Eyre Peninsula, pen., Austl. F7 50

F

Fabens, Tx., U.S. o11 120
Fabius, stm., Mo., U.S. A6 102
Fabriano, Italy F7 14
Facatativá, Col. E5 58
Factoryville, Pa., U.S. C10 115
Fada, Chad E10 42
Fada Ngourma, Burkina F6 42
Faddejevskij, Ostrov, i., U.S.S.R. B22 20
Faenza, Italy E6 14
Faeroe Islands, dep., Eur. C6 4
Fagernes, Nor. F7 6
Fagersta, Swe. F10 6
Fairacres, N.M., U.S. E3 108
Fairbank, Ia., U.S. B5 92
Fairbanks, Ak., U.S. C10 79
Fair Bluff, N.C., U.S. C3 110
Fairborn, Oh., U.S. C1 112
Fairburn, Ga., U.S. C2 87
Fairbury, Il., U.S. C5 90
Fairbury, Ne., U.S. D8 104
Fairchance, Pa., U.S. G2 115
Fairchild Air Force Base, mil., Wa., U.S. g13 124
Fairdale, Ky., U.S. B4 94
Fairfax, Ca., U.S. C2 82
Fairfax, De., U.S. A3 85
Fairfax, Ia., U.S. C6 92
Fairfax, Mn., U.S. F4 100
Fairfax, Mo., U.S. A2 102
Fairfax, Ok., U.S. A5 113
Fairfax, S.C., U.S. F5 117
Fairfax, Va., U.S. B5 123
Fairfax, co., Va., U.S. B5 123
Fairfield, Al., U.S. B3 78
Fairfield, Ca., U.S. C2 82
Fairfield, Ct., U.S. E2 84
Fairfield, Il., U.S. E5 90
Fairfield, Ia., U.S. C6 92
Fairfield, Me., U.S. D3 96
Fairfield, Mt., U.S. C5 103
Fairfield, Oh., U.S. n12 112
Fairfield, Tx., U.S. D4 120
Fairfield, co., Ct., U.S. D2 84
Fairfield, co., Oh., U.S. C3 112
Fairfield, co., S.C., U.S. C5 117
Fairfield Bay, Ar., U.S. B3 81
Fairfield Pond, l., Vt., U.S. B3 122
Fair Grove, Mo., U.S. D4 102
Fair Grove, N.C., U.S. B2 110
Fairhaven, Ma., U.S. C6 98
Fair Haven, Mi., U.S. F8 99
Fair Haven, N.J., U.S. C4 107
Fair Haven, Vt., U.S. D2 122
Fairhope, Al., U.S. E2 78
Fair Isle, i., Scot., U.K. B11 7
Fairland, In., U.S. E6 91
Fairland, Ok., U.S. A7 113
Fair Lawn, N.J., U.S. h8 107
Fairlawn, Va., U.S. C2 123
Fairlea, W.V., U.S. D4 125
Fairmont, Il., U.S. C6 90
Fairmont, Mn., U.S. G4 100
Fairmont, Ne., U.S. D8 104
Fairmont, N.C., U.S. C3 110
Fairmont, W.V., U.S. B4 125
Fairmount, Ga., U.S. B2 87
Fairmount, In., U.S. D6 91
Fairmount Heights, Md., U.S. f9 97
Fair Oaks, Ga., U.S. h7 87
Fairoaks, Pa., U.S. h13 115
Fair Plain, Mi., U.S. F4 99
Fairport, N.Y., U.S. B3 109
Fairport Harbor, Oh., U.S. A4 112
Fairvale, N.B., Can. D4 71
Fairview, Alta., Can. A1 68
Fairview, Mt., U.S. C12 103
Fairview, N.J., U.S. h8 107
Fairview, Ok., U.S. A3 113
Fairview, Pa., U.S. B1 115
Fairview, Tn., U.S. B4 119
Fairview, Ut., U.S. D4 121
Fairview Heights, Il., U.S. E3 90
Fairview Park, In., U.S. E3 91
Fairview Park, Oh., U.S. g9 112
Fairview Peak, mtn., Nv., U.S. D3 105
Fairview Peak, mtn., Or., U.S. D4 114
Fairway, Ks., U.S. k16 93
Fairweather, Mount, mtn., N.A. E5 66
Faisalabad, Pak. E5 38
Faison, N.C., U.S. B4 110
Faizābād, India G10 38
Fakenham, Eng., U.K. I13 7
Fakfak, Indon. F9 32
Falaise, Fr. D6 10
Falam, Burma C2 34
Falconer, N.Y., U.S. C1 109
Falcon Heights, Mn., U.S. n12 100
Falcon Heights, Or., U.S. E5 114
Falcon Reservoir, res., N.A. D10 62
Falfurrias, Tx., U.S. F3 120
Falher, Alta., Can. B2 68
Falkenberg, Swe. H9 6
Falkensee, Ger. C13 8
Falkenstein, Ger. E12 8
Falkland Islands (Islas Malvinas), dep., S.A. G5 56
Falköping, Swe. G9 6
Falkville, Al., U.S. A3 78
Fall, stm., Ks., U.S. E7 93
Fall Branch, Tn., U.S. C11 119
Fallbrook, Ca., U.S. F5 82
Fall City, Wa., U.S. B4 124
Fall Creek, Wi., U.S. D2 126
Falling Creek, stm., Va., U.S. n17 123
Falling Rock Creek, stm., W.V., U.S. m13 125
Fall Mountain Lake, Ct., U.S. C4 84
Fallon, Nv., U.S. D3 105
Fallon, co., Mt., U.S. D12 103
Fallon Indian Reservation, Nv., U.S. D3 105
Fallon Naval Air Station, mil., Nv., U.S. D3 105
Fall River, Ma., U.S. C5 98
Fall River, Wi., U.S. E4 126
Fall River, co., S.D., U.S. D2 118
Fall River Lake, res., Ks., U.S. E7 93
Falls, co., Tx., U.S. D4 120
Falls Church, Va., U.S. g12 123
Falls City, Ne., U.S. D10 104
Falls City, Or., U.S. C3 114
Falls Creek, Pa., U.S. D4 115
Fallston, Md., U.S. A5 97
Falmouth, N.S., Can. E5 71
Falmouth, Eng., U.K. K7 7
Falmouth, Ky., U.S. B5 94
Falmouth, Me., U.S. E2 96
Falmouth, Ma., U.S. C6 98
Falmouth, Va., U.S. B5 123
False Cape, c., Fl., U.S. D6 86
False Cape, c., Va., U.S. D7 123
False Divi Point, c., India E6 37
Falset, Spain D12 12
Falun, Swe. F10 6

Name	Map Ref	Page
Famagusta see Gazimağusa, N. Cyp.	B3	40
Famatina, Nevado de, mts., Arg.	B3	56
Fancy Farm, Ky., U.S.	f9	94
Fangcheng, China	B1	28
Fannin, co., Ga., U.S.	B2	87
Fannin, co., Tx., U.S.	C4	120
Fanny, Mount, mtn., Or., U.S.	B9	114
Fano, Italy	F8	14
Faradje, Zaire	H11	42
Faradofay, Madag.	G9	44
Farafangana, Madag.	F9	44
Farāh, Afg.	C1	36
Faranah, Gui.	F3	42
Farasān, Jazā'ir, is., Sau. Ar.	E3	46
Farewell, Cape, c., N.Z.	D4	52
Fargo, Ga., U.S.	F4	87
Fargo, N.D., U.S.	C9	111
Faribault, Mn., U.S.	F5	100
Faribault, co., Mn., U.S.	G4	100
Farīdpur, Bngl.	I13	38
Färjestaden, Swe.	H11	6
Farley, Ia., U.S.	B6	92
Farmer City, Il., U.S.	C5	90
Farmers Branch, Tx., U.S.	n10	120
Farmersburg, In., U.S.	F3	91
Farmerville, La., U.S.	B3	95
Farmingdale, Me., U.S.	D3	96
Farmington, Ar., U.S.	A1	81
Farmington, Ct., U.S.	C4	84
Farmington, Il., U.S.	C3	90
Farmington, Ia., U.S.	D6	92
Farmington, Me., U.S.	D2	96
Farmington, Mi., U.S.	p15	99
Farmington, Mn., U.S.	F5	100
Farmington, Mo., U.S.	D7	102
Farmington, N.H., U.S.	D4	106
Farmington, N.M., U.S.	A1	108
Farmington, Ut., U.S.	C4	121
Farmington, stm., Ct., U.S.	B4	84
Farmington Hills, Mi., U.S.	o15	99
Farmland, In., U.S.	D7	91
Farmville, N.C., U.S.	B5	110
Farmville, Va., U.S.	C4	123
Farnham, Que., Can.	D5	74
Faro, Braz.	D7	54
Faro, Port.	H4	12
Faro, Punta del, c., Italy	K10	14
Fårösund, Swe.	H12	6
Farquhar Group, is., Sey.	D10	44
Farrell, Pa., U.S.	D1	115
Farrukhābād, India	G8	38
Fartak, Ra's, c., Yemen	E5	46
Farvel, Kap, c., Grnld.	E24	66
Farwell, Mi., U.S.	E6	99
Farwell, Tx., U.S.	B1	120
Fasano, Italy	I12	14
Fatehpur, India	H9	38
Fatehpur, India	G6	38
Faulk, co., S.D., U.S.	B6	118
Faulkland Heights, De., U.S.	i7	85
Faulkner, co., Ar., U.S.	B3	81
Faulkton, S.D., U.S.	B6	118
Fauquier, co., Va., U.S.	B5	123
Fauske, Nor.	C10	6
Favara, Italy	L8	14
Faverges, Fr.	G13	10
Fawnie Nose, mtn., B.C., Can.	C5	69
Fayette, Al., U.S.	B2	78
Fayette, Ia., U.S.	B6	92
Fayette, Ms., U.S.	D2	101
Fayette, Mo., U.S.	B5	102
Fayette, Oh., U.S.	A1	112
Fayette, co., Al., U.S.	B3	78
Fayette, co., Ga., U.S.	C2	87
Fayette, co., Il., U.S.	D5	90
Fayette, co., In., U.S.	E7	91
Fayette, co., Ia., U.S.	B6	92
Fayette, co., Ky., U.S.	B5	94
Fayette, co., Oh., U.S.	C2	112
Fayette, co., Pa., U.S.	G2	115
Fayette, co., Tn., U.S.	B2	119
Fayette, co., Tx., U.S.	E4	120
Fayette, co., W.V., U.S.	C3	125
Fayetteville, Ar., U.S.	A1	81
Fayetteville, Ga., U.S.	C2	87
Fayetteville, N.C., U.S.	B4	110
Fayetteville, Pa., U.S.	G6	115
Fayetteville, Tn., U.S.	B5	119
Fayetteville, W.V., U.S.	C3	125
Fāzilka, India	E6	38
Fazzān (Fezzan), reg., Libya	C8	42
Fdérik, Maur.	D3	42
Fear, Cape, c., N.C., U.S.	D5	110
Feather, stm., Ca., U.S.	C3	82
Fécamp, Fr.	C7	10
Federalsburg, Md., U.S.	C6	97
Feeding Hills, Ma., U.S.	B2	98
Fehmarn Belt, strt., Eur.	A11	8
Feijó, Braz.	E4	54
Feira de Santana, Braz.	B9	57
Felanitx, Spain	F15	12
Feldbach, Aus.	I15	8
Feldkirch, Aus.	H9	8
Feldkirchen in Kärnten, Aus.	I14	8
Félix Gómez, Mex.	C4	62
Felletin, Fr.	G9	10
Fellsmere, Fl., U.S.	E6	86
Felton, Ca., U.S.	D2	82
Felton, De., U.S.	D3	85
Feltre, Italy	C6	14
Femundsenden, Nor.	F8	6
Fence, stm., Mi., U.S.	B2	99
Fence Lake, l., Wi., U.S.	C4	126
Fenelon Falls, Ont., Can.	C6	73
Fengcheng, China	G4	28
Fengzhen, China	C9	26
Fenimore Pass, strt., Ak., U.S.	E4	79
Fennimore, Wi., U.S.	F3	126
Fennville, Mi., U.S.	F4	99
Fenton, Mi., U.S.	F7	99
Fentress, co., Tn., U.S.	C9	119
Fenwick Island, i., S.C., U.S.	k11	117
Fenyang, China	D9	26
Feodosija, U.S.S.R.	H5	18
Fer, Point au, c., La., U.S.	E4	95
Ferdinand, In., U.S.	H4	91
Fergana, U.S.S.R.	I12	18
Fergus, Ont., Can.	D4	73
Fergus, co., Mt., U.S.	C7	103
Fergus Falls, Mn., U.S.	D2	100
Ferguson, Ky., U.S.	C5	94
Ferguson, Mo., U.S.	C7	102
Ferme-Neuve, Que., Can.	C2	74
Fermo, Italy	F8	14
Fermont, Que., Can.	h13	74
Fermoy, Ire.	I4	7
Fernandina Beach, Fl., U.S.	B5	86
Fernando de Noronha, Ilha, i., Braz.	D12	54
Fernandópolis, Braz.	F3	57
Fernando Póo see Bioko, i., Eq. Gui.	H7	42
Fernán-Núñez, Spain	H7	12
Fern Creek, Ky., U.S.	g11	94
Ferndale, Ca., U.S.	B1	82
Ferndale, Md., U.S.	B4	97
Ferndale, Mi., U.S.	P15	99
Ferndale, Pa., U.S.	F4	115
Ferndale, Wa., U.S.	A3	124
Fernie, B.C., Can.	E10	69
Fernley, Nv., U.S.	D2	105
Fern Ridge Lake, res., Or., U.S.	C3	114
Fernwood, Id., U.S.	B2	89
Fernwood, Ms., U.S.	D3	101
Ferrara, Italy	E6	14
Ferreira do Alentejo, Port.	G3	12
Ferrelo, Cape, c., Or., U.S.	E2	114
Ferriday, La., U.S.	C4	95
Ferris, Tx., U.S.	C4	120
Ferris Mountains, mts., Wy., U.S.	D5	127
Ferron, Ut., U.S.	D4	121
Ferrum, Va., U.S.	D2	123
Ferry, co., Wa., U.S.	A7	124
Ferry Farms, Va., U.S.	B5	123
Ferryland, Newf., Can.	E5	72
Ferry Point, c., N.J., U.S.	k7	107
Fertile, Mn., U.S.	C2	100
Fès, Mor.	B5	42
Feshi, Zaire	C3	44
Fessenden, N.D., U.S.	B6	111
Festus, Mo., U.S.	C7	102
Fethiye, Tur.	M13	16
Feuilles, Rivière aux, stm., Que., Can.	g12	74
Feurs, Fr.	G11	10
Feyzābād, Afg.	B4	38
Fez see Fès, Mor.	B5	42
Fianarantsoa, Madag.	F9	44
Ficksburg, S. Afr.	G5	44
Fidalgo Island, i., Wa., U.S.	A3	124
Fidenza, Italy	E5	14
Fieldale, Va., U.S.	D3	123
Fields, Lake, l., Fl., U.S.	B3	86
Fields, Lake, l., La., U.S.	k10	95
Fier, Alb.	I3	16
Fifteenmile Creek, stm., Wy., U.S.	B4	127
Fifteen Mile Falls Reservoir, res., U.S.	C5	122
Figeac, Fr.	H9	10
Figueira da Foz, Port.	E3	12
Figueras, Spain	C14	12
Figuig, Mor.	B5	42
Fiji, ctry., Oc.	H1	2
Filchner Ice Shelf, Ant.	B9	47
Filer, Id., U.S.	G4	89
Fillmore, Ca., U.S.	E4	82
Fillmore, Ut., U.S.	E3	121
Fillmore, co., Mn., U.S.	G6	100
Fillmore, co., Ne., U.S.	D8	104
Finale Ligure, Italy	E3	14
Findlay, Il., U.S.	D5	90
Findlay, Oh., U.S.	A2	112
Finisterre, Cabo de, c., Spain	C2	12
Finland, ctry., Eur.	C13	4
Finland, Gulf of, b., Eur.	G16	6
Finlay, stm., B.C., Can.	E7	66
Finley, Tn., U.S.	A2	119
Finney, co., Ks., U.S.	D3	93
Finn Mountain, mtn., Ak., U.S.	C8	79
Finse, Nor.	F6	6
Finspång, Swe.	G10	6
Finsterwalde, Ger.	D13	8
Fiorenzuola d'Arda, Italy	E4	14
Fircrest, Wa., U.S.	f10	124
Firebaugh, Ca., U.S.	D3	82
Firenze (Florence), Italy	F6	14
Firenzuola, Italy	E6	14
Firestone, Co., U.S.	A6	83
Firminy, Fr.	G11	10
Fīrozābād, India	G8	38
Fīrozpur, India	E6	38
First Connecticut Lake, l., N.H., U.S.	f7	106
Fish, stm., Al., U.S.	E2	78
Fish, stm., Me., U.S.	A4	96
Fish Creek, stm., W.V., U.S.	g8	125
Fisher, Il., U.S.	C5	90
Fisher, co., Tx., U.S.	C2	120
Fisher Bay, b., Man., Can.	D3	70
Fishermans Island, i., Va., U.S.	h15	123
Fishers, In., U.S.	E5	91
Fishers Island, i., N.Y., U.S.	m16	109
Fishers Peak, mtn., Co., U.S.	D6	83
Fisher Strait, strt., N.W. Ter., Can.	D16	66
Fishersville, Va., U.S.	B4	123
Fishing Bay, b., Md., U.S.	D5	97
Fishing Creek, Md., U.S.	D5	97
Fishing Creek, stm., N.C., U.S.	A5	110
Fishing Creek, stm., S.C., U.S.	B5	117
Fishing Creek, stm., W.V., U.S.	B4	125
Fishing Creek Reservoir, res., S.C., U.S.	B6	117
Fishkill, N.Y., U.S.	D7	109
Fish Lake, l., Ut., U.S.	E4	121
Fish River Lake, l., Me., U.S.	B4	96
Fishtrap Lake, res., Ky., U.S.	C7	94
Fiskdale, Ma., U.S.	B3	98
Fitchburg, Ma., U.S.	A4	98
Fitzgerald, Ga., U.S.	E3	87
Fitz Roy, Arg.	F3	56
Fitzroy, stm., Austl.	C4	50
Fitzroy, Monte (Cerro Chaltel), mtn., S.A.	F2	56
Fitzroy Crossing, Austl.	C5	50
Fitzwilliam, N.H., U.S.	E2	106
Fitzwilliam Island, i., Ont., Can.	B3	73
Five Island Lake, l., Ia., U.S.	A3	92
Fivemile Creek, stm., Wy., U.S.	C4	127
Five Points, N.M., U.S.	B3	108
Flagler, co., Fl., U.S.	C5	86
Flagler Beach, Fl., U.S.	C5	86
Flagstaff, Az., U.S.	B4	80
Flagstaff Lake, l., Or., U.S.	E7	114
Flambeau, stm., Wi., U.S.	C3	126
Flamborough Head, c., Eng., U.K.	G12	7
Flaming Gorge Dam, Ut., U.S.	C6	121
Flaming Gorge National Recreation Area, U.S.	E3	127
Flaming Gorge Reservoir, res., U.S.	E3	127
Flanagan, Il., U.S.	C5	90
Flandreau, S.D., U.S.	C9	118
Flandreau Indian Reservation, S.D., U.S.	C9	118
Flat, stm., Mi., U.S.	E5	99
Flat, stm., N.C., U.S.	A4	110
Flat, stm., R.I., U.S.	E2	116
Flat Brook, stm., N.J., U.S.	A3	107
Flathead, co., Mt., U.S.	B2	103
Flathead, South Fork, stm., Mt., U.S.	C3	103
Flathead Indian Reservation, Mt., U.S.	C2	103
Flathead Lake, l., Mt., U.S.	C2	103
Flathead Valley, val., Mt., U.S.	C2	103
Flat Lake, l., La., U.S.	k9	95
Flat Lick, Ky., U.S.	D6	94
Flatonia, Tx., U.S.	E4	120
Flat River, Mo., U.S.	D7	102
Flat River Reservoir, res., R.I., U.S.	D3	116
Flat Rock, Mi., U.S.	F7	99
Flat Rock, N.C., U.S.	f10	110
Flatrock, stm., In., U.S.	F6	91
Flattery, Cape, c., Wa., U.S.	A1	124
Flatwoods, Ky., U.S.	B7	94
Fleetwood, Eng., U.K.	H9	7
Fleetwood, Pa., U.S.	F10	115
Flekkefjord, Nor.	G6	6
Fleming, co., Ky., U.S.	B6	94
Fleming-Neon, Ky., U.S.	C7	94
Flemingsburg, Ky., U.S.	B6	94
Flemington, N.J., U.S.	B3	107
Flemington, Pa., U.S.	D7	115
Flensburg, Ger.	A9	8
Flers, Fr.	D6	10
Fletcher, N.C., U.S.	f10	110
Fletcher, Ok., U.S.	C3	113
Fleurance, Fr.	I7	10
Flinders, stm., Austl.	C8	50
Flinders Island, i., Austl.	G9	50
Flin Flon, Man., Can.	B1	70
Flint, Wales, U.K.	H9	7
Flint, Mi., U.S.	E7	99
Flint, stm., Ga., U.S.	E2	87
Flint City, Al., U.S.	A3	78
Flint Creek Range, mts., Mt., U.S.	D3	103
Flint Run, stm., W.V., U.S.	k9	125
Flippin, Ar., U.S.	A3	81
Flomaton, Al., U.S.	D2	78
Flora, Il., U.S.	E5	90
Flora, In., U.S.	C4	91
Flora, Ms., U.S.	C3	101
Florac, Fr.	H10	10
Florala, Al., U.S.	D3	78
Floral City, Fl., U.S.	D4	86
Florence, Al., U.S.	A2	78
Florence, Az., U.S.	D4	80
Florence, Co., U.S.	C5	83
Florence, Ks., U.S.	D7	93
Florence, Ky., U.S.	A5	94
Florence, Ms., U.S.	C3	101
Florence, N.J., U.S.	C3	107
Florence, Or., U.S.	D2	114
Florence, S.C., U.S.	C8	117
Florence, co., S.C., U.S.	C8	117
Florence, co., Wi., U.S.	C5	126
Florence see Firenze, Italy	F6	14
Florenceville, N.B., Can.	C2	71
Florencia, Col.	G5	58
Flores, i., Indon.	G7	32
Flores, Laut (Flores Sea), Indon.	G6	32
Floresville, Tx., U.S.	E3	120
Florham Park, N.J., U.S.	B4	107
Floriano, Braz.	E10	54
Florianópolis, Braz.	B7	56
Florida, Col.	F4	58
Florida, Cuba	D8	64
Florida, N.Y., U.S.	D6	109
Florida, state, U.S.	E5	86
Florida, Cape, c., Fl., U.S.	G6	86
Florida, Straits of, strt., N.A.	B7	64
Florida Bay, b., Fl., U.S.	H6	86
Floridablanca, Col.	D6	58
Florida City, Fl., U.S.	G6	86
Florida Keys, is., Fl., U.S.	H6	86
Florida Mountains, mts., N.M., U.S.	E2	108
Florida State Indian Reservation, Fl., U.S.	F5	86
Florien, La., U.S.	C2	95
Florissant, Mo., U.S.	f13	102
Florissant Fossil Beds National Monument, Co., U.S.	C5	83
Florø, Nor.	F5	6
Flossmoor, Il., U.S.	k9	90
Flovilla, Ga., U.S.	C3	87
Flower Brook, stm., Vt., U.S.	E2	122
Flowery Branch, Ga., U.S.	B3	87
Flowood, Ms., U.S.	C3	101
Floyd, co., Ga., U.S.	B1	87
Floyd, co., In., U.S.	H6	91
Floyd, co., Ia., U.S.	A5	92
Floyd, co., Ky., U.S.	C7	94
Floyd, co., Tx., U.S.	B2	120
Floyd, co., Va., U.S.	D2	123
Floyd, stm., Ia., U.S.	B1	92
Floydada, Tx., U.S.	C2	120
Floyds Fork, stm., Ky., U.S.	B4	94
Floyds Knobs, In., U.S.	H6	91
Flushing, Mi., U.S.	E7	99
Flushing, Oh., U.S.	B4	112
Flushing see Vlissingen, Neth.	D3	8
Fluvanna, co., Va., U.S.	C4	123
Fly, stm.	m15	50a
Foard, co., Tx., U.S.	B3	120
Foça, Tur.	K10	16
Focşani, Rom.	D11	16
Fogang (Shijiao), China	L2	28
Foggia, Italy	H10	14
Fogland Point, c., R.I., U.S.	E6	116
Fogo, Newf., Can.	D4	72
Fogo, Cape, c., Newf., Can.	D5	72
Fogo Island, i., Newf., Can.	D4	72
Fohnsdorf, Aus.	H14	8
Foix, Fr.	J8	10
Foley, Al., U.S.	E2	78
Foley, Mn., U.S.	E5	100
Foley Island, i., N.W. Ter., Can.	C17	66
Foligno, Italy	G7	14
Folkestone, Eng., U.K.	J14	7
Folkston, Ga., U.S.	F4	87
Follansbee, W.V., U.S.	A4	125
Follonica, Italy	G5	14
Folly Beach, S.C., U.S.	F8	117
Folly Island, i., S.C., U.S.	F8	117
Folsom, Ca., U.S.	C3	82
Fonda, Ia., U.S.	B3	92
Fond du Lac, Wi., U.S.	E5	126
Fond du Lac, co., Wi., U.S.	E5	126
Fond du Lac Indian Reservation, Mn., U.S.	D6	100
Fondi, Italy	H8	14
Fondouk el Aouareb, Tun.	N4	14
Fonni, Italy	I4	14
Fonseca, Col.	B6	58
Fonseca, Golfo de, b., N.A.	H4	64
Fontainebleau, Fr.	D9	10
Fontana, Ca., U.S.	m14	82
Fontana, Wi., U.S.	F5	126
Fontana Lake, res., N.C., U.S.	f9	110
Fontanelle, Ia., U.S.	C3	92
Fonte Boa, Braz.	D5	54
Fontenay-le-Comte, Fr.	F6	10
Fontenelle Reservoir, res., Wy., U.S.	D2	127
Fontur, c., Ice.	B5	4
Foochow see Fuzhou, China	I8	28
Footville, Wi., U.S.	F4	126
Foraker, Mount, mtn., Ak., U.S.	f16	79
Forbach, Fr.	C13	10
Forbach, Ger.	G8	8
Forbes, Mount, mtn., Alta., Can.	D2	68
Forcalquier, Fr.	I12	10
Forchheim, Ger.	F11	8
Ford, co., Il., U.S.	C5	90
Ford, co., Ks., U.S.	E4	93
Ford, stm., Mi., U.S.	C3	99
Ford City, Ca., U.S.	E4	82
Ford City, Pa., U.S.	E2	115
Førde, Nor.	F5	6
Fordoche, La., U.S.	D4	95
Fords Prairie, Wa., U.S.	C2	124
Fordyce, Ar., U.S.	D3	81
Forel, Mont, mtn., Grnld.	C25	66
Foreman, Ar., U.S.	D1	81
Forest, Ont., Can.	D2	73
Forest, Ms., U.S.	C4	101
Forest, Oh., U.S.	B2	112
Forest, co., Pa., U.S.	C3	115
Forest, co., Wi., U.S.	C5	126
Forest, stm., N.D., U.S.	A8	111
Forest Acres, S.C., U.S.	C6	117
Forestburg, Alta., Can.	C4	68
Forest City, Ia., U.S.	A4	92
Forest City, N.C., U.S.	B1	110
Forest City, Pa., U.S.	C11	115
Forestdale, R.I., U.S.	B3	116
Forest Dale, Vt., U.S.	D2	122
Forest Glen, La., U.S.	h12	95
Forest Grove, Or., U.S.	B3	114
Forest Hill, Md., U.S.	A5	97
Forest Hills, Pa., U.S.	k14	115
Forest Knolls, Ca., U.S.	g7	82
Forest Lake, Mn., U.S.	E6	100
Forest Park, Ga., U.S.	h8	87
Forest Park, Il., U.S.	k9	90
Forest Park, La., U.S.	B3	95
Forest Park, Oh., U.S.	n12	112
Forfar, Scot., U.K.	E10	7
Forillon, Parc National de, Que., Can.	k14	74
Fork Creek, stm., W.V., U.S.	m12	125
Forked Deer, stm., Tn., U.S.	B2	119
Forkland, Al., U.S.	C2	78
Forks, Wa., U.S.	B1	124
Forlì, Italy	E7	14
Formia, Italy	H8	14
Formiga, Braz.	F6	57
Formosa, Arg.	B5	56
Formosa, Braz.	C5	57
Formosa, Serra, plat., Braz.	F8	54
Formosa see Taiwan, i., Asia	L9	28
Forney, Tx., U.S.	C4	120
Fornovo di Taro, Italy	E5	14
Forrest, Austl.	F5	50
Forrest, Il., U.S.	C5	90
Forrest, co., Ms., U.S.	D4	101
Forrest City, Ar., U.S.	B5	81
Forrester Island, i., Ak., U.S.	n23	79
Forreston, Il., U.S.	A4	90
Forsayth, Austl.	C8	50
Forst, Ger.	D14	8
Forsyth, Ga., U.S.	C3	87
Forsyth, Il., U.S.	D5	90
Forsyth, Mo., U.S.	E4	102
Forsyth, Mt., U.S.	D10	103
Forsyth, co., Ga., U.S.	B2	87
Forsyth, co., N.C., U.S.	A2	110
Fortaleza, Braz.	D11	54
Fort Apache Indian Reservation, Az., U.S.	D5	80
Fort-Archambault see Sarh, Chad	G9	42
Fort Ashby, W.V., U.S.	B6	125
Fort Atkinson, Wi., U.S.	F5	126
Fort Augustus, Scot., U.K.	D8	7
Fort Beaufort, S. Afr.	H5	44
Fort Belknap Indian Reservation, Mt., U.S.	B8	103
Fort Belvoir, mil., Va., U.S.	g12	123
Fort Bend, co., Tx., U.S.	E5	120
Fort Benjamin Harrison, mil., In., U.S.	k10	91
Fort Benning, mil., Ga., U.S.	D2	87
Fort Benton, Mt., U.S.	C6	103
Fort Berthold Indian Reservation, N.D., U.S.	B3	111
Fort Bidwell Indian Reservation, Ca., U.S.	B3	82
Fort Bliss, mil., Tx., U.S.	o11	120
Fort Bragg, Ca., U.S.	C2	82
Fort Bragg, mil., N.C., U.S.	B3	110
Fort Branch, In., U.S.	H2	91
Fort Calhoun, Ne., U.S.	C9	104
Fort Campbell, mil., U.S.	A4	119
Fort Carson, mil., Co., U.S.	C6	83
Fort Chipewyan, Alta., Can.	f8	68
Fort Clatsop National Memorial, hist., Or., U.S.	A3	114
Fort Cobb, Ok., U.S.	B3	113
Fort Cobb Reservoir, res., Ok., U.S.	B3	113
Fort Collins, Co., U.S.	A5	83
Fort Coulonge, Que., Can.	B8	73
Fort Davis, Tx., U.S.	o13	120
Fort Davis National Historic Site, hist., Tx., U.S.	o13	120
Fort Defiance, Az., U.S.	B6	80
Fort-de-France, Mart.	G17	64
Fort Deposit, Al., U.S.	D3	78
Fort Detrick, mil., Md., U.S.	B3	97
Fort Devens, mil., Ma., U.S.	f9	98
Fort Dix, mil., N.J., U.S.	C3	107
Fort Dodge, Ia., U.S.	B3	92
Fort Donelson National Battlefield, Tn., U.S.	A4	119
Fort Edward, N.Y., U.S.	B7	109
Fort Erie, Ont., Can.	E6	73
Fortescue, stm., Austl.	D3	50
Fort Eustis, mil., Va., U.S.	h14	123
Fort Fairfield, Me., U.S.	B5	96
Fort Frances, Ont., Can.	o16	73
Fort Franklin, N.W. Ter., Can.	C8	66
Fort Gaines, Ga., U.S.	E1	87
Fort Gay, W.V., U.S.	C2	125
Fort Gibson, Ok., U.S.	B6	113
Fort Gibson Lake, res., Ok., U.S.	A6	113
Fort Good Hope, N.W. Ter., Can.	C7	66
Fort Gordon, mil., Ga., U.S.	C4	87
Fort Greely, mil., Ak., U.S.	C10	79
Forth, Firth of, est., Scot., U.K.	E10	7
Fort Hall, Id., U.S.	F6	89
Fort Hall Indian Reservation, Id., U.S.	F6	89
Fort Hood, mil., Tx., U.S.	D4	120
Fort Howard, Md., U.S.	B5	97
Fort Huachuca, mil., Az., U.S.	F5	80
Fortín Coronel Eugenio Garay, Para.	H6	54
Fort Jackson, mil., S.C., U.S.	C6	117
Fort Jefferson National Monument, Fl., U.S.	H4	86
Fort Kent, Me., U.S.	A4	96
Fort Knox, mil., Ky., U.S.	B4	94
Fort-Lamy see N'Djamena, Chad	F9	42
Fort Laramie, Wy., U.S.	D8	127
Fort Laramie National Historic Site, hist., Wy., U.S.	D8	127
Fort Lauderdale, Fl., U.S.	F6	86
Fort Lawn, S.C., U.S.	B6	117
Fort Leavenworth, mil., Ks., U.S.	C9	93
Fort Lee, N.J., U.S.	B5	107
Fort Lee, mil., Va., U.S.	C5	123
Fort Leonard Wood, mil., Mo., U.S.	D5	102
Fort Lewis, mil., Wa., U.S.	B3	124
Fort Liard, N.W. Ter., Can.	D8	66
Fort Loramie, Oh., U.S.	B1	112
Fort Loudon, Pa., U.S.	G6	115
Fort Loudoun Lake, res., Tn., U.S.	D9	119
Fort Lupton, Co., U.S.	A6	83
Fort MacArthur, mil., Ca., U.S.	n12	82
Fort Macleod, Alta., Can.	E4	68
Fort Madison, Ia., U.S.	D6	92
Fort Matanzas National Monument, Fl., U.S.	C5	86
Fort McClellan, mil., Al., U.S.	B4	78
Fort McDermitt Indian Reservation, U.S.	B4	105
Fort McDowell Indian Reservation, Az., U.S.	D4	80
Fort McHenry National Monument And Historic Shrine, Md., U.S.	g11	97
Fort McMurray, Alta., Can.	A5	68
Fort Meade, Fl., U.S.	E5	86
Fort Meade, mil., Md., U.S.	B4	97
Fort Meadow Reservoir, res., Ma., U.S.	g9	98
Fort Mill, S.C., U.S.	A6	117
Fort Mitchell, Al., U.S.	C4	78
Fort Mitchell, Ky., U.S.	h13	94
Fort Mojave Indian Reservation, U.S.	C1	80
Fort Monmouth, mil., N.J., U.S.	C4	107
Fort Monroe, mil., Va., U.S.	h15	123
Fort Morgan, Co., U.S.	A7	83
Fort Myer, mil., Va., U.S.	g12	123
Fort Myers, Fl., U.S.	F5	86
Fort Myers Beach, Fl., U.S.	F5	86
Fort Nelson, B.C., Can.	m18	69
Fort Norman, N.W. Ter., Can.	D7	66
Fort Oglethorpe, Ga., U.S.	B1	87
Fort Ord, mil., Ca., U.S.	D3	82
Fort Payne, Al., U.S.	A4	78
Fort Peck Indian Reservation, Mt., U.S.	B11	103
Fort Peck Lake, res., Mt., U.S.	C9	103
Fort Pierce, Fl., U.S.	E6	86
Fort Pierce Inlet, b., Fl., U.S.	E6	86

Name	Map Ref	Page
Fort Pierre, S.D., U.S.	C5	118
Fort Plain, N.Y., U.S.	C6	109
Fort Polk, mil., La., U.S.	C2	95
Fort Portal, Ug.	A6	44
Fort Providence, N.W. Ter., Can.	D9	66
Fort Randall Dam, S.D., U.S.	D7	118
Fort Recovery, Oh., U.S.	B1	112
Fort Reliance, N.W. Ter., Can.	D11	66
Fort Resolution, N.W. Ter., Can.	D10	66
Fortress Mountain, mtn., Wy., U.S.	B3	127
Fort Richardson, mil., Ak., U.S.	C10	79
Fort Riley, mil., Ks., U.S.	C7	93
Fort Ritchie, mil., Md., U.S.	A3	97
Fort Rucker, mil., Al., U.S.	D4	78
Fort Saint James, B.C., Can.	B5	69
Fort Saint John, B.C., Can.	A7	69
Fort Sam Houston, mil., Tx., U.S.	k7	120
Fort Sandeman, Pak.	E3	38
Fort Saskatchewan, Alta., Can.	C4	68
Fort Scott, Ks., U.S.	E9	93
Fort Shafter, mil., Hi., U.S.	g10	88
Fort Shawnee, Oh., U.S.	B1	112
Fort Sheridan, mil., Il., U.S.	h9	90
Fort Sill, mil., Ok., U.S.	C3	113
Fort Simpson, N.W. Ter., Can.	D8	66
Fort Smith, N.W. Ter., Can.	D10	66
Fort Smith, Ar., U.S.	B1	81
Fort Stewart, mil., Ga., U.S.	D5	87
Fort Stockton, Tx., U.S.	D1	120
Fort Sumner, N.M., U.S.	C5	108
Fort Sumter National Monument, S.C., U.S.	k12	117
Fort Supply Lake, res., Ok., U.S.	A2	113
Fort Thomas, Ky., U.S.	h14	94
Fort Totten, N.D., U.S.	B7	111
Fort Totten Indian Reservation, N.D., U.S.	B7	111
Fortuna, Ca., U.S.	B1	82
Fortune, Newf., Can.	E4	72
Fortune Bay, b., Newf., Can.	E4	72
Fort Union National Monument, N.M., U.S.	B5	108
Fort Valley, Ga., U.S.	D3	87
Fort Vermilion, Alta., Can.	f7	68
Fortville, In., U.S.	E6	91
Fort Wainwright, mil., Ak., U.S.	C10	79
Fort Walton Beach, Fl., U.S.	u15	86
Fort Washington Forest, Md., U.S.	C4	97
Fort Wayne, In., U.S.	B7	91
Fort William, Scot., U.K.	E7	7
Fort Wingate, N.M., U.S.	B1	108
Fort Worth, Tx., U.S.	C4	120
Fort Wright, Ky., U.S.	h13	94
Forty Fort, Pa., U.S.	D10	115
Fort Yukon, Ak., U.S.	B10	79
Fort Yuma Indian Reservation, Ca., U.S.	F6	82
Foshan, China	L2	28
Fossano, Italy	E2	14
Fossil Butte National Monument, Wy., U.S.	E2	127
Fossil Lake, l., Or., U.S.	D6	114
Fossombrone, Italy	F7	14
Foss Reservoir, res., Ok., U.S.	B2	113
Fosston, Mn., U.S.	C3	100
Foster, Or., U.S.	C4	114
Foster, co., N.D., U.S.	B6	111
Foster Village, Hi., U.S.	g10	88
Fostoria, Oh., U.S.	A2	112
Fougamou, Gabon	B2	44
Fougères, Fr.	D5	10
Fouke, Ar., U.S.	D2	81
Foula, i., Scot., U.K.	A10	7
Foumban, Cam.	G8	42
Fountain, Co., U.S.	C6	83
Fountain, co., In., U.S.	D3	91
Fountain City, In., U.S.	E8	91
Fountain City, Wi., U.S.	D2	126
Fountain Hill, Pa., U.S.	E11	115
Fountain Inn, S.C., U.S.	B3	117
Fountain Peak, mtn., Ca., U.S.	E6	82
Fountain Place, La., U.S.	D4	95
Fourche LaFave, stm., Ar., U.S.	C2	81
Fourche Maline, stm., Ok., U.S.	C6	113
Fourmies, Fr.	B11	10
Four Mountains, Islands of, is., Ak., U.S.	E6	79
Four Oaks, N.C., U.S.	B4	110
Fowler, Ca., U.S.	D4	82
Fowler, Co., U.S.	C6	83
Fowler, In., U.S.	C3	91
Fowler, Mi., U.S.	E6	99
Fowlerville, Mi., U.S.	F6	99
Fox, stm., Man., Can.	B4	70
Fox, stm., U.S.	B5	90
Fox, stm., U.S.	A6	102
Fox, stm., Mi., U.S.	B4	99
Fox, stm., Wi., U.S.	D5	126
Foxboro, Ont., Can.	C7	73
Foxboro, Ma., U.S.	B5	98
Fox Creek, Alta., Can.	B2	68
Foxe Basin, b., N.W. Ter., Can.	C17	66
Foxe Channel, strt., N.W. Ter., Can.	D16	66
Foxe Peninsula, pen., N.W. Ter., Can.	D17	66
Fox Island, i., R.I., U.S.	E4	116
Fox Island, i., Wa., U.S.	f10	124
Fox Islands, is., Ak., U.S.	E6	79
Fox Lake, Il., U.S.	A5	90
Fox Lake, Wi., U.S.	E5	126
Fox Lake, l., Il., U.S.	h8	90
Fox Mountain, mtn., Nv., U.S.	B2	105
Fox Point, Wi., U.S.	E6	126
Fox River Grove, Il., U.S.	h8	90
Foxworth, Ms., U.S.	D4	101
Foz do Cunene, Ang.	E2	44
Foz do Iguaçu, Braz.	B6	56
Frackville, Pa., U.S.	E9	115
Fraga, Spain	D12	12
Framingham, Ma., U.S.	B5	98
Franca, Braz.	F5	57
Francavilla Fontana, Italy	I12	14
France, ctry., Eur.	F8	4
Francesville, In., U.S.	C4	91
Franceville, Gabon	B2	44
Francis, Lake, l., N.H., U.S.	f7	106
Francis Case, Lake, res., S.D., U.S.	D6	118
Francistown, Bots.	F5	44
Francofonte, Italy	L9	14
Franconia, N.H., U.S.	B3	106
Franconia Notch, N.H., U.S.	B3	106
Francs Peak, mtn., Wy., U.S.	C3	127
Frankenberg, Ger.	E13	8
Frankenberg-Eder, Ger.	D8	8
Frankenmuth, Mi., U.S.	E7	99
Frankford, Ont., Can.	C7	73
Frankford, De., U.S.	F5	85
Frankfort, Il., U.S.	m9	90
Frankfort, In., U.S.	D4	91
Frankfort, Ks., U.S.	C7	93
Frankfort, Ky., U.S.	B5	94
Frankfort, Mi., U.S.	D4	99
Frankfort, N.Y., U.S.	B5	109
Frankfort, Oh., U.S.	C2	112
Frankfurt am Main, Ger.	E8	8
Frankfurt an der Oder, Ger.	C14	8
Franklin, Ga., U.S.	C1	87
Franklin, In., U.S.	F5	91
Franklin, Ky., U.S.	D3	94
Franklin, La., U.S.	E4	95
Franklin, Ma., U.S.	B5	98
Franklin, Ne., U.S.	D7	104
Franklin, N.H., U.S.	D3	106
Franklin, N.J., U.S.	A3	107
Franklin, N.C., U.S.	f9	110
Franklin, Oh., U.S.	C1	112
Franklin, Pa., U.S.	D2	115
Franklin, Tn., U.S.	B5	119
Franklin, Tx., U.S.	D4	120
Franklin, Va., U.S.	D6	123
Franklin, W.V., U.S.	C5	125
Franklin, Wi., U.S.	n11	126
Franklin, co., Al., U.S.	A2	78
Franklin, co., Ar., U.S.	B2	81
Franklin, co., Fl., U.S.	C2	86
Franklin, co., Ga., U.S.	B3	87
Franklin, co., Id., U.S.	G7	89
Franklin, co., Il., U.S.	E4	90
Franklin, co., In., U.S.	F7	91
Franklin, co., Ia., U.S.	B4	92
Franklin, co., Ks., U.S.	D8	93
Franklin, co., Ky., U.S.	B5	94
Franklin, co., La., U.S.	B4	95
Franklin, co., Me., U.S.	C2	96
Franklin, co., Ma., U.S.	A2	98
Franklin, co., Ms., U.S.	D3	101
Franklin, co., Mo., U.S.	C6	102
Franklin, co., Ne., U.S.	D7	104
Franklin, co., N.Y., U.S.	f10	109
Franklin, co., N.C., U.S.	A4	110
Franklin, co., Oh., U.S.	B2	112
Franklin, co., Pa., U.S.	G6	115
Franklin, co., Tn., U.S.	B5	119
Franklin, co., Tx., U.S.	C5	120
Franklin, co., Vt., U.S.	B2	122
Franklin, co., Va., U.S.	D3	123
Franklin, co., Wa., U.S.	C6	124
Franklin, Point, c., Ak., U.S.	A8	79
Franklin Bay, b., N.W. Ter., Can.	C7	66
Franklin D. Roosevelt Lake, res., Wa., U.S.	B7	124
Franklin Falls Reservoir, res., N.H., U.S.	C3	106
Franklin Grove, Il., U.S.	B4	90
Franklin Lake, l., N.W. Ter., Can.	C13	66
Franklin Lake, l., Nv., U.S.	C6	105
Franklin Mountains, mts., N.W. Ter., Can.	D8	66
Franklin Park, Il., U.S.	k9	90
Franklin Park, Pa., U.S.	h13	115
Franklin Strait, strt., N.W. Ter., Can.	B13	66
Franklinton, La., U.S.	D5	95
Franklinton, N.C., U.S.	A4	110
Franklinville, N.Y., U.S.	C2	109
Frankston, Tx., U.S.	C5	120
Frankton, In., U.S.	D6	91
Frascati, Italy	H7	14
Fraser, stm., B.C., Can.	E7	69
Fraser, stm., Newf., Can.	g9	72
Fraser, Mount, mtn., Can.	C8	69
Fraserburgh, Scot., U.K.	D10	7
Fraser Lake, B.C., Can.	B5	69
Fraser Plateau, plat., B.C., Can.	D6	69
Frauenfeld, Switz.	E15	10
Frazee, Mn., U.S.	D3	100
Frazeysburg, Oh., U.S.	B3	112
Frazier Park, Ca., U.S.	E4	82
Fr'azino, U.S.S.R.	F21	22
Frederic, Wi., U.S.	C1	126
Frederica, De., U.S.	D4	85
Fredericia, Den.	I7	6
Frederick, Co., U.S.	A6	83
Frederick, Md., U.S.	B3	97
Frederick, Ok., U.S.	C2	113
Frederick, co., Md., U.S.	B3	97
Frederick, co., Va., U.S.	A4	123
Fredericksburg, Ia., U.S.	B5	92
Fredericksburg, Tx., U.S.	D3	120
Fredericksburg, Va., U.S.	B5	123
Frederick Sound, strt., Ak., U.S.	m23	79
Fredericktown, Mo., U.S.	D7	102
Fredericktown, Oh., U.S.	B3	112
Fredericktown, Pa., U.S.	F1	115
Fredericton, N.B., Can.	D3	71
Fredericton Junction, N.B., Can.	D3	71
Frederikshåb, Grnld.	D23	66
Frederikshavn, Den.	H8	6
Fredonia, Az., U.S.	A3	80
Fredonia, Ks., U.S.	E8	93
Fredonia, N.Y., U.S.	C1	109
Fredonia, Wi., U.S.	E6	126
Fredrikstad, Nor.	G8	6
Freeborn, co., Mn., U.S.	G5	100
Freeburg, Il., U.S.	E4	90
Freedom, Pa., U.S.	E1	115
Freedom, Wy., U.S.	D2	127
Freehold, N.J., U.S.	C4	107
Freeland, Mi., U.S.	E6	99
Freeland, Pa., U.S.	D10	115
Freelandville, In., U.S.	G3	91
Freel Peak, mtn., Ca., U.S.	C4	82
Freels, Cape, c., Newf., Can.	D5	72
Freels, Cape, c., Newf., Can.	E5	72
Freeman, S.D., U.S.	D8	118
Freeman, Lake, l., In., U.S.	C4	91
Freemansburg, Pa., U.S.	E11	115
Freemason Island, i., La., U.S.	E7	95
Freeport, Bah.	A8	64
Freeport, Il., U.S.	A4	90
Freeport, Me., U.S.	E2	96
Freeport, N.Y., U.S.	n15	109
Freeport, Pa., U.S.	E2	115
Freeport, Tx., U.S.	E5	120
Freer, Tx., U.S.	F3	120
Freestone, co., Tx., U.S.	D4	120
Freetown, S.L.	G3	42
Freetown, In., U.S.	G5	91
Freezeout Mountains, mts., Wy., U.S.	D6	127
Fregenal de la Sierra, Spain	G5	12
Freiberg, Ger.	E13	8
Freiburg [im Breisgau], Ger.	H7	8
Freising, Ger.	G11	8
Freistadt, Aus.	G14	8
Freital, Ger.	D13	8
Fréjus, Fr.	I13	10
Fremont, Ca., U.S.	D2	82
Fremont, In., U.S.	A8	91
Fremont, Ia., U.S.	C5	92
Fremont, Mi., U.S.	E5	99
Fremont, Ne., U.S.	C9	104
Fremont, N.C., U.S.	B5	110
Fremont, Oh., U.S.	A2	112
Fremont, co., Co., U.S.	C5	83
Fremont, co., Id., U.S.	E7	89
Fremont, co., Ia., U.S.	D2	92
Fremont, co., Wy., U.S.	C4	127
Fremont, stm., Ut., U.S.	E4	121
Fremont Island, i., Ut., U.S.	B3	121
Fremont Lake, l., Wy., U.S.	D3	127
Fremont Peak, mtn., Wy., U.S.	C3	127
French Broad, stm., U.S.	D10	119
Frenchburg, Ky., U.S.	C6	94
French Creek, stm., Pa., U.S.	C2	115
French Frigate Shoals, rf., Hi., U.S.	m14	88
French Guiana, dep., S.A.	C8	54
French Lick, In., U.S.	G4	91
Frenchman Bay, b., Me., U.S.	D4	96
Frenchman Creek, stm., U.S.	D4	104
Frenchman Hills, hills, Wa., U.S.	C6	124
Frenchman Lake, l., Nv., U.S.	G6	105
French Polynesia, dep., Oc.	G3	2
French Settlement, La., U.S.	D5	95
Freshfield, Mount, mtn., Can.	D2	68
Fresnillo, Mex.	F8	62
Fresno, Ca., U.S.	D4	82
Fresno, co., Ca., U.S.	D4	82
Fresno Reservoir, res., Mt., U.S.	B6	103
Freudenstadt, Ger.	G8	8
Frewsburg, N.Y., U.S.	C1	109
Fria, Cape, c., Nmb.	E2	44
Friars Point, Ms., U.S.	A3	101
Frías, Arg.	B3	56
Fribourg (Freiburg), Switz.	F14	10
Friday Harbor, Wa., U.S.	A2	124
Fridley, Mn., U.S.	m12	100
Friedberg, Aus.	H16	8
Friedrichshafen, Ger.	H9	8
Friend, Ne., U.S.	D8	104
Friendsville, Tn., U.S.	D9	119
Fries, Va., U.S.	D2	123
Friesland, hist. reg., Neth.	B5	8
Frio, co., Tx., U.S.	E3	120
Frio, stm., Tx., U.S.	E3	120
Frio, Cabo, c., Braz.	G7	57
Friona, Tx., U.S.	B1	120
Fripps Island, i., S.C., U.S.	G7	117
Frisco, Co., U.S.	B4	83
Frisco City, Al., U.S.	D2	78
Frisco Peak, mtn., Ut., U.S.	E2	121
Frissell, Mount, mtn., U.S.	A2	84
Fritch, Tx., U.S.	B2	120
Fritzlar, Ger.	D9	8
Friza, Proliv, strt., U.S.S.R.	H23	20
Frobisher Bay, b., N.W. Ter., Can.	D19	66
Frobisher Lake, l., Sask., Can.	m7	75
Frohnleiten, Aus.	H15	8
Frontenac, Ks., U.S.	E9	93
Frontier, co., Ne., U.S.	D5	104
Front Range, mts., Co., U.S.	A5	83
Front Royal, Va., U.S.	B4	123
Frosinone, Italy	H8	14
Frostburg, Md., U.S.	k13	97
Frostproof, Fl., U.S.	E5	86
Fruita, Co., U.S.	B2	83
Fruit Heights, Ut., U.S.	B4	121
Fruitland, Id., U.S.	F2	89
Fruitland, Md., U.S.	D6	97
Fruitland, N.M., U.S.	A1	108
Fruitland Park, Fl., U.S.	D5	86
Fruitport, Mi., U.S.	E4	99
Fruitvale, B.C., Can.	E9	69
Fruitvale, Co., U.S.	B2	83
Fruitvale, Wa., U.S.	C5	124
Fruitville, Fl., U.S.	E4	86
Frunze, U.S.S.R.	I12	18
Frutigen, Switz.	F14	10
Fryeburg, Me., U.S.	D2	96
Fuchū, Japan	H6	30
Fuencaliente, Spain	G7	12
Fuente de Cantos, Spain	G5	12
Fuente-obejuna, Spain	G6	12
Fuerteventura, i., Spain	C3	42
Fuji, Japan	G11	30
Fuji, Mount see Fuji-san, vol., Japan	G11	30
Fujian, prov., China	F10	26
Fujin, China	B13	26
Fujinomiya, Japan	G11	30
Fuji-san (Fujiyama), vol., Japan	G11	30
Fujisawa, Japan	G12	30
Fujiyama see Fuji-san, vol., Japan	G11	30
Fuji-yoshida, Japan	G11	30
Fukagawa, Japan	p20	30a
Fukaya, Japan	F12	30
Fukuchiyama, Japan	G8	30
Fukue, Japan	J1	30
Fukui, Japan	F9	30
Fukuoka, Japan	I3	30
Fukushima, Japan	E13	30
Fukushima, Japan	r18	30a
Fukuyama, Japan	H6	30
Fūlādī, Kūh-e, mtn., Afg.	C2	38
Fulda, Ger.	E9	8
Fulda, Mn., U.S.	G3	100
Fullerton, Ca., U.S.	n13	82
Fullerton, Ne., U.S.	C8	104
Fulton, Il., U.S.	B3	90
Fulton, Ky., U.S.	f9	94
Fulton, Md., U.S.	B4	97
Fulton, Ms., U.S.	A5	101
Fulton, Mo., U.S.	C6	102
Fulton, N.Y., U.S.	B4	109
Fulton, co., Ar., U.S.	A4	81
Fulton, co., Ga., U.S.	C2	87
Fulton, co., Il., U.S.	C3	90
Fulton, co., In., U.S.	B5	91
Fulton, co., Ky., U.S.	f8	94
Fulton, co., N.Y., U.S.	B6	109
Fulton, co., Oh., U.S.	A1	112
Fulton, co., Pa., U.S.	G5	115
Fultondale, Al., U.S.	f7	78
Funabashi, Japan	G13	30
Funchal, Port.	B2	42
Fundación, Col.	B5	58
Fundy, Bay of, b., Can.	D4	71
Fundy National Park, N.B., Can.	D4	71
Funkstown, Md., U.S.	A2	97
Fuquay-Varina, N.C., U.S.	B4	110
Furano, Japan	p20	30a
Furmanov, U.S.S.R.	D24	22
Furnace Brook, stm., Vt., U.S.	D3	122
Furnas, co., Ne., U.S.	D6	104
Furnas, Reprêsa de, res., Braz.	F5	57
Furneaux Group, is., Austl.	H9	50
Furqlus, Syria	B5	40
Fürstenfeld, Aus.	H16	8
Fürstenfeldbruck, Ger.	G11	8
Fürstenwalde, Ger.	C14	8
Fürth, Ger.	F10	8
Furth im Wald, Ger.	F12	8
Furudal, Swe.	F10	6
Fushun, China	C11	26
Füssen, Ger.	H10	8
Fuxian, China	D11	26
Fuxian, China	D8	26
Fuxinshi, China	C11	26
Fuyang, China	C4	28
Fuzhou, China	G5	28
Fuzhou (Foochow), China	I8	28
Fyffe, Al., U.S.	A4	78

G

Name	Map Ref	Page
Gabbs, Nv., U.S.	E4	105
Gabès, Tun.	B8	42
Gabès, Golfe de, b., Tun.	B8	42
Gabon, ctry., Afr.	B2	44
Gaborone, Bots.	F5	44
Gabriel Strait, strt., N.W. Ter., Can.	D19	66
Gabriola, B.C., Can.	f12	69
Gabrovo, Bul.	G9	16
Gadag, India	E3	37
Gäddede, Swe.	D10	6
Gadsden, Al., U.S.	A3	78
Gadsden, co., Fl., U.S.	B2	86
Gaeta, Italy	H8	14
Gaffney, S.C., U.S.	A4	117
Gafsa, Tun.	B7	42
Gage, co., Ne., U.S.	D9	104
Gagetown, N.B., Can.	D3	71
Gagliano del Capo, Italy	J13	14
Gagnoa, I.C.	G4	42
Gahanna, Oh., U.S.	k11	112
Gaillac, Fr.	I8	10
Gaillard, Lake, l., Ct., U.S.	D5	84
Gaines, co., Tx., U.S.	C1	120
Gainesboro, Tn., U.S.	C8	119
Gaines Creek, stm., Ok., U.S.	C6	113
Gainesville, Fl., U.S.	C4	86
Gainesville, Ga., U.S.	B3	87
Gainesville, Mo., U.S.	E5	102
Gainesville, Tx., U.S.	C4	120
Gainesville, Va., U.S.	g11	123
Gairdner, Lake, l., Austl.	F7	50
Gaithersburg, Md., U.S.	B3	97
Galán, Cerro, mtn., Arg.	B3	56
Galapagos Islands see Colón, Archipiélago de, is., Ec.	m15	58a
Galashiels, Scot., U.K.	F10	7
Galați, Rom.	D12	16
Galatia, Il., U.S.	F5	90
Galatina, Italy	I13	14
Galax, Va., U.S.	D2	123
Galena, Ak., U.S.	C8	79
Galena, Il., U.S.	A3	90
Galena, Ks., U.S.	E9	93
Galeota Point, c., Trin.	I17	64
Galera, Punta, c., Chile	D2	56
Galera, Punta, c., Ec.	G2	58
Galesburg, Il., U.S.	C3	90
Galesburg, Mi., U.S.	F5	99
Gales Ferry, Ct., U.S.	D7	84
Galesville, Md., U.S.	C4	97
Galesville, Wi., U.S.	D2	126
Galeton, Pa., U.S.	C6	115
Galič, U.S.S.R.	C25	22
Galicia, hist. reg., Eur.	F21	8
Galicia, hist. reg., Spain	B3	12
Galilee, Sea of see Kinneret, Yam, l., Isr.	C4	40
Galion, Oh., U.S.	B3	112
Galisteo Creek, stm., N.M., U.S.	k8	108
Galiuro Mountains, mts., Az., U.S.	E5	80
Galka'yo, Som.	G4	46
Gallant, Al., U.S.	B3	78
Gallarate, Italy	D3	14
Gallatin, Mo., U.S.	B4	102
Gallatin, Tn., U.S.	A5	119
Gallatin, co., Il., U.S.	F5	90
Gallatin, co., Ky., U.S.	B5	94
Gallatin, co., Mt., U.S.	E5	103
Gallatin, stm., Mt., U.S.	E5	103
Gallatin Range, mts., Mt., U.S.	E5	103
Gallaway, Tn., U.S.	B2	119
Galle, Sri L.	I6	37
Gallia, co., Oh., U.S.	D3	112
Galliano, La., U.S.	E5	95
Gallinas, Punta, c., Col.	A7	58
Gallinas Mountains, mts., N.M., U.S.	C2	108
Gallipoli, Italy	I12	14
Gallipoli see Gelibolu, Tur.	I10	16
Gallipolis, Oh., U.S.	D3	112
Gallitzin, Pa., U.S.	F4	115
Gällivare, Swe.	C13	6
Gallo Mountains, mts., N.M., U.S.	C1	108
Galloo Island, i., N.Y., U.S.	B4	109
Galloway, Mull of, c., Scot., U.K.	G8	7
Gallup, N.M., U.S.	B1	108
Galt, Ca., U.S.	C3	82
Galtür, Aus.	I10	8
Galty Mountains, mts., Ire.	I4	7
Galva, Il., U.S.	B3	90
Galva, Ks., U.S.	D6	93
Galveston, In., U.S.	C5	91
Galveston, Tx., U.S.	E5	120
Galveston, co., Tx., U.S.	E5	120
Galveston Bay, b., Tx., U.S.	E5	120
Galveston Island, i., Tx., U.S.	E5	120
Gálvez, Arg.	C4	56
Galway, Ire.	H3	7
Gambela, Eth.	G1	46
Gambell, Ak., U.S.	C5	79
Gambia, ctry., Afr.	F2	42
Gambia (Gambie), stm., Afr.	F2	42
Gambier, Oh., U.S.	B3	112
Gambo, Newf., Can.	D4	72
Gambrills, Md., U.S.	B4	97
Gamleby, Swe.	H11	6
Ganado, Az., U.S.	B6	80
Ganado, Tx., U.S.	E4	120
Gananoque, Ont., Can.	C8	73
Ganda, Ang.	D2	44
Gandak, stm., Asia	G11	38
Gander, Newf., Can.	D4	72
Gander, stm., Newf., Can.	D4	72
Ganderkesee, Ger.	B8	8
Gander Lake, l., Newf., Can.	D4	72
Gandesa, Spain	D12	12
Gāndhinagar, India	I5	38
Gāndhi Sāgar, res., India	H6	38
Gandía, Spain	G11	12
Gangāpur, India	G7	38
Gangāwati, India	E4	37
Gangdisê Shan, mts., China	E10	38
Ganges, B.C., Can.	g12	69
Ganges (Ganga) (Padma), stm., Asia	I13	38
Ganges, Mouths of the, mth., Asia	J13	38
Gang Mills, N.Y., U.S.	C3	109
Gangtok, India	G13	38
Gangu, China	E8	26
Gannat, Fr.	F10	10
Gannett Peak, mtn., Wy., U.S.	C3	127
Gansu, prov., China	D7	26
Gantt, S.C., U.S.	B3	117
Gantt Lake, res., Al., U.S.	D3	78
Ganzhou, China	J3	28
Ganzi, China	E7	26
Gao, Mali	E5	42
Gaokeng, China	H2	28
Gaoyou, China	C8	28
Gaozhou, China	D11	34
Gap, Fr.	H13	10
Gap, Pa., U.S.	G9	115
Gar, China	E9	38
Garanhuns, Braz.	E11	54
Garber, Ok., U.S.	A4	113
Garberville, Ca., U.S.	B2	82
Garça, Braz.	G4	57
Garda, Lago di, l., Italy	D5	14
Gardelegen, Ger.	C11	8
Garden, co., Ne., U.S.	C3	104
Gardena, Ca., U.S.	n12	82
Garden City, Ga., U.S.	D5	87
Garden City, Id., U.S.	F2	89
Garden City, Ks., U.S.	E3	93
Garden City, Mi., U.S.	p15	99
Garden City, Mo., U.S.	C3	102
Gardendale, Al., U.S.	B3	78
Garden Grove, Ca., U.S.	n13	82
Garden Island, i., Mi., U.S.	C5	99
Garden Plain, Ks., U.S.	E6	93
Garden Reach, India	I13	38
Gardēz, Afg.	D3	38
Gardiner, Me., U.S.	D3	96
Gardiner, Mt., U.S.	E6	103
Gardiner, Or., U.S.	D2	114
Gardiners Island, i., N.Y., U.S.	m16	109
Gardner, Il., U.S.	B5	90
Gardner, Ks., U.S.	D9	93
Gardner, Ma., U.S.	A4	98
Gardner Canal, strt., B.C., Can.	C3	69
Gardner Lake, l., Ct., U.S.	C6	84
Gardner Lake, l., Me., U.S.	D5	96
Gardner Pinnacles, Hi., U.S.	k14	88
Gardnerville, Nv., U.S.	E2	105
Gardone Val Trompia, Italy	D5	14
Garfield, N.J., U.S.	h8	107
Garfield, co., Co., U.S.	B2	83
Garfield, co., Mt., U.S.	C9	103
Garfield, co., Ne., U.S.	C6	104
Garfield, co., Ok., U.S.	A4	113
Garfield, co., Ut., U.S.	F4	121
Garfield, co., Wa., U.S.	C8	124
Garfield Heights, Oh., U.S.	h9	112
Garfield Mountain, mtn., Mt., U.S.	F4	103
Garfield Peak, mtn., Wy., U.S.	D5	127
Garibaldi, Or., U.S.	B3	114
Garibaldi, Mount, mtn., B.C., Can.	E6	69
Garies, S. Afr.	H3	44
Garissa, Kenya	B7	44
Garland, N.C., U.S.	C4	110
Garland, Tx., U.S.	n10	120
Garland, Ut., U.S.	B3	121
Garland, co., Ar., U.S.	C2	81
Garlin, Fr.	I6	10
Garm āb, Afg.	D1	38
Garmisch-Partenkirchen, Ger.	H11	8
Garnavillo, Ia., U.S.	B6	92

Name	Map Ref	Page
Garner, Ia., U.S.	**A4**	92
Garner, N.C., U.S.	**B4**	110
Garnet Range, mts., Mt., U.S.	**D3**	103
Garnett, Ks., U.S.	**D8**	93
Garnish, Newf., Can.	**E4**	72
Garonne, stm., Eur.	**H6**	10
Garoua, Cam.	**G8**	42
Garrard, co., Ky., U.S.	**C5**	94
Garretson, S.D., U.S.	**D9**	118
Garrett, In., U.S.	**B7**	91
Garrett, co., Md., U.S.	**k12**	97
Garrett Park, Md., U.S.	**B3**	97
Garrettsville, Oh., U.S.	**A4**	112
Garrison, Ky., U.S.	**B6**	94
Garrison, Md., U.S.	**B4**	97
Garrison, N.D., U.S.	**B4**	111
Garrison Dam, N.D., U.S.	**B4**	111
Garrovillas, Spain	**F5**	12
Garry Lake, l., N.W. Ter., Can.	**C12**	66
Garsen, Kenya	**B8**	44
Garut, Indon.	**m13**	33a
Garvin, co., Ok., U.S.	**C4**	113
Gary, In., U.S.	**A3**	91
Gary, W.V., U.S.	**D3**	125
Garysburg, N.C., U.S.	**A5**	110
Garyville, La., U.S.	**D5**	95
Garza, co., Tx., U.S.	**C2**	120
Garza-Little Elm Reservoir, res., Tx., U.S.	**C4**	120
Garzón, Col.	**F5**	58
Gas City, In., U.S.	**D6**	91
Gasconade, co., Mo., U.S.	**C6**	102
Gasconade, stm., Mo., U.S.	**C6**	102
Gascoyne, stm., Austl.	**E3**	50
Gasparilla Island, i., Fl., U.S.	**F4**	86
Gaspé, Que., Can.	**k14**	74
Gaspésie, Péninsule de la, pen., Que., Can.	**k13**	74
Gassaway, W.V., U.S.	**C4**	125
Gassville, Ar., U.S.	**A3**	81
Gaston, In., U.S.	**D7**	91
Gaston, N.C., U.S.	**A5**	110
Gaston, S.C., U.S.	**D5**	117
Gaston, co., N.C., U.S.	**B1**	110
Gaston, Lake, res., U.S.	**A5**	110
Gaston Dam, N.C., U.S.	**A5**	110
Gastonia, N.C., U.S.	**B1**	110
Gátas, Akrotírion, c., Cyp.	**B3**	40
Gatčina, U.S.S.R.	**B13**	22
Gate City, Va., U.S.	**f9**	123
Gates, N.Y., U.S.	**B3**	109
Gates, Tn., U.S.	**B2**	119
Gates, co., N.C., U.S.	**A6**	110
Gateshead, Eng., U.K.	**G11**	7
Gateshead Island, i., N.W. Ter., Can.	**B12**	66
Gates of the Arctic National Park, Ak., U.S.	**B9**	79
Gatesville, Tx., U.S.	**D4**	120
Gatineau, Que., Can.	**D2**	74
Gatineau, stm., Que., Can.	**D2**	74
Gatineau, Parc de la, Que., Can.	**D2**	74
Gatlinburg, Tn., U.S.	**D10**	119
Gaucín, Spain	**I6**	12
Gauhāti, India	**G14**	38
Gauley, stm., W.V., U.S.	**C3**	125
Gauley Bridge, W.V., U.S.	**C3**	125
Gautier, Ms., U.S.	**f8**	101
Gauting, Ger.	**G11**	8
Gavá, Spain	**D14**	12
Gavins Point Dam, U.S.	**B8**	104
Gävle, Swe.	**F11**	6
Gavrilov-Jam, U.S.S.R.	**D22**	22
Gawler Ranges, mts., Austl.	**F7**	50
Gaya, India	**H11**	38
Gay Head, c., Ma., U.S.	**D6**	98
Gaylord, Mi., U.S.	**C6**	99
Gaylord, Mn., U.S.	**F4**	100
Gayndah, Austl.	**E10**	50
Gaza see Ghazzah, Isr. Occ.	**D4**	40
Gaziantep, Tur.	**H15**	4
Gazimağusa, N. Cyp.	**B3**	40
Gazimağusa Körfezi, b., N. Cyp.	**B4**	40
Gbarnga, Lib.	**G4**	42
Gdańsk (Danzig), Pol.	**A18**	8
Gdynia, Pol.	**A18**	8
Gearhart, Or., U.S.	**A3**	114
Gearhart Mountain, mtn., Or., U.S.	**E6**	114
Geary, N.B., Can.	**D3**	71
Geary, Ok., U.S.	**B3**	113
Geary, co., Ks., U.S.	**D7**	93
Geauga, co., Oh., U.S.	**A4**	112
Gebze, Tur.	**I13**	16
Gediz, stm., Tur.	**K11**	16
Geel, Bel.	**D4**	8
Geelong, Austl.	**G8**	50
Ge'ermu, China	**B16**	38
Geesthacht, Ger.	**B10**	8
Geilo, Nor.	**F7**	6
Geislingen, Ger.	**G9**	8
Geistown, Pa., U.S.	**F4**	115
Geist Reservoir, res., In., U.S.	**E6**	91
Gejiu (Kokiu), China	**C7**	34
Gela, Italy	**L9**	14
Gelibolu, Tur.	**I10**	16
Gelibolu Yarımadası (Gallipoli Peninsula), pen., Tur.	**I10**	16
Gelsenkirchen, Ger.	**D7**	8
Gem, co., Id., U.S.	**E2**	89
Gembloux, Bel.	**E4**	8
Gemena, Zaire	**H9**	42
Gemlik, Tur.	**I13**	16
Gemona del Friuli, Italy	**C8**	14
Genale (Juba), stm., Afr.	**G3**	46
General Alvear, Arg.	**C3**	56
General Bravo, Mex.	**E10**	62
General Carneiro, Braz.	**C2**	57
General Levalle, Arg.	**C4**	56
General Pico, Arg.	**D4**	56
General Pinedo, Arg.	**B4**	56
General Roca, Arg.	**D3**	56
General Villegas, Arg.	**D4**	56
Genesee, Id., U.S.	**C2**	89
Genesee, Mi., U.S.	**E7**	99
Genesee, co., Mi., U.S.	**E7**	99
Genesee, co., N.Y., U.S.	**B2**	109
Genesee, stm., N.Y., U.S.	**C2**	109
Geneseo, Il., U.S.	**B3**	90
Geneseo, N.Y., U.S.	**C3**	109
Geneva, Al., U.S.	**D4**	78
Geneva, Il., U.S.	**B5**	90
Geneva, In., U.S.	**C8**	91
Geneva, Ne., U.S.	**D8**	104
Geneva, N.Y., U.S.	**C4**	109
Geneva, Oh., U.S.	**A5**	112
Geneva, co., Al., U.S.	**D4**	78
Geneva, Lake, l., Eur.	**F13**	10
Geneva, Lake, l., Wi., U.S.	**F5**	126
Geneva see Genève, Switz.	**F13**	10
Geneva-on-the-Lake, Oh., U.S.	**A5**	112
Genève, Switz.	**F13**	10
Genk, Bel.	**E5**	8
Genkai-nada, Japan	**I3**	30
Genoa, Il., U.S.	**A5**	90
Genoa, Ne., U.S.	**C8**	104
Genoa, Nv., U.S.	**D2**	105
Genoa, Oh., U.S.	**A2**	112
Genoa City, Wi., U.S.	**F5**	126
Genoa see Genova, Italy	**E3**	14
Genola, Ut., U.S.	**D4**	121
Genova (Genoa), Italy	**E3**	14
Genova, Golfo di, b., Italy	**E3**	14
Gent (Gand), Bel.	**D3**	8
Genteng, Indon.	**n17**	33a
Genthin, Ger.	**C12**	8
Gentry, Ar., U.S.	**A1**	81
Gentry, co., Mo., U.S.	**A3**	102
Geographe Bay, b., Austl.	**F3**	50
George, S. Afr.	**H4**	44
George, Ia., U.S.	**A2**	92
George, co., Ms., U.S.	**E5**	101
George, stm., Que., Can.	**g13**	74
George, Cape, c., N.S., Can.	**D8**	71
George, Lake, l., Ug.	**B6**	44
George, Lake, l., Fl., U.S.	**C5**	86
George, Lake, l., N.Y., U.S.	**B7**	109
George Air Force Base, mil., Ca., U.S.	**E5**	82
George B. Stevenson Reservoir, res., Pa., U.S.	**D6**	115
George Peak, mtn., Ut., U.S.	**B2**	121
Georgetown, P.E.I., Can.	**C7**	71
Georgetown, Cay. Is.	**E7**	64
Georgetown, Gam.	**F3**	42
Georgetown, Guy.	**D13**	58
George Town (Pinang), Malay.	**L6**	34
Georgetown, Ca., U.S.	**C3**	82
Georgetown, Co., U.S.	**B5**	83
Georgetown, Ct., U.S.	**D2**	84
Georgetown, De., U.S.	**F4**	85
Georgetown, Ga., U.S.	**E1**	87
Georgetown, Il., U.S.	**D6**	90
Georgetown, In., U.S.	**H6**	91
Georgetown, Ky., U.S.	**B5**	94
Georgetown, Ma., U.S.	**A6**	98
Georgetown, Oh., U.S.	**D2**	112
Georgetown, S.C., U.S.	**E9**	117
Georgetown, Tx., U.S.	**D4**	120
Georgetown, co., S.C., U.S.	**E9**	117
George Washington Birthplace National Monument, Va., U.S.	**B6**	123
George Washington Carver National Monument, Mo., U.S.	**E3**	102
George West, Tx., U.S.	**E3**	120
Georgia, state, U.S.	**D3**	87
Georgia, Strait of, strt., N.A.	**B2**	76
Georgia see Gruzinskaja Sovetskaja Socialističeskaja Respublika, state, U.S.S.R.	**I6**	18
Georgiana, Al., U.S.	**D3**	78
Georgian Bay, b., Ont., Can.	**B3**	73
Georgina, stm., Austl.	**D7**	50
Gera, Ger.	**E12**	8
Gerald, Mo., U.S.	**C6**	102
Geraldine, Al., U.S.	**A4**	78
Geral do Paranã, Serra, hills, Braz.	**C5**	57
Geraldton, Austl.	**E2**	50
Geraldton, Ont., Can.	**o18**	73
Gérardmer, Fr.	**D13**	10
Gerber Reservoir, res., Or., U.S.	**E5**	114
Gerdine, Mount, mtn., Ak., U.S.	**C9**	79
Gereshk, Afg.	**E1**	38
Gérgal, Spain	**H9**	12
Gering, Ne., U.S.	**C2**	104
Gerlach, Nv., U.S.	**C2**	105
Germantown, Il., U.S.	**E4**	90
Germantown, Md., U.S.	**B3**	97
Germantown, Oh., U.S.	**C1**	112
Germantown, Tn., U.S.	**B2**	119
Germantown, Wi., U.S.	**E5**	126
Germany, ctry., Eur.	**E10**	4
Germiston, S. Afr.	**G5**	44
Gerona, Spain	**D14**	12
Geronimo, Ok., U.S.	**C3**	113
Gervais, Or., U.S.	**B4**	114
Geseke, Ger.	**D8**	8
Getafe, Spain	**E8**	12
Gettysburg, Pa., U.S.	**G7**	115
Gettysburg, S.D., U.S.	**C6**	118
Ghāghra, stm., Asia	**G10**	38
Ghana, ctry., Afr.	**G5**	42
Ghanzi, Bots.	**F4**	44
Gharbīyah, Aṣ-Ṣaḥrā' al- (Western Desert), des., Egypt	**C11**	42
Ghardaïa, Alg.	**B6**	42
Gharyān, Libya	**B8**	42
Ghāt, Libya	**D8**	42
Għawdex, i., Malta	**M9**	14
Ghazāl, Baḥr al-, stm., Sudan	**G12**	42
Ghāziābād, India	**F7**	38
Ghāzīpur, India	**H10**	38
Ghaznī, Afg.	**D3**	38
Ghazzah (Gaza), Isr. Occ.	**D4**	40
Ghedi, Italy	**D5**	14
Gheen, Mn., U.S.	**C6**	100
Ghent see Gent, Bel.	**D3**	8
Gheorghe Gheorghiu-Dej, Rom.	**C10**	16
Ghīn, Tall, mtn., Syria	**C5**	40
Ghudāmis, Libya	**B7**	42
Giants Neck, Ct., U.S.	**D7**	84
Gibbon, Mn., U.S.	**F4**	100
Gibbon, Ne., U.S.	**D7**	104
Gibbons, Alta., Can.	**C4**	68
Gibbstown, N.J., U.S.	**D2**	107
Gibeon, Nmb.	**G3**	44
Gibraltar, Gib.	**I6**	12
Gibraltar, dep., Eur.	**H6**	4
Gibraltar, Strait of (Estrecho de Gibraltar), strt.	**J6**	12
Gibraltar Point, c., Eng., U.K.	**H13**	7
Gibsland, La., U.S.	**B2**	95
Gibson, Ga., U.S.	**C4**	87
Gibson, co., In., U.S.	**H2**	91
Gibson, co., Tn., U.S.	**A3**	119
Gibsonburg, Oh., U.S.	**A2**	112
Gibson City, Il., U.S.	**C5**	90
Gibson Desert, des., Austl.	**D4**	50
Gibsonia, Pa., U.S.	**h14**	115
Gibson Island, i., Md., U.S.	**B5**	97
Gibsons, B.C., Can.	**E6**	69
Gibsonton, Fl., U.S.	**p11**	86
Gibsonville, N.C., U.S.	**A3**	110
Giddings, Tx., U.S.	**D4**	120
Gideon, Mo., U.S.	**E8**	102
Gien, Fr.	**E9**	10
Giessen, Ger.	**E8**	8
Gifford, Fl., U.S.	**E6**	86
Gifford, Il., U.S.	**C5**	90
Gifu, Japan	**G9**	30
Gig Harbor, Wa., U.S.	**B3**	124
Gihon, stm., Vt., U.S.	**B3**	122
Gijón, Spain	**B6**	12
Gila, co., Az., U.S.	**D5**	80
Gila, stm., U.S.	**E4**	76
Gila Bend, Az., U.S.	**E3**	80
Gila Bend Indian Reservation, Az., U.S.	**D3**	80
Gila Bend Mountains, mts., Az., U.S.	**D2**	80
Gila Cliff Dwellings National Monument, N.M., U.S.	**D1**	108
Gila Mountains, mts., Az., U.S.	**D6**	80
Gila Peak, mtn., Az., U.S.	**D6**	80
Gila River Indian Reservation, Az., U.S.	**D4**	80
Gilbert, Az., U.S.	**D4**	80
Gilbert, Ia., U.S.	**B4**	92
Gilbert, La., U.S.	**B4**	95
Gilbert, Mn., U.S.	**C6**	100
Gilbert Islands see Kiribati, ctry., Oc.	**G24**	2
Gilbert Peak, mtn., Wa., U.S.	**C4**	124
Gilbert Plains, Man., Can.	**D1**	70
Gilbertsville, Ky., U.S.	**f9**	94
Gilbertsville, Pa., U.S.	**F10**	115
Gilbertville, Ia., U.S.	**B5**	92
Gilbués, Braz.	**E9**	54
Gilchrist, Or., U.S.	**D5**	114
Gilchrist, co., Fl., U.S.	**C4**	86
Gilcrest, Co., U.S.	**A6**	83
Giles, co., Tn., U.S.	**B4**	119
Giles, co., Va., U.S.	**C2**	123
Gilford Island, i., B.C., Can.	**D4**	69
Gilgit, Pak.	**C6**	38
Gillam, Man., Can.	**A4**	70
Gillespie, Il., U.S.	**D4**	90
Gillespie, co., Tx., U.S.	**D3**	120
Gillespie Dam, Az., U.S.	**D3**	80
Gillett, Ar., U.S.	**C4**	81
Gillett, Wi., U.S.	**D5**	126
Gillette, Wy., U.S.	**B7**	127
Gilliam, co., Or., U.S.	**B6**	114
Gilman, Il., U.S.	**C5**	90
Gilman, Vt., U.S.	**C5**	122
Gilmanton, N.H., U.S.	**D4**	106
Gilmer, Tx., U.S.	**C5**	120
Gilmer, co., Ga., U.S.	**B2**	87
Gilmer, co., W.V., U.S.	**C4**	125
Gilo, stm., Eth.	**G1**	46
Gilpin, co., Co., U.S.	**B5**	83
Gilroy, Ca., U.S.	**D3**	82
Gil'uj, stm., U.S.S.R.	**G19**	20
Giluwe, Mount, mtn., Pap. N. Gui.	**m15**	50a
Gimli, Man., Can.	**D3**	70
Ginosa, Italy	**I11**	14
Ginowan, Japan	**y27**	31b
Gioia del Colle, Italy	**I11**	14
Gioia Tauro, Italy	**K10**	14
Girard, Il., U.S.	**D4**	90
Girard, Ks., U.S.	**E9**	93
Girard, Oh., U.S.	**A5**	112
Girard, Pa., U.S.	**B1**	115
Girardot, Col.	**E5**	58
Girardville, Pa., U.S.	**E9**	115
Giridih, India	**H12**	38
Girifalco, Italy	**K11**	14
Girne, N. Cyp.	**B3**	40
Girwa, stm., Asia	**F9**	38
Gisborne, N.Z.	**C7**	52
Gisenyi, Rw.	**B5**	44
Gisors, Fr.	**C8**	10
Giugliano [in Campania], Italy	**I9**	14
Giulianova, Italy	**G8**	14
Giurgiu, Rom.	**F9**	16
Givet, Fr.	**B11**	10
Givors, Fr.	**G11**	10
Giyon, Eth.	**G2**	46
Giza see Al-Jīzah, Egypt	**B12**	42
Gižiga, U.S.S.R.	**E26**	20
Gižiginskaja Guba, b., U.S.S.R.	**E25**	20
Gjandža, U.S.S.R.	**I7**	18
Gjirokastër, Alb.	**I4**	16
Gjoa Haven, N.W. Ter., Can.	**C13**	66
Glacier, co., Mt., U.S.	**B3**	103
Glacier Bay, b., Ak., U.S.	**k21**	79
Glacier Bay National Park, Ak., U.S.	**D12**	79
Glacier National Park, B.C., Can.	**D9**	69
Glacier National Park, Mt., U.S.	**B2**	103
Glacier Peak, mtn., Wa., U.S.	**A4**	124
Gladbrook, Ia., U.S.	**B5**	92
Glade Creek, stm., Wa., U.S.	**C6**	124
Glade Creek, stm., W.V., U.S.	**n14**	125
Glade Creek, stm., W.V., U.S.	**n13**	125
Glades, co., Fl., U.S.	**F5**	86
Glade Spring, Va., U.S.	**f10**	123
Gladewater, Tx., U.S.	**C5**	120
Gladstone, Austl.	**D10**	50
Gladstone, Man., Can.	**D2**	70
Gladstone, Mi., U.S.	**C4**	99
Gladstone, Mo., U.S.	**h10**	102
Gladstone, Or., U.S.	**B4**	114
Gladwin, Mi., U.S.	**E6**	99
Gladwin, co., Mi., U.S.	**D6**	99
Glåma, stm., Nor.	**F8**	6
Glarner Alpen, mts., Switz.	**F15**	10
Glarus, Switz.	**E16**	10
Glascock, co., Ga., U.S.	**C4**	87
Glasford, Il., U.S.	**C4**	90
Glasgow, Scot., U.K.	**F8**	7
Glasgow, Ky., U.S.	**C4**	94
Glasgow, Mo., U.S.	**B5**	102
Glasgow, Mt., U.S.	**B10**	103
Glasgow, Va., U.S.	**C3**	123
Glasgow, W.V., U.S.	**m13**	125
Glassboro, N.J., U.S.	**D2**	107
Glasscock, co., Tx., U.S.	**D2**	120
Glassport, Pa., U.S.	**F2**	115
Glastonbury, Ct., U.S.	**C5**	84
Glauchau, Ger.	**E12**	8
Glazier Lake, l., Me., U.S.	**A3**	96
Glazov, U.S.S.R.	**F8**	18
Gleason, Tn., U.S.	**A3**	119
Gleisdorf, Aus.	**H15**	8
Glen Allan, Ms., U.S.	**B2**	101
Glen Allen, Va., U.S.	**C5**	123
Glenboro, Man., Can.	**E2**	70
Glenbrook, Nv., U.S.	**D2**	105
Glen Burnie, Md., U.S.	**B4**	97
Glen Canyon Dam, Az., U.S.	**A4**	80
Glen Canyon National Recreation Area, U.S.	**F5**	121
Glencoe, Ont., Can.	**E3**	73
Glencoe, Al., U.S.	**B4**	78
Glencoe, Il., U.S.	**A6**	90
Glencoe, Mn., U.S.	**F4**	100
Glen Cove, N.Y., U.S.	**h13**	109
Glendale, Az., U.S.	**D3**	80
Glendale, Ca., U.S.	**m12**	82
Glendale, Ms., U.S.	**D4**	101
Glendale, Oh., U.S.	**C1**	112
Glendale, Or., U.S.	**E3**	114
Glendale, R.I., U.S.	**B2**	116
Glendale, S.C., U.S.	**B4**	117
Glen Dale, W.V., U.S.	**B4**	125
Glendale, Wi., U.S.	**m12**	126
Glendale Heights, W.V., U.S.	**g8**	125
Glendive, Mt., U.S.	**C12**	103
Glendo, Wy., U.S.	**D7**	127
Glendora, Ca., U.S.	**m13**	82
Glendo Reservoir, res., Wy., U.S.	**D8**	127
Glenelg, Md., U.S.	**B4**	97
Glen Ellis Falls, wtfl, N.H., U.S.	**B4**	106
Glen Ellyn, Il., U.S.	**k8**	90
Glenham, N.Y., U.S.	**D7**	109
Glen Innes, Austl.	**E10**	50
Glen Jean, W.V., U.S.	**D3**	125
Glen Lake, l., Mi., U.S.	**D5**	99
Glen Lyon, Pa., U.S.	**D9**	115
Glenmora, La., U.S.	**D3**	95
Glenn, co., Ca., U.S.	**C2**	82
Glennallen, Ak., U.S.	**f19**	79
Glenns Ferry, Id., U.S.	**G3**	89
Glennville, Ga., U.S.	**E5**	87
Glenolden, Pa., U.S.	**p20**	115
Glenpool, Ok., U.S.	**B5**	113
Glen Raven, N.C., U.S.	**A3**	110
Glen Ridge, N.J., U.S.	**h8**	107
Glen Rock, N.J., U.S.	**h8**	107
Glen Rock, Pa., U.S.	**G8**	115
Glenrock, Wy., U.S.	**D7**	127
Glen Rose, Tx., U.S.	**C4**	120
Glens Falls, N.Y., U.S.	**B7**	109
Glen Ullin, N.D., U.S.	**C4**	111
Glenview, Il., U.S.	**h9**	90
Glenview Naval Air Station, mil., Il., U.S.	**h9**	90
Glenville, Mn., U.S.	**G5**	100
Glenville, W.V., U.S.	**C4**	125
Glenwood, Newf., Can.	**D4**	72
Glenwood, Ar., U.S.	**C2**	81
Glenwood, Ga., U.S.	**D4**	87
Glenwood, Ia., U.S.	**C2**	92
Glenwood, Mn., U.S.	**E3**	100
Glenwood, Va., U.S.	**D3**	123
Glenwood City, Wi., U.S.	**C1**	126
Glenwood Springs, Co., U.S.	**B3**	83
Glidden, Ia., U.S.	**B3**	92
Glide, Or., U.S.	**D3**	114
Glina, Yugo.	**D11**	14
Glittertinden, mtn., Nor.	**F7**	6
Gliwice (Gleiwitz), Pol.	**E18**	8
Globe, Az., U.S.	**D5**	80
Gloggnitz, Aus.	**H15**	8
Gloster, Ms., U.S.	**D2**	101
Gloucester, Ont., Can.	**h12**	73
Gloucester, Eng., U.K.	**J10**	7
Gloucester, Ma., U.S.	**A6**	98
Gloucester, Va., U.S.	**C6**	123
Gloucester, co., N.J., U.S.	**D2**	107
Gloucester, co., Va., U.S.	**C6**	123
Gloucester City, N.J., U.S.	**D2**	107
Gloucester Point, Va., U.S.	**C6**	123
Glouster, Oh., U.S.	**C3**	112
Glover Island, i., Newf., Can.	**D3**	72
Gloversville, N.Y., U.S.	**B6**	109
Glovertown, Newf., Can.	**D4**	72
Gloverville, S.C., U.S.	**E4**	117
Gluck, S.C., U.S.	**C2**	117
Glücksburg, Ger.	**A9**	8
Glückstadt, Ger.	**B9**	8
Glyndon, Md., U.S.	**B4**	97
Glyndon, Mn., U.S.	**D2**	100
Glynn, co., Ga., U.S.	**E5**	87
Gmünd, Aus.	**G14**	8
Gmunden, Aus.	**H13**	8
Gnadenhutten, Oh., U.S.	**B4**	112
Gnarp, Swe.	**E11**	6
Gniezno, Pol.	**C17**	8
Gnjilane, Yugo.	**G5**	16
Gō, stm., Japan	**H5**	30
Goa, ter., India	**E2**	37
Goat Island, i., R.I., U.S.	**F5**	116
Goat Mountain, mtn., Mt., U.S.	**C3**	103
Goat Rock Dam, U.S.	**C4**	78
Goba, Eth.	**G3**	46
Gobabis, Nmb.	**F3**	44
Gobi, des., Asia	**C7**	26
Gobles, Mi., U.S.	**F5**	99
Godāvari, stm., India	**D6**	37
Goddard, Ks., U.S.	**E6**	93
Goderich, Ont., Can.	**D3**	73
Godfrey, Il., U.S.	**E3**	90
Godhavn, Grnld.	**C22**	66
Godhra, India	**I5**	38
Godoy Cruz, Arg.	**C3**	56
Gods, stm., Man., Can.	**A5**	70
Gods Lake, l., Man., Can.	**B4**	70
Godthåb, Grnld.	**D22**	66
Godwin Austen see K2, mtn., Asia	**C7**	38
Goéland, Lac au, l., Que., Can.	**G17**	66
Goélands, Lac aux, l., Que., Can.	**E20**	66
Goff Creek, stm., Ok., U.S.	**e9**	113
Goffstown, N.H., U.S.	**D3**	106
Gogebic, co., Mi., U.S.	**n12**	99
Gogebic, Lake, l., Mi., U.S.	**m12**	99
Goiana, Braz.	**G9**	54
Goiânia, Braz.	**D4**	57
Goiás, Braz.	**C3**	57
Gojra, Pak.	**E5**	38
Gokāk, India	**D3**	37
Gökçeada, i., Tur.	**I9**	16
Gol'čicha, U.S.S.R.	**C10**	20
Golconda, Il., U.S.	**F5**	90
Golconda, Nv., U.S.	**C4**	105
Gold Bar, Wa., U.S.	**B4**	124
Gold Beach, Or., U.S.	**E2**	114
Golden, B.C., Can.	**D9**	69
Golden, Co., U.S.	**B5**	83
Golden City, Mo., U.S.	**D3**	102
Goldendale, Wa., U.S.	**D5**	124
Golden Gate Bridge, Ca., U.S.	**h7**	82
Golden Gate National Recreation Area, Ca., U.S.	**h7**	82
Golden Hinde, mtn., B.C., Can.	**E5**	69
Golden Meadow, La., U.S.	**E5**	95
Golden Spike National Historic Site, hist., Ut., U.S.	**B3**	121
Golden Valley, Mn., U.S.	**n12**	100
Golden Valley, co., Mt., U.S.	**D7**	103
Golden Valley, co., N.D., U.S.	**B2**	111
Goldfield, Ia., U.S.	**B4**	92
Goldfield, Nv., U.S.	**F4**	105
Gold Hill, Or., U.S.	**E3**	114
Goldsboro, N.C., U.S.	**B5**	110
Goldsby, Ok., U.S.	**B4**	113
Goldthwaite, Tx., U.S.	**D3**	120
Golec-Skalistyj, Gora, mtn., U.S.S.R.	**F17**	20
Goleta, Ca., U.S.	**E4**	82
Golf Manor, Oh., U.S.	**o13**	112
Goliad, Tx., U.S.	**E4**	120
Goliad, co., Tx., U.S.	**E4**	120
Golspie, Scot., U.K.	**D9**	7
Gomati, stm., India	**G9**	38
Gombe, stm., Tan.	**B6**	44
Gomel', U.S.S.R.	**I14**	22
Gomera, i., Spain	**C2**	42
Gómez Palacio, Mex.	**E8**	62
Gonābād, Iran	**K9**	18
Gonaïves, Haiti	**E11**	64
Gonam, U.S.S.R.	**F20**	20
Gonam, stm., U.S.S.R.	**F28**	20
Gonâve, Golfe de la, b., Haiti	**E11**	64
Gonâve, Île de la, i., Haiti	**E11**	64
Gonda, India	**G9**	38
Gondal, India	**J4**	38
Gonder, Eth.	**F2**	46
Gondia, India	**B6**	37
Gondomar, Port.	**D3**	12
Gondrecourt-le-Château, Fr.	**D12**	10
Gönen, Tur.	**I11**	16
Gōnoura, Japan	**I2**	30
Gonzales, Ca., U.S.	**D3**	82
Gonzales, La., U.S.	**D5**	95
Gonzales, Tx., U.S.	**E4**	120
Gonzales, co., Tx., U.S.	**E4**	120
Gonzalez, Fl., U.S.	**u14**	86
Goochland, co., Va., U.S.	**C5**	123
Goode, Mount, mtn., Ak., U.S.	**g18**	79
Goodfellow Air Force Base, mil., Tx., U.S.	**D2**	120
Good Hope, Cape of, c., S. Afr.	**H3**	44
Good Hope Mountain, mtn., B.C., Can.	**D5**	69
Goodhue, co., Mn., U.S.	**F6**	100
Gooding, Id., U.S.	**G4**	89
Gooding, co., Id., U.S.	**F4**	89
Goodland, In., U.S.	**C3**	91
Goodland, Ks., U.S.	**C2**	93
Goodlettsville, Tn., U.S.	**g10**	119
Goodman, Ms., U.S.	**C4**	101
Goodman, Mo., U.S.	**E3**	102
Good Pine, La., U.S.	**C3**	95
Goodsprings, Nv., U.S.	**H6**	105
Goodview, Mn., U.S.	**F7**	100
Goodwater, Al., U.S.	**B3**	78
Goodwell, Ok., U.S.	**e9**	113
Goodyear, Az., U.S.	**D3**	80
Goole, Eng., U.K.	**H12**	7
Goondiwindi, Austl.	**E10**	50
Goose, stm., N.D., U.S.	**B8**	111
Goose Bay, b., Newf., Can.	**B1**	72
Gooseberry Creek, stm., Wy., U.S.	**B4**	127
Goose Creek, S.C., U.S.	**F7**	117
Goose Creek, stm., U.S.	**G5**	89
Goose Creek, stm., Va., U.S.	**C3**	123
Goose Creek Reservoir, res., S.C., U.S.	**k11**	117
Goose Lake, l., U.S.	**B3**	82
Goose Pond, l., N.H., U.S.	**C2**	106
Göppingen, Ger.	**G9**	8
Gorakhpur, India	**G10**	38
Gorda, Punta, c., Cuba	**C6**	64
Gordil, Cen. Afr. Rep.	**G10**	42
Gordo, Al., U.S.	**B2**	78

Name	Map Ref	Page
Gordon, Ga., U.S.	D3	87
Gordon, Ne., U.S.	B3	104
Gordon, co., Ga., U.S.	B2	87
Gordonsville, Tn., U.S.	C8	119
Gordonsville, Va., U.S.	B4	123
Gore, Eth.	G2	46
Gore, N.Z.	G2	52
Gore, Ok., U.S.	B6	113
Gore Bay, Ont., Can.	B2	73
Gore Point, c., Ak., U.S.	h16	79
Gore Range, mts., Co., U.S.	B4	83
Goreville, Il., U.S.	F5	90
Gorey, Ire.	I6	7
Gorgān, Iran	J8	18
Gorge High Dam, Wa., U.S.	A4	124
Gorham, Me., U.S.	E2	96
Gorham, N.H., U.S.	B4	106
Gorinchem, Neth.	D4	8
Gorizia, Italy	D8	14
Gorki, U.S.S.R.	G13	22
Gorki see Nižnij Novgorod, U.S.S.R.	E27	22
Gorkovskoje Vodochranilišče, res., U.S.S.R.	D26	22
Görlitz, Ger.	B13	8
Gorlovka, U.S.S.R.	H5	18
Gorman, Tx., U.S.	C3	120
Gornja Radgona, Yugo.	C10	14
Gorno-Altajsk, U.S.S.R.	G11	20
Gorodec, U.S.S.R.	E26	22
Gorontalo, Indon.	E7	32
Gort, Ire.	H4	7
Gorzów Wielkopolski (Landsberg an der Warthe), Pol.	C15	8
Goshen, In., U.S.	A6	91
Goshen, N.Y., U.S.	D6	109
Goshen, Oh., U.S.	C1	112
Goshen, co., Wy., U.S.	D8	127
Goshute Indian Reservation, U.S.	D7	105
Goshute Lake, l., Nv., U.S.	C7	105
Goshute Mountains, mts., Nv., U.S.	C7	105
Goslar, Ger.	D10	8
Gosper, co., Ne., U.S.	D6	104
Gosport, In., U.S.	F4	91
Göteborg (Gothenburg), Swe.	H8	6
Gotemba, Japan	G11	30
Gotha, Ger.	E10	8
Gothenburg, Ne., U.S.	D5	104
Gothenburg see Göteborg, Swe.	H8	6
Gotland, i., Swe.	H12	6
Gotō-rettō, is., Japan	J1	30
Göttingen, Ger.	D9	8
Gottwaldov, Czech.	F17	8
Gouda, Neth.	C4	8
Gouin, Réservoir, res., Que., Can.	k12	74
Goulburn, Austl.	F9	50
Goulburn Islands, is., Austl.	B6	50
Gould, Ar., U.S.	D4	81
Goulding, Fl., U.S.	u14	86
Gould Island, i., R.I., U.S.	E5	116
Goulds, Fl., U.S.	s13	86
Gourdon, Fr.	H8	10
Gouré, Niger	F8	42
Gourin, Fr.	D3	10
Gournay-en-Bray, Fr.	C8	10
Gouverneur, N.Y., U.S.	f9	109
Gove, co., Ks., U.S.	D3	93
Governador Valadares, Braz.	E8	57
Governors Harbour, Bah.	B9	64
Govind Balabh Pant Sāgar, res., India	H10	38
Govind Sāgar, res., India	E7	38
Gowanda, N.Y., U.S.	C2	109
Gower, Mo., U.S.	B3	102
Gowmal (Gumal), stm., Asia	D3	38
Gowmal Kalay, Afg.	D3	38
Gowrie, Ia., U.S.	B3	92
Goya, Arg.	B5	56
Gozo see Għawdex, i., Malta	M9	14
Graaff-Reinet, S. Afr.	H4	44
Grabill, In., U.S.	B8	91
Grace, Id., U.S.	G7	89
Graceville, Fl., U.S.	u16	86
Graceville, Mn., U.S.	E2	100
Gracewood, Ga., U.S.	C4	87
Gracias a Dios, Cabo, c., N.A.	G6	64
Gradaús, Braz.	E8	54
Gradaús, Serra dos, plat., Braz.	E8	54
Grado, Italy	D8	14
Grady, co., Ga., U.S.	F2	87
Grady, co., Ok., U.S.	C4	113
Graettinger, Ia., U.S.	A3	92
Grafton, Austl.	E10	50
Grafton, Il., U.S.	E3	90
Grafton, Ma., U.S.	B4	98
Grafton, N.D., U.S.	A8	111
Grafton, Oh., U.S.	A3	112
Grafton, Va., U.S.	h15	123
Grafton, W.V., U.S.	B4	125
Grafton, Wi., U.S.	E6	126
Grafton, co., N.H., U.S.	C3	106
Grafton, Cape, c., Austl.	C9	50
Graham, N.C., U.S.	A3	110
Graham, Tx., U.S.	C3	120
Graham, co., Az., U.S.	E5	80
Graham, co., Ks., U.S.	C4	93
Graham, co., N.C., U.S.	f9	110
Graham, Lake, res., Tx., U.S.	C3	120
Graham, Mount, mtn., Az., U.S.	E6	80
Graham Island, i., B.C., Can.	C1	69
Graham Lake, l., Me., U.S.	D4	96
Graham Moore, Cape, c., N.W. Ter., Can.	B17	66
Grahamstown, S. Afr.	H5	44
Grahn, Ky., U.S.	B6	94
Grainger, co., Tn., U.S.	C10	119
Grain Valley, Mo., U.S.	B3	102
Grajaú, Braz.	E9	54
Gramat, Fr.	H8	10
Grambling, La., U.S.	B3	95
Gramercy, La., U.S.	h10	95
Grammichele, Italy	L9	14
Grampian Mountains, mts., Scot., U.K.	E8	7
Granada, Col.	F6	58
Granada, Nic.	I5	64
Granada, Spain	H8	12
Granard, Ire.	H5	7
Granbury, Tx., U.S.	C4	120
Granby, Que., Can.	D5	74
Granby, Co., U.S.	A5	83
Granby, Ct., U.S.	B4	84
Granby, Mo., U.S.	E3	102
Granby, Lake, res., Co., U.S.	A5	83
Gran Canaria, i., Spain	C2	42
Gran Chaco, pl., S.A.	A4	56
Grand, co., Co., U.S.	A4	83
Grand, co., Ut., U.S.	E6	121
Grand, stm., Ont., Can.	D4	73
Grand, stm., Mi., U.S.	E5	99
Grand, stm., Mo., U.S.	A3	102
Grand, stm., Oh., U.S.	A4	112
Grand, stm., S.D., U.S.	B4	118
Grandas, Spain	B5	12
Grand Bahama, i., Bah.	A8	64
Grand Bank, Newf., Can.	E4	72
Grand-Bassam, I.C.	G5	42
Grand Bay, N.B., Can.	D3	71
Grand Bay, Al., U.S.	E1	78
Grand Bend, Ont., Can.	D3	73
Grand Blanc, Mi., U.S.	F7	99
Grand Caillou, La., U.S.	E5	95
Grand Canal, Ire.	H5	7
Grand Canal see Da Yunhe, China	E10	26
Grand Canyon, Az., U.S.	A3	80
Grand Canyon, val., Az., U.S.	A3	80
Grand Canyon National Park, Az., U.S.	B3	80
Grand Cayman, i., Cay. Is.	E7	64
Grand Centre, Alta., Can.	B5	68
Grand Coteau, La., U.S.	D3	95
Grand Coulee, Wa., U.S.	B6	124
Grand Coulee Dam, Wa., U.S.	B6	124
Grande, stm., Bol.	G6	54
Grande, stm., Braz.	E3	57
Grande, Bahía, b., Arg.	G3	56
Grande, Boca, mth., Ven.	C12	58
Grande, Ilha, i., Braz.	G6	57
Grande, Ilha, i., Braz.	G1	57
Grande, Rio (Bravo del Norte), stm., N.A.	F7	76
Grande-Anse, N.B., Can.	B4	71
Grande Cache, Alta., Can.	C1	68
Grande Comore, i., Com.	D8	44
Grande de Matagalpa, stm., Nic.	H5	64
Grande de Santiago, Río, stm., Mex.	G7	62
Grande do Gurupá, Ilha, i., Braz.	D8	54
Grande-Entrée, Que., Can.	B8	71
Grande Prairie, Alta., Can.	B1	68
Grand Erg de Bilma, des., Niger	E8	42
Grand Erg Occidental, des., Alg.	B6	42
Grand Erg Oriental, des., Alg.	B7	42
Grande rivière de la Baleine, stm., Que., Can.	g11	74
Grande Ronde, stm., U.S.	C8	124
Grandes, Salinas, pl., Arg.	B4	56
Grandes-Bergeronnes, Que., Can.	A8	74
Grande-Terre, i., Guad.	F17	64
Grand Falls (Grand-Sault), N.B., Can.	B2	71
Grand Falls, Newf., Can.	D4	72
Grand Falls, wtfl, Me., U.S.	C5	96
Grandfather Mountain, mtn., N.C., U.S.	A1	110
Grandfield, Ok., U.S.	C3	113
Grand Forks, B.C., Can.	E8	69
Grand Forks, N.D., U.S.	B8	111
Grand Forks, co., N.D., U.S.	B8	111
Grand Forks Air Force Base, mil., N.D., U.S.	B8	111
Grand-Fougeray, Fr.	E5	10
Grand Harbour, N.B., Can.	E3	71
Grand Haven, Mi., U.S.	E4	99
Grand Island, Ne., U.S.	D7	104
Grand Island, i., La., U.S.	D6	95
Grand Island, i., Mi., U.S.	B4	99
Grand Isle, La., U.S.	E6	95
Grand Isle, co., Vt., U.S.	B2	122
Grand Isle, i., La., U.S.	E6	95
Grand Junction, Co., U.S.	B2	83
Grand Junction, Ia., U.S.	B3	92
Grand Lake, l., N.B., Can.	D3	71
Grand Lake, l., Newf., Can.	D3	72
Grand Lake, l., La., U.S.	E3	95
Grand Lake, l., La., U.S.	E6	95
Grand Lake, l., Mi., U.S.	C7	99
Grand Lake, l., Oh., U.S.	B1	112
Grand Lake Matagamon, l., Me., U.S.	B4	96
Grand Lake Seboeis, l., Me., U.S.	B4	96
Grand Ledge, Mi., U.S.	F6	99
Grand Manan Island, i., N.B., Can.	E3	71
Grand Marais, Mn., U.S.	k9	100
Grand Meadow, Mn., U.S.	G6	100
Grand-Mère, Que., Can.	C5	74
Grand Mound, Ia., U.S.	C7	92
Grand Portage Indian Reservation, Mn., U.S.	k10	100
Grand Portage National Monument, Mn., U.S.	h10	100
Grand Prairie, Tx., U.S.	n10	120
Grand Rapids, Mi., U.S.	F5	99
Grand Rapids, Mn., U.S.	C5	100
Grand Rapids, Oh., U.S.	f6	112
Grand Rivière de la Baleine, stm., Que., Can.	E17	66
Grand-Saint-Bernard, Tunnel du, Eur.	G14	10
Grand Saline, Tx., U.S.	C5	120
Grand Terre Islands, is., La., U.S.	E6	95
Grand Teton, mtn., Wy., U.S.	C2	127
Grand Teton National Park, Wy., U.S.	C2	127
Grand Tower, Il., U.S.	F4	90
Grand Traverse, co., Mi., U.S.	D5	99
Grand Traverse Bay, b., Mi., U.S.	C5	99
Grand Turk, T./C. Is.	D12	64
Grand Valley, Ont., Can.	D4	73
Grandview, Man., Can.	D1	70
Grandview, In., U.S.	I4	91
Grandview, Mo., U.S.	C3	102
Grandview, Wa., U.S.	C6	124
Grandview Heights, Oh., U.S.	m10	112
Grandville, Mi., U.S.	F5	99
Grandy, N.C., U.S.	A7	110
Granger, In., U.S.	A5	91
Granger, Ia., U.S.	C4	92
Granger, Tx., U.S.	D4	120
Granger, Wa., U.S.	C5	124
Grangeville, Id., U.S.	D2	89
Granisle, B.C., Can.	B4	69
Granite, Ok., U.S.	C2	113
Granite, co., Mt., U.S.	D3	103
Granite City, Il., U.S.	E3	90
Granite Falls, Mn., U.S.	F3	100
Granite Falls, N.C., U.S.	B1	110
Granite Falls, Wa., U.S.	A4	124
Granite Lake, res., Newf., Can.	D3	72
Granite Mountain, mtn., Ak., U.S.	B7	79
Granite Mountains, mts., Az., U.S.	E2	80
Granite Mountains, mts., Wy., U.S.	D5	127
Granite Pass, Wy., U.S.	B5	127
Granite Peak, mtn., Mt., U.S.	E7	103
Granite Peak, mtn., Nv., U.S.	B4	105
Granite Peak, mtn., Nv., U.S.	C2	105
Granite Peak, mtn., Ut., U.S.	C2	121
Granite Peak, mtn., Ut., U.S.	E3	121
Granite Peak, mtn., Wy., U.S.	D4	127
Granite Quarry, N.C., U.S.	B2	110
Granite Range, mts., Nv., U.S.	C2	105
Graniteville, S.C., U.S.	D4	117
Graniteville, Vt., U.S.	C4	122
Granollers, Spain	D14	12
Grant, Al., U.S.	A3	78
Grant, Mi., U.S.	E5	99
Grant, Ne., U.S.	D4	104
Grant, co., Ar., U.S.	C3	81
Grant, co., In., U.S.	D6	91
Grant, co., Ks., U.S.	E2	93
Grant, co., Ky., U.S.	B5	94
Grant, co., La., U.S.	C3	95
Grant, co., Mn., U.S.	E2	100
Grant, co., Ne., U.S.	C4	104
Grant, co., N.M., U.S.	E1	108
Grant, co., N.D., U.S.	C4	111
Grant, co., Ok., U.S.	A4	113
Grant, co., Or., U.S.	C7	114
Grant, co., S.D., U.S.	B8	118
Grant, co., Wa., U.S.	B6	124
Grant, co., W.V., U.S.	B5	125
Grant, co., Wi., U.S.	F3	126
Grant, Mount, mtn., Nv., U.S.	E3	105
Grant City, Mo., U.S.	A3	102
Grantham, Eng., U.K.	I12	7
Grant Park, Il., U.S.	B6	90
Grant Range, mts., Nv., U.S.	E6	105
Grants, N.M., U.S.	B2	108
Grantsburg, Wi., U.S.	C1	126
Grants Pass, Or., U.S.	E3	114
Grantsville, Ut., U.S.	C3	121
Grantsville, W.V., U.S.	C3	125
Grant Town, W.V., U.S.	B4	125
Grantville, Ga., U.S.	C2	87
Granville, Fr.	D5	10
Granville, Il., U.S.	B4	90
Granville, N.Y., U.S.	B7	109
Granville, Oh., U.S.	B3	112
Granville, W.V., U.S.	h11	125
Granville, co., N.C., U.S.	A4	110
Granville Lake, l., Man., Can.	A1	70
Granvin, Nor.	F6	6
Grapeland, Tx., U.S.	D5	120
Grapeview, Wa., U.S.	B3	124
Grapevine, Tx., U.S.	C4	120
Grapevine Lake, res., Tx., U.S.	n9	120
Grapevine Peak, mtn., Nv., U.S.	G4	105
Gras, Lac de, l., N.W. Ter., Can.	D10	66
Grasonville, Md., U.S.	C5	97
Grass, stm., Man., Can.	B2	70
Grass, stm., N.Y., U.S.	f9	109
Grasse, Fr.	I13	10
Grass Lake, Il., U.S.	h8	90
Grass Lake, Mi., U.S.	F6	99
Grass Lake, l., Il., U.S.	h8	90
Grass Valley, Ca., U.S.	C3	82
Grassy Brook, stm., Vt., U.S.	E3	122
Grassy Lake, l., La., U.S.	k9	95
Grates Point, c., Newf., Can.	D5	72
Gratiot, co., Mi., U.S.	E6	99
Gratis, Oh., U.S.	C1	112
Grave Creek, stm., W.V., U.S.	g8	125
Gravelly Branch, stm., De., U.S.	F4	85
Gravelly Range, mts., Mt., U.S.	E4	103
Gravenhurst, Ont., Can.	C5	73
Grave Peak, mtn., Id., U.S.	C4	89
Graves, co., Ky., U.S.	f9	94
Gravette, Ar., U.S.	A1	81
Gravina in Puglia, Italy	I11	14
Gray, Fr.	E12	10
Gray, Ga., U.S.	C3	87
Gray, Ky., U.S.	D5	94
Gray, La., U.S.	k10	95
Gray, Me., U.S.	g7	96
Gray, co., Ks., U.S.	E3	93
Gray, co., Tx., U.S.	B2	120
Grayback Mountain, mtn., Or., U.S.	E3	114
Gray Court, S.C., U.S.	B3	117
Grayland, Wa., U.S.	C1	124
Grayling, Mi., U.S.	D6	99
Graylyn Crest, De., U.S.	A3	85
Grays Harbor, co., Wa., U.S.	B2	124
Grays Harbor, b., Wa., U.S.	C1	124
Grayslake, Il., U.S.	A5	90
Grays Lake, sw., Id., U.S.	F7	89
Grayson, Ky., U.S.	B7	94
Grayson, co., Ky., U.S.	C3	94
Grayson, co., Tx., U.S.	C4	120
Grayson, co., Va., U.S.	D1	123
Grayson Lake, res., Ky., U.S.	B7	94
Grays Peak, mtn., Co., U.S.	B5	83
Gray Summit, Mo., U.S.	g12	102
Graysville, Al., U.S.	f7	78
Graysville, Tn., U.S.	D8	119
Grayville, Il., U.S.	E5	90
Graz, Aus.	H15	8
Gr'azi, U.S.S.R.	I22	22
Great Abaco, i., Bah.	A9	64
Great Artesian Basin, Austl.	D8	50
Great Australian Bight, Austl.	F5	50
Great Averill Pond, l., Vt., U.S.	B5	122
Great Barrier Reef, rf., Austl.	C9	50
Great Barrington, Ma., U.S.	B1	98
Great Basin National Park, Nv., U.S.	E7	105
Great Bay, b., N.H., U.S.	D5	106
Great Bay, b., N.J., U.S.	D4	107
Great Bear Lake, l., N.W. Ter., Can.	C9	66
Great Bend, Ks., U.S.	D5	93
Great Captain Island, i., Ct., U.S.	F1	84
Great Channel, strt., Asia	K3	34
Great Dismal Swamp, sw., U.S.	D6	123
Great Divide Basin, Wy., U.S.	E4	127
Great Dividing Range, mts., Austl.	D9	50
Great East Lake, l., U.S.	C5	106
Great Egg Harbor, stm., N.J., U.S.	D3	107
Greater Antilles, is., N.A.	D10	64
Greater Sunda Islands, is., Asia	F4	32
Great Exuma, i., Bah.	C10	64
Great Falls, Mt., U.S.	C5	103
Great Falls, S.C., U.S.	B6	117
Great Falls, wtfl, Md., U.S.	B3	97
Great Falls Dam, Tn., U.S.	D6	119
Great Guana Cay, i., Bah.	B9	64
Great Himalaya Range, mts., Asia	F10	38
Greathouse Peak, mtn., Mt., U.S.	D7	103
Great Inagua, i., Bah.	D11	64
Great Indian Desert (Thar Desert), des., Asia	G4	38
Great Island, spit, Ma., U.S.	C7	98
Great Island, i., N.C., U.S.	B6	110
Great Karroo, plat., S. Afr.	H4	44
Great Lakes Naval Training Center, mil., Il., U.S.	h9	90
Great Miami, stm., U.S.	C1	112
Great Misery Island, i., Ma., U.S.	f12	98
Great Moose Lake, l., Me., U.S.	D3	96
Great Neck, N.Y., U.S.	h13	109
Great Nicobar, i., India	K2	34
Great Pee Dee, stm., U.S.	D9	117
Great Plain of the Koukdjuak, pl., N.W. Ter., Can.	C18	66
Great Plains, pl., N.A.	E10	61
Great Point, c., Ma., U.S.	D7	98
Great Ruaha, stm., Tan.	C7	44
Great Sacandaga Lake, l., N.Y., U.S.	C6	109
Great Salt Lake, l., Ut., U.S.	B3	121
Great Salt Lake Desert, des., Ut., U.S.	C2	121
Great Salt Plains Lake, res., Ok., U.S.	A3	113
Great Salt Pond, b., R.I., U.S.	h7	116
Great Sand Dunes National Monument, Co., U.S.	D5	83
Great Sandy Desert, des., Austl.	D4	50
Great Slave Lake, l., N.W. Ter., Can.	D10	66
Great Smoky Mountains, mts., U.S.	B8	119
Great Smoky Mountains National Park, U.S.	B8	119
Great Swamp, sw., R.I., U.S.	F3	116
Great Victoria Desert, des., Austl.	E5	50
Great Village, N.S., Can.	D6	71
Great Wass Island, i., Me., U.S.	D5	96
Great Yarmouth, Eng., U.K.	I14	7
Greece, N.Y., U.S.	B3	109
Greece, ctry., Eur.	H12	4
Greeley, Co., U.S.	A6	83
Greeley, Pa., U.S.	D12	115
Greeley, co., Ks., U.S.	D2	93
Greeley, co., Ne., U.S.	C7	104
Green, Or., U.S.	D3	114
Green, co., Ky., U.S.	C4	94
Green, co., Wi., U.S.	F4	126
Green, stm., U.S.	D5	76
Green, stm., U.S.	A1	83
Green, stm., U.S.	F3	122
Green, stm., Il., U.S.	B4	90
Green, stm., Ky., U.S.	C2	94
Green, stm., Wa., U.S.	B3	124
Green Acres, De., U.S.	h8	85
Greenacres, Wa., U.S.	B8	124
Greenacres City, Fl., U.S.	F6	86
Greenback, Tn., U.S.	D9	119
Green Bay, Wi., U.S.	D6	126
Green Bay, b., U.S.	D3	99
Greenbelt, Md., U.S.	C4	97
Greenbriar, Va., U.S.	g12	123
Greenbrier, Ar., U.S.	B3	81
Green Brier, Tn., U.S.	A5	119
Greenbrier, co., W.V., U.S.	D4	125
Greenbrier, stm., W.V., U.S.	D4	125
Greenbush, Mn., U.S.	B2	100
Greencastle, In., U.S.	E4	91
Greencastle, Pa., U.S.	G6	115
Green City, Mo., U.S.	A5	102
Green Cove Springs, Fl., U.S.	C5	86
Greendale, In., U.S.	F8	91
Greendale, Wi., U.S.	F6	126
Greene, Ia., U.S.	B5	92
Greene, N.Y., U.S.	C5	109
Greene, co., Al., U.S.	C1	78
Greene, co., Ar., U.S.	A5	81
Greene, co., Ga., U.S.	C3	87
Greene, co., Il., U.S.	D3	90
Greene, co., In., U.S.	F4	91
Greene, co., Ia., U.S.	B3	92
Greene, co., Ms., U.S.	D5	101
Greene, co., Mo., U.S.	D4	102
Greene, co., N.Y., U.S.	C6	109
Greene, co., N.C., U.S.	B5	110
Greene, co., Oh., U.S.	C2	112
Greene, co., Pa., U.S.	G1	115
Greene, co., Tn., U.S.	C11	119
Greene, co., Va., U.S.	B4	123
Greeneville, Tn., U.S.	C11	119
Green Fall, stm., U.S.	F1	116
Greenfield, Ca., U.S.	D3	82
Greenfield, Il., U.S.	D3	90
Greenfield, In., U.S.	E6	91
Greenfield, Ia., U.S.	C3	92
Greenfield, Ma., U.S.	A2	98
Greenfield, Mo., U.S.	D4	102
Greenfield, N.H., U.S.	E3	106
Greenfield, Oh., U.S.	C2	112
Greenfield, Tn., U.S.	A3	119
Greenfield, Wi., U.S.	n11	126
Greenfield Plaza, Ia., U.S.	e8	92
Green Forest, Ar., U.S.	A2	81
Green Harbor, Ma., U.S.	B6	98
Green Hill Pond, l., R.I., U.S.	G3	116
Greenhills, Oh., U.S.	n12	112
Green Lake, Wi., U.S.	E5	126
Green Lake, co., Wi., U.S.	E4	126
Green Lake, l., Me., U.S.	D4	96
Green Lake, l., Wi., U.S.	E5	126
Greenland, Ar., U.S.	B1	81
Greenland, N.H., U.S.	D5	106
Greenland, dep., N.A.	B16	61
Greenland Sea	B13	128
Greenlee, co., Az., U.S.	D6	80
Green Lookout Mountain, mtn., Wa., U.S.	D3	124
Green Mountain, mtn., Wy., U.S.	D5	127
Green Mountain Reservoir, res., Co., U.S.	B4	83
Green Mountains, mts., Vt., U.S.	F2	122
Greenock, Scot., U.K.	F8	7
Greenock, Pa., U.S.	F2	115
Green Peter Lake, res., Or., U.S.	C4	114
Green Pond, Al., U.S.	B2	78
Green Pond, l., N.J., U.S.	A4	107
Greenport, N.Y., U.S.	m16	109
Green River, Ut., U.S.	E5	121
Green River, Wy., U.S.	E3	127
Green River Lake, res., Ky., U.S.	C4	94
Green River Lock and Dam, U.S.	I2	91
Green River Reservoir, res., Vt., U.S.	B3	122
Green Rock, Il., U.S.	B3	90
Greensboro, Al., U.S.	C2	78
Greensboro, Ga., U.S.	C3	87
Greensboro, Md., U.S.	C6	97
Greensboro, N.C., U.S.	A3	110
Greensburg, In., U.S.	F7	91
Greensburg, Ks., U.S.	E4	93
Greensburg, Ky., U.S.	C4	94
Greensburg, Pa., U.S.	F2	115
Greens Peak, mtn., Az., U.S.	C6	80
Green Springs, Oh., U.S.	A2	112
Greensville, co., Va., U.S.	D5	123
Green Swamp, sw., N.C., U.S.	C4	110
Greentown, In., U.S.	D6	91
Greenup, Il., U.S.	D5	90
Greenup, Ky., U.S.	B7	94
Greenup, co., Ky., U.S.	B7	94
Green Valley, Az., U.S.	F5	80
Greenview, Il., U.S.	C4	90
Greenville, Lib.	G4	42
Greenville, Al., U.S.	D3	78
Greenville, Ca., U.S.	B3	82
Greenville, De., U.S.	A3	85
Greenville, Ga., U.S.	C2	87
Greenville, Il., U.S.	E4	90
Greenville, Ky., U.S.	C2	94
Greenville, Me., U.S.	C3	96
Greenville, Mi., U.S.	E5	99
Greenville, Ms., U.S.	B2	101
Greenville, N.H., U.S.	E3	106
Greenville, N.C., U.S.	B5	110
Greenville, Oh., U.S.	B1	112
Greenville, Pa., U.S.	D1	115
Greenville, R.I., U.S.	C3	116
Greenville, S.C., U.S.	B3	117
Greenville, Tx., U.S.	C4	120
Greenville, co., S.C., U.S.	B3	117
Greenville Creek, stm., Oh., U.S.	B1	112
Greenville Junction, Me., U.S.	C3	96
Greenwich, Ct., U.S.	E1	84
Greenwich, N.Y., U.S.	B7	109
Greenwich, Oh., U.S.	A3	112
Greenwich Bay, b., R.I., U.S.	D4	116
Greenwich Point, c., Ct., U.S.	E1	84
Greenwood, B.C., Can.	E8	69
Greenwood, Ar., U.S.	B1	81
Greenwood, De., U.S.	E3	85
Greenwood, In., U.S.	E5	91
Greenwood, La., U.S.	B2	95
Greenwood, Ms., U.S.	B3	101
Greenwood, Mo., U.S.	k11	102
Greenwood, Pa., U.S.	E5	115
Greenwood, S.C., U.S.	C3	117
Greenwood, Wi., U.S.	D3	126
Greenwood, co., Ks., U.S.	E7	93
Greenwood, co., S.C., U.S.	C3	117
Greenwood, Lake, res., In., U.S.	G4	91
Greenwood, Lake, res., S.C., U.S.	C4	117
Greenwood Lake, N.Y., U.S.	D6	109
Greenwood Lake, l., U.S.	A4	107
Greenwood Lake, l., Mn., U.S.	C7	100
Greer, S.C., U.S.	B3	117
Greer, co., Ok., U.S.	C2	113
Greers Ferry Lake, res., Ar., U.S.	B3	81
Greeson, Lake, res., Ar., U.S.	C2	81
Gregg, co., Tx., U.S.	C5	120
Gregory, S.D., U.S.	D6	118
Gregory, co., S.D., U.S.	D6	118
Greifswald, Ger.	A13	8
Greilickville, Mi., U.S.	D5	99
Greiz, Ger.	E12	8
Grenada, Ms., U.S.	B4	101
Grenada, co., Ms., U.S.	B4	101
Grenada, ctry., N.A.	H17	64
Grenada Lake, res., Ms., U.S.	B4	101
Grenadine Islands, is., N.A.	H17	64
Grenchen, Switz.	E14	10
Grenoble, Fr.	G12	10
Grenville, Que., Can.	D3	74
Grenville, Cape, c., Austl.	B8	50
Grenville, Point, c., Wa., U.S.	B1	124
Gresham, Or., U.S.	B4	114
Gresik, Indon.	m16	33a
Gretna, Man., Can.	E3	70
Gretna, Fl., U.S.	B2	86
Gretna, La., U.S.	E5	95
Gretna, Ne., U.S.	C9	104
Gretna, Va., U.S.	D3	123
Greven, Ger.	C7	8
Grevená, Grc.	I5	16
Grevesmühlen, Ger.	B11	8
Grey, stm., Newf., Can.	E3	72
Greybull, Wy., U.S.	B4	127
Greybull, stm., Wy., U.S.	B4	127
Greylock, Mount, mtn., Ma., U.S.	A1	98

Name	Map Ref	Page
Greymouth, N.Z.	**E3**	52
Greys, stm., Wy., U.S.	**C2**	127
Gridley, Ca., U.S.	**C3**	82
Gridley, Il., U.S.	**C5**	90
Griffin, Ga., U.S.	**C2**	87
Griffiss Air Force Base, mil., N.Y., U.S.	**B5**	109
Griffith, Austl.	**F9**	50
Griffith, In., U.S.	**A3**	91
Grifton, N.C., U.S.	**B5**	110
Griggs, co., N.D., U.S.	**B7**	111
Griggsville, Il., U.S.	**D3**	90
Grik, Malay.	**L6**	34
Grimes, Ia., U.S.	**C4**	92
Grimes, co., Tx., U.S.	**D4**	120
Grimmen, Ger.	**A13**	8
Grimsby, Ont., Can.	**D5**	73
Grimsby, Eng., U.K.	**H12**	7
Grimselpass, Switz.	**F15**	10
Grimshaw, Alta., Can.	**A2**	68
Grimsley, Tn., U.S.	**C9**	119
Grimstad, Nor.	**G7**	6
Grindall Creek, Va., U.S.	**n18**	123
Grinnell, Ia., U.S.	**C5**	92
Grinnell Peninsula, pen., N.W. Ter., Can.	**A14**	66
Gris-Nez, Cap, c., Fr.	**B8**	10
Grissom Air Force Base, mil., In., U.S.	**C5**	91
Griswold, Ia., U.S.	**C2**	92
Grizzly Mountain, mtn., Id., U.S.	**B2**	89
Grizzly Mountain, mtn., Or., U.S.	**C6**	114
Grizzly Mountain, mtn., Wa., U.S.	**A7**	124
Groais Island, i., Newf., Can.	**C4**	72
Grodno, U.S.S.R.	**H6**	22
Groesbeck, Tx., U.S.	**D4**	120
Grombalia, Tun.	**M5**	14
Gronau, Ger.	**C6**	8
Grong, Nor.	**D9**	6
Groningen, Neth.	**B6**	8
Groom Lake, l., Nv., U.S.	**F6**	105
Groom Range, mts., Nv., U.S.	**F6**	105
Groote Eylandt, i., Austl.	**B7**	50
Grootfontein, Nmb.	**E3**	44
Gros Morne National Park, Newf., Can.	**D3**	72
Grosse Isle Naval Air Station, mil., Mi., U.S.	**p15**	99
Grossenhain, Ger.	**D13**	8
Grosse Pointe, Mi., U.S.	**p16**	99
Grosse Pointe Park, Mi., U.S.	**p16**	99
Grosse Pointe Woods, Mi., U.S.	**p16**	99
Grosseto, Italy	**G6**	14
Grossglockner, mtn., Aus.	**H12**	8
Grossmont, Ca., U.S.	**o16**	82
Gros Ventre, stm., Wy., U.S.	**C2**	127
Gros Ventre Range, mts., Wy., U.S.	**C2**	127
Groswater Bay, b., Newf., Can.	**F21**	66
Groton, Ct., U.S.	**D7**	84
Groton, N.Y., U.S.	**C4**	109
Groton, S.D., U.S.	**B7**	118
Groton Long Point, Ct., U.S.	**D7**	84
Grottaglie, Italy	**I12**	14
Grottaminarda, Italy	**H10**	14
Grottoes, Va., U.S.	**B4**	123
Grouse Creek, stm., Ut., U.S.	**B2**	121
Grouse Creek Mountain, mtn., Id., U.S.	**E5**	89
Grove, Ok., U.S.	**A7**	113
Grove City, Fl., U.S.	**F4**	86
Grove City, Oh., U.S.	**C2**	112
Grove City, Pa., U.S.	**D1**	115
Grove Hill, Al., U.S.	**D2**	78
Groveland, Fl., U.S.	**D5**	86
Groveland, Ma., U.S.	**A5**	98
Grove Point, c., Md., U.S.	**B5**	97
Groveport, Oh., U.S.	**C3**	112
Grover City, Ca., U.S.	**E3**	82
Groves, Tx., U.S.	**E6**	120
Groveton, N.H., U.S.	**A3**	106
Groveton, Tx., U.S.	**D5**	120
Groveton, Va., U.S.	**g12**	123
Groveton Gardens, Va., U.S.	**B5**	123
Grovetown, Ga., U.S.	**C4**	87
Groveville, N.J., U.S.	**C3**	107
Growler Peak, mtn., Az., U.S.	**E2**	80
Groznyj, U.S.S.R.	**I7**	18
Grudziądz, Pol.	**B18**	8
Gruetli-Laager, Tn., U.S.	**D8**	119
Grulla, Tx., U.S.	**F3**	120
Grundy, Va., U.S.	**e9**	123
Grundy, co., Il., U.S.	**B5**	90
Grundy, co., Ia., U.S.	**B5**	92
Grundy, co., Mo., U.S.	**A4**	102
Grundy, co., Tn., U.S.	**D8**	119
Grundy Center, Ia., U.S.	**B5**	92
Grunthal, Man., Can.	**E3**	70
Gruver, Tx., U.S.	**A2**	120
Gruzinskaja Sovetskaja Socialističeskaja Respublika (Georgia), state, U.S.S.R.	**I6**	18
Guacanayabo, Golfo de, b., Cuba	**D9**	64
Guachochic, Mex.	**D6**	62
Guadalajara, Mex.	**G8**	62
Guadalajara, Spain	**E8**	12
Guadalcanal, i., Sol.Is.	**A11**	50
Guadalquivir, stm., Spain	**H6**	12
Guadalupe, Mex.	**E9**	62
Guadalupe, Az., U.S.	**m9**	80
Guadalupe, Ca., U.S.	**E3**	82
Guadalupe, co., N.M., U.S.	**C5**	108
Guadalupe, co., Tx., U.S.	**E4**	120
Guadalupe Garzarón, Mex.	**E9**	62
Guadalupe Mountains, mts., U.S.	**E5**	108
Guadalupe Mountains National Park, Tx., U.S.	**o12**	120
Guadalupe Peak, mtn., Tx., U.S.	**o12**	120
Guadeloupe, dep., N.A.	**F17**	64
Guadeloupe Passage, strt., N.A.	**F17**	64
Guadiana, stm., Eur.	**H4**	12
Guadix, Spain	**H8**	12
Guafo, Isla, i., Chile	**E2**	56
Guajará Mirim, Braz.	**F5**	54
Gualeguaychú, Arg.	**C5**	56
Gualicho, Salina, pl., Arg.	**E3**	56
Guam, dep., Oc.	**F22**	2
Guaminí, Arg.	**D4**	56
Guamo, Col.	**E5**	58
Guampí, Sierra de, mts., Ven.	**B5**	54
Guanaja, Isla de, i., Hond.	**F5**	64
Guanajuato, Mex.	**G9**	62
Guanambi, Braz.	**C7**	57
Guanare, Ven.	**C8**	58
Guanarito, Ven.	**C8**	58
Guanay, Cerro, mtn., Ven.	**E9**	58
Guane, Cuba	**C5**	64
Guang'an, China	**E8**	26
Guangdong, prov., China	**G9**	26
Guanghua, China	**E9**	26
Guangxi Zhuang Zizhiqu, prov., China	**G8**	26
Guangyuan, China	**E8**	26
Guangzhou (Canton), China	**L2**	28
Guano Lake, l., Or., U.S.	**E7**	114
Guantánamo, Cuba	**D10**	64
Guanxian, China	**E7**	26
Guápiles, C.R.	**I6**	64
Guaporé (Iténez), stm., S.A.	**F6**	54
Guaqui, Bol.	**G5**	54
Guarabira, Braz.	**E11**	54
Guaranda, Ec.	**H3**	58
Guarapuava, Braz.	**B6**	56
Guaratinguetá, Braz.	**G6**	57
Guarda, Port.	**E4**	12
Guardo, Spain	**C7**	12
Guárico, Embalse del, res., Ven.	**C9**	58
Guarulhos, Braz.	**G5**	57
Guarus, Braz.	**F8**	57
Guasave, Mex.	**E5**	62
Guasdualito, Ven.	**D7**	58
Guatemala, Guat.	**G2**	64
Guatemala, ctry., N.A.	**G2**	64
Guaviare, stm., Col.	**F8**	58
Guaxupé, Braz.	**F5**	57
Guayama, P.R.	**F14**	64
Guayaquil, Ec.	**I3**	58
Guayaquil, Golfo de, b., S.A.	**I2**	58
Guaymallén, Arg.	**C3**	56
Guaymas, Mex.	**D4**	62
Gubbio, Italy	**F7**	14
Guchengzi, China	**D7**	26
Güdalūr, India	**G4**	37
Gudiyāttam, India	**F5**	37
Güdūr, India	**E5**	37
Guebwiller, Fr.	**E14**	10
Guelma, Alg.	**A7**	42
Guelph, Ont., Can.	**D4**	73
Guérande, Fr.	**E4**	10
Guéret, Fr.	**F8**	10
Guernsey, Wy., U.S.	**D8**	127
Guernsey, co., Oh., U.S.	**B4**	112
Guernsey, dep., Eur.	**C4**	10
Gueydan, La., U.S.	**D3**	95
Guga, U.S.S.R.	**G21**	20
Guibes, Nmb.	**G3**	44
Güicán, Col.	**D6**	58
Guichen, Fr.	**E5**	10
Guiding, China	**A9**	34
Guijuelo, Spain	**E6**	12
Guilford, Ct., U.S.	**D5**	84
Guilford, Me., U.S.	**C3**	96
Guilford, co., N.C., U.S.	**A3**	110
Guilin (Kweilin), China	**B11**	34
Guillaumes, Fr.	**H13**	10
Guimarães, Port.	**D3**	12
Guin, Al., U.S.	**B2**	78
Guinea, ctry., Afr.	**F3**	42
Guinea, Gulf of, b., Afr.	**H6**	42
Guinea-Bissau, ctry., Afr.	**F2**	42
Güines, Cuba	**C6**	64
Guingamp, Fr.	**D3**	10
Güira de Melena, Cuba	**C6**	64
Guiratinga, Braz.	**G8**	54
Güiria, Ven.	**B11**	58
Guixian, China	**C10**	34
Guiyang (Kweiyang), China	**A9**	34
Guizhou, prov., China	**F8**	26
Gujarat, state, India	**I4**	38
Gūjar Khān, Pak.	**D5**	38
Gujrānwāla, Pak.	**D6**	38
Gujrāt, Pak.	**D6**	38
Gulbarga, India	**D4**	37
Guledagudda, India	**D3**	37
Gulf, co., Fl., U.S.	**C1**	86
Gulf Gate Estates, Fl., U.S.	**E4**	86
Gulf Islands National Seashore, U.S.	**E5**	101
Gulfport, Fl., U.S.	**E4**	86
Gulfport, Ms., U.S.	**E4**	101
Gulf Shores, Al., U.S.	**E2**	78
Gull Island, i., N.C., U.S.	**B7**	110
Gullivan Bay, b., Fl., U.S.	**G5**	86
Gull Lake, l., Alta., Can.	**C4**	68
Gull Lake, l., Mn., U.S.	**D4**	100
Güllük, Tur.	**L11**	16
Gülpınar, Tur.	**J10**	16
Gulu, Ug.	**H12**	42
Gumal (Gowmal), stm., Asia	**D3**	38
Gumboro, De., U.S.	**G4**	85
Gummersbach, Ger.	**D7**	8
Guna, India	**H7**	38
Gunisao, stm., Man., Can.	**C3**	70
Gunnarn, Swe.	**D11**	6
Gunnison, Co., U.S.	**C4**	83
Gunnison, Ms., U.S.	**B3**	101
Gunnison, Ut., U.S.	**D4**	121
Gunnison, co., Co., U.S.	**C3**	83
Gunnison, stm., Co., U.S.	**C2**	83
Gunnison, Mount, mtn., Co., U.S.	**C3**	83
Gunpowder Neck, c., Md., U.S.	**B5**	97
Gunpowder River, b., Md., U.S.	**B5**	97
Guntakal, India	**E4**	37
Gunter Air Force Base, mil., Al., U.S.	**C3**	78
Guntersville, Al., U.S.	**A3**	78
Guntersville Lake, res., Al., U.S.	**A3**	78
Guntown, Ms., U.S.	**A5**	101
Guntūr, India	**D6**	37
Gunungsitoli, Indon.	**N4**	34
Günzburg, Ger.	**G10**	8
Gunzenhausen, Ger.	**F10**	8
Gurdāspur, India	**D6**	38
Gurdon, Ar., U.S.	**D2**	81
Guri, Embalse, res., Ven.	**D11**	58
Gurjev, U.S.S.R.	**H8**	18
Gurley, Al., U.S.	**A3**	78
Gurnee, Il., U.S.	**h9**	90
Gurnet Point, c., Ma., U.S.	**B6**	98
Gurupi, Braz.	**F9**	54
Gurupi, stm., Braz.	**D9**	54
Gusau, Nig.	**F7**	42
Gus'-Chrustal'nyj, U.S.S.R.	**F23**	22
Gusev, U.S.S.R.	**G5**	22
Gushi, China	**C4**	28
Gushikawa, Japan	**y27**	31b
Gusinoozersk, U.S.S.R.	**G15**	20
Guspini, Italy	**J3**	14
Gustav Holm, Kap, c., Grnld.	**C26**	66
Gustine, Ca., U.S.	**D3**	82
Güstrow, Ger.	**B12**	8
Gütersloh, Ger.	**D8**	8
Guthrie, Ky., U.S.	**D2**	94
Guthrie, Ok., U.S.	**B4**	113
Guthrie, W.V., U.S.	**m12**	125
Guthrie, co., Ia., U.S.	**C3**	92
Guthrie Center, Ia., U.S.	**C3**	92
Guttenberg, Ia., U.S.	**B6**	92
Guttenberg, N.J., U.S.	**h8**	107
Guyana, ctry., S.A.	**B7**	54
Guyandotte, stm., W.V., U.S.	**C2**	125
Guymon, Ok., U.S.	**e9**	113
Guysborough, N.S., Can.	**D8**	71
Guyton, Ga., U.S.	**D5**	87
Güzelyurt Körfezi, b., N. Cyp.	**B3**	40
Gwādar, Pak.	**D1**	36
Gwai, Zimb.	**E5**	44
Gwalior, India	**G8**	38
Gwanda, Zimb.	**F5**	44
Gweru, Zimb.	**E5**	44
Gwinhurst, De., U.S.	**h8**	85
Gwinn, Mi., U.S.	**B3**	99
Gwinner, N.D., U.S.	**C8**	111
Gwinnett, co., Ga., U.S.	**C2**	87
Gwydyr Bay, b., Ak., U.S.	**A10**	79
Gwynns Falls, stm., Md., U.S.	**g10**	97
Gympie, Austl.	**E10**	50
Gyöngyös, Hung.	**H19**	8
Győr, Hung.	**H17**	8
Gypsum, Co., U.S.	**B4**	83
H		
Haakon, co., S.D., U.S.	**C4**	118
Haapajärvi, Fin.	**E15**	6
Haapamäki, Fin.	**E15**	6
Haar, Ger.	**G11**	8
Haarlem, Neth.	**C4**	8
Haast, N.Z.	**E2**	52
Habersham, co., Ga., U.S.	**B3**	87
Habiganj, Bngl.	**H14**	38
Hachijō-jima, i., Japan	**E14**	26
Hachinohe, Japan	**B14**	30
Hachiōji, Japan	**G12**	30
Hackberry, La., U.S.	**E2**	95
Hackensack, N.J., U.S.	**B4**	107
Hackensack, stm., N.J., U.S.	**h8**	107
Hackettstown, N.J., U.S.	**B3**	107
Hackleburg, Al., U.S.	**A2**	78
Hadd, Ra's al-, c., Oman	**D6**	46
Haddam, Ct., U.S.	**D5**	84
Haddock, Ga., U.S.	**C3**	87
Haddonfield, N.J., U.S.	**D2**	107
Haddon Heights, N.J., U.S.	**D2**	107
Hadejia, stm., Nig.	**F8**	42
Ḥadera, Isr.	**C4**	40
Haderslev, Den.	**I7**	6
Hadīyah, Sau. Ar.	**C2**	46
Hadjeb el Aïoun, Tun.	**N4**	14
Hadley Bay, b., N.W. Ter., Can.	**B11**	66
Hadley Lake, l., Me., U.S.	**D5**	96
Hadlock, Wa., U.S.	**A3**	124
Ha Dong, Viet.	**D8**	34
Hadramawt, reg., Yemen	**E4**	46
Haeju, N. Kor.	**D12**	26
Hāfizābād, Pak.	**D5**	38
Hafun, Ras, c., Som.	**F5**	46
Hagan, Ga., U.S.	**D5**	87
Hagemeister Island, i., Ak., U.S.	**D7**	79
Hagen, Ger.	**D7**	8
Hagerman, Id., U.S.	**G4**	89
Hagerman, N.M., U.S.	**D5**	108
Hagerstown, In., U.S.	**E7**	91
Hagerstown, Md., U.S.	**A2**	97
Hagfors, Swe.	**F9**	6
Haggin, Mount, mtn., Mt., U.S.	**D3**	103
Hagi, Japan	**H4**	30
Ha Giang, Viet.	**C8**	34
Hague, Sask., Can.	**E2**	75
Hague, Cap de la, c., Fr.	**C5**	10
Haguenau, Fr.	**D14**	10
Hagues Peak, mtn., Co., U.S.	**A5**	83
Ha! Ha!, Baie des, b., Que., Can.	**C2**	72
Hahira, Ga., U.S.	**F3**	87
Hahnville, La., U.S.	**E5**	95
Haian, China	**C9**	28
Haicheng, China	**C11**	26
Hai Duong, Viet.	**D9**	34
Haifa see Ḥefa, Isr.	**C4**	40
Haikou, China	**D11**	34
Haiku, Hi., U.S.	**C5**	88
Hā'il, Sau. Ar.	**C3**	46
Hailaer, China	**B10**	26
Hailey, Id., U.S.	**F4**	89
Haileybury, Ont., Can.	**p20**	73
Haileyville, Ok., U.S.	**C6**	113
Haimen, China	**G10**	28
Haimen, China	**L5**	28
Hainan, China	**H8**	26
Hainan Dao, i., China	**E10**	34
Haines, Ak., U.S.	**D12**	79
Haines City, Fl., U.S.	**D5**	86
Haines Junction, Yukon, Can.	**D5**	66
Hainfeld, Aus.	**G15**	8
Haining, China	**E9**	28
Hai Phong, Viet.	**D9**	34
Haiti (Haïti), ctry., N.A.	**E11**	64
Haizhou, China	**A8**	28
Hakodate, Japan	**r18**	30a
Hāla, Pak.	**H3**	38
Ḥalab (Aleppo), Syria	**A5**	40
Ḥalā'ib, Sudan	**D13**	42
Halawa, Cape, c., Hi., U.S.	**B5**	88
Halawa Heights, Hi., U.S.	**g10**	88
Halbā, Leb.	**B5**	40
Halberstadt, Ger.	**D11**	8
Halden, Nor.	**G8**	6
Haldensleben, Ger.	**C11**	8
Haldimand, Ont., Can.	**E5**	73
Haldwāni, India	**F8**	38
Hale, co., Al., U.S.	**C2**	78
Hale, co., Tx., U.S.	**B2**	120
Haleakala Crater, crat., Hi., U.S.	**C5**	88
Haleakala National Park, Hi., U.S.	**C6**	88
Hale Center, Tx., U.S.	**B2**	120
Haleiwa, Hi., U.S.	**B3**	88
Hales Corners, Wi., U.S.	**n11**	126
Halethorpe, Md., U.S.	**B4**	97
Haleyville, Al., U.S.	**A2**	78
Half Moon Bay, Ca., U.S.	**k8**	82
Halfway, Md., U.S.	**A2**	97
Haliburton, Ont., Can.	**B6**	73
Halibut Point, c., Ma., U.S.	**A6**	98
Halifax, N.S., Can.	**E6**	71
Halifax, Va., U.S.	**D4**	123
Halifax, co., N.C., U.S.	**A5**	110
Halifax, co., Va., U.S.	**D4**	123
Halifax Bay, b., Austl.	**C9**	50
Haliimaile, Hi., U.S.	**C5**	88
Halkirk, Scot., U.K.	**C9**	7
Hall, co., Ga., U.S.	**B3**	87
Hall, co., Ne., U.S.	**D7**	104
Hall, co., Tx., U.S.	**B2**	120
Hallam Peak, mtn., B.C., Can.	**C8**	69
Hallandale, Fl., U.S.	**G6**	86
Halla-san, mtn., S. Kor.	**E12**	26
Halle, Ger.	**D11**	8
Hällefors, Swe.	**G10**	6
Hallein, Aus.	**H13**	8
Hallettsville, Tx., U.S.	**E4**	120
Hallie, Wi., U.S.	**D2**	126
Hall Island, i., Ak., U.S.	**C5**	79
Hall Meadow Brook Reservoir, res., Ct., U.S.	**B3**	84
Hall Mountain, mtn., Wa., U.S.	**A8**	124
Hällnäs, Swe.	**D12**	6
Hallock, Mn., U.S.	**B2**	100
Hallowell, Me., U.S.	**D3**	96
Hall Peninsula, pen., N.W. Ter., Can.	**D19**	66
Halls, Tn., U.S.	**B2**	119
Hallsberg, Swe.	**G10**	6
Halls Creek, Austl.	**C5**	50
Halls Creek, stm., Ut., U.S.	**F5**	121
Halls Crossroads, Tn., U.S.	**m14**	119
Halls Stream, stm., N.H., U.S.	**f7**	106
Hallstavik, Swe.	**F12**	6
Hallstead, Pa., U.S.	**C10**	115
Hallsville, Mo., U.S.	**B5**	102
Hallsville, Tx., U.S.	**C5**	120
Halmahera, i., Indon.	**E8**	32
Halmahera, Laut, Indon.	**F8**	32
Halmstad, Swe.	**H9**	6
Halsey, Or., U.S.	**C3**	114
Hälsingborg see Helsingborg, Swe.	**H9**	6
Halstad, Mn., U.S.	**C2**	100
Halstead, Ks., U.S.	**E6**	93
Haltern, Ger.	**D7**	8
Haltiatunturi, mtn., Eur.	**B13**	6
Halton Hills, Ont., Can.	**D5**	73
Hamada, Japan	**H5**	30
Hamadān, Iran	**B4**	46
Ḥamāh, Syria	**B5**	40
Hamamatsu, Japan	**H10**	30
Hamar, Nor.	**F8**	6
Hamblen, co., Tn., U.S.	**C10**	119
Hamburg, Ger.	**B9**	8
Hamburg, Ar., U.S.	**D4**	81
Hamburg, Ia., U.S.	**D2**	92
Hamburg, N.Y., U.S.	**C2**	109
Hamburg, Pa., U.S.	**E10**	115
Hamden, Ct., U.S.	**D4**	84
Hamden, Oh., U.S.	**C3**	112
Hämeenlinna, Fin.	**F15**	6
Hamel, Mn., U.S.	**m11**	100
Hameln, Ger.	**C9**	8
Hamersley Range, mts., Austl.	**D3**	50
Hamhŭng, N. Kor.	**D12**	26
Hami, China	**C5**	26
Hamilton, Ber.	**E14**	76
Hamilton, Ont., Can.	**D5**	73
Hamilton, N.Z.	**B5**	52
Hamilton, Scot., U.K.	**F8**	7
Hamilton, Al., U.S.	**A2**	78
Hamilton, Il., U.S.	**C2**	90
Hamilton, In., U.S.	**A8**	91
Hamilton, Mi., U.S.	**F4**	99
Hamilton, Ms., U.S.	**B5**	101
Hamilton, Mo., U.S.	**B3**	102
Hamilton, Mt., U.S.	**D2**	103
Hamilton, N.Y., U.S.	**C5**	109
Hamilton, Oh., U.S.	**C1**	112
Hamilton, Tx., U.S.	**D3**	120
Hamilton, Va., U.S.	**A5**	123
Hamilton, co., Fl., U.S.	**B3**	86
Hamilton, co., Il., U.S.	**E5**	90
Hamilton, co., In., U.S.	**D5**	91
Hamilton, co., Ia., U.S.	**B4**	92
Hamilton, co., Ks., U.S.	**E2**	93
Hamilton, co., Ne., U.S.	**D7**	104
Hamilton, co., N.Y., U.S.	**B6**	109
Hamilton, co., Oh., U.S.	**C1**	112
Hamilton, co., Tn., U.S.	**D8**	119
Hamilton, co., Tx., U.S.	**D3**	120
Hamilton, Lake, res., Ar., U.S.	**C2**	81
Hamilton, Mount, mtn., Ak., U.S.	**C8**	79
Hamilton, Mount, mtn., Ca., U.S.	**k9**	82
Hamilton, Mount, mtn., Nv., U.S.	**D6**	105
Hamilton Inlet, b., Newf., Can.	**A2**	72
Hamilton Reservoir, res., Ma., U.S.	**B3**	98
Hamilton Sound, strt., Newf., Can.	**D4**	72
Hamilton Square, N.J., U.S.	**C3**	107
Hamiota, Man., Can.	**D1**	70
Hamlet, In., U.S.	**B4**	91
Hamlet, N.C., U.S.	**C3**	110
Hamlet, Mount, mtn., Ak., U.S.	**B6**	79
Hamlin, Pa., U.S.	**D11**	115
Hamlin, Tx., U.S.	**C2**	120
Hamlin, W.V., U.S.	**C2**	125
Hamlin, co., S.D., U.S.	**C8**	118
Hamlin Lake, l., Mi., U.S.	**D4**	99
Hamm, Ger.	**D7**	8
Hammamet, Tun.	**M5**	14
Hammam Lif, Tun.	**M5**	14
Hammerdal, Swe.	**E10**	6
Hammon, Ok., U.S.	**B2**	113
Hammonasset, stm., Ct., U.S.	**D5**	84
Hammonasset Point, c., Ct., U.S.	**E5**	84
Hammond, In., U.S.	**A2**	91
Hammond, La., U.S.	**D5**	95
Hammond, Wi., U.S.	**D1**	126
Hammond Bay, b., Mi., U.S.	**C6**	99
Hammonton, N.J., U.S.	**D3**	107
Hampden, Newf., Can.	**D3**	72
Hampden, Me., U.S.	**D4**	96
Hampden, co., Ma., U.S.	**B2**	98
Hampden Highlands, Me., U.S.	**D4**	96
Hampshire, Il., U.S.	**A5**	90
Hampshire, co., Ma., U.S.	**B2**	98
Hampshire, co., W.V., U.S.	**B6**	125
Hampstead, Md., U.S.	**A4**	97
Hampstead, N.C., U.S.	**C5**	110
Hampton, N.B., Can.	**D4**	71
Hampton, Ar., U.S.	**D3**	81
Hampton, Ga., U.S.	**C2**	87
Hampton, Ia., U.S.	**B4**	92
Hampton, N.H., U.S.	**E5**	106
Hampton, S.C., U.S.	**F5**	117
Hampton, Tn., U.S.	**C11**	119
Hampton, Va., U.S.	**C6**	123
Hampton, co., S.C., U.S.	**F5**	117
Hampton Bays, N.Y., U.S.	**n16**	109
Hampton Beach, N.H., U.S.	**E5**	106
Hampton Butte, mtn., Or., U.S.	**D6**	114
Hampton Roads, Va., U.S.	**k15**	123
Hampton Roads Bridge-Tunnel, Va., U.S.	**k15**	123
Hams Fork, stm., Wy., U.S.	**E2**	127
Hamtramck, Mi., U.S.	**p15**	99
Hana, Hi., U.S.	**C6**	88
Hanahan, S.C., U.S.	**F7**	117
Hanalei Bay, b., Hi., U.S.	**A2**	88
Hanamaki, Japan	**C14**	30
Hanamaulu, Hi., U.S.	**B2**	88
Hanapepe, Hi., U.S.	**B2**	88
Hanau, Ger.	**E8**	8
Hanceville, Al., U.S.	**A3**	78
Hancock, Md., U.S.	**A1**	97
Hancock, Mi., U.S.	**A2**	99
Hancock, Mn., U.S.	**E3**	100
Hancock, co., Ga., U.S.	**C3**	87
Hancock, co., Il., U.S.	**C2**	90
Hancock, co., In., U.S.	**E6**	91
Hancock, co., Ia., U.S.	**A4**	92
Hancock, co., Ky., U.S.	**C3**	94
Hancock, co., Me., U.S.	**D4**	96
Hancock, co., Ms., U.S.	**E4**	101
Hancock, co., Oh., U.S.	**A2**	112
Hancock, co., Tn., U.S.	**C10**	119
Hancock, co., W.V., U.S.	**A4**	125
Hand, co., S.D., U.S.	**C6**	118
Handa, Japan	**H9**	30
Handan, China	**D9**	26
Hando, Som.	**F5**	46
HaNegev, reg., Isr.	**D4**	40
Hanford, Ca., U.S.	**D4**	82
Hangchow see Hangzhou, China	**E9**	28
Hangman Creek, stm., Wa., U.S.	**B8**	124
Hangö (Hanko), Fin.	**G14**	6
Hangzhou (Hangchow), China	**E9**	28
Hangzhou Wan, b., China	**E9**	28
Hanish, Jazā'ir, is., Yemen	**F3**	46
Hanjiang, China	**J8**	28
Hankinson, N.D., U.S.	**C9**	111
Hanna, Alta., Can.	**D5**	68
Hanna, Wy., U.S.	**E6**	127
Hanna City, Il., U.S.	**C4**	90
Hannahville Indian Reservation, Mi., U.S.	**C3**	99
Hannibal, Mo., U.S.	**B6**	102
Hannover, Ger.	**C9**	8
Ha Noi, Viet.	**D8**	34
Hanover, Ont., Can.	**C3**	73
Hanover, Il., U.S.	**A3**	90
Hanover, In., U.S.	**G7**	91
Hanover, Ks., U.S.	**C7**	93
Hanover, Ma., U.S.	**B6**	98
Hanover, Mn., U.S.	**m11**	100
Hanover, N.H., U.S.	**C2**	106
Hanover, Pa., U.S.	**G8**	115
Hanover, co., Va., U.S.	**C5**	123
Hanover Park, Il., U.S.	**k8**	90
Hansen, Id., U.S.	**G4**	89
Hansford, co., Tx., U.S.	**A2**	120
Hanson, Ma., U.S.	**B6**	98
Hanson, co., S.D., U.S.	**D8**	118
Hantsport, N.S., Can.	**D5**	71
Hanzhong, China	**E8**	26
Haparanda, Swe.	**D15**	6
Hapeville, Ga., U.S.	**C2**	87
Happy Valley, N.M., U.S.	**E5**	108
Happy Valley-Goose Bay, Newf., Can.	**B1**	72
Harahan, La., U.S.	**k11**	95
Haralson, co., Ga., U.S.	**C1**	87
Harare, Zimb.	**E6**	44
Harash, Bi'r al-, well, Libya	**C10**	42
Harbeson, De., U.S.	**F4**	85
Harbin, China	**B12**	26
Harbor, Or., U.S.	**E2**	114
Harbor Beach, Mi., U.S.	**E8**	99
Harborcreek, Pa., U.S.	**B2**	115
Harbor Springs, Mi., U.S.	**C6**	99
Harbour Breton, Newf., Can.	**E4**	72
Harbour Grace, Newf., Can.	**E5**	72

Name — Map Ref — Page

Harcuvar Mountains, mts., Az., U.S. D2 80
Harda, India I7 38
Hardangerfjorden, Nor. F5 6
Hardee, co., Fl., U.S. E5 86
Hardeeville, S.C., U.S. G5 117
Hardeman, co., Tn., U.S. B2 119
Hardeman, co., Tx., U.S. B3 120
Hardin, Il., U.S. D3 90
Hardin, Mt., U.S. E9 103
Hardin, co., Il., U.S. F5 90
Hardin, co., Ia., U.S. B4 92
Hardin, co., Ky., U.S. C4 94
Hardin, co., Oh., U.S. B2 112
Hardin, co., Tn., U.S. B3 119
Hardin, co., Tx., U.S. D5 120
Harding, co., N.M., U.S. B5 108
Harding, co., S.D., U.S. B2 118
Harding, Lake, res., U.S. C4 78
Hardinsburg, Ky., U.S. C3 94
Hardisty, Alta., Can. C5 68
Hardwār, India F8 38
Hardwick, Ga., U.S. C3 87
Hardwick, Vt., U.S. B4 122
Hardwood Ridge, mtn., Pa., U.S. D11 115
Hardy, co., W.V., U.S. B6 125
Hardy Lake, res., In., U.S. G6 91
Hare Bay, Newf., Can. D4 72
Hare Bay, b., Newf., Can. C4 72
Harer, Eth. G3 46
Harford, co., Md., U.S. A5 97
Hargeysa, Som. G3 46
Harihar, India E3 37
Harīrūd (Tedžen), stm., Asia J10 18
Harkers Island, N.C., U.S. C6 110
Harlan, In., U.S. B8 91
Harlan, Ia., U.S. C2 92
Harlan, Ky., U.S. D6 94
Harlan, co., Ky., U.S. D6 94
Harlan, co., Ne., U.S. D6 104
Harlan County Lake, res., Ne., U.S. E6 104
Harlem, Fl., U.S. F6 86
Harlem, Ga., U.S. C4 87
Harlem, Mt., U.S. B8 103
Harleyville, S.C., U.S. E7 117
Harlingen, Neth. B5 8
Harlingen, Tx., U.S. F4 120
Harlow, Eng., U.K. J13 7
Harlowton, Mt., U.S. D7 103
Harmon, co., Ok., U.S. C2 113
Harmon Creek, stm., W.V., U.S. f8 125
Harmony, In., U.S. E3 91
Harmony, Mn., U.S. G6 100
Harmony, Pa., U.S. E1 115
Harmony, R.I., U.S. B3 116
Harnett, co., N.C., U.S. B4 110
Harney, co., Or., U.S. D7 114
Harney, Lake, l., Fl., U.S. D5 86
Harney Lake, l., Or., U.S. D7 114
Harney Peak, mtn., S.D., U.S. D2 118
Härnösand, Swe. E11 6
Haro, Spain C9 12
Haro Strait, strt., Wa., U.S. A2 124
Harper, Lib. H4 42
Harper, Ks., U.S. E5 93
Harper, co., Ks., U.S. E5 93
Harper, co., Ok., U.S. A2 113
Harper, Mount, mtn., Ak., U.S. C11 79
Harpers Ferry, W.V., U.S. B7 125
Harpers Ferry National Historical Park, W.V., U.S. B7 125
Harpersville, Al., U.S. B3 78
Harpeth, stm., Tn., U.S. A5 119
Harquahala Mountain, mtn., Az., U.S. D2 80
Harquahala Mountains, mts., Az., U.S. D2 80
Harrah, Ok., U.S. B4 113
Harricana, stm., Can. F17 66
Harriman, Tn., U.S. D9 119
Harriman Reservoir, res., Vt., U.S. F3 122
Harrington, De., U.S. E8 85
Harrington Park, N.J., U.S. h9 107
Harris, Mn., U.S. E6 100
Harris, R.I., U.S. D3 116
Harris, co., Ga., U.S. D2 87
Harris, co., Tx., U.S. E5 120
Harris, Lake, l., Fl., U.S. D5 86
Harrisburg, Ar., U.S. B5 81
Harrisburg, Il., U.S. F5 90
Harrisburg, Or., U.S. C3 114
Harrisburg, Pa., U.S. F8 115
Harrisburg, S.D., U.S. D9 118
Harrison, Ar., U.S. A2 81
Harrison, Mi., U.S. D6 99
Harrison, N.J., U.S. k8 107
Harrison, N.Y., U.S. h13 109
Harrison, Oh., U.S. C1 112
Harrison, Tn., U.S. h11 119
Harrison, co., In., U.S. H5 91
Harrison, co., Ia., U.S. C2 92
Harrison, co., Ky., U.S. B5 94
Harrison, co., Ms., U.S. E4 101
Harrison, co., Mo., U.S. A3 102
Harrison, co., Oh., U.S. B4 112
Harrison, co., Tx., U.S. C5 120
Harrison, co., W.V., U.S. B4 125
Harrison, Cape, c., Newf., Can. g10 72
Harrison Bay, b., Ak., U.S. A9 79
Harrisonburg, Va., U.S. B4 123
Harrison Hot Springs, B.C., Can. f14 69
Harrison Lake, l., B.C., Can. E7 69
Harrisonville, Mo., U.S. C3 102
Harriston, Ont., Can. D4 73
Harristown, Il., U.S. D4 90
Harrisville, R.I., U.S. B2 116
Harrisville, Ut., U.S. B4 121
Harrisville, W.V., U.S. B3 125
Harrodsburg, Ky., U.S. C5 94
Harrogate, Eng., U.K. G11 7
Harrow, Ont., Can. E2 73
Harry S. Truman Reservoir, res., Mo., U.S. C4 102
Harry Strunk Lake, res., Ne., U.S. D5 104
Harstad, Nor. B11 6
Hart, Mi., U.S. E4 99
Hart, Tx., U.S. B1 120
Hart, co., Ga., U.S. B4 87
Hart, co., Ky., U.S. C4 94
Hart, Lake, l., Fl., U.S. D5 86
Hartford, Al., U.S. D4 78
Hartford, Ar., U.S. B1 81
Hartford, Ct., U.S. B5 84
Hartford, Il., U.S. E3 90
Hartford, Ia., U.S. C4 92
Hartford, Ky., U.S. C3 94
Hartford, Mi., U.S. F4 99
Hartford, S.D., U.S. D9 118
Hartford, Vt., U.S. D4 122
Hartford, Wi., U.S. E5 126
Hartford, co., Ct., U.S. B4 84
Hartford City, In., U.S. D7 91
Hartington, Ne., U.S. B8 104
Hart Lake, l., Or., U.S. E7 114
Hartland, N.B., Can. C2 71
Hartland, Me., U.S. D3 96
Hartland, Wi., U.S. E5 126
Hartland Point, c., Eng., U.K. J8 7
Hartlepool, Eng., U.K. G11 7
Hartley, Ia., U.S. A2 92
Hartley, co., Tx., U.S. B1 120
Hartney, Man., Can. E1 70
Hartselle, Al., U.S. A3 78
Hartshorne, Ok., U.S. C6 113
Hartsville, S.C., U.S. C7 117
Hartsville, Tn., U.S. A5 119
Hartville, Oh., U.S. B4 112
Hartwell, Ga., U.S. B4 87
Hartwell Lake, res., U.S. B1 117
Hārūnābād, Pak. F5 38
Hārūt, stm., Afg. C1 36
Harvard, Il., U.S. A5 90
Harvard, Ne., U.S. D7 104
Harvard, Mount, mtn., Co., U.S. C4 83
Harvey, Il., U.S. B6 90
Harvey, La., U.S. E5 95
Harvey, Mi., U.S. B3 99
Harvey, N.D., U.S. B6 111
Harvey, co., Ks., U.S. D6 93
Harvey Lake, res., Pa., U.S. m16 115
Harveys Creek, stm., Pa., U.S. n16 115
Harwich, Eng., U.K. J14 7
Harwich Port, Ma., U.S. C7 98
Harwinton, Ct., U.S. B3 84
Haryana, state, India F7 38
Harz, mts., Ger. D10 8
Hasbrouck Heights, N.J., U.S. h8 107
Haskell, Ar., U.S. C3 81
Haskell, Ok., U.S. B6 113
Haskell, Tx., U.S. C3 120
Haskell, co., Ks., U.S. E3 93
Haskell, co., Ok., U.S. B6 113
Haskell, co., Tx., U.S. C3 120
Haskovo, Bul. H9 16
Hassan, India F4 37
Hassayampa, stm., Az., U.S. D3 80
Hasselt, Bel. E5 8
Hassfurt, Ger. E10 8
Hässleholm, Swe. H9 6
Hastings, Ont., Can. C7 73
Hastings, N.Z. C6 52
Hastings, Eng., U.K. K13 7
Hastings, Mi., U.S. F5 99
Hastings, Mn., U.S. F6 100
Hastings, Ne., U.S. D7 104
Hastings, Pa., U.S. E4 115
Hastings-on-Hudson, N.Y., U.S. h13 109
Hatch, N.M., U.S. E2 108
Hatchet Lake, N.S., Can. E6 71
Hatchie, stm., Tn., U.S. B2 119
Hatchineha, Lake, l., Fl., U.S. D5 86
Hat Creek, stm., S.D., U.S. E2 118
Hatfield, In., U.S. I3 91
Hatfield, Pa., U.S. F11 115
Hāthras, India G8 38
Ha Tinh, Viet. E8 34
Hat Mountain, mtn., Az., U.S. E3 80
Hatteras, N.C., U.S. B7 110
Hatteras, Cape, c., N.C., U.S. B7 110
Hatteras Inlet, b., N.C., U.S. B7 110
Hattiesburg, Ms., U.S. D4 101
Hatton, N.D., U.S. B8 111
Hat Yai, Thai. K6 34
Haubstadt, In., U.S. H2 91
Haugesund, Nor. G5 6
Haughton, La., U.S. B2 95
Haukivuori, Fin. E16 6
Hauser, Or., U.S. D2 114
Haut, Isle au, i., Me., U.S. D4 96
Haut Atlas, mts., Mor. B4 42
Hauula, Hi., U.S. B4 88
Havana, Fl., U.S. B2 86
Havana, Il., U.S. C3 90
Havana see La Habana, Cuba C6 64
Havant, Eng., U.K. K12 7
Havasu, Lake, res., U.S. C1 80
Havasupai Indian Reservation, Az., U.S. A3 80
Havelberg, Ger. C12 8
Havelock, Ont., Can. C7 73
Havelock, N.C., U.S. C6 110
Haven, Ks., U.S. E6 93
Haverford [Township], Pa., U.S. o20 115
Haverhill, Ma., U.S. A5 98
Hāveri, India E3 37
Haverstraw, N.Y., U.S. D7 109
Haviland, Ks., U.S. E4 93
Havířov, Czech. F18 8
Havre, Mt., U.S. B7 103
Havre de Grace, Md., U.S. A5 97
Havre North, Mt., U.S. B7 103
Haw, stm., N.C., U.S. B3 110
Hawaii, co., Hi., U.S. D6 88
Hawaii, state, U.S. C5 88
Hawaii, i., Hi., U.S. D6 88
Hawaiian Islands, is., Hi., U.S. m14 88
Hawaii Volcanoes National Park, Hi., U.S. D6 88
Hawarden, Ia., U.S. A1 92
Hawesville, Ky., U.S. C3 94
Hawi, Hi., U.S. C6 88
Hawick, Scot., U.K. F10 7
Hawke Bay, b., N.Z. C6 52
Hawkesbury, Ont., Can. B10 73
Hawkesbury Island, i., B.C., Can. C3 69
Hawkins, co., Tn., U.S. C11 119
Hawkinsville, Ga., U.S. D3 87
Hawley, Mn., U.S. D2 100
Hawley, Pa., U.S. D11 115
Haworth, N.J., U.S. h9 107
Haw River, N.C., U.S. A3 110
Hawthorne, Ca., U.S. n12 82
Hawthorne, Fl., U.S. C4 86
Hawthorne, Nv., U.S. E3 105
Hawthorne, N.J., U.S. B4 107
Hawthorne, N.Y., U.S. g13 109
Haxtun, Co., U.S. A8 83
Hay, Austl. F8 50
Hay, stm., Austl. D7 50
Hay, stm., Can. E9 66
Hay, Cape, c., N.W. Ter., Can. B10 66
Hayange, Fr. C13 10
Hayden, Az., U.S. E5 80
Hayden, Co., U.S. A3 83
Hayden Lake, l., Id., U.S. B2 89
Hayes, La., U.S. D3 95
Hayes, co., Ne., U.S. D4 104
Hayes, stm., Man., Can. B5 70
Hayes, Mount, mtn., Ak., U.S. C10 79
Hayfield, Mn., U.S. G6 100
Hayford Peak, mtn., Nv., U.S. G6 105
Haymock Lake, l., Me., U.S. B3 96
Haynesville, La., U.S. B2 95
Hayneville, Al., U.S. C3 78
Hayrabolu, Tur. H11 16
Hay River, N.W. Ter., Can. D9 66
Hays, Ks., U.S. D4 93
Hays, N.C., U.S. A1 110
Hays, co., Tx., U.S. D3 120
Hays Canyon Peak, mtn., Nv., U.S. B2 105
Hay Springs, Ne., U.S. B3 104
Haystack Mountain, mtn., Nv., U.S. B6 105
Haysville, Ks., U.S. g12 93
Hayti, Mo., U.S. E8 102
Hayti Heights, Mo., U.S. E8 102
Hayward, Ca., U.S. h8 82
Hayward, Wi., U.S. B2 126
Haywood, co., N.C., U.S. f9 110
Haywood, co., Tn., U.S. B2 119
Hazard, Ky., U.S. C6 94
Hazardville, Ct., U.S. B5 84
Hazāribāgh, India I11 38
Hazel Crest, Il., U.S. k9 90
Hazel Dell, Wa., U.S. D3 124
Hazel Green, Al., U.S. A3 78
Hazel Green, Wi., U.S. F3 126
Hazel Park, Mi., U.S. p15 99
Hazelton Pyramid, mtn., Wy., U.S. B5 127
Hazelwood, N.C., U.S. f9 110
Hazen, Ar., U.S. C4 81
Hazen, N.D., U.S. B4 111
Hazen Bay, b., Ak., U.S. C6 79
Hazlehurst, Ga., U.S. E4 87
Hazlehurst, Ms., U.S. D3 101
Hazlet, N.J., U.S. C4 107
Hazleton, Ia., U.S. B6 92
Hazleton, Pa., U.S. E10 115
Head Harbor Island, i., Me., U.S. D5 96
Headland, Al., U.S. D4 78
Headley, Mount, mtn., Mt., U.S. C1 103
Healdsburg, Ca., U.S. C2 82
Healdton, Ok., U.S. C4 113
Healy, Ak., U.S. C10 79
Heard, co., Ga., U.S. C1 87
Hearne, Tx., U.S. D4 120
Hearst, Ont., Can. o19 73
Heart, stm., N.D., U.S. C3 111
Heart Butte Dam, N.D., U.S. C4 111
Heart Lake, l., Wy., U.S. B2 127
Heart's Content, Newf., Can. E5 72
Heath, Oh., U.S. B3 112
Heath Springs, S.C., U.S. B6 117
Heavener, Ok., U.S. C7 113
Hebbronville, Tx., U.S. F3 120
Hebei, prov., China D10 26
Heber, Az., U.S. C5 80
Heber City, Ut., U.S. C4 121
Heber Springs, Ar., U.S. B3 81
Hébertville, Que., Can. A6 74
Hebgen Lake, res., Mt., U.S. F5 103
Hebrides, is., Scot., U.K. D6 4
Hebron, N.S., Can. F3 71
Hebron, Il., U.S. A5 90
Hebron, In., U.S. B3 91
Hebron, Ky., U.S. h13 94
Hebron, Md., U.S. D6 97
Hebron, Ne., U.S. D8 104
Hebron, N.D., U.S. C3 111
Hebron, Oh., U.S. C3 112
Hebron see Al-Khalīl, Jord. D4 40
Hecate Strait, strt., B.C., Can. C2 69
Heceta Island, i., Ak., U.S. n23 79
Hechi, China B9 34
Hechingen, Ger. G8 8
Hechuan, China E8 26
Hecla Island, i., Man., Can. D3 70
Hector, Mn., U.S. F4 100
Hedemora, Swe. F10 6
He Devil, mtn., Id., U.S. D2 89
Hedrick, Ia., U.S. C5 92
Heerenveen, Neth. C5 8
Heerlen, Neth. E5 8
Ḥefa (Haifa), Isr. C4 40
Hefei, China D6 28
Heflin, Al., U.S. B4 78
Hefner, Lake, res., Ok., U.S. B4 113
Hegang, China B13 26
Hegins, Pa., U.S. E9 115
Heide, Ger. A9 8
Heidelberg, Ger. F8 8
Heidelberg, Ms., U.S. D5 101
Heidenheim, Ger. F10 8
Heidenreichstein, Aus. G15 8
Heidrick, Ky., U.S. D6 94
Heihe (Naquka), China E14 38
Heilbron, S. Afr. G5 44
Heilbronn, Ger. F9 8
Heiligenstadt, Ger. D10 8
Heilongjiang, prov., China B12 26
Heilongjiang (Amur), stm., Asia G19 20
Heinola, Fin. F16 6
Hejaz see Al-Ḥijāz, reg., Sau. Ar. C2 46
Hekla, vol., Ice. C4 4
Hekou, China C7 34
Helena, Al., U.S. B3 78
Helena, Ar., U.S. C5 81
Helena, Ga., U.S. D4 87
Helena, Mt., U.S. D4 103
Helena, Ok., U.S. A3 113
Helensburgh, Scot., U.K. E8 7
Helgoland, i., Ger. A7 8
Helgoländer Bucht, b., Ger. A8 8
Hellam, Pa., U.S. G8 115
Hellertown, Pa., U.S. E11 115
Hellesylt, Nor. E6 6
Hellín, Spain G10 12
Hells Canyon, val., U.S. B10 114
Hells Canyon National Recreation Area, U.S. B10 114
Hell-Ville, Madag. D9 44
Helmand, stm., Asia C2 36
Helmond, Neth. D5 8
Helmsdale, Scot., U.K. C9 7
Helmstedt, Ger. C10 8
Helotes, Tx., U.S. h7 120
Helper, Ut., U.S. D5 121
Helsingborg, Swe. H9 6
Helsingfors see Helsinki, Fin. F15 6
Helsingør (Elsinore), Den. H9 6
Helsinki (Helsingfors), Fin. F15 6
Hematite, Mo., U.S. C7 102
Hemet, Ca., U.S. F5 82
Hemingford, Ne., U.S. B2 104
Hemingway, S.C., U.S. D9 117
Hemlock, Mi., U.S. E6 99
Hemlock Reservoir, res., Ct., U.S. E2 84
Hemmingford, Que., Can. D4 74
Hemphill, Tx., U.S. D6 120
Hemphill, co., Tx., U.S. B2 120
Hempstead, N.Y., U.S. n15 109
Hempstead, Tx., U.S. D4 120
Hempstead, co., Ar., U.S. D2 81
Hemse, Swe. H12 6
Henagar, Al., U.S. A4 78
Henan, prov., China E9 26
Henderson, Ky., U.S. C2 94
Henderson, La., U.S. D4 95
Henderson, Mn., U.S. F5 100
Henderson, Ne., U.S. D8 104
Henderson, Nv., U.S. G7 105
Henderson, N.C., U.S. A4 110
Henderson, Tn., U.S. B3 119
Henderson, Tx., U.S. C5 120
Henderson, co., Il., U.S. C3 90
Henderson, co., Ky., U.S. C2 94
Henderson, co., N.C., U.S. f10 110
Henderson, co., Tn., U.S. B3 119
Henderson, co., Tx., U.S. C5 120
Henderson's Point, Ms., U.S. g7 101
Hendersonville, N.C., U.S. f10 110
Hendersonville, Tn., U.S. A5 119
Hendricks, Mn., U.S. F2 100
Hendricks, co., In., U.S. E4 91
Hendry, co., Fl., U.S. F5 86
Hengelo, Neth. C6 8
Hengshan, China H1 28
Hengyang, China F9 26
Henlawson, W.V., U.S. n12 125
Henlopen, Cape, c., De., U.S. E5 85
Hennef, Ger. E7 8
Hennepin, co., Mn., U.S. E5 100
Hennessey, Ok., U.S. A4 113
Henniker, N.H., U.S. D3 106
Henning, Mn., U.S. D3 100
Henning, Tn., U.S. B2 119
Henrico, co., Va., U.S. C5 123
Henrietta, N.C., U.S. B1 110
Henrietta, Tx., U.S. C3 120
Henrietta Maria, Cape, c., Ont., Can. n19 73
Henry, Il., U.S. B4 90
Henry, co., Al., U.S. D4 78
Henry, co., Ga., U.S. C2 87
Henry, co., Il., U.S. B3 90
Henry, co., In., U.S. E7 91
Henry, co., Ia., U.S. C6 92
Henry, co., Ky., U.S. B4 94
Henry, co., Mo., U.S. C4 102
Henry, co., Oh., U.S. A1 112
Henry, co., Tn., U.S. A3 119
Henry, co., Va., U.S. D3 123
Henry, Mount, mtn., Mt., U.S. B1 103
Henryetta, Ok., U.S. B6 113
Henry Kater, Cape, c., N.W. Ter., Can. C19 66
Henrys Fork, stm., U.S. E2 127
Henryville, Que., Can. D4 74
Henryville, In., U.S. G6 91
Hensall, Ont., Can. D3 73
Henzada, Burma F3 34
Hephzibah, Ga., U.S. C4 87
Heppner, Or., U.S. B7 114
Hepu (Lianzhou), China D10 34
Herāt, Afg. C1 36
Herbes, Isle aux, i., Al., U.S. E1 78
Herbignac, Fr. E4 10
Herculaneum, Mo., U.S. C7 102
Hereford, Eng., U.K. I10 7
Hereford, Md., U.S. A4 97
Hereford, Tx., U.S. B1 120
Hereford Inlet, b., N.J., U.S. E3 107
Herford, Ger. C8 8
Herington, Ks., U.S. D7 93
Herkimer, N.Y., U.S. B6 109
Herkimer, co., N.Y., U.S. B5 109
Hermann, Mo., U.S. C6 102
Hermano Peak, mtn., Co., U.S. D2 83
Hermantown, Mn., U.S. D6 100
Hermanus, S. Afr. H3 44
Herminie, Pa., U.S. F2 115
Hermiston, Or., U.S. B7 114
Hermitage, Newf., Can. E4 72
Hermitage, Ar., U.S. D3 81
Hermitage Bay, b., Newf., Can. E3 72
Hermosillo, Mex. C4 62
Hernando, Fl., U.S. D4 86
Hernando, Ms., U.S. A4 101
Hernando, co., Fl., U.S. D4 86
Herndon, Va., U.S. B5 123
Herning, Den. H7 6
Heron Lake, Mn., U.S. G3 100
Herrera del Duque, Spain F6 12
Herrera de Pisuerga, Spain C7 12
Herrin, Il., U.S. F4 90
Herring Bay, b., Md., U.S. C4 97
Herring Cove, N.S., Can. E6 71
Herrington Lake, res., Ky., U.S. C5 94
Herscher, Il., U.S. B5 90
Hershey, Pa., U.S. F8 115
Hertford, N.C., U.S. A6 110
Hertford, co., N.C., U.S. A5 110
Hervás, Spain E6 12
Hesdin, Fr. B9 10
Hesperia, Ca., U.S. E5 82
Hesperia, Mi., U.S. E4 99
Hesperus Mountain, mtn., Co., U.S. D2 83
Hesston, Ks., U.S. D6 93
Hetian, China B8 38
Hettinger, N.D., U.S. D3 111
Hettinger, co., N.D., U.S. C3 111
Heyburn, Id., U.S. G5 89
Heyworth, Il., U.S. C5 90
Hialeah, Fl., U.S. G6 86
Hiawatha, Ia., U.S. B6 92
Hiawatha, Ks., U.S. C8 93
Hibbing, Mn., U.S. C6 100
Hickam Air Force Base, mil., Hi., U.S. g10 88
Hickman, Ky., U.S. f8 94
Hickman, Ne., U.S. D9 104
Hickman, co., Ky., U.S. f8 94
Hickman, co., Tn., U.S. B4 119
Hickory, N.C., U.S. B1 110
Hickory, co., Mo., U.S. D4 102
Hicksville, N.Y., U.S. E7 109
Hicksville, Oh., U.S. A1 112
Hico, Tx., U.S. D3 120
Hico, W.V., U.S. C3 125
Hidaka-sammyaku, mts., Japan q20 30a
Hidalgo, Mex. E10 62
Hidalgo, Tx., U.S. F3 120
Hidalgo, co., N.M., U.S. F1 108
Hidalgo, co., Tx., U.S. F3 120
Hidalgo del Parral, Mex. D7 62
Hiddenite, N.C., U.S. B1 110
Hieroglyphic Mountains, mts., Az., U.S. k8 80
Hierro, i., Spain C2 42
Higashiōsaka, Japan H8 30
Higbee, Mo., U.S. B5 102
Higganum, Ct., U.S. D5 84
Higgins Lake, l., Mi., U.S. D6 99
Higgins Millpond, res., Md., U.S. C6 97
Higginsville, Mo., U.S. B4 102
High Bridge, N.J., U.S. B3 107
High Falls Reservoir, res., Wi., U.S. C5 126
High Island, i., Mi., U.S. C5 99
Highland, Il., U.S. E4 90
Highland, In., U.S. A3 91
Highland, Ks., U.S. C8 93
Highland, Mi., U.S. o14 99
Highland, N.Y., U.S. D7 109
Highland, Wi., U.S. E3 126
Highland, co., Oh., U.S. C2 112
Highland, co., Va., U.S. B3 123
Highland Lake, l., Me., U.S. g7 96
Highland Lakes, N.J., U.S. A4 107
Highland Park, Il., U.S. A6 90
Highland Park, Mi., U.S. p15 99
Highland Park, Tx., U.S. n10 120
Highland Peak, mtn., Ca., U.S. C4 82
Highland Point, c., Fl., U.S. G5 86
Highlands, N.J., U.S. C5 107
Highlands, N.C., U.S. f9 110
Highlands, Tx., U.S. r14 120
Highlands, co., Fl., U.S. E5 86
Highland Springs, Va., U.S. C5 123
High Level, Alta., Can. F7 68
Highmore, S.D., U.S. C6 118
High Point, N.C., U.S. B2 110
High Prairie, Alta., Can. B2 68
High Ridge, Mo., U.S. g12 102
High River, Alta., Can. D4 68
Highrock Lake, l., Man., Can. B1 70
High Rock Lake, res., N.C., U.S. B2 110
High Spire, Pa., U.S. F8 115
High Springs, Fl., U.S. C4 86
Hightstown, N.J., U.S. C3 107
Highwood, Il., U.S. A6 90
Highwood Baldy, mtn., Mt., U.S. C6 103
Highwood Mountains, mts., Mt., U.S. C6 103
Higuerote, Ven. B9 58
Higüey, Dom. Rep. E13 64
Híjar, Spain D11 12
Hikari, Japan I4 30
Hikone, Japan G9 30
Hiko Range, mts., Nv., U.S. F6 105
Hilbert, Wi., U.S. D5 126
Hildale, Ut., U.S. F3 121
Hilden, N.S., Can. D6 71
Hildesheim, Ger. C9 8
Hill, co., Mt., U.S. B6 103
Hill, co., Tx., U.S. D4 120
Hill City, Ks., U.S. C4 93
Hill City, S.D., U.S. D2 118
Hillcrest, Il., U.S. B4 90
Hillcrest Heights, Md., U.S. C4 97
Hilliard, Fl., U.S. B5 86
Hilliard, Oh., U.S. k10 112
Hill Island Lake, l., N.W. Ter., Can. D11 66
Hill Lake, l., Ar., U.S. h10 81
Hills, Ia., U.S. C6 92
Hills, Mn., U.S. G2 100
Hillsboro, Il., U.S. D4 90
Hillsboro, Ks., U.S. D6 93
Hillsboro, Mo., U.S. C7 102
Hillsboro, N.H., U.S. D3 106
Hillsboro, N.D., U.S. B8 111
Hillsboro, Oh., U.S. C2 112
Hillsboro, Or., U.S. B4 114
Hillsboro, Tx., U.S. C4 120
Hillsboro, Wi., U.S. E3 126
Hillsboro Canal, Fl., U.S. F6 86

Name	Map Ref	Page
Hillsborough, N.B., Can.	D5	71
Hillsborough, N.C., U.S.	A3	110
Hillsborough, co., Fl., U.S.	E4	86
Hillsborough, co., N.H., U.S.	E3	106
Hillsborough Bay, b., P.E.I., Can.	C6	71
Hillsburgh, Ont., Can.	D4	73
Hills Creek Lake, res., Or., U.S.	D4	114
Hillsdale, Mi., U.S.	G6	99
Hillsdale, N.J., U.S.	g8	107
Hillsdale, co., Mi., U.S.	G6	99
Hillside, N.J., U.S.	k8	107
Hillsville, Pa., U.S.	D1	115
Hillsville, Va., U.S.	D2	123
Hilo, Hi., U.S.	D6	88
Hilo Bay, b., Hi., U.S.	D6	88
Hilton, N.Y., U.S.	B3	109
Hilton Head Island, S.C., U.S.	G6	117
Hilton Head Island, i., S.C., U.S.	G6	117
Hilversum, Neth.	C5	8
Himachal Pradesh, ter., India	E7	38
Himalayas, mts., Asia	F10	38
Himeji, Japan	H7	30
Himi, Japan	F9	30
Himş (Homs), Syria	B5	40
Hinchinbrook Island, i., Austl.	C9	50
Hinchinbrook Island, i., Ak., U.S.	g18	79
Hinckley, Il., U.S.	B5	90
Hinckley, Mn., U.S.	D6	100
Hinckley, Ut., U.S.	D3	121
Hinckley Reservoir, res., N.Y., U.S.	B5	109
Hindaun, India	G7	38
Hindman, Ky., U.S.	C7	94
Hinds, co., Ms., U.S.	C3	101
Hindu Kush, mts., Asia	B4	38
Hindupur, India	F4	37
Hines, Or., U.S.	D7	114
Hinesville, Ga., U.S.	E5	87
Hinganghāt, India	B5	37
Hingham, Ma., U.S.	B6	98
Hingham Bay, b., Ma., U.S.	g12	98
Hingoli, India	C4	37
Hinojosa del Duque, Spain	G6	12
Hinsdale, Il., U.S.	k9	90
Hinsdale, N.H., U.S.	E2	106
Hinsdale, co., Co., U.S.	D3	83
Hinton, Alta., Can.	C2	68
Hinton, Ia., U.S.	B1	92
Hinton, Ok., U.S.	B3	113
Hinton, W.V., U.S.	D4	125
Hirado, Japan	I2	30
Hīrākud, res., India	J10	38
Hiram, Ga., U.S.	C2	87
Hiram, Oh., U.S.	A4	112
Hirara, Japan	G12	26
Hiratsuka, Japan	G12	30
Hirosaki, Japan	B13	30
Hiroshima, Japan	H5	30
Hirson, Fr.	C11	10
Hisār, India	F6	38
Hispaniola, i., N.A.	E12	64
Hita, Japan	I3	30
Hitachi, Japan	F13	30
Hitchcock, Tx., U.S.	r14	120
Hitchcock, co., Ne., U.S.	D4	104
Hitchcock Lake, Ct., U.S.	C4	84
Hitoyoshi, Japan	J3	30
Hitra, i., Nor.	E7	6
Hiwassee, stm., Tn., U.S.	D9	119
Hiwassee Lake, res., N.C., U.S.	f8	110
Hjørring, Den.	H7	6
Ho, Ghana	G6	42
Hoa Binh, Viet.	D8	34
Hoagland, In., U.S.	C8	91
Hoback, stm., Wy., U.S.	C2	127
Hobart, Austl.	H9	50
Hobart, In., U.S.	A3	91
Hobart, Ok., U.S.	B2	113
Hobbs, N.M., U.S.	E6	108
Hobe Sound, Fl., U.S.	E6	86
Hobo, Col.	F5	58
Hoboken, N.J., U.S.	k8	107
Höchstadt an der Aisch, Ger.	F10	8
Hockessin, De., U.S.	A3	85
Hocking, co., Oh., U.S.	C3	112
Hocking, stm., Oh., U.S.	C3	112
Hockley, co., Tx., U.S.	C1	120
Hodgeman, co., Ks., U.S.	D4	93
Hodgenville, Ky., U.S.	C4	94
Hodges Village Reservoir, res., Ma., U.S.	B4	98
Hódmezővásárhely, Hung.	I20	8
Hodna, Chott el, l., Alg.	J16	12
Hodonín, Czech.	G17	8
Hof, Ger.	E11	8
Hoffman Estates, Il., U.S.	h8	90
Hofgeismar, Ger.	D9	8
Hofheim in Unterfranken, Ger.	E10	8
Hofors, Swe.	F11	6
Hōfu, Japan	H4	30
Hogansville, Ga., U.S.	C2	87
Hogback Mountain, mtn., Mt., U.S.	F4	103
Hog Island, i., Fl., U.S.	C3	86
Hog Island, i., Mi., U.S.	C5	99
Hog Island, i., N.C., U.S.	B6	110
Hog Island, i., R.I., U.S.	D5	116
Hog Island, i., Va., U.S.	C7	123
Hoh, stm., Wa., U.S.	B1	124
Hohenau an der March, Aus.	G16	8
Hohenwald, Tn., U.S.	B4	119
Hohe Tauern, mts., Aus.	H12	8
Hoh Head, c., Wa., U.S.	B1	124
Hohhot, China	C9	26
Hohoe, Ghana	G5	42
Hōhoku, Japan	H3	30
Ho-Ho-Kus, N.J., U.S.	h8	107
Hoh Xil Shan, mts., China	C13	38
Hoi An, Viet.	G10	34
Hoisington, Ks., U.S.	D5	93
Hokah, Mn., U.S.	G7	100
Hoke, co., N.C., U.S.	B3	110
Hokes Bluff, Al., U.S.	B4	78
Hokitika, N.Z.	E3	52
Hokkaidō, i., Japan	p20	30a
Holbrook, Az., U.S.	C5	80
Holbrook, Ma., U.S.	B5	98
Holcomb, Ks., U.S.	E3	93
Holden, Ma., U.S.	B4	98
Holden, Mo., U.S.	C4	102
Holden, W.V., U.S.	D2	125
Holden Heights, Fl., U.S.	D5	86
Holdenville, Ok., U.S.	B5	113
Holdrege, Ne., U.S.	D6	104
Hole in the Mountain Peak, mtn., Nv., U.S.	C6	105
Holgate, Oh., U.S.	A1	112
Holguín, Cuba	D9	64
Höljes, Swe.	F9	6
Hollabrunn, Aus.	G16	8
Holladay, Ut., U.S.	C4	121
Holland, In., U.S.	H3	91
Holland, Mi., U.S.	F4	99
Holland, Oh., U.S.	A2	112
Holland, Tx., U.S.	D4	120
Hollandale, Ms., U.S.	B3	101
Holland Island, i., Md., U.S.	D5	97
Holland see Netherlands, ctry., Eur.	E9	4
Holland Point, c., Md., U.S.	C4	97
Holland Straits, strt., Md., U.S.	D5	97
Holley, N.Y., U.S.	B2	109
Holliday, Tx., U.S.	C3	120
Hollidaysburg, Pa., U.S.	F5	115
Hollins, Va., U.S.	C3	123
Hollis, Ok., U.S.	C2	113
Hollister, Ca., U.S.	D3	82
Hollister, Mo., U.S.	E4	102
Holliston, Ma., U.S.	B5	98
Holloman Air Force Base, mil., N.M., U.S.	E3	108
Hollow Rock, Tn., U.S.	A3	119
Hollowtop Mountain, mtn., Mt., U.S.	E4	103
Holly, Co., U.S.	C8	83
Holly, Mi., U.S.	F7	99
Holly Grove, Ar., U.S.	C4	81
Holly Hill, Fl., U.S.	C5	86
Holly Hill, S.C., U.S.	E7	117
Holly Pond, Al., U.S.	A3	78
Holly Ridge, N.C., U.S.	C5	110
Holly Shelter Swamp, sw., N.C., U.S.	C5	110
Holly Springs, Ga., U.S.	B2	87
Holly Springs, Ms., U.S.	A4	101
Holly Springs, N.C., U.S.	B4	110
Hollywood, Al., U.S.	A4	78
Hollywood, Fl., U.S.	F6	86
Hollywood, Md., U.S.	D4	97
Hollywood, S.C., U.S.	k11	117
Hollywood Indian Reservation, Fl., U.S.	r3	86
Holman Island, N.W. Ter., Can.	B9	66
Holmen, Wi., U.S.	E2	126
Holmes, co., Fl., U.S.	u16	86
Holmes, co., Ms., U.S.	B3	101
Holmes, co., Oh., U.S.	B4	112
Holmes, Mount, mtn., Wy., U.S.	B2	127
Holmes Reefs, rf., Austl.	C9	50
Holstebro, Den.	H7	6
Holstein, Ia., U.S.	B2	92
Holsteinsborg, Grnld.	C22	66
Holston, stm., Tn., U.S.	C11	119
Holston, Middle Fork, stm., Va., U.S.	f10	123
Holston High Knob, mtn., Tn., U.S.	C11	119
Holsworthy, Eng., U.K.	K8	7
Holt, Al., U.S.	B2	78
Holt, Mi., U.S.	F6	99
Holt, co., Mo., U.S.	A2	102
Holt, co., Ne., U.S.	B7	104
Holt Lake, res., Al., U.S.	B2	78
Holton, Ks., U.S.	C8	93
Holtville, Ca., U.S.	F6	82
Holualoa, Hi., U.S.	D6	88
Holy Cross, Mountain of the, mtn., Co., U.S.	B4	83
Holyhead, Wales, U.K.	H8	7
Holyoke, Co., U.S.	A8	83
Holyoke, Ma., U.S.	B2	98
Holyoke Range, hills, Ma., U.S.	B2	98
Holzminden, Ger.	D9	8
Hombori Tondo, mtn., Mali	E5	42
Homburg, Ger.	F7	8
Home Bay, b., N.W. Ter., Can.	C19	66
Homecroft, In., U.S.	m10	91
Homedale, Id., U.S.	F2	89
Home Hill, Austl.	C9	50
Homeland, Ga., U.S.	F4	87
Home Place, In., U.S.	E5	91
Homer, Ak., U.S.	D9	79
Homer, Ga., U.S.	B3	87
Homer, Il., U.S.	C6	90
Homer, La., U.S.	B2	95
Homer, Mi., U.S.	F6	99
Homer, N.Y., U.S.	C4	109
Homer City, Pa., U.S.	E3	115
Homerville, Ga., U.S.	E4	87
Homer Youngs Peak, mtn., Mt., U.S.	E3	103
Homestead, Fl., U.S.	G6	86
Homestead, Pa., U.S.	k14	115
Homestead Air Force Base, mil., Fl., U.S.	G6	86
Homestead National Monument of America, Ne., U.S.	D9	104
Homewood, Al., U.S.	g7	78
Homewood, Il., U.S.	B6	90
Homewood, Oh., U.S.	C1	112
Hominy, Ok., U.S.	A5	113
Hominy Creek, stm., Ok., U.S.	A5	113
Homme Dam, N.D., U.S.	A8	111
Homochitto, stm., Ms., U.S.	D2	101
Homosassa, Fl., U.S.	D4	86
Homs see Himş, Syria	B5	40
Honaker, Va., U.S.	e10	123
Honaunau, Hi., U.S.	D6	88
Honda, Col.	E5	58
Hondo, Japan	J3	30
Hondo, Tx., U.S.	E3	120
Hondo, stm., N.A.	H15	62
Hondo, Rio, stm., N.M., U.S.	D4	108
Honduras, ctry., N.A.	G4	64
Honduras, Gulf of, b., N.A.	F4	64
Honea Path, S.C., U.S.	C3	117
Hønefoss, Nor.	F8	6
Honeoye Falls, N.Y., U.S.	C3	109
Honesdale, Pa., U.S.	C11	115
Honey Brook, Pa., U.S.	F10	115
Honey Grove, Tx., U.S.	C5	120
Honey Lake, l., Ca., U.S.	B3	82
Honeypot Glen, Ct., U.S.	C4	84
Honeyville, Ut., U.S.	B3	121
Hon Gai, Viet.	D9	34
Honga River, b., Md., U.S.	D5	97
Hongdong, China	D9	26
Honghu, China	F2	28
Hong Kong, dep., Asia	M3	28
Hongliuyuan, China	C6	26
Honguedo, Détroit d', strt., Que., Can.	G20	66
Hongze Hu, l., China	B7	28
Honiara, Sol.Is.	A11	50
Honjō, Japan	F12	30
Honningsvåg, Nor.	A15	6
Honokaa, Hi., U.S.	C6	88
Honolulu, Hi., U.S.	B4	88
Honolulu, co., Hi., U.S.	B3	88
Honolulu International Airport, Hi., U.S.	g10	88
Honomu, Hi., U.S.	D6	88
Honouliuli, Hi., U.S.	g9	88
Honshū, i., Japan	F10	30
Honuapo Bay, b., Hi., U.S.	D6	88
Hood, co., Tx., U.S.	C4	120
Hood, Mount, mtn., Or., U.S.	B5	114
Hood Canal, b., Wa., U.S.	B2	124
Hoodoo Peak, mtn., Wa., U.S.	A5	124
Hood River, Or., U.S.	B5	114
Hood River, co., Or., U.S.	B5	114
Hoodsport, Wa., U.S.	B2	124
Hoogeveen, Neth.	C6	8
Hooker, Ok., U.S.	e9	113
Hooker, co., Ne., U.S.	C4	104
Hook Head, c., Ire.	I6	7
Hooksett, N.H., U.S.	D4	106
Hoonah, Ak., U.S.	D12	79
Hoopa Valley Indian Reservation, Ca., U.S.	B2	82
Hooper, Ne., U.S.	C9	104
Hooper Bay, Ak., U.S.	C6	79
Hooper Islands, is., Md., U.S.	D5	97
Hooper Strait, strt., Md., U.S.	D5	97
Hoopes Reservoir, res., De., U.S.	A3	85
Hoopeston, Il., U.S.	C6	90
Hoorn, Neth.	C5	8
Hoosac Range, mts., U.S.	A1	98
Hoosic, stm., U.S.	C7	109
Hoosick Falls, N.Y., U.S.	C7	109
Hoover Dam, U.S.	G7	105
Hoover Reservoir, res., Oh., U.S.	B3	112
Hooverson Heights, W.V., U.S.	f8	125
Hopatcong, N.J., U.S.	B3	107
Hopatcong, Lake, l., N.J., U.S.	A3	107
Hope, B.C., Can.	E7	69
Hope, Ar., U.S.	D2	81
Hope, In., U.S.	F6	91
Hope, R.I., U.S.	D3	116
Hope, Ben, mtn., Scot., U.K.	C8	7
Hope, Point, c., Ak., U.S.	B6	79
Hopedale, Il., U.S.	C4	90
Hopedale, Ma., U.S.	B4	98
Hope Island, i., R.I., U.S.	E5	116
Hope Mills, N.C., U.S.	C4	110
Hopes Advance, Cap, c., Que., Can.	f13	74
Hopetown, S. Afr.	G4	44
Hope Valley, R.I., U.S.	E2	116
Hopewell, Va., U.S.	C5	123
Hopewell Junction, N.Y., U.S.	D7	109
Hopi Indian Reservation, Az., U.S.	A5	80
Hopkins, Mn., U.S.	n12	100
Hopkins, S.C., U.S.	D6	117
Hopkins, co., Ky., U.S.	C2	94
Hopkins, co., Tx., U.S.	C5	120
Hopkinsville, Ky., U.S.	D2	94
Hopkinton, Ia., U.S.	B6	92
Hopkinton, Ma., U.S.	B4	98
Hopkinton, R.I., U.S.	F1	116
Hopkinton Lake, res., N.H., U.S.	D3	106
Hopwood, Pa., U.S.	G2	115
Hoquiam, Wa., U.S.	C2	124
Horace, N.D., U.S.	C9	111
Horace Mountain, mtn., Ak., U.S.	B10	79
Horatio, Ar., U.S.	D1	81
Horgen, Switz.	E15	10
Horicon, Wi., U.S.	E5	126
Horine, Mo., U.S.	C7	102
Hormuz, Strait of, strt., Asia	C6	46
Horn, Aus.	G15	8
Horn, Cape see Hornos, Cabo de, c., Chile	H3	56
Hornell, N.Y., U.S.	C3	109
Hornersville, Mo., U.S.	E7	102
Horn Island, i., Ms., U.S.	E5	101
Horn Island Pass, strt., Ms., U.S.	g8	101
Horn Lake, Ms., U.S.	A3	101
Hornos, Cabo de (Cape Horn), c., Chile	H3	56
Horn Plateau, plat., N.W. Ter., Can.	D9	66
Horqin Youyi Qianqi, China	B11	26
Horry, co., S.C., U.S.	D10	117
Horse, stm., Ct., U.S.	C6	84
Horse Cave, Ky., U.S.	C4	94
Horse Creek, stm., U.S.	E8	127
Horse Creek Reservoir, res., Co., U.S.	C7	83
Horsehead Lake, l., N.D., U.S.	B6	111
Horseheads, N.Y., U.S.	C4	109
Horse Heaven Hills, hills, Wa., U.S.	C6	124
Horsens, Den.	I7	6
Horse Peak, mtn., N.M., U.S.	D1	108
Horseshoe Bend, Id., U.S.	F2	89
Horseshoe Bend National Military Park, Al., U.S.	C4	78
Horseshoe Cove, b., Fl., U.S.	C3	86
Horseshoe Point, c., Fl., U.S.	C3	86
Horseshoe Reservoir, res., Az., U.S.	C4	80
Horsham, Austl.	G8	50
Horten, Nor.	G8	6
Horton, Ks., U.S.	C8	93
Hortonia, Lake, l., Vt., U.S.	D2	122
Hortonville, Wi., U.S.	D5	126
Hoschton, Ga., U.S.	B3	87
Hoshangābād, India	I7	38
Hoshiārpur, India	E6	38
Hospers, Ia., U.S.	A2	92
Hospet, India	E4	37
Hospitalet, Spain	D14	12
Hosta Butte, mtn., N.M., U.S.	B1	108
Hoste, Isla, i., Chile	H3	56
Hotchkiss, Co., U.S.	C3	83
Hot Creek Range, mts., Nv., U.S.	E5	105
Hot Creek Valley, val., Nv., U.S.	E5	105
Hoting, Swe.	D11	6
Hot Spring, co., Ar., U.S.	C2	81
Hot Springs, S.D., U.S.	D2	118
Hot Springs, co., Wy., U.S.	C4	127
Hot Springs National Park, Ar., U.S.	C2	81
Hot Springs National Park, Ar., U.S.	C2	81
Hot Springs Peak, mtn., Ca., U.S.	B3	82
Hot Springs Peak, mtn., Nv., U.S.	B4	105
Hottah Lake, l., N.W. Ter., Can.	C9	66
Houghton, Mi., U.S.	A2	99
Houghton, N.Y., U.S.	C2	109
Houghton, co., Mi., U.S.	B2	99
Houghton Lake, Mi., U.S.	D6	99
Houghton Lake, l., Mi., U.S.	D6	99
Houghton Lake Heights, Mi., U.S.	D6	99
Houlton, Me., U.S.	B5	96
Houma, China	D9	26
Houma, La., U.S.	E5	95
Housatonic, stm., U.S.	D3	84
House Springs, Mo., U.S.	g12	102
Houston, De., U.S.	E3	85
Houston, Mn., U.S.	G7	100
Houston, Ms., U.S.	B4	101
Houston, Mo., U.S.	D6	102
Houston, Pa., U.S.	F1	115
Houston, Tx., U.S.	E5	120
Houston, co., Al., U.S.	D4	78
Houston, co., Ga., U.S.	D3	87
Houston, co., Mn., U.S.	G7	100
Houston, co., Tn., U.S.	A4	119
Houston, co., Tx., U.S.	D5	120
Houston, stm., La., U.S.	D2	95
Houston, Lake, res., Tx., U.S.	r14	120
Houston Intercontinental Airport, Tx., U.S.	r14	120
Houtman Rocks, Austl.	E2	50
Houtzdale, Pa., U.S.	E5	115
Hovenweep National Monument, Ut., U.S.	F6	121
Hovmantorp, Swe.	H10	6
Howard, Ks., U.S.	E7	93
Howard, S.D., U.S.	C8	118
Howard, Wi., U.S.	D5	126
Howard, co., Ar., U.S.	C2	81
Howard, co., In., U.S.	C5	91
Howard, co., Ia., U.S.	A5	92
Howard, co., Md., U.S.	B4	97
Howard, co., Mo., U.S.	B5	102
Howard, co., Ne., U.S.	C7	104
Howard, co., Tx., U.S.	C2	120
Howard City, Mi., U.S.	E5	99
Howard Hanson Reservoir, res., Wa., U.S.	B4	124
Howard Lake, Mn., U.S.	E4	100
Howard Prairie Lake, res., Or., U.S.	E4	114
Howards Grove-Millersville, Wi., U.S.	E6	126
Howell, Mi., U.S.	F7	99
Howell, co., Mo., U.S.	E6	102
Howells, Ne., U.S.	C8	104
Howe Sound, strt., B.C., Can.	E6	69
Howick, Que., Can.	D4	74
Howland, Me., U.S.	C4	96
Howrah, India	I13	38
Hoxie, Ar., U.S.	A5	81
Hoxie, Ks., U.S.	C3	93
Höxter, Ger.	D9	8
Hoy, i., Scot., U.K.	C9	7
Høyanger, Nor.	F6	6
Hoyerswerda, Ger.	D14	8
Hoyos, Spain	E5	12
Hoyt Lakes, Mn., U.S.	C6	100
Hradec Králové, Czech.	E15	8
Hsilo, Tai.	L9	28
Hsinchu, Tai.	K9	28
Hsüehchia, Tai.	L9	28
Huacho, Peru	F3	54
Huachuca City, Az., U.S.	F5	80
Hua Hin, Thai.	H5	34
Huahua, stm., Nic.	G6	64
Huaian, China	B8	28
Huainan, China	C6	28
Huaiyang, China	B3	28
Huaiyin, China	B8	28
Huaiyuan, China	C6	28
Hualalai, vol., Hi., U.S.	D6	88
Hualapai Indian Reservation, Az., U.S.	B2	80
Hualapai Mountains, mts., Az., U.S.	C2	80
Hualapai Peak, mtn., Az., U.S.	B2	80
Hualien, Tai.	L10	28
Huallaga, stm., Peru	E3	54
Huallanca, Peru	E3	54
Huamachuco, Peru	E3	54
Huambo, Ang.	D3	44
Huancayo, Peru	F3	54
Huang (Yellow), stm., China	D10	26
Huangchuan, China	C4	28
Huangling, China	D8	26
Huangshi, China	E4	28
Huangyan, China	G10	28
Huánuco, Peru	E3	54
Huaraz, Peru	E3	54
Huascarán, Nevado, mtn., Peru	E3	54
Huasco, Chile	B2	56
Huatabampo, Mex.	D5	62
Huauchinango, Mex.	G10	62
Hubbard, Ia., U.S.	B4	92
Hubbard, Oh., U.S.	A5	112
Hubbard, Or., U.S.	B4	114
Hubbard, Tx., U.S.	D4	120
Hubbard, co., Mn., U.S.	C4	100
Hubbard Creek Lake, res., Tx., U.S.	C3	120
Hubbard Lake, l., Mi., U.S.	D7	99
Hubbardton, stm., Vt., U.S.	D2	122
Hubbell, Mi., U.S.	A2	99
Hubei, prov., China	E9	26
Hubli, India	E3	37
Huckleberry Mountain, mtn., Or., U.S.	D4	114
Huddersfield, Eng., U.K.	H11	7
Huddinge, Swe.	G11	6
Hudiksvall, Swe.	F11	6
Hudson, Que., Can.	D3	74
Hudson, Co., U.S.	A6	83
Hudson, Fl., U.S.	D4	86
Hudson, Il., U.S.	C5	90
Hudson, Ia., U.S.	B5	92
Hudson, Ma., U.S.	B4	98
Hudson, Mi., U.S.	G6	99
Hudson, N.H., U.S.	E4	106
Hudson, N.Y., U.S.	C7	109
Hudson, N.C., U.S.	B1	110
Hudson, Oh., U.S.	A4	112
Hudson, Wi., U.S.	D1	126
Hudson, Wy., U.S.	D4	127
Hudson, co., N.J., U.S.	B4	107
Hudson, stm., U.S.	E7	109
Hudson, Lake, res., Ok., U.S.	A6	113
Hudson Bay, b., Can.	D15	66
Hudson Falls, N.Y., U.S.	B7	109
Hudson Hope, B.C., Can.	A6	69
Hudson Lake, In., U.S.	A4	91
Hudson Strait, strt., Can.	D18	66
Hudsonville, Mi., U.S.	F5	99
Hudspeth, co., Tx., U.S.	o12	120
Hue, Viet.	F9	34
Huehuetenango, Guat.	G2	64
Huelma, Spain	H8	12
Huelva, Spain	H5	12
Huércal-Overa, Spain	H10	12
Huerfano, co., Co., U.S.	D5	83
Huerfano, stm., Co., U.S.	D6	83
Huerfano Mountain, mtn., N.M., U.S.	A2	108
Huesca, Spain	C11	12
Hueytown, Al., U.S.	g6	78
Huffakers, Nv., U.S.	D2	105
Hugh Butler Lake, res., Ne., U.S.	D5	104
Hughenden, Austl.	D8	50
Hughes, Ar., U.S.	C5	81
Hughes, co., Ok., U.S.	B5	113
Hughes, co., S.D., U.S.	C5	118
Hughes, North Fork, stm., W.V., U.S.	B3	125
Hughes, South Fork, stm., W.V., U.S.	B3	125
Hughesville, Md., U.S.	C4	97
Hughesville, Pa., U.S.	D8	115
Hugo, Co., U.S.	B7	83
Hugo, Mn., U.S.	m13	100
Hugo, Ok., U.S.	C6	113
Hugo Lake, res., Ok., U.S.	C6	113
Hugoton, Ks., U.S.	E2	93
Huidong, China	A7	34
Huila, Nevado del, mtn., Col.	F4	58
Huili, China	A7	34
Huinan, China	C12	26
Huittinen (Lauttakylä), Fin.	F14	6
Huitzuco [de los Figueroa], Mex.	H10	62
Huixtla, Mex.	J13	62
Huiyang (Huizhou), China	L3	28
Hulah Lake, res., Ok., U.S.	A5	113
Hulan, China	B12	26
Hulett, Wy., U.S.	B8	127
Hull, Que., Can.	D2	74
Hull, Ia., U.S.	A1	92
Hull, Ma., U.S.	B6	98
Hultsfred, Swe.	H10	6
Hulun Nur, l., China	B10	26
Humaitá, Braz.	E6	54
Humansville, Mo., U.S.	D4	102
Humber, stm., Eng., U.K.	H12	7
Humble, Tx., U.S.	E5	120
Humboldt, Az., U.S.	C3	80
Humboldt, Ia., U.S.	B3	92
Humboldt, Ks., U.S.	E8	93
Humboldt, Ne., U.S.	D10	104
Humboldt, Tn., U.S.	B3	119
Humboldt, co., Ca., U.S.	B2	82
Humboldt, co., Ia., U.S.	B3	92
Humboldt, co., Nv., U.S.	B3	105
Humboldt, stm., Nv., U.S.	C3	105
Humboldt Range, mts., Nv., U.S.	C3	105
Hummels Wharf, Pa., U.S.	E8	115
Humphrey, Ar., U.S.	C4	81
Humphrey, Ne., U.S.	C8	104
Humphreys, co., Ms., U.S.	B3	101
Humphreys, co., Tn., U.S.	A4	119
Humphreys, Mount, mtn., Ca., U.S.	D4	82
Humphreys Peak, mtn., Az., U.S.	B4	80
Hunan, prov., China	F9	26
Hundred Acre Pond, l., R.I., U.S.	E3	116
Hunedoara, Rom.	D6	16
Hünfeld, Ger.	E9	8
Hungary, ctry., Eur.	F11	4
Hungt'ou Hsü, i., Tai.	M10	28
Hŭngnam, N. Kor.	D12	26
Hungry Horse, Mt., U.S.	B2	103
Hungry Horse Reservoir, res., Mt., U.S.	B3	103
Hunsrück, mts., Ger.	F6	8
Hunt, co., Tx., U.S.	C4	120
Hunt, stm., R.I., U.S.	D4	116
Hunterdon, co., N.J., U.S.	B3	107
Hunter Island, i., Austl.	H8	50

Name	Map Ref	Page
Hunter Island, i., B.C., Can.	D3	69
Huntertown, In., U.S.	B7	91
Huntingburg, In., U.S.	H4	91
Huntingdon, Que., Can.	D3	74
Huntingdon, Pa., U.S.	F6	115
Huntingdon, Tn., U.S.	A3	119
Huntingdon, co., Pa., U.S.	F5	115
Hunting Island, i., S.C., U.S.	G7	117
Huntington, Ar., U.S.	B1	81
Huntington, In., U.S.	C7	91
Huntington, N.Y., U.S.	E7	109
Huntington, Tx., U.S.	D5	120
Huntington, Ut., U.S.	D5	121
Huntington, W.V., U.S.	C2	125
Huntington, co., In., U.S.	C6	91
Huntington Beach, Ca., U.S.	F4	82
Huntington Lake, res., In., U.S.	C7	91
Huntington Woods, Mi., U.S.	p15	99
Huntingtown, Md., U.S.	C4	97
Huntland, Tn., U.S.	B5	119
Huntley, Il., U.S.	A5	90
Hunt Mountain, mtn., Wy., U.S.	B5	127
Huntsville, Ont., Can.	B5	73
Huntsville, Al., U.S.	A3	78
Huntsville, Ar., U.S.	A2	81
Huntsville, Mo., U.S.	B5	102
Huntsville, Tn., U.S.	C9	119
Huntsville, Tx., U.S.	D5	120
Huon Gulf, b., Pap. N. Gui.	m16	50a
Hurao, China	B13	26
Hurd, Cape, c., Ont., Can.	B3	73
Hurley, Ms., U.S.	E5	101
Hurley, N.M., U.S.	E1	108
Hurley, N.Y., U.S.	D6	109
Hurley, Wi., U.S.	B3	126
Hurlock, Md., U.S.	C6	97
Huron, Oh., U.S.	A3	112
Huron, S.D., U.S.	C7	118
Huron, co., Mi., U.S.	E7	99
Huron, co., Oh., U.S.	A3	112
Huron, stm., Mi., U.S.	p14	99
Huron, Lake, l., N.A.	C10	76
Huron Mountains, hills, Mi., U.S.	B3	99
Hurricane, Ut., U.S.	F2	121
Hurricane, W.V., U.S.	C2	125
Hurst, Il., U.S.	F4	90
Hurt, Va., U.S.	C3	123
Hurtsboro, Al., U.S.	C4	78
Húsavík, Ice.	B4	4
Huskvarna, Swe.	H10	6
Hustisford, Wi., U.S.	E5	126
Husum, Ger.	A9	8
Hutchins, Tx., U.S.	n10	120
Hutchinson, Ks., U.S.	D6	93
Hutchinson, Mn., U.S.	F4	100
Hutchinson, co., S.D., U.S.	D8	118
Hutchinson, co., Tx., U.S.	B2	120
Hutchinson Island, i., Fl., U.S.	E6	86
Hutchinson Island, i., S.C., U.S.	k11	117
Hutch Mountain, mtn., Az., U.S.	C4	80
Hüttental, Ger.	E8	8
Huttig, Ar., U.S.	D3	81
Huwei, Tai.	L9	28
Huxley, Ia., U.S.	C4	92
Huy, Bel.	E5	8
Huzhou, China	E9	28
Hvannadalshnúkur, mtn., Ice.	C4	4
Hvar, Yugo.	F11	14
Hwange, Zimb.	E5	44
Hwang Ho see Huang, stm., China	D10	26
Hyannis, Ma., U.S.	C7	98
Hyannis Port, Ma., U.S.	C7	98
Hyattsville, Md., U.S.	C4	97
Hybla Valley, Va., U.S.	g12	123
Hyco, stm., Va., U.S.	D3	123
Hyco Lake, res., N.C., U.S.	A3	110
Hydaburg, Ak., U.S.	D13	79
Hyde, Pa., U.S.	D5	115
Hyde, co., N.C., U.S.	B6	110
Hyde, co., S.D., U.S.	C6	118
Hyde Park, Guy.	D13	58
Hyde Park, N.Y., U.S.	D7	109
Hyde Park, Ut., U.S.	B4	121
Hyder, Ak., U.S.	D13	79
Hyderābād, India	D5	37
Hyderābād, Pak.	H3	38
Hydeville, Vt., U.S.	D2	122
Hydro, Ok., U.S.	B3	113
Hyères, Fr.	I13	10
Hyesan, N. Kor.	C12	26
Hymera, In., U.S.	F3	91
Hyndman, Pa., U.S.	G4	115
Hyndman Peak, mtn., Id., U.S.	F4	89
Hyrum, Ut., U.S.	B4	121
Hythe, Alta., Can.	B1	68
Hyūga, Japan	J4	30
Hyūga-nada, Japan	J4	30
Hyvinkää, Fin.	F15	6

I

Name	Map Ref	Page
Iamonia, Lake, l., Fl., U.S.	B2	86
Iași, Rom.	B11	16
Iatt, Lake, res., La., U.S.	C3	95
Ibadan, Nig.	G6	42
Ibagué, Col.	E5	58
Ibapah Peak, mtn., Ut., U.S.	D2	121
Ibarra, Ec.	G3	58
Ibb, Yemen	F3	46
Iberia, Mo., U.S.	C5	102
Iberia, co., La., U.S.	E4	95
Iberville, Que., Can.	D4	74
Iberville, co., La., U.S.	D4	95
Iberville, Mont d' (Mount Caubvick), mtn., Can.	g14	74
Ibiá, Braz.	E5	57
Ibicaraí, Braz.	C9	57
Ibiza, Spain	G13	12
Ibiza, i., Spain	G13	12
Ibo, Moz.	D8	44
Ica, Peru	F3	54
Içá (Putumayo), stm., S.A.	I8	58
Içana, Braz.	C5	54
Içana, stm., S.A.	C5	54
Ice Harbor Dam, Wa., U.S.	C7	124
İçel, Tur.	H14	4
Iceland, ctry., Eur.	B4	4
Ichalkaranji, India	D3	37
Ich Bogd Uul, mts., Mong.	C7	26
Ichinomiya, Japan	G9	30
Ichinoseki, Japan	D14	30
Icicle Creek, stm., Wa., U.S.	B5	124
Icó, Braz.	E11	54
Icy Cape, c., Ak., U.S.	A7	79
Icy Strait, strt., Ak., U.S.	k22	79
Ida, Mi., U.S.	G7	99
Ida, co., Ia., U.S.	B2	92
Ida, Lake, l., Mn., U.S.	D3	100
Idabel, Ok., U.S.	D7	113
Ida Grove, Ia., U.S.	B2	92
Idaho, co., Id., U.S.	D3	89
Idaho, state, U.S.	E3	89
Idaho Falls, Id., U.S.	F6	89
Idaho Springs, Co., U.S.	B5	83
Idalou, Tx., U.S.	C2	120
Idamay, W.V., U.S.	k10	125
Idanha-a-Nova, Port.	F4	12
Idāppādi, India	G4	37
Idar-Oberstein, Ger.	F7	8
Idaville, In., U.S.	C4	91
Ider, Al., U.S.	A4	78
Idfū, Egypt	D12	42
Idlib, Syria	B5	40
Ídolo, Isla del, i., Mex.	G11	62
Ieper, Bel.	E2	8
Ierápetra, Grc.	N9	16
Iesi, Italy	F8	14
Ife, Nig.	G6	42
Iferouâne, Niger	E7	42
Iforas, Adrar des, mts., Afr.	D6	42
Iglesias, Italy	J3	14
Igloolik, N.W. Ter., Can.	C16	66
Ignacio, Co., U.S.	D3	83
Iguaçu, Saltos do (Iguassu Falls), wtfl, S.A.	B6	56
Iguala, Mex.	H10	62
Igualada, Spain	D13	12
Iguape, Braz.	A7	56
Iguatu, Braz.	E11	54
Iguéla, Gabon	B1	44
Iguidi, Erg, dunes, Afr.	C4	42
Ihosy, Madag.	F9	44
Iida, Japan	G10	30
Iisalmi, Fin.	E16	6
Iizuka, Japan	I3	30
IJmuiden, Neth.	C4	8
IJsselmeer (Zuiderzee), Neth.	C5	8
Ika, U.S.S.R.	F15	20
Ikela, Zaire	B4	44
Ikerre, Nig.	G7	42
Ila, Nig.	G6	42
Ilagan, Phil.	B7	32
Ilan, Tai.	K10	28
Ilbenge, U.S.S.R.	E18	20
Île-à-la-Crosse, Lac, l., Sask., Can.	B2	75
Ilebo, Zaire	B4	44
Île-de-France, hist. reg., Fr.	C9	10
Île-Perrot, Que., Can.	q19	74
Ilhéus, Braz.	C9	57
Ili, stm., Asia	I13	18
Iliamna Lake, l., Ak., U.S.	D8	79
Iliamna Volcano, vol., Ak., U.S.	C9	79
Ilion, N.Y., U.S.	B5	109
Ilio Point, c., Hi., U.S.	B4	88
Ilirska Bistrica, Yugo.	D9	14
Il'jinskij, U.S.S.R.	H22	20
Ilkal, India	E4	37
Illampu, Nevado, mtn., Bol.	G5	54
Illapel, Chile	C2	56
Illescas, Mex.	F8	62
Illiers, Fr.	D8	10
Illimani, Nevado, mtn., Bol.	G5	54
Illinois, state, U.S.	C4	90
Illinois, stm., U.S.	A7	113
Illinois, stm., Il., U.S.	B5	90
Illinois, stm., Or., U.S.	E3	114
Illinois Peak, mtn., Id., U.S.	B3	89
Illiopolis, Il., U.S.	D4	90
Illizi, Alg.	C7	42
Illmo, Mo., U.S.	D8	102
Il'men', Ozero, l., U.S.S.R.	C14	22
Ilo, Peru	G4	54
Iloilo, Phil.	C7	32
Ilomantsi, Fin.	E18	6
Ilorin, Nig.	G6	42
Il'pyrskij, U.S.S.R.	F26	20
Ilwaco, Wa., U.S.	C1	124
Imabari, Japan	H6	30
Iman, U.S.S.R.	H20	20
Imari, Japan	I2	30
Imatra, Fin.	F17	6
Imboden, Ar., U.S.	A4	81
Imlay, Nv., U.S.	C3	105
Imlay City, Mi., U.S.	E7	99
Immenstadt, Ger.	H10	8
Immokalee, Fl., U.S.	F5	86
Imnaha, stm., Or., U.S.	B10	114
Imola, Italy	E6	14
Imperatriz, Braz.	E9	54
Imperia, Italy	F3	14
Imperial, Ca., U.S.	F6	82
Imperial, Mo., U.S.	C7	102
Imperial, Ne., U.S.	D4	104
Imperial, Pa., U.S.	k13	115
Imperial, co., Ca., U.S.	F6	82
Imperial Beach, Ca., U.S.	o15	82
Imperial Dam, U.S.	E1	80
Imperial Reservoir, res., U.S.	E1	80
Imperial Valley, val., Ca., U.S.	F6	82
Impfondo, Congo	A3	44
Imphāl, India	H15	38
Imst, Aus.	H10	8
Imuris, Mex.	B4	62
Ina, Japan	G10	30
In'a, stm., U.S.S.R.	E23	20
Inari, Fin.	B16	6
Inca, Spain	F14	12
İncekum Burnu, c., Tur.	A3	40
Inch'ŏn, S. Kor.	D12	26
Incline Village, Nv., U.S.	D2	105
Independence, Ia., U.S.	B6	92
Independence, Ks., U.S.	E8	93
Independence, Ky., U.S.	B5	94
Independence, La., U.S.	D5	95
Independence, Mo., U.S.	B3	102
Independence, Or., U.S.	C3	114
Independence, Va., U.S.	D1	123
Independence, Wi., U.S.	D2	126
Independence, co., Ar., U.S.	B4	81
Independence, stm., N.Y., U.S.	B5	109
Independence Mountains, mts., Nv., U.S.	C5	105
Independence National Historical Park, Pa., U.S.	p21	115
Independence Rock, mtn., Wy., U.S.	D5	127
India, ctry., Asia	E4	36
Indian, stm., Ont., Can.	B7	73
Indian, stm., De., U.S.	F4	85
Indian, stm., Mi., U.S.	B4	99
Indian, stm., N.Y., U.S.	A5	109
Indiana, Pa., U.S.	E3	115
Indiana, co., Pa., U.S.	E3	115
Indiana, state, U.S.	E5	91
Indiana Dunes National Lakeshore, In., U.S.	A3	91
Indianapolis, In., U.S.	E5	91
Indian Bay, b., Fl., U.S.	D4	86
Indian Cedar Swamp, sw., R.I., U.S.	F2	116
Indian Creek, stm., Oh., U.S.	C1	112
Indian Creek, stm., S.D., U.S.	B2	118
Indian Creek, stm., Tn., U.S.	B3	119
Indian Creek, stm., W.V., U.S.	k9	125
Indian Creek, stm., W.V., U.S.	D4	125
Indian Head, Md., U.S.	C3	97
Indian Island, i., N.C., U.S.	B6	110
Indian Lake, l., Mi., U.S.	C4	99
Indian Lake, l., N.Y., U.S.	B6	109
Indian Lake, l., Oh., U.S.	B2	112
Indian Lake, l., R.I., U.S.	F4	116
Indian Neck, Ct., U.S.	D4	84
Indian Ocean	G17	2
Indianola, Ia., U.S.	C4	92
Indianola, Ms., U.S.	B3	101
Indianola, Ne., U.S.	D5	104
Indian Peak, mtn., Ut., U.S.	E2	121
Indian Peak, mtn., Wy., U.S.	B3	127
Indian Prairie Canal, Fl., U.S.	E5	86
Indian Ridge Estates, Az., U.S.	E5	80
Indian River, co., Fl., U.S.	E6	86
Indian River, b., Fl., U.S.	D6	86
Indian River Bay, b., De., U.S.	F5	85
Indian Rock, mtn., Wa., U.S.	D5	124
Indian Rocks Beach, Fl., U.S.	p10	86
Indian Springs, Nv., U.S.	G6	105
Indian Stream, stm., N.H., U.S.	f7	106
Indiantown, Fl., U.S.	E6	86
Indian Trail, N.C., U.S.	B2	110
Indigirka, stm., U.S.S.R.	C23	20
Indio, Ca., U.S.	F5	82
Indispensable Reefs, rf., Sol.Is.	B12	50
Indonesia, ctry., Asia	F6	32
Indore, India	I6	38
Indoukâl-n-Taghès, mtn., Niger	E7	42
Indramayu, Indon.	m14	33a
Indrāvati, stm., India	C6	37
Indus, stm., Asia	H2	38
İnegöl, Tur.	I13	16
Infiernillo, Presa del, res., Mex.	H9	62
I-n-Gall, Niger	E7	42
Ingalls, In., U.S.	E6	91
Ingalls Park, Il., U.S.	B5	90
Ingersoll, Ont., Can.	D4	73
Ingham, Austl.	C9	50
Ingham, co., Mi., U.S.	F6	99
Ingleside, Tx., U.S.	F4	120
Inglewood, Ca., U.S.	n12	82
Ingolstadt, Ger.	G11	8
Ingraham, Lake, l., Fl., U.S.	G5	86
Ingram, Pa., U.S.	k13	115
In Guezzam, Alg.	E7	42
Inhambane, Moz.	F7	44
Inhambupe, Braz.	F11	54
Inhaminga, Moz.	E6	44
Inharrime, Moz.	F7	44
Inírida, stm., Col.	F8	58
Inkerman, N.B., Can.	B5	71
Inkom, Id., U.S.	G6	89
Inkster, Mi., U.S.	p15	99
Inland Sea see Seto-naikai, Japan	H6	30
Inle Lake, l., Burma	D4	34
Inman, Ks., U.S.	D6	93
Inman, S.C., U.S.	A3	117
Inn (En), stm., Eur.	G13	8
Innamincka, Austl.	E8	50
Inner Hebrides, is., Scot., U.K.	E6	7
Innisfail, Alta., Can.	C4	68
Innsbruck, Aus.	H11	8
Inola, Ok., U.S.	A6	113
Inongo, Zaire	B3	44
Inowrocław, Pol.	C18	8
In Salah, Alg.	C6	42
Inscription House Ruin, hist., Az., U.S.	A5	80
Insein, Burma	F4	34
Institute, W.V., U.S.	m12	125
Interlachen, Fl., U.S.	C5	86
Interlaken, Switz.	F14	10
International Falls, Mn., U.S.	B5	100
Inthanon, Doi, mtn., Thai.	E5	34
Intiyaco, Arg.	B4	56
Intracoastal Waterway, U.S.	E4	95
Inukjuak, Que., Can.	g11	74
Inveraray, Scot., U.K.	E7	7
Invercargill, N.Z.	G2	52
Inverell, Austl.	E10	50
Inver Grove Heights, Mn., U.S.	n12	100
Invermere, B.C., Can.	D9	69
Inverness, Scot., U.K.	D8	7
Inverness, Ca., U.S.	C2	82
Inverness, Fl., U.S.	D4	86
Inverness, Ms., U.S.	B3	101
Inverurie, Scot., U.K.	D10	7
Investigator Group, is., Austl.	F6	50
Investigator Strait, strt., Austl.	G7	50
Invisible Mountain, mtn., Id., U.S.	F5	89
Inwood, Ia., U.S.	A1	92
Inwood, N.Y., U.S.	k13	109
Inwood, W.V., U.S.	B6	125
Inyangani, mtn., Zimb.	E6	44
Inyan Kara Creek, stm., Wy., U.S.	B8	127
Inyan Kara Mountain, mtn., Wy., U.S.	B8	127
Inyo, co., Ca., U.S.	D5	82
Inyo, Mount, mtn., Ca., U.S.	D5	82
Inyo Mountains, mts., Ca., U.S.	D4	82
Ioánnina, Grc.	J4	16
Iola, Ks., U.S.	E8	93
Iola, Wi., U.S.	D4	126
Iona, Id., U.S.	F7	89
Ione, Ca., U.S.	C3	82
Ionia, Mi., U.S.	F5	99
Ionia, co., Mi., U.S.	F5	99
Ionian Islands see Iónioi Nísoi, is., Grc.	K4	16
Ionian Sea, Eur.	H11	4
Iónioi Nísoi, is., Grc.	K4	16
Iosco, co., Mi., U.S.	D7	99
Iota, La., U.S.	D3	95
Iowa, La., U.S.	D2	95
Iowa, co., Ia., U.S.	C5	92
Iowa, co., Wi., U.S.	E3	126
Iowa, state, U.S.	C4	92
Iowa, stm., Ia., U.S.	C6	92
Iowa, West Branch, stm., Ia., U.S.	B4	92
Iowa City, Ia., U.S.	C6	92
Iowa Falls, Ia., U.S.	B4	92
Iowa Indian Reservation, U.S.	C8	93
Iowa Lake, l., U.S.	A3	92
Iowa Park, Tx., U.S.	C3	120
Ipameri, Braz.	D4	57
Iphigenia Bay, b., Ak., U.S.	n22	79
Ipiales, Col.	G4	58
Ipiaú, Braz.	C9	57
Ipoh, Malay.	L6	34
Ipswich, Austl.	E10	50
Ipswich, Eng., U.K.	I14	7
Ipswich, Ma., U.S.	A6	98
Ipswich, S.D., U.S.	B6	118
Ipswich, stm., Ma., U.S.	A5	98
Ipu, Braz.	D10	54
Iqaluit, N.W. Ter., Can.	D19	66
Iquique, Chile	H4	54
Iquitos, Peru	D4	54
Iraan, Tx., U.S.	D2	120
Iráklion, Grc.	N9	16
Iran, ctry., Asia	B5	46
Iran Mountains, mts., Asia	E5	32
Īrānshahr, Iran	C7	46
Irapa, Ven.	B11	58
Irapuato, Mex.	G9	62
Iraq, ctry., Asia	B3	46
Irazú, Volcán, vol., C.R.	J6	64
Irbid, Jord.	C4	40
Irbil, Iraq	A3	46
Iredell, co., N.C., U.S.	B2	110
Ireland, ctry., Eur.	E6	4
Iriga, Phil.	r20	32
Iringa, Tan.	C7	44
Irion, co., Tx., U.S.	D2	120
Iriri, stm., Braz.	D8	54
Irish, Mount, mtn., Nv., U.S.	F6	105
Irish Sea, Eur.	H8	7
Irkutsk, U.S.S.R.	G14	20
Irmo, S.C., U.S.	C5	117
Iron, co., Mi., U.S.	B2	99
Iron, co., Mo., U.S.	D7	102
Iron, co., Ut., U.S.	F2	121
Iron, co., Wi., U.S.	B3	126
Irondale, Al., U.S.	f7	78
Irondequoit, N.Y., U.S.	B3	109
Iron Gate, val., Eur.	E6	16
Iron Gate Reservoir, res., Eur.	E6	16
Iron Gate Reservoir, res., Ca., U.S.	B2	82
Iron Mountain, Mi., U.S.	C2	99
Iron Mountain, mtn., Az., U.S.	D4	80
Iron Mountains, mts., U.S.	D1	123
Iron Ridge, Wi., U.S.	E5	126
Iron River, Mi., U.S.	B2	99
Iron River, Wi., U.S.	B2	126
Ironton, Mo., U.S.	D7	102
Ironton, Oh., U.S.	D3	112
Ironwood, Mi., U.S.	n11	99
Iroquois, Ont., Can.	C9	73
Iroquois, co., Il., U.S.	C6	90
Iroquois, stm., U.S.	C6	90
Iroquois, Lake, l., Vt., U.S.	B2	122
Iroquois Falls, Ont., Can.	o19	73
Irrawaddy see Ayeyarwady, stm., Burma	G3	34
Irricana, Alta., Can.	D4	68
Irrigon, Or., U.S.	B7	114
Irtyš (Ertix), stm., Asia	F11	18
Irumu, Zaire	A5	44
Irún, Spain	B10	12
Irurzun, Spain	C10	12
Irú Tepuy, mtn., Ven.	E12	58
Irvine, Scot., U.K.	F8	7
Irvine, Ca., U.S.	n13	82
Irvine, Ky., U.S.	C6	94
Irving, Tx., U.S.	n10	120
Irvington, Al., U.S.	E1	78
Irvington, Il., U.S.	E4	90
Irvington, Ky., U.S.	C3	94
Irvington, N.J., U.S.	k8	107
Irvington, N.Y., U.S.	g13	109
Irwin, Pa., U.S.	F2	115
Irwin, co., Ga., U.S.	E3	87
Irwinton, Ga., U.S.	D3	87
Isabel, Mount, mtn., Wy., U.S.	D2	127
Isabella, co., Mi., U.S.	E6	99
Isabella, Cordillera, mts., Nic.	G5	64
Isabella Indian Reservation, Mi., U.S.	E6	99
Isabella Lake, l., Mn., U.S.	C7	100
Ísafjördur, Ice.	B3	4
Isahaya, Japan	J3	30
Isanti, Mn., U.S.	E5	100
Isanti, co., Mn., U.S.	E5	100
Isar, stm., Eur.	G11	8
Ischia, Italy	I8	14
Ise, Japan	H9	30
Isernia, Italy	H9	14
Isesaki, Japan	F12	30
Ise-wan, b., Japan	H9	30
Isherton, Guy.	F13	58
Ishikari-wan, b., Japan	p18	30a
Ishinomaki, Japan	D14	30
Ishpeming, Mi., U.S.	B3	99
Isinglass, stm., N.H., U.S.	D4	106
Isiolo, Kenya	A7	44
Isiro, Zaire	H11	42
İskele, N. Cyp.	B3	40
İskenderun, Tur.	H15	4
İskenderun Körfezi, b., Tur.	A4	40
Iskitim, U.S.S.R.	G10	20
İslâhiye, Tur.	A5	40
Islāmābād, Pak.	D5	38
Islamorada, Fl., U.S.	H6	86
Isla Mujeres, Mex.	G16	62
Island, co., Wa., U.S.	A3	124
Island Beach, N.J., U.S.	D4	107
Island City, Or., U.S.	B8	114
Island Falls, Me., U.S.	B4	96
Island Lake, l., Man., Can.	C4	70
Island Park, R.I., U.S.	E6	116
Island Park Reservoir, res., Id., U.S.	E7	89
Island Pond, Vt., U.S.	B5	122
Island Pond, l., N.H., U.S.	E4	106
Islands, Bay of, b., Newf., Can.	D2	72
Isla Vista, Ca., U.S.	E4	82
Islay, i., Scot., U.K.	F6	7
Isle-aux-Morts, Newf., Can.	E2	72
Isle of Man, dep., Eur.	E7	4
Isle of Palms, S.C., U.S.	k12	117
Isle of Wight, co., Va., U.S.	D6	123
Isle of Wight Bay, b., Md., U.S.	D7	97
Isle Royale National Park, Mi., U.S.	h9	99
Islesboro Island, i., Me., U.S.	D4	96
Isleta, N.M., U.S.	C3	108
Isleta Indian Reservation, N.M., U.S.	C3	108
Islington, Ma., U.S.	h11	98
Isola, Ms., U.S.	B3	101
Isola della Scala, Italy	D5	14
Ispica, Italy	M9	14
Israel (Yisra'el), ctry., Asia	D4	40
Israel, stm., N.H., U.S.	B3	106
Issano, Guy.	E13	58
Issaquah, Wa., U.S.	B3	124
Issaquena, co., Ms., U.S.	C2	101
Issoire, Fr.	G10	10
Issoudun, Fr.	F8	10
Is-sur-Tille, Fr.	E12	10
İstanbul, Tur.	G13	4
İstanbul Boğazı (Bosporus), strt., Tur.	H13	16
Isto, Mount, mtn., Ak., U.S.	B11	79
Istokpoga, Lake, l., Fl., U.S.	E5	86
Itabaiana, Braz.	F11	54
Itaberaí, Braz.	G9	54
Itabira, Braz.	E7	57
Itabuna, Braz.	C9	57
Itacoatiara, Braz.	D7	54
Itagüí, Col.	D5	58
Itaituba, Braz.	D7	54
Itajaí, Braz.	B7	56
Itajubá, Braz.	G6	57
Italy, Tx., U.S.	C4	120
Italy, ctry., Eur.	G10	4
Itaperuna, Braz.	F8	57
Itapetinga, Braz.	C8	57
Itapetininga, Braz.	G4	57
Itapeva, Braz.	G4	57
Itapicuru, stm., Braz.	D10	54
Itapira, Braz.	G5	57
Itaquari, Braz.	F8	57
Itararé, Braz.	H4	57
Itārsi, India	I7	38
Itasca, Il., U.S.	k8	90
Itasca, Tx., U.S.	C4	120
Itasca, co., Mn., U.S.	C5	100
Itasca, Lake, l., Mn., U.S.	C3	100
Itawamba, co., Ms., U.S.	A5	101
Ithaca, Mi., U.S.	E6	99
Ithaca, N.Y., U.S.	C4	109
Itō, Japan	H12	30
Itta Bena, Ms., U.S.	B3	101
Ittiri, Italy	I3	14
Ituberá, Braz.	B9	57
Ituiutaba, Braz.	E4	57
Itumbiara, Braz.	E4	57
Ituni, Guy.	E13	58
Ituri, stm., Zaire	A5	44
Iturup, Ostrov (Etorofu-tō), i., U.S.S.R.	I23	20
Ituverava, Braz.	F5	57
Ituxi, stm., Braz.	E5	54
Itzehoe, Ger.	B9	8
Iuka, Ms., U.S.	A5	101
Iva, S.C., U.S.	C2	117
Ivalo, Fin.	B16	6
Ivanhoe, Mn., U.S.	F2	100
Ivanić Grad, Yugo.	D11	14
Ivano-Frankovsk, U.S.S.R.	H2	18
Ivanovo, U.S.S.R.	D23	22
Ivigtut, Grnld.	D23	66
Ivinheima, stm., Braz.	G2	57
Ivins, Ut., U.S.	F2	121
Ivory Coast, ctry., Afr.	G4	42
Ivoryton, Ct., U.S.	D6	84
Ivrea, Italy	D2	14
Iwaki (Taira), Japan	E13	30
Iwakuni, Japan	H5	30
Iwanai, Japan	q18	30a
Iwanuma, Japan	D13	30
Iwo, Nig.	G6	42
Ixtacihuatl, vol., Mex.	H10	62
Iyo-nada, Japan	I5	30
Izabal, Lago de, l., Guat.	G3	64
Izard, co., Ar., U.S.	A4	81
Izegem, Bel.	E3	8
Iževsk, U.S.S.R.	F8	18
İzmir, Tur.	H13	4
İzmit, Tur.	G13	4
Iznalloz, Spain	H8	12
İznik Gölü, l., Tur.	I13	16
Izozog, Bañados de, sw., Bol.	G6	54
Izúcar de Matamoros, Mex.	H10	62
Izuhara, Japan	H2	30
Izumo, Japan	G5	30
Izu-shotō, is., Japan	H12	30

Name — Map Ref — Page

Izvestij CIK, Ostrova, is., U.S.S.R. **B10** 20

J

Jabalpur, India **I8** 38
Jabbūl, Sabkhat al-, l., Syria **A5** 40
Jablah, Syria **B4** 40
Jablonec nad Nisou, Czech. **E15** 8
Jablonovyj Chrebet (Yablonovy Range), mts., U.S.S.R. **G16** 20
Jaboatão, Braz. **E11** 54
Jabrīn, well, Sau. Ar. **D4** 46
Jaca, Spain **C11** 12
Jacarèzinho, Braz. **G4** 57
Jáchal, Arg. **C3** 56
Jacinto City, Tx., U.S. **r14** 120
Jack, co., Tx., U.S. **C3** 120
Jackfish Lake, l., Sask., Can. **D1** 75
Jackman, Me., U.S. **C2** 96
Jackman Station, Me., U.S. **C2** 96
Jack Mountain, mtn., Mt., U.S. **D4** 103
Jack Mountain, mtn., Wa., U.S. **A5** 124
Jackpot, Nv., U.S. **B7** 105
Jacksboro, Tn., U.S. **C9** 119
Jacksboro, Tx., U.S. **C3** 120
Jacks Mountain, mtn., Pa., U.S. **E6** 115
Jackson, Al., U.S. **D2** 78
Jackson, Ca., U.S. **C3** 82
Jackson, Ga., U.S. **C3** 87
Jackson, Ky., U.S. **C6** 94
Jackson, La., U.S. **D4** 95
Jackson, Mi., U.S. **F6** 99
Jackson, Mn., U.S. **G4** 100
Jackson, Ms., U.S. **C3** 101
Jackson, Mo., U.S. **D8** 102
Jackson, Oh., U.S. **C3** 112
Jackson, S.C., U.S. **E4** 117
Jackson, Tn., U.S. **B3** 119
Jackson, Wi., U.S. **E5** 126
Jackson, Wy., U.S. **C2** 127
Jackson, co., Al., U.S. **A3** 78
Jackson, co., Ar., U.S. **B4** 81
Jackson, co., Co., U.S. **A4** 83
Jackson, co., Fl., U.S. **B1** 86
Jackson, co., Ga., U.S. **B3** 87
Jackson, co., Il., U.S. **F4** 90
Jackson, co., In., U.S. **G5** 91
Jackson, co., Ia., U.S. **B7** 92
Jackson, co., Ks., U.S. **C8** 93
Jackson, co., Ky., U.S. **C5** 94
Jackson, co., La., U.S. **B3** 95
Jackson, co., Mi., U.S. **F6** 99
Jackson, co., Mn., U.S. **G3** 100
Jackson, co., Ms., U.S. **E5** 101
Jackson, co., Mo., U.S. **B3** 102
Jackson, co., N.C., U.S. **f9** 110
Jackson, co., Oh., U.S. **C3** 112
Jackson, co., Ok., U.S. **C2** 113
Jackson, co., Or., U.S. **E4** 114
Jackson, co., S.D., U.S. **D4** 118
Jackson, co., Tn., U.S. **C8** 119
Jackson, co., Tx., U.S. **E4** 120
Jackson, co., W.V., U.S. **C3** 125
Jackson, co., Wi., U.S. **D3** 126
Jackson, stm., Va., U.S. **C3** 123
Jackson, Lake, l., Fl., U.S. **E5** 86
Jackson, Lake, l., Fl., U.S. **B2** 86
Jackson, Mount, mtn., N.H., U.S. **B4** 106
Jackson Center, Oh., U.S. **B1** 112
Jackson Lake, res., Wy., U.S. **C2** 127
Jackson Mountains, mts., Nv., U.S. **B3** 105
Jackson's Arm, Newf., Can. **D3** 72
Jacksons Gap, Al., U.S. **C4** 78
Jacksonville, Al., U.S. **B4** 78
Jacksonville, Ar., U.S. **C3** 81
Jacksonville, Fl., U.S. **B5** 86
Jacksonville, Il., U.S. **D3** 90
Jacksonville, N.C., U.S. **C5** 110
Jacksonville, Or., U.S. **E4** 114
Jacksonville, Tx., U.S. **D5** 120
Jacksonville Beach, Fl., U.S. **B5** 86
Jacksonville Naval Air Station, mil., Fl., U.S. **B5** 86
Jacks Peak, mtn., Ut., U.S. **E3** 121
Jacmel, Haiti **E11** 64
Jacobābād, Pak. **F3** 38
Jacques-Cartier, stm., Que., Can. **B6** 74
Jacques-Cartier, Détroit de, strt., Que., Can. **h8** 72
Jacquet River, N.B., Can. **B4** 71
Jadraque, Spain **E9** 12
Jaén, Peru **E3** 54
Jaén, Spain **H8** 12
Jaffna, Sri L. **H6** 37
Jaffrey, N.H., U.S. **E2** 106
Jafr, Qāʿ al-, depr., Jord. **D5** 40
Jagādhri, India **E7** 38
Jagdalpur, India **C7** 37
Jagersfontein, S. Afr. **G5** 44
Jagodnoje, U.S.S.R. **E23** 20
Jagtiāl, India **C5** 37
Jaguarão, Braz. **C6** 56
Jahrom, Iran **C5** 46
Jaidak, Afg. **E2** 38
Jaipur, India **G6** 38
Jajce, Yugo. **E12** 14
Jakarta, Indon. **m13** 32
Jakobshavn, Grnld. **C22** 66
Jakobstad (Pietarsaari), Fin. **E14** 6
Jakutsk, U.S.S.R. **E19** 20
Jal, N.M., U.S. **E6** 108
Jalālābād, Afg. **C4** 38
Jalapa, Guat. **G3** 64
Jalapa Enríquez, Mex. **H11** 62
Jālgaon, India **B3** 37
Jālna, India **C3** 37
Jalostotitlán, Mex. **G8** 62
Jalpaiguri, India **G13** 38
Jalta, U.S.S.R. **I4** 18
Jaltepec, stm., Mex. **I12** 62
Jamaica, ctry., N.A. **E9** 64
Jamaica Bay, b., N.Y., U.S. **k13** 109
Jamaica Channel, strt., N.A. **E10** 64
Jamālpur, Bngl. **H13** 38
Jamālpur, India **H12** 38
Jamame, Som. **A8** 44
Jambi, Indon. **F3** 32
Jambol, Bul. **G10** 16
James, stm., U.S. **C7** 76
James, stm., Mo., U.S. **E4** 102
James, stm., Va., U.S. **C5** 123
James, Lake, l., In., U.S. **A7** 91
James, Lake, res., N.C., U.S. **B1** 110
James Bay, b., Can. **F16** 66
James Branch, stm., De., U.S. **F3** 85
Jamesburg, N.J., U.S. **C4** 107
James City, N.C., U.S. **B5** 110
James City, co., Va., U.S. **C6** 123
James Island, S.C., U.S. **k12** 117
James Island, i., Md., U.S. **C5** 97
James Island, i., S.C., U.S. **F8** 117
James River Bridge, Va., U.S. **k15** 123
Jamestown, In., U.S. **E4** 91
Jamestown, Ky., U.S. **D4** 94
Jamestown, N.Y., U.S. **C1** 109
Jamestown, N.C., U.S. **B3** 110
Jamestown, N.D., U.S. **C7** 111
Jamestown, Oh., U.S. **C2** 112
Jamestown, R.I., U.S. **F5** 116
Jamestown, Tn., U.S. **C9** 119
James Town, Wy., U.S. **E3** 127
Jamestown Dam, N.D., U.S. **C7** 111
Jamestown Reservoir, res., N.D., U.S. **C7** 111
Jamiltepec, Mex. **I11** 62
Jamkhandi, India **D3** 37
Jammu, India **D6** 38
Jammu and Kashmir, dep., Asia **C6** 38
Jāmnagar, India **I4** 38
Jāmpur, Pak. **F4** 38
Jämsä, Fin. **F15** 6
Jamshedpur, India **I12** 38
Jamsk, U.S.S.R. **F24** 20
Jamūi, India **H12** 38
Jamuna, stm., Bngl. **H13** 38
Jana, stm., U.S.S.R. **C21** 20
Janaucu, Ilha, i., Braz. **C8** 54
Janesville, Ca., U.S. **B3** 82
Janesville, Ia., U.S. **B5** 92
Janesville, Mn., U.S. **F5** 100
Janesville, Wi., U.S. **F4** 126
Jangipur, India **H13** 38
Janīn, Jord. **C4** 40
Janskij, U.S.S.R. **D20** 20
Janskij Zaliv, b., U.S.S.R. **C21** 20
Januária, Braz. **C6** 57
Jaora, India **I6** 38
Japan, ctry., Asia **D14** 26
Japan, Sea of, Asia **D13** 26
Japurá (Caquetá), stm., S.A. **D5** 54
Jaqué, Pan. **K8** 64
Jarābulus, Syria **A6** 40
Jaraiz de la Vera, Spain **E6** 12
Jarash, Jord. **C4** 40
Jarcevo, U.S.S.R. **F15** 22
Jardines de la Reina, is., Cuba **D8** 64
Jari, stm., Braz. **D8** 54
Jaridih, India **I12** 38
Jaroslavl', U.S.S.R. **D22** 22
Jarosław, Pol. **E22** 8
Jarrettsville, Md., U.S. **A5** 97
Järvenpää, Fin. **F15** 6
Järvsö, Swe. **F11** 6
Jask, Iran **C6** 46
Jasmine Estates, Fl., U.S. **D4** 86
Jasnyj, U.S.S.R. **G19** 20
Jasonville, In., U.S. **F3** 91
Jasper, Al., U.S. **B2** 78
Jasper, Fl., U.S. **B4** 86
Jasper, Ga., U.S. **B2** 87
Jasper, In., U.S. **H4** 91
Jasper, Mo., U.S. **D3** 102
Jasper, Tn., U.S. **D8** 119
Jasper, Tx., U.S. **D6** 120
Jasper, co., Ga., U.S. **C3** 87
Jasper, co., Il., U.S. **D5** 90
Jasper, co., In., U.S. **B3** 91
Jasper, co., Ia., U.S. **C4** 92
Jasper, co., Ms., U.S. **C4** 101
Jasper, co., Mo., U.S. **D3** 102
Jasper, co., S.C., U.S. **G5** 117
Jasper, co., Tx., U.S. **D5** 120
Jasper National Park, Alta., Can. **C1** 68
Jataí, Braz. **D3** 57
Játiva, Spain **G11** 12
Jatni, India **J11** 38
Jaú, Braz. **G4** 57
Jauaperi, stm., Braz. **C6** 54
Jauja, Peru **F3** 54
Jaunpur, India **H10** 38
Java see Jawa, i., Indon. **G4** 32
Javari (Yavarí), stm., S.A. **D4** 54
Java Sea see Jawa, Laut, Indon. **G4** 32
Jävre, Swe. **D13** 6
Jawa, i., Indon. **G4** 32
Jawa, Laut (Java Sea), Indon. **G4** 32
Jaworzno, Pol. **E19** 8
Jay, Ok., U.S. **A7** 113
Jay, co., In., U.S. **D7** 91
Jaya, Puncak, mtn., Indon. **F10** 32
Jayapura, Indon. **F11** 32
Jayb, Wādī al-, val., Asia **D4** 40
J. B. Thomas, Lake, res., Tx., U.S. **C2** 120
Jean, Nv., U.S. **H6** 105
Jeanerette, La., U.S. **E4** 95
Jean Lafitte National Historical Park, La., U.S. **k12** 95
Jeannette, Pa., U.S. **F2** 115
Jebba, Nig. **G6** 42
Jeddore Lake, res., Newf., Can. **D3** 72
Jeff Davis, co., Ga., U.S. **E4** 87
Jeff Davis, co., Tx., U.S. **o12** 120
Jefferson, Ga., U.S. **B3** 87
Jefferson, Ia., U.S. **B3** 92
Jefferson, La., U.S. **k11** 95
Jefferson, N.C., U.S. **A1** 110
Jefferson, Oh., U.S. **A5** 112
Jefferson, Or., U.S. **C3** 114
Jefferson, S.C., U.S. **B7** 117
Jefferson, Tx., U.S. **C5** 120
Jefferson, Wi., U.S. **E5** 126
Jefferson, co., Al., U.S. **B3** 78
Jefferson, co., Ar., U.S. **C3** 81
Jefferson, co., Co., U.S. **B5** 83
Jefferson, co., Fl., U.S. **B3** 86
Jefferson, co., Ga., U.S. **C4** 87
Jefferson, co., Id., U.S. **F6** 89
Jefferson, co., Il., U.S. **E5** 90
Jefferson, co., In., U.S. **G6** 91
Jefferson, co., Ia., U.S. **C5** 92
Jefferson, co., Ks., U.S. **C8** 93
Jefferson, co., Ky., U.S. **B4** 94
Jefferson, co., La., U.S. **E5** 95
Jefferson, co., Ms., U.S. **D2** 101
Jefferson, co., Mo., U.S. **C7** 102
Jefferson, co., Mt., U.S. **D4** 103
Jefferson, co., Ne., U.S. **D8** 104
Jefferson, co., N.Y., U.S. **A5** 109
Jefferson, co., Oh., U.S. **B5** 112
Jefferson, co., Ok., U.S. **C4** 113
Jefferson, co., Or., U.S. **C5** 114
Jefferson, co., Pa., U.S. **D3** 115
Jefferson, co., Tn., U.S. **C10** 119
Jefferson, co., Tx., U.S. **E5** 120
Jefferson, co., Wa., U.S. **B1** 124
Jefferson, co., W.V., U.S. **B7** 125
Jefferson, co., Wi., U.S. **E5** 126
Jefferson, stm., Mt., U.S. **E5** 103
Jefferson, Mount, mtn., Id., U.S. **E7** 89
Jefferson, Mount, mtn., Nv., U.S. **E5** 105
Jefferson, Mount, mtn., Or., U.S. **C5** 114
Jefferson City, Mo., U.S. **C5** 102
Jefferson City, Tn., U.S. **C10** 119
Jefferson Davis, co., La., U.S. **D3** 95
Jefferson Davis, co., Ms., U.S. **D4** 101
Jefferson Farms, De., U.S. **i7** 85
Jefferson Proving Ground, mil., In., U.S. **G7** 91
Jeffersontown, Ky., U.S. **B4** 94
Jeffersonville, Ga., U.S. **D3** 87
Jeffersonville, In., U.S. **H6** 91
Jeffersonville, Ky., U.S. **C6** 94
Jeffersonville, Oh., U.S. **C2** 112
Jeffrey, W.V., U.S. **D3** 125
Jeffrey City, Wy., U.S. **D5** 127
Jeffries Creek, stm., S.C., U.S. **C8** 117
Jefremov, U.S.S.R. **H21** 22
Jegorjevsk, U.S.S.R. **F22** 22
Jehossee Island, i., S.C., U.S. **k11** 117
Jejsk, U.S.S.R. **H5** 18
Jekyll Island, i., Ga., U.S. **E5** 87
Jelec, U.S.S.R. **I21** 22
Jelenia Góra (Hirschberg), Pol. **E15** 8
Jelgava, U.S.S.R. **E6** 22
Jelizavety, Mys, c., U.S.S.R. **G22** 20
Jellico, Tn., U.S. **C9** 119
Jelm Mountain, mtn., Wy., U.S. **E7** 127
Jeloguj, stm., U.S.S.R. **E11** 20
Jember, Indon. **n16** 32
Jemez, stm., N.M., U.S. **k7** 108
Jemez Canyon Dam, N.M., U.S. **k7** 108
Jemez Indian Reservation, N.M., U.S. **h7** 108
Jemez Pueblo, N.M., U.S. **B3** 108
Jemison, Al., U.S. **C3** 78
Jena, Ger. **E11** 8
Jena, La., U.S. **C3** 95
Jenašimskij Polkan, Gora, mtn., U.S.S.R. **F12** 20
Jendouba (Souk el Arba), Tun. **M3** 14
Jenisej, stm., U.S.S.R. **D11** 20
Jenisejsk, U.S.S.R. **F12** 20
Jenisejskij Zaliv, b., U.S.S.R. **C10** 20
Jenkins, Ky., U.S. **C7** 94
Jenkins, co., Ga., U.S. **D5** 87
Jenkintown, Pa., U.S. **o21** 115
Jenks, Ok., U.S. **A6** 113
Jennings, La., U.S. **D3** 95
Jennings, Mo., U.S. **f13** 102
Jennings, co., In., U.S. **G6** 91
Jensen Beach, Fl., U.S. **E6** 86
Jepara, Indon. **m15** 33a
Jequié, Braz. **B8** 57
Jequitinhonha, stm., Braz. **D9** 57
Jerada, Mor. **B5** 42
Jerauld, co., S.D., U.S. **C7** 118
Jérémie, Haiti **E10** 64
Jeremoabo, Braz. **F11** 54
Jerevan, U.S.S.R. **I6** 18
Jerez de García Salinas, Mex. **F8** 62
Jerez de la Frontera, Spain **I5** 12
Jerez de los Caballeros, Spain **G5** 12
Jericho, Vt., U.S. **B3** 122
Jericho see Arīḥā, Jord. **D4** 40
Jerimoth Hill, hill, R.I., U.S. **C1** 116
Jermyn, Pa., U.S. **C10** 115
Jerofej Pavlovič, U.S.S.R. **G18** 20
Jerome, Id., U.S. **G4** 89
Jerome, Pa., U.S. **F4** 115
Jerome, co., Id., U.S. **G4** 89
Jeropol, U.S.S.R. **D27** 20
Jersey, co., Il., U.S. **D3** 90
Jersey, dep., Eur. **C4** 10
Jersey City, N.J., U.S. **B4** 107
Jersey Mountain, mtn., Id., U.S. **E3** 89
Jersey Shore, Pa., U.S. **D7** 115
Jerseyville, Il., U.S. **D3** 90
Jerusalem see Yerushalayim, Isr. **D4** 40
Jervis Inlet, b., B.C., Can. **D6** 69
Jesenice, Yugo. **C9** 14
Jessamine, co., Ky., U.S. **C5** 94
Jessore, Bngl. **I13** 38
Jessup, Md., U.S. **B4** 97
Jessup, Pa., U.S. **m18** 115
Jesup, Ga., U.S. **E5** 87
Jesup, Ia., U.S. **B5** 92
Jesup, Lake, l., Fl., U.S. **D5** 86
Jésus, Île, i., Que., Can. **p19** 74
Jesús Carranza, Mex. **I12** 62
Jetmore, Ks., U.S. **D4** 93
Jeumont, Fr. **B11** 10
Jever, Ger. **B7** 8
Jevpatorija, U.S.S.R. **H4** 18
Jewel Cave National Monument, S.D., U.S. **D2** 118
Jewell, Ia., U.S. **B4** 92
Jewell, co., Ks., U.S. **C5** 93
Jewett City, Ct., U.S. **C8** 84
Jeypore, India **C7** 37
Jhang Maghiāna, Pak. **E5** 38
Jhānsi, India **H8** 38
Jharia, India **I12** 38
Jhelum, Pak. **D5** 38
Jhelum, stm., Asia **E5** 38
Jiading, China **D10** 28
Jiaganj, India **H13** 38
Jiamusi, China **B13** 26
Jian, China **H3** 28
Jianchuan, China **A5** 34
Jiangmen, China **M2** 28
Jiangsu, prov., China **E10** 26
Jiangxi, prov., China **F10** 26
Jiangyin, China **D9** 28
Jiangzi, China **F13** 38
Jianou, China **H7** 28
Jianshui, China **C7** 34
Jiaoxian, China **D10** 26
Jiaozuo, China **D9** 26
Jiashan, China **C6** 28
Jiawang, China **A6** 28
Jiaxian, China **A2** 28
Jiaxing, China **E9** 28
Jiazi, China **M5** 28
Jicarilla Apache Indian Reservation, N.M., U.S. **A2** 108
Jiddah, Sau. Ar. **D2** 46
Jieshou, China **B4** 28
Jieyang, China **L5** 28
Jihlava, Czech. **F15** 8
Jijiga, Eth. **G3** 46
Jijona, Spain **G11** 12
Jilemutu, China **A11** 26
Jilin, China **C12** 26
Jilin, prov., China **C12** 26
Jill, Kediet ej, mtn., Maur. **D3** 42
Jima, Eth. **G2** 46
Jimena de la Frontera, Spain **I6** 12
Jim Hogg, co., Tx., U.S. **F3** 120
Jim Lake, res., N.D., U.S. **B7** 111
Jim Thorpe, Pa., U.S. **E10** 115
Jim Wells, co., Tx., U.S. **F3** 120
Jinan (Tsinan), China **D10** 26
Jind, India **F7** 38
Jingdezhen (Kingtechen), China **F6** 28
Jingjiang, China **C9** 28
Jingxi, China **C9** 34
Jinhua, China **F8** 28
Jining, China **C9** 26
Jining, China **D10** 26
Jinja, Ug. **A6** 44
Jinning (Jiukunyang), China **B7** 34
Jinotega, Nic. **H4** 64
Jinshi, China **F9** 26
Jinxian, China **D11** 26
Jinzhou, China **C11** 26
Jiparaná, stm., Braz. **E6** 54
Jipijapa, Ec. **H2** 58
Jirjā, Egypt **C12** 42
Jisr ash-Shughūr, Syria **B5** 40
Jiujiang, China **F4** 28
Jiuling Shan, mts., China **G3** 28
Jiumangya, China **B14** 38
Jiuquan, China **D6** 26
Jixi, China **B13** 26
Joaçaba, Braz. **B6** 56
Joanna, S.C., U.S. **C4** 117
João Pessoa, Braz. **E12** 54
Joaquín V. González, Arg. **B4** 56
Job Peak, mtn., Nv., U.S. **D3** 105
Jobson (Vera), Arg. **B4** 56
Jocassee, Lake, res., U.S. **B1** 117
Jódar, Spain **H8** 12
Jo Daviess, co., Il., U.S. **A3** 90
Jodhpur, India **G5** 38
Joe Batt's Arm [-Barr'd Islands-Shoal Bay], Newf., Can. **D4** 72
Joensuu, Fin. **E17** 6
Joes Brook, stm., Vt., U.S. **C4** 122
Joes Creek, stm., W.V., U.S. **m12** 125
Joffre, Mount, mtn., Can. **D3** 68
Jogjakarta see Yogyakarta, Indon. **G5** 32
Johannesburg, S. Afr. **G5** 44
Johar, Som. **H4** 46
John, Cape, c., N.S., Can. **D6** 71
John Day, Or., U.S. **C8** 114
John Day, stm., Or., U.S. **B6** 114
John Day Dam, U.S. **D5** 124
John Day Fossil Beds National Monument, Or., U.S. **C6** 114
John F. Kennedy Space Center, sci., Fl., U.S. **D6** 86
John H. Kerr Dam, Va., U.S. **D4** 123
John H. Kerr Reservoir, res., U.S. **D4** 123
John Martin Reservoir, res., Co., U.S. **C7** 83
John Muir National Historical Site, hist., Ca., U.S. **h8** 82
John o' Groats, Scot., U.K. **C9** 7
John Redmond Reservoir, res., Ks., U.S. **D8** 93
John Sevier, Tn., U.S. **m14** 119
Johns Island, i., S.C., U.S. **F7** 117
Johnson, Ks., U.S. **E2** 93
Johnson, Vt., U.S. **B3** 122
Johnson, co., Ar., U.S. **B2** 81
Johnson, co., Ga., U.S. **D4** 87
Johnson, co., Il., U.S. **F5** 90
Johnson, co., In., U.S. **F5** 91
Johnson, co., Ia., U.S. **C6** 92
Johnson, co., Ks., U.S. **D9** 93
Johnson, co., Ky., U.S. **C7** 94
Johnson, co., Mo., U.S. **C4** 102
Johnson, co., Ne., U.S. **D9** 104
Johnson, co., Tn., U.S. **C12** 119
Johnson, co., Tx., U.S. **C4** 120
Johnson, co., Wy., U.S. **B6** 127
Johnsonburg, Pa., U.S. **D4** 115
Johnson City, N.Y., U.S. **C5** 109
Johnson City, Tn., U.S. **C11** 119
Johnson City, Tx., U.S. **D3** 120
Johnson Creek, Wi., U.S. **E5** 126
Johnsonville, S.C., U.S. **D9** 117
Johns Pass, strt., Fl., U.S. **p10** 86
Johnston, Ia., U.S. **e8** 92
Johnston, R.I., U.S. **C4** 116
Johnston, S.C., U.S. **D4** 117
Johnston, co., N.C., U.S. **B4** 110
Johnston, co., Ok., U.S. **C5** 113
Johnston City, Il., U.S. **F5** 90
Johnston Key, i., Fl., U.S. **H5** 86
Johnstown, Co., U.S. **A6** 83
Johnstown, N.Y., U.S. **B6** 109
Johnstown, Oh., U.S. **B3** 112
Johnstown, Pa., U.S. **F4** 115
John W. Flannagan Reservoir, res., Va., U.S. **e9** 123
Johor Baharu, Malay. **N7** 34
Joigny, Fr. **E10** 10
Joiner, Ar., U.S. **B5** 81
Joinvile, Braz. **B7** 56
Joinville, Fr. **D12** 10
Jokkmokk, Swe. **C12** 6
Joliet, Il., U.S. **B5** 90
Joliette, Que., Can. **C4** 74
Jolo Island, i., Phil. **D7** 32
Jombang, Indon. **m16** 33a
Jones, Ok., U.S. **B4** 113
Jones, co., Ga., U.S. **C3** 87
Jones, co., Ia., U.S. **B6** 92
Jones, co., Ms., U.S. **D4** 101
Jones, co., N.C., U.S. **B5** 110
Jones, co., S.D., U.S. **D5** 118
Jones, co., Tx., U.S. **C3** 120
Jonesboro, Ar., U.S. **B5** 81
Jonesboro, Ga., U.S. **C2** 87
Jonesboro, Il., U.S. **F4** 90
Jonesboro, In., U.S. **D6** 91
Jonesboro, La., U.S. **B3** 95
Jonesborough, Tn., U.S. **C11** 119
Jonesburg, Mo., U.S. **C6** 102
Jones Creek, Tx., U.S. **s14** 120
Jones Mill, Ar., U.S. **C3** 81
Jonesport, Me., U.S. **D5** 96
Jones Sound, strt., N.W. Ter., Can. **A15** 66
Jonestown, Ms., U.S. **A3** 101
Jonesville, La., U.S. **C4** 95
Jonesville, Mi., U.S. **G6** 99
Jonesville, N.C., U.S. **A2** 110
Jonesville, S.C., U.S. **B4** 117
Jonesville, Va., U.S. **f8** 123
Jongkha, China **F11** 38
Jönköping, Swe. **H10** 6
Jonquière, Que., Can. **A6** 74
Jonzac, Fr. **G6** 10
Joplin, Mo., U.S. **D3** 102
Joppatowne, Md., U.S. **B5** 97
Jordan, Mn., U.S. **F5** 100
Jordan, ctry., Asia **D5** 40
Jordan, stm., Asia **C4** 40
Jordan, stm., Ut., U.S. **C4** 121
Jordan Creek, stm., U.S. **E9** 114
Jordan Lake, res., Al., U.S. **C3** 78
Jorhāt, India **G16** 38
Jörn, Swe. **D13** 6
Jornado del Muerto, des., N.M., U.S. **D3** 108
Jos, Nig. **G7** 42
José Battle y Ordóñez, Ur. **C5** 56
Joseph, Or., U.S. **B9** 114
Joseph, Lac, l., Newf., Can. **h8** 72
Joseph Bonaparte Gulf, b., Austl. **B5** 50
Joseph City, Az., U.S. **C5** 80
Josephine, co., Or., U.S. **E3** 114
Joshua, Tx., U.S. **n9** 120
Joshua Tree, Ca., U.S. **E5** 82
Joshua Tree National Monument, Ca., U.S. **F6** 82
Joškar-Ola, U.S.S.R. **F7** 18
Jourdanton, Tx., U.S. **E3** 120
Joutsijärvi, Fin. **C16** 6
Jovellanos, Cuba **C7** 64
J. Percy Priest Lake, res., Tn., U.S. **A5** 119
Juab, co., Ut., U.S. **D2** 121
Juan Aldama, Mex. **E8** 62
Juan de Fuca, Strait of, strt., N.A. **G8** 66
Juan de Nova, Île, i., Reu. **E8** 44
Juárez, Arg. **D5** 56
Juàzeiro, Braz. **E10** 54
Juàzeiro do Norte, Braz. **E11** 54
Jūbā, Sudan **H12** 42
Juba (Genale), stm., Afr. **H3** 46
Juchitán [de Zaragoza], Mex. **I12** 62
Judenburg, Aus. **H14** 8
Judith, stm., Mt., U.S. **C7** 103
Judith, Point, c., R.I., U.S. **G4** 85
Judith Basin, co., Mt., U.S. **C6** 103
Judith Island, i., N.C., U.S. **B6** 110
Judith Mountains, mts., Mt., U.S. **C7** 103
Judith Peak, mtn., Mt., U.S. **C7** 103
Judoma, stm., U.S.S.R. **F21** 20
Judsonia, Ar., U.S. **B4** 81
Juigalpa, Nic. **H5** 64
Juiz de Fora, Braz. **F7** 57
Jukagirskoje Ploskogorje, plat., U.S.S.R. **D24** 20
Jukte, U.S.S.R. **E15** 20
Julesburg, Co., U.S. **A8** 83
Juliaca, Peru **G4** 54
Julian, Ca., U.S. **F5** 82
Julian, W.V., U.S. **C3** 125
Julian Alps, mts., Eur. **C8** 14
Juliana Top, mtn., Sur. **C7** 54
Julianehåb, Grnld. **D23** 66
Jülich, Ger. **E6** 8
Jullundur, India **E6** 38
Jumbo Peak, mtn., Nv., U.S. **G7** 105
Jumentos Cays, is., Bah. **C10** 64
Jumet, Bel. **E4** 8
Jumilla, Spain **G10** 12
Jump, stm., Wi., U.S. **C3** 126
Junāgadh, India **J4** 38
Junction, Tx., U.S. **D3** 120
Junction City, Ar., U.S. **D3** 81

Name Map Ref Page

Junction City, Ks., U.S. C7 93
Junction City, Ky., U.S. C5 94
Junction City, La., U.S. A3 95
Junction City, Or., U.S. C3 114
Jundiaí, Braz. G5 57
Juneau, Ak., U.S. D13 79
Juneau, Wi., U.S. E5 126
Juneau, co., Wi., U.S. E3 126
June in Winter, Lake, l., Fl., U.S. E5 86
Jungfrau, mtn., Switz. F14 10
Junggar Pendi, China B4 26
Juniata, Ne., U.S. D7 104
Juniata, co., Pa., U.S. F7 115
Juniata, stm., Pa., U.S. F7 115
Junín, Arg. C4 56
Junín, Lago de, l., Peru F3 54
Junín de los Andes, Arg. D2 56
Junior Lake, l., Me., U.S. C4 96
Juniper Mountains, mts., Az., U.S. B2 80
Junipero Serra Peak, mtn., Ca., U.S. D3 82
Junsele, Swe. E11 6
Jupiter, Fl., U.S. F6 86
Jupiter Inlet, b., Fl., U.S. F6 86
Jupiter Island, i., Fl., U.S. E6 86
Jura, mts., Eur. F13 10
Jura, i., Scot., U.K. F7 7
Jurga, U.S.S.R. F10 20
Jūrmala, U.S.S.R. E6 22
Juruá, stm., S.A. D5 54
Juruena, stm., Braz. E7 54
Justin, Tx., U.S. C4 120
Justo Daract, Arg. C3 56
Jutaí, stm., Braz. D5 54
Jüterbog, Ger. D13 8
Jutiapa, Guat. G3 64
Juticalpa, Hond. G4 64
Jutland see Jylland, pen., Den. H7 6
Juventud, Isla de la (Isle of Pines), i., Cuba D6 64
Juwara, Oman E6 46
Juža, U.S.S.R. E25 22
Južno-Sachalinsk, U.S.S.R. H22 20
Južnyj, Mys, c., U.S.S.R. F25 20
Južnyj Bug, stm., U.S.S.R. H3 18
Jwayyā, Leb. C4 40
Jylland, pen., Den. H7 6
Jyväskylä, Fin. E15 6

K

K2 (Qogir Feng), mtn., Asia C7 38
Kaaawa, Hi., U.S. f10 88
Kaala, mtn., Hi., U.S. f9 88
Kaala Djerda, Tun. N3 14
Kaalualu Bay, b., Hi., U.S. E6 88
Kaaumakua, Puu, mtn., Hi., U.S. f10 88
Kabale, Ug. B5 44
Kabalo, Zaire C5 44
Kabambare, Zaire B5 44
Kåbdalis, Swe. C12 6
Kabetogama Lake, l., Mn., U.S. B5 100
Kabīr Kūh, mts., Iran B4 46
Kabompo, stm., Zam. D4 44
Kabongo, Zaire C5 44
Kābul, Afg. C3 38
Kābul, stm., Asia C4 38
Kabwe (Broken Hill), Zam. D5 44
Kachess Lake, res., Wa., U.S. B4 124
K'achta, U.S.S.R. G15 20
Kačug, U.S.S.R. G15 20
Kadan Kyun, i., Burma H5 34
Kadiri, India E5 37
Kadoka, S.D., U.S. D4 118
Kaduna, Nig. F7 42
Kāduqlī, Sudan F11 42
Kadykčan, U.S.S.R. E23 20
Kaédi, Maur. E3 42
Kaena Point, c., Hi., U.S. B3 88
Kaesŏng, N. Kor. D12 26
Kafia Kingi, Sudan G10 42
Kafue, stm., Zam. D5 44
Kaga, Japan F9 30
Kagamigahara, Japan G9 30
Kagaznagar, India C5 37
Kagoshima, Japan K3 30
Kahaluu, Hi., U.S. D6 88
Kahaluu, Hi., U.S. g10 88
Kahana Bay, b., Hi., U.S. f10 88
Kahemba, Zaire C3 44
Kahoka, Mo., U.S. A6 102
Kahoolawe, i., Hi., U.S. C5 88
Kahramanmaraş, Tur. H15 4
Kahuku, Hi., U.S. B4 88
Kahuku Point, c., Hi., U.S. B4 88
Kahului, Hi., U.S. C5 88
Kahului Bay, b., Hi., U.S. C5 88
Kai, Kepulauan, is., Indon. G9 32
Kaibab Indian Reservation, Az., U.S. A3 80
Kaieteur Fall, wtfl, Guy. E13 58
Kaifeng, China E9 26
Kaikoura, N.Z. E4 52
Kaili, China A10 34
Kailua, Hi., U.S. B4 88
Kailua Bay, b., Hi., U.S. g11 88
Kailua Kona, Hi., U.S. D6 88
Kaimana, Indon. F9 32
Kaimanawa Mountains, mts., N.Z. C5 52
Kainan, Japan H8 30
Kaiserslautern, Ger. F7 8
Kaitangata, N.Z. G2 52
Kaiwi Channel, strt., Hi., U.S. B4 88
Kajaani, Fin. D16 6
Kajakī, Band-e, res., Afg. D1 38
Kajan, stm., Indon. E6 32
Kajang, Malay. M6 34
Kakamas, S. Afr. G4 44
Kaka Point, c., Hi., U.S. C5 88
Kake, Ak., U.S. D13 79
Kakegawa, Japan H11 30
Kakie, Bots. F4 44
Kākināda, India D7 37
Kakogawa, Japan H7 30
Kaladan, stm., Asia D2 34
Ka Lae, c., Hi., U.S. E6 88
Kalahari Desert, des., Afr. F4 44
Kālahasti, India F5 37
Kalaheo, Hi., U.S. B2 88
Kalajoki, Fin. D14 6
Kalakan, U.S.S.R. F17 20
Kalām, Pak. C5 38
Kalama, Wa., U.S. C3 124
Kalámai, Grc. L6 16
Kalamazoo, Mi., U.S. F5 99
Kalamazoo, co., Mi., U.S. F5 99
Kalamazoo, stm., Mi., U.S. F5 99
Kalasin, Thai. F7 34
Kalāt, Pak. F2 38
Kalaupapa Peninsula, pen., Hi., U.S. B5 88
Kalawao, co., Hi., U.S. B5 88
Kalb, Ra's al-, c., Yemen F4 46
Kale, Tur. L12 16
Kaleden, B.C., Can. E8 69
Kalemie (Albertville), Zaire C5 44
Kalena, Puu, mtn., Hi., U.S. g9 88
Kalgin Island, i., Ak., U.S. g16 79
Kalgoorlie, Austl. F4 50
Kalima, Zaire B5 44
Kálimnos, Grc. M10 16
Kaliningrad (Königsberg), U.S.S.R. G3 22
Kalinkoviči, U.S.S.R. I12 22
Kalispel Indian Reservation, Wa., U.S. A8 124
Kalispell, Mt., U.S. B2 103
Kalisz, Pol. D18 8
Kalkaska, Mi., U.S. D5 99
Kalkaska, co., Mi., U.S. D5 99
Kalmar, Swe. H11 6
Kalohi Channel, strt., Hi., U.S. C4 88
Kālol, India I5 38
Kaloli Point, c., Hi., U.S. D7 88
Kalona, Ia., U.S. C6 92
Kalone Peak, mtn., B.C., Can. C4 69
Kaluga, U.S.S.R. G19 22
Kalutara, Sri L. I5 37
Kamaishi, Japan C14 30
Kamakou, mtn., Hi., U.S. B5 88
Kamakura, Japan G12 30
Kamālia, Pak. E5 38
Kamarān, i., Yemen E3 46
Kamas, Ut., U.S. C4 121
Kamba, China F13 38
Kambam, India H4 37
Kambar, Pak. G2 38
Kamčatka, stm., U.S.S.R. F25 20
Kamčatka, Poluostrov, pen., U.S.S.R. F25 20
Kamčatskij Zaliv, b., U.S.S.R. F26 20
Kamen', Gora, mtn., U.S.S.R. D12 20
Kamen'-na-Obi, U.S.S.R. G10 20
Kamenz, Ger. D14 8
Kamiah, Id., U.S. C2 89
Kamiak Butte, mtn., Wa., U.S. C8 124
Kamienna Góra, Pol. E16 8
Kamilukuak Lake, l., N.W. Ter., Can. D12 66
Kamina, Zaire C5 44
Kaminak Lake, l., N.W. Ter., Can. D13 66
Kaminuriak Lake, l., N.W. Ter., Can. D13 66
Kamitsushima, Japan H2 30
Kamloops, B.C., Can. D7 69
Kamo, Japan E12 30
Kāmoke, Pak. E6 38
Kampala, Ug. A6 44
Kampar, Malay. L6 34
Kampen, Neth. C5 8
Kampeska, Lake, l., S.D., U.S. C8 118
Kâmpóng Cham, Camb. H8 34
Kâmpóng Chhnăng, Camb. H8 34
Kâmpóng Saôm, Camb. I7 34
Kâmpóng Saôm, Chhâk, b., Camb. I7 34
Kâmpóng Thum, Camb. H8 34
Kâmpôt, Camb. I8 34
Kāmthi, India B5 37
Kamuela (Waimea), Hi., U.S. C6 88
Kamui-misaki, c., Japan p18 30a
Kan, stm., Asia H9 34
Kanab, Ut., U.S. F3 121
Kanab Creek, stm., U.S. A3 80
Kanabec, co., Mn., U.S. E5 100
Kanaga Island, i., Ak., U.S. E4 79
Kanairiktok, stm., Newf., Can. g9 72
Kananga (Luluabourg), Zaire C4 44
Kanapou Bay, b., Hi., U.S. C5 88
Kanata, Ont., Can. B9 73
Kanawha, Ia., U.S. B4 92
Kanawha, co., W.V., U.S. C3 125
Kanawha, stm., W.V., U.S. C3 125
Kanazawa, Japan F9 30
Kanchanaburi, Thai. G5 34
Kānchenjunga, mtn., Asia G13 38
Kānchipuram, India F5 37
Kandhkot, Pak. F3 38
Kāndi, India I13 38
Kandiyohi, co., Mn., U.S. E3 100
Kandy, Sri L. I6 37
Kane, Pa., U.S. C4 115
Kane, co., Il., U.S. B5 90
Kane, co., Ut., U.S. F3 121
Kaneohe, Hi., U.S. B4 88
Kaneohe Bay, b., Hi., U.S. g10 88
Kaneohe Bay Marine Corps Air Station, mil., Hi., U.S. g10 88
Kangar, Malay. K6 34
Kangaroo Island, i., Austl. G7 50
Kangean, Kepulauan, is., Indon. G6 32
Kangnŭng, S. Kor. D12 26
Kango, Gabon A2 44
Kangto, mtn., Asia G15 38
Kaniama, Zaire C4 44
Kankakee, Il., U.S. B6 90
Kankakee, co., Il., U.S. B6 90
Kankakee, stm., U.S. B5 90
Kankan, Gui. F4 42
Kanmaw Kyun, i., Burma I5 34
Kannapolis, N.C., U.S. B2 110
Kannauj, India G8 38
Kannonkoski, Fin. E15 6
Kannus, Fin. E14 6
Kano, Nig. F7 42
Kanonji, Japan H6 30
Kanopolis, Ks., U.S. D5 93
Kanopolis Lake, res., Ks., U.S. D5 93
Kanoya, Japan K3 30
Kānpur, India G9 38
Kansas, Il., U.S. D6 90
Kansas, state, U.S. D5 93
Kansas, stm., Ks., U.S. C7 93
Kansas City, Ks., U.S. C9 93
Kansas City, Mo., U.S. B3 102
Kansk, U.S.S.R. F13 20
Kantō-sammyaku, mts., Japan F11 30
Kanuma, Japan F12 30
Kanye, Bots. F5 44
Kaohsiung, Tai. M9 28
Kaohsiunghsien, Tai. M9 28
Kaokoveld, plat., Nmb. E2 44
Kaolack, Sen. F2 42
Kapaa, Hi., U.S. A2 88
Kapaau, Hi., U.S. C6 88
Kapadvanj, India I5 38
Kapanga, Zaire C4 44
Kapapa Island, i., Hi., U.S. g10 88
Kapfenberg, Aus. H15 8
Kaplan, La., U.S. D3 95
Kaposvár, Hung. I17 8
Kaptai, Bngl. I15 38
Kapuas, stm., Indon. F4 32
Kapūrthala, India E6 38
Kapuskasing, Ont., Can. o19 73
Karabük, Tur. G14 4
Karacabey, Tur. I12 16
Karacaköy, Tur. H12 16
Karāchi, Pak. H2 38
Karād, India D3 37
Karaganda, U.S.S.R. H8 20
Karaginskij, Ostrov, i., U.S.S.R. F26 20
Karaginskij Zaliv, b., U.S.S.R. F26 20
Karagoš, Gora, mtn., U.S.S.R. G11 20
Kāraikkudi, India G5 37
Karakelong, Pulau, i., Indon. E8 32
Karakoram Range, mts., Asia C7 38
Karakumskij kanal, U.S.S.R. J10 18
Karaman, Tur. H14 4
Karaman, Tur. L13 16
Karamay, China B3 26
Karamürsel, Tur. I13 16
Kāranja, India B4 37
Karasburg, Nmb. G3 44
Karasjok, Nor. B15 6
Karatsu, Japan I2 30
Karaul, U.S.S.R. C10 20
Karauli, India G7 38
Karawang, Indon. m13 33a
Karawanken, mts., Eur. C9 14
Karbalā', Iraq B3 46
Kårböle, Swe. F10 6
Karcag, Hung. H20 8
Kardhítsa, Grc. J5 16
Kărdžali, Bul. H9 16
Kargasok, U.S.S.R. F10 20
Karhula, Fin. F16 6
Kariba, Zimb. E5 44
Kariba, Lake, res., Afr. E5 44
Karibib, Nmb. F3 44
Karigasniemi, Fin. B15 6
Karimata, Kepulauan, is., Indon. F4 32
Karimata, Selat (Karimata Strait), strt., Indon. F4 32
Karīmganj, India H15 38
Karīmnagar, India C5 37
Karin, Som. F4 46
Karis (Karjaa), Fin. F14 6
Kariya, Japan H9 30
Karkabet, Eth. E2 46
Karlovac, Yugo. D10 14
Karlovo, Bul. G8 16
Karlovy Vary, Czech. E12 8
Karlshamn, Swe. H10 6
Karlskoga, Swe. G10 6
Karlskrona, Swe. H10 6
Karlsruhe, Ger. F8 8
Karlstad, Swe. G9 6
Karlstad, Mn., U.S. B2 100
Karnāl, India F7 38
Karnaphuli Reservoir, res., Bngl. I15 38
Karnataka, state, India E3 37
Karnes, co., Tx., U.S. E4 120
Karnes City, Tx., U.S. E4 120
Karns, Tn., U.S. n13 119
Karonga, Mwi. C6 44
Kárpathos, i., Grc. N11 16
Karpenísion, Grc. K5 16
Kars, Tur. G16 4
Kärsämäki, Fin. E15 6
Karši, U.S.S.R. J11 18
Kartal, Tur. I13 16
Karufa, Indon. F9 32
Karungi, Swe. C14 6
Karūr, India G5 37
Karviná, Czech. F18 8
Kārwār, India E3 37
Kasai (Cassai), stm., Afr. B3 44
Kasaji, Zaire D4 44
Kasama, Zam. D6 44
Kasanga, Tan. C6 44
Kasaoka, Japan H6 30
Kāsaragod, India F3 37
Kasba Lake, l., N.W. Ter., Can. D12 66
Kaseda, Japan K3 30
Kasempa, Zam. D5 44
Kasenga, Zaire D5 44
Kasese, Zaire B5 44
Kāsganj, India G8 38
Kāshān, Iran B5 46
Kashi, China D2 26
Kashima-nada, Japan F13 30
Kashīpur, India F8 38
Kashiwa, Japan G12 30
Kashiwazaki, Japan E11 30
Kashmir see Jammu and Kashmir, dep., Asia C6 38
Kasimov, U.S.S.R. G24 22
Kašin, U.S.S.R. D20 22
Kašira, U.S.S.R. G21 22
Kaskaskia, stm., Il., U.S. D5 90
Kaskö (Kaskinen), Fin. E13 6
Kaslo, B.C., Can. E9 69
Kasongo, Zaire B5 44
Kasota, Mn., U.S. F5 100
Kasr, Ra's, c., Sudan E13 42
Kassalā, Sudan E13 42
Kassel, Ger. D9 8
Kasson, Mn., U.S. F6 100
Kastoría, Grc. I5 16
Kasugai, Japan G9 30
Kasūr, Pak. E6 38
Katahdin, Mount, mtn., Me., U.S. C4 96
Katanga, stm., U.S.S.R. F14 20
Katanga Plateau, plat., Zaire D5 44
Katchall Island, i., India K2 34
Kateríni, Grc. I6 16
Kates Needle, mtn., Ak., U.S. m24 79
Katherine, Austl. B6 50
Kāthiāwār, pen., India I4 38
Kathleen, Fl., U.S. D4 86
Kāṭhmāṇḍau, Nepal G11 38
Katihār, India H12 38
Katiola, I.C. G4 42
Katmai, Mount, mtn., Ak., U.S. D9 79
Katmai National Park, Ak., U.S. D9 79
Katmandu see Kāṭhmāṇḍau, Nepal G11 38
Katowice, Pol. E19 8
Kātrīnā, Jabal, mtn., Egypt C12 42
Katrineholm, Swe. G11 6
Katsina, Nig. F7 42
Katsuta, Japan F13 30
Kattegat, strt., Eur. H8 6
Katy, Tx., U.S. r14 120
Kauai, co., Hi., U.S. B1 88
Kauai, i., Hi., U.S. A2 88
Kauai Channel, strt., Hi., U.S. B3 88
Kau Desert, des., Hi., U.S. D6 88
Kaufbeuren, Ger. H10 8
Kaufman, Tx., U.S. C4 120
Kaufman, co., Tx., U.S. C4 120
Kauiki Head, c., Hi., U.S. C6 88
Kaukauna, Wi., U.S. D5 126
Kaukauveld, mts., Afr. F3 44
Kaula Island, i., Hi., U.S. m15 88
Kaulakahi Channel, strt., Hi., U.S. A2 88
Kaumakani, Hi., U.S. B2 88
Kaunakakai, Hi., U.S. B4 88
Kauna Point, c., Hi., U.S. D6 88
Kaunas, U.S.S.R. G6 22
Kaura Namoda, Nig. F7 42
Kaustinen, Fin. E14 6
Kavača, U.S.S.R. E27 20
Kavacık, Tur. J12 16
Kavalerovo, U.S.S.R. I21 20
Kavála, Grc. I8 16
Kavaratti, India G2 37
Kavieng, Pap. N. Gui. k17 50a
Kawagoe, Japan G12 30
Kawaguchi, Japan G12 30
Kawaihoa Point, c., Hi., U.S. B1 88
Kawaikini, mtn., Hi., U.S. A2 88
Kawambwa, Zam. C5 44
Kawanoe, Japan H6 30
Kawasaki, Japan G12 30
Kawich Peak, mtn., Nv., U.S. F5 105
Kawich Range, mts., Nv., U.S. F5 105
Kaw Lake, res., Ok., U.S. A5 113
Kawm Umbū, Egypt D12 42
Kay, co., Ok., U.S. A4 113
Kayankulam, India H4 37
Kaycee, Wy., U.S. C6 127
Kayenta, Az., U.S. A5 80
Kayes, Mali F3 42
Kayseri, Tur. H15 4
Kaysville, Ut., U.S. B4 121
Kazachskaja Sovetskaja Socialističeskaja Respublika (Kazakhstan), state, U.S.S.R. H11 18
Kazačinskoje, U.S.S.R. F12 20
Kazačje, U.S.S.R. C21 20
Kazakhstan see Kazachskaja Sovetskaja Socialističeskaja Respublika, state, U.S.S.R. H11 18
Kazan', U.S.S.R. F7 18
Kazanlăk, Bul. G9 16
Kāzerūn, Iran C5 46
Keaau, Hi., U.S. D6 88
Keahiakahoe, Puu, mtn., Hi., U.S. g10 88
Keahole Point, c., Hi., U.S. D5 88
Kealaikahiki Channel, strt., Hi., U.S. C5 88
Kealaikahiki Point, c., Hi., U.S. C5 88
Kealakekua, Hi., U.S. D6 88
Kealia, Hi., U.S. A2 88
Keams Canyon, Az., U.S. B5 80
Keanapapa Point, c., Hi., U.S. C4 88
Keansburg, N.J., U.S. C4 107
Kearney, Mo., U.S. B3 102
Kearney, Ne., U.S. D6 104
Kearney, co., Ne., U.S. D7 104
Kearns, Ut., U.S. C4 121
Kearny, Az., U.S. D5 80
Kearny, N.J., U.S. h8 107
Kearny, co., Ks., U.S. D2 93
Kebri Dehar, Eth. G3 46
Kechika, stm., B.C., Can. E7 66
Kecskemét, Hung. I19 8
Kedges Straits, strt., Md., U.S. D5 97
Kedgwick, N.B., Can. B2 71
Kediri, Indon. m16 32
Kedon, U.S.S.R. E25 20
Kédougou, Sen. F3 42
Kędzierzyn, Pol. E18 8
Keego Harbor, Mi., U.S. o15 99
Keele Peak, mtn., Yukon, Can. D6 66
Keelung see Chilung, Tai. J10 28
Keene, N.H., U.S. E2 106
Keene, Tx., U.S. n9 120
Keeper Hill, hill, Ire. I4 7
Keeseville, N.Y., U.S. f11 109
Keesler Air Force Base, mil., Ms., U.S. E5 101
Keetmanshoop, Nmb. G3 44
Keet Seel Ruin, hist., Az., U.S. A5 80
Keewatin, Ont., Can. E4 70
Keewatin, Mn., U.S. C5 100
Kefallinía, i., Grc. K4 16
Keffi, Nig. G7 42
Keflavík, Ice. C3 4
Ke Ga, Mui, c., Viet. H10 34
Kegonsa, Lake, l., Wi., U.S. F4 126
Keiser, Ar., U.S. B5 81
Keith, Scot., U.K. D10 7
Keith, co., Ne., U.S. C4 104
Keizer, Or., U.S. C3 114
Kejimkujik National Park, N.S., Can. E4 71
Kekaha, Hi., U.S. B2 88
Kelafo, Eth. G3 46
Kelang, Malay. M6 34
Kelheim, Ger. G11 8
Kelibia, Tun. M6 14
Keller, Tx., U.S. n9 120
Kellett, Cape, c., N.W. Ter., Can. B7 66
Kelleys Island, i., Oh., U.S. A3 112
Kellogg, Id., U.S. B2 89
Kellogg, Ia., U.S. C5 92
Kelloselkä, Fin. C17 6
Kelly Air Force Base, mil., Tx., U.S. k7 120
Kelly Island, i., De., U.S. D4 85
Kellyville, Ok., U.S. B5 113
Kélo, Chad G9 42
Kelottijärvi, Fin. B14 6
Kelowna, B.C., Can. E8 69
Kelso, Wa., U.S. C3 124
Keluang, Malay. M7 34
Kemerovo, U.S.S.R. F11 20
Kemi, Fin. D15 6
Kemijärvi, Fin. C16 6
Kemijoki, stm., Fin. C15 6
Kemmerer, Wy., U.S. E2 127
Kemp, Tx., U.S. C4 120
Kemp, Lake, res., Tx., U.S. C3 120
Kemper, co., Ms., U.S. C5 101
Kemps Bay, Bah. B9 64
Kempt, Lac, l., Que., Can. G18 66
Kempten [Allgäu], Ger. H10 8
Kemptville, Ont., Can. B9 73
Kemul, Kong, mtn., Indon. E6 32
Kenai, Ak., U.S. C9 79
Kenai Fjords National Park, Ak., U.S. D10 79
Kenai Mountains, mts., Ak., U.S. h16 79
Kenai Peninsula, pen., Ak., U.S. h16 79
Kenansville, N.C., U.S. C5 110
Kenbridge, Va., U.S. D4 123
Kendall, Fl., U.S. s13 86
Kendall, co., Il., U.S. B5 90
Kendall, co., Tx., U.S. E3 120
Kendall, Cape, c., N.W. Ter., Can. D15 66
Kendall Park, N.J., U.S. C3 107
Kendallville, In., U.S. B7 91
Kendari, Indon. F7 32
Kenedy, Tx., U.S. E4 120
Kenedy, co., Tx., U.S. F4 120
Kenema, S.L. G3 42
Kenesaw, Ne., U.S. D7 104
Kĕng Tung, Burma D5 34
Kenhardt, S. Afr. G4 44
Kenilworth, Il., U.S. h9 90
Kenitra, Mor. B4 42
Kenly, N.C., U.S. B4 110
Kenmare, N.D., U.S. A3 111
Kenmore, N.Y., U.S. C2 109
Kennaday Peak, mtn., Wy., U.S. E6 127
Kennebago Lake, l., Me., U.S. C2 96
Kennebec, co., Me., U.S. D3 96
Kennebec, stm., Me., U.S. D3 96
Kennebunk, Me., U.S. E2 96
Kennebunkport, Me., U.S. E2 96
Kennedy Entrance, strt., Ak., U.S. D9 79
Kennedy Peak, mtn., Burma C2 34
Kenner, La., U.S. E5 95
Kennesaw, Ga., U.S. B2 87
Kennesaw Mountain, mtn., Ga., U.S. C2 87
Kennett, Mo., U.S. E7 102
Kennett Square, Pa., U.S. G10 115
Kennewick, Wa., U.S. C6 124
Kenn Reefs, rf., Austl. D11 50
Kennydale, Wa., U.S. e11 124
Keno, Or., U.S. E5 114
Kénogami, Lac, l., Que., Can. A6 74
Kenora, Ont., Can. o16 73
Kenosha, Wi., U.S. F6 126
Kenosha, co., Wi., U.S. F5 126
Kenova, W.V., U.S. C2 125
Kensett, Ar., U.S. B4 81
Kensico Reservoir, res., N.Y., U.S. g13 109
Kensington, P.E.I., Can. C6 71
Kensington, Ct., U.S. C4 84
Kensington, Md., U.S. B3 97
Kent, Oh., U.S. A4 112
Kent, Wa., U.S. B3 124
Kent, co., De., U.S. D3 85
Kent, co., Md., U.S. B5 97
Kent, co., Mi., U.S. E5 99
Kent, co., R.I., U.S. D2 116
Kent, co., Tx., U.S. C2 120
Kent City, Mi., U.S. E5 99
Kent Island, i., De., U.S. D4 85
Kent Island, i., Md., U.S. C5 97
Kentland, In., U.S. C3 91
Kenton, De., U.S. D3 85
Kenton, Oh., U.S. B2 112
Kenton, Tn., U.S. A2 119
Kenton, co., Ky., U.S. B5 94
Kent Peninsula, pen., N.W. Ter., Can. C11 66
Kent Point, c., Md., U.S. C5 97
Kentucky, state, U.S. C4 94
Kentucky, stm., Ky., U.S. B5 94
Kentwood, La., U.S. D5 95
Kentwood, Mi., U.S. F5 99
Kenvil, N.J., U.S. B3 107
Kenvir, Ky., U.S. D6 94
Kenya, ctry., Afr. B7 44
Kenya, Mount see Kirinyaga, mtn., Kenya B7 44
Kenyon, Mn., U.S. F6 100
Kenyon, R.I., U.S. F2 116
Keokea, Hi., U.S. C5 88
Keokuk, Ia., U.S. D6 92
Keokuk, co., Ia., U.S. C5 92
Keokuk Lock and Dam, U.S. D6 92
Keosauqua, Ia., U.S. D6 92

Name | Map Ref | Page

Keota, Ia., U.S. C6 92
Keota, Ok., U.S. B7 113
Keowee, Lake, res., S.C., U.S. B2 117
Kepi, Indon. G10 32
Kerala, state, India G4 37
Kerč', U.S.S.R. H5 18
Keremeos, B.C., Can. E8 69
Keren, Eth. E2 46
Kerens, Tx., U.S. C4 120
Kerguélen, Îles, is., F.S.A.T. J17 2
Kerhonkson, N.Y., U.S. D6 109
Kericho, Kenya B7 44
Kerinci, Gunung, mtn., Indon. F3 32
Kerkhoven, Mn., U.S. E3 100
Kérkira (Corfu), Grc. J3 16
Kérkira, i., Grc. J3 16
Kermān, Iran B6 46
Kerme Körfezi, b., Tur. M11 16
Kermit, Tx., U.S. D1 120
Kermode, Mount, mtn., B.C., Can. C2 69
Kern, co., Ca., U.S. E4 82
Kern, stm., Ca., U.S. E4 82
Kernersville, N.C., U.S. A2 110
Kernville, Ca., U.S. E4 82
Kerr, co., Tx., U.S. D3 120
Kerr, Lake, l., Fl., U.S. C5 86
Kerrville, Tx., U.S. D3 120
Kerry Head, c., Ire. I3 7
Kersey, Co., U.S. A6 83
Kershaw, S.C., U.S. B6 117
Kershaw, co., S.C., U.S. C6 117
Kerulen (Cherlen), stm., Asia B9 26
Kesagami Lake, l., Ont., Can. F16 66
Keşan, Tur. I10 16
Kesennuma, Japan D14 30
Keshena, Wi., U.S. D5 126
Ket', stm., U.S.S.R. F11 20
Keta, Ozero, l., U.S.S.R. D11 20
Ketchikan, Ak., U.S. D13 79
Ketchum, Id., U.S. F4 89
Kettering, Eng., U.K. I12 7
Kettering, Oh., U.S. C1 112
Kettle, stm., Mn., U.S. D6 100
Kettle Creek, stm., Pa., U.S. D6 115
Kettle Creek Lake, res., Pa., U.S. D6 115
Kettle Falls, Wa., U.S. A7 124
Keuka Lake, l., N.Y., U.S. C3 109
Kew, T./C. Is. D11 64
Kewanee, Il., U.S. B4 90
Kewaskum, Wi., U.S. E5 126
Kewaunee, Wi., U.S. D6 126
Kewaunee, co., Wi., U.S. D6 126
Keweenaw, co., Mi., U.S. A2 99
Keweenaw Bay, b., Mi., U.S. B2 99
Keweenaw Peninsula, pen., Mi., U.S. A3 99
Keweenaw Point, c., Mi., U.S. A3 99
Keya Paha, co., Ne., U.S. B6 104
Keya Paha, stm., U.S. A5 104
Keyhole Reservoir, res., Wy., U.S. B8 127
Key Largo, Fl., U.S. G6 86
Keyport, N.J., U.S. C4 107
Keyser, W.V., U.S. B6 125
Keystone, W.V., U.S. D3 125
Keystone Heights, Fl., U.S. C4 86
Keystone Lake, res., Ok., U.S. A5 113
Keystone Peak, mtn., Az., U.S. F4 80
Keysville, Va., U.S. C4 123
Key West, Fl., U.S. H5 86
Key West Naval Air Station, mil., Fl., U.S. H5 86
Kezar Falls, Me., U.S. E2 96
Kezar Lake, l., Me., U.S. D2 96
Kežma, U.S.S.R. F14 20
Khadki (Kirkee), India C2 37
Khairpur, Pak. G3 38
Khalkís, Grc. K7 16
Khambhāliya, India I3 38
Khambhāt, Gulf of, b., India B2 37
Khāmgaon, India B4 37
Khammam, India D6 37
Khānābād, Afg. B3 38
Khānaqīn, Iraq B3 46
Khandwa, India B4 37
Khānewāl, Pak. E4 38
Khaniá, Grc. N8 16
Khanna, India E7 38
Khānpur, Pak. F4 38
Khān Yūnus, Isr. Occ. D4 40
Kharagpur, India I12 38
Khargon, India J6 38
Kharkov see Char'kov, U.S.S.R. G5 18
Khartoum see Al-Kharṭūm, Sudan E12 42
Kherson see Cherson, U.S.S.R. H4 18
Khíos, Grc. K10 16
Kholm, Afg. B2 38
Khong, Laos G8 34
Khong Sédone, Laos G8 34
Khon Kaen, Thai. F7 34
Khóra Sfakíon, Grc. N8 16
Khorramābād, Iran B4 46
Khorramshahr, Iran B4 46
Khouribga, Mor. B4 42
Khowst, Afg. D3 38
Khulna, Bngl. I13 38
Khunjerab Pass, Asia B6 38
Khurja, India F7 38
Khūryān Mūryān (Kuria Muria Isls, is., Oman E6 46
Khushāb, Pak. D5 38
Khvājeh Moḥammad, Kūh-e, mts., Afg. B4 38
Khvoy, Iran J6 18
Khyber Pass, Asia C4 38
Kiamichi, stm., Ok., U.S. C6 113
Kiamika, stm., Que., Can. C2 74
Kiana, Ak., U.S. B7 79
Kiawah Island, i., S.C., U.S. F7 117
Kibangou, Congo B2 44
Kibombo, Zaire B5 44
Kibre Mengist, Eth. G2 46
Kičevo, Yugo. H4 16
Kichčik, U.S.S.R. G25 20
Kickamuit, stm., R.I., U.S. D5 116
Kickapoo, stm., Wi., U.S. E3 126
Kickapoo, Lake, res., Tx., U.S. C3 120
Kickapoo Indian Reservation, Ks., U.S. C8 93
Kicking Horse Pass, Can. D2 68
Kidal, Mali E6 42
Kidder, co., N.D., U.S. C6 111
Kidira, Sen. F3 42
Kiefer, Ok., U.S. B5 113
Kiel, Ger. A10 8
Kiel, Wi., U.S. E5 126
Kielce, Pol. E20 8
Kieler Bucht, b., Ger. A10 8
Kiester, Mn., U.S. G5 100
Kiev see Kijev, U.S.S.R. G4 18
Kiffa, Maur. E3 42
Kigali, Rw. B6 44
Kigoma, Tan. B5 44
Kihei, Hi., U.S. C5 88
Kihniö, Fin. E14 6
Kiholo Bay, b., Hi., U.S. D5 88
Kii-suidō, strt., Japan I7 30
Kijev (Kiev), U.S.S.R. G4 18
Kikinda, Yugo. D4 16
Kikládhes, is., Grc. L8 16
Kikwit, Zaire C3 44
Kilauea, Hi., U.S. A2 88
Kilauea Crater, crat., Hi., U.S. D6 88
Kilauea Point, c., Hi., U.S. A2 88
Kilgore, Tx., U.S. C5 120
Kilimanjaro, mtn., Tan. B7 44
Kilis, Tur. A5 40
Kilkee, Ire. I3 7
Kilkenny, Ire. I5 7
Kilkís, Grc. H6 16
Killala, Ire. G3 7
Killaloe Station, Ont., Can. B7 73
Killam, Alta., Can. C5 68
Killarney, Man., Can. E2 70
Killarney, Ire. I3 7
Killarney Provincial Park, Ont., Can. A3 73
Killdeer, N.D., U.S. B3 111
Killeen, Tx., U.S. D4 120
Killen, Al., U.S. A2 78
Killian, La., U.S. h10 95
Killik, stm., Ak., U.S. B9 79
Killona, La., U.S. h11 95
Killorglin, Ire. I3 7
Kilmarnock, Scot., U.K. F8 7
Kilmarnock, Va., U.S. C6 123
Kilmichael, Ms., U.S. B4 101
Kiln, Ms., U.S. E4 101
Kilombero, stm., Tan. C7 44
Kilosa, Tan. C7 44
Kilpisjärvi, Fin. B13 6
Kilwa, Zaire C5 44
Kilwa Kivinje, Tan. C7 44
Kimball, Mn., U.S. E4 100
Kimball, Ne., U.S. C2 104
Kimball, S.D., U.S. D7 118
Kimball, co., Ne., U.S. C2 104
Kimball, Mount, mtn., Ak., U.S. C11 79
Kimberley, B.C., Can. E9 69
Kimberley, S. Afr. G4 44
Kimberley Plateau, plat., Austl. C5 50
Kimberlin Heights, Tn., U.S. n14 119
Kimberly, Al., U.S. B3 78
Kimberly, Id., U.S. G4 89
Kimberly, W.V., U.S. m13 125
Kimberly, Wi., U.S. h9 126
Kimble, co., Tx., U.S. D3 120
Kimch'aek, N. Kor. C12 26
Kimovsk, U.S.S.R. H21 22
Kimry, U.S.S.R. E20 22
Kinabalu, Gunong, mtn., Malay. D6 32
Kinbasket Lake, res., B.C., Can. D8 69
Kincaid, Il., U.S. D4 90
Kincaid, W.V., U.S. m13 125
Kincaid, Lake, res., Il., U.S. D4 90
Kincardine, Ont., Can. C3 73
Kincheloe Air Force Base, mil., Mi., U.S. B6 99
Kinder, La., U.S. D3 95
Kindia, Gui. F3 42
Kindu, Zaire B5 44
Kinešma, U.S.S.R. D25 22
King, N.C., U.S. A2 110
King, Wi., U.S. D4 126
King, co., Tx., U.S. C2 120
King, co., Wa., U.S. B3 124
King and Queen, co., Va., U.S. C6 123
Kingaroy, Austl. E10 50
King City, Ca., U.S. D3 82
King City, Mo., U.S. A3 102
King Cove, Ak., U.S. E7 79
Kingfield, Me., U.S. D2 96
Kingfisher, Ok., U.S. B4 113
Kingfisher, co., Ok., U.S. B3 113
King George, co., Va., U.S. B5 123
King Island, i., Austl. G8 50
King Island, i., B.C., Can. C4 69
King Lear Peak, mtn., Nv., U.S. B3 105
King Leopold Ranges, mts., Austl. C5 50
Kingman, Az., U.S. B1 80
Kingman, Ks., U.S. E5 93
Kingman, co., Ks., U.S. E5 93
King Mountain, mtn., Or., U.S. E3 114
King Mountain, mtn., Or., U.S. D8 114
King Peak, mtn., Ca., U.S. B1 82
Kings, Ms., U.S. C3 101
Kings, co., Ca., U.S. D4 82
Kings, co., N.Y., U.S. E7 109
Kings, stm., Ar., U.S. A2 81
Kings, stm., Ca., U.S. D4 82
Kings, stm., Nv., U.S. B3 105
King Salmon, Ak., U.S. D8 79
Kingsburg, Ca., U.S. D4 82
Kingsbury, co., S.D., U.S. C8 118
Kings Canyon National Park, Ca., U.S. D4 82
Kingsey-Falls, Que., Can. D5 74
Kingsford, Mi., U.S. C2 99
Kingsland, Ga., U.S. F5 87
Kingsland, Tx., U.S. D3 120
Kingsley, Ia., U.S. B2 92
Kingsley, Mi., U.S. D5 99
King's Lynn, Eng., U.K. I13 7
Kings Mountain, N.C., U.S. B1 110
King Sound, strt., Austl. C4 50
Kings Park West, Va., U.S. B5 123
Kings Peak, mtn., Ut., U.S. C5 121
King's Point, Newf., Can. D3 72
Kingsport, Tn., U.S. C11 119
Kingston, Ont., Can. C8 73
Kingston, Jam. E9 64
Kingston, Ga., U.S. B2 87
Kingston, Id., U.S. B2 89
Kingston, Ma., U.S. C6 98
Kingston, N.H., U.S. E4 106
Kingston, N.Y., U.S. D6 109
Kingston, Oh., U.S. C3 112
Kingston, Ok., U.S. D5 113
Kingston, Pa., U.S. D10 115
Kingston, R.I., U.S. F3 116
Kingston, Tn., U.S. D9 119
Kingston Springs, Tn., U.S. A4 119
Kingston upon Hull, Eng., U.K. H12 7
Kingstown, St. Vin. H17 64
Kingstown, Md., U.S. B5 97
Kingstree, S.C., U.S. D8 117
Kingsville, Ont., Can. E2 73
Kingsville, Md., U.S. B5 97
Kingsville (North Kingsville), Oh., U.S. A5 112
Kingsville, Tx., U.S. F4 120
Kingsville Naval Air Station, mil., Tx., U.S. F4 120
King William, co., Va., U.S. C5 123
King William Island, i., N.W. Ter., Can. C13 66
King William's Town, S. Afr. H5 44
Kingwood, W.V., U.S. B5 125
Kinistino, Sask., Can. E3 75
Kinkaid Lake, res., Il., U.S. F4 90
Kinloch, Mo., U.S. f13 102
Kinmundy, Il., U.S. E5 90
Kinna, Swe. H9 6
Kinnairds Head, c., Scot., U.K. D10 7
Kinnelon, N.J., U.S. B4 107
Kinneret, Yam, l., Isr. C4 40
Kinney, co., Tx., U.S. E2 120
Kinross, Scot., U.K. E9 7
Kinsale, Ire. J4 7
Kinsarvik, Nor. F6 6
Kinsey, Al., U.S. D4 78
Kinshasa (Léopoldville), Zaire B3 44
Kinsley, Ks., U.S. E4 93
Kinston, N.C., U.S. B5 110
Kintyre, pen., Scot., U.K. F7 7
Kintyre, Mull of, c., Scot., U.K. F7 7
Kinyeti, mtn., Sudan H12 42
Kiowa, Ks., U.S. E5 93
Kiowa, Ok., U.S. C6 113
Kiowa, co., Co., U.S. C8 83
Kiowa, co., Ks., U.S. E4 93
Kiowa, co., Ok., U.S. C2 113
Kiowa Creek, stm., Ok., U.S. A1 113
Kipembawe, Tan. C6 44
Kipili, Tan. C6 44
Kipnuk, Ak., U.S. C7 79
Kipushi, Zaire D5 44
Kirbyville, Tx., U.S. D6 120
Kirchdorf an der Krems, Aus. H14 8
Kirenga, stm., U.S.S.R. F15 20
Kirensk, U.S.S.R. F15 20
Kirghizia see Kirgizskaja Sovetskaja Socialističeskaja Respublika, state, U.S.S.R. I12 18
Kirgizskaja Sovetskaja Socialističeskaja Respublika, state, U.S.S.R. I12 18
Kiribati, ctry., Oc. G24 2
Kırıkhan, Tur. A5 40
Kırıkkale, Tur. H14 4
Kirin see Jilin, China C12 26
Kirinyaga (Mount Kenya), mtn., Kenya B7 44
Kırkağaç, Tur. J11 16
Kirkcaldy, Scot., U.K. E9 7
Kirkcudbright, Scot., U.K. G8 7
Kirkenes, Nor. B18 6
Kirkland, Il., U.S. A5 90
Kirkland, Wa., U.S. B3 124
Kirkland Lake, Ont., Can. o19 73
Kırklareli, Tur. H11 16
Kirklin, In., U.S. D5 91
Kirksville, Mo., U.S. A5 102
Kirkūk, Iraq A3 46
Kirkwall, Scot., U.K. C10 7
Kirkwood, De., U.S. B3 85
Kirkwood, Il., U.S. C3 90
Kirkwood, Mo., U.S. f13 102
Kirov, U.S.S.R. F7 18
Kirov, U.S.S.R. G17 22
Kirovograd, U.S.S.R. H4 18
Kirovskij, U.S.S.R. G25 20
Kırşehir, Tur. H14 4
Kīrthar Range, mts., Pak. G2 38
Kirtland, N.M., U.S. A1 108
Kirtland Air Force Base, mil., N.M., U.S. k7 108
Kiruna, Swe. C13 6
Kirwin Reservoir, res., Ks., U.S. C4 93
Kiryū, Japan F12 30
Kisa, Swe. H10 6
Kisangani (Stanleyville), Zaire A5 44
Kisarazu, Japan G12 30
K.I. Sawyer Air Force Base, mil., Mi., U.S. B3 99
Kisel'ovsk, U.S.S.R. G11 20
Kishanganj, India G12 38
Kishangarh, India G6 38
Kishinev see Kišin'ov, U.S.S.R. H3 18
Kishiwada, Japan H8 30
Kishorganj, Bngl. H14 38
Kishwaukee, stm., Il., U.S. A5 90
Kišin'ov, U.S.S.R. H3 18
Kiska Island, i., Ak., U.S. E3 79
Kiskunfélegyháza, Hung. I19 8
Kiskunhalas, Hung. I19 8
Kislovodsk, U.S.S.R. I6 18
Kismayu, Som. B8 44
Kissidougou, Gui. G3 42
Kissimmee, Fl., U.S. D5 86
Kissimmee, stm., Fl., U.S. E5 86
Kissimmee, Lake, l., Fl., U.S. E5 86
Kississing Lake, l., Man., Can. B1 70
Kistanje, Yugo. F10 14
Kistler, W.V., U.S. D3 125
Kisumu, Kenya B6 44
Kitaibaraki, Japan F13 30
Kitakami, stm., Japan C14 30
Kitakami-sanchi, mts., Japan C14 30
Kitakyūshū, Japan I3 30
Kitale, Kenya A6 44
Kitami, Japan p21 30a
Kitami-sanchi, mts., Japan o20 30a
Kit Carson, co., Co., U.S. B8 83
Kitchener, Ont., Can. D4 73
Kíthira, i., Grc. M6 16
Kitimat, B.C., Can. B3 69
Kitsap, co., Wa., U.S. B3 124
Kitscoty, Alta., Can. C5 68
Kittanning, Pa., U.S. E2 115
Kittatinny Mountain, mtn., U.S. B2 107
Kittery, Me., U.S. E2 96
Kittery Point, Me., U.S. E2 96
Kittilä, Fin. C15 6
Kittitas, Wa., U.S. C5 124
Kittitas, co., Wa., U.S. B4 124
Kitts, Ky., U.S. D6 94
Kittson, co., Mn., U.S. B2 100
Kitty Hawk, N.C., U.S. A7 110
Kitty Hawk Bay, b., N.C., U.S. A7 110
Kitwe, Zam. D5 44
Kitzbühel, Aus. H12 8
Kitzingen, Ger. F10 8
Kivu, Lac, l., Afr. B5 44
Kızıl, stm., Tur. G14 4
Kjustendil, Bul. G6 16
Kladno, Czech. E14 8
Klagenfurt, Aus. I14 8
Klaipėda (Memel), U.S.S.R. F4 22
Klamath, co., Or., U.S. E5 114
Klamath, stm., U.S. B2 82
Klamath Falls, Or., U.S. E5 114
Klamath Mountains, mts., U.S. E2 114
Klangenan, Indon. m14 33a
Klarälven, stm., Eur. F9 6
Klawock, Ak., U.S. D13 79
Kleberg, co., Tx., U.S. F4 120
Klerksdorp, S. Afr. G5 44
Kleve, Ger. D6 8
Klickitat, Wa., U.S. D4 124
Klickitat, co., Wa., U.S. D4 124
Klickitat, stm., Wa., U.S. C4 124
Klimovsk, U.S.S.R. F20 22
Klin, U.S.S.R. E19 22
Klincy, U.S.S.R. I15 22
Kłodzko, Pol. E16 8
Klondike, hist. reg., Yukon, Can. D5 66
Klondike Gold Rush National Historical Park, Ak., U.S. k22 79
Klosterneuburg, Aus. G16 8
Kluane Lake, l., Yukon, Can. D5 66
Klutina Lake, l., Ak., U.S. g19 79
Knapp Creek, stm., W.V., U.S. C5 125
Knee Lake, l., Man., Can. B4 70
Kneža, Bul. F8 16
Knife, stm., N.D., U.S. B3 111
Knightdale, N.C., U.S. B4 110
Knight Inlet, b., B.C., Can. D5 69
Knight Island, i., Ak., U.S. g18 79
Knightstown, In., U.S. E6 91
Knightsville, In., U.S. E3 91
Knightville Reservoir, res., Ma., U.S. B2 98
Knin, Yugo. E11 14
Knittelfeld, Aus. H14 8
Knob Noster, Mo., U.S. C4 102
Knokke, Bel. D3 8
Knollwood, W.V., U.S. m12 125
Knott, co., Ky., U.S. C6 94
Knox, In., U.S. B4 91
Knox, Pa., U.S. D2 115
Knox, co., Il., U.S. B3 90
Knox, co., In., U.S. G3 91
Knox, co., Ky., U.S. D6 94
Knox, co., Me., U.S. D4 96
Knox, co., Mo., U.S. A5 102
Knox, co., Ne., U.S. B8 104
Knox, co., Oh., U.S. B3 112
Knox, co., Tn., U.S. C10 119
Knox, co., Tx., U.S. C3 120
Knox, Cape, c., B.C., Can. B1 69
Knox City, Tx., U.S. C3 120
Knoxville, Il., U.S. C3 90
Knoxville, Ia., U.S. C4 92
Knoxville, Tn., U.S. D10 119
Knysna, S. Afr. H4 44
Kōbe, Japan H8 30
København (Copenhagen), Den. I9 6
Koblenz, Ger. E7 8
Kobrin, U.S.S.R. I7 22
Kobuk, stm., Ak., U.S. B8 79
Kobuk Valley National Park, Ak., U.S. B8 79
Kočani, Yugo. H6 16
Kočečum, stm., U.S.S.R. D13 20
Kočevje, Yugo. D9 14
Kōchi, Japan I6 30
Koch Peak, mtn., Mt., U.S. E5 103
Kodiak, Ak., U.S. D9 79
Kodiak Island, i., Ak., U.S. D9 79
Koes, Nmb. G3 44
Kofa Mountains, mts., Az., U.S. D2 80
Köflach, Aus. H15 8
Kōfu, Japan G11 30
Koga, Japan F12 30
Kogaluc, Baie, b., Que., Can. E17 66
Kogaluk, stm., Newf., Can. g9 72
Køge Bugt, b., Grnld. D24 66
Kohala Mountains, mts., Hi., U.S. C6 88
Kohāt, Pak. D4 38
Kohīma, India H16 38
Kohler, Wi., U.S. E6 126
Kohtla-Järve, U.S.S.R. B10 22
Kokand, U.S.S.R. I12 18
Kokanee Glacier Provincial Park, B.C., Can. E9 69
Kokemäki, Fin. F14 6
Kokkola (Gamlakarleby), Fin. E14 6
Koko Head, c., Hi., U.S. B4 88
Kokolik, stm., Ak., U.S. B7 79
Kokomo, In., U.S. D5 91
Kokonau, Indon. F10 32
Kokopo, Pap. N. Gui. k17 50a
Kokosing, stm., Oh., U.S. B3 112
Koksoak, stm., Que., Can. E19 66
Kokstad, S. Afr. H5 44
Kolaka, Indon. F7 32
Kola Peninsula see Kol'skij poluostrov, pen., U.S.S.R. D5 18
Kolār, India F5 37
Kolār Gold Fields, India F5 37
Kol'čugino, U.S.S.R. E22 22
Kolda, Sen. F3 42
Kolding, Den. I7 6
Kolhāpur, India D3 37
Kolín, Czech. E15 8
Kollegāl, India F4 37
Köln (Cologne), Ger. E6 8
Koloa, Hi., U.S. B2 88
Kołobrzeg, Pol. A15 8
Kolomna, U.S.S.R. F21 22
Kolpaševo, U.S.S.R. F10 20
Kolpino, U.S.S.R. B13 22
Kol'skij poluostrov (Kola Peninsula), pen., U.S.S.R. D5 18
Kolwezi, Zaire D5 44
Kolyma, stm., U.S.S.R. D25 20
Kolymskaja Nizmennost', pl., U.S.S.R. D24 20
Komárno, Czech. H18 8
Komatsu, Japan F9 30
Komló, Hung. I18 8
Kommunizma, pik, mtn., U.S.S.R. J12 18
Komoé, stm., Afr. G5 42
Komotiní, Grc. H9 16
Komsomolec, Ostrov, i., U.S.S.R. A12 20
Komsomol'sk-na-Amure, U.S.S.R. G21 20
Komsomol'skoj Pravdy, Ostrova, is., U.S.S.R. B15 20
Konahuanui, Puu, mtn., Hi., U.S. g10 88
Konakovo, U.S.S.R. E19 22
Konawa, Ok., U.S. C5 113
Konch, India H8 38
Kondrovo, U.S.S.R. G18 22
Kŏng, Kaôh, i., Camb. I7 34
Kongolo, Zaire C5 44
Kongsberg, Nor. G7 6
Kongsvinger, Nor. F8 6
Kongsvoll, Nor. E7 6
Kongur Shan, mtn., China A6 38
Königs Wusterhausen, Ger. C13 8
Konin, Pol. C18 8
Konjic, Yugo. F12 14
Konomoc, Lake, res., Ct., U.S. D7 84
Konqi, stm., China C4 26
Konstanz, Ger. H9 8
Kontagora, Nig. F7 42
Kontiomäki, Fin. D17 6
Kon Tum, Viet. G10 34
Konya, Tur. H14 4
Konza, Kenya B7 44
Koochiching, co., Mn., U.S. B4 100
Koolau Range, mts., Hi., U.S. f10 88
Koontz Lake, In., U.S. B5 91
Kooskia, Id., U.S. C3 89
Kootenai, co., Id., U.S. B2 89
Kootenay Lake, l., B.C., Can. E9 69
Kootenay National Park, B.C., Can. D9 69
Kopargaon, India C3 37
Koper, Yugo. D8 14
Kopetdag, chrebet, mts., Asia J9 18
Köping, Swe. G10 6
Koppal, India E4 37
Koppang, Nor. F8 6
Koppel, Pa., U.S. E1 115
Koprivnica, Yugo. C11 14
Kor'akskoje Nagorje, mts., U.S.S.R. E27 20
Korba, India I10 38
Korbach, Ger. D8 8
Korçë, Alb. I4 16
Korčula, Yugo. G12 14
Korea, North, ctry., Asia C12 26
Korea, South, ctry., Asia D12 26
Korea Bay, b., Asia D11 26
Korea Strait, strt., Asia E12 26
Korf, U.S.S.R. E27 20
Korhogo, I.C. G4 42
Korinthiakós Kólpos, b., Grc. K6 16
Kórinthos (Corinth), Grc. L6 16
Kōriyama, Japan E13 30
Korliki, U.S.S.R. E10 20
Korogwe, Tan. C7 44
Koronis, Lake, l., Mn., U.S. E4 100
Koro Toro, Chad E9 42
Korovin Volcano, vol., Ak., U.S. E5 79
Korsakov, U.S.S.R. H22 20
Korsnäs, Fin. E13 6
Korso, Fin. F15 6
Kortrijk (Courtrai), Bel. E3 8
Koruçam Burnu, c., N. Cyp. B3 40
Koš-Agač, U.S.S.R. G11 20
Kosciusko, Ms., U.S. B4 101
Kosciusko, co., In., U.S. B6 91
Kosciusko, Mount, mtn., Austl. G9 50
Koshkonong, Lake, l., Wi., U.S. F5 126
Košice, Czech. G21 8
Kosovska Mitrovica, Yugo. G4 16
Kossuth, co., Ia., U.S. A3 92
Kostroma, U.S.S.R. D23 22
Koszalin (Köslin), Pol. A16 8
Kota, India H6 38
Kota Baharu, Malay. K7 34
Kotabumi, Indon. F3 32
Kot Addu, Pak. E4 38
Kota Kinabalu (Jesselton), Malay. D6 32
Kotel'nyj, Ostrov, i., U.S.S.R. B21 20
Köthen, Ger. D11 8
Kotka, Fin. F16 6

Kot Kapūra, India E6 38
Kotlas, U.S.S.R. E7 18
Kotlik, Ak., U.S. C7 79
Kotor Varoš, Yugo. E12 14
Kotovsk, U.S.S.R. I24 22
Kotri, Pak. H3 38
Kötschach [-Mauthen], Aus. I12 8
Kottagūdem, India D6 37
Kottayam, India H4 37
Kotte, Sri L. I5 37
Kotto, stm., Cen. Afr. Rep. G10 42
Kotuj, stm., U.S.S.R. C14 20
Kotzebue, Ak., U.S. B7 79
Kotzebue Sound, strt., Ak., U.S. B7 79
Kouchibouguac National Park, N.B., Can. C5 71
Koudougou, Burkina F5 42
Koula-Moutou, Gabon B2 44
Koumra, Chad G9 42
Kountze, Tx., U.S. D5 120
Koussi, Emi, mtn., Chad E9 42
Koutiala, Mali F4 42
Kouts, In., U.S. B3 91
Kouvola, Fin. F16 6
Kovrov, U.S.S.R. E24 22
Kowkcheh, stm., Afg. B4 38
Kowloon (Jiulong), H.K. M3 28
Kowt-e 'Ashrow, Afg. C3 38
Koyukuk, stm., Ak., U.S. B8 79
Koza, Japan y27 31b
Kozáni, Grc. I5 16
Kra, Isthmus of, Asia I5 34
Krâchéh, Camb. H9 34
Kragerø, Nor. G7 6
Kragujevac, Yugo. E4 16
Kraków, Pol. E19 8
Kraljevica, Yugo. D9 14
Kraljevo, Yugo. F4 16
Kramfors, Swe. E11 6
Krångede, Swe. E11 6
Kranj, Yugo. C9 14
Krasneno, U.S.S.R. E28 20
Krasnodar, U.S.S.R. H5 18
Krasnogorsk, U.S.S.R. F20 22
Krasnojarsk, U.S.S.R. F12 20
Krasnoje, Ozero, l., U.S.S.R. E28 20
Krasnosel'kup, U.S.S.R. D10 20
Krasnozavodsk, U.S.S.R. E21 22
Krebs, Ok., U.S. C6 113
Kremenčug, U.S.S.R. H4 18
Kremmling, Co., U.S. A4 83
Krems an der Donau, Aus. G15 8
Kresta, Zaliv, b., U.S.S.R. D30 20
Kribi, Cam. H7 42
Kričov, U.S.S.R. H14 22
Krishna, stm., India D5 37
Krishnanagar, India I13 38
Kristiansand, Nor. G7 6
Kristianstad, Swe. H10 6
Kristiansund, Nor. E6 6
Kristinehamn, Swe. G10 6
Kríti, i., Grc. N8 16
Kritikón Pélagos, Grc. N8 16
Krivoj Rog, U.S.S.R. H4 18
Krivoy Rog see Krivoj Rog, U.S.S.R. H4 18
Krnov, Czech. E17 8
Kroken, Nor. D10 6
Kroměříž, Czech. F17 8
Kronach, Ger. E11 8
Krŏng Khémôreăh Phumint, Camb. I7 34
Kronockij Zaliv, b., U.S.S.R. G26 20
Kronoki, U.S.S.R. G26 20
Kronštadt, U.S.S.R. B12 22
Kroonstad, S. Afr. G5 44
Kropotkin, U.S.S.R. F17 20
Krosno, Pol. F21 8
Krotz Springs, La., U.S. D4 95
Krško, Yugo. D10 14
Kr'ukovo, U.S.S.R. D25 20
Krung Thep (Bangkok), Thai. H6 34
Kruševac, Yugo. F5 16
Krušné hory (Erzgebirge), mts., Eur. E12 8
Kruzenšterna, Proliv, strt., U.S.S.R. H24 20
Kruzof Island, i., Ak., U.S. m21 79
Krymskij poluostrov (Crimea), pen., U.S.S.R. H4 18
Ksar-es-Souk, Mor. B5 42
Ksenjevka, U.S.S.R. G17 20
Ksour Essaf, Tun. N5 14
Kuala Kangsar, Malay. L6 34
Kualakapuas, Indon. F5 32
Kuala Krai, Malay. L7 34
Kuala Kubu Baharu, Malay. M6 34
Kuala Lumpur, Malay. M6 34
Kuala Nerang, Malay. K6 34
Kuala Pilah, Malay. M7 34
Kuala Terengganu, Malay. L7 34
Kuantan, Malay. M7 34
Kubokawa, Japan I6 30
Kuche, China C3 26
Kuching, Malay. E5 32
Kudat, Malay. D6 32
Kudus, Indon. m15 32
Kuee Ruins, hist., Hi., U.S. D6 88
Kufstein, Aus. H12 8
Kuhmo, Fin. D17 6
Kuito, Ang. D3 44
Kuiu Island, i., Ak., U.S. m23 79
Kuivaniemi, Fin. D15 6
Kukawa, Nig. F8 42
Kula, Tur. K12 16
Kula, Hi., U.S. C5 88
Kul'ab, U.S.S.R. B3 38
Kula Kangri, mtn., Bhu. F14 38
Kulebaki, U.S.S.R. F25 22
Kulen Vakuf, Yugo. E11 14
Kulim, Malay. L6 34
Kulmbach, Ger. E11 8
Kulpmont, Pa., U.S. E9 115
Kulundinskoje, Ozero, l., U.S.S.R. G9 20
Kulunqi, China C11 26
Kumagaya, Japan F12 30
Kumamoto, Japan J3 30
Kumano, Japan I9 30
Kumano-nada, Japan I9 30
Kumanovo, Yugo. G5 16
Kumasi, Ghana G5 42
Kumbakonam, India G5 37
Kume-shima, i., Japan y26 31b
Kumo, Nig. F8 42
Kumon Range, mts., Burma B4 34
Kumukahi, Cape, c., Hi., U.S. D7 88
Kuna, Id., U.S. F2 89
Kunašir, Ostrov (Kunashiri-tō), i., U.S.S.R. I23 20
Kundiān, Pak. D4 38
Kundla, India J4 38
Kunes, Nor. A16 6
Kunghit Island, i., B.C., Can. C2 69
Kuningan, Indon. m14 33a
Kunlun Shan, mts., China B12 38
Kunming, China B7 34
Kunsan, S. Kor. D12 26
Kunshan, China D9 28
Kuopio, Fin. E16 6
Kupang, Indon. H7 32
Kupreanof Island, i., Ak., U.S. m23 79
Kupres, Yugo. E12 14
Kura, stm., Asia I7 18
Kurashiki, Japan H6 30
Kurayoshi, Japan G6 30
Kure, Japan H5 30
Kure Island, i., Hi., U.S. k12 88
Kurejka, stm., U.S.S.R. D11 20
Kurenalus, Fin. D16 6
Kurgan-T'ube, U.S.S.R. B3 38
Kurikka, Fin. E14 6
Kuril Islands see Kuril'skije Ostrova, is., U.S.S.R. H23 20
Kuril'sk, U.S.S.R. H23 20
Kuril'skije Ostrova (Kuril Islands), is., U.S.S.R. H23 20
Kurmuk, Sudan F12 42
Kurnool, India E5 37
Kurow, N.Z. F3 52
Kursk, U.S.S.R. G5 18
Kurtistown, Hi., U.S. D6 88
Kuruman, S. Afr. G4 44
Kurume, Japan I3 30
Kurumkan, U.S.S.R. G16 20
Kurunegala, Sri L. I6 37
Kuşadası Körfezi, b., Tur. L11 16
Kuş Gölü, l., Tur. I11 16
Kushima, Japan K4 30
Kushiro, Japan q22 30a
Kushtia, Bngl. I13 38
Kushui, China C5 26
Kuskokwim, stm., Ak., U.S. C8 79
Kuskokwim Bay, b., Ak., U.S. D7 79
Kuskokwim Mountains, mts., Ak., U.S. C8 79
Kūstī, Sudan F12 42
K'us'ur, U.S.S.R. C19 20
Kut, Ko, i., Thai. I7 34
Kutaisi, U.S.S.R. I6 18
Kūt al-Imāra, Iraq B4 46
Kutch, Gulf of, b., India I3 38
Kutina, Yugo. D11 14
Kutno, Pol. C19 8
Kutu, Zaire B3 44
Kutztown, Pa., U.S. E10 115
Kuujjuaq, Que., Can. g13 74
Kuusamo, Fin. D17 6
Kuusankoski, Fin. F16 6
Kuvango, Ang. D3 44
Kuwait, ctry., Asia C4 46
Kuwait see Al-Kuwayt, Kuw. C4 46
Kuwana, Japan G9 30
Kuybyshev see Kujbyšev, U.S.S.R. G8 18
Kuzneck, U.S.S.R. G7 18
Kvikkjokk, Swe. C11 6
Kwando (Cuando), stm., Afr. E4 44
Kwangchow see Guangzhou, China L2 28
Kwangju, S. Kor. D12 26
Kwango (Cuango), stm., Afr. B3 44
Kwekwe, Zimb. E5 44
Kwethluk, Ak., U.S. C7 79
Kwidzyn, Pol. B18 8
Kwigillingok, Ak., U.S. D7 79
Kwilu (Cuilo), stm., Afr. B3 44
Kyaiklat, Burma F3 34
Kyaikto, Burma F4 34
Kyle, Tx., U.S. E4 120
Kyle of Lochalsh, Scot., U.K. D7 7
Kyoga, Lake, l., Ug. A6 44
Kyōto, Japan G8 30
Kyuquot Sound, strt., B.C., Can. E4 69
Kyūshū, i., Japan I3 30
Kyūshū-sanchi, mts., Japan J4 30
Kyyjärvi, Fin. E15 6
Kyzyl, U.S.S.R. G12 20
Kzyl-Orda, U.S.S.R. I11 18

L

Logan, Mount, mtn., Yukon, Can. D4 66
Laa an der Thaya, Aus. G16 8
La Almunia de Doña Godina, Spain D10 12
La Asunción, Ven. B11 58
Laau Point, c., Hi., U.S. B4 88
L'Abacou, Pointe, c., Haiti E11 64
Labadieville, La., U.S. E5 95
La Bañeza, Spain C6 12
La Barca, Mex. G8 62
La Barge, Wy., U.S. D2 127
La Barge Creek, stm., Wy., U.S. D2 127
La Baule, Fr. E4 10
Labé, Gui. F3 42
Labe (Elbe), stm., Eur. E14 8
La Belle, Fl., U.S. F5 86
La Belle, Mo., U.S. A6 102
Labette, co., Ks., U.S. E8 93
Labin, Yugo. D9 14
La Bisbal, Spain D15 12
Labouheyre, Fr. H6 10
Labrador, reg., Newf., Can. g9 72
Labrador City, Newf., Can. h8 72
Labrador Sea, N.A. E22 66
Lábrea, Braz. E6 54
Labutta, Burma F3 34
La Canada Flintridge, Ca., U.S. m12 82
Lacanau, Fr. H5 10
La Cañiza, Spain C3 12
La Canourgue, Fr. H10 10
La Carolina, Spain G8 12
Lacaune, Fr. I9 10
Lac-Bouchette, Que., Can. A5 74
Lac-Brome, Que., Can. D5 74
Laccadive Sea, Asia H3 37
Lac-Carré, Que., Can. C3 74
Lac Courte Oreilles Indian Reservation, Wi., U.S. C2 126
Lac du Bonnet, Man., Can. D3 70
Lac du Flambeau, Wi., U.S. C4 126
Lac du Flambeau Indian Reservation, Wi., U.S. C3 126
La Ceiba, Hond. G4 64
La Ceiba, Ven. C7 58
La Center, Ky., U.S. e9 94
Lac-Etchemin, Que., Can. C7 74
Lacey, Wa., U.S. B3 124
La Charité [-sur-Loire], Fr. E10 10
La Châtre, Fr. F8 10
La Chaux-de-Fonds, Switz. E13 10
Lachine, Que., Can. D4 74
La Chorrera, Col. H6 58
La Chorrera, Pan. J8 64
Lachute, Que., Can. D3 74
La Ciotat, Fr. I12 10
Lackawanna, N.Y., U.S. C2 109
Lackawanna, co., Pa., U.S. D10 115
Lackland Air Force Base, mil., Tx., U.S. k7 120
Lac La Biche, Alta., Can. B5 68
Lac la Hache, B.C., Can. D7 69
Laclede, co., Mo., U.S. D5 102
Lac-Mégantic, Que., Can. D7 74
Lacolle, Que., Can. D4 74
Lacombe, Alta., Can. C4 68
Lacombe, La., U.S. D6 95
Lacon, Il., U.S. B4 90
Laconia, N.H., U.S. C4 106
La Conner, Wa., U.S. A3 124
Lacoochee, Fl., U.S. D4 86
La Coruña, Spain B3 12
Lac qui Parle, co., Mn., U.S. F2 100
Lac qui Parle, stm., Mn., U.S. F2 100
La Creek Lake, l., S.D., U.S. D4 118
La Crescent, Mn., U.S. G7 100
La Crete, Alta., Can. f7 68
La Crosse, In., U.S. B4 91
La Crosse, Ks., U.S. D4 93
La Crosse, Wi., U.S. E2 126
La Crosse, co., Wi., U.S. E2 126
La Crosse, stm., Wi., U.S. E3 126
La Cruz, Nic. H5 64
La Cygne, Ks., U.S. D9 93
Ladd, Il., U.S. B4 90
Ladies Island, i., S.C., U.S. G6 117
Lādīz, Iran C7 46
Lādnun, India G6 38
Ladoga, In., U.S. E4 91
Ladoga, Lake see Ladožskoje Ozero, l., U.S.S.R. F18 6
La Dorada, Col. E5 58
Ladožskoje Ozero (Lake Ladoga), l., U.S.S.R. F18 6
Ladson, S.C., U.S. F7 117
Lady Lake, Fl., U.S. D5 86
Lady Laurier, Mount, mtn., B.C., Can. A6 69
Ladysmith, B.C., Can. E6 69
Ladysmith, S. Afr. G5 44
Ladysmith, Wi., U.S. C2 126
Lae, Pap. N. Gui. m16 50a
La Encantada, Cerro de, mtn., Mex. B2 62
La Esmeralda, Ven. F10 58
La Esperanza, Hond. G3 64
La Estrada, Spain C3 12
La Farge, Wi., U.S. E3 126
Lafayette, Al., U.S. C4 78
Lafayette, Co., U.S. B5 83
Lafayette, Ga., U.S. B1 87
Lafayette, In., U.S. D4 91
Lafayette, La., U.S. D3 95
Lafayette, N.C., U.S. B4 110
Lafayette, Or., U.S. B3 114
La Fayette, R.I., U.S. E4 116
Lafayette, Tn., U.S. A5 119
Lafayette, co., Ar., U.S. D2 81
Lafayette, co., Fl., U.S. C3 86
Lafayette, co., La., U.S. D3 95
Lafayette, co., Ms., U.S. A4 101
Lafayette, co., Mo., U.S. B4 102
Lafayette, co., Wi., U.S. F3 126
Lafayette, Mount, mtn., N.H., U.S. B3 106
La Feria, Tx., U.S. F4 120
La Ferté-Bernard, Fr. D7 10
La Ferté-Macé, Fr. D6 10
La Ferté-Saint-Aubin, Fr. E8 10
Lafia, Nig. G7 42
Lafitte, La., U.S. k11 95
La Flèche, Fr. E6 10
La Follette, Tn., U.S. C9 119
La Fontaine, In., U.S. C6 91
La Fortuna, C.R. I5 64
Lafourche, La., U.S. E5 95
Lafourche, co., La., U.S. E5 95
La France, S.C., U.S. B2 117
La Fregeneda, Spain E5 12
La Fria, Ven. C6 58
La Fuente de San Esteban, Spain E5 12
Lågen, stm., Nor. F8 6
Laghouat, Alg. B6 42
Lago, Mount, mtn., Wa., U.S. A5 124
Lagonegro, Italy I10 14
Lagos, Nig. G6 42
Lagos de Moreno, Mex. G9 62
La Goulette, Tun. M5 14
La Grand'Combe, Fr. H11 10
La Grande, Or., U.S. B8 114
La Grande, stm., Que., Can. h11 74
La Grande Deux, Réservoir, res., Que., Can. h11 74
La Grange, Austl. C4 50
La Grange, Ga., U.S. C1 87
La Grange, Il., U.S. B6 90
Lagrange, In., U.S. A7 91
La Grange, Ky., U.S. B4 94
La Grange, Mo., U.S. A6 102
La Grange, N.C., U.S. B5 110
Lagrange, Oh., U.S. A3 112
La Grange, Tx., U.S. E4 120
Lagrange, co., In., U.S. A7 91
La Grange Park, Il., U.S. k9 90
La Gran Sabana, pl., Ven. E12 58
La Grita, Ven. C7 58
La Guadeloupe (Saint-Evariste), Que., Can. D7 74
La Guaira, Ven. B9 58
La Guajira, Península de, pen., S.A. A7 58
Laguardia, Spain C9 12
La Guardia, Spain D3 12
La Guerche-de-Bretagne, Fr. E5 10
La Guerche-sur-l'aubois, Fr. F9 10
Laguiole, Fr. H9 10
Laguna, N.M., U.S. B2 108
Laguna Beach, Ca., U.S. F5 82
Laguna Dam, U.S. E1 80
Laguna Indian Reservation, N.M., U.S. C2 108
Lagunillas, Bol. G6 54
La Habana (Havana), Cuba C6 64
La Habra, Ca., U.S. n13 82
Lahaina, Hi., U.S. C5 88
La Harpe, Il., U.S. C3 90
La Harpe, Ks., U.S. E8 93
Lahat, Indon. F3 32
La Have, stm., N.S., Can. E5 71
La Haye-du-Puits, Fr. C5 10
Lahij, Yemen F3 46
Laholm, Swe. H9 6
Lahoma, Ok., U.S. A3 113
Lahontan Reservoir, res., Nv., U.S. D2 105
Lahore, Pak. E6 38
Lahr, Ger. G7 8
Lahti, Fin. F15 6
Laie, Hi., U.S. B4 88
L'Aigle, Fr. D7 10
Laignes, Fr. E11 10
Laihia, Fin. E14 6
Laingsburg, S. Afr. H4 44
Laingsburg, Mi., U.S. F6 99
Lairg, Scot., U.K. C8 7
Laissac, Fr. H9 10
Laiyang, China D11 26
La Jara, Co., U.S. D5 83
Lajes, Braz. E11 54
La Jolla, Point, c., Ca., U.S. o15 82
La Joya, Mex. A2 62
La Junta, Mex. C6 62
La Junta, Co., U.S. D7 83
Lake, co., Ca., U.S. C2 82
Lake, co., Co., U.S. B4 83
Lake, co., Fl., U.S. D5 86
Lake, co., Il., U.S. A6 90
Lake, co., In., U.S. B3 91
Lake, co., Mi., U.S. E5 99
Lake, co., Mn., U.S. C7 100
Lake, co., Mt., U.S. C2 103
Lake, co., Oh., U.S. A4 112
Lake, co., Or., U.S. E6 114
Lake, co., S.D., U.S. C8 118
Lake, co., Tn., U.S. A2 119
Lake Alfred, Fl., U.S. D5 86
Lake Andes, S.D., U.S. D7 118
Lake Ariel, Pa., U.S. D11 115
Lake Arrowhead, Ca., U.S. E5 82
Lake Arthur, La., U.S. D3 95
Lake Barcroft, Va., U.S. B5 123
Lake Benton, Mn., U.S. F2 100
Lake Bluff, Il., U.S. A6 90
Lake Butler, Fl., U.S. B4 86
Lake Charles, La., U.S. D2 95
Lake Chelan National Recreation Area, Wa., U.S. A5 124
Lake City, Ar., U.S. B5 81
Lake City, Fl., U.S. B4 86
Lake City, Ia., U.S. B3 92
Lake City, Mi., U.S. D5 99
Lake City, Mn., U.S. F6 100
Lake City, Pa., U.S. B1 115
Lake City, S.C., U.S. D8 117
Lake City, Tn., U.S. C9 119
Lake Clark National Park, Ak., U.S. C9 79
Lake Cowichan, B.C., Can. g11 69
Lake Creek, stm., Wa., U.S. B7 124
Lake Crystal, Mn., U.S. F4 100
Lake Delta, N.Y., U.S. B5 109
Lake Delton, Wi., U.S. E4 126
Lake District National Park, Eng., U.K. G9 7
Lake Elsinore, Ca., U.S. F5 82
Lake Erie Beach, N.Y., U.S. C1 109
Lakefield, Ont., Can. C6 73
Lakefield, Mn., U.S. G3 100
Lake Forest, Il., U.S. A6 90
Lake Fork, stm., Ut., U.S. C5 121
Lake Geneva, Wi., U.S. F5 126
Lake Hamilton, Ar., U.S. g7 81
Lake Harbour, N.W. Ter., Can. D19 66
Lake Havasu City, Az., U.S. C1 80
Lake Helen, Fl., U.S. D5 86
Lakehurst, N.J., U.S. C4 107
Lakehurst Naval Air Station, mil., N.J., U.S. C4 107
Lake in the Hills, Il., U.S. h8 90
Lake Jackson, Tx., U.S. E5 120
Lake Katrine, N.Y., U.S. D7 109
Lakeland, Fl., U.S. D5 86
Lakeland, Ga., U.S. E3 87
Lake Linden, Mi., U.S. A2 99
Lake Louise, Alta., Can. D2 68
Lake Magdalene, Fl., U.S. o11 86
Lake Mary, Fl., U.S. D5 86
Lake Mead National Recreation Area, U.S. H7 105
Lake Meredith National Recreation Area, Tx., U.S. B2 120
Lake Mills, Ia., U.S. A4 92
Lake Mills, Wi., U.S. E5 126
Lakemore, Oh., U.S. A4 112
Lake Mountain, mtn., Wy., U.S. E6 127
Lake Nebagamon, Wi., U.S. B2 126
Lake Odessa, Mi., U.S. F5 99
Lake Of The Woods, co., Mn., U.S. B4 100
Lake Orion, Mi., U.S. F7 99
Lake Oswego, Or., U.S. B4 114
Lake Ozark, Mo., U.S. C5 102
Lake Park, Fl., U.S. F6 86
Lake Park, Ia., U.S. A2 92
Lake Park, Mn., U.S. D2 100
Lake Placid, Fl., U.S. E5 86
Lake Placid, N.Y., U.S. A7 109
Lake Pontchartrain Causeway, La., U.S. h11 95
Lakeport, Ca., U.S. C2 82
Lake Preston, S.D., U.S. C8 118
Lake Providence, La., U.S. B4 95
Lake Range, mts., Nv., U.S. C2 105
Lake Ridge, Va., U.S. B5 123
Lake Shore, Md., U.S. B5 97
Lakeshore, Ms., U.S. E4 101
Lakeside, Ca., U.S. F5 82
Lakeside, Ct., U.S. D3 84
Lakeside, Mt., U.S. B2 103
Lakeside, Oh., U.S. A3 112
Lakeside, Or., U.S. D2 114
Lakeside Park, Ky., U.S. h13 94
Lakeside-Pinetop, Az., U.S. C6 80
Lake Station, In., U.S. A3 91
Lake Station, Ok., U.S. A5 113
Lake Stevens, Wa., U.S. A3 124
Lake Superior Provincial Park, Ont., Can. p18 73
Lake Swamp, stm., S.C., U.S. D8 117
Lake Tansi Village, Tn., U.S. D8 119
Lake Valley, val., Nv., U.S. E7 105
Lake View, Ia., U.S. B2 92
Lakeview, Mi., U.S. E5 99
Lakeview, Oh., U.S. B2 112
Lakeview, Or., U.S. E6 114
Lake View, S.C., U.S. C9 117
Lake Villa, Il., U.S. h8 90
Lake Village, Ar., U.S. D4 81
Lake Village, In., U.S. B3 91
Lakeville, Ct., U.S. B2 84
Lakeville, In., U.S. A5 91
Lakeville, Ma., U.S. C6 98
Lakeville, Mn., U.S. F5 100
Lake Waccamaw, N.C., U.S. C4 110
Lake Wales, Fl., U.S. E5 86
Lakewood, Ca., U.S. n12 82
Lakewood, Co., U.S. B5 83
Lakewood, Il., U.S. D5 90
Lakewood, Ia., U.S. f8 92
Lakewood, N.J., U.S. C4 107
Lakewood, N.Y., U.S. C1 109
Lakewood, Oh., U.S. A4 112
Lakewood Center, Wa., U.S. B3 124
Lake Worth, Fl., U.S. F6 86
Lake Worth Inlet, b., Fl., U.S. F7 86
Lake Zurich, Il., U.S. h8 90
Lakhīmpur, India G9 38
Lakin, Ks., U.S. E2 93
Lakota, N.D., U.S. A7 111
Lakselv, Nor. A15 6
Lakshadweep, state, India H3 37
Lakshadweep, is., India H2 37
Lalbenque, Fr. H8 10
La Libertad, Guat. F2 64
La Libertad, Mex. C3 62
Lalinde, Fr. H7 10
La Línea, Spain I6 12
Lalitpur, India H8 38
Lalitpur, Nepal G11 38
La Loupe, Fr. D8 10
La Luz, N.M., U.S. E4 108
Lama, Ozero, l., U.S.S.R. D12 20
La Maddalena, Italy H4 14
La Madrid, Arg. B3 56
La Malbaie, Que., Can. B7 74
La Mancha, Mex. E8 62
La Mancha, reg., Spain G8 12
Lamar, Ar., U.S. B2 81
Lamar, Co., U.S. C8 83
Lamar, Mo., U.S. D3 102
Lamar, Pa., U.S. D7 115
Lamar, S.C., U.S. C7 117
Lamar, co., Al., U.S. B1 78
Lamar, co., Ga., U.S. C2 87
Lamar, co., Ms., U.S. D4 101
Lamar, co., Tx., U.S. C5 120
Lamar, stm., Wy., U.S. B2 127
Lamarche, Fr. D12 10
La Mauricie, Parc National de, Que., Can. C5 74
Lamb, co., Tx., U.S. B1 120
Lamballe, Fr. D4 10
Lambaréné, Gabon B2 44
Lambert, Ms., U.S. A3 101
Lambert Glacier, Ant. B19 47
Lamberton, Mn., U.S. F3 100
Lambert's Bay, S. Afr. H3 44
Lambertville, Mi., U.S. G7 99
Lambertville, N.J., U.S. C3 107
Lambton, Cape, c., N.W. Ter., Can. B8 66
Lame Deer, Mt., U.S. E10 103
Lamego, Port. D4 12
Lamèque, N.B., Can. B5 71
Lamèque, Île, i., N.B., Can. B5 71
La Mesa, Ca., U.S. F5 82
La Mesa, N.M., U.S. E3 108
Lamesa, Tx., U.S. C2 120
Lamía, Grc. K6 16
Lamoille, Nv., U.S. C6 105
Lamoille, co., Vt., U.S. B3 122
Lamoille, stm., Vt., U.S. B3 122
La Moine, stm., Il., U.S. C3 90
Lamoni, Ia., U.S. D4 92
Lamont, Alta., Can. C4 68
Lamont, Ca., U.S. E4 82
La Monte, Mo., U.S. C4 102
La Motte, Isle, i., Vt., U.S. B2 122
Lamotte-Beuvron, Fr. E9 10

Name	Map Ref	Page
La Moure, N.D., U.S.	C7	111
La Moure, co., N.D., U.S.	C7	111
Lampang, Thai.	E5	34
Lampasas, Tx., U.S.	D3	120
Lampasas, co., Tx., U.S.	D3	120
Lampedusa, Isola di, i., Italy	N7	14
Lampertheim, Ger.	F8	8
Lampman, Sask., Can.	H4	75
Lamprey, stm., N.H., U.S.	D4	106
Lamu, Kenya	B8	44
La Mure, Fr.	H12	10
Lanai, i., Hi., U.S.	C4	88
Lanai City, Hi., U.S.	C5	88
Lanaihale, mtn., Hi., U.S.	C5	88
Lanark, Ont., Can.	C8	73
Lanark, Il., U.S.	A4	90
Lanark, W.V., U.S.	D3	125
Lanbi Kyun, i., Burma	I5	34
Lancaster, Ont., Can.	B10	73
Lancaster, Eng., U.K.	G10	7
Lancaster, Ca., U.S.	E4	82
Lancaster, Ky., U.S.	C5	94
Lancaster, Mo., U.S.	A5	102
Lancaster, N.H., U.S.	B3	106
Lancaster, N.Y., U.S.	C2	109
Lancaster, Oh., U.S.	C3	112
Lancaster, Pa., U.S.	F9	115
Lancaster, S.C., U.S.	B6	117
Lancaster, Tx., U.S.	n10	120
Lancaster, Wi., U.S.	F3	126
Lancaster, co., Ne., U.S.	D9	104
Lancaster, co., Pa., U.S.	G9	115
Lancaster, co., S.C., U.S.	B6	117
Lancaster, co., Va., U.S.	C6	123
Lancaster Sound, strt., N.W. Ter., Can.	B16	66
Lance Creek, stm., Wy., U.S.	C8	127
Lanciano, Italy	G9	14
Landau, Ger.	F8	8
Landau an der Isar, Ger.	G12	8
Land Between the Lakes, U.S.	f9	94
Lander, Wy., U.S.	D4	127
Lander, co., Nv., U.S.	C4	105
Landerneau, Fr.	D2	10
Landess, In., U.S.	C6	91
Landete, Spain	F10	12
Landis, N.C., U.S.	B2	110
Lando, S.C., U.S.	B5	117
Landquart, Switz.	F16	10
Landrum, S.C., U.S.	A3	117
Land's End, c., Eng., U.K.	K7	7
Lands End, c., R.I., U.S.	F5	116
Landshut, Ger.	G12	8
Landskrona, Swe.	I9	6
Lane, co., Ks., U.S.	D3	93
Lane, co., Or., U.S.	C4	114
Lanesboro, Mn., U.S.	G7	100
Lanett, Al., U.S.	C4	78
Langar, Afg.	B5	38
Långban, Swe.	G10	6
Langdon, N.D., U.S.	A7	111
Langeac, Fr.	G10	10
Langeais, Fr.	E7	10
Langeloth, Pa., U.S.	F1	115
Langenhagen, Ger.	C9	8
Langenthal, Switz.	E14	10
Langholm, Scot., U.K.	F9	7
Langhorne, Pa., U.S.	F12	115
Langlade, co., Wi., U.S.	C4	126
Langley, B.C., Can.	f13	69
Langley, S.C., U.S.	E4	117
Langley, Wa., U.S.	A3	124
Langley Air Force Base, mil., Va., U.S.	h15	123
Langley Park, Md., U.S.	f9	97
Langnau, Switz.	F14	10
Langogne, Fr.	H10	10
Langon, Fr.	H6	10
Langres, Fr.	E1	10
Langsa, Indon.	E2	32
Lang Son, Viet.	D9	34
Langston, Ok., U.S.	B4	113
Languedoc, hist. reg., Fr.	I9	10
L'Anguille, stm., Ar., U.S.	B5	81
Langzhong, China	E8	26
Lanham, Md., U.S.	C4	97
Lanier, co., Ga., U.S.	E3	87
Lannemezan, Fr.	I7	10
Lannilis, Fr.	D2	10
Lannion, Fr.	D3	10
Lannon, Wi., U.S.	m11	126
L'Annonciation, Que., Can.	C3	74
Lansdale, Pa., U.S.	F11	115
Lansdowne, Md., U.S.	B4	97
L'Anse, Mi., U.S.	B2	99
L'Anse-au-Loup, Newf., Can.	C3	72
L'Anse Indian Reservation, Mi., U.S.	B2	99
Lansford, Pa., U.S.	E10	115
Lansing, Il., U.S.	B6	90
Lansing, Ia., U.S.	A6	92
Lansing, Ks., U.S.	C9	93
Lansing, Mi., U.S.	F6	99
Lantana, Fl., U.S.	F6	86
Lantau Island, i., H.K.	M2	28
Lanusei, Italy	J4	14
Lanxi, China	F8	28
Lanzarote, i., Spain	C3	42
Lanzhou, China	D7	26
Laoag, Phil.	B7	32
Lao Cai, Viet.	C7	34
Laon, Fr.	C10	10
La Oroya, Peru	F3	54
Laos, ctry., Asia	B3	32
Lapalisse, Fr.	F10	10
La Palma, Col.	E5	58
La Palma, Pan.	J8	64
La Palma, i., Spain	C2	42
La Paragua, Ven.	D11	58
La Paz, Arg.	C5	56
La Paz, Arg.	C3	56
La Paz, Bol.	G5	54
La Paz, Mex.	E4	62
La Paz, co., Az., U.S.	D2	80
La Paz, Bahía de, b., Mex.	E4	62
Lapeer, Mi., U.S.	E7	99
Lapeer, co., Mi., U.S.	E7	99
Lapel, In., U.S.	D6	91
La Perouse Strait, strt., Asia	B15	26
La Piedad [Cavadas], Mex.	G8	62
La Pine, Or., U.S.	D5	114
Lapinlahti, Fin.	E16	6
La Place, La., U.S.	h11	95
Lapland, reg., Eur.	C14	6
La Plata, Arg.	C5	56
La Plata, Md., U.S.	C4	97
La Plata, Mo., U.S.	A5	102
La Plata, co., Co., U.S.	D3	83
La Plata Mountains, mts., Co., U.S.	D3	83
La Plata Peak, mtn., Co., U.S.	B4	83
La Platte, stm., Vt., U.S.	C2	122
La Pocatière, Que., Can.	B7	74
Laporte, Co., U.S.	A5	83
La Porte, In., U.S.	A4	91
La Porte, Tx., U.S.	r14	120
La Porte, co., In., U.S.	A4	91
La Porte City, Ia., U.S.	B5	92
Lappeenranta, Fin.	F17	6
La Prairie, Que., Can.	D4	74
La Pryor, Tx., U.S.	E3	120
Laptevych, More (Laptev Sea), U.S.S.R.	B19	20
Lapua, Fin.	E14	6
La Puebla, Spain	F15	12
La Puebla de Montalbán, Spain	F7	12
La Push, Wa., U.S.	B1	124
Lapwai, Id., U.S.	C2	89
La Quiaca, Arg.	A3	56
L'Aquila, Italy	G8	14
Lār, Iran	C5	46
Larache, Mor.	A4	42
Laramie, Wy., U.S.	E7	127
Laramie, co., Wy., U.S.	E8	127
Laramie, stm., U.S.	E7	127
Laramie Mountains, mts., Wy., U.S.	D7	127
Laramie Peak, mtn., Wy., U.S.	D7	127
Larantuka, Indon.	G7	32
L'Arbresle, Fr.	G11	10
Lärbro, Swe.	H12	6
Larche, Col de, Eur.	H13	10
Larchmont, N.Y., U.S.	h13	109
Larchwood, Ia., U.S.	A1	92
Laredo, Tx., U.S.	F3	120
La Réole, Fr.	H6	10
Largeau, Chad	E9	42
L'argentière-la-Bessée, Fr.	H13	10
Lar Gerd, Afg.	C2	38
Largo, Fl., U.S.	E4	86
Largo, Cañon, val., N.M., U.S.	A2	108
Largo, Key, i., Fl., U.S.	G6	86
Largs, Scot., U.K.	F8	7
Larimer, co., Co., U.S.	A5	83
Larimore, N.D., U.S.	B8	111
La Rioja, Arg.	B3	56
Lárisa, Grc.	J6	16
Larjak, U.S.S.R.	E10	20
Lārkāna, Pak.	G3	38
Lark Harbour, Newf., Can.	D2	72
Larkspur, Ca., U.S.	h7	82
Larksville, Pa., U.S.	n17	115
Lárnax (Larnaca), Cyp.	B3	40
Larne, N. Ire., U.K.	G7	7
Larned, Ks., U.S.	D4	93
La Robla, Spain	C6	12
La Roca de la Sierra, Spain	F5	12
La Rochefoucauld, Fr.	G7	10
La Rochelle, Fr.	F5	10
La Roche-sur-Yon, Fr.	F5	10
La Roda, Spain	F9	12
La Romana, Dom. Rep.	E13	64
Laroquebrou, Fr.	H9	10
Larose, La., U.S.	E5	95
La Rubia, Arg.	C4	56
Larue, co., Ky., U.S.	C4	94
Laruns, Fr.	J6	10
Larvik, Nor.	G7	6
LaSalle, Que., Can.	q19	74
La Salle, Co., U.S.	A6	83
La Salle, Il., U.S.	B4	90
La Salle, co., Il., U.S.	B4	90
La Salle, co., La., U.S.	C3	95
La Salle, co., Tx., U.S.	E3	120
Las Animas, Co., U.S.	C7	83
Las Animas, co., Co., U.S.	D6	83
Las Anod, Som.	G4	46
La Sarre, Que., Can.	k11	74
Las Casitas, Cerro, mtn., Mex.	F5	62
Las Choapas, Mex.	I12	62
La Scie, Newf., Can.	D4	72
Las Colimas, Mex.	E10	62
Las Cruces, N.M., U.S.	E3	108
Las Delicias, Mex.	J14	62
La Selle, Pic, mtn., Haiti	E11	64
La Serena, Chile	B2	56
Las Escobas, Mex.	B2	62
La Seyne, Fr.	I12	10
Las Flores, Arg.	D5	56
Lashio, Burma	C4	34
Laško, Yugo.	C10	14
Las Lomitas, Arg.	A4	56
Las Minas, Cerro, mtn., Hond.	G3	64
La Solana, Spain	G8	12
Las Palmas de Gran Canaria, Spain	C2	42
La Spezia, Italy	E4	14
Las Piedras, Ur.	C5	56
Las Plumas, Arg.	E3	56
Lassen, co., Ca., U.S.	B3	82
Lassen Peak, vol., Ca., U.S.	B3	82
Lassen Volcanic National Park, Ca., U.S.	B3	82
L'Assomption, Que., Can.	D4	74
Las Termas, Arg.	B4	56
Last Mountain Lake, l., Sask., Can.	F3	75
Las Tórtolas, Cerro, mtn., S.A.	B3	56
Las Varas, Mex.	C5	62
Las Vegas, Nv., U.S.	G6	105
Las Vegas, N.M., U.S.	B4	108
Latacunga, Ec.	H3	58
Latah, co., Id., U.S.	C2	89
Latakia see Al-Lādhiqīyah, Syria	B4	40
La Teste-de-Buch, Fr.	H5	10
Lathrop, Mo., U.S.	B3	102
Lathrop Wells, Nv., U.S.	G5	105
Latimer, co., Ok., U.S.	C6	113
Latina, Italy	H7	14
Laton, Ca., U.S.	D4	82
La Tortuga, Isla, i., Ven.	B10	58
Latour Peak, mtn., Id., U.S.	B2	89
Latrobe, Pa., U.S.	F3	115
Latta, S.C., U.S.	C9	117
La Tuque, Que., Can.	B5	74
Lātūr, India	C4	37
Latvia see Latvijskaja Sovetskaja Socialističeskaja Respublika, state, U.S.S.R.	F3	18
Latvijskaja Sovetskaja Socialističeskaja Respublika, state, U.S.S.R.	F3	18
Lauchhammer, Ger.	D13	8
Lauderdale, Ms., U.S.	C5	101
Lauderdale, co., Al., U.S.	A2	78
Lauderdale, co., Ms., U.S.	C5	101
Lauderdale, co., Tn., U.S.	B2	119
Lauderdale Lakes, Fl., U.S.	r13	86
Lauenburg, Ger.	B10	8
Laughlin, Nv., U.S.	H7	105
Laughlin Air Force Base, mil., Tx., U.S.	E2	120
Laughlin Peak, mtn., N.M., U.S.	A5	108
Laughlintown, Pa., U.S.	F3	115
Launceston, Austl.	H9	50
Launceston, Eng., U.K.	K8	7
Launching Point, c., P.E.I., Can.	C7	71
La Union, El Sal.	H4	64
La Unión, Spain	H11	12
La Unión, Ven.	C9	58
La Urbana, Ven.	D9	58
Laurel, De., U.S.	F3	85
Laurel, Fl., U.S.	E4	86
Laurel, Md., U.S.	B4	97
Laurel, Ms., U.S.	D4	101
Laurel, Mt., U.S.	E8	103
Laurel, Ne., U.S.	B8	104
Laurel, Va., U.S.	C5	123
Laurel, co., Ky., U.S.	C5	94
Laurel, stm., Ky., U.S.	D5	94
Laurel Bay, S.C., U.S.	G6	117
Laurel Creek, stm., W.V., U.S.	n14	125
Laurel Creek, stm., W.V., U.S.	m12	125
Laureldale, Pa., U.S.	F10	115
Laurel Fork, stm., W.V., U.S.	C5	125
Laurel Hill, N.C., U.S.	C3	110
Laurel River Lake, res., Ky., U.S.	D5	94
Laurence G. Hanscom Air Force Base, mil., Ma., U.S.	g10	98
Laurence Harbor, N.J., U.S.	C4	107
Laurens, Ia., U.S.	B3	92
Laurens, S.C., U.S.	C3	117
Laurens, co., Ga., U.S.	D4	87
Laurens, co., S.C., U.S.	C4	117
Laurentides, Que., Can.	D4	74
Laurentides, Parc Provincial des, Que., Can.	B6	74
Laurier, Que., Can.	C6	74
Laurière, Fr.	F8	10
Laurierville, Que., Can.	C6	74
Laurinburg, N.C., U.S.	C3	110
Laurium, Mi., U.S.	A2	99
Lausanne, Switz.	F13	10
Laut, Pulau, i., Indon.	F6	32
Laut, Pulau, i., Indon.	L9	34
Lautaro, Chile	D2	56
Lauterbach, Ger.	E9	8
Laut Kecil, Kepulauan, is., Indon.	F6	32
Lauzon, Que., Can.	C6	74
Lava Beds National Monument, Ca., U.S.	B3	82
Lavaca, Ar., U.S.	B1	81
Lavaca, co., Tx., U.S.	E4	120
Lavagh More, mtn., Ire.	G4	7
Laval, Que., Can.	D4	74
Laval, Fr.	D6	10
La Vale, Md., U.S.	k13	97
Lavaltrie, Que., Can.	D4	74
Lavapié, Punta, c., Chile	D2	56
Laveen, Az., U.S.	m8	80
La Vega, Dom. Rep.	E12	64
La Vela, Cabo de, c., Col.	A6	58
Lavello, Italy	H10	14
L'Avenir, Que., Can.	D5	74
La Vergne, Tn., U.S.	A5	119
La Verkin, Ut., U.S.	F2	121
La Verne, Ca., U.S.	m13	82
Laverne, Ok., U.S.	A2	113
La Veta, Co., U.S.	D5	83
Lavia, Fin.	F14	6
La Vista, Ga., U.S.	h8	87
La Vista, Ne., U.S.	g12	104
Lavonia, Ga., U.S.	B3	87
Lavon Lake, res., Tx., U.S.	m10	120
La Voulte-sur-Rhône, Fr.	H11	10
Lavras, Braz.	F6	57
Lawai, Hi., U.S.	B2	88
Lawang, Indon.	m16	33a
Lawers, Ben, mtn., Scot., U.K.	E8	7
Lawn, Newf., Can.	E4	72
Lawrence, In., U.S.	E5	91
Lawrence, Ks., U.S.	D8	93
Lawrence, Ma., U.S.	A5	98
Lawrence, Mi., U.S.	F4	99
Lawrence, N.Y., U.S.	k13	109
Lawrence, co., Al., U.S.	A2	78
Lawrence, co., Ar., U.S.	A4	81
Lawrence, co., Il., U.S.	E6	90
Lawrence, co., In., U.S.	G4	91
Lawrence, co., Ky., U.S.	B7	94
Lawrence, co., Ms., U.S.	D3	101
Lawrence, co., Mo., U.S.	D4	102
Lawrence, co., Oh., U.S.	D3	112
Lawrence, co., Pa., U.S.	E1	115
Lawrence, co., Tn., U.S.	B4	119
Lawrenceburg, In., U.S.	F8	91
Lawrenceburg, Ky., U.S.	B5	94
Lawrenceburg, Tn., U.S.	B4	119
Lawrence Park, Pa., U.S.	B1	115
Lawrenceville, Ga., U.S.	C3	87
Lawrenceville, Il., U.S.	E6	90
Lawrenceville, Va., U.S.	D5	123
Lawson, Mo., U.S.	B3	102
Lawsonia, Md., U.S.	E6	97
Lawtell, La., U.S.	D3	95
Lawton, Mi., U.S.	F5	99
Lawton, Ok., U.S.	C3	113
Lawz, Jabal al-, mtn., Sau. Ar.	C2	46
Lay Lake, res., Al., U.S.	B3	78
Laysan Island, i., Hi., U.S.	k13	88
Layton, Ut., U.S.	B4	121
La Zarca, Mex.	E7	62
Lazarev, U.S.S.R.	G22	20
Lazi, China	F12	38
Lea, co., N.M., U.S.	D6	108
Leachville, Ar., U.S.	B5	81
Lead, S.D., U.S.	C2	118
Leadbetter Point, c., Wa., U.S.	C1	124
Leadville, Co., U.S.	B4	83
Leadwood, Mo., U.S.	D7	102
Leaf, stm., Ms., U.S.	D5	101
Leaf Rapids, Man., Can.	A1	70
Leake, co., Ms., U.S.	C4	101
Leakesville, Ms., U.S.	D5	101
Lealman, Fl., U.S.	p10	86
Leamington, Ont., Can.	E2	73
Leary, Ga., U.S.	E2	87
Leatherman Peak, mtn., Id., U.S.	E5	89
Leavenworth, Ks., U.S.	C9	93
Leavenworth, Wa., U.S.	B5	124
Leavenworth, co., Ks., U.S.	C8	93
Leavittsburg, Oh., U.S.	A5	112
Leawood, Ks., U.S.	D9	93
Lebanon, De., U.S.	D4	85
Lebanon, Il., U.S.	E4	90
Lebanon, In., U.S.	D5	91
Lebanon, Ky., U.S.	C4	94
Lebanon, Mo., U.S.	D5	102
Lebanon, N.H., U.S.	C2	106
Lebanon, Oh., U.S.	C1	112
Lebanon, Or., U.S.	C4	114
Lebanon, Pa., U.S.	F9	115
Lebanon, Tn., U.S.	A5	119
Lebanon, Va., U.S.	f9	123
Lebanon, co., Pa., U.S.	F8	115
Lebanon, ctry., Asia	C4	40
Lebanon Junction, Ky., U.S.	C4	94
Le Blanc, Fr.	F8	10
Lebo, Ks., U.S.	D8	93
Lębork, Pol.	A17	8
Lebrija, Spain	I5	12
Lecce, Italy	I13	14
Lecco, Italy	D4	14
Le Center, Mn., U.S.	F5	100
Le Cheylard, Fr.	H11	10
Le Claire, Ia., U.S.	C7	92
Lecompte, La., U.S.	C3	95
Lecompton, Ks., U.S.	C8	93
Le Creusot, Fr.	F11	10
Led'anaja, Gora, mtn., U.S.S.R.	E31	20
Le Dorat, Fr.	F8	10
Leduc, Alta., Can.	C4	68
Lee, Ma., U.S.	B1	98
Lee, co., Al., U.S.	C4	78
Lee, co., Ar., U.S.	C5	81
Lee, co., Fl., U.S.	F5	86
Lee, co., Ga., U.S.	E2	87
Lee, co., Il., U.S.	B4	90
Lee, co., Ia., U.S.	D6	92
Lee, co., Ky., U.S.	C6	94
Lee, co., Ms., U.S.	A5	101
Lee, co., N.C., U.S.	B3	110
Lee, co., S.C., U.S.	C7	117
Lee, co., Tx., U.S.	D4	120
Lee, co., Va., U.S.	f8	123
Lee, Lake, l., Ms., U.S.	B3	101
Leechburg, Pa., U.S.	E2	115
Leech Lake, l., Mn., U.S.	C4	100
Leech Lake Indian Reservation, Mn., U.S.	C4	100
Lee Creek, stm., U.S.	B1	81
Leeds, Eng., U.K.	H11	7
Leeds, Al., U.S.	B3	78
Leelanau, co., Mi., U.S.	D5	99
Leelanau, Lake, l., Mi., U.S.	C5	99
Lee Park, Pa., U.S.	n17	115
Leer, Ger.	B7	8
Leesburg, Fl., U.S.	D5	86
Leesburg, Ga., U.S.	E2	87
Leesburg, Oh., U.S.	C2	112
Leesburg, Va., U.S.	A5	123
Lees Summit, Mo., U.S.	C3	102
Leesville, La., U.S.	C2	95
Leesville, S.C., U.S.	D4	117
Leesville Lake, res., Va., U.S.	C3	123
Leeton, Mo., U.S.	C4	102
Leetonia, Oh., U.S.	B5	112
Leetsdale, Pa., U.S.	h13	115
Leeuwarden, Neth.	B5	8
Leeuwin, Cape, c., Austl.	F3	50
Leeward Islands, is., N.A.	F17	64
Leflore, co., Ms., U.S.	B3	101
Le Flore, co., Ok., U.S.	C7	113
Legal, Alta., Can.	C4	68
Legazpi, Phil.	r20	33b
Leghorn see Livorno, Italy	F5	14
Legnago, Italy	D6	14
Legnano, Italy	D3	14
Legnica (Liegnitz), Pol.	D16	8
Le Grand, Ca., U.S.	D3	82
Le Grand, Ia., U.S.	B5	92
Le Havre, Fr.	C7	10
Lehi, Ut., U.S.	C4	121
Lehigh, co., Pa., U.S.	E10	115
Lehigh, stm., Pa., U.S.	E10	115
Lehigh Acres, Fl., U.S.	F5	86
Lehighton, Pa., U.S.	E10	115
Lehua Island, i., Hi., U.S.	A1	88
Lehututu, Bots.	F4	44
Leiah, Pak.	E4	38
Leibnitz, Aus.	I15	8
Leicester, Eng., U.K.	I11	7
Leicester, Ma., U.S.	B4	98
Leichhardt, stm., Austl.	C7	50
Leiden, Neth.	C4	8
Leighton, Al., U.S.	A2	78
Leikanger, Nor.	F6	6
Leinster, hist. reg., Ire.	H5	7
Leinster, Mount, mtn., Ire.	I6	7
Leipsic, De., U.S.	D3	85
Leipsic, Oh., U.S.	A2	112
Leipsic, stm., De., U.S.	C3	85
Leipzig, Ger.	D12	8
Leiria, Port.	F3	12
Leisler, Mount, mtn., Austl.	D5	50
Leisure City, Fl., U.S.	s13	86
Leitchfield, Ky., U.S.	C3	94
Leitrim, Ire.	G4	7
Leiyang, China	I1	28
Leizhou Bandao, pen., China	D11	34
Leland, Il., U.S.	B5	90
Leland, Ms., U.S.	B3	101
Leleiwi Point, c., Hi., U.S.	D7	88
Leleque, Arg.	E2	56
Le Lion-d'Angers, Fr.	E6	10
Leli Shan, mtn., China	D9	38
Le Locle, Switz.	E13	10
Le Lude, Fr.	E7	10
Le Maire, Estrecho de, strt., Arg.	G4	56
Le Mans, Fr.	D7	10
Le Mars, Ia., U.S.	B1	92
Leme, Braz.	G5	57
Lemesós (Limassol), Cyp.	B3	40
Lemgo, Ger.	C8	8
Lemhi, co., Id., U.S.	E4	89
Lemhi, stm., Id., U.S.	E5	89
Lemhi Pass, Id., U.S.	E5	89
Lemhi Range, mts., Id., U.S.	E5	89
Lemmon, S.D., U.S.	B3	118
Lemmon, Mount, mtn., Az., U.S.	E5	80
Lemmon Valley, Nv., U.S.	D2	105
Lemon, Lake, l., In., U.S.	F5	91
Lemon Fair, stm., Vt., U.S.	C2	122
Lemon Grove, Ca., U.S.	o15	82
Lemon Island, i., S.C., U.S.	G6	117
Lemont, Il., U.S.	B5	90
Lemont, Pa., U.S.	E6	115
Lemonweir, stm., Wi., U.S.	D3	126
Lemoore, Ca., U.S.	D4	82
Lemoore Naval Air Station, mil., Ca., U.S.	D4	82
Lempa, stm., N.A.	H3	64
Lem Peak, mtn., Id., U.S.	E5	89
Lena, Il., U.S.	A4	90
Lena, stm., U.S.S.R.	C19	20
Lenawee, co., Mi., U.S.	G6	99
Lencloître, Fr.	F7	10
Lenexa, Ks., U.S.	D9	93
Lenghu, China	D5	26
Leninabad, U.S.S.R.	I11	18
Leninakan, U.S.S.R.	I6	18
Leningrad (Saint Petersburg)	B13	22
Leninogorsk, U.S.S.R.	G10	20
Leninsk-Kuzneckij, U.S.S.R.	G11	20
Leninskoje, U.S.S.R.	H20	20
Lennox, S.D., U.S.	D9	118
Lennoxville, Que., Can.	D6	74
Lenoir, N.C., U.S.	B1	110
Lenoir, co., N.C., U.S.	B5	110
Lenoir City, Tn., U.S.	D9	119
Lenore Lake, l., Sask., Can.	E3	75
Lenore Lake, l., Wa., U.S.	B6	124
Lenox, Ga., U.S.	E3	87
Lenox, Ia., U.S.	D3	92
Lenox, Ma., U.S.	B1	98
Lens, Fr.	B9	10
Lensk, U.S.S.R.	E16	20
Lentini, Italy	L10	14
Leo, In., U.S.	B7	91
Leoben, Aus.	H15	8
Leominster, Eng., U.K.	I10	7
Leominster, Ma., U.S.	A4	98
León, Nic.	H4	64
León, Spain	C6	12
Leon, Ia., U.S.	D4	92
Leon, Ks., U.S.	E7	93
Leon, co., Fl., U.S.	B2	86
Leon, co., Tx., U.S.	D4	120
Leonard, Tx., U.S.	C4	120
Leonardo, N.J., U.S.	C4	107
Leonardtown, Md., U.S.	D4	97
Leonberg, Ger.	G9	8
León [de los Aldamas], Mex.	G9	62
Leonia, N.J., U.S.	h9	107
Leonora, Austl.	E4	50
Leonville, La., U.S.	D4	95
Léopold II, Lac see Mai-Ndombe, Lac, l., Zaire	B3	44
Leopoldina, Braz.	F7	57
Léopoldville see Kinshasa, Zaire	B3	44
Leoti, Ks., U.S.	D2	93
Le Palais, Fr.	E3	10
Lepanto, Ar., U.S.	B5	81
Lepe, Spain	H4	12
Leping, China	G6	28
L'Épiphanie, Que., Can.	D4	74
Lepontine, Alpi, mts., Eur.	F15	10
Le Puy, Fr.	G10	10
Lercara Friddi, Italy	L8	14
Lerici, Italy	E4	14
Lérida, Col.	G7	58
Lérida, Spain	D12	12
Lerma, Spain	C8	12
Le Roy, Il., U.S.	C5	90
Le Roy, Mn., U.S.	G6	100
Le Roy, N.Y., U.S.	C3	109
Lerwick, Scot., U.K.	A11	7
Léry, Que., Can.	q19	74
Léry, Lake, l., La., U.S.	k12	95
Les Andelys, Fr.	C8	10
Lesbos see Lésvos, i., Grc.	J10	16
Les Cayes, Haiti	E11	64
Les Échelles, Fr.	G12	10
Les Herbiers, Fr.	F5	10
Leskovac, Yugo.	G5	16
Leslie, Mi., U.S.	F6	99
Leslie, S.C., U.S.	B6	117
Leslie, co., Ky., U.S.	C6	94
Lesotho, ctry., Afr.	G5	44
Lesozavodsk, U.S.S.R.	H20	20

Name | Map Ref | Page

Les Sables-d'Olonne, Fr. F5 10
Lesser Antilles, is. G17 64
Lesser Slave Lake, l., Alta., Can. B3 68
Lesser Sunda Islands, is., Indon. G6 32
Lester Prairie, Mn., U.S. F4 100
Le Sueur, Mn., U.S. F5 100
Le Sueur, co., Mn., U.S. F5 100
Lésvos (Lesbos), i., Grc. J10 16
Leszno, Pol. D16 8
Letcher, co., Ky., U.S. C7 94
Lethbridge, Alta., Can. E4 68
Lethbridge, Newf., Can. D5 72
Lethem, Guy. F13 58
Le Thillot, Fr. E13 10
Leti, Kepulauan, is., Indon. G8 32
Leticia, Col. J8 58
Le Tréport, Fr. B8 10
Letsôk-Aw Kyun, i., Burma I5 34
Letterkenny, Ire. G5 7
Leutkirch, Ger. H10 8
Leuven, Bel. E4 8
Levádhia, Grc. K6 16
Levante, Riviera di, Italy E4 14
Levelland, Tx., U.S. C1 120
Leveque, Cape, c., Austl. C4 50
Leverkusen, Ger. D6 8
Le Vigan, Fr. I10 10
Lévis, Que., Can. C6 74
Levisa Fork, stm., U.S. C7 94
Levittown, N.Y., U.S. E7 109
Levittown, Pa., U.S. F12 115
Levy, co., Fl., U.S. C4 86
Levy Lake, l., Fl., U.S. C4 86
Lewes, Eng., U.K. K13 7
Lewes, De., U.S. E5 85
Lewes and Rehoboth Canal, De., U.S. F5 85
Lewis, co., Id., U.S. C2 89
Lewis, co., Ky., U.S. B6 94
Lewis, co., Mo., U.S. A6 102
Lewis, co., N.Y., U.S. B5 109
Lewis, co., Tn., U.S. B4 119
Lewis, co., Wa., U.S. C3 124
Lewis, co., W.V., U.S. C4 125
Lewis, stm., Wa., U.S. C4 124
Lewis, stm., Wy., U.S. B2 127
Lewis, Isle of, i., Scot., U.K. C6 7
Lewis, Mount, mtn., Nv., U.S. C5 105
Lewis and Clark, co., Mt., U.S. C4 103
Lewis and Clark Cavern, Mt., U.S. D5 103
Lewis and Clark Lake, res., U.S. E8 118
Lewisburg, Ky., U.S. D3 94
Lewisburg, Oh., U.S. C1 112
Lewisburg, Pa., U.S. E8 115
Lewisburg, Tn., U.S. B5 119
Lewisburg, W.V., U.S. D4 125
Lewis Creek, stm., Vt., U.S. C2 122
Lewis Lake, l., Wy., U.S. B2 127
Lewisport, Ky., U.S. C3 94
Lewisporte, Newf., Can. D4 72
Lewis Smith Lake, res., Al., U.S. B2 78
Lewiston, Id., U.S. C1 89
Lewiston, Me., U.S. D2 96
Lewiston, Mn., U.S. G7 100
Lewiston, N.Y., U.S. B1 109
Lewiston, Ut., U.S. B4 121
Lewiston Peak, mtn., Ut., U.S. C3 121
Lewiston Woodville, N.C., U.S. A5 110
Lewistown, Il., U.S. C3 90
Lewistown, Mt., U.S. C7 103
Lewistown, Pa., U.S. E6 115
Lewisville, Ar., U.S. D2 81
Lewisville, Tx., U.S. C4 120
Lewisville Lake, res., Tx., U.S. C4 120
Lexington, Al., U.S. A2 78
Lexington, Il., U.S. C5 90
Lexington, Ky., U.S. B5 94
Lexington, Ma., U.S. B5 98
Lexington, Mi., U.S. E8 99
Lexington, Ms., U.S. B3 101
Lexington, Mo., U.S. B4 102
Lexington, Ne., U.S. D6 104
Lexington, N.C., U.S. B2 110
Lexington, Oh., U.S. B3 112
Lexington, Ok., U.S. B4 113
Lexington, S.C., U.S. D5 117
Lexington, Tn., U.S. B3 119
Lexington, Va., U.S. C3 123
Lexington, co., S.C., U.S. D5 117
Lexington Park, Md., U.S. D5 97
Leyte, i., Phil. C7 32
Leyte Gulf, b., Phil. C8 32
Lhasa, China F14 38
Lhokseumawe, Indon. D2 32
Lianhua Shan, mts., China L4 28
Lianxian, China G9 26
Lianyungang, China E10 26
Liao, stm., China C11 26
Liaocheng, China D10 26
Liaodong Wan, b., China C11 26
Liaoning, prov., China C11 26
Liaotung, Gulf of see Liaodong Wan, b., China C11 26
Liaoyang, China C11 26
Liaoyuan, China C12 26
Liard, stm., Can. E8 66
Libby, Mt., U.S. B1 103
Libenge, Zaire H9 42
Liberal, Ks., U.S. E3 93
Liberal, Mo., U.S. D3 102
Liberec, Czech. E15 8
Liberia, C.R. I5 64
Liberia, ctry., Afr. G4 42
Libertad, Ven. C8 58
Liberty, In., U.S. E8 91
Liberty, Ky., U.S. C5 94
Liberty, Ms., U.S. D3 101
Liberty, Mo., U.S. B3 102
Liberty, N.Y., U.S. D6 109
Liberty, N.C., U.S. B3 110
Liberty, S.C., U.S. B2 117
Liberty, Tx., U.S. D5 120
Liberty, co., Fl., U.S. B2 86
Liberty, co., Ga., U.S. E5 87
Liberty, co., Mt., U.S. B5 103
Liberty, co., Tx., U.S. D5 120
Liberty Center, Oh., U.S. A1 112
Liberty Lake, Wa., U.S. g14 124
Liberty Lake, res., Md., U.S. B4 97
Libertyville, Il., U.S. A6 90
Lībīyah, Aṣ-Ṣaḥrā' al- (Libyan Desert), des., Afr. D11 42
Libourne, Fr. H6 10
Libreville, Gabon A1 44
Libuse, La., U.S. C3 95
Libya, ctry., Afr. C9 42
Libyan Desert see Lībīyah, Aṣ-Ṣaḥrā' al-, des., Afr. D11 42
Licata, Italy L8 14
Lichinga, Moz. D7 44
Lichtenfels, Ger. E11 8
Lick Creek, stm., Tn., U.S. C11 119
Licking, Mo., U.S. D6 102
Licking, co., Oh., U.S. B3 112
Licking, stm., Ky., U.S. B6 94
Lida, U.S.S.R. H8 22
Lida, Lake, l., Mn., U.S. D3 100
Lidgerwood, N.D., U.S. C8 111
Lidköping, Swe. G9 6
Lido di Ostia, Italy H7 14
Liechtenstein, ctry., Eur. F9 4
Liège, Bel. E5 8
Lieksa, Fin. E18 6
Lienz, Aus. I12 8
Liepāja, U.S.S.R. E4 22
Lier, Bel. D4 8
Liestal, Switz. E14 10
Liévin, Fr. B9 10
Lièvre, Rivière du, stm., Que., Can. D2 74
Liezen, Aus. H14 8
Lifford, Ire. G5 7
Ligao, Phil. r20 33b
Lighthouse Inlet, b., S.C., U.S. k12 117
Lighthouse Point, c., Fl., U.S. C2 86
Lighthouse Point, c., La., U.S. E3 95
Lighthouse Point, c., Mi., U.S. C5 99
Lightning Creek, stm., Wy., U.S. C8 127
Ligny-en-Barrois, Fr. D12 10
Ligonier, In., U.S. B6 91
Ligonier, Pa., U.S. F3 115
Ligurian Sea, Eur. F3 14
Lihou Reefs, rf., Austl. C10 50
Lihue, Hi., U.S. B2 88
Lijiang, China F7 26
Likasi (Jadotville), Zaire D5 44
Likino-Dulevo, U.S.S.R. F22 22
Liknes, Nor. G6 6
Likouala, stm., Congo B3 44
Lilbourn, Mo., U.S. E8 102
Lilburn, Ga., U.S. h8 87
Liling, China H2 28
Lille, Fr. B10 10
Lillehammer, Nor. F8 6
Lillestrøm, Nor. G8 6
Lillian, Al., U.S. E2 78
Lillington, N.C., U.S. B4 110
Lillinonah, Lake, l., Ct., U.S. C2 84
Lillo, Spain F8 12
Lillooet, B.C., Can. D7 69
Lillooet, stm., B.C., Can. D6 69
Lilly, Pa., U.S. F4 115
Lilly Fork, stm., W.V., U.S. m13 125
Lilly Grove, W.V., U.S. D3 125
Lilongwe, Mwi. D6 44
Lily, Ky., U.S. C5 94
Lima, Peru F3 54
Lima, N.Y., U.S. C3 109
Lima, Oh., U.S. B1 112
Lima Reservoir, res., Mt., U.S. F4 103
Limassol see Lemesós, Cyp. B3 40
Limbdi, India I4 38
Limburg an der Lahn, Ger. E8 8
Limeira, Braz. G5 57
Limerick, Ire. I4 7
Limestone, Me., U.S. B5 96
Limestone, co., Al., U.S. A2 78
Limestone, co., Tx., U.S. D4 120
Limestone Point, pen., Man., Can. C2 70
Liminka, Fin. D15 6
Limmen Bight, Austl. B7 50
Límnos, i., Grc. J9 16
Limoges, Ont., Can. B9 73
Limoges, Fr. G8 10
Limón, C.R. I6 64
Limón, Hond. G5 64
Limon, Co., U.S. B7 83
Limousins, Plateau du, plat., Fr. G8 10
Limoux, Fr. I9 10
Limpopo, stm., Afr. F6 44
Linares, Chile D2 56
Linares, Col. G4 58
Linares, Mex. E10 62
Linares, Spain G8 12
Lincoln, Arg. C4 56
Lincoln, Ont., Can. D5 73
Lincoln, Eng., U.K. H12 7
Lincoln, Al., U.S. B3 78
Lincoln, Ar., U.S. B1 81
Lincoln, Ca., U.S. C3 82
Lincoln, De., U.S. E4 85
Lincoln, Id., U.S. F7 89
Lincoln, Il., U.S. C4 90
Lincoln, Ks., U.S. C5 93
Lincoln, Me., U.S. C4 96
Lincoln, Ma., U.S. g10 98
Lincoln, Mo., U.S. C4 102
Lincoln, Ne., U.S. D9 104
Lincoln, N.H., U.S. B3 106
Lincoln, co., Ar., U.S. D4 81
Lincoln, co., Co., U.S. C7 83
Lincoln, co., Ga., U.S. C4 87
Lincoln, co., Id., U.S. G4 89
Lincoln, co., Ks., U.S. C5 93
Lincoln, co., Ky., U.S. C5 94
Lincoln, co., La., U.S. B3 95
Lincoln, co., Me., U.S. D3 96
Lincoln, co., Mn., U.S. F2 100
Lincoln, co., Ms., U.S. D3 101
Lincoln, co., Mo., U.S. B7 102
Lincoln, co., Mt., U.S. B1 103
Lincoln, co., Ne., U.S. D5 104
Lincoln, co., Nv., U.S. F6 105
Lincoln, co., N.M., U.S. D4 108
Lincoln, co., N.C., U.S. B1 110
Lincoln, co., Ok., U.S. B5 113
Lincoln, co., Or., U.S. C3 114
Lincoln, co., S.D., U.S. D9 118
Lincoln, co., Tn., U.S. B5 119
Lincoln, co., Wa., U.S. B7 124
Lincoln, co., W.V., U.S. C2 125
Lincoln, co., Wi., U.S. C4 126
Lincoln, co., Wy., U.S. D2 127
Lincoln, Mount, mtn., Co., U.S. B4 83
Lincoln Acres, Ca., U.S. o15 82
Lincoln City, Or., U.S. C3 114
Lincoln Heights, Oh., U.S. o13 112
Lincoln Park, Co., U.S. C5 83
Lincoln Park, Ga., U.S. D2 87
Lincoln Park, Mi., U.S. p15 99
Lincoln Park, N.J., U.S. B4 107
Lincolnshire, Il., U.S. h9 90
Lincoln Tomb State Memorial, hist., Il., U.S. D4 90
Lincolnton, Ga., U.S. C4 87
Lincolnton, N.C., U.S. B1 110
Lincolnville, S.C., U.S. h11 117
Lincolnwood, Il., U.S. h9 90
Lincroft, N.J., U.S. C4 107
Lindale, Ga., U.S. B1 87
Lindale, Tx., U.S. C5 120
Lindau, Ger. H9 8
Linden, Al., U.S. C2 78
Linden, In., U.S. D4 91
Linden, Mi., U.S. F7 99
Linden, N.J., U.S. k8 107
Linden, Tn., U.S. B4 119
Linden, Tx., U.S. C5 120
Lindenhurst, Il., U.S. h8 90
Lindenhurst, N.Y., U.S. n15 109
Lindenwold, N.J., U.S. D3 107
Lindesnes, c., Nor. G6 6
Lindi, Tan. C7 44
Lindon, Ut., U.S. C4 121
Lindsay, Ont., Can. C6 73
Lindsay, Ca., U.S. D4 82
Lindsay, Ok., U.S. C4 113
Lindsborg, Ks., U.S. D6 93
Lindstrom, Mn., U.S. E6 100
Linesville, Pa., U.S. C1 115
Lineville, Al., U.S. B4 78
Lingao, China D10 34
Lingayen, Phil. B7 32
Lingen, Ger. C7 8
Lingga, Kepulauan, is., Indon. F3 32
Lingle, Wy., U.S. D8 127
Linglestown, Pa., U.S. F8 115
Lingling, China A11 34
Linh, Ngoc, mtn., Viet. G9 34
Linhai, China G10 28
Linière, Que., Can. C7 74
Linjiang, China C12 26
Linköping, Swe. G10 6
Linkou, China B13 26
Linn, Mo., U.S. C6 102
Linn, co., Ia., U.S. B6 92
Linn, co., Ks., U.S. D9 93
Linn, co., Mo., U.S. B4 102
Linn, co., Or., U.S. C4 114
Lino Lakes, Mn., U.S. m12 100
Linqing, China D10 26
Linru, China A1 28
Lins, Braz. F4 57
Lintao, China D7 26
Linthicum Heights, Md., U.S. B4 97
Linton, In., U.S. F3 91
Linton, N.D., U.S. C5 111
Linwood, N.J., U.S. E3 107
Linxi, China C10 26
Linxia, China D7 26
Linyi, China D10 26
Linz, Aus. G14 8
Lion, Golfe du, b., Fr. I11 10
Lipa, Phil. r19 33b
Lipeck, U.S.S.R. I22 22
Lippstadt, Ger. D8 8
Lipscomb, Al., U.S. B3 78
Lipscomb, co., Tx., U.S. A2 120
Lira, Ug. H12 42
Liria, Spain F11 12
Lisala, Zaire A4 44
Lisboa (Lisbon), Port. G2 12
Lisbon, Ia., U.S. C6 92
Lisbon, Me., U.S. D2 96
Lisbon, Md., U.S. B3 97
Lisbon, N.H., U.S. B3 106
Lisbon, N.D., U.S. C8 111
Lisbon, Oh., U.S. B5 112
Lisbon Center, Me., U.S. f7 96
Lisbon Falls, Me., U.S. E2 96
Lisbon see Lisboa, Port. G2 12
Lisburne, Cape, c., Ak., U.S. B6 79
Lishui, China G8 28
Lisianski Island, i., Hi., U.S. k13 88
Lisičansk, U.S.S.R. H5 18
Lisieux, Fr. C7 10
Lisle, Il., U.S. k8 90
L'Isle-Jourdain, Fr. I8 10
L'Isle Jourdain, Fr. F7 10
L'Islet-sur-Mer, Que., Can. B7 74
L'Isle-Verte, Que., Can. A8 74
Lismore, Austl. E10 50
Listowel, Ont., Can. D4 73
Listowel, Ire. I3 7
Lit, Swe. E10 6
Litang, China G8 26
Litchfield, Ct., U.S. C3 84
Litchfield, Il., U.S. D4 90
Litchfield, Mi., U.S. F6 99
Litchfield, Mn., U.S. E4 100
Litchfield, co., Ct., U.S. B2 84
Litchfield Park, Az., U.S. m8 80
Lithia Springs, Ga., U.S. h7 87
Lithonia, Ga., U.S. C2 87
Lithuania see Litovskaja Sovetskaja Socialističeskaja Respublika, state, U.S.S.R. F2 18
Litija, Yugo. C9 14
Lititz, Pa., U.S. F9 115
Litovko, U.S.S.R. H21 20
Litovskaja Sovetskaja Socialističeskaja Respublika, state, U.S.S.R. F2 18
Little, stm., U.S. B5 81
Little, stm., U.S. D7 113
Little, stm., Ct., U.S. C7 84
Little, stm., Ky., U.S. D2 94
Little, stm., La., U.S. C3 95
Little, stm., N.C., U.S. B3 110
Little, stm., Ok., U.S. B5 113
Little, stm., S.C., U.S. C2 117
Little, stm., Tn., U.S. n14 119
Little, stm., Vt., U.S. C3 122
Little, stm., Va., U.S. D2 123
Little Abaco Island, i., Bah. A9 64
Little Acres, Az., U.S. D5 80
Little Andaman, i., India I2 34
Little Arkansas, stm., Ks., U.S. D6 93
Little Belt Mountains, mts., Mt., U.S. D6 103
Little Bighorn, stm., U.S. E9 103
Little Black, stm., Me., U.S. A3 96
Little Blue, stm., U.S. C6 93
Little Blue, stm., In., U.S. H5 91
Little Bow, stm., Alta., Can. D4 68
Little Cacapon, stm., W.V., U.S. B6 125
Little Catalina, Newf., Can. D5 72
Little Cayman, i., Cay. Is. E7 64
Little Cedar, stm., Ia., U.S. A5 92
Little Churchill, stm., Man., Can. A4 70
Little Chute, Wi., U.S. D5 126
Little Coal, stm., W.V., U.S. C3 125
Little Colorado, stm., Az., U.S. B4 80
Little Compton, R.I., U.S. E6 116
Little Creek, De., U.S. D4 85
Little Creek Naval Amphibious Base, mil., Va., U.S. k15 123
Little Creek Peak, mtn., Ut., U.S. F3 121
Little Current, Ont., Can. B3 73
Little Diomede Island, i., Ak., U.S. B6 79
Little Egg Harbor, b., N.J., U.S. D4 107
Little Egg Inlet, b., N.J., U.S. E4 107
Little Falls, Mn., U.S. E4 100
Little Falls, N.J., U.S. B4 107
Little Falls, N.Y., U.S. B6 109
Little Ferry, N.J., U.S. h8 107
Littlefield, Tx., U.S. C1 120
Little Fishing Creek, stm., W.V., U.S. h9 125
Littlefork, Mn., U.S. B5 100
Little Fork, stm., Mn., U.S. B5 100
Little Goose Creek, stm., Wy., U.S. B6 127
Little Gunpowder Falls, stm., Md., U.S. A4 97
Little Humboldt, stm., Nv., U.S. B4 105
Little Inagua, i., Bah. D11 64
Little Kanawha, stm., W.V., U.S. C4 125
Little Lake, Mi., U.S. B3 99
Little Lake, l., La., U.S. E5 95
Little Lynches, stm., S.C., U.S. C7 117
Little Manatee, stm., Fl., U.S. p11 86
Little Mecatina, stm., Can. h9 72
Little Miami, stm., Oh., U.S. C1 112
Little Minch, strt., Scot., U.K. D6 7
Little Missouri, stm., U.S. B6 76
Little Missouri, stm., Ar., U.S. D2 81
Little Muddy, stm., Il., U.S. E4 90
Little Muddy, stm., N.D., U.S. A2 111
Little Nicobar, i., India K2 34
Little Osage, stm., U.S. E9 93
Little Otter Creek, stm., Vt., U.S. C2 122
Little Owyhee, stm., U.S. B5 105
Little Pee Dee, stm., S.C., U.S. C9 117
Little Powder, stm., U.S. F11 103
Little Red, stm., Ar., U.S. B4 81
Little River, co., Ar., U.S. D1 81
Little River Inlet, b., S.C., U.S. D10 117
Little Rock, Ar., U.S. C3 81
Little Rock, stm., U.S. A1 92
Little Rock Air Force Base, mil., Ar., U.S. C3 81
Little Sable Point, c., Mi., U.S. E4 99
Little Salt Lake, l., Ut., U.S. F3 121
Little Sandy, stm., Ky., U.S. B6 94
Little Sandy Creek, stm., Wy., U.S. D3 127
Little Sebago Lake, l., Me., U.S. g7 96
Little Silver, N.J., U.S. C4 107
Little Sioux, stm., U.S. B2 92
Little Sioux, West Fork, stm., Ia., U.S. B2 92
Little Smoky, stm., Alta., Can. B2 68
Little Snake, stm., U.S. A2 83
Little Spokane, stm., Wa., U.S. B8 124
Littlestown, Pa., U.S. G7 115
Little Tallapoosa, stm., U.S. B4 78
Little Tenmile Creek, stm., W.V., U.S. k10 125
Little Tennessee, stm., U.S. D9 119
Littleton, Co., U.S. B6 83
Littleton, Me., U.S. B5 96
Littleton, Ma., U.S. f10 98
Littleton, N.H., U.S. B3 106
Littleton, N.C., U.S. A5 110
Littleville, Al., U.S. A2 78
Little Wabash, stm., Il., U.S. E5 90
Little Walnut, stm., Ks., U.S. g13 93
Little White, stm., S.D., U.S. D5 118
Little Wolf, stm., Wi., U.S. D4 126
Little Wood, stm., Id., U.S. F4 89
Liuan, China D5 28
Liuhe, China C7 28
Liuzhou, China B10 34
Live Oak, Ca., U.S. C3 82
Live Oak, Fl., U.S. B4 86
Live Oak, co., Tx., U.S. E3 120
Livermore, Ca., U.S. h9 82
Livermore, Ky., U.S. C2 94
Livermore, Mount, mtn., Tx., U.S. o12 120
Livermore Falls, Me., U.S. D2 96
Liverpool, Eng., U.K. H10 7
Liverpool, Cape, c., N.W. Ter., Can. B17 66
Livingston, Al., U.S. C1 78
Livingston, Ca., U.S. D3 82
Livingston, Il., U.S. E4 90
Livingston, La., U.S. D5 95
Livingston, Mt., U.S. E6 103
Livingston, N.J., U.S. B4 107
Livingston, Tn., U.S. C8 119
Livingston, Tx., U.S. D5 120
Livingston, co., Il., U.S. C5 90
Livingston, co., Ky., U.S. e9 94
Livingston, co., La., U.S. D5 95
Livingston, co., Mi., U.S. F7 99
Livingston, co., Mo., U.S. B4 102
Livingston, co., N.Y., U.S. C3 109
Livingston, Lake, res., Tx., U.S. D5 120
Livingstone, Zam. E5 44
Livingstonia, Mwi. D6 44
Livno, Yugo. F12 14
Livny, U.S.S.R. I20 22
Livonia, La., U.S. D4 95
Livonia, Mi., U.S. F7 99
Livorno (Leghorn), Italy F5 14
Liyang, China D8 28
Lizard Head Pass, Co., U.S. D3 83
Lizard Head Peak, mtn., Wy., U.S. D3 127
Lizard Point, c., Eng., U.K. L7 7
Lizella, Ga., U.S. D3 87
Ljubljana, Yugo. C9 14
Ljungby, Swe. H9 6
Ljusdal, Swe. F11 6
Llandudno, Wales, U.K. H9 7
Llanelli, Wales, U.K. J8 7
Llanes, Spain B7 12
Llanidloes, Wales, U.K. I9 7
Llano, Tx., U.S. D3 120
Llano, co., Tx., U.S. D3 120
Llano, stm., Tx., U.S. D3 120
Llanos, pl., S.A. E7 58
Llanwrtyd Wells, Wales, U.K. I9 7
Llera, Mex. F10 62
Llerena, Spain G5 12
Lloyd, Ky., U.S. B7 94
Lloydminster, Alta., Can. C5 68
Lloyds, stm., Newf., Can. D3 72
Lluchmayor, Spain F14 12
Llullaillaco, Volcán, vol., S.A. A3 56
Lo, stm., Viet. C8 34
Loami, Il., U.S. D4 90
Loange, stm., Afr. C3 44
Löbau, Ger. D14 8
Lobaye, stm., Cen. Afr. Rep. G9 42
Lobelville, Tn., U.S. B4 119
Lobito, Ang. D2 44
Lobos de Afuera, Islas, is., Peru E2 54
Lobos de Tierra, Isla, i., Peru E2 54
Lobster Lake, l., Me., U.S. C3 96
Locarno, Switz. F15 10
Lochaline, Scot., U.K. E7 7
Lochboisdale, Scot., U.K. D5 7
Loches, Fr. E7 10
Lochgilphead, Scot., U.K. E7 7
Loch Lomond, Va., U.S. B5 123
Loch Raven Reservoir, res., Md., U.S. B4 97
Lochsa, stm., Id., U.S. C3 89
Lockeport, N.S., Can. F4 71
Lockesburg, Ar., U.S. D1 81
Lockhart, Tx., U.S. E4 120
Lock Haven, Pa., U.S. D7 115
Lockland, Oh., U.S. o13 112
Lockney, Tx., U.S. B2 120
Lockport, Il., U.S. B5 90
Lockport, La., U.S. E5 95
Lockport, N.Y., U.S. B2 109
Lockwood, Mo., U.S. D4 102
Lockwood, Mt., U.S. E8 103
Loc Ninh, Viet. I9 34
Locust, N.C., U.S. B2 110
Locust Fork, stm., Al., U.S. B3 78
Locust Grove, Ga., U.S. C2 87
Locust Grove, Ok., U.S. A6 113
Lod, Isr. D4 40
Lodejnoje Polje, U.S.S.R. A16 22
Lodève, Fr. I10 10
Lodgepole Creek, stm., U.S. C3 104
Lodi, Italy D4 14
Lodi, Ca., U.S. C3 82
Lodi, N.J., U.S. h8 107
Lodi, Oh., U.S. A3 112
Lodi, Wi., U.S. E4 126
Lodja, Zaire B4 44
Lodore, Canyon of, val., Co., U.S. A2 83
Lodwar, Kenya H2 46
Łodź, Pol. D19 8
Loffa, stm., Afr. G3 42
Logan, Ia., U.S. C2 92
Logan, Ks., U.S. C4 93
Logan, N.M., U.S. B6 108
Logan, Oh., U.S. C3 112
Logan, Ut., U.S. B4 121
Logan, W.V., U.S. D3 125
Logan, co., Ar., U.S. B2 81
Logan, co., Co., U.S. A7 83
Logan, co., Il., U.S. C4 90
Logan, co., Ks., U.S. D2 93
Logan, co., Ky., U.S. D3 94
Logan, co., Ne., U.S. C5 104
Logan, co., N.D., U.S. C6 111
Logan, co., Oh., U.S. B2 112
Logan, co., Ok., U.S. B4 113
Logan, co., W.V., U.S. D3 125
Logan, Mount, mtn., Yukon, Can. D4 66
Logan, Mount, mtn., Wa., U.S. A5 124
Logandale, Nv., U.S. G7 105
Logan Lake, B.C., Can. D7 69
Logan Martin Lake, res., Al., U.S. B3 78
Logan Pass, Mt., U.S. B2 103
Logansport, In., U.S. C5 91
Logansport, La., U.S. C2 95
Loganville, Ga., U.S. C3 87
Loganville, Pa., U.S. G8 115
Loggieville, N.B., Can. B4 71
Log Lane Village, Co., U.S. A7 83
Logone, stm., Afr. F9 42
Logroño, Spain C9 12
Logrosán, Spain F6 12
Lohr, Ger. E9 8
Loi-Kaw, Burma E4 34
Loimaa, Fin. F14 6
Loire, stm., Fr. E5 10
Loja, Ec. J3 58
Loja, Spain H7 12
Lokolama, Zaire B3 44
Lol, stm., Sudan G11 42
Lola, Mount, mtn., Ca., U.S. C3 82
Lolo, Mt., U.S. D2 103

Name	Map Ref	Page
Lolo Pass, U.S.	C4	89
Lomami, stm., Zaire	B4	44
Lombard, Il., U.S.	k8	90
Lomblen, Pulau, i., Indon.	G7	32
Lombok, i., Indon.	G6	32
Lomé, Togo	G6	42
Lomela, Zaire	B4	44
Lomela, stm., Zaire	B4	44
Lomira, Wi., U.S.	E5	126
Lomond, Loch, l., Scot., U.K.	E8	7
Lomonosov, U.S.S.R.	B12	22
Lompoc, Ca., U.S.	E3	82
Łomża, Pol.	B22	8
Lonaconing, Md., U.S.	k13	97
Lonāvale, India	C2	37
Loncoche, Chile	D2	56
London, Ont., Can.	E3	73
London, Eng., U.K.	J12	7
London, Ar., U.S.	B2	81
London, Ky., U.S.	C5	94
London, Oh., U.S.	C2	112
Londonderry, N. Ire., U.K.	G5	7
Londonderry, N.H., U.S.	E4	106
Londonderry, Cape, c., Austl.	B5	50
Londonderry, Isla, i., Chile	H2	56
Londontown, Md., U.S.	C4	97
Londrina, Braz.	G3	57
Lone Grove, Ok., U.S.	C4	113
Lone Mountain, mtn., Nv., U.S.	E4	105
Lone Pine, Ca., U.S.	D4	82
Lone Tree, Ia., U.S.	C6	92
Long, co., Ga., U.S.	E5	87
Longa, Proliv, strt., U.S.S.R.	C29	20
Longarone, Italy	C7	14
Long Bar Harbor, Md., U.S.	B5	97
Long Beach, Ca., U.S.	F4	82
Long Beach, In., U.S.	A4	91
Long Beach, Md., U.S.	D5	97
Long Beach, Ms., U.S.	g7	101
Long Beach, N.Y., U.S.	E7	109
Long Beach, Wa., U.S.	C1	124
Long Beach Naval Shipyard, mil., Ca., U.S.	n12	82
Longboat Key, Fl., U.S.	q10	86
Longboat Key, i., Fl., U.S.	E4	86
Longboat Pass, strt., Fl., U.S.	q10	86
Long Branch, N.J., U.S.	C5	107
Longbranch, Wa., U.S.	B3	124
Long Creek Mountain, mtn., Wy., U.S.	D5	127
Longeau, Fr.	E12	10
Long Grove, Ia., U.S.	C7	92
Long Harbour [-Mount Arlington Heights], Newf., Can.	E5	72
Long Island, i., Bah.	C10	64
Long Island, i., N.S., Can.	E3	71
Long Island, i., Me., U.S.	g7	96
Long Island, i., Ma., U.S.	g12	98
Long Island, i., N.Y., U.S.	E7	109
Long Island Sound, strt., U.S.	E7	109
Longjiang, China	B11	26
Long Key, i., Fl., U.S.	H6	86
Long Lake, Il., U.S.	h8	90
Long Lake, l., Me., U.S.	D2	96
Long Lake, l., Me., U.S.	A4	96
Long Lake, l., Mi., U.S.	D5	99
Long Lake, l., Mi., U.S.	C7	99
Long Lake, l., Mn., U.S.	D4	100
Long Lake, l., N.Y., U.S.	B6	109
Long Lake, l., N.D., U.S.	C6	111
Long Lake, l., Wa., U.S.	f10	124
Long Lake, l., Wi., U.S.	C2	126
Longli, China	A9	34
Longmeadow, Ma., U.S.	B2	98
Longmont, Co., U.S.	A5	83
Long Point, c., Man., Can.	C2	70
Long Point, pen., Ont., Can.	E4	73
Long Pond, res., Fl., U.S.	C4	86
Long Prairie, Mn., U.S.	E4	100
Long Range Mountains, mts., Newf., Can.	D3	72
Longreach, Austl.	D8	50
Longsheng, China	B11	34
Longs Peak, mtn., Co., U.S.	A5	83
Longué, Fr.	E6	10
Longueuil, Que., Can.	D4	74
Longuyon, Fr.	C12	10
Long View, N.C., U.S.	B1	110
Longview, Tx., U.S.	C5	120
Longview, Wa., U.S.	C3	124
Longwy, Fr.	C12	10
Long Xuyen, Viet.	I8	34
Lonigo, Italy	D6	14
Löningen, Ger.	C7	8
Lonoke, Ar., U.S.	C4	81
Lonoke, co., Ar., U.S.	C4	81
Lønsdal, Nor.	C10	6
Lonsdale, Mn., U.S.	F5	100
Lonsdale, R.I., U.S.	B4	116
Lons-le-Saunier, Fr.	F12	10
Loogootee, In., U.S.	G4	91
Lookout, Ky., U.S.	C7	94
Lookout, Cape, c., N.C., U.S.	C6	110
Lookout, Point, c., Mi., U.S.	d7	99
Lookout Mountain, Tn., U.S.	h11	119
Lookout Mountain, mtn., U.S.	D8	119
Lookout Mountain, mtn., Or., U.S.	C6	114
Lookout Pass, U.S.	B3	89
Lookout Point Lake, res., Or., U.S.	D4	114
Loon Lake, Wa., U.S.	A8	124
Loon Lake, l., Me., U.S.	B3	96
Loop Creek, stm., W.V., U.S.	m13	125
Loop Head, c., Ire.	I3	7
Loosahatchie, stm., Tn., U.S.	B2	119
Lopatina, Gora, mtn., U.S.S.R.	G22	20
Lopatka, Mys, c., U.S.S.R.	G25	20
Lop Buri, Thai.	G6	34
Lopez, Cap, c., Gabon	B1	44
López Collada, Mex.	B3	62
Lopez Island, i., Wa., U.S.	A3	124
Lop Nur, l., China	C5	26
Lora del Río, Spain	H6	12
Lorain, Oh., U.S.	A3	112
Lorain, co., Oh., U.S.	A3	112
Loramie, Lake, res., Oh., U.S.	B1	112
Lorca, Spain	H10	12
Lord Howe Island, i., Austl.	F11	50
Lordsburg, N.M., U.S.	E1	108
Loreauville, La., U.S.	D4	95
Lorena, Braz.	G6	57
Lorenzo, Tx., U.S.	C2	120
Loreto, Braz.	E9	54
Loreto, Col.	I7	58
Loreto, Mex.	F9	62
Lorette, Man., Can.	E3	70
Loretteville, Que., Can.	C6	74
Loretto, Ky., U.S.	C4	94
Loretto, Pa., U.S.	F4	115
Loretto, Tn., U.S.	B4	119
Lorica, Col.	C5	58
Lorient, Fr.	E3	10
L'Orignal, Ont., Can.	B10	73
Loring Air Force Base, mil., Me., U.S.	B5	96
Loriol [-du-Comtat], Fr.	H11	10
Loris, S.C., U.S.	C10	117
Lorne, N.B., Can.	B3	71
Lörrach, Ger.	H7	8
Lorraine, hist. reg., Fr.	D13	10
Los Alamos, N.M., U.S.	B3	108
Los Alamos, co., N.M., U.S.	B3	108
Los Aldamas, Mex.	D10	62
Los Altos, Ca., U.S.	k8	82
Los Ángeles, Chile	D2	56
Los Angeles, Ca., U.S.	E4	82
Los Angeles, co., Ca., U.S.	E4	82
Los Angeles Aqueduct, Ca., U.S.	E4	82
Los Banos, Ca., U.S.	D3	82
Los Blancos, Arg.	A4	56
Los Fresnos, Tx., U.S.	F4	120
Los Gatos, Ca., U.S.	D2	82
Los Lagos, Chile	D2	56
Los Lunas, N.M., U.S.	C3	108
Los Mochis, Mex.	E5	62
Los Palacios y Villafranca, Spain	H6	12
Los Pinos, stm., Co., U.S.	D3	83
Los Ranchos de Albuquerque, N.M., U.S.	B3	108
Los Roques, Islas, is., Ven.	B9	58
Lost, stm., In., U.S.	G4	91
Lost, stm., Wa., U.S.	A5	124
Lost, stm., W.V., U.S.	B6	125
Lost Creek, stm., Wy., U.S.	D4	127
Los Teques, Ven.	B9	58
Los Testigos, Islas, is., Ven.	B11	58
Lost Peak, mtn., Ut., U.S.	F2	121
Lost Ranger Peak, mtn., Co., U.S.	A4	83
Lost River Glacial Caverns, N.H., U.S.	B3	106
Lost River Range, mts., Id., U.S.	E5	89
Lost Trail Pass, U.S.	D5	89
Los Vilos, Chile	C2	56
Los Yébenes, Spain	F8	12
Lota, Chile	D2	56
Lotawana, Lake, res., Mo., U.S.	k11	102
Lotbinière, Que., Can.	C6	74
Louang Namtha, Laos	D6	34
Louangphrabang, Laos	E7	34
Loudéac, Fr.	D4	10
Loudon, Tn., U.S.	D9	119
Loudon, co., Tn., U.S.	D9	119
Loudonville, Oh., U.S.	B3	112
Loudoun, co., Va., U.S.	A5	123
Loudun, Fr.	E7	10
Louga, Sen.	E2	42
Loughrea, Ire.	H4	7
Louhans, Fr.	F12	10
Louisa, Ky., U.S.	B7	94
Louisa, Va., U.S.	B4	123
Louisa, co., Ia., U.S.	C6	92
Louisa, co., Va., U.S.	C5	123
Louisa, Lake, l., Fl., U.S.	D5	86
Louisbourg, N.S., Can.	D10	71
Louisburg, Ks., U.S.	D9	93
Louisburg, N.C., U.S.	A4	110
Louisdale, N.S., Can.	D8	71
Louise, Lake, l., Ak., U.S.	f18	79
Louise Island, i., B.C., Can.	C2	69
Louiseville, Que., Can.	C5	74
Louisiade Archipelago, is., Pap. N. Gui.	B10	50
Louisiana, Mo., U.S.	B6	102
Louisiana, state, U.S.	C3	95
Louisiana Point, c., La., U.S.	E2	95
Louis Trichardt, S. Afr.	F5	44
Louisville, Al., U.S.	D4	78
Louisville, Co., U.S.	B5	83
Louisville, Ga., U.S.	C4	87
Louisville, Il., U.S.	E5	90
Louisville, Ky., U.S.	B4	94
Louisville, Ms., U.S.	B4	101
Louisville, Ne., U.S.	D9	104
Louisville, Oh., U.S.	B4	112
Louis-XIV, Pointe, c., Que., Can.	h11	74
Loulé, Port.	H3	12
Loup, co., Ne., U.S.	C6	104
Loup, stm., Ne., U.S.	C8	104
Loup City, Ne., U.S.	C7	104
Lourdes, Newf., Can.	D2	72
Lourdes, Fr.	I6	10
Lourenço Marques see Maputo, Moz.	G6	44
Louth, Eng., U.K.	H12	7
Louviers, Fr.	C8	10
Louviers, Co., U.S.	B6	83
Love, co., Ok., U.S.	D4	113
Loveč, Bul.	F8	16
Loveland, Co., U.S.	A5	83
Loveland, Oh., U.S.	n13	112
Loveland Park, Oh., U.S.	C1	112
Loveland Pass, Co., U.S.	B5	83
Lovell, Wy., U.S.	B4	127
Lovelock, Nv., U.S.	C3	105
Lovely, Ky., U.S.	C7	94
Lovenia, Mount, mtn., Ut., U.S.	C5	121
Love Point, c., Md., U.S.	B5	97
Lovere, Italy	D5	14
Loves Park, Il., U.S.	A4	90
Lovettsville, Va., U.S.	A5	123
Loving, N.M., U.S.	E5	108
Loving, co., Tx., U.S.	D1	120
Lovington, Il., U.S.	D5	90
Lovington, Ia., U.S.	e8	92
Lovington, N.M., U.S.	E6	108
Lövstabruk, Swe.	F11	6
Low, Cape, c., N.W. Ter., Can.	D15	66
Lowden, Ia., U.S.	C7	92
Lowell, Ar., U.S.	A1	81
Lowell, In., U.S.	B3	91
Lowell, Ma., U.S.	A5	98
Lowell, Mi., U.S.	F5	99
Lowell, N.C., U.S.	B1	110
Lowell, Or., U.S.	D4	114
Lowell, Lake, res., Id., U.S.	F2	89
Lowellville, Oh., U.S.	A5	112
Lower Arrow Lake, res., B.C., Can.	E8	69
Lower Brule Indian Reservation, S.D., U.S.	C6	118
Lower California see Baja California, pen., Mex.	D3	62
Lower Hutt, N.Z.	D5	52
Lower Klamath Lake, l., Ca., U.S.	B3	82
Lower Matecumbe Key, i., Fl., U.S.	H6	86
Lower Monumental Lake, res., Wa., U.S.	C7	124
Lower New York Bay, b., N.J., U.S.	B4	107
Lower Otay Lake, res., Ca., U.S.	o16	82
Lower Paia, Hi., U.S.	C5	88
Lower Red Lake, l., Mn., U.S.	C3	100
Lower Rice Lake, l., Mn., U.S.	C3	100
Lower Salmon Dam, Id., U.S.	G4	89
Lower West Pubnico, N.S., Can.	F4	71
Lowestoft, Eng., U.K.	I14	7
Lowndes, co., Al., U.S.	C3	78
Lowndes, co., Ga., U.S.	F3	87
Lowndes, co., Ms., U.S.	B5	101
Lowry Air Force Base, mil., Co., U.S.	B6	83
Lowry City, Mo., U.S.	C4	102
Lowville, N.Y., U.S.	B5	109
Loxley, Al., U.S.	E2	78
Loyal, Wi., U.S.	D3	126
Loyall, Ky., U.S.	D6	94
Loyalsock Creek, stm., Pa., U.S.	D8	115
Loznica, Yugo.	E3	16
Lozoyuela, Spain	E8	12
Lua, stm., Zaire	H9	42
Lualaba, stm., Zaire	B5	44
Lua Makika, crat., Hi., U.S.	C5	88
Luanda, Ang.	C2	44
Luang Praban Range, mts., Asia	E6	34
Luanguinga, stm., Afr.	D4	44
Luangwa, stm., Afr.	D6	44
Luanshya, Zam.	D5	44
Luarca, Spain	B5	12
Luau, Ang.	D4	44
Lubang Island, i., Phil.	C7	32
Lubango, Ang.	D2	44
Lübben, Ger.	D13	8
Lübbenau, Ger.	D13	8
Lubbock, Tx., U.S.	C2	120
Lubbock, co., Tx., U.S.	C2	120
Lubec, Me., U.S.	D6	96
Lübeck, Ger.	B10	8
Lübecker Bucht, b., Ger.	A11	8
L'ubercy, U.S.S.R.	F20	22
Lubilash, stm., Zaire	C4	44
Lubin, Pol.	D16	8
Lublin, Pol.	D22	8
Lubudi, Zaire	C4	44
Lubuksikaping, Indon.	N6	34
Lubumbashi (Élisabethville), Zaire	D5	44
Lubutu, Zaire	B5	44
Lucama, N.C., U.S.	B4	110
Lucan, Ont., Can.	D3	73
Lucania, Mount, mtn., Yukon, Can.	D4	66
L'uca-Ongokton, Gora, mtn., U.S.S.R.	D15	20
Lucas, co., Ia., U.S.	C4	92
Lucas, co., Oh., U.S.	A2	112
Lucasville, Oh., U.S.	D3	112
Lucca, Italy	F5	14
Luce, co., Mi., U.S.	B5	99
Luce Bay, b., Scot., U.K.	G8	7
Lucedale, Ms., U.S.	E5	101
Lucena, Phil.	r19	33b
Lucena, Spain	H7	12
Lucena del Cid, Spain	E11	12
Luc-en-Diois, Fr.	H12	10
Lucera, Italy	H10	14
Lucerne, Ca., U.S.	C2	82
Lucerne see Luzern, Switz.	E15	10
Lucernemines, Pa., U.S.	E3	115
Lucerne Valley, Ca., U.S.	E5	82
Luceville, Que., Can.	A9	74
Luchiang, Tai.	K9	28
Lüchow, Ger.	C11	8
Lucira, Ang.	D2	44
Luck, U.S.S.R.	G3	18
Luck, Wi., U.S.	C1	126
Luckeesarai, India	H12	38
Luckenwalde, Ger.	C13	8
Lucknow, Ont., Can.	D3	73
Lucknow, India	G9	38
Lucky Peak Lake, res., Id., U.S.	F3	89
Luçon, Fr.	F5	10
Lüderitz, Nmb.	G3	44
Ludhiāna, India	E6	38
Ludington, Mi., U.S.	E4	99
L'udinovo, U.S.S.R.	H17	22
Ludlow, Ky., U.S.	h13	94
Ludlow, Ma., U.S.	B3	98
Ludlow, Vt., U.S.	E3	122
Ludowici, Ga., U.S.	E5	87
Ludvika, Swe.	F10	6
Ludwigsburg, Ger.	G9	8
Ludwigsfelde, Ger.	C13	8
Ludwigshafen, Ger.	F8	8
Luena, stm., Ang.	D4	44
Luene, Ang.	D3	44
Lufeng, China	M4	28
Lufkin, Tx., U.S.	D5	120
Luga, U.S.S.R.	C12	22
Lugano, Switz.	F15	10
Lugansk, U.S.S.R.	H5	18
Lugenda, stm., Moz.	D7	44
Lugh Ganane, Som.	H3	46
Lugnaquillia Mountain, mtn., Ire.	I6	7
Lugo, Italy	E6	14
Lugo, Spain	B4	12
Lugoff, S.C., U.S.	C6	117
Lugoj, Rom.	D5	16
Luhit, stm., Asia	G16	38
Luilaka, stm., Zaire	B4	44
Luino, Italy	C3	14
Lukachukai, Az., U.S.	A6	80
Luke Air Force Base, mil., Az., U.S.	D3	80
Lukulu, Zam.	D4	44
Lula, Ga., U.S.	B3	87
Luleå, Swe.	D14	6
Lüleburgaz, Tur.	H11	16
Luling, La., U.S.	k11	95
Luling, Tx., U.S.	E4	120
Lulonga, stm., Zaire	A3	44
Lumajang, Indon.	n16	33a
Lumber, stm., U.S.	C9	117
Lumber City, Ga., U.S.	E4	87
Lumberport, W.V., U.S.	B4	125
Lumberton, Ms., U.S.	D4	101
Lumberton, N.C., U.S.	C3	110
Lumbrales, Spain	E5	12
Lumby, B.C., Can.	D8	69
Lumding, India	H15	38
Lummi Indian Reservation, Wa., U.S.	A3	124
Lumpkin, Ga., U.S.	D2	87
Lumpkin, co., Ga., U.S.	B2	87
Lumsden, Newf., Can.	D5	72
Luna, co., N.M., U.S.	E2	108
Luna Pier, Mi., U.S.	G7	99
Lund, Swe.	I9	6
Lund, Nv., U.S.	E6	105
Lundar, Man., Can.	D2	70
Lundazi, Zam.	D6	44
Lüneburg, Ger.	B10	8
Lüneburger Heide, reg., Ger.	B10	8
Lunel, Fr.	I11	10
Lunenburg, Ma., U.S.	A4	98
Lunenburg, co., Va., U.S.	D4	123
Lunéville, Fr.	D13	10
Lunga, stm., Zam.	D5	44
Luohe, China	B3	28
Luolong, China	E17	38
Luopu, China	B9	38
Luoyang, China	E9	26
Lūrah, stm., Afg.	D2	38
Luray, Va., U.S.	B4	123
Lure, Fr.	E13	10
Lure, Lake, res., N.C., U.S.	f10	110
Lurgan, N. Ire., U.K.	G6	7
Lúrio, stm., Moz.	D7	44
Lusaka, Zam.	E5	44
Lusambo, Zaire	B4	44
Lusby, Md., U.S.	D5	97
Luseland, Sask., Can.	E1	75
Lushan, China	B1	28
Lushnje, Alb.	I3	16
Lushoto, Tan.	B7	44
Lüshun (Port Arthur), China	D11	26
Lusk, Wy., U.S.	D8	127
Lussac-les-Châteaux, Fr.	F7	10
Lūt, Dasht-e, des., Iran	B6	46
Lutcher, La., U.S.	D5	95
Luther, Ok., U.S.	B4	113
Luthersville, Ga., U.S.	C2	87
Lutherville-Timonium, Md., U.S.	B4	97
Luton, Eng., U.K.	J12	7
Lutsk see Luck, U.S.S.R.	G3	18
Luttrell, Tn., U.S.	C10	119
Lutz, Fl., U.S.	D4	86
Luverne, Al., U.S.	D3	78
Luverne, Mn., U.S.	G2	100
Luwegu, stm., Tan.	C7	44
Luxapallila Creek, stm., U.S.	B5	101
Luxembourg, Lux.	F6	8
Luxembourg, ctry., Eur.	F9	4
Luxemburg, Wi., U.S.	D6	126
Luxomni, Ga., U.S.	h8	87
Luxora, Ar., U.S.	B6	81
Luzern, Switz.	E15	10
Luzerne, Pa., U.S.	n17	115
Luzerne, co., Pa., U.S.	D9	115
Luzhou, China	F8	26
Luzon, i., Phil.	B7	32
Luzon Strait, strt., Asia	G11	26
Luzy, Fr.	F10	10
L'vov, U.S.S.R.	H2	18
Lycksele, Swe.	D12	6
Lycoming, co., Pa., U.S.	D7	115
Lycoming Creek, stm., Pa., U.S.	D7	115
Lydenburg, S. Afr.	G6	44
Lyell, Mount, mtn., Can.	D2	68
Lyford, Tx., U.S.	F4	120
Lykens, Pa., U.S.	E8	115
Lyle, Wa., U.S.	D4	124
Lyman, S.C., U.S.	B3	117
Lyman, Wy., U.S.	E2	127
Lyman, co., S.D., U.S.	D6	118
Lyman Lake, res., Az., U.S.	C6	80
Lynch, Ky., U.S.	D7	94
Lynchburg, Oh., U.S.	C2	112
Lynchburg, Tn., U.S.	B5	119
Lynchburg, Va., U.S.	C3	123
Lynches, stm., S.C., U.S.	D8	117
Lynden, Wa., U.S.	A3	124
Lynde Point, c., Ct., U.S.	D6	84
Lyndhurst, N.J., U.S.	h8	107
Lyndhurst, Oh., U.S.	g10	112
Lyndon, Ks., U.S.	D8	93
Lyndon, Ky., U.S.	g11	94
Lyndon B. Johnson National Historical Site, hist., Tx., U.S.	D3	120
Lyndon B. Johnson Space Center, sci., Tx., U.S.	r14	120
Lyndonville, Vt., U.S.	B4	122
Lyndora, Pa., U.S.	E2	115
Lynher Reef, rf., Austl.	C4	50
Lynn, Al., U.S.	A2	78
Lynn, In., U.S.	D8	91
Lynn, Ma., U.S.	B6	98
Lynn, co., Tx., U.S.	C2	120
Lynn, Lake, res., W.V., U.S.	B5	125
Lynn Canal, b., Ak., U.S.	k22	79
Lynne Acres, Md., U.S.	B4	97
Lynnfield, Ma., U.S.	f11	98
Lynn Garden, Tn., U.S.	A9	119
Lynn Garden, Tn., U.S.	C11	119
Lynn Haven, Fl., U.S.	u16	86
Lynnhaven Roads, b., Va., U.S.	k15	123
Lynnville, In., U.S.	H3	91
Lynnwood, Wa., U.S.	B3	124
Lynton, Eng., U.K.	J9	7
Lynwood, Ca., U.S.	n12	82
Lyon, Fr.	G11	10
Lyon, co., Ia., U.S.	A1	92
Lyon, co., Ks., U.S.	D7	93
Lyon, co., Ky., U.S.	C1	94
Lyon, co., Mn., U.S.	F3	100
Lyon, co., Nv., U.S.	D2	105
Lyons, Co., U.S.	A5	83
Lyons, Ga., U.S.	D4	87
Lyons, Il., U.S.	k9	90
Lyons, In., U.S.	G3	91
Lyons, Ks., U.S.	D5	93
Lyons, Mi., U.S.	F6	99
Lyons, Ne., U.S.	C9	104
Lyons, N.Y., U.S.	B3	109
Lyons, Or., U.S.	C4	114
Lyster Station, Que., Can.	C6	74
Lytle, Tx., U.S.	E3	120
M		
Ma, stm., Asia	D8	34
Maalaea Bay, b., Hi., U.S.	C5	88
Ma'ān, Jord.	D4	40
Maanshan, China	D7	28
Ma'arrat an-Nu'mān, Syria	B5	40
Maas (Meuse), stm., Eur.	D5	8
Maastricht, Neth.	E5	8
Mabank, Tx., U.S.	C4	120
Mabaruma, Guy.	C13	58
Mabel, Mn., U.S.	G7	100
Maben, Ms., U.S.	B4	101
Mableton, Ga., U.S.	h7	87
Mabscott, W.V., U.S.	D3	125
Mabton, Wa., U.S.	C5	124
Mača, U.S.S.R.	F17	20
Macaé, Braz.	G8	57
Macão, Port.	F3	12
Macao see Macau, dep., Asia	M2	28
Macapá, Braz.	C8	54
Macará, Ec.	J3	58
Macarani, Braz.	C8	57
Macas, Ec.	I3	58
Macau, Braz.	E11	54
Macau (Aomen), Macao	M2	28
Macau (Aomen), dep., Asia	M2	28
MacClenny, Fl., U.S.	B4	86
MacDill Air Force Base, mil., Fl., U.S.	E4	86
Macdonnell Ranges, mts., Austl.	D6	50
MacDowell Reservoir, res., N.H., U.S.	E2	106
Macduff, Scot., U.K.	D10	7
Macdui, Ben, mtn., Scot., U.K.	D9	7
Macedo de Cavaleiros, Port.	D5	12
Macedonia, Oh., U.S.	A4	112
Macedonia, hist. reg., Eur.	H6	16
Maceió, Braz.	E11	54
Macerata, Italy	F8	14
Maces Bay, b., N.B., Can.	D3	71
MacGregor, Man., Can.	E2	70
Machačkala, U.S.S.R.	I7	18
Machagai, Arg.	B4	56
Machala, Ec.	I3	58
Machecoul, Fr.	E5	10
Machias, Me., U.S.	D5	96
Machias, stm., Me., U.S.	B4	96
Machias, stm., Me., U.S.	D5	96
Machias Bay, b., Me., U.S.	D5	96
Machias Lakes, l., Me., U.S.	C5	96
Machilīpatnam (Bandar), India	D6	37
Machiques, Ven.	B6	58
Macho, Arroyo del, val., N.M., U.S.	C4	108
Machupicchu, Peru	F4	54
Macina, reg., Mali	F4	42
Mackay, Austl.	D9	50
Mackay, Lake, l., Austl.	D5	50
MacKenzie, B.C., Can.	B6	69
Mackenzie, stm., N.W. Ter., Can.	C6	66
Mackenzie Bay, b., Can.	C5	66
Mackenzie Mountains, mts., Can.	D7	66
Mackinac, co., Mi., U.S.	B5	99
Mackinac, Straits of, strt., Mi., U.S.	C6	99
Mackinac Bridge, Mi., U.S.	C6	99
Mackinac Island, i., Mi., U.S.	C6	99
Mackinaw, Il., U.S.	C4	90
Mackinaw, stm., Il., U.S.	C4	90
Mackinaw City, Mi., U.S.	C6	99
Maclear, S. Afr.	H5	44
Macmillan, stm., Yukon, Can.	D6	66
Macomb, Il., U.S.	C3	90
Macomb, co., Mi., U.S.	F8	99
Macomer, Italy	I3	14
Mâcon, Fr.	F11	10
Macon, Ga., U.S.	D3	87
Macon, Il., U.S.	D5	90
Macon, Ms., U.S.	B5	101
Macon, Mo., U.S.	B5	102
Macon, co., Al., U.S.	C4	78
Macon, co., Ga., U.S.	D2	87
Macon, co., Il., U.S.	D4	90
Macon, co., Mo., U.S.	B5	102
Macon, co., N.C., U.S.	f9	110
Macon, co., Tn., U.S.	A5	119
Macon, Bayou, stm., U.S.	B4	95
Macoupin, co., Il., U.S.	D4	90
MacTier, Ont., Can.	B5	73

Macungie, Pa., U.S. E10 115
Mad, stm., Ca., U.S. B2 82
Mad, stm., Ct., U.S. B3 84
Mad, stm., N.H., U.S. C3 106
Mad, stm., Oh., U.S. C2 112
Mad, stm., Vt., U.S. C3 122
Ma'dabā, Jord. D4 40
Madagascar, ctry., Afr. E9 44
Madame, Isle, i., N.S., Can. D9 71
Madanapalle, India F5 37
Madang, Pap. N. Gui. m16 50a
Mādārīpur, Bngl. I14 38
Madawaska, Me., U.S. A4 96
Madawaska, stm., Can. B9 74
Madawaska, stm., Ont., Can. B7 73
Madawaska Lake, l., Me., U.S. A4 96
Maddaloni, Italy H9 14
Madeira, Oh., U.S. o13 112
Madeira, i., Port. B2 42
Madeira, stm., S.A. E6 54
Madeira, Arquipélago da (Madeira Islands), is., Port. B2 42
Mädelegabel, mtn., Eur. E17 10
Madeleine, Îles de la, is., Que., Can. B8 71
Madelia, Mn., U.S. F4 100
Madeline Island, i., Wi., U.S. B3 126
Madera, Ca., U.S. D3 82
Madera, co., Ca., U.S. D4 82
Madhubani, India G12 38
Madhya Pradesh, state, India I8 38
Madill, Ok., U.S. C5 113
Madīnat ash-Sha'b, Yemen F3 46
Madingou, Congo B2 44
Madison, Al., U.S. A3 78
Madison, Ar., U.S. B5 81
Madison, Ct., U.S. D5 84
Madison, Fl., U.S. B3 86
Madison, Ga., U.S. C3 87
Madison, Il., U.S. E3 90
Madison, In., U.S. G7 91
Madison, Ks., U.S. D7 93
Madison, Me., U.S. D3 96
Madison, Mn., U.S. E2 100
Madison, Ms., U.S. C3 101
Madison, Ne., U.S. C8 104
Madison, N.J., U.S. B4 107
Madison, N.C., U.S. A3 110
Madison, Oh., U.S. A4 112
Madison, S.D., U.S. C8 118
Madison, W.V., U.S. C3 125
Madison, Wi., U.S. E4 126
Madison, co., Al., U.S. A3 78
Madison, co., Ar., U.S. B2 81
Madison, co., Fl., U.S. B3 86
Madison, co., Ga., U.S. B3 87
Madison, co., Id., U.S. F7 89
Madison, co., Il., U.S. E4 90
Madison, co., In., U.S. D6 91
Madison, co., Ia., U.S. C3 92
Madison, co., Ky., U.S. C5 94
Madison, co., La., U.S. B4 95
Madison, co., Ms., U.S. C4 101
Madison, co., Mo., U.S. D7 102
Madison, co., Mt., U.S. E5 103
Madison, co., Ne., U.S. C8 104
Madison, co., N.Y., U.S. C5 109
Madison, co., N.C., U.S. f10 110
Madison, co., Oh., U.S. C2 112
Madison, co., Tn., U.S. B3 119
Madison, co., Tx., U.S. D5 120
Madison, co., Va., U.S. B4 123
Madison, stm., Mt., U.S. E5 103
Madison Heights, Mi., U.S. o15 99
Madison Heights, Va., U.S. C3 123
Madison Lake, Mn., U.S. F5 100
Madison Range, mts., Mt., U.S. E5 103
Madisonville, Ky., U.S. C2 94
Madisonville, La., U.S. D5 95
Madisonville, Tn., U.S. D9 119
Madisonville, Tx., U.S. D5 120
Madiun, Indon. m15 32
Madoc, Ont., Can. C7 73
Mado Gashi, Kenya B7 44
Madras, India F6 37
Madras, Or., U.S. C5 114
Madre, Laguna, b., Mex. E11 62
Madre, Laguna, b., Tx., U.S. F4 120
Madre, Sierra, mts., N.A. J14 62
Madre, Sierra, mts., Phil. B7 32
Madre de Dios, stm., S.A. F5 54
Madre de Dios, Isla, i., Chile G1 56
Madre del Sur, Sierra, mts., Mex. I10 62
Madre Occidental, Sierra, mts., Mex. E6 62
Madre Oriental, Sierra, mts., Mex. F9 62
Madrid, Spain E8 12
Madrid, Ia., U.S. C4 92
Madridejos, Spain F8 12
Maduo, China E6 26
Madura, i., Indon. G5 32
Madurai, India H5 37
Maebashi, Japan F12 30
Mae Hong Son, Thai. E4 34
Maeser, Ut., U.S. C6 121
Mae Sot, Thai. F5 34
Maestra, Sierra, mts., Cuba D9 64
Maevatanana, Madag. E9 44
Mafia Island, i., Tan. C7 44
Mafikeng, S. Afr. G5 44
Mafra, Braz. B7 56
Magadan, U.S.S.R. F24 20
Magadi, Kenya B7 44
Magallanes, Estrecho de (Strait of Magellan), strt., S.A. G2 56
Magangué, Col. C5 58
Magazine, Ar., U.S. B2 81
Magazine Mountain, mtn., Ar., U.S. B2 81
Magdagači, U.S.S.R. G19 20
Magdalena, Bol. F6 54
Magdalena, Mex. B4 62
Magdalena, N.M., U.S. C2 108
Magdalena, stm., Col. B5 58
Magdalena, Bahía, b., Mex. E3 62
Magdalena, Isla, i., Chile E2 56
Magdalena Mountains, mts., N.M., U.S. D2 108
Magdeburg, Ger. C11 8
Magee, Ms., U.S. D4 101
Magelang, Indon. m15 33a
Magellan, Strait of see Magallanes, Estrecho de, strt., S.A. G2 56
Magenta, Italy D3 14
Maggie Creek, stm., Nv., U.S. C5 105
Maggiore, Lago, l., Eur. C3 14
Magic Reservoir, res., Id., U.S. F4 89
Magione, Italy F7 14
Magna, Ut., U.S. C3 121
Magnetawan, stm., Ont., Can. B4 73
Magnitogorsk, U.S.S.R. G9 18
Magnolia, Ar., U.S. D2 81
Magnolia, Ky., U.S. C4 94
Magnolia, Ms., U.S. D3 101
Magnolia, N.C., U.S. C4 110
Magnolia, Oh., U.S. B4 112
Magoffin, co., Ky., U.S. C6 94
Magog, Que., Can. D5 74
Magothy River, b., Md., U.S. B4 97
Magpie, Lac, l., Que., Can. F20 66
Magrath, Alta., Can. E4 68
Magruder Mountain, mtn., Nv., U.S. F4 105
Maguarinho, Cabo, c., Braz. D9 54
Magway, Burma D3 34
Mahābād, Iran J7 18
Mahābhārat Range, mts., Nepal F10 38
Mahaicony Village, Guy. D14 58
Mahajamba, Baie de la, b., Madag. E9 44
Mahajanga, Madag. E9 44
Mahakam, stm., Indon. E6 32
Mahānadi, stm., India J11 38
Mahanoro, Madag. E9 44
Mahanoy City, Pa., U.S. E9 115
Mahārāshtra, state, India C3 37
Maha Sarakham, Thai. F7 34
Mahaska, co., Ia., U.S. C5 92
Mahaṭṭat al-Qaṭrānah, Jord. D5 40
Mahaṭṭat Ḥaraḍ, Sau. Ar. D4 46
Mahbūbnagar, India D4 37
Mahé Island, i., Sey. B11 44
Mahenge, Tan. C7 44
Mahi, stm., India I5 38
Mahmūd-e 'Erāqī, Afg. C3 38
Mahnomen, Mn., U.S. C3 100
Mahnomen, co., Mn., U.S. C3 100
Mahoba, India H8 38
Mahogany Mountain, mtn., Or., U.S. D9 114
Mahomet, Il., U.S. C5 90
Mahón, Spain F16 12
Mahone Bay, N.S., Can. E5 71
Mahoning, co., Oh., U.S. B5 112
Mahoning, stm., U.S. A5 112
Mahopac, N.Y., U.S. D7 109
Mahuva, India J4 38
Mahwah, N.J., U.S. A4 107
Maiden, N.C., U.S. B1 110
Maidstone, Eng., U.K. J13 7
Maidstone Lake, l., Vt., U.S. B5 122
Maiduguri, Nig. F8 42
Maili, Hi., U.S. g9 88
Maili Point, c., Hi., U.S. g9 88
Maillezais, Fr. F6 10
Main, stm., Ger. F9 8
Mainburg, Ger. G11 8
Main Channel, strt., Ont., Can. B3 73
Mai-Ndombe, Lac, l., Zaire B3 44
Maine, state, U.S. C3 96
Mainland, i., Scot., U.K. B9 7
Mainland, i., Scot., U.K. A11 7
Main Pass, strt., La., U.S. E6 95
Mainz, Ger. E8 8
Maipo, Volcán, vol., S.A. C3 56
Maipú, Arg. D5 56
Maiquetía, Ven. B9 58
Maisonnette, N.B., Can. B4 71
Maitland, Austl. F10 50
Maitland, Ont., Can. C9 73
Maize, Ks., U.S. g12 93
Maizuru, Japan G8 30
Maja, stm., U.S.S.R. F20 20
Majene, Indon. F6 32
Maji, Eth. G2 46
Majkop, U.S.S.R. I6 18
Majno-Pyl'gino, U.S.S.R. E29 20
Major, co., Ok., U.S. A3 113
Majorca see Mallorca, i., Spain F15 12
Makaha, Hi., U.S. g9 88
Makaha Point, c., Hi., U.S. A2 88
Makah Indian Reservation, Wa., U.S. A1 124
Makahuena Point, c., Hi., U.S. B2 88
Makakilo City, Hi., U.S. g9 88
Makale, Indon. F6 32
Makapuu Head, c., Hi., U.S. B4 88
Makarska, Yugo. F12 14
Makasar, Selat (Makassar Strait), strt., Indon. F6 32
Makassar see Ujungpandang, Indon. G6 32
Makawao, Hi., U.S. C5 88
Makaweli, Hi., U.S. B2 88
Makeni, S.L. G3 42
Makgadikgadi Pans, pl., Bots. F5 44
Makhachkala see Machačkala, U.S.S.R. I7 18
Makindu, Kenya B7 44
M'akit, U.S.S.R. E24 20
Makkah (Mecca), Sau. Ar. D2 46
Maklakovo, U.S.S.R. F12 20
Makó, Hung. I20 8
Makokou, Gabon A2 44
Makthar, Tun. N4 14
Makumbi, Zaire C4 44
Makurazaki, Japan K3 30
Makurdi, Nig. G7 42
Makushin Volcano, vol., Ak., U.S. E6 79
Malabar, Fl., U.S. D6 86
Malabar Coast, India G4 37
Malabo, Eq. Gui. H7 42
Malacca, Strait of, strt., Asia M6 34
Malad City, Id., U.S. G6 89
Málaga, Col. D6 58
Málaga, Spain I7 12
Malagón, Spain F8 12
Malaimbandy, Madag. F9 44
Malaja Kuril'skaja Gr'ada (Habomai-shotō), is., U.S.S.R. p24 30a
Malakāl, Sudan G12 42
Malakoff, Tx., U.S. C4 120
Malang, Indon. m16 32
Malanje, Ang. C3 44
Malanville, Benin F6 42
Mälaren, l., Swe. G11 6
Malargüe, Arg. D3 56
Malartic, Que., Can. k11 74
Malaspina Glacier, Ak., U.S. D11 79
Malatya, Tur. H15 4
Malawi, ctry., Afr. D6 44
Malaya, reg., Malay. M7 34
Malay Peninsula, pen., Asia K6 34
Malaysia, ctry., Asia E3 32
Malbaie, stm., Que., Can. B7 74
Malbork, Pol. A19 8
Malcolm, Austl. E4 50
Malden, Ma., U.S. B5 98
Malden, Mo., U.S. E8 102
Malden, W.V., U.S. m12 125
Maldives, ctry., Asia I2 37
Maldonado, Ur. C6 56
Mālegaon, India B3 37
Malek Dīn, Afg. D3 38
Malha Wells, Sudan E11 42
Malheur, co., Or., U.S. D9 114
Malheur, stm., Or., U.S. D9 114
Malheur Lake, l., Or., U.S. D8 114
Mali, ctry., Afr. E5 42
Malibu, Ca., U.S. m11 82
Malik, Wādī al-, val., Sudan E11 42
Malin, Or., U.S. E5 114
Malindi, Kenya B8 44
Malino, Bukit, mtn., Indon. E7 32
Malka, U.S.S.R. G25 20
Malkāpur, India B4 37
Malkara, Tur. I10 16
Mallaig, Scot., U.K. D7 7
Mallawī, Egypt C12 42
Malletts Bay, b., Vt., U.S. B2 122
Mallnitz, Aus. I13 8
Mallorca, i., Spain F14 12
Mallow, Ire. I4 7
Malmberget, Swe. C13 6
Malmédy, Bel. E6 8
Malmesbury, S. Afr. H3 44
Malmö, Swe. I9 6
Malmstrom Air Force Base, mil., Mt., U.S. C5 103
Malolos, Phil. q19 33b
Malone, N.Y., U.S. f10 109
Maloney Reservoir, res., Ne., U.S. C5 104
Måløy, Nor. F5 6
Malpaso, Presa de, res., Mex. I13 62
Malpelo, Isla de, i., Col. C2 54
Malpeque Bay, b., P.E.I., Can. C6 71
Malta, Il., U.S. B5 90
Malta, Mt., U.S. B9 103
Malta, ctry., Eur. H10 4
Malta Channel, strt., Eur. M9 14
Maltahöhe, Nmb. F3 44
Maluku (Moluccas), is., Indon. F8 32
Maluku, Laut (Molucca Sea), Indon. F7 32
Malung, Swe. F9 6
Malvern, Ar., U.S. C3 81
Malvern, Ia., U.S. D2 92
Malvern, Oh., U.S. B4 112
Malvern, Pa., U.S. o19 115
Malverne, N.Y., U.S. k13 109
Malyj An'uj, stm., U.S.S.R. D26 20
Malyj L'achovskij, Ostrov, i., U.S.S.R. C22 20
Malyj Tajmyr, Ostrov, i., U.S.S.R. B15 20
Mama, U.S.S.R. F16 20
Mamala Bay, b., Hi., U.S. g10 88
Mamaroneck, N.Y., U.S. h13 109
Mamberamo, stm., Indon. F10 32
Mamers, Fr. D7 10
Mamfe, Cam. G7 42
Mammoth, Az., U.S. E5 80
Mammoth Cave National Park, Ky., U.S. C4 94
Mammoth Lakes, Ca., U.S. D4 82
Mammoth Spring, Ar., U.S. A4 81
Mamoré, stm., S.A. F5 54
Mamou, Gui. F3 42
Mamou, La., U.S. D3 95
Man, I.C. G4 42
Man, W.V., U.S. D3 125
Manacapuru, Braz. D6 54
Manacor, Spain F15 12
Manado, Indon. E7 32
Managua, Nic. H4 64
Managua, Lago de, l., Nic. H4 64
Manakara, Madag. F9 44
Manama see Al-Manāmah, Bahr. C5 46
Manana Island, i., Hi., U.S. g11 88
Mananara, Madag. E9 44
Mananjary, Madag. F9 44
Manantico Creek, stm., N.J., U.S. E3 107
Mana Point, c., Hi., U.S. A2 88
Manas, China C4 26
Manasquan, N.J., U.S. C4 107
Manasquan, stm., N.J., U.S. C4 107
Manassa, Co., U.S. D5 83
Manassas, Va., U.S. B5 123
Manassas National Battlefield Park, Va., U.S. g11 123
Manassas Park, Va., U.S. B5 123
Manatee, co., Fl., U.S. E4 86
Manatee, stm., Fl., U.S. E4 86
Manaus, Braz. D6 54
Manawa, Wi., U.S. D5 126
Manbij, Syria A5 40
Mancelona, Mi., U.S. D5 99
Mancha Real, Spain H8 12
Manchester, Eng., U.K. H10 7
Manchester, Ct., U.S. B5 84
Manchester, Ga., U.S. D2 87
Manchester, Ia., U.S. B6 92
Manchester, Ky., U.S. C6 94
Manchester, Me., U.S. D3 96
Manchester, Md., U.S. A4 97
Manchester, Ma., U.S. A6 98
Manchester, Mi., U.S. F6 99
Manchester, Mo., U.S. f12 102
Manchester, N.H., U.S. E4 106
Manchester, N.Y., U.S. C3 109
Manchester, Oh., U.S. D2 112
Manchester, Pa., U.S. F8 115
Manchester, Tn., U.S. B5 119
Manchester, Vt., U.S. E2 122
Manchester Center, Vt., U.S. E2 122
Manchuria, reg., China B12 26
Manciano, Italy G6 14
Mancos, Co., U.S. D2 83
Mancos, stm., U.S. D2 83
Mand, stm., Iran C5 46
Manda, Tan. D6 44
Mandal, Nor. G6 6
Mandalay, Burma C4 34
Mandalgov', Mong. B8 26
Mandan, N.D., U.S. C5 111
Mandas, Italy J4 14
Mandasor, India H6 38
Mandeb, Bāb el-, strt. F3 46
Mandeville, Ar., U.S. D2 81
Mandeville, La., U.S. D5 95
Mandi Bahāuddīn, Pak. D5 38
Mandimba, Moz. D7 44
Mandla, India I9 38
Manduria, Italy I12 14
Māndvi, India I3 38
Mandya, India F4 37
Manerbio, Italy D5 14
Manfredonia, Italy H10 14
Mangabeiras, Chapada das, hills, Braz. F9 54
Mangalore, India F3 37
Mangkalihat, Tanjung, c., Indon. E6 32
Manglares, Cabo, c., Col. G3 58
Mangoche, Mwi. D7 44
Mangoky, stm., Madag. F8 44
Mangole, Pulau, i., Indon. F8 32
Māngrol, India J4 38
Mangrove Cay, i., Bah. B9 64
Mangualde, Port. E4 12
Mangum, Ok., U.S. C2 113
Mangya, China D5 26
Manhattan, Ks., U.S. C7 93
Manhattan, Mt., U.S. E5 103
Manhattan Beach, Ca., U.S. n12 82
Manhattan Island, i., N.Y., U.S. h13 109
Manheim, Pa., U.S. F9 115
Manhuaçu, Braz. F7 57
Manicoré, Braz. E6 54
Manicouagan, stm., Que., Can. F19 66
Manicouagan, Réservoir, res., Que., Can. h13 74
Manila, Phil. q19 32
Manila, Ar., U.S. B5 81
Manila Bay, b., Phil. C7 32
Manilla, Ia., U.S. C2 92
Manipur, ter., India H15 38
Manisa, Tur. K11 16
Manistee, Mi., U.S. D4 99
Manistee, co., Mi., U.S. D4 99
Manistee, stm., Mi., U.S. D5 99
Manistique, Mi., U.S. C4 99
Manistique, stm., Mi., U.S. B4 99
Manistique Lake, l., Mi., U.S. B5 99
Manito, Il., U.S. C4 90
Manitoba, prov., Can. C3 70
Manitoba, Lake, l., Man., Can. D2 70
Manitou, Man., Can. E2 70
Manitou, Lake, l., Ont., Can. B3 73
Manitou Island, i., Mi., U.S. A3 99
Manitou Lake, l., Sask., Can. E1 75
Manitoulin Island, i., Ont., Can. B2 73
Manitou Springs, Co., U.S. C6 83
Manitowoc, Wi., U.S. D6 126
Manitowoc, co., Wi., U.S. D6 126
Manitowoc, stm., Wi., U.S. h10 126
Maniwaki, Que., Can. C2 74
Manizales, Col. E5 58
Manjacaze, Moz. F6 44
Mānjra, stm., India C4 37
Mankato, Ks., U.S. C5 93
Mankato, Mn., U.S. F5 100
Mankoya, Zam. D4 44
Manlius, N.Y., U.S. C5 109
Manlléu, Spain C14 12
Manly, Ia., U.S. A4 92
Manmād, India B3 37
Mannar, Gulf of, b., Asia H5 37
Mannārgudi, India G5 37
Mannar Island, i., Sri L. H5 37
Mannford, Ok., U.S. A5 113
Mannheim, Ger. F8 8
Manning, Alta., Can. A2 68
Manning, Ia., U.S. C2 92
Manning, S.C., U.S. D7 117
Mannington, W.V., U.S. B4 125
Manns Creek, stm., W.V., U.S. n14 125
Mannville, Alta., Can. C5 68
Manokin, stm., Md., U.S. D6 97
Manokotak, Ak., U.S. D8 79
Manokwari, Indon. F9 32
Manomet, Ma., U.S. C6 98
Manomet Point, c., Ma., U.S. C6 98
Manono, Zaire C5 44
Manor, Tx., U.S. D4 120
Manosque, Fr. I12 10
Manouane, Lac, l., Que., Can. h12 74
Manresa, Spain D13 12
Mānsa, India F6 38
Mansa, Zam. D5 44
Manseau, Que., Can. C5 74
Mansel Island, i., N.W. Ter., Can. D17 66
Mansfield, Eng., U.K. H11 7
Mansfield, Ar., U.S. B1 81
Mansfield, Il., U.S. C5 90
Mansfield, La., U.S. B2 95
Mansfield, Ma., U.S. B5 98
Mansfield, Mo., U.S. D5 102
Mansfield, Oh., U.S. B3 112
Mansfield, Pa., U.S. C7 115
Mansfield, Tx., U.S. n9 120
Mansfield, Mount, mtn., Vt., U.S. B3 122
Mansfield Center, Ct., U.S. B7 84
Mansfield Hollow Lake, res., Ct., U.S. B7 84
Manson, Ia., U.S. B3 92
Manson, Wa., U.S. B5 124
Mansonville, Que., Can. D5 74
Mansura, La., U.S. C3 95
Manta, Ec. H2 58
Mantachie, Ms., U.S. A5 101
Manteca, Ca., U.S. D3 82
Manteno, Il., U.S. B6 90
Manteo, N.C., U.S. B7 110
Mantes-la-Jolie, Fr. D8 10
Manti, Ut., U.S. D4 121
Mantiqueira, Serra da, mts., Braz. F6 57
Manton, Mi., U.S. D5 99
Mantorville, Mn., U.S. F6 100
Mantova, Italy D5 14
Mantua, Oh., U.S. A4 112
Mantua, Ut., U.S. B4 121
Manturovo, U.S.S.R. C27 22
Manukau Harbour, b., N.Z. B5 52
Manumuskin, stm., N.J., U.S. E3 107
Manus Island, i., Pap. N. Gui. k16 50a
Manvel, Tx., U.S. r14 120
Manville, N.J., U.S. B3 107
Manville, R.I., U.S. B4 116
Many, La., U.S. C2 95
Many Farms, Az., U.S. A6 80
Manzanares, Spain F8 12
Manzanillo, Cuba D9 64
Manzanillo, Mex. H7 62
Manzano Mountains, mts., N.M., U.S. C3 108
Manzano Peak, mtn., N.M., U.S. C3 108
Manzhouli, China B10 26
Mao, Chad F9 42
Maoke, Pegunungan, mts., Indon. F10 32
Mapastepec, Mex. J13 62
Mapi, Indon. G10 32
Mapia, Kepulauan, is., Indon. E9 32
Mapimí, Mex. E8 62
Mapimí, Bolsón de, des., Mex. D8 62
Mapire, Ven. D10 58
Maple, stm., U.S. A7 118
Maple, stm., Ia., U.S. B2 92
Maple, stm., N.D., U.S. C8 111
Maple Bluff, Wi., U.S. E4 126
Maple Grove, Mn., U.S. m12 100
Maple Heights, Oh., U.S. h9 112
Maple Lake, Mn., U.S. E5 100
Maple Plain, Mn., U.S. m11 100
Maple Shade, N.J., U.S. D2 107
Maplesville, Al., U.S. C3 78
Mapleton, Ia., U.S. B2 92
Mapleton, Mn., U.S. G5 100
Mapleton, N.D., U.S. C8 111
Mapleton, Or., U.S. C3 114
Mapleton, Ut., U.S. C4 121
Maple Valley, Wa., U.S. f11 124
Mapleville, R.I., U.S. B2 116
Maplewood, Mn., U.S. n12 100
Maplewood, Mo., U.S. f13 102
Maplewood, N.J., U.S. B4 107
Mapuera, stm., Braz. D7 54
Maputo (Lourenço Marques), Moz. G6 44
Maqueda, Spain E7 12
Maquela do Zombo, Ang. C3 44
Maquinchao, Arg. E3 56
Maquoketa, Ia., U.S. B7 92
Maquoketa, stm., Ia., U.S. B6 92
Maquoketa, North Fork, stm., Ia., U.S. B7 92
Mar, Serra do, clf, Braz. A7 56
Marabá, Braz. E9 54
Maracá, Ilha de, i., Braz. C8 54
Maracaibo, Ven. B7 58
Maracaibo, Lago de, l., Ven. C7 58
Maracay, Ven. B9 58
Marādah, Libya C9 42
Maradi, Niger F7 42
Marāgheh, Iran J7 18
Maragogipe, Braz. B9 57
Marahuaca, Cerro, mtn., Ven. F10 58
Marais des Cygnes, stm., U.S. D8 93
Marajó, Baía de, b., Braz. D9 54
Marajó, Ilha de, i., Braz. D9 54
Maralal, Kenya A7 44
Marambaia, Ilha da, i., Braz. G7 57
Marana, Az., U.S. E4 80
Marang, Malay. L7 34
Marañón, stm., Peru D3 54
Marans, Fr. F5 10
Marapanim, Braz. D9 54
Marathon, Fl., U.S. H5 86
Marathon, Wi., U.S. D4 126
Marathon, co., Wi., U.S. D4 126
Marawī, Sudan E1 46
Marble, Mn., U.S. C5 100
Marble, N.C., U.S. f9 110
Marble Bar, Austl. D3 50
Marble Canyon, val., Az., U.S. A4 80
Marble Falls, Tx., U.S. D3 120
Marblehead, Ma., U.S. B6 98
Marble Hill, Mo., U.S. D8 102
Marbleton, Wy., U.S. D2 127
Marburg an der Lahn, Ger. E8 8
Marbury, Md., U.S. C3 97
Marcaria, Italy D5 14
Marceline, Mo., U.S. B5 102
Marcellus, Mi., U.S. F5 99
March (Morava), stm., Eur. G16 8
Marcha, U.S.S.R. E18 20
Marcha, stm., U.S.S.R. E17 20
March Air Force Base, mil., Ca., U.S. F5 82
Marche-en-Famenne, Bel. E5 8
Marchena, Spain H6 12
Mar Chiquita, Laguna, l., Arg. C4 56
Marco, Fl., U.S. G5 86
Marcus, Ia., U.S. B2 92
Marcus Baker, Mount, mtn., Ak., U.S. g18 79
Marcus Hook, Pa., U.S. G11 115
Marcy, Mount, mtn., N.Y., U.S. A7 109
Mardān, Pak. C5 38
Mar del Plata, Arg. D5 56
Mardin, Tur. H16 4

Name | Map Ref | Page

Mareeba, Austl. C9 50
Mareg, Som. H4 46
Marengo, Il., U.S. A5 90
Marengo, In., U.S. H5 91
Marengo, Ia., U.S. C5 92
Marengo, co., Al., U.S. C2 78
Marennes, Fr. G5 10
Marfa, Tx., U.S. o12 120
Margaret, Al., U.S. B3 78
Margarita, Isla de, i., Ven. B10 58
Margate, Fl., U.S. F6 86
Margate City, N.J., U.S. E3 107
Margherita Peak, mtn., Afr. A5 44
Marghī, Afg. C2 38
Margrethe, Lake, l., Mi., U.S. D6 99
María Cleofas, Isla, i., Mex. G6 62
María Madre, Isla, i., Mex. G6 62
María Magdalena, Isla, i., Mex. G6 62
Marian, Lake, l., Fl., U.S. E5 86
Marianao, Cuba C6 64
Marianna, Ar., U.S. C5 81
Marianna, Fl., U.S. B1 86
Marias, stm., Mt., U.S. B4 103
Marias, Islas, is., Mex. G6 62
Marias Pass, Mt., U.S. B3 103
Mariato, Punta, c., Pan. K7 64
Mariazell, Aus. H15 8
Maribor, Yugo. C10 14
Marica (Évros) (Meriç), stm., Eur. G9 16
Maricopa, Az., U.S. E3 80
Maricopa, Ca., U.S. E4 82
Maricopa, co., Az., U.S. D3 80
Maricopa Mountains, mts., Az., U.S. m7 80
Marie-Galante, i., Guad. G17 64
Mariehamn, Fin. F12 6
Mariemont, Oh., U.S. o13 112
Mariental, Nmb. F3 44
Marienville, Pa., U.S. D3 115
Maries, co., Mo., U.S. C6 102
Mariestad, Swe. G9 6
Marietta, Ga., U.S. C2 87
Marietta, Oh., U.S. C4 112
Marietta, Ok., U.S. D4 113
Marietta, S.C., U.S. A2 117
Marieville, Que., Can. D4 74
Marília, Braz. G4 57
Marimba, Ang. C3 44
Marín, Spain C3 12
Marin, co., Ca., U.S. C2 82
Marinduque Island, i., Phil. C7 32
Marine, Il., U.S. E4 90
Marine City, Mi., U.S. F8 99
Marine On St. Croix, Mn., U.S. E6 100
Marinette, Wi., U.S. C6 126
Marinette, co., Wi., U.S. C5 126
Maringá, Braz. G3 57
Maringouin, La., U.S. D4 95
Marinha Grande, Port. F3 12
Marion, Al., U.S. C2 78
Marion, Ar., U.S. B5 81
Marion, Il., U.S. F5 90
Marion, In., U.S. C6 91
Marion, Ia., U.S. B6 92
Marion, Ks., U.S. D6 93
Marion, Ky., U.S. e9 94
Marion, La., U.S. B3 95
Marion, Mi., U.S. D5 99
Marion, Ms., U.S. C5 101
Marion, N.C., U.S. B1 110
Marion, Oh., U.S. B2 112
Marion, Pa., U.S. G6 115
Marion, S.C., U.S. C9 117
Marion, S.D., U.S. D8 118
Marion, Va., U.S. f10 123
Marion, Wi., U.S. D5 126
Marion, co., Al., U.S. A2 78
Marion, co., Ar., U.S. A3 81
Marion, co., Fl., U.S. C4 86
Marion, co., Ga., U.S. D2 87
Marion, co., Il., U.S. E4 90
Marion, co., In., U.S. E5 91
Marion, co., Ia., U.S. C4 92
Marion, co., Ks., U.S. D6 93
Marion, co., Ky., U.S. C4 94
Marion, co., Ms., U.S. D4 101
Marion, co., Mo., U.S. B6 102
Marion, co., Oh., U.S. B2 112
Marion, co., Or., U.S. C4 114
Marion, co., S.C., U.S. C9 117
Marion, co., Tn., U.S. D8 119
Marion, co., Tx., U.S. C5 120
Marion, co., W.V., U.S. B4 125
Marion, Lake, res., S.C., U.S. E7 117
Marion Station, Md., U.S. D6 97
Marionville, Mo., U.S. D4 102
Maripa, Ven. D10 58
Mariposa, co., Ca., U.S. D3 82
Mariscal Estigarribia, Para. A4 56
Marissa, Il., U.S. E4 90
Maritime Alps, mts., Eur. H14 10
Mariupol' (Ždanov), U.S.S.R. H5 18
Marka, Som. H3 46
Markaryd, Swe. H9 6
Markdale, Ont., Can. C4 73
Marked Tree, Ar., U.S. B5 81
Markesan, Wi., U.S. E5 126
Markham, Ont., Can. D5 73
Markham, Il., U.S. k9 90
Markham, Tx., U.S. E4 120
Markham, Mount, mtn., Ant. A29 47
Markland Lock and Dam, U.S. B5 94
Markle, In., U.S. C7 91
Markovo, U.S.S.R. E28 20
Marks, Ms., U.S. A3 101
Marksville, La., U.S. C3 95
Marktredwitz, Ger. E12 8
Mark Twain Lake, res., Mo., U.S. B6 102
Marlboro, N.Y., U.S. D6 109
Marlboro, Va., U.S. n17 123
Marlboro, co., S.C., U.S. B8 117
Marlborough, Ct., U.S. C6 84
Marlborough, Ma., U.S. B4 98
Marlborough, N.H., U.S. E2 106
Marle, Fr. C10 10
Marlette, Mi., U.S. E7 99
Marley, Md., U.S. B4 97
Marlin, Tx., U.S. D4 120
Marlinton, W.V., U.S. C4 125
Marlow, Ok., U.S. C4 113
Marlowe, W.V., U.S. B7 125
Marlton, N.J., U.S. D3 107
Marmaduke, Ar., U.S. A5 81
Marmande, Fr. H7 10
Marmara Adası, i., Tur. I11 16
Marmara Denizi (Sea of Marmara), Tur. I12 16
Marmaris, Tur. M12 16
Marmet, W.V., U.S. C3 125
Marmora, Ont., Can. C7 73
Marne, stm., Fr. C10 10
Maroa, Il., U.S. C5 90
Maroa, Ven. F9 58
Maroantsetra, Madag. E9 44
Maromokotro, mtn., Madag. D9 44
Marondera, Zimb. E6 44
Maros (Mureş), stm., Eur. C4 16
Maroua, Cam. F8 42
Marovoay, Madag. E9 44
Marquesas Keys, is., Fl., U.S. H4 86
Marquette, Mi., U.S. B3 99
Marquette, co., Mi., U.S. B3 99
Marquette, co., Wi., U.S. E4 126
Marquette Heights, Il., U.S. C4 90
Marquise, Fr. B8 10
Marrah, Jabal, mtn., Sudan F10 42
Marrakech, Mor. B4 42
Marrero, La., U.S. E5 95
Mars, Pa., U.S. E1 115
Marsabit, Kenya H2 46
Marsala, Italy L7 14
Marsā Maṭrūḥ, Egypt B11 42
Marseille, Fr. J12 10
Marseille-en-Beauvaisis, Fr. C8 10
Marseilles, Il., U.S. B5 90
Marshall, Sask., Can. D1 75
Marshall, Ar., U.S. B3 81
Marshall, Il., U.S. D6 90
Marshall, Mi., U.S. F6 99
Marshall, Mn., U.S. F3 100
Marshall, Mo., U.S. B4 102
Marshall, N.C., U.S. f10 110
Marshall, Tx., U.S. C5 120
Marshall, Va., U.S. B5 123
Marshall, Wi., U.S. E4 126
Marshall, co., Al., U.S. A3 78
Marshall, co., Il., U.S. B4 90
Marshall, co., In., U.S. B5 91
Marshall, co., Ia., U.S. C4 92
Marshall, co., Ks., U.S. C7 93
Marshall, co., Ky., U.S. f9 94
Marshall, co., Mn., U.S. B2 100
Marshall, co., Ms., U.S. A4 101
Marshall, co., Ok., U.S. C5 113
Marshall, co., S.D., U.S. B8 118
Marshall, co., Tn., U.S. B5 119
Marshall, co., W.V., U.S. B4 125
Marshallton, De., U.S. B3 85
Marshalltown, Ia., U.S. B5 92
Marshallville, Ga., U.S. D3 87
Marshes Siding, Ky., U.S. D5 94
Marshfield, Ma., U.S. B6 98
Marshfield, Mo., U.S. D5 102
Marshfield, Wi., U.S. D3 126
Marshfield Hills, Ma., U.S. B6 98
Marsh Fork, stm., W.V., U.S. n13 125
Marsh Harbour, Bah. A9 64
Mars Hill, Me., U.S. B5 96
Mars Hill, N.C., U.S. f10 110
Marsh Island, i., La., U.S. E4 95
Marsh Lake, res., Mn., U.S. E2 100
Marsh Peak, mtn., Ut., U.S. C6 121
Marshville, N.C., U.S. C2 110
Marsing, Id., U.S. F2 89
Märsta, Swe. G11 6
Marston, Mo., U.S. E8 102
Mart, Tx., U.S. D4 120
Martaban, Gulf of, b., Burma F4 34
Marthasville, Mo., U.S. C6 102
Martha's Vineyard, i., Ma., U.S. D6 98
Martigny, Switz. F14 10
Martigues, Fr. I12 10
Martin, Czech. F18 8
Martin, Ky., U.S. C7 94
Martin, S.D., U.S. D4 118
Martin, Tn., U.S. A3 119
Martin, co., Fl., U.S. E6 86
Martin, co., In., U.S. G4 91
Martin, co., Ky., U.S. C7 94
Martin, co., Mn., U.S. G4 100
Martin, co., N.C., U.S. B5 110
Martin, co., Tx., U.S. C2 120
Martina Franca, Italy I12 14
Martinez, Ca., U.S. C2 82
Martinez, Ga., U.S. C4 87
Martínez de la Torre, Mex. G11 62
Martinique, dep., N.A. G17 64
Martin Lake, res., Al., U.S. C4 78
Martin Point, c., Ak., U.S. A11 79
Martinsberg, Aus. G15 8
Martinsburg, Pa., U.S. F5 115
Martinsburg, W.V., U.S. B7 125
Martins Ferry, Oh., U.S. B5 112
Martinsville, Il., U.S. D6 90
Martinsville, In., U.S. F5 91
Martinsville, Va., U.S. D3 123
Martos, Spain H8 12
Martre, Lac la, l., N.W. Ter., Can. D9 66
Marttí, Fin. C17 6
Marugame, Japan H6 30
Ma'rūt, Afg. E2 38
Marvejols, Fr. H10 10
Marvell, Ar., U.S. C5 81
Marvine, Mount, mtn., Ut., U.S. E4 121
Mary, U.S.S.R. J10 18
Mary, Lake, l., Mn., U.S. E3 100
Mary, Lake, l., Ms., U.S. D2 101
Maryborough, Austl. E10 50
Maryland, state, U.S. B4 97
Maryland City, Md., U.S. B4 97
Maryland Heights, Mo., U.S. f13 102
Maryland Point, c., Md., U.S. D3 97
Maryport, Eng., U.K. G9 7
Marys, stm., Nv., U.S. B6 105
Marys Peak, mtn., Or., U.S. C3 114
Marystown, Newf., Can. E4 72
Marysville, Ca., U.S. C3 82
Marysville, Ks., U.S. C7 93
Marysville, Mi., U.S. F8 99
Marysville, Oh., U.S. B2 112
Marysville, Pa., U.S. F8 115
Marysville, Wa., U.S. A3 124
Maryville, Mo., U.S. A3 102
Maryville, Tn., U.S. D10 119
Marzūq, Libya C8 42
Marzūq, Idehan, reg., Libya C8 42
Masai Steppe, plat., Tan. B7 44
Masaka, Ug. B6 44
Masan, S. Kor. D12 26
Masasi, Tan. D7 44
Masaya, Nic. I4 64
Masbate Island, i., Phil. C7 32
Mascarene Islands, is., Afr. F11 44
Mascoma, stm., N.H., U.S. C2 106
Mascoma Lake, l., N.H., U.S. C2 106
Mascot, Tn., U.S. C10 119
Mascota, Mex. G7 62
Mascouche, Que., Can. D4 74
Mascoutah, Il., U.S. E4 90
Maseru, Leso. G5 44
Mashābih, i., Sau. Ar. C2 46
Mashapaug Pond, l., Ct., U.S. A7 84
Masherbrum, mtn., Pak. C7 38
Mashhad, Iran J9 18
Masi Manimba, Zaire B3 44
Masindi, Ug. H12 42
Masjed Soleymān, Iran B4 46
Mask, Lough, l., Ire. H3 7
Maskanah, Syria A6 40
Maskinongé, Que., Can. C4 74
Mason, Mi., U.S. F6 99
Mason, Nv., U.S. E2 105
Mason, Oh., U.S. C1 112
Mason, Tx., U.S. D3 120
Mason, W.V., U.S. B2 125
Mason, co., Il., U.S. C4 90
Mason, co., Ky., U.S. B6 94
Mason, co., Mi., U.S. D4 99
Mason, co., Tx., U.S. D3 120
Mason, co., Wa., U.S. B2 124
Mason, co., W.V., U.S. C3 125
Mason City, Il., U.S. C4 90
Mason City, Ia., U.S. A4 92
Masontown, Pa., U.S. G2 115
Masontown, W.V., U.S. B5 125
Masqaṭ (Muscat), Oman D6 46
Massa, Italy E5 14
Massabesic Lake, l., N.H., U.S. E4 106
Massac, co., Il., U.S. F5 90
Massachusetts, state, U.S. B4 98
Massachusetts Bay, b., Ma., U.S. B6 98
Massacre Lake, l., Nv., U.S. B2 105
Massafra, Italy I12 14
Massa Marittima, Italy F5 14
Massangena, Moz. F6 44
Massapoag Lake, l., Ma., U.S. h11 98
Massarosa, Italy F5 14
Massasecum, Lake, l., N.H., U.S. D3 106
Massena, N.Y., U.S. f10 109
Massenya, Chad F9 42
Masset, B.C., Can. C1 69
Massey, Ont., Can. A2 73
Massif Central see Central, Massif, mts., Fr. G10 10
Massillon, Oh., U.S. B4 112
Massive, Mount, mtn., Co., U.S. B4 83
Masterton, N.Z. D5 52
Mastic Beach, N.Y., U.S. n16 109
Mastung, Pak. F2 38
Masuda, Japan H4 30
Masury, Oh., U.S. A5 112
Matadi, Zaire C2 44
Matagalpa, Nic. H5 64
Matagorda, co., Tx., U.S. E5 120
Matagorda Bay, b., Tx., U.S. E4 120
Matagorda Island, i., Tx., U.S. E4 120
Matagorda Peninsula, pen., Tx., U.S. E5 120
Matale, Sri L. I6 37
Matamoras, Pa., U.S. D12 115
Matamoros, Mex. E11 62
Matamoros de la Laguna, Mex. E8 62
Matandu, stm., Tan. C7 44
Matane, Que., Can. k13 74
Matanuska, stm., Ak., U.S. g18 79
Matanzas, Cuba C7 64
Matanzas Inlet, b., Fl., U.S. C5 86
Matara, Sri L. J6 37
Mataró, Spain D14 12
Matatiele, S. Afr. H5 44
Matawan, N.J., U.S. C4 107
Matehuala, Mex. F9 62
Mateira, Braz. E3 57
Matelica, Italy F7 14
Matera, Italy I11 14
Mateur, Tun. L4 14
Matewan, W.V., U.S. D2 125
Mather, Pa., U.S. G1 115
Mather Air Force Base, mil., Ca., U.S. C3 82
Mather Peaks, mts., Wy., U.S. B5 127
Mathews, La., U.S. E5 95
Mathews, Va., U.S. C6 123
Mathews, co., Va., U.S. C6 123
Mathews, Lake, l., Ca., U.S. n14 82
Mathis, Tx., U.S. E4 120
Mathiston, Ms., U.S. B4 101
Mathura, India G7 38
Matías Romero, Mex. I12 62
Matinicus Island, i., Me., U.S. E3 96
Mātli, Pak. H3 38
Mato, Cerro, mtn., Ven. D10 58
Matoaca, Va., U.S. n18 123
Mato Grosso, Braz. F7 54
Mato Grosso, Planalto do, plat., Braz. G7 54
Matosinhos, Port. D3 12
Matou, Tai. L9 28
Maṭraḥ, Oman D6 46
Matsqui, B.C., Can. f13 69
Matsudo, Japan G12 30
Matsue, Japan G6 30
Matsumae, Japan r18 30a
Matsumoto, Japan F10 30
Matsusaka, Japan H9 30
Matsu Tao, i., Tai. I8 28
Matsuyama, Japan I5 30
Mattagami, stm., Ont., Can. F16 66
Mattamiscontis Lake, l., Me., U.S. C4 96
Mattamuskeet, Lake, l., N.C., U.S. B6 110
Mattāncheri, India H4 37
Mattapoisett, Ma., U.S. C6 98
Mattaponi, stm., Va., U.S. C5 123
Mattawa, Ont., Can. A6 73
Mattawamkeag, Me., U.S. C4 96
Mattawamkeag, stm., Me., U.S. C4 96
Mattawamkeag Lake, l., Me., U.S. C4 96
Matterhorn, mtn., Eur. G14 10
Matterhorn, mtn., Nv., U.S. B6 105
Matteson, Il., U.S. k9 90
Matthews, Mo., U.S. E8 102
Matthews, N.C., U.S. B2 110
Matthews Ridge, Guy. D12 58
Matthew Town, Bah. D11 64
Mattighofen, Aus. G13 8
Mattituck, N.Y., U.S. n16 109
Mattoon, Il., U.S. D5 90
Mattoon, Lake, res., Il., U.S. D5 90
Mattydale, N.Y., U.S. B4 109
Matunuck, R.I., U.S. G3 116
Maturín, Ven. C11 58
Maúa, Moz. D7 44
Maubeuge, Fr. B10 10
Maud, Ok., U.S. B5 113
Maugansville, Md., U.S. A2 97
Maui, co., Hi., U.S. B5 88
Maui, i., Hi., U.S. C6 88
Mauldin, S.C., U.S. B3 117
Mauléon-Licharre, Fr. I6 10
Maulvi Bāzār, Bngl. H14 38
Maumee, Oh., U.S. A2 112
Maumee, stm., U.S. A2 112
Maumee Bay, b., U.S. G7 99
Maumelle, Lake, res., Ar., U.S. C3 81
Maun, Bots. E4 44
Mauna Kea, vol., Hi., U.S. D6 88
Maunaloa, Hi., U.S. B4 88
Mauna Loa, vol., Hi., U.S. D6 88
Maunalua Bay, b., Hi., U.S. g10 88
Maunath Bhanjan, India H10 38
Maunawili, Hi., U.S. g10 88
Mau Rānīpur, India H8 38
Maurepas, Lake, l., La., U.S. D5 95
Mauriac, Fr. G9 10
Maurice, Ia., U.S. B1 92
Maurice, stm., N.J., U.S. E2 107
Mauritania, ctry., Afr. D3 42
Mauritius, ctry., Afr. F11 44
Maurs, Fr. H9 10
Maury, co., Tn., U.S. B4 119
Maury City, Tn., U.S. B2 119
Maury Island, i., Wa., U.S. f11 124
Mauston, Wi., U.S. E3 126
Mauterndorf, Aus. H13 8
Mauthausen, Aus. G14 8
Maverick, co., Tx., U.S. E2 120
Maw-Daung Pass, Asia I5 34
Mawlaik, Burma C3 34
Mawlamyine (Moulmein), Burma F4 34
Maw Taung, mtn., Asia I5 34
Maxinkuckee, Lake, l., In., U.S. B5 91
Max Meadows, Va., U.S. D2 123
Maxton, N.C., U.S. C3 110
Maxville, Ont., Can. B10 73
Maxwell, Ia., U.S. C4 92
Maxwell Acres, W.V., U.S. g8 125
Maxwell Air Force Base, mil., Al., U.S. C3 78
Mayaguana, i., Bah. C11 64
Mayaguana Passage, strt., Bah. C11 64
Mayagüez, P.R. E14 64
Maya Mountains, mts., N.A. F3 64
Maybole, Scot., U.K. F8 7
Mayen, Ger. E7 8
Mayenne, Fr. D6 10
Mayer, Az., U.S. C3 80
Mayerthorpe, Alta., Can. C3 68
Mayes, co., Ok., U.S. A6 113
Mayesville, S.C., U.S. D7 117
Mayfield, Ky., U.S. f9 94
Mayfield, Pa., U.S. C10 115
Mayfield Heights, Oh., U.S. A4 112
Mayfield Lake, res., Wa., U.S. C3 124
Mayflower, Ar., U.S. C3 81
Mayking, Ky., U.S. C7 94
Maykop see Majkop, U.S.S.R. I6 18
Maymyo, Burma C4 34
Maynard, Ma., U.S. B5 98
Maynardville, Tn., U.S. C10 119
Mayne, B.C., Can. g12 69
Mayo, Yukon, Can. D5 66
Mayo, Md., U.S. C4 97
Mayo, S.C., U.S. A4 117
Mayodan, N.C., U.S. A3 110
Mayotte, ter., Afr. D9 44
Mayotte, i., May. D9 44
May Park, Or., U.S. B8 114
Mayport Naval Station, mil., Fl., U.S. B5 86
Maysville, Ga., U.S. B3 87
Maysville, Ky., U.S. B6 94
Maysville, Mo., U.S. B3 102
Maysville, N.C., U.S. C5 110
Maysville, Ok., U.S. C4 113
Mayumba, Gabon B2 44
Māyūram, India G5 37
Mayville, Mi., U.S. E7 99
Mayville, N.Y., U.S. C1 109
Mayville, N.D., U.S. B8 111
Mayville, Wi., U.S. E5 126
Maywood, Il., U.S. k9 90
Maywood, N.J., U.S. h8 107
Maywood Park, Or., U.S. B4 114
Mazabuka, Zam. E5 44
Mazamet, Fr. I9 10
Mazara del Vallo, Italy L7 14
Mazār-e Sharīf, Afg. B2 38
Mazaruni, stm., Guy. E13 58
Mazatenango, Guat. G2 64
Mazatlán, Mex. F6 62
Mazatzal Mountains, mts., Az., U.S. C4 80
Mazatzal Peak, mtn., Az., U.S. C4 80
Mazeppa, Mn., U.S. F6 100
Mazoe, stm., Afr. E6 44
Mazomanie, Wi., U.S. E4 126
Mazon, Il., U.S. B5 90
Mbabane, Swaz. G6 44
Mbaïki, Cen. Afr. Rep. H9 42
Mbala, Zam. C6 44
Mbale, Ug. A6 44
Mbandaka (Coquilhatville), Zaire A3 44
Mbanza-Ngungu, Zaire C2 44
M'banz Congo, Ang. C2 44
Mbeya, Tan. C6 44
Mbomou (Bomu), stm., Afr. H10 42
Mbout, Maur. E3 42
Mbuji-Mayi (Bakwanga), Zaire C4 44
McAdam, N.B., Can. D2 71
McAdoo, Pa., U.S. E9 115
McAfee Peak, mtn., Nv., U.S. B6 105
McAlester, Ok., U.S. C6 113
McAlester, Lake, res., Ok., U.S. B6 113
McAllen, Tx., U.S. F3 120
McAlmont, Ar., U.S. h10 81
McAlpine, Md., U.S. B4 97
McAlpine Lock and Dam, U.S. H6 91
McArthur, Oh., U.S. C3 112
McBee, S.C., U.S. C7 117
McCall, Id., U.S. E2 89
McCalla, Al., U.S. g6 78
McCamey, Tx., U.S. D1 120
McCammon, Id., U.S. G6 89
McCandless, Pa., U.S. h13 115
McCartney Mountain, mtn., Mt., U.S. E4 103
McCaysville, Ga., U.S. B2 87
McChord Air Force Base, mil., Wa., U.S. f11 124
McClain, co., Ok., U.S. C4 113
McCleary, Wa., U.S. B2 124
McClellan Air Force Base, mil., Ca., U.S. C3 82
McClintock, Mount, mtn., Ant. A28 47
McCloud, Ca., U.S. B2 82
McClure, Pa., U.S. E7 115
McColl, S.C., U.S. B8 117
McComas, W.V., U.S. D3 125
McComb, Ms., U.S. D3 101
McComb, Oh., U.S. A2 112
McCone, co., Mt., U.S. C11 103
McConnell Air Force Base, mil., Ks., U.S. g12 93
McConnellsburg, Pa., U.S. G6 115
McConnelsville, Oh., U.S. C4 112
McCook, Ne., U.S. D5 104
McCook, co., S.D., U.S. D8 118
McCordsville, In., U.S. E6 91
McCormick, S.C., U.S. D3 117
McCormick, co., S.C., U.S. D3 117
McCracken, co., Ky., U.S. e9 94
McCreary, Man., Can. D2 70
McCreary, co., Ky., U.S. D5 94
McCrory, Ar., U.S. B4 81
McCulloch, co., Tx., U.S. D3 120
McCullough Mountain, mtn., Nv., U.S. H6 105
McCurtain, co., Ok., U.S. C7 113
McDermitt, Nv., U.S. B4 105
McDonald, co., Mo., U.S. E3 102
McDonough, Ga., U.S. C2 87
McDonough, co., Il., U.S. C3 90
McDougall, Mount, mtn., Wy., U.S. D2 127
McDowell, Ky., U.S. C7 94
McDowell, co., N.C., U.S. f10 110
McDowell, co., W.V., U.S. D3 125
McDowell Mountains, mts., Az., U.S. k9 80
McDowell Peak, mtn., Az., U.S. k9 80
McDuffie, co., Ga., U.S. C4 87
McElroy Creek, stm., W.V., U.S. k9 125
Mcensk, U.S.S.R. H19 22
McEwen, Tn., U.S. A4 119
McFarland, Ca., U.S. E4 82
McFarland, Wi., U.S. E4 126
McGehee, Ar., U.S. D4 81
McGill, Nv., U.S. D7 105
McGrath, Ak., U.S. C8 79
McGregor, Ia., U.S. A6 92
McGregor, Tx., U.S. D4 120
McGregor, stm., B.C., Can. B7 69
McGregor Lake, l., Alta., Can. D4 68
McGuire, Mount, mtn., Id., U.S. D4 89
McGuire Air Force Base, mil., N.J., U.S. C3 107
McHenry, Il., U.S. A5 90
McHenry, Md., U.S. k12 97
McHenry, co., Il., U.S. A5 90
McHenry, co., N.D., U.S. A5 111
McIntosh, Mn., U.S. C3 100
McIntosh, co., Ga., U.S. E5 87
McIntosh, co., N.D., U.S. C6 111
McIntosh, co., Ok., U.S. B6 113
McKean, co., Pa., U.S. C4 115
McKee, Ky., U.S. C6 94
McKeesport, Pa., U.S. F2 115
McKees Rocks, Pa., U.S. F1 115
McKenzie, Tn., U.S. A3 119
McKenzie, co., N.D., U.S. B2 111
McKenzie, stm., Or., U.S. C4 114
McKinley, co., N.M., U.S. B1 108
McKinley, Mount, mtn., Ak., U.S. C9 79
McKinleyville, Ca., U.S. B1 82
McKinney, Tx., U.S. C4 120
McKinney, Lake, l., Ks., U.S. E2 93
McKittrick Summit, mtn., Ca., U.S. E4 82
McLaughlin, S.D., U.S. B5 118
McLean, Il., U.S. C4 90
McLean, Va., U.S. g12 123

Name	Map Ref	Page
McLean, co., Il., U.S.	C4	90
McLean, co., Ky., U.S.	C2	94
McLean, co., N.D., U.S.	B4	111
McLeansboro, Il., U.S.	E5	90
McLennan, Alta., Can.	B2	68
McLennan, co., Tx., U.S.	D4	120
McLeod, co., Mn., U.S.	F4	100
McLeod, Lake, l., Austl.	D2	50
M'Clintock Channel, strt., N.W. Ter., Can.	B12	66
McLoud, Ok., U.S.	B4	113
McLoughlin, Mount, mtn., Or., U.S.	D4	114
McLouth, Ks., U.S.	C8	93
McMechen, W.V., U.S.	B4	125
McMillan, Lake, res., N.M., U.S.	E5	108
McMinn, co., Tn., U.S.	D9	119
McMinnville, Or., U.S.	B3	114
McMinnville, Tn., U.S.	D8	119
McMullen, co., Tx., U.S.	E3	120
McNairy, co., Tn., U.S.	B3	119
McNary, Az., U.S.	C6	80
McNary Dam, U.S.	B7	114
McNeil, Ar., U.S.	D2	81
McNeil, Mount, mtn., B.C., Can.	B2	69
McNeil Island, i., Wa., U.S.	f10	124
McNeill, Ms., U.S.	E4	101
McPherson, Ks., U.S.	D6	93
McPherson, co., Ks., U.S.	D6	93
McPherson, co., Ne., U.S.	C4	104
McPherson, co., S.D., U.S.	B6	118
McQueeney, Tx., U.S.	h7	120
McRae, Ar., U.S.	B4	81
McRae, Ga., U.S.	D4	87
McRoberts, Ky., U.S.	C7	94
McSherrystown, Pa., U.S.	G7	115
Mead, Wa., U.S.	B8	124
Mead, Lake, res., U.S.	A1	80
Meade, Ks., U.S.	E3	93
Meade, co., Ks., U.S.	E3	93
Meade, co., Ky., U.S.	C3	94
Meade, co., S.D., U.S.	C3	118
Meade, stm., Ak., U.S.	B8	79
Meaden Peak, mtn., Co., U.S.	A3	83
Meade Peak, mtn., Id., U.S.	G7	89
Meadow, stm., W.V., U.S.	C4	125
Meadow Creek, stm., W.V., U.S.	n14	125
Meadow Lands, Pa., U.S.	F1	115
Meadow Valley Wash, val., Nv., U.S.	F7	105
Meadowview, Va., U.S.	f10	123
Meadville, Pa., U.S.	C1	115
Meaford, Ont., Can.	C4	73
Meagher, co., Mt., U.S.	D6	103
Mealhada, Port.	E3	12
Meander Creek Reservoir, res., Oh., U.S.	A5	112
Meath, hist. reg., Ire.	H5	7
Meaux, Fr.	D9	10
Mebane, N.C., U.S.	A3	110
Mecca, Ca., U.S.	F5	82
Mecca see Makkah, Sau. Ar.	D2	46
Mechanic Falls, Me., U.S.	D2	96
Mechanicsburg, Oh., U.S.	B2	112
Mechanicsburg, Pa., U.S.	F7	115
Mechanicsville, Ia., U.S.	C6	92
Mechanicsville, Md., U.S.	D4	97
Mechanicsville, Va., U.S.	C5	123
Mechanicville, N.Y., U.S.	C7	109
Mechant, Lake, l., La., U.S.	E4	95
Mechelen, Bel.	D4	8
Mecklenburg, co., N.C., U.S.	B2	110
Mecklenburg, co., Va., U.S.	D4	123
Mecklenburg, hist. reg., Ger.	B12	8
Mecklenburger Bucht, b., Ger.	A11	8
Mecosta, co., Mi., U.S.	E5	99
Medan, Indon.	E2	32
Medanosa, Punta, c., Arg.	F3	56
Medaryville, In., U.S.	B4	91
Meddybumps Lake, l., Me., U.S.	C5	96
Medeiros Neto, Braz.	D8	57
Medellín, Col.	D5	58
Médenine, Tun.	B8	42
Medfield, Ma., U.S.	h10	98
Medford, Ma., U.S.	B5	98
Medford, Mn., U.S.	F5	100
Medford, Ok., U.S.	A4	113
Medford, Or., U.S.	E4	114
Medford, Wi., U.S.	C3	126
Medford Lakes, N.J., U.S.	D3	107
Medgidia, Rom.	E12	16
Media, Pa., U.S.	G11	115
Mediapolis, Ia., U.S.	C6	92
Mediaş, Rom.	C8	16
Medical Lake, Wa., U.S.	B8	124
Medicine Bow, Wy., U.S.	E6	127
Medicine Bow, stm., Wy., U.S.	E6	127
Medicine Bow Mountains, mts., U.S.	E6	127
Medicine Bow Peak, mtn., Wy., U.S.	E6	127
Medicine Hat, Alta., Can.	D5	68
Medicine Lodge, Ks., U.S.	E5	93
Medicine Lodge, stm., U.S.	E4	93
Medina, N.Y., U.S.	B2	109
Medina, Oh., U.S.	A4	112
Medina, Tn., U.S.	B3	119
Medina, Wa., U.S.	e11	124
Medina, co., Oh., U.S.	A4	112
Medina, co., Tx., U.S.	E3	120
Medina, stm., Tx., U.S.	k7	120
Medina see Al-Madīnah, Sau. Ar.	D2	46
Medinaceli, Spain	D9	12
Medina del Campo, Spain	D7	12
Medina de Ríoseco, Spain	D6	12
Mediterranean Sea	D14	2
Medjez el Bab, Tun.	M4	14
Médoc, reg., Fr.	G5	10
Medora, In., U.S.	G5	91
Médouneu, Gabon	A2	44
Medway, Me., U.S.	C4	96
Medway, Ma., U.S.	B5	98
Medway, stm., N.S., Can.	E5	71
Meekatharra, Austl.	E3	50
Meeker, Co., U.S.	A3	83
Meeker, Ok., U.S.	B5	113
Meeker, co., Mn., U.S.	E4	100
Meelpaeg Lake, res., Newf., Can.	D3	72
Meerut, India	F7	38
Meeteetse, Wy., U.S.	B4	127
Mega, Eth.	H2	46
Mégantic, Lac, l., Que., Can.	D7	74
Mégantic, Mont, mtn., Que., Can.	D6	74
Mégara, Grc.	K7	16
Meggett, S.C., U.S.	F7	117
Meghalaya, state, India	H14	38
Meherrin, stm., U.S.	A4	110
Mehlville, Mo., U.S.	f13	102
Mehsāna, India	I5	38
Mehtar Lām, Afg.	C4	38
Mehun-sur-Yèvre, Fr.	E9	10
Meigs, Ga., U.S.	E2	87
Meigs, co., Oh., U.S.	C3	112
Meigs, co., Tn., U.S.	D9	119
Meiktila, Burma	D3	34
Meiningen, Ger.	E10	8
Meissen, Ger.	D13	8
Meixian, China	K5	28
Mekambo, Gabon	A2	44
Mekele, Eth.	F2	46
Meknès, Mor.	B4	42
Mekong, stm., Asia	H8	34
Melaka, Malay.	M7	34
Melanesia, is., Oc.	G23	2
Melbourne, Austl.	G8	50
Melbourne, Ar., U.S.	A4	81
Melbourne, Fl., U.S.	D6	86
Melbourne, Ia., U.S.	C4	92
Melbourne, Ky., U.S.	h14	94
Melbourne Beach, Fl., U.S.	D6	86
Melcher, Ia., U.S.	C4	92
Meldorf, Ger.	A9	8
Mélèzes, Rivière aux, stm., Que., Can.	g12	74
Melfi, Chad	F9	42
Melfi, Italy	I10	14
Melgaço, Port.	C3	12
Melhus, Nor.	E8	6
Melilla, Sp. N. Afr.	A5	42
Melita, Man., Can.	E1	70
Melito di Porto Salvo, Italy	L10	14
Melitopol', U.S.S.R.	H5	18
Melk, Aus.	G15	8
Mellansel, Swe.	E12	6
Melle, Fr.	F6	10
Mellen, Wi., U.S.	B3	126
Mellerud, Swe.	G9	6
Mellette, co., S.D., U.S.	D5	118
Mellish Reef, atoll, Austl.	C11	50
Melo, Ur.	C6	56
Melocheville, Que., Can.	q19	74
Melrhir, Chott, l., Alg.	B7	42
Melrose, Fl., U.S.	C4	86
Melrose, Ma., U.S.	B5	98
Melrose, Mn., U.S.	E4	100
Melrose, N.M., U.S.	C6	108
Melrose Park, Fl., U.S.	r13	86
Meltaus, Fin.	C15	6
Melton Hill Lake, res., Tn., U.S.	D9	119
Melton Mowbray, Eng., U.K.	I12	7
Melun, Fr.	D9	10
Melvern Lake, res., Ks., U.S.	D8	93
Melville, La., U.S.	D4	95
Melville, Lake, l., Newf., Can.	B2	72
Melville Hills, hills, N.W. Ter., Can.	C8	66
Melville Island, i., Austl.	B6	50
Melville Island, i., N.W. Ter., Can.	A10	66
Melville Peninsula, pen., N.W. Ter., Can.	C16	66
Melvin, Ky., U.S.	C7	94
Memmingen, Ger.	H10	8
Memphis, Fl., U.S.	p10	86
Memphis, Mi., U.S.	F8	99
Memphis, Mo., U.S.	A5	102
Memphis, Tn., U.S.	B1	119
Memphis, Tx., U.S.	B2	120
Memphis Naval Air Station, mil., Tn., U.S.	B2	119
Mena, Ar., U.S.	C1	81
Menahga, Mn., U.S.	D3	100
Ménaka, Mali	E6	42
Menan, Id., U.S.	F7	89
Menands, N.Y., U.S.	C7	109
Menard, Tx., U.S.	D3	120
Menard, co., Il., U.S.	C4	90
Menard, co., Tx., U.S.	D3	120
Menasha, Wi., U.S.	D5	126
Mendawai, stm., Indon.	F5	32
Mende, Fr.	H10	10
Mendenhall, Ms., U.S.	D4	101
Méndez, Ec.	I3	58
Mendham, N.J., U.S.	B3	107
Mendi, Eth.	G2	46
Mendip Hills, hills, Eng., U.K.	J10	7
Mendocino, co., Ca., U.S.	C2	82
Mendon, Il., U.S.	C2	90
Mendon, Mi., U.S.	F5	99
Mendon, Ut., U.S.	B4	121
Mendota, Ca., U.S.	D3	82
Mendota, Il., U.S.	B4	90
Mendota, Lake, l., Wi., U.S.	E4	126
Mendoza, Arg.	C3	56
Mene de Mauroa, Ven.	B7	58
Mene Grande, Ven.	C7	58
Menemen, Tur.	K11	16
Menfi, Italy	L7	14
Mengzhi, China	C7	34
Mengzi, China	B5	34
Menifee, co., Ky., U.S.	C6	94
Menlo Park, Ca., U.S.	k8	82
Menno, S.D., U.S.	D8	118
Menominee, Mi., U.S.	C3	99
Menominee, co., Mi., U.S.	C3	99
Menominee, co., Wi., U.S.	C5	126
Menominee, stm., U.S.	C6	126
Menominee Indian Reservation, Wi., U.S.	C5	126
Menomonee, stm., Wi., U.S.	m11	126
Menomonee Falls, Wi., U.S.	E5	126
Menomonie, Wi., U.S.	D2	126
Menongue, Ang.	D3	44
Menorca, i., Spain	F16	12
Mentawai, Kepulauan, is., Indon.	F2	32
Menton, Fr.	I14	10
Mentone, In., U.S.	B5	91
Mentor, Oh., U.S.	A4	112
Mentor-on-the-Lake, Oh., U.S.	A4	112
Menzel Bourguiba, Tun.	L4	14
Meoqui, Mex.	C7	62
Meppel, Neth.	C6	8
Meppen, Ger.	C7	8
Mequon, Wi., U.S.	E6	126
Mer, Fr.	E8	10
Meramec, stm., Mo., U.S.	C7	102
Merano (Meran), Italy	C6	14
Merasheen Island, i., Newf., Can.	E4	72
Merauke, Indon.	G11	32
Meraux, La., U.S.	k12	95
Mercaderes, Col.	G4	58
Merced, Ca., U.S.	D3	82
Merced, co., Ca., U.S.	D3	82
Merced, stm., Ca., U.S.	D3	82
Mercedes, Arg.	C3	56
Mercedes, Arg.	B5	56
Mercedes, Tx., U.S.	F4	120
Mercedes, Ur.	C5	56
Mercer, Pa., U.S.	D1	115
Mercer, Wi., U.S.	B3	126
Mercer, co., Il., U.S.	B3	90
Mercer, co., Ky., U.S.	C5	94
Mercer, co., Mo., U.S.	A4	102
Mercer, co., N.J., U.S.	C3	107
Mercer, co., N.D., U.S.	B4	111
Mercer, co., Oh., U.S.	B1	112
Mercer, co., Pa., U.S.	D1	115
Mercer, co., W.V., U.S.	D3	125
Mercer Island, Wa., U.S.	B3	124
Mercer Island, i., Wa., U.S.	e11	124
Mercersburg, Pa., U.S.	G6	115
Mercerville, N.J., U.S.	C3	107
Mercier, Que., Can.	D4	74
Meredith, N.H., U.S.	C3	106
Meredith, Lake, l., Co., U.S.	C7	83
Meredith, Lake, res., Tx., U.S.	B2	120
Meredosia, Il., U.S.	D3	90
Meredosia Lake, l., Il., U.S.	D3	90
Mergui (Myeik), Burma	H5	34
Mergui Archipelago, is., Burma	H4	34
Meriç (Marica) Évros, stm., Eur.	H10	16
Mérida, Mex.	G15	62
Mérida, Spain	G5	12
Mérida, Ven.	C7	58
Meriden, Ct., U.S.	C4	84
Meriden, Ks., U.S.	C8	93
Meridian, Id., U.S.	F2	89
Meridian, Ms., U.S.	C5	101
Meridian, Pa., U.S.	E2	115
Meridian, Tx., U.S.	D4	120
Meridian Hills, In., U.S.	k10	91
Meridian Naval Air Station, mil., Ms., U.S.	C5	101
Meridianville, Al., U.S.	A3	78
Mérignac, Fr.	H6	10
Merikarvia, Fin.	F13	6
Meriwether, co., Ga., U.S.	C2	87
Merkel, Tx., U.S.	C2	120
Merlin, Ont., Can.	E2	73
Mermentau, La., U.S.	D3	95
Mermentau, stm., La., U.S.	E3	95
Meron, Hare, mtn., Isr.	C4	40
Merriam, Ks., U.S.	k16	93
Merrick, co., Ne., U.S.	C7	104
Merrickville, Ont., Can.	C9	73
Merrill, Ia., U.S.	B1	92
Merrill, Mi., U.S.	E6	99
Merrill, Or., U.S.	E5	114
Merrill, Wi., U.S.	C4	126
Merrillville, In., U.S.	B3	91
Merrimac, Ma., U.S.	A5	98
Merrimack, N.H., U.S.	E4	106
Merrimack, co., N.H., U.S.	D3	106
Merrimack, stm., U.S.	A5	98
Merritt, B.C., Can.	D7	69
Merritt Island, Fl., U.S.	D6	86
Merritt Reservoir, res., Ne., U.S.	B5	104
Merrymeeting Lake, l., N.H., U.S.	D4	106
Merryville, La., U.S.	D2	95
Merseburg, Ger.	D11	8
Merthyr Tydfil, Wales, U.K.	J9	7
Mértola, Port.	H4	12
Merton, Wi., U.S.	m11	126
Méru, Fr.	C9	10
Merwin Lake, res., Wa., U.S.	C3	124
Merzig, Ger.	F6	8
Mesa, Az., U.S.	D4	80
Mesa, co., Co., U.S.	C2	83
Mesabi Range, hills, Mn., U.S.	C6	100
Mesagne, Italy	I12	14
Mesa Mountain, mtn., Co., U.S.	D4	83
Mesa Verde National Park, Co., U.S.	D2	83
Mescalero, N.M., U.S.	D4	108
Mescalero Indian Reservation, N.M., U.S.	D4	108
Mesilla, N.M., U.S.	E3	108
Mesolóngion, Grc.	K5	16
Mesopotamia, reg., Asia	B3	46
Mesquite, Nv., U.S.	G7	105
Mesquite, N.M., U.S.	E3	108
Mesquite, Tx., U.S.	n10	120
Messalo, stm., Moz.	D7	44
Messalonskee Lake, l., Me., U.S.	D3	96
Messina, Italy	K10	14
Messina, S. Afr.	F5	44
Messina, Stretto di, strt., Italy	K10	14
Mesta (Néstos), stm., Eur.	H7	16
Mestre, Italy	D7	14
Meta, stm., S.A.	D9	58
Métabetchouan, Que., Can.	A6	74
Métabetchouane, stm., Que., Can.	A5	74
Metairie, La., U.S.	k11	95
Metamora, Il., U.S.	C4	90
Metán, Arg.	B3	56
Metcalfe, Ont., Can.	B9	73
Metcalfe, Ms., U.S.	B2	101
Metcalfe, co., Ky., U.S.	C4	94
Metedeconk, North Branch, stm., N.J., U.S.	C4	107
Metedeconk, South Branch, stm., N.J., U.S.	C3	107
Meteghan, N.S., Can.	E3	71
Meteghan River, N.S., Can.	E3	71
Meteor Crater, crat., Az., U.S.	C4	80
Methow, stm., Wa., U.S.	A5	124
Methuen, Ma., U.S.	A5	98
Metković, Yugo.	F12	14
Metlakatla, Ak., U.S.	D13	79
Metlatonoc, Mex.	I10	62
Metlika, Yugo.	D10	14
Metonga, Lake, l., Wi., U.S.	C5	126
Metro, Indon.	k12	33a
Metropolis, Il., U.S.	F5	90
Mettawee, stm., U.S.	E2	122
Metter, Ga., U.S.	D4	87
Mettūr, India	G4	37
Metuchen, N.J., U.S.	B4	107
Metz, Fr.	C13	10
Metzger, Or., U.S.	h12	114
Meuse (Maas), stm., Eur.	E5	8
Mexia, Tx., U.S.	D4	120
Mexia, Lake, res., Tx., U.S.	D4	120
Mexiana, Ilha, i., Braz.	D9	54
Mexicali, Mex.	A2	62
Mexico, In., U.S.	C5	91
Mexico, Me., U.S.	D2	96
Mexico, Mo., U.S.	B6	102
Mexico (México), ctry., N.A.	F8	62
Mexico, Gulf of, b., N.A.	F9	76
Mexico City see Ciudad de México, Mex.	H10	62
Meximieux, Fr.	G12	10
Meycauayan, Phil.	q19	33b
Meyersdale, Pa., U.S.	G3	115
Meymaneh, Afg.	C1	38
Meyrueis, Fr.	H10	10
Meždurečensk, U.S.S.R.	G11	20
Mèze, Fr.	I10	10
Mezőtúr, Hung.	H20	8
Mezquital, Mex.	F7	62
Mezzolombardo, Italy	C6	14
Mhow, India	I6	38
Miami, Az., U.S.	D5	80
Miami, Fl., U.S.	G6	86
Miami, Ok., U.S.	A7	113
Miami, co., In., U.S.	C5	91
Miami, co., Ks., U.S.	D9	93
Miami, co., Oh., U.S.	B1	112
Miami Beach, Fl., U.S.	G6	86
Miami Canal, Fl., U.S.	F6	86
Miami International Airport, Fl., U.S.	G6	86
Miamisburg, Oh., U.S.	C1	112
Miami Shores, Fl., U.S.	G6	86
Miami Springs, Fl., U.S.	G6	86
Miandrivazo, Madag.	E9	44
Miāneh, Iran	J7	18
Mianus Reservoir, res., U.S.	E1	84
Miānwāli, Pak.	D4	38
Mica Mountain, mtn., Az., U.S.	E5	80
Micco, Fl., U.S.	E6	86
Miccosukee, Lake, res., Fl., U.S.	B2	86
Michelson, Mount, mtn., Ak., U.S.	B11	79
Michie, Tn., U.S.	B3	119
Michigamme, Lake, l., Mi., U.S.	B2	99
Michigamme Reservoir, res., Mi., U.S.	B2	99
Michigan, state, U.S.	E6	99
Michigan, stm., Co., U.S.	A4	83
Michigan, Lake, l., U.S.	C9	76
Michigan Center, Mi., U.S.	F6	99
Michigan City, In., U.S.	A4	91
Michigan Island, i., Wi., U.S.	B3	126
Michikamau Lake, l., Newf., Can.	F20	66
Michipicoten Island, i., Ont., Can.	G15	66
Micronesia, is., Oc.	F23	2
Mičurinsk, U.S.S.R.	I23	22
Middelburg, Neth.	D3	8
Middelburg, S. Afr.	H4	44
Middelharnis, Neth.	D4	8
Middle, stm., Ia., U.S.	C3	92
Middle, stm., Mn., U.S.	B2	100
Middle Andaman, i., India	H2	34
Middleboro (Middleborough Center), Ma., U.S.	C6	98
Middlebourne, W.V., U.S.	B4	125
Middleburg, Fl., U.S.	B5	86
Middleburg, Pa., U.S.	E7	115
Middleburg Heights, Oh., U.S.	h9	112
Middlebury, Ct., U.S.	C3	84
Middlebury, In., U.S.	A6	91
Middlebury, Vt., U.S.	C2	122
Middlefield, Ct., U.S.	C5	84
Middlefield, Oh., U.S.	A4	112
Middle Island Creek, stm., W.V., U.S.	B3	125
Middle Nodaway, stm., Ia., U.S.	C3	92
Middle Park, val., Co., U.S.	A4	83
Middle Patuxent, stm., Md., U.S.	B4	97
Middleport, N.Y., U.S.	B2	109
Middleport, Oh., U.S.	C3	112
Middle Raccoon, stm., Ia., U.S.	C3	92
Middle River, Md., U.S.	B5	97
Middlesboro, Ky., U.S.	D6	94
Middlesex, N.J., U.S.	B4	107
Middlesex, N.C., U.S.	B4	110
Middlesex, co., Ct., U.S.	D5	84
Middlesex, co., Ma., U.S.	A5	98
Middlesex, co., N.J., U.S.	C4	107
Middlesex, co., Va., U.S.	C6	123
Middlesex Fells Reservation, Ma., U.S.	g11	98
Middleton, N.S., Can.	E4	71
Middleton, Id., U.S.	F2	89
Middleton, Ma., U.S.	A5	98
Middleton, Wi., U.S.	E4	126
Middleton Reef, atoll, Austl.	E11	50
Middletown, Ca., U.S.	C2	82
Middletown, Ct., U.S.	C5	84
Middletown, De., U.S.	C3	85
Middletown, In., U.S.	D6	91
Middletown, Ky., U.S.	g11	94
Middletown, Md., U.S.	B2	97
Middletown, N.J., U.S.	C4	107
Middletown, N.Y., U.S.	D6	109
Middletown, Oh., U.S.	C1	112
Middletown, Pa., U.S.	F8	115
Middletown, R.I., U.S.	E5	116
Middletown, Va., U.S.	A4	123
Middleville, Mi., U.S.	F5	99
Midfield, Al., U.S.	g7	78
Midland, Ont., Can.	C5	73
Midland, Mi., U.S.	E6	99
Midland, N.C., U.S.	B2	110
Midland, Pa., U.S.	E1	115
Midland, Tx., U.S.	D1	120
Midland, co., Mi., U.S.	E6	99
Midland, co., Tx., U.S.	D1	120
Midland City, Al., U.S.	D4	78
Midland Park, Ks., U.S.	g12	93
Midland Park, N.J., U.S.	B4	107
Midland Park, S.C., U.S.	k11	117
Midleton, Ire.	J4	7
Midlothian, Il., U.S.	k9	90
Midlothian, Tx., U.S.	C4	120
Midnapore, India	I12	38
Midongy Sud, Madag.	F9	44
Midvale, Ut., U.S.	C4	121
Midville, Ga., U.S.	D4	87
Midway, B.C., Can.	E8	69
Midway, De., U.S.	F5	85
Midway, Ky., U.S.	B5	94
Midway, Pa., U.S.	G7	115
Midway, Ut., U.S.	C4	121
Midway Islands, dep., Oc.	E1	2
Midwest, Wy., U.S.	C6	127
Midwest City, Ok., U.S.	B4	113
Mielec, Pol.	E21	8
Mieres, Spain	B6	12
Miesbach, Ger.	H11	8
Mifflin, co., Pa., U.S.	E6	115
Mifflinburg, Pa., U.S.	E7	115
Mifflinville, Pa., U.S.	D9	115
Miguel Alemán, Presa, res., Mex.	H11	62
Miguel Auza, Mex.	E8	62
Mihajlovgrad, Bul.	F7	16
Mihara, Japan	H6	30
Mikasa, Japan	p19	30a
Mikkeli, Fin.	F16	6
Mikumi, Tan.	C7	44
Milaca, Mn., U.S.	E5	100
Milagro, Arg.	C3	56
Milagro, Ec.	I3	58
Milam, co., Tx., U.S.	D4	120
Milan, Ga., U.S.	D3	87
Milan, Il., U.S.	B3	90
Milan, In., U.S.	F7	91
Milan, Mi., U.S.	F7	99
Milan, Mo., U.S.	A4	102
Milan, N.M., U.S.	B2	108
Milan, Oh., U.S.	A3	112
Milan, Tn., U.S.	B3	119
Milan see Milano, Italy	D4	14
Milano (Milan), Italy	D4	14
Milâs, Tur.	L11	16
Milazzo, Italy	K10	14
Milbank, S.D., U.S.	B9	118
Mildmay, Ont., Can.	C3	73
Mildura, Austl.	F8	50
Milesburg, Pa., U.S.	E6	115
Miles City, Mt., U.S.	D11	103
Milestone, Sask., Can.	G3	75
Milford, Ct., U.S.	E3	84
Milford, De., U.S.	E4	85
Milford, Il., U.S.	C6	90
Milford, In., U.S.	B6	91
Milford, Ia., U.S.	A2	92
Milford, Me., U.S.	D4	96
Milford, Ma., U.S.	B4	98
Milford, Mi., U.S.	F7	99
Milford, Ne., U.S.	D8	104
Milford, N.H., U.S.	E3	106
Milford, Oh., U.S.	C1	112
Milford, Pa., U.S.	D12	115
Milford, Ut., U.S.	E2	121
Milford Haven, Wales, U.K.	J7	7
Milford Lake, res., Ks., U.S.	C6	93
Milford Station, N.S., Can.	D6	71
Mililani Town, Hi., U.S.	g9	88
Mil'kovo, U.S.S.R.	G25	20
Milk River, Alta., Can.	E4	68
Mill, stm., Ma., U.S.	h9	98
Millard, co., Ut., U.S.	D2	121
Millau, Fr.	H10	10
Millbrae, Ca., U.S.	h8	82
Millbrook, Ont., Can.	C6	73
Millbrook, Al., U.S.	C3	78
Mill Brook, stm., Vt., U.S.	B5	122
Millburn, N.J., U.S.	B4	107
Millbury, Ma., U.S.	B4	98
Millbury, Oh., U.S.	e7	112
Mill City, Or., U.S.	C4	114
Millcreek, Ut., U.S.	C4	121
Mill Creek, W.V., U.S.	C5	125
Mill Creek, stm., N.J., U.S.	D4	107
Mill Creek, stm., Oh., U.S.	B2	112
Mill Creek, stm., Tn., U.S.	g10	119
Mill Creek, stm., W.V., U.S.	C3	125
Mill Creek, stm., W.V., U.S.	m13	125
Millcreek Township, Pa., U.S.	B1	115
Milledgeville, Ga., U.S.	C3	87
Milledgeville, Il., U.S.	B4	90
Mille Îles, Rivière des, stm., Que., Can.	p19	74
Mille Lacs, co., Mn., U.S.	E5	100
Mille Lacs, Lac des, l., Ont., Can.	G14	66
Mille Lacs Indian Reservation, Mn., U.S.	D5	100
Mille Lacs Lake, l., Mn., U.S.	D5	100
Millen, Ga., U.S.	D5	87
Miller, S.D., U.S.	C7	118
Miller, co., Ar., U.S.	D2	81
Miller, co., Ga., U.S.	E2	87
Miller, co., Mo., U.S.	C5	102
Miller, Mount, mtn., Ak., U.S.	C11	79
Miller Peak, mtn., Az., U.S.	F5	80
Miller Run, stm., Vt., U.S.	B4	122
Millers, stm., Ma., U.S.	A3	98
Millersburg, In., U.S.	A6	91
Millersburg, Ky., U.S.	B5	94
Millersburg, Oh., U.S.	B4	112
Millersburg, Pa., U.S.	E8	115
Millersport, Oh., U.S.	C3	112
Millersville, Pa., U.S.	F9	115
Millet, Alta., Can.	C4	68
Mill Hall, Pa., U.S.	D7	115
Milliken, Co., U.S.	A6	83
Millington, Mi., U.S.	E7	99
Millington, Tn., U.S.	B2	119
Millinocket, Me., U.S.	C4	96
Millinocket Lake, l., Me., U.S.	C4	96

Name	Map Ref	Page
Millinocket Lake, l., Me., U.S.	B4	96
Millis, Ma., U.S.	B5	98
Millport, Al., U.S.	B1	78
Millry, Al., U.S.	D1	78
Mills, Wy., U.S.	D6	127
Mills, co., Ia., U.S.	C2	92
Mills, co., Tx., U.S.	D3	120
Millsboro, De., U.S.	F4	85
Millsboro, Pa., U.S.	G1	115
Millstadt, Il., U.S.	E3	90
Millstone, stm., N.J., U.S.	C4	107
Milltown, In., U.S.	H5	91
Milltown, N.J., U.S.	C4	107
Milltown, Wi., U.S.	C1	126
Milltown [-Head of Bay d'Espoir], Newf., Can.	E4	72
Milltown Malbay, Ire.	I3	7
Millvale, Pa., U.S.	k14	115
Mill Valley, Ca., U.S.	D2	82
Millville, Ma., U.S.	B4	98
Millville, N.J., U.S.	E2	107
Millville, Pa., U.S.	D9	115
Millville, Ut., U.S.	B4	121
Millville Lake, N.H., U.S.	E4	106
Millwood, Wa., U.S.	g14	124
Millwood Lake, res., Ar., U.S.	D1	81
Milner Dam, Id., U.S.	G5	89
Milnor, N.D., U.S.	C8	111
Milo, Ia., U.S.	C4	92
Milo, Me., U.S.	C4	96
Milparinka, Austl.	E8	50
Milroy, In., U.S.	F7	91
Milroy, Pa., U.S.	E6	115
Milstead, Ga., U.S.	C3	87
Milton, Ont., Can.	D5	73
Milton, De., U.S.	E4	85
Milton, Fl., U.S.	u14	86
Milton, In., U.S.	E7	91
Milton, Ma., U.S.	B5	98
Milton, N.H., U.S.	D5	106
Milton, Pa., U.S.	D8	115
Milton, Vt., U.S.	B2	122
Milton, Wa., U.S.	f11	124
Milton, W.V., U.S.	C2	125
Milton, Wi., U.S.	F5	126
Milton, Lake, l., Oh., U.S.	A4	112
Miltona, Lake, l., Mn., U.S.	D3	100
Milton-Freewater, Or., U.S.	B8	114
Milton Reservoir, res., Co., U.S.	A6	83
Milverton, Ont., Can.	D4	73
Milwaukee, Wi., U.S.	E6	126
Milwaukee, co., Wi., U.S.	E6	126
Milwaukee, stm., Wi., U.S.	m12	126
Milwaukie, Or., U.S.	B4	114
Mimizan, Fr.	H5	10
Mims, Fl., U.S.	D6	86
Min, stm., China	I7	28
Mina, Nv., U.S.	E3	105
Minahasa, pen., Indon.	E7	32
Minamata, Japan	J3	30
Minas, Ur.	C5	56
Minas, Sierra de las, mts., Guat.	G3	64
Minas Basin, b., N.S., Can.	D5	71
Minas Channel, strt., N.S., Can.	D5	71
Minas de Barroterán, Mex.	D9	62
Minas Novas, Braz.	D7	57
Minatare, Ne., U.S.	C2	104
Minatitlán, Mex.	I12	62
Minco, Ok., U.S.	B4	113
Mindanao, i., Phil.	D7	32
Mindanao, stm., Phil.	D7	32
Mindanao Sea, Phil.	D7	32
Mindelheim, Ger.	G10	8
Minden, Ger.	C8	8
Minden, La., U.S.	B2	95
Minden, Ne., U.S.	D7	104
Minden, Nv., U.S.	E2	105
Minden, W.V., U.S.	D3	125
Mindoro, i., Phil.	C7	32
Mindoro Strait, strt., Phil.	C7	32
Mine Hill, N.J., U.S.	B3	107
Mineiros, Braz.	D2	57
Mineola, N.Y., U.S.	E7	109
Mineola, Tx., U.S.	C5	120
Miner, Mo., U.S.	E8	102
Miner, co., S.D., U.S.	D8	118
Mineral, co., Co., U.S.	D4	83
Mineral, co., Mt., U.S.	C1	103
Mineral, co., Nv., U.S.	E3	105
Mineral, co., W.V., U.S.	B6	125
Mineral Point, Wi., U.S.	F3	126
Mineral Springs, Ar., U.S.	D2	81
Mineral Wells, Tx., U.S.	C3	120
Minersville, Pa., U.S.	E9	115
Minersville, Ut., U.S.	E3	121
Minerva, Oh., U.S.	B4	112
Minervino Murge, Italy	H11	14
Minetto, N.Y., U.S.	B4	109
Mingo, co., W.V., U.S.	D2	125
Mingo Junction, Oh., U.S.	B5	112
Minho (Miño), stm., Eur.	D3	12
Minidoka, co., Id., U.S.	G5	89
Minidoka Dam, Id., U.S.	G5	89
Minier, Il., U.S.	C4	90
Minisink Island, i., N.J., U.S.	A3	107
Minitonas, Man., Can.	C1	70
Minna, Nig.	G7	42
Minneapolis, Ks., U.S.	C6	93
Minneapolis, Mn., U.S.	F5	100
Minnedosa, Man., Can.	D2	70
Minnedosa, stm., Man., Can.	D1	70
Minnehaha, co., S.D., U.S.	D9	118
Minneola, Ks., U.S.	E3	93
Minneota, Mn., U.S.	F3	100
Minnesota, state, U.S.	E4	100
Minnesota, stm., Mn., U.S.	F2	100
Minnesota Lake, Mn., U.S.	G5	100
Minnetonka, Mn., U.S.	n12	100
Minnetonka, Lake, l., Mn., U.S.	n11	100
Minnewaska, Lake, l., Mn., U.S.	E3	100
Miño (Minho), stm., Eur.	D3	12
Minocqua, Wi., U.S.	C4	126
Minonk, Il., U.S.	C4	90
Minooka, Il., U.S.	B5	90
Minot, N.D., U.S.	A4	111
Minot Air Force Base, mil., N.D., U.S.	A4	111
Minquadale, De., U.S.	i7	85
Minsk, U.S.S.R.	H10	22
Mińsk Mazowiecki, Pol.	C21	8
Minster, Oh., U.S.	B1	112
Mint Hill, N.C., U.S.	B2	110
Minto, N.B., Can.	C3	71
Minto Inlet, b., N.W. Ter., Can.	B9	66
Minturn, Co., U.S.	B4	83
Minturno, Italy	H8	14
Minusinsk, U.S.S.R.	G12	20
Minute Man National Historical Park, Ma., U.S.	g10	98
Minxian, China	E7	26
Mio, Mi., U.S.	D6	99
Mira, Italy	D7	14
Mirabel, Que., Can.	D3	74
Miraflores, Col.	E6	58
Miraflores, Col.	G6	58
Miraj, India	D3	37
Miramar, Fl., U.S.	s13	86
Miramar Naval Air Station, mil., Ca., U.S.	F5	82
Miramas, Fr.	I11	10
Mirambeau, Fr.	G6	10
Miramichi Bay, b., N.B., Can.	B5	71
Miranda de Ebro, Spain	C9	12
Miranda do Douro, Port.	D5	12
Mirande, Fr.	I7	10
Mirandela, Port.	D4	12
Mirandola, Italy	E6	14
Mirbāṭ, Oman	E5	46
Mirebeau-sur-Bèze, Fr.	E12	10
Miri, Malay.	E5	32
Mirnyj, U.S.S.R.	E16	20
Mīrpur Khās, Pak.	H3	38
Mirror Lake, l., N.H., U.S.	C4	106
Mirzāpur, India	H10	38
Misawa, Japan	B14	30
Miscouche, P.E.I., Can.	C6	71
Miscou Island, i., N.B., Can.	B5	71
Miscou Point, c., N.B., Can.	A5	71
Misenheimer, N.C., U.S.	B2	110
Mishawaka, In., U.S.	A5	91
Misheguk Mountain, mtn., Ak., U.S.	B7	79
Mishicot, Wi., U.S.	D6	126
Mishmi Hills, hills, Asia	F16	38
Misima Island, i., Pap. N. Gui.	B10	50
Miskitos, Cayos, is., Nic.	G6	64
Miskolc, Hung.	G20	8
Misool, Pulau, i., Indon.	F9	32
Mispillion, stm., De., U.S.	E4	85
Misrātah, Libya	B9	42
Missaukee, co., Mi., U.S.	D5	99
Missaukee, Lake, l., Mi., U.S.	D5	99
Mission, Ks., U.S.	m16	93
Mission, S.D., U.S.	D5	118
Mission, Tx., U.S.	F3	120
Mission Range, mts., Mt., U.S.	C3	103
Mission Viejo, Ca., U.S.	n13	82
Missisquoi, stm., Vt., U.S.	B3	122
Missisquoi Bay, b., Vt., U.S.	A2	122
Mississauga, Ont., Can.	D5	73
Mississinewa, stm., U.S.	D7	91
Mississinewa Lake, res., In., U.S.	C6	91
Mississippi, co., Ar., U.S.	B5	81
Mississippi, co., Mo., U.S.	E8	102
Mississippi, state, U.S.	C4	101
Mississippi, stm., U.S.	E8	76
Mississippi Delta, La., U.S.	E6	95
Mississippi Sound, strt., U.S.	E5	101
Mississippi State, Ms., U.S.	B5	101
Missoula, Mt., U.S.	D2	103
Missoula, co., Mt., U.S.	D2	103
Missouri, state, U.S.	C5	102
Missouri, stm., U.S.	C7	76
Missouri City, Tx., U.S.	r14	120
Missouri Valley, Ia., U.S.	C2	92
Mistassini, Que., Can.	h12	74
Mistassini, Lac, l., Que., Can.	h12	74
Misti, Volcán, vol., Peru	G4	54
Mistretta, Italy	L9	14
Mita, Punta de, c., Mex.	G7	62
Mitchell, Austl.	E9	50
Mitchell, Ont., Can.	D3	73
Mitchell, Il., U.S.	E3	90
Mitchell, In., U.S.	G5	91
Mitchell, Ne., U.S.	C2	104
Mitchell, S.D., U.S.	D7	118
Mitchell, co., Ga., U.S.	E2	87
Mitchell, co., Ia., U.S.	A5	92
Mitchell, co., Ks., U.S.	C5	93
Mitchell, co., N.C., U.S.	e10	110
Mitchell, co., Tx., U.S.	C2	120
Mitchell, stm., Austl.	C8	50
Mitchell, Lake, l., Mi., U.S.	D5	99
Mitchell, Lake, res., Al., U.S.	C3	78
Mitchell, Mount, mtn., N.C., U.S.	f10	110
Mitchell Island, i., La., U.S.	E6	95
Mitchellville, Ia., U.S.	C4	92
Mitilíni, Grc.	J10	16
Mitkof Island, i., Ak., U.S.	m23	79
Mito, Japan	F13	30
Mitsiwa, Eth.	E2	46
Mitsuke, Japan	E11	30
Mittenwald, Ger.	H11	8
Mittweida, Ger.	E12	8
Mitú, Col.	G7	58
Mitumba, Monts, mts., Zaire	C5	44
Mitwaba, Zaire	C5	44
Mitzic, Gabon	A2	44
Miura, Japan	G12	30
Mixian, China	A2	28
Miyako, Japan	C14	30
Miyako-jima, i., Japan	G12	26
Miyakonojō, Japan	K4	30
Miyazaki, Japan	K4	30
Miyoshi, Japan	H5	30
Miyun, China	C10	26
Mizdah, Libya	B8	42
Mizen Head, c., Ire.	J3	7
Mizoram, ter., India	I15	38
Mizpe Ramon, Isr.	D4	40
Mizque, Bol.	G5	54
Mjölby, Swe.	G10	6
Mjøsa, l., Nor.	F8	6
Mkalama, Tan.	B6	44
Mladá Boleslav, Czech.	E14	8
Mława, Pol.	B20	8
Mo, Nor.	C10	6
Moab, Ut., U.S.	E6	121
Moanda, Gabon	B2	44
Moapa River Indian Reservation, Nv., U.S.	G7	105
Moate, Ire.	H5	7
Mobara, Japan	G13	30
Mobaye, Cen. Afr. Rep.	H10	42
Moberly, Mo., U.S.	B5	102
Mobile, Al., U.S.	E1	78
Mobile, co., Al., U.S.	E1	78
Mobile, stm., Al., U.S.	E1	78
Mobile Bay, b., Al., U.S.	E1	83
Mobridge, S.D., U.S.	B5	118
Moçambique, Moz.	E8	44
Mocanaqua, Pa., U.S.	D9	115
Mocha, Isla, i., Chile	D2	56
Mochudi, Bots.	F5	44
Mocksville, N.C., U.S.	B2	110
Moclips, Wa., U.S.	B1	124
Môco, Serra do, mtn., Ang.	D3	44
Mocoa, Col.	G4	58
Mococa, Braz.	F5	57
Moctezuma, Mex.	C5	62
Mocuba, Moz.	E7	44
Modane, Fr.	G13	10
Model Reservoir, res., Co., U.S.	D6	83
Modena, Italy	E5	14
Modesto, Ca., U.S.	D3	82
Modica, Italy	M9	14
Mödling, Aus.	G16	8
Modoc, co., Ca., U.S.	B3	82
Modowi, Indon.	F9	32
Moengo, Sur.	B8	54
Moenkopi, Az., U.S.	A4	80
Moffat, Scot., U.K.	F9	7
Moffat, co., Co., U.S.	A2	83
Moffat Tunnel, Co., U.S.	B5	83
Moffett Field Naval Air Station, mil., Ca., U.S.	k8	82
Moga, India	E6	38
Mogadisho see Muqdisho, Som.	H4	46
Mogadore, Oh., U.S.	A4	112
Mogadouro, Port.	D5	12
Mogaung, Burma	B4	34
Mogi das Cruzes, Braz.	G5	57
Mogil'ov, U.S.S.R.	H13	22
Mogi-Mirim, Braz.	G5	57
Mogincual, Moz.	E8	44
Mogoča, U.S.S.R.	G17	20
Mogočin, U.S.S.R.	F10	20
Mogok, Burma	C4	34
Mogollon Mountains, mts., N.M., U.S.	D1	108
Mogollon Rim, clf, Az., U.S.	C5	80
Mogotón, Pico, mtn., N.A.	H4	64
Mohall, N.D., U.S.	A4	111
Mohave, co., Az., U.S.	B1	80
Mohave, Lake, res., U.S.	H7	105
Mohave Mountains, mts., Az., U.S.	C1	80
Mohave Valley, Az., U.S.	C1	80
Mohawk, N.Y., U.S.	C5	109
Mohawk, stm., N.H., U.S.	g7	106
Mohawk, stm., N.Y., U.S.	C6	109
Mohawk Lake, l., N.J., U.S.	A3	107
Mohawk Mountains, mts., Az., U.S.	E2	80
Moheli, i., Com.	D8	44
Mohican, stm., Oh., U.S.	B3	112
Mohinora, Cerro, mtn., Mex.	D6	62
Mohnton, Pa., U.S.	F10	115
Moi, Nor.	G6	6
Moisie, Que., Can.	h8	72
Moisie, stm., Que., Can.	F19	66
Moissac, Fr.	H8	10
Mojave, Ca., U.S.	E4	82
Mojave, stm., Ca., U.S.	E5	82
Mojave Desert, des., Ca., U.S.	E5	82
Mojjero, stm., U.S.S.R.	D14	20
Mojo, Eth.	G2	46
Mokapu Peninsula, pen., Hi., U.S.	g10	88
Mokapu Point, c., Hi., U.S.	g11	88
Mokelumne, stm., Ca., U.S.	C3	82
Mokena, Il., U.S.	k9	90
Mokp'o, S. Kor.	E12	26
Moku Manu, i., Hi., U.S.	g11	88
Mol, Bel.	D5	8
Molalla, Or., U.S.	B4	114
Moldau see Vltava, stm., Czech.	F14	8
Moldavia see Moldavskaja Sovetskaja Socialističeskaja Respublika, state, U.S.S.R.	H3	18
Moldavskaja Sovetskaja Socialističeskaja Respublika, state, U.S.S.R.	H3	18
Molde, Nor.	E6	6
Molepolole, Bots.	F5	44
Molfetta, Italy	H11	14
Molina de Aragón, Spain	E10	12
Molina de Segura, Spain	G10	12
Moline, Il., U.S.	B3	90
Moline, Mi., U.S.	F5	99
Molino, Fl., U.S.	u14	86
Molins de Rey, Spain	D14	12
Mollendo, Peru	G4	54
Mölln, Ger.	B10	8
Mölndal, Swe.	H9	6
Molodečno, U.S.S.R.	G9	22
Molokai, i., Hi., U.S.	B5	88
Molokini, i., Hi., U.S.	C5	88
Molson Lake, l., Man., Can.	B3	70
Molucca Sea see Maluku, Laut, Indon.	F7	32
Moluccas see Maluku, is., Indon.	F8	32
Moma, Moz.	E7	44
Moma, stm., U.S.S.R.	D22	20
Mombasa, Kenya	B7	44
Mombetsu, Japan	o21	30a
Momence, Il., U.S.	B6	90
Momotombo, Volcán, vol., Nic.	H4	64
Mon, stm., Burma	D3	34
Mona, Canal de la, strt., N.A.	E14	64
Mona, Isla, i., P.R.	E14	64
Monaca, Pa., U.S.	E1	115
Monaco, ctry., Eur.	G9	4
Monadhliath Mountains, mts., Scot., U.K.	D8	7
Monadnock, Mount, mtn., N.H., U.S.	E2	106
Monadnock Mountain, mtn., Vt., U.S.	B5	122
Monahans, Tx., U.S.	D1	120
Monarch Mills, S.C., U.S.	B4	117
Monarch Pass, Co., U.S.	C4	83
Monashee Mountains, mts., B.C., Can.	D8	69
Monastir, Tun.	N5	14
Moncalieri, Italy	D2	14
Monção, Braz.	D9	54
Mönchengladbach, Ger.	D6	8
Monchique, Port.	H3	12
Moncks Corner, S.C., U.S.	E7	117
Monclova, Mex.	D9	62
Moncton, N.B., Can.	C5	71
Mondoñedo, Spain	B4	12
Mondovì, Italy	E2	14
Mondovi, Wi., U.S.	D2	126
Mondragone, Italy	H8	14
Monee, Il., U.S.	B6	90
Monessen, Pa., U.S.	F2	115
Monett, Mo., U.S.	E4	102
Monette, Ar., U.S.	B5	81
Monfalcone, Italy	D8	14
Monforte de Lemos, Spain	C4	12
Monfort Heights, Oh., U.S.	o12	112
Mong Cai, Viet.	D9	34
Möng Hsat, Burma	D5	34
Monghyr, India	H12	38
Mongo, Chad	F9	42
Mongol Altajn Nuruu, mts., Asia	B5	26
Mongolia, ctry., Asia	B7	26
Mongu, Zam.	E4	44
Monhegan Island, i., Me., U.S.	E3	96
Monida Pass, U.S.	E6	89
Moniteau, co., Mo., U.S.	C5	102
Monitor Range, mts., Nv., U.S.	E5	105
Monitor Valley, val., Nv., U.S.	D5	105
Monmouth, Il., U.S.	C3	90
Monmouth, Or., U.S.	C3	114
Monmouth, co., N.J., U.S.	C4	107
Monmouth Beach, N.J., U.S.	C5	107
Monmouth Mountain, mtn., B.C., Can.	D6	69
Mono, co., Ca., U.S.	D4	82
Monocacy, stm., Md., U.S.	B3	97
Mono Lake, l., Ca., U.S.	D4	82
Monomonac, Lake, l., U.S.	E3	106
Monomoy Island, i., Ma., U.S.	C7	98
Monomoy Point, c., Ma., U.S.	C7	98
Monon, In., U.S.	C4	91
Monona, Ia., U.S.	A6	92
Monona, Wi., U.S.	E4	126
Monona, co., Ia., U.S.	B1	92
Monona, Lake, l., Wi., U.S.	E4	126
Monongah, W.V., U.S.	B4	125
Monongahela, Pa., U.S.	F2	115
Monongahela, stm., U.S.	G2	115
Monongalia, co., W.V., U.S.	B4	125
Monopoli, Italy	I12	14
Monóvar, Spain	G11	12
Monreal del Campo, Spain	E10	12
Monroe, Ga., U.S.	C3	87
Monroe, In., U.S.	C8	91
Monroe, Ia., U.S.	C4	92
Monroe, La., U.S.	B3	95
Monroe, Mi., U.S.	G7	99
Monroe, N.Y., U.S.	D6	109
Monroe, N.C., U.S.	C2	110
Monroe, Oh., U.S.	C1	112
Monroe, Ut., U.S.	E3	121
Monroe, Wa., U.S.	B4	124
Monroe, Wi., U.S.	F4	126
Monroe, co., Al., U.S.	D2	78
Monroe, co., Ar., U.S.	C4	81
Monroe, co., Fl., U.S.	G5	86
Monroe, co., Ga., U.S.	D3	87
Monroe, co., Il., U.S.	E3	90
Monroe, co., In., U.S.	F4	91
Monroe, co., Ia., U.S.	D5	92
Monroe, co., Ky., U.S.	D4	94
Monroe, co., Mi., U.S.	G7	99
Monroe, co., Ms., U.S.	B5	101
Monroe, co., Mo., U.S.	B5	102
Monroe, co., N.Y., U.S.	B3	109
Monroe, co., Oh., U.S.	C4	112
Monroe, co., Pa., U.S.	D11	115
Monroe, co., Tn., U.S.	D9	119
Monroe, co., W.V., U.S.	D4	125
Monroe, co., Wi., U.S.	E3	126
Monroe Center, Ct., U.S.	D3	84
Monroe City, Mo., U.S.	B6	102
Monroe Lake, res., In., U.S.	F5	91
Monroe Park, De., U.S.	h7	85
Monroeville, Al., U.S.	D2	78
Monroeville, In., U.S.	C8	91
Monroeville, Oh., U.S.	A3	112
Monroeville, Pa., U.S.	k14	115
Monrovia, Lib.	G3	42
Monrovia, Ca., U.S.	m13	82
Monrovia, In., U.S.	E5	91
Mons, Bel.	E3	8
Monson, Ma., U.S.	B3	98
Montague, P.E.I., Can.	C7	71
Montague, Ca., U.S.	B2	82
Montague, Mi., U.S.	E4	99
Montague, co., Tx., U.S.	C4	120
Montague, Isla, i., Mex.	B2	62
Montague Island, i., Ak., U.S.	D10	79
Montague Peak, mtn., Ak., U.S.	g18	79
Montague Strait, strt., Ak., U.S.	h18	79
Montaigu, Fr.	F5	10
Montalbán, Spain	E11	12
Montalcino, Italy	F6	14
Montalegre, Port.	D4	12
Mont Alto, Pa., U.S.	G6	115
Montana, state, U.S.	D7	103
Montánchez, Spain	F5	12
Montargis, Fr.	D9	10
Montauban, Fr.	H8	10
Montauk, N.Y., U.S.	m17	109
Montbard, Fr.	E11	10
Montbéliard, Fr.	E13	10
Mont Belvieu, Tx., U.S.	E5	120
Montblanch, Spain	D13	12
Montbrison, Fr.	G11	10
Montcalm, co., Mi., U.S.	E5	99
Montchanin, De., U.S.	h7	85
Montclair, Ca., U.S.	m13	82
Montclair, N.J., U.S.	B4	107
Mont Clare, Pa., U.S.	o19	115
Mont-de-Marsan, Fr.	I6	10
Montdidier, Fr.	C9	10
Monteagle, Tn., U.S.	D8	119
Monteagudo, Bol.	G6	54
Monte Azul, Braz.	C7	57
Montebello, Que., Can.	D3	74
Montebello, Ca., U.S.	m12	82
Monte Caseros, Arg.	C5	56
Montecatini Terme, Italy	F5	14
Monte Comán, Arg.	C3	56
Montecristi, Dom. Rep.	E12	64
Montecristi, Ec.	H2	58
Montefiascone, Italy	G7	14
Montego Bay, Jam.	E9	64
Montegut, La., U.S.	E5	95
Montélimar, Fr.	H11	10
Montello, Nv., U.S.	B7	105
Montello, Wi., U.S.	E4	126
Montemorelos, Mex.	E10	62
Montemor-o-Novo, Port.	G3	12
Montendre, Fr.	G6	10
Montenero di Bisaccia, Italy	H9	14
Montepuez, Moz.	D8	44
Montepulciano, Italy	F6	14
Monte Quemado, Arg.	B4	56
Montereau-faut-Yonne, Fr.	D9	10
Monterey, Ca., U.S.	D3	82
Monterey, Tn., U.S.	C8	119
Monterey, co., Ca., U.S.	D3	82
Monterey Bay, b., Ca., U.S.	D2	82
Monterey Park, Ca., U.S.	m12	82
Montería, Col.	C5	58
Monterotondo, Italy	G7	14
Monterrey, Mex.	E9	62
Montesano, Wa., U.S.	C2	124
Monte Sant'Angelo, Italy	H10	14
Montes Claros, Braz.	D7	57
Montevallo, Al., U.S.	B3	78
Montevarchi, Italy	F6	14
Montevideo, Mn., U.S.	F3	100
Montevideo, Ur.	C5	56
Monte Vista, Co., U.S.	D4	83
Montezuma, Ga., U.S.	D2	87
Montezuma, In., U.S.	E3	91
Montezuma, Ia., U.S.	C5	92
Montezuma, Ks., U.S.	E3	93
Montezuma, co., Co., U.S.	D2	83
Montezuma Castle National Monument, Az., U.S.	C4	80
Montezuma Peak, mtn., Az., U.S.	D3	80
Montgomery, Al., U.S.	C3	78
Montgomery, Il., U.S.	B5	90
Montgomery, La., U.S.	C3	95
Montgomery, Mn., U.S.	F5	100
Montgomery, N.Y., U.S.	D6	109
Montgomery, Oh., U.S.	o13	112
Montgomery, Pa., U.S.	D8	115
Montgomery, W.V., U.S.	C3	125
Montgomery, co., Al., U.S.	C3	78
Montgomery, co., Ar., U.S.	C2	81
Montgomery, co., Ga., U.S.	D4	87
Montgomery, co., Il., U.S.	D4	90
Montgomery, co., In., U.S.	D4	91
Montgomery, co., Ia., U.S.	C2	92
Montgomery, co., Ks., U.S.	E8	93
Montgomery, co., Ky., U.S.	B6	94
Montgomery, co., Md., U.S.	B3	97
Montgomery, co., Ms., U.S.	B4	101
Montgomery, co., Mo., U.S.	C6	102
Montgomery, co., N.Y., U.S.	C6	109
Montgomery, co., N.C., U.S.	B3	110
Montgomery, co., Oh., U.S.	C1	112
Montgomery, co., Pa., U.S.	F11	115
Montgomery, co., Tn., U.S.	A4	119
Montgomery, co., Tx., U.S.	D5	120
Montgomery, co., Va., U.S.	C2	123
Montgomery City, Mo., U.S.	C6	102
Monthey, Switz.	F13	10
Monticello, Ar., U.S.	D4	81
Monticello, Fl., U.S.	B3	86
Monticello, Ga., U.S.	C3	87
Monticello, Il., U.S.	C5	90
Monticello, In., U.S.	C4	91
Monticello, Ia., U.S.	B6	92
Monticello, Ky., U.S.	D5	94
Monticello, Mn., U.S.	E5	100
Monticello, Ms., U.S.	D3	101
Monticello, N.Y., U.S.	D6	109
Monticello, Ut., U.S.	F6	121
Monticello, Wi., U.S.	F4	126
Montichiari, Italy	D5	14
Montignac, Fr.	G8	10
Montijo, Port.	G3	12
Montijo, Spain	G5	12
Montilla, Spain	H7	12
Montivilliers, Fr.	C7	10
Mont-Joli, Que., Can.	A9	74
Mont-Laurier, Que., Can.	C2	74
Mont-Louis, Fr.	J9	10
Montluçon, Fr.	F9	10
Montmagny, Que., Can.	C7	74
Montmorenci, S.C., U.S.	D4	117
Montmorency, co., Mi., U.S.	C6	99
Montmorillon, Fr.	F7	10
Montmort, Fr.	D10	10
Montoro, Spain	G7	12
Montour, co., Pa., U.S.	D8	115
Montour Falls, N.Y., U.S.	C4	109
Montoursville, Pa., U.S.	D8	115
Montpelier, Id., U.S.	G7	89
Montpelier, In., U.S.	C7	91
Montpelier, Oh., U.S.	A1	112

Name	Map Ref	Page
Montpelier, Vt., U.S.	C3	122
Montpellier, Fr.	I10	10
Montréal, Que., Can.	D4	74
Montreal, Wi., U.S.	B3	126
Montréal, Île de, i., Que., Can.	q19	74
Montreal Lake, l., Sask., Can.	C3	75
Montréal-Nord, Que., Can.	p19	74
Montreat, N.C., U.S.	f10	110
Montreuil-Bellay, Fr.	E6	10
Montreux, Switz.	F13	10
Mont-Rolland, Que., Can.	D3	74
Montrose, B.C., Can.	E9	69
Montrose, Scot., U.K.	E10	7
Montrose, Al., U.S.	E2	78
Montrose, Co., U.S.	C3	83
Montrose, Ia., U.S.	D6	92
Montrose, Mi., U.S.	E7	99
Montrose, Pa., U.S.	C10	115
Montrose, Va., U.S.	m18	123
Montrose, co., Co., U.S.	C2	83
Mont-Royal, Que., Can.	p19	74
Montserrat, dep., N.A.	F16	64
Mont-Tremblant, Parc Provincial du, Que., Can.	C3	74
Montvale, N.J., U.S.	A4	107
Montville, Ct., U.S.	D7	84
Monument, Co., U.S.	B6	83
Monument Beach, Ma., U.S.	C6	98
Monument Peak, mtn., Co., U.S.	B3	83
Monument Peak, mtn., Id., U.S.	G4	89
Monument Valley, val., Az., U.S.	A5	80
Monywa, Burma	C3	34
Monza, Italy	D4	14
Monzón, Spain	D12	12
Moodus, Ct., U.S.	D6	84
Moodus Reservoir, res., Ct., U.S.	C6	84
Moody, Tx., U.S.	D4	120
Moody, co., S.D., U.S.	C9	118
Moon Lake, l., Ms., U.S.	A3	101
Moora, Austl.	F3	50
Moorcroft, Wy., U.S.	B8	127
Moore, Ok., U.S.	B4	113
Moore, co., N.C., U.S.	B3	110
Moore, co., Tn., U.S.	B5	119
Moore, co., Tx., U.S.	B2	120
Moore Dam, U.S.	B3	106
Moorefield, W.V., U.S.	B6	125
Moore Haven, Fl., U.S.	F5	86
Mooreland, Ok., U.S.	A2	113
Moore Reservoir, res., U.S.	B3	106
Moores Creek National Military Park, N.C., U.S.	C4	110
Moores Hill, In., U.S.	F7	91
Moorestown, N.J., U.S.	D3	107
Mooresville, In., U.S.	E5	91
Mooresville, N.C., U.S.	B2	110
Moorhead, Mn., U.S.	D2	100
Moorhead, Ms., U.S.	B3	101
Mooringsport, La., U.S.	B2	95
Moose, stm., N.H., U.S.	B4	106
Moose, stm., N.Y., U.S.	B5	109
Moose, stm., Vt., U.S.	B5	122
Moosehead Lake, l., Me., U.S.	C3	96
Moose Jaw, stm., Sask., Can.	G3	75
Moose Lake, Man., Can.	C1	70
Moose Lake, Mn., U.S.	D6	100
Moose Lake, l., Wi., U.S.	B2	126
Mooseleuk Stream, stm., Me., U.S.	B4	96
Mooselookmeguntic Lake, l., Me., U.S.	D2	96
Moose Mountain Creek, stm., Sask., Can.	H4	75
Moose Mountain Provincial Park, Sask., Can.	H4	75
Moosic, Pa., U.S.	m18	115
Moosup, Ct., U.S.	C8	84
Moosup, stm., U.S.	C1	116
Mopang Lake, l., Me., U.S.	D5	96
Mopti, Mali	F5	42
Moquegua, Peru	G4	54
Mora, Port.	G3	12
Mora, Spain	F8	12
Mora, Swe.	F10	6
Mora, Mn., U.S.	E5	100
Mora, N.M., U.S.	B4	108
Mora, co., N.M., U.S.	A5	108
Mora, stm., N.M., U.S.	B5	108
Morādābād, India	F8	38
Morada Nova de Minas, Braz.	E6	57
Morafenobe, Madag.	E8	44
Moraleda, Canal, strt., Chile	E2	56
Morant Cays, is., Jam.	F9	64
Mor'arovskij Zaton, U.S.S.R.	F10	20
Moratuwa, Sri L.	I5	37
Morava, hist. reg., Czech.	F17	8
Morava (March), stm., Eur.	G16	8
Moravia, Ia., U.S.	D5	92
Moravia see Morava, hist. reg., Czech.	F17	8
Morawhanna, Guy.	C13	58
Moray Firth, est., Scot., U.K.	D9	7
Morden, Man., Can.	E2	70
More, Ben, mtn., Scot., U.K.	E8	7
More Assynt, Ben, mtn., Scot., U.K.	C8	7
Moreau, stm., S.D., U.S.	B3	118
Moreauville, La., U.S.	C4	95
Morecambe, Eng., U.K.	G10	7
Moree, Austl.	E9	50
Morehead, Ky., U.S.	B6	94
Morehead City, N.C., U.S.	C6	110
Morehouse, Mo., U.S.	E8	102
Morehouse, co., La., U.S.	B4	95
Morelia, Mex.	H9	62
Morella, Spain	E11	12
Morena, India	G8	38
Morenci, Az., U.S.	D6	80
Morenci, Mi., U.S.	G6	99
Moresby Island, i., B.C., Can.	C2	69
Moreuil, Fr.	C9	10
Morey, Lake, l., Vt., U.S.	D4	122
Morey Peak, mtn., Nv., U.S.	E5	105
Morgan, Mn., U.S.	F4	100
Morgan, Ut., U.S.	B4	121
Morgan, co., Al., U.S.	A3	78
Morgan, co., Co., U.S.	A7	83
Morgan, co., Ga., U.S.	C3	87
Morgan, co., Il., U.S.	D3	90
Morgan, co., In., U.S.	F5	91
Morgan, co., Ky., U.S.	C6	94
Morgan, co., Mo., U.S.	C5	102
Morgan, co., Oh., U.S.	C4	112
Morgan, co., Tn., U.S.	C9	119
Morgan, co., Ut., U.S.	B4	121
Morgan, co., W.V., U.S.	B6	125
Morgan City, La., U.S.	E4	95
Morganfield, Ky., U.S.	C2	94
Morgan Hill, Ca., U.S.	D3	82
Morgan Island, i., S.C., U.S.	G6	117
Morgan Point, c., Ct., U.S.	E4	84
Morganton, N.C., U.S.	B1	110
Morgantown, In., U.S.	F5	91
Morgantown, Ky., U.S.	C3	94
Morgantown, Ms., U.S.	D2	101
Morgantown, Tn., U.S.	D8	119
Morgantown, W.V., U.S.	B5	125
Morganza, La., U.S.	D4	95
Mori, Japan	q18	30a
Moriah, Mount, mtn., Nv., U.S.	D7	105
Moriarty, N.M., U.S.	C3	108
Morinville, Alta., Can.	C4	68
Morioka, Japan	C14	30
Morkoka, stm., U.S.S.R.	D16	20
Morlaix, Fr.	D3	10
Morley, Mo., U.S.	D8	102
Mormon Peak, mtn., Nv., U.S.	G7	105
Morning Sun, Ia., U.S.	C6	92
Mornington Island, i., Austl.	C7	50
Morobe, Pap. N. Gui.	m16	50a
Morocco, In., U.S.	C3	91
Morocco, ctry., Afr.	B4	42
Morogoro, Tan.	C7	44
Moro Gulf, b., Phil.	D7	32
Morombe, Madag.	F8	44
Morón, Cuba	C8	64
Morondava, Madag.	F8	44
Morón de la Frontera, Spain	H6	12
Moroni, Com.	D8	44
Moroni, Ut., U.S.	D4	121
Morošečnoje, U.S.S.R.	F25	20
Morotai, i., Indon.	E8	32
Morrill, Ne., U.S.	C2	104
Morrill, co., Ne., U.S.	C2	104
Morrilton, Ar., U.S.	B3	81
Morrinhos, Braz.	D4	57
Morris, Man., Can.	E3	70
Morris, Al., U.S.	B3	78
Morris, Il., U.S.	B5	90
Morris, Mn., U.S.	E3	100
Morris, Ok., U.S.	B6	113
Morris, co., Ks., U.S.	D7	93
Morris, co., N.J., U.S.	B3	107
Morris, co., Tx., U.S.	C5	120
Morrisburg, Ont., Can.	C9	73
Morris Island, i., S.C., U.S.	F8	117
Morrison, Il., U.S.	B4	90
Morrison, Ok., U.S.	A4	113
Morrison, co., Mn., U.S.	D4	100
Morrison City, Tn., U.S.	C11	119
Morrisonville, Il., U.S.	D4	90
Morrisonville, N.Y., U.S.	f11	109
Morris Plains, N.J., U.S.	B4	107
Morristown, In., U.S.	E6	91
Morristown, Mn., U.S.	F5	100
Morristown, N.J., U.S.	B4	107
Morristown, Tn., U.S.	C10	119
Morristown National Historical Park, N.J., U.S.	B3	107
Morrisville, N.Y., U.S.	C5	109
Morrisville, Pa., U.S.	F12	115
Morrisville, Vt., U.S.	B3	122
Morro, Ec.	I2	58
Morro, Punta, c., Chile	B2	56
Morro Bay, Ca., U.S.	E3	82
Morro do Chapéu, Braz.	F10	54
Morrow, Ga., U.S.	C2	87
Morrow, Oh., U.S.	C1	112
Morrow, co., Oh., U.S.	B3	112
Morrow, co., Or., U.S.	B7	114
Moršansk, U.S.S.R.	H24	22
Morse, La., U.S.	D3	95
Morse Reservoir, res., In., U.S.	D5	91
Morses Creek, stm., N.J., U.S.	k8	107
Mortagne, Fr.	D7	10
Mortagne-sur-Sèvre, Fr.	E6	10
Mortara, Italy	D3	14
Mortes, Rio das, stm., Braz.	G8	54
Morton, Il., U.S.	C4	90
Morton, Ms., U.S.	C4	101
Morton, Tx., U.S.	C1	120
Morton, Wa., U.S.	C3	124
Morton, co., Ks., U.S.	E2	93
Morton, co., N.D., U.S.	C4	111
Morton Grove, Il., U.S.	h9	90
Morton Pass, Wy., U.S.	E7	127
Mortons Gap, Ky., U.S.	C2	94
Morven, mtn., Scot., U.K.	C9	7
Morvi, India	I4	38
Morwell, Austl.	G9	50
Mosbach, Ger.	F9	8
Moscos Islands, is., Burma	G4	34
Moscow, Id., U.S.	C2	89
Moscow, Pa., U.S.	m18	115
Moscow Mills, Mo., U.S.	C7	102
Moscow see Moskva, U.S.S.R.	F20	22
Mosel (Moselle), stm., Eur.	F6	8
Moselle, Ms., U.S.	D4	101
Moselle (Mosel), stm., Eur.	F6	8
Moses Coulee, val., Wa., U.S.	B6	124
Moses Lake, Wa., U.S.	B6	124
Moses Lake, l., Wa., U.S.	B6	124
Mosheim, Tn., U.S.	C11	119
Moshi, Tan.	B7	44
Mosinee, Wi., U.S.	D4	126
Mosjøen, Nor.	D9	6
Moskva (Moscow), U.S.S.R.	F20	22
Mosquera, Col.	F3	58
Mosquito Creek Lake, res., Oh., U.S.	A5	112
Mosquito Lagoon, b., Fl., U.S.	D6	86
Mosquitos, Golfo de los, b., Pan.	J7	64
Moss, Nor.	G8	6
Mossaka, Congo	B3	44
Moss Bluff, La., U.S.	D2	95
Mosselbaai, S. Afr.	H4	44
Mossendjo, Congo	B2	44
Mossoró, Braz.	E11	54
Moss Point, Ms., U.S.	E5	101
Most, Czech.	E13	8
Mostaganem, Alg.	A6	42
Mostar, Yugo.	F12	14
Mostardas, Braz.	C6	56
Møsting, Kap, c., Grnld.	D24	66
Moswansicut Pond, l., R.I., U.S.	C3	116
Mota del Marqués, Spain	D6	12
Motala, Swe.	G10	6
Motherwell, Scot., U.K.	F8	7
Motīhāri, India	G11	38
Motilla del Palancar, Spain	F10	12
Motley, co., Tx., U.S.	B2	120
Motril, Spain	I8	12
Mott, N.D., U.S.	C3	111
Motueka, N.Z.	D4	52
Motul de Felipe Carrillo Puerto, Mex.	G15	62
Motygino, U.S.S.R.	F12	20
Mouchoir Passage, strt., N.A.	D12	64
Moudjéria, Maur.	E3	42
Mouila, Gabon	B2	44
Moulamein Creek, stm., Austl.	G8	50
Moulins, Fr.	F10	10
Moulmeingyun, Burma	F3	34
Moulouya, Oued, stm., Mor.	B5	42
Moulton, Al., U.S.	A2	78
Moulton, Ia., U.S.	D5	92
Moultrie, Ga., U.S.	E3	87
Moultrie, co., Il., U.S.	D5	90
Moultrie, Lake, res., S.C., U.S.	E7	117
Mound, Mn., U.S.	n11	100
Mound Bayou, Ms., U.S.	B3	101
Mound City, Il., U.S.	F4	90
Mound City, Ks., U.S.	D9	93
Mound City, Mo., U.S.	A2	102
Mound City Group National Monument, Oh., U.S.	C2	112
Moundou, Chad	G9	42
Moundridge, Ks., U.S.	D6	93
Mounds, Il., U.S.	F4	90
Mounds, Ok., U.S.	B5	113
Mounds View, Mn., U.S.	m12	100
Moundsville, W.V., U.S.	B4	125
Moundville, Al., U.S.	C2	78
Mountainair, N.M., U.S.	C3	108
Mountainaire, Az., U.S.	B4	80
Mountain Brook, Al., U.S.	g7	78
Mountain City, Ga., U.S.	B3	87
Mountain City, Nv., U.S.	B6	105
Mountain City, Tn., U.S.	C12	119
Mountain Fork, stm., U.S.	C7	113
Mountain Grove, Mo., U.S.	D5	102
Mountain Home, Ar., U.S.	A3	81
Mountain Home, Id., U.S.	F3	89
Mountain Home Air Force Base, mil., Id., U.S.	F3	89
Mountain Iron, Mn., U.S.	C6	100
Mountain Lake, Mn., U.S.	G4	100
Mountain Lake Park, Md., U.S.	m12	97
Mountain Nile (Bahr al-Jabal), stm., Sudan	G12	42
Mountain Pine, Ar., U.S.	C2	81
Mountainside, N.J., U.S.	B4	107
Mountain View, Ar., U.S.	B3	81
Mountain View, Ca., U.S.	k8	82
Mountain View, Mo., U.S.	D6	102
Mountain View, N.M., U.S.	C3	108
Mountain View, Ok., U.S.	B3	113
Mountain View, Wy., U.S.	E2	127
Mountain Village, Ak., U.S.	C7	79
Mount Airy, Md., U.S.	B3	97
Mount Airy, N.C., U.S.	A2	110
Mount Albert, Ont., Can.	C5	73
Mount Angel, Or., U.S.	B4	114
Mount Arlington, N.J., U.S.	B3	107
Mount Ayr, Ia., U.S.	D3	92
Mount Carmel, Il., U.S.	E6	90
Mount Carmel, Oh., U.S.	o13	112
Mount Carmel, Pa., U.S.	E9	115
Mount Carmel [-Mitchell's Brook-Saint Catherine's], Newf., Can.	E5	72
Mount Carroll, Il., U.S.	A4	90
Mount Clare, W.V., U.S.	B4	125
Mount Clemens, Mi., U.S.	F8	99
Mount Desert Island, i., Me., U.S.	D4	96
Mount Dora, Fl., U.S.	D5	86
Mount Forest, Ont., Can.	D4	73
Mount Gambier, Austl.	G8	50
Mount Gay, W.V., U.S.	D2	125
Mount Gilead, N.C., U.S.	B3	110
Mount Gilead, Oh., U.S.	B3	112
Mount Healthy, Oh., U.S.	o12	112
Mount Holly, N.J., U.S.	D3	107
Mount Holly, N.C., U.S.	B1	110
Mount Holly Springs, Pa., U.S.	F7	115
Mount Hope, Austl.	F7	50
Mount Hope, Ks., U.S.	E6	93
Mount Hope, W.V., U.S.	D3	125
Mount Hope, stm., Ct., U.S.	B7	84
Mount Hope Bay, b., U.S.	D6	116
Mount Horeb, Wi., U.S.	E4	126
Mount Ida, Ar., U.S.	C2	81
Mount Isa, Austl.	D7	50
Mount Jackson, Va., U.S.	B4	123
Mount Jewett, Pa., U.S.	C4	115
Mount Joy, Pa., U.S.	F9	115
Mount Juliet, Tn., U.S.	A5	119
Mount Kisco, N.Y., U.S.	D7	109
Mount Lebanon, Pa., U.S.	F1	115
Mount Magnet, Austl.	E3	50
Mount Morris, Il., U.S.	A4	90
Mount Morris, Mi., U.S.	E7	99
Mount Morris, N.Y., U.S.	C3	109
Mount Olive, Al., U.S.	B3	78
Mount Olive, Il., U.S.	D4	90
Mount Olive, Ms., U.S.	D4	101
Mount Olive, N.C., U.S.	B4	110
Mount Olive, Tn., U.S.	n14	119
Mount Orab, Oh., U.S.	C2	112
Mount Pearl, Newf., Can.	E5	72
Mount Penn, Pa., U.S.	F10	115
Mount Pleasant, Ia., U.S.	D6	92
Mount Pleasant, Mi., U.S.	E6	99
Mount Pleasant, N.C., U.S.	B2	110
Mount Pleasant, Pa., U.S.	F2	115
Mount Pleasant, S.C., U.S.	F8	117
Mount Pleasant, Tn., U.S.	B4	119
Mount Pleasant, Tx., U.S.	C5	120
Mount Pleasant, Ut., U.S.	D4	121
Mount Pocono, Pa., U.S.	D11	115
Mount Prospect, Il., U.S.	A6	90
Mount Pulaski, Il., U.S.	C4	90
Mountrail, co., N.D., U.S.	A3	111
Mount Rainier, Md., U.S.	f9	97
Mount Rainier National Park, Wa., U.S.	C4	124
Mount Revelstoke National Park, B.C., Can.	D8	69
Mount Rogers National Recreation Area, Va., U.S.	D1	123
Mount Rushmore National Memorial, hist., S.D., U.S.	D2	118
Mount Savage, Md., U.S.	k13	97
Mount Shasta, Ca., U.S.	B2	82
Mount Sterling, Il., U.S.	D3	90
Mount Sterling, Ky., U.S.	B6	94
Mount Sterling, Oh., U.S.	C2	112
Mount Uniacke, N.S., Can.	E6	71
Mount Union, Pa., U.S.	F6	115
Mount Vernon, Al., U.S.	D1	78
Mount Vernon, Ga., U.S.	D4	87
Mount Vernon, Il., U.S.	E5	90
Mount Vernon, In., U.S.	I2	91
Mount Vernon, Ia., U.S.	C6	92
Mount Vernon, Ky., U.S.	C5	94
Mount Vernon, Mo., U.S.	D4	102
Mount Vernon, N.Y., U.S.	h13	109
Mount Vernon, Oh., U.S.	B3	112
Mount Vernon, Tx., U.S.	C5	120
Mount Vernon, Wa., U.S.	A3	124
Mount View, R.I., U.S.	D4	116
Mount Washington, Ky., U.S.	B4	94
Mount Wolf, Pa., U.S.	F8	115
Mount Zion, Il., U.S.	D5	90
Moura, Braz.	D6	54
Moura, Port.	G4	12
Mourne Mountains, mts., N. Ire., U.K.	G6	7
Moussoro, Chad	F9	42
Moutong, Indon.	E7	32
Moville, Ia., U.S.	B1	92
Moweaqua, Il., U.S.	D4	90
Mower, co., Mn., U.S.	G6	100
Moxee City, Wa., U.S.	C5	124
Moxos, Llanos de, pl., Bol.	G6	54
Moyahua, Mex.	G8	62
Moyale, Kenya	H2	46
Moyen Atlas, mts., Mor.	B5	42
Moyeuvre-Grande, Fr.	C13	10
Moyock, N.C., U.S.	A6	110
Moyu, China	B8	38
Možajsk, U.S.S.R.	F19	22
Mozambique, ctry., Afr.	E6	44
Mozambique Channel, strt., Afr.	E8	44
Mozyr', U.S.S.R.	G3	18
Mpanda, Tan.	C6	44
Mpika, Zam.	D6	44
Mrkonjić Grad, Yugo.	E12	14
Msaken, Tun.	N5	14
Mtwara, Tan.	D8	44
Muang Khammouan, Laos	F8	34
Muang Pakxan, Laos	E7	34
Muar, Malay.	M7	34
Muaratewe, Indon.	F5	32
Muāri, Rās, c., Pak.	H2	38
Mücheln, Ger.	D11	8
Muchinga Mountains, mts., Zam.	D6	44
Muckleshoot Indian Reservation, Wa., U.S.	f11	124
Mud, stm., Ky., U.S.	C3	94
Mud, stm., Mn., U.S.	B3	100
Mud, stm., W.V., U.S.	C2	125
Mudanjiang, China	C12	26
Mud Creek, stm., Ok., U.S.	C4	113
Muddy Boggy Creek, stm., Ok., U.S.	C6	113
Muddy Creek, stm., Ut., U.S.	E4	121
Muddy Creek, stm., Wy., U.S.	E2	127
Muddy Creek, stm., Wy., U.S.	E5	127
Muddy Creek, stm., Wy., U.S.	D6	127
Muddy Creek, stm., Wy., U.S.	C4	127
Muddy Mountains, mts., Nv., U.S.	G7	105
Muddy Peak, mtn., Nv., U.S.	G7	105
Mud Lake, l., Me., U.S.	A4	96
Mud Lake, l., Nv., U.S.	F4	105
Mudon, Burma	F4	34
Muenster, Tx., U.S.	C4	120
Mufulira, Zam.	D5	44
Mu Gia, Deo (Mu Gia Pass), Asia	F8	34
Muğla, Tur.	H13	4
Mühldorf, Ger.	G12	8
Muhlenberg, co., Ky., U.S.	C2	94
Mühlhausen, Ger.	D10	8
Mühlviertel, reg., Aus.	G14	8
Muhola, Fin.	E15	6
Muirkirk, Md., U.S.	B4	97
Muiron Islands, is., Austl.	D2	50
Muir Woods National Monument, Ca., U.S.	h7	82
Mukden see Shenyang, China	C11	26
Mukilteo, Wa., U.S.	B3	124
Mukwonago, Wi., U.S.	F5	126
Mula, Spain	G10	12
Mulanje, Mwi.	E7	44
Mulberry, Ar., U.S.	B1	81
Mulberry, Fl., U.S.	E4	86
Mulberry, In., U.S.	D4	91
Mulberry, N.C., U.S.	A1	110
Mulberry, stm., Ar., U.S.	B1	81
Mulberry Fork, stm., Al., U.S.	B3	78
Muldraugh, Ky., U.S.	C4	94
Muldrow, Ok., U.S.	B7	113
Muleshoe, Tx., U.S.	B1	120
Mulgrave, N.S., Can.	D8	71
Mulhacén, mtn., Spain	H8	12
Mulhouse, Fr.	E14	10
Mull, Island of, i., Scot., U.K.	E6	7
Mullan, Id., U.S.	B3	89
Mullan Pass, Mt., U.S.	D4	103
Mullens, W.V., U.S.	D3	125
Muller, Pegunungan, mts., Indon.	E5	32
Mullet Key, i., Fl., U.S.	p10	86
Mullett Lake, l., Mi., U.S.	C6	99
Mullewa, Austl.	E3	50
Mullica, stm., N.J., U.S.	D3	107
Mullins, S.C., U.S.	C9	117
Multān, Pak.	E4	38
Multnomah, co., Or., U.S.	B4	114
Mulvane, Ks., U.S.	E6	93
Mumbwa, Zam.	D5	44
Mummy Range, mts., Co., U.S.	A5	83
Muna, Pulau, i., Indon.	F7	32
Muncar, Indon.	n17	33a
München (Munich), Ger.	G11	8
Muncie, In., U.S.	D7	91
Muncy, Pa., U.S.	D8	115
Munday, Tx., U.S.	C3	120
Mundelein, Il., U.S.	A5	90
Münden, Ger.	D9	8
Munford, Al., U.S.	B4	78
Munford, Tn., U.S.	B2	119
Munfordville, Ky., U.S.	C4	94
Mungbere, Zaire	H11	42
Munhall, Pa., U.S.	k14	115
Munhango, Ang.	D3	44
Munich see München, Ger.	G11	8
Munising, Mi., U.S.	B4	99
Munster, Ger.	C10	8
Münster, Ger.	D7	8
Munster, In., U.S.	A2	91
Munster, hist. reg., Ire.	I4	7
Munsungan Lake, l., Me., U.S.	B3	96
Munuscong Lake, l., Mi., U.S.	B6	99
Muong Sing, Laos	D6	34
Muqayshit, i., U.A.E.	D5	46
Muqdisho, Som.	H4	46
Mur (Mura), stm., Eur.	I15	8
Mura (Mur), stm., Eur.	I16	8
Murat, Fr.	G9	10
Murat, stm., Tur.	H16	4
Murau, Aus.	H14	8
Muravera, Italy	J4	14
Murça, Port.	D4	12
Murchison, stm., Austl.	E3	50
Murcia, Spain	H10	12
Murderkill, stm., De., U.S.	D4	85
Murdo, S.D., U.S.	D5	118
Mureş (Maros), stm., Eur.	C5	16
Muret, Fr.	I8	10
Murfreesboro, Ar., U.S.	C2	81
Murfreesboro, N.C., U.S.	A5	110
Murfreesboro, Tn., U.S.	B5	119
Mūrīān, Hāmūn-e, l., Iran	C6	46
Murmansk, U.S.S.R.	D4	18
Murom, U.S.S.R.	F25	22
Muroran, Japan	q18	30a
Muros, Spain	C2	12
Muroto, Japan	I7	30
Muroto-zaki, c., Japan	I7	30
Murphy, Mo., U.S.	g13	102
Murphy, N.C., U.S.	f8	110
Murphy Island, i., S.C., U.S.	E9	117
Murphysboro, Il., U.S.	F4	90
Murray, Ia., U.S.	C4	92
Murray, Ky., U.S.	f9	94
Murray, Ut., U.S.	C4	121
Murray, co., Ga., U.S.	B2	87
Murray, co., Mn., U.S.	F3	100
Murray, co., Ok., U.S.	C4	113
Murray, stm., Austl.	F7	50
Murray, Lake, res., Ok., U.S.	C4	113
Murray, Lake, res., S.C., U.S.	C5	117
Murray Head, c., P.E.I., Can.	C7	71
Murraysburg, S. Afr.	H4	44
Murrayville, Ga., U.S.	B3	87
Murrells Inlet, S.C., U.S.	D9	117
Murrells Inlet, b., S.C., U.S.	D10	117
Murten, Switz.	F14	10
Murukta, U.S.S.R.	D14	20
Murwāra, India	I9	38
Murwillumbah, Austl.	E10	50
Mürzzuschlag, Aus.	H15	8
Muş, Tur.	H16	4
Musay'īd, Qatar	D5	46
Muscat and Oman see Oman, ctry., Asia	D6	46
Muscatatuck, stm., In., U.S.	G5	91
Muscatine, Ia., U.S.	C6	92
Muscatine, co., Ia., U.S.	C6	92
Muscat see Masqaṭ, Oman	D6	46
Mus-Chaja, Gora, mtn., U.S.S.R.	E22	20
Muscle Shoals, Al., U.S.	A2	78
Muscow, Mount, mtn., B.C., Can.	C4	69
Muscoda, Wi., U.S.	E3	126
Muscogee, co., Ga., U.S.	D2	87
Musconetcong, stm., N.J., U.S.	B4	107
Muscooten Bay, l., Il., U.S.	C3	90
Muse, Pa., U.S.	F1	115
Musgrave, Austl.	B8	50
Musgrave Harbour, Newf., Can.	D5	72
Musgrave Ranges, mts., Austl.	E6	50
Musgravetown, Newf., Can.	D5	72
Mushin, Nig.	G6	42
Muskeg Bay, b., Mn., U.S.	B3	100
Muskeget Island, i., Ma., U.S.	D7	98
Muskego, Wi., U.S.	F5	126
Muskego Lake, l., Wi., U.S.	n11	126
Muskegon, Mi., U.S.	E4	99
Muskegon, co., Mi., U.S.	E4	99
Muskegon, stm., Mi., U.S.	E4	99
Muskegon Heights, Mi., U.S.	E4	99
Muskegon Lake, l., Mi., U.S.	E4	99
Muskingum, co., Oh., U.S.	B4	112
Muskingum, stm., Oh., U.S.	C4	112
Muskogee, Ok., U.S.	B6	113
Muskogee, co., Ok., U.S.	B6	113
Musoma, Tan.	B6	44
Musquacook Lakes, l., Me., U.S.	B3	96
Musquodoboit Harbour, N.S., Can.	E6	71
Musselshell, co., Mt., U.S.	D8	103
Musselshell, stm., Mt., U.S.	D9	103
Mussidan, Fr.	G7	10
Mussuma, Ang.	D4	44
Mustafakemalpaşa, Tur.	I12	16
Mustang, Ok., U.S.	B4	113
Mustinka, stm., Mn., U.S.	E2	100
Mut, Tur.	A3	40
Mutare, Zimb.	E6	44
Mutoraj, U.S.S.R.	E14	20
Mutsu, Japan	A14	30

Name — Map Ref — Page

Mutsu-wan, b., Japan **A13** 30
Mutton Mountains, mts., Or., U.S. **C5** 114
Muzaffarābād, Pak. **C5** 38
Muzaffarnagar, India **F7** 38
Muzaffarpur, India **G11** 38
Muzon, Cape, c., Ak., U.S. **n23** 79
Muztag, mtn., China **B9** 38
Muztag, mtn., China **B12** 38
Mvuma, Zimb. **E6** 44
Mwanza, Tan. **B6** 44
Mweelrea, mtn., Ire. **H3** 7
Mweka, Zaire **B4** 44
Mwenezi, Zimb. **F6** 44
Mweru, Lake, l., Afr. **C5** 44
Mwinilunga, Zam. **D4** 44
Myakka, stm., Fl., U.S. **E4** 86
Myanaung, Burma **E3** 34
Myaungmya, Burma **F3** 34
Myerstown, Pa., U.S. **F9** 115
Myingyan, Burma **D3** 34
Myitkyinā, Burma **B4** 34
Myllymäki, Fin. **E15** 6
Mymensingh, Bngl. **H14** 38
Mynämäki, Fin. **F13** 6
Myrskylä (Mörskom), Fin. **F15** 6
Myrtle Beach, S.C., U.S. **D10** 117
Myrtle Beach Air Force Base, mil., S.C., U.S. **D10** 117
Myrtle Creek, Or., U.S. **D3** 114
Myrtle Grove, Fl., U.S. **u14** 86
Myrtle Point, Or., U.S. **D2** 114
Mysen, Nor. **G8** 6
Mysore, India **F4** 37
Mys Šmidta, U.S.S.R. **D30** 20
Mystic, Ct., U.S. **D8** 84
Mystic Lakes, l., Ma., U.S. **g11** 98
My Tho, Viet. **I9** 34
Mytišči, U.S.S.R. **F20** 22
Mzimba, Mwi. **D6** 44
Mzuzu, Mwi. **D6** 44

N

Naalehu, Hi., U.S. **D6** 88
Naas, Ire. **H6** 7
Nabadwīp, India **I13** 38
Naberežnyje Čelny, U.S.S.R. **F8** 18
Nabeul, Tun. **M5** 14
Nabī Shu'ayb, Jabal an-, mtn., Yemen **E3** 46
Nabnasset, Ma., U.S. **A5** 98
Nābulus, Isr. Occ. **C4** 40
Nacala-Velha, Moz. **D8** 44
Naches, stm., Wa., U.S. **C5** 124
Nachingwea, Tan. **D7** 44
Nachodka, U.S.S.R. **I20** 20
Nacimiento, Lake, res., Ca., U.S. **E3** 82
Naco, Mex. **B5** 62
Naco, Az., U.S. **F6** 80
Nacogdoches, Tx., U.S. **D5** 120
Nacogdoches, co., Tx., U.S. **D5** 120
Nadiād, India **I5** 38
Nadym, stm., U.S.S.R. **E8** 20
Næstved, Den. **I8** 6
Naga, Phil. **r20** 32
Nagahama, Japan **G9** 30
Nagaland, state, India **H16** 38
Nagano, Japan **F11** 30
Nagaoka, Japan **E11** 30
Nāgappattinam, India **G5** 37
Nagasaki, Japan **J2** 30
Nāgaur, India **G5** 38
Nāgda, India **I6** 38
Nāgercoil, India **H4** 37
Nago, Japan **y27** 31b
Nagornyj, U.S.S.R. **F18** 20
Nagoya, Japan **G9** 30
Nāgpur, India **B5** 37
Nags Head, N.C., U.S. **B7** 110
Nagykanizsa, Hung. **I16** 8
Nagykőrös, Hung. **H19** 8
Naha, Japan **y27** 31b
Nahant, Ma., U.S. **g12** 98
Nahariya, Isr. **C4** 40
Nahmakanta Lake, l., Me., U.S. **C3** 96
Nahunta, Ga., U.S. **E5** 87
Naidong, China **F14** 38
Nain, Newf., Can. **g9** 72
Nā'īn, Iran **B5** 46
Nairn, Scot., U.K. **D9** 7
Nairobi, Kenya **B7** 44
Najafābād, Iran **B5** 46
Nájera, Spain **C9** 12
Najin, N. Kor. **C13** 26
Nakaminato, Japan **F13** 30
Nakatsu, Japan **I4** 30
Nakatsugawa, Japan **G10** 30
Nakhon Pathom, Thai. **H6** 34
Nakhon Phanom, Thai. **F8** 34
Nakhon Ratchasima, Thai. **G7** 34
Nakhon Sawan, Thai. **G6** 34
Nakhon Si Thammarat, Thai. **J5** 34
Nakina, Ont., Can. **o18** 73
Naknek, Ak., U.S. **D8** 79
Naknek Lake, l., Ak., U.S. **D8** 79
Nakskov, Den. **I8** 6
Nakuru, Kenya **B7** 44
Nakusp, B.C., Can. **D9** 69
Nalchik see Nal'čik, U.S.S.R. **I6** 18
Nal'čik, U.S.S.R. **I6** 18
Nalgonda, India **D5** 37
Nālūt, Libya **B8** 42
Namak, Daryācheh-ye, l., Iran **K8** 18
Namangan, U.S.S.R. **I12** 18
Namanock Island, i., N.J., U.S. **A3** 107
Namapa, Moz. **D7** 44
Namatanai, Pap. N. Gui. **k17** 50a
Nambour, Austl. **E10** 50
Namcha Barwa see Namjagbarwa Feng, mtn., China **F16** 38
Nam Co, l., China **E14** 38
Nam Dinh, Viet. **D9** 34
Namekagon, stm., Wi., U.S. **B2** 126
Namekagon Lake, l., Wi., U.S. **B2** 126
Namhkam, Burma **C4** 34
Namib Desert, des., Nmb. **F2** 44
Namibe, Ang. **E2** 44
Namibia, ctry., Afr. **F3** 44
Namjagbarwa Feng, mtn., China **F16** 38
Namlea, Indon. **F8** 32
Nampa, Id., U.S. **F2** 89
Namp'o, N. Kor. **D12** 26
Nampula, Moz. **E7** 44
Namsos, Nor. **D8** 6
Namur, Bel. **E4** 8
Nanaimo, B.C., Can. **E5** 69
Nanakuli, Hi., U.S. **B3** 88
Nanao, Japan **E9** 30
Nance, co., Ne., U.S. **C7** 104
Nanchang, China **G4** 28
Nanchong, China **E8** 26
Nancy, Fr. **D13** 10
Nanda Devi, mtn., India **E8** 38
Nānded, India **C4** 37
Nandurbār, India **B3** 37
Nandyāl, India **E5** 37
Nānga Parbat, mtn., Pak. **C6** 38
Nangqian (Xiangda), China **D17** 38
Nanjing (Nanking), China **C7** 28
Nanking see Nanjing, China **C7** 28
Nankoku, Japan **I6** 30
Nankou, China **C10** 26
Nan Ling, mts., China **F9** 26
Nanning, China **C10** 34
Nanping, China **I7** 28
Nansei-shotō (Ryukyu Islands), is., Japan **F12** 26
Nansemond, stm., Va., U.S. **k14** 123
Nantes, Fr. **E5** 10
Nanticoke, Ont., Can. **E4** 73
Nanticoke, Pa., U.S. **D10** 115
Nanticoke, stm., U.S. **D6** 97
Nanton, Alta., Can. **D4** 68
Nantong, China **C9** 28
Nant'ou, Tai. **L9** 28
Nantua, Fr. **F12** 10
Nantucket, Ma., U.S. **D7** 98
Nantucket, co., Ma., U.S. **D7** 98
Nantucket Island, i., Ma., U.S. **D7** 98
Nantucket Sound, strt., Ma., U.S. **C7** 98
Nantuxent Point, c., N.J., U.S. **E2** 107
Nanty Glo, Pa., U.S. **F4** 115
Nanuet, N.Y., U.S. **g12** 109
Nanuque, Braz. **D8** 57
Nanxiang, China **D10** 28
Nanxiong, China **J3** 28
Nanyang, China **B1** 28
Naoetsu, Japan **E11** 30
Naoma, W.V., U.S. **n13** 125
Naomi Peak, mtn., Ut., U.S. **B4** 121
Náousa, Grc. **I6** 16
Napa, Ca., U.S. **C2** 82
Napa, co., Ca., U.S. **C2** 82
Napanee, Ont., Can. **C8** 73
Napatree Point, c., R.I., U.S. **G1** 116
Napavine, Wa., U.S. **C3** 124
Naperville, Il., U.S. **B5** 90
Napier, N.Z. **C6** 52
Napierville, Que., Can. **D4** 74
Naples, Fl., U.S. **F5** 86
Naples, Tx., U.S. **C5** 120
Naples, Ut., U.S. **C6** 121
Naples see Napoli, Italy **I9** 14
Napo, stm., S.A. **I6** 58
Napoleon, N.D., U.S. **C6** 111
Napoleon, Oh., U.S. **A1** 112
Napoleonville, La., U.S. **E4** 95
Napoli (Naples), Italy **I9** 14
Nappanee, In., U.S. **B5** 91
Nara, Japan **H8** 30
Nara, Mali **E4** 42
Naracoorte, Austl. **G8** 50
Naramata, B.C., Can. **E8** 69
Naranja, Fl., U.S. **G6** 86
Narasapur, India **D6** 37
Narasaraopet, India **D6** 37
Narathiwat, Thai. **K6** 34
Nārāyanganj, Bngl. **I14** 38
Narberth, Pa., U.S. **p20** 115
Narbonne, Fr. **I9** 10
Nardò, Italy **I13** 14
Narew, stm., Eur. **C21** 8
Nārīn Ghar, Afg. **B3** 38
Narita, Japan **G13** 30
Narmada, stm., India **J5** 38
Nārnaul, India **F7** 38
Narni, Italy **G7** 14
Naro-Fominsk, U.S.S.R. **F19** 22
Narragansett, R.I., U.S. **F4** 116
Narragansett Bay, b., R.I., U.S. **E5** 116
Narraguagus, stm., Me., U.S. **D5** 96
Narrows, Va., U.S. **C2** 123
Narsimhapur, India **I8** 38
Narssag, Grnld. **D23** 66
Naruto, Japan **H7** 30
Narva, U.S.S.R. **B11** 22
Narvik, Nor. **B11** 6
Naselle, Wa., U.S. **C2** 124
Nash, Tx., U.S. **C5** 120
Nash, co., N.C., U.S. **A4** 110
Nashawena Island, i., Ma., U.S. **D6** 98
Nash Stream, stm., N.H., U.S. **A4** 106
Nashua, Ia., U.S. **B5** 92
Nashua, N.H., U.S. **E4** 106
Nashua, stm., U.S. **E3** 106
Nashville, Ar., U.S. **D2** 81
Nashville, Ga., U.S. **E3** 87
Nashville, Il., U.S. **E4** 90
Nashville, In., U.S. **F5** 91
Nashville, Mi., U.S. **F5** 99
Nashville, N.C., U.S. **B5** 110
Nashville, Tn., U.S. **A5** 119
Nashwauk, Mn., U.S. **C5** 100
Nāsik, India **C2** 37
Nāsir, Sudan **G12** 42
Naskaupi, stm., Newf., Can. **g9** 72
Nassau, Bah. **B9** 64
Nassau, co., Fl., U.S. **B5** 86
Nassau, co., N.Y., U.S. **E7** 109
Nassau, stm., Fl., U.S. **k8** 86
Nassau Sound, b., Fl., U.S. **B5** 86
Nasser, Lake, res., Afr. **D12** 42
Nässjö, Swe. **H10** 6
Nasukoin Mountain, mtn., Mt., U.S. **B2** 103
Natal, Braz. **E11** 54
Natalbany, La., U.S. **D5** 95
Natalia, Tx., U.S. **E3** 120
Natashquan, stm., Can. **h9** 72
Natchaug, stm., Ct., U.S. **B7** 84
Natchez, Ms., U.S. **D2** 101
Natchitoches, La., U.S. **C2** 95
Natchitoches, co., La., U.S. **C2** 95
Nāthdwāra, India **H5** 38
Natick, Ma., U.S. **B5** 98
National City, Ca., U.S. **F5** 82
Natron, Lake, l., Afr. **B7** 44
Natrona, co., Wy., U.S. **D5** 127
Natrona Heights, Pa., U.S. **E2** 115
Nattaung, mtn., Burma **E4** 34
Natuna Besar, i., Indon. **M10** 34
Natuna Besar, Kepulauan, is., Indon. **M10** 34
Natuna Selatan, Kepulauan, is., Indon. **M10** 34
Natural Bridge, Ut., U.S. **F3** 121
Natural Bridge, Va., U.S. **C3** 123
Natural Bridges National Monument, Ut., U.S. **F6** 121
Naturaliste, Cape, c., Austl. **F3** 50
Nauen, Ger. **C12** 8
Naugatuck, Ct., U.S. **D3** 84
Naugatuck, stm., Ct., U.S. **D3** 84
Naumburg, Ger. **D11** 8
Naushon Island, i., Ma., U.S. **D6** 98
Nautilus Park, Ct., U.S. **D7** 84
Nauvoo, Il., U.S. **C2** 90
Nava del Rey, Spain **D6** 12
Navahermosa, Spain **F7** 12
Navajo, co., Az., U.S. **B5** 80
Navajo Dam, N.M., U.S. **A2** 108
Navajo Indian Reservation, U.S. **A4** 80
Navajo Mountain, mtn., Ut., U.S. **F5** 121
Navajo National Monument, Az., U.S. **A5** 80
Navajo Reservoir, res., U.S. **A2** 108
Navalcarnero, Spain **E7** 12
Navalmoral de la Mata, Spain **F6** 12
Navalvillar de Pela, Spain **F6** 12
Navan, Ont., Can. **B9** 73
Navan, Ire. **H6** 7
Navarin, Mys, c., U.S.S.R. **E29** 20
Navarino, Isla, i., Chile **H3** 56
Navarre, Oh., U.S. **B4** 112
Navarro, co., Tx., U.S. **D4** 120
Navasota, Tx., U.S. **D4** 120
Navassa Island, i., N.A. **E10** 64
Navoi, U.S.S.R. **I11** 18
Navojoa, Mex. **D5** 62
Navolato, Mex. **E6** 62
Navsāri, India **B2** 37
Nawābganj, Bngl. **H13** 38
Nawābganj, India **G9** 38
Nawābshāh, Pak. **G3** 38
Nāwah, Afg. **D2** 38
Nawalgarh, India **G6** 38
Nawiliwili Bay, b., Hi., U.S. **B2** 88
Náxos, i., Grc. **L9** 16
Nayak, Afg. **C2** 38
Naylor, Mo., U.S. **E7** 102
Nayoro, Japan **o20** 30a
Nazaré, Braz. **B9** 57
Nazaré, Port. **F2** 12
Nazareth, Pa., U.S. **E11** 115
Nazca, Peru **F4** 54
Naze, Japan **w29** 31b
Nazilli, Tur. **L12** 16
Nazko, stm., B.C., Can. **C6** 69
Ndélé, Cen. Afr. Rep. **G10** 42
N'Djamena (Fort-Lamy), Chad **F9** 42
Ndola, Zam. **D5** 44
Neagh, Lough, l., N. Ire., U.K. **G6** 7
Neah Bay, Wa., U.S. **A1** 124
Néa Páfos (Paphos), Cyp. **B3** 40
Neápolis, Grc. **M7** 16
Near Islands, is., Ak., U.S. **E2** 79
Nebo, Mount, mtn., Ut., U.S. **D4** 121
Nebraska, state, U.S. **C6** 104
Nebraska City, Ne., U.S. **D10** 104
Nechako, stm., B.C., Can. **C5** 69
Neches, stm., Tx., U.S. **D5** 120
Nechí, Col. **C5** 58
Neckar, stm., Ger. **F9** 8
Necker Island, i., Hi., U.S. **m15** 88
Necochea, Arg. **D5** 56
Nederland, Co., U.S. **B5** 83
Nederland, Tx., U.S. **E6** 120
Nedrow, N.Y., U.S. **C4** 109
Needham, Ma., U.S. **g11** 98
Needle Mountain, mtn., Wy., U.S. **B3** 127
Needles, Ca., U.S. **E6** 82
Needville, Tx., U.S. **r14** 120
Neenah, Wi., U.S. **D5** 126
Neepawa, Man., Can. **D2** 70
Neffs, Oh., U.S. **B5** 112
Neffsville, Pa., U.S. **F9** 115
Negage, Ang. **C3** 44
Negaunee, Mi., U.S. **B3** 99
Negele, Eth. **G2** 46
Negev Desert see Hanegev, reg., Isr. **D4** 40
Negley, Oh., U.S. **B5** 112
Negombo, Sri L. **I5** 37
Negra, Punta, c., Peru **E2** 54
Negro, stm., Arg. **E4** 56
Negro, stm., S.A. **H12** 58
Negros, i., Phil. **C7** 32
Neguac, N.B., Can. **B4** 71
Nehalem, stm., Or., U.S. **A3** 114
Nehbandān, Iran **B7** 46
Neheim-Hüsten, Ger. **D7** 8
Neiba, Bahía de, b., Dom. Rep. **E12** 64
Neijiang, China **F8** 26
Neill Point, c., Wa., U.S. **f11** 124
Neillsville, Wi., U.S. **D3** 126
Nei Monggol Zizhiqu (Inner Mongolia), prov., China **C10** 26
Neisse (Nysa Łużycka), stm., Eur. **D14** 8
Neiva, Col. **F5** 58
Neja, U.S.S.R. **C26** 22
Nekemte, Eth. **G2** 46
Nekoosa, Wi., U.S. **D4** 126
Nelidovo, U.S.S.R. **E15** 22
Neligh, Ne., U.S. **B7** 104
Nel'kan, U.S.S.R. **F21** 20
Nellikuppam, India **G5** 37
Nellis Air Force Base, mil., Nv., U.S. **G6** 105
Nellore, India **E5** 37
Nelson, B.C., Can. **E9** 69
Nelson, N.Z. **D4** 52
Nelson, Ne., U.S. **D7** 104
Nelson, co., Ky., U.S. **C4** 94
Nelson, co., N.D., U.S. **B7** 111
Nelson, co., Va., U.S. **C4** 123
Nelson, stm., Man., Can. **A4** 70
Nelsonville, Oh., U.S. **C3** 112
Néma, Maur. **E4** 42
Nemacolin, Pa., U.S. **G2** 115
Nemadji, stm., U.S. **B1** 126
Nemaha, co., Ks., U.S. **C7** 93
Nemaha, co., Ne., U.S. **D10** 104
Nemours, Fr. **D9** 10
Nemuro, Japan **p23** 30a
Nemuro Strait, strt., Asia **o23** 30a
Nenagh, Ire. **I4** 7
Nenana, Ak., U.S. **C10** 79
Neodesha, Ks., U.S. **E8** 93
Neoga, Il., U.S. **D5** 90
Neola, Ia., U.S. **C2** 92
Neola, Ut., U.S. **C5** 121
Neopit, Wi., U.S. **D5** 126
Neosho, Mo., U.S. **E3** 102
Neosho, co., Ks., U.S. **E8** 93
Neosho, stm., Ok., U.S. **A6** 113
Nepal (Nepāl), ctry., Asia **D5** 36
Nepālganj, Nepal **F9** 38
Nepaug Reservoir, res., Ct., U.S. **B3** 84
Nepean, Ont., Can. **B9** 73
Nepewassi Lake, l., Ont., Can. **A4** 73
Nephi, Ut., U.S. **D4** 121
Nepisiguit, stm., N.B., Can. **B3** 71
Nepisiguit Bay, b., N.B., Can. **B4** 71
Neponset, stm., Ma., U.S. **h11** 98
Neptune, N.J., U.S. **C4** 107
Neptune Beach, Fl., U.S. **B5** 86
Neptune City, N.J., U.S. **C4** 107
Nérac, Fr. **H7** 10
Nerastro, Sarīr, des., Libya **D10** 42
Nerčinskij Zavod, U.S.S.R. **G17** 20
Nerechta, U.S.S.R. **D23** 22
Neriquinha, Ang. **E4** 44
Nerva, Spain **H5** 12
Nesbyen, Nor. **F7** 6
Nescopeck, Pa., U.S. **D9** 115
Neshanic, stm., N.J., U.S. **C3** 107
Neshoba, co., Ms., U.S. **C4** 101
Neskaupstadur, Ice. **B5** 4
Nesna, Nor. **C9** 6
Nesowadnehunk, l., Me., U.S. **B3** 96
Nesquehoning, Pa., U.S. **E10** 115
Ness, co., Ks., U.S. **D4** 93
Ness, Loch, l., Scot., U.K. **D8** 7
Ness City, Ks., U.S. **D4** 93
Néstos (Mesta), stm., Eur. **H8** 16
Netanya, Isr. **C4** 40
Netcong, N.J., U.S. **B3** 107
Netherlands, ctry., Eur. **E9** 4
Netherlands Antilles (Nederlandse Antillen), dep., N.A. **H13** 64
Netrakona, Bngl. **H14** 38
Nettie, W.V., U.S. **C4** 125
Nettilling Lake, l., N.W. Ter., Can. **C18** 66
Nett Lake, l., Mn., U.S. **B5** 100
Nett Lake Indian Reservation, Mn., U.S. **B6** 100
Nettleton, Ms., U.S. **A5** 101
Nettuno, Italy **H7** 14
Neubrandenburg, Ger. **B13** 8
Neuburg an der Donau, Ger. **G11** 8
Neuchâtel, Switz. **F13** 10
Neuchâtel, Lac de, l., Switz. **F13** 10
Neufchâteau, Bel. **F5** 8
Neufchâteau, Fr. **D12** 10
Neufchâtel-en-Bray, Fr. **C8** 10
Neuillé-Pont-Pierre, Fr. **E7** 10
Neumarkt in der Oberpfalz, Ger. **F11** 8
Neumünster, Ger. **A9** 8
Neunkirchen, Aus. **H16** 8
Neunkirchen/Saar, Ger. **F7** 8
Neuquén, Arg. **D3** 56
Neuruppin, Ger. **C12** 8
Neuse, stm., N.C., U.S. **B6** 110
Neusiedler See, l., Eur. **H16** 8
Neuss, Ger. **D6** 8
Neustadt [an der Aisch], Ger. **F10** 8
Neustadt an der Weinstrasse, Ger. **F8** 8
Neustadt in Holstein, Ger. **A10** 8
Neustrelitz, Ger. **B13** 8
Neu-Ulm, Ger. **G10** 8
Neuville, Que., Can. **C6** 74
Neuville-de-Poitou, Fr. **F7** 10
Neuwied, Ger. **E7** 8
Nevada, Ia., U.S. **B4** 92
Nevada, Mo., U.S. **D3** 102
Nevada, co., Ar., U.S. **D2** 81
Nevada, co., Ca., U.S. **C3** 82
Nevada, state, U.S. **D5** 105
Nevada, Sierra, mts., Spain **H8** 12
Nevada, Sierra, mts., Ca., U.S. **D4** 82
Nevada City, Ca., U.S. **C3** 82
Nevado, Cerro, mtn., Arg. **D3** 56
Nevado, Cerro, mtn., Col. **F5** 58
Never, U.S.S.R. **G18** 20
Nevers, Fr. **E10** 10
Neversink, stm., N.Y., U.S. **D6** 109
Nevis, i., St. K./N. **F16** 64
Nevis, Ben, mtn., Scot., U.K. **E7** 7
New, stm., U.S. **C3** 125
New, stm., Az., U.S. **k8** 80
New, stm., N.C., U.S. **C5** 110
New Albany, In., U.S. **H6** 91
New Albany, Ms., U.S. **A4** 101
New Albany, Oh., U.S. **k11** 112
New Amsterdam, Guy. **D14** 58
Newark, Ar., U.S. **B4** 81
Newark, Ca., U.S. **h8** 82
Newark, De., U.S. **B3** 85
Newark, Il., U.S. **B5** 90
Newark, N.J., U.S. **B4** 107
Newark, N.Y., U.S. **B3** 109
Newark, Oh., U.S. **B3** 112
Newark Bay, b., N.J., U.S. **k8** 107
Newark Lake, l., Nv., U.S. **D6** 105
New Athens, Il., U.S. **E4** 90
New Augusta, Ms., U.S. **D4** 101
Newaygo, Mi., U.S. **E5** 99
Newaygo, co., Mi., U.S. **E5** 99
New Baden, Il., U.S. **E4** 90
New Baltimore, Mi., U.S. **F8** 99
New Bedford, Ma., U.S. **C6** 98
New Bedford, Pa., U.S. **D1** 115
Newberg, Or., U.S. **B4** 114
New Berlin, Il., U.S. **D4** 90
New Berlin, Wi., U.S. **n11** 126
New Bern, N.C., U.S. **B5** 110
Newbern, Tn., U.S. **A2** 119
Newberry, Fl., U.S. **C4** 86
Newberry, Mi., U.S. **B5** 99
Newberry, S.C., U.S. **C4** 117
Newberry, co., S.C., U.S. **C4** 117
New Bethlehem, Pa., U.S. **D3** 115
New Bloomfield, Pa., U.S. **F7** 115
New Boston, Mi., U.S. **p15** 99
New Boston, Oh., U.S. **D3** 112
New Boston, Tx., U.S. **C5** 120
New Braunfels, Tx., U.S. **E3** 120
New Bremen, Oh., U.S. **B1** 112
New Brighton, Mn., U.S. **m12** 100
New Brighton, Pa., U.S. **E1** 115
New Britain, Ct., U.S. **C4** 84
New Britain, i., Pap. N. Gui. **m16** 50a
New Brockton, Al., U.S. **D4** 78
New Brunswick, N.J., U.S. **C4** 107
New Brunswick, prov., Can. **C3** 71
New Buffalo, Mi., U.S. **G4** 99
Newburg, Wi., U.S. **E5** 126
Newburgh, Ont., Can. **C8** 73
Newburgh, In., U.S. **I3** 91
Newburgh, N.Y., U.S. **D6** 109
Newburgh Heights, Oh., U.S. **h9** 112
Newburyport, Ma., U.S. **A6** 98
New Caledonia, dep., Oc. **H24** 2
New Canaan, Ct., U.S. **E2** 84
New Carlisle, In., U.S. **A4** 91
New Carlisle, Oh., U.S. **C1** 112
Newcastle, Austl. **F10** 50
Newcastle, N.B., Can. **C4** 71
Newcastle, Ont., Can. **D6** 73
Newcastle, S. Afr. **G5** 44
Newcastle, N. Ire., U.K. **G7** 7
New Castle, Al., U.S. **B3** 78
New Castle, Co., U.S. **B3** 83
New Castle, De., U.S. **B3** 85
New Castle, In., U.S. **E7** 91
New Castle, Ky., U.S. **B4** 94
Newcastle, Ok., U.S. **B4** 113
New Castle, Pa., U.S. **D1** 115
Newcastle, Wy., U.S. **C8** 127
New Castle, co., De., U.S. **B3** 85
Newcastle upon Tyne, Eng., U.K. **G11** 7
Newcastle Waters, Austl. **C6** 50
New City, N.Y., U.S. **D6** 109
Newcomerstown, Oh., U.S. **B4** 112
New Concord, Oh., U.S. **C4** 112
New Cumberland, Pa., U.S. **F8** 115
New Cumberland, W.V., U.S. **A4** 125
Newdegate, Austl. **F3** 50
New Delhi, India **F7** 38
Newell, Ia., U.S. **B2** 92
Newell, S.D., U.S. **C2** 118
Newell, W.V., U.S. **A4** 125
New Ellenton, S.C., U.S. **E4** 117
Newellton, La., U.S. **B4** 95
New England, N.D., U.S. **C3** 111
Newenham, Cape, c., Ak., U.S. **D7** 79
New Fairfield, Ct., U.S. **D2** 84
Newfane, N.Y., U.S. **B2** 109
Newfields, N.H., U.S. **D5** 106
New Florence, Mo., U.S. **C6** 102
Newfound Gap, U.S. **f9** 110
Newfound Lake, l., N.H., U.S. **C3** 106
Newfoundland, prov., Can. **D4** 72
Newfoundland, i., Newf., Can. **D3** 72
New Franklin, Mo., U.S. **B5** 102
New Freedom, Pa., U.S. **G8** 115
New Georgia, i., Sol.Is. **A11** 50
New Germany, N.S., Can. **E5** 71
New Glarus, Wi., U.S. **F4** 126
New Guinea, i. **m14** 50a
Newhall, Ia., U.S. **C6** 92
New Hampshire, state, U.S. **C3** 106
New Hampton, Ia., U.S. **A5** 92
New Hanover, co., N.C., U.S. **C5** 110
New Hanover, i., Pap. N. Gui. **k17** 50a
New Harbour, Newf., Can. **E5** 72
New Harmony, In., U.S. **H2** 91
New Hartford, Ct., U.S. **B4** 84
New Hartford, Ia., U.S. **B5** 92
New Haven, Ct., U.S. **D4** 84
New Haven, In., U.S. **B7** 91
New Haven, Ky., U.S. **C4** 94
New Haven, Mi., U.S. **F8** 99
New Haven, Mo., U.S. **C6** 102
New Haven, W.V., U.S. **C3** 125
New Haven, co., Ct., U.S. **D4** 84
New Haven, stm., Vt., U.S. **C2** 122
New Haven Harbor, b., Ct., U.S. **E4** 84
New Hazelton, B.C., Can. **B4** 69
New Hebrides see Vanuatu, ctry., Oc. **H24** 2
New Holland, Ga., U.S. **B3** 87
New Holland, Pa., U.S. **F9** 115
New Holstein, Wi., U.S. **E5** 126
New Hope, Al., U.S. **A3** 78
New Hope, Ky., U.S. **C4** 94

Name | Map Ref | Page

New Hope, Mn., U.S. m12 100
New Hope, Pa., U.S. F12 115
New Hudson, Mi., U.S. o14 99
New Iberia, La., U.S. D4 95
Newington, Ct., U.S. C5 84
New Inlet, b., N.C., U.S. D5 110
New Ireland, i., Pap. N. Gui. k17 50a
New Jersey, state, U.S. C4 107
New Johnsonville, Tn., U.S. A4 119
New Kensington, Pa., U.S. E2 115
New Kent, co., Va., U.S. C5 123
Newkirk, Ok., U.S. A4 113
New Laguna, N.M., U.S. B2 108
New Lake, l., N.C., U.S. B6 110
New Lenox, Il., U.S. B6 90
New Lexington, Oh., U.S. C3 112
New Lisbon, Wi., U.S. E3 126
New Liskeard, Ont., Can. p20 73
Newllano, La., U.S. C2 95
New London, Ct., U.S. D7 84
New London, Ia., U.S. D6 92
New London, Mn., U.S. E4 100
New London, Mo., U.S. B6 102
New London, N.H., U.S. D3 106
New London, Oh., U.S. A3 112
New London, Wi., U.S. D5 126
New London, co., Ct., U.S. C7 84
New London Submarine Base, mil., Ct., U.S. D7 84
New Madison, Oh., U.S. C1 112
New Madrid, Mo., U.S. E8 102
New Madrid, co., Mo., U.S. E8 102
Newman, Ca., U.S. D3 82
Newman, Il., U.S. D6 90
New Manchester, W.V., U.S. e8 125
Newman Grove, Ne., U.S. C8 104
Newman Lake, l., Wa., U.S. B8 124
Newmanstown, Pa., U.S. F9 115
Newmarket, Ont., Can. C5 73
New Market, Al., U.S. A3 78
New Market, In., U.S. E4 91
Newmarket, N.H., U.S. D5 106
New Market, Tn., U.S. C10 119
New Market, Va., U.S. B4 123
New Martinsville, W.V., U.S. B4 125
New Matamoras, Oh., U.S. C4 112
New Mexico, state, U.S. C3 108
New Miami, Oh., U.S. C1 112
New Milford, Ct., U.S. C2 84
New Milford, N.J., U.S. h8 107
New Milford, Pa., U.S. C10 115
Newnan, Ga., U.S. C2 87
Newnans Lake, l., Fl., U.S. C4 86
New Norfolk, Austl. H9 50
New Orleans, La., U.S. E5 95
New Orleans Naval Air Station, mil., La., U.S. k11 95
New Oxford, Pa., U.S. G7 115
New Palestine, In., U.S. E6 91
New Paltz, N.Y., U.S. D6 109
New Paris, In., U.S. B6 91
New Paris, Oh., U.S. C1 112
New Philadelphia, Oh., U.S. B4 112
New Philadelphia, Pa., U.S. E9 115
New Plymouth, N.Z. C5 52
New Plymouth, Id., U.S. F2 89
New Point Comfort, c., Va., U.S. C6 123
Newport, Eng., U.K. K11 7
Newport, Wales, U.K. J9 7
Newport, Ar., U.S. B4 81
Newport, De., U.S. B3 85
Newport, In., U.S. E3 91
Newport, Ky., U.S. A5 94
Newport, Me., U.S. D3 96
Newport, Mi., U.S. G7 99
Newport, Mn., U.S. n13 100
Newport, N.H., U.S. D2 106
Newport, N.C., U.S. C6 110
Newport, Oh., U.S. C4 112
Newport, Or., U.S. C2 114
Newport, Pa., U.S. F7 115
Newport, R.I., U.S. F5 116
Newport, Tn., U.S. D10 119
Newport, Vt., U.S. B4 122
Newport, Wa., U.S. A8 124
Newport, co., R.I., U.S. E5 116
Newport Beach, Ca., U.S. n13 82
Newport News, Va., U.S. D6 123
New Port Richey, Fl., U.S. D4 86
New Prague, Mn., U.S. F5 100
New Preston, Ct., U.S. C2 84
New Providence, N.J., U.S. B4 107
New Providence, i., Bah. B9 64
Newquay, Eng., U.K. K7 7
New Richland, Mn., U.S. G5 100
New Richmond, Que., Can. A4 71
New Richmond, Oh., U.S. D1 112
New Richmond, Wi., U.S. C1 126
New River Inlet, b., N.C., U.S. C5 110
New Roads, La., U.S. D4 95
New Rochelle, N.Y., U.S. E7 109
New Rockford, N.D., U.S. B6 111
New Ross, Ire. I6 7
Newry, N. Ire., U.K. G6 7
New Salem, N.D., U.S. C4 111
New Sarpy, La., U.S. k11 95
New Sharon, Ia., U.S. C5 92
New Site, Al., U.S. B4 78
New Smyrna Beach, Fl., U.S. C6 86
New South Wales, state, Austl. F9 50
New Straitsville, Oh., U.S. C3 112
New Tazewell, Tn., U.S. C10 119
Newton, Al., U.S. D4 78
Newton, Ga., U.S. E2 87
Newton, Il., U.S. E5 90
Newton, Ia., U.S. C4 92
Newton, Ks., U.S. D6 93
Newton, Ma., U.S. B5 98
Newton, Ms., U.S. C4 101
Newton, N.J., U.S. A3 107
Newton, N.C., U.S. B1 110
Newton, Tx., U.S. D6 120
Newton, Ut., U.S. B4 121
Newton, co., Ar., U.S. B2 81
Newton, co., Ga., U.S. C3 87
Newton, co., In., U.S. B3 91
Newton, co., Ms., U.S. C4 101
Newton, co., Mo., U.S. E3 102
Newton, co., Tx., U.S. D6 120
Newton Falls, Oh., U.S. A5 112
Newton Lake, res., Il., U.S. E5 90
Newton Stewart, Scot., U.K. G8 7
Newtown, Ct., U.S. D2 84
New Town, N.D., U.S. B3 111
Newtown, Oh., U.S. C1 112
Newtownabbey, N. Ire., U.K. G7 7
Newtownards, N. Ire., U.K. G7 7
Newtown Square, Pa., U.S. p20 115
New Ulm, Mn., U.S. F4 100
New Vienna, Oh., U.S. C2 112
Newville, Pa., U.S. F7 115
New Washington, In., U.S. G6 91
New Washington, Oh., U.S. B3 112
New Waterford, Oh., U.S. B5 112
New Westminster, B.C., Can. E6 69
New Whiteland, In., U.S. E5 91
New Wilmington, Pa., U.S. D1 115
New Windsor, Il., U.S. B3 90
New Windsor, Md., U.S. A3 97
New Windsor, N.Y., U.S. D6 109
New World Island, i., Newf., Can. D4 72
New York, N.Y., U.S. E7 109
New York, co., N.Y., U.S. k13 109
New York, state, U.S. C6 109
New York Mills, Mn., U.S. D3 100
New Zealand, ctry., Oc. D4 52
Nežin, U.S.S.R. G4 18
Nez Perce, co., Id., U.S. C2 89
Nez Perce Indian Reservation, Id., U.S. C2 89
Ngami, Lake, l., Bots. F4 44
Nganglong Kangri, mts., China D10 38
Nganjuk, Indon. m15 33a
Ngaoundéré, Cam. G8 42
Nguigmi, Niger F8 42
Nguru, Nig. F8 42
Nha Trang, Viet. H10 34
Niafounké, Mali E5 42
Niagara, Wi., U.S. C6 126
Niagara, co., N.Y., U.S. B2 109
Niagara Falls, Ont., Can. D5 73
Niagara Falls, N.Y., U.S. B1 109
Niagara-on-the-Lake, Ont., Can. D5 73
Niamey, Niger F6 42
Niangara, Zaire H11 42
Niangua, stm., Mo., U.S. D5 102
Niantic, Ct., U.S. D7 84
Nias, Pulau, i., Indon. N4 34
Nibley, Ut., U.S. B4 121
Nicaragua, ctry., N.A. H5 64
Nicaragua, Lago de, l., Nic. I5 64
Nicastro (Lamezia Terme), Italy K11 14
Nicatous Lake, l., Me., U.S. C4 96
Nice, Fr. I14 10
Niceville, Fl., U.S. u15 86
Nichinan, Japan K4 30
Nicholas, co., Ky., U.S. B6 94
Nicholas, co., W.V., U.S. C4 125
Nicholas Channel, strt., N.A. C7 64
Nicholasville, Ky., U.S. C5 94
Nicholls, Ga., U.S. E4 87
Nichols Hills, Ok., U.S. B4 113
Nicholson, Ms., U.S. E4 101
Nickajack Lake, res., Tn., U.S. D8 119
Nickel Centre, Ont., Can. p19 73
Nickerson, Ks., U.S. D5 93
Nicobar Islands, is., India J2 34
Nicolet, Que., Can. C5 74
Nicolet, stm., Que., Can. C5 74
Nicolet, Lake, l., Mi., U.S. B6 99
Nicollet, Mn., U.S. F4 100
Nicollet, co., Mn., U.S. F4 100
Nicolls Town, Bah. B8 64
Nicoma Park, Ok., U.S. B4 113
Nicosia, Cyp. B3 40
Nicosia, N. Cyp. B3 40
Nicosia, Italy L9 14
Nicoya, Golfo de, b., C.R. J5 64
Nicoya, Península de, pen., C.R. I5 64
Niebüll, Ger. A8 8
Nienburg, Ger. C9 8
Nieuw Nickerie, Sur. B7 54
Nieves, Mex. E8 62
Nigadoo, N.B., Can. B4 71
Niger, ctry., Afr. E7 42
Niger, stm., Afr. G7 42
Nigeria, ctry., Afr. G7 42
Nigríta, Grc. I7 16
Nihoa, i., Hi., U.S. m15 88
Niigata, Japan E12 30
Niihama, Japan I6 30
Niihau, i., Hi., U.S. B1 88
Niinisalo, Fin. F14 6
Niitsu, Japan E12 30
Níjar, Spain I9 12
Nijmegen, Neth. D5 8
Nikishka, Ak., U.S. g16 79
Nikkō, Japan F12 30
Nikolajev, U.S.S.R. H4 18
Nikolajevsk-na-Amure, U.S.S.R. G22 20
Nikolayev see Nikolajev, U.S.S.R. H4 18
Nikšić, Yugo. G2 16
Niland, Ca., U.S. F6 82
Nile (Nahr an-Nīl), stm., Afr. C12 42
Niles, Il., U.S. h9 90
Niles, Mi., U.S. G4 99
Niles, Oh., U.S. A5 112
Nileshwar, India F3 37
Nīmach, India H6 38
Nimba, Mont, mtn., Afr. G4 42
Nîmes, Fr. I11 10
Nimrod Lake, res., Ar., U.S. C2 81
Nine Degree Channel, strt., India H2 37
Nine Mile Creek, stm., Ut., U.S. D5 121
Ninemile Point, c., Mi., U.S. C6 99
Ninety Six, S.C., U.S. C3 117
Ningbo, China F10 28
Ningming, China C9 34
Ningxia Huizu Zizhiqu, prov., China D8 26
Ninh Binh, Viet. D8 34
Ninigret Pond, l., R.I., U.S. G2 116
Ninilchik, Ak., U.S. C9 79
Ninnescah, stm., Ks., U.S. E6 93
Niobrara, co., Wy., U.S. C8 127
Niobrara, stm., U.S. B7 104
Niono, Mali F4 42
Nioro du Sahel, Mali E4 42
Niort, Fr. F6 10
Niota, Tn., U.S. D9 119
Nipāni, India D3 37
Nipigon, Lake, l., Ont., Can. o17 73
Nipissing, Lake, l., Ont., Can. A5 73
Nipomo, Ca., U.S. E3 82
Nipple Mountain, mtn., Co., U.S. D2 83
Nirmal, India C5 37
Niš, Yugo. F5 16
Nisa, Port. F4 12
Nishinoomote, Japan u30 31b
Nishiwaki, Japan H7 30
Niskayuna, N.Y., U.S. C7 109
Nisqually, stm., Wa., U.S. C3 124
Nisswa, Mn., U.S. D4 100
Niterói, Braz. G7 57
Nitra, Czech. G18 8
Nitro, W.V., U.S. C3 125
Niue, dep., Oc. H1 2
Nivelles, Bel. E4 8
Niverville, Man., Can. E3 70
Niwot, Co., U.S. A5 83
Nixa, Mo., U.S. D4 102
Nixon, Nv., U.S. D2 105
Nixon, Tx., U.S. E4 120
Nizāmābād, India C5 37
Nizip, Tur. A5 40
Nižn'aja Pojma, U.S.S.R. F13 20
Nižn'aja Tunguska, stm., U.S.S.R. E12 20
Nižneangarsk, U.S.S.R. F15 20
Nižneilimsk, U.S.S.R. F14 20
Nižneudinsk, U.S.S.R. G13 20
Nižnij Novgorod (Gorki), U.S.S.R. E27 22
Nizza Monferrato, Italy E3 14
Njombe, Tan. C6 44
Nkhota Kota, Mwi. D6 44
Nkongsamba, Cam. H7 42
Noākhāli, Bngl. I14 38
Noank, Ct., U.S. D8 84
Noatak, Ak., U.S. B7 79
Noatak, stm., Ak., U.S. B7 79
Nobel, Ont., Can. B4 73
Nobeoka, Japan J4 30
Noble, Ok., U.S. B4 113
Noble, co., In., U.S. B7 91
Noble, co., Oh., U.S. C4 112
Noble, co., Ok., U.S. A4 113
Nobles, co., Mn., U.S. G3 100
Noblesville, In., U.S. D6 91
Noboribetsu, Japan q19 30a
Nocatee, Fl., U.S. E5 86
Nocera [Inferiore], Italy I9 14
Nochixtlán, Mex. I11 62
Nocona, Tx., U.S. C4 120
Nodaway, co., Mo., U.S. A3 102
Nodaway, stm., U.S. A2 102
Noel, Mo., U.S. E3 102
Nogales, Mex. B4 62
Nogales, Az., U.S. F5 80
Nōgata, Japan I3 30
Nogent-le-Rotrou, Fr. D7 10
Noginsk, U.S.S.R. F21 22
Nogoyá, Arg. C5 56
Noirmoutier, Fr. E4 10
Nojima-zaki, c., Japan H12 30
Nokia, Fin. F14 6
Nokomis, Fl., U.S. E4 86
Nokomis, Il., U.S. D4 90
Nokomis, Lake, res., Wi., U.S. C4 126
Nolan, co., Tx., U.S. C2 120
Nolichucky, stm., Tn., U.S. C10 119
Nolin, stm., Ky., U.S. C3 94
Nolin Lake, res., Ky., U.S. C3 94
Nomans Land, i., Ma., U.S. D6 98
Nombre de Dios, Mex. F7 62
Nome, Ak., U.S. C6 79
Nominingue, Que., Can. C2 74
Nonacho Lake, l., N.W. Ter., Can. D11 66
Nonesuch, stm., Me., U.S. g7 96
Nong'an, China C12 26
Nong Khai, Thai. F7 34
Nonquit Pond, l., R.I., U.S. E6 116
Nontron, Fr. G7 10
Nooksack, North Fork, stm., Wa., U.S. A4 124
Nooksack, South Fork, stm., Wa., U.S. A3 124
Noordoost Polder, reg., Neth. C5 8
Noorvik, Ak., U.S. B7 79
Nootka Island, i., B.C., Can. G7 66
Nootka Sound, strt., B.C., Can. E4 69
No Point, Point, c., Md., U.S. D5 97
Noquebay, Lake, l., Wi., U.S. C6 126
Nora, Que., Can. k11 74
Nora Springs, Ia., U.S. A5 92
Norborne, Mo., U.S. B4 102
Norco, La., U.S. E5 95
Norcross, Ga., U.S. C2 87
Norden, Ger. B7 8
Nordenham, Ger. B8 8
Nordenšel'da, Archipelag, is., U.S.S.R. B13 20
Norderney, i., Ger. B7 8
Nordfjordeid, Nor. F5 6
Nordfold, Nor. C10 6
Nordhausen, Ger. D10 8
Nordhorn, Ger. C7 8
Nordkapp, c., Nor. A15 6
Nordkjosbotn, Nor. B12 6
Nördlingen, Ger. G10 8
Nordmaling, Swe. E12 6
Nordreisa, Nor. B13 6
Nordre Strømfjord, Grnld. C22 66
Nordvik, U.S.S.R. C16 20
Norfolk, Ct., U.S. B3 84
Norfolk, Ne., U.S. B8 104
Norfolk, N.Y., U.S. f9 109
Norfolk, Va., U.S. D6 123
Norfolk, co., Ma., U.S. B5 98
Norfolk Naval Base, mil., Va., U.S. k15 123
Norfolk Naval Shipyard, mil., Va., U.S. k15 123
Norfork Dam, Ar., U.S. A3 81
Norfork Lake, res., U.S. A3 81
Noril'sk, U.S.S.R. D11 20
Norland, Fl., U.S. s13 86
Norlina, N.C., U.S. A4 110
Normal, Il., U.S. C5 90
Norman, Ok., U.S. B4 113
Norman, co., Mn., U.S. C2 100
Norman, Lake, res., N.C., U.S. B2 110
Normandie, hist. reg., Fr. D6 10
Normandy, Mo., U.S. f13 102
Normandy see Normandie, hist. reg., Fr. D6 10
Norman Park, Ga., U.S. E3 87
Normanton, Austl. C8 50
Norman Wells, N.W. Ter., Can. C7 66
Norphlet, Ar., U.S. D3 81
Ñorquincó, Arg. E2 56
Norridge, Il., U.S. k9 90
Norridgewock, Me., U.S. D3 96
Norris, S.C., U.S. B2 117
Norris, Tn., U.S. C9 119
Norris Arm, Newf., Can. D4 72
Norris City, Il., U.S. F5 90
Norris Dam, Tn., U.S. C9 119
Norris Lake, res., Tn., U.S. C10 119
Norris Point, Newf., Can. D3 72
Norristown, Pa., U.S. F11 115
Norrköping, Swe. G11 6
Norrtälje, Swe. G12 6
Norseman, Austl. F4 50
Norsk, U.S.S.R. G19 20
Norte, Serra do, plat., Braz. F7 54
North, S.C., U.S. D5 117
North, stm., Al., U.S. B2 78
North, stm., Ia., U.S. f8 92
North, stm., Ma., U.S. h12 98
North, stm., W.V., U.S. B6 125
North, Cape, c., N.S., Can. B9 71
North Adams, Ma., U.S. A1 98
North Albany, Or., U.S. k11 114
Northam, Austl. F3 50
North America E10 61
North Amherst, Ma., U.S. B2 98
Northampton, Eng., U.K. I12 7
Northampton, Ma., U.S. B2 98
Northampton, Pa., U.S. E11 115
Northampton, co., N.C., U.S. A5 110
Northampton, co., Pa., U.S. E11 115
Northampton, co., Va., U.S. C7 123
North Andaman, i., India H2 34
North Andover, Ma., U.S. A5 98
North Andrews Gardens, Fl., U.S. r13 86
North Anna, stm., Va., U.S. B5 123
North Anson, Me., U.S. D3 96
North Apollo, Pa., U.S. E2 115
North Arapaho Peak, mtn., Co., U.S. A5 83
North Arlington, N.J., U.S. h8 107
North Atlanta, Ga., U.S. h8 87
North Attleboro, Ma., U.S. C5 98
North Augusta, S.C., U.S. D4 117
North Aurora, Il., U.S. k8 90
North Baltimore, Oh., U.S. A2 112
North Bay, Ont., Can. A5 73
North Beach, Md., U.S. C4 97
North Belmont, N.C., U.S. B1 110
North Bend, Ne., U.S. C9 104
North Bend, Or., U.S. D2 114
North Bend, Wa., U.S. B4 124
North Bennington, Vt., U.S. F2 122
North Bergen, N.J., U.S. h8 107
North Berwick, Me., U.S. E2 96
North Billerica, Ma., U.S. A5 98
Northborough, Ma., U.S. B4 98
North Branch, Mi., U.S. E7 99
North Branch, Mn., U.S. E6 100
North Branch, N.H., U.S. D3 106
North Branch, N.J., U.S. B3 107
North Branford, Ct., U.S. D4 84
Northbridge, Ma., U.S. B4 98
Northbrook, Il., U.S. h9 90
North Brookfield, Ma., U.S. B3 98
North Brunswick, N.J., U.S. C4 107
North Caldwell, N.J., U.S. B4 107
North Canadian, stm., Ok., U.S. A5 113
North Canton, Ga., U.S. B2 87
North Canton, Oh., U.S. B4 112
North Cape, c., P.E.I., Can. B6 71
North Cape May, N.J., U.S. F3 107
North Cape see Nordkapp, c., Nor. A15 6
North Caribou Lake, l., Ont., Can. F14 66
North Carolina, state, U.S. B3 110
North Cascades National Park, Wa., U.S. A4 124
North Channel, strt., Ont., Can. A2 73
North Channel, strt., U.K. F7 7
North Charleston, S.C., U.S. F8 117
North Chicago, Il., U.S. A6 90
North Clarendon, Vt., U.S. D3 122
North College Hill, Oh., U.S. o12 112
North Conway, N.H., U.S. B4 106
North Corbin, Ky., U.S. D5 94
North Crossett, Ar., U.S. D4 81
North Cyprus, ctry., Asia B3 40
North Dakota, state, U.S. B5 111
North Dartmouth, Ma., U.S. C6 98
North Druid Hills, Ga., U.S. h8 87
North Eagle Butte, S.D., U.S. B4 118
North East, Md., U.S. A6 97
North East, Pa., U.S. B2 115
Northeast, stm., Md., U.S. A6 97
Northeast Cape, c., Ak., U.S. C6 79
Northeast Cape Fear, stm., N.C., U.S. C5 110
Northeast Harbor, Me., U.S. D4 96
Northeast Henrietta, N.Y., U.S. B3 109
North Easton, Ma., U.S. B5 98
Northeast Pond, l., N.H., U.S. D5 106
Northeast Providence Channel, strt., Bah. B9 64
North Edisto, stm., S.C., U.S. k11 117
Northeim, Ger. D9 8
North English, Ia., U.S. C5 92
North English, stm., Ia., U.S. C5 92
North Enid, Ok., U.S. A4 113
Northern Cheyenne Indian Reservation, Mt., U.S. E10 103
Northern Indian Lake, l., Man., Can. A3 70
Northern Ireland, ter., U.K. G6 7
Northern Territory, ter., Austl. C6 50
North Falmouth, Ma., U.S. C6 98
Northfield, Mn., U.S. F5 100
Northfield, N.H., U.S. D3 106
Northfield, N.J., U.S. E3 107
Northfield, Oh., U.S. h9 112
Northfield, Vt., U.S. C3 122
Northfield Falls, Vt., U.S. C3 122
North Flinders Ranges, mts., Austl. F7 50
North Fond du Lac, Wi., U.S. E5 126
Northford, Ct., U.S. D4 84
North Fork Reservoir, res., Or., U.S. B4 114
North Fort Myers, Fl., U.S. F5 86
North Fox Island, i., Mi., U.S. C5 99
North Frisian Islands, is., Eur. A8 8
Northglenn, Co., U.S. B6 83
North Gower, Ont., Can. B9 73
North Grafton, Ma., U.S. B4 98
North Grosvenordale, Ct., U.S. B8 84
North Gulfport, Ms., U.S. E4 101
North Haledon, N.J., U.S. B4 107
North Hampton, N.H., U.S. E5 106
North Hartland Reservoir, res., Vt., U.S. D4 122
North Hatley, Que., Can. D6 74
North Haven, Ct., U.S. D4 84
North Head, N.B., Can. E3 71
North Hero Island, i., Vt., U.S. B2 122
North Horn Lake, l., Tn., U.S. e8 119
North Industry, Oh., U.S. B4 112
North Inlet, b., S.C., U.S. E9 117
North Island, i., N.Z. C5 52
North Island, i., S.C., U.S. E9 117
North Island Naval Air Station, mil., Ca., U.S. o15 82
North Islands, is., La., U.S. E7 95
North Judson, In., U.S. B4 91
North Kansas City, Mo., U.S. h10 102
North Kingstown, R.I., U.S. E4 116
North Kingsville, Oh., U.S. A5 112
North La Junta, Co., U.S. C7 83
Northlake, Il., U.S. k9 90
North Laramie, stm., Wy., U.S. D7 127
North Las Vegas, Nv., U.S. G6 105
North La Veta Pass, Co., U.S. D5 83
North Lewisburg, Oh., U.S. B2 112
North Liberty, In., U.S. A5 91
North Liberty, Ia., U.S. C6 92
North Lima, Oh., U.S. B5 112
North Little Rock, Ar., U.S. C3 81
North Logan, Ut., U.S. B4 121
North Loon Mountain, mtn., Id., U.S. D3 89
North Magnetic Pole B22 128
North Mamm Peak, mtn., Co., U.S. B3 83
North Manchester, In., U.S. C6 91
North Manitou Island, i., Mi., U.S. C4 99
North Mankato, Mn., U.S. F4 100
North Merrydale, La., U.S. D4 95
North Miami, Fl., U.S. G6 86
North Miami Beach, Fl., U.S. s13 86
North Middletown, Ky., U.S. B5 94
North Moose Lake, l., Man., Can. B1 70
North Mountain, mtn., Pa., U.S. D9 115
North Muskegon, Mi., U.S. E4 99
North Myrtle Beach, S.C., U.S. D10 117
North Naples, Fl., U.S. F5 86
North New River Canal, Fl., U.S. F6 86
North Ogden, Ut., U.S. B4 121
North Olmsted, Oh., U.S. h9 112
North Palisade, mtn., Ca., U.S. D4 82
North Park, Il., U.S. A4 90
North Park, val., Co., U.S. A4 83
North Pass, strt., La., U.S. E7 95
North Pembroke, Ma., U.S. B6 98
North Plainfield, N.J., U.S. B4 107
North Plains, Or., U.S. B4 114
North Plains, pl., N.M., U.S. C1 108
North Platte, Ne., U.S. C5 104
North Platte, stm., U.S. C6 76
North Point, c., Md., U.S. B5 97
North Point, c., Mi., U.S. C7 99
North Pole A12 128
Northport, Al., U.S. B2 78
North Prairie, Wi., U.S. F5 126
North Providence, R.I., U.S. C4 116
North Raccoon, stm., Ia., U.S. C3 92
North Reading, Ma., U.S. f11 98
North Richland Hills, Tx., U.S. n9 120
Northridge, Oh., U.S. C2 112
North Ridgeville, Oh., U.S. A3 112
North Royalton, Oh., U.S. h9 112
North Rustico, P.E.I., Can. C6 71
North Salem, N.H., U.S. E4 106
North Salt Lake, Ut., U.S. C4 121
North Santee, stm., S.C., U.S. E9 117
North Saskatchewan, stm., Can. F10 66
North Schell Peak, mtn., Nv., U.S. D7 105
North Scituate, Ma., U.S. h12 98
North Sea, Eur. D8 4
North Shoshone Peak, mtn., Nv., U.S. D4 105
North Sioux City, S.D., U.S. E9 118
North Skunk, stm., Ia., U.S. C5 92
North Springfield, Vt., U.S. E3 122
North Springfield Reservoir, res., Vt., U.S. E4 122
North Star, De., U.S. A3 85
North St. Paul, Mn., U.S. m13 100
North Stratford, N.H., U.S. A3 106
North Sudbury, Ma., U.S. g10 98
North Swanzey, N.H., U.S. E2 106
North Syracuse, N.Y., U.S. B4 109
North Tarrytown, N.Y., U.S. D7 109
North Terre Haute, In., U.S. E3 91
North Thompson, stm., B.C., Can. D8 69
North Tonawanda, N.Y., U.S. B2 109
North Troy, Vt., U.S. B4 122
North Tunica, Ms., U.S. A3 101
North Twin Lake, l., Wi., U.S. B4 126
Northumberland, Pa., U.S. E8 115
Northumberland, co., Pa., U.S. D8 115
Northumberland, co., Va., U.S. C6 123
Northumberland National Park, Eng., U.K. F10 7

Name	Map Ref	Page
Northumberland Strait, strt., Can.	C6	71
North Umpqua, stm., Or., U.S.	D3	114
North Uxbridge, Ma., U.S.	B4	98
Northvale, N.J., U.S.	g9	107
North Vancouver, B.C., Can.	E6	69
North Vassalboro, Me., U.S.	D3	96
North Vernon, In., U.S.	F6	91
Northville, Mi., U.S.	p15	99
North Wales, Pa., U.S.	F11	115
North Walpole, N.H., U.S.	D2	106
North Warren, Pa., U.S.	C3	115
North Webster, In., U.S.	B6	91
North West Cape, c., Austl.	D2	50
Northwest Miramichi, stm., N.B., Can.	B3	71
Northwest Providence Channel, strt., Bah.	A8	64
Northwest Territories, prov., Can.	C13	66
North Wildwood, N.J., U.S.	E3	107
North Wilkesboro, N.C., U.S.	A1	110
North Windham, Ct., U.S.	C7	84
North Windham, Me., U.S.	E2	96
Northwood, Ia., U.S.	A4	92
Northwood, N.D., U.S.	B8	111
North Woodstock, N.H., U.S.	B3	106
North York, Ont., Can.	D5	73
North York, Pa., U.S.	G8	115
North York Moors National Park, Eng., U.K.	G12	7
Norton, N.B., Can.	D4	71
Norton, Ks., U.S.	C4	93
Norton, Ma., U.S.	C5	98
Norton, Oh., U.S.	A4	112
Norton, Va., U.S.	f9	123
Norton, co., Ks., U.S.	C4	93
Norton Air Force Base, mil., Ca., U.S.	E5	82
Norton Bay, b., Ak., U.S.	C7	79
Norton Pond, l., Vt., U.S.	B5	122
Norton Reservoir, res., Ks., U.S.	C3	93
Norton Shores, Mi., U.S.	E4	99
Norton Sound, strt., Ak., U.S.	C6	79
Nortonville, Ks., U.S.	C8	93
Nortonville, Ky., U.S.	C2	94
Norwalk, Ca., U.S.	n12	82
Norwalk, Ct., U.S.	E2	84
Norwalk, Ia., U.S.	C4	92
Norwalk, Oh., U.S.	A3	112
Norwalk, stm., Ct., U.S.	E2	84
Norwalk Islands, is., Ct., U.S.	E2	84
Norway, Me., U.S.	D2	96
Norway, Mi., U.S.	C3	99
Norway, ctry., Eur.	C9	4
Norway Bay, b., N.W. Ter., Can.	B12	66
Norway House, Man., Can.	C3	70
Norway Lake, l., Mn., U.S.	E3	100
Norwegian Sea, Eur.	C12	128
Norwich, Eng., U.K.	I14	7
Norwich, Ct., U.S.	C7	84
Norwich, N.Y., U.S.	C5	109
Norwich, Vt., U.S.	D4	122
Norwood, Ont., Can.	C7	73
Norwood, Ma., U.S.	B5	98
Norwood, Mn., U.S.	F5	100
Norwood, N.J., U.S.	h9	107
Norwood, N.Y., U.S.	f10	109
Norwood, N.C., U.S.	B2	110
Norwood, Oh., U.S.	o13	112
Norwood, Pa., U.S.	p20	115
Norwoodville, Ia., U.S.	e8	92
Noshiro, Japan	B13	30
Notasulga, Al., U.S.	C4	78
Notch Peak, mtn., Ut., U.S.	D2	121
Noto, Italy	M10	14
Notodden, Nor.	G7	6
Notre Dame, Monts, mts., Que., Can.	k13	74
Notre Dame Bay, b., Newf., Can.	D4	72
Notre Dame de Lourdes, Man., Can.	E2	70
Notre-Dame-du-Lac, Que., Can.	B9	74
Nottawasaga Bay, b., Ont., Can.	C4	73
Nottaway, stm., Que., Can.	h11	74
Nottingham, Eng., U.K.	I11	7
Nottingham Island, i., N.W. Ter., Can.	D17	66
Nottoway, co., Va., U.S.	C4	123
Nottoway, stm., Va., U.S.	D5	123
Nouadhibou, Maur.	D2	42
Nouakchott, Maur.	E2	42
Nouamrhar, Maur.	E2	42
Noupoort, S. Afr.	H4	44
Nouveau-Québec, Cratère du, crat., Que., Can.	D18	66
Nova América, Braz.	C4	57
Nova Cruz, Braz.	E11	54
Nova Freixo, Moz.	D7	44
Nova Friburgo, Braz.	G7	57
Nova Gaia, Ang.	D3	44
Nova Gradiška, Yugo.	D12	14
Nova Iguaçu, Braz.	G7	57
Novaja Sibir', Ostrov, i., U.S.S.R.	B23	20
Novaja Zeml'a, is., U.S.S.R.	C5	20
Nova Lima, Braz.	E7	57
Nova Lisboa see Huambo, Ang.	D3	44
Nova Mambone, Moz.	F7	44
Novara, Italy	D3	14
Nova Scotia, prov., Can.	D6	71
Nova Sofala, Moz.	F6	44
Novato, Ca., U.S.	C2	82
Novelda, Spain	G11	12
Nové Zámky, Czech.	H18	8
Novgorod, U.S.S.R.	C14	22
Novi, Mi., U.S.	p15	99
Novi Ligure, Italy	E3	14
Novi Pazar, Bul.	F11	16
Novi Pazar, Yugo.	F4	16
Novi Sad, Yugo.	D3	16
Novoaltajsk, U.S.S.R.	G10	20
Novo Aripuanã, Braz.	E6	54
Novogrudok, U.S.S.R.	H8	22
Novokuzneck, U.S.S.R.	G11	20
Novo Mesto, Yugo.	D10	14
Novo Redondo, Ang.	D2	44
Novorossijsk, U.S.S.R.	I5	18
Novorybnoje, U.S.S.R.	C15	20
Novosibirsk, U.S.S.R.	D4	128
Novosibirskije Ostrova, is., U.S.S.R.	B22	20
Novosibirskoje Vodochranilišče, res., U.S.S.R.	G10	20
Novotroick, U.S.S.R.	G9	18
Novozybkov, U.S.S.R.	I14	22
Novska, Yugo.	D11	14
Nowa Sól (Neusalz), Pol.	D15	8
Nowata, Ok., U.S.	A6	113
Nowata, co., Ok., U.S.	A6	113
Nowgong, India	G15	38
Nowood, stm., Wy., U.S.	B5	127
Nowshāk, mtn., Asia	B4	38
Nowshera, Pak.	C4	38
Nowy Sącz, Pol.	F20	8
Nowy Targ, Pol.	F20	8
Noxon Reservoir, res., Mt., U.S.	C1	103
Noxontown Lake, res., De., U.S.	C3	85
Noxubee, co., Ms., U.S.	B5	101
Noxubee, stm., U.S.	B5	101
Noyes Island, i., Ak., U.S.	n22	79
Noyon, Fr.	C9	10
Nozay, Fr.	E5	10
Nsanje, Mwi.	E7	44
Nsawam, Ghana	G5	42
Nubanusit Lake, l., N.H., U.S.	E2	106
Nubian Desert, des., Sudan	D12	42
Nuckolls, co., Ne., U.S.	D7	104
Nucla, Co., U.S.	C2	83
Nueces, co., Tx., U.S.	F4	120
Nueces, stm., Tx., U.S.	E3	120
Nueltin Lake, l., Can.	E13	66
Nueva Casas Grandes, Mex.	B6	62
Nueva Rosita, Mex.	D9	62
Nueva San Salvador, El Sal.	H3	64
Nueve de Julio, Arg.	D4	56
Nuevitas, Cuba	D9	64
Nuevo, Golfo, b., Arg.	E4	56
Nuevo Laredo, Mex.	D10	62
Nuevo Rocafuerte, Ec.	H5	58
Nuits-Saint-Georges, Fr.	E11	10
Nukus, U.S.S.R.	I9	18
Nulato, Ak., U.S.	C8	79
Nulhegan, stm., Vt., U.S.	B5	122
Nullagine, Austl.	D4	50
Nullarbor Plain, pl., Austl.	F5	50
Numata, Japan	F12	30
Numazu, Japan	G11	30
Numfoor, Pulau, i., Indon.	F9	32
Nun, stm., China	A12	26
Nunivak Island, i., Ak., U.S.	D6	79
Nunjiang, China	B12	26
Nuoro, Italy	I4	14
N'urba, U.S.S.R.	E17	20
Nuremberg, Pa., U.S.	E9	115
Nuremberg see Nürnberg, Ger.	F11	8
Nürnberg, Ger.	F11	8
Nurri, Italy	J4	14
Nutley, N.J., U.S.	B4	107
Nutter Fort, W.V., U.S.	k10	125
Nutting Lake, Ma., U.S.	f10	98
Nuuanu Pali, Hi., U.S.	g10	88
Nyack, N.Y., U.S.	D7	109
Nyainqêntanglha Shan, mts., China	E13	38
Nyala, Sudan	F10	42
Nyanda, Zimb.	F6	44
Nyasa, Lake, l., Afr.	D6	44
Nyaunglebin, Burma	F4	34
Nybro, Swe.	H10	6
Nye, co., Nv., U.S.	E5	105
Nyenyam, China	F11	38
Nyeri, Kenya	B7	44
Nyíregyháza, Hung.	H21	8
Nykøbing, Den.	I8	6
Nyköping, Swe.	G11	6
Nylstroom, S. Afr.	F5	44
Nynäshamn, Swe.	G11	6
Nyngan, Austl.	F9	50
Nyon, Switz.	F13	10
Nyons, Fr.	H12	10
Nysa, Pol.	E17	8
Nysa Łużycka (Neisse) (Nisa), stm., Eur.	D14	8
Nyssa, Or., U.S.	D9	114
Nzérékoré, Gui.	G4	42
N'zeto, Ang.	C2	44

O

Name	Map Ref	Page
Oahe, Lake, res., U.S.	B6	76
Oahe Dam, S.D., U.S.	C5	118
Oahu, i., Hi., U.S.	B4	88
Oak Bay, B.C., Can.	h12	69
Oak Bluffs, Ma., U.S.	D6	98
Oak Creek, Co., U.S.	A4	83
Oak Creek, Wi., U.S.	n12	126
Oakdale, Ca., U.S.	D3	82
Oakdale, Ga., U.S.	h8	87
Oakdale, La., U.S.	D3	95
Oakdale, Pa., U.S.	k13	115
Oakes, N.D., U.S.	C7	111
Oakfield, N.Y., U.S.	B2	109
Oakfield, Wi., U.S.	E5	126
Oak Forest, Il., U.S.	k9	90
Oak Grove, Ky., U.S.	D2	94
Oak Grove, La., U.S.	B4	95
Oak Grove, Or., U.S.	B4	114
Oak Harbor, Oh., U.S.	A2	112
Oak Harbor, Wa., U.S.	A3	124
Oak Hill, Mi., U.S.	D4	99
Oak Hill, Oh., U.S.	D3	112
Oak Hill, W.V., U.S.	D3	125
Oak Hill, mtn., Ma., U.S.	f9	98
Oakhurst, Ok., U.S.	A5	113
Oak Island, i., Wi., U.S.	B3	126
Oak Lake, l., Man., Can.	E1	70
Oakland, Ca., U.S.	D2	82
Oakland, Il., U.S.	D5	90
Oakland, Ia., U.S.	C2	92
Oakland, Me., U.S.	D3	96
Oakland, Md., U.S.	m12	97
Oakland, Ne., U.S.	C9	104
Oakland, N.J., U.S.	A4	107
Oakland, Ok., U.S.	C5	113
Oakland, Or., U.S.	D3	114
Oakland, R.I., U.S.	B2	116
Oakland, co., Mi., U.S.	F7	99
Oakland City, In., U.S.	H3	91
Oakland Park, Fl., U.S.	r13	86
Oak Lawn, Il., U.S.	B6	90
Oaklawn, Ks., U.S.	g12	93
Oakley, Id., U.S.	G5	89
Oakley, Ks., U.S.	C3	93
Oakman, Al., U.S.	B2	78
Oakmont, Pa., U.S.	E2	115
Oak Mountain, mtn., Ga., U.S.	D2	87
Oak Orchard, De., U.S.	F5	85
Oak Park, Il., U.S.	B6	90
Oak Park, Mi., U.S.	p15	99
Oak Ridge, N.C., U.S.	A3	110
Oakridge, Or., U.S.	D4	114
Oak Ridge, Tn., U.S.	C9	119
Oak Ridge Reservoir, res., N.J., U.S.	A3	107
Oakton, Va., U.S.	g12	123
Oaktown, In., U.S.	G3	91
Oak Valley, N.J., U.S.	D2	107
Oakville, Ont., Can.	D5	73
Oakville, Ct., U.S.	C3	84
Oakville, Mo., U.S.	g13	102
Oakwood, Ga., U.S.	B3	87
Oakwood, Il., U.S.	C6	90
Oakwood, Oh., U.S.	C1	112
Oamaru, N.Z.	F3	52
Oaxaca [de Juárez], Mex.	I11	62
Ob', stm., U.S.S.R.	D7	20
Oban, Scot., U.K.	E7	7
Obbia, Som.	G4	46
Obed, stm., Tn., U.S.	C9	119
Oberlin, Ks., U.S.	C3	93
Oberlin, La., U.S.	D3	95
Oberlin, Oh., U.S.	A3	112
Oberwart, Aus.	H16	8
Obetz, Oh., U.S.	C3	112
Obi, Kepulauan, is., Indon.	F8	32
Obi, Pulau, i., Indon.	F8	32
Óbidos, Braz.	D7	54
Obihiro, Japan	q21	30a
Obion, Tn., U.S.	A2	119
Obion, co., Tn., U.S.	A2	119
Obion, stm., Tn., U.S.	A2	119
Oblong, Il., U.S.	D6	90
Oblučje, U.S.S.R.	H20	20
Obninsk, U.S.S.R.	F19	22
Obock, Dji.	F3	46
O'Brien, co., Ia., U.S.	A2	92
Obrovac, Yugo.	E10	14
Observation Peak, mtn., Ca., U.S.	B3	82
Observatoire, Caye de l', i., N. Cal.	D11	50
Obuasi, Ghana	G5	42
Ocala, Fl., U.S.	C4	86
Ocaña, Col.	C6	58
Ocaña, Spain	F8	12
Occidental, Cordillera, mts., Col.	E4	58
Occidental, Cordillera, mts., Peru	F4	54
Ocean, co., N.J., U.S.	D4	107
Oceana, W.V., U.S.	D3	125
Oceana, co., Mi., U.S.	E4	99
Oceana Naval Air Station, mil., Va., U.S.	k15	123
Ocean Bluff, Ma., U.S.	B6	98
Ocean City, Fl., U.S.	u15	86
Ocean City, Md., U.S.	D7	97
Ocean City, N.J., U.S.	E3	107
Ocean Grove, Ma., U.S.	C5	98
Ocean Park, Wa., U.S.	C1	124
Ocean Port, N.J., U.S.	C4	107
Oceanside, Ca., U.S.	F5	82
Ocean Springs, Ms., U.S.	E5	101
Ocean [Township], N.J., U.S.	C4	107
Ocean View, De., U.S.	F5	85
Ocha, U.S.S.R.	G22	20
Ocheda Lake, l., Mn., U.S.	G3	100
Ocheyedan, stm., Ia., U.S.	A2	92
Ochiltree, co., Tx., U.S.	A2	120
Ochlockonee, stm., Fl., U.S.	B2	86
Ochoco Lake, res., Or., U.S.	C6	114
Ocho Rios, Jam.	E9	64
Ochota, stm., U.S.S.R.	F22	20
Ochotsk, U.S.S.R.	F22	20
Ochsenfurt, Ger.	F10	8
Ocilla, Ga., U.S.	E3	87
Ockelbo, Swe.	F11	6
Ocmulgee, stm., Ga., U.S.	D3	87
Ocoee, Fl., U.S.	D5	86
Ocoee, Lake, res., Tn., U.S.	D9	119
Oconee, co., Ga., U.S.	C3	87
Oconee, co., S.C., U.S.	B1	117
Oconee, stm., Ga., U.S.	C3	87
Oconee, Lake, res., Ga., U.S.	C3	87
Oconomowoc, Wi., U.S.	E5	126
Oconto, Wi., U.S.	D6	126
Oconto, co., Wi., U.S.	D5	126
Oconto, stm., Wi., U.S.	D5	126
Oconto Falls, Wi., U.S.	D5	126
Ocotal, Nic.	H4	64
Ocotlán, Mex.	G8	62
Ocracoke Inlet, b., N.C., U.S.	B6	110
Ocracoke Island, i., N.C., U.S.	B7	110
Octoraro Creek, stm., U.S.	A5	97
Ocumare del Tuy, Ven.	B9	58
Ocussi, Indon.	G7	32
Oda, Ghana	G5	42
Oda, Jabal, mtn., Sudan	D13	42
Ōdate, Japan	B13	30
Odawara, Japan	G12	30
Odda, Nor.	F6	6
Odebolt, Ia., U.S.	B2	92
Odell, Il., U.S.	B5	90
Odell, Or., U.S.	B5	114
Odell Lake, l., Or., U.S.	E5	114
Odem, Tx., U.S.	F4	120
Odemira, Port.	H3	12
Ödemiş, Tur.	K11	16
Odense, Den.	I8	6
Odenton, Md., U.S.	B4	97
Odenville, Al., U.S.	B3	78
Oder (Odra), stm., Eur.	C14	8
Oderberg, Ger.	C14	8
Odessa, Ont., Can.	C8	73
Odessa, U.S.S.R.	H4	18
Odessa, De., U.S.	C3	85
Odessa, Mo., U.S.	C4	102
Odessa, Tx., U.S.	D1	120
Odessa, Wa., U.S.	B7	124
Odienné, I.C.	G4	42
Odin, Il., U.S.	E4	90
Odincovo, U.S.S.R.	F20	22
Odon, In., U.S.	G4	91
O'Donnell, Tx., U.S.	C2	120
Odra (Oder), stm., Eur.	C14	8
Oelsnitz, Ger.	E12	8
Oelwein, Ia., U.S.	B6	92
O'Fallon, Il., U.S.	E4	90
O'Fallon, Mo., U.S.	f12	102
Offenbach, Ger.	E8	8
Offenburg, Ger.	G7	8
Offutt Air Force Base, mil., Ne., U.S.	g3	104
Ōfunato, Japan	C14	30
Ōgaki, Japan	G9	30
Ogallala, Ne., U.S.	C4	104
Ogbomosho, Nig.	G6	42
Ogden, Ia., U.S.	B3	92
Ogden, Ks., U.S.	C7	93
Ogden, Ut., U.S.	B4	121
Ogden, Mount, mtn., N.A.	k23	79
Ogdensburg, N.J., U.S.	A3	107
Ogdensburg, N.Y., U.S.	f9	109
Ogeechee, stm., Ga., U.S.	D5	87
Ogemaw, co., Mi., U.S.	D6	99
Ogilvie Mountains, mts., Yukon, Can.	D5	66
Ogle, co., Il., U.S.	A4	90
Oglesby, Il., U.S.	B4	90
Oglethorpe, Ga., U.S.	D2	87
Oglethorpe, co., Ga., U.S.	C3	87
Oglethorpe, Mount, mtn., Ga., U.S.	B2	87
Ogooué, stm., Afr.	B2	44
Ogulin, Yugo.	D10	14
Ogunquit, Me., U.S.	E2	96
Oğuzeli, Tur.	A5	40
Ohanet, Alg.	C7	42
Ōhata, Japan	A14	30
Ohatchee, Al., U.S.	B3	78
O'Higgins, Lago (Lago San Martín), l., S.A.	F2	56
Ohio, co., In., U.S.	G7	91
Ohio, co., Ky., U.S.	C3	94
Ohio, co., W.V., U.S.	A4	125
Ohio, state, U.S.	B3	112
Ohio, stm., U.S.	D9	76
Ohio Brush Creek, stm., Oh., U.S.	D2	112
Ohio City, Oh., U.S.	B1	112
Ohio Peak, mtn., Co., U.S.	C3	83
Ohioville, Pa., U.S.	E1	115
Ohoopee, stm., Ga., U.S.	D4	87
Ohrid, Lake, l., Eur.	H4	16
Öhringen, Ger.	F9	8
Oiapoque, Braz.	C8	54
Oil City, La., U.S.	B2	95
Oil City, Pa., U.S.	D2	115
Oil Creek, stm., Pa., U.S.	C2	115
Oildale, Ca., U.S.	E4	82
Oil Springs, Ont., Can.	E2	73
Oilton, Ok., U.S.	A5	113
Ōita, Japan	I4	30
Ojai, Ca., U.S.	E4	82
Ojinaga, Mex.	C7	62
Ojm'akon, U.S.S.R.	E22	20
Ojo de Liebre, Laguna, b., Mex.	D2	62
Ojos del Salado, Cerro, mtn., S.A.	B3	56
Oka, stm., U.S.S.R.	G14	20
Oka, stm., U.S.S.R.	F25	22
Okaba, Indon.	G10	32
Okahandja, Nmb.	F3	44
Okaloosa, co., Fl., U.S.	u15	86
Okamanpeedan Lake, l., U.S.	A3	92
Okanagan Falls, B.C., Can.	E8	69
Okanagan Lake, l., B.C., Can.	D8	69
Okanagan Landing, B.C., Can.	D8	69
Okanogan, Wa., U.S.	A6	124
Okanogan, co., Wa., U.S.	A5	124
Okāra, Pak.	E5	38
Okarche, Ok., U.S.	B4	113
Okatibee Reservoir, res., Ms., U.S.	C5	101
Okauchee Lake, Wi., U.S.	E5	126
Okavango (Cubango), stm., Afr.	E3	44
Okavango Swamp, sw., Bots.	E4	44
Ōkawa, Japan	I3	30
Okawville, Il., U.S.	E4	90
Okaya, Japan	F11	30
Okayama, Japan	H6	30
Okazaki, Japan	H10	30
Okeechobee, Fl., U.S.	E6	86
Okeechobee, co., Fl., U.S.	E6	86
Okeechobee, Lake, l., Fl., U.S.	F6	86
Okeene, Ok., U.S.	A3	113
Okefenokee Swamp, sw., U.S.	F4	87
Okemah, Ok., U.S.	B5	113
Okfuskee, co., Ok., U.S.	B5	113
Okhotsk, Sea of (Ochotskoje More), Asia	G23	20
Oki-guntō, is., Japan	F6	30
Okinawa-jima, i., Japan	y27	31b
Okinoerabu-shima, i., Japan	x28	31b
Okino-Tori-shima, i., Japan	G14	26
Oklahoma, co., Ok., U.S.	B4	113
Oklahoma, state, U.S.	B4	113
Oklahoma City, Ok., U.S.	B4	113
Oklawaha, Fl., U.S.	C5	86
Oklawaha, stm., Fl., U.S.	C5	86
Oklawaha, Lake, res., Fl., U.S.	C5	86
Okmulgee, Ok., U.S.	B6	113
Okmulgee, co., Ok., U.S.	B5	113
Okoboji, Ia., U.S.	A2	92
Okobojo Creek, stm., S.D., U.S.	C5	118
Okolona, Ky., U.S.	g11	94
Okolona, Ms., U.S.	B5	101
Okotoks, Alta., Can.	D4	68
Okt'abr'skoj Revol'ucii, Ostrov, i., U.S.S.R.	B13	20
Oktibbeha, co., Ms., U.S.	B5	101
Ola, Ar., U.S.	B2	81
Olancha Peak, mtn., Ca., U.S.	D4	82
Olanchito, Hond.	G4	64
Öland, i., Swe.	H11	6
Olanta, S.C., U.S.	D8	117
Olathe, Co., U.S.	C3	83
Olathe, Ks., U.S.	D9	93
Olavarría, Arg.	D4	56
Olbia, Italy	I4	14
Ol'chon, Ostrov, i., U.S.S.R.	G15	20
Olcott, N.Y., U.S.	B2	109
Old Bahama Channel, strt., N.A.	C8	64
Old Bridge, N.J., U.S.	C4	107
Oldenburg, Ger.	B8	8
Oldenburg, In., U.S.	F7	91
Oldenburg [in Holstein], Ger.	A10	8
Old Faithful Geyser, Wy., U.S.	B2	127
Old Forge, Pa., U.S.	D10	115
Old Fort, N.C., U.S.	f10	110
Oldham, co., Ky., U.S.	B4	94
Oldham, co., Tx., U.S.	B1	120
Old Harbor, Ak., U.S.	D9	79
Old Head of Kinsale, c., Ire.	J4	7
Old Hickory Lake, res., Tn., U.S.	A5	119
Oldman, stm., Alta., Can.	E4	68
Old Man of the Mountain, N.H., U.S.	B3	106
Oldmans Creek, stm., N.J., U.S.	D2	107
Old Orchard Beach, Me., U.S.	E2	96
Old Perlican, Newf., Can.	D5	72
Old Point Comfort, c., Va., U.S.	h15	123
Old Rhodes Key, i., Fl., U.S.	G6	86
Old River Lake, l., Ar., U.S.	k10	81
Olds, Alta., Can.	D3	68
Old Saybrook, Ct., U.S.	D6	84
Oldsmar, Fl., U.S.	o10	86
Old Tampa Bay, b., Fl., U.S.	p10	86
Old Tappan, N.J., U.S.	g9	107
Old Topsail Inlet, b., N.C., U.S.	C5	110
Old Town, Me., U.S.	D4	96
Old Wives Lake, l., Sask., Can.	G2	75
Olean, N.Y., U.S.	C2	109
O'Leary, P.E.I., Can.	C5	71
Ølen, Nor.	G5	6
Olenij, Ostrov, i., U.S.S.R.	C9	20
Olen'ok, U.S.S.R.	D16	20
Olen'ok, stm., U.S.S.R.	C18	20
Olen'okskij Zaliv, b., U.S.S.R.	C18	20
Olentangy, stm., Oh., U.S.	B3	112
Oleśnica, Pol.	D17	8
Ol'ga, U.S.S.R.	I21	20
Olga, Mount, mtn., Austl.	E6	50
Olhão, Port.	H3	12
Ólimbos, mtn., Cyp.	B3	40
Ólimbos, Óros, mtn., Grc.	I6	16
Olímpia, Braz.	F4	57
Olin, Ia., U.S.	B6	92
Olinda, Braz.	E12	54
Olite, Spain	C10	12
Oliva, Arg.	C4	56
Oliva, Spain	G11	12
Oliva de la Frontera, Spain	G5	12
Olive Branch, Ms., U.S.	A4	101
Olive Hill, Ky., U.S.	B6	94
Olivehurst, Ca., U.S.	C3	82
Oliveira, Braz.	F6	57
Olivenza, Spain	G4	12
Oliver, B.C., Can.	E8	69
Oliver, Pa., U.S.	G2	115
Oliver, co., N.D., U.S.	B4	111
Oliver Dam, U.S.	C5	78
Oliver Springs, Tn., U.S.	C9	119
Olivet, Mi., U.S.	F6	99
Olivia, Mn., U.S.	F4	100
Olla, La., U.S.	C3	95
Ollagüe, Chile	A3	56
Olmedo, Spain	D7	12
Olmito, Tx., U.S.	F4	120
Olmos, Peru	E3	54
Olmos Park, Tx., U.S.	k7	120
Olmsted, co., Mn., U.S.	G6	100
Olmsted Falls, Oh., U.S.	h9	112
Olney, Il., U.S.	E5	90
Olney, Md., U.S.	B3	97
Olney, Tx., U.S.	C3	120
Oloj, stm., U.S.S.R.	D26	20
Ol'okma, stm., U.S.S.R.	F18	20
Ol'okminsk, U.S.S.R.	E18	20
Olomouc, Czech.	F17	8
Olongapo, Phil.	q19	33b
Oloron-Sainte-Marie, Fr.	I6	10
Olot, Spain	C14	12
Olov'annaja, U.S.S.R.	G17	20
Olsztyn (Allenstein), Pol.	B20	8
Olten, Switz.	E14	10
Olton, Tx., U.S.	B1	120
Oluan Pi, c., Tai.	N9	28
Olustee, Ok., U.S.	C2	113
Ol'utorskij, Mys, c., U.S.S.R.	F28	20
Ol'utorskij Zaliv, b., U.S.S.R.	E27	20
Olympia, Wa., U.S.	B3	124
Olympic Mountains, mts., Wa., U.S.	B2	124
Olympic National Park, Wa., U.S.	B2	124
Olympus, Mount, mtn., Wa., U.S.	B2	124
Olympus, Mount see Ólimbos, Óros, mtn., Grc.	I6	16
Olyphant, Pa., U.S.	D10	115
Omae-zaki, c., Japan	H11	30
Omagh, N. Ire., U.K.	G5	7
Omaha, Ne., U.S.	C10	104
Omaha Indian Reservation, Ne., U.S.	B9	104
Omak, Wa., U.S.	A6	124
Omak Lake, l., Wa., U.S.	A6	124
Oman, ctry., Asia	D6	46
Oman, Gulf of, b., Asia	D6	46
Omar, W.V., U.S.	D3	125
Ōma-zaki, c., Japan	A13	30
Omčak, U.S.S.R.	E23	20
Omega, Ga., U.S.	E3	87
Omegna, Italy	D3	14
Omemee, Ont., Can.	C6	73

Name | Map Ref | Page
Omerville, Que., Can. D5 74
Ometepe, Isla de, i., Nic. I5 64
Ometepec, Mex. I10 62
Omineca, stm., B.C., Can. B5 69
Omineca Mountains, mts., B.C., Can. A4 69
Ōmiya, Japan G12 30
Ommaney, Cape, c., Ak., U.S. D12 79
Ommanney Bay, b., N.W. Ter., Can. B12 66
Ommen, Neth. C6 8
Omo, stm., Eth. G2 46
Omolon, stm., U.S.S.R. D25 20
Ompompanoosuc, stm., Vt., U.S. D4 122
Omro, Wi., U.S. D5 126
Omsk, U.S.S.R. F8 20
Omsukčan, U.S.S.R. E25 20
Ōmura, Japan J2 30
Ōmuta, Japan I3 30
Onaga, Ks., U.S. C7 93
Onalaska, Wa., U.S. C3 124
Onalaska, Wi., U.S. E2 126
Onamia, Mn., U.S. D5 100
Onancock, Va., U.S. C7 123
Onarga, Il., U.S. C6 90
Onawa, Ia., U.S. B1 92
Onawa, Lake, l., Me., U.S. C3 96
Onaway, Mi., U.S. C6 99
Onda, Spain F11 12
Ondangua, Nmb. E3 44
Ondjiva, Ang. E3 44
Öndörchaan, Mong. B9 26
Oneco, Fl., U.S. E4 86
Onega, Lake see Onežskoje ozero, l., U.S.S.R. E5 18
One Hundred Fifty Mile House, B.C., Can. C7 69
One Hundred Mile House, B.C., Can. D7 69
Oneida, Ky., U.S. C6 94
Oneida, N.Y., U.S. B5 109
Oneida, Oh., U.S. C1 112
Oneida, Tn., U.S. C9 119
Oneida, co., Id., U.S. G6 89
Oneida, co., N.Y., U.S. B5 109
Oneida, co., Wi., U.S. C4 126
Oneida Lake, l., N.Y., U.S. B5 109
O'Neill, Ne., U.S. B7 104
Onekotan, Ostrov, i., U.S.S.R. H24 20
Oneonta, Al., U.S. B3 78
Oneonta, N.Y., U.S. C5 109
Onežskoje ozero, l., U.S.S.R. E5 18
Ongole, India E6 37
Onida, S.D., U.S. C5 118
Onitsha, Nig. G7 42
Onoda, Japan I4 30
Onomichi, Japan H6 30
Onondaga, co., N.Y., U.S. C4 109
Onondaga Indian Reservation, N.Y., U.S. C4 109
Onota Lake, l., Ma., U.S. B1 98
Onoway, Alta., Can. C3 68
Onset, Ma., U.S. C6 98
Onslow, Austl. D3 50
Onslow, co., N.C., U.S. C5 110
Onslow Bay, b., N.C., U.S. C5 110
Onsted, Mi., U.S. F6 99
Ontario, Ca., U.S. E5 82
Ontario, Oh., U.S. B3 112
Ontario, Or., U.S. C10 114
Ontario, co., N.Y., U.S. C3 109
Ontario, prov., Can. C6 73
Ontario, Lake, l., N.A. C11 76
Onteniente, Spain G11 12
Ontonagon, Mi., U.S. m12 99
Ontonagon, co., Mi., U.S. m12 99
Ontonagon Indian Reservation, Mi., U.S. B1 99
Onverwacht, Sur. B7 54
Oodnadatta, Austl. E7 50
Ooldea, Austl. F6 50
Oolitic, In., U.S. G4 91
Oologah, Ok., U.S. A6 113
Oologah Lake, res., Ok., U.S. A6 113
Ooltewah, Tn., U.S. D8 119
Oostburg, Wi., U.S. E6 126
Oostende (Ostende), Bel. D2 8
Oosterhout, Neth. D4 8
Ootacamund, India G4 37
Ootsa Lake, l., B.C., Can. C4 69
Opala, Zaire B4 44
Opa-Locka, Fl., U.S. s13 86
Opatija, Yugo. D9 14
Opava, Czech. F17 8
Opelika, Al., U.S. C4 78
Opelousas, La., U.S. D3 95
Opequon Creek, stm., W.V., U.S. B6 125
Opiscotéo, Lac, l., Que., Can. F19 66
Opole (Oppeln), Pol. E17 8
Opotiki, N.Z. C6 52
Opp, Al., U.S. D3 78
Oppdal, Nor. E7 6
Oppelo, Ar., U.S. B3 81
Opportunity, Wa., U.S. B8 124
Optima Reservoir, res., Ok., U.S. e9 113
Oquawka, Il., U.S. C3 90
Ora, Italy C6 14
Oracle, Az., U.S. E5 80
Oradea, Rom. B5 16
Oradell, N.J., U.S. h8 107
Oradell Reservoir, res., N.J., U.S. h9 107
Orai, India H8 38
Oraibi, Az., U.S. B5 80
Oran, Alg. A5 42
Oran, Mo., U.S. D8 102
Orange, Austl. F9 50
Orange, Fr. H11 10
Orange, Ca., U.S. n13 82
Orange, Ct., U.S. D3 84
Orange, Ma., U.S. A3 98
Orange, N.J., U.S. B4 107
Orange, Tx., U.S. D6 120
Orange, Va., U.S. B4 123
Orange, co., Ca., U.S. F5 82
Orange, co., Fl., U.S. D5 86
Orange, co., In., U.S. G4 91
Orange, co., N.Y., U.S. D6 109
Orange, co., N.C., U.S. A3 110
Orange, co., Tx., U.S. D6 120
Orange, co., Vt., U.S. D3 122
Orange, co., Va., U.S. B4 123
Orange (Oranje), stm., Afr. G3 44
Orange, Cabo, c., Braz. C8 54
Orange Beach, Al., U.S. E2 78
Orangeburg, S.C., U.S. E6 117
Orangeburg, co., S.C., U.S. E6 117
Orange City, Fl., U.S. D5 86
Orange City, Ia., U.S. B1 92
Orange Grove, Ms., U.S. E5 101
Orange Grove, Tx., U.S. F4 120
Orange Lake, l., Fl., U.S. C4 86
Orange Park, Fl., U.S. B5 86
Orangeville, Ont., Can. D4 73
Orangeville, Ut., U.S. D4 121
Orange Walk, Belize E3 64
Orani, Phil. q19 33b
Oranienburg, Ger. C13 8
Oranjestad, Aruba H12 64
Orbetello, Italy G6 14
Orbost, Austl. G9 50
Örbyhus, Swe. F11 6
Orcas Island, i., Wa., U.S. A3 124
Orcera, Spain G9 12
Orchard City, Co., U.S. C3 83
Orchard Homes, Mt., U.S. D2 103
Orchard Park, N.Y., U.S. C2 109
Orchards, Wa., U.S. D3 124
Orchard Valley, Wy., U.S. E8 127
Orchila, Isla, i., Ven. B9 58
Orchon, stm., Mong. B7 26
Orcutt, Ca., U.S. E3 82
Ord, Ne., U.S. C7 104
Ord, Mount, mtn., Austl. C5 50
Ordenes, Spain B3 12
Ordway, Co., U.S. C7 83
Ordzhonikidze see Ordžonikidze, U.S.S.R. I6 18
Oreana, Il., U.S. D5 90
Örebro, Swe. G10 6
Orechovo-Zujevo, U.S.S.R. F21 22
Oregon, Il., U.S. A4 90
Oregon, Mo., U.S. B2 102
Oregon, Oh., U.S. A2 112
Oregon, Wi., U.S. F4 126
Oregon, co., Mo., U.S. E6 102
Oregon, state, U.S. C6 114
Oregon Caves National Monument, Or., U.S. E2 114
Oregon City, Or., U.S. B4 114
Oregon Inlet, b., N.C., U.S. B7 110
Orem, Ut., U.S. C4 121
Orenburg, U.S.S.R. G9 18
Orense, Spain C4 12
Orestiás, Grc. H10 16
Orfordville, Wi., U.S. F4 126
Organ Mountains, mts., N.M., U.S. E3 108
Organ Pipe Cactus National Monument, Az., U.S. E3 80
Orgūn, Afg. D3 38
Oriental, N.C., U.S. B6 110
Oriental, Cordillera, mts., Col. E6 58
Oriental, Cordillera, mts., Peru F4 54
Orihuela, Spain G11 12
Orillia, Ont., Can. C5 73
Orinoco, stm., S.A. C11 58
Orinoco, Delta del, Ven. C12 58
Orion, Il., U.S. B3 90
Oripää, Fin. F14 6
Orissa, state, India J11 38
Oristano, Italy I3 14
Orivesi, Fin. F15 6
Orizaba, Mex. H11 62
Orizaba, Pico de (Volcán Citlaltépetl), vol., Mex. H11 62
Orkney Islands, is., Scot., U.K. B9 7
Orland, Ca., U.S. C2 82
Orlando, Fl., U.S. D5 86
Orland Park, Il., U.S. k9 90
Orléans, Fr. E8 10
Orleans, In., U.S. G5 91
Orleans, Ma., U.S. C7 98
Orleans, Vt., U.S. B4 122
Orleans, co., La., U.S. E6 95
Orleans, co., N.Y., U.S. B2 109
Orleans, co., Vt., U.S. B4 122
Orléans, Île d', i., Que., Can. C6 74
Orman Dam, S.D., U.S. C2 118
Ormond Beach, Fl., U.S. C5 86
Ormož, Yugo. C11 14
Ormstown, Que., Can. D3 74
Ornans, Fr. E13 10
Örnsköldsvik, Swe. E12 6
Orocué, Col. E7 58
Orofino, Id., U.S. C2 89
Or'ol, U.S.S.R. I19 22
Oromocto, N.B., Can. D3 71
Oromocto Lake, l., N.B., Can. D2 71
Orono, Me., U.S. D4 96
Oronoco, Mn., U.S. F6 100
Oroville, Ca., U.S. C3 82
Oroville, Wa., U.S. A6 124
Oroville, Lake, res., Ca., U.S. C3 82
Orrick, Mo., U.S. B3 102
Orrville, Oh., U.S. B4 112
Orsk, U.S.S.R. G9 18
Orta Nova, Italy H10 14
Ortegal, Cabo, c., Spain B4 12
Orting, Wa., U.S. B3 124
Ortiz, Ven. C9 58
Ortona, Italy G9 14
Ortonville, Mi., U.S. F7 99
Ortonville, Mn., U.S. E2 100
Orūmīyeh (Rezā'īyeh), Iran J7 18
Orūmīyeh, Daryācheh-ye, l., Iran J7 18
Oruro, Bol. G5 54
Orūzgān (Qala-I-Hazār Qadam), Afg. D2 38
Orvieto, Italy G7 14
Orwell, Oh., U.S. A5 112
Orwigsburg, Pa., U.S. E9 115
Oš, U.S.S.R. I12 18
Osa, Península de, pen., C.R. J6 64
Osage, Ia., U.S. A5 92
Osage, Wy., U.S. C8 127
Osage, co., Ks., U.S. D8 93
Osage, co., Mo., U.S. C6 102
Osage, co., Ok., U.S. A5 113
Osage, stm., Mo., U.S. C3 102
Osage Beach, Mo., U.S. C5 102
Osage City, Ks., U.S. D8 93
Ōsaka, Japan H8 30
Ōsaka-wan, b., Japan H8 30
Osakis, Mn., U.S. E3 100
Osakis, Lake, l., Mn., U.S. E3 100
Osawatomie, Ks., U.S. D9 93
Osborne, Ks., U.S. C5 93
Osborne, co., Ks., U.S. C5 93
Osburn, Id., U.S. B3 89
Osceola, Ar., U.S. B6 81
Osceola, In., U.S. A5 91
Osceola, Ia., U.S. C4 92
Osceola, Mo., U.S. C4 102
Osceola, Ne., U.S. C8 104
Osceola, Wi., U.S. C1 126
Osceola, co., Fl., U.S. E5 86
Osceola, co., Ia., U.S. A2 92
Osceola, co., Mi., U.S. E5 99
Osceola Mills, Pa., U.S. E5 115
Oschersleben, Ger. C11 8
Oscoda, Mi., U.S. D7 99
Oscoda, co., Mi., U.S. D6 99
Oscura Mountains, mts., N.M., U.S. D3 108
Osen, Nor. D8 6
Osgood, In., U.S. F7 91
Oshawa, Ont., Can. D6 73
Oshima-hantō, pen., Japan q18 30a
Oshkosh, Ne., U.S. C3 104
Oshkosh, Wi., U.S. D5 126
Oshogbo, Nig. G6 42
Osh see Oš, U.S.S.R. I12 18
Oshwe, Zaire B3 44
Osijek, Yugo. D2 16
Osimo, Italy F8 14
Osinniki, U.S.S.R. G11 20
Osipoviči, U.S.S.R. H11 22
Oskaloosa, Ia., U.S. C5 92
Oskaloosa, Ks., U.S. C8 93
Oskarshamn, Swe. H11 6
Oslo, Nor. G8 6
Osmānābād, India C4 37
Osmaniye, Tur. A5 40
Osmond, Ne., U.S. B8 104
Osnabrück, Ger. C8 8
Osorno, Chile E2 56
Osorno, Spain C7 12
Osoyoos, B.C., Can. E8 69
Osoyoos Lake, l., Wa., U.S. A6 124
Ospino, Ven. C8 58
Osprey, Fl., U.S. E4 86
Osprey Reef, rf., Austl. B9 50
Ossa, Mount, mtn., Austl. H9 50
Ossabaw Island, i., Ga., U.S. E5 87
Osseo, Mn., U.S. m12 100
Osseo, Wi., U.S. D2 126
Ossian, In., U.S. C7 91
Ossian, Ia., U.S. A6 92
Ossining, N.Y., U.S. D7 109
Ossipee, stm., U.S. C5 106
Ossipee Lake, l., N.H., U.S. C4 106
Ostaškov, U.S.S.R. D16 22
Osterholz-Scharmbeck, Ger. B8 8
Osterode, Ger. D10 8
Östersund, Swe. E10 6
Osterville, Ma., U.S. C7 98
Ostrava, Czech. F18 8
Ostrołęka, Pol. B21 8
Ostrov, U.S.S.R. D11 22
Ostrowiec Świętokrzyski, Pol. E21 8
Ostrów Wielkopolski, Pol. D17 8
Ostuni, Italy I12 14
Ōsumi-kaikyō, strt., Japan L3 30
Ōsumi-shotō, is., Japan u30 31b
Osuna, Spain H6 12
Osvaldo Cruz, Braz. F3 57
Oswegatchie, stm., N.Y., U.S. f9 109
Oswego, Il., U.S. B5 90
Oswego, Ks., U.S. E8 93
Oswego, N.Y., U.S. B4 109
Oswego, co., N.Y., U.S. B4 109
Oswego, stm., N.J., U.S. D4 107
Oswego, stm., N.Y., U.S. B4 109
Oswestry, Eng., U.K. I9 7
Oświęcim, Pol. E19 8
Ōta, Japan F12 30
Otaki, N.Z. D5 52
Otaru, Japan p18 30a
Otavi, Nmb. E3 44
Oteen, N.C., U.S. f10 110
Otero, co., Co., U.S. D7 83
Otero, co., N.M., U.S. E3 108
Othello, Wa., U.S. C6 124
Oti, stm., Afr. G6 42
Otish, Monts, mts., Que., Can. F18 66
Otis Orchards, Wa., U.S. g14 124
Otis Reservoir, res., Ma., U.S. B1 98
Otisville, Mi., U.S. E7 99
Otjiwarongo, Nmb. F3 44
Otočac, Yugo. E10 14
Otoe, co., Ne., U.S. D9 104
Otranto, Italy I13 14
Otranto, Strait of, mth., Eur. I2 16
Otsego, Mi., U.S. F5 99
Otsego, co., Mi., U.S. C6 99
Otsego, co., N.Y., U.S. C5 109
Otsego Lake, l., N.Y., U.S. C6 109
Ōtsu, Japan G8 30
Otta, Nor. F7 6
Ottauquechee, stm., Vt., U.S. D4 122
Ottawa, Ont., Can. B9 73
Ottawa, Il., U.S. B5 90
Ottawa, Ks., U.S. D8 93
Ottawa, Oh., U.S. A1 112
Ottawa, co., Ks., U.S. C6 93
Ottawa, co., Mi., U.S. F4 99
Ottawa, co., Oh., U.S. A2 112
Ottawa, co., Ok., U.S. A7 113
Ottawa, stm., Can. G17 66
Ottawa, stm., Oh., U.S. e6 112
Ottawa Hills, Oh., U.S. e6 112
Ottawa Islands, is., N.W. Ter., Can. E16 66
Ottenby, Swe. H11 6
Otterbein, In., U.S. D3 91
Otter Brook, stm., N.H., U.S. E2 106
Otter Brook Lake, res., N.H., U.S. E2 106
Otter Creek, stm., Ut., U.S. E4 121
Otter Creek, stm., Vt., U.S. C2 122
Otter Creek Reservoir, res., Ut., U.S. E4 121
Otter Islands, is., S.C., U.S. m11 117
Otter Tail, co., Mn., U.S. D3 100
Otter Tail, stm., Mn., U.S. D2 100
Otter Tail Lake, l., Mn., U.S. D3 100
Otterville, Ont., Can. E4 73
Ottumwa, Ia., U.S. C5 92
Otwock, Pol. C21 8
Ötztaler Alpen, mts., Eur. C5 14
Ouachita, co., Ar., U.S. D3 81
Ouachita, co., La., U.S. B3 95
Ouachita, Lake, res., Ar., U.S. C2 81
Ouachita Mountains, mts., U.S. E8 76
Ouadda, Cen. Afr. Rep. G10 42
Ouagadougou, Burkina F5 42
Ouahigouya, Burkina F5 42
Oualâta, Maur. E4 42
Ouallene, Alg. D6 42
Ouanda Djallé, Cen. Afr. Rep. G10 42
Ouarane, reg., Maur. D3 42
Ouargla, Alg. B7 42
Ouarzazate, Mor. B4 42
Oubangui, stm., Afr. A3 44
Oudtshoorn, S. Afr. H4 44
Oued Meliz, Tun. M3 14
Oued Zarga, Tun. M4 14
Ouémé, stm., Benin G6 42
Ouesso, Congo A3 44
Ouezzane, Mor. B4 42
Oujda, Mor. B5 42
Oulu, Fin. D15 6
Oulujärvi, l., Fin. D16 6
Oum Chalouba, Chad E10 42
Ounianga Kébir, Chad E10 42
Ouray, Co., U.S. C3 83
Ouray, co., Co., U.S. C3 83
Ouray, Mount, mtn., Co., U.S. C4 83
Ourinhos, Braz. G4 57
Ourique, Port. H3 12
Ouro Prêto, Braz. F7 57
Ou-sammyaku, mts., Japan D13 30
Outagamie, co., Wi., U.S. D5 126
Outardes Quatre, Réservoir, res., Que., Can. h13 74
Outer Hebrides, is., Scot., U.K. D5 7
Outer Island, i., Wi., U.S. A3 126
Outer Santa Barbara Passage, strt., Ca., U.S. F4 82
Outpost Mountain, mtn., Ak., U.S. B9 79
Outremont, Que., Can. p19 74
Ovalle, Chile C2 56
Ovamboland, hist. reg., Nmb. E3 44
Ovana, Cerro, mtn., Ven. E9 58
Ovar, Port. E3 12
Overbrook, Ks., U.S. D8 93
Overgaard, Az., U.S. C5 80
Overland, Mo., U.S. f13 102
Overland Park, Ks., U.S. m16 93
Overlea, Md., U.S. B5 97
Overton, Nv., U.S. G7 105
Overton, Tx., U.S. C5 120
Overton, co., Tn., U.S. C8 119
Övertorneå, Swe. C14 6
Ovett, Ms., U.S. D4 101
Ovid, Mi., U.S. E6 99
Oviedo, Spain B6 12
Owando, Congo B3 44
Owasco Lake, l., N.Y., U.S. C4 109
Owase, Japan H9 30
Owasso, Ok., U.S. A6 113
Owatonna, Mn., U.S. F5 100
Owego, N.Y., U.S. C4 109
Owen, Wi., U.S. D3 126
Owen, co., In., U.S. F4 91
Owen, co., Ky., U.S. B5 94
Owen, Lake, l., Wi., U.S. B2 126
Owen, Mount, mtn., Co., U.S. C3 83
Owens, stm., Ca., U.S. D4 82
Owensboro, Ky., U.S. C2 94
Owens Cross Roads, Al., U.S. A3 78
Owens Lake, l., Ca., U.S. D5 82
Owen Sound, Ont., Can. C4 73
Owen Sound, b., Ont., Can. C4 73
Owen Stanley Range, mts., Pap. N. Gui. m16 50a
Owensville, In., U.S. H2 91
Owensville, Mo., U.S. C6 102
Owensville, Oh., U.S. C1 112
Owenton, Ky., U.S. B5 94
Owings Mills, Md., U.S. B4 97
Owingsville, Ky., U.S. B6 94
Owl Creek, stm., Wy., U.S. C4 127
Owl Creek Mountains, mts., Wy., U.S. C4 127
Owo, Nig. G7 42
Owosso, Mi., U.S. E6 99
Owsley, co., Ky., U.S. C6 94
Owyhee, Nv., U.S. B5 105
Owyhee, co., Id., U.S. G2 89
Owyhee, stm., U.S. E9 114
Owyhee, Lake, res., Or., U.S. D9 114
Owyhee Dam, Or., U.S. D9 114
Owyhee Mountains, mts., U.S. G2 89
Oxbow Dam, U.S. E2 89
Oxelösund, Swe. G11 6
Oxford, N.S., Can. D6 71
Oxford, N.Z. E4 52
Oxford, Eng., U.K. J11 7
Oxford, Al., U.S. B4 78
Oxford, Ct., U.S. D3 84
Oxford, Ga., U.S. C3 87
Oxford, In., U.S. C3 91
Oxford, Ia., U.S. C6 92
Oxford, Ks., U.S. E6 93
Oxford, Me., U.S. D2 96
Oxford, Md., U.S. C5 97
Oxford, Ma., U.S. B4 98
Oxford, Mi., U.S. F7 99
Oxford, Ms., U.S. A4 101
Oxford, Ne., U.S. D6 104
Oxford, N.Y., U.S. C5 109
Oxford, N.C., U.S. A4 110
Oxford, Oh., U.S. C1 112
Oxford, Pa., U.S. G10 115
Oxford, co., Me., U.S. D2 96
Oxford Lake, l., Man., Can. B4 70
Oxford Peak, mtn., Id., U.S. G6 89
Oxnard, Ca., U.S. E4 82
Oxon Hill, Md., U.S. f9 97
Oxus see Amu Darya, stm., Asia I10 18
Oyama, B.C., Can. D8 69
Oyama, Japan F12 30
Oyem, Gabon A2 44
Oyen, Alta., Can. D5 68
Oyonnax, Fr. F12 10
Oyster Bay, N.Y., U.S. E7 109
Oyster Keys, is., Fl., U.S. G6 86
Ozamiz, Phil. D7 32
Ozark, Al., U.S. D4 78
Ozark, Ar., U.S. B2 81
Ozark, Mo., U.S. D4 102
Ozark, co., Mo., U.S. E5 102
Ozark Plateau, plat., U.S. D8 76
Ozark Reservoir, res., Ar., U.S. B1 81
Ozarks, Lake of the, res., Mo., U.S. C5 102
Ozaukee, co., Wi., U.S. E6 126
Ózd, Hung. G20 8
Ozernovskij, U.S.S.R. G25 20
Ozette Lake, l., Wa., U.S. A1 124
Ozieri, Italy I3 14
Ožogino, Ozero, l., U.S.S.R. D23 20
Ozona, Fl., U.S. o10 86
Ozona, Tx., U.S. D2 120
Ōzu, Japan I5 30

P

Paarl, S. Afr. H3 44
Paauilo, Hi., U.S. C6 88
Pabianice, Pol. D19 8
Pābna, Bngl. H13 38
Pacasmayo, Peru E3 54
Pace, Fl., U.S. u14 86
Pachaug Pond, l., Ct., U.S. C8 84
Pachino, Italy M10 14
Pachuca [de Soto], Mex. G10 62
Pacific, Mo., U.S. C7 102
Pacific, Wa., U.S. f11 124
Pacific, co., Wa., U.S. C2 124
Pacifica, Ca., U.S. h8 82
Pacific Beach, Wa., U.S. B1 124
Pacific City, Or., U.S. B3 114
Pacific Creek, stm., Wy., U.S. D3 127
Pacific Grove, Ca., U.S. D3 82
Pacific Ocean F2 2
Pacific Palisades, Hi., U.S. g10 88
Pacific Ranges, mts., B.C., Can. D4 69
Pacific Rim National Park, B.C., Can. E5 69
Pack Monadnock Mountain, mtn., N.H., U.S. E3 106
Packwood, Wa., U.S. C4 124
Pacolet, S.C., U.S. B4 117
Pacolet, stm., S.C., U.S. A4 117
Pacolet Mills, S.C., U.S. B4 117
Pactola Reservoir, res., S.D., U.S. C2 118
Padang, Indon. F3 32
Padangpanjang, Indon. O6 34
Padangsidempuan, Indon. N5 34
Paddock Lake, Wi., U.S. n11 126
Paden City, W.V., U.S. B4 125
Paderborn, Ger. D8 8
Padova, Italy D6 14
Padre Island, i., Tx., U.S. F4 120
Padre Island National Seashore, Tx., U.S. F4 120
Padrón, Spain C3 12
Padstow, Eng., U.K. K8 7
Padua see Padova, Italy D6 14
Paducah, Ky., U.S. e9 94
Paducah, Tx., U.S. B2 120
Paektu-san, mtn., Asia C12 26
Pafúri, Moz. F6 44
Pag, Yugo. E10 14
Pagai Selatan, Pulau, i., Indon. F3 32
Pagai Utara, Pulau, i., Indon. F3 32
Page, Az., U.S. A4 80
Page, W.V., U.S. C3 125
Page, co., Ia., U.S. D2 92
Page, co., Va., U.S. B4 123
Pageland, S.C., U.S. B7 117
Pagoda Peak, mtn., Co., U.S. A3 83
Pagoda Point, c., Burma G3 34
Pagosa Springs, Co., U.S. D3 83
Paguate, N.M., U.S. B2 108
Pahala, Hi., U.S. D6 88
Pahang, stm., Malay. M7 34
Pahoa, Hi., U.S. D7 88
Pahokee, Fl., U.S. F6 86
Pahrump, Nv., U.S. G6 105
Pahute Mesa, mtn., Nv., U.S. F5 105
Paia, Hi., U.S. C5 88
Päijänne, l., Fin. F15 6
Pailolo Channel, strt., Hi., U.S. B5 88
Paimpol, Fr. D3 10
Paincourtville, La., U.S. k9 95
Painesville, Oh., U.S. A4 112
Paint, stm., Mi., U.S. B2 99
Paint Creek, stm., Oh., U.S. C2 112
Paint Creek, stm., W.V., U.S. m13 125
Paint Creek, North Fork, stm., Oh., U.S. C2 112
Paint Creek Lake, res., Oh., U.S. C2 112
Painted Desert, des., Az., U.S. B4 80
Painted Post, N.Y., U.S. C3 109
Painted Rock Reservoir, res., Az., U.S. D3 80
Paintsville, Ky., U.S. C7 94
Paisley, Ont., Can. C3 73
Paisley, Scot., U.K. F8 7
Paita, Peru E2 54
Pajala, Swe. C14 6
Paján, Ec. H2 58
Pakanbaru, Indon. E3 32
Pakaraima Mountains, mts., S.A. E12 58
Pakistan (Pākistān), ctry., Asia D2 36

Name — Map Ref — Page

Pakistan, East see Bangladesh, ctry., Asia E6 36
Pakokku, Burma D3 34
Pakowki Lake, l., Alta., Can. E5 68
P'akupur, stm., U.S.S.R. E9 20
Pakxé, Laos G8 34
Pala, Chad G8 42
Palacios, Tx., U.S. E4 120
Palamós, Spain D15 12
Palana, U.S.S.R. F25 20
Pālanpur, India H5 38
Palaoa Point, c., Hi., U.S. C4 88
Palapye, Bots. F5 44
Palatine, Il., U.S. A5 90
Palatka, U.S.S.R. E24 20
Palatka, Fl., U.S. C5 86
Palawan, i., Phil. D6 32
Pālayankottai, India H4 37
Palembang, Indon. F3 32
Palencia, Spain C7 12
Palermo, Italy K8 14
Palestine, Ar., U.S. C5 81
Palestine, Il., U.S. D6 90
Palestine, Tx., U.S. D5 120
Palestine, ctry., Asia C4 40
Palestine, Lake, res., Tx., U.S. C5 120
Paletwa, Burma D2 34
Pālghāt, India G4 37
Pāli, India H5 38
Palikea, mtn., Hi., U.S. g9 88
Palisade, Co., U.S. B2 83
Palisades Park, N.J., U.S. h8 107
Palisades Reservoir, res., U.S. F7 89
Pālitāna, India J4 38
Palk Strait, strt., Asia H5 37
Pallastunturi, mtn., Fin. B14 6
Palma, Moz. D8 44
Palma del Río, Spain H6 12
Palma [de Mallorca], Spain F14 12
Palma di Montechiaro, Italy L8 14
Palmanova, Italy D8 14
Palmarito, Ven. D7 58
Palmas, Cape, c., Lib. H4 42
Palma Soriano, Cuba D9 64
Palm Bay, Fl., U.S. D6 86
Palm Beach, Fl., U.S. F6 86
Palm Beach, co., Fl., U.S. F6 86
Palm Beach Gardens, Fl., U.S. F6 86
Palmdale, Ca., U.S. E4 82
Palmelo, Braz. D4 57
Palmer, Ak., U.S. C10 79
Palmer, Ma., U.S. B3 98
Palmer, Mi., U.S. B3 99
Palmer, Ms., U.S. D4 101
Palmer, Ne., U.S. C7 104
Palmer, Tn., U.S. D8 119
Palmer, Tx., U.S. n10 120
Palmer Lake, Co., U.S. B6 83
Palmerston, Ont., Can. D4 73
Palmerston, Cape, c., Austl. D9 50
Palmerston North, N.Z. D5 52
Palmerton, Pa., U.S. E10 115
Palmetto, Fl., U.S. E4 86
Palmetto, Ga., U.S. C2 87
Palm Harbor, Fl., U.S. o10 86
Palmi, Italy K10 14
Palmira, Col. F4 58
Palmira, Ec. I3 58
Palms, Isle of, i., S.C., U.S. F8 117
Palm Springs, Ca., U.S. F5 82
Palm Springs, Fl., U.S. F6 86
Palmyra, In., U.S. H5 91
Palmyra, Mo., U.S. B6 102
Palmyra, N.J., U.S. C2 107
Palmyra, N.Y., U.S. B3 109
Palmyra, Pa., U.S. F8 115
Palmyra, Wi., U.S. F5 126
Palni, India G4 37
Palo Alto, Ca., U.S. D2 82
Palo Alto, co., Ia., U.S. A3 92
Paloich, Sudan F12 42
Palomar Mountain, mtn., Ca., U.S. F5 82
Palomas Mountains, mts., Az., U.S. D2 80
Palo Pinto, co., Tx., U.S. C3 120
Palos Park, Il., U.S. k9 90
Palos Verdes Estates, Ca., U.S. n12 82
Palourde, Lake, l., La., U.S. k9 95
Palouse, Wa., U.S. C8 124
Palouse, stm., Wa., U.S. C7 124
Palu, Indon. F6 32
Palwal, India F7 38
Pamekasan, Indon. m16 33a
Pamiers, Fr. I8 10
Pamir, mts., Asia B3 36
Pamlico, co., N.C., U.S. B6 110
Pamlico, stm., N.C., U.S. B6 110
Pamlico Sound, strt., N.C., U.S. B6 110
Pampa, Tx., U.S. B2 120
Pampas, reg., Arg. C4 56
Pamplico, S.C., U.S. D8 117
Pamplona, Col. D6 58
Pamplona, Spain C10 12
Pamunkey, stm., Va., U.S. C5 123
Pana, Il., U.S. D4 90
Panaca, Nv., U.S. F7 105
Panache, Lake, l., Ont., Can. A3 73
Panaji (Panjim), India E2 37
Panamá, Pan. J8 64
Panama, Ok., U.S. B7 113
Panama, ctry., N.A. J7 64
Panama, Gulf of, b., Pan. J8 64
Panama, Isthmus of, Pan. J8 64
Panama Canal, Pan. J8 64
Panama City, Fl., U.S. u16 86
Panama City Beach, Fl., U.S. u16 86
Panamint Range, mts., Ca., U.S. D5 82
Panay, i., Phil. C7 32
Pancake Range, mts., Nv., U.S. E6 105
Pandharpur, India D3 37
Pandora, Oh., U.S. B2 112
P'andž (Panj), stm., Asia A4 38
Panevėžys, U.S.S.R. F7 22
Pangala, Congo B2 44
Pangburn, Ar., U.S. B4 81
Pangkalanbuun, Indon. F5 32
Pangkalpinang, Indon. F4 32
Pangnirtung, N.W. Ter., Can. C19 66
Panguitch, Ut., U.S. F3 121
Pangutaran Group, is., Phil. D7 32
Panhandle, Tx., U.S. B2 120
Paniau, mtn., Hi., U.S. B1 88
Pānīpat, India F7 38
Panj (P'andž), stm., Asia B4 38
Panjāb, Afg. C2 38
Panjgūr, Pak. D1 36
Panola, co., Ms., U.S. A3 101
Panola, co., Tx., U.S. C5 120
Panora, Ia., U.S. C3 92
Pantelleria, Italy M6 14
Panvel, India C2 37
Panxian, China B8 34
Panyam, Nig. G7 42
Panyu, China M2 28
Paola, Italy J11 14
Paola, Ks., U.S. D9 93
Paoli, In., U.S. G5 91
Paoli, Pa., U.S. o20 115
Paonia, Co., U.S. C3 83
Pápa, Hung. H17 8
Papago Indian Reservation, Az., U.S. E3 80
Papaikou, Hi., U.S. D6 88
Papantla [de Olarte], Mex. G11 62
Papawai Point, c., Hi., U.S. C5 88
Papenburg, Ger. B7 8
Papillion, Ne., U.S. C9 104
Papineauville, Que., Can. D2 74
Papua, Gulf of, b., Pap. N. Gui. m15 50a
Papua New Guinea, ctry., Oc. m15 50a
Pará, stm., Braz. D9 54
Paracatu, Braz. D5 57
Paracatu, stm., Braz. D6 57
Paracel Islands, is., Asia B5 32
Parachute, Co., U.S. B2 83
Paradis, La., U.S. k11 95
Paradise, Ca., U.S. C3 82
Paradise, Nv., U.S. G6 105
Paradise, stm., Newf., Can. B3 72
Paradise Hills, N.M., U.S. B3 108
Paradise Valley, Az., U.S. k9 80
Paradise Valley, Nv., U.S. B4 105
Paragould, Ar., U.S. A5 81
Paraguaçu Paulista, Braz. G3 57
Paraguaipoa, Ven. B7 58
Paraguaná, Península de, pen., Ven. B7 58
Paraguarí, Para. B5 56
Paraguay, ctry., S.A. A5 56
Paraguay, stm., S.A. B5 56
Paraíba do Sul, stm., Braz. F7 57
Parakou, Benin G6 42
Paramagudi, India H5 37
Paramaribo, Sur. B7 54
Paramirim, Braz. B7 57
Paramount, Md., U.S. A2 97
Paramus, N.J., U.S. h8 107
Paramušir, Ostrov, i., U.S.S.R. G25 20
Paraná, Arg. C4 56
Paranã, Braz. B5 57
Paranã, stm., Braz. B5 57
Paraná, stm., S.A. C5 56
Paranaguá, Braz. B7 56
Paranaíba, Braz. E3 57
Paranaíba, stm., Braz. E3 57
Paranapanema, stm., Braz. G3 57
Paranavaí, Braz. G2 57
Parangaba, Braz. D11 54
Paratinga, Braz. B7 57
Paraúna, Braz. D3 57
Paray-le-Monial, Fr. F11 10
Pārbati, stm., India H7 38
Parbhani, India C4 37
Parchim, Ger. B11 8
Parchment, Mi., U.S. F5 99
Pardeeville, Wi., U.S. E4 126
Pardo, stm., Braz. F5 57
Pardubice, Czech. E15 8
Parece Vela see Okino-Tori-shima, i., Japan G14 26
Parecis, Serra dos, mts., Braz. F7 54
Paredes de Nava, Spain C7 12
Paren', U.S.S.R. E26 20
Parepare, Indon. F6 32
Pargas (Parainen), Fin. F14 6
Paria, stm., U.S. A4 80
Paria, Gulf of, b. I16 64
Pariaguán, Ven. C10 58
Pariaman, Indon. O6 34
Parícutin, vol., Mex. H8 62
Parikkala, Fin. F17 6
Parima, Sierra, mts., S.A. F10 58
Pariñas, Punta, c., Peru D2 54
Parintins, Braz. D7 54
Paris, Ont., Can. D4 73
Paris, Fr. D9 10
Paris, Ar., U.S. B2 81
Paris, Il., U.S. D6 90
Paris, Ky., U.S. B5 94
Paris, Mo., U.S. B5 102
Paris, Tn., U.S. A3 119
Paris, Tx., U.S. C5 120
Paris Peak, mtn., Id., U.S. G7 89
Parit Buntar, Malay. L6 34
Park, co., Co., U.S. B5 83
Park, co., Mt., U.S. E6 103
Park, co., Wy., U.S. B3 127
Park, stm., N.D., U.S. A8 111
Parkano, Fin. E14 6
Park City, Ks., U.S. g12 93
Park City, Ut., U.S. C4 121
Parkdale, P.E.I., Can. C6 71
Parke, co., In., U.S. E3 91
Parker, Az., U.S. C1 80
Parker, Co., U.S. B6 83
Parker, Fl., U.S. u16 86
Parker, S.D., U.S. D8 118
Parker, co., Tx., U.S. C4 120
Parker, Cape, c., N.W. Ter., Can. A17 66
Parker City, In., U.S. D7 91
Parker Dam, U.S. C1 80
Parkersburg, Ia., U.S. B5 92
Parkersburg, W.V., U.S. B3 125
Parkers Prairie, Mn., U.S. D3 100
Parkesburg, Pa., U.S. G10 115
Park Falls, Wi., U.S. C3 126
Park Forest, Il., U.S. B6 90
Park Hall, Md., U.S. D5 97
Parkhill, Ont., Can. D3 73
Park Hills, Ky., U.S. h13 94
Parkin, Ar., U.S. B5 81
Parkland, Wa., U.S. f11 124
Park Layne, Oh., U.S. C1 112
Park Range, mts., Co., U.S. A4 83
Park Rapids, Mn., U.S. D3 100
Park Ridge, Il., U.S. B6 90
Park Ridge, N.J., U.S. g8 107
Park River, N.D., U.S. A8 111
Parkrose, Or., U.S. B4 114
Parksley, Va., U.S. C7 123
Parkston, S.D., U.S. D8 118
Parksville, B.C., Can. E5 69
Parkville, Md., U.S. B4 97
Parkville, Mo., U.S. B3 102
Parkwater, Wa., U.S. g14 124
Parkwood, N.C., U.S. B4 110
Parlākimidi, India C8 37
Parle, Lac qui, l., Mn., U.S. E3 100
Parlier, Ca., U.S. D4 82
Parma, Italy E5 14
Parma, Id., U.S. F2 89
Parma, Mi., U.S. F6 99
Parma, Mo., U.S. E8 102
Parma, Oh., U.S. A4 112
Parmachenee Lake, l., Me., U.S. C2 96
Parma Heights, Oh., U.S. h9 112
Parmer, co., Tx., U.S. B1 120
Parnaíba, Braz. D10 54
Parnaíba, stm., Braz. D10 54
Pärnu, U.S.S.R. C7 22
Paro, Bhu. G13 38
Parowan, Ut., U.S. F3 121
Par Pond, res., S.C., U.S. D5 117
Parral, Chile D2 56
Parramore Island, i., Va., U.S. C7 123
Parras de la Fuente, Mex. E8 62
Parrish, Al., U.S. B2 78
Parrsboro, N.S., Can. D5 71
Parry, Cape, c., N.W. Ter., Can. B8 66
Parry, Mount, mtn., B.C., Can. C3 69
Parry Bay, b., N.W. Ter., Can. C16 66
Parry Sound, Ont., Can. B4 73
Parshall, N.D., U.S. B3 111
Parsons, Ks., U.S. E8 93
Parsons, Tn., U.S. B3 119
Parsons, W.V., U.S. B5 125
Parsonsburg, Md., U.S. D7 97
Parthenay, Fr. F6 10
Partinico, Italy K8 14
Partridge Point, c., Newf., Can. C3 72
Paru, stm., Braz. D8 54
Pārvatīpuram, India C7 37
Parys, S. Afr. G5 44
Pasadena, Newf., Can. D3 72
Pasadena, Ca., U.S. E4 82
Pasadena, Md., U.S. B4 97
Pasadena, Tx., U.S. r14 120
Pascagoula, Ms., U.S. E5 101
Pascagoula, stm., Ms., U.S. E5 101
Pascagoula Bay, b., Ms., U.S. f8 101
Pasco, Wa., U.S. C6 124
Pasco, co., Fl., U.S. D4 86
Pascoag, R.I., U.S. B2 116
Pascoag Reservoir, res., R.I., U.S. B2 116
Pascua, Isla de (Easter Island), i., Chile H5 2
Pasewalk, Ger. B13 8
Pasig, Phil. q19 33b
P'asina, stm., U.S.S.R. C11 20
P'asino, Ozero, l., U.S.S.R. D11 20
P'asinskij Zaliv, b., U.S.S.R. C10 20
Pasirpengarajan, Indon. N6 34
Pasir Puteh, Malay. L7 34
Pasni, Pak. D1 36
Paso de Indios, Arg. E3 56
Paso de los Libres, Arg. B5 56
Paso Robles, Ca., U.S. E3 82
Pasque Island, i., Ma., U.S. D6 98
Pasquotank, co., N.C., U.S. A6 110
Passagem, Braz. B7 57
Passaic, N.J., U.S. B4 107
Passaic, co., N.J., U.S. A4 107
Passaic, stm., N.J., U.S. h8 107
Passamaquoddy Bay, b., Me., U.S. C6 96
Passau, Ger. G13 8
Pass Christian, Ms., U.S. E4 101
Passo Fundo, Braz. B6 56
Passos, Braz. F5 57
Passumpsic, stm., Vt., U.S. C4 122
Pasto, Col. G4 58
Pastora Peak, mtn., Az., U.S. A6 80
Pastrana, Spain E9 12
Pasuruan, Indon. m16 33a
Patagonia, Az., U.S. F5 80
Patagonia, reg., Arg. E3 56
Pātan, India I5 38
Patapsco, stm., Md., U.S. B4 97
Pataskala, Oh., U.S. C3 112
Patchet Brook Reservoir, res., R.I., U.S. E6 116
Patchogue, N.Y., U.S. n15 109
Pate Island, i., Kenya B8 44
Paternò, Italy L9 14
Paterson, N.J., U.S. B4 107
Pathānkot, India D6 38
Pathein, Burma F3 34
Pathfinder Reservoir, res., Wy., U.S. D6 127
Pati, Indon. m15 33a
Patiāla, India E7 38
Patience Island, i., R.I., U.S. D5 116
P'atigorsk, U.S.S.R. I6 18
Pātkai Range, mts., Asia G16 38
Patman, Lake, res., Tx., U.S. C5 120
Patna, India H11 38
Patoka, In., U.S. H2 91
Patoka, stm., In., U.S. H2 91
Patoka Lake, res., In., U.S. H4 91
Patos, Braz. E11 54
Patos, Lagoa dos, b., Braz. C6 56
Patos de Minas, Braz. E5 57
Patquía, Arg. C3 56
Pátrai, Grc. K5 16
Patricio Lynch, Isla, i., Chile F1 56
Patrick, co., Va., U.S. D2 123
Patrick Air Force Base, mil., Fl., U.S. D6 86
Patrocínio, Braz. E5 57
Pattani, Thai. K6 34
Patten, Me., U.S. C4 96
Patterson, Ga., U.S. E4 87
Patterson, La., U.S. E4 95
Patterson Creek, stm., W.V., U.S. B5 125
Pattoki, Pak. E5 38
Patton, Pa., U.S. E4 115
Patuākhāli, Bngl. I14 38
Patuca, stm., Hond. G5 64
Patuxent, stm., Md., U.S. D4 97
Patuxent Naval Air Test Center, mil., Md., U.S. D5 97
Pátzcuaro, Mex. H9 62
Pau, Fr. I6 10
Paul, Id., U.S. G5 89
Paulding, Oh., U.S. A1 112
Paulding, co., Ga., U.S. C2 87
Paulding, co., Oh., U.S. A1 112
Paulina, La., U.S. h10 95
Paulina Mountains, mts., Or., U.S. D5 114
Paulina Peak, mtn., Or., U.S. E5 114
Paulins Kill, stm., N.J., U.S. A3 107
Paulistana, Braz. E10 54
Paulistas, Braz. E7 57
Paullina, Ia., U.S. B2 92
Paulo Afonso, Braz. E11 54
Paulsboro, N.J., U.S. D2 107
Paul Stream, stm., Vt., U.S. B5 122
Pauls Valley, Ok., U.S. C4 113
Paungde, Burma E3 34
Pavia, Italy D4 14
Pavilion Key, i., Fl., U.S. G5 86
Pavlodar, U.S.S.R. G9 20
Pavlof Volcano, vol., Ak., U.S. D7 79
Pavlovo, U.S.S.R. F26 22
Pavlovsk, U.S.S.R. G7 20
Pavlovskij Posad, U.S.S.R. F21 22
Pavo, Ga., U.S. F3 87
Pavón, Col. F6 58
Pavullo nel Frignano, Italy E5 14
Pawcatuck, Ct., U.S. D8 84
Pawcatuck, stm., R.I., U.S. G1 116
Paw Creek, N.C., U.S. B2 110
Pawhuska, Ok., U.S. A5 113
Pawling, N.Y., U.S. D7 109
Pawnee, Il., U.S. D4 90
Pawnee, Ok., U.S. A5 113
Pawnee, co., Ks., U.S. D4 93
Pawnee, co., Ne., U.S. D9 104
Pawnee, co., Ok., U.S. A5 113
Pawnee, stm., Ks., U.S. D3 93
Pawnee City, Ne., U.S. D9 104
Pawpaw, Il., U.S. B5 90
Paw Paw, Mi., U.S. F5 99
Paw Paw, stm., Mi., U.S. F4 99
Pawpaw Creek, stm., W.V., U.S. h10 125
Pawtuckaway Pond, l., N.H., U.S. D4 106
Pawtucket, R.I., U.S. C4 116
Pawtuxet, stm., R.I., U.S. C4 116
Paxton, Il., U.S. C5 90
Paxton, Ma., U.S. B4 98
Payakumbuh, Indon. O6 34
Payette, Id., U.S. E2 89
Payette, co., Id., U.S. E2 89
Payette, North Fork, stm., Id., U.S. E2 89
Payette, South Fork, stm., Id., U.S. E3 89
Payette Lake, res., Id., U.S. E3 89
Payne, Oh., U.S. A1 112
Payne, co., Ok., U.S. A4 113
Paynesville, Mn., U.S. E4 100
Paysandú, Ur. C5 56
Payson, Az., U.S. C4 80
Payson, Il., U.S. D2 90
Payson, Ut., U.S. C4 121
Pazardžik, Bul. G8 16
Pazarköy, Tur. J11 16
Paz de Río, Col. E6 58
Pazin, Yugo. D8 14
Pea, stm., Al., U.S. D3 78
Peabody, Ks., U.S. D6 93
Peabody, Ma., U.S. A6 98
Peabody, stm., N.H., U.S. B4 106
Peace, stm., Can. E9 66
Peace, stm., Fl., U.S. E5 86
Peace Dale, R.I., U.S. F3 116
Peace River, Alta., Can. A2 68
Peach, co., Ga., U.S. D3 87
Peacham Pond, res., Vt., U.S. C4 122
Peach Point, c., Ma., U.S. f12 98
Peach Springs, Az., U.S. B2 80
Peak District National Park, Eng., U.K. H11 7
Peaks Island, i., Me., U.S. g7 96
Peale, Mount, mtn., Ut., U.S. E6 121
Pea Patch Island, i., De., U.S. B3 85
Pea Ridge, Ar., U.S. A1 81
Pea Ridge National Military Park, Ar., U.S. A1 81
Pearisburg, Va., U.S. C2 123
Pearl, Ms., U.S. C3 101
Pearl, stm., U.S. D3 101
Pearland, Tx., U.S. r14 120
Pearl and Hermes Reef, rf., Hi., U.S. k12 88
Pearl City, Hi., U.S. B4 88
Pearl Harbor, b., Hi., U.S. B3 88
Pearl Harbor Naval Station, mil., Hi., U.S. g10 88
Pearlington, Ms., U.S. E4 101
Pearl River, La., U.S. D6 95
Pearl River, N.Y., U.S. g12 109
Pearl River, co., Ms., U.S. E4 101
Pearsall, Tx., U.S. E3 120
Pearsoll Peak, mtn., Or., U.S. E3 114
Pearson, Ga., U.S. E4 87
Peary Land, reg., Grnld. A16 128
Pease, stm., Tx., U.S. B3 120
Pease Air Force Base, mil., N.H., U.S. D5 106
Pebane, Moz. E7 44
Peć, Yugo. G4 16
Pecatonica, Il., U.S. A4 90
Pecatonica, stm., U.S. A4 90
Pecatonica, East Branch, stm., Wi., U.S. F4 126
Peckerwood Lake, res., Ar., U.S. C4 81
Pečora, stm., U.S.S.R. D5 20
Pecos, N.M., U.S. B4 108
Pecos, Tx., U.S. D1 120
Pecos, co., Tx., U.S. D1 120
Pecos, stm., U.S. E6 76
Pecos National Monument, N.M., U.S. B4 108
Pécs, Hung. I18 8
Peculiar, Mo., U.S. C3 102
Peddocks Island, i., Ma., U.S. g12 98
Pedernales, Ven. C11 58
Pedregal, Ven. B7 58
Pedro, Point, c., Sri L. H6 37
Pedro de Valdivia, Chile A3 56
Pedro Juan Caballero, Para. G1 57
Peebles, Oh., U.S. D2 112
Peekskill, N.Y., U.S. D7 109
Peel, I. of Man G8 7
Peel, stm., Can. C5 66
Peel Point, c., N.W. Ter., Can. B10 66
Peel Sound, strt., N.W. Ter., Can. B13 66
Pegram, Tn., U.S. A4 119
Pehuajó, Arg. D4 56
Peikang, Tai. L9 28
Peine, Ger. C10 8
Pekalongan, Indon. m14 32
Pekin, Il., U.S. C4 90
Pekin, In., U.S. G5 91
Peking see Beijing, China D10 26
Pelagie, Isole, is., Italy N7 14
Pelahatchie, Ms., U.S. C4 101
Pelée, Montagne, mtn., Mart. G17 64
Pelee Island, i., Ont., Can. F2 73
Peleng, Pulau, i., Indon. F7 32
Pelham, Ont., Can. D5 73
Pelham, Al., U.S. B3 78
Pelham, Ga., U.S. E2 87
Pelham, N.H., U.S. E4 106
Pelham Manor, N.Y., U.S. h13 109
Pelican Bay, b., Man., Can. C1 70
Pelican Lake, l., Man., Can. C1 70
Pelican Lake, l., Mn., U.S. D4 100
Pelican Lake, l., Mn., U.S. D3 100
Pelican Lake, l., Mn., U.S. B6 100
Pelican Lake, l., Mn., U.S. E5 100
Pelican Lake, l., Wi., U.S. C4 126
Pelican Mountain, mtn., Alta., Can. B4 68
Pelican Rapids, Mn., U.S. D2 100
Pella, Ia., U.S. C5 92
Pell City, Al., U.S. B3 78
Pell Lake, Wi., U.S. n11 126
Pello, Fin. C14 6
Pelly Mountains, mts., Yukon, Can. D6 66
Pelopónnisos, reg., Grc. L5 16
Pelotas, Braz. C6 56
Pelton, Lake, l., La., U.S. E5 95
Pemadumcook Lake, l., Me., U.S. C3 96
Pemalang, Indon. m14 33a
Pematangsiantar, Indon. E2 32
Pemba, Moz. D8 44
Pemba Island, i., Tan. C7 44
Pemberton, Austl. F3 50
Pemberville, Oh., U.S. A2 112
Pembina, N.D., U.S. A8 111
Pembina, co., N.D., U.S. A8 111
Pembina, stm., Alta., Can. C3 68
Pembroke, Ont., Can. B7 73
Pembroke, Wales, U.K. J8 7
Pembroke, Ga., U.S. D5 87
Pembroke, Ky., U.S. D2 94
Pembroke, Ma., U.S. B6 98
Pembroke, N.C., U.S. C3 110
Pembroke, Va., U.S. C2 123
Pembroke Pines, Fl., U.S. r13 86
Pemigewasset, stm., N.H., U.S. C3 106
Pemiscot, co., Mo., U.S. E8 102
Peñafiel, Spain D7 12
Penápolis, Braz. F3 57
Peñaranda de Bracamonte, Spain E6 12
Pen Argyl, Pa., U.S. E11 115
Peñarroya-Pueblonuevo, Spain G6 12
Penas, Golfo de, b., Chile F1 56
Penasco, N.M., U.S. A4 108
Peñasco, Río, stm., N.M., U.S. E4 108
Penbrook, Pa., U.S. F8 115
Pender, Ne., U.S. B9 104
Pender, co., N.C., U.S. C4 110
Pendleton, In., U.S. E6 91
Pendleton, Or., U.S. B8 114
Pendleton, S.C., U.S. B2 117
Pendleton, co., Ky., U.S. B5 94
Pendleton, co., W.V., U.S. C5 125
Pendley Hills, Ga., U.S. h8 87
Pend Oreille, co., Wa., U.S. A8 124
Pend Oreille, Lake, l., Id., U.S. A2 89
Pend Oreille, Mount, mtn., Id., U.S. A2 89
Penetanguishene, Ont., Can. C5 73
P'enghu Liehtao, is., Tai. L8 28
Penglai, China D11 26
Penhold, Alta., Can. C4 68
Peniche, Port. F2 12
Penjamo, Mex. G9 62
Pennant Point, c., N.S., Can. E6 71
Pennask Mountain, mtn., B.C., Can. E7 69
Penne, Italy G8 14
Pennell, Mount, mtn., Ut., U.S. F5 121
Penner, stm., India E5 37
Penn Hills, Pa., U.S. k14 115
Pennines, mts., Eng., U.K. G10 7

Name Map Ref Page

Pennines, Alpes, mts., Eur. F14 10
Pennington, co., Mn., U.S. B2 100
Pennington, co., S.D., U.S. D2 118
Pennington Gap, Va., U.S. f8 123
Pennsauken, N.J., U.S. D2 107
Pennsboro, W.V., U.S. B4 125
Pennsburg, Pa., U.S. F11 115
Penns Grove, N.J., U.S. D2 107
Pennsville, N.J., U.S. D1 107
Pennsylvania, state, U.S. E7 115
Pennville, In., U.S. D7 91
Penn Yan, N.Y., U.S. C3 109
Penobscot, co., Me., U.S. C4 96
Penobscot, stm., Me., U.S. C4 96
Penobscot Bay, b., Me., U.S. D3 96
Penobscot Lake, l., Me., U.S. C2 96
Penonomé, Pan. J7 64
Penrith, Eng., U.K. G10 7
Pensacola, Fl., U.S. u14 86
Pensacola Bay, b., Fl., U.S. u14 86
Pensacola Dam, Ok., U.S. A6 113
Pensacola Naval Air Station, mil., Fl., U.S. u14 86
Pentagon Mountain, mtn., Mt., U.S. C3 103
Penticton, B.C., Can. E8 69
Pentland Firth, strt., Scot., U.K. C9 7
Pentwater, Mi., U.S. E4 99
Penyu, Kepulauan, is., Indon. G8 32
Penza, U.S.S.R. G7 18
Penzance, Eng., U.K. K7 7
Penžina, stm., U.S.S.R. E27 20
Penžinskaja Guba, b., U.S.S.R. E26 20
Penžinskij Chrebet, mts., U.S.S.R. E27 20
Peonan Point, c., Man., Can. D2 70
Peoria, Az., U.S. D3 80
Peoria, Il., U.S. C4 90
Peoria, co., Il., U.S. C4 90
Peoria Heights, Il., U.S. C4 90
Peotone, Il., U.S. B6 90
Pepacton Reservoir, res., N.Y., U.S. C6 109
Pepeekeo, Hi., U.S. D6 88
Pepin, Wi., U.S. D1 126
Pepin, co., Wi., U.S. D2 126
Pepin, Lake, l., U.S. D1 126
Pepperell, Ma., U.S. A4 98
Pequannock, N.J., U.S. B4 107
Pequest, stm., N.J., U.S. B2 107
Pequop Mountains, mts., Nv., U.S. C7 105
Pequot Lakes, Mn., U.S. D4 100
Perabumulih, Indon. F3 32
Percy, Il., U.S. E4 90
Perdido, Al., U.S. D2 78
Perdido, stm., U.S. E2 78
Perdido Bay, b., Al., U.S. E2 78
Pereira, Col. E5 58
Pere Marquette, stm., Mi., U.S. E4 99
Pereslavl'-Zalesskij, U.S.S.R. E21 22
Pergamino, Arg. C4 56
Pergine Valsugana, Italy C6 14
Perham, Mn., U.S. D3 100
Péribonca, stm., Que., Can. G18 66
Peridot, Az., U.S. D5 80
Périgueux, Fr. G7 10
Perijá, Sierra de, mts., S.A. B6 58
Perkasie, Pa., U.S. F11 115
Perkins, Ok., U.S. B4 113
Perkins, co., Ne., U.S. D4 104
Perkins, co., S.D., U.S. B3 118
Perkinston, Ms., U.S. E4 101
Perlas, Archipiélago de las, is., Pan. J8 64
Perlas, Laguna de, b., Nic. H6 64
Perleberg, Ger. B11 8
Perm', U.S.S.R. F9 18
Pernik, Bul. G7 16
Péronne, Fr. C9 10
Perpignan, Fr. J9 10
Perquimans, co., N.C., U.S. A6 110
Perrine, Fl., U.S. G6 86
Perris, Ca., U.S. F5 82
Perro, Laguna del, l., N.M., U.S. C4 108
Perros-Guirec, Fr. D3 10
Perrot, Île, i., Que., Can. q19 74
Perry, Fl., U.S. B3 86
Perry, Ga., U.S. D3 87
Perry, Ia., U.S. C3 92
Perry, Ks., U.S. C8 93
Perry, Mi., U.S. F6 99
Perry, Mo., U.S. B6 102
Perry, N.Y., U.S. C2 109
Perry, Oh., U.S. A4 112
Perry, Ok., U.S. A4 113
Perry, Ut., U.S. B3 121
Perry, co., Al., U.S. C2 78
Perry, co., Ar., U.S. C3 81
Perry, co., Il., U.S. E4 90
Perry, co., In., U.S. H4 91
Perry, co., Ky., U.S. C6 94
Perry, co., Ms., U.S. D4 101
Perry, co., Mo., U.S. D8 102
Perry, co., Oh., U.S. C3 112
Perry, co., Pa., U.S. F7 115
Perry, co., Tn., U.S. B4 119
Perry Hall, Md., U.S. B5 97
Perry Lake, res., Ks., U.S. C8 93
Perryman, Md., U.S. B5 97
Perrysburg, Oh., U.S. A2 112
Perry Stream, stm., N.H., U.S. f7 106
Perry's Victory and International Peace Memorial, hist., Oh., U.S. A2 112
Perryton, Tx., U.S. A2 120
Perryville, Ar., U.S. B3 81
Perryville, Ky., U.S. C5 94
Perryville, Md., U.S. A5 97
Perryville, Mo., U.S. D8 102
Pershing, co., Nv., U.S. C3 105
Persia see Iran, ctry., Asia B5 46
Persian Gulf, b., Asia C5 46
Person, co., N.C., U.S. A3 110
Perth, Austl. F3 50
Perth, Ont., Can. C8 73
Perth, Scot., U.K. E9 7
Perth Amboy, N.J., U.S. B4 107
Perth-Andover, N.B., Can. D10 71
Pertuis, Fr. I12 10
Peru, Il., U.S. B4 90
Peru, In., U.S. C5 91
Peru, Ne., U.S. D10 104
Peru, N.Y., U.S. f11 109
Peru (Perú), ctry., S.A. E3 54
Perugia, Italy F7 14
Perušić, Yugo. E10 14
Pesaro, Italy F7 14
Pescadores see P'enghu Liehtao, is., Tai. L8 28
Pescara, Italy G9 14
Pescia, Italy F5 14
Peshastin, Wa., U.S. B5 124
Peshāwar, Pak. C4 38
Peshtigo, Wi., U.S. C6 126
Peshtigo, stm., Wi., U.S. C5 126
Pesqueira, Braz. E11 54
Pessac, Fr. H6 10
Petaḥ Tiqwa, Isr. C4 40
Petal, Ms., U.S. D4 101
Petaluma, Ca., U.S. C2 82
Petatlán, Mex. I9 62
Petawawa, Ont., Can. B7 73
Petawawa, stm., Ont., Can. A6 73
Petenwell Lake, res., Wi., U.S. D4 126
Peterborough, Austl. F7 50
Peterborough, Ont., Can. C6 73
Peterborough, Eng., U.K. I12 7
Peterborough, N.H., U.S. E3 106
Peterhead, Scot., U.K. D11 7
Peter Pond Lake, l., Sask., Can. m7 75
Petersburg, Ak., U.S. D13 79
Petersburg, Il., U.S. C4 90
Petersburg, In., U.S. H3 91
Petersburg, Mi., U.S. G7 99
Petersburg, Oh., U.S. B5 112
Petersburg, Tx., U.S. C2 120
Petersburg, Va., U.S. C5 123
Petersburg, W.V., U.S. B5 125
Peters Creek, stm., W.V., U.S. m14 125
Peterson, Al., U.S. B2 78
Peterson Field, mil., Co., U.S. C6 83
Petersville, Al., U.S. A2 78
Petit Bois Island, i., Ms., U.S. E5 101
Petitcodiac, N.B., Can. D4 71
Petitcodiac, stm., N.B., Can. C5 71
Petite Amite, stm., La., U.S. h10 95
Petit Jean, stm., Ar., U.S. B2 81
Petit Lac Des Allemands, l., La., U.S. k11 95
Petit Lake, l., La., U.S. k12 95
Petitot, stm., Can. E8 66
Petit-Rocher, N.B., Can. B4 71
Petitsikapau Lake, l., Newf., Can. g8 72
Petlād, India I5 38
Petone, N.Z. D5 52
Petoskey, Mi., U.S. C6 99
Petrified Forest National Park, Az., U.S. B6 80
Petrila, Rom. D7 16
Petrinja, Yugo. D11 14
Petrograd see Leningrad, U.S.S.R. B13 22
Petroleum, co., Mt., U.S. C8 103
Petrolia, Ont., Can. E2 73
Petrolina, Braz. E10 54
Petropavlovsk-Kamčatskij, U.S.S.R. G25 20
Petrópolis, Braz. G7 57
Petros, Tn., U.S. C9 119
Petroșani, Rom. D7 16
Petrovsk-Zabajkal'skij, U.S.S.R. G15 20
Petrozavodsk, U.S.S.R. E4 18
Pettaquamscutt Lake Shores, R.I., U.S. F4 116
Pettingell Peak, mtn., Co., U.S. B5 83
Pettis, co., Mo., U.S. C4 102
Pevek, U.S.S.R. D28 20
Pevely, Mo., U.S. g13 102
Pewaukee, Wi., U.S. E5 126
Pewaukee Lake, l., Wi., U.S. m11 126
Pewee Valley, Ky., U.S. B4 94
Pézenas, Fr. I10 10
Pforzheim, Ger. G8 8
Pfungstadt, Ger. F8 8
Pha-an, Burma F4 34
Phagwāra, India E6 38
Phalsbourg, Fr. D14 10
Phaltan, India D3 37
Phangan, Ko, i., Thai. J6 34
Phangnga, Thai. J5 34
Phanom Dongrak, Thiu Khao, mts., Asia G7 34
Phan Rang, Viet. I10 34
Phan Si Pan, mtn., Viet. C7 34
Phan Thiet, Viet. I10 34
Pharr, Tx., U.S. F3 120
Phatthalung, Thai. K6 34
Phayao, Thai. E5 34
Phelps, Ky., U.S. C7 94
Phelps, N.Y., U.S. C3 109
Phelps, Wi., U.S. B4 126
Phelps, co., Mo., U.S. D6 102
Phelps, co., Ne., U.S. D6 104
Phelps Lake, l., N.C., U.S. B6 110
Phenix City, Al., U.S. C4 78
Phetchaburi, Thai. H5 34
Philadelphia, Ms., U.S. C4 101
Philadelphia, Pa., U.S. G11 115
Philadelphia, co., Pa., U.S. G12 115
Philadelphia Naval Shipyard, mil., Pa., U.S. P21 115
Phil Campbell, Al., U.S. A2 78
Philip, S.D., U.S. C4 118
Philippeville, Bel. E4 8
Philippi, W.V., U.S. B4 125
Philippines, ctry., Asia C7 32
Philippine Sea E21 2
Philipsburg, Mt., U.S. D3 103
Philipsburg, Pa., U.S. E5 115
Philleo Lake, l., Wa., U.S. h14 124
Phillips, Me., U.S. D2 96
Phillips, Tx., U.S. B2 120
Phillips, Wi., U.S. C3 126
Phillips, co., Ar., U.S. C5 81
Phillips, co., Co., U.S. A8 83
Phillips, co., Ks., U.S. C4 93
Phillips, co., Mt., U.S. B8 103
Phillips Brook, stm., N.H., U.S. A4 106
Phillipsburg, Ks., U.S. C4 93
Phillipsburg, N.J., U.S. B2 107
Philmont, N.Y., U.S. C7 109
Philo, Il., U.S. C5 90
Philomath, Or., U.S. C3 114
Philpots Island, i., N.W. Ter., Can. B17 66
Philpott Reservoir, res., Va., U.S. D2 123
Phitsanulok, Thai. F6 34
Phnom Penh see Phnum Pénh, Camb. I8 34
Phnum Pénh (Phnom Penh), Camb. I8 34
Phoenix, Az., U.S. D3 80
Phoenix, Il., U.S. k9 90
Phoenix, N.Y., U.S. B4 109
Phoenix, Or., U.S. E4 114
Phoenixville, Pa., U.S. F10 115
Phôngsali, Laos D7 34
Phrae, Thai. E6 34
Phra Nakhon Si Ayutthaya, Thai. G6 34
Phuket, Thai. K5 34
Phuket, Ko, i., Thai. K5 34
Phu Ly, Viet. D8 34
Phumĭ Béng, Camb. H8 34
Phumĭ Kâmpóng Trâbêk, Camb. H8 34
Phu Quoc, Dao, i., Viet. I7 34
Phu Tho, Viet. D8 34
Piacenza, Italy D4 14
Piatra-Neamț, Rom. C10 16
Piatt, co., Il., U.S. D5 90
Piazza Armerina, Italy L9 14
Pibor Post, Sudan G12 42
Picacho, Az., U.S. E4 80
Picardie, hist. reg., Fr. C9 10
Picayune, Ms., U.S. E4 101
Piccadilly, Newf., Can. D2 72
Pichanal, Arg. A4 56
Picher, Ok., U.S. A7 113
Pickaway, co., Oh., U.S. C2 112
Pickens, Ms., U.S. C4 101
Pickens, S.C., U.S. B2 117
Pickens, co., Al., U.S. B1 78
Pickens, co., Ga., U.S. B2 87
Pickens, co., S.C., U.S. B2 117
Pickerel Lake, l., Wi., U.S. C5 126
Pickering, Ont., Can. D5 73
Pickerington, Oh., U.S. C3 112
Pickett, co., Tn., U.S. C8 119
Pickwick Lake, res., U.S. A6 101
Pickworth Point, c., Ma., U.S. f12 98
Pico Rivera, Ca., U.S. n12 82
Picos, Braz. E10 54
Picquigny, Fr. C9 10
Picton, Ont., Can. D7 73
Pictou Island, i., N.S., Can. D7 71
Picture Butte, Alta., Can. E4 68
Pictured Rocks National Lakeshore, Mi., U.S. B4 99
Pidálion, Akrotírion, c., Cyp. B4 40
Pidurutalagala, mtn., Sri L. I6 37
Piedmont, Al., U.S. B4 78
Piedmont, Ca., U.S. h8 82
Piedmont, Mo., U.S. D7 102
Piedmont, Ok., U.S. B4 113
Piedmont, S.C., U.S. B3 117
Piedmont, W.V., U.S. B5 125
Piedmont Lake, res., Oh., U.S. B4 112
Piedra, stm., Co., U.S. D3 83
Piedrabuena, Spain F7 12
Piedrahita, Spain E6 12
Piedras Blancas, Point, c., Ca., U.S. E3 82
Piedras Negras, Guat. F2 64
Piedras Negras, Mex. C9 62
Pieksämäki, Fin. E16 6
Pierce, Co., U.S. A6 83
Pierce, Id., U.S. C3 89
Pierce, Ne., U.S. B8 104
Pierce, co., Ga., U.S. E4 87
Pierce, co., Ne., U.S. B8 104
Pierce, co., N.D., U.S. A5 111
Pierce, co., Wa., U.S. C3 124
Pierce, co., Wi., U.S. D1 126
Pierce, Lake, l., Fl., U.S. E5 86
Pierce City, Mo., U.S. E3 102
Pierceton, In., U.S. B6 91
Pierre, S.D., U.S. C5 118
Pierre-Buffière, Fr. G8 10
Pierrefonds, Que., Can. q19 74
Pierre Part, La., U.S. k9 95
Pierreville, Que., Can. C5 74
Pierson, Fl., U.S. C5 86
Pierz, Mn., U.S. E4 100
Pietermaritzburg, S. Afr. G6 44
Pietersburg, S. Afr. F5 44
Pietrasanta, Italy F5 14
Piet Retief, S. Afr. G6 44
Pigeon, Mi., U.S. E7 99
Pigeon, stm., U.S. f9 110
Pigeon, stm., In., U.S. A6 91
Pigeon, stm., Mn., U.S. h10 100
Pigeon, stm., Wi., U.S. k10 126
Pigeon Cove, Ma., U.S. A6 98
Pigeon Forge, Tn., U.S. D10 119
Pigeon Point, c., Mn., U.S. h10 100
Pigg, stm., Va., U.S. D3 123
Piggott, Ar., U.S. A5 81
Pihlajavesi, l., Fin. F17 6
Pihtipudas, Fin. E15 6
Pijijiapan, Mex. J13 62
Pikal'ovo, U.S.S.R. B17 22
Pike, co., Al., U.S. D4 78
Pike, co., Ar., U.S. C2 81
Pike, co., Ga., U.S. C2 87
Pike, co., Il., U.S. D2 90
Pike, co., In., U.S. H3 91
Pike, co., Ky., U.S. C7 94
Pike, co., Ms., U.S. D3 101
Pike, co., Mo., U.S. B6 102
Pike, co., Oh., U.S. C2 112
Pike, co., Pa., U.S. D11 115
Pike, stm., Wi., U.S. C6 126
Pike Island Dam, U.S. f8 125
Pike Lake, Mn., U.S. D6 100
Pikes Peak, mtn., Co., U.S. C5 83
Pikesville, Md., U.S. B4 97
Piketberg, S. Afr. H3 44
Piketon, Oh., U.S. C2 112
Pikeville, Ky., U.S. C7 94
Pikeville, Tn., U.S. D8 119
Piła (Schneidemühl), Pol. B16 8
Pilar do Sul, Braz. G5 57
Pilcomayo, stm., S.A. A4 56
Pīlībhīt, India F8 38
Pillar Point, c., Ca., U.S. k7 82
Pilot Grove, Mo., U.S. C5 102
Pilot Knob, Mo., U.S. D7 102
Pilot Knob, mtn., Id., U.S. D3 89
Pilot Mound, Man., Can. E2 70
Pilot Mountain, N.C., U.S. A2 110
Pilot Peak, mtn., Nv., U.S. E4 105
Pilot Peak, mtn., Nv., U.S. B7 105
Pilot Peak, mtn., Wy., U.S. B3 127
Pilot Point, Tx., U.S. C4 120
Pilot Range, mts., Nv., U.S. B7 105
Pilot Rock, Or., U.S. B8 114
Pilot Station, Ak., U.S. C7 79
Pima, Az., U.S. E6 80
Pima, co., Az., U.S. E3 80
Pimentel, Peru E3 54
Pimmit Hills, Va., U.S. g12 123
Pina, Spain D11 12
Pinal, co., Az., U.S. E4 80
Pinaleno Mountains, mts., Az., U.S. E5 80
Pinal Mountains, mts., Az., U.S. D5 80
Pinang see George Town, Malay. L6 34
Pinar del Río, Cuba C6 64
Pinardville, N.H., U.S. E3 106
Pincher Creek, Alta., Can. E4 68
Pinckard, Al., U.S. D4 78
Pinckney, Mi., U.S. F7 99
Pinckney Island, i., S.C., U.S. G6 117
Pinckneyville, Il., U.S. E4 90
Pinconning, Mi., U.S. E7 99
Píndhos Óros, mts., Grc. J5 16
Pindi Gheb, Pak. D5 38
Pindus Mountains see Píndhos Óros, mts., Grc. J5 16
Pine, Az., U.S. C4 80
Pine, co., Mn., U.S. D6 100
Pine, stm., Mi., U.S. D7 99
Pine, stm., Mi., U.S. D5 99
Pine, stm., N.H., U.S. C4 106
Pine, stm., Wi., U.S. C5 126
Pine, stm., Wi., U.S. C4 126
Pine Barrens, reg., N.J., U.S. D3 107
Pine Bluff, Ar., U.S. C3 81
Pinebluff, N.C., U.S. B3 110
Pine Bluffs, Wy., U.S. E8 127
Pine Bridge, Ct., U.S. D3 84
Pine Castle, Fl., U.S. D5 86
Pine City, Mn., U.S. E6 100
Pine Creek, stm., Nv., U.S. C5 105
Pine Creek, stm., Pa., U.S. C6 115
Pine Creek, stm., Wa., U.S. B8 124
Pine Creek Lake, res., Ok., U.S. C6 113
Pinedale, Wy., U.S. D3 127
Pine Falls, Man., Can. D3 70
Pine Forest Range, mts., Nv., U.S. B3 105
Pine Grove, Pa., U.S. E9 115
Pine Grove Mills, Pa., U.S. E6 115
Pine Hill, N.J., U.S. D3 107
Pine Hills, Fl., U.S. D5 86
Pinehouse Lake, Sask., Can. B2 75
Pinehouse Lake, l., Sask., Can. B2 75
Pinehurst, Ma., U.S. f11 98
Pinehurst, N.C., U.S. B3 110
Pine Island, Mn., U.S. F6 100
Pine Island, i., Fl., U.S. F4 86
Pine Island Sound, strt., Fl., U.S. F4 86
Pine Key, i., Fl., U.S. p10 86
Pine Knot, Ky., U.S. D5 94
Pine Lake, Ga., U.S. h8 87
Pine Lake, l., In., U.S. A4 91
Pine Lake, l., Wi., U.S. C5 126
Pine Lawn, Mo., U.S. f13 102
Pine Level, N.C., U.S. B4 110
Pinellas, co., Fl., U.S. D4 86
Pinellas, Point, c., Fl., U.S. p10 86
Pinellas Park, Fl., U.S. E4 86
Pine Mountain, Ga., U.S. D2 87
Pine Mountain, mtn., Or., U.S. D6 114
Pine Mountain, mtn., Wy., U.S. E3 127
Pine Point, N.W. Ter., Can. D10 66
Pine Point, Me., U.S. E2 96
Pine Prairie, La., U.S. D3 95
Pine Ridge, S.D., U.S. D3 118
Pine Ridge Indian Reservation, S.D., U.S. D3 118
Pine River, Mn., U.S. D4 100
Pinerolo, Italy E2 14
Pines, Lake O' the, res., Tx., U.S. C5 120
Pinesdale, Mt., U.S. D2 103
Pinetops, N.C., U.S. B5 110
Pine Valley, val., Ut., U.S. E2 121
Pineville, Ky., U.S. D6 94
Pineville, La., U.S. C3 95
Pineville, N.C., U.S. B2 110
Pineville, W.V., U.S. D3 125
Pinewood, Fl., U.S. s13 86
Pinewood, S.C., U.S. D7 117
Piney Creek, stm., W.V., U.S. n13 125
Piney Fork, stm., W.V., U.S. h9 125
Piney Point, Md., U.S. D4 97
Piney View, W.V., U.S. n13 125
Ping, stm., Thai. F5 34
Pingdingshan, China E9 26
Pinghu, China E10 28
Pingliang, China D8 26
Pingtan Dao, i., China J8 28
P'ingtung, Tai. M9 28
Pingxiang, China H2 28
Pingyao, China D9 26
Pinhel, Port. E4 12
Pinnacles National Monument, Ca., U.S. D3 82
Pinneberg, Ger. B9 8
Pinole, Ca., U.S. h8 82
Pinopolis Dam, S.C., U.S. E8 117
Pinos, Mount, mtn., Ca., U.S. E4 82
Pins, Pointe aux, c., Ont., Can. E3 73
Pinsk, U.S.S.R. I9 22
Pinson, Al., U.S. f7 78
Pinta, Sierra, mts., Az., U.S. E2 80
Pintwater Range, mts., Nv., U.S. G6 105
Pioche, Nv., U.S. F7 105
Piombino, Italy G5 14
Pioneer, Oh., U.S. A1 112
Pioneer Mountains, mts., Id., U.S. F5 89
Pioneer Mountains, mts., Mt., U.S. E3 103
Pioner, Ostrov, i., U.S.S.R. B12 20
Piotrków Trybunalski, Pol. D19 8
Pipe Spring National Monument, Az., U.S. A3 80
Pipestem Creek, stm., N.D., U.S. B6 111
Pipestone, Mn., U.S. G2 100
Pipestone, co., Mn., U.S. F2 100
Pipestone, stm., Ont., Can. F14 66
Pipestone National Monument, Mn., U.S. G2 100
Pipestone Pass, Mt., U.S. E4 103
Pipmuacan, Réservoir, res., Que., Can. k12 74
Piqua, Oh., U.S. B1 112
Piracicaba, Braz. G5 57
Piraeus see Piraiévs, Grc. L7 16
Piraí do Sul, Braz. A7 56
Piraiévs (Piraeus), Grc. L7 16
Piraju, Braz. G4 57
Piran, Yugo. D8 14
Pirané, Arg. B5 56
Pirapora, Braz. D6 57
Pires do Rio, Braz. D4 57
Pírgos, Grc. L5 16
Pirmasens, Ger. F7 8
Pirna, Ger. E13 8
Pirtleville, Az., U.S. F6 80
Piru, Indon. F8 32
Pisa, Italy F5 14
Pisagua, Chile G4 54
Piscataqua, stm., N.H., U.S. D5 106
Piscataquis, co., Me., U.S. C3 96
Piscataquis, stm., Me., U.S. C3 96
Piscataquog, stm., N.H., U.S. D3 106
Piscataway, N.J., U.S. B4 107
Pisco, Peru F3 54
Piseco Lake, l., N.Y., U.S. B6 109
Písek, Czech. F14 8
Pisgah, Al., U.S. A4 78
Pisgah, Oh., U.S. n13 112
Pisgah, Mount, mtn., Wy., U.S. B8 127
Pisgah Forest, N.C., U.S. f10 110
Pishan, China B8 38
Pismo Beach, Ca., U.S. E3 82
Pisticci, Italy I11 14
Pistoia, Italy F5 14
Pistolet Bay, b., Newf., Can. C4 72
Pit, stm., Ca., U.S. B3 82
Pitalito, Col. G4 58
Pitcairn, Pa., U.S. k14 115
Pitcairn, dep., Oc. H4 2
Piteå, Swe. D13 6
Pitești, Rom. E8 16
Pithāpuram, India D7 37
Pithiviers, Fr. D9 10
Pitiquito, Mex. B3 62
Pitkin, co., Co., U.S. B4 83
Pitlochry, Scot., U.K. E9 7
Pitman, N.J., U.S. D2 107
Pitt, co., N.C., U.S. B5 110
Pitt Island, i., B.C., Can. C3 69
Pittsboro, In., U.S. E5 91
Pittsboro, N.C., U.S. B3 110
Pittsburg, Ca., U.S. g9 82
Pittsburg, Ks., U.S. E9 93
Pittsburg, Ky., U.S. C5 94
Pittsburg, Tx., U.S. C5 120
Pittsburg, co., Ok., U.S. C6 113
Pittsburgh, Pa., U.S. F1 115
Pittsfield, Il., U.S. D3 90
Pittsfield, Me., U.S. D3 96
Pittsfield, Ma., U.S. B1 98
Pittsfield, N.H., U.S. D4 106
Pittsford, Vt., U.S. D2 122
Pittston, Pa., U.S. D10 115
Pittsville, Md., U.S. D7 97
Pittsville, Wi., U.S. D3 126
Pittsylvania, co., Va., U.S. D3 123
Piu, Cerro, mtn., Nic. H5 64
Piura, Peru E2 54
Piute, co., Ut., U.S. E3 121
Piute Peak, mtn., Ca., U.S. E4 82
Piute Reservoir, res., Ut., U.S. E3 121
Pixley, Ca., U.S. E4 82
Pizzo, Italy K11 14
Placentia, Newf., Can. E5 72
Placentia Bay, b., Newf., Can. E4 72
Placer, co., Ca., U.S. C3 82
Placer Mountain, mtn., N.M., U.S. k8 108
Placerville, Ca., U.S. C3 82
Placetas, Cuba C8 64
Placid, Lake, l., Fl., U.S. E5 86
Placid, Lake, l., N.Y., U.S. f11 109
Placitas, N.M., U.S. B3 108
Plain City, Oh., U.S. B2 112
Plain City, Ut., U.S. B3 121
Plain Dealing, La., U.S. B2 95
Plainfield, Ct., U.S. C8 84
Plainfield, Il., U.S. B5 90
Plainfield, In., U.S. E5 91
Plainfield, N.J., U.S. B4 107
Plainfield, Vt., U.S. C4 122
Plainfield, Wi., U.S. D4 126
Plainfield Heights, Mi., U.S. E5 99
Plains, Ga., U.S. D2 87
Plains, Ks., U.S. E3 93
Plains, Mt., U.S. C2 103
Plains, Pa., U.S. n17 115
Plains, Tx., U.S. C1 120
Plainview, Ar., U.S. C2 81
Plainview, Mn., U.S. F6 100
Plainview, Ne., U.S. B8 104
Plainview, Tx., U.S. B2 120
Plainville, Ct., U.S. C4 84
Plainville, Ks., U.S. C4 93
Plainville, Ma., U.S. B5 98
Plainwell, Mi., U.S. F5 99
Plaistow, N.H., U.S. E4 106
Plankinton, S.D., U.S. D7 118
Plano, Il., U.S. B5 90

Name Map Ref Page

Plano, Tx., U.S. C4 120
Plantagenet, Ont., Can. B9 73
Plantation, Fl., U.S. r13 86
Plant City, Fl., U.S. D4 86
Plantersville, Al., U.S. C3 78
Plantersville, Ms., U.S. A5 101
Plantsite, Az., U.S. D6 80
Plantsville, Ct., U.S. C4 84
Plaquemine, La., U.S. D4 95
Plaquemines, co., La., U.S. E6 95
Plasencia, Spain E5 12
Plaški, Yugo. D10 14
Plaster Rock, N.B., Can. C2 71
Plata, Río de la, est., S.A. D5 56
Platte, S.D., U.S. D7 118
Platte, co., Mo., U.S. B3 102
Platte, co., Ne., U.S. C8 104
Platte, co., Wy., U.S. D7 127
Platte, stm., U.S. B3 102
Platte, stm., Mn., U.S. E4 100
Platte, stm., Ne., U.S. D6 104
Platte City, Mo., U.S. B3 102
Platte Island, i., Sey. C11 44
Platteville, Co., U.S. A6 83
Platteville, Wi., U.S. F3 126
Plattling, Ger. G12 8
Plattsburg, Mo., U.S. B3 102
Plattsburgh, N.Y., U.S. f11 109
Plattsburgh Air Force Base, mil., N.Y., U.S. f11 109
Plattsmouth, Ne., U.S. D10 104
Plau, Ger. B12 8
Plauen, Ger. E12 8
Playas Lake, l., N.M., U.S. F2 108
Play Cu, Viet. H9 34
Playgreen Lake, l., Man., Can. B2 70
Pleasant, stm., Me., U.S. C3 96
Pleasant, Lake, res., Az., U.S. D3 80
Pleasant Gap, Pa., U.S. E6 115
Pleasant Garden, N.C., U.S. B3 110
Pleasant Grove, Al., U.S. g7 78
Pleasant Grove, Ut., U.S. C4 121
Pleasant Hill, Ca., U.S. h8 82
Pleasant Hill, Il., U.S. D3 90
Pleasant Hill, Ia., U.S. e8 92
Pleasant Hill, La., U.S. C2 95
Pleasant Hill, Mo., U.S. C3 102
Pleasant Hill, Oh., U.S. B1 112
Pleasant Lake, In., U.S. A7 91
Pleasant Lake, l., Me., U.S. C5 96
Pleasant Lake, l., N.H., U.S. D4 106
Pleasanton, Ca., U.S. h9 82
Pleasanton, Ks., U.S. D9 93
Pleasanton, Tx., U.S. E3 120
Pleasant Prairie, Wi., U.S. n12 126
Pleasants, co., W.V., U.S. B3 125
Pleasant Valley, Ia., U.S. g11 92
Pleasant Valley, Mo., U.S. h11 102
Pleasant View, Ut., U.S. B3 121
Pleasantville, Ia., U.S. C4 92
Pleasantville, N.J., U.S. E3 107
Pleasantville, N.Y., U.S. D7 109
Pleasantville, Oh., U.S. C3 112
Pleasure Beach, Ct., U.S. D7 84
Pleasure Ridge Park, Ky., U.S. g11 94
Pleasureville, Ky., U.S. B4 94
Pleiku see Play Cu, Viet. H9 34
Pléneuf, Fr. D4 10
Plenty, Bay of, b., N.Z. B6 52
Plentywood, Mt., U.S. B12 103
Plessisville, Que., Can. C6 74
Pleternica, Yugo. D12 14
Plétipi, Lac, l., Que., Can. F18 66
Pleven, Bul. F8 16
Pljevlja, Yugo. F3 16
Ploče, Yugo. F12 14
Płock, Pol. C19 8
Ploërmel, Fr. E4 10
Ploiești, Rom. E10 16
Plomosa Mountains, mts., Az., U.S. D1 80
Plonge, Lac la, l., Sask., Can. B2 75
Plouguenast, Fr. D4 10
Plovdiv, Bul. G8 16
Plover, Wi., U.S. D4 126
Plover, stm., Wi., U.S. D4 126
Plum, Pa., U.S. k14 115
Plumas, co., Ca., U.S. B3 82
Plum Coulee, Man., Can. E3 70
Plumerville, Ar., U.S. B3 81
Plum Island, i., Ma., U.S. A6 98
Plummer, Id., U.S. B2 89
Plumsteadville, Pa., U.S. F11 115
Plumtree, Zimb. F5 44
Plymouth, Monts. F16 64
Plymouth, Eng., U.K. K8 7
Plymouth, Ct., U.S. C3 84
Plymouth, Fl., U.S. D5 86
Plymouth, In., U.S. B5 91
Plymouth, Ma., U.S. C6 98
Plymouth, Mi., U.S. p15 99
Plymouth, Mn., U.S. m12 100
Plymouth, N.H., U.S. C3 106
Plymouth, N.C., U.S. B6 110
Plymouth, Oh., U.S. A3 112
Plymouth, Pa., U.S. D10 115
Plymouth, Wi., U.S. E6 126
Plymouth, co., Ia., U.S. B1 92
Plymouth, co., Ma., U.S. C6 98
Plymouth Bay, b., Ma., U.S. C6 98
Plzeň, Czech. F13 8
Po, stm., Italy E7 14
Po, stm., Va., U.S. B5 123
Pobeda, Gora, mtn., U.S.S.R. D23 20
Pocahontas, Ar., U.S. A5 81
Pocahontas, Il., U.S. E4 90
Pocahontas, Ia., U.S. B3 92
Pocahontas, co., Ia., U.S. B3 92
Pocahontas, co., W.V., U.S. C4 125
Pocasset, Ma., U.S. C6 98
Pocatalico, W.V., U.S. C3 125
Pocatalico, stm., W.V., U.S. C3 125
Pocatello, Id., U.S. G6 89
Počep, U.S.S.R. I16 22
Pochutla, Mex. J11 62
Poções, Braz. C8 57
Pocola, Ok., U.S. B7 113
Pocomoke, stm., Md., U.S. D7 97
Pocomoke City, Md., U.S. D6 97
Pocomoke Sound, strt., Md., U.S. E6 97
Pocono Mountains, hills, Pa., U.S. E11 115
Pocono Pines, Pa., U.S. D11 115
Poços de Caldas, Braz. F5 57
Pocotopaug Lake, res., Ct., U.S. C6 84
Podensac, Fr. H6 10
Podkamennaja Tunguska, U.S.S.R. E12 20
Podkamennaja Tunguska, stm., U.S.S.R. E13 20
Podol'sk, U.S.S.R. F20 22
Podor, Sen. E3 42
Podravska Slatina, Yugo. D12 14
Pofadder, S. Afr. G3 44
Poge, Cape, c., Ma., U.S. D7 98
Poggibonsi, Italy F6 14
P'ohang, S. Kor. D12 26
Pohénégamook, Que., Can. B8 74
Pohue Bay, b., Hi., U.S. E6 88
Poinsett, co., Ar., U.S. B5 81
Poinsett, Lake, l., Fl., U.S. D6 86
Poinsett, Lake, l., S.D., U.S. C8 118
Point Clear, Al., U.S. E2 78
Pointe a la Hache, La., U.S. E6 95
Pointe-à-Pitre, Guad. F17 64
Pointe-au-Pic, Que., Can. B7 74
Pointe-Calumet, Que., Can. p19 74
Pointe-Claire, Que., Can. D4 74
Pointe Coupee, co., La., U.S. D4 95
Pointe-des-Cascades, Que., Can. q19 74
Point Edward, Ont., Can. D2 73
Pointe-Noire, Congo B2 44
Pointe-Verte, N.B., Can. B4 71
Point Fortin, Trin. I17 64
Point Hope, Ak., U.S. B6 79
Point Imperial, mtn., Az., U.S. A4 80
Point Judith Pond, l., R.I., U.S. F4 116
Point Lake, l., N.W. Ter., Can. C10 66
Point Leamington, Newf., Can. D4 72
Point Marion, Pa., U.S. G2 115
Point Mugu Naval Air Station, mil., Ca., U.S. E4 82
Point of Rocks, Md., U.S. B2 97
Point Pelee National Park, Ont., Can. F2 73
Point Pleasant, N.J., U.S. C4 107
Point Pleasant, W.V., U.S. C2 125
Point Pleasant Beach, N.J., U.S. C4 107
Point Reyes National Seashore, Ca., U.S. C2 82
Point Roberts, Wa., U.S. A2 124
Poipu, Hi., U.S. B2 88
Poison Creek, stm., Wy., U.S. C5 127
Poisson Blanc, Lac du, res., Que., Can. C2 74
Poitiers, Fr. F7 10
Poitou, reg., Fr. F6 10
Poix, Fr. C8 10
Pokegama Lake, l., Mn., U.S. C5 100
Pokegama Lake, l., Wi., U.S. C2 126
Polacca, Az., U.S. B5 80
Poland, ctry., Eur. E11 4
Polar Bear Provincial Park, Ont., Can. n18 73
Polecat Creek, stm., Ok., U.S. B5 113
Pol-e Khomrī, Afg. C3 38
Polesje, reg., U.S.S.R. I10 22
Pólis, Cyp. B3 40
Polistena, Italy K11 14
Polk, Pa., U.S. D2 115
Polk, co., Ar., U.S. C1 81
Polk, co., Fl., U.S. E5 86
Polk, co., Ga., U.S. C1 87
Polk, co., Ia., U.S. C4 92
Polk, co., Mn., U.S. C2 100
Polk, co., Mo., U.S. D4 102
Polk, co., Ne., U.S. C8 104
Polk, co., N.C., U.S. f10 110
Polk, co., Or., U.S. C3 114
Polk, co., Tn., U.S. D9 119
Polk, co., Tx., U.S. D5 120
Polk, co., Wi., U.S. C1 126
Polk City, Fl., U.S. D5 86
Polk City, Ia., U.S. C4 92
Pol'kino, U.S.S.R. C13 20
Pollāchi, India G4 37
Polo, Il., U.S. B4 90
Polock, U.S.S.R. F11 22
Polson, Mt., U.S. C2 103
Poltava, U.S.S.R. H4 18
Polynesia, is., Oc. G2 2
Pomabamba, Peru E3 54
Pomaro, Mex. H8 62
Pombal, Port. F3 12
Pomerania, hist. reg., Pol. A16 8
Pomeranian Bay, b., Eur. A14 8
Pomeroy, Ia., U.S. B3 92
Pomeroy, Oh., U.S. C3 112
Pomeroy, Wa., U.S. C8 124
Pomme de Terre, stm., Mn., U.S. E3 100
Pomme de Terre, stm., Mo., U.S. D4 102
Pomme de Terre Lake, res., Mo., U.S. D4 102
Pomona, Ca., U.S. E5 82
Pomona, Ks., U.S. D8 93
Pomona Lake, res., Ks., U.S. D7 93
Pompano Beach, Fl., U.S. F6 86
Pompton Lakes, N.J., U.S. A4 107
Ponaganset, stm., R.I., U.S. C2 116
Ponaganset Reservoir, res., R.I., U.S. B2 116
Ponca, Ne., U.S. B9 104
Ponca City, Ok., U.S. A4 113
Ponca Creek, stm., U.S. A6 104
Ponca Indian Reservation, Ne., U.S. B7 104
Ponce, P.R. E14 64
Ponce de Leon Bay, b., Fl., U.S. G5 86
Ponce de Leon Inlet, b., Fl., U.S. C6 86
Poncha Pass, Co., U.S. C4 83
Ponchatoula, La., U.S. D5 95
Pond, stm., Ky., U.S. C2 94
Pond Creek, Ok., U.S. A3 113
Pondera, co., Mt., U.S. B4 103
Pond Fork, stm., W.V., U.S. D3 125
Pondicherry, India G5 37
Pondicherry, ter., India G5 37
Pond Inlet, N.W. Ter., Can. B17 66
Pone Island, i., Md., U.S. D5 97
Ponferrada, Spain C5 12
Ponoka, Alta., Can. C4 68
Ponorogo, Indon. m15 33a
Pons, Fr. G6 10
Ponta Grossa, Braz. B6 56
Pont-à-Mousson, Fr. D13 10
Ponta Porã, Braz. G1 57
Pontarlier, Fr. F13 10
Pontassieve, Italy F6 14
Pont-Audemer, Fr. C7 10
Pontchartrain, Lake, l., La., U.S. D5 95
Pontchâteau, Fr. E4 10
Pont de Suert, Spain C12 12
Ponte Branca, Braz. D2 57
Ponte da Barca, Port. D3 12
Pontedera, Italy F5 14
Ponte de Sor, Port. F3 12
Ponteix, Sask., Can. H2 75
Ponte Nova, Braz. F7 57
Pontevedra, Spain C3 12
Ponte Vedra Beach, Fl., U.S. B5 86
Pontgibaud, Fr. F9 10
Pontiac, Il., U.S. C5 90
Pontiac, Mi., U.S. F7 99
Pontianak, Indon. F4 32
Pontivy, Fr. D4 10
Pont-l'Abbé, Fr. E2 10
Pontoise, Fr. C9 10
Pontoosuc Lake, l., Ma., U.S. B1 98
Pontorson, Fr. D5 10
Pontotoc, Ms., U.S. A4 101
Pontotoc, co., Ms., U.S. A4 101
Pontotoc, co., Ok., U.S. C5 113
Pont-Rouge, Que., Can. C6 74
Pontypool, Ont., Can. C6 73
Pontypool, Wales, U.K. J9 7
Poole, Eng., U.K. K11 7
Pooler, Ga., U.S. D5 87
Pooles Island, i., Md., U.S. B5 97
Poolesville, Md., U.S. B3 97
Poopó, Lago de, l., Bol. G5 54
Popayán, Col. F4 58
Pope, co., Ar., U.S. B2 81
Pope, co., Il., U.S. F5 90
Pope, co., Mn., U.S. E3 100
Pope Air Force Base, mil., N.C., U.S. B3 110
Poplar, Mt., U.S. B11 103
Poplar, stm., Can. C3 70
Poplar, stm., Mn., U.S. C2 100
Poplar Bluff, Mo., U.S. E7 102
Poplar Island, i., Md., U.S. C5 97
Poplarville, Ms., U.S. E4 101
Popocatépetl, Volcán, vol., Mex. H10 62
Popokabaka, Zaire C3 44
Popomanasiu, Mount, mtn., Sol.Is. A11 50
Popondetta, Pap. N. Gui. m16 50a
Popple, stm., Wi., U.S. C5 126
Poquonock, Ct., U.S. B5 84
Poquonock Bridge, Ct., U.S. D7 84
Poquoson, Va., U.S. C6 123
Porangatu, Braz. F9 54
Porbandar, India J3 38
Porcher Island, i., B.C., Can. C2 69
Porcupine Mountains, mts., Mi., U.S. m12 99
Pordenone, Italy D7 14
Poreč, Yugo. D8 14
Pori, Fin. F13 6
Porkkala, Fin. G15 6
Porlamar, Ven. B11 58
Poronajsk, U.S.S.R. H22 20
Porsgrunn, Nor. G7 6
Portadown, N. Ire., U.K. G6 7
Portage, In., U.S. A3 91
Portage, Mi., U.S. F5 99
Portage, Pa., U.S. F4 115
Portage, Wi., U.S. E4 126
Portage, co., Oh., U.S. A4 112
Portage, co., Wi., U.S. D4 126
Portage, stm., Oh., U.S. B2 112
Portage Bay, b., Man., Can. D2 70
Portage Head, c., Wa., U.S. A1 124
Portage Lake, l., Me., U.S. B4 96
Portage Lakes, Oh., U.S. B4 112
Portage la Prairie, Man., Can. E2 70
Portageville, Mo., U.S. E8 102
Port Alberni, B.C., Can. E5 69
Portalegre, Port. F4 12
Portales, N.M., U.S. C6 108
Port Alice, B.C., Can. D4 69
Port Allegany, Pa., U.S. C5 115
Port Allen, La., U.S. D4 95
Port Angeles, Wa., U.S. A2 124
Port Antonio, Jam. E9 64
Port Aransas, Tx., U.S. F4 120
Port Arthur, Tx., U.S. E6 120
Port Arthur see Lüshun, China D11 26
Port Augusta, Austl. F7 50
Port au Port Bay, b., Newf., Can. D2 72
Port au Port [West-Aguathuna-Felix Cove], Newf., Can. D2 72
Port-au-Prince, Haiti E11 64
Port au Prince Peninsula, pen., Newf., Can. D2 72
Port Austin, Mi., U.S. D7 99
Port Barre, La., U.S. D4 95
Port-Bergé, Madag. E9 44
Port Blair, India I2 34
Port Blandford, Newf., Can. D4 72
Port Bolivar, Tx., U.S. E5 120
Port Burwell, Ont., Can. E4 73
Port Byron, Il., U.S. B3 90
Port Carbon, Pa., U.S. E9 115
Port Carling, Ont., Can. B5 73
Port-Cartier-Ouest, Que., Can. k13 74
Port Chalmers, N.Z. F3 52
Port Charlotte, Fl., U.S. F4 86
Port Chester, N.Y., U.S. E7 109
Port Clinton, Oh., U.S. A3 112
Port Colborne, Ont., Can. E5 73
Port Coquitlam, B.C., Can. E6 69
Port Deposit, Md., U.S. A5 97
Port Dickinson, N.Y., U.S. C5 109
Port Dickson, Malay. M6 34
Port Edward, B.C., Can. B2 69
Port Edwards, Wi., U.S. D4 126
Portel, Braz. D8 54
Portel, Port. G4 12
Port Elgin, Ont., Can. C3 73
Port Elizabeth, S. Afr. H5 44
Port Ellen, Scot., U.K. F6 7
Porter, In., U.S. A3 91
Porter, Tx., U.S. D5 120
Porter, co., In., U.S. B3 91
Porter Creek, stm., W.V., U.S. m13 125
Porterdale, Ga., U.S. C3 87
Porterville, Ca., U.S. D4 82
Port Ewen, N.Y., U.S. D7 109
Port Gamble Indian Reservation, Wa., U.S. B3 124
Port-Gentil, Gabon B1 44
Port Gibson, Ms., U.S. D3 101
Port Harcourt, Nig. H7 42
Port Hedland, Austl. D3 50
Port Hood, N.S., Can. C8 71
Port Hope, Ont., Can. D6 73
Port Hope Simpson, Newf., Can. B3 72
Port Hueneme, Ca., U.S. E4 82
Port Huron, Mi., U.S. F8 99
Portimão, Port. H3 12
Port Isabel, Tx., U.S. F4 120
Port Jefferson, N.Y., U.S. n15 109
Port Jervis, N.Y., U.S. D6 109
Portland, Austl. G8 50
Portland, Ct., U.S. C5 84
Portland, In., U.S. D8 91
Portland, Me., U.S. E2 96
Portland, Mi., U.S. F6 99
Portland, N.D., U.S. B8 111
Portland, Or., U.S. B4 114
Portland, Tn., U.S. A5 119
Portland, Tx., U.S. F4 120
Portland, Bill of, c., Eng., U.K. K10 7
Portland Inlet, b., B.C., Can. B2 69
Portland Point, c., Jam. F9 64
Port Lavaca, Tx., U.S. E4 120
Port Lincoln, Austl. F7 50
Port Loko, S.L. G3 42
Port Louis, Mrts. F11 44
Port Ludlow, Wa., U.S. B3 124
Port-Lyautey see Kenitra, Mor. B4 42
Port Macquarie, Austl. F10 50
Port Madison Indian Reservation, Wa., U.S. B3 124
Port McNeil, B.C., Can. D4 69
Port McNicoll, Ont., Can. C5 73
Port Monmouth, N.J., U.S. C4 107
Port Moresby, Pap. N. Gui. m16 50a
Port Morien, N.S., Can. C10 71
Port Neches, Tx., U.S. E6 120
Portneuf, Que., Can. C6 74
Port Nolloth, S. Afr. G3 44
Porto, Port. D3 12
Porto Alegre, Braz. C6 56
Porto Amboim, Ang. D2 44
Portobelo, Pan. J8 64
Porto de Moz, Braz. D8 54
Porto Esperança, Braz. G7 54
Porto Esperidião, Braz. G7 54
Pôrto Feliz, Braz. G5 57
Portoferraio, Italy G5 14
Pôrto Ferreira, Braz. F5 57
Port of Spain, Trin. I17 64
Portogruaro, Italy D7 14
Portola, Ca., U.S. C3 82
Porto Murtinho, Braz. H7 54
Porto Nacional, Braz. F9 54
Porto-Novo, Benin G6 42
Port Orange, Fl., U.S. C6 86
Port Orchard, Wa., U.S. B3 124
Port Orford, Or., U.S. E2 114
Porto San Giorgio, Italy F8 14
Porto Santo Stefano, Italy G6 14
Pôrto São José, Braz. G2 57
Pôrto Seguro, Braz. D9 57
Porto Torres, Italy I3 14
Porto União, Braz. B6 56
Porto Velho, Braz. E6 54
Portoviejo, Ec. H2 58
Port Penn, De., U.S. B3 85
Port Pirie, Austl. F7 50
Port Richey, Fl., U.S. D4 86
Port Rowan, Ont., Can. E4 73
Port Royal, S.C., U.S. G6 117
Port Royal Island, i., S.C., U.S. G6 117
Port Royal Sound, strt., S.C., U.S. G6 117
Port Said see Būr Sa'īd, Egypt B12 42
Port-Sainte-Marie, Fr. H7 10
Port Saint Joe, Fl., U.S. C1 86
Port Saint Johns, S. Afr. H5 44
Port Saint Lucie, Fl., U.S. E6 86
Port Salerno, Fl., U.S. E6 86
Port Saunders, Newf., Can. C3 72
Port Shepstone, S. Afr. H6 44
Portsmouth, Eng., U.K. K11 7
Portsmouth, N.H., U.S. D5 106
Portsmouth, Oh., U.S. D3 112
Portsmouth, R.I., U.S. E6 116
Portsmouth, Va., U.S. D6 123
Portsmouth Naval Shipyard, mil., Me., U.S. D5 106
Port Stanley, Ont., Can. E3 73
Port Sulphur, La., U.S. E6 95
Port Talbot, Wales, U.K. J9 7
Port Townsend, Wa., U.S. A3 124
Portugal, ctry., Eur. H6 4
Portugalete, Spain B8 12
Portuguese Guinea see Guinea-Bissau, ctry., Afr. F2 42
Portumna, Ire. H4 7
Port Union, Newf., Can. D5 72
Port-Vendres, Fr. J10 10
Port Washington, N.Y., U.S. h13 109
Port Washington, Wi., U.S. E6 126
Port Wentworth, Ga., U.S. D5 87
Porum, Ok., U.S. B6 113
Porz, Ger. E7 8
Porzuna, Spain F7 12
Posadas, Arg. B5 56
Poschiavo, Switz. F17 10
Posen, Il., U.S. k9 90
Posey, co., In., U.S. H2 91
Poseyville, In., U.S. H2 91
Poso, Indon. F7 32
Posse, Braz. C5 57
Pössneck, Ger. E11 8
Post, Tx., U.S. C2 120
Post Falls, Id., U.S. B2 89
Post Maurice Cortier (Bidon Cinq), Alg. D6 42
Postojna, Yugo. D9 14
P'ostraja Dresva, U.S.S.R. E25 20
Postville, Ia., U.S. A6 92
Potawatomi Indian Reservation, Ks., U.S. C8 93
Potchefstroom, S. Afr. G5 44
Poté, Braz. D8 57
Poteau, Ok., U.S. B7 113
Poteau, stm., U.S. B7 113
Poteet, Tx., U.S. E3 120
Potenza, Italy I10 14
Potes, Spain B7 12
Potgietersrus, S. Afr. F5 44
Poth, Tx., U.S. E3 120
Potholes Reservoir, res., Wa., U.S. B6 124
Potiraguá, Braz. C9 57
Potiskum, Nig. F8 42
Potlatch, Id., U.S. C2 89
Potomac, Md., U.S. B3 97
Potomac, stm., U.S. D4 97
Potomac Heights, Md., U.S. C3 97
Potomac Park, Md., U.S. k13 97
Potosí, Bol. G5 54
Potosi, Mo., U.S. D7 102
Potosí, Cerro, mtn., Mex. E9 62
Potsdam, Ger. C13 8
Potsdam, N.Y., U.S. f10 109
Pottawatomie, co., Ks., U.S. C7 93
Pottawatomie, co., Ok., U.S. B4 113
Pottawattamie, co., Ia., U.S. C2 92
Potter, co., Pa., U.S. C6 115
Potter, co., S.D., U.S. B6 118
Potter, co., Tx., U.S. B2 120
Potter Valley, Ca., U.S. C2 82
Potts Creek, stm., U.S. C2 123
Pottstown, Pa., U.S. F10 115
Pottsville, Ar., U.S. B2 81
Pottsville, Pa., U.S. E9 115
P'otzu, Tai. L9 28
Pouce Coupe, B.C., Can. B7 69
Pouch Cove, Newf., Can. E5 72
Poughkeepsie, N.Y., U.S. D7 109
Poulan, Ga., U.S. E3 87
Poulsbo, Wa., U.S. B3 124
Poultney, Vt., U.S. D2 122
Poultney, stm., Vt., U.S. D2 122
Pound, Va., U.S. e9 123
Pound Gap, U.S. C7 94
Pouso Alegre, Braz. G6 57
Poŭthĭsăt, Camb. H7 34
Pouzauges, Fr. F6 10
Póvoa de Varzim, Port. D3 12
Povungnituk, Que., Can. f11 74
Powassan, Ont., Can. A5 73
Poway, Ca., U.S. F5 82
Powder, stm., U.S. B5 76
Powder, stm., Or., U.S. C9 114
Powder, Middle Fork, stm., Wy., U.S. C6 127
Powder, North Fork, stm., Wy., U.S. C6 127
Powder, South Fork, stm., Wy., U.S. C6 127
Powder River, co., Mt., U.S. E11 103
Powder River Pass, Wy., U.S. B5 127
Powder Springs, Ga., U.S. h8 87
Powell, Oh., U.S. B2 112
Powell, Tn., U.S. m13 119
Powell, Wy., U.S. B4 127
Powell, co., Ky., U.S. C6 94
Powell, co., Mt., U.S. D4 103
Powell, stm., U.S. C10 119
Powell, Lake, res., U.S. F5 121
Powell, Mount, mtn., Co., U.S. B4 83
Powell, Mount, mtn., N.M., U.S. B1 108
Powell Butte, Or., U.S. C5 114
Powell Park, reg., Co., U.S. A2 83
Powell River, B.C., Can. E5 69
Powellton, W.V., U.S. C3 125
Power, co., Id., U.S. G5 89
Powers, Or., U.S. E2 114
Powerview, Man., Can. D3 70
Poweshiek, co., Ia., U.S. C5 92
Powhatan, Va., U.S. C5 123
Powhatan, co., Va., U.S. C5 123
Powhatan Point, Oh., U.S. C5 112
Poxoreu, Braz. C1 57
Poyang, China G5 28
Poyang Hu, l., China F5 28
Poygan, Lake, l., Wi., U.S. D5 126
Poynette, Wi., U.S. E4 126
Poza Rica de Hidalgo, Mex. G11 62
Poznań, Pol. C16 8
Pozo Alcón, Spain H9 12
Pozoblanco, Spain G7 12
Pozo Redondo Mountains, mts., Az., U.S. E3 80
Pozuelo de Alarcón, Spain E8 12
Pozzuoli, Italy I9 14
Prachin Buri, Thai. G6 34
Prachuap Khiri Khan, Thai. I5 34
Prague, Ok., U.S. B5 113
Prague see Praha, Czech. E14 8
Praha (Prague), Czech. E14 8
Prainha, Braz. E6 54
Prairie, co., Ar., U.S. C4 81
Prairie, co., Mt., U.S. D11 103
Prairie, stm., Mn., U.S. C5 100
Prairie, stm., Wi., U.S. C4 126
Prairie City, Ia., U.S. C4 92

Name Map Ref Page

Prairie City, Or., U.S. C8 114
Prairie Creek Reservoir, res., In., U.S. D7 91
Prairie Dog Creek, stm., U.S. C3 93
Prairie du Chien, Wi., U.S. E2 126
Prairie du Sac, Wi., U.S. E4 126
Prairie Grove, Ar., U.S. B1 81
Prairies, Rivière des, stm., Que., Can. p19 74
Prairie View, Tx., U.S. D5 120
Prairie Village, Ks., U.S. m16 93
Praslin Island, i., Sey. B11 44
Pratas Islands see Tungsha Tao, is., Tai. G10 26
Prat de Llobregat, Spain D14 12
Prater Mountain, mtn., Wy., U.S. C2 127
Prato, Italy F6 14
Pratt, Ks., U.S. E5 93
Pratt, co., Ks., U.S. E5 93
Prattville, Al., U.S. C3 78
Pravia, Spain B5 12
Preble, co., Oh., U.S. C1 112
Predazzo, Italy C6 14
Predlitz [-Turrach], Aus. H13 8
Pré-en-Pail, Fr. D6 10
Preetz, Ger. A10 8
Premont, Tx., U.S. F3 120
Prentiss, Ms., U.S. D4 101
Prentiss, co., Ms., U.S. A5 101
Prenzlau, Ger. B13 8
Preparis Island, i., Burma G2 34
Preparis North Channel, strt., Burma G2 34
Preparis South Channel, strt., Burma G2 34
Přerov, Czech. F17 8
Prescott, Ont., Can. C9 73
Prescott, Az., U.S. C3 80
Prescott, Ar., U.S. D2 81
Prescott, Wi., U.S. D1 126
Presho, S.D., U.S. D5 118
Presidencia Roca, Arg. B5 56
Presidente Epitácio, Braz. F2 57
Presidente Prudente, Braz. G3 57
Presidential Range, mts., N.H., U.S. B4 106
Presidio, Tx., U.S. p12 120
Presidio, co., Tx., U.S. o12 120
Presidio of San Francisco, mil., Ca., U.S. h8 82
Prešov, Czech. F21 8
Prespa, Lake, l., Eur. I4 16
Presque Isle, Me., U.S. B5 96
Presque Isle, co., Mi., U.S. C6 99
Preston, Eng., U.K. H10 7
Preston, Id., U.S. G7 89
Preston, Ia., U.S. B7 92
Preston, Mn., U.S. G6 100
Preston, co., W.V., U.S. B5 125
Preston Peak, mtn., Ca., U.S. B2 82
Prestonsburg, Ky., U.S. C7 94
Presumpscot, stm., Me., U.S. g7 96
Pretoria, S. Afr. G5 44
Prettyboy Reservoir, res., Md., U.S. A4 97
Pretty Prairie, Ks., U.S. E5 93
Préveza, Grc. K4 16
Prewitt Reservoir, res., Co., U.S. A7 83
Prey Vêng, Camb. I8 34
Pribilof Islands, is., Ak., U.S. D5 79
Příbram, Czech. F14 8
Price, Ut., U.S. D5 121
Price, co., Wi., U.S. C3 126
Price, stm., Ut., U.S. D5 121
Price Inlet, b., S.C., U.S. k12 117
Prichard, Al., U.S. E1 78
Priego, Spain E9 12
Priego de Córdoba, Spain H7 12
Prien, Ger. H12 8
Prieska, S. Afr. G4 44
Priest Lake, l., Id., U.S. A2 89
Priest Rapids Dam, Wa., U.S. C6 124
Priest Rapids Lake, res., Wa., U.S. C6 124
Priest River, Id., U.S. A2 89
Prievidza, Czech. G18 8
Prijedor, Yugo. E11 14
Prilep, Yugo. H5 16
Prim, Point, c., P.E.I., Can. C6 71
Primghar, Ia., U.S. A2 92
Primrose, R.I., U.S. B3 116
Primrose Lake, l., Can. F11 66
Prince, Lake, res., Va., U.S. k14 123
Prince Albert National Park, Sask., Can. C2 75
Prince Albert Sound, strt., N.W. Ter., Can. B9 66
Prince Charles Island, i., N.W. Ter., Can. C17 66
Prince-de-Galles, Cap du, c., Que., Can. D18 66
Prince Edward, co., Va., U.S. C4 123
Prince Edward Island, prov., Can. C6 71
Prince Edward Island National Park, P.E.I., Can. C6 71
Prince Frederick, Md., U.S. C4 97
Prince George, B.C., Can. C6 69
Prince George, co., Va., U.S. C5 123
Prince Georges, co., Md., U.S. C4 97
Prince of Wales, Cape, c., Ak., U.S. B6 79
Prince of Wales Island, i., Austl. B8 50
Prince of Wales Island, i., N.W. Ter., Can. B13 66
Prince of Wales Island, i., Ak., U.S. n23 79
Prince of Wales Strait, strt., N.W. Ter., Can. B9 66
Prince Regent Inlet, b., N.W. Ter., Can. B14 66
Prince Rupert, B.C., Can. B2 69
Princes Lakes, In., U.S. F5 91
Princess Anne, Md., U.S. D6 97
Princess Royal Channel, strt., B.C., Can. C3 69
Princess Royal Island, i., B.C., Can. C3 69
Princeton, B.C., Can. E7 69
Princeton, Fl., U.S. G6 86
Princeton, Il., U.S. B4 90
Princeton, In., U.S. H2 91
Princeton, Ia., U.S. C7 92
Princeton, Ky., U.S. C2 94
Princeton, Me., U.S. C5 96
Princeton, Mn., U.S. E5 100
Princeton, Mo., U.S. A4 102
Princeton, N.J., U.S. C3 107
Princeton, N.C., U.S. B4 110
Princeton, W.V., U.S. D3 125
Princeton, Wi., U.S. E4 126
Princeton, Mount, mtn., Co., U.S. C4 83
Princeville, Que., Can. C6 74
Princeville, Il., U.S. C4 90
Princeville, N.C., U.S. B5 110
Prince William, co., Va., U.S. B5 123
Prince William Sound, strt., Ak., U.S. g18 79
Príncipe, i., S. Tom./P. A1 44
Principe Channel, strt., B.C., Can. C3 69
Príncipe da Beira, Braz. F6 54
Prineville, Or., U.S. C6 114
Prineville Reservoir, res., Or., U.S. C6 114
Pringsewu, Indon. k12 33a
Prinzapolca, Nic. H6 64
Prior Lake, Mn., U.S. F5 100
Priština, Yugo. G5 16
Pritchards Island, i., S.C., U.S. G6 117
Pritzwalk, Ger. B12 8
Privas, Fr. H11 10
Privolžsk, U.S.S.R. D24 22
Probolinggo, Indon. m16 33a
Proctor, Mn., U.S. D6 100
Proctor, Vt., U.S. D2 122
Proctor Lake, res., Tx., U.S. C3 120
Proctorsville, Vt., U.S. E3 122
Proddatūr, India E5 37
Professor Dr. Ir. W.J. van Blommestein Meer, res., Sur. C7 54
Progreso, Mex. G15 62
Prokopjevsk, U.S.S.R. G11 20
Prokuplje, Yugo. F5 16
Promontory Mountains, mts., Ut., U.S. B3 121
Prophetstown, Il., U.S. B4 90
Propriá, Braz. F11 54
Prospect, Ct., U.S. C4 84
Prospect, Ky., U.S. g11 94
Prospect, Oh., U.S. B2 112
Prospect, Or., U.S. E4 114
Prospect, Pa., U.S. E1 115
Prospect Hill, mtn., Or., U.S. k11 114
Prospect Park, N.J., U.S. B4 107
Prospect Park, Pa., U.S. p20 115
Prosperity, S.C., U.S. C4 117
Prosperity, W.V., U.S. n13 125
Prosser, Wa., U.S. C6 124
Prostějov, Czech. F17 8
Protection, Ks., U.S. E4 93
Protville, Tun. M5 14
Provence, hist. reg., Fr. I13 10
Providence, Ky., U.S. C2 94
Providence, R.I., U.S. C4 116
Providence, Ut., U.S. B4 121
Providence, co., R.I., U.S. C2 116
Providence, stm., R.I., U.S. C5 116
Providence Island, i., Sey. C10 44
Providence Point, c., R.I., U.S. D5 116
Providencia, Isla de, i., Col. H7 64
Providenija, U.S.S.R. E31 20
Province Lake, l., N.H., U.S. C5 106
Provincetown, Ma., U.S. B7 98
Provins, Fr. D10 10
Provo, Ut., U.S. C4 121
Provo, stm., Ut., U.S. C4 121
Provost, Alta., Can. C5 68
Prowers, co., Co., U.S. D8 83
Prozor, Yugo. F12 14
Prudence Island, i., R.I., U.S. E5 116
Prudenville, Mi., U.S. D6 99
Prudhoe Bay, Ak., U.S. A10 79
Prudhoe Bay, b., Ak., U.S. A10 79
Prüm, Ger. E6 8
Pruszków, Pol. C20 8
Prut, stm., Eur. D12 16
Pryor, Mt., U.S. E8 103
Pryor, Ok., U.S. A6 113
Pryor Mountains, mts., Mt., U.S. E8 103
Przemyśl, Pol. F22 8
Pskov, U.S.S.R. D11 22
Ptolemaís, Grc. I5 16
Ptuj, Yugo. C10 14
Pucallpa, Peru E4 54
Pucheng, China H7 28
Puckaway Lake, l., Wi., U.S. E4 126
Pudukkottai, India G5 37
Puebla de Sanabria, Spain C5 12
Puebla de Trives, Spain C4 12
Puebla [de Zaragoza], Mex. H10 62
Pueblo, Co., U.S. C6 83
Pueblo, co., Co., U.S. C6 83
Pueblo Hundido, Chile B2 56
Pueblo Mountain, mtn., Or., U.S. E8 114
Pueblo Mountains, mts., Or., U.S. E8 114
Pueblo Reservoir, res., Co., U.S. C6 83
Puentedeume, Spain B3 12
Puente-Genil, Spain H7 12
Pueo Point, c., Hi., U.S. B1 88
Puerco, stm., U.S. C6 80
Puerco, Rio, stm., N.M., U.S. B2 108
Puerto Aisén, Chile F2 56
Puerto Alfonso, Col. I7 58
Puerto Ángel, Mex. J11 62
Puerto Armuelles, Pan. J6 64
Puerto Asís, Col. G4 58
Puerto Ayacucho, Ven. E9 58
Puerto Barrios, Guat. G3 64
Puerto Berrío, Col. D5 58
Puerto Boyacá, Col. E5 58
Puerto Cabello, Ven. B8 58
Puerto Cabezas, Nic. G6 64
Puerto Carreño, Col. D9 58
Puerto Casado, Para. A5 56
Puerto Chicama, Peru E3 54
Puerto Cortés, C.R. J6 64
Puerto Cortés, Hond. G4 64
Puerto Cumarebo, Ven. B8 58
Puerto de Pollensa, Spain F15 12
Puerto de San José, Guat. H2 64
Puerto Deseado, Arg. F3 56
Puerto Escondido, Mex. J11 62
Puerto Francisco de Orellana, Ec. H4 58
Puerto Inírida, Col. F9 58
Puerto Juárez, Mex. G16 62
Puerto la Cruz, Ven. B10 58
Puerto Leguízamo, Col. H5 58
Puerto Limón, Col. F6 58
Puertollano, Spain G7 12
Puerto Lobos, Arg. E3 56
Puerto Madryn, Arg. E3 56
Puerto Maldonado, Peru F5 54
Puerto Montt, Chile E2 56
Puerto Morelos, Mex. G16 62
Puerto Nariño, Col. E9 58
Puerto Natales, Chile G2 56
Puerto Padre, Cuba D9 64
Puerto Peñasco, Mex. B3 62
Puerto Plata, Dom. Rep. E12 64
Puerto Princesa, Phil. D6 32
Puerto Real, Spain I5 12
Puerto Rico, dep., N.A. E14 64
Puerto Rondón, Col. D7 58
Puerto Suárez, Bol. G7 54
Puerto Tejada, Col. F4 58
Puerto Vallarta, Mex. G7 62
Puerto Wilches, Col. D6 58
Puget Sound, strt., Wa., U.S. B3 124
Puget Sound Naval Shipyard, mil., Wa., U.S. e10 124
Pugwash, N.S., Can. D6 71
Puhi, Hi., U.S. B2 88
Puigcerdá, Spain C13 12
Pukalani, Hi., U.S. C5 88
Pukaskwa National Park, Ont., Can. o18 73
Pukch'ŏng, N. Kor. C12 26
Pukë, Alb. G3 16
Pukeashun Mountain, mtn., B.C., Can. D8 69
Pukekohe, N.Z. B5 52
Pukou, China C7 28
Pula, Yugo. E8 14
Pulacayo, Bol. H5 54
Pulaski, N.Y., U.S. B4 109
Pulaski, Tn., U.S. B4 119
Pulaski, Va., U.S. C2 123
Pulaski, Wi., U.S. D5 126
Pulaski, co., Ar., U.S. C3 81
Pulaski, co., Ga., U.S. D3 87
Pulaski, co., Il., U.S. F4 90
Pulaski, co., In., U.S. B4 91
Pulaski, co., Ky., U.S. C5 94
Pulaski, co., Mo., U.S. D5 102
Pulaski, co., Va., U.S. C2 123
Puli, Tai. L9 28
Puliyangudi, India H4 37
Pulkkila, Fin. D15 6
Pullman, Wa., U.S. C8 124
Pulog, Mount, mtn., Phil. B7 32
Pumphrey, Md., U.S. h11 97
Puná, Isla, i., Ec. I2 58
Punakha, Bhu. G13 38
Pūnch, India D6 38
Pune (Poona), India C2 37
Pungo Lake, l., N.C., U.S. B6 110
Punjab, state, India E6 38
Puno, Peru G4 54
Punta, Cerro de, mtn., P.R. E14 64
Punta Alta, Arg. D4 56
Punta Arenas, Chile G2 56
Punta Delgada, Arg. E4 56
Punta de Mata, Ven. C11 58
Punta Gorda, Belize F3 64
Punta Gorda, Nic. I6 64
Punta Gorda, Fl., U.S. F4 86
Puntarenas, C.R. J5 64
Punto Fijo, Ven. B7 58
Punxsutawney, Pa., U.S. E4 115
Puolanka, Fin. D16 6
Purcell, Ok., U.S. B4 113
Purcellville, Va., U.S. A5 123
Purdy, Mo., U.S. E4 102
Purgatoire, stm., Co., U.S. D7 83
Purgatoire Peak, mtn., Co., U.S. D5 83
Puri, India K11 38
Purli, India C4 37
Purnea, India H12 38
Purūlia, India I12 38
Purus (Purús), stm., S.A. D6 54
Purvis, Ms., U.S. D4 101
Purwakarta, Indon. m13 33a
Purwokerto, Indon. m14 32
Purworejo, Indon. m15 33a
Pusan, S. Kor. D12 26
Pushaw Lake, l., Me., U.S. D4 96
Pushmataha, co., Ok., U.S. C6 113
Puškin, U.S.S.R. B13 22
Puškino, U.S.S.R. E20 22
Putao, Burma F6 26
Putian, China J8 28
Puting, Tanjung, c., Indon. F5 32
Putnam, Ct., U.S. B8 84
Putnam, co., Fl., U.S. C5 86
Putnam, co., Ga., U.S. C3 87
Putnam, co., Il., U.S. B4 90
Putnam, co., In., U.S. E4 91
Putnam, co., Mo., U.S. A4 102
Putnam, co., N.Y., U.S. D7 109
Putnam, co., Oh., U.S. B1 112
Putnam, co., Tn., U.S. C8 119
Putnam, co., W.V., U.S. C3 125
Putney, Ga., U.S. E2 87
Putney, Vt., U.S. F3 122
Putorana, Plato, plat., U.S.S.R. D12 20
Puttalam, Sri L. H5 37
Puttgarden, Ger. A11 8
Putumayo (Içá), stm., S.A. I7 58
Putuo, China F11 28
Puukohola Heiau National Historic Site, hist., Hi., U.S. D6 88
Puxico, Mo., U.S. E7 102
Puyallup, Wa., U.S. B3 124
Puyallup, stm., Wa., U.S. C3 124
Puy de Dôme, mtn., Fr. G9 10
Puy de Sancy, mtn., Fr. G9 10
Puylaurens, Fr. I9 10
Puyo, Ec. H4 58
Pweto, Zaire C5 44
Pwllheli, Wales, U.K. I8 7
Pyapon, Burma F3 34
Pyatigorsk see P'atigorsk, U.S.S.R. I6 18
Pyè (Prome), Burma E3 34
Pyhäjoki, Fin. D15 6
Pyhäselkä, Fin. E17 6
Pyinmana, Burma E4 34
Pyles Fork, stm., W.V., U.S. h10 125
Pymatuning Reservoir, res., U.S. C1 115
P'yŏngyang, N. Kor. D12 26
Pyramid Lake, l., Nv., U.S. C2 105
Pyramid Lake Indian Reservation, Nv., U.S. D2 105
Pyramid Mountains, mts., N.M., U.S. E1 108
Pyramid Peak, mtn., N.M., U.S. E1 108
Pyramid Peak, mtn., Wy., U.S. C2 127
Pyrenees, mts., Eur. C12 12
Pyskowice, Pol. E18 8
Pyu, Burma E4 34

Q

Qaidam Pendi, China B16 38
Qalāt, Afg. D2 38
Qal'at Bīshah, Sau. Ar. E3 46
Qal'eh-ye Kānsī, Afg. C2 36
Qal'eh-ye Sarkārī, Afg. C2 38
Qallābāt, Sudan F13 42
Qamar, Ghubbat al-, b., Yemen E5 46
Qamdo, China E6 26
Qandahār, Afg. E1 38
Qandala, Som. F4 46
Qarqan, stm., China B11 38
Qarqīn, Afg. B2 38
Qaṣr al-Burayqah, Libya B9 42
Qaṣr al-Farāfirah, Egypt C11 42
Qaṭanā, Syria C5 40
Qatar, ctry., Asia C5 46
Qazvīn, Iran J8 18
Qeshm, i., Iran C6 46
Qeyṣār, Afg. C1 38
Qeẕi'ot, Isr. D4 40
Qiemo, China A11 38
Qijiang, China F8 26
Qinā, Egypt C12 42
Qingdao (Tsingtao), China D11 26
Qinghai, prov., China D6 26
Qinghai Hu, l., China D7 26
Qingjiang, China G4 28
Qinglong, China B8 34
Qingyang, China D8 26
Qingyuan, China G8 26
Qingyuan, China L2 28
Qinhuangdao, China D10 26
Qin Ling, mts., China E8 26
Qinzhou, China D10 34
Qiongzhou Haixia, strt., China D11 34
Qiqihar, China B11 26
Qiryat Shemona, Isr. C4 40
Qitai, China C4 26
Qīzān, Sau. Ar. E3 46
Qom, Iran B5 46
Qomsheh, Iran B5 46
Qondūz, Afg. B3 38
Qondūz, stm., Afg. C3 38
Quabbin Reservoir, res., Ma., U.S. B3 98
Quaddick Reservoir, res., Ct., U.S. B8 84
Quail Oaks, Va., U.S. n18 123
Quaker Hill, Ct., U.S. D7 84
Quakertown, Pa., U.S. F11 115
Qualicum Beach, B.C., Can. E5 69
Quanah, Tx., U.S. B3 120
Quang Ngai, Viet. G10 34
Quannapowitt, Lake, l., Ma., U.S. f11 98
Quantico, Va., U.S. B5 123
Quantico Marine Corps Air Station, mil., Va., U.S. B5 123
Quanzhou, China K7 28
Quapaw, Ok., U.S. A7 113
Qu'Appelle, Sask., Can. G4 75
Qu'Appelle, stm., Can. G4 75
Quarryville, Pa., U.S. G9 115
Quartu Sant'Elena, Italy J4 14
Quartz Lake, l., N.W. Ter., Can. B16 66
Quartz Mountain, mtn., Or., U.S. D4 114
Quartzsite, Az., U.S. D1 80
Quassapaug, Lake, l., Ct., U.S. C3 84
Quatsino Sound, strt., B.C., Can. D3 69
Quay, co., N.M., U.S. C6 108
Qūchān, Iran J9 18
Québec, Que., Can. C6 74
Quebec, prov., Can. C5 74
Quechee, Vt., U.S. D4 122
Quedlinburg, Ger. D11 8
Queen, stm., R.I., U.S. E3 116
Queen Annes, co., Md., U.S. B5 97
Queen Bess, Mount, mtn., B.C., Can. D5 69
Queen Charlotte, B.C., Can. C1 69
Queen Charlotte Islands, is., B.C., Can. C1 69
Queen Charlotte Mountains, mts., B.C., Can. C1 69
Queen Charlotte Sound, strt., B.C., Can. n17 69
Queen Charlotte Strait, strt., B.C., Can. D4 69
Queen City, Mo., U.S. A5 102
Queen City, Tx., U.S. C5 120
Queen Creek, Az., U.S. m9 80
Queen Maud Gulf, b., N.W. Ter., Can. C12 66
Queen Maud Land, reg., Ant. B14 47
Queens, co., N.Y., U.S. E7 109
Queens Channel, strt., N.W. Ter., Can. A13 66
Queensland, state, Austl. D8 50
Queenstown, N.Z. F2 52
Queenstown, S. Afr. H5 44
Quelimane, Moz. E7 44
Quemoy see Chinmen Tao, i., Tai. K7 28
Querétaro, Mex. G9 62
Querobabi, Mex. B4 62
Quesnel, B.C., Can. C6 69
Quesnel, stm., B.C., Can. C6 69
Quesnel Lake, l., B.C., Can. C7 69
Questa, N.M., U.S. A4 108
Questembert, Fr. E4 10
Quetico Provincial Park, Ont., Can. o17 73
Quetta, Pak. E2 38
Quevedo, Ec. H3 58
Quevedo, stm., Ec. H3 58
Quezaltenango, Guat. G2 64
Quezon City, Phil. q19 32
Qufu, China D10 26
Quibdó, Col. E4 58
Quiberon, Fr. E3 10
Quicksand Pond, l., R.I., U.S. E6 116
Quidnessett, R.I., U.S. E4 116
Quidnick, R.I., U.S. D3 116
Quidnick Reservoir, res., R.I., U.S. D2 116
Quilá, Mex. E6 62
Quilcene, Wa., U.S. B3 124
Quileute Indian Reservation, Wa., U.S. B1 124
Quillan, Fr. J9 10
Quilon, India H4 37
Quilpie, Austl. E8 50
Quimilí, Arg. B4 56
Quimper, Fr. D2 10
Quimperlé, Fr. E3 10
Quinault, stm., Wa., U.S. B1 124
Quinault, Lake, l., Wa., U.S. B2 124
Quinault Indian Reservation, Wa., U.S. B1 124
Quincemil, Peru F4 54
Quincy, Ca., U.S. C3 82
Quincy, Fl., U.S. B2 86
Quincy, Il., U.S. D2 90
Quincy, Ma., U.S. B5 98
Quincy, Mi., U.S. G6 99
Quincy, Wa., U.S. B6 124
Quincy Bay, b., Ma., U.S. g12 98
Quinebaug, Ct., U.S. A8 84
Quinebaug, stm., Ct., U.S. C8 84
Quinhagak, Ak., U.S. D7 79
Qui Nhon, Viet. H10 34
Quinlan, Tx., U.S. C4 120
Quinn, stm., Nv., U.S. B3 105
Quinn Canyon Range, mts., Nv., U.S. F6 105
Quinnesec, Mi., U.S. C3 99
Quinnipiac, stm., Ct., U.S. D4 84
Quintanar de la Orden, Spain F8 12
Quinter, Ks., U.S. C3 93
Quinton, Ok., U.S. B6 113
Quiroga, Spain C4 12
Quitman, Ar., U.S. B3 81
Quitman, Ga., U.S. F3 87
Quitman, Ms., U.S. C5 101
Quitman, Tx., U.S. C5 120
Quitman, co., Ga., U.S. E1 87
Quitman, co., Ms., U.S. A3 101
Quito, Ec. H3 58
Quixadá, Braz. D11 54
Qujing, China B7 34
Qumalai (Sewugou), China C16 38
Quoich, stm., N.W. Ter., Can. D14 66
Quonnipaug Lake, l., Ct., U.S. D5 84
Quonochontaug, R.I., U.S. G2 116
Quonochontaug Pond, l., R.I., U.S. G2 116
Quonset Point, c., R.I., U.S. E4 116
Qutdligssat, Grnld. B22 66
Quthing, Leso. H5 44
Quxian, China G7 28

R

Raalte, Neth. C6 8
Rab, Yugo. E9 14
Raba, Indon. G6 32
Rába (Raab), stm., Eur. H17 8
Rábade, Spain B4 12
Rabat (Victoria), Malta M9 14
Rabat, Mor. B4 42
Rabaul, Pap. N. Gui. k17 50a
Rabbit Creek, stm., S.D., U.S. B3 118
Rabbit Ears Pass, Co., U.S. A4 83
Rābigh, Sau. Ar. D2 46
Rabun, co., Ga., U.S. B3 87
Rabun Bald, mtn., Ga., U.S. B3 87
Raccoon Creek, stm., Oh., U.S. D3 112
Raccourci Island, i., La., U.S. D4 95
Race, Cape, c., Newf., Can. E5 72
Raceland, Ky., U.S. B7 94
Raceland, La., U.S. E5 95
Race Point, c., Ma., U.S. B7 98
Rach Gia, Viet. I8 34
Racibórz (Ratibor), Pol. E18 8
Racine, W.V., U.S. C3 125
Racine, Wi., U.S. F6 126
Racine, co., Wi., U.S. F5 126
Racine Dam, U.S. C3 125
Radcliff, Ky., U.S. C4 94
Radeberg, Ger. D13 8
Radebeul, Ger. D13 8
Radeče, Yugo. C10 14
Radford, Va., U.S. C2 123
Radolfzell, Ger. H8 8
Radom, Pol. D21 8
Radomsko, Pol. D19 8
Rae, N.W. Ter., Can. D9 66
Rāe Bareli, India G9 38
Raeford, N.C., U.S. C3 110
Rae Isthmus, N.W. Ter., Can. C15 66
Rae Strait, strt., N.W. Ter., Can. C13 66
Raetihi, N.Z. C5 52
Rafaela, Arg. C4 56
Rafah, Isr. Occ. D4 40
Rafhā', Sau. Ar. C3 46
Rafsanjān, Iran K9 18
Rafsanjān, Iran B6 46
Raft, stm., Id., U.S. G5 89

Name	Map Ref	Page
Raft River Mountains, mts., Ut., U.S.	B2	121
Raga, Sudan	G11	42
Ragged Island, i., Me., U.S.	E4	96
Ragged Lake, l., Me., U.S.	C3	96
Ragged Top Mountain, mtn., Wy., U.S.	E7	127
Ragland, Al., U.S.	B3	78
Ragusa, Italy	M9	14
Ragusa see Dubrovnik, Yugo.	G13	14
Rahīmyār Khān, Pak.	F4	38
Rahway, N.J., U.S.	B4	107
Rahway, stm., N.J., U.S.	k7	107
Rāichūr, India	D4	37
Raigarh, India	B7	37
Railroad Valley, val., Nv., U.S.	E6	105
Rainbow Bridge National Monument, Ut., U.S.	F5	121
Rainbow Falls, wtfl, Tn., U.S.	D10	119
Rainbow Flowage, res., Wi., U.S.	C4	126
Rainbow Lake, l., Me., U.S.	C3	96
Rainelle, W.V., U.S.	D4	125
Rainier, Or., U.S.	A4	114
Rainier, Wa., U.S.	C3	124
Rainier, Mount, mtn., Wa., U.S.	C4	124
Rains, co., Tx., U.S.	C5	120
Rainsville, Al., U.S.	A4	78
Rainy Lake, l., N.A.	G14	66
Rainy Lake, l., Mn., U.S.	B5	100
Rainy River, Ont., Can.	o16	73
Raipur, India	B6	37
Rājahmundry, India	D6	37
Raja-Jooseppi, Fin.	B17	6
Rājapālaiyam, India	H4	37
Rājasthān, prov., India	G5	38
Rājasthān Canal, India	F5	38
Rajčichinsk, U.S.S.R.	H19	20
Rājkot, India	I4	38
Rāj-Nāndgaon, India	B6	37
Rājpīpla, India	J5	38
Rājshāhi, Bngl.	H13	38
Rakaposhi, mtn., Pak.	B6	38
Rakata, Pulau, i., Indon.	m12	33a
Råkvåg, Nor.	E8	6
Raleigh, Ms., U.S.	C4	101
Raleigh, N.C., U.S.	B4	110
Raleigh, W.V., U.S.	n13	125
Raleigh, co., W.V., U.S.	D3	125
Raleigh Bay, b., N.C., U.S.	C6	110
Ralls, Tx., U.S.	C2	120
Ralls, co., Mo., U.S.	B6	102
Ralston, Ne., U.S.	g12	104
Ralston Valley, val., Nv., U.S.	E4	105
Rama, Nic.	H5	64
Ramah, N.M., U.S.	B1	108
Ramah Indian Reservation, N.M., U.S.	C1	108
Rām Allāh, Jord.	D4	40
Ramapo, stm., N.J., U.S.	A4	107
Ramblewood, N.J., U.S.	D3	107
Rambouillet, Fr.	D8	10
Ramea, Newf., Can.	E3	72
Ramenskoje, U.S.S.R.	F21	22
Rāmeswaram, India	H5	37
Rāmgarh, Bngl.	I14	38
Ramla, Isr.	D4	40
Ramlo, mtn., Eth.	F3	46
Ramona, Ca., U.S.	F5	82
Rampart Range, mts., Co., U.S.	B5	83
Rāmpur, India	F8	38
Ramree Island, i., Burma	E2	34
Ramsay, Mi., U.S.	n12	99
Ramseur, N.C., U.S.	B3	110
Ramsey, I. of Man	G8	7
Ramsey, Il., U.S.	D4	90
Ramsey, Mn., U.S.	E5	100
Ramsey, N.J., U.S.	A4	107
Ramsey, co., Mn., U.S.	E5	100
Ramsey, co., N.D., U.S.	A7	111
Ramsgate, Eng., U.K.	J14	7
Ramshorn Peak, mtn., Mt., U.S.	E5	103
Ramshorn Peak, mtn., Wy., U.S.	C3	127
Rāmu, Bngl.	J15	38
Ramu, stm., Pap. N. Gui.	m16	50a
Rancagua, Chile	C2	56
Rancharia, Braz.	G3	57
Rancheria Rock, mtn., Or., U.S.	C6	114
Ranchester, Wy., U.S.	B5	127
Rānchī, India	I11	38
Rancho Palos Verdes, Ca., U.S.	n12	82
Ranchos de Taos, N.M., U.S.	A4	108
Rancocas Creek, stm., N.J., U.S.	C3	107
Rand, W.V., U.S.	C3	125
Randall, co., Tx., U.S.	B2	120
Randallstown, Md., U.S.	B4	97
Randazzo, Italy	L9	14
Randers, Den.	H8	6
Randle, Wa., U.S.	C4	124
Randleman, N.C., U.S.	B3	110
Randolph, Me., U.S.	D3	96
Randolph, Ma., U.S.	B5	98
Randolph, Ne., U.S.	B8	104
Randolph, Vt., U.S.	D3	122
Randolph, Wi., U.S.	E4	126
Randolph, co., Al., U.S.	B4	78
Randolph, co., Ar., U.S.	A4	81
Randolph, co., Ga., U.S.	E2	87
Randolph, co., Il., U.S.	E4	90
Randolph, co., In., U.S.	D7	91
Randolph, co., Mo., U.S.	B5	102
Randolph, co., N.C., U.S.	B3	110
Randolph, co., W.V., U.S.	C5	125
Randolph Air Force Base, mil., Tx., U.S.	h7	120
Randolph Hills, Md., U.S.	B3	97
Random Island, i., Newf., Can.	D5	72
Random Lake, Wi., U.S.	E6	126
Rangeley, Me., U.S.	D2	96
Rangeley Lake, l., Me., U.S.	D2	96
Rangely, Co., U.S.	A2	83
Ranger, Tx., U.S.	C3	120
Ranger Lake, l., N.M., U.S.	D6	108
Rangoon see Yangon, Burma	B2	32
Rangpur, Bngl.	H13	38
Rankin, Pa., U.S.	k14	115
Rankin, co., Ms., U.S.	C4	101
Rankin Inlet, N.W. Ter., Can.	D14	66
Rann of Kutch, pl., Asia	H3	38
Ransom, co., N.D., U.S.	C8	111
Ranson, W.V., U.S.	B7	125
Rantauprapat, Indon.	E2	32
Rantekombola, Bulu, mtn., Indon.	F7	32
Rantoul, Il., U.S.	C5	90
Raoping, China	L6	28
Raoul, Ga., U.S.	B3	87
Rapallo, Italy	E4	14
Rapid, stm., Mn., U.S.	B4	100
Rapid City, S.D., U.S.	C2	118
Rapides, co., La., U.S.	C3	95
Rapid River, Mi., U.S.	C4	99
Rapids City, Il., U.S.	B3	90
Rappahannock, co., Va., U.S.	B4	123
Rappahannock, stm., Va., U.S.	B5	123
Raquette, stm., N.Y., U.S.	f10	109
Raquette Lake, l., N.Y., U.S.	B6	109
Raritan, N.J., U.S.	B3	107
Raritan, stm., N.J., U.S.	C4	107
Raritan Bay, b., N.J., U.S.	C4	107
Ra's al-'Ayn, Syria	A7	40
Ra's an-Naqb, Jord.	D4	40
Ras Dashen, mtn., Eth.	F2	46
Ras Djebel, Tun.	L5	14
Rasht, Iran	J7	18
Rāsipuram, India	G5	37
Rasskazovo, U.S.S.R.	I24	22
Rastatt, Ger.	G8	8
Ratangarh, India	F6	38
Rätansbyn, Swe.	E10	6
Rathbun Lake, res., Ia., U.S.	D5	92
Rathdrum, Id., U.S.	B2	89
Rathenow, Ger.	C12	8
Rathkeale, Ire.	I4	7
Rathlin Island, i., N. Ire., U.K.	F6	7
Rat Islands, is., Ak., U.S.	E3	79
Ratlām, India	I6	38
Ratnāgiri, India	D2	37
Ratnapura, Sri L.	I6	37
Raton, N.M., U.S.	A5	108
Raton Pass, N.M., U.S.	A5	108
Rattlesnake Creek, stm., Oh., U.S.	C2	112
Rattlesnake Creek, stm., Wa., U.S.	C6	124
Rättvik, Swe.	F10	6
Ratz, Mount, mtn., B.C., Can.	E6	66
Ratzeburg, Ger.	B10	8
Raub, Malay.	M6	34
Rauch, Arg.	D5	56
Rauma, Fin.	F13	6
Raurkela, India	I11	38
Ravalli, co., Mt., U.S.	D2	103
Raven, Va., U.S.	e10	123
Ravena, N.Y., U.S.	C7	109
Ravenel, S.C., U.S.	k11	117
Ravenna, Italy	E7	14
Ravenna, Ky., U.S.	C6	94
Ravenna, Mi., U.S.	E5	99
Ravenna, Ne., U.S.	C7	104
Ravenna, Oh., U.S.	A4	112
Raven Park, reg., Co., U.S.	A2	83
Ravensburg, Ger.	H9	8
Ravenshoe, Austl.	C9	50
Ravensthorpe, Austl.	F3	50
Ravenswood, W.V., U.S.	C3	125
Rāwalpindi, Pak.	D5	38
Rawdon, Que., Can.	C4	74
Rawhide Creek, stm., Wy., U.S.	D8	127
Rawlings, Md., U.S.	k13	97
Rawlinna, Austl.	F5	50
Rawlins, Wy., U.S.	E5	127
Rawlins, co., Ks., U.S.	C2	93
Rawson, Arg.	E3	56
Ray, N.D., U.S.	A2	111
Ray, co., Mo., U.S.	B3	102
Ray, Cape, c., Newf., Can.	E2	72
Raya, Bukit, mtn., Indon.	F5	32
Rāyadrug, India	E4	37
Ray City, Ga., U.S.	E3	87
Raymond, Alta., Can.	E4	68
Raymond, Il., U.S.	D4	90
Raymond, Mn., U.S.	E3	100
Raymond, Ms., U.S.	C3	101
Raymond, N.H., U.S.	D4	106
Raymond, Wa., U.S.	C2	124
Raymondville, Tx., U.S.	F4	120
Raymore, Sask., Can.	F3	75
Raymore, Mo., U.S.	C3	102
Rayne, La., U.S.	D3	95
Raynham, Ma., U.S.	C5	98
Raynham Center, Ma., U.S.	C5	98
Raytown, Mo., U.S.	h11	102
Rayville, La., U.S.	B4	95
R'azan', U.S.S.R.	G22	22
Razgrad, Bul.	F10	16
R'ažsk, U.S.S.R.	H23	22
Reader, W.V., U.S.	B4	125
Reading, Eng., U.K.	J12	7
Reading, Ma., U.S.	A5	98
Reading, Mi., U.S.	G6	99
Reading, Oh., U.S.	C1	112
Reading, Pa., U.S.	F10	115
Readlyn, Ia., U.S.	B5	92
Reagan, co., Tx., U.S.	D2	120
Real, co., Tx., U.S.	E3	120
Realicó, Arg.	D4	56
Réalmont, Fr.	I9	10
Reamstown, Pa., U.S.	F9	115
Recanati, Italy	F8	14
Recherche, Archipelago of the, is., Austl.	F4	50
Rečica, U.S.S.R.	I13	22
Recife, Braz.	E12	54
Recklinghausen, Ger.	D7	8
Recreo, Arg.	B3	56
Rector, Ar., U.S.	A5	81
Red (Hong) (Yuan), stm., Asia	C8	34
Red, stm., N.A.	B7	76
Red, stm., U.S.	E8	76
Red, stm., Ky., U.S.	C6	94
Red, stm., Tn., U.S.	A4	119
Red Bank, N.J., U.S.	C4	107
Red Bank, Tn., U.S.	D8	119
Red Bay, Al., U.S.	A1	78
Redberry Lake, l., Sask., Can.	E2	75
Redbird, Oh., U.S.	A4	112
Red Bird, stm., Ky., U.S.	C6	94
Red Bluff, Ca., U.S.	B2	82
Red Bluff Lake, res., U.S.	o12	120
Red Boiling Springs, Tn., U.S.	C8	119
Red Bud, Il., U.S.	E4	90
Red Butte, mtn., Ut., U.S.	B2	121
Red Cedar, stm., Wi., U.S.	C2	126
Red Cedar Lake, l., Wi., U.S.	C2	126
Redcliff, Alta., Can.	D5	68
Redcliffe, Mount, mtn., Austl.	E4	50
Red Cliff Indian Reservation, Wi., U.S.	B2	126
Red Cloud, Ne., U.S.	D7	104
Redcloud Peak, mtn., Co., U.S.	D3	83
Red Deer, Alta., Can.	C4	68
Red Deer, stm., Can.	D4	68
Red Deer, stm., Can.	E4	75
Redding, Ca., U.S.	B2	82
Redding, Ct., U.S.	D2	84
Redeye, stm., Mn., U.S.	D3	100
Redfield, Ar., U.S.	C3	81
Redfield, Ia., U.S.	C3	92
Redfield, S.D., U.S.	C7	118
Redford, Mi., U.S.	F7	99
Redgranite, Wi., U.S.	D4	126
Red Hook, N.Y., U.S.	C7	109
Red Indian Lake, l., Newf., Can.	D3	72
Red Jacket, W.V., U.S.	D2	125
Redkey, In., U.S.	D7	91
Redlake, Mn., U.S.	C3	100
Red Lake, co., Mn., U.S.	C2	100
Red Lake, l., Az., U.S.	B1	80
Red Lake, stm., Mn., U.S.	C2	100
Red Lake Falls, Mn., U.S.	C2	100
Red Lake Indian Reservation, Mn., U.S.	B3	100
Redlands, Ca., U.S.	E5	82
Red Lion, Pa., U.S.	G8	115
Red Lodge, Mt., U.S.	E7	103
Red Mill Pond, l., De., U.S.	E5	85
Redmond, Or., U.S.	C5	114
Redmond, Ut., U.S.	E4	121
Redmond, Wa., U.S.	e11	124
Red Mountain, mtn., Ca., U.S.	B2	82
Red Mountain, mtn., Mt., U.S.	C4	103
Red Mountain Pass, Co., U.S.	D3	83
Red Oak, Ga., U.S.	h7	87
Red Oak, Ia., U.S.	D2	92
Red Oak, Ok., U.S.	C6	113
Red Oak, Tx., U.S.	n10	120
Red Oaks, La., U.S.	h9	95
Redon, Fr.	E4	10
Redondela, Spain	C3	12
Redondo, Port.	G4	12
Redondo, Wa., U.S.	f11	124
Redondo Beach, Ca., U.S.	n12	82
Redoubt Volcano, vol., Ak., U.S.	g15	79
Red Peak, mtn., Co., U.S.	B4	83
Red River, co., La., U.S.	B2	95
Red River, co., Tx., U.S.	C5	120
Red Rock, stm., Mt., U.S.	F4	103
Red Rock, Lake, res., Ia., U.S.	C4	92
Red Sea	D2	46
Red Springs, N.C., U.S.	C3	110
Red Table Mountain, mts., Co., U.S.	B4	83
Redwater, Alta., Can.	C4	68
Redwater, stm., Mt., U.S.	C11	103
Red Willow, co., Ne., U.S.	D5	104
Redwillow, stm., Can.	B7	69
Red Wing, Mn., U.S.	F6	100
Redwood, co., Mn., U.S.	F3	100
Redwood, stm., Mn., U.S.	F3	100
Redwood City, Ca., U.S.	D2	82
Redwood Falls, Mn., U.S.	F3	100
Redwood National Park, Ca., U.S.	B2	82
Redwood Valley, Ca., U.S.	C2	82
Ree, Lough, l., Ire.	H4	7
Reed City, Mi., U.S.	E5	99
Reedley, Ca., U.S.	D4	82
Reedsburg, Wi., U.S.	E3	126
Reeds Peak, mtn., N.M., U.S.	D2	108
Reedsport, Or., U.S.	D2	114
Reedsville, Pa., U.S.	E6	115
Reedsville, Wi., U.S.	D6	126
Reedy, stm., S.C., U.S.	C3	117
Reedy Lake, l., Fl., U.S.	E5	86
Reelfoot Lake, l., Tn., U.S.	A2	119
Reese, Mi., U.S.	E7	99
Reese, stm., Nv., U.S.	C4	105
Reese Air Force Base, mil., Tx., U.S.	C1	120
Reeves, co., Tx., U.S.	o13	120
Reform, Al., U.S.	B1	78
Refugio, Tx., U.S.	E4	120
Refugio, co., Tx., U.S.	E4	120
Regen, Ger.	G13	8
Regencia, Braz.	E9	57
Regensburg, Ger.	F12	8
Reggane, Alg.	C6	42
Reggio di Calabria, Italy	K10	14
Reggio nell'Emilia, Italy	E5	14
Regina, Sask., Can.	G3	75
Regina Beach, Sask., Can.	G3	75
Rehoboth, Nmb.	F3	44
Rehoboth, Nmb.	E3	44
Rehoboth Bay, b., De., U.S.	F5	85
Rehoboth Beach, De., U.S.	F5	85
Rehovot, Isr.	D4	40
Reichenbach, Ger.	E12	8
Reid, Mount, mtn., Ak., U.S.	n24	79
Reidland, Ky., U.S.	e9	94
Reidsville, Ga., U.S.	D4	87
Reidsville, N.C., U.S.	A3	110
Reims, Fr.	C11	10
Reina Adelaida, Archipiélago, is., Chile	G2	56
Reinbeck, Ia., U.S.	B5	92
Reindeer Island, i., Man., Can.	C3	70
Reindeer Lake, l., Can.	m8	75
Reinosa, Spain	B7	12
Reisterstown, Md., U.S.	B4	97
Reliance, Wy., U.S.	E3	127
Remada, Tun.	B8	42
Remanso, Braz.	E10	54
Rembang, Indon.	m15	33a
Remington, In., U.S.	C3	91
Remiremont, Fr.	D13	10
Remmel Dam, Ar., U.S.	g8	81
Remscheid, Ger.	D7	8
Remsen, Ia., U.S.	B2	92
Rend Lake, res., Il., U.S.	E5	90
Rendova, i., Sol.Is.	A11	50
Rendsburg, Ger.	A9	8
Renforth, N.B., Can.	D4	71
Renfrew, Ont., Can.	B8	73
Rengat, Indon.	O7	34
Rennell Island, i., Sol.Is.	B12	50
Rennes, Fr.	D5	10
Reno, Nv., U.S.	D2	105
Reno, co., Ks., U.S.	E5	93
Reno, Lake, l., Mn., U.S.	E3	100
Reno Hill, mtn., Wy., U.S.	D6	127
Renovo, Pa., U.S.	D6	115
Rensselaer, In., U.S.	C3	91
Rensselaer, N.Y., U.S.	C7	109
Rensselaer, co., N.Y., U.S.	C7	109
Renton, Wa., U.S.	B3	124
Renville, Mn., U.S.	F3	100
Renville, co., Mn., U.S.	F4	100
Renville, co., N.D., U.S.	A4	111
Reo, Indon.	G7	32
Repentigny, Que., Can.	D4	74
Republic, Mi., U.S.	B3	99
Republic, Mo., U.S.	D4	102
Republic, Pa., U.S.	G2	115
Republic, Wa., U.S.	A7	124
Republic, co., Ks., U.S.	C6	93
Republican, stm., U.S.	C6	93
Repulse Bay, N.W. Ter., Can.	C15	66
Repvåg, Nor.	A15	6
Réquista, Fr.	H9	10
Reschenpass, Eur.	C5	14
Reserve, La., U.S.	h10	95
Resistencia, Arg.	B5	56
Reșița, Rom.	D5	16
Resolute, N.W. Ter., Can.	B14	66
Resolution Island, i., N.W. Ter., Can.	D20	66
Reston, Man., Can.	E1	70
Reston, Va., U.S.	B5	123
Resülhınzır, c., Tur.	A4	40
Retalhuleu, Guat.	G2	64
Rethel, Fr.	C11	10
Réthimnon, Grc.	N8	16
Reunion (Réunion), dep., Afr.	F11	44
Reus, Spain	D13	12
Reutlingen, Ger.	G9	8
Revelo, Ky., U.S.	D5	94
Revelstoke, B.C., Can.	D8	69
Revelstoke, Lake, res., B.C., Can.	D8	69
Revere, Ma., U.S.	g11	98
Revillagigedo, Islas de, is., Mex.	H4	62
Revillagigedo Island, i., Ak., U.S.	n24	79
Revin, Fr.	C11	10
Rewa, India	H9	38
Rewāri, India	F7	38
Rex, Ga., U.S.	h8	87
Rexburg, Id., U.S.	F7	89
Rexton, N.B., Can.	C5	71
Rey, Iran	J8	18
Rey, Isla del, i., Pan.	J8	64
Reyes, Bol.	F5	54
Reyes, Point, c., Ca., U.S.	C2	82
Reyhanlı, Tur.	A5	40
Reykjavík, Ice.	C3	4
Reynolds, Ga., U.S.	D2	87
Reynolds, co., Mo., U.S.	D6	102
Reynoldsburg, Oh., U.S.	C3	112
Reynoldsville, Pa., U.S.	D4	115
Reynosa, Mex.	D10	62
Rēzekne, U.S.S.R.	E10	22
Rhaetian Alps, mts., Eur.	F16	10
Rhea, co., Tn., U.S.	D9	119
Rheine, Ger.	C7	8
Rheydt, Ger.	D6	8
Rhine (Rhein) (Rhin), stm., Eur.	D6	8
Rhinebeck, N.Y., U.S.	D7	109
Rhinelander, Wi., U.S.	C4	126
Rho, Italy	D4	14
Rhode Island, state, U.S.	D3	116
Rhode Island, i., R.I., U.S.	E5	116
Rhode Island Sound, strt., U.S.	F5	116
Rhodesia see Zimbabwe, ctry., Afr.	E5	44
Rhodes Peak, mtn., Id., U.S.	C4	89
Rhodes see Ródhos, Grc.	M12	16
Rhodope Mountains, mts., Eur.	H8	16
Rhondda, Wales, U.K.	J9	7
Rhône, stm., Eur.	H11	10
Rialto, Ca., U.S.	m14	82
Riau, Kepulauan, is., Indon.	N8	34
Riaza, Spain	D8	12
Ribadeo, Spain	B4	12
Ribadesella, Spain	B6	12
Ribeirão Prêto, Braz.	F5	57
Ribera, Italy	L8	14
Riberalta, Bol.	F5	54
Rib Lake, Wi., U.S.	C3	126
Ribnitz-Damgarten, Ger.	A12	8
Riccione, Italy	F7	14
Rice, Mn., U.S.	E4	100
Rice, co., Ks., U.S.	D5	93
Rice, co., Mn., U.S.	F5	100
Riceboro, Ga., U.S.	E5	87
Rice Lake, Wi., U.S.	C2	126
Rice Lake, l., Ont., Can.	C6	73
Rice Lake, l., Mn., U.S.	D5	100
Riceville, Ia., U.S.	A5	92
Rich, co., Ut., U.S.	B4	121
Rich, Cape, c., Ont., Can.	C4	73
Richards-Gebaur Air Force Base, mil., Mo., U.S.	C3	102
Richards Island, i., N.W. Ter., Can.	C6	66
Richardson, Tx., U.S.	n10	120
Richardson, co., Ne., U.S.	D10	104
Richardson Lakes, l., Me., U.S.	D2	96
Richardson Mountains, mts., Can.	C5	66
Richardton, N.D., U.S.	C3	111
Rich Creek, Va., U.S.	C2	123
Riche, Pointe, c., Newf., Can.	C3	72
Richfield, Mn., U.S.	F5	100
Richfield, Ut., U.S.	E3	121
Richford, Vt., U.S.	B3	122
Rich Hill, Mo., U.S.	C3	102
Richibucto, N.B., Can.	C5	71
Richland, Ga., U.S.	D2	87
Richland, Mo., U.S.	D5	102
Richland, Wa., U.S.	C6	124
Richland, co., Il., U.S.	E5	90
Richland, co., La., U.S.	B4	95
Richland, co., Mt., U.S.	C12	103
Richland, co., N.D., U.S.	C8	111
Richland, co., Oh., U.S.	B3	112
Richland, co., S.C., U.S.	D6	117
Richland, co., Wi., U.S.	E3	126
Richland Balsam, mtn., N.C., U.S.	f10	110
Richland Center, Wi., U.S.	E3	126
Richland Creek, stm., Tn., U.S.	B5	119
Richlands, N.C., U.S.	C5	110
Richlands, Va., U.S.	e10	123
Richlandtown, Pa., U.S.	F11	115
Richmond, Austl.	D8	50
Richmond, B.C., Can.	E6	69
Richmond, Que., Can.	D5	74
Richmond, Ca., U.S.	D2	82
Richmond, Il., U.S.	A5	90
Richmond, In., U.S.	E8	91
Richmond, Ky., U.S.	C5	94
Richmond, Me., U.S.	D3	96
Richmond, Mi., U.S.	F8	99
Richmond, Mn., U.S.	E4	100
Richmond, Mo., U.S.	B4	102
Richmond, Tx., U.S.	E5	120
Richmond, Ut., U.S.	B4	121
Richmond, Vt., U.S.	C3	122
Richmond, Va., U.S.	C5	123
Richmond, co., Ga., U.S.	C4	87
Richmond, co., N.Y., U.S.	E6	109
Richmond, co., N.C., U.S.	B3	110
Richmond, co., Va., U.S.	C6	123
Richmond Beach, Wa., U.S.	B3	124
Richmond Heights, Fl., U.S.	s13	86
Richmond Heights, Mo., U.S.	f13	102
Richmond Highlands, Wa., U.S.	B3	124
Richmond Hill, Ont., Can.	D5	73
Richmond Hill, Ga., U.S.	E5	87
Richmond National Battlefield Park, Va., U.S.	n18	123
Rich Square, N.C., U.S.	A5	110
Richthofen, Mount, mtn., Co., U.S.	A5	83
Richton, Ms., U.S.	D5	101
Richwood, Oh., U.S.	B2	112
Richwood, W.V., U.S.	C4	125
Rickenbacker Air Force Base, mil., Oh., U.S.	m11	112
Rickman, Tn., U.S.	C8	119
Riddle, Or., U.S.	E3	114
Riddle Mountain, mtn., Or., U.S.	D8	114
Rideau, stm., Ont., Can.	B9	73
Ridgecrest, Ca., U.S.	E5	82
Ridge Farm, Il., U.S.	D6	90
Ridgefield, Ct., U.S.	D2	84
Ridgefield, N.J., U.S.	h8	107
Ridgefield, Wa., U.S.	D3	124
Ridgefield Park, N.J., U.S.	B4	107
Ridgeland, Ms., U.S.	C3	101
Ridgeland, S.C., U.S.	G6	117
Ridgeley, W.V., U.S.	B6	125
Ridgely, Md., U.S.	C6	97
Ridgely, Tn., U.S.	A2	119
Ridge Spring, S.C., U.S.	D4	117
Ridgetop, Tn., U.S.	A5	119
Ridgetown, Ont., Can.	E3	73
Ridgeview, W.V., U.S.	C3	125
Ridgeville, In., U.S.	D7	91
Ridgeville, S.C., U.S.	E7	117
Ridgeway, Va., U.S.	D3	123
Ridgewood, N.J., U.S.	B4	107
Ridgway, Il., U.S.	F5	90
Ridgway, Pa., U.S.	D4	115
Riding Mountain National Park, Man., Can.	D1	70
Ridley Park, Pa., U.S.	p20	115
Ried im Innkreis, Aus.	G13	8
Riesa, Ger.	D13	8
Riesi, Italy	L9	14
Rieti, Italy	G7	14
Rif, mts., Mor.	A5	42
Riffe Lake, res., Wa., U.S.	C3	124
Rifle, Co., U.S.	B3	83
Rifle, stm., Mi., U.S.	D6	99
Rift Valley, val., Afr.	B5	44
Rīga, U.S.S.R.	E7	22
Rigaud, Que., Can.	D3	74
Rigby, Id., U.S.	F7	89
Rīgestān, reg., Afg.	C1	36
Riihimäki, Fin.	F15	6
Rijeka, Yugo.	D9	14
Riley, Ks., U.S.	C7	93
Riley, co., Ks., U.S.	C7	93
Riley, Mount, mtn., N.M., U.S.	F2	108
Rimbey, Alta., Can.	C3	68
Rimersburg, Pa., U.S.	D3	115
Rimini, Italy	E7	14
Rimouski, Que., Can.	A9	74
Rimouski, stm., Que., Can.	A9	74
Rimouski-Est, Que., Can.	A9	74
Rimrock Lake, res., Wa., U.S.	C4	124
Rincon, Ga., U.S.	D5	87
Rincon Mountains, mts., Az., U.S.	E5	80
Rindal, Nor.	E7	6
Ringebu, Nor.	F8	6
Ringgold, Ga., U.S.	B1	87
Ringgold, La., U.S.	B2	95
Ringgold, co., Ia., U.S.	D3	92
Ringling, Ok., U.S.	C4	113
Ringwood, N.J., U.S.	A4	107
Rio, Fl., U.S.	E6	86
Rio, Wi., U.S.	E4	126
Rio Arriba, co., N.M., U.S.	A2	108
Riobamba, Ec.	H3	58
Río Benito, Eq. Gui.	H7	42

Name | Map Ref | Page

Rio Blanco, co., Co., U.S. B2 83
Rio Branco, Braz. E5 54
Rio Claro, Braz. G5 57
Río Colorado, Arg. D4 56
Río Cuarto, Arg. C4 56
Rio de Janeiro, Braz. G7 57
Rio Dell, Ca., U.S. B1 82
Rio do Sul, Braz. B7 56
Río Gallegos, Arg. G3 56
Río Grande, Arg. G3 56
Rio Grande, Braz. C6 56
Río Grande, Mex. F8 62
Río Grande, Nic. H6 64
Rio Grande, Oh., U.S. D3 112
Rio Grande, co., Co., U.S. D4 83
Rio Grande City, Tx., U.S. F3 120
Rio Grande Reservoir, res., Co., U.S. D3 83
Ríohacha, Col. B6 58
Rio Hondo, Tx., U.S. F4 120
Rioja, Peru E3 54
Riom, Fr. G10 10
Río Mayo, Arg. F2 56
Río Negro, Embalse del, res., Ur. C5 56
Rio Negro, Pantanal do, sw., Braz. G7 54
Rionero in Vulture, Italy I10 14
Rio Pardo, Braz. B6 56
Rio Pardo de Minas, Braz. G10 54
Rio Rancho, N.M., U.S. B3 108
Río Sucio, Col. E5 58
Rio Verde, Braz. D3 57
Ríoverde, Mex. G10 62
Rio Vista, Ca., U.S. C3 82
Rioz, Fr. E13 10
Ripley, Ms., U.S. A5 101
Ripley, Oh., U.S. D2 112
Ripley, Tn., U.S. B2 119
Ripley, W.V., U.S. C3 125
Ripley, co., In., U.S. F7 91
Ripley, co., Mo., U.S. E7 102
Ripoll, Spain C14 12
Ripon, Eng., U.K. G11 7
Ripon, Wi., U.S. E5 126
Rippowam, stm., Ct., U.S. E1 84
Ririe Lake, res., Id., U.S. F7 89
Rishon leẔiyyon, Isr. D4 40
Rising Sun, De., U.S. D3 85
Rising Sun, In., U.S. G8 91
Rising Sun, Md., U.S. A5 97
Rison, Ar., U.S. D3 81
Ritchie, co., W.V., U.S. B3 125
Ritter, Mount, mtn., Ca., U.S. D4 82
Rittman, Oh., U.S. B4 112
Ritzville, Wa., U.S. B7 124
Riva, Italy D5 14
Rivanna, stm., Va., U.S. C4 123
Rivas, Nic. I5 64
Rivera, Ur. C5 56
Riverbank, Ca., U.S. D3 82
River Bourgeois, N.S., Can. D9 71
Riverdale, Ca., U.S. D4 82
Riverdale, Il., U.S. k9 90
Riverdale, Md., U.S. C4 97
River Edge, N.J., U.S. h8 107
River Falls, Al., U.S. D3 78
River Falls, Wi., U.S. D1 126
River Forest, Il., U.S. k9 90
River Grove, Il., U.S. k9 90
Riverhead, N.Y., U.S. n16 109
River Hebert, N.S., Can. D5 71
River Heights, Ut., U.S. B4 121
River Hills, Wi., U.S. m12 126
River Pines, Ma., U.S. f10 98
River Ridge, La., U.S. k11 95
River Road, Or., U.S. C3 114
River Rouge, Mi., U.S. p15 99
Rivers, Man., Can. D1 70
Riverside, Al., U.S. B3 78
Riverside, Ca., U.S. F5 82
Riverside, Il., U.S. k9 90
Riverside, Ia., U.S. C6 92
Riverside, N.J., U.S. C3 107
Riverside, Pa., U.S. E8 115
Riverside, co., Ca., U.S. F5 82
Riverside Reservoir, res., Co., U.S. A6 83
Riverton, Man., Can. D3 70
Riverton, Il., U.S. D4 90
Riverton, Ks., U.S. E9 93
Riverton, N.J., U.S. C3 107
Riverton, Ut., U.S. C4 121
Riverton, Vt., U.S. C3 122
Riverton, Wy., U.S. C4 127
Riverton Heights, Wa., U.S. f11 124
River Vale, N.J., U.S. h8 107
Riverview, Fl., U.S. p11 86
Riverview, Mi., U.S. p15 99
Rivesaltes, Fr. J9 10
Rivesville, W.V., U.S. B4 125
Riviera Beach, Fl., U.S. F6 86
Riviera Beach, Md., U.S. B4 97
Rivière-du-Loup, Que., Can. B8 74
Rivière-Verte, N.B., Can. B1 71
Rivoli, Italy D2 14
Riyadh see Ar-Riyāḍ, Sau. Ar. D4 46
Rize, Tur. G16 4
Rižskij Zaliv, b., U.S.S.R. D6 22
Roa, Spain D8 12
Roachdale, In., U.S. E4 91
Roane, co., Tn., U.S. D9 119
Roane, co., W.V., U.S. C3 125
Roan Mountain, Tn., U.S. C11 119
Roanne, Fr. F11 10
Roanoke, Al., U.S. B4 78
Roanoke, Il., U.S. C4 90
Roanoke, In., U.S. C7 91
Roanoke, La., U.S. D3 95
Roanoke, Tx., U.S. m9 120
Roanoke, Va., U.S. C3 123
Roanoke, co., Va., U.S. C2 123
Roanoke, stm., U.S. A5 110
Roanoke Island, i., N.C., U.S. B7 110
Roanoke Rapids, N.C., U.S. A5 110
Roanoke Rapids Lake, res., U.S. A5 110
Roaring Fork, stm., Co., U.S. C4 83
Roaring Spring, Pa., U.S. F5 115
Roatán, Isla de, i., Hond. F4 64
Robbins, Il., U.S. k9 90
Robbins, N.C., U.S. B3 110
Robbinsdale, Mn., U.S. m12 100
Robbinsville, N.C., U.S. f9 110
Röbel, Ger. B12 8
Robersonville, N.C., U.S. B5 110
Roberta, Ga., U.S. D2 87
Robert Lee, Tx., U.S. D2 120
Roberts, Wi., U.S. C1 126
Roberts, co., S.D., U.S. B8 118
Roberts, co., Tx., U.S. B2 120
Roberts, Point, c., Wa., U.S. A2 124
Robert's Arm, Newf., Can. D4 72
Roberts Creek Mountain, mtn., Nv., U.S. D5 105
Robertsdale, Al., U.S. E2 78
Robertsfors, Swe. D13 6
Robert S. Kerr Reservoir, res., Ok., U.S. B6 113
Roberts Mountain, mtn., Ak., U.S. C6 79
Roberts Mountain, mtn., Wy., U.S. D3 127
Robertson, co., Ky., U.S. B5 94
Robertson, co., Tn., U.S. A5 119
Robertson, co., Tx., U.S. D4 120
Robertsonville, Que., Can. C6 74
Roberts Peak, mtn., B.C., Can. F8 66
Robertsport, Lib. G3 42
Robertville, N.B., Can. B4 71
Roberval, Que., Can. A5 74
Robeson, co., N.C., U.S. C3 110
Robins, Ia., U.S. B6 92
Robinson, Il., U.S. D6 90
Robinson Fork, stm., W.V., U.S. k9 125
Robinson Fork, stm., W.V., U.S. m14 125
Roblin, Man., Can. D1 70
Roboré, Bol. G7 54
Robson, Mount, mtn., B.C., Can. C8 69
Robstown, Tx., U.S. F4 120
Roca Partida, Isla, i., Mex. H3 62
Roca Partida, Punta, c., Mex. H12 62
Rocas, Atol das, atoll, Braz. D12 54
Roccastrada, Italy F6 14
Rocha, Ur. C6 56
Rochefort, Fr. G6 10
Rochelle, Ga., U.S. E3 87
Rochelle, Il., U.S. B4 90
Rochelle Park, N.J., U.S. h8 107
Rochester, Il., U.S. D4 90
Rochester, In., U.S. B5 91
Rochester, Mi., U.S. F7 99
Rochester, Mn., U.S. F6 100
Rochester, N.H., U.S. D5 106
Rochester, N.Y., U.S. B3 109
Rochester, Pa., U.S. E1 115
Rochester, Vt., U.S. D3 122
Rochester, Wa., U.S. C2 124
Rochester, Wi., U.S. n11 126
Rock, co., Mn., U.S. G2 100
Rock, co., Ne., U.S. B6 104
Rock, co., Wi., U.S. F4 126
Rock, stm., U.S. B3 90
Rock, stm., U.S. A1 92
Rockall, i., Scot., U.K. D5 4
Rockaway, N.J., U.S. B3 107
Rockaway, Or., U.S. B3 114
Rockbridge, co., Va., U.S. C3 123
Rockcastle, co., Ky., U.S. C5 94
Rockcastle, stm., Ky., U.S. C5 94
Rockcliffe Park, Ont., Can. h12 73
Rock Creek, Mn., U.S. E6 100
Rock Creek, stm., U.S. D3 113
Rock Creek, stm., U.S. h14 124
Rock Creek, stm., Nv., U.S. C5 105
Rock Creek, stm., Or., U.S. B6 114
Rock Creek, stm., Wa., U.S. B8 124
Rock Creek, stm., Wa., U.S. D5 124
Rock Creek, stm., Wy., U.S. E6 127
Rock Creek Butte, mtn., Or., U.S. C8 114
Rockdale, Il., U.S. B5 90
Rockdale, Md., U.S. B4 97
Rockdale, Tx., U.S. D4 120
Rockdale, co., Ga., U.S. C3 87
Rockfall, Ct., U.S. C5 84
Rock Falls, Il., U.S. B4 90
Rockford, Il., U.S. A4 90
Rockford, Ia., U.S. A5 92
Rockford, Mi., U.S. E5 99
Rockford, Mn., U.S. E5 100
Rockford, Oh., U.S. B1 112
Rockford, Tn., U.S. D10 119
Rock Hall, Md., U.S. B5 97
Rockhampton, Austl. D10 50
Rock Hill, S.C., U.S. B5 117
Rockingham, N.C., U.S. C3 110
Rockingham, co., N.H., U.S. D4 106
Rockingham, co., N.C., U.S. A3 110
Rockingham, co., Va., U.S. B4 123
Rock Island, Que., Can. D5 74
Rock Island, Il., U.S. B3 90
Rock Island, co., Il., U.S. B3 90
Rock Island, i., Fl., U.S. C3 86
Rock Island, i., Wi., U.S. C7 126
Rock Lake, l., Wa., U.S. B8 124
Rockland, Ont., Can. B9 73
Rockland, Me., U.S. D3 96
Rockland, Ma., U.S. B6 98
Rockland, co., N.Y., U.S. D6 109
Rockledge, Fl., U.S. D6 86
Rockledge, Pa., U.S. o20 115
Rocklin, Ca., U.S. C3 82
Rockmart, Ga., U.S. B1 87
Rock Mountain, mtn., Co., U.S. D3 83
Rockport, In., U.S. I3 91
Rockport, Me., U.S. D3 96
Rockport, Ma., U.S. A6 98
Rock Port, Mo., U.S. A2 102
Rockport, Tx., U.S. E4 120
Rock Rapids, Ia., U.S. A1 92
Rock River, Wy., U.S. E7 127
Rock Sound, Bah. B9 64
Rocksprings, Tx., U.S. D2 120
Rock Springs, Wy., U.S. E3 127
Rockstone, Guy. E13 58
Rockton, Il., U.S. A4 90
Rock Valley, Ia., U.S. A1 92
Rockville, In., U.S. E3 91
Rockville, Md., U.S. B3 97
Rockville Centre, N.Y., U.S. n15 109
Rockwall, Tx., U.S. C4 120
Rockwall, co., Tx., U.S. C4 120
Rockwell, Ia., U.S. B4 92
Rockwell, N.C., U.S. B2 110
Rockwell City, Ia., U.S. B3 92
Rockwell Park, N.C., U.S. B2 110
Rockwood, Mi., U.S. F7 99
Rockwood, Pa., U.S. G3 115
Rockwood, Tn., U.S. D9 119
Rocky, stm., N.C., U.S. B2 110
Rocky, stm., S.C., U.S. C2 117
Rocky, East Branch, stm., Oh., U.S. h9 112
Rocky, West Branch, stm., Oh., U.S. h9 112
Rocky Boys Indian Reservation, Mt., U.S. B7 103
Rocky Ford, Co., U.S. C7 83
Rocky Fork Lake, l., Oh., U.S. C2 112
Rocky Harbour, Newf., Can. D3 72
Rocky Hill, Ct., U.S. C5 84
Rocky Lake, l., Me., U.S. D5 96
Rocky Mount, N.C., U.S. B5 110
Rocky Mount, Va., U.S. D3 123
Rocky Mountain, mtn., Mt., U.S. C4 103
Rocky Mountain House, Alta., Can. C3 68
Rocky Mountain National Park, Co., U.S. A5 83
Rocky Mountains, mts., N.A. E9 61
Rocky Ripple, In., U.S. k10 91
Rocky River, Oh., U.S. A4 112
Rocky Top, mtn., Or., U.S. C4 114
Roddickton, Newf., Can. C3 72
Roderfield, W.V., U.S. D3 125
Rodez, Fr. H9 10
Ródhos (Rhodes), Grc. M12 16
Ródhos, i., Grc. M11 16
Rodney, Ont., Can. E3 73
Rodney, Cape, c., Ak., U.S. C6 79
Rodney Village, De., U.S. D3 85
Rodniki, U.S.S.R. D24 22
Roebourne, Austl. D3 50
Roebuck, S.C., U.S. B4 117
Roeland Park, Ks., U.S. k16 93
Roeselare, Bel. E3 8
Roes Welcome Sound, strt., N.W. Ter., Can. D15 66
Roff, Ok., U.S. C5 113
Rogagua, Lago, l., Bol. F5 54
Roger Mills, co., Ok., U.S. B2 113
Rogers, Ar., U.S. A1 81
Rogers, Mn., U.S. E5 100
Rogers, Tx., U.S. D4 120
Rogers, co., Ok., U.S. A6 113
Rogers, Mount, mtn., Va., U.S. f10 123
Rogers City, Mi., U.S. C7 99
Rogers Lake, res., Ct., U.S. D6 84
Rogers Pass, Mt., U.S. C4 103
Rogersville, N.B., Can. C4 71
Rogersville, Al., U.S. A2 78
Rogersville, Mo., U.S. D4 102
Rogersville, Tn., U.S. C10 119
Roggiano Gravina, Italy J11 14
Rogue, stm., Or., U.S. E2 114
Rogue River, Or., U.S. E3 114
Rohtak, India F7 38
Roi Et, Thai. F7 34
Rojo, Cabo, c., Mex. G11 62
Roland, Ia., U.S. B4 92
Roland, Ok., U.S. B7 113
Roland, Lake, res., Md., U.S. g11 97
Rolândia, Braz. G3 57
Røldal, Nor. G6 6
Rolette, N.D., U.S. A6 111
Rolette, co., N.D., U.S. A6 111
Rolfe, Ia., U.S. B3 92
Rolla, Mo., U.S. D6 102
Rolla, N.D., U.S. A6 111
Rollingbay, Wa., U.S. e10 124
Rolling Fork, Ms., U.S. C3 101
Rolling Fork, stm., Ar., U.S. C1 81
Rolling Fork, stm., Ky., U.S. C4 94
Rolling Meadows, Il., U.S. h8 90
Rollingstone, Mn., U.S. F7 100
Rollinsford, N.H., U.S. D5 106
Roma (Rome), Italy H7 14
Roma, Tx., U.S. F3 120
Romain, Cape, c., S.C., U.S. F9 117
Roman, Rom. C10 16
Romania, ctry., Eur. F13 4
Roman Nose Mountain, mtn., Or., U.S. D3 114
Romano, Cape, c., Fl., U.S. G5 86
Romano, Cayo, i., Cuba C8 64
Romans [-sur-Isère], Fr. G12 10
Romanzof, Cape, c., Ak., U.S. C6 79
Romanzof Mountains, mts., Ak., U.S. B11 79
Rome, Ga., U.S. B1 87
Rome, Il., U.S. C4 90
Rome, N.Y., U.S. B5 109
Rome City, In., U.S. B7 91
Romeo, Mi., U.S. F7 99
Romeoville, Il., U.S. k8 90
Rome see Roma, Italy H7 14
Romilly-sur-Seine, Fr. D10 10
Romney, W.V., U.S. B6 125
Romorantin-Lanthenay, Fr. E8 10
Romulus, Mi., U.S. p15 99
Ron, Mui, c., Viet. E9 34
Ronan, Mt., U.S. C2 103
Roncador, Serra do, plat., Braz. F8 54
Roncesvalles, Spain B10 12
Ronceverte, W.V., U.S. D4 125
Ronda, Spain I6 12
Rondônia, Braz. F6 54
Rondonópolis, Braz. D1 57
Ronge, Lac la, l., Sask., Can. B3 75
Rønne, Den. I10 6
Ronneby, Swe. H10 6
Ronne Ice Shelf, Ant. B6 47
Ronse, Bel. E3 8
Roodhouse, Il., U.S. D3 90
Rooks, co., Ks., U.S. C4 93
Roorkee, India F7 38
Roosendaal, Neth. D4 8
Roosevelt, Ut., U.S. C5 121
Roosevelt, co., Mt., U.S. B11 103
Roosevelt, co., N.M., U.S. C6 108
Roosevelt, stm., Braz. E6 54
Roosevelt Park, Mi., U.S. E4 99
Root, stm., Mn., U.S. G7 100
Root, stm., Wi., U.S. n12 126
Roper, N.C., U.S. B6 110
Roquefort, Fr. H6 10
Roraima, Mount, mtn., S.A. E12 58
Røros, Nor. E8 6
Rorschach, Switz. E16 10
Rørvik, Nor. D8 6
Rošal', U.S.S.R. F22 22
Rosamond, Ca., U.S. E4 82
Rosamorada, Mex. F7 62
Rosario, Arg. C4 56
Rosário, Braz. D10 54
Rosario, Mex. B2 62
Rosario, Mex. F7 62
Rosario, Ven. B6 58
Rosário Oeste, Braz. F7 54
Rosarno, Italy K10 14
Rosas, Golfo de, b., Spain C15 12
Roscoe, Il., U.S. A5 90
Roscoe, Tx., U.S. C2 120
Roscommon, Ire. H4 7
Roscommon, Mi., U.S. D6 99
Roscommon, co., Mi., U.S. D6 99
Roscrea, Ire. I5 7
Rose, Mount, mtn., Nv., U.S. D2 105
Roseau, Dom. G17 64
Roseau, Mn., U.S. B3 100
Roseau, co., Mn., U.S. B3 100
Roseau, South Fork, stm., Mn., U.S. B3 100
Rose-Blanche [-Harbour le Cou], Newf., Can. E2 72
Roseboro, N.C., U.S. C4 110
Rosebud, S.D., U.S. D5 118
Rosebud, Tx., U.S. D4 120
Rosebud, co., Mt., U.S. D10 103
Rosebud Indian Reservation, S.D., U.S. D5 118
Roseburg, Or., U.S. D3 114
Rosedale, In., U.S. E3 91
Rosedale, Md., U.S. g11 97
Rosedale, Ms., U.S. B2 101
Rose Hill, Ks., U.S. E6 93
Rose Hill, N.C., U.S. C4 110
Rose Hill, Va., U.S. f8 123
Roseland, Fl., U.S. E6 86
Roseland, In., U.S. A5 91
Roseland, La., U.S. D5 95
Roseland, Oh., U.S. B3 112
Roselle, Il., U.S. k8 90
Roselle, N.J., U.S. k7 107
Roselle Park, N.J., U.S. k7 107
Rosemère, Que., Can. p19 74
Rosemount, Mn., U.S. F5 100
Rosenberg, Tx., U.S. E5 120
Rosendale, Wi., U.S. E5 126
Rosenheim, Ger. H12 8
Rose Peak, mtn., Az., U.S. D6 80
Rosepine, La., U.S. D2 95
Rose Point, c., B.C., Can. B2 69
Roseto, Pa., U.S. E11 115
Roseville, Ca., U.S. C3 82
Roseville, Il., U.S. C3 90
Roseville, Mi., U.S. o16 99
Roseville, Mn., U.S. m12 100
Roseville, Oh., U.S. C3 112
Rosewood Heights, Il., U.S. E3 90
Rosiclare, Il., U.S. F5 90
Rosignano Marittimo, Italy F5 14
Roskilde, Den. I9 6
Roslags-Näsby, Swe. G12 6
Roslavl', U.S.S.R. H15 22
Roslyn, Wa., U.S. B4 124
Roslyn Heights, N.Y., U.S. h13 109
Ross, Oh., U.S. C1 112
Ross, co., Oh., U.S. C2 112
Rossano, Italy J11 14
Rossan Point, c., Ire. G4 7
Ross Barnett Reservoir, res., Ms., U.S. C3 101
Rossburn, Man., Can. D1 70
Ross Dam, Wa., U.S. A4 124
Rossel Island, i., Pap. N. Gui. B10 50
Rossford, Oh., U.S. A2 112
Ross Ice Shelf, Ant. A31 47
Rossignol, Lake, l., N.S., Can. E4 71
Rossijskaja Sovetskaja Federativnaja Socialističeskaja Respublika (Russia), state, U.S.S.R. E15 18
Rossijskaja Sovetskaja Federativnaja Socialističeskaja Respublika (Russia), state, U.S.S.R. E13 20
Ross Island, i., Man., Can. B3 70
Ross Lake National Recreation Area, Wa., U.S. A5 124
Rossland, B.C., Can. E9 69
Rosslare, Ire. I6 7
Rosso, Maur. E2 42
Ross River, Yukon, Can. D6 66
Ross Sea, Ant. B31 47
Rossville, Ga., U.S. B1 87
Rossville, Il., U.S. C6 90
Rossville, In., U.S. D4 91
Rossville, Ks., U.S. C8 93
Rostock, Ger. A12 8
Rostov, U.S.S.R. D22 22
Rostov-na-Donu, U.S.S.R. H5 18
Roswell, Ga., U.S. B2 87
Roswell, N.M., U.S. D5 108
Rotan, Tx., U.S. C2 120
Rotenburg, Ger. B9 8
Rothaargebirge, mts., Ger. D8 8
Rothenburg ob der Tauber, Ger. F10 8
Rothesay, N.B., Can. D4 71
Rothschild, Wi., U.S. D4 126
Rothsville, Pa., U.S. F9 115
Roti, Pulau, i., Indon. H7 32
Rotondella, Italy I11 14
Rotorua, N.Z. C6 52
Rotterdam, Neth. D4 8
Rotterdam, N.Y., U.S. C6 109
Rottweil, Ger. G8 8
Roubaix, Fr. B10 10
Rouen, Fr. C8 10
Rouge, stm., Que., Can. D3 74
Rough, stm., Ky., U.S. C3 94
Rough River Lake, res., Ky., U.S. C3 94
Roulette, Pa., U.S. C5 115
Round Island, i., Ms., U.S. g8 101
Round Lake, Il., U.S. h8 90
Round Lake Beach, Il., U.S. h8 90
Round Mountain, Nv., U.S. E4 105
Round Rock, Tx., U.S. D4 120
Roundup, Mt., U.S. D8 103
Round Valley Indian Reservation, Ca., U.S. C2 82
Round Valley Reservoir, res., N.J., U.S. B3 107
Rouses Point, N.Y., U.S. f11 109
Roussillon, hist. reg., Fr. J9 10
Routt, co., Co., U.S. A3 83
Rouyn, Que., Can. k11 74
Rouzerville, Pa., U.S. G6 115
Rovaniemi, Fin. C15 6
Rovato, Italy D4 14
Rovereto, Italy D6 14
Rovigo, Italy D6 14
Rovinj, Yugo. D8 14
Rovno, U.S.S.R. G3 18
Rowan, co., Ky., U.S. B6 94
Rowan, co., N.C., U.S. B2 110
Rowland, N.C., U.S. C3 110
Rowlesburg, W.V., U.S. B5 125
Rowley Island, i., N.W. Ter., Can. C17 66
Rowley Shoals, rf., Austl. C3 50
Roxboro, N.C., U.S. A4 110
Roxton Falls, Que., Can. D5 74
Roxton Pond, Que., Can. D5 74
Roy, Ut., U.S. B3 121
Royal, stm., Me., U.S. g7 96
Royal Canal, Ire. H5 7
Royal Center, In., U.S. C4 91
Royale, Isle, i., Mi., U.S. h9 99
Royal Gorge, val., Co., U.S. C5 83
Royal Oak, Mi., U.S. F7 99
Royal Pines, N.C., U.S. f10 110
Royalton, Il., U.S. F4 90
Royalton, Mn., U.S. E4 100
Royan, Fr. G5 10
Royersford, Pa., U.S. F10 115
Royerton, In., U.S. D7 91
Royse City, Tx., U.S. C4 120
Royston, B.C., Can. E5 69
Royston, Ga., U.S. B3 87
Rubbestadneset, Nor. G5 6
Rubcovsk, U.S.S.R. G10 20
Rubidoux, Ca., U.S. n14 82
Rubio, Ven. D6 58
Ruby Dome, mtn., Nv., U.S. C6 105
Ruby Lake, l., Nv., U.S. C6 105
Ruby Mountains, mts., Nv., U.S. C6 105
Ruby Range, mts., Co., U.S. C3 83
Ruby Range, mts., Mt., U.S. E4 103
Rudolf, Lake, l., Afr. H2 46
Rudolstadt, Ger. E11 8
Rudyard, Mi., U.S. B6 99
Rue, Fr. B8 10
Rufā'ah, Sudan F12 42
Ruffec, Fr. F7 10
Rufino, Arg. C4 56
Rufus Woods Lake, res., Wa., U.S. A6 124
Rugao, China C9 28
Rugby, Eng., U.K. I11 7
Rugby, N.D., U.S. A5 111
Ruian, China H9 28
Ruidoso, N.M., U.S. D4 108
Ruidoso Downs, N.M., U.S. D4 108
Ruijin, China F10 26
Ruijin, China J4 28
Rukwa, Lake, l., Tan. C6 44
Ruleville, Ms., U.S. B3 101
Rum, stm., Mn., U.S. D5 100
Ruma, Yugo. D3 16
Rumbek, Sudan G11 42
Rum Cay, i., Bah. C10 64
Rum Creek, stm., W.V., U.S. n12 125
Rumford, Me., U.S. D2 96
Rumia, Pol. A18 8
Rum Jungle, Austl. B6 50
Rumoi, Japan p19 30a
Rumson, N.J., U.S. C4 107
Rumstick Point, c., R.I., U.S. D5 116
Ru'nan, China B3 28
Runanga, N.Z. E3 52
Runge, Tx., U.S. E4 120
Rungwa, Tan. C6 44
Runnels, co., Tx., U.S. D3 120
Runnemede, N.J., U.S. D2 107
Ruoqiang, China D4 26
Rupert, Id., U.S. G5 89
Rupert, W.V., U.S. D4 125
Rupert, Rivière de, stm., Que., Can. h11 74
Rural Hall, N.C., U.S. A2 110
Rural Retreat, Va., U.S. D1 123
Rusagonis, N.B., Can. D3 71
Ruse, Bul. F9 16
Rush, co., In., U.S. E6 91
Rush, co., Ks., U.S. D4 93
Rush, stm., Mn., U.S. F4 100
Rush, stm., Wi., U.S. D1 126
Rush City, Mn., U.S. E6 100
Rush Creek, stm., Oh., U.S. B2 112
Rush Creek, stm., Ok., U.S. C4 113
Rushford, Mn., U.S. G7 100
Rush Lake, l., Mn., U.S. E3 100
Rush Lake, l., Mn., U.S. D3 100
Rush Lake, l., Wi., U.S. E5 126
Rushmere, Va., U.S. h14 123
Rush Springs, Ok., U.S. C4 113
Rushville, Il., U.S. C3 90
Rushville, In., U.S. E7 91
Rushville, Ne., U.S. B3 104
Rusk, Tx., U.S. D5 120
Rusk, co., Tx., U.S. C5 120
Rusk, co., Wi., U.S. C2 126
Ruskin, Fl., U.S. E4 86

Name	Map Ref	Page
Russas, Braz.	D11	54
Russell, Man., Can.	D1	70
Russell, Ont., Can.	B9	73
Russell, Ks., U.S.	D5	93
Russell, Ky., U.S.	B7	94
Russell, Pa., U.S.	C3	115
Russell, co., Al., U.S.	C4	78
Russell, co., Ks., U.S.	D5	93
Russell, co., Ky., U.S.	D4	94
Russell, co., Va., U.S.	f9	123
Russell, Mount, mtn., Ak., U.S.	f16	79
Russell Cave National Monument, Al., U.S.	A4	78
Russell Fork, stm., U.S.	C7	94
Russell Island, i., N.W. Ter., Can.	B13	66
Russell Springs, Ky., U.S.	C4	94
Russellville, Al., U.S.	A2	78
Russellville, Ar., U.S.	B2	81
Russellville, Ky., U.S.	D3	94
Russellville, Mo., U.S.	C5	102
Russellville, Tn., U.S.	C10	119
Rüsselsheim, Ger.	E8	8
Russian, stm., Ca., U.S.	C2	82
Russia see Rossijskaja Sovetskaja Federativnaja Socialističeskaja Respublika, state, U.S.S.R.	E13	20
Russiaville, In., U.S.	D5	91
Rustavi, U.S.S.R.	I7	18
Rustburg, Va., U.S.	C3	123
Rustenburg, S. Afr.	G5	44
Ruston, La., U.S.	B3	95
Ruston, Wa., U.S.	B3	124
Ruth, Nv., U.S.	D6	105
Rutherford, N.J., U.S.	B4	107
Rutherford, Tn., U.S.	A3	119
Rutherford, co., N.C., U.S.	B1	110
Rutherford, co., Tn., U.S.	B5	119
Rutherfordton, N.C., U.S.	B1	110
Ruthven, Ia., U.S.	A3	92
Rutland, Ma., U.S.	B4	98
Rutland, Vt., U.S.	D3	122
Rutland, co., Vt., U.S.	D2	122
Rutledge, Ga., U.S.	C3	87
Rutledge, Tn., U.S.	C10	119
Ruukki, Fin.	D15	6
Ruvuma (Rovuma), stm., Afr.	D7	44
Ružomberok, Czech.	F19	8
Rwanda, ctry., Afr.	B5	44
Ryan, Ok., U.S.	C4	113
Ryan Peak, mtn., Id., U.S.	F4	89
Rybačje, U.S.S.R.	I9	20
Rybinsk, U.S.S.R.	C21	22
Rybinskoje Vodochranilišče, res., U.S.S.R.	C21	22
Rybnik, Pol.	E18	8
Rycroft, Alta., Can.	B1	68
Ryde, Eng., U.K.	K11	7
Rye, N.H., U.S.	D5	106
Rye, N.Y., U.S.	h13	109
Rye Beach, N.H., U.S.	E5	106
Rye Patch Dam, Nv., U.S.	C3	105
Rye Patch Reservoir, res., Nv., U.S.	C3	105
Ryfoss, Nor.	F7	6
Ryōtsu, Japan	D11	30
Rysy, mtn., Eur.	F20	8
Ryukyu Islands see Nansei-shotō, is., Japan	F12	26
Rzeszów, Pol.	E21	8
Ržev, U.S.S.R.	E17	22

S

Name	Map Ref	Page
Saalfeld, Ger.	E11	8
Saarbrücken, Ger.	F6	8
Saaremaa, i., U.S.S.R.	C5	22
Saarijärvi, Fin.	E15	6
Saarlouis, Ger.	F6	8
Sab, Tônlé, l., Camb.	H7	34
Saba, i., Neth. Ant.	F16	64
Sabadell, Spain	D14	12
Sabae, Japan	G9	30
Sabana, Archipiélago de, is., Cuba	C8	64
Sabanagrande, Hond.	H4	64
Sabanalarga, Col.	B5	58
Sabang, Indon.	E6	32
Sabanilla, Mex.	E9	62
Sabará, Braz.	E7	57
Sabattus, Me., U.S.	D2	96
Sabetha, Ks., U.S.	C8	93
Sabhah, Libya	C8	42
Sabi (Save), stm., Afr.	F6	44
Sabillasville, Md., U.S.	A3	97
Sabina, Oh., U.S.	C2	112
Sabinal, Tx., U.S.	E3	120
Sabiñánigo, Spain	C11	12
Sabinas, Mex.	D9	62
Sabinas Hidalgo, Mex.	D9	62
Sabine, co., La., U.S.	C2	95
Sabine, co., Tx., U.S.	D6	120
Sabine, stm., U.S.	D6	120
Sabine Lake, l., U.S.	E2	95
Sabine Pass, strt., U.S.	E2	95
Sable, Cape, c., N.S., Can.	H19	66
Sable, Cape, c., Fl., U.S.	G5	86
Sable, Îles de, i., N. Cal.	C11	50
Sable Island, i., N.S., Can.	F10	71
Sabula, Ia., U.S.	B7	92
Sabzevār, Iran	J9	18
Sac, co., Ia., U.S.	B2	92
Sac, stm., Mo., U.S.	D4	102
Sacajawea, Lake, res., Wa., U.S.	C7	124
Sacajawea Peak, mtn., Or., U.S.	B9	114
Sacandaga Lake, l., N.Y., U.S.	B6	109
Sac and Fox Indian Reservation, Ia., U.S.	C5	92
Sacaton, Az., U.S.	D4	80
Sac City, Ia., U.S.	B2	92
Sacedón, Spain	E9	12
Sachalin, Ostrov (Sakhalin), i., U.S.S.R.	G22	20
Sachalinskij Zaliv, b., U.S.S.R.	G22	20
Sachigo, stm., Ont., Can.	F14	66
Sachse, Tx., U.S.	n10	120
Sachs Harbour, N.W. Ter., Can.	B8	66
Šachty, U.S.S.R.	H6	18
Sachuest Point, c., R.I., U.S.	F6	116
Sackville, N.B., Can.	D5	71
Saco, Me., U.S.	E2	96
Saco, stm., U.S.	E2	96
Saco, East Branch, stm., N.H., U.S.	B4	106
Sacramento, Ca., U.S.	C3	82
Sacramento, co., Ca., U.S.	C3	82
Sacramento, stm., Ca., U.S.	C3	82
Sacramento, stm., N.M., U.S.	E4	108
Sacramento Mountains, mts., N.M., U.S.	E4	108
Sacramento Valley, val., Ca., U.S.	C2	82
Sacré-Coeur-Saguenay, Que., Can.	A8	74
Sacred Heart, Mn., U.S.	F3	100
Sádaba, Spain	C10	12
Şa'dah, Yemen	E3	46
Saddle, stm., N.J., U.S.	h8	107
Saddleback Mountain, mtn., Az., U.S.	k8	80
Saddle Brook, N.J., U.S.	h8	107
Saddlebunch Keys, is., Fl., U.S.	H5	86
Saddle Mountain, mtn., Or., U.S.	B3	114
Saddle Mountains, mts., Wa., U.S.	C5	124
Saddle River, N.J., U.S.	A4	107
Sa Dec, Viet.	I8	34
Sādiqābad, Pak.	F4	38
Sado, i., Japan	D11	30
Sado-kaikyō, strt., Japan	E11	30
Saegertown, Pa., U.S.	C1	115
Safety Harbor, Fl., U.S.	E4	86
Säffle, Swe.	G9	6
Safford, Az., U.S.	E6	80
Safi, Mor.	B4	42
Safīd, stm., Afg.	B1	38
Sāfīd Kūh, Selseleh-ye, mts., Afg.	C1	36
Safonovo, U.S.S.R.	F16	22
Saga, Japan	I3	30
Sagadahoc, co., Me., U.S.	E3	96
Sagaing, Burma	D3	34
Sagamihara, Japan	G12	30
Sagami-nada, b., Japan	G12	30
Sagamore Hills, Oh., U.S.	h9	112
Saganaga Lake, l., Mn., U.S.	B7	100
Sāgar, India	E3	37
Sāgar, India	I8	38
Sag Harbor, N.Y., U.S.	m16	109
Saginaw, Mi., U.S.	E7	99
Saginaw, Tx., U.S.	n9	120
Saginaw, co., Mi., U.S.	E6	99
Saginaw Bay, b., Mi., U.S.	E7	99
Saglek Bay, b., Newf., Can.	f9	72
Sagres, Port.	H3	12
Saguache, co., Co., U.S.	C4	83
Sagua de Tánamo, Cuba	D10	64
Sagua la Grande, Cuba	C7	64
Saguaro Lake, res., Az., U.S.	k10	80
Saguaro National Monument, Az., U.S.	E5	80
Saguaro National Monument (Tucson Mountain Section), Az., U.S.	E4	80
Saguenay, stm., Que., Can.	A7	74
Sagunto, Spain	F11	12
Sahagún, Col.	C5	58
Sahagún, Spain	C6	12
Sahara, des., Afr.	D6	42
Sahāranpur, India	F7	38
Sāhīwāl (Montgomery), Pak.	E5	38
Sahuaripa, Mex.	C5	62
Sahuarita, Az., U.S.	F5	80
Sahuayo, Mex.	G8	62
Saibai, i., Austl.	A8	50
Saïda, Alg.	B6	42
Saidpur, Bngl.	H13	38
Saidu, Pak.	C5	38
Saigō, Japan	F6	30
Saigon see Thanh Pho Ho Chi Minh, Viet.	I9	34
Saijō, Japan	I6	30
Saimaa, l., Fin.	F16	6
Saint Abb's Head, c., Scot., U.K.	F10	7
Saint Adolphe, Man., Can.	E3	70
Saint-Affrique, Fr.	I9	10
Sainte-Agathe, Que., Can.	C6	74
Sainte-Agathe-des-Monts, Que., Can.	C3	74
Saint-Aimé (Massueville), Que., Can.	D5	74
Saint-Alban, Que., Can.	C5	74
Saint Alban's, Newf., Can.	E4	72
Saint Albans, Eng., U.K.	J12	7
Saint Albans, Vt., U.S.	B2	122
Saint Albans, W.V., U.S.	C3	125
Saint Albans Bay, b., Vt., U.S.	B2	122
Saint Albert, Alta., Can.	C4	68
Saint-Amand-Mont-Rond, Fr.	F9	10
Saint-Ambroise, Que., Can.	A6	74
Saint-Ambroix, Fr.	H11	10
Saint-André, Cap, c., Madag.	E8	44
Saint-André-Avellin, Que., Can.	D2	74
Saint-André-Est, Que., Can.	D3	74
Saint-André-les-Alpes, Fr.	I13	10
Saint Andrew Bay, b., Fl., U.S.	u16	86
Saint Andrews, N.B., Can.	D2	71
Saint Andrews, Scot., U.K.	E10	7
Saint Andrews, S.C., U.S.	C5	117
Saint Andrews, S.C., U.S.	F7	117
Saint Anne, Il., U.S.	B6	90
Sainte-Anne-de-Beaupré, Que., Can.	B7	74
Sainte-Anne [-de-Bellevue], Que., Can.	q19	74
Sainte Anne-de-Madawaska, N.B., Can.	B1	71
Sainte Anne-des-Chênes, Man., Can.	E3	70
Saint-Anselme, Que., Can.	C7	74
Saint Ansgar, Ia., U.S.	A5	92
Saint Anthony, Newf., Can.	C4	72
Saint Anthony, Id., U.S.	F7	89
Saint Antoine, N.B., Can.	C5	71
Saint-Apollinaire, Que., Can.	C6	74
Saint Arthur, N.B., Can.	B3	71
Saint-Astier, Fr.	G7	10
Saint-Aubert, Que., Can.	B7	74
Saint Augustin, stm., Can.	C2	72
Saint Augustine, Fl., U.S.	C5	86
Saint Austell, Eng., U.K.	K8	7
Saint-Avold, Fr.	C13	10
Saint-Barthélemy, i., Guad.	F16	64
Saint Basile, N.B., Can.	B1	71
Saint-Basile [-Sud], Que., Can.	C6	74
Saint-Benoît-du-Sault, Fr.	F8	10
Saint-Bernard, Que., Can.	C6	74
Saint Bernard, Al., U.S.	A3	78
Saint Bernard, La., U.S.	E6	95
Saint Bernard, Oh., U.S.	o13	112
Saint Bernard, co., La., U.S.	E6	95
Saint Bernice, In., U.S.	E2	91
Saint Bride, Mount, mtn., Alta., Can.	D3	68
Saint Bride's, Newf., Can.	E4	72
Saint-Brieuc, Fr.	D4	10
Saint-Bruno, Que., Can.	A6	74
Saint-Calais, Fr.	E7	10
Saint-Casimir, Que., Can.	C5	74
Saint Catharines, Ont., Can.	D5	73
Saint Catherine, Lake, l., Vt., U.S.	E2	122
Saint Catherines Island, i., Ga., U.S.	E5	87
Saint-Célestin (Annaville), Que., Can.	C5	74
Saint-Céré, Fr.	H8	10
Saint-Césaire, Que., Can.	D4	74
Saint-Chamond, Fr.	G11	10
Saint-Charles, Que., Can.	C7	74
Saint Charles, Il., U.S.	B5	90
Saint Charles, Mi., U.S.	E6	99
Saint Charles, Mn., U.S.	G6	100
Saint Charles, Mo., U.S.	C7	102
Saint Charles, co., La., U.S.	E5	95
Saint Charles, co., Mo., U.S.	C7	102
Saint-Chély-d'Apcher, Fr.	H10	10
Saint Christopher (Saint Kitts), i., St. K./N.	F16	64
Saint Christopher-Nevis see Saint Kitts and Nevis, ctry., N.A.	F16	64
Saint-Chrysostome, Que., Can.	D4	74
Saint Clair, Mi., U.S.	F8	99
Saint Clair, Mn., U.S.	F5	100
Saint Clair, Mo., U.S.	C6	102
Saint Clair, Pa., U.S.	E9	115
Saint Clair, co., Al., U.S.	B3	78
Saint Clair, co., Il., U.S.	E3	90
Saint Clair, co., Mi., U.S.	F8	99
Saint Clair, co., Mo., U.S.	C4	102
Saint Clair Shores, Mi., U.S.	p16	99
Saint Clairsville, Oh., U.S.	B5	112
Saint Claude, Man., Can.	E2	70
Saint-Claude, Fr.	F12	10
Saint Cloud, Fl., U.S.	D5	86
Saint Cloud, Mn., U.S.	E4	100
Saint-Coeur-de-Marie, Que., Can.	A6	74
Saint-Constant, Que., Can.	q19	74
Sainte-Croix, Que., Can.	C6	74
Saint Croix, co., Wi., U.S.	C1	126
Saint Croix, i., V.I.U.S.	F15	64
Saint Croix, stm., U.S.	C1	126
Saint Croix, Lake, l., U.S.	D1	126
Saint Croix Falls, Wi., U.S.	C1	126
Saint Croix Stream, stm., Me., U.S.	B4	96
Saint-Damase, Que., Can.	D4	74
Saint David, Az., U.S.	F5	80
Saint-David-de-l'Auberivière, Que., Can.	n17	74
Saint David's, Wales, U.K.	J7	7
Saint-Denis, Que., Can.	D4	74
Saint-Denis, Fr.	D9	10
Saint-Denis, Reu.	F11	44
Saint-Dié, Fr.	D13	10
Saint-Dizier, Fr.	D11	10
Saint-Dominique, Que., Can.	D5	74
Saint Edward, Ne., U.S.	C8	104
Saint Eleanor's, P.E.I., Can.	C6	71
Saint Elias, Cape, c., Ak., U.S.	D11	79
Saint Elmo, Al., U.S.	E1	78
Saint Elmo, Il., U.S.	D5	90
Saint-Éphrem [-de-Tring], Que., Can.	C7	74
Saint Étienne, Fr.	G11	10
Saint-Eustache, Que., Can.	D4	74
Saint-Félicien, Que., Can.	A5	74
Saint-Félix-de-Valois, Que., Can.	C4	74
Saint-Ferdinand (Bernierville), Que., Can.	C6	74
Saint-Ferréol [-les-Neiges], Que., Can.	B7	74
Saint-Flavien, Que., Can.	C6	74
Saint-Florentin, Fr.	D10	10
Saint-Florent-sur-Cher, Fr.	F9	10
Saint-Flour, Fr.	G10	10
Sainte-Foy, Que., Can.	n17	74
Sainte-Foy-la-Grande, Fr.	H7	10
Saint Francis, Ks., U.S.	C2	93
Saint Francis, Mn., U.S.	E5	100
Saint Francis, S.D., U.S.	D5	118
Saint Francis, Wi., U.S.	n12	126
Saint Francis, co., Ar., U.S.	B5	81
Saint Francis, stm., U.S.	A5	81
Saint Francis, Cape, c., Newf., Can.	E5	72
Saint Francisville, Il., U.S.	E6	90
Saint Francisville, La., U.S.	D4	95
Saint Francois, co., Mo., U.S.	D7	102
Saint-François, stm., Que., Can.	D5	74
Saint-François, Lac, l., Que., Can.	D6	74
Saint Francois Mountains, hills, Mo., U.S.	D7	102
Saint Froid Lake, l., Me., U.S.	B4	96
Saint-Fulgence, Que., Can.	A7	74
Saint-Gabriel, Que., Can.	C4	74
Saint-Gaudens, Fr.	I7	10
Saint-Gédéon, Que., Can.	D7	74
Sainte Genevieve, Mo., U.S.	D7	102
Sainte Genevieve, co., Mo., U.S.	D7	102
Saint George, Austl.	E9	50
Saint George, N.B., Can.	D3	71
Saint George, Ont., Can.	D4	73
Saint George, S.C., U.S.	E6	117
Saint George, Ut., U.S.	F2	121
Saint George, Cape, c., Newf., Can.	D2	72
Saint George, Cape, c., Fl., U.S.	C1	86
Saint George Island, i., Ak., U.S.	D6	79
Saint George Island, i., Fl., U.S.	C2	86
Saint George's, Newf., Can.	D2	72
Saint-Georges, Que., Can.	C5	74
Saint-Georges, Fr. Gu.	C8	54
Saint George's, Gren.	H17	64
Saint Georges, De., U.S.	B3	85
Saint George's Bay, b., Newf., Can.	D2	72
Saint Georges Bay, b., N.S., Can.	D8	71
Saint George's Channel, strt., Eur.	J6	7
Saint-Georges-Ouest, Que., Can.	C7	74
Saint-Germain, Fr.	D9	10
Saint-Gervais, Que., Can.	C7	74
Saint-Gilles, Que., Can.	C6	74
Saint-Gilles-Croix-de-Vie, Fr.	F5	10
Saint-Girons, Fr.	J8	10
Saint-Grégoire (Larochelle), Que., Can.	C5	74
Saint-Guénolé, Fr.	E2	10
Saint-Guillaume-d'Upton, Que., Can.	D5	74
Saint Helen, Lake, l., Mi., U.S.	D6	99
Saint Helena, Ca., U.S.	C2	82
Saint Helena, co., La., U.S.	D5	95
Saint Helena Bay, b., S. Afr.	H3	44
Saint Helena Island, i., S.C., U.S.	G6	117
Saint Helena Sound, strt., S.C., U.S.	G7	117
Saint Helens, Or., U.S.	B4	114
Saint Helens, Mount, vol., Wa., U.S.	C3	124
Saint Helier, Jersey	C4	10
Saint Henry, Oh., U.S.	B1	112
Saint-Hippolyte, Fr.	E13	10
Saint-Honoré, Que., Can.	D7	74
Saint-Hubert, Que., Can.	q20	74
Saint-Hubert-de-Témiscouata, Que., Can.	B8	74
Saint-Hyacinthe, Que., Can.	D5	74
Saint Ignace, Mi., U.S.	C6	99
Saint Ignace Island, i., Ont., Can.	G15	66
Saint Ignatius, Mt., U.S.	C2	103
Saint Isidore de Prescott, Ont., Can.	B10	73
Saint Jacobs, Ont., Can.	D4	73
Saint Jacques, N.B., Can.	B1	71
Saint-Jacques, Que., Can.	D4	74
Saint James, Mn., U.S.	G4	100
Saint James, Mo., U.S.	D6	102
Saint James, co., La., U.S.	D5	95
Saint James, Cape, c., B.C., Can.	D2	69
Saint James City, Fl., U.S.	F4	86
Saint-Jean, stm., Que., Can.	A7	74
Saint-Jean, Lac, l., Que., Can.	A5	74
Saint Jean Baptiste, Man., Can.	E3	70
Saint-Jean-Chrysostome, Que., Can.	o17	74
Saint-Jean-d'Angély, Fr.	G6	10
Saint-Jean-de-Luz, Fr.	I5	10
Saint-Jean-de-Maurienne, Fr.	G13	10
Saint-Jean-de-Monts, Fr.	F4	10
Saint-Jean-Pied-de-Port, Fr.	I5	10
Saint-Jean-sur-Richelieu, Que., Can.	D4	74
Saint-Jérôme, Que., Can.	D3	74
Saint Jo, Tx., U.S.	C4	120
Saint-Joachim, Que., Can.	B7	74
Saint Joe, stm., Id., U.S.	B3	89
Saint John, N.B., Can.	D3	71
Saint John, In., U.S.	B3	91
Saint John, Ks., U.S.	E5	93
Saint John, i., V.I.U.S.	E15	64
Saint John, stm., N.A.	G19	66
Saint John, Cape, c., Newf., Can.	D4	72
Saint John Bay, b., Newf., Can.	C3	72
Saint Johns, Antig.	F17	64
Saint John's, Newf., Can.	E5	72
Saint Johns, Az., U.S.	C6	80
Saint Johns, Mi., U.S.	F6	99
Saint Johns, co., Fl., U.S.	C5	86
Saint Johns, stm., Fl., U.S.	B5	86
Saint Johnsbury, Vt., U.S.	C4	122
Saint Johnsville, N.Y., U.S.	B6	109
Saint John the Baptist, co., La., U.S.	D5	95
Saint Jones, stm., De., U.S.	D4	85
Saint Joseph, N.B., Can.	D5	71
Saint Joseph, Il., U.S.	C5	90
Saint Joseph, La., U.S.	C4	95
Saint Joseph, Mi., U.S.	F4	99
Saint Joseph, Mn., U.S.	E4	100
Saint Joseph, Mo., U.S.	B3	102
Saint Joseph, Tn., U.S.	B4	119
Saint Joseph, co., In., U.S.	A5	91
Saint Joseph, co., Mi., U.S.	G5	99
Saint Joseph, stm., U.S.	F5	99
Saint-Joseph, Lac, l., Que., Can.	n16	74
Saint Joseph, Lake, l., Ont., Can.	o17	73
Saint Joseph Bay, b., Fl., U.S.	C1	86
Saint-Joseph-de-Beauce, Que., Can.	C7	74
Saint Joseph Point, c., Fl., U.S.	v16	86
Saint Joseph Sound, strt., Fl., U.S.	o10	86
Saint-Jovite, Que., Can.	C3	74
Saint-Julien-en-Born, Fr.	H5	10
Saint-Junien, Fr.	G7	10
Saint-Just-en-Chaussée, Fr.	C9	10
Saint Kilda, i., Scot., U.K.	D4	7
Saint Kitts-Nevis, ctry., N.A.	F16	64
Saint-Lambert, Que., Can.	p19	74
Saint Landry, co., La., U.S.	D3	95
Saint-Laurent, Que., Can.	p19	74
Saint Lawrence, Newf., Can.	E4	72
Saint Lawrence, co., N.Y., U.S.	A5	109
Saint Lawrence, stm., N.A.	G19	66
Saint Lawrence, Cape, c., N.S., Can.	B9	71
Saint Lawrence, Gulf of, b., Can.	G20	66
Saint Lawrence Island, i., Ak., U.S.	C5	79
Saint Lawrence Islands National Park, Ont., Can.	C9	73
Saint Léonard, N.B., Can.	B2	71
Saint-Léonard [-d'Aston], Que., Can.	C5	74
Saint-Liboire, Que., Can.	D5	74
Saint-Lô, Fr.	C5	10
Saint-Louis, Sen.	E2	42
Saint Louis, Mi., U.S.	E6	99
Saint Louis, Mo., U.S.	C7	102
Saint Louis, co., Mn., U.S.	C6	100
Saint Louis, co., Mo., U.S.	C7	102
Saint Louis, stm., U.S.	D6	100
Saint-Louis, Lac, l., Que., Can.	q19	74
Saint Louis Bay, b., Ms., U.S.	f7	101
Saint-Louis-de-Gonzague, Que., Can.	D3	74
Saint-Louis-de-Kent, N.B., Can.	C5	71
Saint-Louis-du-Ha! Ha!, Que., Can.	B8	74
Saint Louis Park, Mn., U.S.	n12	100
Saint-Luc, Que., Can.	D4	74
Saint Lucia, ctry., N.A.	H17	64
Saint Lucia Channel, strt., N.A.	G17	64
Saint Lucie, co., Fl., U.S.	E6	86
Saint Lucie Canal, Fl., U.S.	F6	86
Saint Lucie Inlet, b., Fl., U.S.	E6	86
Sainte-Madeleine, Que., Can.	D4	74
Saint Malo, Man., Can.	E3	70
Saint-Malo, Fr.	D4	10
Saint-Malo, Golfe de, b., Fr.	D4	10
Saint-Marc, Haiti	E11	64
Saint-Marc [-des-Carrières], Que., Can.	C5	74
Saint-Marcellin, Fr.	G12	10
Saint Margaret Bay, b., Newf., Can.	C3	72
Sainte-Marguerite, stm., Que., Can.	A7	74
Sainte-Marie, Que., Can.	C6	74
Sainte-Marie, Cap, c., Madag.	G9	44
Saint Maries, Id., U.S.	B2	89
Sainte-Marthe, Que., Can.	D3	74
Saint Martin, co., La., U.S.	D4	95
Saint-Martin (Sint Maarten), i., N.A.	E16	64
Saint Martin, Lake, l., Man., Can.	D2	70
Saint Martin Island, i., Mi., U.S.	C4	99
Saint Martinville, La., U.S.	D4	95
Saint Mary, co., La., U.S.	E4	95
Saint Mary-of-the-Woods, In., U.S.	E3	91
Saint Mary Peak, mtn., Austl.	F7	50
Saint Marys, Austl.	H9	50
Saint Mary's, Newf., Can.	E5	72
Saint Mary's, Ont., Can.	D3	73
Saint Marys, Ak., U.S.	C7	79
Saint Marys, Ga., U.S.	F5	87
Saint Marys, In., U.S.	A5	91
Saint Marys, Ks., U.S.	C7	93
Saint Marys, Oh., U.S.	B1	112
Saint Marys, Pa., U.S.	D4	115
Saint Marys, W.V., U.S.	B3	125
Saint Marys, co., Md., U.S.	D4	97
Saint Marys, stm., N.S., Can.	D8	71
Saint Marys, stm., U.S.	F5	87
Saint Marys, stm., U.S.	C8	91
Saint Marys, stm., Md., U.S.	D5	97
Saint Mary's, Cape, c., Newf., Can.	E4	72
Saint Mary's Bay, b., Newf., Can.	E5	72
Saint Marys Bay, b., N.S., Can.	E3	71
Saint Marys City, Md., U.S.	D5	97
Saint-Mathieu, Pointe de, c., Fr.	D2	10
Saint Matthew Island, i., Ak., U.S.	C5	79
Saint Matthews, Ky., U.S.	B4	94
Saint Matthews, S.C., U.S.	D6	117
Sainte-Maure-du-Touraine, Fr.	E7	10
Saint-Maurice, stm., Que., Can.	C5	74
Sainte-Maxime, Fr.	I13	10
Saint-Méen-le-Grand, Fr.	D4	10
Sainte-Menehould, Fr.	C11	10
Sainte-Mère-Église, Fr.	C5	10
Saint Michael, Mn., U.S.	E5	100
Saint Michaels, Md., U.S.	C5	97
Saint-Michel [-de-Bellechasse], Que., Can.	C7	74
Saint-Mihiel, Fr.	D12	10
Saint-Moritz see Sankt Moritz, Switz.	F16	10
Saint-Nazaire, Fr.	E4	10
Saint-Nicolas, Que., Can.	o17	74
Saint-Odilon, Que., Can.	C7	74
Saint-Omer, Fr.	B9	10
Saint-Ours, Que., Can.	D4	74
Saint-Pacôme, Que., Can.	B8	74
Saint-Pamphile, Que., Can.	C8	74
Saint Paris, Oh., U.S.	B2	112
Saint-Pascal, Que., Can.	B8	74
Saint Paul, Alta., Can.	B5	68
Saint Paul, Ak., U.S.	D5	79
Saint Paul, In., U.S.	F6	91
Saint Paul, Ks., U.S.	E8	93
Saint Paul, Mn., U.S.	F5	100
Saint Paul, Mo., U.S.	f12	102
Saint Paul, Ne., U.S.	C7	104
Saint Paul, Va., U.S.	f9	123
Saint Paul Island, i., Ak., U.S.	D5	79
Saint Paul Park, Mn., U.S.	n12	100
Saint Pauls, N.C., U.S.	C4	110
Sainte-Perpétue-de-L'Islet, Que., Can.	B8	74
Saint Peter, Mn., U.S.	F5	100
Saint Peter Port, Guernsey	C4	10
Saint Peters, N.S., Can.	D9	71
Saint Peters, Mo., U.S.	C7	102
Saint Petersburg, Fl., U.S.	E4	86
Saint Petersburg Beach, Fl., U.S.	p10	86
Saint Petersburg see Leningrad, U.S.S.R.	B13	22
Saint Phillips Island, i., S.C., U.S.	G6	117
Saint-Pie, Que., Can.	D5	74

Saint-Pierre, Reu. **F11** 44
Saint-Pierre, St. P./M. **E3** 72
Saint-Pierre, Lac, l., Que., Can. **C5** 74
Saint Pierre and Miquelon, dep., N.A. **G21** 66
Saint Pierre Island, i., Sey. **C10** 44
Saint Pierre-Jolys, Man., Can. **E3** 70
Saint-Pierre-le-Moûtier, Fr. **F10** 10
Saint-Pol-de-Léon, Fr. **D3** 10
Saint-Pons, Fr. **I9** 10
Saint-Pourçain-sur-Sioule, Fr. **F10** 10
Saint-Prime, Que., Can. **A5** 74
Saint Quentin, N.B., Can. **B2** 71
Saint-Quentin, Fr. **C10** 10
Saint-Raphaël, Que., Can. **C7** 74
Saint-Raphaël, Fr. **I13** 10
Saint-Raymond, Que., Can. **C6** 74
Saint-Rédempteur, Que., Can. **o17** 74
Saint Regis, Mt., U.S. **C1** 103
Saint Regis, West Branch, stm., N.Y., U.S. **f10** 109
Saint-Rémi, Que., Can. **D4** 74
Saint-Romuald, Que., Can. **C6** 74
Saint Rose, La., U.S. **k11** 95
Sainte Rose du Lac, Man., Can. **D2** 70
Saintes, Fr. **G6** 10
Saint Sauveur, N.B., Can. **B4** 71
Saint-Sauveur-des-Monts, Que., Can. **D3** 74
Saint-Sébastien, Cap, c., Madag. **D9** 44
Saint-Siméon, Que., Can. **B8** 74
Saint Simons Island, Ga., U.S. **E5** 87
Saint Simons Island, i., Ga., U.S. **E5** 87
Saint Stephen, N.B., Can. **D2** 71
Saint Stephen, S.C., U.S. **E8** 117
Saint Tammany, co., La., U.S. **D5** 95
Sainte-Thècle, Que., Can. **C5** 74
Sainte-Thérèse, Que., Can. **D4** 74
Saint Thomas, Ont., Can. **E3** 73
Saint Thomas, i., V.I.U.S. **E15** 64
Saint Timothée, Que., Can. **q18** 74
Saint-Tite, Que., Can. **C5** 74
Saint-Tropez, Fr. **I13** 10
Saint-Valéry-en-Caux, Fr. **C7** 10
Saint-Varent, Fr. **F6** 10
Sainte-Véronique, Que., Can. **C3** 74
Saint-Victor, Que., Can. **C7** 74
Saint-Vincent, Cap, c., Madag. **F8** 44
Saint Vincent, Gulf, b., Austl. **F7** 50
Saint Vincent and the Grenadines, ctry., N.A. **H17** 64
Saint Vincent Island, i., Fl., U.S. **C1** 86
Saint Vincent Passage, strt., N.A. **H17** 64
Saint Vincent's [-Saint Stephens-Peter's River], Newf., Can. **E5** 72
Saint-Vith, Bel. **E6** 8
Saint Walburg, Sask., Can. **D1** 75
Saint-Zacharie, Que., Can. **C7** 74
Sairecábur, Cerro, mtn., S.A. **A3** 56
Saito, Japan **J4** 30
Saitula, China **B8** 38
Sajama, Nevado, mtn., Bol. **G5** 54
Sajia, China **F13** 38
Sajnšand, Mong. **C9** 26
Sakai, Japan **H8** 30
Sakaide, Japan **H6** 30
Sakai-minato, Japan **G6** 30
Sakakawea, Lake, res., N.D., U.S. **B3** 111
Sakami, Lac, l., Que., Can. **F17** 66
Sakata, Japan **D12** 30
Sakhalin see Sachalin, Ostrov, i., U.S.S.R. **G22** 20
Sākhar, Afg. **D1** 38
Sakishima-shotō, is., Japan **G11** 26
Sakon Nakhon, Thai. **F8** 34
Sakonnet, stm., R.I., U.S. **E6** 116
Sakonnet Point, c., R.I., U.S. **F6** 116
Saku, Japan **F11** 30
Sakurai, Japan **H8** 30
Sal, Point, c., Ca., U.S. **E3** 82
Sala, Swe. **G11** 6
Salaberry-de-Valleyfield, Que., Can. **D3** 74
Sala Consilina, Italy **I10** 14
Salado, stm., Arg. **C4** 56
Salado, Rio, stm., N.M., U.S. **C2** 108
Şalālah, Oman **E5** 46
Salamanca, Mex. **G9** 62
Salamanca, Spain **E6** 12
Salamanca, N.Y., U.S. **C2** 109
Salamina, Col. **E5** 58
Salamonie, stm., In., U.S. **C6** 91
Salamonie Lake, res., In., U.S. **C6** 91
Salatiga, Indon. **m15** 33a
Salavat, U.S.S.R. **G9** 18
Salawati, i., Indon. **F9** 32
Saldanha, S. Afr. **H3** 44
Sale, Austl. **G9** 50
Sale Creek, Tn., U.S. **D8** 119
Salem, India **G5** 37
Salem, Ar., U.S. **A4** 81
Salem, Il., U.S. **E5** 90
Salem, In., U.S. **G5** 91
Salem, Ky., U.S. **e9** 94
Salem, Ma., U.S. **A6** 98
Salem, Mo., U.S. **D6** 102
Salem, N.H., U.S. **E4** 106
Salem, N.J., U.S. **D2** 107
Salem, Oh., U.S. **B5** 112
Salem, Or., U.S. **C4** 114
Salem, S.D., U.S. **D8** 118
Salem, Ut., U.S. **C4** 121
Salem, Va., U.S. **C2** 123
Salem, W.V., U.S. **B4** 125
Salem, Wi., U.S. **n11** 126
Salem, co., N.J., U.S. **D2** 107
Salem, stm., N.J., U.S. **D2** 107
Salem, Lake, l., Vt., U.S. **B4** 122
Salemi, Italy **L7** 14
Sälen, Swe. **F9** 6
Salerno, Italy **I9** 14
Salford, Eng., U.K. **H10** 7
Salgótarján, Hung. **G19** 8
Sali, Yugo. **F10** 14
Salida, Co., U.S. **C5** 83
Salies-de-Béarn, Fr. **I6** 10
Salihli, Tur. **K12** 16
Salina, Ks., U.S. **D6** 93
Salina, Ok., U.S. **A6** 113
Salina, Ut., U.S. **E4** 121
Salina Cruz, Mex. **I12** 62
Salinas, Braz. **D7** 57
Salinas, Ca., U.S. **D3** 82
Salinas, stm., Ca., U.S. **D3** 82
Salinas de Hidalgo, Mex. **F9** 62
Salinas Peak, mtn., N.M., U.S. **D3** 108
Salinas Pueblo Missions National Monument, N.M., U.S. **C3** 108
Saline, Mi., U.S. **F7** 99
Saline, co., Ar., U.S. **C3** 81
Saline, co., Il., U.S. **F5** 90
Saline, co., Ks., U.S. **D6** 93
Saline, co., Mo., U.S. **B4** 102
Saline, co., Ne., U.S. **D8** 104
Saline, stm., Ar., U.S. **C1** 81
Saline, stm., Ar., U.S. **D4** 81
Saline, stm., Ks., U.S. **C3** 93
Saline, North Fork, stm., Il., U.S. **F5** 90
Saline Lake, res., La., U.S. **C3** 95
Salineville, Oh., U.S. **B5** 112
Salisbury, N.B., Can. **C4** 71
Salisbury, Eng., U.K. **J11** 7
Salisbury, Ct., U.S. **B2** 84
Salisbury, Md., U.S. **D6** 97
Salisbury, Ma., U.S. **A6** 98
Salisbury, Mo., U.S. **B5** 102
Salisbury, N.C., U.S. **B2** 110
Salisbury see Harare, Zimb. **E6** 44
Salisbury Island, i., N.W. Ter., Can. **D17** 66
Salisbury Plain, pl., Eng., U.K. **J11** 7
Salish Mountains, mts., Mt., U.S. **B2** 103
Salkehatchie, stm., S.C., U.S. **E5** 117
Şalkhad, Syria **C5** 40
Salles-Curan, Fr. **H9** 10
Sallisaw, Ok., U.S. **B7** 113
Salluit, Que., Can. **f11** 74
Salmo, B.C., Can. **E9** 69
Salmon, Id., U.S. **D5** 89
Salmon, stm., N.B., Can. **C4** 71
Salmon, stm., Id., U.S. **D3** 89
Salmon Creek, Wa., U.S. **D3** 124
Salmon Creek Reservoir, res., Id., U.S. **G4** 89
Salmon Falls, stm., U.S. **D5** 106
Salmon Falls Creek, stm., U.S. **G4** 89
Salmon Mountains, mts., Ca., U.S. **B2** 82
Salmon Point, c., Ont., Can. **D7** 73
Salmon River Mountains, mts., Id., U.S. **E3** 89
Salmon River Reservoir, res., N.Y., U.S. **B5** 109
Salo, Fin. **F14** 6
Salome, Az., U.S. **D2** 80
Salon-De-Provence, Fr. **I12** 10
Salonika see Thessaloníki, Grc. **I6** 16
Salsomaggiore Terme, Italy **E4** 14
Salt, stm., Az., U.S. **D4** 80
Salt, stm., Ky., U.S. **C4** 94
Salt, stm., Mo., U.S. **B6** 102
Salta, Arg. **A3** 56
Salt Creek, stm., N.M., U.S. **D5** 108
Salt Creek, stm., Oh., U.S. **C3** 112
Salt Creek, stm., Wy., U.S. **C6** 127
Salter Path, N.C., U.S. **C6** 110
Salt Fork Lake, res., Oh., U.S. **B4** 112
Saltillo, Mex. **E9** 62
Saltillo, Ms., U.S. **A5** 101
Salt Lake, co., Ut., U.S. **C3** 121
Salt Lake, l., Hi., U.S. **g10** 88
Salt Lake, l., N.M., U.S. **E6** 108
Salt Lake City, Ut., U.S. **C4** 121
Salto, Ur. **C5** 56
Salton Sea, l., Ca., U.S. **F5** 82
Saltonstall, Lake, l., Ct., U.S. **D4** 84
Salt Point, c., Ca., U.S. **C2** 82
Salt River Indian Reservation, Az., U.S. **k9** 80
Salt River Range, mts., Wy., U.S. **D2** 127
Saltsburg, Pa., U.S. **F3** 115
Salt Springs, Fl., U.S. **C5** 86
Saltville, Va., U.S. **f10** 123
Salt Wells Creek, stm., Wy., U.S. **E4** 127
Saluda, S.C., U.S. **C4** 117
Saluda, co., S.C., U.S. **C4** 117
Saluda, stm., S.C., U.S. **C4** 117
Saluda Dam, S.C., U.S. **C5** 117
Sālūr, India **C7** 37
Saluzzo, Italy **E2** 14
Salvador, Braz. **B9** 57
Salvador, Lake, l., La., U.S. **E5** 95
Salvatierra, Mex. **G9** 62
Salween (Nu) (Thanlwin), stm., Asia **D5** 34
Salyersville, Ky., U.S. **C6** 94
Salzburg, Aus. **H13** 8
Salzgitter, Ger. **C10** 8
Salzwedel, Ger. **C11** 8
Sama [de Langreo], Spain **B6** 12
Samaná, Bahía de, b., Dom. Rep. **E13** 64
Samana Cay, i., Bah. **C11** 64
Samandağı, Tur. **A4** 40
Samar, i., Phil. **C8** 32
Samara, U.S.S.R. **G8** 18
Samarai, Pap. N. Gui. **n17** 50a
Samariapo, Ven. **E9** 58
Samarinda, Indon. **F6** 32
Samarkand, U.S.S.R. **J11** 18
Sāmarrā', Iraq **B3** 46
Samāstipur, India **H11** 38
Sambalpur, India **J10** 38
Sambas, Indon. **E4** 32
Sambava, Madag. **D10** 44
Sambhal, India **F8** 38
Sāmbhar, India **G6** 38
Samborondón, Ec. **H3** 58
Sammamish Lake, l., Wa., U.S. **e11** 124
Samneua, Laos **D8** 34
Samobor, Yugo. **D10** 14
Sámos, i., Grc. **L10** 16
Samoset, Fl., U.S. **q10** 86
Sampit, Indon. **F5** 32
Sampit, stm., S.C., U.S. **E9** 117
Sampson, co., N.C., U.S. **B4** 110
Sam Rayburn Reservoir, res., Tx., U.S. **D5** 120
Samson, Al., U.S. **D3** 78
Samsun, Tur. **G15** 4
Samuels, Id., U.S. **A2** 89
Samui, Ko, i., Thai. **J6** 34
Samut Prakan, Thai. **H6** 34
Samut Sakhon, Thai. **H6** 34
San, Mali **F5** 42
San, stm., Eur. **E22** 8
Şan'ā', Yemen **E3** 46
Sanaga, stm., Cam. **H7** 42
San Agustín, Col. **G4** 58
San Agustin, Cape, c., Phil. **D8** 32
San Agustin, Plains of, pl., N.M., U.S. **C2** 108
Sanak Islands, is., Ak., U.S. **E7** 79
Sanana, Pulau, i., Indon. **F8** 32
Sanandaj, Iran **A4** 46
San Andreas, Ca., U.S. **C3** 82
San Andrés, Isla de, i., Col. **H7** 64
San Andres Mountains, mts., N.M., U.S. **E3** 108
San Andres Peak, mtn., N.M., U.S. **E3** 108
San Andrés Tuxtla, Mex. **H12** 62
San Angelo, Tx., U.S. **D2** 120
San Anselmo, Ca., U.S. **h7** 82
San Antonio, Tx., U.S. **E3** 120
San Antonio, Cabo, c., Arg. **D5** 56
San Antonio, Cabo, c., Cuba **D5** 64
San Antonio Abad, Spain **G13** 12
San Antonio Bay, b., Tx., U.S. **E4** 120
San Antonio de Bravo, Mex. **B7** 62
San Antonio de los Cobres, Arg. **A3** 56
San Antonio del Táchira, Ven. **D6** 58
San Antonio Mountain, mtn., N.M., U.S. **A3** 108
San Antonio Oeste, Arg. **E4** 56
San Augustine, Tx., U.S. **D5** 120
San Augustine, co., Tx., U.S. **D5** 120
San Benedetto del Tronto, Italy **G8** 14
San Benedicto, Isla, i., Mex. **H4** 62
San Benito, Guat. **F3** 64
San Benito, Tx., U.S. **F4** 120
San Benito, co., Ca., U.S. **D3** 82
San Benito Mountain, mtn., Ca., U.S. **D3** 82
San Bernardino, Ca., U.S. **E5** 82
San Bernardino, co., Ca., U.S. **E5** 82
San Bernardo, Chile **C2** 56
San Blas, Mex. **G7** 62
San Blas, Mex. **D5** 62
San Blas, Cape, c., Fl., U.S. **v16** 86
San Borja, Bol. **F5** 54
Sanborn, Ia., U.S. **A2** 92
Sanborn, co., S.D., U.S. **D7** 118
Sanbornville, N.H., U.S. **C4** 106
San Bruno, Ca., U.S. **D2** 82
San Carlos, Nic. **I5** 64
San Carlos, Az., U.S. **D5** 80
San Carlos, Ca., U.S. **k8** 82
San Carlos, Ven. **C8** 58
San Carlos de Bariloche, Arg. **E2** 56
San Carlos de Guaroa, Col. **F6** 58
San Carlos de la Rápita, Spain **E12** 12
San Carlos del Zulia, Ven. **C7** 58
San Carlos de Río Negro, Ven. **G9** 58
San Carlos Indian Reservation, Az., U.S. **D5** 80
San Carlos Lake, res., Az., U.S. **D5** 80
San Cataldo, Italy **L9** 14
Sancerre, Fr. **E9** 10
Sánchez, Mex. **D10** 62
San Clemente, Ca., U.S. **F5** 82
San Clemente Island, i., Ca., U.S. **F4** 82
Sancoins, Fr. **F9** 10
San Cristóbal, Arg. **C4** 56
San Cristóbal, Ven. **D6** 58
San Cristóbal, Volcán, vol., Nic. **H4** 64
San Cristóbal las Casas, Mex. **I13** 62
Sancti-Spíritus, Cuba **D8** 64
Sand, Nor. **G6** 6
Sandakan, Malay. **D6** 32
Sanday, i., Scot., U.K. **B10** 7
Sand Creek, stm., Wy., U.S. **C7** 127
Sanders, Az., U.S. **B6** 80
Sanders, co., Mt., U.S. **C1** 103
Sanderson, Tx., U.S. **D1** 120
Sandersville, Ga., U.S. **D4** 87
Sandersville, Ms., U.S. **D4** 101
Sand Hill, Ma., U.S. **h13** 98
Sand Hill, stm., Mn., U.S. **C2** 100
Sandia, Peru **F5** 54
Sandia Crest, mtn., N.M., U.S. **k8** 108
Sandia Indian Reservation, N.M., U.S. **k7** 108
Sandia Mountains, mts., N.M., U.S. **k8** 108
San Diego, Ca., U.S. **F5** 82
San Diego, Tx., U.S. **F3** 120
San Diego, co., Ca., U.S. **F5** 82
San Diego, stm., Ca., U.S. **o15** 82
San Diego Naval Station, mil., Ca., U.S. **o15** 82
San Diego Naval Training Center, mil., Ca., U.S. **o15** 82
Sand Island, i., Hi., U.S. **g10** 88
Sand Island, i., Wi., U.S. **B3** 126
Sand Key, i., Fl., U.S. **E4** 86
Sandlick Creek, stm., W.V., U.S. **n13** 125
Sandnes, Nor. **G5** 6
Sandoa, Zaire **C4** 44
San Donà di Piave, Italy **D7** 14
Sandoval, Il., U.S. **E4** 90
Sandoval, co., N.M., U.S. **B2** 108
Sandoway, Burma **E3** 34
Sand Point, Ak., U.S. **D7** 79
Sandpoint, Id., U.S. **A2** 89
Sands Key, i., Fl., U.S. **s3** 86
Sand Springs, Ok., U.S. **A5** 113
Sandston, Va., U.S. **m18** 123
Sandstone, Austl. **E3** 50
Sandstone, Mn., U.S. **D6** 100
Sandusky, Mi., U.S. **E8** 99
Sandusky, Oh., U.S. **A3** 112
Sandusky, co., Oh., U.S. **A2** 112
Sandusky, stm., Oh., U.S. **B2** 112
Sandviken, Swe. **F11** 6
Sandwich, Il., U.S. **B5** 90
Sandwich, Ma., U.S. **C7** 98
Sandwich Bay, b., Newf., Can. **B3** 72
Sandy, Or., U.S. **B4** 114
Sandy, Ut., U.S. **C4** 121
Sandy, stm., Me., U.S. **D2** 96
Sandy Creek, stm., Oh., U.S. **B4** 112
Sandy Creek, stm., Ok., U.S. **C2** 113
Sandy Hook, Ct., U.S. **D2** 84
Sandy Hook, spit, N.J., U.S. **C5** 107
Sandy Island, i., S.C., U.S. **D9** 117
Sandy Lake, l., Newf., Can. **D3** 72
Sandy Lake, l., Ont., Can. **n16** 73
Sandy Neck, pen., Ma., U.S. **C7** 98
Sandy Point, c., R.I., U.S. **h7** 116
Sandy Springs, Ga., U.S. **h8** 87
Sandy Springs, S.C., U.S. **B2** 117
Sandyville, Md., U.S. **A4** 97
San Felipe, Ven. **B8** 58
San Felipe Indian Reservation, N.M., U.S. **k8** 108
San Felipe Pueblo, N.M., U.S. **B3** 108
San Feliu de Guixols, Spain **D15** 12
San Fernando, Chile **C2** 56
San Fernando, Mex. **E10** 62
San Fernando, Phil. **q19** 32
San Fernando, Phil. **B7** 32
San Fernando, Spain **I5** 12
San Fernando, Trin. **I17** 64
San Fernando, Ca., U.S. **m12** 82
San Fernando de Apure, Ven. **D9** 58
San Fernando de Atabapo, Ven. **E9** 58
Sanford, Co., U.S. **D5** 83
Sanford, Fl., U.S. **D5** 86
Sanford, Me., U.S. **E2** 96
Sanford, Mi., U.S. **E6** 99
Sanford, N.C., U.S. **B3** 110
Sanford, Mount, mtn., Ak., U.S. **C11** 79
San Francisco, Arg. **C4** 56
San Francisco, Ca., U.S. **D2** 82
San Francisco, co., Ca., U.S. **D2** 82
San Francisco, stm., U.S. **D6** 80
San Francisco Bay, b., Ca., U.S. **h8** 82
San Francisco de Borja, Mex. **D6** 62
San Francisco del Oro, Mex. **D7** 62
San Francisco del Rincón, Mex. **G9** 62
San Francisco de Macorís, Dom. Rep. **E12** 64
San Fratello, Italy **K9** 14
San Gabriel, Ec. **G4** 58
San Gabriel, Ca., U.S. **m12** 82
San Gabriel Mountains, mts., Ca., U.S. **m12** 82
Sangamner, India **C3** 37
Sangamon, co., Il., U.S. **D4** 90
Sangamon, stm., Il., U.S. **C3** 90
San Gavino Monreale, Italy **J3** 14
Sangay, Volcán, vol., Ec. **H3** 58
Sang-e Māsheh, Afg. **D2** 38
Sanger, Ca., U.S. **D4** 82
Sanger, Tx., U.S. **C4** 120
Sangerhausen, Ger. **D11** 8
Sangha, stm., Afr. **B3** 44
Sanghar, Pak. **G3** 38
Sangihe, Kepulauan, is., Indon. **E8** 32
Sangihe, Pulau, i., Indon. **E8** 32
San Gil, Col. **D6** 58
San Giovanni in Fiore, Italy **J11** 14
San Giovanni in Persiceto, Italy **E6** 14
San Giovanni Valdarno, Italy **F6** 14
Sāngli, India **D3** 37
Sangolquí, Ec. **H3** 58
San Gorgonio Mountain, mtn., Ca., U.S. **E5** 82
San Gregorio, Ur. **C5** 56
Sangrūr, India **E6** 38
Sangüesa, Spain **C10** 12
Sanibel, Fl., U.S. **F4** 86
Sanibel Island, i., Fl., U.S. **F4** 86
San Ignacio, Arg. **B5** 56
San Ignacio, Hond. **G4** 64
Sanilac, co., Mi., U.S. **E8** 99
San Isidro, Arg. **C5** 56
San Isidro, C.R. **J6** 64
San Jacinto, Col. **C5** 58
San Jacinto, Ca., U.S. **F5** 82
San Jacinto, co., Tx., U.S. **D5** 120
San Jacinto, stm., Tx., U.S. **r14** 120
Sanjō, Japan **E11** 30
San Joaquin, co., Ca., U.S. **D3** 82
San Joaquin, stm., Ca., U.S. **D3** 82
San Joaquin Valley, val., Ca., U.S. **D3** 82
San Jorge, Golfo, b., Arg. **F3** 56
San Jorge, Golfo de, b., Spain **E12** 12
San José, C.R. **J5** 64
San Jose, Ca., U.S. **D3** 82
San José, Isla, i., Mex. **E4** 62
San José de Chiquitos, Bol. **G6** 54
San José de Guanipa, Ven. **C10** 58
San José del Cabo, Mex. **F5** 62
San José del Guaviare, Col. **F6** 58
San José de Mayo, Ur. **C5** 56
San José de Ocuné, Col. **E7** 58
San José de Raíces, Mex. **E9** 62
San Jose Island, i., Tx., U.S. **E4** 120
San Juan, Arg. **C3** 56
San Juan, Mex. **D8** 62
San Juan, P.R. **E14** 64
San Juan, Tx., U.S. **F3** 120
San Juan, co., Co., U.S. **D3** 83
San Juan, co., N.M., U.S. **A1** 108
San Juan, co., Ut., U.S. **F5** 121
San Juan, co., Wa., U.S. **A2** 124
San Juan, stm., N.A. **I6** 64
San Juan Capistrano, Ca., U.S. **F5** 82
San Juan de Colón, Ven. **C6** 58
San Juan [de la Maguana], Dom. Rep. **E12** 64
San Juan del Norte, Nic. **I6** 64
San Juan de los Cayos, Ven. **B8** 58
San Juan de los Morros, Ven. **C9** 58
San Juan del Río, Mex. **G9** 62
San Juan del Sur, Nic. **I5** 64
San Juan Island, i., Wa., U.S. **A2** 124
San Juan Mountains, mts., Co., U.S. **D3** 83
San Julián, Arg. **F3** 56
San Justo, Arg. **C4** 56
Sankt Gallen, Aus. **H14** 8
Sankt Gallen, Switz. **E16** 10
Sankt Johann im Pongau, Aus. **H13** 8
Sankt Moritz, Switz. **F16** 10
Sankt Peter, Ger. **A8** 8
Sankt Pölten, Aus. **G15** 8
Sankt Veit an der Glan, Aus. **I14** 8
Sankt Wendel, Ger. **F7** 8
Sankuru, stm., Zaire **B4** 44
San Lázaro, Cabo, c., Mex. **E3** 62
San Leandro, Ca., U.S. **h8** 82
San Lope, Col. **D7** 58
San Lorenzo, Arg. **C4** 56
San Lorenzo, Ec. **G3** 58
San Lorenzo, Isla, i., Peru **F3** 54
San Lorenzo de El Escorial, Spain **E7** 12
San Lorenzo de la Parrilla, Spain **F9** 12
Sanlúcar de Barrameda, Spain **I5** 12
San Lucas, Ec. **I3** 58
San Lucas, Cabo, c., Mex. **F5** 62
San Luis, Arg. **C3** 56
San Luis, Cuba **D10** 64
San Luis, Guat. **F3** 64
San Luis, Az., U.S. **E3** 80
San Luis, Co., U.S. **D5** 83
San Luis, Ven. **B8** 58
San Luis, Lago de, l., Bol. **F6** 54
San Luis, Point, c., Ca., U.S. **E3** 82
San Luis de la Paz, Mex. **G9** 62
San Luis Obispo, Ca., U.S. **E3** 82
San Luis Obispo, co., Ca., U.S. **E3** 82
San Luis Pass, strt., Tx., U.S. **r14** 120
San Luis Peak, mtn., Co., U.S. **D4** 83
San Luis Potosí, Mex. **F9** 62
San Luis Río Colorado, Mex. **A2** 62
San Luis Valley, val., Co., U.S. **D4** 83
San Manuel, Az., U.S. **E5** 80
San Marcos, Col. **C5** 58
San Marcos, Mex. **D8** 62
San Marcos, Mex. **I10** 62
San Marcos, Tx., U.S. **E4** 120
San Marcos, stm., Tx., U.S. **h8** 120
San Marino, Ca., U.S. **m12** 82
San Marino, ctry., Eur. **G10** 4
San Martín de Valdeiglesias, Spain **E7** 12
San Mateo, Spain **E12** 12
San Mateo, Ca., U.S. **D2** 82
San Mateo, co., Ca., U.S. **D2** 82
San Mateo Mountains, mts., N.M., U.S. **D2** 108
San Mateo Mountains, mts., N.M., U.S. **B2** 108
San Matías, Golfo, b., Arg. **E4** 56
San Miguel, El Sal. **H3** 64
San Miguel, co., Co., U.S. **D2** 83
San Miguel, co., N.M., U.S. **B5** 108
San Miguel, stm., Bol. **F6** 54
San Miguel, stm., Co., U.S. **C2** 83
San Miguel de Allende, Mex. **G9** 62
San Miguel del Monte, Arg. **D5** 56
San Miguel de Tucumán, Arg. **B3** 56
San Miguel el Alto, Mex. **G8** 62
San Miguel Island, i., Ca., U.S. **E3** 82
San Miguel Mountains, mts., Co., U.S. **D2** 83
Sannār, Sudan **F12** 42
Sannicandro Garganico, Italy **H10** 14
San Nicolas, Phil. **o19** 33b
San Nicolás de los Arroyos, Arg. **C4** 56
San Nicolas Island, i., Ca., U.S. **F4** 82
Sannikova, Proliv, strt., U.S.S.R. **C21** 20
Sanniquellie, Lib. **G4** 42
Sano, Japan **F12** 30
Sanok, Pol. **F22** 8
San Onofre, Col. **C5** 58
San Pablo, Col. **G4** 58
San Pablo, Phil. **q19** 32
San Pablo Balleza, Mex. **D6** 62
San Pablo Bay, b., Ca., U.S. **g8** 82
San Patricio, co., Tx., U.S. **E4** 120
San Pedro, stm., Az., U.S. **E5** 80
San Pedro, Punta, c., Chile **B2** 56
San Pedro, Volcán, vol., Chile **A3** 56
San Pedro Bay, b., Ca., U.S. **n12** 82
San Pedro Carchá, Guat. **G2** 64
San Pedro de las Colonias, Mex. **E8** 62
San Pedro de Macorís, Dom. Rep. **E13** 64
San Pedro Mártir, Sierra, mts., Mex. **B2** 62
San Pedro Peaks, mts., N.M., U.S. **A3** 108
San Pedro Sula, Hond. **G4** 64
Sanpete, co., Ut., U.S. **D4** 121
Sanpoil, stm., Wa., U.S. **A7** 124
San Quintín, Cabo, c., Mex. **B1** 62
San Rafael, Arg. **C3** 56
San Rafael, Mex. **E9** 62
San Rafael, Ca., U.S. **D2** 82
San Rafael, N.M., U.S. **B2** 108
San Rafael, stm., Ut., U.S. **D5** 121
San Rafael Knob, mtn., Ut., U.S. **E5** 121
San Rafael Mountains, mts., Ca., U.S. **E4** 82
San Ramón, Nic. **G5** 64
San Ramon, Ca., U.S. **h9** 82
San Remo, Italy **F2** 14
San Saba, Tx., U.S. **D3** 120
San Saba, co., Tx., U.S. **D3** 120
San Salvador, El Sal. **H3** 64
San Salvador (Watling Island), i., Bah. **B10** 64
San Salvador de Jujuy, Arg. **A3** 56
Sansanné-Mango, Togo **F6** 42
San Sebastián, Spain **B10** 12
Sansepolcro, Italy **F7** 14
San Severo, Italy **H10** 14
San Simon, stm., Az., U.S. **E6** 80
Sanski Most, Yugo. **E11** 14
Santa Ana, Bol. **G5** 54
Santa Ana, Bol. **F5** 54
Santa Ana, El Sal. **H3** 64
Santa Ana, Mex. **E9** 62
Santa Ana, Mex. **B4** 62
Santa Ana, Ca., U.S. **F5** 82
Santa Ana, stm., Ca., U.S. **n13** 82

Name	Map Ref	Page
Santa Ana Indian Reservation, N.M., U.S.	h7	108
Santa Ana Mountains, mts., Ca., U.S.	n13	82
Santa Anna, Tx., U.S.	D3	120
Santa Bárbara, Mex.	D7	62
Santa Barbara, Ca., U.S.	E4	82
Santa Barbara, co., Ca., U.S.	E3	82
Santa Barbara Channel, strt., Ca., U.S.	E3	82
Santa Barbara Island, i., Ca., U.S.	F4	82
Santa Catalina, Gulf of, b., Ca., U.S.	F5	82
Santa Catalina Island, i., Ca., U.S.	F4	82
Santa Catalina Mountains, mts., Az., U.S.	E5	80
Santa Catarina, Ilha de, i., Braz.	B7	56
Santa Clara, Cuba	C8	64
Santa Clara, Ca., U.S.	D2	82
Santa Clara, Ut., U.S.	F2	121
Santa Clara, co., Ca., U.S.	D3	82
Santa Clara, stm., Ca., U.S.	E4	82
Santa Claus, In., U.S.	H4	91
Santa Coloma de Farnés, Spain	D14	12
Santa Comba Dão, Port.	E3	12
Santa Cruz, Arg.	F3	56
Santa Cruz, Bol.	G6	54
Santa Cruz, C.R.	I5	64
Santa Cruz, Phil.	q19	33b
Santa Cruz, Ca., U.S.	D2	82
Santa Cruz, N.M., U.S.	B3	108
Santa Cruz, co., Az., U.S.	F5	80
Santa Cruz, co., Ca., U.S.	D2	82
Santa Cruz, stm., Az., U.S.	E4	80
Santa Cruz del Quiché, Guat.	G2	64
Santa Cruz de Tenerife, Spain	C2	42
Santa Cruz do Rio Pardo, Braz.	G4	57
Santa Cruz Island, i., Ca., U.S.	F4	82
Santa Elena, Ec.	I2	58
Santa Elena, Punta, c., Ec.	I2	58
Santa Eugenia, Spain	C2	12
Santa Eulalia, Spain	E10	12
Santa Eulalia del Río, Spain	G13	12
Santa Fe, Arg.	C4	56
Santa Fé, Braz.	C3	57
Santa Fé, Cuba	D6	64
Santa Fe, Spain	H8	12
Santa Fe, N.M., U.S.	B4	108
Santa Fe, Tx., U.S.	r14	120
Santa Fe, co., N.M., U.S.	B3	108
Santa Fe, stm., N.M., U.S.	h8	108
Santa Fe Baldy, mtn., N.M., U.S.	B4	108
Santa Inés, Isla, i., Chile	G2	56
Santa Isabel, Ec.	I3	58
Santa Isabel, i., Sol.Is.	A11	50
Santa Isabel see Malabo, Eq. Gui.	H7	42
Santa Lucia Range, mts., Ca., U.S.	E3	82
Santa Magdalena, Isla, i., Mex.	E3	62
Santa Margarita, Ca., U.S.	E3	82
Santa Margarita, Isla de, i., Mex.	E4	62
Santa Maria, Braz.	B6	56
Santa Maria, Ca., U.S.	E3	82
Santa Maria, stm., Az., U.S.	C2	80
Santa Maria, Cabo de, c., Ang.	D2	44
Santa Maria do Suaçuí, Braz.	E7	57
Santa Maria Mountains, mts., Az., U.S.	C3	80
Santa Marta, Col.	B5	58
Santa Monica, Ca., U.S.	m12	82
Santana do Livramento, Braz.	C5	56
Santander, Col.	F4	58
Santander, Spain	B8	12
Sant' Antioco, Italy	J3	14
Santa Paula, Ca., U.S.	E4	82
Santaquin, Ut., U.S.	D4	121
Sant'Arcangelo, Italy	I11	14
Santarém, Braz.	D8	54
Santarém, Port.	F3	12
Santa Rita, Col.	G6	58
Santa Rita, Hond.	G4	64
Santa Rosa, Arg.	D4	56
Santa Rosa, Arg.	C3	56
Santa Rosa, Ec.	I3	58
Santa Rosa, Ca., U.S.	C2	82
Santa Rosa, N.M., U.S.	C5	108
Santa Rosa, co., Fl., U.S.	u14	86
Santa Rosa de Cabal, Col.	E5	58
Santa Rosa [de Copán], Hond.	G3	64
Santa Rosa Island, i., Ca., U.S.	F3	82
Santa Rosa Island, i., Fl., U.S.	u14	86
Santa Rosa Range, mts., Nv., U.S.	B4	105
Šantarskije Ostrova, is., U.S.S.R.	F21	20
Santa Teresa Gallura, Italy	H4	14
Santa Vitória do Palmar, Braz.	C6	56
Santa Ynez, Ca., U.S.	E3	82
Santee, Ca., U.S.	o16	82
Santee, stm., S.C., U.S.	E8	117
Santee Dam, S.C., U.S.	E7	117
Santee Indian Reservation, Ne., U.S.	B8	104
Santhià, Italy	D3	14
Santiago, Chile	C2	56
Santiago, Dom. Rep.	E12	64
Santiago, Pan.	J7	64
Santiago de Compostela, Spain	C3	12
Santiago de Cuba, Cuba	D10	64
Santiago del Estero, Arg.	B4	56
Santiago do Cacém, Port.	G3	12
Santiago Ixcuintla, Mex.	G7	62
Santiago Papasquiaro, Mex.	E7	62
Santiago Peak, mtn., Ca., U.S.	n13	82
Santiago Reservoir, res., Ca., U.S.	n13	82
Santiaguillo, Laguna de, l., Mex.	E7	62
Santiam Pass, Or., U.S.	C4	114
Sāntipur, India	I13	38
Santisteban del Puerto, Spain	G8	12
Santo Amaro, Braz.	B9	57
Santo Anastácio, Braz.	F3	57
Santo André, Braz.	G5	57
Santo Ângelo, Braz.	B6	56
Santo Antônio de Jesus, Braz.	B9	57
Santo Antônio do Içá, Braz.	D5	54
Santo Domingo, Dom. Rep.	E13	64
Santo Domingo, Nic.	H5	64
Santo Domingo de la Calzada, Spain	C9	12
Santo Domingo de los Colorados, Ec.	H3	58
Santo Domingo Indian Reservation, N.M., U.S.	h8	108
Santo Domingo Pueblo, N.M., U.S.	B3	108
Santoña, Spain	B8	12
Santos, Braz.	G5	57
Santos Dumont, Braz.	F7	57
Santo Tomás, Mex.	B1	62
Santo Tomé, Arg.	B5	56
San Valentín, Monte, mtn., Chile	F2	56
San Vicente, El Sal.	H3	64
San Vicente, Mex.	B1	62
San Vicente de Baracaldo, Spain	B9	12
San Vicente de la Barquera, Spain	B7	12
San Vicente del Caguán, Col.	F5	58
San Vicente Reservoir, res., Ca., U.S.	o16	82
San Xavier Indian Reservation, Az., U.S.	E4	80
Sanzao Dao, i., China	M2	28
Sanza Pombo, Ang.	C3	44
São Bento, Braz.	D10	54
São Borja, Braz.	B5	56
São Caetano do Sul, Braz.	G5	57
São Carlos, Braz.	G5	57
São Domingos, Braz.	B5	57
São Francisco, stm., Braz.	E11	54
São Francisco do Sul, Braz.	B7	56
São Gabriel, Braz.	E8	57
São João da Boa Vista, Braz.	F5	57
São João da Madeira, Port.	E3	12
São João del Rei, Braz.	F6	57
São Joaquim da Barra, Braz.	F5	57
São José do Rio Prêto, Braz.	F4	57
São José dos Campos, Braz.	G6	57
São Leopoldo, Braz.	B6	56
São Lourenço, Braz.	G6	57
São Lourenço, Pantanal de, sw., Braz.	G7	54
São Luís, Braz.	D10	54
São Manuel, Braz.	G4	57
São Mateus, Braz.	E9	57
Saona, Isla, i., Dom. Rep.	E13	64
Saône, stm., Fr.	F11	10
São Paulo, Braz.	G5	57
São Pedro do Ivaí, Braz.	G3	57
São Pedro do Sul, Port.	E3	12
São Romão, Braz.	D6	57
São Roque, Cabo de, c., Braz.	E11	54
São Sebastião, Ponta, c., Moz.	F7	44
São Sebastião do Paraíso, Braz.	F5	57
São Tomé, S. Tom./P.	A1	44
São Tomé, i., S. Tom./P.	A1	44
São Tomé, Cabo de, c., Braz.	F8	57
Sao Tome and Principe, ctry., Afr.	A1	44
São Vicente, Braz.	G5	57
São Vicente, Cabo de, c., Port.	H2	12
Sapé, Braz.	E11	54
Sapele, Nig.	G7	42
Sapelo Island, i., Ga., U.S.	E5	87
Sapitwa, mtn., Mwi.	E7	44
Sappa Creek, stm., U.S.	E5	104
Sapphire Mountains, mts., Mt., U.S.	D3	103
Sappington, Mo., U.S.	f13	102
Sapporo, Japan	p19	30a
Sapri, Italy	I10	14
Sapulpa, Ok., U.S.	B5	113
Sara Buri, Thai.	G6	34
Sarajevo, Yugo.	F2	16
Saraland, Al., U.S.	E1	78
Saranac, Mi., U.S.	F5	99
Saranac, stm., N.Y., U.S.	F11	109
Saranac Lake, N.Y., U.S.	f10	109
Saranac Lakes, l., N.Y., U.S.	f10	109
Sarangani Islands, is., Phil.	D8	32
Saransk, U.S.S.R.	G7	18
Sarapul, U.S.S.R.	F8	18
Sarasota, Fl., U.S.	E4	86
Sarasota, co., Fl., U.S.	E4	86
Sarasota Bay, b., Fl., U.S.	E4	86
Saratoga, Ca., U.S.	k8	82
Saratoga, Tx., U.S.	D5	120
Saratoga, Wy., U.S.	E6	127
Saratoga, co., N.Y., U.S.	B7	109
Saratoga Lake, l., N.Y., U.S.	C7	109
Saratoga National Historical Park, N.Y., U.S.	B7	109
Saratoga Springs, N.Y., U.S.	B7	109
Saratov, U.S.S.R.	G7	18
Saravane, Laos	G9	34
Saraxie, Mo., U.S.	D3	102
Sardalas, Libya	C8	42
Sardārshahr, India	F6	38
Sardegna, i., Italy	I3	14
Sardinia see Sardegna, i., Italy	I3	14
Sardis, Ga., U.S.	D5	87
Sardis, Ms., U.S.	A4	101
Sardis Lake, res., Ms., U.S.	A4	101
Sar-e Pol, Afg.	B1	38
Sarepta, La., U.S.	B2	95
Sarera, Teluk, b., Indon.	F10	32
Sargent, Ga., U.S.	C2	87
Sargent, Ne., U.S.	C6	104
Sargent, co., N.D., U.S.	C8	111
Sargodha, Pak.	D5	38
Sarh, Chad	G9	42
Sariñena, Spain	D11	12
Şarköy, Tur.	I11	16
Sarlat-la-Canéda, Fr.	H8	10
Sarmi, Indon.	F10	32
Sarmiento, Arg.	F3	56
Särna, Swe.	F9	6
Sarnia, Ont., Can.	E2	73
Sarpy, co., Ne., U.S.	C9	104
Sarralbe, Fr.	C14	10
Sarrebourg, Fr.	D14	10
Sarreguemines, Fr.	C14	10
Sarria, Spain	C4	12
Sartang, stm., U.S.S.R.	D20	20
Sartell, Mn., U.S.	E4	100
Sarthe, stm., Fr.	E6	10
Sarufutsu, Japan	n20	30a
Sarzeau, Fr.	E4	10
Sasarām, India	H11	38
Sasebo, Japan	I2	30
Saskatchewan, prov., Can.	E3	75
Saskatchewan, stm., Can.	F12	66
Saskylach, U.S.S.R.	C16	20
Sasovo, U.S.S.R.	G24	22
Sassafras, stm., Md., U.S.	B5	97
Sassafras Mountain, mtn., U.S.	A2	117
Sassandra, I.C.	H4	42
Sassandra, stm., I.C.	G4	42
Sassari, Italy	I3	14
Sassnitz, Ger.	A13	8
Sassuolo, Italy	E5	14
Sastown, Lib.	H4	42
Satah Mountain, mtn., B.C., Can.	C5	69
Sata-misaki, c., Japan	L3	30
Satanta, Ks., U.S.	E3	93
Sātāra, India	D2	37
Satilla, stm., Ga., U.S.	E5	87
Satkānia, Bngl.	I15	38
Satna, India	H9	38
Sātpura Range, mts., India	B4	37
Satsuma, Al., U.S.	E1	78
Satsunan-shotō, is., Japan	v29	31b
Şatu Mare, Rom.	B6	16
Šatura, U.S.S.R.	F22	22
Satus Creek, stm., Wa., U.S.	C5	124
Sauceda Mountains, mts., Az., U.S.	E3	80
Sauda, Nor.	G6	6
Saudi Arabia, ctry., Asia	D4	46
Saufley Field Naval Air Station, mil., Fl., U.S.	u14	86
Saugatuck, Mi., U.S.	F4	99
Saugatuck, stm., Ct., U.S.	D2	84
Saugatucket, stm., R.I., U.S.	F4	116
Saugatuck Reservoir, res., Ct., U.S.	D2	84
Saugerties, N.Y., U.S.	C7	109
Saugus, Ma., U.S.	B5	98
Saugus, stm., Ma., U.S.	g11	98
Sauk, co., Wi., U.S.	E4	126
Sauk, stm., Mn., U.S.	E4	100
Sauk, stm., Wa., U.S.	A4	124
Sauk Centre, Mn., U.S.	E4	100
Sauk City, Wi., U.S.	E4	126
Sauk Rapids, Mn., U.S.	E4	100
Saukville, Wi., U.S.	E6	126
Saulgau, Ger.	G9	8
Saulnierville, N.S., Can.	E3	71
Sault-au-Mouton, Que., Can.	A8	74
Sault Sainte Marie, Ont., Can.	p18	73
Sault Sainte Marie, Mi., U.S.	B6	99
Saumarez Reef, rf., Austl.	D10	50
Saumur, Fr.	E6	10
Saunders, co., Ne., U.S.	C9	104
Saunderstown, R.I., U.S.	E4	116
Saurimo, Ang.	C4	44
Sausalito, Ca., U.S.	D2	82
Sava, Italy	I12	14
Sava, stm., Yugo.	E3	16
Savage, Md., U.S.	B4	97
Savage, stm., Md., U.S.	k12	97
Savage River Reservoir, res., Md., U.S.	k12	97
Savanna, Il., U.S.	A3	90
Savanna, Ok., U.S.	C6	113
Savannah, Ga., U.S.	D5	87
Savannah, Mo., U.S.	B3	102
Savannah, Tn., U.S.	B3	119
Savannah, stm., U.S.	F5	117
Savannah River Plant, sci., S.C., U.S.	E4	117
Savannakhet, Laos	F8	34
Savanna Lake, l., Md., U.S.	D6	97
Savanna-la-Mar, Jam.	E8	64
Savaştepe, Tur.	J11	16
Save (Sabi), stm., Afr.	F6	44
Savenay, Fr.	E5	10
Saverdun, Fr.	I8	10
Saverne, Fr.	D14	10
Savigliano, Italy	E2	14
Saville Dam, Ct., U.S.	B4	84
Savona, Italy	E3	14
Savonlinna, Fin.	F17	6
Savonranta, Fin.	E17	6
Savoonga, Ak., U.S.	C5	79
Savoy, Il., U.S.	C5	90
Savu Sea see Sawu, Laut, Indon.	G7	32
Sawai Mādhopur, India	G7	38
Sawākin, Sudan	E13	42
Sawang, Indon.	N7	34
Sawatch Range, mts., Co., U.S.	B4	83
Sawdā', Qurnat as-, mtn., Leb.	B5	40
Sawel Mountain, mtn., N. Ire., U.K.	G5	7
Sawhāj, Egypt	C12	42
Sawknah, Libya	C9	42
Sawnee Mountain, mtn., Ga., U.S.	B2	87
Sawtooth Mountains, mts., Id., U.S.	F4	89
Sawtooth National Recreation Area, Id., U.S.	E3	89
Sawu, Laut (Savu Sea), Indon.	G7	32
Sawu, Pulau, i., Indon.	H7	32
Sawwān, Ard aş-, pl., Jord.	D5	40
Sawyer, co., Wi., U.S.	C2	126
Sawyerville, Que., Can.	D6	74
Saxmundham, Eng., U.K.	I14	7
Saxonburg, Pa., U.S.	E2	115
Saxtons, stm., Vt., U.S.	E3	122
Saxtons River, Vt., U.S.	E3	122
Sayaboury, Laos	E6	34
Sayan Mountains (Sajany), mts., Asia	G12	20
Sayaxché, Guat.	F2	64
Saybrook, Il., U.S.	C5	90
Saybrook Manor, Ct., U.S.	D6	84
Şaydā (Sidon), Leb.	C4	40
Saydel, Ia., U.S.	e8	92
Sayhūt, Yemen	E5	46
Saylesville, R.I., U.S.	B4	116
Saylorsburg, Pa., U.S.	E11	115
Saylorville, Ia., U.S.	e8	92
Saylorville Lake, res., Ia., U.S.	C4	92
Sayre, Al., U.S.	B3	78
Sayre, Ok., U.S.	B2	113
Sayre, Pa., U.S.	C8	115
Sayreville, N.J., U.S.	C4	107
Sayula, Mex.	H8	62
Say'ūn, Yemen	E4	46
Sayville, N.Y., U.S.	n15	109
Scafell Pikes, mtn., Eng., U.K.	G9	7
Scalp Level, Pa., U.S.	F4	115
Scanlon, Mn., U.S.	D6	100
Scapegoat Mountain, mtn., Mt., U.S.	C3	103
Ščapino, U.S.S.R.	F25	20
Scappoose, Or., U.S.	B4	114
Scarborough, Ont., Can.	m15	73
Scarborough, Trin.	I17	64
Scarborough, Me., U.S.	E2	96
Scarbro, W.V., U.S.	n13	125
Scarsdale, N.Y., U.S.	h13	109
Ščelkovo, U.S.S.R.	F21	22
Ščerbakovo, U.S.S.R.	D26	20
Schaefferstown, Pa., U.S.	F9	115
Schaffhausen, Switz.	E15	10
Schaller, Ia., U.S.	B2	92
Schaumburg, Il., U.S.	h8	90
Schell Creek Range, mts., Nv., U.S.	D7	105
Schenectady, N.Y., U.S.	C7	109
Schenectady, co., N.Y., U.S.	C6	109
Schererville, In., U.S.	B3	91
Schertz, Tx., U.S.	h7	120
Schiller Park, Il., U.S.	k9	90
Schio, Italy	D6	14
Schladming, Aus.	H13	8
Schleicher, co., Tx., U.S.	D2	120
Schleiden, Ger.	E6	8
Schleswig, Ger.	A9	8
Schleswig, Ia., U.S.	B2	92
Schley, co., Ga., U.S.	D2	87
Schneverdingen, Ger.	B9	8
Schofield, Wi., U.S.	D4	126
Schofield Barracks, mil., Hi., U.S.	g9	88
Schoharie, co., N.Y., U.S.	C6	109
Schoharie Creek, stm., N.Y., U.S.	C6	109
Schönebeck, Ger.	B13	8
Schongau, Ger.	H10	8
Schoodic Lake, l., Me., U.S.	C4	96
Schoolcraft, Mi., U.S.	F5	99
Schoolcraft, co., Mi., U.S.	B4	99
Schramberg, Ger.	G8	8
Schrobenhausen, Ger.	G11	8
Schroon Lake, l., N.Y., U.S.	B7	109
Schulenburg, Tx., U.S.	E4	120
Schuler, Ok., U.S.	B6	113
Schurz, Nv., U.S.	E3	105
Schuyler, Ne., U.S.	C8	104
Schuyler, co., Il., U.S.	C3	90
Schuyler, co., Mo., U.S.	A5	102
Schuyler, co., N.Y., U.S.	C4	109
Schuylkill, co., Pa., U.S.	E9	115
Schuylkill, stm., Pa., U.S.	F10	115
Schuylkill Haven, Pa., U.S.	E9	115
Schwabach, Ger.	F11	8
Schwaben, hist. reg., Ger.	G10	8
Schwäbische Alb, mts., Ger.	G9	8
Schwäbisch Gmünd, Ger.	G9	8
Schwäbisch Hall, Ger.	F9	8
Schwandorf in Bayern, Ger.	F12	8
Schwaner, Pegunungan, mts., Indon.	F5	32
Schwarzwald, mts., Ger.	G8	8
Schwaz, Aus.	H11	8
Schwechat, Aus.	G16	8
Schwedt, Ger.	B14	8
Schweinfurt, Ger.	E10	8
Schwerin, Ger.	B11	8
Schwyz, Switz.	E15	10
Sciacca, Italy	L8	14
Scicli, Italy	M9	14
Science Hill, Ky., U.S.	C5	94
Scilly, Isles of, is., Eng., U.K.	L6	7
Scio, Or., U.S.	C4	114
Scioto, co., Oh., U.S.	D3	112
Scioto, stm., Oh., U.S.	B2	112
Scituate, Ma., U.S.	B6	98
Scituate Reservoir, res., R.I., U.S.	C3	116
Scobey, Mt., U.S.	B11	103
Scofield Reservoir, res., Ut., U.S.	D4	121
Ščokino, U.S.S.R.	G20	22
Scotch Plains, N.J., U.S.	B4	107
Scotia, Ca., U.S.	B1	82
Scotia, N.Y., U.S.	C7	109
Scotland, Ont., Can.	D4	73
Scotland, S.D., U.S.	D8	118
Scotland, co., Mo., U.S.	A5	102
Scotland, co., N.C., U.S.	C3	110
Scotland, ter., U.K.	D8	7
Scotland Neck, N.C., U.S.	A5	110
Scotlandville, La., U.S.	D4	95
Scotrun, Pa., U.S.	D11	115
Scotstown, Que., Can.	D6	74
Scott, La., U.S.	D3	95
Scott, co., Ar., U.S.	C1	81
Scott, co., Il., U.S.	D3	90
Scott, co., In., U.S.	G6	91
Scott, co., Ia., U.S.	C7	92
Scott, co., Ks., U.S.	D3	93
Scott, co., Ky., U.S.	B5	94
Scott, co., Mn., U.S.	F5	100
Scott, co., Ms., U.S.	C4	101
Scott, co., Mo., U.S.	D8	102
Scott, co., Tn., U.S.	C9	119
Scott, co., Va., U.S.	f9	123
Scott, Cape, c., B.C., Can.	D3	69
Scott, Mount, mtn., Or., U.S.	E4	114
Scott Air Force Base, mil., Il., U.S.	E4	90
Scott City, Ks., U.S.	D3	93
Scott City, Mo., U.S.	D8	102
Scottdale, Ga., U.S.	h8	87
Scottdale, Pa., U.S.	F2	115
Scott Islands, is., B.C., Can.	F7	66
Scott Mountain, mtn., Id., U.S.	E3	89
Scott Peak, mtn., Id., U.S.	E6	89
Scott Reef, rf., Austl.	B4	50
Scott Reservoir, res., N.C., U.S.	A1	110
Scottsbluff, Ne., U.S.	C2	104
Scotts Bluff, co., Ne., U.S.	C2	104
Scotts Bluff National Monument, Ne., U.S.	C2	104
Scottsboro, Al., U.S.	A3	78
Scottsburg, In., U.S.	G6	91
Scottsdale, Austl.	H9	50
Scottsdale, Az., U.S.	D4	80
Scottsville, Ky., U.S.	D3	94
Scottsville, N.Y., U.S.	B3	109
Scottville, Mi., U.S.	E4	99
Scourie, Scot., U.K.	C7	7
Scraggly Lake, l., Me., U.S.	B4	96
Scranton, Ks., U.S.	D8	93
Scranton, Pa., U.S.	D10	115
Scranton, S.C., U.S.	D8	117
Screven, Ga., U.S.	E4	87
Screven, co., Ga., U.S.	D5	87
Scribner, Ne., U.S.	C9	104
Scugog, Lake, l., Ont., Can.	C6	73
Scurry, co., Tx., U.S.	C2	120
Scutari, Lake, l., Eur.	G3	16
Seaboard, N.C., U.S.	A5	110
Seabreeze, De., U.S.	F5	85
Seabrook, N.H., U.S.	E5	106
Seabrook, Tx., U.S.	r14	120
Seabrook Island, i., S.C., U.S.	F7	117
Seadrift, Tx., U.S.	E4	120
Seaford, De., U.S.	F3	85
Seaford, Va., U.S.	h15	123
Seaforth, Ont., Can.	D3	73
Seagoville, Tx., U.S.	n10	120
Seagraves, Tx., U.S.	C1	120
Seaham, Eng., U.K.	G11	7
Sea Isle City, N.J., U.S.	E3	107
Seal, stm., Man., Can.	E13	66
Seal Cove, Newf., Can.	D3	72
Seal Point, c., P.E.I., Can.	C5	71
Seal Rock, Or., U.S.	C2	114
Sealy, Tx., U.S.	E4	120
Seaman, Oh., U.S.	D2	112
Seaman Range, mts., Nv., U.S.	F6	105
Searchlight, Nv., U.S.	H7	105
Searcy, Ar., U.S.	B4	81
Searcy, co., Ar., U.S.	B3	81
Searles Lake, l., Ca., U.S.	E5	82
Searsport, Me., U.S.	D4	96
Seaside, Or., U.S.	B3	114
Seat Pleasant, Md., U.S.	C4	97
Seattle, Wa., U.S.	B3	124
Seattle-Tacoma International Airport, Wa., U.S.	f11	124
Seaview, Wa., U.S.	C1	124
Sebago Lake, Me., U.S.	E2	96
Sebalino, U.S.S.R.	G11	20
Sebastian, Fl., U.S.	E6	86
Sebastian, co., Ar., U.S.	B1	81
Sebastian, Cape, c., Or., U.S.	E2	114
Sebastian Inlet, b., Fl., U.S.	E6	86
Sebastián Vizcaíno, Bahía, b., Mex.	C2	62
Sebasticook Lake, l., Me., U.S.	D3	96
Sebec Lake, l., Me., U.S.	C3	96
Sebeka, Mn., U.S.	D3	100
Sebewaing, Mi., U.S.	E7	99
Seboeis, stm., Me., U.S.	B4	96
Seboeis Lake, l., Me., U.S.	C4	96
Seboomook Lake, l., Me., U.S.	C3	96
Sebree, Ky., U.S.	C2	94
Sebring, Fl., U.S.	E5	86
Sebring, Oh., U.S.	B4	112
Secaucus, N.J., U.S.	h8	107
Sechelt, B.C., Can.	E6	69
Second Lake, l., N.H., U.S.	f7	106
Second Mesa, Az., U.S.	B5	80
Secret Lake, l., R.I., U.S.	E4	116
Section, Al., U.S.	A4	78
Security, Co., U.S.	C6	83
Sedalia, Mo., U.S.	C4	102
Sedan, Fr.	C11	10
Sedan, Ks., U.S.	E7	93
Sedano, Spain	C8	12
Sedgewick, Alta., Can.	C5	68
Sedgewick, Mount, mtn., N.M., U.S.	B1	108
Sedgwick, Ks., U.S.	E6	93
Sedgwick, co., Co., U.S.	A8	83
Sedgwick, co., Ks., U.S.	E6	93
Sedley, Va., U.S.	D6	123
Sedona, Az., U.S.	C4	80
Sedro Woolley, Wa., U.S.	A3	124
Seeheim, Nmb.	G3	44
Seekonk, Ma., U.S.	C5	98
Seekonk, stm., R.I., U.S.	C4	116
Seeley, Ca., U.S.	F6	82
Seeley Lake, Mt., U.S.	C3	103
Seelyville, In., U.S.	F3	91
Sées, Fr.	D7	10
Segamat, Malay.	M7	34
Ségou, Mali	F4	42
Segovia, Col.	D5	58
Segovia, Spain	E7	12
Segré, Fr.	E6	10
Seguam Island, i., Ak., U.S.	E5	79
Seguam Pass, strt., Ak., U.S.	E5	79
Séguédine, Niger	D8	42
Seguin, Tx., U.S.	E4	120
Sehore, India	I7	38
Seia, Port.	E4	12
Seiling, Ok., U.S.	A3	113
Seinäjoki, Fin.	E14	6
Seine, stm., Fr.	C7	10
Seki, Tur.	M13	16
Sekiu, Wa., U.S.	A1	124
Sekondi-Takoradi, Ghana	H5	42
Šelagskij, Mys, c., U.S.S.R.	C28	20
Selah, Wa., U.S.	C5	124
Selaru, Pulau, i., Indon.	G9	32
Selatan, Tanjung, c., Indon.	F5	32
Selawik, Ak., U.S.	B7	79
Selawik Lake, l., Ak., U.S.	B7	79
Selayar, Pulau, i., Indon.	G7	32
Selb, Ger.	E12	8
Selby, S.D., U.S.	B5	118
Selbyville, De., U.S.	G5	85
Selçuk, Tur.	L11	16

Name	Map Ref	Page
Seldovia, Ak., U.S.	D9	79
Selemdža, stm., U.S.S.R.	G20	20
Selenn'ach, stm., U.S.S.R.	D21	20
Sélestat, Fr.	D14	10
Sélibaby, Maur.	E3	42
Šelichova, Zaliv, b., U.S.S.R.	E25	20
Seligman, Az., U.S.	B3	80
Selinsgrove, Pa., U.S.	E8	115
Selkirk, Man., Can.	D3	70
Selkirk, Scot., U.K.	F10	7
Selkirk Mountains, mts., N.A.	F9	66
Sellersburg, In., U.S.	H6	91
Sellersville, Pa., U.S.	F11	115
Selles-sur-Cher, Fr.	E8	10
Sells, Az., U.S.	F4	80
Selma, Al., U.S.	C2	78
Selma, Ca., U.S.	D4	82
Selma, In., U.S.	D7	91
Selma, N.C., U.S.	B4	110
Selmer, Tn., U.S.	B3	119
Selva, Arg.	B4	56
Selvas, for., Braz.	E6	54
Selway, stm., Id., U.S.	C3	89
Selwyn Mountains, mts., Can.	D6	66
Semara, W. Sah.	C3	42
Semarang, Indon.	m15	32
Semeru, Gunung, vol., Indon.	n16	33a
Seminoe Mountains, mts., Wy., U.S.	D6	127
Seminoe Reservoir, res., Wy., U.S.	D6	127
Seminole, Ok., U.S.	B5	113
Seminole, Tx., U.S.	C1	120
Seminole, co., Fl., U.S.	D5	86
Seminole, co., Ga., U.S.	F2	87
Seminole, co., Ok., U.S.	B5	113
Seminole, Lake, res., U.S.	F2	87
Semipalatinsk, U.S.S.R.	G10	20
Semisopochnoi Island, i., Ak., U.S.	E3	79
Semmes, Al., U.S.	E1	78
Šemonaicha, U.S.S.R.	G10	20
Semur-en-Auxois, Fr.	E11	10
Sên, stm., Camb.	H8	34
Sena, Moz.	E6	44
Senachwine Lake, l., Il., U.S.	B4	90
Senador Pompeu, Braz.	E11	54
Sena Madureira, Braz.	E5	54
Senanga, Zam.	E4	44
Senath, Mo., U.S.	E7	102
Senatobia, Ms., U.S.	A4	101
Sendai, Japan	K3	30
Sendai, Japan	D13	30
Seneca, Il., U.S.	B5	90
Seneca, Ks., U.S.	C7	93
Seneca, Mo., U.S.	E3	102
Seneca, Pa., U.S.	D2	115
Seneca, S.C., U.S.	B2	117
Seneca, co., N.Y., U.S.	C4	109
Seneca, co., Oh., U.S.	A2	112
Seneca Falls, N.Y., U.S.	C4	109
Seneca Lake, l., N.Y., U.S.	C4	109
Senecaville Lake, res., Oh., U.S.	C4	112
Senegal (Sénégal), ctry., Afr.	F3	42
Sénégal, stm., Afr.	E3	42
Senekal, S. Afr.	G5	44
Senftenberg, Ger.	D13	8
Senigallia, Italy	F8	14
Senise, Italy	I11	14
Senmonorom, Camb.	H9	34
Senneterre, Que., Can.	k11	74
Sennori, Italy	I3	14
Senoia, Ga., U.S.	C2	87
Sens, Fr.	D10	10
Senta, Yugo.	D4	16
Sentinel, Ok., U.S.	B2	113
Seo de Urgel, Spain	C13	12
Seoni, India	I8	38
Seoul see Sŏul, S. Kor.	D12	26
Sept-Îles (Seven Islands), Que., Can.	h13	74
Sepulga, stm., Al., U.S.	D3	78
Sepúlveda, Spain	D8	12
Sequatchie, co., Tn., U.S.	D8	119
Sequatchie, stm., Tn., U.S.	D8	119
Sequim, Wa., U.S.	A2	124
Sequoia National Park, Ca., U.S.	D4	82
Sequoyah, co., Ok., U.S.	B7	113
Seraing, Bel.	E5	8
Seram, i., Indon.	F8	32
Seram, Laut (Ceram Sea), Indon.	F8	32
Serang, Indon.	m13	33a
Seremban, Malay.	M6	34
Serengeti Plain, pl., Tan.	B6	44
Serenje, Zam.	D6	44
Sergeant Bluff, Ia., U.S.	B1	92
Sergeja Kirova, Ostrova, is., U.S.S.R.	B11	20
Šerlovaja Gora, mtn., U.S.S.R.	G17	20
Serowe, Bots.	F5	44
Serpa, Port.	H4	12
Serpuchov, U.S.S.R.	G20	22
Sérrai, Grc.	H7	16
Serra San Bruno, Italy	K11	14
Serra Talhada, Braz.	E11	54
Serres, Fr.	H12	10
Serrezuela, Arg.	C3	56
Serri, Italy	J4	14
Serrinha, Braz.	F11	54
Sertã, Port.	F3	12
Sesfontein, Nmb.	E2	44
Sesheke, Zam.	E4	44
Sessa Aurunca, Italy	H8	14
Sesser, Il., U.S.	E4	90
Sestri Levante, Italy	E4	14
Sète, Fr.	I10	10
Sete Lagoas, Braz.	E6	57
Seth, W.V., U.S.	C3	125
Sétif, Alg.	A7	42
Seto, Japan	G10	30
Seto-naikai, Japan	H6	30
Setúbal, Port.	G3	12
Seul, Lac, l., Ont., Can.	o16	73
Seul Choix Point, c., Mi., U.S.	C5	99
Sevan, ozero, l., U.S.S.R.	I7	18
Sevastopol', U.S.S.R.	I4	18
Sevčenko, U.S.S.R.	I8	18
Seven Devils Lake, res., Ar., U.S.	D4	81
Seven Devils Mountains, mts., Id., U.S.	D2	89
Seven Hills, Oh., U.S.	h9	112
Seven Mile Beach, N.J., U.S.	E3	107
Sévérac-le-Château, Fr.	H10	10
Severn, Md., U.S.	B4	97
Severn, stm., Ont., Can.	n17	73
Severn, stm., Eng., U.K.	J10	7
Severnaja Dvina, stm., U.S.S.R.	E6	18
Severnaja Zeml'a, is., U.S.S.R.	B13	20
Severna Park, Md., U.S.	B4	97
Severn River, b., Md., U.S.	B4	97
Severodvinsk, U.S.S.R.	E5	18
Severo-Kuril'sk, U.S.S.R.	G25	20
Severo-Sibirskaja Nizmennost', pl., U.S.S.R.	C13	20
Severo-Zadonsk, U.S.S.R.	G21	22
Sevettijärvi, Fin.	B17	6
Sevier, co., Ar., U.S.	D1	81
Sevier, co., Tn., U.S.	D10	119
Sevier, co., Ut., U.S.	E4	121
Sevier, stm., Ut., U.S.	D3	121
Sevier Bridge Reservoir, res., Ut., U.S.	D4	121
Sevier Lake, l., Ut., U.S.	E2	121
Sevierville, Tn., U.S.	D10	119
Sevilla, Col.	E5	58
Sevilla, Spain	H6	12
Seville, Oh., U.S.	A4	112
Seville see Sevilla, Spain	H6	12
Sewanee, Tn., U.S.	D8	119
Seward, Ak., U.S.	C10	79
Seward, Ne., U.S.	D8	104
Seward, co., Ks., U.S.	E3	93
Seward, co., Ne., U.S.	D8	104
Seward Peninsula, pen., Ak., U.S.	B7	79
Sewickley, Pa., U.S.	E1	115
Sexsmith, Alta., Can.	B1	68
Seychelles, ctry., Afr.	B11	44
Seydisfjördur, Ice.	B5	4
Seymour, Ct., U.S.	D3	84
Seymour, In., U.S.	G6	91
Seymour, Ia., U.S.	D4	92
Seymour, Mo., U.S.	D5	102
Seymour, Tx., U.S.	C3	120
Seymour, Wi., U.S.	D5	126
Seymour Inlet, b., B.C., Can.	D4	69
Seymour Johnson Air Force Base, mil., N.C., U.S.	B5	110
Seymour Lake, l., Vt., U.S.	B4	122
Seymourville, La., U.S.	h9	95
Seyne, Fr.	H13	10
Seyssel, Fr.	G12	10
Sézanne, Fr.	D10	10
Sezze, Italy	H8	14
Sfax, Tun.	B8	42
's-Gravenhage (The Hague), Neth.	C4	8
Shabbona, Il., U.S.	B5	90
Shache, China	A7	38
Shackelford, co., Tx., U.S.	C3	120
Shackleton Ice Shelf, Ant.	C22	47
Shaddādī, Syria	A7	40
Shadehill Dam, S.D., U.S.	B3	118
Shadehill Reservoir, res., S.D., U.S.	B3	118
Shadow Mountain National Recreation Area, Co., U.S.	A4	83
Shady Cove, Or., U.S.	E4	114
Shady Side, Md., U.S.	C4	97
Shadyside, Oh., U.S.	C5	112
Shady Spring, W.V., U.S.	D3	125
Shafer, Lake, l., In., U.S.	C4	91
Shafer Butte, mtn., Id., U.S.	F2	89
Shafter, Ca., U.S.	E4	82
Shaftsbury, Vt., U.S.	E2	122
Shāhdādkot, Pak.	G2	38
Shahdol, India	I9	38
Shāhjahānpur, India	G8	38
Shāh Jūy, Afg.	D2	38
Shahrak, Afg.	C1	38
Shājāpur, India	I7	38
Shakawe, Bots.	E4	44
Shaker Heights, Oh., U.S.	A4	112
Shakhty see Šachty, U.S.S.R.	H6	18
Shaki, Nig.	G6	42
Shakopee, Mn., U.S.	F5	100
Shaler Mountains, mts., N.W. Ter., Can.	B10	66
Shallotte, N.C., U.S.	D4	110
Shallotte Inlet, b., N.C., U.S.	D4	110
Shallowater, Tx., U.S.	C2	120
Shām, Bādiyat ash-, des., Asia	C6	40
Shām, Jabal ash-, mtn., Oman	D6	46
Shamokin, Pa., U.S.	E8	115
Shamokin Dam, Pa., U.S.	E8	115
Shamrock, Tx., U.S.	B2	120
Shandī, Sudan	E12	42
Shandong, prov., China	D10	26
Shandong Bandao, pen., China	D11	26
Shanghai, China	D10	28
Shanghai Shih, China	E11	26
Shangqiu, China	A4	28
Shangrao, China	G6	28
Shangshui, China	B3	28
Shangzhi, China	B12	26
Shannock, R.I., U.S.	F2	116
Shannon, Ga., U.S.	B1	87
Shannon, Il., U.S.	A4	90
Shannon, Ms., U.S.	A5	101
Shannon, co., Mo., U.S.	D6	102
Shannon, co., S.D., U.S.	D3	118
Shannon, stm., Ire.	I3	7
Shannon, Lake, l., Wa., U.S.	A4	124
Shannontown, S.C., U.S.	D7	117
Shantou (Swatow), China	L5	28
Shantung Peninsula see Shandong Bandao, pen., China	D11	26
Shānxī, prov., China	D8	26
Shănxī, prov., China	D9	26
Shanyin, China	D9	26
Shaoguan, China	K2	28
Shaowu, China	H6	28
Shaoxing, China	E9	28
Shaoyang, China	F9	26
Shark Bay, b., Austl.	E2	50
Sharkey, co., Ms., U.S.	C3	101
Shark Point, c., Fl., U.S.	H5	86
Sharktooth Mountain, mtn., B.C., Can.	E7	66
Sharon, Ct., U.S.	B2	84
Sharon, Ma., U.S.	B5	98
Sharon, Pa., U.S.	D1	115
Sharon, Tn., U.S.	A3	119
Sharon, Wi., U.S.	F5	126
Sharon Hill, Pa., U.S.	p20	115
Sharon Park, Oh., U.S.	n12	112
Sharon Springs, Ks., U.S.	D2	93
Sharonville, Oh., U.S.	n13	112
Sharp, co., Ar., U.S.	A4	81
Sharpe, Lake, res., S.D., U.S.	C6	118
Sharpes, Fl., U.S.	D6	86
Sharpley, De., U.S.	h7	85
Sharpsburg, Md., U.S.	B2	97
Sharpsburg, N.C., U.S.	B5	110
Sharpsburg, Pa., U.S.	k14	115
Sharpsville, In., U.S.	D5	91
Sharpsville, Pa., U.S.	D1	115
Sharptown, Md., U.S.	C6	97
Sharqīyah, Aṣ-Ṣaḥrā' ash- (Arabian Desert), des., Egypt	C12	42
Shashi, China	E9	26
Shashi, stm., Afr.	F5	44
Shasta, co., Ca., U.S.	B3	82
Shasta, Mount, vol., Ca., U.S.	B2	82
Shasta Lake, res., Ca., U.S.	B2	82
Shattuck, Ok., U.S.	A2	113
Shaw, Ms., U.S.	B3	101
Shaw Air Force Base, mil., S.C., U.S.	D7	117
Shawano, Wi., U.S.	D5	126
Shawano, co., Wi., U.S.	D5	126
Shawano Lake, l., Wi., U.S.	D5	126
Shawinigan, Que., Can.	C5	74
Shawinigan-Sud, Que., Can.	C5	74
Shawnee, Ks., U.S.	k16	93
Shawnee, Ok., U.S.	B5	113
Shawnee, co., Ks., U.S.	D8	93
Shawneetown, Il., U.S.	F5	90
Shawsheen, stm., Ma., U.S.	f11	98
Shaybārā, i., Sau. Ar.	C2	46
Shaykh, Jabal ash-, mtn., Asia	C4	40
Shebele (Shebelle), stm., Afr.	G3	46
Sheberghān, Afg.	B1	38
Sheboygan, Wi., U.S.	E6	126
Sheboygan, co., Wi., U.S.	E6	126
Sheboygan, stm., Wi., U.S.	k10	126
Sheboygan Falls, Wi., U.S.	E6	126
Shediac, N.B., Can.	C5	71
Sheenjek, stm., Ak., U.S.	B11	79
Sheep Mountain, mtn., Az., U.S.	E1	80
Sheep Mountain, mtn., Wy., U.S.	C2	127
Sheep Mountain, mtn., Wy., U.S.	B5	127
Sheep Peak, mtn., Nv., U.S.	G6	105
Sheep Range, mts., Nv., U.S.	G6	105
Sheet Harbour, N.S., Can.	E7	71
Sheffield, Eng., U.K.	H11	7
Sheffield, Al., U.S.	A2	78
Sheffield, Il., U.S.	B4	90
Sheffield, Ia., U.S.	B4	92
Sheffield, Pa., U.S.	C3	115
Sheffield Lake, Oh., U.S.	A3	112
Sheila, N.B., Can.	B5	71
Shēkhābād, Afg.	C3	38
Shekhūpura, Pak.	E5	38
Shelagyote Peak, mtn., B.C., Can.	B4	69
Shelbiana, Ky., U.S.	C7	94
Shelbina, Mo., U.S.	B5	102
Shelburn, In., U.S.	F3	91
Shelburne, Ont., Can.	C4	73
Shelburne Falls, Ma., U.S.	A2	98
Shelburne Pond, l., Vt., U.S.	C2	122
Shelby, Al., U.S.	B3	78
Shelby, In., U.S.	B3	91
Shelby, Ia., U.S.	C2	92
Shelby, Mi., U.S.	E4	99
Shelby, Ms., U.S.	B3	101
Shelby, Mt., U.S.	B5	103
Shelby, Ne., U.S.	C8	104
Shelby, N.C., U.S.	B1	110
Shelby, Oh., U.S.	B3	112
Shelby, co., Al., U.S.	B3	78
Shelby, co., Il., U.S.	D5	90
Shelby, co., In., U.S.	E6	91
Shelby, co., Ia., U.S.	C2	92
Shelby, co., Ky., U.S.	B4	94
Shelby, co., Mo., U.S.	B5	102
Shelby, co., Oh., U.S.	B1	112
Shelby, co., Tn., U.S.	B2	119
Shelby, co., Tx., U.S.	D5	120
Shelbyville, Il., U.S.	D5	90
Shelbyville, In., U.S.	F6	91
Shelbyville, Ky., U.S.	B4	94
Shelbyville, Tn., U.S.	B5	119
Shelbyville, Lake, res., Il., U.S.	D5	90
Sheldon, Il., U.S.	C6	90
Sheldon, Ia., U.S.	A2	92
Sheldon, Tx., U.S.	r14	120
Shelikof Strait, strt., Ak., U.S.	D9	79
Shell Creek, stm., U.S.	A2	83
Shell Creek, stm., Wy., U.S.	B5	127
Shelley, Id., U.S.	F6	89
Shell Lake, Wi., U.S.	C2	126
Shell Lake, l., Mn., U.S.	D3	100
Shell Lake, l., Wi., U.S.	C2	126
Shellman, Ga., U.S.	E2	87
Shell Rock, Ia., U.S.	B5	92
Shell Rock, stm., Ia., U.S.	B5	92
Shellsburg, Ia., U.S.	B6	92
Shelly Mountain, mtn., Id., U.S.	F5	89
Shelter Island, N.Y., U.S.	m16	109
Shelton, Ct., U.S.	D3	84
Shelton, Ne., U.S.	D7	104
Shelton, Wa., U.S.	B2	124
Shemya Air Force Base, mil., Ak., U.S.	E2	79
Shenandoah, Ia., U.S.	D2	92
Shenandoah, Pa., U.S.	E9	115
Shenandoah, Va., U.S.	B4	123
Shenandoah, co., Va., U.S.	B4	123
Shenandoah, stm., U.S.	A5	123
Shenandoah, North Fork, stm., Va., U.S.	B4	123
Shenandoah, South Fork, stm., Va., U.S.	B4	123
Shenandoah Mountain, mtn., U.S.	B3	123
Shenandoah National Park, Va., U.S.	B4	123
Shenango River Lake, res., U.S.	D1	115
Shengfang, China	D10	26
Shengze, China	E9	28
Shenipsit Lake, l., Ct., U.S.	B6	84
Shenyang (Mukden), China	C11	26
Shenzha, China	E13	38
Shepaug, stm., Ct., U.S.	C2	84
Shepaug Dam, Ct., U.S.	D2	84
Shepaug Reservoir, res., Ct., U.S.	C2	84
Shepherd, Mi., U.S.	E6	99
Shepherd, Tx., U.S.	D5	120
Shepherdstown, W.V., U.S.	B7	125
Shepherdsville, Ky., U.S.	C4	94
Sheppard Air Force Base, mil., Tx., U.S.	C3	120
Shepparton, Austl.	G9	50
Sherborn, Ma., U.S.	h10	98
Sherbro Island, i., S.L.	G3	42
Sherbrooke, Que., Can.	D6	74
Sherburn, Mn., U.S.	G4	100
Sherburne, co., Mn., U.S.	E5	100
Sheridan, Ar., U.S.	C3	81
Sheridan, Il., U.S.	B5	90
Sheridan, In., U.S.	D5	91
Sheridan, Mi., U.S.	E5	99
Sheridan, Mt., U.S.	E4	103
Sheridan, Or., U.S.	B3	114
Sheridan, Wy., U.S.	B6	127
Sheridan, co., Ks., U.S.	C3	93
Sheridan, co., Mt., U.S.	B12	103
Sheridan, co., Ne., U.S.	B3	104
Sheridan, co., N.D., U.S.	B5	111
Sheridan, co., Wy., U.S.	B5	127
Sheridan, Mount, mtn., Wy., U.S.	B2	127
Sheringham Cromer, Eng., U.K.	I14	7
Sherman, Tx., U.S.	C4	120
Sherman, co., Ks., U.S.	C2	93
Sherman, co., Ne., U.S.	C6	104
Sherman, co., Or., U.S.	B6	114
Sherman, co., Tx., U.S.	A2	120
Sherman Reservoir, res., Ne., U.S.	C7	104
Sherrelwood, Co., U.S.	B6	83
Sherrill, N.Y., U.S.	B5	109
's-Hertogenbosch, Neth.	D5	8
Sherwood, P.E.I., Can.	C6	71
Sherwood, Ar., U.S.	C3	81
Sherwood, Or., U.S.	h12	114
Sherwood, Wi., U.S.	h9	126
Sherwood Manor, Ct., U.S.	A5	84
Sherwood Park, De., U.S.	i7	85
Shetek, Lake, l., Mn., U.S.	G3	100
Shetland Islands, is., Scot., U.K.	A11	7
Shetucket, stm., Ct., U.S.	C7	84
Sheyenne, stm., N.D., U.S.	C8	111
Sheyenne Lake, res., N.D., U.S.	B5	111
Shiawassee, co., Mi., U.S.	F6	99
Shibata, Japan	E12	30
Shibetsu, Japan	p23	30a
Shibukawa, Japan	F11	30
Shickshinny, Pa., U.S.	D9	115
Shijiazhuang, China	D9	26
Shijushan, China	D8	26
Shikārpur, Pak.	G3	38
Shikohābād, India	G8	38
Shikoku, i., Japan	I6	30
Shikoku-sanchi, mts., Japan	I6	30
Shikotsu-ko, l., Japan	q19	30a
Shillington, Pa., U.S.	F10	115
Shillong, India	H14	38
Shiloh National Military Park, Tn., U.S.	B3	119
Shilong, China	L2	28
Shimabara, Japan	J3	30
Shimada, Japan	H11	30
Shimbiris, mtn., Som.	F4	46
Shimizu, Japan	G11	30
Shimminato, Japan	F10	30
Shimodate, Japan	F12	30
Shimoga, India	F3	37
Shimonoseki, Japan	I3	30
Shinano, stm., Japan	E11	30
Shīndand, Afg.	C1	36
Shiner, Tx., U.S.	E4	120
Shinglehouse, Pa., U.S.	C5	115
Shingū, Japan	I8	30
Shinjō, Japan	D13	30
Shinnston, W.V., U.S.	B4	125
Shinshār, Syria	B5	40
Shinyanga, Tan.	B6	44
Shiocton, Wi., U.S.	D5	126
Shiogama, Japan	D14	30
Shiojiri, Japan	F10	30
Shiping, China	C7	34
Ship Island, i., Ms., U.S.	E5	101
Ship Island Pass, strt., Ms., U.S.	g7	101
Shippegan, N.B., Can.	B5	71
Shippensburg, Pa., U.S.	F6	115
Shiprock, N.M., U.S.	A1	108
Ship Rock, mtn., N.M., U.S.	A1	108
Shirakawa, Japan	E13	30
Shīrāz, Iran	C5	46
Shire, stm., Afr.	E6	44
Shiretoko-misaki, c., Japan	o23	30a
Shirley, In., U.S.	E6	91
Shirley, Ma., U.S.	A4	98
Shirley Mountains, mts., Wy., U.S.	D6	127
Shirpur, India	B3	37
Shishaldin Volcano, vol., Ak., U.S.	E7	79
Shishmaref, Ak., U.S.	B6	79
Shively, Ky., U.S.	B4	94
Shivpuri, India	H7	38
Shizuoka, Japan	H11	30
Shkodër, Alb.	G3	16
Shoal Creek, stm., U.S.	B4	119
Shoal Harbour, Newf., Can.	D4	72
Shoal Lake, Man., Can.	D1	70
Shoals, In., U.S.	G4	91
Shoals, Isles of, is., Me., U.S.	E2	96
Shoalwater, Cape, c., Wa., U.S.	C1	124
Shōdo-shima, i., Japan	H7	30
Shoemakersville, Pa., U.S.	F10	115
Sholāpur, India	D3	37
Shongopovi, Az., U.S.	B5	80
Shonto, Az., U.S.	A5	80
Shoreham, Mi., U.S.	F4	99
Shores Acres, R.I., U.S.	E4	116
Shoreview, Mn., U.S.	m12	100
Shorewood, Il., U.S.	k8	90
Shorewood, Mn., U.S.	n11	100
Shorewood, Wi., U.S.	E6	126
Short Beach, Ct., U.S.	D4	84
Shoshone, Id., U.S.	G4	89
Shoshone, co., Id., U.S.	B2	89
Shoshone, stm., Wy., U.S.	B4	127
Shoshone Falls, wtfl, Id., U.S.	G4	89
Shoshone Lake, l., Wy., U.S.	B2	127
Shoshone Mountains, mts., Nv., U.S.	E4	105
Shoshone Peak, mtn., Nv., U.S.	G5	105
Shoshone Range, mts., Nv., U.S.	C5	105
Shoshong, Bots.	F5	44
Shoshoni, Wy., U.S.	C4	127
Shoup, Id., U.S.	D4	89
Shouxian, China	C5	28
Show Low, Az., U.S.	C5	80
Shreve, Oh., U.S.	B3	112
Shreveport, La., U.S.	B2	95
Shrewsbury, Eng., U.K.	I10	7
Shrewsbury, Ma., U.S.	B4	98
Shrewsbury, N.J., U.S.	C4	107
Shrewsbury, Pa., U.S.	G8	115
Shuajingsi, China	E7	26
Shuangcheng, China	B12	26
Shuangyashan, China	B13	26
Shubenacadie, N.S., Can.	D6	71
Shuksan, Mount, mtn., Wa., U.S.	A4	124
Shullsburg, Wi., U.S.	F3	126
Shumagin Islands, is., Ak., U.S.	E7	79
Shunde, China	M2	28
Shungnak, Ak., U.S.	B8	79
Shuqrā', Yemen	F4	46
Shūshtar, Iran	B4	46
Shuswap Lake, l., B.C., Can.	D8	69
Shwebo, Burma	C3	34
Siaksriinderapura, Indon.	N7	34
Siālkot, Pak.	D6	38
Siam, Gulf of see Thailand, Gulf of, b., Asia	J6	34
Sian see Xi'an, China	E8	26
Siargao Island, i., Phil.	D8	32
Šiaškotan, Ostrov, i., U.S.S.R.	H24	20
Šiauliai, U.S.S.R.	F6	22
Šibenik, Yugo.	F10	14
Siberia see Sibir', reg., U.S.S.R.	D16	20
Siberut, Pulau, i., Indon.	F2	32
Sibi, Pak.	F2	38
Sibir' (Siberia), reg., U.S.S.R.	D16	20
Sibir'akova, Ostrov, i., U.S.S.R.	C9	20
Sibiti, Congo	B2	44
Sibiu, Rom.	D8	16
Sibley, Ia., U.S.	A2	92
Sibley, La., U.S.	B2	95
Sibley, co., Mn., U.S.	F4	100
Sibolga, Indon.	E2	32
Sibsāgar, India	G16	38
Sibu, Malay.	E5	32
Sibutu Island, i., Phil.	E6	32
Sibuyan Island, i., Phil.	C7	32
Sibuyan Sea, Phil.	C7	32
Sicamous, B.C., Can.	D8	69
Sichote-Alin', mts., U.S.S.R.	H21	20
Sichuan, prov., China	E7	26
Sicié, Cap, c., Fr.	I12	10
Sicilia, i., Italy	L9	14
Sicily, Strait of, strt.	L7	14
Sicily see Sicilia, i., Italy	L9	14
Sico, stm., Hond.	G5	64
Sicuani, Peru	F4	54
Siddipet, India	C5	37
Siderno, Italy	K11	14
Sidhpur, India	I5	38
Sidi bel Abbès, Alg.	A5	42
Sidi Ifni, Mor.	C3	42
Sidmouth, Eng., U.K.	K9	7
Sidney, B.C., Can.	E6	69
Sidney, Il., U.S.	C5	90
Sidney, Ia., U.S.	D2	92
Sidney, Mt., U.S.	C12	103
Sidney, Ne., U.S.	C3	104
Sidney, N.Y., U.S.	C5	109
Sidney, Oh., U.S.	B1	112
Sidney Lanier, Lake, res., Ga., U.S.	B2	87
Sidon see Şaydā, Leb.	C4	40
Sidra, Gulf of see Surt, Khalīj, b., Libya	B9	42
Siedlce, Pol.	C22	8
Siegburg, Ger.	E7	8
Siegen, Ger.	E8	8
Siĕmréab, Camb.	H7	34
Siena, Italy	F6	14
Sierra, co., Ca., U.S.	C3	82
Sierra, co., N.M., U.S.	D2	108
Sierra Blanca Peak, mtn., N.M., U.S.	D4	108
Sierra Colorada, Arg.	E3	56
Sierra Estrella, mts., Az., U.S.	m8	80
Sierra Leone, ctry., Afr.	G3	42
Sierra Madre, Ca., U.S.	m12	82
Sierra Vista, Az., U.S.	F5	80
Sierre, Switz.	F14	10
Siesta Key, i., Fl., U.S.	E4	86
Sighetul Marmaţiei, Rom.	B7	16
Sighişoara, Rom.	C8	16
Siglufjördur, Ice.	B4	4
Signal Mountain, Tn., U.S.	D8	119
Signal Peak, mtn., Az., U.S.	D1	80
Signal Peak, mtn., Ut., U.S.	F2	121
Signy-l'Abbaye, Fr.	C11	10
Sigourney, Ia., U.S.	C5	92
Sigüenza, Spain	D9	12
Sigües, Spain	C10	12
Siguiri, Gui.	F4	42
Siilinjärvi, Fin.	E16	6
Si-Kacha, Thai.	H6	34
Sīkar, India	G6	38
Sikasso, Mali	F4	42
Sikeston, Mo., U.S.	E8	102
Sikiá, Grc.	I7	16
Síkinos, Grc.	M9	16
Sikkim, state, India	G13	38
Šikotan, Ostrov (Shikotan-tō), i., U.S.S.R.	I23	20

Name — Map Ref — Page

Sikt'ach, U.S.S.R. D19 20
Silandro, Italy C5 14
Silao, Mex. G9 62
Silay, Phil. C7 32
Silba, Yugo. E9 14
Silchar, India H15 38
Siler City, N.C., U.S. B3 110
Silesia, hist. reg., Pol. E16 8
Siletz, Or., U.S. C3 114
Silifke, Tur. A3 40
Silīguri, India G13 38
Siling Co, l., China E13 38
Silistra, Bul. E11 16
Šilka, U.S.S.R. G18 20
Šilka, stm., U.S.S.R. G17 20
Silkeborg, Den. H7 6
Sillamäe, U.S.S.R. B10 22
Sillé-le-Guillaume, Fr. D6 10
Sillery, Que., Can. n17 74
Sillon de Talbert, pen., Fr. D3 10
Siloam Springs, Ar., U.S. A1 81
Silsbee, Tx., U.S. D5 120
Silt, Co., U.S. B3 83
Silvânia, Braz. G9 54
Silvassa, India B2 37
Silver Bay, Mn., U.S. C7 100
Silver Bow, co., Mt., U.S. E4 103
Silver City, Nv., U.S. D2 105
Silver City, N.M., U.S. E1 108
Silver Creek, Ne., U.S. C8 104
Silver Creek, N.Y., U.S. C1 109
Silver Creek, stm., Or., U.S. D7 114
Silverdale, Wa., U.S. B3 124
Silver Grove, Ky., U.S. h14 94
Silver Hill, Md., U.S. f9 97
Silver Lake, Ks., U.S. C8 93
Silver Lake, Ma., U.S. f11 98
Silver Lake, Mn., U.S. F4 100
Silver Lake, Wi., U.S. F5 126
Silver Lake, l., De., U.S. D3 85
Silver Lake, l., Ia., U.S. A3 92
Silver Lake, l., Me., U.S. C3 96
Silver Lake, l., N.H., U.S. E2 106
Silver Lake, l., N.H., U.S. C4 106
Silver Lake, l., Or., U.S. D7 114
Silver Lake, l., Wa., U.S. g13 124
Silverpeak, Nv., U.S. F4 105
Silver Peak Range, mts., Nv., U.S. F4 105
Silver Spring, Md., U.S. C3 97
Silver Springs, Nv., U.S. D2 105
Silver Star Mountain, mtn., Wa., U.S. A5 124
Silverthrone Mountain, mtn., B.C., Can. D4 69
Silvertip Mountain, mtn., Mt., U.S. C3 103
Silverton, Co., U.S. D3 83
Silverton, Id., U.S. B3 89
Silverton, N.J., U.S. C4 107
Silverton, Oh., U.S. o13 112
Silverton, Or., U.S. C4 114
Silvi, Italy G9 14
Silvies, stm., Or., U.S. D7 114
Silview, De., U.S. B3 85
Silvis, Il., U.S. B3 90
Simanggang, Malay. E5 32
Šimanovsk, U.S.S.R. G19 20
Simav, Tur. J12 16
Simcoe, Ont., Can. E4 73
Simcoe, Lake, l., Ont., Can. C5 73
Simeulue, Pulau, i., Indon. M3 34
Simferopol', U.S.S.R. I4 18
Simi Valley, Ca., U.S. E4 82
Simla, India E7 38
Simmesport, La., U.S. D4 95
Simms Stream, stm., N.H., U.S. g7 106
Simojovel [de Allende], Mex. I13 62
Simonette, stm., Alta., Can. B1 68
Simplon Pass, Switz. F15 10
Simpson, Pa., U.S. C11 115
Simpson, co., Ky., U.S. D3 94
Simpson, co., Ms., U.S. D4 101
Simpson Creek, stm., W.V., U.S. k10 125
Simpson Desert, des., Austl. D7 50
Simpson Peninsula, pen., N.W. Ter., Can. C15 66
Simpsonville, Ky., U.S. B4 94
Simpsonville, S.C., U.S. B3 117
Simsboro, La., U.S. B3 95
Simsbury, Ct., U.S. B4 84
Simušir, Ostrov, i., U.S.S.R. H24 20
Sīnā', Shibh Jazīrat (Sinai Peninsula), pen., Egypt C12 42
Sinabang, Indon. M4 34
Sinai Peninsula see Sīnā', Shibh Jazīrat, pen., Egypt C12 42
Sin'aja, stm., U.S.S.R. E18 20
Sinaloa, state, Mex. E5 62
Sīnāwan, Libya B8 42
Sincé, Col. C5 58
Sincé, Col. J10 64
Sincelejo, Col. C5 58
Sinclair, Wy., U.S. E5 127
Sindri, India I12 38
Sines, Port. H3 12
Sinfães, Port. D3 12
Singānallūr, India G4 37
Singapore, Sing. N7 34
Singapore, ctry., Asia E3 32
Singapore Strait, strt., Asia N7 34
Singen [Hohentwiel], Ger. H8 8
Singida, Tan. B6 44
Singkang, Indon. F7 32
Singkawang, Indon. E4 32
Siniscola, Italy I4 14
Sinj, Yugo. F11 14
Sinjah, Sudan F12 42
Sinkāt, Sudan E13 42
Sinnamary, Fr. Gu. B8 54
Sinnemahoning Creek, stm., Pa., U.S. D5 115
Sinop, Tur. G15 4
Sinskoje, U.S.S.R. E19 20
Sintang, Indon. E5 32
Sint Eustatius, i., Neth. Ant. F16 64
Sint Marten (Saint-Martin), i., N.A. E16 64
Sint-Niklaas, Bel. D4 8
Sinton, Tx., U.S. E4 120
Sintra, Port. G2 12
Sinŭiju, N. Kor. C11 26
Sion, Switz. F14 10
Sioux, co., Ia., U.S. A1 92
Sioux, co., Ne., U.S. B2 104
Sioux, co., N.D., U.S. C4 111
Sioux Center, Ia., U.S. A1 92
Sioux City, Ia., U.S. B1 92
Sioux Falls, S.D., U.S. D9 118
Sioux Lookout, Ont., Can. o17 73
Sioux Rapids, Ia., U.S. B2 92
Siping, China C11 26
Sipiwesk Lake, l., Man., Can. B3 70
Sipsey, stm., Al., U.S. B2 78
Sipsey Fork, stm., Al., U.S. A2 78
Siracusa, Italy L10 14
Sirājganj, Bngl. H13 38
Sir Douglas, Mount, mtn., Can. D3 68
Sir Edward Pellew Group, is., Austl. C7 50
Siren, Wi., U.S. C1 126
Siret, stm., Eur. C11 16
Sirevåg, Nor. G5 6
Sir James MacBrien, Mount, mtn., N.W. Ter., Can. D7 66
Sirohi, India H5 38
Sirsa, India F6 38
Sir Sandford, Mount, mtn., B.C., Can. D9 69
Sirsi, India E3 37
Sir Wilfrid Laurier, Mount, mtn., B.C., Can. C8 69
Sisak, Yugo. D11 14
Siskiyou, co., Ca., U.S. B2 82
Siskiyou Mountains, mts., U.S. F3 114
Siskiyou Pass, Or., U.S. E4 114
Sisseton, S.D., U.S. B8 118
Sisseton Indian Reservation, U.S. B8 118
Sissiboo, stm., N.S., Can. E4 71
Sisson Branch Reservoir, res., N.B., Can. B2 71
Sissonville, W.V., U.S. C3 125
Sisteron, Fr. H12 10
Sisters, Or., U.S. C5 114
Sistersville, W.V., U.S. B4 125
Sītāpur, India G9 38
Sitka, Ak., U.S. D12 79
Sitka National Historical Park, Ak., U.S. m22 79
Sitka Sound, strt., Ak., U.S. m22 79
Sittard, Neth. D5 8
Sittoung, stm., Burma E4 34
Sittwe (Akyab), Burma D2 34
Situbondo, Indon. m16 33a
Sivas, Tur. H15 4
Sīwah, Egypt C11 42
Siwān, India G11 38
Sjælland, i., Den. I8 6
Skagen, Den. H8 6
Skagerrak, strt., Eur. H7 6
Skagit, co., Wa., U.S. A4 124
Skagway, Ak., U.S. D12 79
Skaidi, Nor. A15 6
Skamania, co., Wa., U.S. D3 124
Skaneateles, N.Y., U.S. C4 109
Skaneateles Lake, l., N.Y., U.S. C4 109
Skārdu, Pak. C6 38
Skarżysko-Kamienna, Pol. D20 8
Skeena Mountains, mts., B.C., Can. E7 66
Skegness, Eng., U.K. H13 7
Skeleton Lake, l., Ont., Can. B5 73
Skellefteå, Swe. D13 6
Skelleftehamn, Swe. D13 6
Skiatook, Ok., U.S. A5 113
Skiatook Reservoir, res., Ok., U.S. A5 113
Skibotn, Nor. B13 6
Skiddaw, mtn., Eng., U.K. G9 7
Skien, Nor. G7 6
Skierniewice, Pol. D20 8
Skihist Mountain, mtn., B.C., Can. D7 69
Skikda, Alg. A7 42
Skillet Fork, stm., Il., U.S. E5 90
Skillingaryd, Swe. H10 6
Šklad, U.S.S.R. C18 20
Škofja Loka, Yugo. C9 14
Skokie, Il., U.S. A6 90
Skokomish Indian Reservation, Wa., U.S. B2 124
Skopje, Yugo. H5 16
Skövde, Swe. G9 6
Skovorodino, U.S.S.R. G18 20
Skowhegan, Me., U.S. D3 96
Skull Valley, val., Ut., U.S. C3 121
Skull Valley Indian Reservation, Ut., U.S. C3 121
Skuna, stm., Ms., U.S. B4 101
Skunk, stm., Ia., U.S. D6 92
Skwentna, stm., Ak., U.S. g15 79
Skye, Island of, i., Scot., U.K. D6 7
Skykomish, stm., Wa., U.S. B4 124
Skyland, Nv., U.S. D2 105
Skyland, N.C., U.S. f10 110
Skyline, Al., U.S. A3 78
Slagnäs, Swe. D12 6
Slamet, Gunung, vol., Indon. m14 33a
Slancy, U.S.S.R. B11 22
Slano, Yugo. G12 14
Slater, Ia., U.S. C4 92
Slater, Mo., U.S. B4 102
Slater, S.C., U.S. A3 117
Slatersville, R.I., U.S. A3 116
Slatersville Reservoir, res., R.I., U.S. B3 116
Slatington, Pa., U.S. E10 115
Slaton, Tx., U.S. C2 120
Slaughter, La., U.S. D4 95
Slave, stm., Can. D10 66
Slave Lake, Alta., Can. B3 68
Slavonia see Slavonija, reg., Yugo. D12 14
Slavonija, reg., Yugo. D12 14
Slavonska Požega, Yugo. D12 14
Slavonski Brod, Yugo. D2 16
Slayton, Mn., U.S. G3 100
Sleeping Bear Dunes National Lakeshore, Mi., U.S. D4 99
Sleeping Bear Point, c., Mi., U.S. D4 99
Sleepy Eye, Mn., U.S. F4 100
Slickville, Pa., U.S. F2 115
Slidell, La., U.S. D6 95
Sliderock Mountain, mtn., Mt., U.S. D3 103
Sligo, Ire. G4 7
Slinger, Wi., U.S. E5 126
Slippery Rock, Pa., U.S. D1 115
Sliven, Bul. G10 16
Sloan, Ia., U.S. B1 92
Sloan, N.Y., U.S. C2 109
Slocomb, Al., U.S. D4 78
Slonim, U.S.S.R. H8 22
Slope, co., N.D., U.S. C2 111
Slovakia see Slovensko, hist. reg., Czech. G19 8
Slovenjgradec, Yugo. C10 14
Slovenska Bistrica, Yugo. C10 14
Slovensko, hist. reg., Czech. G19 8
Sluck, U.S.S.R. H10 22
Sl'ud'anka, U.S.S.R. G14 20
Słupsk (Stolp), Pol. A17 8
Smackover, Ar., U.S. D3 81
Small Point, c., Me., U.S. g8 96
Smallwood Reservoir, res., Newf., Can. g8 72
Smederevo, Yugo. E4 16
Smethport, Pa., U.S. C5 115
Šmidovič, U.S.S.R. H20 20
Šmidta, Ostrov, i., U.S.S.R. A12 20
Smith, co., Ks., U.S. C5 93
Smith, co., Ms., U.S. C4 101
Smith, co., Tn., U.S. A5 119
Smith, co., Tx., U.S. C5 120
Smith, stm., U.S. D3 123
Smith, stm., Mt., U.S. D5 103
Smith and Sayles Reservoir, res., R.I., U.S. B2 116
Smith Bay, b., Ak., U.S. A9 79
Smith Canyon, val., Co., U.S. D7 83
Smith Center, Ks., U.S. C5 93
Smithers, B.C., Can. B4 69
Smithers, W.V., U.S. C3 125
Smithfield, N.C., U.S. B4 110
Smithfield, Pa., U.S. G2 115
Smithfield, Ut., U.S. B4 121
Smithfield, Va., U.S. D6 123
Smith Island, i., U.S. D5 97
Smith Island, i., Va., U.S. C7 123
Smith Mountain Lake, res., Va., U.S. C3 123
Smith Peak, mtn., Id., U.S. A2 89
Smith Point, c., Ma., U.S. D7 98
Smith Point, c., Va., U.S. C6 123
Smiths, Al., U.S. C4 78
Smithsburg, Md., U.S. A2 97
Smiths Falls, Ont., Can. C8 73
Smiths Grove, Ky., U.S. C3 94
Smithton, Austl. H9 50
Smithton, Il., U.S. E4 90
Smithtown, N.Y., U.S. n15 109
Smithville, Ga., U.S. E2 87
Smithville, Ms., U.S. A5 101
Smithville, Mo., U.S. B3 102
Smithville, Oh., U.S. B4 112
Smithville, Tn., U.S. D8 119
Smithville, Tx., U.S. D4 120
Smithville Lake, res., Mo., U.S. B3 102
Smoke Creek Desert, des., Nv., U.S. C2 105
Smokey, Cape, c., N.S., Can. C9 71
Smokey Dome, mtn., Id., U.S. F4 89
Smoky, stm., Alta., Can. B1 68
Smoky Hill, stm., U.S. D5 93
Smoky Lake, Alta., Can. B4 68
Smoky Mountains, mts., Id., U.S. F4 89
Smolensk, U.S.S.R. G15 22
Smooth Rock Falls, Ont., Can. o19 73
Smoothstone Lake, l., Sask., Can. C2 75
Smyrna, De., U.S. C3 85
Smyrna, Ga., U.S. C2 87
Smyrna, Tn., U.S. B5 119
Smyrna, stm., De., U.S. C3 85
Smyth, co., Va., U.S. f10 123
Smythe, Mount, mtn., B.C., Can. E8 66
Snake, stm., U.S. D5 100
Snake, stm., Mn., U.S. B1 100
Snake, stm., Ne., U.S. B4 104
Snake Range, mts., Nv., U.S. E7 105
Snake River Plain, pl., Id., U.S. F2 89
Snake River Range, mts., U.S. C2 127
Sneads, Fl., U.S. B2 86
Sneedville, Tn., U.S. C10 119
Sneek, Neth. B5 8
Snipe Keys, is., Fl., U.S. H5 86
Snohomish, Wa., U.S. B3 124
Snohomish, co., Wa., U.S. A4 124
Snoqualmie, Wa., U.S. B4 124
Snoqualmie, stm., Wa., U.S. B4 124
Snoqualmie Pass, Wa., U.S. B4 124
Snowbank Lake, l., Mn., U.S. B7 100
Snowdon, mtn., Wales, U.K. H8 7
Snowdonia National Park, Wales, U.K. I9 7
Snowdrift, N.W. Ter., Can. D10 66
Snowflake, Az., U.S. C5 80
Snow Hill, Md., U.S. D7 97
Snow Hill, N.C., U.S. B5 110
Snowking Mountain, mtn., Wa., U.S. A4 124
Snow Lake, Man., Can. B1 70
Snowmass Mountain, mtn., Co., U.S. B3 83
Snow Peak, mtn., Wa., U.S. A7 124
Snowshoe Lake, l., Me., U.S. B4 96
Snowshoe Peak, mtn., Mt., U.S. B1 103
Snow Water Lake, l., Nv., U.S. C7 105
Snowyside Peak, mtn., Id., U.S. F4 89
Snyder, Ok., U.S. C3 113
Snyder, Tx., U.S. C2 120
Snyder, co., Pa., U.S. E7 115
Soacha, Col. E5 58
Soalala, Madag. E9 44
Soap Lake, Wa., U.S. B6 124
Sobat, stm., Sudan G12 42
Sobinka, U.S.S.R. F23 22
Sobral, Braz. D10 54
Socastee, S.C., U.S. D9 117
Sochi see Soči, U.S.S.R. I5 18
Soči, U.S.S.R. I5 18
Social Circle, Ga., U.S. C3 87
Society Hill, S.C., U.S. C8 117
Socorro, Col. D6 58
Socorro, N.M., U.S. C3 108
Socorro, co., N.M., U.S. D2 108
Socorro, Isla, i., Mex. H4 62
Socotra see Suquṭrā, i., Yemen F5 46
Soc Trang, Viet. J8 34
Socuéllamos, Spain F9 12
Sodankylä, Fin. C16 6
Soda Springs, Id., U.S. G7 89
Soddy-Daisy, Tn., U.S. D8 119
Söderhamn, Swe. F11 6
Södertälje, Swe. G11 6
Sodo, Eth. G2 46
Sodus, N.Y., U.S. B3 109
Soest, Ger. D8 8
Sofia, stm., Madag. E9 44
Sofia see Sofija, Bul. G7 16
Sofija (Sofia), Bul. G7 16
Sogamoso, Col. E6 58
Sognafjorden, Nor. F5 6
Søgne, Nor. G6 6
Soignies, Bel. E4 8
Sointula, B.C., Can. D4 69
Soissons, Fr. C10 10
Sokal'skogo, Proliv, strt., U.S.S.R. B14 20
Söke, Tur. L11 16
Sokodé, Togo G6 42
Sokol, U.S.S.R. C19 20
Sokol, U.S.S.R. B23 22
Sokoto, Nig. F7 42
Sol, Costa del, Spain I7 12
Solana, Fl., U.S. F5 86
Solano, Phil. p19 33b
Solano, co., Ca., U.S. C3 82
Solbad Hall in Tirol, Aus. H11 8
Soldier, stm., Ia., U.S. C2 92
Soldier Key, i., Fl., U.S. s3 86
Soldotna, Ak., U.S. g16 79
Soledad, Col. B5 58
Soledad, Ca., U.S. D3 82
Soledad, Ven. C11 58
Soleduck, stm., Wa., U.S. B1 124
Solingen, Ger. D7 8
Sollefteå, Swe. E11 6
Sollentuna, Swe. G11 6
Sóller, Spain F14 12
Solnečnogorsk, U.S.S.R. E19 22
Sologoncy, U.S.S.R. D16 20
Solok, Indon. O6 34
Solomon, Ks., U.S. D6 93
Solomon, stm., Ks., U.S. C6 93
Solomon Islands, ctry., Oc. G23 2
Solomons, Md., U.S. D5 97
Solomon Sea, Oc. A10 50
Solon, Ia., U.S. C6 92
Solon, Oh., U.S. A4 112
Solothurn, Switz. E14 10
Solsona, Spain D13 12
Soltau, Ger. C9 8
Solvay, N.Y., U.S. B4 109
Solwezi, Zam. D5 44
Soma, Tur. J11 16
Somalia, ctry., Afr. G4 46
Sombor, Yugo. D3 16
Sombrerete, Mex. F8 62
Somerdale, N.J., U.S. D2 107
Somers, Ct., U.S. B6 84
Somers, Mt., U.S. B2 103
Somerset, Man., Can. E2 70
Somerset, Ky., U.S. C5 94
Somerset, Ma., U.S. C5 98
Somerset, N.J., U.S. B3 107
Somerset, Oh., U.S. C3 112
Somerset, Pa., U.S. F3 115
Somerset, Tx., U.S. k7 120
Somerset, Wi., U.S. C1 126
Somerset, co., Me., U.S. C2 96
Somerset, co., Md., U.S. D6 97
Somerset, co., N.J., U.S. B3 107
Somerset, co., Pa., U.S. G3 115
Somerset Island, i., N.W. Ter., Can. B14 66
Somerset Reservoir, res., Vt., U.S. E3 122
Somers Point, N.J., U.S. E3 107
Somersville, Ct., U.S. B6 84
Somersworth, N.H., U.S. D5 106
Somerton, Az., U.S. E1 80
Somervell, co., Tx., U.S. C4 120
Somerville, Ma., U.S. B5 98
Somerville, N.J., U.S. B3 107
Somerville, Tn., U.S. B2 119
Somerville, Tx., U.S. D4 120
Somerville Lake, res., Tx., U.S. D4 120
Someș (Szamos), stm., Eur. B6 16
Sömmerda, Ger. D11 8
Somonauk, Il., U.S. B5 90
Somoto, Nic. H4 64
Son, stm., India H10 38
Sønderborg, Den. I7 6
Sondershausen, Ger. D10 8
Søndre Strømfjord, Grnld. C22 66
Sondrio, Italy C4 14
Song Cau, Viet. H10 34
Songea, Tan. D7 44
Songhua, stm., China B12 26
Songjiang, China D10 28
Songkhla, Thai. K6 34
Songnim, N. Kor. D12 26
Sonīpat, India F7 38
Son La, Viet. D7 34
Sonmiāni Bay, b., Pak. H2 38
Sonneberg, Ger. E11 8
Sonoita, Mex. B3 62
Sonoma, Ca., U.S. C2 82
Sonoma, co., Ca., U.S. C2 82
Sonoma Peak, mtn., Nv., U.S. C4 105
Sonoma Range, mts., Nv., U.S. C4 105
Sonora, Ca., U.S. D3 82
Sonora, Tx., U.S. D2 120
Sonora, stm., Mex. C4 62
Sonseca, Spain F8 12
Sonsón, Col. E5 58
Sonsonate, El Sal. H3 64
Sonsorol Islands, is., T.T.P.I. D9 32
Son Tay, Viet. D8 34
Sonthofen, Ger. H10 8
Soochow see Suzhou, China D9 28
Soperton, Ga., U.S. D4 87
Sophia, W.V., U.S. D3 125
Sopot, Pol. A18 8
Sopron, Hung. H16 8
Sopur, India C6 38
Sora, Italy H8 14
Sore, Fr. H6 10
Sorel, Que., Can. C4 74
Sorgono, Italy I4 14
Sorgues, Fr. H11 10
Soria, Spain D9 12
Sorocaba, Braz. G5 57
Sorong, Indon. F9 32
Soroti, Ug. H12 42
Sorrento, Italy I9 14
Sorrento, La., U.S. D5 95
Sorsele, Swe. D11 6
Sorsogon, Phil. C7 32
Sort, Spain C13 12
Sorūbī, Afg. C3 38
Sos del Rey Católico, Spain C10 12
Sosnovo-Oz'orskoje, U.S.S.R. G16 20
Sosnowiec, Pol. E19 8
Šoštanj, Yugo. C10 14
Sotkamo, Fin. D17 6
Soto la Marina, Mex. F10 62
Sotteville, Fr. C8 10
Soucook, stm., N.H., U.S. D4 106
Soudan, Mn., U.S. C6 100
Souderton, Pa., U.S. F11 115
Souhegan, stm., N.H., U.S. E3 106
Souillac, Fr. H8 10
Soŭl (Seoul), S. Kor. D12 26
Soulac-sur-Mer, Fr. G5 10
Souris, Man., Can. E1 70
Souris, P.E.I., Can. C7 71
Sousa, Braz. E11 54
Sousse, Tun. N5 14
South, stm., Ia., U.S. C4 92
South, stm., N.C., U.S. C4 110
South Acton, Ma., U.S. g10 98
South Africa, ctry., Afr. G5 44
South Amboy, N.J., U.S. C4 107
South America E4 53
South Amherst, Ma., U.S. B2 98
South Amherst, Oh., U.S. A3 112
Southampton, Ont., Can. C3 73
Southampton, Eng., U.K. K11 7
Southampton, N.Y., U.S. n16 109
Southampton, co., Va., U.S. D5 123
Southampton Island, i., N.W. Ter., Can. D16 66
South Andaman, i., India I2 34
South Anna, stm., Va., U.S. C5 123
South Aulatsivik Island, i., Newf., Can. E20 66
South Australia, state, Austl. F7 50
Southaven, Ms., U.S. A3 101
South Bald Mountain, mtn., Co., U.S. A5 83
South Baldy, mtn., N.M., U.S. D2 108
South Barre, Vt., U.S. C3 122
South Bay, Fl., U.S. F6 86
South Beloit, Il., U.S. A4 90
South Bend, In., U.S. A5 91
South Bend, Wa., U.S. C2 124
South Berwick, Me., U.S. E2 96
South Bloomfield, Oh., U.S. C3 112
South Boston, Va., U.S. D4 123
South Bound Brook, N.J., U.S. B3 107
South Branch Lake, l., Me., U.S. C4 96
Southbridge, Ma., U.S. B3 98
South Bristol, Me., U.S. E3 96
South Britain, Ct., U.S. D3 84
South Broadway, Wa., U.S. C5 124
South Bruny, i., Austl. H9 50
South Burlington, Vt., U.S. C2 122
Southbury, Ct., U.S. D3 84
South Carolina, state, U.S. D6 117
South Charleston, Oh., U.S. C2 112
South Charleston, W.V., U.S. C3 125
South Chicago Heights, Il., U.S. m9 90
South China Sea, Asia C5 32
South Coffeyville, Ok., U.S. A6 113
South Congaree, S.C., U.S. D5 117
South Connellsville, Pa., U.S. G2 115
South Dakota, state, U.S. C5 118
South Dartmouth, Ma., U.S. C6 98
South Daytona, Fl., U.S. C5 86
South Deerfield, Ma., U.S. B2 98
South Dennis, Ma., U.S. C7 98
South Duxbury, Ma., U.S. B6 98
Southeast Cape, c., Austl. H9 50
Southeast Cape, c., Ak., U.S. C6 79
South Easton, Ma., U.S. B5 98
Southeast Pass, strt., La., U.S. E7 95
Southeast Point, c., R.I., U.S. h7 116
South Elgin, Il., U.S. B5 90
Southend-on-Sea, Eng., U.K. J13 7
Southern Alps, mts., N.Z. E3 52
Southern Cross, Austl. F3 50
Southern Indian Lake, l., Man., Can. f8 70
Southern Pines, N.C., U.S. B3 110
Southern Ute Indian Reservation, Co., U.S. D2 83
South Euclid, Oh., U.S. g9 112
Southey, Sask., Can. G3 75
South Fabius, stm., Mo., U.S. A5 102
South Fallsburg, N.Y., U.S. D6 109
Southfield, Mi., U.S. o15 99
South Fork, Pa., U.S. F4 115
South Fox Island, i., Mi., U.S. C5 99
South Fulton, Tn., U.S. A3 119

Name | Map Ref | Page

South Gastonia, N.C., U.S. **B1** 110
South Gate, Ca., U.S. **n12** 82
Southgate, Ky., U.S. **h14** 94
Southgate, Mi., U.S. **p15** 99
South Georgia, i., Falk. Is. **G9** 56
South Glastonbury, Ct., U.S. **C5** 84
South Glens Falls, N.Y., U.S. **B7** 109
South Grafton, Ma., U.S. **B4** 98
South Grand, stm., Mo., U.S. **C3** 102
South Hadley, Ma., U.S. **B2** 98
South Hadley Falls, Ma., U.S. **B2** 98
South Hamilton, Ma., U.S. **A6** 98
South Haven, In., U.S. **A3** 91
South Haven, Mi., U.S. **F4** 99
South Henik Lake, l., N.W. Ter., Can. **D13** 66
South Hero Island, i., Vt., U.S. **B2** 122
South Hill, Va., U.S. **D4** 123
South Hingham, Ma., U.S. **h12** 98
South Holland, Il., U.S. **k9** 90
South Holston Lake, res., U.S. **A9** 119
South Hooksett, N.H., U.S. **D4** 106
South Hopkinton, R.I., U.S. **F1** 116
South Houston, Tx., U.S. **r14** 120
South Hutchinson, Ks., U.S. **f11** 93
South Indian Lake, Man., Can. **A2** 70
Southington, Ct., U.S. **C4** 84
South International Falls, Mn., U.S. **B5** 100
South Island, i., N.Z. **E3** 52
South Island, i., S.C., U.S. **E9** 117
South Jacksonville, Il., U.S. **D3** 90
South Jordan, Ut., U.S. **C3** 121
South Kenosha, Wi., U.S. **F6** 126
South Lake Tahoe, Ca., U.S. **C4** 82
South Lancaster, Ma., U.S. **B4** 98
South Laurel, Md., U.S. **B4** 97
South Lebanon, Oh., U.S. **C1** 112
South Lyon, Mi., U.S. **F7** 99
South Magnetic Pole **C26** 47
South Manitou Island, i., Mi., U.S. **C4** 99
South Marsh Island, i., Md., U.S. **D5** 97
South Miami, Fl., U.S. **G6** 86
South Miami Heights, Fl., U.S. **s13** 86
South Mills, N.C., U.S. **A6** 110
South Milwaukee, Wi., U.S. **F6** 126
Southmont, N.C., U.S. **B2** 110
South Moose Lake, l., Man., Can. **C1** 70
South Mountain, mtn., Id., U.S. **G2** 89
South Mountain, mtn., N.M., U.S. **k8** 108
South Mountains, mts., Az., U.S. **m8** 80
South Mountains, mts., N.C., U.S. **B1** 110
South Nahanni, stm., N.W. Ter., Can. **D7** 66
South New River Canal, Fl., U.S. **r3** 86
South Ogden, Ut., U.S. **B4** 121
Southold, N.Y., U.S. **m16** 109
South Orange, N.J., U.S. **B4** 107
South Orkney Islands, is., B.A.T. **C8** 47
South Paris, Me., U.S. **D2** 96
South Park, val., Co., U.S. **B5** 83
South Pass, Wy., U.S. **D4** 127
South Pass, strt., La., U.S. **F6** 95
South Patrick Shores, Fl., U.S. **D6** 86
South Pekin, Il., U.S. **C4** 90
South Pittsburg, Tn., U.S. **D8** 119
South Plainfield, N.J., U.S. **B4** 107
South Platte, stm., U.S. **C6** 76
South Point, c., Mi., U.S. **D7** 99
South Pole, Ant. **A12** 47
Southport, Eng., U.K. **H9** 7
Southport, Fl., U.S. **u16** 86
Southport, In., U.S. **E5** 91
Southport, N.Y., U.S. **C4** 109
Southport, N.C., U.S. **D4** 110
South Portland, Me., U.S. **E2** 96
South Portsmouth, Ky., U.S. **B6** 94
South Range, Mi., U.S. **A2** 99
South River, Ont., Can. **B5** 73
South River, N.J., U.S. **C4** 107
South River, b., Md., U.S. **C4** 97
South Ronaldsay, i., Scot., U.K. **C10** 7
South Royalton, Vt., U.S. **D3** 122
South Sandwich Islands, is., Falk. Is. **D10** 47
South San Francisco, Ca., U.S. **h8** 82
South Saskatchewan, stm., Can. **F11** 66
South Shetland Islands, is., B.A.T. **C7** 47
South Shields, Eng., U.K. **F11** 7
Southside, Al., U.S. **B3** 78
Southside Place, Tx., U.S. **r14** 120
South Sioux City, Ne., U.S. **B9** 104
South Skunk, stm., Ia., U.S. **C4** 92
South Stony Brook, N.Y., U.S. **n15** 109
South St. Paul, Mn., U.S. **n12** 100
South Streator, Il., U.S. **B5** 90
South Toms River, N.J., U.S. **D4** 107
South Torrington, Wy., U.S. **D8** 127
South Tucson, Az., U.S. **E5** 80
South Valley Stream, N.Y., U.S. **n15** 109
South Venice, Fl., U.S. **E4** 86
South Ventana Cone, vol., Ca., U.S. **D3** 82
South Waverly, Pa., U.S. **C8** 115
South Wellfleet, Ma., U.S. **C8** 98
South Wellington, B.C., Can. **f12** 69
South West Africa see Namibia, ctry., Afr. **F3** 44
South Westbury, N.Y., U.S. **n15** 109
South West Cape, c., Austl. **H9** 50
Southwest Channel, strt., Fl., U.S. **E4** 86
South West City, Mo., U.S. **E3** 102
Southwest Harbor, Me., U.S. **D4** 96
Southwest Head, c., N.B., Can. **E3** 71
Southwest Miramichi, stm., N.B., Can. **C3** 71
Southwest Pass, strt., La., U.S. **F6** 95
Southwest Pass, strt., La., U.S. **E3** 95
Southwest Point, c., R.I., U.S. **h7** 116
South Weymouth Naval Air Station, mil., Ma., U.S. **h12** 98
South Whitley, In., U.S. **B6** 91
South Williamson, Ky., U.S. **C7** 94
South Williamsport, Pa., U.S. **D7** 115
South Windham, Ct., U.S. **C7** 84
South Windham, Me., U.S. **E2** 96
South Windsor, Ct., U.S. **B5** 84
Southwood, Co., U.S. **B6** 83
Southwood Acres, Ct., U.S. **A5** 84
South Woodstock, Ct., U.S. **B8** 84
South Yarmouth, Ma., U.S. **C7** 98
South Zanesville, Oh., U.S. **C3** 112
Sovetsk (Tilsit), U.S.S.R. **F4** 22
Sovetskaja Gavan', U.S.S.R. **H22** 20
Soviet Union see Union of Soviet Socialist Republics, ctry., Eur. **E13** 18
Soviet Union see Union of Soviet Socialist Republics, ctry., Eur. **D10** 24
Spa, Bel. **E5** 8
Spain, ctry., Eur. **G7** 4
Spalding, co., Ga., U.S. **C2** 87
Spanaway, Wa., U.S. **B3** 124
Spangler, Pa., U.S. **E4** 115
Spaniard's Bay, Newf., Can. **E5** 72
Spanish Fork, Ut., U.S. **C4** 121
Spanish Fort, Al., U.S. **E2** 78
Spanish Lake, Mo., U.S. **f13** 102
Spanish North Africa, dep., Afr. **A4** 42
Spanish Peak, mtn., Or., U.S. **C7** 114
Spanish Sahara see Western Sahara, dep., Afr. **D3** 42
Spanish Town, Jam. **E9** 64
Sparks, Ga., U.S. **E3** 87
Sparks, Nv., U.S. **D2** 105
Sparta, Ga., U.S. **C4** 87
Sparta, Il., U.S. **E4** 90
Sparta, Mi., U.S. **E5** 99
Sparta, Mo., U.S. **D4** 102
Sparta (Lake Mohawk), N.J., U.S. **A3** 107
Sparta, N.C., U.S. **A1** 110
Sparta, Tn., U.S. **D8** 119
Sparta, Wi., U.S. **E3** 126
Spartanburg, S.C., U.S. **B4** 117
Spartanburg, co., S.C., U.S. **B3** 117
Sparta see Spárti, Grc. **L6** 16
Spartel, Cap, c., Mor. **J6** 12
Spárti (Sparta), Grc. **L6** 16
Spartivento, Capo, c., Italy **K3** 14
Sparwood, B.C., Can. **E10** 69
Spassk-Dal'nij, U.S.S.R. **I20** 20
Spavinaw Creek, stm., Ok., U.S. **A7** 113
Spear, Cape, c., Newf., Can. **E5** 72
Spearfish, S.D., U.S. **C2** 118
Spearman, Tx., U.S. **A2** 120
Spearville, Ks., U.S. **E4** 93
Speed, In., U.S. **H6** 91
Speedway, In., U.S. **E5** 91
Spence Bay, N.W. Ter., Can. **C14** 66
Spencer, In., U.S. **F4** 91
Spencer, Ia., U.S. **A2** 92
Spencer, Ma., U.S. **B4** 98
Spencer, N.C., U.S. **B2** 110
Spencer, Tn., U.S. **D8** 119
Spencer, W.V., U.S. **C3** 125
Spencer, Wi., U.S. **D3** 126
Spencer, co., In., U.S. **H4** 91
Spencer, co., Ky., U.S. **B4** 94
Spencer, Cape, c., Ak., U.S. **k21** 79
Spencer Gulf, b., Austl. **F7** 50
Spencer Lake, l., Me., U.S. **C2** 96
Spencerport, N.Y., U.S. **B3** 109
Spencerville, Md., U.S. **B4** 97
Spencerville, Oh., U.S. **B1** 112
Sperry, Ok., U.S. **A6** 113
Spesutie Island, i., Md., U.S. **B5** 97
Spey, stm., Scot., U.K. **D9** 7
Speyer, Ger. **F8** 8
Spiceland, In., U.S. **E7** 91
Spicer, Mn., U.S. **E4** 100
Spider Lake, l., Wi., U.S. **B2** 126
Spindale, N.C., U.S. **B1** 110
Spink, co., S.D., U.S. **C7** 118
Spirit Lake, Id., U.S. **B2** 89
Spirit Lake, Ia., U.S. **A2** 92
Spirit Lake, l., Ia., U.S. **A2** 92
Spirit Lake, l., Wa., U.S. **C3** 124
Spirit River, Alta., Can. **B1** 68
Spirit River Flowage, res., Wi., U.S. **C4** 126
Spiro, Ok., U.S. **B7** 113
Spittal an der Drau, Aus. **I13** 8
Spitz, Aus. **G15** 8
Split, Yugo. **F11** 14
Split, Cape, c., N.S., Can. **D5** 71
Split Lake, l., Man., Can. **A4** 70
Split Rock Creek, stm., U.S. **G2** 100
Splügen, Switz. **F16** 10
Spofford Lake, l., N.H., U.S. **E2** 106
Spokane, Wa., U.S. **B8** 124
Spokane, co., Wa., U.S. **B8** 124
Spokane, stm., U.S. **B8** 124
Spokane, Mount, mtn., Wa., U.S. **B8** 124
Spokane Indian Reservation, Wa., U.S. **B8** 124
Spoleto, Italy **G7** 14
Spoon, stm., Il., U.S. **C3** 90
Spooner, Wi., U.S. **C2** 126
Spooner Lake, l., Wi., U.S. **C2** 126
Spornoje, U.S.S.R. **E24** 20
Spotswood, N.J., U.S. **C4** 107
Spotsylvania, co., Va., U.S. **B5** 123
Sprague, W.V., U.S. **n13** 125
Sprague, stm., Or., U.S. **E5** 114
Sprague Lake, l., Wa., U.S. **B7** 124
Spratly Island, i., Asia **D5** 32
Spremberg, Ger. **D14** 8
Spring, stm., Ar., U.S. **A4** 81
Spring Arbor, Mi., U.S. **F6** 99
Spring Bay, b., Ut., U.S. **B3** 121
Springbok, S. Afr. **G3** 44
Springboro, Oh., U.S. **C1** 112
Spring Brook, stm., Pa., U.S. **n18** 115
Spring City, Pa., U.S. **F10** 115
Spring City, Tn., U.S. **D9** 119
Spring City, Ut., U.S. **D4** 121
Spring Creek, stm., U.S. **D4** 104
Spring Creek, stm., Nv., U.S. **C4** 105
Spring Creek, stm., N.D., U.S. **B3** 111
Springdale, Newf., Can. **D3** 72
Springdale, Ar., U.S. **A1** 81
Springdale, Oh., U.S. **n13** 112
Springdale, Pa., U.S. **E2** 115
Springdale, S.C., U.S. **D5** 117
Springer, N.M., U.S. **A5** 108
Springerville, Az., U.S. **C6** 80
Springfield, Co., U.S. **D8** 83
Springfield, Fl., U.S. **u16** 86
Springfield, Ga., U.S. **D5** 87
Springfield, Il., U.S. **D4** 90
Springfield, Ky., U.S. **C4** 94
Springfield, Ma., U.S. **B2** 98
Springfield, Mn., U.S. **F4** 100
Springfield, Mo., U.S. **D4** 102
Springfield, Ne., U.S. **C9** 104
Springfield, N.J., U.S. **B4** 107
Springfield, Oh., U.S. **C2** 112
Springfield, Or., U.S. **C4** 114
Springfield, Pa., U.S. **p20** 115
Springfield, S.D., U.S. **E8** 118
Springfield, Tn., U.S. **A5** 119
Springfield, Vt., U.S. **E4** 122
Springfield, Va., U.S. **g12** 123
Springfield, Lake, res., Il., U.S. **D4** 90
Springfontein, S. Afr. **H5** 44
Spring Garden, Guy. **D13** 58
Spring Glen, Ut., U.S. **D5** 121
Spring Green, Wi., U.S. **E3** 126
Spring Grove, Il., U.S. **h8** 90
Spring Grove, Mn., U.S. **G7** 100
Spring Grove, Pa., U.S. **G8** 115
Spring Hill, Fl., U.S. **D4** 86
Spring Hill, Ks., U.S. **D9** 93
Springhill, La., U.S. **A2** 95
Spring Hill, Tn., U.S. **B5** 119
Spring Hope, N.C., U.S. **B4** 110
Spring Island, i., S.C., U.S. **G6** 117
Spring Lake, Mi., U.S. **E4** 99
Spring Lake, N.J., U.S. **C4** 107
Spring Lake, N.C., U.S. **B4** 110
Spring Lake, l., Me., U.S. **C2** 96
Spring Lake, res., U.S. **B3** 90
Spring Lake Heights, N.J., U.S. **C4** 107
Spring Mountains, mts., Nv., U.S. **G6** 105
Springport, Mi., U.S. **F6** 99
Springs, S. Afr. **G5** 44
Springside, Sask., Can. **F4** 75
Springvale, Me., U.S. **E2** 96
Spring Valley, Ca., U.S. **o16** 82
Spring Valley, Il., U.S. **B4** 90
Spring Valley, Mn., U.S. **G6** 100
Spring Valley, N.Y., U.S. **g12** 109
Spring Valley, Wi., U.S. **D1** 126
Springville, Al., U.S. **B3** 78
Springville, Ia., U.S. **B6** 92
Springville, N.Y., U.S. **C2** 109
Springville, Ut., U.S. **C4** 121
Spruce Fork, stm., W.V., U.S. **m12** 125
Spruce Grove, Alta., Can. **C4** 68
Spruce Knob, mtn., W.V., U.S. **C6** 125
Spruce Knob-Seneca Rocks National Recreation Area, W.V., U.S. **C5** 125
Spruce Mountain, mtn., Az., U.S. **C3** 80
Spruce Mountain, mtn., Nv., U.S. **C7** 105
Spruce Pine, N.C., U.S. **f10** 110
Spruce Run Reservoir, res., N.J., U.S. **B3** 107
Spur, Tx., U.S. **C2** 120
Spurr, Mount, mtn., Ak., U.S. **g15** 79
Squam Lake, l., N.H., U.S. **C4** 106
Squapan Lake, l., Me., U.S. **B4** 96
Square Lake, l., Me., U.S. **A4** 96
Squatec, Que., Can. **B9** 74
Squaw Cap Mountain, mtn., N.B., Can. **B3** 71
Squaw Hill, mtn., Wy., U.S. **E7** 127
Squaw Peak, mtn., Mt., U.S. **C2** 103
Squibnocket Point, c., Ma., U.S. **D6** 98
Squinzano, Italy **I13** 14
Squire, W.V., U.S. **D3** 125
Sragen, Indon. **m15** 33a
Sredinnyj Chrebet, mts., U.S.S.R. **F26** 20
Srednekolymsk, U.S.S.R. **D24** 20
Srednerusskaja Vozvyšennost', plat., U.S.S.R. **H20** 22
Srednesibirskoje Ploskogorje, plat., U.S.S.R. **D14** 20
Sremska Mitrovica, Yugo. **E3** 16
Sri Gangānagar, India **F5** 38
Srīkākulam, India **C7** 37
Sri Lanka, ctry., Asia **H5** 36
Srīnagar, India **C6** 38
Srīrampur, India **C3** 37
Stack Reservoir, res., R.I., U.S. **C3** 116
Stade, Ger. **B9** 8
Stadthagen, Ger. **C9** 8
Stafford, Eng., U.K. **I10** 7
Stafford, Ks., U.S. **E5** 93
Stafford, Va., U.S. **B5** 123
Stafford, co., Ks., U.S. **D5** 93
Stafford, co., Va., U.S. **B5** 123
Stafford Pond, l., R.I., U.S. **D6** 116
Stafford Springs, Ct., U.S. **B6** 84
Staked Plain see Estacado, Llano, pl., U.S. **E6** 76
Stalheim, Nor. **F6** 6
Stalingrad see Volgograd, U.S.S.R. **H6** 18
Stalowa Wola, Pol. **E22** 8
Stambaugh, Mi., U.S. **B2** 99
Stamford, Ct., U.S. **E1** 84
Stamford, Tx., U.S. **C3** 120
Stamford, Vt., U.S. **F2** 122
Stamford, Lake, res., Tx., U.S. **C3** 120
Stamping Ground, Ky., U.S. **B5** 94
Stamps, Ar., U.S. **D2** 81
Stanaford, W.V., U.S. **D3** 125
Stanberry, Mo., U.S. **A3** 102
Standerton, S. Afr. **G5** 44
Standing Rock Indian Reservation, U.S. **B4** 118
Standish, Mi., U.S. **E7** 99
Stanfield, Az., U.S. **E3** 80
Stanfield, Or., U.S. **B7** 114
Stanford, Ky., U.S. **C5** 94
Stanhope, N.J., U.S. **B3** 107
Stanislaus, co., Ca., U.S. **D3** 82
Stanke Dimitrov, Bul. **G7** 16
Stanley, Falk. Is. **G5** 56
Stanley, N.C., U.S. **B1** 110
Stanley, N.D., U.S. **A3** 111
Stanley, Va., U.S. **B4** 123
Stanley, Wi., U.S. **D3** 126
Stanley, co., S.D., U.S. **C5** 118
Stanley Falls, wtfl, Zaire **A5** 44
Stanleytown, Va., U.S. **D3** 123
Stanleyville, N.C., U.S. **A2** 110
Stanleyville see Kisangani, Zaire **A5** 44
Stanly, co., N.C., U.S. **B2** 110
Stann Creek, Belize **F3** 64
Stanovoj Chrebet, mts., U.S.S.R. **F19** 20
Stanovoje Nagorje (Stanovoy Mountains), mts., U.S.S.R. **F16** 20
Stanstead, Que., Can. **D5** 74
Stanton, Ia., U.S. **D2** 92
Stanton, Ky., U.S. **C6** 94
Stanton, Mi., U.S. **E5** 99
Stanton, Ne., U.S. **C8** 104
Stanton, Tx., U.S. **C2** 120
Stanton, co., Ks., U.S. **E2** 93
Stanton, co., Ne., U.S. **C8** 104
Stantonsburg, N.C., U.S. **B5** 110
Stanwood, Ia., U.S. **C6** 92
Stanwood, Wa., U.S. **A3** 124
Staples, Mn., U.S. **D4** 100
Stapleton, Al., U.S. **E2** 78
Star, Id., U.S. **F2** 89
Star, N.C., U.S. **B3** 110
Starachowice, Pol. **D21** 8
Staraja Russa, U.S.S.R. **C14** 22
Stara Planina (Balkan Mountains), mts., Eur. **G8** 16
Stara Zagora, Bul. **G9** 16
Starbuck, Mn., U.S. **E3** 100
Star City, Ar., U.S. **D4** 81
Star City, W.V., U.S. **B5** 125
Stargard Szczeciński (Stargard in Pommern), Pol. **B15** 8
Stargo, Az., U.S. **D6** 80
Stark, co., Il., U.S. **B4** 90
Stark, co., N.D., U.S. **C3** 111
Stark, co., Oh., U.S. **B4** 112
Starke, Fl., U.S. **C4** 86
Starke, co., In., U.S. **B4** 91
Starks, La., U.S. **D2** 95
Starkville, Ms., U.S. **B5** 101
Star Lake, l., Mn., U.S. **D3** 100
Starnberg, Ger. **G11** 8
Starogard Gdański, Pol. **B18** 8
Star Peak, mtn., Nv., U.S. **C3** 105
Starr, co., Tx., U.S. **F3** 120
Startex, S.C., U.S. **B3** 117
Start Point, c., Eng., U.K. **K9** 7
Startup, Wa., U.S. **B4** 124
State Center, Ia., U.S. **B4** 92
State College, Pa., U.S. **E6** 115
Stateline, Nv., U.S. **E2** 105
State Line, Pa., U.S. **G6** 115
Staten Island, i., N.Y., U.S. **k12** 109
Statenville, Ga., U.S. **F4** 87
Statesboro, Ga., U.S. **D5** 87
Statesville, N.C., U.S. **B2** 110
Statham, Ga., U.S. **C3** 87
Statue of Liberty National Monument, N.J., U.S. **k8** 107
Staunton, Il., U.S. **D4** 90
Staunton, Va., U.S. **B3** 123
Stavanger, Nor. **G5** 6
Stavropol', U.S.S.R. **H6** 18
Stayner, Ont., Can. **C4** 73
Stayton, Or., U.S. **C4** 114
Steamboat, Nv., U.S. **D2** 105
Steamboat Mountain, mtn., Mt., U.S. **C4** 103
Steamboat Mountain, mtn., Wy., U.S. **E4** 127
Steamboat Springs, Co., U.S. **A4** 83
Stearns, Ky., U.S. **D5** 94
Stearns, co., Mn., U.S. **E4** 100
Stearns Brook, stm., N.H., U.S. **A4** 106
Stebbins, Ak., U.S. **C7** 79
Steele, Al., U.S. **B3** 78
Steele, Mo., U.S. **E8** 102
Steele, N.D., U.S. **C6** 111
Steele, co., Mn., U.S. **F5** 100
Steele, co., N.D., U.S. **B8** 111
Steele, Mount, mtn., Wy., U.S. **E6** 127
Steeleville, Il., U.S. **E4** 90
Steelton, Pa., U.S. **F8** 115
Steelville, Mo., U.S. **D6** 102
Steenkool, Indon. **F9** 32
Steens Mountain, mts., Or., U.S. **E8** 114
Stefansson Island, i., N.W. Ter., Can. **B11** 66
Steger, Il., U.S. **B6** 90
Steilacoom, Wa., U.S. **f10** 124
Steinbach, Man., Can. **E3** 70
Steinhatchee, stm., Fl., U.S. **C3** 86
Steinkjer, Nor. **D8** 6
Stellenbosch, S. Afr. **H3** 44
Stenay, Fr. **C12** 10
Stendal, Ger. **C11** 8
Stephen, Mn., U.S. **B2** 100
Stephens, Ar., U.S. **D2** 81
Stephens, co., Ga., U.S. **B3** 87
Stephens, co., Ok., U.S. **C4** 113
Stephens, co., Tx., U.S. **C3** 120
Stephens City, Va., U.S. **A4** 123
Stephens Lake, res., Man., Can. **A4** 70
Stephenson, Mi., U.S. **C3** 99
Stephenson, co., Il., U.S. **A4** 90
Stephens Passage, strt., Ak., U.S. **m23** 79
Stephenville, Newf., Can. **D2** 72
Stephenville, Tx., U.S. **C3** 120
Stephenville Crossing, Newf., Can. **D2** 72
Sterling, Ak., U.S. **g16** 79
Sterling, Co., U.S. **A7** 83
Sterling, Il., U.S. **B4** 90
Sterling, Ks., U.S. **D5** 93
Sterling, Ok., U.S. **C3** 113
Sterling, Va., U.S. **A5** 123
Sterling, co., Tx., U.S. **D2** 120
Sterling City, Tx., U.S. **D2** 120
Sterling Heights, Mi., U.S. **o15** 99
Sterling Reservoir, res., Co., U.S. **A7** 83
Sterlington, La., U.S. **B3** 95
Sterlitamak, U.S.S.R. **G9** 18
Stettin see Szczecin, Pol. **B14** 8
Stettler, Alta., Can. **C4** 68
Steuben, co., In., U.S. **A7** 91
Steuben, co., N.Y., U.S. **C3** 109
Steubenville, Oh., U.S. **B5** 112
Stevenage, Eng., U.K. **J12** 7
Stevens, co., Ks., U.S. **E2** 93
Stevens, co., Mn., U.S. **E3** 100
Stevens, co., Wa., U.S. **A7** 124
Stevens Creek Dam, U.S. **C4** 87
Stevenson, Al., U.S. **A4** 78
Stevenson, Ct., U.S. **D3** 84
Stevenson, Wa., U.S. **D4** 124
Stevenson Lake, l., Man., Can. **C4** 70
Stevens Pass, Wa., U.S. **B4** 124
Stevens Peak, mtn., Id., U.S. **B3** 89
Stevens Point, Wi., U.S. **D4** 126
Stevensville, Md., U.S. **C5** 97
Stevensville, Mi., U.S. **F4** 99
Stevensville, Mt., U.S. **D2** 103
Stewart, co., Ga., U.S. **D2** 87
Stewart, co., Tn., U.S. **A4** 119
Stewart Island, i., N.Z. **G1** 52
Stewart Mountain, mtn., Az., U.S. **k9** 80
Stewartstown, Pa., U.S. **G8** 115
Stewartsville, Mo., U.S. **B3** 102
Stewartville, Mn., U.S. **G6** 100
Stewiacke, N.S., Can. **D6** 71
Steyr, Aus. **G14** 8
Stigler, Ok., U.S. **B6** 113
Stigliano, Italy **I11** 14
Stikine, stm., B.C., Can. **E7** 66
Stikine, stm., Ak., U.S. **D13** 79
Stikine Ranges, mts., B.C., Can. **E6** 66
Still, stm., Ct., U.S. **B3** 84
Stillaguamish, North Fork, stm., Wa., U.S. **A4** 124
Stillaguamish, South Fork, stm., Wa., U.S. **A4** 124
Stillhouse Hollow Lake, res., Tx., U.S. **D4** 120
Stillman Valley, Il., U.S. **A4** 90
Stillmore, Ga., U.S. **D4** 87
Stillwater, Mn., U.S. **E6** 100
Stillwater, Ok., U.S. **A4** 113
Stillwater, co., Mt., U.S. **E7** 103
Stillwater Range, mts., Nv., U.S. **D3** 105
Stillwater Reservoir, res., N.Y., U.S. **B5** 109
Stillwater Reservoir, res., R.I., U.S. **B3** 116
Stilwell, Ok., U.S. **B7** 113
Stimson, Mount, mtn., Mt., U.S. **B3** 103
Stine Mountain, mtn., Mt., U.S. **E3** 103
Stinking Lake, l., N.M., U.S. **A3** 108
Stinnett, Tx., U.S. **B2** 120
Štip, Yugo. **H6** 16
Stirling, Alta., Can. **E4** 68
Stirling, Ont., Can. **C7** 73
Stirling, Scot., U.K. **E9** 7
Stjørdalshalsen, Nor. **E8** 6
Stockbridge, Ga., U.S. **C2** 87
Stockbridge, Mi., U.S. **F6** 99
Stockbridge-Munsee Indian Reservation, Wi., U.S. **D5** 126
Stockdale, Tx., U.S. **E4** 120
Stockerau, Aus. **G16** 8
Stockholm, Swe. **G12** 6
Stockton, Ca., U.S. **D3** 82
Stockton, Il., U.S. **A3** 90
Stockton, Ks., U.S. **C4** 93
Stockton, Md., U.S. **D7** 97
Stockton, Mo., U.S. **D4** 102
Stockton Island, i., Wi., U.S. **B3** 126
Stockton Lake, res., Mo., U.S. **D4** 102
Stoddard, Wi., U.S. **E2** 126
Stoddard, co., Mo., U.S. **E8** 102
Stoke-on-Trent, Eng., U.K. **H10** 7
Stokes, co., N.C., U.S. **A2** 110
Stokesdale, N.C., U.S. **A3** 110
Stolbovoj, Ostrov, i., U.S.S.R. **C21** 20
Stollings, W.V., U.S. **n12** 125
Ston, Yugo. **G12** 14
Stone, co., Ar., U.S. **B3** 81
Stone, co., Ms., U.S. **E4** 101
Stone, co., Mo., U.S. **E4** 102
Stoneboro, Pa., U.S. **D1** 115
Stone Corral Lake, l., Or., U.S. **E7** 114
Stoneham, Ma., U.S. **g11** 98
Stonehaven, Scot., U.K. **E10** 7
Stone Mountain, Ga., U.S. **C2** 87
Stone Mountain, mtn., Ga., U.S. **C2** 87
Stones River National Battlefield, hist., Tn., U.S. **B4** 119
Stoneville, N.C., U.S. **A3** 110
Stonewall, Man., Can. **D3** 70
Stonewall, La., U.S. **B2** 95
Stonewall, Ms., U.S. **C5** 101
Stonewall, co., Tx., U.S. **C2** 120
Stonewood, W.V., U.S. **k10** 125
Stoney Creek, Ont., Can. **D5** 73
Stonington, Ct., U.S. **D8** 84
Stonington, Il., U.S. **D4** 90
Stonington, Me., U.S. **D4** 96
Stono, stm., S.C., U.S. **k11** 117
Stono Inlet, b., S.C., U.S. **F8** 117
Stony Brook, N.Y., U.S. **n15** 109
Stony Brook, stm., N.J., U.S. **C3** 107
Stony Creek, stm., Va., U.S. **C5** 123
Stony Island, i., N.Y., U.S. **B4** 109
Stony Plain, Alta., Can. **C3** 68
Stony Point, N.C., U.S. **B1** 110
Storby, Fin. **F12** 6
Støren, Nor. **E8** 6
Storey, co., Nv., U.S. **D2** 105
Storfors, Swe. **G10** 6
Storkerson Peninsula, pen., N.W. Ter., Can. **B11** 66
Storlien, Swe. **E9** 6
Storm Lake, Ia., U.S. **B2** 92
Storm Lake, l., Ia., U.S. **B2** 92
Storm Mountain, mtn., Ak., U.S. **h16** 79
Stornoway, Scot., U.K. **C6** 7
Storrs, Ct., U.S. **B7** 84
Storuman, Swe. **D11** 6
Storvreta, Swe. **G11** 6
Story, Wy., U.S. **B6** 127
Story, co., Ia., U.S. **B4** 92
Story City, Ia., U.S. **B4** 92
Stoughton, Sask., Can. **H4** 75
Stoughton, Ma., U.S. **B5** 98
Stoughton, Wi., U.S. **F4** 126

Name — **Map Ref** — **Page**

Stover, Mo., U.S. C5 102
Stow, Oh., U.S. A4 112
Stow Creek, stm., N.J., U.S. E2 107
Stowe, Pa., U.S. F10 115
Stowe, Vt., U.S. C3 122
Stoyoma Mountain, mtn., B.C., Can. E7 69
Strabane, Pa., U.S. F1 115
Strafford, Mo., U.S. D4 102
Strafford, co., N.H., U.S. D4 106
Straffordville, Ont., Can. E4 73
Strahan, Austl. H9 50
Strakonice, Czech. F13 8
Stralsund, Ger. A13 8
Stranraer, Scot., U.K. G7 7
Strasbourg, Fr. D14 10
Strasburg, Co., U.S. B6 83
Strasburg, Oh., U.S. B4 112
Strasburg, Pa., U.S. G9 115
Strasburg, Va., U.S. B4 123
Stratford, Ont., Can. D3 73
Stratford, Ct., U.S. E3 84
Stratford, Ia., U.S. B4 92
Stratford, N.J., U.S. D2 107
Stratford, Ok., U.S. C5 113
Stratford, Tx., U.S. A1 120
Stratford, Wi., U.S. D3 126
Stratford Point, c., Ct., U.S. E3 84
Stratford-upon-Avon, Eng., U.K. I11 7
Stratham, N.H., U.S. D5 106
Strathmore, Alta., Can. D4 68
Strathmore, Ca., U.S. D4 82
Strathroy, Ont., Can. E3 73
Stratton, Co., U.S. B8 83
Straubing, Ger. G12 8
Strausberg, Ger. C13 8
Strawberry, stm., Ar., U.S. A4 81
Strawberry, stm., Ut., U.S. C5 121
Strawberry Mountain, mtn., Or., U.S. C8 114
Strawberry Point, Ia., U.S. B6 92
Strawberry Point, c., Ma., U.S. B6 98
Strawberry Range, mts., Or., U.S. C8 114
Strawberry Reservoir, res., Ut., U.S. C4 121
Streator, Il., U.S. B5 90
Stretensk, U.S.S.R. G17 20
Strickland, stm., Pap. N. Gui. m15 50a
Strimón (Struma), stm., Eur. I7 16
Stromness, Scot., U.K. C9 7
Stromsburg, Ne., U.S. C8 104
Strömstad, Swe. G8 6
Strömsund, Swe. E10 6
Strong, Ar., U.S. D3 81
Strong, Me., U.S. D2 96
Strong, stm., Ms., U.S. C4 101
Strong City, Ks., U.S. D7 93
Stronghurst, Il., U.S. C3 90
Strongsville, Oh., U.S. A4 112
Stronsay, i., Scot., U.K. B10 7
Stroud, Ok., U.S. B5 113
Stroudsburg, Pa., U.S. E11 115
Stroudwater, stm., Me., U.S. g7 96
Strum, Wi., U.S. D2 126
Struma (Strimón), stm., Eur. H7 16
Strumble Head, c., Wales, U.K. I7 7
Strumica, Yugo. H6 16
Strunino, U.S.S.R. E21 22
Struthers, Oh., U.S. A5 112
Stryker, Oh., U.S. A1 112
Stuart, Fl., U.S. E6 86
Stuart, Ia., U.S. C3 92
Stuart, Ne., U.S. B6 104
Stuart, Va., U.S. D2 123
Stuart, Mount, mtn., Wa., U.S. B5 124
Stuart Lake, l., B.C., Can. B5 69
Stuarts Draft, Va., U.S. B3 123
Stull, stm., Can. B5 70
Stump Lake, l., N.D., U.S. B7 111
Stump Pond, res., R.I., U.S. D2 116
Stung Treng, Camb. H8 34
Stupino, U.S.S.R. G21 22
Sturbridge, Ma., U.S. B3 98
Sturgeon, Mo., U.S. B5 102
Sturgeon, stm., Mi., U.S. B4 99
Sturgeon Bay, Wi., U.S. D6 126
Sturgeon Bay, b., Man., Can. C3 70
Sturgeon Falls, Ont., Can. A5 73
Sturgeon Lake, l., Ont., Can. C6 73
Sturgis, Sask., Can. F4 75
Sturgis, Ky., U.S. e10 94
Sturgis, Mi., U.S. G5 99
Sturgis, S.D., U.S. C2 118
Sturtevant, Wi., U.S. F6 126
Stutsman, co., N.D., U.S. B6 111
Stuttgart, Ger. G9 8
Stuttgart, Ar., U.S. C4 81
Suaita, Col. D6 58
Subang, Indon. m13 33a
Subansiri, stm., Asia G16 38
Subiaco, Italy H8 14
Sublette, Ks., U.S. E3 93
Sublette, co., Wy., U.S. D2 127
Sublett Range, mts., Id., U.S. G6 89
Sublimity, Or., U.S. C4 114
Subotica, Yugo. C3 16
Sučan, U.S.S.R. I20 20
Sucarnoochee, stm., Al., U.S. C1 78
Succasunna, N.J., U.S. B3 107
Suceava, Rom. B10 16
Süchbaatar, Mong. A8 26
Suchumi, U.S.S.R. I6 18
Sucre, Bol. G5 54
Sucuaro, Col. E8 58
Sudan, ctry., Afr. F12 42
Sudan, reg., Afr. F7 42
Sudbury, Ont., Can. A4 73
Sudbury, Ma., U.S. B5 98
Sudbury, stm., Ma., U.S. B5 98
Sudbury Center, Ma., U.S. g10 98
Sudbury Reservoir, res., Ma., U.S. g10 98
Sudeten see Sudety, mts., Eur. E15 8
Sudety, mts., Eur. E15 8
Sue, stm., Sudan G11 42
Sueca, Spain F11 12
Suez see As-Suways, Egypt C12 42
Suez Canal see Suways, Qanāt as-, Egypt D3 40
Suffern, N.Y., U.S. D6 109
Suffield, Ct., U.S. B5 84
Suffolk, Va., U.S. D6 123
Suffolk, co., Ma., U.S. B5 98
Suffolk, co., N.Y., U.S. n15 109
Sugar, stm., U.S. F4 126
Sugar, stm., N.H., U.S. D2 106
Sugar City, Id., U.S. F7 89
Sugar Creek, Mo., U.S. h11 102
Sugarcreek, Pa., U.S. D2 115
Sugar Creek, stm., Oh., U.S. C2 112
Sugar Creek, stm., Pa., U.S. C8 115
Sugar Grove, Va., U.S. D1 123
Sugar Hill, Ga., U.S. B2 87
Sugar Island, i., Mi., U.S. B6 99
Sugar Land, Tx., U.S. E5 120
Sugarland Run, Va., U.S. A5 123
Sugar Loaf, Va., U.S. C3 123
Sugarloaf Mountain, mtn., Mt., U.S. C4 103
Sugar Notch, Pa., U.S. n17 115
Suggi Lake, l., Sask., Can. C4 75
Sugoj, stm., U.S.S.R. E25 20
Suḥār, Oman D6 46
Suhl, Ger. E10 8
Suiattle, stm., Wa., U.S. A4 124
Suide, China D9 26
Suihua, China B12 26
Suining, China E8 26
Suiping, China B2 28
Suitland, Md., U.S. C4 97
Suizhong, China C11 26
Suja, U.S.S.R. E24 22
Sukabumi, Indon. m13 32
Sukagawa, Japan E13 30
Sukhumi see Suchumi, U.S.S.R. I6 18
Sukkertoppen, Grnld. C22 66
Sukkur, Pak. G3 38
Sukumo, Japan J5 30
Sula, Kepulauan, is., Indon. F8 32
Sulaimān Range, mts., Pak. F3 38
Sulawesi (Celebes), i., Indon. F7 32
Sullana, Peru D2 54
Sulligent, Al., U.S. B1 78
Sullivan, Il., U.S. D5 90
Sullivan, In., U.S. F3 91
Sullivan, Mo., U.S. C6 102
Sullivan, co., In., U.S. F3 91
Sullivan, co., Mo., U.S. A4 102
Sullivan, co., N.H., U.S. D2 106
Sullivan, co., N.Y., U.S. D6 109
Sullivan, co., Pa., U.S. D9 115
Sullivan, co., Tn., U.S. C11 119
Sullivan Lake, l., Alta., Can. D5 68
Sullivans Island, S.C., U.S. k12 117
Sully, Fr. E9 10
Sully, Ia., U.S. C5 92
Sully, co., S.D., U.S. C5 118
Sulmona, Italy G8 14
Sulphur, La., U.S. D2 95
Sulphur, Ok., U.S. C5 113
Sulphur, stm., U.S. D2 81
Sulphur Spring Range, mts., Nv., U.S. C5 105
Sulphur Springs, Tx., U.S. C5 120
Sultan, Wa., U.S. B4 124
Sultānpur, India G10 38
Sulu Archipelago, is., Phil. D7 32
Sulu Sea, Asia D6 32
Sulzbach-Rosenberg, Ger. F11 8
Sumas, Wa., U.S. A3 124
Sumatera (Sumatra), i., Indon. F3 32
Sumatra see Sumatera, i., Indon. F3 32
Sumba, i., Indon. G7 32
Sumbawa, i., Indon. G6 32
Sumbawanga, Tan. C6 44
Sumedang, Indon. m13 33a
Šumen, Bul. F10 16
Sumenep, Indon. m16 33a
Sumgait, U.S.S.R. I7 18
Sumiton, Al., U.S. B2 78
Summerfield, N.C., U.S. A3 110
Summerford, Newf., Can. D4 72
Summer Island, i., Mi., U.S. C4 99
Summer Lake, l., Or., U.S. E6 114
Summerland, B.C., Can. E8 69
Summers, co., W.V., U.S. D4 125
Summerside, P.E.I., Can. C6 71
Summersville, W.V., U.S. C4 125
Summersville Lake, res., W.V., U.S. C4 125
Summerton, S.C., U.S. D7 117
Summertown, Tn., U.S. B4 119
Summerville, Ga., U.S. B1 87
Summerville, S.C., U.S. E7 117
Summit, Il., U.S. k9 90
Summit, Ms., U.S. D3 101
Summit, N.J., U.S. B4 107
Summit, Tn., U.S. h11 119
Summit, co., Co., U.S. B4 83
Summit, co., Oh., U.S. A4 112
Summit, co., Ut., U.S. C5 121
Summit Hill, Pa., U.S. E10 115
Summit Lake, l., Ia., U.S. C3 92
Summit Lake Indian Reservation, Nv., U.S. B2 105
Summit Mountain, mtn., Nv., U.S. D5 105
Summit Peak, mtn., Co., U.S. D4 83
Summitville, In., U.S. D6 91
Sumner, Il., U.S. E6 90
Sumner, Ia., U.S. B5 92
Sumner, Wa., U.S. B3 124
Sumner, co., Ks., U.S. E6 93
Sumner, co., Tn., U.S. A5 119
Sumner, Lake, res., N.M., U.S. C5 108
Sumner Dam, N.M., U.S. C5 108
Sumner Strait, strt., Ak., U.S. m23 79
Sumoto, Japan H7 30
Šumperk, Czech. F16 8
Sumrall, Ms., U.S. D4 101
Šumšu, Ostrov, i., U.S.S.R. G25 20
Sumter, S.C., U.S. D7 117
Sumter, co., Al., U.S. C1 78
Sumter, co., Fl., U.S. D4 86
Sumter, co., Ga., U.S. D2 87
Sumter, co., S.C., U.S. D7 117
Sumy, U.S.S.R. G4 18
Sun, stm., Mt., U.S. C4 103
Sunagawa, Japan p19 30a
Sunapee, N.H., U.S. D2 106
Sunapee Lake, l., N.H., U.S. D2 106
Sunbright, Tn., U.S. C9 119
Sunbury, Oh., U.S. B3 112
Sunbury, Pa., U.S. E8 115
Sunchales, Arg. C4 56
Sun City, Az., U.S. k8 80
Suncook, N.H., U.S. D4 106
Suncook, stm., N.H., U.S. D4 106
Suncook Lakes, l., N.H., U.S. D4 106
Sunda, Selat, strt., Indon. G4 32
Sundance, Wy., U.S. B8 127
Sundance Mountain, mtn., Wy., U.S. B8 127
Sundarbans, reg., Asia J13 38
Sunderland, Ont., Can. C5 73
Sunderland, Eng., U.K. G11 7
Sundown, Tx., U.S. C1 120
Sundre, Alta., Can. D3 68
Sundridge, Ont., Can. B5 73
Sundsvall, Swe. E11 6
Sunflower, Ms., U.S. B3 101
Sunflower, co., Ms., U.S. B3 101
Sunflower, Mount, mtn., Ks., U.S. C2 93
Sungaidareh, Indon. O6 34
Sungei Patani, Malay. L6 34
Suniteyouqi, China C9 26
Sunland Park, N.M., U.S. F3 108
Sunlight Creek, stm., Wy., U.S. B3 127
Sunman, In., U.S. F7 91
Sunndalsøra, Nor. E7 6
Sunnyside, Newf., Can. E5 72
Sunnyside, Wa., U.S. C5 124
Sunnyvale, Ca., U.S. k8 82
Sun Prairie, Wi., U.S. E4 126
Sunray, Tx., U.S. A2 120
Sunrise Manor, Nv., U.S. G6 105
Sunset, La., U.S. D3 95
Sunset, Ut., U.S. B4 121
Sunset Beach, Hi., U.S. f9 88
Sunset Crater National Monument, Az., U.S. B4 80
Sunset Lake, l., Vt., U.S. D2 122
Suntar, U.S.S.R. E17 20
Suntar-Chajata, Chrebet, mts., U.S.S.R. E22 20
Suntaug Lake, l., Ma., U.S. f11 98
Sun Valley, Id., U.S. F4 89
Sun Valley, Nv., U.S. D2 105
Sunyani, Ghana G5 42
Suō-nada, Japan I4 30
Suonenjoki, Fin. E16 6
Suordach, U.S.S.R. D20 20
Superior, Az., U.S. D4 80
Superior, Mt., U.S. C2 103
Superior, Ne., U.S. D7 104
Superior, Wi., U.S. B1 126
Superior, Wy., U.S. E4 127
Superior, Lake, l., N.A. B9 76
Superstition Mountains, mts., Az., U.S. m10 80
Supetar, Yugo. F11 14
Suphan Buri, Thai. G6 34
Suqian, China B7 28
Suquamish, Wa., U.S. B3 124
Suquṭrā (Socotra), i., Yemen F5 46
Şūr (Tyre), Leb. C4 40
Şūr, Oman D6 46
Sur, Point, c., Ca., U.S. D3 82
Surabaya, Indon. m16 32
Surakarta, Indon. m15 32
Şūrān, Syria B5 40
Surat, India B2 37
Surat Thani (Ban Don), Thai. J5 34
Surendranagar, India I4 38
Surfside, Fl., U.S. s13 86
Surfside Beach, S.C., U.S. D10 117
Surgoinsville, Tn., U.S. C11 119
Sūri, India I12 38
Surigao, Phil. D8 32
Surin, Thai. G7 34
Suriname, ctry., S.A. C7 54
Sūrmaq, Iran B5 46
Surprise, Az., U.S. k8 80
Surrey, N.D., U.S. A4 111
Surry, co., N.C., U.S. A2 110
Surry, co., Va., U.S. C6 123
Surry Mountain Lake, res., N.H., U.S. D2 106
Surt, Libya B9 42
Surt, Khalīj, b., Libya B9 42
Sürüç, Tur. A6 40
Suruga-wan, b., Japan H11 30
Susa, Italy D2 14
Susanville, Ca., U.S. B3 82
Susitna, stm., Ak., U.S. C10 79
Susquehanna, Pa., U.S. C10 115
Susquehanna, co., Pa., U.S. C10 115
Susquehanna, stm., U.S. A5 97
Susquehanna, West Branch, stm., Pa., U.S. D5 115
Sussex, N.B., Can. D4 71
Sussex, N.J., U.S. A3 107
Sussex, Wi., U.S. m11 126
Sussex, co., De., U.S. F4 85
Sussex, co., N.J., U.S. A3 107
Sussex, co., Va., U.S. D5 123
Susurluk, Tur. J12 16
Sutherland, S. Afr. H4 44
Sutherland, Ia., U.S. B2 92
Sutherland, Ne., U.S. C4 104
Sutherlin, Or., U.S. D3 114
Sutlej (Satluj) (Langqên), stm., Asia F4 38
Sutter, co., Ca., U.S. C3 82
Sutter Creek, Ca., U.S. C3 82
Sutton, Que., Can. D5 74
Sutton, Ne., U.S. D8 104
Sutton, W.V., U.S. C4 125
Sutton, co., Tx., U.S. D2 120
Sutton Lake, res., W.V., U.S. C4 125
Sutwik Island, i., Ak., U.S. D8 79
Suwa, Japan F11 30
Suwałki, Pol. A22 8
Suwanee, Ga., U.S. B2 87
Suwannee, co., Fl., U.S. B3 86
Suwannee, stm., U.S. C4 86
Suwannee Sound, strt., Fl., U.S. C3 86
Suways, Qanāt as- (Suez Canal), Egypt D3 40
Suwŏn, S. Kor. D12 26
Suxian, China B5 28
Suzaka, Japan F11 30
Suzhou (Soochow), China D9 28
Suzuka, Japan H9 30
Suzu-misaki, c., Japan E10 30
Suzzara, Italy D5 14
Svappavaara, Swe. C13 6
Svartenhuk, pen., Grnld. B22 66
Sv'atoj Nos, Mys, c., U.S.S.R. C22 20
Sveg, Swe. E10 6
Svenljunga, Swe. H9 6
Svensen, Or., U.S. A3 114
Sverdlovsk, U.S.S.R. F10 18
Svetlaja, U.S.S.R. H21 20
Svetlyj, U.S.S.R. F17 20
Svištov, Bul. F9 16
Svobodnyj, U.S.S.R. G19 20
Svolvær, Nor. B10 6
Swain, co., N.C., U.S. f9 110
Swainsboro, Ga., U.S. D4 87
Swakopmund, Nmb. F2 44
Swampscott, Ma., U.S. B6 98
Swan, stm., Can. C1 70
Swan Creek, stm., Oh., U.S. e6 112
Swan Falls, wtfl, Id., U.S. F2 89
Swan Hill, Austl. G8 50
Swan Hills, Alta., Can. B3 68
Swan Islands, is., Hond. F6 64
Swan Lake, l., Man., Can. C1 70
Swan Lake, l., Me., U.S. D4 96
Swan Lake, l., Ne., U.S. C3 104
Swannanoa, N.C., U.S. f10 110
Swan Peak, mtn., Mt., U.S. C3 103
Swan Range, mts., Mt., U.S. C3 103
Swan River, Man., Can. C1 70
Swansboro, N.C., U.S. C5 110
Swansea, Wales, U.K. J9 7
Swansea, Il., U.S. E4 90
Swanson Lake, res., Ne., U.S. D4 104
Swanton, Oh., U.S. A2 112
Swanton, Vt., U.S. B2 122
Swanzey Center, N.H., U.S. E2 106
Swarthmore, Pa., U.S. p20 115
Swartswood Lake, l., N.J., U.S. A3 107
Swartz Creek, Mi., U.S. F7 99
Swayzee, In., U.S. C6 91
Swaziland, ctry., Afr. G6 44
Swea City, Ia., U.S. A3 92
Sweden, ctry., Eur. C10 4
Sweeny, Tx., U.S. r14 120
Sweet Grass, co., Mt., U.S. E7 103
Sweet Home, Or., U.S. C4 114
Sweetser, In., U.S. C6 91
Sweet Springs, Mo., U.S. C4 102
Sweetwater, Tn., U.S. D9 119
Sweetwater, Tx., U.S. C2 120
Sweetwater, co., Wy., U.S. E3 127
Sweetwater, stm., Wy., U.S. D4 127
Sweetwater Creek, Fl., U.S. p10 86
Sweetwater Creek, stm., Ok., U.S. B1 113
Swellendam, S. Afr. H4 44
Swepsonville, N.C., U.S. A3 110
Świdnica (Schweidnitz), Pol. E16 8
Swift, co., Mn., U.S. E3 100
Swift, stm., N.H., U.S. B4 106
Swift Creek, stm., N.C., U.S. B5 110
Swift Creek, stm., Va., U.S. n17 123
Swift Creek Reservoir, res., Wa., U.S. C3 124
Swift Diamond, stm., N.H., U.S. g7 106
Swifton, Ar., U.S. B4 81
Swinburne, Cape, c., N.W. Ter., Can. B13 66
Swindon, Eng., U.K. J11 7
Swinford, Ire. H4 7
Swinomish Indian Reservation, Wa., U.S. A3 124
Świnoujście (Swinemünde), Pol. B14 8
Swisher, Ia., U.S. C6 92
Swisher, co., Tx., U.S. B2 120
Swissvale, Pa., U.S. k14 115
Switzer, W.V., U.S. D3 125
Switzerland, Fl., U.S. m8 86
Switzerland, co., In., U.S. G7 91
Switzerland, ctry., Eur. F9 4
Swoyerville, Pa., U.S. D10 115
Syalach, U.S.S.R. D18 20
Sycamore, Al., U.S. B3 78
Sycamore, Il., U.S. B5 90
Sycamore, Oh., U.S. B2 112
Sycamore Creek, stm., W.V., U.S. m13 125
Sydenham, Ont., Can. C8 73
Sydney, Austl. F10 50
Syke, Ger. C8 8
Sykesville, Md., U.S. B4 97
Sykesville, Pa., U.S. D4 115
Sykkylven, Nor. E6 6
Syktyvkar, U.S.S.R. E8 18
Sylacauga, Al., U.S. B3 78
Sylhet, Bngl. H14 38
Sylva, N.C., U.S. f9 110
Sylvania, Al., U.S. A4 78
Sylvania, Ga., U.S. D5 87
Sylvania, Oh., U.S. A2 112
Sylvan Lake, Alta., Can. C3 68
Sylvan Lake, Mi., U.S. o15 99
Sylvan Lake, l., In., U.S. B7 91
Sylvan Pass, Wy., U.S. B2 127
Sylvester, Ga., U.S. E3 87
Sym, U.S.S.R. E11 20
Symmes Creek, stm., Oh., U.S. D3 112
Symsonia, Ky., U.S. f9 94
Syracuse, In., U.S. B6 91
Syracuse, Ks., U.S. E2 93
Syracuse, Ne., U.S. D9 104
Syracuse, N.Y., U.S. B4 109
Syracuse, Ut., U.S. B3 121
Syrdarja (Syr Darya), stm., U.S.S.R. I11 18
Syria, ctry., Asia B5 40
Syriam, Burma F4 34
Syrian Desert see Shām, Bādiyat ash-, des., Asia C6 40
Sysladobsis Lake, l., Me., U.S. C4 96
Syzran', U.S.S.R. G7 18
Szamos (Someş), stm., Eur. B6 16
Szczecin (Stettin), Pol. B14 8
Szczecinek (Neustettin), Pol. B16 8
Szeged, Hung. I20 8
Székesfehérvár, Hung. H18 8
Szentes, Hung. I20 8
Szolnok, Hung. H20 8
Szombathely, Hung. H16 8

T

Taal, Lake, l., Phil. r19 33b
Tabaco, Phil. r20 33b
Tabarka, Tun. M3 14
Tabatinga, Serra da, hills, Braz. F10 54
Tabbys Peak, mtn., Ut., U.S. C3 121
Tabelbala, Alg. C5 42
Taber, Alta., Can. E4 68
Tabernes de Valldigna, Spain F11 12
Tablas Island, i., Phil. C7 32
Table Head, c., Newf., Can. B4 72
Table Mountain, mtn., Az., U.S. E5 80
Table Rock Lake, res., U.S. E4 102
Table Top, mtn., Az., U.S. E3 80
Tabor, U.S.S.R. C24 20
Tabor, Ia., U.S. D2 92
Tabora, Tan. C6 44
Tabor City, N.C., U.S. C4 110
Tabou, I.C. H4 42
Tabrīz, Iran J7 18
Tabūk, Sau. Ar. C2 46
Tacámbaro de Codallos, Mex. H9 62
Tachikawa, Japan G12 30
Tacna, Peru G4 54
Tacoma, Wa., U.S. B3 124
Taconic Range, mts., U.S. A1 98
Tacuarembó, Ur. C5 56
Tacubaya, Mex. C7 62
Tadjerouine, Tun. N3 14
Tadoule Lake, l., Man., Can. E13 66
Tadoussac, Que., Can. A8 74
Tādpatri, India E5 37
Tadžikskaja Sovetskaja Socialističeskaja Respublika, state, U.S.S.R. J12 18
Taegu, S. Kor. D12 26
Taejŏn, S. Kor. D12 26
Tafalla, Spain C10 12
Taft, Ca., U.S. E4 82
Taft, Tx., U.S. F4 120
Tagajō, Japan D13 30
Taganrog, U.S.S.R. H5 18
Taglio di Po, Italy D7 14
Taguatinga, Braz. B5 57
Taguke, China D11 38
Tagula Island, i., Pap. N. Gui. B10 50
Tagus (Tejo) (Tajo), stm., Eur. F3 12
Tahan, Gunong, mtn., Malay. L7 34
Tahat, mtn., Alg. D7 42
Tahlequah, Ok., U.S. B7 113
Tahoe, Lake, l., U.S. E1 105
Tahoe City, Ca., U.S. C3 82
Tahoka, Tx., U.S. C2 120
Taholah, Wa., U.S. B1 124
Tahoua, Niger F7 42
Tahquamenon, stm., Mi., U.S. B5 99
Tahsis, B.C., Can. E4 69
Tahtsa Peak, mtn., B.C., Can. C4 69
T'aichung, Tai. K9 28
T'aichunghsien, Tai. K9 28
Taihape, N.Z. C5 52
Tai Hu, l., China D9 28
Tailai, China B11 26
Tain, Scot., U.K. D8 7
T'ainan, Tai. L9 28
T'aipei, Tai. J10 28
T'aipeihsien, Tai. J10 28
Taiping, Malay. L6 34
Taishun, China H8 28
Taitao, Península de, pen., Chile F2 56
T'aitung, Tai. M10 28
Taivalkoski, Fin. D17 6
Taiwan (T'aiwan), ctry., Asia G11 26
Taiwan Strait, strt., Asia K8 28
Taixian, China C9 28
Taixing, China C9 28
Taiyuan, China D9 26
Taizhou, China C8 28
Ta'izz, Yemen F3 46
Tajikistan see Tadžikskaja Sovetskaja Socialističeskaja Respublika, state, U.S.S.R. J12 18
Tajitos, Mex. B3 62
Tajmura, stm., U.S.S.R. E13 20
Tajmyr, Ozero, l., U.S.S.R. C14 20
Tajmyr, Poluostrov, pen., U.S.S.R. B14 20
Tajšet, U.S.S.R. F13 20
Tajumulco, Volcán, vol., Guat. G2 64
Tak, Thai. F5 34
Takada, Japan E11 30
Takalar, Indon. G6 32
Takamatsu, Japan H7 30
Takaoka, Japan F10 30
Takapuna, N.Z. B5 52
Takasaki, Japan F12 30
Takatsuki, Japan H8 30
Takawa, Japan I3 30
Takayama, Japan F10 30
Takefu, Japan G9 30
Takêv, Camb. I8 34
Takijuq Lake, l., N.W. Ter., Can. C10 66
Takikawa, Japan p19 30a
Takla Lake, l., B.C., Can. B5 69
Taklimakan Shamo, des., China D3 26

Takoma Park, Md., U.S. **f8** 97
Taku Glacier, Ak., U.S. **k22** 79
Tala, Mex. **G8** 62
Talagang, Pak. **D5** 38
Talaimannar, Sri L. **H5** 37
Talara, Peru **D2** 54
Talarrubias, Spain **F6** 12
Talasea, Pap. N. Gui. **m17** 50a
Talaud, Kepulauan, is., Indon. **E8** 32
Talavera de la Reina, Spain **F7** 12
Talawdī, Sudan **F12** 42
Talbot, co., Ga., U.S. **D2** 87
Talbot, co., Md., U.S. **C5** 97
Talbot Island, i., Fl., U.S. **B5** 86
Talbot Lake, l., Man., Can. **B2** 70
Talbotton, Ga., U.S. **D2** 87
Talca, Chile **D2** 56
Talcahuano, Chile **D2** 56
Talent, Or., U.S. **E4** 114
Taliabu, Pulau, i., Indon. **F7** 32
Taliaferro, co., Ga., U.S. **C4** 87
Talihina, Ok., U.S. **C6** 113
Talkeetna, Ak., U.S. **C10** 79
Talkeetna Mountains, mts., Ak., U.S. **f17** 79
Talladega, Al., U.S. **B3** 78
Talladega, co., Al., U.S. **B3** 78
Tallahassee, Fl., U.S. **B2** 86
Tallahatchie, co., Ms., U.S. **B3** 101
Tallahatchie, stm., Ms., U.S. **B3** 101
Tallapoosa, Ga., U.S. **C1** 87
Tallapoosa, co., Al., U.S. **C4** 78
Tallapoosa, stm., Al., U.S. **C3** 78
Tallassee, Al., U.S. **C4** 78
Talleyville, De., U.S. **A3** 85
Tallinn, U.S.S.R. **B7** 22
Tall Kalakh, Syria **B5** 40
Tallmadge, Oh., U.S. **A4** 112
Tall Tamir, Syria **A7** 40
Tallulah, La., U.S. **B4** 95
Tal'menka, U.S.S.R. **G10** 20
Talo, mtn., Eth. **F2** 46
Tāloqān, Afg. **B3** 38
Talquin, Lake, res., Fl., U.S. **B2** 86
Talu, Indon. **N5** 34
Taluk, Indon. **O6** 34
Tama, Ia., U.S. **C5** 92
Tama, co., Ia., U.S. **B5** 92
Tamale, Ghana **G5** 42
Tamalpais, Mount, mtn., Ca., U.S. **h7** 82
Tamana, Japan **J3** 30
Tamanrasset, Alg. **D7** 42
Tamaqua, Pa., U.S. **E10** 115
Tamaroa, Il., U.S. **E4** 90
Tamazula de Gordiano, Mex. **H8** 62
Tamazunchale, Mex. **G10** 62
Tambacounda, Sen. **F3** 42
Tambohorano, Madag. **E8** 44
Tambov, U.S.S.R. **I24** 22
Tambura, Sudan **G11** 42
Tamchaket, Maur. **E3** 42
Tamel Aike, Arg. **F2** 56
Tamiahua, Laguna de, b., Mex. **G11** 62
Tamiami Canal, Fl., U.S. **G6** 86
Tamil Nadu, state, India **G5** 37
Tam Ky, Viet. **G10** 34
Tampa, Fl., U.S. **E4** 86
Tampa Bay, b., Fl., U.S. **E4** 86
Tampere, Fin. **F14** 6
Tampico, Mex. **F11** 62
Tampico, Il., U.S. **B4** 90
Tamrida, Yemen **F5** 46
Tamsagbulag, Mong. **B10** 26
Tamworth, Austl. **F10** 50
Tana, Nor. **A17** 6
Tana, stm., Eur. **A16** 6
Tana, stm., Kenya **B7** 44
Tana, Lake, l., Eth. **F2** 46
Tanabe, Japan **I8** 30
Tanaga Island, i., Ak., U.S. **E4** 79
Tanahjampea, Pulau, i., Indon. **G7** 32
Tanami Desert, des., Austl. **C5** 50
Tanana, Ak., U.S. **B9** 79
Tanana, stm., Ak., U.S. **C10** 79
Tananarive see Antananarivo, Madag. **E9** 44
Tānda, India **G10** 38
Tandil, Arg. **D5** 56
Tando Ādam, Pak. **H3** 38
Tando Muhammad Khān, Pak. **H3** 38
Tanega-shima, i., Japan **u30** 31b
Taney, co., Mo., U.S. **E4** 102
Taneycomo, Lake, res., Mo., U.S. **E4** 102
Taneytown, Md., U.S. **A3** 97
Tanezrouft, des., Afr. **D5** 42
Tanga, Tan. **C7** 44
Tangail, Bngl. **H13** 38
Tanganyika, Lake, l., Afr. **C5** 44
Tanger (Tangier), Mor. **A4** 42
Tangerang, Indon. **m13** 33a
Tangermünde, Ger. **C11** 8
Tanggula Shan, mts., China **D13** 38
Tangier, Va., U.S. **C7** 123
Tangier Island, i., Va., U.S. **C6** 123
Tangier Sound, strt., Md., U.S. **D6** 97
Tangier see Tanger, Mor. **A4** 42
Tangipahoa, co., La., U.S. **D5** 95
Tangipahoa, stm., La., U.S. **D5** 95
Tangra Yumco, l., China **E12** 38
Tangshan, China **D10** 26
Tanimbar, Kepulauan, is., Indon. **G9** 32
Tanjungbalai, Indon. **M5** 34
Tanjungkarang-Telukbetung, Indon. **k12** 32
Tanjungpinang, Indon. **N8** 34
Tanjungselor, Indon. **E6** 32
Tānk, Pak. **D4** 38
Tännäs, Swe. **E9** 6
Tanner, Al., U.S. **A3** 78
Tânout, Niger **F7** 42
Tanshui, Tai. **J10** 28
Ṭanṭā, Egypt **B12** 42
Tanuku, India **D6** 37
Tanzania, ctry., Afr. **C6** 44
Taos, Mo., U.S. **C5** 102
Taos, N.M., U.S. **A4** 108
Taos, co., N.M., U.S. **A4** 108
Taos Pueblo, N.M., U.S. **A4** 108
Taoudenni, Mali **D5** 42
Tapachula, Mex. **J13** 62
Tapah, Malay. **L6** 34
Tapajós, stm., Braz. **E7** 54
Taphan Hin, Thai. **F6** 34
Tāpi, stm., India **B2** 37
Tappahannock, Va., U.S. **C6** 123
Tappan, N.Y., U.S. **g13** 109
Tappan, Lake, res., N.J., U.S. **g9** 107
Tappan Lake, res., Oh., U.S. **B4** 112
Taqātu' Hayyā, Sudan **E13** 42
Taquaritinga, Braz. **F4** 57
Tar, stm., N.C., U.S. **B5** 110
Tara, Ont., Can. **C3** 73
Tarābulus (Tripoli), Leb. **B4** 40
Tarābulus (Tripoli), Libya **B8** 42
Tarābulus (Tripolitania), reg., Libya **B8** 42
Tarakan, Indon. **E6** 32
Tarancón, Spain **E8** 12
Taranto, Italy **I12** 14
Taranto, Golfo di, b., Italy **I12** 14
Tarapacá, Col. **I8** 58
Tarare, Fr. **G11** 10
Tarascon, Fr. **J8** 10
Tarata, Bol. **G5** 54
Tarazona, Spain **D10** 12
Tarazona de la Mancha, Spain **F10** 12
Tarbert, Scot., U.K. **F7** 7
Tarbert, Scot., U.K. **D6** 7
Tarbes, Fr. **I7** 10
Tarboro, N.C., U.S. **B5** 110
Tarcento, Italy **C8** 14
Taree, Austl. **F10** 50
Tareja, U.S.S.R. **C12** 20
Tarentum, Pa., U.S. **E2** 115
Tarfaya, Mor. **C3** 42
Targhee Pass, U.S. **E7** 89
Tarifa, Punta de, c., Spain **I6** 12
Tariffville, Ct., U.S. **B4** 84
Tarija, Bol. **H6** 54
Tarim, stm., China **C3** 26
Tarīn Kowt, Afg. **D1** 38
Tarkio, Mo., U.S. **A2** 102
Tarkwa, Ghana **G5** 42
Tarlac, Phil. **q19** 32
Tarn, stm., Fr. **I8** 10
Tärnaby, Swe. **D10** 6
Tarnak, stm., Afg. **D2** 38
Tarnów, Pol. **E20** 8
Tarnowskie Góry, Pol. **E18** 8
Tarpey, Ca., U.S. **D4** 82
Tarpon, Lake, l., Fl., U.S. **o10** 86
Tarpon Springs, Fl., U.S. **D4** 86
Tarquinia, Italy **G6** 14
Tarragona, Spain **D13** 12
Tarrant, Al., U.S. **B3** 78
Tarrant, co., Tx., U.S. **C4** 120
Tarrasa, Spain **D14** 12
Tarryall Mountains, mts., Co., U.S. **B5** 83
Tarrytown, N.Y., U.S. **D7** 109
Tarsus, Tur. **A4** 40
Tartagal, Arg. **A4** 56
Tartas, Fr. **I6** 10
Tartu, U.S.S.R. **C9** 22
Tarṭūs, Syria **B4** 40
Tarutung, Indon. **M5** 34
Tašauz, U.S.S.R. **I9** 18
Tasejeva, stm., U.S.S.R. **F12** 20
Tasejevo, U.S.S.R. **F12** 20
Taseko Mountain, mtn., B.C., Can. **D6** 69
Tashi Gang Dzong, Bhu. **G14** 38
Tashkent see Taškent, U.S.S.R. **I11** 18
Tasikmalaya, Indon. **m14** 32
Taškent, U.S.S.R. **I11** 18
Tasmania, state, Austl. **H9** 50
Tasman Sea, Oc. **G11** 50
Tasso, Tn., U.S. **D9** 119
Taštagol, U.S.S.R. **G11** 20
Tatabánya, Hung. **H18** 8
Tatarskij Proliv, strt., U.S.S.R. **H22** 20
Tate, Ga., U.S. **B2** 87
Tate, co., Ms., U.S. **A4** 101
Tateville, Ky., U.S. **D5** 94
Tateyama, Japan **H12** 30
Tathlina Lake, l., N.W. Ter., Can. **D9** 66
Tatnam, Cape, c., Man., Can. **f9** 70
Tatta, Pak. **H2** 38
Tattnall, co., Ga., U.S. **D4** 87
Tatum, N.M., U.S. **D6** 108
Tatvan, Tur. **H16** 4
Tau, Nor. **G5** 6
Taubaté, Braz. **G6** 57
Tauberbischofsheim, Ger. **F9** 8
Taujskaja Guba, b., U.S.S.R. **F24** 20
Taumarunui, N.Z. **C5** 52
Taum Sauk Mountain, mtn., Mo., U.S. **D6** 102
Taungdwingyi, Burma **D3** 34
Taunggyi, Burma **D4** 34
Taungup Pass, Burma **E3** 34
Taunton, Eng., U.K. **J9** 7
Taunton, Ma., U.S. **C5** 98
Taunton, stm., Ma., U.S. **C5** 98
Taupo, Lake, l., N.Z. **C5** 52
Tauranga, N.Z. **B6** 52
Taureau, Réservoir, res., Que., Can. **C4** 74
Taurus Mountains see Toros Dağları, mts., Tur. **H14** 4
Tauste, Spain **D10** 12
Tavares, Fl., U.S. **D5** 86
Tavernier, Fl., U.S. **G6** 86
Tavira, Port. **H4** 12
Tavoy Point, c., Burma **H5** 34
Tavşanlı, Tur. **J13** 16
Tawakoni, Lake, res., Tx., U.S. **C4** 120
Tawas City, Mi., U.S. **D7** 99
Tawas Lake, l., Mi., U.S. **D7** 99
Tawau, Malay. **E6** 32
Tawitawi Island, i., Phil. **D6** 32
Ṭawkar, Sudan **E13** 42
Taxco de Alarcón, Mex. **H10** 62
Tay, Loch, l., Scot., U.K. **E8** 7
Taylor, B.C., Can. **A7** 69
Taylor, Az., U.S. **C5** 80
Taylor, Ar., U.S. **D2** 81
Taylor, Mi., U.S. **p15** 99
Taylor, Pa., U.S. **D10** 115
Taylor, Tx., U.S. **D4** 120
Taylor, co., Fl., U.S. **B3** 86
Taylor, co., Ga., U.S. **D2** 87
Taylor, co., Ia., U.S. **D3** 92
Taylor, co., Ky., U.S. **C4** 94
Taylor, co., Tx., U.S. **C3** 120
Taylor, co., W.V., U.S. **B4** 125
Taylor, co., Wi., U.S. **C3** 126
Taylor, stm., Co., U.S. **C4** 83
Taylor, Mount, mtn., N.M., U.S. **B2** 108
Taylor Mill, Ky., U.S. **k14** 94
Taylor Mountain, mtn., Id., U.S. **E4** 89
Taylor Park Reservoir, res., Co., U.S. **C4** 83
Taylors, S.C., U.S. **B3** 117
Taylors Falls, Mn., U.S. **E6** 100
Taylors Island, i., Md., U.S. **D5** 97
Taylorsville, In., U.S. **F6** 91
Taylorsville, Ky., U.S. **B4** 94
Taylorsville, Ms., U.S. **D4** 101
Taylorsville, N.C., U.S. **B1** 110
Taylorville, Il., U.S. **D4** 90
Taymā', Sau. Ar. **C2** 46
Tay Ninh, Viet. **I9** 34
Tayoltita, Mex. **E7** 62
Taytay, Phil. **C6** 32
Taz, stm., U.S.S.R. **D10** 20
Taza, Mor. **B5** 42
Tazewell, Tn., U.S. **C10** 119
Tazewell, Va., U.S. **e10** 123
Tazewell, co., Il., U.S. **C4** 90
Tazewell, co., Va., U.S. **e10** 123
Tazin Lake, l., Sask., Can. **E11** 66
Tbessa, Alg. **A7** 42
Tbilisi, U.S.S.R. **I6** 18
Tbong, Camb. **H8** 34
Tchefuncta, stm., La., U.S. **D5** 95
Tchibanga, Gabon **B2** 44
Tchien, Lib. **G4** 42
Tchula, Ms., U.S. **B3** 101
Tczew, Pol. **A18** 8
Tea, S.D., U.S. **D9** 118
Teacapán, Mex. **F7** 62
Teague, Tx., U.S. **D4** 120
Teakean Butte, mtn., Id., U.S. **C2** 89
Te Anau, Lake, l., N.Z. **F1** 52
Teaneck, N.J., U.S. **h8** 107
Teano, Italy **H9** 14
Teaticket, Ma., U.S. **C6** 98
Tebingtinggi, Indon. **M5** 34
Téboursouk, Tun. **M4** 14
Tecate, Mex. **A1** 62
Tecolotlan, Mex. **G7** 62
Tecomán, Mex. **H8** 62
Tecpan de Galeana, Mex. **I9** 62
Tecuala, Mex. **F7** 62
Tecuci, Rom. **D11** 16
Tecumseh, Ont., Can. **E2** 73
Tecumseh, Ks., U.S. **k14** 93
Tecumseh, Mi., U.S. **G7** 99
Tecumseh, Ne., U.S. **D9** 104
Tecumseh, Ok., U.S. **B5** 113
Tedžen (Harīrūd), stm., Asia **J10** 18
Teeswater, Ont., Can. **C3** 73
Tefé, Braz. **D6** 54
Tegal, Indon. **m14** 32
Tegucigalpa, Hond. **G4** 64
Tehachapi, Ca., U.S. **E4** 82
Tehachapi Mountains, mts., Ca., U.S. **E4** 82
Tehama, co., Ca., U.S. **B2** 82
Tehrān, Iran **J8** 18
Tehuacán, Mex. **H11** 62
Tehuantepec, Mex. **I12** 62
Tehuantepec, Golfo de, b., Mex. **J12** 62
Tehuantepec, Istmo de, Mex. **I12** 62
Teide, Pico de, mtn., Spain **C2** 42
Tejamén, Mex. **E7** 62
Tejkovo, U.S.S.R. **E23** 22
Tejupan, Punta, c., Mex. **H8** 62
Tekamah, Ne., U.S. **C9** 104
Tekirdağ, Tur. **I11** 16
Tekoa, Wa., U.S. **B8** 124
Tekonsha, Mi., U.S. **F5** 99
Tela, Hond. **G4** 64
Telavåg, Nor. **F5** 6
Tel Aviv-Yafo, Isr. **C4** 40
Teleckoje, Ozero, l., U.S.S.R. **G11** 20
Telén, Arg. **D3** 56
Telescope Peak, mtn., Ca., U.S. **D5** 82
Teles Pires, stm., Braz. **E7** 54
Telfair, co., Ga., U.S. **E4** 87
Telford, Pa., U.S. **F11** 115
Telfs, Aus. **H11** 8
Teli, U.S.S.R. **G12** 20
Telkwa, B.C., Can. **B4** 69
Tell City, In., U.S. **I4** 91
Teller, co., Co., U.S. **C5** 83
Tellicherry, India **G3** 37
Tellico Plains, Tn., U.S. **D9** 119
Telluride, Co., U.S. **D3** 83
Telok Anson, Malay. **L6** 34
Telos Lake, l., Me., U.S. **B3** 96
Temagami, Lake, l., Ont., Can. **G16** 66
Tembeling, stm., Malay. **L7** 34
Tembenči, stm., U.S.S.R. **D13** 20
Temecula, Ca., U.S. **F5** 82
Temerloh, Malay. **M7** 34
Teminabuan, Indon. **F9** 32
Témiscouata, Lac, l., Que., Can. **B9** 74
Te-Moak Indian Reservation, Nv., U.S. **C6** 105
Temósachic, Mex. **C6** 62
Tempe, Az., U.S. **D4** 80
Temperance, Mi., U.S. **G7** 99
Temperance, stm., Mn., U.S. **C8** 100
Tempio Pausania, Italy **I4** 14
Temple, Ga., U.S. **C1** 87
Temple, Ok., U.S. **C3** 113
Temple, Pa., U.S. **F10** 115
Temple, Tx., U.S. **D4** 120
Temple Terrace, Fl., U.S. **o11** 86
Templin, Ger. **B13** 8
Temuco, Chile **D2** 56
Tena, Ec. **H4** 58
Tenafly, N.J., U.S. **B5** 107
Tenaha, Tx., U.S. **D5** 120
Tenāli, India **D6** 37
Tendaho, Eth. **F3** 46
Tende, Col de, Eur. **H14** 10
Ten Degree Channel, strt., India **J2** 34
Ténéré, des., Niger **E8** 42
Tenerife, i., Spain **C2** 42
Tengchong, China **B5** 34
Tenino, Wa., U.S. **C3** 124
Tenkāsi, India **H4** 37
Tenkiller Ferry Lake, res., Ok., U.S. **B6** 113
Tenkodogo, Burkina **F5** 42
Tenmile, stm., U.S. **B5** 116
Tenmile Creek, stm., W.V., U.S. **k10** 125
Tenmile Lake, l., Mn., U.S. **D4** 100
Tennant Creek, Austl. **C6** 50
Tennessee, state, U.S. **B5** 119
Tennessee, stm., U.S. **D9** 76
Tennessee Pass, Co., U.S. **B4** 83
Tennessee Ridge, Tn., U.S. **A4** 119
Tennille, Ga., U.S. **D4** 87
Tenom, Malay. **D6** 32
Tenryū, stm., Japan **G10** 30
Tensas, co., La., U.S. **B4** 95
Tensas, stm., La., U.S. **B4** 95
Tensaw, stm., Al., U.S. **E2** 78
Ten Sleep, Wy., U.S. **B5** 127
Tenterfield, Austl. **E10** 50
Ten Thousand Islands, is., Fl., U.S. **G5** 86
Teocaltiche, Mex. **G8** 62
Teófilo Otoni, Braz. **D8** 57
Tepa, Indon. **G8** 32
Tepatitlán [de Morelos], Mex. **G8** 62
Tepic, Mex. **G7** 62
Teplice, Czech. **E13** 8
Teramo, Italy **G8** 14
Teresina, Braz. **E10** 54
Teresópolis, Braz. **G7** 57
Termez, U.S.S.R. **B2** 38
Termini Imerese, Italy **L8** 14
Términos, Laguna de, b., Mex. **H14** 62
Termoli, Italy **G9** 14
Ternej, U.S.S.R. **H21** 20
Terni, Italy **G7** 14
Ternopol', U.S.S.R. **H3** 18
Terpenija, Mys, c., U.S.S.R. **H22** 20
Terpenija, Zaliv, b., U.S.S.R. **H22** 20
Terra Alta, W.V., U.S. **B5** 125
Terrace, B.C., Can. **B3** 69
Terracina, Italy **H8** 14
Terralba, Italy **J3** 14
Terra Nova National Park, Newf., Can. **D4** 72
Terrebonne, Que., Can. **D4** 74
Terrebonne, Or., U.S. **C5** 114
Terrebonne, co., La., U.S. **E5** 95
Terrebonne Bay, b., La., U.S. **E5** 95
Terre Haute, In., U.S. **F3** 91
Terre Hill, Pa., U.S. **F9** 115
Terrell, Tx., U.S. **C4** 120
Terrell, co., Ga., U.S. **E2** 87
Terrell, co., Tx., U.S. **D1** 120
Terrell Hills, Tx., U.S. **k7** 120
Terrenceville, Newf., Can. **E4** 72
Terry, Ms., U.S. **C3** 101
Terry, Mt., U.S. **D11** 103
Terry, co., Tx., U.S. **C1** 120
Terrytown, Ne., U.S. **C2** 104
Terryville, Ct., U.S. **C3** 84
Teruel, Spain **E10** 12
Tervola, Fin. **C15** 6
Teseney, Eth. **E2** 46
Teshekpuk Lake, l., Ak., U.S. **A9** 79
Teshio, Japan **o19** 30a
Teslin, Yukon, Can. **D6** 66
Teslin, stm., Can. **D6** 66
Tesouro, Braz. **D2** 57
Tessalit, Mali **D6** 42
Tesuque, N.M., U.S. **B4** 108
Tete, Moz. **E6** 44
Teterow, Ger. **B12** 8
Teton, co., Id., U.S. **F7** 89
Teton, co., Mt., U.S. **C4** 103
Teton, co., Wy., U.S. **C2** 127
Teton, stm., Mt., U.S. **C5** 103
Teton Pass, Wy., U.S. **C2** 127
Teton Range, mts., Wy., U.S. **C2** 127
Teton Village, Wy., U.S. **C2** 127
Tétouan, Mor. **A4** 42
Tetovo, Yugo. **G4** 16
Tet'uche, U.S.S.R. **I21** 20
Teulada, Italy **K3** 14
Teulon, Man., Can. **D3** 70
Teutopolis, Il., U.S. **D5** 90
Teuva, Fin. **E13** 6
Tevere (Tiber), stm., Italy **G7** 14
Teverya, Isr. **C4** 40
Tewksbury, Ma., U.S. **A5** 98
Texada Island, i., B.C., Can. **E5** 69
Texarkana, Ar., U.S. **D1** 81
Texarkana, Tx., U.S. **C5** 120
Texas, co., Mo., U.S. **D5** 102
Texas, co., Ok., U.S. **e9** 113
Texas, state, U.S. **D3** 120
Texas City, Tx., U.S. **E5** 120
Texhoma, Ok., U.S. **e9** 113
Texico, N.M., U.S. **C6** 108
Texoma, Lake, res., U.S. **D5** 113
Teyvareh, Afg. **D1** 38
Teziutlán, Mex. **H11** 62
Tezpur, India **G15** 38
Thabazimbi, S. Afr. **F5** 44
Thai Binh, Viet. **D9** 34
Thailand, ctry., Asia **B3** 32
Thailand, Gulf of, b., Asia **J6** 34
Thai Nguyen, Viet. **D8** 34
Thal, Pak. **D4** 38
Thames, stm., Ont., Can. **E3** 73
Thames, stm., Eng., U.K. **J14** 7
Thames, stm., Ct., U.S. **D7** 84
Thamesville, Ont., Can. **E3** 73
Thāna, India **C2** 37
Thanh Hoa, Viet. **E8** 34
Thanh Pho Ho Chi Minh (Saigon), Viet. **I9** 34
Thanjāvūr, India **G5** 37
Thar Desert (Great Indian Desert), des., Asia **G3** 38
Thargomindah, Austl. **E8** 50
Thatcher, Az., U.S. **E6** 80
Thaton, Burma **F4** 34
Thayer, Mo., U.S. **E6** 102
Thayer, co., Ne., U.S. **D8** 104
Thayetmyo, Burma **E3** 34
Thayne, Wy., U.S. **D1** 127
Thealka, Ky., U.S. **C7** 94
The Barrens, plat., Tn., U.S. **B5** 119
The Bight, Bah. **B10** 64
The Cheviot, mtn., Eng., U.K. **F10** 7
The Colony, Tx., U.S. **C4** 120
The Dalles, Or., U.S. **B5** 114
The Dells, val., Wi., U.S. **E4** 126
Thedford, Ont., Can. **D3** 73
The English Company's Islands, is., Austl. **B7** 50
The Everglades, sw., Fl., U.S. **G6** 86
The Fens, sw., Eng., U.K. **I12** 7
The Flat Tops, mts., Co., U.S. **B3** 83
The Flume, wtfl, N.H., U.S. **B3** 106
The Graves, is., Ma., U.S. **g12** 98
The Hague see 's-Gravenhage, Neth. **C4** 8
The Heads, c., Or., U.S. **E2** 114
Thelon, stm., N.W. Ter., Can. **D12** 66
The Narrows, strt., Wa., U.S. **f10** 124
Theodore, Austl. **D10** 50
Theodore, Al., U.S. **E1** 78
Theodore Roosevelt Lake, res., Az., U.S. **D4** 80
Theodore Roosevelt National Park (South Unit), N.D., U.S. **C2** 111
Theodore Roosevelt National Park (North Unit), N.D., U.S. **B2** 111
The Pas, Man., Can. **C1** 70
The Plains, Oh., U.S. **C3** 112
Theresa, Wi., U.S. **E5** 126
Thermopolis, Wy., U.S. **C4** 127
The Rockies, mts., Wa., U.S. **C3** 124
Thessalon, Ont., Can. **p19** 73
Thessaloníki (Salonika), Grc. **I6** 16
Thetford Mines, Que., Can. **C6** 74
The Thimbles, is., Ct., U.S. **E5** 84
The Village, Ok., U.S. **B4** 113
The Warburton, stm., Austl. **E7** 50
The Wash, b., Eng., U.K. **I13** 7
The Weald, reg., Eng., U.K. **J13** 7
Thibodaux, La., U.S. **E5** 95
Thief, stm., Mn., U.S. **B2** 100
Thief Lake, l., Mn., U.S. **B3** 100
Thief River Falls, Mn., U.S. **B2** 100
Thielsen, Mount, mtn., Or., U.S. **D4** 114
Thiene, Italy **D6** 14
Thiensville, Wi., U.S. **E6** 126
Thiers, Fr. **G10** 10
Thiès, Sen. **F2** 42
Thika, Kenya **B7** 44
Thimphu, Bhu. **G13** 38
Thingangyun, Burma **F4** 34
Thionville, Fr. **C13** 10
Thíra, i., Grc. **M9** 16
Third Lake, l., N.H., U.S. **f7** 106
Thirsk, Eng., U.K. **G11** 7
Thisted, Den. **H7** 6
Thívai (Thebes), Grc. **K7** 16
Thiviers, Fr. **G7** 10
Thomas, Ok., U.S. **B3** 113
Thomas, co., Ga., U.S. **F3** 87
Thomas, co., Ks., U.S. **C2** 93
Thomas, co., Ne., U.S. **C5** 104
Thomasboro, Il., U.S. **C5** 90
Thomaston, Ct., U.S. **C3** 84
Thomaston, Ga., U.S. **D2** 87
Thomaston, Me., U.S. **D3** 96
Thomaston Reservoir, res., Ct., U.S. **C3** 84
Thomastown, Ire. **I5** 7
Thomasville, Al., U.S. **D2** 78
Thomasville, Ga., U.S. **F3** 87
Thomasville, N.C., U.S. **B2** 110
Thompson, Man., Can. **B3** 70
Thompson, Ct., U.S. **B8** 84
Thompson, N.D., U.S. **B8** 111
Thompson, stm., U.S. **A4** 102
Thompson Falls, Mt., U.S. **C1** 103
Thompson Island, i., Ma., U.S. **g11** 98
Thompson Lake, l., U.S. **D2** 96
Thompson Peak, mtn., Ca., U.S. **B2** 82
Thompson Peak, mtn., N.M., U.S. **h9** 108
Thompson Reservoir, res., Or., U.S. **E5** 114
Thomsen, stm., N.W. Ter., Can. **B9** 66
Thomson, Ga., U.S. **C4** 87
Thon Buri, Thai. **H6** 34
Thongwa, Burma **F4** 34
Thonon-les-Bains, Fr. **F13** 10
Thonotosassa, Fl., U.S. **D4** 86
Thonze, Burma **F3** 34
Thorburn, N.S., Can. **D7** 71
Thoreau, N.M., U.S. **B1** 108
Thornbury, Ont., Can. **C4** 73
Thorndale, Tx., U.S. **D4** 120
Thornton, Ont., Can. **C5** 73
Thorntown, In., U.S. **D4** 91
Thorold, Ont., Can. **D5** 73
Thorp, Wi., U.S. **D3** 126
Thorsby, Al., U.S. **C3** 78
Thouars, Fr. **F6** 10
Thousand Islands, is., N.Y., U.S. **A4** 109
Thousand Lake Mountain, mtn., Ut., U.S. **E4** 121
Thousand Springs Creek, stm., U.S. **B7** 105
Thrace, hist. reg., Eur. **G13** 4
Thrakikón Pélagos, Grc. **I8** 16
Three Fingered Jack, mtn., Or., U.S. **C5** 114
Three Forks, Mt., U.S. **E5** 103
Three Hills, Alta., Can. **D4** 68
Three Lakes, Wi., U.S. **C4** 126
Three Mile Plains, N.S., Can. **E5** 71
Three Oaks, Mi., U.S. **G4** 99
Three Pagodas Pass, Asia **G5** 34
Three Points, Cape, c., Ghana **H5** 42
Three Rivers, Ma., U.S. **B3** 98

Name	Map Ref	Page
Three Rivers, Mi., U.S.	G5	99
Three Rivers, Tx., U.S.	E3	120
Three Sisters, mtn., Or., U.S.	C5	114
Three Springs, Austl.	E3	50
Throckmorton, co., Tx., U.S.	C3	120
Throop, Pa., U.S.	m18	115
Throssell Range, mts., Austl.	D4	50
Thu Dao Mot, Viet.	I9	34
Thule, Grnld.	B19	128
Thun, Switz.	F14	10
Thunder Bay, Ont., Can.	o17	73
Thunder Bay, b., Mi., U.S.	D7	99
Thunder Bay, stm., Mi., U.S.	D6	99
Thunderbird, Lake, res., Ok., U.S.	B4	113
Thunderbolt, Ga., U.S.	D5	87
Thunder Butte Creek, stm., S.D., U.S.	B3	118
Thunersee, l., Switz.	F14	10
Thüringen, hist. reg., Ger.	D11	8
Thurles, Ire.	I5	7
Thurmont, Md., U.S.	A3	97
Thurso, Que., Can.	D2	74
Thurso, Scot., U.K.	C9	7
Thurston, co., Ne., U.S.	B9	104
Thurston, co., Wa., U.S.	C2	124
Tiancang, China	C7	26
Tiandong, China	C9	34
Tianjin (Tientsin), China	D10	26
Tianjun, China	D6	26
Tianmen, China	E2	28
Tianshui, China	E8	26
Tiaret, Alg.	A6	42
Tibagi, Braz.	A6	56
Tibasti, Sarīr, des., Libya	D9	42
Tiber see Tevere, stm., Italy	G7	14
Tibesti, mts., Chad	D9	42
Tibet, hist. reg., China	E12	38
Tiburón, Isla, i., Mex.	C3	62
Tice, Fl., U.S.	F5	86
Tīchīt, Maur.	E4	42
Tichvin, U.S.S.R.	B16	22
Tickfaw, stm., La., U.S.	C5	95
Ticonderoga, N.Y., U.S.	B7	109
Ticul, Mex.	G15	62
Tide Head, N.B., Can.	B3	71
Tidjikdja, Maur.	E3	42
Tieling, China	C11	26
Tienen, Bel.	E4	8
Tien Shan, mts., Asia	C2	26
Tientsin see Tianjin, China	D10	26
Tierra Amarilla, N.M., U.S.	A3	108
Tierra Blanca, Mex.	H11	62
Tierra del Fuego, Isla Grande de, i., S.A.	G3	56
Tierralta, Col.	C4	58
Tietê, stm., Braz.	F3	57
Tieton, Wa., U.S.	C5	124
Tieton, stm., Wa., U.S.	C4	124
Tieton Dam, Wa., U.S.	C4	124
Tiffany Mountain, mtn., Wa., U.S.	A6	124
Tiffin, Oh., U.S.	A2	112
Tiffin, stm., Oh., U.S.	A1	112
Tift, co., Ga., U.S.	E3	87
Tifton, Ga., U.S.	E3	87
Tigard, Or., U.S.	h12	114
Tigerton, Wi., U.S.	D4	126
Tigil', U.S.S.R.	F25	20
Tignall, Ga., U.S.	C4	87
Tignish, P.E.I., Can.	C5	71
Tigre, stm., Peru	D3	54
Tigris (Dijlah), stm., Asia	A3	46
Tiguentourine, Alg.	C7	42
Tijesno, Yugo.	F10	14
Tijuana, Mex.	A1	62
Tikamgarh, India	H8	38
Tikrīt, Iraq	B3	46
Tilburg, Neth.	D5	8
Tilbury, Ont., Can.	E2	73
Tilden, Il., U.S.	E4	90
Tilden, Ne., U.S.	B8	104
Tilghman, Md., U.S.	C5	97
Tilghman Island, i., Md., U.S.	C5	97
Tilhar, India	G8	38
Tillabéry, Niger	F6	42
Tillamook, Or., U.S.	B3	114
Tillamook, co., Or., U.S.	B3	114
Tillanchong Island, i., India	J2	34
Tillery, Lake, res., N.C., U.S.	B2	110
Tillman, co., Ok., U.S.	C2	113
Tillmans Corner, Al., U.S.	E1	78
Tillsonburg, Ont., Can.	E4	73
Tilton, Il., U.S.	C6	90
Tilton, N.H., U.S.	D3	106
Tiltonsville, Oh., U.S.	B5	112
Timaru, N.Z.	F3	52
Timbalier Island, i., La., U.S.	E5	95
Timberlake, Va., U.S.	C3	123
Timberville, Va., U.S.	B4	123
Timbuktu see Tombouctou, Mali	E5	42
Timimoun, Alg.	C6	42
Timiris, Cap, c., Maur.	E2	42
Timișoara, Rom.	D5	16
Timmins, Ont., Can.	o19	73
Timmonsville, S.C., U.S.	C8	117
Timms Hill, hill, Wi., U.S.	C3	126
Timor, i., Indon.	G8	32
Timor Sea	B5	50
Timotes, Ven.	C7	58
Timpanogos Cave National Monument, Ut., U.S.	C4	121
Timpton, stm., U.S.S.R.	F19	20
Tims Ford Lake, res., Tn., U.S.	B5	119
Tinaquillo, Ven.	C8	58
Tindivanam, India	F5	37
Tindouf, Alg.	C4	42
Tingmerkpuk Mountain, mtn., Ak., U.S.	B7	79
Tingo María, Peru	E3	54
Tingvoll, Nor.	E7	6
Tinharé, Ilha de, i., Braz.	F11	54
Tinker Air Force Base, mil., Ok., U.S.	B4	113
Tinley Park, Il., U.S.	k9	90
Tinniswood, Mount, mtn., B.C., Can.	D6	69
Tinogasta, Arg.	B3	56
Tinsukia, India	G16	38
Tinton Falls, N.J., U.S.	C4	107
Tioga, La., U.S.	C3	95
Tioga, N.D., U.S.	A3	111
Tioga, co., N.Y., U.S.	C4	109
Tioga, co., Pa., U.S.	C7	115
Tioga, stm., Pa., U.S.	B7	115
Tiogue Lake, res., R.I., U.S.	D3	116
Tioman, Pulau, i., Malay.	M8	34
Tionesta Creek, stm., Pa., U.S.	C3	115
Tionesta Lake, res., Pa., U.S.	D3	115
Tioughnioga, stm., N.Y., U.S.	C4	109
Tippah, co., Ms., U.S.	A5	101
Tippah, stm., Ms., U.S.	A4	101
Tipp City, Oh., U.S.	C1	112
Tippecanoe, co., In., U.S.	D4	91
Tippecanoe, stm., In., U.S.	C4	91
Tipperary, Ire.	I4	7
Tipton, Ca., U.S.	D4	82
Tipton, In., U.S.	D5	91
Tipton, Ia., U.S.	C6	92
Tipton, Mo., U.S.	C5	102
Tipton, Ok., U.S.	C2	113
Tipton, co., In., U.S.	D5	91
Tipton, co., Tn., U.S.	B2	119
Tipton, Mount, mtn., Az., U.S.	B1	80
Tiptonville, Tn., U.S.	A2	119
Tiquisate, Guat.	G2	64
Tiracambu, Serra do, plat., Braz.	D9	54
Tīrān, Maḍīq, strt.	F4	40
Tiran, Strait of see Tīrān, Maḍīq, strt.	F4	40
Tiranë, Alb.	H3	16
Tirano, Italy	C5	14
Tiraspol', U.S.S.R.	H3	18
Tirat Karmel, Isr.	C4	40
Tire, Tur.	K11	16
Tiree, i., Scot., U.K.	E6	7
Tîrgoviște, Rom.	E9	16
Tîrgu-Jiu, Rom.	D7	16
Tîrgu Mureș, Rom.	C8	16
Tîrgu-Ocna, Rom.	C10	16
Tîrnavos, Grc.	J6	16
Tirschenreuth, Ger.	F12	8
Tiruchchirāppalli, India	G5	37
Tirunelveli, India	H4	37
Tirupati, India	F5	37
Tiruppattūr, India	F5	37
Tiruppur, India	G4	37
Tiruvannāmalai, India	F5	37
Tishomingo, Ok., U.S.	C5	113
Tishomingo, co., Ms., U.S.	A5	101
Tiskilwa, Il., U.S.	B4	90
Tisza (Tisa), stm., Eur.	C4	16
Tit-Ary, U.S.S.R.	C19	20
Titicaca, Lago, l., S.A.	G5	54
Titograd, Yugo.	G3	16
Titonka, Ia., U.S.	A3	92
Titovo Užice, Yugo.	F3	16
Titov Veles, Yugo.	H5	16
Titule, Zaire	H11	42
Titus, co., Tx., U.S.	C5	120
Titusville, Fl., U.S.	D6	86
Titusville, Pa., U.S.	C2	115
Tiverton, Ont., Can.	C3	73
Tiverton, Eng., U.K.	K9	7
Tiverton, R.I., U.S.	D6	116
Tivoli, Italy	H7	14
Tizimín, Mex.	G15	62
Tizi-Ouzou, Alg.	A6	42
Tlahualilo de Zaragoza, Mex.	D8	62
Tlaltenango de Sánchez Román, Mex.	G8	62
Tlaxiaco, Mex.	I11	62
Tlemcen, Alg.	B5	42
Tlētē Ouāte Gharbī, Jabal, mtn., Syria	B6	40
Toamasina, Madag.	E9	44
Toano, Va., U.S.	C6	123
Toano Range, mts., Nv., U.S.	C7	105
Toast, N.C., U.S.	A2	110
Toba, Japan	H9	30
Toba, Danau, l., Indon.	M5	34
Tobacco Root Mountains, mts., Mt., U.S.	E5	103
Tobago, i., Trin.	I17	64
Toba Inlet, b., B.C., Can.	D5	69
Toba Kākar Range, mts., Pak.	E2	38
Tobarra, Spain	G10	12
Tobermory, Scot., U.K.	E6	7
Tobin, Mount, mtn., Nv., U.S.	C4	105
Tobin Lake, l., Sask., Can.	D4	75
Tobin Range, mts., Nv., U.S.	C4	105
Tobique, stm., N.B., Can.	B2	71
Tobruk see Ṭubruq, Libya	B10	42
Tobyhanna, Pa., U.S.	D11	115
Tocantínia, Braz.	E9	54
Tocantinópolis, Braz.	E9	54
Tocantins, stm., Braz.	D9	54
Toccoa, Ga., U.S.	B3	87
Toccoa, stm., Ga., U.S.	B2	87
Toccoa Falls, Ga., U.S.	B3	87
Tochigi, Japan	F12	30
Töcksfors, Swe.	G8	6
Toco, Chile	A3	56
Tocopilla, Chile	A2	56
Todd, co., Ky., U.S.	D2	94
Todd, co., Mn., U.S.	D4	100
Todd, co., S.D., U.S.	D5	118
Todi, Italy	G7	14
Todos Santos, Mex.	F4	62
Todtnau, Ger.	H7	8
Tofield, Alta., Can.	C4	68
Tofino, B.C., Can.	E5	69
Togiak, Ak., U.S.	D7	79
Togian, Kepulauan, is., Indon.	F7	32
Togo, ctry., Afr.	G6	42
Togwotee Pass, Wy., U.S.	C2	127
Tohakum Peak, mtn., Nv., U.S.	C2	105
Tohatchi, N.M., U.S.	B1	108
Tohopekaliga, Lake, l., Fl., U.S.	D5	86
Toiyabe Range, mts., Nv., U.S.	D4	105
Tok, Ak., U.S.	C11	79
Tōkamachi, Japan	E11	30
Tokara-kaikyō, strt., Japan	u30	31b
Tokara-rettō, is., Japan	v29	31b
Tokat, Tur.	G15	4
Tokelau Islands, dep., Oc.	G1	2
Toki, Japan	G10	30
Tokuno-shima, i., Japan	x28	31b
Tokushima, Japan	H7	30
Tokuyama, Japan	H4	30
Tōkyō, Japan	G12	30
Tokzār, Afg.	C2	38
Tolbuhin, Bul.	F11	16
Toleak Point, c., Wa., U.S.	B1	124
Toledo, Spain	F7	12
Toledo, Il., U.S.	D5	90
Toledo, Ia., U.S.	B5	92
Toledo, Oh., U.S.	A2	112
Toledo, Or., U.S.	C3	114
Toledo Bend Reservoir, res., U.S.	C2	95
Tolentino, Italy	F8	14
Toler, Ky., U.S.	C7	94
Toliara, Madag.	F8	44
Toljatti, U.S.S.R.	G7	18
Tol'ka, U.S.S.R.	E10	20
Tolland, Ct., U.S.	B6	84
Tolland, co., Ct., U.S.	B6	84
Tollesboro, Ky., U.S.	B6	94
Tolleson, Az., U.S.	m8	80
Tolmezzo, Italy	C8	14
Tolmin, Yugo.	C8	14
Tolo, Teluk, b., Indon.	F7	32
Tolono, Il., U.S.	D5	90
Tolosa, Spain	B9	12
Tolstoj, Mys, c., U.S.S.R.	F25	20
Tolt Reservoir, res., Wa., U.S.	B4	124
Toluca, Il., U.S.	C4	90
Toluca, Nevado de, vol., Mex.	H10	62
Toluca [de Lerdo], Mex.	H10	62
Tom', stm., U.S.S.R.	F11	20
Tomah, Wi., U.S.	E3	126
Tomahawk, Wi., U.S.	C4	126
Tomahawk Lake, l., Wi., U.S.	C4	126
Tomakomai, Japan	q19	30a
Tomar, Port.	F3	12
Tomaszów Mazowiecki, Pol.	D20	8
Tomatlán, Mex.	H7	62
Tombador, Serra do, plat., Braz.	F7	54
Tomball, Tx., U.S.	D5	120
Tombigbee, stm., U.S.	D1	78
Tombouctou (Timbuktu), Mali	E5	42
Tombstone, Az., U.S.	F5	80
Tombua, Ang.	E2	44
Tomelloso, Spain	F9	12
Tom Green, co., Tx., U.S.	D2	120
Tomini, Teluk, b., Indon.	F7	32
Tommot, U.S.S.R.	F19	20
Tom Nevers Head, c., Ma., U.S.	D8	98
Tomo, stm., Col.	E8	58
Tompkins, co., N.Y., U.S.	C4	109
Tompkinsville, Ky., U.S.	D4	94
Tomptokan, U.S.S.R.	F20	20
Tomra, Nor.	E6	6
Toms, stm., N.J., U.S.	C4	107
Tomsk, U.S.S.R.	F10	20
Toms River, N.J., U.S.	D4	107
Tonalá, Mex.	I13	62
Tonasket, Wa., U.S.	A6	124
Tonawanda, N.Y., U.S.	B2	109
Tonawanda Indian Reservation, N.Y., U.S.	B2	109
Tondabayashi, Japan	H8	30
Tone, stm., Japan	F12	30
Tonga, ctry., Oc.	H1	2
Tonganoxie, Ks., U.S.	C8	93
Tongbai, China	C2	28
Tongchuan, China	D8	26
Tongeren, Bel.	E5	8
Tongguan, China	E9	26
Tonghai, China	B7	34
Tonghua, China	C12	26
Tongliao, China	C11	26
Tongling, China	E6	28
Tongsa Dzong, Bhu.	G14	38
Tongtianheyan, China	D15	38
Tongue, Scot., U.K.	C8	7
Tongue, stm., Mt., U.S.	E10	103
Tongue, stm., Tx., U.S.	p13	120
Tongzi, China	F8	26
Tonk, India	G6	38
Tonkawa, Ok., U.S.	A4	113
Tonkin, Gulf of, b., Asia	E9	34
Tonle Sap see Sab, Tônlé, l., Camb.	H7	34
Tonneins, Fr.	H7	10
Tonnerre, Fr.	E10	10
Tonopah, Nv., U.S.	E4	105
Tønsberg, Nor.	G8	6
Tonstad, Nor.	G6	6
Tonto National Monument, Az., U.S.	D4	80
Tonto Natural Bridge, Az., U.S.	C4	80
Tooele, Ut., U.S.	C3	121
Tooele, co., Ut., U.S.	C2	121
Toole, co., Mt., U.S.	B5	103
Toombs, co., Ga., U.S.	D4	87
Toomsboro, Ga., U.S.	D3	87
Toowoomba, Austl.	E10	50
Topeka, In., U.S.	A6	91
Topeka, Ks., U.S.	C8	93
Topia, Mex.	E6	62
Topka, Gora, mtn., U.S.S.R.	F21	20
Topock, Az., U.S.	C1	80
Toppenish, Wa., U.S.	C5	124
Topsfield, Ma., U.S.	A6	98
Topsham, Me., U.S.	E3	96
Topton, Pa., U.S.	F10	115
Toquima Range, mts., Nv., U.S.	E5	105
Torbay, Newf., Can.	E5	72
Torbert, Mount, mtn., Ak., U.S.	g15	79
Torch Lake, l., Mi., U.S.	D5	99
Tordesillas, Spain	D6	12
Töre, Swe.	D14	6
Torgau, Ger.	D12	8
Torhout, Bel.	D3	8
Torino (Turin), Italy	D2	14
Torit, Sudan	H12	42
Torkestān, Band-e, mts., Afg.	C2	38
Torneälven, stm., Eur.	B12	4
Torngat Mountains, mts., Can.	f8	72
Toro, Spain	D6	12
Toronto, Ont., Can.	D5	73
Toronto, Oh., U.S.	B5	112
Toronto Lake, res., Ks., U.S.	E7	93
Toro Peak, mtn., Ca., U.S.	F5	82
Tororo, Ug.	A6	44
Toros Dağlan, mts., Tur.	H14	4
Torquay (Torbay), Eng., U.K.	K9	7
Torquemada, Spain	C7	12
Torrance, Ca., U.S.	n12	82
Torrance, co., N.M., U.S.	C3	108
Torrão, Port.	G3	12
Torre Annunziata, Italy	I9	14
Torre Baja, Spain	E10	12
Torreblanca, Spain	E12	12
Torrecilla en Cameros, Spain	C9	12
Torre de Moncorvo, Port.	D4	12
Torredonjimeno, Spain	H8	12
Torrelaguna, Spain	E8	12
Torrelavega, Spain	B7	12
Torremaggiore, Italy	H10	14
Torremolinos, Spain	I7	12
Torrens, Lake, l., Austl.	F7	50
Torrente, Spain	F11	12
Torreón, Mex.	E8	62
Torres Novas, Port.	F3	12
Torres Strait, strt., Oc.	B8	50
Torres Vedras, Port.	F2	12
Torrevieja, Spain	H11	12
Torridon, Scot., U.K.	D7	7
Torriglia, Italy	E4	14
Torrijos, Spain	F7	12
Torrington, Ct., U.S.	B3	84
Torrington, Wy., U.S.	D8	127
Torrox, Spain	I8	12
Torsby, Swe.	F9	6
Tórshavn, Faer. Is.	C6	4
Tortola, i., Br. Vir. Is.	E15	64
Tortolì, Italy	J4	14
Tortona, Italy	E3	14
Tortosa, Spain	E12	12
Tortue, Île de la, i., Haiti	D11	64
Toruń, Pol.	B18	8
Toržok, U.S.S.R.	D17	22
Tosa-shimizu, Japan	J5	30
Tosa-wan, b., Japan	I6	30
Tostado, Arg.	B4	56
Totagatic, stm., Wi., U.S.	B2	126
Totana, Spain	H10	12
Toteng, Bots.	F4	44
Tôtes, Fr.	C8	10
Tot'ma, U.S.S.R.	B25	22
Totowa, N.J., U.S.	B4	107
Totson Mountain, mtn., Ak., U.S.	C8	79
Tottenham, Ont., Can.	C5	73
Tottori, Japan	G7	30
Toubkal, Jbel, mtn., Mor.	B4	42
Touchet, stm., Wa., U.S.	C7	124
Touggourt, Alg.	B7	42
Touisset, Ma., U.S.	C5	98
Toul, Fr.	D12	10
Toulon, Fr.	I12	10
Toulon, Il., U.S.	B4	90
Toulouse, Fr.	I8	10
Tounan, Tai.	L9	28
Toungoo, Burma	E4	34
Tourcoing, Fr.	B10	10
Tournai, Bel.	E3	8
Tournon, Fr.	G11	10
Tournus, Fr.	F11	10
Tours, Fr.	E7	10
Touside, Pic, mtn., Chad	D9	42
Toussaint Creek, stm., Oh., U.S.	f7	112
Toutle, North Fork, stm., Wa., U.S.	C3	124
Tovar, Ven.	C7	58
Towanda, Il., U.S.	C5	90
Towanda, Ks., U.S.	E7	93
Towanda, Pa., U.S.	C9	115
Towanda Creek, stm., Pa., U.S.	C8	115
Tower City, Pa., U.S.	E8	115
Town Creek, Al., U.S.	A2	78
Towner, N.D., U.S.	A5	111
Towner, co., N.D., U.S.	A6	111
Towns, co., Ga., U.S.	B3	87
Townsend, De., U.S.	C3	85
Townsend, Mt., U.S.	D5	103
Townshend Reservoir, res., Vt., U.S.	E3	122
Townsville, Austl.	C9	50
Towson, Md., U.S.	B4	97
Toyama, Japan	F10	30
Toyohashi, Japan	H10	30
Toyokawa, Japan	H10	30
Toyonaka, Japan	H8	30
Toyooka, Japan	G7	30
Toyota, Japan	G10	30
Tozeur, Tun.	B7	42
Trabzon, Tur.	G15	4
Tracadie, N.B., Can.	B5	71
Tracy, N.B., Can.	D3	71
Tracy, Que., Can.	C4	74
Tracy, Ca., U.S.	D3	82
Tracy, Mn., U.S.	F3	100
Tracy City, Tn., U.S.	D8	119
Tracyton, Wa., U.S.	e10	124
Tradewater, stm., Ky., U.S.	C2	94
Traer, Ia., U.S.	B5	92
Trafford, Pa., U.S.	k14	115
Trafford, Lake, l., Fl., U.S.	F5	86
Trail, B.C., Can.	E9	69
Trail Creek, In., U.S.	A4	91
Traill, co., N.D., U.S.	B8	111
Trail Ridge, mtn., U.S.	F4	87
Tralee, Ire.	I3	7
Tranås, Swe.	G10	6
Trancas, Arg.	B3	56
Trang, Thai.	K5	34
Trangan, Pulau, i., Indon.	G9	32
Trani, Italy	H11	14
Transylvania, co., N.C., U.S.	f10	110
Transylvania, hist. reg., Rom.	C7	16
Transylvanian Alps see Carpații Meridionali, mts., Rom.	D8	16
Trapani, Italy	K7	14
Trappe, Md., U.S.	C5	97
Trapper Peak, mtn., Mt., U.S.	E2	103
Traun, Aus.	G14	8
Traunstein, Ger.	H12	8
Travelers Rest, S.C., U.S.	B3	117
Traverse, co., Mn., U.S.	E2	100
Traverse, Lake, l., U.S.	B9	118
Traverse City, Mi., U.S.	D5	99
Tra Vinh, Viet.	J9	34
Travis, co., Tx., U.S.	D4	120
Travis Air Force Base, mil., Ca., U.S.	C2	82
Travnik, Yugo.	E12	14
Tray Mountain, mtn., Ga., U.S.	B3	87
Treasure, co., Mt., U.S.	D9	103
Treasure Island Naval Station, mil., Ca., U.S.	h8	82
Trecate, Italy	D3	14
Trego, co., Ks., U.S.	D4	93
Tregosse Islets, is., Austl.	C10	50
Tréguier, Fr.	D3	10
Treherne, Man., Can.	E2	70
Treinta y Tres, Ur.	C6	56
Trélazé, Fr.	E6	10
Trelew, Arg.	E3	56
Trelleborg, Swe.	I9	6
Tremblant, Mont, mtn., Que., Can.	C3	74
Tremont, Il., U.S.	C4	90
Tremont, Pa., U.S.	E9	115
Tremonton, Ut., U.S.	B3	121
Tremp, Spain	C12	12
Trempealeau, Wi., U.S.	D2	126
Trempealeau, co., Wi., U.S.	D2	126
Trempealeau, stm., Wi., U.S.	D2	126
Trenche, stm., Que., Can.	B5	74
Trenčín, Czech.	G18	8
Trenque Lauquen, Arg.	D4	56
Trent, stm., N.C., U.S.	B5	110
Trente et un Milles, Lac des, l., Que., Can.	C2	74
Trento, Italy	C6	14
Trenton, Ont., Can.	C7	73
Trenton, Fl., U.S.	C4	86
Trenton, Ga., U.S.	B1	87
Trenton, Il., U.S.	E4	90
Trenton, Mi., U.S.	F7	99
Trenton, Mo., U.S.	A4	102
Trenton, Ne., U.S.	D4	104
Trenton, N.J., U.S.	C3	107
Trenton, Oh., U.S.	C1	112
Trenton, Tn., U.S.	B3	119
Trepassey, Newf., Can.	E5	72
Trepassey Bay, b., Newf., Can.	E5	72
Tres Arroyos, Arg.	D4	56
Tresckow, Pa., U.S.	E10	115
Três Corações, Braz.	F6	57
Tres Esquinas, Col.	G5	58
Três Lagoas, Braz.	F3	57
Três Marias, Represa, res., Braz.	E6	57
Tres Picos, Cerro, mtn., Arg.	D4	56
Três Pontas, Braz.	F6	57
Tres Puntas, Cabo, c., Arg.	F3	56
Três Rios, Braz.	G7	57
Treutlen, co., Ga., U.S.	D4	87
Treviglio, Italy	D4	14
Treviso, Italy	D7	14
Trevor, Wi., U.S.	n11	126
Trevorton, Pa., U.S.	E8	115
Treynor, Ia., U.S.	C2	92
Trezevant, Tn., U.S.	A3	119
Triadelphia, W.V., U.S.	A4	125
Triadelphia Reservoir, res., Md., U.S.	B3	97
Triangle, Va., U.S.	B5	123
Tribune, Ks., U.S.	D2	93
Trichūr, India	G4	37
Tri City, Or., U.S.	E3	114
Trident Peak, mtn., Nv., U.S.	B3	105
Trieben, Aus.	H14	8
Trier, Ger.	F6	8
Trieste, Italy	D8	14
Trigg, co., Ky., U.S.	D2	94
Triglav, mtn., Yugo.	C8	14
Trigo Mountains, mts., Az., U.S.	D1	80
Trikala, Grc.	J5	16
Trikora, Puncak, mtn., Indon.	F10	32
Tri Lakes, In., U.S.	B7	91
Trim, Ire.	H6	7
Trimble, Tn., U.S.	A2	119
Trimble, co., Ky., U.S.	B4	94
Trimont, Mn., U.S.	G4	100
Trincheras, Mex.	B4	62
Trincomalee, Sri L.	H6	37
Třinec, Czech.	F18	8
Tring Jonction, Que., Can.	C6	74
Trinidad, Bol.	F6	54
Trinidad, Col.	E7	58
Trinidad, Cuba	D8	64
Trinidad, Co., U.S.	D6	83
Trinidad, Tx., U.S.	C4	120
Trinidad, i., Trin.	I17	64
Trinidad and Tobago, ctry., N.A.	I17	64
Trinidad Head, c., Ca., U.S.	B1	82
Trinity, Al., U.S.	A2	78
Trinity, Tx., U.S.	D5	120
Trinity, co., Ca., U.S.	B2	82
Trinity, co., Tx., U.S.	D5	120
Trinity, stm., Ca., U.S.	B2	82
Trinity, stm., Tx., U.S.	D5	120
Trinity Bay, b., Newf., Can.	D5	72
Trinity Islands, is., Ak., U.S.	D9	79
Trinity Mountain, mtn., Id., U.S.	F3	89
Trinity Mountains, mts., Ca., U.S.	B2	82
Trinity Peak, mtn., Nv., U.S.	C3	105
Trinity Range, mts., Nv., U.S.	C3	105
Trion, Ga., U.S.	B1	87
Tripoli, Ia., U.S.	B5	92
Tripolis, Grc.	L6	16
Tripoli see Ṭarābulus, Leb.	B4	40
Tripoli see Ṭarābulus, Libya	B8	42
Tripp, S.D., U.S.	D8	118
Tripp, co., S.D., U.S.	D6	118
Triumph, La., U.S.	E6	95
Trivandrum, India	H4	37
Trnava, Czech.	G17	8
Troarn, Fr.	C6	10
Trobriand Islands, is., Pap. N. Gui.	A10	50

Name | Map Ref | Page

Trochu, Alta., Can. **D4** 68
Trogir, Yugo. **F11** 14
Trois-Pistoles, Que., Can. **A8** 74
Trois-Rivières, Que., Can. **C5** 74
Trois-Rivières-Ouest, Que., Can. **C5** 74
Trojan, Bul. **G8** 16
Trollhättan, Swe. **G9** 6
Trombetas, stm., Braz. **C7** 54
Tromelin, i., Afr. **E10** 44
Tromsø, Nor. **B12** 6
Trona, Ca., U.S. **E5** 82
Tronador, Monte, mtn., S.A. **E2** 56
Trondheim, Nor. **E8** 6
Trondheimsfjorden, Nor. **E8** 6
Tropea, Italy **K10** 14
Trophy Mountain, mtn., B.C., Can. **D8** 69
Trotwood, Oh., U.S. **C1** 112
Troup, co., Ga., U.S. **C1** 87
Trousdale, co., Tn., U.S. **A5** 119
Trout, stm., Fl., U.S. **m8** 86
Trout, stm., Vt., U.S. **B3** 122
Trout Creek, Ont., Can. **B5** 73
Trout Creek Pass, Co., U.S. **C5** 83
Trout Lake, Wa., U.S. **D4** 124
Trout Lake, l., N.W. Ter., Can. **D8** 66
Trout Lake, l., Ont., Can. **o16** 73
Trout Lake, l., Mn., U.S. **B6** 100
Trout Lake, l., Wi., U.S. **B4** 126
Troutman, N.C., U.S. **B2** 110
Trout Peak, mtn., Wy., U.S. **B3** 127
Trout River, Newf., Can. **D2** 72
Trouville [-sur-Mer], Fr. **C7** 10
Troy, Al., U.S. **D4** 78
Troy, Id., U.S. **C2** 89
Troy, Il., U.S. **E4** 90
Troy, Ks., U.S. **C8** 93
Troy, Mi., U.S. **o15** 99
Troy, Mo., U.S. **C7** 102
Troy, Mt., U.S. **B1** 103
Troy, N.H., U.S. **E2** 106
Troy, N.Y., U.S. **C7** 109
Troy, N.C., U.S. **B3** 110
Troy, Oh., U.S. **B1** 112
Troy, Pa., U.S. **C8** 115
Troy, Tn., U.S. **A2** 119
Troyes, Fr. **D11** 10
Troy Peak, mtn., Nv., U.S. **E6** 105
Truchas Peak, mtn., N.M., U.S. **B4** 108
Trucial States see United Arab Emirates, ctry., Asia **D5** 46
Truckee, Ca., U.S. **C3** 82
Truckee, stm., U.S. **D2** 105
Trujillo, Hond. **G4** 64
Trujillo, Peru **E3** 54
Trujillo, Spain **F6** 12
Trujillo, Ven. **C7** 58
Truman, Mn., U.S. **G4** 100
Trumann, Ar., U.S. **B5** 81
Trumansburg, N.Y., U.S. **C4** 109
Trumbull, Ct., U.S. **E3** 84
Trumbull, co., Oh., U.S. **A5** 112
Trumbull, Mount, mtn., Az., U.S. **A2** 80
Truro, Eng., U.K. **K7** 7
Trussville, Al., U.S. **B3** 78
Trustom Pond, l., R.I., U.S. **G3** 116
Truth or Consequences (Hot Springs), N.M., U.S. **D2** 108
Trutnov, Czech. **E15** 8
Tryon, N.C., U.S. **f10** 110
Tržič, Yugo. **C9** 14
Tsala Apopka Lake, l., Fl., U.S. **D4** 86
Tsaratanana, Madag. **E9** 44
Tsaratanana, Massif du, mts., Madag. **D9** 44
Tschida, Lake, res., N.D., U.S. **C4** 111
Tshabong, Bots. **G4** 44
Tshangalele, Lac, l., Zaire **D5** 44
Tshikapa, Zaire **C4** 44
Tshofa, Zaire **C5** 44
Tshuapa, stm., Zaire **B4** 44
Tsoying, Tai. **M9** 28
Tsu, Japan **H9** 30
Tsubame, Japan **E11** 30
Tsuchiura, Japan **F13** 30
Tsugaru-kaikyō, strt., Japan **A13** 30
Tsukumi, Japan **I4** 30
Tsukushi-sanchi, mts., Japan **I3** 30
Tsumeb, Nmb. **E3** 44
Tsuruga, Japan **G9** 30
Tsuruoka, Japan **D12** 30
Tsushima, is., Japan **H2** 30
Tsushima-kaikyō, strt., Japan **I2** 30
Tsuyama, Japan **G7** 30
Tual, Indon. **G9** 32
Tualatin, stm., Or., U.S. **h11** 114
Tuba City, Az., U.S. **A4** 80
Tuban, Indon. **m16** 33a
Tubarão, Braz. **B7** 56
Ţubruq, Libya **B10** 42
Tucannon, stm., Wa., U.S. **C8** 124
Tucano, Braz. **F11** 54
Tuckahoe, N.Y., U.S. **h13** 109
Tuckahoe, stm., N.J., U.S. **E3** 107
Tucker, Ga., U.S. **h8** 87
Tucker, co., W.V., U.S. **B5** 125
Tucker Island, i., N.J., U.S. **E4** 107
Tuckerman, Ar., U.S. **B4** 81
Tuckernuck Island, i., Ma., U.S. **D7** 98
Tuckerton, N.J., U.S. **D4** 107
Tucson, Az., U.S. **E5** 80
Tucumcari, N.M., U.S. **B6** 108
Tucumcari Mountain, mtn., N.M., U.S. **B6** 108
Tucupita, Ven. **C11** 58
Tucuruí, Braz. **D9** 54
Tudela, Spain **C10** 12
Tudmur (Palmyra), Syria **B6** 40
Tugaloo Lake, res., U.S. **B1** 117
Tug Fork, stm., U.S. **C2** 125
Tuguegarao, Phil. **p19** 32
Tugur, U.S.S.R. **G21** 20
Tukangbesi, Kepulauan, is., Indon. **G7** 32
Tuktoyaktuk, N.W. Ter., Can. **C6** 66
Tukwila, Wa., U.S. **f11** 124
Tula, Mex. **F10** 62
Tula, U.S.S.R. **G20** 22
Tulalip Indian Reservation, Wa., U.S. **A3** 124
Tulancingo, Mex. **G10** 62
Tulare, Ca., U.S. **D4** 82
Tulare, co., Ca., U.S. **D4** 82
Tulare Lake, l., Ca., U.S. **D4** 82
Tularosa, N.M., U.S. **D3** 108
Tularosa Mountains, mts., N.M., U.S. **D1** 108
Tularosa Valley, val., N.M., U.S. **E3** 108
Tulcán, Ec. **G4** 58
Tulcea, Rom. **D12** 16
Tule Lake, sw., Ca., U.S. **B3** 82
Tule River Indian Reservation, Ca., U.S. **E4** 82
Tule Valley, val., Ut., U.S. **D2** 121
Tulia, Tx., U.S. **B2** 120
Ţūlkarm, Jord. **C4** 40
Tullahoma, Tn., U.S. **B5** 119
Tullamore, Ire. **H5** 7
Tulle, Fr. **G8** 10
Tullins, Fr. **G12** 10
Tulsa, Ok., U.S. **A6** 113
Tulsa, co., Ok., U.S. **B6** 113
Tuluá, Col. **E4** 58
Tulum, Mex. **G16** 62
Tulun, U.S.S.R. **G14** 20
Tulungagung, Indon. **n15** 33a
Tuma, stm., Nic. **H5** 64
Tumacacori National Monument, Az., U.S. **F4** 80
Tumaco, Col. **G3** 58
Tuman-gang, stm., Asia **C12** 26
Tumany, U.S.S.R. **E25** 20
Tumatumari, Guy. **E13** 58
Tumba, Lac, l., Zaire **B3** 44
Tumbes, Peru **D2** 54
Tumble Mountain, mtn., Mt., U.S. **E7** 103
Tumbler Ridge, B.C., Can. **B7** 69
Tumen, China **C12** 26
Tumiritinga, Braz. **E8** 57
Tumkūr, India **F4** 37
Tummo, Libya **D8** 42
Tumsar, India **B5** 37
Tumuc-Humac Mountains, mts., S.A. **C8** 54
Tumwater, Wa., U.S. **B3** 124
Tunbridge Wells, Eng., U.K. **J13** 7
Tunduru, Tan. **D7** 44
Tundža, stm., Eur. **G10** 16
T'ung, stm., U.S.S.R. **D17** 20
Tungabhadra, stm., India **E4** 37
Tungabhadra Reservoir, res., India **E4** 37
Tungchiang, Tai. **M9** 28
Tungsha Tao (Pratas Islands), is., Tai. **G10** 26
Tungshih, Tai. **K9** 28
Tunica, Ms., U.S. **A3** 101
Tunica, co., Ms., U.S. **A3** 101
Tunis, Tun. **M5** 14
Tunisia, ctry., Afr. **B7** 42
Tunja, Col. **E6** 58
Tunkhannock, Pa., U.S. **C10** 115
Tunk Lake, l., Me., U.S. **D4** 96
Tunnel Hill, Ga., U.S. **B1** 87
Tunp Range, mts., Wy., U.S. **D2** 127
Tununak, Ak., U.S. **C6** 79
Tunxi, China **F7** 28
Tuobuja, U.S.S.R. **E18** 20
Tuolumne, Ca., U.S. **D3** 82
Tuolumne, co., Ca., U.S. **C4** 82
Tuolumne, stm., Ca., U.S. **D3** 82
Tupã, Braz. **F3** 57
Tupaciguara, Braz. **E4** 57
Tupanciretã, Braz. **B6** 56
Tupelo, Ms., U.S. **A5** 101
Tupiza, Bol. **H5** 54
Tupper Lake, N.Y., U.S. **A6** 109
Tupper Lake, l., N.Y., U.S. **A6** 109
Túquerres, Col. **G4** 58
Tura, India **H14** 38
Tura, U.S.S.R. **E14** 20
Turan, U.S.S.R. **G12** 20
Turbat, Pak. **D1** 36
Turbeville, S.C., U.S. **D7** 117
Turbo, Col. **C4** 58
Turda, Rom. **C7** 16
Turgutlu, Tur. **K11** 16
Turimiquire, Cerro, mtn., Ven. **B11** 58
Turin see Torino, Italy **D2** 14
Turkey, ctry., Asia **H14** 4
Turkey, stm., Ia., U.S. **B6** 92
Turkey Creek, stm., Ok., U.S. **A3** 113
Turkey Point, c., Md., U.S. **B5** 97
Turkmenistan see Turkmenskaja Sovetskaja Socialističeskaja Respublika, state, U.S.S.R. **I9** 18
Turkmenskaja Sovetskaja Socialističeskaja Respublika, state, U.S.S.R. **I9** 18
Turks and Caicos Islands, dep., N.A. **D12** 64
Turks Islands, is., T./C. Is. **D12** 64
Turku (Åbo), Fin. **F14** 6
Turley, Ok., U.S. **A6** 113
Turlock, Ca., U.S. **D3** 82
Turnbull, Mount, mtn., Az., U.S. **D5** 80
Turneffe Islands, is., Belize **F4** 64
Turner, Or., U.S. **C4** 114
Turner, co., Ga., U.S. **E3** 87
Turner, co., S.D., U.S. **D8** 118
Turners Falls, Ma., U.S. **A2** 98
Turner Valley, Alta., Can. **D3** 68
Turnhout, Bel. **D4** 8
Turnor Lake, l., Sask., Can. **m7** 75
Turnu-Măgurele, Rom. **F8** 16
Turpan, China **C4** 26
Turquino, Pico, mtn., Cuba **E9** 64
Turrell, Ar., U.S. **B5** 81
Turret Peak, mtn., Az., U.S. **C4** 80
Turtle Creek, Pa., U.S. **k14** 115
Turtle Flambeau Flowage, res., Wi., U.S. **B3** 126
Turtle Lake, N.D., U.S. **B5** 111
Turtle Lake, Wi., U.S. **C1** 126
Turtle Lake, l., Sask., Can. **D1** 75
Turtle Mountain Indian Reservation, N.D., U.S. **A6** 111
Turu, stm., U.S.S.R. **D14** 20
Turuchan, stm., U.S.S.R. **D11** 20
Turuchansk, U.S.S.R. **D11** 20
Tuscaloosa, Al., U.S. **B2** 78
Tuscaloosa, co., Al., U.S. **B2** 78
Tuscarawas, co., Oh., U.S. **B4** 112
Tuscarawas, stm., Oh., U.S. **B4** 112
Tuscarora Indian Reservation, N.Y., U.S. **B2** 109
Tuscarora Mountain, mtn., Pa., U.S. **F6** 115
Tuscarora Mountains, mts., Nv., U.S. **B5** 105
Tuscola, Il., U.S. **D5** 90
Tuscola, co., Mi., U.S. **E7** 99
Tuscumbia, Al., U.S. **A2** 78
Tuskegee, Al., U.S. **C4** 78
Tusket, stm., N.S., Can. **E4** 71
Tustumena Lake, l., Ak., U.S. **g16** 79
Tuticorin, India **H5** 37
Tutóia, Braz. **D10** 54
Tuttle, Ok., U.S. **B4** 113
Tuttle Creek Lake, res., Ks., U.S. **C7** 93
Tututalak Mountain, mtn., Ak., U.S. **B7** 79
Tutwiler, Ms., U.S. **A3** 101
Tuvalu, ctry., Oc. **G24** 2
Tuwayq, Jabal, mts., Sau. Ar. **D4** 46
Tuxedo, N.C., U.S. **f10** 110
Tuxedo Park, De., U.S. **i7** 85
Tuxpan, Mex. **G7** 62
Tuxpan de Rodríguez Cano, Mex. **G11** 62
Tuxtla Gutiérrez, Mex. **I13** 62
Túy, Spain **C3** 12
Tuy Hoa, Viet. **H10** 34
Tuz Gölü, l., Tur. **H14** 4
Tuzigoot National Monument, Az., U.S. **C4** 80
Tuzla, Yugo. **E2** 16
Tveitsund, Nor. **G7** 6
Tver', U.S.S.R. **E18** 22
Tweed, Ont., Can. **C7** 73
Tweedsmuir Provincial Park, B.C., Can. **C4** 69
Tweedy Mountain, mtn., Mt., U.S. **E4** 103
Twelvepole Creek, stm., W.V., U.S. **C2** 125
Twentymile Creek, stm., W.V., U.S. **C3** 125
Twentynine Palms, Ca., U.S. **E5** 82
Twentynine Palms Marine Corps Base, mil., Ca., U.S. **E5** 82
Twiggs, co., Ga., U.S. **D3** 87
Twillingate, Newf., Can. **D4** 72
Twin Buttes, mtn., Or., U.S. **C4** 114
Twin Buttes Reservoir, res., Tx., U.S. **D2** 120
Twin City, Ga., U.S. **D4** 87
Twin Creek, stm., Oh., U.S. **C1** 112
Twin Falls, Id., U.S. **G4** 89
Twin Falls, co., Id., U.S. **G4** 89
Twin Knolls, Az., U.S. **m9** 80
Twin Lakes, Ga., U.S. **F3** 87
Twin Lakes, Wi., U.S. **F5** 126
Twin Lakes, l., Ct., U.S. **A2** 84
Twin Lakes, l., Ia., U.S. **B3** 92
Twin Lakes, l., Me., U.S. **C4** 96
Twin Mountains, mtn., Wy., U.S. **E7** 127
Twin Peaks, mts., Id., U.S. **E4** 89
Twin Rivers, N.J., U.S. **C4** 107
Twinsburg, Oh., U.S. **A4** 112
Twin Valley, Mn., U.S. **C2** 100
Twisp, Wa., U.S. **A5** 124
Two Harbors, Mn., U.S. **C7** 100
Two Hills, Alta., Can. **C5** 68
Two Mile Beach, N.J., U.S. **F3** 107
Two Rivers, Wi., U.S. **D6** 126
Two Rivers, North Branch, stm., Mn., U.S. **B2** 100
Two Rivers, South Branch, stm., Mn., U.S. **B2** 100
Tybee Island, Ga., U.S. **D6** 87
Tychy, Pol. **E18** 8
Tygart Lake, res., W.V., U.S. **B5** 125
Tygart River, Falls of the, wtfl, W.V., U.S. **k10** 125
Tygart Valley, stm., W.V., U.S. **B4** 125
Tyger, stm., S.C., U.S. **B4** 117
Tyler, Mn., U.S. **F2** 100
Tyler, Tx., U.S. **C5** 120
Tyler, co., Tx., U.S. **D5** 120
Tyler, co., W.V., U.S. **B4** 125
Tyler, Lake, res., Tx., U.S. **C5** 120
Tyler Branch, stm., Vt., U.S. **B3** 122
Tyler Heights, W.V., U.S. **C3** 125
Tylertown, Ms., U.S. **D3** 101
Tymochtee Creek, stm., Oh., U.S. **B2** 112
Tyndall, S.D., U.S. **E8** 118
Tyndall Air Force Base, mil., Fl., U.S. **u16** 86
Tyonek, Ak., U.S. **C9** 79
Tyre see Şūr, Leb. **C4** 40
Tyrma, U.S.S.R. **G20** 20
Tyrone, N.M., U.S. **E1** 108
Tyrone, Ok., U.S. **e9** 113
Tyrone, Pa., U.S. **E5** 115
Tyronza, Ar., U.S. **B5** 81
Tyrrell, co., N.C., U.S. **B6** 110
Tyrrhenian Sea (Mare Tirreno), Eur. **I6** 14
Tysse, Nor. **F5** 6
Tzaneen, S. Afr. **F6** 44

U

Uatumã, stm., Braz. **D7** 54
Uaupés, Braz. **D5** 54
Ubá, Braz. **F7** 57
Ubangi (Oubangui), stm., Afr. **H9** 42
Ube, Japan **I4** 30
Úbeda, Spain **G8** 12
Uberaba, Braz. **E5** 57
Uberlândia, Braz. **E4** 57
Ubly, Mi., U.S. **E8** 99
Ubon Ratchathani, Thai. **G8** 34
Ubundi, Zaire **B5** 44
Učami, U.S.S.R. **E13** 20
Ucayali, stm., Peru **E4** 54
Uchiura-wan, b., Japan **q18** 30a
Ucluelet, B.C., Can. **E5** 69
Ucon, Id., U.S. **F7** 89
Uda, stm., U.S.S.R. **G13** 20
Uda, stm., U.S.S.R. **G20** 20
Udaipur, India **H5** 38
Udall, Ks., U.S. **E6** 93
Uddevalla, Swe. **G8** 6
Udgīr, India **C4** 37
Udine, Italy **C8** 14
Udipi, India **F3** 37
Udon Thani, Thai. **F7** 34
Udskaja Guba, b., U.S.S.R. **G21** 20
Udža, U.S.S.R. **C17** 20
Ueckermünde, Ger. **B14** 8
Ueda, Japan **F11** 30
Uele, stm., Zaire **H10** 42
Uelen, U.S.S.R. **D31** 20
Uelzen, Ger. **C10** 8
Ueno, Japan **H9** 30
Uere, stm., Zaire **H11** 42
Ufa, U.S.S.R. **G9** 18
Uganda, ctry., Afr. **A6** 44
Ugashik Lakes, l., Ak., U.S. **D8** 79
Ugine, Fr. **G13** 10
Uglegorsk, U.S.S.R. **H22** 20
Uglič, U.S.S.R. **D21** 22
Uhrichsville, Oh., U.S. **B4** 112
Uíge, Ang. **C3** 44
Uinta, co., Wy., U.S. **E2** 127
Uinta, stm., Ut., U.S. **C5** 121
Uintah, co., Ut., U.S. **D6** 121
Uintah and Ouray Indian Reservation, Ut., U.S. **C5** 121
Uinta Mountains, mts., Ut., U.S. **C5** 121
Uitenhage, S. Afr. **H5** 44
Uivak, Cape, c., Newf., Can. **f9** 72
Ujandina, stm., U.S.S.R. **D22** 20
Uji, Japan **H8** 30
Ujiji, Tan. **B5** 44
Ujjain, India **I6** 38
Ujungpandang, Indon. **G6** 32
Uka, U.S.S.R. **F26** 20
Ukiah, Ca., U.S. **C2** 82
Ukraine see Ukrainskaja Sovetskaja Socialističeskaja Respublika, state, U.S.S.R. **H4** 18
Ukrainskaja Sovetskaja Socialističeskaja Respublika (Ukraine), state, U.S.S.R. **H4** 18
Ulaanbaatar (Ulan Bator), Mong. **B8** 26
Ulaangom, Mong. **B5** 26
Ulak Island, i., Ak., U.S. **E4** 79
Ulan Bator see Ulaanbaatar, Mong. **B8** 26
Ulan-Ude, U.S.S.R. **G15** 20
Ulhāsnagar, India **C2** 37
Uliastaj, Mong. **B6** 26
Ulindi, stm., Zaire **B5** 44
Ulja, U.S.S.R. **F22** 20
Uljanovsk, U.S.S.R. **G7** 18
Ullapool, Scot., U.K. **D7** 7
Ullŭng-do, i., S. Kor. **D13** 26
Ulm, Ger. **G10** 8
Ulsan, S. Kor. **D12** 26
Ulster, co., N.Y., U.S. **D6** 109
Ulster, hist. reg., Eur. **G5** 7
Ulu, U.S.S.R. **E19** 20
Ulubat Gölü, l., Tur. **I12** 16
Ulungur Hu, l., China **B4** 26
Ulysses, Ks., U.S. **E2** 93
Umag, Yugo. **D8** 14
Uman', U.S.S.R. **H4** 18
Umanak, Grnld. **B22** 66
Umanak Fjord, Grnld. **B22** 66
Umatilla, Fl., U.S. **D5** 86
Umatilla, Or., U.S. **B7** 114
Umatilla, co., Or., U.S. **B8** 114
Umatilla, stm., Or., U.S. **B7** 114
Umatilla Indian Reservation, Or., U.S. **B8** 114
Umbagog Lake, l., U.S. **A4** 106
Umcolcus Lake, l., Me., U.S. **B4** 96
Umeå, Swe. **E13** 6
Umm Durmān (Omdurman), Sudan **E12** 42
Umnak Island, i., Ak., U.S. **E6** 79
Umnäs, Swe. **D11** 6
Umpqua, stm., Or., U.S. **D3** 114
Umsaskis Lake, l., Me., U.S. **B3** 96
Umtata, S. Afr. **H5** 44
Umzinto, S. Afr. **H6** 44
Unadilla, Ga., U.S. **D3** 87
Unadilla, stm., N.Y., U.S. **C5** 109
Unalakleet, Ak., U.S. **C7** 79
Unalaska Island, i., Ak., U.S. **E6** 79
'Unayzah, Sau. Ar. **C3** 46
Uncasville, Ct., U.S. **D7** 84
Uncompahgre, stm., Co., U.S. **C3** 83
Uncompahgre Mountains, mts., Co., U.S. **C3** 83
Uncompahgre Peak, mtn., Co., U.S. **C3** 83
Underwood, Al., U.S. **B3** 78
Underwood, N.D., U.S. **B4** 111
Ungava, Péninsule d', pen., Que., Can. **g12** 74
Ungava Bay, b., Can. **E19** 66
União dos Palmares, Braz. **E11** 54
Unicoi, Tn., U.S. **C11** 119
Unicoi, co., Tn., U.S. **C11** 119
Unicoi Mountains, mts., U.S. **D9** 119
Unimak Island, i., Ak., U.S. **D7** 79
Unimak Pass, strt., Ak., U.S. **E6** 79
Union, Ky., U.S. **k13** 94
Union, Ms., U.S. **C4** 101
Union, Mo., U.S. **C6** 102
Union, Or., U.S. **B9** 114
Union, S.C., U.S. **B4** 117
Union, Wa., U.S. **B2** 124
Union, co., Ar., U.S. **D3** 81
Union, co., Fl., U.S. **B4** 86
Union, co., Ga., U.S. **B2** 87
Union, co., Il., U.S. **F4** 90
Union, co., In., U.S. **E8** 91
Union, co., Ia., U.S. **C3** 92
Union, co., Ky., U.S. **C2** 94
Union, co., La., U.S. **B3** 95
Union, co., Ms., U.S. **A4** 101
Union, co., N.J., U.S. **B4** 107
Union, co., N.M., U.S. **A6** 108
Union, co., N.C., U.S. **B2** 110
Union, co., Oh., U.S. **B2** 112
Union, co., Or., U.S. **B8** 114
Union, co., Pa., U.S. **E7** 115
Union, co., S.C., U.S. **B4** 117
Union, co., S.D., U.S. **E9** 118
Union, co., Tn., U.S. **C10** 119
Union, West Branch, stm., Me., U.S. **D4** 96
Union Beach, N.J., U.S. **C4** 107
Union Bridge, Md., U.S. **A3** 97
Union City, Ca., U.S. **h8** 82
Union City, Ga., U.S. **C2** 87
Union City, In., U.S. **D8** 91
Union City, Mi., U.S. **F5** 99
Union City, N.J., U.S. **h8** 107
Union City, Oh., U.S. **B1** 112
Union City, Ok., U.S. **B4** 113
Union City, Pa., U.S. **C2** 115
Union City, Tn., U.S. **A2** 119
Union Flat Creek, stm., Wa., U.S. **C8** 124
Union Gap, Wa., U.S. **C5** 124
Union Grove, Wi., U.S. **F5** 126
Union Lake, l., N.J., U.S. **E2** 107
Union of Soviet Socialist Republics, ctry., Eur. **D10** 24
Union Pier, Mi., U.S. **G4** 99
Union Point, Ga., U.S. **C3** 87
Union Springs, Al., U.S. **C4** 78
Uniontown, Al., U.S. **C2** 78
Uniontown, Ky., U.S. **C2** 94
Uniontown, Oh., U.S. **B4** 112
Uniontown, Pa., U.S. **G2** 115
Union Village, R.I., U.S. **B3** 116
Union Village Reservoir, res., Vt., U.S. **D4** 122
Unionville, Ct., U.S. **B4** 84
Unionville, Mo., U.S. **A4** 102
United Arab Emirates, ctry., Asia **D5** 46
United Kingdom, ctry., Eur. **E7** 4
United Nations Headquarters, N.Y., U.S. **h12** 109
United States, ctry., N.A. **D7** 76
United States Air Force Academy, mil., Co., U.S. **B6** 83
United States Military Academy, mil., N.Y., U.S. **C6** 109
United States Naval Academy, mil., Md., U.S. **C4** 97
Unity Reservoir, res., Or., U.S. **C8** 114
University City, Mo., U.S. **C7** 102
University Heights, Ia., U.S. **C6** 92
University Heights, Oh., U.S. **h9** 112
University Park, Ia., U.S. **C5** 92
University Park, N.M., U.S. **E3** 108
University Park, Tx., U.S. **n10** 120
University Place, Wa., U.S. **f10** 124
Unnão, India **G9** 38
Uozu, Japan **F10** 30
Upata, Ven. **C11** 58
Upemba, Lac, l., Zaire **C5** 44
Upernavik, Grnld. **B21** 66
Upington, S. Afr. **G4** 44
Upland, Ca., U.S. **E5** 82
Upland, In., U.S. **D7** 91
Upleta, India **J4** 38
Upolu Point, c., Hi., U.S. **C6** 88
Upper Ammonoosuc, stm., N.H., U.S. **A4** 106
Upper Arlington, Oh., U.S. **B2** 112
Upper Arrow Lake, l., B.C., Can. **F9** 66
Upper Arrow Lake, res., B.C., Can. **D9** 69
Upperco, Md., U.S. **A4** 97
Upper Darby, Pa., U.S. **G11** 115
Upper Greenwood Lake, N.J., U.S. **A4** 107
Upper Humber, stm., Newf., Can. **D3** 72
Upper Iowa, stm., Ia., U.S. **A5** 92
Upper Island Cove, Newf., Can. **E5** 72
Upper Kapuas Mountains, mts., Asia **E5** 32
Upper Klamath Lake, l., Or., U.S. **E4** 114
Upper Marlboro, Md., U.S. **C4** 97
Upper New York Bay, b., U.S. **k8** 107
Upper Red Lake, l., Mn., U.S. **B4** 100
Upper Saddle River, N.J., U.S. **A4** 107
Upper Sandusky, Oh., U.S. **B2** 112
Upper Sheila, N.B., Can. **B5** 71
Upper Volta see Burkina Faso, ctry., Afr. **F5** 42
Uppsala, Swe. **G11** 6
Upright, Cape, c., Ak., U.S. **C5** 79
Upshur, co., Tx., U.S. **C5** 120
Upshur, co., W.V., U.S. **C4** 125
Upson, co., Ga., U.S. **D2** 87
Upton, Que., Can. **D5** 74
Upton, Ky., U.S. **C4** 94
Upton, Ma., U.S. **B4** 98
Upton, Wy., U.S. **B8** 127
Upton, co., Tx., U.S. **D2** 120
Uquía, Cerro, mtn., Ven. **E11** 58
Urabá, Golfo de, b., Col. **C4** 58
Ural, stm., U.S.S.R. **H8** 18
Ural Mountains see Ural'skije gory, mts., U.S.S.R. **F9** 18
Ural'sk, U.S.S.R. **G8** 18
Ural'skije gory (Ural Mountains), mts., U.S.S.R. **F9** 18
Urania, La., U.S. **C3** 95
Urbana, Il., U.S. **C5** 90
Urbana, Oh., U.S. **B2** 112
Urbancrest, Oh., U.S. **m10** 112
Urbandale, Ia., U.S. **C4** 92
Urbino, Italy **F7** 14
Urfa, Tur. **H15** 4
Urgenč, U.S.S.R. **I10** 18
Uribe, Col. **F5** 58
Uribia, Col. **B6** 58
Urla, Tur. **K10** 16
Uruaçu, Braz. **C4** 57
Uruapan [del Progreso], Mex. **H8** 62
Urubamba, stm., Peru **F4** 54
Urucuia, stm., Braz. **D6** 57
Uruguaiana, Braz. **B5** 56
Uruguay, ctry., S.A. **C5** 56

Name	Map Ref	Page
Uruguay (Uruguai), stm., S.A.	C5	56
Ürümqi, China	C4	26
Ur'ung-Chaja, U.S.S.R.	C16	20
Urun-Islāmpur, India	D3	37
Urup, Ostrov, i., U.S.S.R.	H23	20
Usa, Japan	I4	30
Uşak, Tur.	K13	16
Usedom, i., Eur.	B14	8
Ushibuka, Japan	J3	30
Ushuaia, Arg.	G3	56
Usolje-Sibirskoje, U.S.S.R.	G14	20
Usquepaug, R.I., U.S.	F3	116
Ussel, Fr.	G9	10
Ussuri (Wusuli), stm., Asia	B14	26
Ussurijsk, U.S.S.R.	I20	20
Ust'-Barguzin, U.S.S.R.	G15	20
Ust'-Belaja, U.S.S.R.	D28	20
Ust'Čaun, U.S.S.R.	D28	20
Ústí nad Labem, Czech.	E14	8
Ust'-Kamčatsk, U.S.S.R.	F26	20
Ust'-Kamenogorsk, U.S.S.R.	H10	20
Ust'-Kut, U.S.S.R.	F15	20
Ust'-Maja, U.S.S.R.	E20	20
Ust'-Nera, U.S.S.R.	E22	20
Usu, China	C3	26
Usuki, Japan	I4	30
Usulután, El Sal.	H3	64
Usumacinta, stm., N.A.	I14	62
Utah, co., Ut., U.S.	C4	121
Utah, state, U.S.	D4	121
Utah Lake, l., Ut., U.S.	C4	121
Utashinai, Japan	p20	30a
Ute Creek, stm., N.M., U.S.	A6	108
Ute Mountain Indian Reservation, U.S.	D2	83
Ute Reservoir, res., N.M., U.S.	B6	108
Utete, Tan.	C7	44
Uthai Thani, Thai.	G6	34
Utiariti, Braz.	F7	54
Utica, Il., U.S.	B5	90
Utica, Mi., U.S.	F7	99
Utica, Ms., U.S.	C3	101
Utica, Ne., U.S.	D8	104
Utica, N.Y., U.S.	B5	109
Utica, Oh., U.S.	B3	112
Utiel, Spain	F10	12
Utikuma Lake, l., Alta., Can.	B3	68
Utrecht, Neth.	C5	8
Utrera, Spain	H6	12
Utsunomiya, Japan	F12	30
Uttar Pradesh, state, India	G8	38
Uusikaupunki (Nystad), Fin.	F13	6
Uvá, stm., Col.	F8	58
Uvalde, Tx., U.S.	E3	120
Uvalde, co., Tx., U.S.	E3	120
Uvdal, Nor.	F7	6
Uvinza, Tan.	C6	44
Uvs Nuur, l., Asia	A5	26
Uwajima, Japan	I5	30
'Uwaynāt, Jabal al-, mtn., Afr.	D10	42
Uwharrie, stm., N.C., U.S.	B3	110
Uxbridge, Ma., U.S.	B4	98
Uyuni, Bol.	H5	54
Uyuni, Salar de, pl., Bol.	H5	54
Uzbekistan see Uzbekskaja Sovetskaja Socialističeskaja Respublika, state, U.S.S.R.	I10	18
Uzbekskaja Sovetskaja Socialističeskaja Respublika, state, U.S.S.R.	I10	18
Uzerche, Fr.	G8	10
Uzès, Fr.	H11	10
Uzlovaja, U.S.S.R.	H21	22
Uzunköprü, Tur.	H10	16
Užur, U.S.S.R.	F11	20

V

Name	Map Ref	Page
Vaala, Fin.	D16	6
Vaasa (Vasa), Fin.	E13	6
Vác, Hung.	H19	8
Vaca Key, i., Fl., U.S.	H5	86
Vacaville, Ca., U.S.	C3	82
Vaccarès, Étang de, b., Fr.	I11	10
Vach, stm., U.S.S.R.	E9	20
Vacherie, La., U.S.	h10	95
Vadsø, Nor.	A17	6
Vaduz, Liech.	H9	8
Váh, stm., Czech.	G18	8
Vaiden, Ms., U.S.	B4	101
Vail, Co., U.S.	B4	83
Vākhān, stm., Afg.	B5	38
Vākhān, reg., Afg.	B5	38
Vålådalen, Swe.	E9	6
Val-Bélair, Que., Can.	n17	74
Valcheta, Arg.	E3	56
Valcourt, Que., Can.	D5	74
Valdagno, Italy	D6	14
Val-David, Que., Can.	C3	74
Valdecañas, Embalse de, res., Spain	F6	12
Valdemarsvik, Swe.	G11	6
Valdepeñas, Spain	G8	12
Valderrobres, Spain	E12	12
Valders, Wi., U.S.	D6	126
Valdés, Península, pen., Arg.	E4	56
Valdese, N.C., U.S.	B1	110
Valdez, Ak., U.S.	C10	79
Val-d'Isère, Fr.	G13	10
Valdivia, Chile	D2	56
Valdivia, Col.	D5	58
Val-d'Or, Que., Can.	k11	74
Valdosta, Ga., U.S.	F3	87
Vale, Or., U.S.	D9	114
Valemount, B.C., Can.	C8	69
Valença, Braz.	B9	57
Valença, Port.	C3	12
Valençay, Fr.	E8	10
Valence, Fr.	H11	10
Valencia, Spain	F11	12
Valencia, Az., U.S.	m7	80
Valencia, Ven.	C8	58
Valencia, co., N.M., U.S.	C3	108
Valencia, Golfo de, b., Spain	F12	12
Valencia de Alcántata, Spain	F4	12
Valencia de Don Juan, Spain	C6	12
Valencia Heights, S.C., U.S.	D6	117
Valenciennes, Fr.	B10	10
Valentine, Ne., U.S.	B5	104
Valenza, Italy	D3	14
Valera, Ven.	C7	58
Valga, U.S.S.R.	D9	22
Valhalla, N.Y., U.S.	D7	109
Valhermoso Springs, Al., U.S.	A3	78
Valjevo, Yugo.	E3	16
Valkeakoski, Fin.	F15	6
Valkenswaard, Neth.	D5	8
Valladolid, Mex.	G15	62
Valladolid, Spain	D7	12
Vall de Uxó, Spain	F11	12
Vallecito Reservoir, res., Co., U.S.	D3	83
Valle de Guanape, Ven.	C10	58
Valle de la Pascua, Ven.	C9	58
Valle de Santiago, Mex.	G9	62
Valle de Zaragoza, Mex.	D7	62
Valledupar, Col.	B6	58
Vallée-Jonction, Que., Can.	C7	74
Valle Hermoso, Mex.	E11	62
Vallejo, Ca., U.S.	C2	82
Vallelunga Pratameno, Italy	L8	14
Vallenar, Chile	B2	56
Valletta, Malta	N9	14
Valley, Ne., U.S.	C9	104
Valley, co., Id., U.S.	E3	89
Valley, co., Mt., U.S.	B10	103
Valley, co., Ne., U.S.	C6	104
Valley, stm., Man., Can.	D1	70
Valley Center, Ks., U.S.	E6	93
Valley City, N.D., U.S.	C8	111
Valley Cottage, N.Y., U.S.	g13	109
Valley East, Ont., Can.	p19	73
Valley Falls, Ks., U.S.	C8	93
Valley Falls, R.I., U.S.	B4	116
Valley Forge, Pa., U.S.	o20	115
Valley Mills, Tx., U.S.	D4	120
Valley Park, Mo., U.S.	f12	102
Valley Springs, S.D., U.S.	D9	118
Valley Station, Ky., U.S.	g11	94
Valley Stream, N.Y., U.S.	n15	109
Valleyview, Alta., Can.	B2	68
Valley View, Pa., U.S.	E8	115
Valliant, Ok., U.S.	D6	113
Vallo della Lucania, Italy	I10	14
Valls, Spain	D13	12
Vallscreek, W.V., U.S.	D3	125
Valmeyer, Il., U.S.	E3	90
Valognes, Fr.	C5	10
Valparai, India	G4	37
Valparaíso, Chile	C2	56
Valparaíso, Mex.	F8	62
Valparaiso, Fl., U.S.	u15	86
Valparaiso, In., U.S.	B3	91
Valréas, Fr.	H11	10
Vals, Tanjung, c., Indon.	G10	32
Valtimo, Fin.	E17	6
Val Verda, Ut., U.S.	C4	121
Valverde, Dom. Rep.	E12	64
Val Verde, co., Tx., U.S.	E2	120
Valverde del Camino, Spain	H5	12
Van, Tur.	H16	4
Van, Tx., U.S.	C5	120
Van, W.V., U.S.	n12	125
Van Alstyne, Tx., U.S.	C4	120
Vanavara, U.S.S.R.	E14	20
Van Buren, Ar., U.S.	B1	81
Van Buren, In., U.S.	C6	91
Van Buren, Me., U.S.	A5	96
Van Buren, Mo., U.S.	E6	102
Van Buren, co., Ar., U.S.	B3	81
Van Buren, co., Ia., U.S.	D6	92
Van Buren, co., Mi., U.S.	F4	99
Van Buren, co., Tn., U.S.	D8	119
Vance, co., N.C., U.S.	A4	110
Vance Air Force Base, mil., Ok., U.S.	A3	113
Vanceboro, N.C., U.S.	B5	110
Vanceburg, Ky., U.S.	B6	94
Vancleave, Ms., U.S.	E5	101
Vancouver, B.C., Can.	E6	69
Vancouver, Wa., U.S.	D3	124
Vancouver, Cape, c., Austl.	G3	50
Vancouver Island, i., B.C., Can.	E4	69
Vancouver Island Ranges, mts., B.C., Can.	D4	69
Vandalia, Il., U.S.	E4	90
Vandalia, Mo., U.S.	B6	102
Vandenberg Air Force Base, mil., Ca., U.S.	E3	82
Vander, N.C., U.S.	B4	110
Vanderbilt Peak, mtn., N.M., U.S.	E1	108
Vanderburgh, co., In., U.S.	H2	91
Vandergrift, Pa., U.S.	E2	115
Vanderhoof, B.C., Can.	C5	69
Van Diemen Gulf, b., Austl.	B6	50
Vänern, l., Swe.	G9	6
Vänersborg, Swe.	G9	6
Vangaindrano, Madag.	F9	44
Van Gölü, l., Tur.	H16	4
Vangunu, i., Sol.Is.	A11	50
Van Horn, Tx., U.S.	o12	120
Van Horne, Ia., U.S.	B5	92
Vanier, Ont., Can.	h12	73
Vāniyambādi, India	F5	37
Vankarem, U.S.S.R.	D30	20
Vankleek Hill, Ont., Can.	B10	73
Van Kull, Kill, stm., N.J., U.S.	k8	107
Van Lear, Ky., U.S.	C7	94
Van Meter, Ia., U.S.	C4	92
Vännäs, Swe.	E12	6
Vannes, Fr.	E4	10
Van Rees, Pegunungan, mts., Indon.	F10	32
Vanrhynsdorp, S. Afr.	H3	44
Vansant, Va., U.S.	e9	123
Vansbro, Swe.	F10	6
Vansittart Island, i., N.W. Ter., Can.	C16	66
Vanuatu, ctry., Oc.	H24	2
Van Vleck, Tx., U.S.	r14	120
Van Wert, Oh., U.S.	B1	112
Van Wert, co., Oh., U.S.	B1	112
Van Zandt, co., Tx., U.S.	C5	120
Varades, Fr.	E5	10
Vārānasi (Benares), India	H10	38
Varaždin, Yugo.	C11	14
Varazze, Italy	E3	14
Varberg, Swe.	H9	6
Vardaman, Ms., U.S.	B4	101
Vardar (Axiós), stm., Eur.	H6	16
Vardø, Nor.	A18	6
Varennes, Que., Can.	D4	74
Varennes-sur-Allier, Fr.	F10	10
Varese, Italy	D3	14
Varginha, Braz.	F6	57
Varina, Va., U.S.	C5	123
Varkaus, Fin.	E16	6
Varkhān, stm., Afg.	D1	38
Varna, Bul.	F11	16
Värnamo, Swe.	H10	6
Varnville, S.C., U.S.	F5	117
Varzy, Fr.	E10	10
Vasai (Bassein), India	C2	37
Vashon, Point, c., Wa., U.S.	e11	124
Vashon Island, i., Wa., U.S.	f11	124
Vass, N.C., U.S.	B3	110
Vassar, Mi., U.S.	E7	99
Västerås, Swe.	G11	6
Västervik, Swe.	H11	6
Vasto, Italy	G9	14
Vas'ugan, stm., U.S.S.R.	F9	20
Vatican City (Città del Vaticano), ctry., Eur.	H7	14
Vatnajökull, Ice.	C4	4
Vättern, l., Swe.	G10	6
Vaucouleurs, Fr.	D12	10
Vaudreuil, Que., Can.	D3	74
Vaughan, Ont., Can.	D5	73
Vaughn, Mt., U.S.	C5	103
Vaughn, N.M., U.S.	C4	108
Vaupés (Uaupés), stm., S.A.	G7	58
Vauxhall, Alta., Can.	D4	68
Växjö, Swe.	H10	6
Vazante, Braz.	D5	57
V'azemskij, U.S.S.R.	H20	20
V'az'ma, U.S.S.R.	F17	22
V'azniki, U.S.S.R.	E25	22
Veazie, Me., U.S.	D4	96
Vechta, Ger.	C8	8
Veedersburg, In., U.S.	D3	91
Veendam, Neth.	B6	8
Vegreville, Alta., Can.	C4	68
Vejer de la Frontera, Spain	I6	12
Vejle, Den.	I7	6
Vela Luka, Yugo.	G11	14
Velda Rose Estates, Az., U.S.	D4	80
Velenje, Yugo.	C10	14
Vélez-Málaga, Spain	I7	12
Vélez Rubio, Spain	H9	12
Velhas, Rio das, stm., Braz.	D6	57
Velike Lašče, Yugo.	D9	14
Velikije Luki, U.S.S.R.	E13	22
Veliko Tărnovo, Bul.	F9	16
Vella Lavella, i., Sol.Is.	A11	50
Velletri, Italy	H7	14
Vellore, India	F5	37
Velma, Ok., U.S.	C4	113
Velva, N.D., U.S.	A5	111
Venado Tuerto, Arg.	C4	56
Venango, co., Pa., U.S.	D2	115
Venda Nova, Braz.	E7	57
Vendeuvre-sur-Barse, Fr.	D11	10
Vendôme, Fr.	E8	10
Veneta, Or., U.S.	C3	114
Venezia (Venice), Italy	D7	14
Venezuela, ctry., S.A.	B5	54
Venezuela, Golfo de, b., S.A.	B7	58
Veniaminof, Mount, mtn., Ak., U.S.	D8	79
Venice, Fl., U.S.	E4	86
Venice, Il., U.S.	E3	90
Venice, Gulf of, b., Eur.	D7	14
Venice see Venezia, Italy	D7	14
Vénissieux, Fr.	G11	10
Venlo, Neth.	D6	8
Venosa, Italy	I10	14
Ventanas, Ec.	H3	58
Ventnor City, N.J., U.S.	E4	107
Ventspils, U.S.S.R.	D4	22
Ventuari, stm., Ven.	E9	58
Ventura (San Buenaventura), Ca., U.S.	E4	82
Ventura, co., Ca., U.S.	E4	82
Venustiano Carranza, Mex.	I13	62
Vera, Spain	H10	12
Veracruz [Llave], Mex.	H11	62
Verāval, India	J4	38
Verbania, Italy	D3	14
Vercelli, Italy	D3	14
Verchères, Que., Can.	D4	74
Verchn'aja Amga, U.S.S.R.	F19	20
Verchneimbatskoje, U.S.S.R.	E11	20
Verchojansk, U.S.S.R.	D20	20
Verchojanskij Chrebet, mts., U.S.S.R.	D19	20
Verda, Ky., U.S.	D6	94
Verde, stm., Az., U.S.	C4	80
Verden, Ger.	C9	8
Verdi, Nv., U.S.	D2	105
Verdigre, Ne., U.S.	B7	104
Verdigris, Ok., U.S.	A6	113
Verdigris, stm., U.S.	A6	113
Verdi Peak, mtn., Nv., U.S.	C6	105
Verdun, Que., Can.	q19	74
Verdun, Fr.	C12	10
Vereeniging, S. Afr.	G5	44
Vergara, Spain	B9	12
Vergennes, Vt., U.S.	C2	122
Veríssimo, Braz.	E4	57
Vermilion, Alta., Can.	C5	68
Vermilion, Oh., U.S.	A3	112
Vermilion, co., Il., U.S.	C6	90
Vermilion, co., La., U.S.	E3	95
Vermilion, stm., Alta., Can.	C5	68
Vermilion, stm., Il., U.S.	C5	90
Vermilion, stm., La., U.S.	E3	95
Vermilion, stm., Mn., U.S.	B6	100
Vermilion, stm., Oh., U.S.	A3	112
Vermilion Bay, b., La., U.S.	E3	95
Vermilion Lake, l., Mn., U.S.	C6	100
Vermilion Pass, Can.	D2	68
Vermillion, S.D., U.S.	E9	118
Vermillion, co., In., U.S.	E2	91
Vermillion, East Fork, stm., S.D., U.S.	D8	118
Vermillon, stm., Que., Can.	B4	74
Vermont, Il., U.S.	C3	90
Vermont, state, U.S.	D3	122
Vermontville, Mi., U.S.	F5	99
Vernal, Ut., U.S.	C6	121
Verneuil-sur-Avre, Fr.	D7	10
Vernon, B.C., Can.	D8	69
Vernon, Fr.	C8	10
Vernon, Al., U.S.	B1	78
Vernon, Tx., U.S.	B3	120
Vernon, co., La., U.S.	C2	95
Vernon, co., Mo., U.S.	D3	102
Vernon, co., Wi., U.S.	E3	126
Vernon Hills, Il., U.S.	h9	90
Vernonia, Or., U.S.	B3	114
Vero Beach, Fl., U.S.	E6	86
Véroia, Grc.	I6	16
Verona, Ont., Can.	C8	73
Verona, Italy	D6	14
Verona, Ms., U.S.	A5	101
Verona, N.J., U.S.	B4	107
Verona, Pa., U.S.	k14	115
Verona, Wi., U.S.	F4	126
Verret, Lake, l., La., U.S.	E4	95
Versailles, Fr.	D9	10
Versailles, In., U.S.	F7	91
Versailles, Ky., U.S.	B5	94
Versailles, Mo., U.S.	C5	102
Versailles, Oh., U.S.	B1	112
Vert, Cap, c., Sen.	F2	42
Vertientes, Cuba	D8	64
Vertou, Fr.	E5	10
Verviers, Bel.	E5	8
Vesoul, Fr.	E13	10
Vestal, N.Y., U.S.	C4	109
Vestavia Hills, Al., U.S.	g7	78
Vestmannaeyjar, Ice.	C3	4
Vesuvio, vol., Italy	I9	14
Vesuvius see Vesuvio, vol., Italy	I9	14
Veszprém, Hung.	H17	8
Vetlanda, Swe.	H10	6
Vevay, In., U.S.	G7	91
Vevey, Switz.	F13	10
Veynes, Fr.	H12	10
Viadana, Italy	E5	14
Vian, Ok., U.S.	B7	113
Viana del Bollo, Spain	C4	12
Viana do Alentejo, Port.	G3	12
Viana do Castelo, Port.	D3	12
Viangchan, Laos	F7	34
Viareggio, Italy	F5	14
Viborg, Den.	H7	6
Viborg, S.D., U.S.	D8	118
Vibo Valentia, Italy	K11	14
Viburnum, Mo., U.S.	D6	102
Vic-en-Bigorre, Fr.	I7	10
Vicente, Point, c., Ca., U.S.	n12	82
Vicenza, Italy	D6	14
Vich, Spain	D14	12
Vichada, stm., Col.	E8	58
Vichy, Fr.	F10	10
Vici, Ok., U.S.	A2	113
Vicksburg, Mi., U.S.	F5	99
Vicksburg, Ms., U.S.	C3	101
Vicksburg National Military Park, Ms., U.S.	C3	101
Viçosa, Braz.	F7	57
Victor, Ia., U.S.	C5	92
Victor, N.Y., U.S.	C3	109
Victoria, B.C., Can.	E6	69
Victoria, Newf., Can.	E5	72
Victoria (Xianggang), H.K.	M3	28
Victoria, Sey.	B11	44
Victoria, Ks., U.S.	D4	93
Victoria, Tx., U.S.	E4	120
Victoria, Va., U.S.	D4	123
Victoria, state, Austl.	G9	50
Victoria, co., Tx., U.S.	E4	120
Victoria, Lake, l., Afr.	B6	44
Victoria, Mount, mtn., Burma	D2	34
Victoria de las Tunas, Cuba	D9	64
Victoria Falls, wtfl, Afr.	E5	44
Victoria Harbour, Ont., Can.	C5	73
Victoria Island, i., N.W. Ter., Can.	B10	66
Victoria Lake, res., Newf., Can.	D3	72
Victoria Land, reg., Ant.	B28	47
Victoria Nile, stm., Ug.	H12	42
Victoria Peak, mtn., Belize	F3	64
Victoria Strait, strt., N.W. Ter., Can.	C12	66
Victoriaville, Que., Can.	C6	74
Victoria West, S. Afr.	H4	44
Victorville, Ca., U.S.	E5	82
Vičuga, U.S.S.R.	D24	22
Vidalia, Ga., U.S.	D4	87
Vidalia, La., U.S.	C4	95
Vidisha, India	I7	38
Vidor, Tx., U.S.	D5	120
Viechtach, Ger.	F12	8
Viedma, Arg.	E4	56
Viedma, Lago, l., Arg.	F2	56
Viella, Spain	C12	12
Vienna, Ga., U.S.	D3	87
Vienna, Il., U.S.	F5	90
Vienna, Mo., U.S.	C6	102
Vienna, Va., U.S.	B5	123
Vienna, W.V., U.S.	B3	125
Vienna see Wien, Aus.	G16	8
Vienne, Fr.	G11	10
Vientiane see Viangchan, Laos	F7	34
Vieques, Isla de, i., P.R.	E15	64
Vieremä, Fin.	E16	6
Vierwaldstätter See, l., Switz.	F15	10
Vierzon, Fr.	E9	10
Vieste, Italy	H11	14
Vietnam, ctry., Asia	B4	32
Vieux Desert, Lac, l., Wi., U.S.	B4	126
Vigan, Phil.	p19	33b
Vigevano, Italy	D3	14
Vignola, Italy	E5	14
Vigo, Spain	C3	12
Vigo, co., In., U.S.	F3	91
Vihti, Fin.	F15	6
Vijayawāda, India	D6	37
Vijosë (Aóös), stm., Eur.	I3	16
Vikajärvi, Fin.	C16	6
Viking, Alta., Can.	C5	68
Vila Coutinho, Moz.	D6	44
Vila do Conde, Port.	D3	12
Vila Fontes, Moz.	E7	44
Vilafranca del Panadés, Spain	D13	12
Vila Franca de Xira, Port.	G3	12
Vilanculos, Moz.	F7	44
Vila Nova de Famalicão, Port.	D3	12
Vila Nova de Foz Côa, Port.	D4	12
Vila Nova de Gaia, Port.	D3	12
Vila Pery, Moz.	E6	44
Vila Real, Port.	D4	12
Vilas, co., Wi., U.S.	B4	126
Vila Velha, Braz.	F8	57
Vila Velha de Ródão, Port.	F4	12
Vilhelmina, Swe.	D11	6
Vilhena, Braz.	F6	54
Vil'kickogo, Proliv, strt., U.S.S.R.	B14	20
Villa Ahumada, Mex.	B6	62
Villa Bella, Bol.	F5	54
Villablino, Spain	C5	12
Villa Bruzual, Ven.	C8	58
Villacañas, Spain	F8	12
Villacarriedo, Spain	B8	12
Villacarrillo, Spain	G8	12
Villach, Aus.	I13	8
Villacidro, Italy	J3	14
Villa Colón (Caucete), Arg.	C3	56
Villa del Rosario, Ven.	I11	64
Villa de Méndez, Mex.	E10	62
Villadiego, Spain	C7	12
Villafranca del Bierzo, Spain	C5	12
Villafranca de los Barros, Spain	G5	12
Villafranca di Verona, Italy	D5	14
Villa Frontera, Mex.	D9	62
Villagarcía, Spain	C3	12
Villa Grove, Il., U.S.	D5	90
Villaguay, Arg.	C5	56
Villa Hayes, Para.	B5	56
Villahermosa, Mex.	I13	62
Villajoyosa, Spain	G11	12
Villalón de Campos, Spain	C6	12
Villalonga, Arg.	D4	56
Villalpando, Spain	D6	12
Villa María, Arg.	C4	56
Villamartín, Spain	I6	12
Villa Montes, Bol.	H6	54
Villanova Monteleone, Italy	I3	14
Villanueva, Col.	B6	58
Villanueva de Córdoba, Spain	G7	12
Villanueva de la Serena, Spain	G6	12
Villanueva de los Infantes, Spain	G9	12
Villanueva del Río y Minas, Spain	H6	12
Villanueva y Geltrú, Spain	D13	12
Villa Park, Il., U.S.	k8	90
Villa Pedro Montoya, Mex.	G10	62
Villarcayo, Spain	C8	12
Villa Rica, Ga., U.S.	C2	87
Villarreal, Spain	F11	12
Villarrica, Chile	D2	56
Villarrobledo, Spain	F9	12
Villas, N.J., U.S.	E3	107
Villa San Giovanni, Italy	K10	14
Villasayas, Spain	D9	12
Villa Unión, Arg.	B4	56
Villavicencio, Col.	E6	58
Villaviciosa de Córdoba, Spain	G6	12
Villedieu, Fr.	D5	10
Villefort, Fr.	H10	10
Villefranche, Fr.	G11	10
Villefranche-de-Rouergue, Fr.	H9	10
Villena, Spain	G11	12
Villeneuve-de-Berg, Fr.	H11	10
Villeneuve-Saint-Georges, Fr.	D9	10
Villeneuve-sur-Lot, Fr.	H7	10
Ville Platte, La., U.S.	D3	95
Villers-Bocage, Fr.	C6	10
Villers-Cotterêts, Fr.	C10	10
Ville Saint-Georges, Que., Can.	C7	74
Villeurbanne, Fr.	G11	10
Villingen-Schwenningen, Ger.	G8	8
Villisca, Ia., U.S.	D3	92
Villupuram, India	G5	37
Vilnius, U.S.S.R.	G8	22
Vilonia, Ar., U.S.	B3	81
Vilsbiburg, Ger.	G12	8
Vil'uj, stm., U.S.S.R.	E18	20
Vil'ujsk, U.S.S.R.	E18	20
Vimianzo, Spain	B2	12
Vimoutiers, Fr.	D7	10
Vina, stm., Cam.	G8	42
Viña del Mar, Chile	C2	56
Vinalhaven, Me., U.S.	D4	96
Vinalhaven Island, i., Me., U.S.	D4	96
Vinaroz, Spain	E12	12
Vincennes, In., U.S.	G2	91
Vincent, Al., U.S.	B3	78
Vinces, Ec.	H3	58
Vindeln, Swe.	D12	6
Vindhya Range, mts., India	I7	38
Vine Brook, stm., Ma., U.S.	g11	98
Vinegar Hill, mtn., Or., U.S.	C8	114
Vine Grove, Ky., U.S.	C4	94
Vineland, N.J., U.S.	E2	107
Vineyard Haven, Ma., U.S.	D6	98
Vineyard Sound, strt., Ma., U.S.	D6	98
Vinh, Viet.	E8	34
Vinhais, Port.	D4	12
Vinh Long, Viet.	I8	34
Vinita, Ok., U.S.	A6	113
Vinkovci, Yugo.	D2	16
Vinnica, U.S.S.R.	H3	18
Vinnitsa see Vinnica, U.S.S.R.	H3	18
Vinson Massif, mtn., Ant.	B4	47
Vinton, Ia., U.S.	B5	92
Vinton, La., U.S.	D2	95
Vinton, Va., U.S.	C3	123
Vinton, co., Oh., U.S.	C3	112

Name — Map Ref — Page

Viola, Il., U.S. **B3** 90
Violet, La., U.S. **k12** 95
Vipava, Yugo. **D8** 14
Vipiteno, Italy **C6** 14
Virac, Phil. **C7** 32
Viramgām, India **I5** 38
Viranşehir, Tur. **A6** 40
Virden, Man., Can. **E1** 70
Virden, Il., U.S. **D4** 90
Vire, Fr. **D6** 10
Virgin, stm., U.S. **G8** 105
Virginia, S. Afr. **G5** 44
Virginia, Al., U.S. **g6** 78
Virginia, Il., U.S. **D3** 90
Virginia, Mn., U.S. **C6** 100
Virginia, state, U.S. **C4** 123
Virginia Beach, Va., U.S. **D7** 123
Virginia City, Nv., U.S. **D2** 105
Virginia Peak, mtn., Nv., U.S. **D2** 105
Virgin Islands, dep., N.A. **E15** 64
Virje, Yugo. **C11** 14
Virkie, Scot., U.K. **B11** 7
Viroqua, Wi., U.S. **E3** 126
Virovitica, Yugo. **D12** 14
Virtaniemi, Fin. **B17** 6
Virudunagar, India **H4** 37
Vis, Yugo. **F11** 14
Visalia, Ca., U.S. **D4** 82
Visby, Swe. **H12** 6
Viscount Melville Sound, strt., N.W. Ter., Can. **B10** 66
Viseu, Port. **E4** 12
Vishākhapatnam, India **D7** 37
Vislinskij Zaliv, b., Eur. **A19** 8
Visnagar, India **I5** 38
Vista, Ca., U.S. **F5** 82
Vistula see Wisła, stm., Pol. **A18** 8
Vitarte, Peru **F3** 54
Vitebsk, U.S.S.R. **F13** 22
Viterbo, Italy **G7** 14
Vitigudino, Spain **D5** 12
Vitim, U.S.S.R. **F16** 20
Vitim, stm., U.S.S.R. **F16** 20
Vitória, Braz. **F8** 57
Vitoria, Spain **C9** 12
Vitória da Conquista, Braz. **C8** 57
Vitré, Fr. **D5** 10
Vitry-le-François, Fr. **D11** 10
Vitteaux, Fr. **E11** 10
Vittel, Fr. **D12** 10
Vittoria, Italy **M9** 14
Vittorio Veneto, Italy **D7** 14
Viver, Spain **F11** 12
Vivero, Spain **B4** 12
Vivian, La., U.S. **B2** 95
Viviers, Fr. **H11** 10
Vivonne, Fr. **F7** 10
Vizcachas, Meseta de las, plat., Arg. **G2** 56
Vizcaíno, Desierto de, des., Mex. **D3** 62
Vizianagaram, India **C7** 37
Vizille, Fr. **G12** 10
Vlaardingen, Neth. **D4** 8
Vladikavkaz, U.S.S.R. **I6** 18
Vladimir, U.S.S.R. **E23** 22
Vladivostok, U.S.S.R. **E35** 128
Vlissingen (Flushing), Neth. **D3** 8
Vlorë, Alb. **I3** 16
Vltava, stm., Czech. **F14** 8
Vöcklabruck, Aus. **G13** 8
Vodnjan, Yugo. **E8** 14
Vogelsberg, mts., Ger. **E9** 8
Voghera, Italy **E4** 14
Vohenstrauss, Ger. **F12** 8
Vohibinany, Madag. **E9** 44
Vohimarina, Madag. **D10** 44
Voi, Kenya **B7** 44
Voinjama, Lib. **G4** 42
Voiron, Fr. **G12** 10
Voitsberg, Aus. **H15** 8
Volcano, Hi., U.S. **D6** 88
Volchov, U.S.S.R. **B15** 22
Volda, Nor. **E6** 6
Volga, S.D., U.S. **C9** 118
Volga, stm., U.S.S.R. **H7** 18
Volgograd (Stalingrad), U.S.S.R. **H6** 18
Volkovysk, U.S.S.R. **H7** 22
Voločanka, U.S.S.R. **C12** 20
Vologda, U.S.S.R. **B22** 22
Volokolamsk, U.S.S.R. **E18** 22
Vólos, Grc. **J6** 16
Volta, Lake, res., Ghana **G5** 42
Volta Blanche (White Volta), stm., Afr. **F5** 42
Volta Noire (Black Volta), stm., Afr. **F6** 42
Volta Redonda, Braz. **G6** 57
Volterra, Italy **F5** 14
Volusia, co., Fl., U.S. **C5** 86
Volžskij, U.S.S.R. **H6** 18
Von Frank Mountain, mtn., Ak., U.S. **C9** 79
Vonore, Tn., U.S. **D9** 119
Voríai Sporádhes, is., Grc. **J7** 16
Voronež, U.S.S.R. **G5** 18
Voronezh see Voronež, U.S.S.R. **G5** 18
Vosges, mts., Fr. **D14** 10
Voskresensk, U.S.S.R. **F21** 22
Voss, Nor. **F6** 6
Vostočno-Sibirskoje More (East Siberian Sea), U.S.S.R. **C25** 20
Vostočnyj Sajan, mts., U.S.S.R. **G13** 20
Votkinsk, U.S.S.R. **F8** 18
Votuporanga, Braz. **F4** 57
Vouziers, Fr. **C11** 10
Voyageurs National Park, Mn., U.S. **B5** 100
Vraca, Bul. **F7** 16
Vrangel'a, Ostrov, i., U.S.S.R. **C29** 20
Vranje, Yugo. **G5** 16
Vrhnika, Yugo. **D9** 14
Vryburg, S. Afr. **G4** 44
Vryheid, S. Afr. **G6** 44
Vsevidof, Mount, mtn., Ak., U.S. **E6** 79
Vsevoložsk, U.S.S.R. **A13** 22
Vukovar, Yugo. **D2** 16
Vulcan, Alta., Can. **D4** 68
Vung Tau (Cap-St.-Jacques), Viet. **I9** 34
Vuoggatjålme, Swe. **C11** 6
Vuoksenniska, Fin. **F17** 6
Vyborg, U.S.S.R. **A11** 22
Vyška, U.S.S.R. **D18** 22
Vyšnij Voloček, U.S.S.R. **D17** 22
Vysokogornyj, U.S.S.R. **G21** 20

W

Wa, Ghana **F5** 42
Waawaa, Puu, mtn., Hi., U.S. **D6** 88
Wabana (Bell Island), Newf., Can. **E5** 72
Wabasca, Alta., Can. **B4** 68
Wabasca, stm., Alta., Can. **f1** 68
Wabash, In., U.S. **C6** 91
Wabash, co., Il., U.S. **E6** 90
Wabash, co., In., U.S. **C6** 91
Wabash, stm., U.S. **H2** 91
Wabasha, Mn., U.S. **F6** 100
Wabasha, co., Mn., U.S. **F6** 100
Wabasso, Fl., U.S. **E6** 86
Wabasso, Mn., U.S. **F3** 100
Wabaunsee, co., Ks., U.S. **D7** 93
Wabeno, Wi., U.S. **C5** 126
Wabowden, Man., Can. **B2** 70
Wabush, Newf., Can. **h8** 72
Waccamaw, stm., U.S. **D9** 117
Waccamaw, Lake, l., N.C., U.S. **C4** 110
Waccasassa Bay, b., Fl., U.S. **C4** 86
Wachusett Mountain, mtn., Ma., U.S. **B4** 98
Wachusett Reservoir, res., Ma., U.S. **B4** 98
Waco, Tx., U.S. **D4** 120
Waco Lake, res., Tx., U.S. **D4** 120
Waconda Lake, res., Ks., U.S. **C5** 93
Waconia, Mn., U.S. **F5** 100
Waddeneilanden, is., Neth. **B5** 8
Waddenzee, Neth. **B5** 8
Waddi, Chappal, mtn., Nig. **G8** 42
Waddington, Mount, mtn., B.C., Can. **D5** 69
Wadena, Mn., U.S. **D3** 100
Wadena, co., Mn., U.S. **D4** 100
Wädenswil, Switz. **E15** 10
Wadesboro, N.C., U.S. **C2** 110
Wādī Halfā', Sudan **D12** 42
Wading, stm., N.J., U.S. **D3** 107
Wadley, Ga., U.S. **D4** 87
Wad Madanī, Sudan **F12** 42
Wadmalaw Island, i., S.C., U.S. **F7** 117
Wadsworth, Il., U.S. **h9** 90
Wadsworth, Nv., U.S. **D2** 105
Wadsworth, Oh., U.S. **A4** 112
Wagener, S.C., U.S. **D5** 117
Wageningen, Neth. **D5** 8
Wager Bay, b., N.W. Ter., Can. **C15** 66
Wagga Wagga, Austl. **G9** 50
Wagin, Austl. **F3** 50
Wagner, S.D., U.S. **D7** 118
Wagoner, Ok., U.S. **B6** 113
Wagoner, co., Ok., U.S. **B6** 113
Wagontire Mountain, mtn., Or., U.S. **D7** 114
Wągrowiec, Pol. **C17** 8
Wah, Pak. **D5** 38
Waha, Libya **C9** 42
Wahiawa, Hi., U.S. **B3** 88
Wahiawa Reservoir, res., Hi., U.S. **g9** 88
Wahkiakum, co., Wa., U.S. **C2** 124
Wahoo, Ne., U.S. **C9** 104
Wahpeton, N.D., U.S. **C9** 111
Wahweap Creek, stm., Ut., U.S. **F4** 121
Waialua, Hi., U.S. **B3** 88
Waialua Bay, b., Hi., U.S. **B3** 88
Waianae, Hi., U.S. **B3** 88
Waianae Range, mts., Hi., U.S. **f9** 88
Waidhofen an der Ybbs, Aus. **H14** 8
Waigeo, Pulau, i., Indon. **F9** 32
Waihi, N.Z. **B5** 52
Waikapu, Hi., U.S. **C5** 88
Waikiki Beach, Hi., U.S. **g10** 88
Wailua, Hi., U.S. **A2** 88
Wailuku, Hi., U.S. **C5** 88
Waimanalo, Hi., U.S. **B4** 88
Waimanalo Bay, b., Hi., U.S. **g11** 88
Waimea, Hi., U.S. **B2** 88
Waimea, Hi., U.S. **f9** 88
Wainwright, Alta., Can. **C5** 68
Wainwright, Ak., U.S. **A8** 79
Waipahu, Hi., U.S. **B3** 88
Waipio Acres, Hi., U.S. **g9** 88
Waipio Peninsula, pen., Hi., U.S. **g10** 88
Waipukurau, N.Z. **D6** 52
Waite Park, Mn., U.S. **E4** 100
Waits, stm., Vt., U.S. **C4** 122
Waitsburg, Wa., U.S. **C7** 124
Wajir, Kenya **H3** 46
Wakarusa, In., U.S. **A5** 91
Wakarusa, stm., Ks., U.S. **D8** 93
Wakasa-wan, b., Japan **G8** 30
Wakatomika Creek, stm., Oh., U.S. **B3** 112
Wakayama, Japan **H8** 30
Wake, co., N.C., U.S. **B4** 110
Wa Keeney, Ks., U.S. **C4** 93
Wakefield, Que., Can. **D2** 74
Wakefield, Ks., U.S. **C6** 93
Wakefield, Ma., U.S. **B5** 98
Wakefield, Mi., U.S. **n12** 99
Wakefield, Ne., U.S. **B9** 104
Wakefield, R.I., U.S. **F3** 116
Wakefield, Va., U.S. **D6** 123
Wake Forest, N.C., U.S. **B4** 110
Wake Island, dep., Oc. **E24** 2
Wakema, Burma **F3** 34
Wakeman, Oh., U.S. **A3** 112
Wakkanai, Japan **n19** 30a
Wakulla, co., Fl., U.S. **B2** 86
Walbridge, Oh., U.S. **e6** 112
Wałbrzych (Waldenburg), Pol. **E16** 8
Walcott, Ia., U.S. **C7** 92
Walcott, Lake, res., Id., U.S. **G5** 89
Walden, Ont., Can. **A3** 73
Walden, Co., U.S. **A4** 83
Walden, N.Y., U.S. **D6** 109
Walden Ridge, mtn., Tn., U.S. **D8** 119
Waldheim, Sask., Can. **E2** 75
Waldo, Ar., U.S. **D2** 81
Waldo, co., Me., U.S. **D3** 96
Waldoboro, Me., U.S. **D3** 96
Waldo Lake, l., Ma., U.S. **h11** 98
Waldo Lake, l., Or., U.S. **D4** 114
Waldport, Or., U.S. **C2** 114
Waldron, Ar., U.S. **C1** 81
Waldron, In., U.S. **F6** 91
Waldshut, Ger. **H8** 8
Waldwick, N.J., U.S. **A4** 107
Wales, ter., U.K. **I9** 7
Wales Island, i., N.W. Ter., Can. **C15** 66
Waleska, Ga., U.S. **B2** 87
Walgett, Austl. **E9** 50
Walhalla, N.D., U.S. **A8** 111
Walhalla, S.C., U.S. **B1** 117
Walhonding, stm., Oh., U.S. **B3** 112
Walker, Ia., U.S. **B6** 92
Walker, La., U.S. **g10** 95
Walker, Mi., U.S. **E5** 99
Walker, Mn., U.S. **C4** 100
Walker, co., Al., U.S. **B2** 78
Walker, co., Ga., U.S. **B1** 87
Walker, co., Tx., U.S. **D5** 120
Walker, stm., Nv., U.S. **D3** 105
Walker Lake, l., Nv., U.S. **E3** 105
Walker River Indian Reservation, Nv., U.S. **D3** 105
Walkersville, Md., U.S. **B3** 97
Walkerton, Ont., Can. **C3** 73
Walkerton, In., U.S. **B5** 91
Walkertown, N.C., U.S. **A2** 110
Walkerville, Mt., U.S. **D4** 103
Wall, S.D., U.S. **D3** 118
Wallace, Id., U.S. **B3** 89
Wallace, N.C., U.S. **C5** 110
Wallace, co., Ks., U.S. **D2** 93
Wallaceburg, Ont., Can. **E2** 73
Wallace Lake, res., La., U.S. **B2** 95
Walla Walla, Wa., U.S. **C7** 124
Walla Walla, co., Wa., U.S. **C7** 124
Walla Walla, stm., U.S. **C7** 124
Walled Lake, Mi., U.S. **o15** 99
Wallen, In., U.S. **B7** 91
Wallenpaupack, Lake, l., Pa., U.S. **D11** 115
Waller, Tx., U.S. **q14** 120
Waller, co., Tx., U.S. **E4** 120
Wallingford, Ct., U.S. **D4** 84
Wallingford, Vt., U.S. **E3** 122
Wallington, N.J., U.S. **h8** 107
Wallis and Futuna, dep., Oc. **G1** 2
Wallkill, N.Y., U.S. **D6** 109
Wallkill, stm., N.Y., U.S. **D6** 109
Wall Lake, Ia., U.S. **B2** 92
Wall Lake, l., Ia., U.S. **B4** 92
Walloomsac, stm., U.S. **F2** 122
Walloon Lake, l., Mi., U.S. **C6** 99
Wallowa, Or., U.S. **B9** 114
Wallowa, co., Or., U.S. **B9** 114
Wallowa Mountains, mts., Or., U.S. **B9** 114
Wallula, Lake, res., U.S. **C7** 124
Wallum Lake, l., U.S. **A1** 116
Walnut, Il., U.S. **B4** 90
Walnut, Ia., U.S. **C2** 92
Walnut, stm., Ks., U.S. **E6** 93
Walnut Canyon National Monument, Az., U.S. **B4** 80
Walnut Cove, N.C., U.S. **A2** 110
Walnut Creek, Ca., U.S. **h8** 82
Walnut Creek, stm., Ks., U.S. **D4** 93
Walnut Grove, Al., U.S. **A3** 78
Walnut Grove, Mn., U.S. **F3** 100
Walnutport, Pa., U.S. **E10** 115
Walnut Ridge, Ar., U.S. **A5** 81
Walpole, Ma., U.S. **B5** 98
Walpole, N.H., U.S. **D2** 106
Walsall, Eng., U.K. **I11** 7
Walsenburg, Co., U.S. **D6** 83
Walsh, Co., U.S. **D8** 83
Walsh, co., N.D., U.S. **A8** 111
Walsrode, Ger. **C9** 8
Walterboro, S.C., U.S. **F6** 117
Walter F. George Dam, U.S. **D4** 78
Walter F. George Lake, res., U.S. **D4** 78
Walters, Ok., U.S. **C3** 113
Walthall, co., Ms., U.S. **D3** 101
Waltham, Ma., U.S. **B5** 98
Walthill, Ne., U.S. **B9** 104
Walthourville, Ga., U.S. **E5** 87
Walton, In., U.S. **C5** 91
Walton, Ky., U.S. **B5** 94
Walton, N.Y., U.S. **C5** 109
Walton, co., Fl., U.S. **u15** 86
Walton, co., Ga., U.S. **C3** 87
Walvisbaai (Walvis Bay), S. Afr. **F2** 44
Walworth, Wi., U.S. **F5** 126
Walworth, co., S.D., U.S. **B5** 118
Walworth, co., Wi., U.S. **F5** 126
Wamac, Il., U.S. **E4** 90
Wamba, stm., Afr. **C3** 44
Wamego, Ks., U.S. **C7** 93
Wamesit, Ma., U.S. **A5** 98
Wamsutter, Wy., U.S. **E5** 127
Wanaka, N.Z. **F2** 52
Wanamingo, Mn., U.S. **F6** 100
Wanapum Dam, Wa., U.S. **C6** 124
Wanapum Lake, res., Wa., U.S. **B6** 124
Wanaque, N.J., U.S. **A4** 107
Wanaque Reservoir, res., N.J., U.S. **A4** 107
Wanatah, In., U.S. **B4** 91
Wanchese, N.C., U.S. **B7** 110
Wando, stm., S.C., U.S. **F8** 117
Wando Woods, S.C., U.S. **k11** 117
Wanganui, N.Z. **C5** 52
Wanganui, stm., N.Z. **C5** 52
Wangaratta, Austl. **G9** 50
Wangen [im Allgäu], Ger. **H9** 8
Wangpan Yang, b., China **E10** 28
Wānkāner, India **I4** 38
Wanxian, China **E8** 26
Wapakoneta, Oh., U.S. **B1** 112
Wapato, Wa., U.S. **C5** 124
Wapawekka Lake, l., Sask., Can. **C3** 75
Wapello, Ia., U.S. **C6** 92
Wapello, co., Ia., U.S. **C5** 92
Wapiti, stm., Can. **B1** 68
Wappapello, Lake, res., Mo., U.S. **D7** 102
Wappingers Falls, N.Y., U.S. **D7** 109
Wapsipinicon, stm., Ia., U.S. **B6** 92
War, W.V., U.S. **D3** 125
Waramaug, Lake, l., Ct., U.S. **C2** 84
Warangal, India **C5** 37
Ward, Ar., U.S. **B4** 81
Ward, co., N.D., U.S. **A4** 111
Ward, co., Tx., U.S. **D1** 120
Warden, Wa., U.S. **C6** 124
Wardha, India **B5** 37
Ward Mountain, mtn., Mt., U.S. **D2** 103
Ware, Ma., U.S. **B3** 98
Ware, co., Ga., U.S. **E4** 87
Ware, stm., Ma., U.S. **B3** 98
War Eagle Mountain, mtn., Id., U.S. **G2** 89
Wareham, Ma., U.S. **C6** 98
Warehouse Point, Ct., U.S. **B5** 84
Waren, Ger. **B12** 8
Warendorf, Ger. **D7** 8
Ware Shoals, S.C., U.S. **C3** 117
Warfield, B.C., Can. **E9** 69
Warminster, Eng., U.K. **J10** 7
Warminster, Pa., U.S. **F11** 115
Warm Springs Indian Reservation, Or., U.S. **C5** 114
Warm Springs Reservoir, res., Or., U.S. **D8** 114
Warnemünde, Ger. **A12** 8
Warner, N.H., U.S. **D3** 106
Warner, Ok., U.S. **B6** 113
Warner, stm., N.H., U.S. **D3** 106
Warner Mountains, mts., Ca., U.S. **B3** 82
Warner Peak, mtn., Or., U.S. **E7** 114
Warner Robins, Ga., U.S. **D3** 87
Warr Acres, Ok., U.S. **B4** 113
Warren, Ar., U.S. **D3** 81
Warren, Il., U.S. **A4** 90
Warren, In., U.S. **C7** 91
Warren, Ma., U.S. **B3** 98
Warren, Mi., U.S. **F7** 99
Warren, Mn., U.S. **B2** 100
Warren, Oh., U.S. **A5** 112
Warren, Or., U.S. **B4** 114
Warren, Pa., U.S. **C3** 115
Warren, R.I., U.S. **D5** 116
Warren, Vt., U.S. **C3** 122
Warren, co., Ga., U.S. **C4** 87
Warren, co., Il., U.S. **C3** 90
Warren, co., In., U.S. **D3** 91
Warren, co., Ia., U.S. **C4** 92
Warren, co., Ky., U.S. **C3** 94
Warren, co., Ms., U.S. **C3** 101
Warren, co., Mo., U.S. **C6** 102
Warren, co., N.J., U.S. **B3** 107
Warren, co., N.Y., U.S. **B7** 109
Warren, co., N.C., U.S. **A4** 110
Warren, co., Oh., U.S. **C1** 112
Warren, co., Pa., U.S. **C3** 115
Warren, co., Tn., U.S. **D8** 119
Warren, co., Va., U.S. **B4** 123
Warren, stm., U.S. **D5** 116
Warren Park, In., U.S. **k10** 91
Warren Peaks, mts., Wy., U.S. **B8** 127
Warrensburg, Il., U.S. **D4** 90
Warrensburg, Mo., U.S. **C4** 102
Warrensburg, N.Y., U.S. **B7** 109
Warrensville Heights, Oh., U.S. **h9** 112
Warrenton, S. Afr. **G4** 44
Warrenton, Ga., U.S. **C4** 87
Warrenton, Mo., U.S. **C6** 102
Warrenton, N.C., U.S. **A4** 110
Warrenton, Or., U.S. **A3** 114
Warrenton, Va., U.S. **B5** 123
Warrenville, Il., U.S. **k8** 90
Warrenville, S.C., U.S. **D4** 117
Warri, Nig. **G7** 42
Warrick, co., In., U.S. **H3** 91
Warrina, Austl. **E7** 50
Warrington, Eng., U.K. **H10** 7
Warrington, Fl., U.S. **u14** 86
Warrior, Al., U.S. **B3** 78
Warrior Lake, res., Al., U.S. **C2** 78
Warrnambool, Austl. **G8** 50
Warroad, Mn., U.S. **B3** 100
Warsaw, Il., U.S. **C2** 90
Warsaw, In., U.S. **B6** 91
Warsaw, Ky., U.S. **B5** 94
Warsaw, Mo., U.S. **C4** 102
Warsaw, N.Y., U.S. **C2** 109
Warsaw, N.C., U.S. **B4** 110
Warsaw, Va., U.S. **C6** 123
Warsaw see Warszawa, Pol. **C21** 8
Warszawa (Warsaw), Pol. **C21** 8
Warta, stm., Pol. **C15** 8
Wartburg, Tn., U.S. **C9** 119
Warthe see Warta, stm., Pol. **C15** 8
Warwick, Austl. **E10** 50
Warwick, Que., Can. **D6** 74
Warwick, Eng., U.K. **I11** 7
Warwick, Md., U.S. **B6** 97
Warwick, N.Y., U.S. **D6** 109
Warwick, R.I., U.S. **D4** 116
Wasaga Beach, Ont., Can. **C4** 73
Wasatch, co., Ut., U.S. **C4** 121
Wasco, Ca., U.S. **E4** 82
Wasco, co., Or., U.S. **B5** 114
Waseca, Mn., U.S. **F5** 100
Waseca, co., Mn., U.S. **F5** 100
Washakie, co., Wy., U.S. **C4** 127
Washakie Needles, mts., Wy., U.S. **C3** 127
Washburn, Il., U.S. **C4** 90
Washburn, Ia., U.S. **B5** 92
Washburn, Me., U.S. **B4** 96
Washburn, N.D., U.S. **B5** 111
Washburn, Wi., U.S. **B3** 126
Washburn, co., Wi., U.S. **C2** 126
Washburn, Mount, mtn., Wy., U.S. **B2** 127
Washington, D.C., U.S. **C3** 97
Washington, Ga., U.S. **C4** 87
Washington, Il., U.S. **C4** 90
Washington, In., U.S. **G3** 91
Washington, Ia., U.S. **C6** 92
Washington, Ks., U.S. **C6** 93
Washington, Ky., U.S. **B6** 94
Washington, La., U.S. **D3** 95
Washington, Ms., U.S. **D2** 101
Washington, Mo., U.S. **C6** 102
Washington, N.J., U.S. **B3** 107
Washington, N.C., U.S. **B5** 110
Washington, Pa., U.S. **F1** 115
Washington, Ut., U.S. **F2** 121
Washington, co., Al., U.S. **D1** 78
Washington, co., Ar., U.S. **A1** 81
Washington, co., Co., U.S. **B7** 83
Washington, co., Fl., U.S. **u16** 86
Washington, co., Ga., U.S. **C4** 87
Washington, co., Id., U.S. **E2** 89
Washington, co., Il., U.S. **E4** 90
Washington, co., In., U.S. **G5** 91
Washington, co., Ia., U.S. **C6** 92
Washington, co., Ks., U.S. **C6** 93
Washington, co., Ky., U.S. **C4** 94
Washington, co., La., U.S. **D5** 95
Washington, co., Me., U.S. **D5** 96
Washington, co., Md., U.S. **A2** 97
Washington, co., Mn., U.S. **E6** 100
Washington, co., Ms., U.S. **B3** 101
Washington, co., Mo., U.S. **D7** 102
Washington, co., Ne., U.S. **C9** 104
Washington, co., N.Y., U.S. **B7** 109
Washington, co., N.C., U.S. **B6** 110
Washington, co., Oh., U.S. **C4** 112
Washington, co., Ok., U.S. **A6** 113
Washington, co., Or., U.S. **B3** 114
Washington, co., Pa., U.S. **F1** 115
Washington, co., R.I., U.S. **E2** 116
Washington, co., Tn., U.S. **C11** 119
Washington, co., Tx., U.S. **D4** 120
Washington, co., Ut., U.S. **F2** 121
Washington, co., Vt., U.S. **C3** 122
Washington, co., Va., U.S. **f9** 123
Washington, co., Wi., U.S. **E5** 126
Washington, state, U.S. **B5** 124
Washington, Lake, l., Fl., U.S. **D6** 86
Washington, Lake, l., Mn., U.S. **E4** 100
Washington, Lake, l., Ms., U.S. **B3** 101
Washington, Lake, l., Wa., U.S. **e11** 124
Washington, Mount, mtn., N.H., U.S. **B4** 106
Washington Court House, Oh., U.S. **C2** 112
Washington Island, i., Wi., U.S. **C7** 126
Washington Park, Il., U.S. **E3** 90
Washington Terrace, Ut., U.S. **B4** 121
Washita, co., Ok., U.S. **B2** 113
Washita, stm., Ok., U.S. **C4** 113
Washoe, co., Nv., U.S. **C2** 105
Washoe City, Nv., U.S. **D2** 105
Washougal, Wa., U.S. **D3** 124
Washow Bay, b., Man., Can. **D3** 70
Washtenaw, co., Mi., U.S. **F7** 99
Wasilla, Ak., U.S. **C10** 79
Wasior, Indon. **F9** 32
Waskom, Tx., U.S. **C5** 120
Waspán, Nic. **G5** 64
Wasque Point, c., Ma., U.S. **D7** 98
Wassen, Switz. **F15** 10
Wassookeag, Lake, l., Me., U.S. **C3** 96
Wassuk Range, mts., Nv., U.S. **E3** 105
Wataga, Il., U.S. **B3** 90
Watauga, co., N.C., U.S. **A1** 110
Watauga, stm., Tn., U.S. **C12** 119
Watauga Lake, res., Tn., U.S. **C12** 119
Watchaug Pond, l., R.I., U.S. **F2** 116
Watch Hill Point, c., R.I., U.S. **G1** 116
Watchung, N.J., U.S. **B4** 107
Waterbury, Ct., U.S. **C3** 84
Waterbury, Vt., U.S. **C3** 122
Waterbury Center, Vt., U.S. **C3** 122
Waterbury Reservoir, res., Vt., U.S. **C3** 122
Wateree, stm., S.C., U.S. **D6** 117
Wateree Lake, res., S.C., U.S. **C6** 117
Waterford, Ire. **I5** 7
Waterford, Ct., U.S. **D7** 84
Waterford, N.Y., U.S. **C7** 109
Waterford, Pa., U.S. **C2** 115
Waterford, Wi., U.S. **F5** 126
Waterhen Lake, l., Man., Can. **C2** 70
Waterloo, Bel. **E4** 8
Waterloo, Ont., Can. **D4** 73
Waterloo, Que., Can. **D5** 74
Waterloo, Il., U.S. **E3** 90
Waterloo, In., U.S. **B7** 91
Waterloo, Ia., U.S. **B5** 92
Waterloo, N.Y., U.S. **C4** 109
Waterloo, Wi., U.S. **E5** 126
Waterman, Il., U.S. **B5** 90
Waterman Reservoir, res., R.I., U.S. **B3** 116
Waterproof, La., U.S. **C4** 95
Watersmeet, Mi., U.S. **n12** 99
Waterton Lakes National Park, Alta., Can. **E3** 68
Watertown, Ct., U.S. **C3** 84
Watertown, Ma., U.S. **g11** 98
Watertown, N.Y., U.S. **B5** 109
Watertown, S.D., U.S. **C8** 118
Watertown, Tn., U.S. **A5** 119
Watertown, Wi., U.S. **E5** 126
Water Valley, Ms., U.S. **A4** 101
Waterville, Ks., U.S. **C7** 93
Waterville, Me., U.S. **D3** 96
Waterville, Mn., U.S. **F5** 100
Waterville, N.Y., U.S. **C5** 109
Waterville, Oh., U.S. **A2** 112
Waterville, Wa., U.S. **B5** 124
Watervliet, Mi., U.S. **F4** 99
Watervliet, N.Y., U.S. **C7** 109
Watford, Ont., Can. **E3** 73
Watford City, N.D., U.S. **B2** 111
Wathena, Ks., U.S. **C9** 93
Watkins, Mn., U.S. **E4** 100
Watkins Glen, N.Y., U.S. **C4** 109
Watkinsville, Ga., U.S. **C3** 87
Watonga, Ok., U.S. **B3** 113
Watonwan, co., Mn., U.S. **F4** 100
Watonwan, stm., Mn., U.S. **G4** 100
Watseka, Il., U.S. **C6** 90
Watson Lake, Yukon, Can. **D7** 66
Watsontown, Pa., U.S. **D8** 115

Name — Map Ref — Page

Watsonville, Ca., U.S. D3 82
Watts Bar Dam, Tn., U.S. D9 119
Watts Bar Lake, res., Tn., U.S. D9 119
Wattsville, S.C., U.S. B4 117
Wattwil, Switz. E16 10
Watubela, Kepulauan, is., Indon. F9 32
Waubaushene, Ont., Can. C5 73
Waubay, S.D., U.S. B8 118
Waubay Lake, l., S.D., U.S. B8 118
Wauchula, Fl., U.S. E5 86
Wauconda, Il., U.S. h8 90
Waugh Mountain, mtn., Id., U.S. D4 89
Waukee, Ia., U.S. C4 92
Waukegan, Il., U.S. A6 90
Waukesha, Wi., U.S. F5 126
Waukesha, co., Wi., U.S. E5 126
Waukewan, Lake, l., N.H., U.S. C3 106
Waukomis, Ok., U.S. A4 113
Waukon, Ia., U.S. A6 92
Waunakee, Wi., U.S. E4 126
Wauneta, Ne., U.S. D4 104
Waungumbaug Lake, l., Ct., U.S. B6 84
Waupaca, Wi., U.S. D4 126
Waupaca, co., Wi., U.S. D5 126
Waupun, Wi., U.S. E5 126
Wauregan, Ct., U.S. C8 84
Waurika, Ok., U.S. C4 113
Waurika Lake, res., Ok., U.S. C3 113
Wausau, Wi., U.S. D4 126
Wausau, Lake, res., Wi., U.S. D4 126
Wauseon, Oh., U.S. A1 112
Waushara, co., Wi., U.S. D4 126
Wautoma, Wi., U.S. D4 126
Wauwatosa, Wi., U.S. m12 126
Wave Hill, Austl. C6 50
Waveland, Ms., U.S. E4 101
Waverley, N.S., Can. E6 71
Waverly, Il., U.S. D4 90
Waverly, Ia., U.S. B5 92
Waverly, Ks., U.S. D8 93
Waverly, Mn., U.S. E5 100
Waverly, Mo., U.S. B4 102
Waverly, Ne., U.S. D9 104
Waverly, N.Y., U.S. C4 109
Waverly, Oh., U.S. C3 112
Waverly, Tn., U.S. A4 119
Waverly, Va., U.S. C5 123
Waverly, W.V., U.S. B3 125
Waverly Hall, Ga., U.S. D2 87
Wāw, Sudan G11 42
Wawanesa, Man., Can. E2 70
Wawasee, Lake, l., In., U.S. B6 91
Wawayanda Lake, l., N.J., U.S. A4 107
Wawota, Sask., Can. H4 75
Waxahachie, Tx., U.S. C4 120
Waxhaw, N.C., U.S. C2 110
Waycross, Ga., U.S. E4 87
Wayland, Ia., U.S. C6 92
Wayland, Ma., U.S. g10 98
Wayland, Mi., U.S. F5 99
Wayland, N.Y., U.S. C3 109
Waylyn, S.C., U.S. k12 117
Waymart, Pa., U.S. C11 115
Wayne, Mi., U.S. p15 99
Wayne, Ne., U.S. B8 104
Wayne, N.J., U.S. B4 107
Wayne, W.V., U.S. C2 125
Wayne, co., Ga., U.S. E5 87
Wayne, co., Il., U.S. E5 90
Wayne, co., In., U.S. E7 91
Wayne, co., Ia., U.S. D4 92
Wayne, co., Ky., U.S. D5 94
Wayne, co., Mi., U.S. F7 99
Wayne, co., Ms., U.S. D5 101
Wayne, co., Mo., U.S. D7 102
Wayne, co., Ne., U.S. B8 104
Wayne, co., N.Y., U.S. B3 109
Wayne, co., N.C., U.S. B4 110
Wayne, co., Oh., U.S. B4 112
Wayne, co., Pa., U.S. C11 115
Wayne, co., Tn., U.S. B4 119
Wayne, co., Ut., U.S. E4 121
Wayne, co., W.V., U.S. C2 125
Wayne City, Il., U.S. E5 90
Waynesboro, Ga., U.S. C4 87
Waynesboro, Ms., U.S. D5 101
Waynesboro, Pa., U.S. G6 115
Waynesboro, Tn., U.S. B4 119
Waynesboro, Va., U.S. B4 123
Waynesburg, Oh., U.S. B4 112
Waynesburg, Pa., U.S. G1 115
Waynesville, Mo., U.S. D5 102
Waynesville, N.C., U.S. f10 110
Waynesville, Oh., U.S. C1 112
Waynetown, In., U.S. D3 91
Waynewood, Va., U.S. g12 123
Waynoka, Ok., U.S. A3 113
Wayzata, Mn., U.S. n11 100
Wazīrābād, Pak. D6 38
Weakley, co., Tn., U.S. A3 119
Weatherford, Ok., U.S. B3 113
Weatherford, Tx., U.S. C4 120
Weatherly, Pa., U.S. E10 115
Weatogue, Ct., U.S. B4 84
Weaver, Al., U.S. B4 78
Weaver Mountains, mts., Az., U.S. C3 80
Weaverville, Ca., U.S. B2 82
Weaverville, N.C., U.S. f10 110
Webb, Al., U.S. D4 78
Webb, Ms., U.S. B3 101
Webb, co., Tx., U.S. F3 120
Webb City, Mo., U.S. D3 102
Webbers Falls, Ok., U.S. B6 113
Webberville, Mi., U.S. F6 99
Webb Lake, l., Me., U.S. D2 96
Weber, co., Ut., U.S. B4 121
Weber City, Va., U.S. f9 123
Webster, Ma., U.S. B4 98
Webster, N.Y., U.S. B3 109
Webster, Pa., U.S. F2 115
Webster, S.D., U.S. B8 118
Webster, co., Ga., U.S. D2 87
Webster, co., Ia., U.S. B3 92
Webster, co., Ky., U.S. C2 94
Webster, co., La., U.S. B2 95
Webster, co., Ms., U.S. B4 101
Webster, co., Mo., U.S. D5 102
Webster, co., Ne., U.S. D7 104
Webster, co., W.V., U.S. C4 125
Webster City, Ia., U.S. B4 92
Webster Groves, Mo., U.S. f13 102
Webster Reservoir, res., Ks., U.S. C4 93
Webster Springs, W.V., U.S. C4 125
Websterville, Vt., U.S. C4 122
Weddell Sea, Ant. B8 47
Wedgeport, N.S., Can. F4 71
Wedgewood, Mo., U.S. f13 102
Wedowee, Al., U.S. B4 78
Weed, Ca., U.S. B2 82
Weed Heights, Nv., U.S. E2 105
Weedon, Que., Can. D6 74
Weedsport, N.Y., U.S. B4 109
Weedville, Pa., U.S. D5 115
Weehawken, N.J., U.S. h8 107
Weeksbury, Ky., U.S. C7 94
Weeping Water, Ne., U.S. D9 104
Wegscheid, Ger. G13 8
Weiden in der Oberpfalz, Ger. F12 8
Weifang, China D10 26
Weihai, China D11 26
Weilburg, Ger. E8 8
Weilheim, Ger. H11 8
Weimar, Ger. E11 8
Weimar, Tx., U.S. E4 120
Weiner, Ar., U.S. B5 81
Weinheim, Ger. F8 8
Weipa, Austl. B8 50
Weippe, Id., U.S. C3 89
Weir, Ks., U.S. E9 93
Weir, Lake, l., Fl., U.S. C5 86
Weirsdale, Fl., U.S. D5 86
Weirton, W.V., U.S. A4 125
Weiser, Id., U.S. E2 89
Weiser, stm., Id., U.S. E2 89
Weishi, China A3 28
Weissenburg in Bayern, Ger. F10 8
Weissenfels, Ger. D11 8
Weiss Lake, res., U.S. A4 78
Weisswasser, Ger. D14 8
Weiz, Aus. H15 8
Wejherowo, Pol. A18 8
Welch, W.V., U.S. D3 125
Welcome, Mn., U.S. G4 100
Welcome, S.C., U.S. B3 117
Weld, co., Co., U.S. A6 83
Weldon, N.C., U.S. A5 110
Weldon Spring, Mo., U.S. f12 102
Weleetka, Ok., U.S. B5 113
Welkom, S. Afr. G5 44
Welland, Ont., Can. E5 73
Wellesley, Ont., Can. D4 73
Wellesley, Ma., U.S. B5 98
Wellesley Islands, is., Austl. C7 50
Wellford, S.C., U.S. B3 117
Wellington, Ont., Can. D7 73
Wellington, N.Z. D5 52
Wellington, Co., U.S. A5 83
Wellington, Ks., U.S. E6 93
Wellington, Mo., U.S. B4 102
Wellington, Nv., U.S. E2 105
Wellington, Oh., U.S. A3 112
Wellington, Tx., U.S. B2 120
Wellington, Ut., U.S. D5 121
Wellington, Isla, i., Chile F2 56
Wellington Channel, strt., N.W. Ter., Can. A14 66
Wellman, Ia., U.S. C6 92
Wells, Me., U.S. E2 96
Wells, Mi., U.S. C3 99
Wells, Mn., U.S. G5 100
Wells, Nv., U.S. B7 105
Wells, co., In., U.S. C7 91
Wells, co., N.D., U.S. B6 111
Wells, stm., Vt., U.S. C4 122
Wellsboro, Pa., U.S. C7 115
Wellsburg, Ia., U.S. B5 92
Wellsburg, W.V., U.S. A4 125
Wellston, Oh., U.S. C3 112
Wellston, Ok., U.S. B4 113
Wellsville, Ks., U.S. D8 93
Wellsville, Mo., U.S. B6 102
Wellsville, N.Y., U.S. C3 109
Wellsville, Oh., U.S. B5 112
Wellsville, Ut., U.S. B4 121
Wellton, Az., U.S. E1 80
Wels, Aus. G14 8
Welsh, La., U.S. D3 95
Welshpool, Wales, U.K. I9 7
Wembley, Alta., Can. B1 68
Wenatchee, Wa., U.S. B5 124
Wenatchee, stm., Wa., U.S. B5 124
Wenatchee Lake, l., Wa., U.S. B5 124
Wenatchee Mountains, mts., Wa., U.S. B5 124
Wendell, Id., U.S. G4 89
Wendell, N.C., U.S. B4 110
Wendover, Ut., U.S. C1 121
Wenham, Ma., U.S. A6 98
Wenham Lake, l., Ma., U.S. f12 98
Wenona, Il., U.S. B4 90
Wenshan, China C8 34
Wentworth, Lake, l., N.H., U.S. C4 106
Wentzville, Mo., U.S. C7 102
Wenzhou, China G9 28
Weohyakapka, Lake, l., Fl., U.S. E5 86
Wernigerode, Ger. D10 8
Wertheim, Ger. F9 8
Wesel, Ger. D6 8
Weser, stm., Ger. B8 8
Weslaco, Tx., U.S. F4 120
Wesleyville, Newf., Can. D5 72
Wesleyville, Pa., U.S. B2 115
Wessel Islands, is., Austl. B7 50
Wesserunsett Lake, l., Me., U.S. D3 96
Wessington Springs, S.D., U.S. C7 118
Wesson, Ms., U.S. D3 101
West, Tx., U.S. D4 120
West, stm., Ct., U.S. D5 84
West, stm., Ma., U.S. h9 98
West, stm., Vt., U.S. E3 122
West Acton, Ma., U.S. g10 98
West Alexandria, Oh., U.S. C1 112
West Allis, Wi., U.S. m11 126
West Alton, Mo., U.S. f13 102
West Andover, Ma., U.S. A5 98
West Baden Springs, In., U.S. G4 91
West Baton Rouge, co., La., U.S. D4 95
West Bay, b., Fl., U.S. u16 86
West Bay, b., N.C., U.S. B6 110
West Bay, b., Tx., U.S. r15 120
West Bend, Ia., U.S. B3 92
West Bend, Wi., U.S. E5 126
West Bengal, state, India I12 38
West Berlin, N.J., U.S. D3 107
West-Berlin see Berlin (West), Ger. C13 8
West Billerica, Ma., U.S. f10 98
West Blocton, Al., U.S. B2 78
Westborough, Ma., U.S. B4 98
West Bountiful, Ut., U.S. C4 121
West Boylston, Ma., U.S. B4 98
West Branch, Ia., U.S. C6 92
West Branch, Mi., U.S. D6 99
West Branch Reservoir, res., Ct., U.S. B3 84
West Bridgewater, Ma., U.S. B5 98
Westbrook, Ct., U.S. D6 84
Westbrook, Me., U.S. E2 96
Westbrook, Mn., U.S. F3 100
West Burlington, Ia., U.S. D6 92
West Butte, mtn., Mt., U.S. B5 103
Westby, Wi., U.S. E3 126
West Cache Creek, stm., Ok., U.S. C3 113
West Caldwell, N.J., U.S. B4 107
West Canada Creek, stm., N.Y., U.S. B6 109
West Carroll, co., La., U.S. B4 95
West Carrollton, Oh., U.S. C1 112
West Carthage, N.Y., U.S. B5 109
Westchester, Il., U.S. k9 90
West Chester, Pa., U.S. G10 115
Westchester, co., N.Y., U.S. D7 109
West Chicago, Il., U.S. k8 90
West Chop, c., Ma., U.S. D6 98
West College Corner, In., U.S. E8 91
West Columbia, S.C., U.S. D5 117
West Columbia, Tx., U.S. E5 120
West Concord, Ma., U.S. B5 98
West Concord, Mn., U.S. F6 100
West Concord, N.C., U.S. B2 110
Westconnaug Reservoir, res., R.I., U.S. C2 116
West Cote Blanche Bay, b., La., U.S. E4 95
West Covina, Ca., U.S. m13 82
West Crossett, Ar., U.S. D4 81
West Cumberland, Me., U.S. E2 96
West Dennis, Ma., U.S. C7 98
West Des Moines, Ia., U.S. C4 92
West Elk Mountains, mts., Co., U.S. C3 83
West Elk Peak, mtn., Co., U.S. C3 83
Westerly, R.I., U.S. F1 116
Western Australia, state, Austl. D4 50
Western Desert see Gharbīyah, Aṣ-Ṣaḥrā' al-, des., Egypt C11 42
Western Ghāts, mts., India E3 37
Westernport, Md., U.S. m12 97
Western Sahara, dep., Afr. D3 42
Western Samoa, ctry., Oc. G1 2
Western Springs, Il., U.S. k9 90
Westerstede, Ger. B7 8
Westerville, Oh., U.S. B3 112
West Falkland, i., Falk. Is. G4 56
West Falmouth, Ma., U.S. C6 98
West Fargo, N.D., U.S. C9 111
West Feliciana, co., La., U.S. D4 95
Westfield, N.B., Can. D3 71
Westfield, In., U.S. D5 91
Westfield, Ma., U.S. B2 98
Westfield, N.J., U.S. B4 107
Westfield, N.Y., U.S. C1 109
Westfield, Pa., U.S. C6 115
Westfield, Wi., U.S. E4 126
Westfield, stm., Ma., U.S. B2 98
West Fork, Ar., U.S. B1 81
West Fork, stm., W.V., U.S. B4 125
West Frankfort, Il., U.S. F5 90
West Freehold, N.J., U.S. C4 107
West Friendship, Md., U.S. B4 97
Westgate, Fl., U.S. F6 86
West Grand Lake, l., Me., U.S. C5 96
West Grove, Pa., U.S. G10 115
West Hanover, Ma., U.S. h12 98
West Hartford, Ct., U.S. B4 84
West Haven, Ct., U.S. D4 84
West Hazleton, Pa., U.S. E9 115
West Helena, Ar., U.S. C5 81
West Hill Reservoir, res., Ma., U.S. B4 98
Westhope, N.D., U.S. A4 111
West Indies, is. E12 64
West Island, i., Ma., U.S. C6 98
West Jefferson, N.C., U.S. A1 110
West Jefferson, Oh., U.S. C2 112
West Jordan, Ut., U.S. C4 121
West Kingston, R.I., U.S. F3 116
West Lafayette, In., U.S. D4 91
West Lafayette, Oh., U.S. B4 112
Westlake, La., U.S. D2 95
Westlake, Oh., U.S. h9 112
West Lake, l., Me., U.S. C4 96
Westland, Mi., U.S. F7 99
West Laramie, Wy., U.S. E7 127
West Lawn, Pa., U.S. F10 115
West Lebanon, In., U.S. D3 91
West Liberty, Ia., U.S. C6 92
West Liberty, Ky., U.S. C6 94
West Liberty, Oh., U.S. B2 112
West Liberty, W.V., U.S. f8 125
West Linn, Or., U.S. B4 114
Westlock, Alta., Can. B4 68
West Long Branch, N.J., U.S. C4 107
West Lorne, Ont., Can. E3 73
West Marion, N.C., U.S. f10 110
West Medway, Ma., U.S. B5 98
West Memphis, Ar., U.S. B5 81
West Miami, Fl., U.S. s13 86
West Middlesex, Pa., U.S. D1 115
West Mifflin, Pa., U.S. F2 115
West Milton, Oh., U.S. C1 112
West Milwaukee, Wi., U.S. m12 126
Westminster, Ca., U.S. n12 82
Westminster, Co., U.S. B5 83
Westminster, Md., U.S. A4 97
Westminster, S.C., U.S. B1 117
West Monroe, La., U.S. B3 95
Westmont, Ca., U.S. n12 82
Westmont, Il., U.S. k9 90
Westmont, N.J., U.S. D2 107
Westmont, Pa., U.S. F4 115
Westmoreland, Tn., U.S. A5 119
Westmoreland, co., Pa., U.S. F2 115
Westmoreland, co., Va., U.S. B6 123
Westmorland, Ca., U.S. F6 82
West Musquash Lake, l., Me., U.S. C5 96
West Mystic, Ct., U.S. D8 84
West Newton, Pa., U.S. F2 115
West New York, N.J., U.S. h8 107
West Nishnabotna, stm., Ia., U.S. C2 92
West Norriton, Pa., U.S. o20 115
Weston, Ct., U.S. E2 84
Weston, Ma., U.S. g10 98
Weston, Mo., U.S. B3 102
Weston, Oh., U.S. A2 112
Weston, Or., U.S. B8 114
Weston, W.V., U.S. B4 125
Weston, Wi., U.S. D4 126
Weston, co., Wy., U.S. C8 127
Weston-super-Mare, Eng., U.K. J10 7
West Orange, N.J., U.S. B4 107
Westover, Md., U.S. D6 97
Westover, W.V., U.S. B5 125
Westover Air Force Base, mil., Ma., U.S. B2 98
West Palm Beach, Fl., U.S. F6 86
West Pawlet, Vt., U.S. E2 122
West Pearl, stm., La., U.S. D6 95
West Pelzer, S.C., U.S. B3 117
West Pensacola, Fl., U.S. u14 86
West Peoria, Il., U.S. C4 90
Westphalia, Mi., U.S. F6 99
West Pittsburg, Pa., U.S. E1 115
West Pittston, Pa., U.S. m17 115
West Plains, Mo., U.S. E6 102
West Point, Ca., U.S. C3 82
West Point, Ga., U.S. D1 87
West Point, Ia., U.S. D6 92
West Point, Ky., U.S. C4 94
West Point, Ms., U.S. B5 101
West Point, Ne., U.S. C9 104
West Point, N.Y., U.S. D7 109
West Point, Va., U.S. C6 123
West Point, mtn., Ak., U.S. C11 79
West Point Lake, res., U.S. C1 87
Westport, Ont., Can. C8 73
Westport, N.Z. D3 52
Westport, Ct., U.S. E2 84
Westport, In., U.S. F6 91
Westport, Wa., U.S. C1 124
West Portsmouth, Oh., U.S. D2 112
West Quoddy Head, c., Me., U.S. D6 96
Westray, i., Scot., U.K. B10 7
Westray Firth, strt., Scot., U.K. B9 7
West Reading, Pa., U.S. F10 115
West Rutland, Vt., U.S. D2 122
West Saint Paul, Mn., U.S. n12 100
West Salem, Il., U.S. E5 90
West Salem, Oh., U.S. B3 112
West Salem, Wi., U.S. E2 126
West Scarborough, Me., U.S. E2 96
West Seneca, N.Y., U.S. C2 109
West Simsbury, Ct., U.S. B4 84
West Slope, Or., U.S. g12 114
West Spanish Peak, mtn., Co., U.S. D6 83
West Springfield, Ma., U.S. B2 98
West Springfield, Va., U.S. g12 123
West Swanzey, N.H., U.S. E2 106
West Terre Haute, In., U.S. F3 91
West Thompson Lake, res., Ct., U.S. B8 84
West Union, Ia., U.S. B6 92
West Union, Oh., U.S. D2 112
West Union, W.V., U.S. B4 125
West Unity, Oh., U.S. A1 112
West University Place, Tx., U.S. r14 120
West Valley City, Ut., U.S. C4 121
West Vancouver, B.C., Can. f12 69
West Van Lear, Ky., U.S. C7 94
West View, Pa., U.S. h13 115
Westville, Il., U.S. C6 90
Westville, In., U.S. A4 91
Westville, N.H., U.S. E4 106
Westville, N.J., U.S. D2 107
Westville, Ok., U.S. A7 113
Westville Lake, res., Ma., U.S. B3 98
West Virginia, state, U.S. C4 125
West Walker, stm., U.S. E2 105
West Wareham, Ma., U.S. C6 98
West Warwick, R.I., U.S. D3 116
Westwego, La., U.S. k11 95
Westwood, Ca., U.S. B3 82
Westwood, Ks., U.S. k16 93
Westwood, Ky., U.S. B7 94
Westwood, Ma., U.S. B5 98
Westwood, N.J., U.S. B4 107
Westwood Lakes, Fl., U.S. s13 86
West Wyoming, Pa., U.S. n17 115
West Yarmouth, Ma., U.S. C7 98
West Yellowstone, Mt., U.S. F5 103
West York, Pa., U.S. G8 115
Wetar, Pulau, i., Indon. G8 32
Wetaskiwin, Alta., Can. C4 68
Wethersfield, Ct., U.S. C5 84
Wet Mountains, mts., Co., U.S. C5 83
Wetumka, Ok., U.S. B5 113
Wetumpka, Al., U.S. C3 78
Wetzel, co., W.V., U.S. B4 125
Wetzlar, Ger. E8 8
Wewahitchka, Fl., U.S. B1 86
Wewak, Pap. N. Gui. k15 50a
Wewoka, Ok., U.S. B5 113
Wexford, Ire. I6 7
Wexford, co., Mi., U.S. D5 99
Weyauwega, Wi., U.S. D5 126
Weymouth, Eng., U.K. K10 7
Weymouth, Ma., U.S. B6 98
Whaleysville, Md., U.S. D7 97
Whalsay, i., Scot., U.K. A12 7
Whangarei, N.Z. A5 52
Wharton, N.J., U.S. B3 107
Wharton, Tx., U.S. E4 120
Wharton, co., Tx., U.S. E4 120
What Cheer, Ia., U.S. C5 92
Whatcom, co., Wa., U.S. A4 124
Whatcom, Lake, l., Wa., U.S. A3 124
Wheatfield, In., U.S. B3 91
Wheatland, Ca., U.S. C3 82
Wheatland, Ia., U.S. C7 92
Wheatland, Wy., U.S. D8 127
Wheatland, co., Mt., U.S. D7 103
Wheatland Reservoir, res., Wy., U.S. E7 127
Wheatley, Ont., Can. E2 73
Wheaton, Il., U.S. B5 90
Wheaton, Md., U.S. B3 97
Wheaton, Mn., U.S. E2 100
Wheaton, Mo., U.S. E3 102
Wheat Ridge, Co., U.S. B5 83
Wheelbarrow Peak, mtn., Nv., U.S. F5 105
Wheeler, Ms., U.S. A5 101
Wheeler, Tx., U.S. B2 120
Wheeler, co., Ga., U.S. D4 87
Wheeler, co., Ne., U.S. C7 104
Wheeler, co., Or., U.S. C6 114
Wheeler, co., Tx., U.S. B2 120
Wheeler Air Force Base, mil., Hi., U.S. g9 88
Wheeler Lake, res., Al., U.S. A2 78
Wheeler Peak, mtn., Ca., U.S. C4 82
Wheeler Peak, mtn., Nv., U.S. E7 105
Wheeler Peak, mtn., N.M., U.S. A4 108
Wheelersburg, Oh., U.S. D3 112
Wheeling, Il., U.S. h9 90
Wheeling, W.V., U.S. A4 125
Wheeling Creek, stm., W.V., U.S. f8 125
Wheelwright, Ky., U.S. C7 94
Whetstone, stm., U.S. E2 100
Whidbey Island, i., Wa., U.S. A3 124
Whidbey Island Naval Air Station, mil., Wa., U.S. A3 124
Whigham, Ga., U.S. F2 87
Whiskey Peak, mtn., Wy., U.S. D5 127
Whiskeytown-Shasta-Trinity National Recreation Area, Ca., U.S. B2 82
Whistler, B.C., Can. D6 69
Whitacres, Ct., U.S. A5 84
Whitakers, N.C., U.S. A5 110
Whitbourne, Newf., Can. E5 72
Whitby, Ont., Can. D6 73
Whitchurch-Stouffville, Ont., Can. D5 73
White, co., Ar., U.S. B4 81
White, co., Ga., U.S. B3 87
White, co., Il., U.S. E5 90
White, co., In., U.S. C4 91
White, co., Tn., U.S. D8 119
White, stm., N.A. D4 66
White, stm., U.S. C4 81
White, stm., U.S. D5 118
White, stm., U.S. C7 121
White, stm., Az., U.S. D5 80
White, stm., In., U.S. H2 91
White, stm., Mi., U.S. E4 99
White, stm., Nv., U.S. E6 105
White, stm., Tx., U.S. C2 120
White, stm., Vt., U.S. D4 122
White, stm., Wa., U.S. B4 124
White, stm., Wa., U.S. B5 124
White, Lake, l., Austl. D5 50
White Bay, b., Newf., Can. D3 72
White Bear, stm., Newf., Can. E3 72
White Bear Lake, Mn., U.S. E5 100
White Bluff, Tn., U.S. A4 119
White Butte, mtn., N.D., U.S. C2 111
White Castle, La., U.S. D4 95
White Center, Wa., U.S. e11 124
White City, Or., U.S. E4 114
White Clay Creek, stm., U.S. A3 104
White Cloud, Mi., U.S. E5 99
Whitecourt, Alta., Can. B3 68
White Creek, stm., U.S. E2 122
Whiteday, stm., W.V., U.S. h10 125
White Deer, Tx., U.S. B2 120
White Earth Indian Reservation, Mn., U.S. C3 100
White Earth Lake, l., Mn., U.S. C3 100
Whiteface, stm., Mn., U.S. C6 100
Whiteface Mountain, mtn., N.Y., U.S. f11 109
Whitefield, N.H., U.S. B3 106
Whitefish, Mt., U.S. B2 103
Whitefish Bay, Wi., U.S. m12 126
Whitefish Bay, b., Mi., U.S. B6 99
Whitefish Lake, l., Mn., U.S. D4 100
Whitefish Range, mts., Mt., U.S. B2 103
Whiteford, Md., U.S. A5 97
White Hall, Al., U.S. C3 78
White Hall, Ar., U.S. C3 81
White Hall, Il., U.S. D3 90
Whitehall, Mi., U.S. E4 99
Whitehall, Mt., U.S. E4 103
Whitehall, N.Y., U.S. B7 109
Whitehall, Oh., U.S. m11 112
Whitehall, Wi., U.S. D2 126
Whitehall Reservoir, res., Ma., U.S. h9 98
Whitehaven, Eng., U.K. G9 7
White Haven, Pa., U.S. D10 115
Whitehorn, Point, c., Wa., U.S. A3 124
Whitehorse, Yukon, Can. D5 66
White Horse, N.J., U.S. C3 107
Whitehouse, Oh., U.S. A2 112
White House, Tn., U.S. A5 119
White Island Shores, Ma., U.S. C6 98

Name | Map Ref | Page

White Knob Mountains, mts., Id., U.S. F5 89
White Lake, l., La., U.S. E3 95
Whiteman Air Force Base, mil., Mo., U.S. C4 102
White Meadow Lake, N.J., U.S. B3 107
White Mesa Natural Bridge, Az., U.S. A4 80
White Mountain Peak, mtn., Ca., U.S. D4 82
White Mountains, mts., U.S. D4 82
White Mountains, mts., N.H., U.S. B3 106
Whitemouth, stm., Man., Can. E4 70
Whitemouth Lake, l., Man., Can. E4 70
White Nile (Al-Bahr al-Abyad), stm., Sudan F12 42
White Oak, Oh., U.S. o12 112
White Oak Creek, stm., Oh., U.S. D2 112
Whiteoak Creek, stm., Tn., U.S. A4 119
White Oak Lake, res., Ar., U.S. D2 81
White Pigeon, Mi., U.S. G5 99
White Pine, Mi., U.S. m12 99
White Pine, Tn., U.S. C10 119
White Pine, co., Nv., U.S. D6 105
White Plains, Md., U.S. C4 97
White Plains, N.Y., U.S. D7 109
Whiteriver, Az., U.S. D6 80
White River Junction, Vt., U.S. D4 122
White Rock, B.C., Can. E6 69
White Russia see Belorusskaja Sovetskaja Socialističeskaja Respublika, state, U.S.S.R. G3 18
White Salmon, Wa., U.S. D4 124
White Salmon, stm., Wa., U.S. D4 124
White Sands Missile Range, mil., N.M., U.S. E3 108
White Sands National Monument, N.M., U.S. E3 108
Whitesboro, N.Y., U.S. B5 109
Whitesboro, Tx., U.S. C4 120
Whitesburg, Ga., U.S. C2 87
Whitesburg, Ky., U.S. C7 94
Whites Creek, stm., Tn., U.S. g10 119
White Sea see Beloje more, U.S.S.R. D5 18
Whiteside, co., Il., U.S. B3 90
White Sulphur Springs, Mt., U.S. D6 103
White Sulphur Springs, W.V., U.S. D4 125
Whitesville, Ky., U.S. C3 94
White Swan, Wa., U.S. C5 124
White Tank Mountains, mts., Az., U.S. k7 80
Whiteville, N.C., U.S. C4 110
Whiteville, Tn., U.S. B2 119
White Volta (Volta Blanche), stm., Afr. F5 42
Whitewater, Ks., U.S. E6 93
Whitewater, Wi., U.S. F5 126
Whitewater, stm., U.S. F7 91
Whitewater, stm., Ks., U.S. E6 93
Whitewater Baldy, mtn., N.M., U.S. D1 108
Whitewater Bay, b., Fl., U.S. G6 86
Whitewood, S.D., U.S. C2 118
Whitewright, Tx., U.S. C4 120
Whitfield, co., Ga., U.S. B2 87
Whitfield Estates, Fl., U.S. q10 86
Whiting, In., U.S. A3 91
Whiting, Ia., U.S. B1 92
Whiting, Wi., U.S. D4 126
Whiting Field Naval Air Station, mil., Fl., U.S. u14 86
Whitinsville, Ma., U.S. B4 98
Whitley, co., In., U.S. B6 91
Whitley, co., Ky., U.S. D5 94
Whitley City, Ky., U.S. D5 94
Whitman, Ma., U.S. B6 98
Whitman, W.V., U.S. D2 125
Whitman, co., Wa., U.S. B8 124
Whitman Square, N.J., U.S. D2 107
Whitmire, S.C., U.S. B4 117
Whitmore Lake, Mi., U.S. p14 99
Whitmore Village, Hi., U.S. f9 88
Whitney, S.C., U.S. B4 117
Whitney, Tx., U.S. D4 120
Whitney, Lake, res., Tx., U.S. D4 120
Whitney, Mount, mtn., Ca., U.S. D4 82
Whitney Point Lake, res., N.Y., U.S. C5 109
Whittier, Ak., U.S. C10 79
Whittier, Ca., U.S. F4 82
Whitwell, Tn., U.S. D8 119
Wholdaia Lake, l., N.W. Ter., Can. D12 66
Whyalla, Austl. F7 50
Wiarton, Ont., Can. C3 73
Wibaux, Mt., U.S. D12 103
Wibaux, co., Mt., U.S. D12 103
Wichita, Ks., U.S. E6 93
Wichita, co., Ks., U.S. D2 93
Wichita, co., Tx., U.S. B3 120
Wichita Falls, Tx., U.S. C3 120
Wichita Mountains, mts., Ok., U.S. C3 113
Wick, Scot., U.K. C9 7
Wickenburg, Az., U.S. D3 80
Wickiup Reservoir, res., Or., U.S. E5 114
Wickliffe, Ky., U.S. f8 94
Wickliffe, Oh., U.S. A4 112
Wicklow, Ire. I6 7
Wicklow Head, c., Ire. I6 7
Wicklow Mountains, mts., Ire. H6 7
Wicomico, co., Md., U.S. D6 97
Wicomico, stm., Md., U.S. D6 97
Wiconisco, Pa., U.S. E8 115
Widefield, Co., U.S. C6 83
Wielkopolska, reg., Pol. D17 8
Wien (Vienna), Aus. G16 8
Wiener Neustadt, Aus. H16 8
Wiesbaden, Ger. E8 8
Wiesloch, Ger. F8 8
Wiggins, Ms., U.S. E4 101
Wiggins Peak, mtn., Wy., U.S. C3 127
Wikwemikong, Ont., Can. B3 73
Wilbarger, co., Tx., U.S. B3 120
Wilber, Ne., U.S. D9 104
Wilberforce, Oh., U.S. C2 112
Wilbraham, Ma., U.S. B3 98
Wilbur, Wa., U.S. B7 124
Wilburton, Ok., U.S. C6 113
Wilcannia, Austl. F8 50
Wilcox, Pa., U.S. C4 115
Wilcox, co., Al., U.S. D2 78
Wilcox, co., Ga., U.S. E3 87
Wild, stm., U.S. B4 106
Wild Ammonoosuc, stm., N.H., U.S. B3 106
Wild Branch, stm., Vt., U.S. B4 122
Wilder, Id., U.S. F2 89
Wilder, Vt., U.S. D4 122
Wilder Dam, U.S. C2 106
Wildhorse Creek, stm., Ok., U.S. C4 113
Wild Horse Reservoir, res., Nv., U.S. B6 105
Wildorado, Tx., U.S. B1 120
Wild Rice, stm., Mn., U.S. C2 100
Wild Rice, stm., N.D., U.S. C8 111
Wildwood, Fl., U.S. D4 86
Wildwood, N.J., U.S. F3 107
Wildwood Crest, N.J., U.S. F3 107
Wilhelm, Mount, mtn., Pap. N. Gui. m16 50a
Wilhelmina Gebergte, mts., Sur. C7 54
Wilhelmina Peak see Trikora, Puntjak, mtn., Indon. F10 32
Wilhelm-Pieck-Stadt Guben, Ger. D14 8
Wilhelmshaven, Ger. B8 8
Wilkes, co., Ga., U.S. C4 87
Wilkes, co., N.C., U.S. A1 110
Wilkes-Barre, Pa., U.S. D10 115
Wilkesboro, N.C., U.S. A1 110
Wilkes Land, reg., Ant. C24 47
Wilkin, co., Mn., U.S. D2 100
Wilkinsburg, Pa., U.S. F2 115
Wilkinson, W.V., U.S. D3 125
Wilkinson, co., Ga., U.S. D3 87
Wilkinson, co., Ms., U.S. D2 101
Will, co., Il., U.S. B6 90
Willacoochee, Ga., U.S. E3 87
Willacy, co., Tx., U.S. F4 120
Willamette, stm., Or., U.S. C3 114
Willamette Pass, Or., U.S. D4 114
Willamina, Or., U.S. B3 114
Willapa Bay, b., Wa., U.S. C1 124
Willard, Mo., U.S. D4 102
Willard, Oh., U.S. A3 112
Willard, Ut., U.S. B3 121
Willard Bay, b., Ut., U.S. B3 121
Willards, Md., U.S. D7 97
Willard Stream, stm., Vt., U.S. B5 122
Willcox, Az., U.S. E6 80
Willcox Playa, l., Az., U.S. E5 80
Willemstad, Neth. Ant. H13 64
William "Bill" Dannelly Reservoir, res., Al., U.S. C2 78
Williams, Az., U.S. B3 80
Williams, Ca., U.S. C2 82
Williams, co., N.D., U.S. A2 111
Williams, co., Oh., U.S. A1 112
Williams, stm., Vt., U.S. E3 122
Williams, stm., W.V., U.S. C4 125
Williams Air Force Base, mil., Az., U.S. D4 80
Williams Bay, Wi., U.S. F5 126
Williamsburg, In., U.S. E8 91
Williamsburg, Ia., U.S. C5 92
Williamsburg, Ky., U.S. D5 94
Williamsburg, Oh., U.S. C1 112
Williamsburg, Pa., U.S. F5 115
Williamsburg, Va., U.S. C6 123
Williamsburg, co., S.C., U.S. D8 117
Williams Fork, stm., Co., U.S. A3 83
Williams Lake, B.C., Can. C6 69
Williamson, N.Y., U.S. B3 109
Williamson, W.V., U.S. D2 125
Williamson, co., Il., U.S. F4 90
Williamson, co., Tn., U.S. B5 119
Williamson, co., Tx., U.S. D4 120
Williamsport, In., U.S. D3 91
Williamsport, Md., U.S. A2 97
Williamsport, Pa., U.S. D7 115
Williamston, Mi., U.S. F6 99
Williamston, N.C., U.S. B5 110
Williamston, S.C., U.S. B3 117
Williamstown, Ky., U.S. B5 94
Williamstown, Ma., U.S. A1 98
Williamstown, N.J., U.S. D3 107
Williamstown, Pa., U.S. E8 115
Williamstown, Vt., U.S. C3 122
Williamstown, W.V., U.S. B3 125
Williamsville, Il., U.S. D4 90
Williamsville, N.Y., U.S. C2 109
Willimantic, Ct., U.S. C7 84
Willimantic, stm., Ct., U.S. B6 84
Willimantic Reservoir, res., Ct., U.S. C7 84
Willingboro, N.J., U.S. C3 107
Willis, Tx., U.S. D5 120
Willis Islets, is., Austl. C9 50
Williston, Fl., U.S. C4 86
Williston, N.D., U.S. A2 111
Williston, S.C., U.S. E5 117
Williston Lake, res., B.C., Can. B6 69
Willits, Ca., U.S. C2 82
Willmar, Mn., U.S. E3 100
Willoughby, Oh., U.S. A4 112
Willoughby, Lake, l., Vt., U.S. B4 122
Willoughby Hills, Oh., U.S. A4 112
Willow, Ak., U.S. g17 79
Willow Creek, stm., Nv., U.S. E5 105
Willow Creek, stm., Ut., U.S. D6 121
Willow Creek, stm., Wy., U.S. C6 127
Willow Grove Naval Air Station, mil., Pa., U.S. F11 115
Willowick, Oh., U.S. A4 112
Willowmore, S. Afr. H4 44
Willow Reservoir, res., Wi., U.S. C3 126
Willow Run, De., U.S. i7 85
Willow Run, Mi., U.S. p14 99
Willows, Ca., U.S. C2 82
Willow Springs, Il., U.S. k9 90
Willow Springs, Mo., U.S. E6 102
Willston, Va., U.S. B5 123
Wilmar, Ar., U.S. D4 81
Wilmerding, Pa., U.S. k14 115
Wilmette, Il., U.S. A6 90
Wilmington, De., U.S. B3 85
Wilmington, Il., U.S. B5 90
Wilmington, Ma., U.S. A5 98
Wilmington, N.C., U.S. C5 110
Wilmington, Oh., U.S. C2 112
Wilmington, Vt., U.S. F3 122
Wilmington Manor, De., U.S. i7 85
Wilmore, Ky., U.S. C5 94
Wilmot, Ar., U.S. D4 81
Wilson, Ar., U.S. B5 81
Wilson, Ks., U.S. D5 93
Wilson, La., U.S. D4 95
Wilson, N.C., U.S. B5 110
Wilson, Ok., U.S. C4 113
Wilson, Pa., U.S. E11 115
Wilson, Wy., U.S. C2 127
Wilson, co., Ks., U.S. E8 93
Wilson, co., N.C., U.S. C2 110
Wilson, co., Tn., U.S. A5 119
Wilson, co., Tx., U.S. E3 120
Wilson, Cape, c., N.W. Ter., Can. C16 66
Wilson, Mount, mtn., Az., U.S. B1 80
Wilson, Mount, mtn., Ca., U.S. m12 82
Wilson, Mount, mtn., Co., U.S. D2 83
Wilson, Mount, mtn., Nv., U.S. E7 105
Wilson, Mount, mtn., Or., U.S. B5 114
Wilson Creek, stm., Wa., U.S. B5 124
Wilson Creek, stm., Wa., U.S. B6 124
Wilson Lake, res., Al., U.S. A2 78
Wilson Lake, res., Ks., U.S. D4 93
Wilsons Beach, N.B., Can. E3 71
Wilsonville, Al., U.S. B3 78
Wilsonville, Or., U.S. h12 114
Wilton, Al., U.S. B3 78
Wilton, Ct., U.S. E2 84
Wilton, Ia., U.S. C6 92
Wilton, Me., U.S. D2 96
Wilton, N.H., U.S. E3 106
Wilton, N.D., U.S. B5 111
Wiluna, Austl. E4 50
Wimauma, Fl., U.S. E4 86
Wimico, Lake, l., Fl., U.S. C1 86
Winamac, In., U.S. B4 91
Winchek Pond, l., R.I., U.S. E1 116
Winchendon, Ma., U.S. A3 98
Winchester, Ont., Can. B9 73
Winchester, Eng., U.K. J11 7
Winchester, Il., U.S. D3 90
Winchester, In., U.S. D8 91
Winchester, Ks., U.S. k15 93
Winchester, Ky., U.S. C5 94
Winchester, Ma., U.S. g11 98
Winchester, Nv., U.S. G6 105
Winchester, N.H., U.S. E2 106
Winchester, Oh., U.S. D2 112
Winchester, Tn., U.S. B5 119
Winchester, Va., U.S. A4 123
Winchester Bay, Or., U.S. D2 114
Wind, stm., Wa., U.S. D4 124
Wind, stm., Wy., U.S. C4 127
Windber, Pa., U.S. F4 115
Wind Cave National Park, S.D., U.S. D2 118
Winder, Ga., U.S. C3 87
Windermere, Eng., U.K. G10 7
Windfall, In., U.S. D6 91
Windgap, Pa., U.S. E11 115
Windham, Ct., U.S. C7 84
Windham, Oh., U.S. A4 112
Windham, co., Ct., U.S. B7 84
Windham, co., Vt., U.S. F3 122
Windhoek, Nmb. F3 44
Wind Lake, Wi., U.S. F5 126
Wind Lake, l., Wi., U.S. n11 126
Windmill Point, c., Va., U.S. C6 123
Windom, Mn., U.S. G3 100
Windom Peak, mtn., Co., U.S. D3 83
Windorah, Austl. E8 50
Window Rock, Az., U.S. B6 80
Wind Point, Wi., U.S. n12 126
Wind River Indian Reservation, Wy., U.S. C4 127
Wind River Peak, mtn., Wy., U.S. D3 127
Wind River Range, mts., Wy., U.S. C3 127
Windsor, Newf., Can. D4 72
Windsor, Ont., Can. E1 73
Windsor, Que., Can. D5 74
Windsor, Eng., U.K. J12 7
Windsor, Co., U.S. A6 83
Windsor, Ct., U.S. B5 84
Windsor, Il., U.S. D5 90
Windsor, Mo., U.S. C4 102
Windsor, N.C., U.S. B6 110
Windsor, Pa., U.S. G8 115
Windsor, Vt., U.S. E4 122
Windsor, Va., U.S. D6 123
Windsor, co., Vt., U.S. D3 122
Windsor Heights, Ia., U.S. e8 92
Windsor Locks, Ct., U.S. B5 84
Windward Islands, is., N.A. H17 64
Windward Passage, strt., N.A. E10 64
Windy Hill, S.C., U.S. C8 117
Windy Peak, mtn., Wa., U.S. A6 124
Winefred Lake, l., Alta., Can. B5 68
Winfield, Al., U.S. B2 78
Winfield, Ia., U.S. C6 92
Winfield, Ks., U.S. E7 93
Winfield, Mo., U.S. C7 102
Winfield, W.V., U.S. C3 125
Wing, stm., Mn., U.S. D3 100
Wingate, N.C., U.S. C2 110
Wingham, Ont., Can. D3 73
Winifrede, W.V., U.S. m12 125
Winisk, stm., Ont., Can. n18 73
Winisk Lake, l., Ont., Can. F16 66
Wink, Tx., U.S. D1 120
Winkelman, Az., U.S. E5 80
Winkler, Man., Can. E3 70
Winkler, co., Tx., U.S. D1 120
Winlock, Wa., U.S. C3 124
Winn, co., La., U.S. C3 95
Winnebago, Il., U.S. A4 90
Winnebago, Mn., U.S. G4 100
Winnebago, Ne., U.S. B9 104
Winnebago, Wi., U.S. h8 126
Winnebago, co., Il., U.S. A4 90
Winnebago, co., Ia., U.S. A4 92
Winnebago, co., Wi., U.S. D5 126
Winnebago, stm., Ia., U.S. A4 92
Winnebago, Lake, l., Wi., U.S. E5 126
Winnebago Indian Reservation, Ne., U.S. B9 104
Winneconne, Wi., U.S. D5 126
Winnemucca, Nv., U.S. C4 105
Winnemucca Lake, l., Nv., U.S. C2 105
Winner, S.D., U.S. D6 118
Winneshiek, co., Ia., U.S. A6 92
Winnetka, Il., U.S. A6 90
Winnfield, La., U.S. C3 95
Winnibigoshish, Lake, l., Mn., U.S. C4 100
Winnipeg, Man., Can. E3 70
Winnipeg, stm., Can. D4 70
Winnipeg, Lake, l., Man., Can. C3 70
Winnipeg Beach, Man., Can. D3 70
Winnipegosis, Man., Can. D2 70
Winnipegosis, Lake, l., Man., Can. C2 70
Winnipesaukee, Lake, l., N.H., U.S. C4 106
Winnisquam, N.H., U.S. C3 106
Winnisquam Lake, l., N.H., U.S. C3 106
Winnsboro, La., U.S. B4 95
Winnsboro, S.C., U.S. C5 117
Winnsboro, Tx., U.S. C5 120
Winnsboro Mills, S.C., U.S. C5 117
Winona, Mn., U.S. F7 100
Winona, Ms., U.S. B4 101
Winona, Mo., U.S. D6 102
Winona, co., Mn., U.S. F7 100
Winona Lake, In., U.S. B6 91
Winona Lake, l., Vt., U.S. C2 122
Winooski, Vt., U.S. C2 122
Winooski, stm., Vt., U.S. C3 122
Winslow, Az., U.S. C5 80
Winslow, In., U.S. H3 91
Winslow, Me., U.S. D3 96
Winsted, Ct., U.S. B3 84
Winsted, Mn., U.S. F4 100
Winston, Fl., U.S. D4 86
Winston, Or., U.S. D3 114
Winston, co., Al., U.S. A2 78
Winston, co., Ms., U.S. B4 101
Winston-Salem, N.C., U.S. A2 110
Winter Garden, Fl., U.S. D5 86
Winter Harbor, Me., U.S. D4 96
Winter Haven, Fl., U.S. D5 86
Winter Park, Fl., U.S. D5 86
Winter Park, N.C., U.S. C5 110
Winterport, Me., U.S. D4 96
Winter Ridge, mtn., Or., U.S. E6 114
Winters, Ca., U.S. C2 82
Winters, Tx., U.S. D3 120
Winterset, Ia., U.S. C4 92
Wintersville, Oh., U.S. B5 112
Winterswijk, Neth. D6 8
Winterthur, Switz. E15 10
Winterton, Newf., Can. E5 72
Winterville, Ga., U.S. C3 87
Winterville, N.C., U.S. B5 110
Winthrop, Ia., U.S. B6 92
Winthrop, Me., U.S. D3 96
Winthrop, Ma., U.S. B6 98
Winthrop, Mn., U.S. F4 100
Winthrop, Lake, l., Ma., U.S. h10 98
Winthrop Harbor, Il., U.S. A6 90
Winton, Austl. D8 50
Winton, N.C., U.S. A6 110
Winton Lake, res., Oh., U.S. o12 113
Winyah Bay, b., S.C., U.S. E9 117
Wirt, co., W.V., U.S. B3 125
Wiscasset, Me., U.S. D3 96
Wisconsin, state, U.S. D4 126
Wisconsin, stm., Wi., U.S. E3 126
Wisconsin, Lake, res., Wi., U.S. E4 126
Wisconsin Dells, Wi., U.S. E4 126
Wisconsin Rapids, Wi., U.S. D4 126
Wise, Va., U.S. f9 123
Wise, co., Tx., U.S. C4 120
Wise, co., Va., U.S. e9 123
Wishek, N.D., U.S. C6 111
Wishram, Wa., U.S. D4 124
Wisła, stm., Pol. A18 8
Wismar, Ger. B11 8
Wisner, La., U.S. C4 95
Wisner, Ne., U.S. C9 104
Wissota, Lake, res., Wi., U.S. D2 126
Wister, Ok., U.S. C7 113
Wister Lake, res., Ok., U.S. C7 113
Witbank, S. Afr. G5 44
Withamsville, Oh., U.S. C1 112
Witherspoon, Mount, mtn., Ak., U.S. g18 79
Withlacoochee, stm., U.S. B3 86
Withlacoochee, stm., Fl., U.S. C4 86
Witless Bay, Newf., Can. E5 72
Witt, Il., U.S. D4 90
Wittenberg, Ger. D12 8
Wittenberg, Wi., U.S. D4 126
Wittenberge, Ger. B11 8
Wittlich, Ger. F6 8
Wittman, Md., U.S. C5 97
Wittmann, Az., U.S. D3 80
Wittstock, Ger. B12 8
Wixom, Mi., U.S. o14 99
Wixom Lake, res., Mi., U.S. E6 99
Włocławek, Pol. C19 8
Woburn, Ma., U.S. B5 98
Wokam, Pulau, i., Indon. G9 32
Woking, Eng., U.K. J12 7
Wolcott, Ct., U.S. C4 84
Wolcott, In., U.S. C3 91
Wolcottville, In., U.S. A7 91
Wolf, stm., Ms., U.S. E4 101
Wolf, stm., Tn., U.S. e9 119
Wolf, stm., Wi., U.S. C5 126
Wolf Creek, Or., U.S. E3 114
Wolf Creek, stm., U.S. A2 113
Wolf Creek, stm., W.V., U.S. m13 125
Wolf Creek Pass, Co., U.S. D3 83
Wolfe, co., Ky., U.S. C6 94
Wolfeboro, N.H., U.S. C4 106
Wolfeboro Falls, N.H., U.S. C4 106
Wolfe City, Tx., U.S. C4 120
Wolfen, Ger. D12 8
Wolfenbüttel, Ger. C10 8
Wolf Lake, Mi., U.S. E4 99
Wolf Lake, l., Il., U.S. k9 90
Wolf Mountain, mtn., Ak., U.S. B9 79
Wolf Point, Mt., U.S. B11 103
Wolfsberg, Aus. I14 8
Wolfsburg, Ger. C10 8
Wolf Swamp, sw., N.C., U.S. C5 110
Wolgast, Ger. A13 8
Wollaston, Cape, c., N.W. Ter., Can. B9 66
Wollaston, Islas, is., Chile H3 56
Wollaston Lake, l., Sask., Can. m8 75
Wollaston Peninsula, pen., N.W. Ter., Can. C10 66
Wollongong, Austl. F10 50
Wolverhampton, Eng., U.K. I10 7
Woman Lake, l., Mn., U.S. D4 100
Womelsdorf, Pa., U.S. F9 115
Wonder Lake, Il., U.S. A5 90
Wonewoc, Wi., U.S. E3 126
Wŏnsan, N. Kor. D12 26
Wood, co., Oh., U.S. A2 112
Wood, co., Tx., U.S. C5 120
Wood, co., W.V., U.S. B3 125
Wood, co., Wi., U.S. D3 126
Wood, stm., Sask., Can. H2 75
Wood, stm., R.I., U.S. F2 116
Wood, stm., Wy., U.S. C3 127
Wood, Mount, mtn., Mt., U.S. E7 103
Woodall Mountain, mtn., Ms., U.S. A5 101
Woodbine, Ga., U.S. F5 87
Woodbine, Ia., U.S. C2 92
Woodbine, Ky., U.S. D5 94
Woodbine, N.J., U.S. E3 107
Woodbridge, Ct., U.S. D3 84
Woodbridge, Va., U.S. B5 123
Woodbridge [Township], N.J., U.S. B4 107
Woodburn, In., U.S. B8 91
Woodburn, Or., U.S. B4 114
Woodbury, Ct., U.S. C3 84
Woodbury, Ga., U.S. D2 87
Woodbury, Mn., U.S. F6 100
Woodbury, N.J., U.S. D2 107
Woodbury, Tn., U.S. B5 119
Woodbury, co., Ia., U.S. B1 92
Woodcliff Lake, N.J., U.S. g8 107
Woodcliff Lake, l., N.J., U.S. g8 107
Wood Dale, Il., U.S. k9 90
Wood End, spit, Ma., U.S. B7 98
Woodfield, S.C., U.S. C6 117
Woodford, co., Il., U.S. C4 90
Woodford, co., Ky., U.S. B5 94
Woodhull, Il., U.S. B3 90
Woodlake, Ca., U.S. D4 82
Woodland, Ca., U.S. C3 82
Woodland, Me., U.S. C5 96
Woodland, N.C., U.S. A5 110
Woodland, Wa., U.S. D3 124
Woodland Acres, Co., U.S. D6 83
Woodland Park, Co., U.S. C5 83
Woodlark Island, i., Pap. N. Gui. A10 50
Woodlawn, Ky., U.S. e9 94
Woodlawn, Md., U.S. g10 97
Woodlawn, Oh., U.S. n13 112
Woodlawn, Va., U.S. D2 123
Woodmont, Ct., U.S. E4 84
Woodmoor, Md., U.S. B4 97
Woodridge, Il., U.S. k8 90
Wood-Ridge, N.J., U.S. h8 107
Wood River, Il., U.S. E3 90
Wood River, Ne., U.S. D7 104
Woodroffe, Mount, mtn., Austl. E6 50
Woodruff, S.C., U.S. B3 117
Woodruff, Wi., U.S. C4 126
Woodruff, co., Ar., U.S. B4 81
Woods, co., Ok., U.S. A3 113
Woods, Lake, res., Tn., U.S. B5 119
Woods, Lake of the, l., N.A. G14 66
Woodsboro, Tx., U.S. E4 120
Woods Cross, Ut., U.S. C4 121
Woodsfield, Oh., U.S. C4 112
Woods Hole, Ma., U.S. C6 98
Woodson, Ar., U.S. C3 81
Woodson, co., Ks., U.S. E8 93
Woodstock, N.B., Can. C2 71
Woodstock, Ont., Can. D4 73
Woodstock, Ga., U.S. B2 87
Woodstock, Il., U.S. A5 90
Woodstock, Md., U.S. B4 97
Woodstock, N.Y., U.S. C6 109
Woodstock, Vt., U.S. D3 122
Woodstock, Va., U.S. B4 123
Woodstown, N.J., U.S. D2 107
Woodsville, N.H., U.S. B2 106
Woodville, N.Z. D5 52
Woodville, Fl., U.S. B2 86
Woodville, Ms., U.S. D2 101
Woodville, Oh., U.S. A2 112
Woodville, Tx., U.S. D5 120
Woodville, Wi., U.S. D1 126
Woodward, Ia., U.S. C4 92
Woodward, Ok., U.S. A2 113
Woodward, co., Ok., U.S. A2 113
Woodworth, La., U.S. C3 95
Woolmarket, Ms., U.S. E5 101
Woolrich, Pa., U.S. D7 115
Woolsey Peak, mtn., Az., U.S. D3 80
Woomera, Austl. F7 50
Woonsocket, R.I., U.S. A3 116
Woonsocket, S.D., U.S. C7 118
Woonsocket Reservoir Number Three, res., R.I., U.S. B3 116
Wooramel, Austl. E2 50
Wooster, Oh., U.S. B4 112
Worcester, S. Afr. H3 44
Worcester, Eng., U.K. I10 7
Worcester, Ma., U.S. B4 98
Worcester, co., Md., U.S. D7 97
Worcester, co., Ma., U.S. A3 98
Worden, Il., U.S. E4 90
Worden Pond, l., R.I., U.S. F3 116
Workington, Eng., U.K. G9 7
Worland, Wy., U.S. B5 127
Worms, Ger. F8 8
Worth, Il., U.S. k9 90
Worth, co., Ga., U.S. E3 87
Worth, co., Ia., U.S. A4 92
Worth, co., Mo., U.S. A3 102
Worthing, Eng., U.K. K12 7

Name — Map Ref — Page

Worthington, In., U.S. **F4** 91
Worthington, Ky., U.S. **B7** 94
Worthington, Mn., U.S. **G3** 100
Worthington, Oh., U.S. **B2** 112
Worthington Peak, mtn., Nv., U.S. **F6** 105
Wowoni, Pulau, i., Indon. **F7** 32
Wrangell, Ak., U.S. **D13** 79
Wrangell, Mount, mtn., Ak., U.S. **f19** 79
Wrangell Island, i., Ak., U.S. **m24** 79
Wrangell Mountains, mts., Ak., U.S. **C11** 79
Wrangell-Saint Elias National Park, Ak., U.S. **C11** 79
Wrath, Cape, c., Scot., U.K. **C7** 7
Wray, Co., U.S. **A8** 83
Wreck Reefs, rf., Austl. **D11** 50
Wrens, Ga., U.S. **C4** 87
Wrentham, Ma., U.S. **B5** 98
Wrexham, Wales, U.K. **H9** 7
Wright, co., Ia., U.S. **B4** 92
Wright, co., Mn., U.S. **E4** 100
Wright, co., Mo., U.S. **D5** 102
Wright, Mount, mtn., Mt., U.S. **C4** 103
Wright Brothers National Memorial, hist., N.C., U.S. **A7** 110
Wright City, Mo., U.S. **C8** 102
Wright City, Ok., U.S. **C6** 113
Wright-Patterson Air Force Base, mil., Oh., U.S. **C1** 112
Wrightson, Mount, mtn., Az., U.S. **F5** 80
Wrightstown, N.J., U.S. **C3** 107
Wrightstown, Wi., U.S. **D5** 126
Wrightsville, Ar., U.S. **C3** 81
Wrightsville, Ga., U.S. **D4** 87
Wrightsville, Pa., U.S. **F8** 115
Wrightsville Beach, N.C., U.S. **C5** 110
Wrightsville Reservoir, res., Vt., U.S. **C3** 122
Wrigley, N.W. Ter., Can. **D8** 66
Wrocław (Breslau), Pol. **D17** 8
Wuchuan, China **D11** 34
Wudu, China **E7** 26
Wugang, China **F9** 26
Wuhan, China **E3** 28
Wuhu, China **D7** 28
Wunstorf, Ger. **C9** 8
Wupatki National Monument, Az., U.S. **B4** 80
Wuppertal, Ger. **D7** 8
Wurtsmith Air Force Base, mil., Mi., U.S. **D7** 99
Würzburg, Ger. **F9** 8
Wurzen, Ger. **D12** 8
Wushan, China **E8** 26
Wushenqi, China **D8** 26
Wusong, China **D10** 28
Wutongqiao, China **F7** 26
Wuwei, China **D7** 26
Wuwei, China **D6** 28
Wuxi (Wuhsi), China **D9** 28
Wuyi Shan, mts., China **I5** 28
Wuyuan, China **C8** 26
Wuzhong, China **D8** 26
Wuzhou (Wuchow), China **C11** 34
Wyaconda, stm., Mo., U.S. **A6** 102
Wyandot, co., Oh., U.S. **B2** 112
Wyandotte, Mi., U.S. **F7** 99
Wyandotte, co., Ks., U.S. **C9** 93
Wyanet, Il., U.S. **B4** 90
Wyk, Ger. **A8** 8
Wylie, Lake, res., U.S. **A5** 117
Wyman Lake, res., Me., U.S. **C3** 96
Wymore, Ne., U.S. **D9** 104
Wyndham, Austl. **C5** 50
Wynndel, B.C., Can. **E9** 69
Wynne, Ar., U.S. **B5** 81
Wynnewood, Ok., U.S. **C4** 113
Wynoochee, stm., Wa., U.S. **B2** 124
Wyoming, Ont., Can. **E2** 73
Wyoming, De., U.S. **D3** 85
Wyoming, Il., U.S. **B4** 90
Wyoming, Ia., U.S. **B6** 92
Wyoming, Mi., U.S. **F5** 99
Wyoming, Mn., U.S. **E6** 100
Wyoming, Oh., U.S. **o13** 112
Wyoming, Pa., U.S. **n17** 115
Wyoming, R.I., U.S. **E2** 116
Wyoming, co., N.Y., U.S. **C2** 109
Wyoming, co., Pa., U.S. **D9** 115
Wyoming, co., W.V., U.S. **D3** 125
Wyoming, state, U.S. **C5** 127
Wyoming Peak, mtn., Wy., U.S. **D2** 127
Wyoming Range, mts., Wy., U.S. **D2** 127
Wyomissing, Pa., U.S. **F10** 115
Wysocking Bay, b., N.C., U.S. **B7** 110
Wythe, co., Va., U.S. **D1** 123
Wytheville, Va., U.S. **D1** 123

X

Xai-Xai, Moz. **G6** 44
Xangongo, Ang. **E3** 44
Xánthi, Grc. **H8** 16
Xapuri, Braz. **F5** 54
Xenia, Oh., U.S. **C2** 112
Xertigny, Fr. **D13** 10
Xi, stm., China **G9** 26
Xiaguan, China **E9** 26
Xiahe, China **D7** 26
Xiamen (Amoy), China **K7** 28
Xi'an (Sian), China **E8** 26
Xiangcheng, China **B2** 28
Xiangfan, China **E9** 26
Xiangkhoang, Laos **E7** 34
Xiangride, China **D6** 26
Xiangtan, China **H1** 28
Xianyou, China **J7** 28
Xiaogan, China **E2** 28
Xiaolan, China **M2** 28
Xiashi, China **E9** 28
Xichang, China **F7** 26
Xiegeer, China **F12** 38
Xigazê, China **F13** 38
Xihua, China **B3** 28
Xilinhaote, China **C10** 26
Xinavane, Moz. **G6** 44
Xingtai, China **D9** 26
Xingu, stm., Braz. **D8** 54
Xingyi, China **B8** 34
Xinhui, China **M2** 28
Xining, China **D7** 26
Xinjiang Uygur Zizhiqu, prov., China **B9** 38
Xinxiang, China **D9** 26
Xinyang, China **C3** 28
Xiping, China **B3** 28
Xique-Xique, Braz. **F10** 54
Xizang Zizhiqu, prov., China **D12** 38
Xuancheng, China **E7** 28
Xuanhua, China **C10** 26
Xuchang, China **A2** 28
Xuwen, China **D11** 34
Xuyong, China **F8** 26
Xuzhou (Süchow), China **A6** 28

Y

Yaan, China **E7** 26
Yacolt, Wa., U.S. **D3** 124
Yacuiba, Bol. **H6** 54
Yādgīr, India **D4** 37
Yadkin, co., N.C., U.S. **A2** 110
Yadkin, stm., N.C., U.S. **B2** 110
Yadkinville, N.C., U.S. **A2** 110
Yainax Butte, mtn., Or., U.S. **E5** 114
Yaizu, Japan **H11** 30
Yakima, Wa., U.S. **C5** 124
Yakima, co., Wa., U.S. **C4** 124
Yakima, stm., Wa., U.S. **C6** 124
Yakima Indian Reservation, Wa., U.S. **C5** 124
Yakobi Island, i., Ak., U.S. **m21** 79
Yakumo, Japan **q18** 30a
Yaku-shima, i., Japan **u30** 31b
Yakutat, Ak., U.S. **D12** 79
Yakutat Bay, b., Ak., U.S. **D11** 79
Yala, Thai. **K6** 34
Yale, Mi., U.S. **E8** 99
Yale, Ok., U.S. **A5** 113
Yale, Mount, mtn., Co., U.S. **C5** 83
Yale Lake, res., Wa., U.S. **D3** 124
Yalobusha, co., Ms., U.S. **A4** 101
Yalobusha, stm., Ms., U.S. **B4** 101
Yalu (Amnok-kang), stm., Asia **C12** 26
Yamachiche, Que., Can. **C5** 74
Yamagata, Japan **D13** 30
Yamaguchi, Japan **H4** 30
Yamato-takada, Japan **H8** 30
Yambio, Sudan **H11** 42
Yamdena, Pulau, i., Indon. **G9** 32
Yamethin, Burma **D4** 34
Yamhill, Or., U.S. **h11** 114
Yamhill, co., Or., U.S. **B3** 114
Yamoussoukro, I.C. **G4** 42
Yampa, stm., Co., U.S. **A2** 83
Yamsay Mountain, mtn., Or., U.S. **E5** 114
Yamuna, stm., India **H9** 38
Yanbu', Sau. Ar. **D2** 46
Yancey, co., N.C., U.S. **f10** 110
Yanceyville, N.C., U.S. **A3** 110
Yanchang, China **D9** 26
Yancheng, China **B9** 28
Yandoon, Burma **F3** 34
Yangjiang, China **G9** 26
Yangon (Rangoon), Burma **B2** 32
Yangquan, China **D9** 26
Yangtze see Chang, stm., China **E10** 26
Yangzhou, China **C8** 28
Yanji, China **C12** 26
Yankton, S.D., U.S. **E8** 118
Yankton, co., S.D., U.S. **D8** 118
Yanqi, China **C4** 26
Yantai (Chefoo), China **D11** 26
Yantic, stm., Ct., U.S. **C7** 84
Yaoundé, Cam. **H8** 42
Yapen, Pulau, i., Indon. **F10** 32
Yaqui, stm., Mex. **C5** 62
Yaraka, Austl. **D8** 50
Yardley, Pa., U.S. **F12** 115
Yardville, N.J., U.S. **C3** 107
Yaritagua, Ven. **B8** 58
Yarmouth, Me., U.S. **E2** 96
Yarnell, Az., U.S. **C3** 80
Yarumal, Col. **D5** 58
Yashiro-jima, i., Japan **I5** 30
Yates, co., N.Y., U.S. **C3** 109
Yates Center, Ks., U.S. **E8** 93
Yates City, Il., U.S. **C3** 90
Yathkyed Lake, l., N.W. Ter., Can. **D13** 66
Yatsushiro, Japan **J3** 30
Yatta Plateau, plat., Kenya **B7** 44
Yaupi, Ec. **I4** 58
Yavapai, co., Az., U.S. **C3** 80
Yavarí (Javari), stm., S.A. **D4** 54
Yavatmāl, India **B5** 37
Yaví, Cerro, mtn., Ven. **E10** 58
Yaviza, Pan. **J9** 64
Yawatahama, Japan **I5** 30
Yawgoog Pond, l., R.I., U.S. **E1** 116
Yaxian, China **E10** 34
Yazd, Iran **B5** 46
Yazoo, co., Ms., U.S. **C3** 101
Yazoo, stm., Ms., U.S. **C3** 101
Yazoo City, Ms., U.S. **C3** 101
Ye, Burma **G4** 34
Yeadon, Pa., U.S. **p21** 115
Yeagertown, Pa., U.S. **E6** 115
Yecheng, China **B7** 38
Yecla, Spain **G10** 12
Yei, stm., Sudan **G12** 42
Yell, co., Ar., U.S. **B2** 81
Yell, i., Scot., U.K. **A11** 7
Yellow, stm., U.S. **u15** 86
Yellow, stm., In., U.S. **B4** 91
Yellow, stm., Wi., U.S. **D3** 126
Yellow, stm., Wi., U.S. **C3** 126
Yellow Creek, stm., Tn., U.S. **A4** 119
Yellowhead Pass, Can. **C1** 68
Yellow see Huang, stm., China **D10** 26
Yellowjacket Mountains, mts., Id., U.S. **D4** 89
Yellowknife, N.W. Ter., Can. **D10** 66
Yellow Lake, l., Wi., U.S. **C1** 126
Yellow Medicine, co., Mn., U.S. **F2** 100
Yellow Sea, Asia **D11** 26
Yellow Springs, Oh., U.S. **C2** 112
Yellowstone, co., Mt., U.S. **D8** 103
Yellowstone, stm., U.S. **D10** 103
Yellowstone Lake, l., Wy., U.S. **B2** 127
Yellowstone National Park, co., Mt., U.S. **E6** 103
Yellville, Ar., U.S. **A3** 81
Yelm, Wa., U.S. **C3** 124
Yemassee, S.C., U.S. **F6** 117
Yemen, ctry., Asia **E4** 46
Yenangyaung, Burma **D3** 34
Yen Bai, Viet. **D8** 34
Yendéré, Burkina **F5** 42
Yendi, Ghana **G5** 42
Yenisey see Jenisej, stm., U.S.S.R. **D11** 20
Yenshui, Tai. **L9** 28
Yentna, stm., Ak., U.S. **f16** 79
Yeovil, Eng., U.K. **K10** 7
Yerevan see Jerevan, U.S.S.R. **I6** 18
Yerington, Nv., U.S. **E2** 105
Yerington Indian Reservation, Nv., U.S. **D2** 105
Yermasóyia, Cyp. **B3** 40
Yermo, Ca., U.S. **E5** 82
Yerupajá, Nevado, mtn., Peru **F3** 54
Yerushalayim (Jerusalem), Isr. **D4** 40
Yeste, Spain **G9** 12
Yexian, China **B2** 28
Yiannitsá, Grc. **I6** 16
Yibin, China **F7** 26
Yichang, China **E9** 26
Yichuan, China **B12** 26
Yichun, China **H3** 28
Yilan, China **B12** 26
Yiliang, China **B7** 34
Yinchuan, China **D8** 26
Yingde, China **K2** 28
Yingkou, China **C11** 26
Yining, China **C3** 26
Yirga Alem, Eth. **G2** 46
Yishan, China **B10** 34
Yíthion, Grc. **M6** 16
Yitulihe, China **A11** 26
Yiyang, China **F9** 26
Ylivieska, Fin. **D15** 6
Ynykčanskij, U.S.S.R. **E21** 20
Yoakum, Tx., U.S. **E4** 120
Yoakum, co., Tx., U.S. **C1** 120
Yockanookany, stm., Ms., U.S. **C4** 101
Yocona, stm., Ms., U.S. **A4** 101
Yogyakarta, Indon. **m15** 32
Yoho National Park, B.C., Can. **D9** 69
Yokkaichi, Japan **H9** 30
Yokohama, Japan **G12** 30
Yokosuka, Japan **G12** 30
Yokote, Japan **C13** 30
Yola, Nig. **G8** 42
Yolo, co., Ca., U.S. **C2** 82
Yolombó, Col. **D5** 58
Yomba Indian Reservation, Nv., U.S. **D4** 105
Yonago, Japan **G6** 30
Yoncalla, Or., U.S. **D3** 114
Yonezawa, Japan **E13** 30
Yongdeng, China **D7** 26
Yongdingzhen, China **A6** 34
Yongfeng, China **H4** 28
Yonkers, N.Y., U.S. **E7** 109
Yopal, Col. **E6** 58
York, Ont., Can. **D5** 73
York, Eng., U.K. **H11** 7
York, Al., U.S. **C1** 78
York, Me., U.S. **E2** 96
York, Ne., U.S. **D8** 104
York, Pa., U.S. **G8** 115
York, S.C., U.S. **B5** 117
York, co., Me., U.S. **E2** 96
York, co., Ne., U.S. **D8** 104
York, co., Pa., U.S. **G8** 115
York, co., S.C., U.S. **A5** 117
York, co., Va., U.S. **C6** 123
York, stm., Ont., Can. **B7** 73
York, stm., Va., U.S. **C6** 123
York, Cape, c., Austl. **B8** 50
York Beach, Me., U.S. **E2** 96
York Harbor, Me., U.S. **E2** 96
Yorklyn, De., U.S. **A3** 85
Yorktown, In., U.S. **D7** 91
Yorktown, Tx., U.S. **E4** 120
Yorktown, Va., U.S. **C6** 123
Yorktown Manor, R.I., U.S. **C3** 116
Yorkville, Il., U.S. **B5** 90
Yorkville, N.Y., U.S. **B5** 109
Yorkville, Oh., U.S. **B5** 112
Yoro, Hond. **G4** 64
Yoron-jima, i., Japan **x28** 31b
Yosemite National Park, Ca., U.S. **D4** 82
Yŏsu, S. Kor. **E12** 26
Youbou, B.C., Can. **g11** 69
Youghal, Ire. **J5** 7
Youghiogheny, stm., U.S. **F2** 115
Youghiogheny River Lake, res., U.S. **G3** 115
Young, Az., U.S. **C5** 80
Young, co., Tx., U.S. **C3** 120
Young Harris, Ga., U.S. **B3** 87
Youngs, Lake, l., Wa., U.S. **f11** 124
Youngstown, N.Y., U.S. **B1** 109
Youngstown, Oh., U.S. **A5** 112
Youngsville, La., U.S. **D3** 95
Youngsville, Pa., U.S. **C3** 115
Youngtown, Az., U.S. **k8** 80
Youngwood, Pa., U.S. **F2** 115
Youyang, China **F8** 26
Ypres see Ieper, Bel. **E2** 8
Ypsilanti, Mi., U.S. **F7** 99
Yreka, Ca., U.S. **B2** 82
Yssingeaux, Fr. **G11** 10
Ystad, Swe. **I9** 6
Yu, stm., China **C10** 34
Yuanling, China **F9** 26
Yuba, co., Ca., U.S. **C3** 82
Yuba, stm., Ca., U.S. **C3** 82
Yuba City, Ca., U.S. **C3** 82
Yūbari, Japan **p19** 30a
Yucatan Channel, strt., N.A. **C4** 64
Yucatan Peninsula, pen., N.A. **H15** 62
Yucca Lake, l., Nv., U.S. **F5** 105
Yucca Mountain, mtn., Nv., U.S. **G5** 105
Yuci, China **D9** 26
Yueyang, China **F2** 28
Yugoslavia, ctry., Eur. **G11** 4
Yukon, Ok., U.S. **B4** 113
Yukon, prov., Can. **D6** 66
Yukon, stm., N.A. **m19** 76a
Yukuhashi, Japan **I3** 30
Yulee, Fl., U.S. **B5** 86
Yulin, China **D8** 26
Yulin, China **C11** 34
Yuma, Az., U.S. **E1** 80
Yuma, Co., U.S. **A8** 83
Yuma, co., Az., U.S. **E1** 80
Yuma, co., Co., U.S. **A8** 83
Yuma Marine Corps Air Station, mil., Az., U.S. **E1** 80
Yumen, China **D6** 26
Yuncheng, China **D9** 26
Yunnan, prov., China **F7** 26
Yurimaguas, Peru **E3** 54
Yuriria, Mex. **G9** 62
Yü Shan, mtn., Tai. **L9** 28
Yushu, China **E6** 26
Yutan, Ne., U.S. **C9** 104
Yutian, China **B9** 38
Yuty, Para. **B5** 56
Yuxian, China **A2** 28
Yuyao, China **E10** 28
Yverdon, Switz. **F13** 10
Yvetot, Fr. **C7** 10

Z

Zaandam, Neth. **C4** 8
Zabīd, Yemen **F3** 46
Zabrze, Pol. **E18** 8
Zacapa, Guat. **G3** 64
Zacapu, Mex. **H9** 62
Zacatecas, Mex. **F8** 62
Zachary, La., U.S. **D4** 95
Zacualtipán, Mex. **G10** 62
Zadar, Yugo. **E10** 14
Zadetkyi Kyun, i., Burma **J5** 34
Zafer Burnu, c., N. Cyp. **B4** 40
Zafra, Spain **G5** 12
Zagorsk, U.S.S.R. **E21** 22
Zagreb, Yugo. **D10** 14
Zāgros, Kūhhā-ye, mts., Iran **B5** 46
Zāhedān, Iran **C7** 46
Zahlah, Leb. **C4** 40
Zaire, ctry., Afr. **B4** 44
Zajsan, U.S.S.R. **H10** 20
Zajsan, Ozero, l., U.S.S.R. **H10** 20
Zákinthos, i., Grc. **L4** 16
Zakopane, Pol. **F19** 8
Zalaegerszeg, Hung. **I16** 8
Zambezi (Zambeze), stm., Afr. **E6** 44
Zambia, ctry., Afr. **D5** 44
Zamboanga, Phil. **D7** 32
Zamfara, stm., Nig. **F7** 42
Zamora, Ec. **J3** 58
Zamora, Spain **D6** 12
Zamora de Hidalgo, Mex. **H8** 62
Zamość, Pol. **E23** 8
Zanesville, Oh., U.S. **C4** 112
Zanjān, Iran **J7** 18
Zanzibar, Tan. **C7** 44
Zanzibar, i., Tan. **C7** 44
Zaouia el Kahla, Alg. **C7** 42
Zaouiet el Mgaïz, Tun. **M5** 14
Zaoz'ornyj, U.S.S.R. **F12** 20
Zapadno-Sibirskaja Nizmennost', pl., U.S.S.R. **E8** 20
Zapadnyj Sajan, mts., U.S.S.R. **G12** 20
Zapala, Arg. **D2** 56
Zapata, Tx., U.S. **F3** 120
Zapata, co., Tx., U.S. **F3** 120
Zapata, Península de, pen., Cuba **C7** 64
Zaporozh'ye see Zaporožje, U.S.S.R. **H5** 18
Zaporožje, U.S.S.R. **H5** 18
Zaragoza, Spain **D11** 12
Zarajsk, U.S.S.R. **G21** 22
Zárate, Arg. **C5** 56
Zaraza, Ven. **C10** 58
Zard Kūh, mtn., Iran **B5** 46
Zarembo Island, i., Ak., U.S. **m23** 79
Zarghūn Shahr, Afg. **D3** 38
Zaria, Nig. **F7** 42
Żary (Sorau), Pol. **D15** 8
Zarzal, Col. **E4** 58
Zāskār, stm., India **D7** 38
Zāskār Mountains, mts., Asia **C4** 36
Zavala, co., Tx., U.S. **E3** 120
Zavolžje, U.S.S.R. **E26** 22
Zavolžsk, U.S.S.R. **D25** 22
Zawiercie, Pol. **E19** 8
Zduńska Wola, Pol. **D18** 8
Zearing, Ia., U.S. **B4** 92
Zebulon, Ga., U.S. **C2** 87
Zebulon, N.C., U.S. **B4** 110
Zeehan, Austl. **H9** 50
Zeeland, Mi., U.S. **F5** 99
Zeerust, S. Afr. **G5** 44
Zehdenick, Ger. **C13** 8
Zeigler, Il., U.S. **F4** 90
Zeila, Som. **F3** 46
Zeitz, Ger. **D12** 8
Zeja, U.S.S.R. **G19** 20
Zeja, stm., U.S.S.R. **G19** 20
Železnogorsk-Ilimskij, U.S.S.R. **F14** 20
Zelienople, Pa., U.S. **E1** 115
Zelina, Yugo. **D11** 14
Zell, Ger. **E7** 8
Zell am See, Aus. **H12** 8
Zemio, Cen. Afr. Rep. **G11** 42
Zenica, Yugo. **E12** 14
Zenith, Wa., U.S. **f11** 124
Zenobia Peak, mtn., Co., U.S. **A2** 83
Zephyr Cove, Nv., U.S. **E2** 105
Zephyrhills, Fl., U.S. **D4** 86
Zerbst, Ger. **D12** 8
Zereh, Gowd-e, l., Afg. **D1** 36
Zermatt, Switz. **F14** 10
Zeytindağ, Tur. **K11** 16
Zgierz, Pol. **D19** 8
Zhalutegi, China **C11** 26
Zhangjiakou (Kalgan), China **C9** 26
Zhangzhou (Longxi), China **K6** 28
Zhanjiang, China **D11** 34
Zhaoan, China **L6** 28
Zhaotong, China **F7** 26
Zhaxigang, China **D8** 38
Zhejiang, prov., China **F10** 26
Zhengzhou, China **E9** 26
Zhenjiang, China **C8** 28
Zhenyuan, China **F8** 26
Zhitomir see Žitomir, U.S.S.R. **G3** 18
Zhob, stm., Pak. **E3** 38
Zhongba, China **F10** 38
Zhongshan, China **M2** 28
Zhoushan Dao, i., China **E11** 28
Zhoushan Qundao, is., China **E10** 28
Zhujiangkou, stm., Asia **M2** 28
Zhumadian, China **C3** 28
Zhungeerqi, China **D9** 26
Zhuoxian, China **D10** 26
Zhuzhou, China **H2** 28
Zia Indian Reservation, N.M., U.S. **h7** 108
Zibo, China **D10** 26
Ziebach, co., S.D., U.S. **C4** 118
Ziel, Mount, mtn., Austl. **D6** 50
Zielona Góra (Grünberg), Pol. **D15** 8
Žigalovo, U.S.S.R. **G15** 20
Žigansk, U.S.S.R. **D18** 20
Zigong, China **F7** 26
Ziguinchor, Sen. **F2** 42
Zihuatanejo, Mex. **I9** 62
Žilina, Czech. **F18** 8
Zillah, Wa., U.S. **C5** 124
Zillertaler Alpen, mts., Eur. **B6** 14
Zilwaukee, Mi., U.S. **E7** 99
Zima, U.S.S.R. **G14** 20
Zimbabwe, ctry., Afr. **E5** 44
Zimmerman, Mn., U.S. **E5** 100
Zinder, Niger **F7** 42
Zion, Il., U.S. **A6** 90
Zion National Park, Ut., U.S. **F3** 121
Zion Reservoir, res., Az., U.S. **C6** 80
Zionsville, In., U.S. **E5** 91
Zipaquirá, Col. **E5** 58
Zirkel, Mount, mtn., Co., U.S. **A4** 83
Ziro, India **G15** 38
Zitácuaro, Mex. **H9** 62
Žitomir, U.S.S.R. **G3** 18
Zittau, Ger. **E14** 8
Ziway, Lake, l., Eth. **G2** 46
Žižickoje, Ozero, l., U.S.S.R. **E14** 22
Zlarin, Yugo. **F10** 14
Žlobin, U.S.S.R. **I13** 22
Zmeinogorsk, U.S.S.R. **G10** 20
Znojmo, Czech. **G16** 8
Zolfo Springs, Fl., U.S. **E5** 86
Zomba, Mwi. **E7** 44
Zonguldak, Tur. **G14** 4
Zorita, Spain **F6** 12
Zouar, Chad **D9** 42
Zrenjanin, Yugo. **D4** 16
Zuckerhütl, mtn., Aus. **I11** 8
Zudañez, Bol. **G6** 54
Zuera, Spain **D11** 12
Zug, Switz. **E15** 10
Zugspitze, mtn., Eur. **H10** 8
Zuiderzee see IJsselmeer, Neth. **C5** 8
Zumba, Ec. **J3** 58
Zumbo, Moz. **E6** 44
Zumbro, stm., Mn., U.S. **F6** 100
Zumbrota, Mn., U.S. **F6** 100
Zuni (Zuni Pueblo), N.M., U.S. **B1** 108
Zuni, stm., U.S. **C6** 80
Zuni Indian Reservation, N.M., U.S. **B1** 108
Zuni Mountains, mts., N.M., U.S. **B1** 108
Zunyi, China **F8** 26
Zuqar, Jazīrat, i., Yemen **F3** 46
Zurich, Ont., Can. **D3** 73
Zürich, Switz. **E15** 10
Zürichsee, l., Switz. **E15** 10
Zutphen, Neth. **C6** 8
Zvishavane, Zimb. **F6** 44
Zvolen, Czech. **G19** 8
Zwettl, Aus. **G15** 8
Zwickau, Ger. **E12** 8
Zwolle, Neth. **C6** 8
Zwolle, La., U.S. **C2** 95
Zyr'anka, U.S.S.R. **D24** 20
Zyr'anovsk, U.S.S.R. **H10** 20
Żyrardów, Pol. **C20** 8

World Political Information

This table lists the area, population, population density, form of government, political status, and capital for every country in the world.

The populations are estimates for January 1, 1991 made by Rand McNally on the basis of official data, United Nations estimates, and other available information. Area figures include inland water.

The political units listed in the table are categorized by political status, as follows: A–independent countries; B–internally independent political entities which are under the protection of other countries in matters of defense and foreign affairs; C–colonies and other dependent political units; D–the major administrative subdivisions of Australia, Canada, China, the Soviet Union, the United Kingdom, the United States, and Yugoslavia. For comparison, the table also includes the continents and the world.

All footnotes to this table appear on page 196.

Country, Division or Region English (Conventional)	Area in sq. mi.	Area in sq. km.	Estimated Population 1/1/91	Pop. per sq. mi.	Pop. per sq. km.	Form of Government and Political Status	Capital
† Afghanistan	251,826	652,225	16,400,000	65	25	Republic ... A	Kābul
Africa	11,700,000	30,300,000	671,800,000	57	22		
Alabama	51,704	133,913	4,063,000	79	30	State (U.S.) ... D	Montgomery
Alaska	591,004	1,530,693	560,000	0.9	0.4	State (U.S.) ... D	Juneau
† Albania	11,100	28,748	3,318,000	299	115	Socialist republic ... A	Tiranë
Alberta	255,287	661,190	2,473,000	9.7	3.7	Province (Canada) ... D	Edmonton
† Algeria	919,595	2,381,741	26,115,000	28	11	Socialist republic ... A	Alger (Algiers)
American Samoa	77	199	42,000	545	211	Unincorporated territory (U.S.) ... C	Pago Pago
Andorra	175	453	52,000	297	115	Coprincipality (Spanish and French protection) .. B	Andorra
† Angola	481,354	1,246,700	10,155,000	21	8.1	Socialist republic ... A	Luanda
Anguilla	35	91	7,000	200	77	Dependent territory (U.K. protection) ... B	The Valley
Anhui	53,668	139,000	56,390,000	1,051	406	Province (China) ... D	Hefei
Antarctica	5,400,000	14,000,000	[1]	—	—		
† Antigua and Barbuda	171	443	80,000	468	181	Parliamentary state ... A	St. Johns
† Argentina	1,073,400	2,780,092	32,485,000	30	12	Republic ... A	Buenos Aires
Arizona	114,002	295,264	3,700,000	32	13	State (U.S.) ... D	Phoenix
Arkansas	53,191	137,764	2,384,000	45	17	State (U.S.) ... D	Little Rock
Arm'anskaja S.S.R. (Armenia)	11,506	29,800	3,350,000	291	112	Soviet socialist republic (U.S.S.R.) ... D	Jerevan
Aruba	75	193	66,000	880	342	Self-governing terr. (Netherlands protection) ... B	Oranjestad
Asia	17,300,000	44,900,000	3,232,000,000	187	72		
† Australia	2,966,155	7,682,300	17,260,000	5.8	2.2	Federal parliamentary state ... A	Canberra
Australian Capital Territory	927	2,400	286,000	309	119	Territory (Australia) ... D	Canberra
† Austria	32,377	83,855	7,681,000	237	92	Federal republic ... A	Wien (Vienna)
Azerbajdžanskaja S.S.R. (Azerbaijan)	33,436	86,600	7,140,000	214	82	Soviet socialist republic (U.S.S.R.) ... D	Baku
† Bahamas	5,380	13,934	256,000	48	18	Parliamentary state ... A	Nassau
† Bahrain	267	691	501,000	1,876	725	Monarchy ... A	Al-Manāmah
† Bangladesh	55,598	143,998	109,540,000	1,970	761	Islamic republic ... A	Dhaka
† Barbados	166	430	259,000	1,560	602	Parliamentary state ... A	Bridgetown
Beijing Shi	6,487	16,800	10,470,000	1,614	623	Autonomous City ... D	Beijing (Peking)
† Belgium	11,783	30,518	9,927,000	842	325	Constitutional monarchy ... A	Bruxelles (Brussels)
† Belize	8,866	22,963	204,000	23	8.9	Parliamentary state ... A	Belmopan
† Belorusskaja S.S.R. (Byelorussia)	80,155	207,600	10,370,000	129	50	Soviet socialist republic (U.S.S.R.) ... D	Minsk
† Benin	43,475	112,600	4,819,000	111	43	Republic ... A	Porto-Novo and Cotonou
Bermuda	21	54	60,000	2,857	1,111	Dependent territory (U.K.) ... C	Hamilton
† Bhutan	17,954	46,500	1,580,000	88	34	Monarchy (Indian protection) ... B	Thimphu
† Bolivia	424,165	1,098,581	7,507,000	18	6.8	Republic ... A	La Paz and Sucre
Bosnia-Hercegovina	19,741	51,129	4,492,000	228	88	Republic (Yugoslavia) ... D	Sarajevo
† Botswana	224,711	582,000	1,324,000	5.9	2.3	Republic ... A	Gaborone
† Brazil	3,286,488	8,511,965	152,050,000	46	18	Federal republic ... A	Brasília
British Columbia	365,948	947,800	3,075,000	8.4	3.2	Province (Canada) ... D	Victoria
British Indian Ocean Territory	23	60	—	—	—	Dependent territory (U.K.) ... C	
† Brunei	2,226	5,765	261,000	117	45	Monarchy ... A	Bandar Seri Begawan
† Bulgaria	42,823	110,912	9,008,000	210	81	Republic ... A	Sofija (Sofia)
† Burkina Faso	105,869	274,200	9,247,000	87	34	Provisional military government ... A	Ouagadougou
† Burma (Myanmar)	261,228	676,577	41,690,000	160	62	Provisional military government ... A	Yangon (Rangoon)
† Burundi	10,745	27,830	5,541,000	516	199	Provisional military government ... A	Bujumbura
California	158,704	411,041	29,905,000	188	73	State (U.S.) ... D	Sacramento
† Cambodia	69,898	181,035	8,345,000	119	46	Socialist republic ... A	Phnum Pénh (Phnom Penh)
† Cameroon	183,569	475,442	12,110,000	66	25	Republic ... A	Yaoundé
† Canada	3,849,674	9,970,610	26,710,000	6.9	2.7	Federal parliamentary state ... A	Ottawa
† Cape Verde	1,557	4,033	381,000	245	94	Republic ... A	Praia
Cayman Islands	100	259	26,000	260	100	Dependent territory (U.K.) ... C	Georgetown
† Central African Republic	240,535	622,984	2,917,000	12	4.7	Republic ... A	Bangui
† Chad	495,755	1,284,000	5,122,000	10	4.0	Republic ... A	N'Djamena
† Chile	292,135	756,626	13,270,000	45	18	Republic ... A	Santiago
† China (excl. Taiwan)	3,689,631	9,556,100	1,141,530,000	309	119	Socialist republic ... A	Beijing (Peking)
Christmas Island	52	135	1,500	29	11	External territory (Australia) ... C	
Cocos (Keeling) Islands	5.4	14	700	130	50	Part of Australia ... C	
† Colombia	440,831	1,141,748	31,370,000	71	27	Republic ... A	Bogotá
Colorado	104,094	269,602	3,400,000	33	13	State (U.S.) ... D	Denver
† Comoros	863	2,235	498,000	577	223	Federal Islamic republic ... A	Moroni
† Congo	132,047	342,000	2,346,000	18	6.9	Socialist republic ... A	Brazzaville
Connecticut	5,019	12,999	3,285,000	655	253	State (U.S.) ... D	Hartford
Cook Islands	91	236	18,000	198	76	Self-governing territory (New Zealand protection) ... B	Avarua
† Costa Rica	19,730	51,100	3,032,000	154	59	Republic ... A	San José
Croatia[9]	21,829	56,538	4,772,000	219	84	Republic (Yugoslavia) ... D	Zagreb
† Cuba	42,804	110,861	10,805,000	252	97	Socialist republic ... A	La Habana (Havana)
† Cyprus (excl. North Cyprus)	2,276	5,896	528,000	232	90	Republic ... A	Nicosia (Levkosía)
Cyprus, North[2]	1,295	3,355	176,000	136	52	Republic ... A	Nicosia (Lefkoşa)
† Czechoslovakia	49,382	127,899	15,690,000	318	123	Federal republic ... A	Praha (Prague)
Delaware	2,045	5,297	677,000	331	128	State (U.S.) ... D	Dover
† Denmark	16,638	43,093	5,138,000	309	119	Constitutional monarchy ... A	København (Copenhagen)
District of Columbia	69	179	577,000	8,362	3,223	Federal district (U.S.) ... D	Washington
† Djibouti	8,958	23,200	341,000	38	15	Republic ... A	Djibouti
† Dominica	305	790	89,000	292	113	Republic ... A	Roseau
† Dominican Republic	18,704	48,442	7,245,000	387	150	Republic ... A	Santo Domingo
† Ecuador	109,484	283,561	10,930,000	100	39	Republic ... A	Quito
† Egypt	386,662	1,001,449	54,910,000	142	55	Socialist republic ... A	Al-Qāhirah (Cairo)
† El Salvador	8,124	21,041	5,363,000	660	255	Republic ... A	San Salvador
England	50,363	130,439	47,820,000	950	367	Administrative division (U.K.) ... D	London
† Equatorial Guinea	10,831	28,051	353,000	33	13	Republic ... A	Malabo
Estonskaja S.S.R. (Estonia)	17,413	45,100	1,602,000	92	36	Soviet socialist republic (U.S.S.R.) ... D	Tallinn
† Ethiopia	483,123	1,251,282	52,206,000	108	42	Socialist republic ... A	Adis Abeba
Europe	3,800,000	9,800,000	693,500,000	183	71		
Faeroe Islands	540	1,399	48,000	89	34	Self-governing territory (Danish protection) ... B	Tórshavn
Falkland Islands[3]	4,700	12,173	2,200	0.5	0.2	Dependent territory (U.K.) ... C	Stanley
† Fiji	7,078	18,333	732,000	103	40	Republic ... A	Suva
† Finland	130,559	338,145	4,984,000	38	15	Republic ... A	Helsinki (Helsingfors)
Florida	58,668	151,949	13,150,000	224	87	State (U.S.) ... D	Tallahassee

World Political Information

Country, Division or Region English (Conventional)	Area in sq. mi.	Area in sq. km.	Estimated Population 1/1/91	Pop. per sq. mi.	Pop. per sq. km.	Form of Government and Political Status	Capital
† France (excl. Overseas Departments)	211,208	547,026	56,580,000	268	103	Republic A	Paris
French Guiana	35,135	91,000	100,000	2.8	1.1	Overseas department (France) C	Cayenne
French Polynesia	1,544	4,000	199,000	129	50	Overseas territory (France) C	Papeete
Fujian	46,332	120,000	29,795,000	643	248	Province (China) D	Fuzhou
† Gabon	103,347	267,667	1,074,000	10	4.0	Republic A	Libreville
† Gambia	4,361	11,295	831,000	191	74	Republic A	Banjul
Gansu	173,746	450,000	22,375,000	129	50	Province (China) D	Lanzhou
Georgia	58,914	152,587	6,540,000	111	43	State (U.S.) D	Atlanta
Gruzinskaja S.S.R. (Georgia)	26,911	69,700	5,535,000	206	79	Soviet socialist republic (U.S.S.R.) D	Tbilisi
† Germany	108,333	357,040	79,220,000	575	222	Federal republic A	Berlin and Bonn
† Ghana	92,098	238,533	15,550,000	169	65	Provisional military government A	Accra
Gibraltar	2.3	6.0	33,000	14,348	5,500	Dependent territory (U.K.) C	Gibraltar
† Greece	50,962	131,990	10,075,000	198	76	Republic A	Athínai (Athens)
Greenland	840,004	2,175,600	57,000	0.1	—	Self-governing territory (Danish protection) B	Godthåb
† Grenada	133	344	114,000	857	331	Parliamentary state A	St. George's
Guadeloupe (incl. Dependencies)	687	1,780	350,000	509	197	Overseas department (France) C	Basse-Terre
Guam	209	541	144,000	689	266	Unincorporated territory (U.S.) C	Agana
Guangdong	68,726	178,000	61,850,000	900	347	Province (China) D	Guangzhou (Canton)
† Guatemala	42,042	108,889	9,324,000	222	86	Republic A	Guatemala
Guernsey (incl. Dependencies)	30	78	56,000	1,867	718	Bailiwick (Channel Islands) C	St. Peter Port
† Guinea	94,926	245,857	7,364,000	78	30	Provisional military government A	Conakry
† Guinea-Bissau	13,948	36,125	1,011,000	72	28	Republic A	Bissau
Guizhou	65,637	170,000	32,650,000	497	192	Province (China) D	Guiyang
† Guyana	83,000	214,969	1,000,000	12	4.7	Republic A	Georgetown
Hainan	13,127	34,000	6,872,000	524	202	Province (China) D	Haikou
† Haiti	10,714	27,750	5,745,000	536	207	Republic A	Port-au-Prince
Hawaii	6,473	16,765	1,140,000	176	68	State (U.S.) D	Honolulu
Hebei	73,359	190,000	61,070,000	832	321	Province (China) D	Shijiazhuang
Heilongjiang	181,082	469,000	36,300,000	200	77	Province (China) D	Harbin
Henan	64,479	167,000	84,700,000	1,314	507	Province (China) D	Zhengzhou
† Honduras	43,277	112,088	5,181,000	120	46	Republic A	Tegucigalpa
Hong Kong	414	1,072	6,009,000	14,514	5,605	Chinese territory under British administration C	Victoria (Xianggang)
Hubei	72,356	187,400	54,110,000	748	289	Province (China) D	Wuhan
Hunan	81,081	210,000	61,640,000	760	294	Province (China) D	Changsha
† Hungary	35,920	93,033	10,540,000	293	113	Republic A	Budapest
† Iceland	39,769	103,000	260,000	6.5	2.5	Republic A	Reykjavík
Idaho	83,566	216,435	1,028,000	12	4.8	State (U.S.) D	Boise
Illinois	57,872	149,888	11,560,000	200	77	State (U.S.) D	Springfield
† India (incl. part of Jammu and Kashmir)	1,237,062	3,203,975	836,170,000	676	261	Federal republic A	New Delhi
Indiana	36,417	94,320	5,618,000	154	60	State (U.S.) D	Indianapolis
† Indonesia	741,101	1,919,443	193,080,000	261	101	Republic A	Jakarta
Inner Mongolia (Nei Mongol Zizhiqu)	456,759	1,183,000	21,915,000	48	19	Autonomous region (China) D	Hohhot
Iowa	56,275	145,752	2,765,000	49	19	State (U.S.) D	Des Moines
† Iran	636,372	1,648,196	56,810,000	89	34	Islamic republic A	Tehrān
† Iraq	169,235	438,317	18,920,000	112	43	Republic A	Baghdād
† Ireland	27,137	70,285	3,471,000	128	49	Republic A	Dublin (Baile Átha Cliath)
Isle of Man	221	572	68,000	308	119	Self-governing territory (U.K. protection) B	Douglas
† Israel	8,019	20,770	4,518,000	563	218	Republic A	Yerushalayim (Jerusalem)
Israeli Occupied Areas[4]	2,947	7,632	1,989,000	675	261		
† Italy	116,324	301,277	57,630,000	495	191	Republic A	Roma (Rome)
† Ivory Coast	124,518	322,500	12,305,000	99	38	Republic A	Abidjan and Yamoussoukro[5]
† Jamaica	4,244	10,991	2,425,000	571	221	Parliamentary state A	Kingston
† Japan	145,870	377,801	123,850,000	849	328	Constitutional monarchy A	Tōkyō
Jersey	45	116	82,000	1,822	707	Bailiwick (Channel Islands) C	St. Helier
Jiangsu	39,614	102,600	67,580,000	1,706	659	Province (China) D	Nanjing
Jiangxi	64,325	166,600	38,015,000	591	228	Province (China) D	Nanchang
Jilin	72,201	187,000	25,115,000	348	134	Province (China) D	Changchun
† Jordan	35,135	91,000	3,112,000	89	34	Constitutional monarchy A	'Ammān
Kansas	82,282	213,109	2,508,000	30	12	State (U.S.) D	Topeka
Kazachskaja S.S.R. (Kazakhstan)	1,049,156	2,717,300	16,810,000	16	6.2	Soviet socialist republic (U.S.S.R.) D	Alma-Ata
Kentucky	40,414	104,672	3,737,000	92	36	State (U.S.) D	Frankfort
† Kenya	224,961	582,646	26,400,000	117	45	Republic A	Nairobi
Kirgizskaja S.S.R. (Kirghizia)	76,641	198,500	4,370,000	57	22	Soviet socialist republic (U.S.S.R.) D	Frunze (Pišpek)
Kiribati	280	726	74,000	264	102	Republic A	Bairiki
Korea, North	46,540	120,538	23,335,000	501	194	Socialist republic A	P'yŏngyang
Korea, South	38,230	99,016	42,975,000	1,124	434	Republic A	Sŏul (Seoul)
† Kuwait	6,880	17,818	2,189,000	318	123	Constitutional monarchy A	Al-Kuwayt (Kuwait)
Kwangsi Chuang (Guangxi Zhuang Zizhiqu)	91,236	236,300	42,695,000	468	181	Autonomous region (China) D	Nanning
† Laos	91,429	236,800	4,069,000	45	17	Socialist republic A	Viangchan (Vientiane)
Latvijskaja S.S.R. (Latvia)	24,595	63,700	2,738,000	111	43	Soviet socialist republic (U.S.S.R.) D	Rīga
† Lebanon	4,015	10,400	3,360,000	837	323	Republic A	Bayrūt (Beirut)
† Lesotho	11,720	30,355	1,764,000	151	58	Constitutional monarchy A	Maseru
Liaoning	56,255	145,700	40,295,000	716	277	Province (China) D	Shenyang (Mukden)
† Liberia	38,250	99,067	2,689,000	70	27	Republic A	Monrovia
† Libya	679,362	1,759,540	4,271,000	6.3	2.4	Socialist republic A	Ṭarābulus (Tripoli)
† Liechtenstein	62	160	31,000	500	194	Constitutional monarchy A	Vaduz
Litovskaja S.S.R. (Lithuania)[6]	25,174	65,200	3,760,000	149	58	Soviet socialist republic (U.S.S.R.) D	Vilnius
Louisiana	47,750	123,672	4,180,000	88	34	State (U.S.) D	Baton Rouge
† Luxembourg	998	2,586	379,000	380	147	Constitutional monarchy A	Luxembourg
Macau	6.6	17	462,000	70,000	27,176	Chinese territory under Portuguese administration C	Macau (Aomen)
Macedonia	9,928	25,713	2,109,000	212	82	Republic (Yugoslavia) D	Skopje
† Madagascar	226,658	587,041	11,995,000	53	20	Republic A	Antananarivo
Maine	33,265	86,156	1,254,000	38	15	State (U.S.) D	Augusta
† Malawi	45,747	118,484	8,432,000	184	71	Republic A	Lilongwe
† Malaysia	129,251	334,758	17,915,000	139	54	Federal constitutional monarchy A	Kuala Lumpur
† Maldives	115	298	215,000	1,870	721	Republic A	Male
† Mali	478,767	1,240,000	8,205,000	17	6.6	Republic A	Bamako
† Malta	122	316	354,000	2,902	1,120	Republic A	Valletta
Manitoba	250,947	649,950	1,116,000	4.4	1.7	Province (Canada) D	Winnipeg
Marshall Islands	70	181	44,000	629	243	Republic (U.S. protection) B	Majuro (island)
Martinique	425	1,100	341,000	802	310	Overseas department (France) C	Fort-de-France
Maryland	10,461	27,094	4,900,000	468	181	State (U.S.) D	Annapolis
Massachusetts	8,286	21,461	6,044,000	729	282	State (U.S.) D	Boston

Country, Division or Region English (Conventional)	Area in sq. mi.	Area in sq. km.	Estimated Population 1/1/91	Pop. per sq. mi.	Pop. per sq. km.	Form of Government and Political Status	Capital
† Mauritania	395,956	*1,025,520*	2,070,000	5.2	*2.0*	Provisional military government A	Nouakchott
† Mauritius (incl. Dependencies)	788	*2,040*	1,091,000	1,385	*535*	Parliamentary state A	Port Louis
Mayotte[7]	144	*374*	85,000	590	*227*	Territorial collectivity (France) C	Dzaoudzi and Mamoudzou[5]
† Mexico	756,066	*1,958,201*	86,675,000	115	*44*	Federal republic A	Ciudad de México (Mexico City)
Michigan	97,107	*251,506*	9,180,000	95	*37*	State (U.S.) D	Lansing
Micronesia, Federated States of	271	*702*	94,000	347	*134*	Republic (U.S. protection) B	Kolonia
Midway Islands	2.0	*5.2*	500	250	*96*	Unincorporated territory (U.S.) C	
Minnesota	86,614	*224,329*	4,439,000	51	*20*	State (U.S.) D	St. Paul
Mississippi	47,691	*123,519*	2,583,000	54	*21*	State (U.S.) D	Jackson
Missouri	69,697	*180,514*	5,192,000	74	*29*	State (U.S.) D	Jefferson City
Moldavskaja S.S.R. (Moldavia)	13,012	*33,700*	4,400,000	338	*131*	Soviet socialist republic (U.S.S.R.) D	Kišin'ov (Kishinev)
Monaco	0.7	*1.9*	29,000	41,429	*15,263*	Constitutional monarchy A	Monaco
† Mongolia	604,829	*1,566,500*	2,203,000	3.6	*1.4*	Socialist republic A	Ulaanbaatar (Ulan Bator)
Montana	147,045	*380,845*	803,000	5.5	*2.1*	State (U.S.) D	Helena
Montenegro	5,333	*13,812*	638,000	120	*66*	Republic (Yugoslavia) D	Titograd
Montserrat	39	*102*	12,000	308	*118*	Dependent territory (U.K.) C	Plymouth
† Morocco (excl. Western Sahara)	172,414	*446,550*	26,575,000	154	*60*	Constitutional monarchy A	Rabat
† Mozambique	308,642	*799,379*	15,785,000	51	*20*	Republic A	Maputo
† Namibia (excl. Walvis Bay)	317,818	*823,144*	1,904,000	6.0	*2.3*	Republic A	Windhoek
Nauru	8.1	*21*	9,000	1,111	*429*	Republic A	Yaren District
Nebraska	77,350	*200,336*	1,605,000	21	*8.0*	State (U.S.) D	Lincoln
† Nepal	56,827	*147,181*	19,390,000	341	*132*	Constitutional monarchy A	Kāṭhmāṇḍāũ
† Netherlands	16,133	*41,785*	14,980,000	929	*359*	Constitutional monarchy A	Amsterdam and 's-Gravenhage (The Hague)
Netherlands Antilles	309	*800*	194,000	628	*243*	Self-governing territory (Netherlands protection) B	Willemstad
Nevada	110,562	*286,354*	1,400,000	13	*4.9*	State (U.S.) D	Carson City
New Brunswick	28,355	*73,440*	737,000	26	*10*	Province (Canada) D	Fredericton
New Caledonia	7,358	*19,058*	170,000	23	*8.9*	Overseas territory (France) C	Nouméa
Newfoundland	156,649	*405,720*	585,000	3.7	*1.4*	Province (Canada) D	St. John's
New Hampshire	9,278	*24,030*	1,129,000	122	*47*	State (U.S.) D	Concord
New Jersey	7,787	*20,168*	7,775,000	998	*386*	State (U.S.) D	Trenton
New Mexico	121,594	*314,927*	1,550,000	13	*4.9*	State (U.S.) D	Santa Fe
New South Wales	309,500	*801,600*	5,902,000	19	*7.4*	State (Australia) D	Sydney
New York	52,737	*136,588*	17,980,000	341	*132*	State (U.S.) D	Albany
† New Zealand	103,519	*268,112*	3,483,000	34	*13*	Parliamentary state A	Wellington
† Nicaragua	50,054	*129,640*	3,659,000	73	*28*	Republic A	Managua
† Niger	489,191	*1,267,000*	7,848,000	16	*6.2*	Provisional military government A	Niamey
† Nigeria	356,669	*923,768*	112,830,000	316	*122*	Provisional military government A	Lagos and Abuja[5]
Ningsia Hui (Ningxia Huizu Zizhiqu)	25,637	*66,400*	4,566,000	178	*69*	Autonomous region (China) D	Yinchuan
Niue	102	*263*	1,800	18	*6.8*	Self-governing terr. (New Zealand protection) B	Alofi
Norfolk Island	14	*36*	2,000	143	*56*	External territory (Australia) C	Kingston
North America	9,400,000	*24,400,000*	426,800,000	45	*17*		
North Carolina	52,669	*136,412*	6,696,000	127	*49*	State (U.S.) D	Raleigh
North Dakota	70,702	*183,117*	634,000	9.0	*3.5*	State (U.S.) D	Bismarck
Northern Ireland	5,452	*14,121*	1,596,000	293	*113*	Administrative division (U.K.) D	Belfast
Northern Mariana Islands	184	*477*	24,000	130	*50*	Commonwealth (U.S. protection) B	Saipan (island)
Northern Territory	519,771	*1,346,200*	159,000	0.3	*0.1*	Territory (Australia) D	Darwin
Northwest Territories	1,322,910	*3,426,320*	53,000	—	—	Territory (Canada) D	Yellowknife
† Norway (incl. Svalbard and Jan Mayen)	149,412	*386,975*	4,271,000	29	*11*	Constitutional monarchy A	Oslo
Nova Scotia	21,425	*55,490*	911,000	43	*16*	Province (Canada) D	Halifax
Oceania (incl. Australia)	3,300,000	*8,500,000*	26,700,000	8.1	*3.1*		
Ohio	44,786	*115,995*	10,770,000	240	*93*	State (U.S.) D	Columbus
Oklahoma	69,957	*181,188*	3,185,000	46	*18*	State (U.S.) D	Oklahoma City
† Oman	82,030	*212,457*	1,366,000	17	*6.4*	Monarchy A	Masqaṭ (Muscat)
Ontario	412,581	*1,068,580*	9,717,000	24	*9.1*	Province (Canada) D	Toronto
Oregon	97,076	*251,426*	2,884,000	30	*11*	State (U.S.) D	Salem
Pacific Islands, Trust Territory of the	196	*508*	15,000	77	*30*	U.N. trusteeship (U.S. administration) B	
† Pakistan (incl. part of Jammu and Kashmir)	339,732	*879,902*	114,380,000	337	*130*	Federal Islamic republic A	Islāmābād
Palau	196	*508*	15,000	77	*30*	Part of Trust Territory of the Pacific Islands B	Koror
† Panama	29,157	*75,517*	2,445,000	84	*32*	Republic A	Panamá
† Papua New Guinea	178,704	*462,840*	3,641,000	20	*7.9*	Parliamentary state A	Port Moresby
† Paraguay	157,048	*406,752*	4,338,000	28	*11*	Republic A	Asunción
Pennsylvania	46,047	*119,261*	11,765,000	256	*99*	State (U.S.) D	Harrisburg
† Peru	496,225	*1,285,216*	22,610,000	46	*18*	Republic A	Lima
† Philippines	115,831	*300,000*	62,170,000	537	*207*	Republic A	Manila
Pitcairn (incl. Dependencies)	19	*49*	50	2.6	*1.0*	Dependent territory (U.K.) C	Adamstown
† Poland	120,728	*312,683*	38, ,000	315	*122*	Republic A	Warszawa (Warsaw)
† Portugal	35,516	*91,985*	10,560,000	297	*115*	Republic A	Lisboa (Lisbon)
Prince Edward Island	2,185	*5,660*	134,000	61	*24*	Province (Canada) D	Charlottetown
Puerto Rico	3,515	*9,104*	3,604,000	1,025	*396*	Commonwealth (U.S. protection) B	San Juan
† Qatar	4,416	*11,437*	514,000	116	*45*	Monarchy A	Ad-Dawḥah (Doha)
Qinghai	277,994	*720,000*	4,452,000	16	*6.2*	Province (China) D	Xining
Quebec	594,860	*1,540,680*	6,840,000	11	*4.4*	Province (Canada) D	Québec
Queensland	666,876	*1,727,200*	2,923,000	4.4	*1.7*	State (Australia) D	Brisbane
Reunion	969	*2,510*	600,000	619	*239*	Overseas department (France) C	Saint-Denis
Rhode Island	1,212	*3,139*	1,003,000	828	*320*	State (U.S.) D	Providence
† Romania	91,699	*237,500*	23,325,000	254	*98*	Republic A	București (Bucharest)
Russian Soviet Federative Socialist Republic	6,592,849	*17,075,400*	149,730,000	23	*8.8*	Soviet socialist republic (U.S.S.R.) D	Moskva (Moscow)
† Rwanda	10,169	*26,338*	7,748,000	762	*294*	Provisional military government A	Kigali
St. Helena (incl. Dependencies)	121	*314*	7,700	64	*25*	Dependent territory (U.K.) C	Jamestown
† St. Kitts and Nevis	104	*269*	44,000	423	*164*	Parliamentary state A	Basseterre
† St. Lucia	238	*616*	152,000	639	*247*	Parliamentary state A	Castries
St. Pierre and Miquelon	93	*242*	6,800	73	*28*	Territorial collectivity (France) C	Saint-Pierre
† St. Vincent and the Grenadines	150	*388*	115,000	767	*296*	Parliamentary state A	Kingstown
San Marino	24	*61*	24,000	1,000	*393*	Republic A	San Marino
† Sao Tome and Principe	372	*964*	127,000	341	*132*	Republic A	São Tomé
Saskatchewan	251,866	*652,330*	1,042,000	4.1	*1.6*	Province (Canada) D	Regina
† Saudi Arabia	830,000	*2,149,690*	15,285,000	18	*7.1*	Monarchy A	Ar-Riyāḍ (Riyadh)
Scotland	30,414	*78,772*	5,090,000	167	*65*	Administrative division (U.K.) D	Edinburgh
† Senegal	75,951	*196,712*	7,257,000	96	*37*	Republic A	Dakar
Serbia	34,116	*88,361*	9,919,000	290	*112*	Republic (Yugoslavia) D	Beograd
† Seychelles	175	*453*	68,000	389	*150*	Republic A	Victoria

World Political Information

Country, Division or Region English (Conventional)	Area in sq. mi.	Area in sq. km.	Estimated Population 1/1/91	Pop. per sq. mi.	Pop. per sq. km.	Form of Government and Political Status	Capital
Shandong	59,074	*153,000*	84,470,000	1,430	*552*	Province (China) D	Jinan (Tsinan)
Shanghai Shi	2,394	*6,200*	13,240,000	5,530	*2,135*	Autonomous city (China) D	Shanghai
Shansi (Shānxī)	60,232	*156,000*	28,765,000	478	*184*	Province (China) D	Taiyuan
Shensi (Shǎnxī)	79,151	*205,000*	33,105,000	418	*161*	Province (China) D	Xi'an (Sian)
Sichuan	220,078	*570,000*	111,640,000	507	*196*	Province (China) D	Chengdu
† Sierra Leone	27,925	*72,325*	4,222,000	151	*58*	Republic A	Freetown
† Singapore	246	*636*	2,757,000	11,207	*4,335*	Republic A	Singapore
Sinkiang (Xinjiang Uygur Zizhiqu)	617,764	*1,600,000*	15,070,000	24	*9.4*	Autonomous region (China) D	Ürümqi
Slovenia[9]	7,819	*20,251*	1,977,000	253	*98*	Republic (Yugoslavia) D	Ljubljana
† Solomon Islands	10,954	*28,370*	322,000	29	*11*	Parliamentary state A	Honiara
† Somalia	246,201	*637,657*	8,499,000	35	*13*	Provisional military government A	Muqdisho (Mogadishu)
† South Africa (incl. Walvis Bay)	433,680	*1,123,226*	40,055,000	92	*36*	Republic A	Pretoria and Cape Town
South America	6,900,000	*17,800,000*	299,200,000	43	*17*		
South Australia	379,925	*984,000*	1,458,000	3.8	*1.5*	State (Australia) D	Adelaide
South Carolina	31,116	*80,590*	3,550,000	114	*44*	State (U.S.) D	Columbia
South Dakota	77,120	*199,740*	702,000	9.1	*3.5*	State (U.S.) D	Pierre
South Georgia and the South Sandwich Islands	1,450	*3,755*	—	—	—	Dependent territory (U.K.) C	
† Spain	194,885	*504,750*	40,190,000	206	*80*	Constitutional monarchy A	Madrid
Spanish North Africa[8]	12	*32*	121,000	10,083	*3,781*	Five possessions (Spain) C	
† Sri Lanka	24,962	*64,652*	17,135,000	686	*265*	Socialist republic A	Colombo and Kotte
† Sudan	967,500	*2,505,813*	25,515,000	26	*10*	Islamic Republic A	Al-Kharṭūm (Khartoum)
† Suriname	63,251	*163,820*	412,000	6.5	*2.5*	Republic A	Paramaribo
† Swaziland	6,704	*17,364*	791,000	118	*46*	Monarchy A	Mbabane and Lobamba
† Sweden	173,732	*449,964*	8,602,000	50	*19*	Constitutional monarchy A	Stockholm
Switzerland	15,943	*41,293*	6,737,000	423	*163*	Federal republic A	Bern (Berne)
† Syria	71,498	*185,180*	12,315,000	172	*67*	Socialist republic A	Dimashq (Damascus)
Taiwan	13,900	*36,002*	20,565,000	1,479	*571*	Republic A	T'aipei
Tadžikskaja S.S.R. (Tajikstan)	55,251	*143,100*	5,185,000	94	*36*	Soviet socialist republic (U.S.S.R.) D	Dušanbe
† Tanzania	364,900	*945,087*	26,065,000	71	*28*	Republic A	Dar es Salaam and Dodoma[5]
Tasmania	26,178	*67,800*	461,000	18	*6.8*	State (Australia) D	Hobart
Tennessee	42,143	*109,150*	4,916,000	117	*45*	State (U.S.) D	Nashville
Texas	266,805	*691,022*	17,300,000	65	*25*	State (U.S.) D	Austin
† Thailand	198,115	*513,115*	56,860,000	287	*111*	Constitutional monarchy A	Krung Thep (Bangkok)
Tianjin Shi	4,363	*11,300*	8,790,000	2,015	*778*	Autonomous city (China) D	Tianjin (Tientsin)
Tibet (Xizang Zizhiqu)	471,045	*1,220,000*	2,283,000	4.8	*1.9*	Autonomous region (China) D	Lhasa
† Togo	21,925	*56,785*	3,627,000	165	*64*	Republic A	Lomé
Tokelau Islands	4.6	*12*	1,800	391	*150*	Island territory (New Zealand) C	
Tonga	290	*750*	102,000	352	*136*	Constitutional monarchy A	Nuku'alofa
† Trinidad and Tobago	1,980	*5,128*	1,242,000	627	*242*	Republic A	Port of Spain
† Tunisia	63,170	*163,610*	8,188,000	130	*50*	Republic A	Tunis
† Turkey	300,948	*779,452*	63,720,000	212	*82*	Republic A	Ankara
Turkmenskaja S.S.R. (Turkmenistan)	188,456	*488,100*	3,585,000	19	*7.3*	Soviet socialist republic (U.S.S.R.) D	Aščhabad
Turks and Caicos Islands	193	*500*	13,000	67	*26*	Dependent territory (U.K.) C	Grand Turk
Tuvalu	10	*26*	8,900	890	*342*	Parliamentary state A	Funafuti
† Uganda	93,104	*241,139*	17,890,000	192	*74*	Republic A	Kampala
† Ukrainskaja S.S.R. (Ukraine)	233,090	*603,700*	52,520,000	225	*87*	Soviet socialist republic (U.S.S.R.) D	Kijev (Kiev)
† Union of Soviet Socialist Republics	8,600,387	*22,274,900*	291,310,000	34	*13*	Federal socialist republic A	Moskva (Moscow)
† United Arab Emirates	32,278	*83,600*	2,321,000	72	*28*	Federation of monarchs A	Abū Ẓaby (Abu Dhabi)
† United Kingdom	94,248	*244,100*	57,380,000	609	*235*	Constitutional monarchy A	London
† United States	3,679,245	*9,529,202*	250,800,000	68	*26*	Federal republic A	Washington
† Uruguay	68,500	*177,414*	3,105,000	45	*18*	Republic A	Montevideo
Utah	84,902	*219,895*	1,765,000	21	*8.0*	State (U.S.) D	Salt Lake City
Uzbekskaja S.S.R. (Uzbekistan)	172,742	*447,400*	20,215,000	117	*45*	Soviet socialist republic (U.S.S.R.) D	Taškent
† Vanuatu	4,707	*12,190*	148,000	31	*12*	Republic A	Port Vila
Vatican City	0.2	*0.4*	800	4,000	*2,000*	Ecclesiastical city-state A	Città del Vaticano (Vatican City)
† Venezuela	352,145	*912,050*	19,995,000	57	*22*	Federal republic A	Caracas
Vermont	9,614	*24,900*	577,000	60	*23*	State (U.S.) D	Montpelier
Victoria	87,877	*227,600*	4,428,000	50	*19*	State (Australia) D	Melbourne
† Vietnam	128,066	*331,689*	67,850,000	530	*205*	Socialist republic A	Ha Noi
Virginia	40,763	*105,576*	6,275,000	154	*59*	State (U.S.) D	Richmond
Virgin Islands (U.S.)	133	*344*	117,000	880	*340*	Unincorporated territory (U.S.) C	Charlotte Amalie
Virgin Islands, British	59	*153*	14,000	237	*92*	Dependent territory (U.K.) C	Road Town
Wake Island	3.0	*7.8*	300	100	*38*	Unincorporated territory (U.S.) C	
Wales	8,019	*20,768*	2,874,000	358	*138*	Administrative division (U.K.) D	Cardiff
Wallis and Futuna	98	*255*	16,000	163	*63*	Overseas territory (France) C	Mata-Utu
Washington	68,139	*176,479*	4,920,000	72	*28*	State (U.S.) D	Olympia
Western Australia	975,101	*2,525,500*	1,643,000	1.7	*0.7*	State (Australia) D	Perth
Western Sahara	102,703	*266,000*	200,000	1.9	*0.8*	Occupied by Morocco	
† Western Samoa	1,093	*2,831*	188,000	172	*66*	Constitutional monarchy A	Apia
West Virginia	24,236	*62,771*	1,831,000	76	*29*	State (U.S.) D	Charleston
Wisconsin	66,213	*171,491*	4,966,000	75	*29*	State (U.S.) D	Madison
Wyoming	97,808	*253,322*	450,000	4.6	*1.8*	State (U.S.) D	Cheyenne
† Yemen	205,356	*531,869*	13,310,000	65	*25*	Republic A	Ṣan'ā'
† Yugoslavia[9]	98,766	*255,804*	23,907,000	242	*93*	Federal socialist republic A	Beograd (Belgrade)
Yukon Territory	186,661	*483,450*	27,000	0.1	*0.1*	Territory (Canada) D	Whitehorse
Yunnan	152,124	*394,000*	37,440,000	246	*95*	Province (China) D	Kunming
† Zaire	905,446	*2,345,095*	36,095,000	40	*15*	Republic A	Kinshasa
† Zambia	290,586	*752,614*	8,226,000	28	*11*	Republic A	Lusaka
Zhejiang	39,305	*101,800*	43,835,000	1,115	*431*	Province (China) D	Hangzhou
† Zimbabwe	150,873	*390,759*	9,491,000	63	*24*	Republic A	Harare
WORLD	57,800,000	*149,700,000*	5,350,000,000	93	*36*		

† Member of the United Nations (1990).
(1) No permanent population.
(2) North Cyprus unilaterally declared its independence from Cyprus in 1983.
(3) Claimed by Argentina.
(4) Includes West Bank, Golan Heights, and Gaza Strip.
(5) Future capital.
(6) Lithuania unilaterally declared its independence from the Soviet Union in 1990.
(7) Claimed by Comoros.
(8) Comprises Ceuta, Melilla, and several small islands.
(9) In June, 1991, the republics of Croatia (Hrvatska) and Slovenia (Slovenija) declared independence from Yugoslavia.

World Geographical Information

General

MOVEMENTS OF THE EARTH

The earth makes one complete revolution around the sun every 365 days, 5 hours, 48 minutes, and 46 seconds.

The earth makes one complete rotation on its axis in 23 hours, 56 minutes and 4 seconds.

The earth revolves in its orbit around the sun at a speed of 66,700 miles per hour (107,343 kilometers per hour).

The earth rotates on its axis at an equatorial speed of more than 1,000 miles per hour (1,600 kilometers per hour).

MEASUREMENTS OF THE EARTH

Estimated age of the earth, at least 4.6 billion years.

Equatorial diameter of the earth, 7,926.38 miles *(12,756.27 kilometers).*

Polar diameter of the earth, 7,899.80 miles *(12,713.50 kilometers).*

Mean diameter of the earth, 7,917.52 miles *(12,742.01 kilometers).*

Equatorial circumference of the earth, 24,901.46 miles *(40,075.02 kilometers).*

Polar circumference of the earth, 24,855.34 miles *(40,000.79 kilometers).*

Difference between equatorial and polar circumferences of the earth, 46.12 miles *(74.23 kilometers).*

Weight of the earth, 6,600,000,000,000,000,000,000 tons, or 6,600 billion billion tons *(6,000 billion billion metric tons).*

THE EARTH'S SURFACE

Total area of the earth, 197,000,000 square miles *(510,000,000 square kilometers).*

Total land area of the earth (including inland water and Antarctica), 57,800,000 square miles *(149,700,000 square kilometers).*

Highest point on the earth's surface, Mt. Everest, Asia, 29,028 feet *(8,848 meters).*

Lowest point on the earth's land surface, shores of the Dead Sea, Asia, 1,299 feet *(396 meters)* below sea level.

Greatest known depth of the ocean, the Mariana Trench, southwest of Guam, Pacific Ocean, 35,810 feet *(10,915 meters).*

THE EARTH'S INHABITANTS

Population of the earth is estimated to be 5,350,000,000 *(January 1, 1991).*

Estimated population density of the earth, 93 per square mile *(36 per square kilometer).*

EXTREMES OF TEMPERATURE AND RAINFALL OF THE EARTH

Highest temperature ever recorded, 136° F. *(58° C.)* at Al-'Azīzīyah, Libya, Africa, on September 13, 1922.

Lowest temperature ever recorded, -129° F. *(-89° C.)* at Vostok, Antarctica on July 21, 1983.

Highest mean annual temperature, 94° F. *(34° C.)* at Dallol, Ethiopia.

Lowest mean annual temperature, -70° F. *(-50° C.)* at Plateau Station, Antarctica.

The greatest local average annual rainfall is at Mt. Waialeale, Kauai, Hawaii, 460 inches *(11,680 millimeters).*

The greatest 24-hour rainfall, 74 inches *(1,880 millimeters),* is at Cilaos, Reunion Island, March 15-16, 1952.

The lowest local average annual rainfall is at Arica, Chile, .03 inches *(8 millimeters).*

The longest dry period, over 14 years, is at Arica, Chile, October 1903 to January 1918.

The Continents

CONTINENT	Area (sq. mi.) (sq. km.)	Estimated Population Jan. 1, 1991	Population per sq. mi. (sq. km.)	Mean Elevation (feet) (M.)	Highest Elevation (Feet) (M.)	Lowest Elevation (Feet) (M.)	Highest Recorded Temperature	Lowest Recorded Temperature
North America	9,400,000 *(24,400,000)*	426,800,000	45 *(17)*	2,000 *(610)*	Mt. McKinley, Alaska, United States 20,320 *(6,194)*	Death Valley, California, United States 282 *(84)* below sea level	Death Valley, California 134° F *(57° C)*	Northice, Greenland -87° F *(-66° C)*
South America	6,900,000 *(17,800,000)*	299,200,000	43 *(17)*	1,800 *(550)*	Cerro Aconcagua, Argentina 22,831 *(6,959)*	Salinas Chicas, Argentina 138 *(42)* below sea level	Rivadavia, Argentina 120° F *(49° C)*	Sarmiento, Argentina -27° F *(-33° C)*
Europe	3,800,000 *(9,800,000)*	693,500,000	183 *(71)*	980 *(300)*	Gora El'brus, U.S.S.R. 18,510 *(5,642)*	Caspian Sea, Soviet Union-Iran 92 *(28)* *below sea level*	Sevilla, Spain 122° F *(50° C)*	Ust' Ščugor, U.S.S.R. -67° F *(-55° C)*
Asia	17,300,000 *(44,900,000)*	3,232,000,000	187 *(72)*	3,000 *(910)*	Mt. Everest, China-Nepal 29,028 *(8,848)*	Dead Sea, Israel-Jordan 1,299 *(396)* below sea level	Tirat Ẓevi, Israel 129° F *(54° C)*	Ojm'akon and Verchojansk, Soviet Union -90° F *(-68° C)*
Africa	11,700,000 *(30,300,000)*	671,800,000	57 *(22)*	1,900 *(580)*	Kilimanjaro, Tanzania 19,340 *(5,895)*	Lac Assal, Djibouti 502 *(153)* below sea level	Al-'Azīzīyah, Libya 136° F *(58° C)*	Ifrane, Morocco -11° F *(-24° C)*
Oceania, incl. Australia	3,300,000 *(8,500,000)*	26,700,000	8.1 *(3.1)*	....	Mt. Wilhelm, Papua New Guinea 14,793 *(4,509)*	Lake Eyre, South Australia, Australia 52 *(16)* below sea level	Cloncurry, Queensland, Australia 128° F *(53° C)*	Charlotte Pass, New South Wales, Australia -8° F *(-22° C)*
Australia	2,966,155 *(7,682,300)*	17,260,000	5.8 *(2.2)*	1,000 *(300)*	Mt. Kosciusko, New South Wales 7,316 *(2,230)*	Lake Eyre, South Australia 52 *(16)* below sea level	Cloncurry, Queensland 128° F *(53° C)*	Charlotte Pass, New South Wales -8° F *(-22° C)*
Antarctica	5,400,000 *(14,000,000)*	....	....	6,000 *(1830)*	Vinson Massif 16,066 *(4,897)*	sea level	Vanda Station 59° F *(15° C)*	Vostok -129° F *(-89° C)*
World	57,800,000 *(149,700,000)*	5,350,000,000	93 *(36)*	....	Mt. Everest, China-Nepal 29,028 *(8,848)*	Dead Sea, Israel-Jordan 1,299 *(396)* below sea level	Al-'Azīzīyah, Libya 136° F *(58° C)*	Vostok, Antarctica -129° F *(-89° C)*

Historical Populations *

AREA	1650	1750	1800	1850	1900	1920	1950	1970	1980	1990
North America	*5,000,000*	*5,000,000*	*13,000,000*	*39,000,000*	106,000,000	147,000,000	219,000,000	316,600,000	365,000,000	423,600,000
South America	*8,000,000*	*7,000,000*	*12,000,000*	*20,000,000*	38,000,000	61,000,000	111,000,000	187,400,000	239,000,000	293,700,000
Europe	*100,000,000*	*140,000,000*	*190,000,000*	265,000,000	400,000,000	453,000,000	530,000,000	623,700,000	660,300,000	688,000,000
Asia	*335,000,000*	*476,000,000*	*593,000,000*	*754,000,000*	*932,000,000*	*1,000,000,000*	*1,418,000,000*	2,086,200,000	2,581,000,000	3,156,100,000
Africa	*100,000,000*	*95,000,000*	*90,000,000*	*95,000,000*	*118,000,000*	*140,000,000*	*199,000,000*	346,900,000	463,800,000	648,300,000
Oceania, incl. Australia	*2,000,000*	*2,000,000*	*2,000,000*	*2,000,000*	6,000,000	9,000,000	13,000,000	19,200,000	22,700,000	26,300,000
Australia	*	*	*	*	4,000,000	6,000,000	8,000,000	12,460,000	14,510,000	16,950,000
World	*550,000,000*	*725,000,000*	*900,000,000*	*1,175,000,000*	*1,600,000,000*	*1,810,000,000*	*2,490,000,000*	3,580,000,000	4,332,000,000	5,236,000,000

** Figures prior to 1970 are rounded to the nearest million. Figures in italics represent very rough estimates.*

Largest Countries : Population

		Population 1/1/91
1	China (excl. Taiwan)	1,141,530,000
2	India (incl. part of Jammu and Kashmir)	836,170,000
3	Union of Soviet Socialist Republics	291,310,000
4	United States	250,800,000
5	Indonesia	193,080,000
6	Brazil	152,050,000
7	Japan	123,850,000
8	Pakistan (incl. part of Jammu and Kashmir)	114,380,000
9	Nigeria	112,830,000
10	Bangladesh	109,540,000
11	Mexico	86,675,000
12	Germany	79,220,000
13	Vietnam	67,850,000
14	Turkey	63,720,000
15	Philippines	62,170,000
16	Italy	57,630,000
17	United Kingdom	57,380,000
18	Thailand	56,860,000
19	Iran	56,810,000
20	France	56,580,000
21	Egypt	54,910,000
22	Ethiopia	52,206,000
23	Korea, South	42,975,000
24	Burma (Myanmar)	41,690,000
25	Spain	40,190,000
26	South Africa	40,055,000
27	Poland	38,010,000

Largest Countries : Area

		Area (sq. mi.)	Area (sq. km.)
1	Union of Soviet Socialist Republics	8,600,387	*22,274,900*
2	Canada	3,849,674	*9,970,610*
3	China (excl. Taiwan)	3,689,631	*9,556,100*
4	United States	3,679,245	*9,529,202*
5	Brazil	3,286,488	*8,511,965*
6	Australia	2,966,155	*7,682,300*
7	India (incl. part of Jammu and Kashmir)	1,237,062	*3,203,975*
8	Argentina	1,073,400	*2,780,092*
9	Sudan	967,500	*2,505,813*
10	Algeria	919,595	*2,381,741*
11	Zaire	905,446	*2,345,095*
12	Greenland	840,004	*2,175,600*
13	Saudi Arabia	830,000	*2,149,690*
14	Mexico	756,066	*1,958,201*
15	Indonesia	741,101	*1,919,443*
16	Libya	679,362	*1,759,540*
17	Iran	636,372	*1,648,196*
18	Mongolia	604,829	*1,566,500*
19	Peru	496,225	*1,285,216*
20	Chad	495,755	*1,284,000*
21	Niger	489,191	*1,267,000*
22	Ethiopia	483,123	*1,251,282*
23	Angola	481,354	*1,246,700*
24	Mali	478,767	*1,240,000*
25	Colombia	440,831	*1,141,748*
26	South Africa	433,680	*1,123,226*
27	Bolivia	424,165	*1,098,581*
28	Mauritania	395,956	*1,025,520*

Principal Mountains

NORTH AMERICA

	Height (feet)	Height (meters)
McKinley, Mt., ▲ Alaska (▲ United States; ▲ North America)	20,320	*6,194*
Logan, Mt., ▲ Canada (▲ Yukon; ▲ St. Elias Mts.)	19,524	*5,951*
Orizaba, Pico de, ▲ Mexico	18,406	*5,610*
St. Elias, Mt., Alaska-Canada	18,008	*5,489*
Popocatépetl, Volcán, Mexico	17,930	*5,465*
Foraker, Mt., Alaska	17,400	*5,304*
Ixtacihuatl, Mexico	17,159	*5,230*
Lucania, Mt., Canada	17,147	*5,226*
Fairweather, Mt., Alaska-Canada (▲ British Columbia)	15,300	*4,663*
Whitney, Mt., ▲ California,	14,494	*4,418*
Elbert, Mt., ▲ Colorado (▲ Rocky Mts.)	14,433	*4,399*
Massive, Mt., Colorado	14,421	*4,396*
Harvard, Mt., Colorado	14,420	*4,395*
Rainier, Mt., ▲ Washington (▲ Cascade Range)	14,410	*4,392*
Williamson, Mt., California	14,375	*4,382*
Blanca Pk., Colorado (▲ Sangre de Cristo Mts.)	14,345	*4,372*
La Plata Pk., Colorado	14,336	*4,370*
Uncompahgre Pk., Colorado (▲ San Juan Mts.)	14,309	*4,361*
Grays Pk., Colorado (▲ Front Range)	14,270	*4,349*
Evans, Mt., Colorado	14,264	*4,348*
Longs Pk., Colorado	14,255	*4,345*
Wrangell, Mt., Alaska	14,163	*4,317*
Shasta, Mt., California	14,162	*4,317*
Pikes Pk., Colorado	14,110	*4,301*
Colima, Nevado de, Mexico	13,993	*4,265*
Tajumulco, Volcán, ▲ Guatemala (▲ Central America)	13,846	*4,220*
Gannett Pk., ▲ Wyoming	13,804	*4,207*
Mauna Kea, ▲ Hawaii	13,796	*4,205*
Grand Teton, Wyoming	13,770	*4,197*
Mauna Loa, Hawaii	13,679	*4,169*
Kings Pk., ▲ Utah	13,528	*4,123*
Cloud Pk., Wyoming (▲ Bighorn Mts.)	13,167	*4,013*
Wheeler Pk., ▲ New Mexico	13,161	*4,011*
Boundary Pk., ▲ Nevada	13,143	*4,006*
Waddington, Mt., Canada (▲ Coast Mts.)	13,104	*3,994*
Robson, Mt., Canada (▲ Canadian Rockies)	12,972	*3,954*
Granite Pk., ▲ Montana	12,799	*3,901*
Borah Pk., ▲ Idaho	12,662	*3,859*
Humphreys Pk., ▲ Arizona	12,633	*3,851*
Chirripó, Cerro, ▲ Costa Rica	12,533	*3,819*
Columbia, Mt., Canada (▲ Alberta)	12,294	*3,747*
Adams, Mt., Washington	12,276	*3,742*
Gunnbjørn Mtn., ▲ Greenland	12,139	*3,700*
San Gorgonio Mtn., California	11,499	*3,505*
Barú, Volcán, ▲ Panama	11,411	*3,475*
Hood, Mt., ▲ Oregon	11,235	*3,424*
Lassen Pk., California	10,457	*3,187*
Duarte, Pico, ▲ Dominican Rep. (▲ West Indies)	10,417	*3,175*
Haleakala Crater, Hawaii (▲ Maui)	10,023	*3,055*
Paricutín, Mexico	9,213	*2,808*
El Pital, Cerro, ▲ El Salvador-Honduras	8,957	*2,730*
La Selle, Pic, ▲ Haiti	8,773	*2,674*
Guadalupe Pk., ▲ Texas	8,749	*2,667*
Olympus, Mt., Washington (▲ Olympic Mts.)	7,965	*2,428*
Blue Mountain Pk., ▲ Jamaica	7,402	*2,256*
Harney Pk., ▲ South Dakota (▲ Black Hills)	7,242	*2,207*
Mitchell, Mt., ▲ North Carolina (▲ Appalachian Mts.)	6,684	*2,037*
Clingmans Dome, North Carolina-▲ Tennessee (▲ Great Smoky Mts.)	6,643	*2,025*
Turquino, Pico, ▲ Cuba	6,470	*1,972*
Washington, Mt., ▲ New Hampshire (▲ White Mts.)	6,288	*1,917*
Rogers, Mt., ▲ Virginia	5,729	*1,746*
Marcy, Mt., ▲ New York (▲ Adirondack Mts.)	5,344	*1,629*
Katahdin, Mt., ▲ Maine	5,268	*1,606*
Kawaikini, Hawaii (▲ Kauai)	5,243	*1,598*
Spruce Knob, ▲ West Virginia	4,862	*1,482*
Pelée, Montagne, ▲ Martinique	4,583	*1,397*
Mansfield, Mt., ▲ Vermont (▲ Green Mts.)	4,393	*1,339*
Punta, Cerro de, ▲ Puerto Rico	4,389	*1,338*
Black Mtn., ▲ Kentucky-Virginia	4,145	*1,263*
Kaala, Hawaii (▲ Oahu)	4,040	*1,231*

SOUTH AMERICA

	Height (feet)	Height (meters)
Aconcagua, Cerro, ▲ Argentina; ▲ Andes; (▲ South America)	22,831	*6,959*
Ojos del Salado, Nevado, Argentina-▲ Chile	22,615	*6,893*
Illimani, Nevado, ▲ Bolivia	22,579	*6,882*
Bonete, Cerro, Argentina	22,546	*6,872*
Huascarán, Nevado, ▲ Peru	22,133	*6,746*
Llullaillaco, Volcán, Argentina-Chile	22,057	*6,723*
Yerupaja, Nevado, Peru	21,765	*6,634*
Tupungato, Cerro, Argentina-Chile	21,555	*6,570*
Sajama, Nevado, Bolivia	21,463	*6,542*
Illampu, Nevado, Bolivia	20,873	*6,362*
Chimborazo, ▲ Ecuador	20,702	*6,310*
Antofalla, Volcán, Argentina	20,013	*6,100*
Cotopaxi, Ecuador	19,347	*5,897*
Misti, Volcán, Peru	19,101	*5,822*
Huila, Nevado del, Colombia (▲ Cordillera Central)	16,896	*5,150*
Bolívar, Pico, ▲ Venezuela	16,427	*5,007*
Fitzroy, Monte (Cerro Chaltel), Argentina-Chile	11,073	*3,375*
Neblina, Pico da, ▲ Brazil-Venezuela	9,888	*3,014*

EUROPE

	Height (feet)	Height (meters)
El'brus, gora, U.S.S.R. (▲ Caucasus; ▲ Europe)	18,510	*5,642*
Dykh-Tau, Mt., U.S.S.R.	17,073	*5,204*
Shkhara, Mt., U.S.S.R.	16,512	*5,033*
Blanc, Mont (Monte Bianco), ▲ France-▲ Italy (▲ Alps)	15,771	*4,807*
Dufourspitze, Italy-▲ Switzerland	15,203	*4,634*
Weisshorn, Switzerland	14,783	*4,506*
Matterhorn, Italy-Switzerland	14,692	*4,478*
Finsteraarhorn, Switzerland	14,022	*4,274*
Jungfrau, Switzerland	13,642	*4,158*
Écrins, Barre des, France	13,458	*4,102*
Viso, Monte, Italy (▲ Alpes Cottiennes)	12,602	*3,841*
Grossglockner, ▲ Austria	12,457	*3,797*
Teide, Pico de, ▲ Spain (▲ Canary Is.)	12,188	*3,715*
Mulhacén, ▲ Spain (continental)	11,410	*3,478*
Aneto, Pico de, Spain (▲ Pyrenees)	11,168	*3,404*
Perdido, Monte, Spain	11,007	*3,355*
Etna, Monte, Italy (▲ Sicily)	10,902	*3,323*
Zugspitze, Austria-▲ Germany	9,721	*2,963*
Musala, ▲ Bulgaria	9,596	*2,925*
Olympus, Mount (Óros Ólimbos), ▲ Greece	9,570	*2,917*
Corno Grande, Italy (▲ Apennines)	9,554	*2,912*
Triglav, ▲ Yugoslavia	9,393	*2,863*
Korab, ▲ Albania-Yugoslavia	9,026	*2,751*
Cinto, Monte, France (▲ Corsica)	8,878	*2,706*
Gerlachovský Štít, ▲ Czechoslovakia (▲ Carpathian Mts.)	8,711	*2,655*
Moldoveanu, ▲ Romania	8,346	*2,544*
Rysy, Czechoslovakia-▲ Poland	8,199	*2,499*
Glittertinden, ▲ Norway (▲ Scandinavia)	8,110	*2,472*
Parnassos, Greece	8,061	*2,457*
Ídhi, Óros, Greece (▲ Crete)	8,057	*2,456*
Pico, Ponta do, ▲ Portugal (▲ Azores Is.)	7,713	*2,351*
Hvannadalshnúkur, ▲ Iceland	6,952	*2,119*
Kebnekaise, ▲ Sweden	6,926	*2,111*
Estrela, ▲ Portugal (continental)	6,539	*1,993*
Narodnaja, gora, U.S.S.R. (▲ Ural Mts.)	6,213	*1,894*
Sancy, Puy de, France (▲ Massif Central)	6,184	*1,885*
Marmora, Punta la, Italy (▲ Sardinia)	6,017	*1,834*
Hekla, Iceland	4,892	*1,491*
Nevis, Ben, ▲ United Kingdom (▲ Scotland)	4,406	*1,343*
Haltiatunturi, ▲ Finland-Norway	4,357	*1,328*
Vesuvio, Italy	4,190	*1,277*
Snowdon, United Kingdom (▲ Wales)	3,560	*1,085*
Carrauntoohil, ▲ Ireland	3,406	*1,038*
Kékes, ▲ Hungary	3,330	*1,015*
Scafell Pikes, United Kingdom (▲ England)	3,210	*978*

ASIA

	Height (feet)	Height (meters)
Everest, Mount, ▲ China-▲ Nepal (▲ Tibet; ▲ Himalayas; ▲ Asia; ▲ World)	29,028	*8,848*
K2 (Qogir Feng), China-▲ Pakistan (▲ Kashmir; ▲ Karakoram Range)	28,250	*8,611*
Kānchenjunga, ▲ India-Nepal	28,208	*8,598*
Makālu, China-Nepal	27,825	*8,481*
Dhawlagiri, Nepal	26,810	*8,172*
Nānga Parbat, Pakistan	26,660	*8,126*
Annapurna, Nepal	26,504	*8,078*
Gasherbrum, China-Pakistan	26,470	*8,068*
Xixabangma Feng, China	26,286	*8,012*
Nanda Devi, India	25,645	*7,817*
Kamet, China-India	25,447	*7,756*
Namjagbarwa Feng, China	25,442	*7,755*
Muztag, China (▲ Kunlun Shan)	25,338	*7,723*
Tirich Mir, Pakistan (▲ Hindu Kush)	25,230	*7,690*
Gongga Shan, China	24,790	*7,556*
Kula Kangri, ▲ Bhutan	24,784	*7,554*
Kommunizma, pik, ▲ U.S.S.R. (▲ Pamir)	24,590	*7,495*
Nowshāk, ▲ Afghanistan-Pakistan	24,557	*7,485*
Pobedy, pik, China-U.S.S.R.	24,406	*7,439*
Chomo Lhari, Bhutan-China	23,997	*7,314*
Muztag, China	23,891	*7,282*
Lenin, pik, U.S.S.R.	23,406	*7,134*
Api, Nepal	23,399	*7,132*
Kangrinboqê Feng, China	22,028	*6,714*
Hkakabo Razi, ▲ Burma	19,296	*5,881*
Damāvend, Qollah-ye, ▲ Iran	18,386	*5,604*
Ağrı Dağı, ▲ Turkey	16,804	*5,122*
Jaya, Puncak, ▲ Indonesia (▲ New Guinea)	16,503	*5,030*
Fūlādī, Kūh-e, Afghanistan	16,243	*4,951*
Kl'učevskaja Sopka, vulkan, U.S.S.R. (▲ Puluostrov Kamčatka)	15,584	*4,750*
Trikora, Puncak, Indonesia	15,584	*4,750*
Belucha, gora, U.S.S.R.	14,783	*4,506*
Turgen, Mount, Mongolia	14,311	*4,362*
Kinabalu, Gunong, ▲ Malaysia (▲ Borneo)	13,455	*4,101*
Yü Shan, ▲ Taiwan	13,114	*3,997*
Erciyes Dağı, Turkey	12,851	*3,917*
Kerinci, Gunung, Indonesia (▲ Sumatra)	12,467	*3,800*
Fuji-san, ▲ Japan (▲ Honshu)	12,388	*3,776*
Rinjani, Indonesia (▲ Lombok)	12,224	*3,726*
Semeru, Indonesia (▲ Java)	12,060	*3,676*
Nabī Shu'ayb, Jabal an-, ▲ Yemen (▲ Arabian Peninsula)	12,008	*3,660*
Rantekombola, Bulu, Indonesia (▲ Celebes)	11,335	*3,455*
Slamet, Indonesia	11,247	*3,428*
Phan Si Pan, ▲ Vietnam	10,312	*3,143*
Shām, Jabal ash-, ▲ Oman	9,957	*3,035*
Apo, Mount, ▲ Philippines (▲ Mindanao)	9,692	*2,954*
Pulog, Mount, Philippines (▲ Luzon)	9,626	*2,934*
Bia, Phou, ▲ Laos	9,249	*2,819*
Shaykh, Jabal ash-, Lebanon-▲ Syria	9,232	*2,814*
Paektu-san, ▲ North Korea-China	9,003	*2,744*
Inthanon, Doi, ▲ Thailand	8,530	*2,600*
Pidurutalagala, ▲ Sri Lanka	8,281	*2,524*
Mayon Volcano, Philippines	8,077	*2,462*
Asahi-dake, Japan (▲ Hokkaidō)	7,513	*2,290*
Tahan, Gunong, Malaysia (▲ Malaya)	7,174	*2,187*
Ólimbos, ▲ Cyprus	6,401	*1,951*
Halla-san, ▲ South Korea	6,398	*1,950*
Aôral, Phnum, ▲ Cambodia	5,948	*1,813*
Kujū-san, Japan (▲ Kyūshū)	5,863	*1,787*
Ramm, Jabal, ▲ Jordan	5,755	*1,754*
Meron, Hare, ▲ Israel	3,963	*1,208*
Carmel, Mt., Israel	1,791	*546*

AFRICA

	Height (feet)	Height (meters)
Kilimanjaro, ▲ Tanzania (▲ Africa)	19,340	*5,895*
Kirinyaga (Mount Kenya), ▲ Kenya	17,058	*5,199*
Margherita Peak, ▲ Uganda-▲ Zaire	16,763	*5,109*
Ras Dashen Terara, ▲ Ethiopia	15,158	*4,620*
Meru, Mount, Tanzania	14,978	*4,565*
Karisimbi, Volcan, ▲ Rwanda-Zaire	14,787	*4,507*
Elgon, Mount, Kenya-Uganda	14,178	*4,321*
Toubkal, Jbel, ▲ Morocco (▲ Atlas Mts.)	13,665	*4,165*
Cameroon Mountain, ▲ Cameroon	13,451	*4,100*
Ntlenyana, Thabana, ▲ Lesotho	11,425	*3,482*
eNjesuthi, ▲ South Africa	11,306	*3,446*
Koussi, Emi, ▲ Chad (▲ Tibesti)	11,204	*3,415*
Kinyeti, ▲ Sudan	10,456	*3,187*
Santa Isabel, Pico de, ▲ Equatorial Guinea (▲ Bioko)	9,869	*3,008*
Tahat, ▲ Algeria (▲ Ahaggar)	9,541	*2,908*
Maromokotro, ▲ Madagascar	9,436	*2,876*
Kātrīnā, Jabal, ▲ Egypt	8,668	*2,642*
Sao Tome, Pico de, ▲ Sao Tome	6,640	*2,024*

OCEANIA

	Height (feet)	Height (meters)
Wilhelm, Mount, ▲ Papua New Guinea	14,793	*4,509*
Giluwe, Mount, Papua New Guinea	14,330	*4,368*
Bangeta, Mt., Papua New Guinea	13,520	*4,121*
Victoria, Mount, Papua New Guinea (▲ Owen Stanley Range)	13,238	*4,035*
Cook, Mount, ▲ New Zealand (▲ South Island)	12,349	*3,764*
Ruapehu, New Zealand (▲ North Island)	9,177	*2,797*
Balbi, Papua New Guinea (▲ Solomon Is.)	9,000	*2,743*
Egmont, Mount, New Zealand	8,260	*2,518*
Orohena, Mont, ▲ French Polynesia (▲ Tahiti)	7,352	*2,241*
Kosciusko, Mount, ▲ Australia (▲ New South Wales)	7,316	*2,230*
Silisili, Mount, ▲ Western Samoa	6,096	*1,858*
Panié, Mont, ▲ New Caledonia	5,341	*1,628*
Bartle Frere, Australia (▲ Queensland)	5,322	*1,622*
Ossa, Mount, Australia (▲ Tasmania)	5,305	*1,617*
Woodroffe, Mount, Australia (▲ South Australia)	4,724	*1,440*
Sinewit, Mt., Papua New Guinea (▲ Bismarck Archipelago)	4,462	*1,360*
Tomanivi, ▲ Fiji (▲ Viti Levu)	4,341	*1,323*
Meharry, Mt., Australia (▲ Western Australia)	4,104	*1,251*
Ayers Rock, Australia	2,844	*867*

ANTARCTICA

	Height (feet)	Height (meters)
Vinson Massif, ▲ Antarctica	16,066	*4,897*
Kirkpatrick, Mount, Antarctica	14,856	*4,528*
Markham, Mount, Antarctica	14,049	*4,282*
Jackson, Mount, Antarctica	13,747	*4,190*
Sidley, Mount, Antarctica	13,717	*4,181*
Wade, Mount, Antarctica	13,399	*4,084*

▲ Highest mountain in state, country, range, or region named.

Oceans, Seas and Gulfs

	Area (sq. mi.)	Area (sq. km.)
Pacific Ocean	63,800,000	*165,200,000*
Atlantic Ocean	31,800,000	*82,400,000*
Indian Ocean	28,900,000	*74,900,000*
Arctic Ocean	5,400,000	*14,000,000*
Arabian Sea	1,492,000	*3,864,000*
South China Sea	1,331,000	*3,447,000*
Caribbean Sea	1,063,000	*2,753,000*
Mediterranean Sea	967,000	*2,505,000*
Bering Sea	876,000	*2,269,000*
Bengal, Bay of	839,000	*2,173,000*
Okhotsk, Sea of	619,000	*1,603,000*
Norwegian Sea	597,000	*1,546,000*
Mexico, Gulf of	596,000	*1,544,000*
Hudson Bay	475,000	*1,230,000*
Greenland Sea	465,000	*1,204,000*

Principal Lakes

	Area (sq. mi.)	Area (sq. km.)
Caspian Sea, Iran—U.S.S.R. (Salt)	143,240	*370,990*
Superior, Lake, Canada—U.S.	31,700	*82,100*
Victoria, Lake, Kenya—Tanzania—Uganda	26,820	*69,463*
Aral'skoje more (Aral Sea), U.S.S.R. (Salt)	24,700	*64,100*
Huron, Lake, Canada—U.S.	23,000	*60,000*
Michigan, Lake, U.S.	22,300	*57,800*
Tanganyika, Lake, Africa	12,350	*31,986*
Bajkal, ozero, U.S.S.R.	12,200	*31,500*
Great Bear Lake, Canada	12,095	*31,326*
Malawi, Lake (Lake Nyasa), Malawi—Mozambique—Tanzania	11,150	*28,878*
Great Slave Lake, Canada	11,030	*28,568*
Erie, Lake, Canada—U.S.	9,910	*25,667*
Winnipeg, Lake, Canada	9,416	*24,387*
Ontario, Lake, Canada—U.S.	7,540	*19,529*
Balchaš, ozero, U.S.S.R.	Δ 7,100	*18,300*
Ladožskoje ozero, U.S.S.R.	6,833	*17,700*
Chad, Lake (Lac Tchad), Cameroon—Chad—Nigeria	6,300	*16,300*
Onežskoje ozero, U.S.S.R.	3,753	*9,720*
Eyre, Lake, Australia (Salt)	Δ 3,700	*9,500*
Titicaca, Lago, Bolivia—Peru	3,200	*8,300*
Nicaragua, Lago de, Nicaragua	3,150	*8,158*
Mai—Ndombe, Lac, Zaire	Δ 3,100	*8,000*
Athabasca, Lake, Canada	3,064	*7,935*
Reindeer Lake, Canada	2,568	*6,650*
Tônlé Sab, Cambodia	Δ 2,500	*6,500*
Rudolf, Lake, Ethiopia—Kenya (Salt)	2,473	*6,405*
Issyk-Kul', ozero, U.S.S.R. (Salt)	2,425	*6,280*
Torrens, Lake, Australia (Salt)	2,300	*5,900*
Albert, Lake, Uganda—Zaire	2,160	*5,594*
Vänern, Sweden	2,156	*5,584*
Nettilling Lake, Canada	2,140	*5,542*
Winnipegosis, Lake, Canada	2,075	*5,374*
Bangweulu, Lake, Zambia	1,930	*4,999*
Nipigon, Lake, Canada	1,872	*4,848*
Orūmīyeh, Daryācheh-ye, Iran (Salt)	Δ 1,815	*4,701*
Manitoba, Lake, Canada	1,785	*4,624*
Woods, Lake of the, Canada—U.S.	1,727	*4,472*
Kyoga, Lake, Uganda	1,710	*4,429*
Gairdner, Lake, Australia (Salt)	Δ 1,700	*4,300*
Great Salt Lake, U.S. (Salt)	1,680	*4,351*

Δ *Due to seasonal fluctuations in water level, areas of these lakes vary considerably.*

Principal Rivers

	Length (miles)	Length (km.)
Nile, Africa	4,145	*6,671*
Amazon-Ucayali, South America	4,000	*6,400*
Yangtze (Chang), Asia	3,900	*6,300*
Mississippi-Missouri, North America	3,740	*6,019*
Huang (Yellow), Asia	3,395	*5,464*
Ob'-Irtyš, Asia	3,362	*5,410*
Río de la Plata-Paraná, South America	3,030	*4,876*
Congo (Zaïre), Africa	2,900	*4,700*
Paraná, South America	2,800	*4,500*
Amur-Argun', Asia	2,761	*4,444*
Amur (Heilong), Asia	2,744	*4,416*
Lena, Asia	2,700	*4,400*
Mackenzie, North America	2,635	*4,241*
Mekong, Asia	2,600	*4,200*
Niger, Africa	2,600	*4,200*
Jenisej, Asia	2,543	*4,092*
Missouri-Red Rock, North America	2,533	*4,076*
Mississippi, North America	2,348	*3,779*
Murray-Darling, Australia	2,330	*3,750*
Missouri, North America	2,315	*3,726*
Volga, Europe	2,194	*3,531*
Madeira, South America	2,013	*3,240*
São Francisco, South America	1,988	*3,199*
Grande, Rio (Río Bravo), North America	1,885	*3,034*
Purús, South America	1,860	*2,993*
Indus, Asia	1,800	*2,900*
Danube, Europe	1,776	*2,858*
Brahmaputra, Asia	1,770	*2,849*
Yukon, North America	1,770	*2,849*
Salween (Nu), Asia	1,750	*2,816*
Zambezi, Africa	1,700	*2,700*
Vil'uj, Asia	1,647	*2,650*
Tocantins, South America	1,640	*2,639*
Orinoco South America,	1,600	*2,600*
Paraguay, South America	1,610	*2,591*
Amu Darya, Asia	1,578	*2,540*
Murray, Australia	1,566	*2,520*
Ganges, Asia	1,560	*2,511*
Pilcomayo, South America	1,550	*2,494*
Euphrates, Asia	1,510	*2,430*
Ural, Asia	1,509	*2,428*
Arkansas, North America	1,459	*2,348*
Colorado, North America (U.S.-Mexico)	1,450	*2,334*
Aldan, Asia	1,412	*2,273*
Syrdarja, Asia	1,370	*2,205*
Dnepr, Europe	1,400	*2,200*
Araguaia, South America	1,400	*2,200*
Kasai (Cassai), Africa	1,338	*2,153*
Tarim, Asia	1,328	*2,137*
Kolyma, Asia	1,323	*2,129*
Orange, Africa	1,300	*2,100*
Negro, South America	1,300	*2,100*
Ayeyarwady, Asia	1,300	*2,100*
Red, North America	1,270	*2,044*
Juruá, South America	1,250	*2,012*
Columbia, North America	1,200	*2,000*
Xingu, South America	1,230	*1,979*
Ucayali, South America	1,220	*1,963*
Saskatchewan-Bow, North America	1,205	*1,939*
Peace North America,	1,195	*1,923*
Tigris, Asia	1,180	*1,899*
Don, Europe	1,162	*1,870*
Songhua, Asia	1,140	*1,835*
Pečora, Europe	1,124	*1,809*
Kama, Europe	1,122	*1,805*
Limpopo, Africa	1,100	*1,800*
Angara, Asia	1,105	*1,779*
Snake, North America	1,038	*1,670*
Uruguay, South America	1,025	*1,650*
Churchill, North America	1,000	*1,600*
Marañón, South America	1,000	*1,600*
Tobol, Asia	989	*1,591*
Ohio, North America	981	*1,579*
Magdalena, South America	950	*1,529*
Roosevelt, South America	950	*1,529*
Oka, Europe	900	*1,500*
Xiang, Asia	930	*1,497*
Godāvari, Asia	930	*1,497*
Canadian, North America	906	*1,458*
Brazos, North America	900	*1,400*
Salado, South America	900	*1,400*
Darling, Australia	864	*1,390*
Fraser, North America	851	*1,370*
Parnaíba, South America	850	*1,368*
Colorado, North America (Texas)	840	*1,352*
Dnestr, Europe	840	*1,352*
Rhine, Europe	820	*1,320*
Narmada, Asia	800	*1,300*
St. Lawrence, North America	800	*1,300*
Ottawa, North America	790	*1,271*
Athabasca, North America	765	*1,231*
Pecos, North America	735	*1,183*
Severskij Donec, Europe	735	*1,183*
Green, North America	730	*1,175*
White, North America (Ar.-Mo.)	720	*1,159*
Cumberland, North America	720	*1,159*
Elbe (Labe), Europe	720	*1,159*
James, North America (N./S. Dakota)	710	*1,143*
Gambia, Africa	680	*1,094*
Yellowstone, North America	671	*1,080*
Tennessee, North America	652	*1,049*
Gila, North America	630	*1,014*
Wisła (Vistula), Europe	630	*1,014*
Tagus (Tejo) (Tajo), Europe	625	*1,006*
Loire, Europe	625	*1,006*
Cimarron, North America	600	*1,000*
North Platte, North America	618	*995*
Albany, North America	610	*982*
Tisza (Tisa), Europe	607	*977*
Back, North America	605	*974*
Ouachita, North America	605	*974*
Sava, Europe	585	*941*
Nemunas (Neman), Europe	582	*937*
Branco, South America	580	*933*
Meuse (Maas), Europe	575	*925*
Oder (Odra), Europe	565	*909*
Rhône, Europe	500	*800*

Principal Islands

	Area (sq. mi.)	Area (sq. km.)
Grønland (Greenland), North America	840,000	*2,175,600*
New Guinea, Asia—Oceania	309,000	*800,000*
Borneo (Kalimantan), Asia	287,300	*744,100*
Madagascar, Africa	226,500	*587,000*
Baffin Island, Canada	195,928	*507,451*
Sumatera (Sumatra), Indonesia	182,860	*473,606*
Honshū, Japan	89,176	*230,966*
Great Britain, United Kingdom	88,795	*229,978*
Victoria Island, Canada	83,897	*217,291*
Ellesmere Island, Canada	75,767	*196,236*
Sulawesi (Celebes), Indonesia	73,057	*189,216*
South Island, New Zealand	57,708	*149,463*
Jawa (Java), Indonesia	51,038	*132,187*
Seram (Ceram), Indonesia	45,801	*118,625*
North Island, New Zealand	44,332	*114,821*
Cuba, North America	42,800	*110,800*
Newfoundland, Canada	42,031	*108,860*
Luzon, Philippines	40,420	*104,688*
Ísland (Iceland), Europe	39,800	*103,000*
Mindanao, Philippines	36,537	*94,630*
Ireland, Europe	32,600	*84,400*
Hokkaidō, Japan	32,245	*83,515*
Novaja Zeml'a (Novaya Zemlya), U.S.S.R.	31,900	*82,600*
Sachalin, ostrov (Sakhalin), U.S.S.R.	29,500	*76,400*
Hispaniola, North America	29,400	*76,200*
Banks Island, Canada	27,038	*70,028*
Tasmania, Australia	26,200	*67,800*
Sri Lanka, Asia	24,900	*64,600*
Devon Island, Canada	21,331	*55,247*
Tierra del Fuego, Isla Grande de, South America	18,600	*48,200*
Kyūshū, Japan	17,129	*44,363*
Melville Island, Canada	16,274	*42,149*
Southampton Island, Canada	15,913	*41,214*
Spitsbergen, Norway	15,260	*39,523*
New Britain, Papua New Guinea	14,093	*36,500*
T'aiwan, Asia	13,900	*36,000*
Hainan Dao, China	13,100	*34,000*
Prince of Wales Island, Canada	12,872	*33,339*
Vancouver Island, Canada	12,079	*31,285*
Sicilia (Sicily), Italy	9,926	*25,709*
Somerset Island, Canada	9,570	*24,786*
Sardegna (Sardinia), Italy	9,301	*24,090*
Shikoku, Japan	7,258	*18,799*
Nordaustlandet (North East Land), Norway	6,350	*16,446*
New Caledonia, Oceania	6,252	*16,192*
Timor, Indonesia	5,743	*14,874*
Flores, Indonesia	5,502	*14,250*
Samar, Philippines	5,100	*13,080*
Negros, Philippines	4,907	*12,710*
Palawan, Philippines	4,550	*11,785*
Panay, Philippines	4,446	*11,515*
Jamaica, North America	4,200	*11,000*
Hawaii, United States	4,034	*10,448*
Cape Breton Island, Canada	3,981	*10,311*
Mindoro, Philippines	3,759	*9,735*
Kodiak Island, United States	3,670	*9,505*
Bougainville, Papua New Guinea	3,600	*9,300*
Cyprus, Asia	3,572	*9,251*
Puerto Rico, North America	3,500	*9,100*
New Ireland, Papua New Guinea	3,500	*9,000*
Corse (Corsica), France	3,367	*8,720*
Kriti (Crete), Greece	3,189	*8,259*
Vrangel'a, ostrov (Wrangel Island), U.S.S.R.	2,800	*7,300*
Leyte, Philippines	2,785	*7,214*
Guadalcanal, Solomon Islands	2,060	*5,336*
Long Island, United States	1,377	*3,566*

World Populations

This table includes every urban center of 50,000 or more population in the world, as well as many other important or well-known cities and towns.

The population figures are all from recent censuses (designated C) or official estimates (designated E), except for a few cities for which only unofficial estimates are available (designated U). The date of the census or estimate is specified for each country. Individual exceptions are dated in parentheses.

For many cities, a second population figure is given accompanied by a star (★). The starred population refers to the city's entire metropolitan area, including suburbs. These metropolitan areas have been defined by Rand McNally, following consistent rules to facilitate comparisons among the urban centers of various countries. Where a place is part of the metropolitan area of another city, that city's name is specified in parentheses preceded by a (★). Some important places that are considered to be secondary central cities of their areas are designated by (★★) preceding the name of the metropolitan area's main city. A population preceded by a triangle (▲) refers to an entire municipality, commune, or other district, which includes rural areas in addition to the urban center itself. The names of capital cities appear in CAPITALS; the largest city in each country is designated by the symbol (•).

For more recent population totals for countries, see the Rand McNally population estimates in the World Political Information table.

AFGHANISTAN / Afghānestān

1988 E ... 15,513,000

Cities and Towns

Herāt ... 177,300
Jalālābād (1982 E) ... 58,000
• KĀBUL ... 1,424,400
Mazār-e Sharīf ... 130,600
Qandahār ... 225,500
Qondūz (1982 E) ... 57,000

ALBANIA / Shqipëri

1987 E ... 3,084,000

Cities and Towns

Durrës ... 78,700
Elbasan ... 78,300
Korçë ... 61,500
Shkodër ... 76,300
• TIRANË ... 255,700
Vlorë ... 67,700

ALGERIA / Algérie / Djazaïr

1987 C ... 23,038,942

Cities and Towns

Aïn el Beïda ... 61,997
Aïn Oussera ... 44,270
Aïn Témouchent ... 47,479
• ALGER (ALGIERS) (★ 2,547,983) ... 1,507,241
Annaba (Bône) ... 305,526
Bab Ezzouar (★ El Djazaïr) ... 55,211
Barika ... 56,488
Batna ... 181,601
Béchar ... 107,311
Bejaïa (Bougie) ... 114,534
Biskra ... 128,281
Blida ... 170,935
Bordj Bou Arreridj ... 84,264
Bordj el Kiffan (★ El Djazaïr) ... 61,035
Boufarik ... 41,305
Bou Saada ... 66,688
Constantine ... 440,842
El Asnam ... 129,976
El Djelfa ... 84,207
El Eulma ... 67,933
El Wad ... 70,073
Ghardaïa ... 89,415
Ghilizane ... 80,091
Guelma ... 77,821
Jijel ... 62,793
Khemis ... 55,335
Khenchla ... 69,743
Laghouat ... 67,214
Lemdiyya ... 85,195
Maghniyya ... 52,275
Messaad ... 47,460
Mostaganem ... 114,037
Mouaskar ... 64,691
M'Sila ... 65,805
Oran ... 628,558
Saïda ... 80,825
Sidi bel Abbès ... 152,778
Skikda ... 128,747
Souq Ahras ... 83,015
Stif ... 170,182
Tébessa ... 107,559
Tihert ... 95,821
Tizi-Ouzou ... 61,163
Tlemcen ... 126,882
Touggourt ... 70,645
Wargla ... 81,721

AMERICAN SAMOA / Amerika Samoa

1980 C ... 32,279

Cities and Towns

• PAGO PAGO ... 3,075

ANDORRA

1986 C ... 46,976

Cities and Towns

• ANDORRA ... 18,463

ANGOLA

1989 E ... 9,739,100

Cities and Towns

Benguela (1983 E) ... 155,000
Cabinda (1970 C) ... 21,124
Huambo (Nova Lisboa) (1983 E) ... 203,000
Lobito (1983 E) ... 150,000
• LUANDA ... 1,459,900
Lubango (1984 E) ... 95,915
Namibe (1981 E) ... 100,000

ANGUILLA

1984 C ... 6,680

Cities and Towns

South Hill ... 961
• THE VALLEY ... 1,042

ANTIGUA AND BARBUDA

1977 E ... 72,000

Cities and Towns

• SAINT JOHNS ... 24,359

ARGENTINA

1980 C ... 27,947,446

Cities and Towns

Almirante Brown (★ Buenos Aires) ... 331,919
Avellaneda (★ Buenos Aires) ... 334,145
Bahía Blanca ... 223,818
Berazategui (★ Buenos Aires) ... 201,862
Berisso (★ Buenos Aires) ... 66,152
• BUENOS AIRES (★ 10,750,000) ... 2,922,829
Campana (★ Buenos Aires) ... 54,832
Caseros (Tres de Febrero) (★ Buenos Aires) ... 345,424
Catamarca (★ 90,000) ... 78,799
Comodoro Rivadavia ... 96,817
Concordia ... 94,222
Córdoba (★ 1,070,000) ... 993,055
Corrientes ... 180,612
Esteban Echeverría (★ Buenos Aires) ... 188,923
Florencio Varela (★ Buenos Aires) ... 173,452
Formosa ... 93,603
General San Martín (★ Buenos Aires) ... 385,625
General Sarmiento (San Miguel) (★ Buenos Aires) ... 502,926
Godoy Cruz (★ Mendoza) ... 142,408
Gualeguaychú ... 51,400
Junín ... 62,458
Lanús (★ Buenos Aires) ... 466,980
La Plata (★★ Buenos Aires) ... 477,175
La Rioja ... 67,043
Las Heras (★ Mendoza) ... 101,579
Lomas de Zamora (★ Buenos Aires) ... 510,130
Mar del Plata ... 414,696
Mendoza (★ 650,000) ... 119,088
Mercedes ... 50,992
Merlo (★ Buenos Aires) ... 292,587
Moreno (★ Buenos Aires) ... 194,440
Morón (★ Buenos Aires) ... 598,420
Necochea ... 51,069
Neuquén ... 90,089
Olavarría ... 64,097
Paraná ... 161,638
Pergamino ... 68,612
Pilar (★ Buenos Aires) ... 84,429
Posadas ... 143,889
Presidencia Roque Sáenz Peña ... 49,341
Punta Alta ... 56,620
Quilmes (★ Buenos Aires) ... 446,587
Rafaela ... 53,273
Resistencia ... 220,104
Río Cuarto ... 110,254
Rosario (★ 1,045,000) ... 938,120
Salta ... 260,744
San Carlos de Bariloche ... 48,980
San Fernando (★ Buenos Aires) ... 133,624
San Francisco (★ 58,536) ... 51,932
San Isidro (★ Buenos Aires) ... 289,170
San Juan (★ 300,000) ... 118,046
San Justo (★ Buenos Aires) ... 949,566
San Lorenzo (★ Rosario) ... 96,891
San Luis ... 70,999
San Miguel de Tucumán (★ 525,000) ... 392,888
San Nicolás de los Arroyos ... 98,495
San Rafael ... 70,959
San Salvador de Jujuy ... 124,950
Santa Fe ... 292,165
Santiago del Estero (★ 200,000) ... 148,758
San Vincente (★ Buenos Aires) ... 55,803
Tandil ... 79,429
Tigre (★ Buenos Aires) ... 206,349
Trelew ... 52,372
Vicente López (★ Buenos Aires) ... 291,072
Villa Krause (★ San Juan) ... 66,693
Villa María ... 67,560
Villa Nueva (★ Mendoza) ... 164,670
Zárate ... 67,143

ARUBA

1987 E ... 64,763

Cities and Towns

• ORANJESTAD ... 19,800

AUSTRALIA

1989 E ... 16,833,100

Cities and Towns

Adelaide (★ 1,036,747) ... 12,340
Albury (★ 66,530) ... 40,730
Auburn (★ Sydney) ... 49,950
Ballarat (★ 80,090) ... 36,680
Bankstown (★ Sydney) ... 158,750
Bendigo (★ 67,920) ... 32,050
Berwick (★ Melbourne) ... 64,100
Blacktown (★ Sydney) ... 210,900
Blue Mountains (★ Sydney) ... 70,800
Botany (★ Sydney) ... 35,650
Brisbane (★ 1,273,511) ... 744,828
Broadmeadows (★ Melbourne) ... 105,500
Cairns (★ 80,875) ... 42,839
Camberwell (★ Melbourne) ... 87,700
Campbelltown (★ Sydney) ... 139,500
CANBERRA (★ 271,362) (1986 C) ... 247,194
Canning (★ Perth) ... 69,104
Canterbury (★ Sydney) ... 135,200
Caulfield (★ Melbourne) ... 70,100
Coburg (★ Melbourne) ... 54,500
Cockburn (★ Perth) ... 49,802
Coffs Harbour ... 47,890
Dandenong (★ Melbourne) ... 59,400
Darwin (★ 72,937) ... 63,900
Doncaster (★ Melbourne) ... 107,300
Enfield (★ Adelaide) ... 64,058
Essendon (★ Melbourne) ... 55,300
Fairfield (★ Sydney) ... 176,350
Footscray (★ Melbourne) ... 48,700
Frankston (★ Melbourne) ... 90,500
Geelong (★ 148,980) ... 13,190
Gosford ... 126,600
Gosnells (★ Perth) ... 71,862
Heidelberg (★ Melbourne) ... 63,500
Hobart (★ 181,210) ... 47,280
Holroyd (★ Sydney) ... 82,500
Hurstville (★ Sydney) ... 66,350
Ipswich (★ Brisbane) ... 75,283
Keilor (★ Melbourne) ... 103,700
Knox (★ Melbourne) ... 121,300
Kogarah (★ Sydney) ... 47,850
Lake Macquarie (★ Newcastle) ... 161,700
Launceston (★ 92,350) ... 32,150
Leichhardt (★ Sydney) ... 58,950
Liverpool (★ Sydney) ... 99,750
Logan (★ Brisbane) ... 142,222
Mackay (★ 50,885) ... 22,583
Malvern (★ Melbourne) ... 43,400
Marion (★ Adelaide) ... 74,631
Marrickville (★ Sydney) ... 84,650
Melbourne (★ 3,039,100) ... 55,300
Melville (★ Perth) ... 85,590
Mitcham (★ Adelaide) ... 63,301
Moorabbin (★ Melbourne) ... 98,900
Newcastle (★ 425,610) ... 130,940
Noarlunga (★ Adelaide) ... 77,352
Northcote (★ Melbourne) ... 49,100
North Sydney (★ Sydney) ... 53,400
Nunawading (★ Melbourne) ... 96,400
Oakleigh (★ Melbourne) ... 57,600
Parramatta (★ Sydney) ... 134,600
Penrith (★ Sydney) ... 152,650
Perth (★ 1,158,387) ... 82,413
Prahran (★ Melbourne) ... 43,900
Preston (★ Melbourne) ... 82,000
Randwick (★ Sydney) ... 119,200
Redcliffe (★ Brisbane) ... 48,123
Rockdale (★ Sydney) ... 88,200
Rockhampton (★ 61,694) ... 58,890
Ryde (★ Sydney) ... 94,400
Saint Kilda (★ Melbourne) ... 46,400
Salisbury (★ Adelaide) ... 106,129
Shoalhaven ... 64,070
Southport (★ 254,861) ... 135,408
South Sydney (★ Sydney) ... 74,100
Springvale (★ Melbourne) ... 88,700
Stirling (★ Perth) ... 181,556
Sunshine (★ Melbourne) ... 97,700
• Sydney (★ 3,623,550) ... 9,800
Tea Tree Gully (★ Adelaide) ... 82,324
Toowoomba ... 81,071
Townsville (★ 111,972) ... 83,339
Wagga Wagga ... 52,180
Wanneroo (★ Perth) ... 163,324
Waverley (★ Melbourne) ... 126,300
Waverley (★ Sydney) ... 61,850
West Torrens (★ Adelaide) ... 44,711
Willoughby (★ Sydney) ... 53,950
Wollongong (★ 236,690) ... 174,770
Woodville (★ Adelaide) ... 82,590
Woollahra (★ Sydney) ... 53,850

AUSTRIA / Österreich

1981 C ... 7,555,338

Cities and Towns

Graz (★ 325,000) ... 243,166
Innsbruck (★ 185,000) ... 117,287
Klagenfurt (★ 115,000) ... 87,321
Linz (★ 335,000) ... 199,910
Salzburg (★ 220,000) ... 139,426
Sankt Pölten (★ 67,000) ... 50,419
Villach (★ 65,000) ... 52,692
Wels (★ 76,000) ... 51,060
• WIEN (VIENNA) (★ 1,875,000) (1988 E) ... 1,482,800

BAHAMAS

1982 E ... 218,000

Cities and Towns

Freeport ... 25,000
• NASSAU ... 135,000

BAHRAIN / Al-Baḥrayn

1981 C ... 350,798

Cities and Towns

• AL-MANĀMAH (★ 224,643) ... 115,054
Al-Muḥarraq (★ Al-Manāmah) ... 57,688

BANGLADESH

1981 C ... 87,119,965

Cities and Towns

Barisāl ... 172,905
Begamganj ... 69,623
Bhairab Bāzār ... 63,563
Bogra ... 68,749
Brāhmanbāria ... 87,570
Chāndpur ... 85,656
Chittagong (★ 1,391,877) ... 980,000
Chuādanga ... 76,000
Comilla ... 184,132
• DHAKA (DACCA) (★ 3,430,312) ... 2,365,695
Dinājpur ... 96,718
Farīdpur ... 66,579
Gulshan (★ Dhaka) ... 215,444
Jamālpur ... 91,815
Jessore ... 148,927
Khulna ... 648,359
Kishorganj ... 52,302
Kushtia ... 74,892
Mādārīpur ... 63,917
Mīrpur (★ Dhaka) ... 349,031
Mymensingh ... 190,991
Naogaon ... 52,975
Nārāyanganj (★★ Dhaka) ... 405,562
Narsinghdi ... 76,841
Nawābganj ... 87,724
Noākhāli ... 59,065
Pābna ... 109,065
Patuākhāli ... 48,121
Rājshāhi ... 253,740
Rangpur ... 153,174
Saidpur ... 126,608
Sātkhira ... 52,156
Sherpur ... 48,214
Sirājganj ... 106,774
Sītākunda (★ Chittagong) ... 237,520
Sylhet ... 168,371
Tangail ... 77,518
Tongi (★ Dhaka) ... 94,580

BARBADOS

1980 C ... 244,228

Cities and Towns

• BRIDGETOWN (★ 115,000) ... 7,466

BELGIUM / België / Belgique

1987 E ... 9,864,751

Cities and Towns

Aalst (Alost) (★ Bruxelles) ... 77,113
Anderlecht (★ Bruxelles) ... 88,849
Antwerpen (★ 1,100,000) ... 479,748
Bastogne (▲ 11,699) ... 6,900
Brugge (Bruges) (★ 223,000) ... 117,755
• BRUXELLES (BRUSSEL) (★ 2,385,000) ... 136,920
Charleroi (★ 480,000) ... 209,395
Etterbeek (★ Bruxelles) ... 44,240
Forest (★ Bruxelles) ... 48,266
Genk (★★ Hasselt) ... 61,391
Gent (Gand) (★ 465,000) ... 233,856
Hasselt (★ 290,000) ... 65,563
Ixelles (★ Bruxelles) ... 76,241
Knokke [-Heist] ... 30,618
Kortrijk (Courtrai) (★ 202,000) ... 76,216
La Louvière (★ 147,000) ... 76,340
Leuven (Louvain) (★ 173,000) ... 84,583
Liège (Luik) (★ 750,000) ... 200,891
Mechelen (Malines) (★ 121,000) ... 75,808
Molenbeek-St.-Jean (★ Bruxelles) ... 69,764
Mons (Bergen) (★ 242,000) ... 89,697
Mouscron (★ Lille, France) ... 53,713
Namur (★ 147,000) ... 102,670
Oostende (Ostende) (★ 122,000) ... 68,318
Roeselare (Roulers) ... 51,963
Saint-Gilles (★ Bruxelles) ... 42,482
Schaerbeek (★ Bruxelles) ... 104,919
Seraing (★ Liège) ... 61,731
Sint-Niklaas (Saint-Nicolas) ... 68,082
Spa ... 9,645
Tournai (Doornik) (▲ 66,998) ... 44,900
Uccle (★ Bruxelles) ... 75,876
Verviers (★ 101,000) ... 53,498
Waterloo (★ Bruxelles) ... 25,232

BELIZE

1985 E ... 166,400

C Census. E Official estimate. U Unofficial estimate.
• Largest city in country.

★ Population or designation of metropolitan area, including suburbs (see headnote).
▲ Population of an entire municipality, commune, or district, including rural area.

Cities and Towns

• Belize City ... 47,000
BELMOPAN ... 4,500

BENIN / Bénin

1984 E ... 3,825,000

Cities and Towns

Abomey ... 53,000
• COTONOU ... 478,000
Natitingou (1975 E) ... 51,000
Ouidah (1979 E) ... 53,000
Parakou ... 92,000
PORTO-NOVO ... 164,000

BERMUDA

1985 E ... 56,000

Cities and Towns

• HAMILTON (★ 15,000) ... 1,676

BHUTAN / Druk-Yul

1982 E ... 1,333,000

Cities and Towns

• THIMPHU ... 12,000

BOLIVIA

1985 E ... 6,429,226

Cities and Towns

Cochabamba ... 317,251
• LA PAZ ... 992,592
Oruro ... 178,393
Potosí ... 113,380
Santa Cruz ... 441,717
SUCRE ... 86,609
Tarija ... 60,621

BOTSWANA

1987 E ... 1,169,000

Cities and Towns

Francistown (1986 E) ... 43,837
• GABORONE ... 107,677
Selebi Phikwe (1986 E) ... 41,382

BRAZIL / Brasil

1985 E ... 135,564,395

Cities and Towns

Alagoinhas (▲ 116,959) ... 87,500
Alegrete (▲ 71,898) ... 56,700
Alvorada ... 105,730
Americana ... 156,030
Anápolis ... 225,840
Apucarana (▲ 92,812) ... 73,700
Aracaju ... 360,013
Araçatuba ... 129,304
Araguari (▲ 96,035) ... 84,300
Arapiraca (▲ 147,879) ... 91,400
Araraquara (▲ 145,042) ... 87,500
Araras (▲ 71,652) ... 59,900
Araxá ... 61,418
Assis (▲ 74,238) ... 63,100
Bagé (▲ 106,155) ... 70,800
Barbacena (▲ 99,337) ... 80,200
Barra do Piraí (▲ 78,189) ... 55,700
Barra Mansa (★ Volta Redonda) ... 149,200
Barretos ... 80,202
Bauru ... 220,105
Bayeux (★ João Pessoa) ... 67,182
Belém (★ 1,200,000) ... 1,116,578
Belford Roxo (★ Rio de Janeiro) ... 340,700
Belo Horizonte (★ 2,950,000) ... 2,114,429
Betim (★ Belo Horizonte) ... 96,810
Blumenau ... 192,074
Boa Vista ... 66,028
Botucatu (▲ 71,139) ... 62,600
Bragança Paulista (▲ 105,099) ... 76,300
BRASÍLIA ... 1,567,709
Caçapava (▲ 64,213) ... 56,600
Cachoeira do Sul (▲ 91,492) ... 58,900
Cachoeirinha (★ Porto Alegre) ... 73,117
Cachoeiro de Itapemirim (▲ 138,156) ... 95,000
Campina Grande ... 279,929
Campinas (★ 1,125,000) ... 841,016
Campo Grande ... 384,398
Campos (▲ 366,716) ... 187,900
Campos Elyseos (★ Rio de Janeiro) ... 188,200
Canoas (★ Porto Alegre) ... 261,222
Carapicuíba (★ São Paulo) ... 265,856
Carazinho (▲ 62,108) ... 48,500
Cariacica (★ Vitória) ... 74,300
Caruaru (▲ 190,794) ... 152,100
Cascavel (▲ 200,485) ... 123,100
Castanhal (▲ 89,703) ... 71,200
Catanduva (▲ 80,309) ... 71,400
Caucaia (★ Fortaleza) ... 78,500
Cavaleiro (★ Recife) ... 106,600
Caxias (▲ 148,230) ... 66,300
Caxias do Sul ... 266,809
Chapecó (▲ 100,997) ... 64,200
Coelho da Rocha (★ Rio de Janeiro) ... 164,400
Colatina (▲ 106,260) ... 58,600
Colombo (★ Curitiba) ... 65,900
Conselheiro Lafaiete ... 77,958
Contagem (★ Belo Horizonte) ... 152,700
Corumbá (▲ 80,666) ... 65,800
Crato (▲ 86,371) ... 52,700
Criciúma (▲ 128,410) ... 85,900
Cruz Alta (▲ 71,817) ... 58,300
Cruzeiro ... 63,918
Cubatão (★ Santos) ... 98,322
Cuiabá (▲ 279,651) ... 220,400
Curitiba (★ 1,700,000) ... 1,279,205
Diadema (★ São Paulo) ... 320,187
Divinópolis ... 139,940
Dourados (▲ 123,757) ... 89,200
Duque de Caxias (★ Rio de Janeiro) ... 353,200
Embu (★ São Paulo) ... 119,791
Erechim (▲ 70,709) ... 54,300
Esteio (★ Porto Alegre) ... 58,964
Feira de Santana (▲ 355,201) ... 278,600
Ferraz de Vasconcelos (★ São Paulo) ... 68,831
Florianópolis (★ 365,000) ... 178,400
Fortaleza (★ 1,825,000) ... 1,582,414
Foz do Iguaçu (▲ 182,101) ... 124,900
Franca ... 182,820
Garanhuns ... 73,100
Goiânia (★ 990,000) ... 923,333
Governador Valadares (▲ 216,957) ... 192,300
Guaratinguetá (▲ 93,534) ... 80,400
Guarujá (★ Santos) ... 83,500
Guarulhos (★ São Paulo) ... 571,700
Ijuí (▲ 82,064) ... 64,400
Ilhéus (▲ 145,810) ... 79,400
Imperatriz (▲ 235,453) ... 119,500
Ipatinga (★ 270,000) ... 149,100
Ipiíba (★ Rio de Janeiro) ... 116,200
Itabira (▲ 81,771) ... 66,300
Itabuna (▲ 167,543) ... 142,200
Itajaí ... 104,232
Itajubá (▲ 69,675) ... 61,500
Itapecerica da Serra (★ São Paulo) ... 65,500
Itapetininga (▲ 105,512) ... 76,700
Itapevi (★ São Paulo) ... 66,825
Itaquaquecetuba (★ São Paulo) ... 91,366
Itaquari (★ Vitória) ... 163,900
Itaúna ... 61,446
Itu (▲ 92,786) ... 77,900
Ituiutaba (▲ 85,365) ... 74,900
Itumbiara (▲ 78,844) ... 57,200
Jaboatão (★ Recife) ... 82,900
Jacareí ... 149,061
Jaú (▲ 92,547) ... 74,500
Jequié (▲ 127,070) ... 92,100
João Pessoa (★ 550,000) ... 348,500
Joinvile ... 302,877
Juàzeiro (★ Petrolina) ... 78,600
Juàzeiro do Norte ... 159,806
Juiz de Fora ... 349,720
Jundiaí (▲ 313,652) ... 268,900
Lajes (▲ 143,246) ... 103,600
Lavras ... 52,100
Limeira ... 186,986
Linhares (▲ 122,453) ... 53,400
Londrina (▲ 346,676) ... 296,400
Lorena ... 63,230
Luziânia (▲ 98,408) ... 71,400
Macapá (▲ 168,839) ... 109,400
Maceió ... 482,195
Manaus ... 809,914
Marabá (▲ 133,559) ... 92,700
Marília (▲ 136,187) ... 116,100
Maringá ... 196,871
Mauá (★ São Paulo) ... 269,321
Mesquita (★ Rio de Janeiro) ... 161,300
Mogi das Cruzes (★ São Paulo) ... 144,800
Mogi-Guaçu (▲ 91,994) ... 81,800
Mogi-Mirim (▲ 63,313) ... 52,300
Monjolo (★ Rio de Janeiro) ... 113,900
Montes Claros (▲ 214,472) ... 183,500
Mossoró (▲ 158,723) ... 128,300
Muriaé (▲ 80,466) ... 57,600
Muribeca dos Guararapes (★ Recife) ... 171,200
Natal ... 510,106
Neves (★ Rio de Janeiro) ... 163,600
Nilópolis (★ Rio de Janeiro) ... 112,800
Niterói (★ Rio de Janeiro) ... 441,684
Nova Friburgo (▲ 143,529) ... 103,500
Nova Iguaçu (★ Rio de Janeiro) ... 592,800
Novo Hamburgo (★ Porto Alegre) ... 167,744
Olinda (★ Recife) ... 316,600
Osasco (★ São Paulo) ... 591,568
Ourinhos (▲ 65,841) ... 58,100
Paranaguá (▲ 94,809) ... 82,300
Paranavaí (▲ 75,511) ... 60,900
Parnaíba (▲ 116,206) ... 90,200
Parque Industrial (★ Belo Horizonte) ... 228,400
Passo Fundo (▲ 137,843) ... 117,500
Passos (▲ 79,393) ... 65,500
Patos ... 74,298
Patos de Minas (▲ 99,027) ... 69,000
Paulo Afonso (▲ 86,182) ... 75,300
Pelotas (▲ 277,730) ... 210,300
Petrolina (★ 225,000) ... 92,100
Petrópolis (★ Rio de Janeiro) ... 170,300
Pindamonhangaba (▲ 86,990) ... 64,100
Pinheirinho (★ Curitiba) ... 51,600
Piracicaba (▲ 252,079) ... 211,000
Poá (★ São Paulo) ... 66,006
Poços de Caldas ... 100,004
Ponta Grossa ... 223,154
Porto Alegre (★ 2,600,000) ... 1,272,121
Porto Velho (▲ 202,011) ... 152,700
Pouso Alegre (▲ 65,958) ... 58,300
Praia Grande (★ Santos) ... 67,800
Presidente Prudente ... 155,883
Queimados (★ Rio de Janeiro) ... 113,700
Recife (★ 2,625,000) ... 1,287,623
Ribeirão Prêto ... 383,125
Rio Branco (▲ 145,486) ... 109,800
Rio Claro ... 129,859
Rio de Janeiro (★ 10,150,000) ... 5,603,388
Rio Grande ... 164,221
Rio Verde (▲ 92,954) ... 59,400
Rondonópolis (▲ 101,642) ... 65,500
Salvador (★ 2,050,000) ... 1,804,438
Santa Bárbara d'Oeste ... 95,818
Santa Cruz do Sul (▲ 115,288) ... 60,300
Santa Maria (▲ 196,827) ... 163,900
Santana do Livramento (▲ 70,489) ... 60,100
Santarém (▲ 226,618) ... 120,800
Santa Rita (★ João Pessoa) ... 60,100
Santo André (★ São Paulo) ... 635,129
Santo Ângelo (▲ 107,559) ... 57,700
Santos (★ 1,065,000) ... 460,100
São Bernardo do Campo (★ São Paulo) ... 562,485
São Caetano do Sul (★ São Paulo) ... 171,005
São Carlos ... 140,383
São Gonçalo (★ Rio de Janeiro) ... 262,400
São João da Boa Vista (▲ 61,653) ... 50,400
São João del Rei (▲ 74,385) ... 61,400
São João de Meriti (★ Rio de Janeiro) ... 241,700
São José do Rio Prêto ... 229,221
São José dos Campos ... 372,578
São José dos Pinhais (★ Curitiba) ... 64,100
São Leopoldo (★ Porto Alegre) ... 114,065
São Lourenco da Mata (★ Recife) ... 65,936
São Luís (★ 600,000) ... 227,900
• São Paulo (★ 15,175,000) ... 10,063,110
São Vicente (★ Santos) ... 239,778
Sapucaia do Sul (★ Porto Alegre) ... 91,820
Sete Lagoas ... 121,418
Sete Pontes (★ Rio de Janeiro) ... 72,300
Sobral (▲ 112,275) ... 69,400
Sorocaba ... 327,468
Suzano (★ São Paulo) ... 128,924
Taboão da Serra (★ São Paulo) ... 122,112
Tatuí (▲ 69,358) ... 56,000
Taubaté ... 205,120
Teófilo Otoni (▲ 126,265) ... 82,700
Teresina (★ 525,000) ... 425,300
Teresópolis (▲ 115,859) ... 92,600
Timon (★ Teresina) ... 68,300
Tubarão (▲ 82,082) ... 70,400
Uberaba ... 244,875
Uberlândia ... 312,024
Uruguaiana (▲ 105,862) ... 91,500
Varginha ... 74,630
Vicente de Carvalho (★ Santos) ... 102,700
Vila Velha (★ Vitória) ... 91,900
Vitória (★ 735,000) ... 201,500
Vitória da Conquista (▲ 198,150) ... 145,800
Vitória de Santo Antão (▲ 100,450) ... 67,800
Volta Redonda (★ 375,000) ... 219,267

BRITISH VIRGIN ISLANDS

1980 C ... 12,034

Cities and Towns

• ROAD TOWN ... 2,479

BRUNEI

1981 C ... 192,832

Cities and Towns

• BANDAR SERI BEGAWAN (★ 64,000) ... 22,777

BULGARIA / Bâlgarija

1986 E ... 9,913,000

Cities and Towns

Blagoevgrad ... 67,766
Burgas ... 186,369
Dimitrovgrad ... 54,898
Gabrovo ... 81,688
Haskovo ... 89,273
Jambol ... 92,321
Kârdžali ... 56,906
Kazanlâk ... 61,780
Kjustendil ... 54,773
Loveč (1985 E) ... 48,862
Mihajlovgrad ... 53,529
Pazardžik ... 79,198
Pernik ... 96,277
Pleven ... 132,206
Plovdiv ... 349,148
Razgrad ... 51,277
Ruse ... 186,428
Silistra ... 54,627
Sliven ... 104,345
• SOFIJA (SOFIA) (★ 1,205,000) ... 1,119,152
Stara Zagora ... 153,538
Šumen ... 102,886
Tolbuhin ... 110,471
Varna ... 303,071
Veliko Târnovo ... 70,610
Vidin ... 63,813
Vraca ... 77,934

BURKINA FASO

1985 C ... 7,964,705

Cities and Towns

Bobo Dioulasso ... 228,668
Koudougou ... 51,926
• OUAGADOUGOU ... 441,514

BURMA / Myanmar

1983 C ... 34,124,908

Cities and Towns

Bago (Pegu) ... 150,528
Chauk ... 51,437
Dawei (Tavoy) ... 69,882
Henzada ... 82,005
Kale ... 52,628
Lashio ... 88,590
Magway ... 54,881
Mandalay ... 532,949
Mawlamyine (Moulmein) ... 219,961
Maymyo ... 63,782
Meiktila ... 96,496
Mergui (Myeik) ... 88,600
Mogok ... 49,392
Monywa ... 106,843
Myingyan ... 77,060
Myitkyinā ... 56,427
Pakokku ... 71,860
Pathein (Bassein) ... 144,096
Pyè (Prome) ... 83,332
Pyinmana ... 52,962
Shwebo ... 52,185
Sittwe (Akyab) ... 107,621
Taunggyi ... 108,231
Thaton ... 61,790
Toungoo ... 65,861
• YANGON (RANGOON) (★ 2,800,000) ... 2,705,039
Yenangyaung ... 62,582

BURUNDI

1986 E ... 4,782,000

Cities and Towns

• BUJUMBURA ... 273,000
Gitega ... 95,000

CAMBODIA / Kâmpŭchéa

1986 E ... 7,492,000

Cities and Towns

Kâmpóng Saôm (1981 E) ... 53,000
• PHNUM PÉNH ... 700,000

CAMEROON / Cameroun

1986 E ... 10,446,409

Cities and Towns

Bafoussam (1985 E) ... 89,000
Bamenda (1985 E) ... 72,000
• Douala ... 1,029,731
Foumban (1985 E) ... 50,000
Garoua (1985 E) ... 96,000
Kumba (1985 E) ... 67,000
Maroua ... 103,653
Ngaoundéré (1985 E) ... 61,000
Nkongsamba ... 123,149
YAOUNDÉ ... 653,670

CANADA

1986 C ... 25,354,064

CANADA: ALBERTA

1986 C ... 2,375,278

Cities and Towns

Calgary (★ 671,326) ... 636,104
Edmonton (★ 785,465) ... 573,982
Fort McMurray (★ 48,497) ... 34,949
Lethbridge ... 58,841
Medicine Hat (★ 50,734) ... 41,804
Red Deer ... 54,425

CANADA: BRITISH COLUMBIA

1986 C ... 2,889,207

Cities and Towns

Burnaby (★ Vancouver) ... 145,161
Chilliwack (★ 50,288) ... 41,337
Kamloops ... 61,773
Kelowna (★ 89,730) ... 61,213
Matsqui (★ 88,420) ... 51,449
Nanaimo (★ 60,420) ... 49,029
Prince George ... 67,621
Richmond (★ Vancouver) ... 108,492
Vancouver (★ 1,380,729) ... 431,147
Victoria (★ 255,547) ... 66,303

CANADA: MANITOBA

1986 C ... 1,071,232

Cities and Towns

Brandon ... 38,708
Portage la Prairie ... 13,198
Winnipeg (★ 625,304) ... 594,551

CANADA: NEW BRUNSWICK

1986 C ... 710,422

Cities and Towns

Fredericton (★ 65,768) ... 44,352
Moncton (★ 102,084) ... 55,468
Saint John (★ 121,265) ... 76,381

CANADA: NEWFOUNDLAND

1986 C ... 568,349

Cities and Towns

Corner Brook (★ 33,730) ... 22,719
Gander ... 10,207
Saint John's (★ 161,901) ... 96,216

CANADA: NORTHWEST TERRITORIES

1986 C ... 52,238

Cities and Towns

Inuvik ... 3,389
Yellowknife ... 11,753

CANADA: NOVA SCOTIA

1986 C ... 873,199

Cities and Towns

Dartmouth (★ Halifax) ... 65,243
Halifax (★ 295,990) ... 113,577
Sydney (★ 119,470) ... 27,754

CANADA: ONTARIO

1986 C ... 9,113,515

Cities and Towns

Barrie (★ 67,703) ... 48,287
Belleville (★ 87,530) ... 36,041
Brampton (★ Toronto) ... 188,498
Brantford (★ 90,521) ... 76,146

C Census. E Official estimate. U Unofficial estimate.
• Largest city in country.
★ Population or designation of metropolitan area, including suburbs (see headnote).
▲ Population of an entire municipality, commune, or district, including rural area.

Burlington (★ Hamilton) 116,675
Cambridge (Galt) (★★ Kitchener) 79,920
Cornwall (★ 51,719) 46,425
East York (★ Toronto) 101,085
Etobicoke (★ Toronto) 302,973
Gloucester (★ Ottawa) 89,810
Guelph (★ 85,962) 78,235
Hamilton (★ 557,029) 306,728
Kingston (★ 122,350) 55,050
Kitchener (★ 311,195) 150,604
London (★ 342,302) 269,140
Markham (★ Toronto) 114,597
Mississauga (★ Toronto) 374,005
Nepean (★ Ottawa) 95,490
Niagara Falls (★★ Saint Catharines) 72,107
North Bay (★ 57,422) 50,623
North York (★ Toronto) 556,297
Oakville (★ Toronto) 87,107
Oshawa (★ 203,543) 123,651
OTTAWA (★ 819,263) 300,763
Peterborough (★ 87,083) 61,049
Saint Catharines (★ 343,258) 123,455
Sarnia (★ 85,700) 49,033
Sault Sainte Marie (★ 84,617) 80,905
Scarborough (★ Toronto) 484,676
Sudbury (★ 148,877) 88,717
Thunder Bay (★ 122,217) 112,272
Timmins 46,657
• Toronto (★ 3,427,168) 612,289
Vaughan (★ Toronto) 65,058
Waterloo (★ Kitchener) 58,718
Windsor (★ 253,988) 193,111
York (★ Toronto) 135,401

CANADA: PRINCE EDWARD ISLAND

1986 C 126,646

Cities and Towns

Charlottetown (★ 53,868) 15,776
Summerside (★ 15,614) 8,020

CANADA: QUÉBEC

1986 C 6,540,276

Cities and Towns

Beauport (★ Québec) 62,869
Brossard (★ Montréal) 57,441
Charlesbourg (★ Québec) 68,996
Chicoutimi (★ 158,468) 61,083
Drummondville (★ 56,283) 36,020
Gatineau (★ Ottawa) 81,244
Hull (★ Ottawa) 58,722
Jonquière (★★ Chicoutimi) 58,467
LaSalle (★ Montréal) 75,621
Laval (★ Montréal) 284,164
Longueuil (★ Montréal) 125,441
Montréal (★ 2,921,357) 1,015,420
Montréal-Nord (★ Montréal) 90,303
Québec (★ 603,267) 164,580
Sainte-Foy (★ Québec) 69,615
Saint-Hubert (★ Montréal) 66,218
Saint-Jean-sur-Richelieu (★ 59,958) 34,745
Saint-Laurent (★ Montréal) 67,002
Saint-Léonard (★ Montréal) 75,947
Shawinigan (★ 61,965) 21,470
Sherbrooke (★ 129,960) 74,438
Trois-Rivières (★ 128,888) 50,122
Verdun (★ Montréal) 60,246

CANADA: SASKATCHEWAN

1986 C 1,010,198

Cities and Towns

Moose Jaw (★ 37,219) 35,073
Prince Albert (★ 40,841) 33,686
Regina (★ 186,521) 175,064
Saskatoon (★ 200,665) 177,641

CANADA: YUKON

1986 C 23,504

Cities and Towns

Dawson (1986 C) 896
Whitehorse (1986 C) 15,199

CAPE VERDE / Cabo Verde

1990 C 336,798,000

Cities and Towns

• PRAIA 61,797

CAYMAN ISLANDS

1988 E 25,900

Cities and Towns

• GEORGETOWN 13,700

CENTRAL AFRICAN REPUBLIC / République centrafricaine

1984 E 2,517,000

Cities and Towns

• BANGUI 473,817
Bouar (1982 E) 48,000

CHAD / Tchad

1979 E 4,405,000

Cities and Towns

Abéché 54,000
Moundou 66,000
• N'DJAMENA 303,000
Sarh 65,000

CHILE

1982 C 11,329,736

Cities and Towns

Antofagasta 185,486
Apoquindo (★ Santiago) 175,735
Arica 139,320
Calama 81,684
Cerrillos (★ Santiago) 67,013
Cerro Navia (★ Santiago) 137,777
Chillán 118,163
Concepción (★ 675,000) 267,891
Conchalí (★ Santiago) 157,884
Copiapó 69,045
Coquimbo 62,186
Coronel (★ Concepción) 65,918
Curicó 60,550
El Bosque (★ Santiago) 143,717
Huechuraba (★ Santiago) 56,313
Independencia (★ Santiago) 86,724
Iquique 110,153
La Cisterna (★ Santiago) 95,863
La Florida (★ Santiago) 191,883
La Granja (★ Santiago) 109,168
La Pintana (★ Santiago) 73,932
La Reina (★ Santiago) 80,452
La Serena 83,283
Las Rejas (★ Santiago) 147,918
Linares 46,433
Lo Espejo (★ Santiago) 124,462
Lo Prado (★ Santiago) 103,575
Los Ángeles 70,529
Lota (★ Concepción) 47,133
Macul (★ Santiago) 113,100
Maipú (★ Santiago) 114,117
Ñuñoa (★ Santiago) 168,919
Osorno 95,286
Ovalle 43,023
Pedro Aguirre Cerda (★ Santiago) 145,207
Peñalolén (★ Santiago) 137,298
Providencia (★ Santiago) 115,449
Pudahuel (★ Santiago) 97,578
Puente Alto (★ Santiago) 109,239
Puerto Montt 84,410
Punta Arenas 95,332
Quilpué (★ Valparaíso) 84,136
Quinta Normal (★ Santiago) 128,989
Rancagua 139,925
Recoleta (★ Santiago) 164,292
Renca (★ Santiago) 93,928
San Antonio 61,486
San Bernardo (★ Santiago) 117,132
San Joaquín (★ Santiago) 123,904
San Miguel (★ Santiago) 88,764
San Ramón (★ Santiago) 99,410
• SANTIAGO (★ 4,100,000) 232,667
Talca 128,544
Talcahuano (★★ Concepción) 202,368
Temuco 157,297
Valdivia 100,046
Valparaíso (★ 675,000) 265,355
Villa Alemana (★ Valparaíso) 55,766
Viña del Mar (★ Valparaíso) 244,899
Vitacura (★ Santiago) 72,038

CHINA / Zhongguo

1988 E 999,999,999

Cities and Towns

Abagnar Qi (▲ 100,700) (1986 E) 71,700
Acheng (1985 E) 100,304
Aihui (▲ 135,000) (1986 E) 76,700
Akesu (▲ 345,900) (1986 E) 143,100
Altay (▲ 141,700) (1986 E) 62,800
Anci (Langfang) (▲ 522,800) (1986 E) 122,100
Anda (▲ 425,500) (1986 E) 130,200
Andong (1986 E) 579,800
Ankang (1985 E) 89,188
Anqing (▲ 433,900) (1986 E) 213,200
Anshan 1,330,000
Anshun (▲ 214,700) (1986 E) 128,800
Anyang (▲ 541,900) (1986 E) 361,200
Baicheng (▲ 282,000) (1986 E) 198,600
Baiquan (1985 E) 50,996
Baiyin (▲ 301,900) (1986 E) 157,100
Baoding (▲ 535,100) (1986 E) 423,200
Baoji (▲ 359,500) (1986 E) 286,200
Baoshan (▲ 688,400) (1986 E) 52,300
Baotou (Paotow) 1,130,000
Baoying (1985 E) 50,479
Bei'an (▲ 440,500) (1986 E) 199,500
Beihai (▲ 175,900) (1986 E) 119,000
BEIJING (PEKING) (★ 7,200,000) 6,710,000
Beipiao (▲ 603,700) (1986 E) 180,900
Bengbu (▲ 612,600) (1986 E) 403,900
Benxi (Penhsi) 860,000
Bijie (1985 E) 54,871
Binxian (▲ 177,900) (1986 E) 86,700
Binxian (1982 C) 127,326
Boli (1985 E) 61,990
Bose (▲ 271,400) (1986 E) 82,000
Boshan (1975 U) 100,000
Boxian (1985 E) 63,222
Boxing (1982 C) 57,554
Boyang (1985 E) 60,688
Butha Qi (Zalantun) (▲ 389,500) (1986 E) 111,300
Cangshan (Bianzhuang) (1982 C) 79,334
Cangzhou (▲ 293,600) (1986 E) 196,700
Changchun (▲ 2,000,000) 1,822,000
Changde (▲ 220,800) (1986 E) 178,200
Changge (1982 C) 67,002
Changji (▲ 233,400) (1986 E) 110,500
Changqing (1982 C) 65,094
Changsha 1,230,000
Changshou (1985 E) 51,923
Changshu (▲ 998,000) (1986 E) 281,300
Changtu (1985 E) 49,937
Changyi (1982 C) 64,513
Changzhi (▲ 463,400) (1986 E) 273,000
Changzhou (Changchow) (1986 E) 522,700
Chaoan (▲ 1,214,500) (1986 E) 265,400
Chaoxian (▲ 739,500) (1986 E) 116,800
Chaoyang, Guangdong prov. (1985 E) 85,968
Chaoyang, Liaoning prov. (▲ 318,900) (1986 E) 180,300
Chengde (▲ 330,400) (1986 E) 226,600
Chengdu (Chengtu) (▲ 2,960,000) 1,884,000
Chenghai (1985 E) 50,631
Chenxian (▲ 191,900) (1986 E) 143,500
Chifeng (Ulanhad) (▲ 882,900) (1986 E) 299,000
Chongqing (Chungking) (▲ 2,890,000) 2,502,000
Chuxian (▲ 365,000) (1986 E) 113,300
Chuxiong (▲ 379,400) (1986 E) 67,700
Da'an (1985 E) 70,552
Dachangzhen (1975 U) 50,000
Dalian (Dairen) 2,280,000
Danyang (1985 E) 48,449
Daqing (▲ 880,000) 640,000
Dashiqiao (1985 E) 68,898
Datong (1985 E) 55,529
Datong (▲ 1,040,000) 810,000
Dawa (1985 E) 142,581
Daxian (▲ 209,400) (1986 E) 142,000
Dehui (1985 E) 60,247
Dengfeng (1982 C) 49,746
Deqing (1982 C) 48,726
Deyang (▲ 753,400) (1986 E) 184,800
Dezhou (▲ 276,200) (1986 E) 161,300
Didao (1975 U) 50,000
Dinghai (1985 E) 50,161
Dongchuan (Xincun) (▲ 275,100) (1986 E) 67,400
Dongguan (▲ 1,208,500) (1986 E) 254,900
Dongsheng (▲ 121,300) (1986 E) 57,500
Dongtai (1985 E) 65,788
Dongying (▲ 514,400) (1986 E) 178,100
Dukou (▲ 551,200) (1986 E) 380,200
Dunhua (▲ 448,000) (1986 E) 217,100
Duyun (▲ 386,600) (1986 E) 123,800
Echeng (▲ 938,000) (1986 E) 217,400
Enshi (▲ 679,000) (1986 E) 84,300
Erenhot (1986 E) 7,200
Ergun Zuoqi (1985 E) 55,970
Feixian (1982 C) 73,246
Fengcheng (1985 E) 66,745
Foshan (▲ 312,700) (1986 E) 243,500
Fujin (1985 E) 60,948
Fuling (▲ 973,500) (1986 E) 166,300
Fushun (Funan) 1,290,000
Fuxian (Wafangdian) (▲ 960,700) (1986 E) 246,200
Fuxinshi 700,000
Fuyang (▲ 195,200) (1986 E) 143,400
Fuyu, Heilongjiang prov. (1985 E) 48,670
Fuyu, Jilin prov. (1985 E) 98,373
Fuzhou, Fujian prov. (▲ 1,240,000) 910,000
Fuzhou, Jiangxi prov. (▲ 171,800) (1986 E) 106,700
Gaixian (1985 E) 67,587
Ganhe (1985 E) 48,128
Ganzhou (▲ 346,000) (1986 E) 191,600
Gaoqing (Tianzhen) (1982 C) 70,411
Gaoyou (1985 E) 57,844
Gejiu (Kokiu) (▲ 341,700) (1986 E) 193,600
Golmud (1986 E) 60,300
Gongchangling (1982 C) 49,281
Guanghua (▲ 420,000) (1986 E) 104,400
Guangyuan (▲ 805,500) (1986 E) 162,200
Guangzhou (Canton) (▲ 3,420,000) 3,100,000
Guanxian, Shandong prov. (1982 C) 49,782
Guanxian, Sichuan prov. (1985 E) 65,039
Guilin (Kweilin) (▲ 457,500) (1986 E) 324,200
Guixian (1985 E) 61,970
Guiyang (Kweiyang) (▲ 1,430,000) 1,030,000
Haicheng (▲ 984,800) (1986 E) 210,700
Haifeng (1985 E) 50,401
Haikou (▲ 289,600) (1986 E) 209,200
Hailaer (1986 E) 180,000
Hailin (1985 E) 58,909
Hailong (Meihekou) (▲ 534,200) (1986 E) 117,500
Hailun (1985 E) 83,448
Haiyang (Dongcun) (1982 C) 77,098
Hami (Kumul) (▲ 270,300) (1986 E) 146,400
Hancheng (▲ 304,200) (1986 E) 66,600
Handan (▲ 1,030,000) 870,000
Hangu (1975 U) 100,000
Hangzhou (Hangchow) 1,290,000
Hanzhong (▲ 415,000) (1986 E) 151,700
Harbin 2,710,000
Hebi (▲ 321,600) (1986 E) 158,500
Hechi (▲ 266,800) (1986 E) 74,400
Hechuan (1985 E) 65,237
Hefei (▲ 930,000) 740,000
Hegang (1986 E) 588,300
Helong (1985 E) 62,665
Hengshui (▲ 286,500) (1986 E) 83,100
Hengyang (▲ 601,300) (1986 E) 419,200
Heshan (▲ 109,600) (1986 E) 42,000
Heze (Caozhou) (▲ 1,001,500) (1986 E) 115,400
Hohhot (▲ 830,000) 670,000
Hongjiang (▲ 67,000) (1986 E) 54,300
Horqin Youyi Qianqi (Ulan Hot) (▲ 192,100) (1986 E) 129,100
Hotan (▲ 122,800) (1986 E) 71,700
Houma (▲ 158,500) (1986 E) 67,000
Huadian (1985 E) 75,183
Huaian (1985 E) 65,673
Huaibei (▲ 447,200) (1986 E) 252,100
Huaide (▲ 899,400) (1986 E) 187,600
Huaihua (▲ 427,100) (1986 E) 102,000
Huainan (▲ 1,110,000) 700,000
Huaiyin (Wangying) (▲ 382,500) (1986 E) 201,700
Huanan (1985 E) 66,596
Huanggang (1982 C) 65,961
Huangshi (1986 E) 451,900
Huayun (Huarong) (▲ 313,500) (1986 E) 81,000
Huinan (Chaoyang) (1985 E) 52,429
Huizhou (▲ 182,100) (1986 E) 117,000
Hulan (1985 E) 74,989
Hunjiang (Badaojiang) (▲ 687,700) (1986 E) 442,600
Huzhou (▲ 964,400) (1986 E) 208,500
Jiading (1985 E) 60,718
Jiamusi (Kiamusze) (▲ 557,700) (1986 E) 429,800
Jian (▲ 184,300) (1986 E) 132,200
Jiangling (1985 E) 77,887
Jiangmen (▲ 231,700) (1986 E) 168,800
Jiangyin (1985 E) 66,476
Jiangyou (1985 E) 72,663
Jianou (1985 E) 55,180
Jiaohe (1985 E) 51,504
Jiaojiang (▲ 385,200) (1986 E) 82,300
Jiaoxian (1985 E) 51,869
Jiaozuo (▲ 509,900) (1986 E) 335,400
Jiawang (1975 U) 50,000
Jiaxing (▲ 686,500) (1986 E) 210,200
Jiayuguan (▲ 102,100) (1986 E) 73,800
Jiexiu (1985 E) 51,300
Jieyang (1985 E) 98,531
Jilin (Kirin) 1,200,000
Jinan (Tsinan) (▲ 2,140,000) 1,546,000
Jinchang (Baijiazui) (▲ 136,000) (1986 E) 90,500
Jincheng (▲ 612,700) (1986 E) 99,900
Jingdezhen (Kingtechen) (▲ 569,700) (1986 E) 304,000
Jingmen (▲ 946,500) (1986 E) 227,000
Jinhua (▲ 799,900) (1986 E) 147,800
Jining, Nei Monggol prov. (1986 E) 163,300
Jining, Shandong prov. (▲ 765,700) (1986 E) 222,600
Jinshi (▲ 219,700) (1986 E) 73,700
Jinxi (▲ 634,300) (1986 E) 223,100
Jinxian (1985 E) 95,761
Jinzhou (Chinchou) (▲ 810,000) 710,000
Jishou (▲ 194,500) (1986 E) 59,500
Jishu (1985 E) 75,587
Jiujiang (▲ 382,300) (1986 E) 248,500
Jiuquan (Suzhou) (▲ 269,900) (1986 E) 56,300
Jiutai (1985 E) 63,021
Jixi (▲ 820,000) 700,000
Jixian (1985 E) 59,725
Juancheng (1982 C) 54,110
Junan (Shizilu) (1982 C) 90,222
Junxian (▲ 423,400) (1986 E) 97,000
Juxian (1982 C) 51,666
Kaifeng (▲ 629,100) (1986 E) 458,800
Kaili (▲ 342,100) (1986 E) 96,600
Kaiping (1985 E) 54,145
Kaiyuan (▲ 342,100) (1986 E) 96,600
Kaiyuan (1985 E) 85,762
Karamay (1986 E) 185,300
Kashi (▲ 194,500) (1986 E) 146,300
Keshan (1985 E) 65,088
Korla (▲ 219,000) (1986 E) 129,400
Kunming (▲ 1,550,000) 1,310,000
Kunshan (1985 E) 44,645
Kuqa (1985 E) 63,847

C Census. E Official estimate. U Unofficial estimate.
• Largest city in country.
★ Population or designation of metropolitan area, including suburbs (see headnote).
▲ Population of an entire municipality, commune, or district, including rural area.

Kuytun (1986 E) ... 60,200
Laiwu (▲ 1,041,800) (1986 E) ... 143,500
Langxiang (1985 E) ... 64,658
Lanxi (1985 E) ... 53,236
Lanxi (▲ 606,800) (1986 E) ... 70,500
Lanzhou (Lanchow) (▲ 1,420,000) ... 1,297,000
Lechang (1986 E) ... 56,913
Lengshuijiang (▲ 277,600) (1986 E) ... 101,700
Lengshuitan (▲ 362,000) (1986 E) ... 60,900
Leshan (▲ 972,300) (1986 E) ... 307,300
Lhasa (▲ 107,700) (1986 E) ... 84,400
Lianyungang (Xinpu) (▲ 459,400) (1986 E) ... 288,000
Liaocheng (▲ 724,300) (1986 E) ... 119,000
Liaoyang (▲ 576,900) (1986 E) ... 442,600
Liaoyuan (1986 E) ... 370,400
Liling (▲ 856,300) (1986 E) ... 107,100
Linfen (▲ 530,100) (1986 E) ... 157,600
Lingling (▲ 515,300) (1986 E) ... 72,700
Lingyuan (1985 E) ... 66,825
Linhai (1985 E) ... 52,653
Linhe (▲ 365,900) (1986 E) ... 99,800
Linkou (1985 E) ... 52,936
Linqing (▲ 603,000) (1986 E) ... 87,000
Linqu (1982 C) ... 84,196
Linxia (▲ 150,200) (1986 E) ... 72,900
Linyi (▲ 1,365,000) (1986 E) ... 190,000
Liuzhou ... 680,000
Longjiang (1985 E) ... 51,156
Longyan (▲ 378,500) (1986 E) ... 114,500
Loudi (▲ 254,300) (1986 E) ... 84,200
Lu'an (▲ 163,400) (1986 E) ... 122,600
Lufeng (1985 E) ... 53,015
Luohe (▲ 159,100) (1986 E) ... 102,300
Luoyang (Loyang) (▲ 1,090,000) ... 760,000
Luzhou (▲ 360,300) (1986 E) ... 237,800
Maanshan (▲ 367,000) (1986 E) ... 258,900
Manzhouli (1986 E) ... 116,600
Maoming (▲ 434,900) (1986 E) ... 118,600
Meixian (▲ 740,600) (1986 E) ... 169,100
Mengxian ... 55,000
Mengyin (1982 C) ... 70,602
Mianyang, Sichuan prov. (▲ 848,500) (1986 E) ... 233,900
Minhang (1975 U) ... 60,000
Mishan (1985 E) ... 54,919
Mixian (1982 C) ... 64,776
Mudanjiang ... 650,000
Nahe (1985 E) ... 49,725
N'aizishen (1985 E) ... 51,982
Nancha (1975 U) ... 50,000
Nanchang (▲ 1,260,000) ... 1,090,000
Nanchong (▲ 238,100) (1986 E) ... 158,000
Nanjing (Nanking) ... 2,390,000
Nanning (▲ 1,000,000) ... 720,000
Nanpiao (1982 C) ... 67,274
Nanping (▲ 420,800) (1986 E) ... 157,100
Nantong (▲ 411,000) (1986 E) ... 308,800
Nanyang (▲ 294,800) (1986 E) ... 199,400
Neihuang (1982 C) ... 56,039
Neijiang (▲ 298,500) (1986 E) ... 191,100
Ning'an (1985 E) ... 49,334
Ningbo (▲ 1,050,000) ... 570,000
Ningyang (1982 C) ... 55,424
Nong'an (1985 E) ... 55,966
Nunjiang (1985 E) ... 59,276
Orogen Zizhiqi (1985 E) ... 48,042
Panshan (▲ 343,100) (1986 E) ... 248,100
Panshi (1985 E) ... 59,270
Pingdingshan (▲ 819,900) (1986 E) ... 363,200
Pingliang (▲ 362,500) (1986 E) ... 85,400
Pingxiang (▲ 1,286,700) (1986 E) ... 368,700
Pingyi (1982 C) ... 89,373
Pingyin (1982 C) ... 62,827
Potou (▲ 456,100) (1986 E) ... 59,000
Puqi (1985 E) ... 65,239
Putian (▲ 265,400) (1986 E) ... 64,600
Putuo (1985 E) ... 50,962
Puyang (▲ 1,086,100) (1986 E) ... 131,000
Qian Gorlos (1985 E) ... 79,494
Qingdao (Tsingtao) ... 1,300,000
Qinggang (1985 E) ... 43,075
Qingjiang, Jiangsu prov. (▲ 246,617) (1982 C) ... 150,000
Qingjiang, Jiangxi prov. (1985 E) ... 42,698
Qingyuan (1985 E) ... 51,756
Qinhuangdao (Chinwangtao) (★ 436,000) (1986 E) ... 307,500
Qinzhou (▲ 923,400) (1986 E) ... 97,100
Qiqihar (Tsitsihar) (▲ 1,330,000) ... 1,180,000
Qitaihe (▲ 309,900) (1986 E) ... 166,400
Qixia (1982 C) ... 54,158
Qixian (1982 C) ... 53,041
Quanzhou (Chuanchou) (▲ 436,000) (1986 E) ... 157,000
Qujing (▲ 758,000) (1986 E) ... 135,000
Quxian (▲ 704,800) (1986 E) ... 124,000
Raoping (1985 E) ... 54,831
Rizhao (▲ 970,300) (1986 E) ... 93,300
Rongcheng (1982 C) ... 52,878
Rugao (1985 E) ... 50,643
Ruian (1985 E) ... 57,993
Sanmenxia (Shanxian) (▲ 150,000) (1986 E) ... 79,000
Sanming (▲ 214,300) (1986 E) ... 144,900
Shache (Yarkand) (1985 E) ... 45,331
• Shanghai (★ 9,300,000) ... 7,220,000
Shangqiu (Zhuji) (▲ 199,400) (1986 E) ... 135,400
Shangrao (▲ 142,500) (1986 E) ... 113,000
Shangshui (1982 C) ... 50,191
Shantou (Swatow) (▲ 790,000) ... 560,000
Shanwei (1985 E) ... 61,234
Shaoguan (1986 E) ... 363,100
Shaowu (▲ 266,700) (1986 E) ... 81,400
Shaoxing (▲ 250,900) (1986 E) ... 167,100
Shaoyang (▲ 465,900) (1986 E) ... 218,600
Shashi (1986 E) ... 253,700
Shenxian (1982 C) ... 50,208
Shenyang (Mukden) (▲ 4,370,000) ... 3,910,000
Shenzhen (▲ 231,900) (1986 E) ... 189,600
Shiguaigou (1975 U) ... 50,000
Shihezi (▲ 549,300) (1987 E) ... 304,700
Shijiazhuang ... 1,220,000
Shiyan (▲ 332,600) (1986 E) ... 227,300
Shizuishan (▲ 317,400) (1986 E) ... 225,500
Shouguang (1982 C) ... 83,400
Shuangcheng (1985 E) ... 91,163
Shuangliao (1985 E) ... 67,326
Shuangyashan (1986 E) ... 427,300
Shuicheng (▲ 2,216,500) (1986 E) ... 363,500
Shulan (1986 E) ... 50,582
Shunde (1985 E) ... 50,262
Siping (▲ 357,800) (1986 E) ... 280,100
Sishui (1982 C) ... 82,990
Songjiang (1985 E) ... 71,864
Songjianghe (1985 E) ... 53,023
Suihua (▲ 732,100) (1986 E) ... 200,400
Suileng (1985 E) ... 68,399
Suining (▲ 1,174,900) (1986 E) ... 118,500
Suixian (▲ 1,281,600) (1986 E) ... 187,700
Suqian (1985 E) ... 50,742
Suxian (▲ 218,600) (1986 E) ... 123,300
Suzhou (Soochow) ... 740,000
Tai'an (▲ 1,325,400) (1986 E) ... 215,900
Taiyuan (▲ 1,980,000) ... 1,700,000
Taizhou (▲ 210,800) (1987 E) ... 143,200
Tancheng (1982 C) ... 61,857
Tangshan (▲ 1,440,000) ... 1,080,000
Tao'an (1985 E) ... 76,269
Tengxian (1985 E) ... 53,254
Tianjin (Tientsin) (▲ 5,540,000) ... 4,950,000
Tianshui (▲ 953,200) (1986 E) ... 209,500
Tiefa (▲ 146,367) (1982 C) ... 60,000
Tieli (1985 E) ... 102,527
Tieling (▲ 454,100) (1986 E) ... 326,100
Tongchuan (▲ 393,200) (1986 E) ... 268,900
Tonghua (▲ 367,400) (1986 E) ... 290,200
Tongliao (▲ 253,100) (1986 E) ... 190,100
Tongling (▲ 216,400) (1986 E) ... 182,900
Tongren (1985 E) ... 50,307
Tongxian (1985 E) ... 97,168
Tumen (▲ 99,700) (1986 E) ... 77,600
Tunxi (▲ 104,500) (1986 E) ... 61,800
Turpan (▲ 196,800) (1986 E) ... 52,300
Ürümqi ... 1,060,000
Wangkui (1985 E) ... 52,021
Wangqing (1985 E) ... 61,237
Wanxian (▲ 280,800) (1986 E) ... 138,700
Weifang (▲ 1,042,200) (1986 E) ... 312,500
Weihai (▲ 220,800) (1986 E) ... 83,000
Weinan (▲ 699,400) (1986 E) ... 111,300
Weishan (Xiazhen) (1982 C) ... 57,932
Weixian (Hanting) (1982 C) ... 50,180
Wenzhou (▲ 530,600) (1986 E) ... 372,200
Wuchang (1985 E) ... 64,403
Wuhai (1986 E) ... 266,000
Wuhan ... 3,570,000
Wuhu (▲ 502,200) (1986 E) ... 396,000
Wulian (Hongning) (1982 C) ... 51,718
Wusong (1982 C) ... 64,017
Wuwei (Liangzhou) (▲ 804,000) (1986 E) ... 115,500
Wuxi (Wuhsi) ... 880,000
Wuzhong (▲ 402,400) (1986 E) ... 48,600
Wuzhou (Wuchow) (▲ 261,500) (1986 E) ... 194,800
Xiaguan (▲ 395,800) (1986 E) ... 112,100
Xiamen (Amoy) (▲ 546,400) (1986 E) ... 343,700
Xi'an (Sian) (▲ 2,580,000) ... 2,210,000
Xiangfan (▲ 421,200) (1986 E) ... 314,900
Xiangtan (▲ 511,100) (1986 E) ... 389,500
Xianning (▲ 402,200) (1986 E) ... 122,200
Xianyang (▲ 641,800) (1986 E) ... 285,900
Xiaogan (▲ 1,204,400) (1986 E) ... 125,500
Xiaoshan (1985 E) ... 63,074
Xichang (▲ 161,000) (1986 E) ... 105,000
Xinghua (1985 E) ... 75,573
Xinglongzhen (1982 C) ... 52,961
Xingtai (▲ 350,800) (1986 E) ... 265,600
Xinhui (1985 E) ... 77,381
Xining (Sining) ... 620,000
Xinmin (1985 E) ... 47,900
Xintai (▲ 1,157,300) (1986 E) ... 171,400
Xinwen (Suncun) (1975 U) ... 50,000
Xinxian (▲ 398,600) (1986 E) ... 74,200
Xinxiang (▲ 540,500) (1986 E) ... 411,000
Xinyang (▲ 234,200) (1986 E) ... 169,100
Xinyu (▲ 610,600) (1986 E) ... 140,200
Xuancheng (1985 E) ... 52,387
Xuanhua (1975 U) ... 140,000
Xuanwei (1982 C) ... 70,081
Xuchang (▲ 247,200) (1986 E) ... 167,800
Xuguit Qi (Yakeshi) (1986 E) ... 390,000
Xuzhou (Süchow) ... 860,000
Yaan (▲ 277,600) (1986 E) ... 89,200
Yan'an (▲ 259,800) (1986 E) ... 86,700
Yancheng (▲ 1,251,400) (1986 E) ... 258,400
Yangcheng (1982 C) ... 57,255
Yangjiang (1986 E) ... 91,433
Yangquan (▲ 478,900) (1986 E) ... 295,100
Yangzhou (▲ 417,300) (1986 E) ... 321,500
Yanji (▲ 216,900) (1986 E) ... 175,000
Yanji (Longjing) (1985 E) ... 55,035
Yanling (1982 C) ... 52,679
Yantai (Chefoo) (▲ 717,300) (1986 E) ... 327,000
Yanzhou (1985 E) ... 48,972
Yaxian (Sanya) (▲ 321,700) (1986 E) ... 70,500
Yi'an (1986 E) ... 54,253
Yibin (Ipin) (▲ 636,500) (1986 E) ... 218,800
Yichang (Ichang) (1986 E) ... 410,500
Yichuan (1982 C) ... 58,914
Yichun, Heilongjiang prov. ... 840,000
Yichun, Jiangxi prov. (▲ 770,200) (1986 E) ... 132,600
Yidu (1985 E) ... 54,838
Yilan (1985 E) ... 50,436
Yima (▲ 84,800) (1986 E) ... 53,700
Yinan (Jiehu) (1982 C) ... 67,803
Yinchuan (▲ 396,900) (1986 E) ... 268,200
Yingchengzi (1985 E) ... 59,072
Yingkou (▲ 480,000) (1986 E) ... 366,900
Yingtan (▲ 116,200) (1986 E) ... 64,500
Yining (Kuldja) (▲ 232,000) (1986 E) ... 153,200
Yiyang (▲ 365,000) (1986 E) ... 155,300
Yiyuan (Nanma) (1982 C) ... 53,800
Yongan (▲ 269,000) (1986 E) ... 105,100
Yongchuan (1985 E) ... 70,444
Yuci (▲ 420,700) (1986 E) ... 171,000
Yueyang (▲ 411,300) (1986 E) ... 239,500
Yulin, Guangxi Zhuangzu prov. (▲ 1,228,800) (1986 E) ... 115,600
Yulin, Shaanxi prov. (1985 E) ... 51,610
Yumen (Laojunmiao) (▲ 160,100) (1986 E) ... 84,300
Yuncheng, Shandong prov. (1982 C) ... 54,262
Yuncheng, Shansi prov. (▲ 434,900) (1986 E) ... 87,000
Yunyang (1982 C) ... 54,903
Yushu (1985 E) ... 57,222
Yuyao (▲ 772,700) (1986 E) ... 169,700
Zaozhuang (▲ 1,592,000) (1986 E) ... 292,200
Zhangjiakou (Kalgan) (▲ 640,000) ... 500,000
Zhangye (▲ 394,200) (1986 E) ... 73,000
Zhangzhou (Longxi) (▲ 310,400) (1986 E) ... 159,400
Zhanhua (Fuguo) (1982 C) ... 48,193
Zhanjiang (▲ 920,900) (1986 E) ... 335,500
Zhaodong (1985 E) ... 99,836
Zhaoqing (Gaoyao) (▲ 187,600) (1986 E) ... 145,700
Zhaotong (▲ 546,600) (1986 E) ... 77,500
Zhaoyuan (1985 E) ... 42,426
Zhaoyuan (1982 C) ... 56,389
Zhengzhou (Chengchow) (▲ 1,580,000) ... 1,150,000
Zhenjiang (1986 E) ... 412,400
Zhongshan (Shiqizhen) (▲ 1,059,700) (1986 E) ... 238,700
Zhoucun (1975 U) ... 50,000
Zhoukouzhen (▲ 220,400) (1986 E) ... 110,500
Zhuhai (▲ 155,000) (1986 E) ... 88,800
Zhumadian (▲ 149,500) (1986 E) ... 99,400
Zhuoxian (1985 E) ... 54,523
Zhuzhou (Chuchow) (▲ 499,600) (1986 E) ... 344,800
Zibo (Zhangdian) (▲ 2,370,000) ... 840,000
Zigong (Tzukung) (▲ 909,300) (1986 E) ... 361,700
Zixing (▲ 334,300) (1986 E) ... 97,100
Ziyang (1985 E) ... 57,349
Zouping (1982 C) ... 49,274
Zouxian (1985 E) ... 61,578
Zunyi (▲ 347,600) (1986 E) ... 236,600

COLOMBIA

1985 C ... 27,867,326

Cities and Towns

Armenia ... 187,130
Barrancabermeja ... 137,406
Barranquilla (★ 1,140,000) ... 899,781
Bello (★ Medellín) ... 212,861
• BOGOTÁ (★ 4,260,000) ... 3,982,941
Bucaramanga (★ 550,000) ... 352,326
Buenaventura ... 160,342
Buga ... 82,992
Cali (★ 1,400,000) ... 1,350,565
Cartagena ... 531,426
Cartago ... 97,791
Ciénaga ... 56,860
Cúcuta (★ 445,000) ... 379,478
Dos Quebradas (★ Pereira) ... 101,480
Duitama ... 56,390
Envigado (★ Medellín) ... 91,391
Florencia ... 66,430
Floridablanca (★ Bucaramanga) ... 143,824
Girardot ... 70,078
Ibagué ... 292,965
Itagüí (★ Medellín) ... 137,623
Magangué ... 49,160
Malambo (★ Barranquilla) ... 52,584
Manizales (★ 330,000) ... 299,352
Medellín (★ 2,095,000) ... 1,468,089
Montería ... 157,466
Neiva ... 194,556
Ocaña ... 51,443
Palmira ... 175,186
Pasto ... 197,407
Pereira (★ 390,000) ... 233,271
Popayán ... 141,964
Santa Marta ... 177,922
Sincelejo ... 120,537
Soacha (★ Bogotá) ... 109,051
Sogamoso ... 64,437
Soledad (★ Barranquilla) ... 165,791
Tuluá ... 99,721
Tunja ... 93,792
Valledupar ... 142,771
Villa Rosario (★ Cúcuta) ... 63,615
Villavicencio ... 178,685

COMOROS / Al-Qumur / Comores

1990 E ... 452,742

Cities and Towns

• MORONI ... 23,432

CONGO

1984 C ... 1,912,429

Cities and Towns

• BRAZZAVILLE ... 585,812
Dolisie ... 49,134
Pointe-Noire ... 294,203

COOK ISLANDS

1986 C ... 18,155

Cities and Towns

• AVARUA ... 9,678

COSTA RICA

1988 E ... 2,851,000

Cities and Towns

Desamparados (★ San José) (1984 C) ... 43,352
Limón (▲ 62,600) ... 40,400
• SAN JOSÉ (★ 670,000) ... 278,600

CUBA

1987 E ... 10,288,000

Cities and Towns

Bayamo ... 108,716
Camagüey ... 265,588
Cárdenas (1981 C) ... 59,352
Cienfuegos ... 112,225
Guantánamo ... 179,091
Holguín ... 199,861
• LA HABANA (HAVANA) (★ 2,125,000) ... 2,036,800
Manzanillo (1981 C) ... 87,830
Matanzas ... 106,954
Palma Soriano (1981 C) ... 55,851
Pinar del Río ... 108,109
Santa Clara ... 182,349
Santiago de Cuba ... 364,554
Victoria de las Tunas (1985 E) ... 91,400

CYPRUS / Kıbrıs / Kípros

1982 C ... 512,097

Cities and Towns

Lemesós (Limassol) (★ 107,161) ... 74,782
• NICOSIA (LEVKOSÍA) (★ 185,000) ... 48,221

CYPRUS, NORTH / Kuzey Kıbrıs

1985 E ... 160,287

Cities and Towns

• NICOSIA (LEFKOŞA) ... 37,400

C Census. E Official estimate. U Unofficial estimate.
• Largest city in country.
★ Population or designation of metropolitan area, including suburbs (see headnote).
▲ Population of an entire municipality, commune, or district, including rural area.

CZECHOSLOVAKIA / Československo

1990 E ... 15,661,734

Cities and Towns

Banská Bystrica ... 87,834
Bratislava ... 442,999
Brno (★ 450,000) ... 392,285
České Budějovice (★ 114,000) ... 99,428
Chomutov (★ 80,000) ... 55,735
Děčín (★ 72,000) ... 56,034
Frýdek-Místek (★ Ostrava) ... 66,791
Gottwaldov (★ 124,000) ... 87,189
Havířov (★ Ostrava) ... 92,037
Hradec Králové (★ 113,000) ... 101,302
Jihlava ... 54,855
Karlovy Vary (Carlsbad) ... 58,039
Karviná (★★ Ostrava) ... 69,521
Kladno (★ 88,500) ... 73,347
Košice ... 237,099
Liberec (★ 175,000) ... 104,256
Martin ... 66,678
Mladá Boleslav ... 49,195
Most (★ 135,000) ... 71,360
Nitra ... 91,297
Olomouc (★ 126,000) ... 107,044
Opava (★ 77,500) ... 63,440
Ostrava (★ 760,000) ... 331,557
Pardubice ... 95,909
Plzeň (★ 210,000) ... 175,038
Poprad ... 53,039
• PRAHA (PRAGUE) (★ 1,325,000) ... 1,215,656
Přerov ... 51,996
Prešov ... 90,121
Prievidza ... 52,624
Prostějov ... 52,074
Teplice (★ 94,000) ... 55,287
Trenčín ... 57,813
Trnava ... 72,866
Ústí nad Labem (★ 115,000) ... 106,499
Žilina ... 97,508

DENMARK / Danmark

1990 E ... 5,135,409

Cities and Towns

Ålborg (▲ 155,019) ... 114,000
Århus (▲ 261,437) ... 202,300
Ballerup (★ København) ... 45,218
Esbjerg (▲ 81,504) ... 71,900
Frederiksberg (★ København) ... 85,611
Gentofte (★ København) ... 65,303
Gladsakse (★ København) ... 60,882
Helsingør (Elsinore) (★ København) ... 56,701
• KØBENHAVN (★ 1,685,000) ... 466,723
Kongens Lyngby (★ København) ... 49,317
Odense (▲ 176,133) ... 140,100
Randers ... 61,020

DJIBOUTI

1976 E ... 226,000

Cities and Towns

• DJIBOUTI ... 120,000

DOMINICA

1984 E ... 77,000

Cities and Towns

• ROSEAU ... 9,348

DOMINICAN REPUBLIC / República Dominicana

1981 C ... 5,647,977

Cities and Towns

Barahona ... 49,334
La Romana ... 91,571
San Cristóbal ... 0
San Francisco de Macorís ... 64,906
San Juan [de la Maguana] ... 49,764
San Pedro de Macorís ... 78,562
Santiago [de los Caballeros] ... 278,638
• SANTO DOMINGO ... 1,313,172

ECUADOR

1987 E ... 9,923,000

Cities and Towns

Alfaro (★ Guayaquil) (1982 C) ... 51,023
Ambato ... 126,067
Cuenca ... 201,490
Esmeraldas ... 120,387
• Guayaquil (★ 1,580,000) ... 1,572,615
Ibarra (1982 C) ... 53,428
Loja (1982 C) ... 71,652
Machala ... 144,396
Manta ... 135,990
Milagro ... 102,884
Portoviejo ... 141,568
Quevedo (1982 C) ... 67,023
QUITO (★ 1,300,000) ... 1,137,705
Riobamba (1982 C) ... 75,455
Santo Domingo de los Colorados ... 104,059

EGYPT / Mişr

1986 C ... 48,205,049

Cities and Towns

Abū Kabīr ... 69,509
Akhmīm ... 70,602
Al-ʻArīsh ... 67,638
Al-Fayyūm ... 212,523
Al-Ḥawāmidīyah (★ Al-Qāhirah) ... 73,060
Al-Iskandarīyah (Alexandria) (★ 3,350,000) ... 2,917,327
Al-Ismāʻīlīyah (★ 235,000) ... 212,567
Al-Jīzah (Giza) (★ Al-Qāhirah) ... 1,870,508
Al-Maḥallah al-Kubrā ... 358,844
Al-Manṣūrah (★ 375,000) ... 316,870
Al-Manzilah ... 55,090
Al-Maṭarīyah ... 74,554
Al-Minyā ... 179,136
• AL-QĀHIRAH (CAIRO) (★ 9,300,000) ... 6,052,836
Al-Uqṣur (Luxor) ... 125,404
Armant ... 54,650
Ashmūn ... 54,450
As-Sinbillāwayn ... 60,285
As-Suways (Suez) ... 326,820
Aswān ... 191,461
Asyūṭ ... 273,191
Az-Zaqāzīq ... 245,496
Bahtīm (★ Al-Qāhirah) ... 275,807
Banhā ... 115,571
Banī Suwayf ... 151,813
Bilbays ... 96,540
Bilqās Qism Awwal ... 73,162
Būlāq ad-Dakrūr (★ Al-Qāhirah) ... 148,787
Būr Saʻīd (Port Said) ... 399,793
Būsh ... 54,482
Damanhūr ... 190,840
Disūq ... 78,119
Dumyāṭ (Damietta) ... 89,498
Hawsh ʻĪsā (1980 C) ... 53,619
Idkū ... 70,729
Jirjā ... 70,899
Kafr ad-Dawwār (★ Al-Iskandarīyah) ... 195,102
Kafr ash-Shaykh ... 102,910
Kafr az-Zayyāt ... 58,061
Kawm Umbū ... 52,131
Maghāghah ... 50,807
Mallawī ... 99,062
Manfalūṭ ... 52,644
Minūf ... 69,883
Mīt Ghamr (★ 100,000) ... 92,253
Qalyūb ... 86,684
Qinā ... 119,794
Rashīd (Rosetta) ... 52,014
Rummānah ... 50,014
Samālūṭ ... 62,404
Sāqiyat Makkī ... 51,062
Sawhāj ... 132,965
Shibīn al-Kawm ... 132,751
Shubrā al-Khaymah (★ Al-Qāhirah) ... 710,794
Sinnūris ... 55,323
Ṭahṭā ... 58,516
Ṭalkhā (★ Al-Manṣūrah) ... 55,757
Ṭanṭā ... 334,505
Warrāq al-ʻArab (★ Al-Qāhirah) ... 127,108
Ziftā (★★ Mīt Ghamr) ... 69,050

EL SALVADOR

1985 E ... 5,337,896

Cities and Towns

Delgado (★ San Salvador) ... 67,684
Mejicanos (★ San Salvador) ... 91,465
Nueva San Salvador (★ San Salvador) ... 53,688
San Miguel ... 88,520
• SAN SALVADOR (★ 920,000) ... 462,652
Santa Ana ... 137,879
Soyapango (★ San Salvador) ... 60,000

EQUATORIAL GUINEA / Guinea Ecuatorial

1983 C ... 300,000

Cities and Towns

• MALABO ... 31,630

ETHIOPIA / Ityopiya

1984 C ... 42,019,418

Cities and Towns

• ADIS ABEBA (★ 1,760,000) (1988 E) ... 1,686,300
Akaki Beseka (★ Adis Abeba) ... 54,146
Asmera (1988 E) ... 319,353
Bahir Dar ... 54,800
Debre Zeyit ... 51,143
Dese ... 68,848
Dire Dawa (1988 E) ... 117,042
Gonder ... 68,958
Harer ... 62,160
Jima ... 60,992
Mekele ... 61,583
Nazret ... 76,284

FAEROE ISLANDS / Føroyar

1990 E ... 47,946

Cities and Towns

• TÓRSHAVN ... 14,767

FALKLAND ISLANDS / Islas Malvinas

1986 C ... 1,916

Cities and Towns

• STANLEY ... 1,200

FIJI

1986 C ... 715,375

Cities and Towns

Lautoka (★ 39,057) ... 28,728
• SUVA (★ 141,273) ... 69,665

FINLAND / Suomi

1988 E ... 4,938,602

Cities and Towns

Espoo (Esbo) (★ Helsinki) ... 164,569
Hämeenlinna ... 42,486
• HELSINKI (HELSINGFORS) (★ 1,040,000) ... 490,034
Joensuu ... 47,099
Jyväskylä (★ 93,000) ... 65,719
Kotka ... 57,745
Kouvola (★ 53,821) ... 31,933
Kuopio ... 78,916
Lahti (★ 108,000) ... 74,300
Lappeenranta (▲ 53,780) ... 47,400
Oulu (★ 121,000) ... 98,582
Pori ... 77,395
Tampere (★ 241,000) ... 170,533
Turku (Åbo) (★ 228,000) ... 160,456
Vaasa (Vasa) ... 53,737
Vantaa (Vanda) (★ Helsinki) ... 149,063

FRANCE

1982 C ... 54,334,871

Cities and Towns

Aix-en-Provence (★ 126,552) ... 121,327
Ajaccio ... 54,089
Albi (★ 60,181) ... 45,947
Alès (★ 70,180) ... 43,268
Amiens (★ 154,498) ... 131,332
Angers (★ 195,859) ... 136,038
Angoulême (★ 103,552) ... 46,197
Annecy (★ 112,632) ... 49,965
Antibes (★★ Cannes) ... 62,859
Antony (★ Paris) ... 54,610
Argenteuil (★ Paris) ... 95,347
Arras (★ 80,477) ... 41,736
Asnières [-sur-Seine] (★ Paris) ... 71,077
Aubervilliers (★ Paris) ... 67,719
Aulnay-sous-Bois (★ Paris) ... 75,996
Avignon (★ 174,264) ... 89,132
Bayonne (★ 127,477) ... 41,381
Beauvais (★ 55,817) ... 52,365
Belfort (★ 76,221) ... 51,206
Besançon (★ 120,772) ... 113,283
Béthune (★ 258,383) ... 25,508
Béziers (★ 81,347) ... 76,647
Bordeaux (★ 640,012) ... 208,159
Boulogne-Billancourt (★ Paris) ... 102,582
Boulogne-sur-Mer (★ 98,566) ... 47,653
Bourges (★ 92,202) ... 76,432
Brest (★ 201,145) ... 156,060
Brive-la-Gaillarde (★ 64,301) ... 51,511
Caen (★ 183,526) ... 114,068
Calais (★ 100,823) ... 76,527
Cannes (★ 295,525) ... 72,259
Châlons-sur-Marne (★ 63,061) ... 51,137
Chalon-sur-Saône (★ 78,064) ... 56,194
Chambéry (★ 96,163) ... 53,427
Champigny-sur-Marne (★ Paris) ... 76,176
Charleville-Mézières (★ 67,694) ... 58,667
Châteauroux (★ 66,851) ... 51,942
Cherbourg (★ 85,485) ... 28,442
Cholet ... 55,524
Clermont-Ferrand (★ 256,189) ... 147,361
Colmar (★ 82,468) ... 62,483
Colombes (★ Paris) ... 78,777
Courbevoie (★ Paris) ... 59,830
Créteil (★ Paris) ... 71,693
Dieppe (★ 41,812) ... 35,957
Dijon (★ 215,865) ... 140,942
Douai (★ 202,366) ... 42,576
Drancy (★ Paris) ... 60,183
Dunkerque (★ 195,705) ... 73,120
Épinay-sur-Seine (★ Paris) ... 50,314
Fontenay-sous-Bois (★ Paris) ... 52,627
Forbach (★ 99,606) ... 27,187
Grenoble (★ 392,021) ... 156,637
Hagondange (★ 119,669) ... 9,091
Ivry-sur-Seine (★ Paris) ... 55,699
La Rochelle (★ 102,143) ... 75,840
La Seyne [-sur-Mer] (★ Toulon) ... 57,659
Laval (★ 55,984) ... 50,360
Le Havre (★ 254,595) ... 199,388
Le Mans (★ 191,080) ... 147,697
Levallois-Perret (★ Paris) ... 53,500
Lille (★ 1,020,000) ... 168,424
Limoges (★ 171,689) ... 140,400
Lorient (★ 104,025) ... 62,554
Lyon (★ 1,275,000) ... 413,095
Maisons-Alfort (★ Paris) ... 51,065
Mantes-la-Jolie (★ 170,265) ... 43,564
Marseille (★ 1,225,000) ... 874,436
Maubeuge (★ 105,714) ... 36,061
Melun (★ 82,479) ... 35,005
Mérignac (★ Bordeaux) ... 51,306
Metz (★ 186,437) ... 114,232
Montbéliard (★ 128,194) ... 31,836
Montluçon (★ 67,963) ... 49,912
Montpellier (★ 221,307) ... 197,231
Montreuil-sous-Bois (★ Paris) ... 93,368
Mulhouse (Mülhausen) (★ 220,613) ... 112,157
Nancy (★ 306,982) ... 96,317
Nanterre (★ Paris) ... 88,578
Nantes (★ 464,857) ... 240,539
Neuilly-sur-Seine (★ Paris) ... 64,170
Nice (★ 449,496) ... 337,085
Nîmes (★ 132,343) ... 124,220
Niort (★ 61,959) ... 58,203
Orléans (★ 220,478) ... 102,710
• PARIS (★ 9,775,000) (1987 E) ... 2,078,900
Pau (★ 131,265) ... 83,790
Perpignan (★ 137,915) ... 111,669
Pessac (★ Bordeaux) ... 50,267
Poitiers (★ 103,204) ... 79,350
Quimper ... 56,907
Reims (★ 199,388) ... 194,656
Rennes (★ 234,418) ... 117,234
Roanne (★ 81,786) ... 48,705
Roubaix (★★ Lille) ... 101,602
Rouen (★ 379,879) ... 101,945
Rueil-Malmaison (★ Paris) ... 63,412
Saint-Brieuc (★ 83,900) ... 48,563
Saint-Chamond (★ 82,059) ... 40,267
Saint-Denis (★ Paris) ... 90,829
Saint-Étienne (★ 317,228) ... 204,955
Saint-Maur-des-Fossés (★ Paris) ... 80,811
Saint-Nazaire (★ 130,271) ... 68,348
Saint-Quentin (★ 71,887) ... 63,567
Sarcelles (★ Paris) ... 53,630
Strasbourg (★ 400,000) ... 248,712
Tarbes (★ 78,056) ... 51,422
Thionville (★ 138,034) ... 40,573
Toulon (★ 410,393) ... 179,423
Toulouse (★ 541,271) ... 347,995
Tourcoing (★★ Lille) ... 96,908
Tours (★ 262,786) ... 132,209
Troyes (★ 125,240) ... 63,581
Valence (★ 106,041) ... 66,356
Valenciennes (★ 349,505) ... 40,275
Vénissieux (★ Lyon) ... 64,804
Versailles (★ Paris) ... 91,494
Villejuif (★ Paris) ... 52,448
Villeneuve-d'Ascq (★ Lille) ... 59,527
Villeurbanne (★ Lyon) ... 115,960
Vitry-sur-Seine (★ Paris) ... 85,263

FRENCH GUIANA / Guyane française

1982 C ... 73,022

Cities and Towns

• CAYENNE ... 38,091

FRENCH POLYNESIA / Polynésie française

1988 C ... 188,814

Cities and Towns

• PAPEETE (★ 80,000) ... 23,555

GABON

1985 E ... 1,312,000

Cities and Towns

Franceville ... 58,800
Lambaréné ... 49,500
• LIBREVILLE ... 235,700
Port Gentil ... 124,400

GAMBIA

1983 C ... 696,000

Cities and Towns

• BANJUL (★ 95,000) ... 44,536

GERMANY / Deutschland

1989 E ... 78,389,735

Cities and Towns

Aachen (★ 535,000) ... 233,255
Aalen (★ 80,000) ... 62,812
Ahlen ... 52,836
Altenburg ... 53,288
Arnsberg ... 73,912
Aschaffenburg (★ 145,000) ... 62,048
Augsburg (★ 405,000) ... 247,731
Baden-Baden ... 50,761
Bad Homburg (★ Frankfurt am Main) ... 51,035
Bad Salzuflen (★★ Herford) ... 50,875
Bamberg (★ 120,000) ... 69,809
Bautzen ... 52,394
Bayreuth (★ 90,000) ... 70,933
Bergheim (★ Köln) ... 55,997
Bergisch Gladbach (★ Köln) ... 101,983
Bergkamen (★ Essen) ... 48,489
BERLIN (★ 3,825,000) ... 3,352,848
Bielefeld (★ 515,000) ... 311,946
Bitterfeld (★ 105,000) ... 20,513
Bocholt ... 67,565
Bochum (★★ Essen) ... 389,087
BONN (★ 570,000) ... 282,190
Bottrop (★ Essen) ... 116,363
Brandenburg ... 94,872
Braunschweig (★ 330,000) ... 253,794
Bremen (★ 800,000) ... 535,058
Bremerhaven (★ 190,000) ... 126,934
Castrop-Rauxel (★ Essen) ... 77,660
Celle ... 71,050
Chemnitz (★ 450,000) ... 311,765
Cottbus ... 128,639
Cuxhaven ... 55,249
Darmstadt (★ 305,000) ... 136,067
Delmenhorst (★★ Bremen) ... 72,901
Dessau (★ 140,000) ... 103,867
Detmold ... 66,809
Dinslaken (★ Essen) ... 63,246
Dormagen (★ Köln) ... 55,935
Dorsten (★ Essen) ... 75,518
Dortmund (★★ Essen) ... 587,328
Dresden (★ 670,000) ... 518,057
Duisburg (★★ Essen) ... 527,447
Düren (★ 110,000) ... 83,120
Düsseldorf (★ 1,190,000) ... 569,641
Eberswalde ... 54,822
Eisenhüttenstadt ... 53,048
Emden ... 49,803
Erfurt ... 220,016
Erlangen (★★ Nürnberg) ... 100,583
Eschweiler (★★ Aachen) ... 53,516
• Essen (★ 4,950,000) ... 620,594
Esslingen (★ Stuttgart) ... 90,537
Flensburg (★ 103,000) ... 85,830
Frankfurt am Main (★ 1,855,000) ... 625,258
Frankfurt an der Oder ... 87,863
Freiberg ... 51,341
Freiburg [im Breisgau] (★ 225,000) ... 183,979
Friedrichshafen ... 52,295
Fulda (★ 79,000) ... 54,320
Fürth (★★ Nürnberg) ... 98,832
Garbsen (★ Hannover) ... 59,225
Garmisch-Partenkirchen ... 25,908
Gelsenkirchen (★★ Essen) ... 287,255
Gera ... 134,834

C Census. E Official estimate. U Unofficial estimate.
• Largest city in country.
★ Population or designation of metropolitan area, including suburbs (see headnote).
▲ Population of an entire municipality, commune, or district, including rural area.

Giessen (★ 160,000) 71,751
Gladbeck (★ Essen) 79,187
Göppingen (★ 155,000) 52,873
Görlitz 77,609
Goslar (★ 84,000) 45,614
Gotha 57,365
Göttingen 118,073
Greifswald 68,597
Grevenbroich (★ Düsseldorf) 59,204
Gummersbach 49,017
Gütersloh (★★ Bielefeld) 83,407
Hagen (★★ Essen) 210,640
Halle (★ 475,000) 236,044
Halle-Neustadt (★ Halle) 93,446
Hamburg (★ 2,225,000) .. 1,603,070
Hameln (★ 72,000) 57,642
Hamm 173,611
Hanau (★★ Frankfurt am Main) 84,300
Hannover (★ 1,000,000) 498,495
Hattingen (★ Essen) 56,242
Heidelberg (★★ Mannheim) 131,429
Heidenheim (★ 89,000) 48,497
Heilbronn (★ 230,000) 112,278
Herford (★ 120,000) 61,700
Herne (★ Essen) 174,664
Herten (★ Essen) 68,111
Hilden (★ Düsseldorf) 53,725
Hildesheim (★ 140,000) 103,512
Hof 50,938
Hoyerswerda 69,361
Hürth (★ Köln) 49,094
Ingolstadt (★ 138,000) 97,702
Iserlohn 93,337
Jena 108,010
Kaiserslautern (★ 138,000) 96,990
Karlsruhe (★ 485,000) 265,100
Kassel (★ 360,000) 189,156
Kempten (Allgäu) 60,052
Kerpen (★ Köln) 54,699
Kiel (★ 335,000) 240,675
Kleve 44,416
Koblenz (★ 180,000) 107,286
Köln (Cologne) (★ 1,760,000) 937,482
Konstanz 72,862
Krefeld (★★ Essen) 235,423
Landshut 57,194
Langenfeld (★ Düsseldorf) 50,777
Leipzig (★ 700,000) 545,307
Leverkusen (★ Köln) 157,358
Lippstadt 60,396
Lübeck (★ 260,000) 210,681
Lüdenscheid 76,118
Ludwigsburg (★ Stuttgart) 79,342
Ludwigshafen (★★ Mannheim) 158,478
Lüneburg 60,053
Lünen (★ Essen) 85,584
Magdeburg (★ 400,000) 290,579
Mainz (★★ Wiesbaden) 174,828
Mannheim (★ 1,400,000) 300,468
Marburg an der Lahn 70,905
Marl (★ Essen) 89,651
Meerbusch (★ Düsseldorf) 50,452
Menden 54,899
Minden (★ 125,000) 75,169
Moers (★ Essen) 101,809
Mönchengladbach (★ 410,000) 252,910
Mülheim an der Ruhr (★ Essen) 175,454
München (Munich) (★ 1,955,000) 1,211,617
Münster 248,919
Neubrandenburg 90,471
Neumünster 79,574
Neunkirchen (★ 135,000) 50,784
Neuss (★ Düsseldorf) 143,976
Neustadt an der Weinstrasse 50,453
Neuwied (★ 150,000) 60,665
Norderstedt (★ Hamburg) 66,747
Nürnberg (★ 1,030,000) 480,078
Oberhausen (★★ Essen) 221,017
Offenbach (★ Frankfurt am Main) 112,450
Offenburg 51,730
Oldenburg 140,785
Osnabrück (★ 270,000) 154,594
Paderborn 114,148
Passau 49,137
Pforzheim (★ 220,000) 108,887
Plauen 77,593
Potsdam (★ Berlin) 142,862
Pulheim (★ Köln) 48,158
Ratingen (★ Düsseldorf) 89,880
Ravensburg (★ 75,000) 44,146
Recklinghausen (★ Essen) 121,666
Regensburg (★ 205,000) 119,078
Remscheid (★★ Wuppertal) 120,979
Reutlingen (★ 160,000) 100,400
Rheine 69,324
Rosenheim 54,304
Rostock 253,990
Rüsselsheim (★★ Wiesbaden) 58,426
Saarbrücken (★ 385,000) 188,467
Saarlouis (★ 115,000) 37,662
Salzgitter 111,674
Sankt Augustin (★ Bonn) 50,230
Schwäbisch Gmünd 57,861
Schwedt 52,419
Schweinfurt (★ 110,000) 52,818
Schwerin 130,685
Schwerte (★ Essen) 49,017
Siegburg (★ 170,000) 34,402
Siegen (★ 200,000) 106,160
Sindelfingen (★ Stuttgart) 57,524
Solingen (★★ Wuppertal) 160,824
Stendal 49,906
Stolberg (★★ Aachen) 56,182
Stralsund 75,498
Stuttgart (★ 1,925,000) 562,658
Suhl 56,345
Trier (★ 125,000) 95,692
Troisdorf (★★ Siegburg) 62,011
Tübingen 76,046
Ulm (★ 210,000) 106,508
Unna (★ Essen) 61,989
Velbert (★ Essen) 88,058
Viersen (★★ Mönchengladbach) 76,163
Villingen-Schwenningen 76,258
Weimar 63,412
Wesel 57,986
Wetzlar (★ 105,000) 50,299
Wiesbaden (★ 795,000) 254,209
Wilhelmshaven (★ 135,000) 89,892
Wismar 58,058
Witten (★ Essen) 109,637
Wittenberg 53,358
Wolfenbüttel (★★ Braunschweig) 50,960
Wolfsburg 125,831
Worms (★★ Mannheim) 74,809
Wuppertal (★ 830,000) 371,283
Würzburg (★ 210,000) 125,589
Zweibrücken (★ 105,000) 33,377
Zwickau (★ 165,000) 121,749

GHANA

1984 C 12,205,574

Cities and Towns

• ACCRA (★ 1,250,000) 859,640
Ashiaman (★ Accra) 49,427
Cape Coast 86,620
Koforidua 54,400
Kumasi (★ 600,000) 348,880
Obuasi 60,146
Sekondi-Takoradi (★ 175,352) 93,882
Tafo (★ Kumasi) 50,432
Tamale (★ 168,091) 136,828
Tema (★★ Accra) 99,608
Teshie (★ Accra) 62,954

GIBRALTAR

1988 E 30,077

Cities and Towns

• GIBRALTAR 30,077

GREECE / Ellás

1981 C 9,740,417

Cities and Towns

Aiyáleo (★ Athínai) 81,906
• ATHÍNAI (ATHENS) (★ 3,027,331) 885,737
Áyios Dhimítrios (★ Athínai) 51,421
Galátsion (★ Athínai) 50,096
Ilioúpolis (★ Athínai) 69,560
Iráklion (★ 110,958) 102,398
Kalamariá (★ Thessaloníki) 51,676
Kallithéa (★ Athínai) 117,319
Kardhítsa 27,291
Kavála 56,375
Keratsínion (★ Athínai) 74,179
Kérkira (Corfu) 33,561
Khalándrion (★ Athínai) 54,320
Khaniá (★ 61,976) 47,451
Khíos (★ 29,742) 24,070
Koridhallós (★ Athínai) 61,313
Kórinthos (Corinth) 22,658
Lárisa 102,048
Néa Ionía (★ Athínai) 59,202
Néa Liósia (★ Athínai) 72,427
Néa Smírni (★ Athínai) 67,408
Níkaia (★ Athínai) 90,368
Palaión Fáliron (★ Athínai) 53,273
Pátrai (★ 154,596) 142,163
Peristérion (★ Athínai) 140,858
Piraiévs (Piraeus) (★★ Athínai) 196,389
Ródhos (Rhodes) 40,392
Spárti (Sparta) (★ 14,388) 12,975
Thessaloníki (Salonika) (★ 706,180) 406,413
Víron (★ Athínai) 57,880
Vólos (★ 107,407) 71,378
Zográfos (★ Athínai) 84,548

GREENLAND / Grønland / Kalaallit Nunaat

1990 E 55,558

Cities and Towns

• GODTHÅB (NUUK) 12,217
Thule 551

GRENADA

1981 C 89,088

Cities and Towns

• SAINT GEORGE'S (★ 25,000) 4,788

GUADELOUPE

1982 C 328,400

Cities and Towns

BASSE-TERRE (★ 26,600) 13,656
Les Abymes (★ Pointe-à-Pitre) 56,165
• Pointe-à-Pitre (★ 83,000) 25,310

GUAM

1980 C 105,979

Cities and Towns

• AGANA (★ 44,000) 896

GUATEMALA

1989 E 8,935,395

Cities and Towns

Escuintla 60,673
• GUATEMALA (★ 1,400,000) 1,057,210
Quetzaltenango 88,769

GUERNSEY

1986 C 55,482

Cities and Towns

• SAINT PETER PORT (★ 36,000) 16,085

GUINEA / Guinée

1986 E 6,225,000

Cities and Towns

• CONAKRY 800,000
Kankan 100,000
Kindia 80,000
Labé 110,000
Nzérékoré (1983 C) 55,356

GUINEA-BISSAU / Guiné-Bissau

1988 E 945,000

Cities and Towns

• BISSAU 125,000

GUYANA

1983 E 918,000

Cities and Towns

• GEORGETOWN (★ 188,000) 78,500

HAITI / Haïti

1987 E 5,531,802

Cities and Towns

Cap-Haïtien 72,161
• PORT-AU-PRINCE (★ 880,000) 797,000

HONDURAS

1988 C 4,376,839

Cities and Towns

Choluteca 53,799
El Progreso 55,523
La Ceiba 68,289
San Pedro Sula 279,356
• TEGUCIGALPA 551,606

HONG KONG

1986 C 5,395,997

Cities and Towns

Kowloon (Jiulong) (★★ Victoria) 774,781
Kwai Chung (★ Victoria) 131,362
New Kowloon (Xinjiulong) (★★ Victoria) 1,526,910
Sha Tin (★ Victoria) 355,810
Sheung Shui 87,206
Tai Po 119,679
Tsuen Wan (Quanwan) (★ Victoria) 514,241
Tuen Mun (★ Victoria) 262,458
• VICTORIA (★ 4,770,000) 1,175,860
Yuen Long 75,740

HUNGARY / Magyarország

1990 C 10,375,000

Cities and Towns

Békéscsaba (▲ 67,621) 58,800
• BUDAPEST (★ 2,565,000) 2,016,132
Debrecen 212,247
Dunaújváros 59,049
Eger 61,908
Győr 129,356
Kaposvár 71,793
Kecskemét (▲ 102,528) 81,200
Miskolc 196,449
Nagykanizsa 54,059
Nyíregyháza (▲ 114,166) 88,500
Pécs 170,119
Sopron 55,088
Szeged 175,338
Székesfehérvár 108,990
Szolnok 78,333
Szombathely 85,418
Tatabánya 74,271
Veszprém 63,902
Zalaegerszeg 62,221

ICELAND / Ísland

1987 E 247,357

Cities and Towns

• REYKJAVÍK (★ 137,941) 93,425

INDIA / Bharat

1981 C 685,184,692

Cities and Towns

Abohar 86,334
Achalpur 81,186
Ādilābād 53,482
Adityapur (★ Jamshedpur) 53,421
Ādoni 108,939
Agartala 132,186
Āgra (★ 747,318) 694,191
Ahmadābād (★ 2,400,000) 2,059,725
Ahmadnagar (★ 181,210) 143,937
Ajmer 375,593
Akola 225,412
Akot 51,936
Alandur (★ Madras) 97,449
Alīgarh 320,861
Alījal 74,493
Allahābād (★ 650,070) 616,051
Alleppey 169,940
Alwar 145,795
Amalner 67,516
Amarnāth (★ Bombay) 96,347
Ambāla (★ 233,110) 104,565
Ambāla Sadar (★ Ambāla) 80,741
Ambattur (★ Madras) 115,901
Āmbūr 66,042
Amrāvati 261,404
Amreli (★ 58,241) 56,598
Amritsar 594,844
Amroha 112,682
Anakāpalle 73,179
Ānand 83,936
Anantapur 119,531
Arcot (★ 94,363) 38,836
Arkonam 59,405
Arni 49,365
Arrah 125,111
Aruppukkottai 72,245
Asansol (★ 1,050,000) 183,375
Ashoknagar-Kalyangarh (★ Hābra) 55,176
Āttūr 50,517
Aurangābād (★ 316,421) 284,607
Avadi (★ Madras) 124,701
Azamgarh 66,523
Badagara 64,174
Bāgalkot 67,858
Baharampur (★ 102,311) 92,889
Bahraich 99,889
Baidyabāti (★ Calcutta) 70,573
Bālāghāt (★ 53,183) 49,564
Balāngīr 54,943
Balasore 65,779
Ballālpur 61,398
Ballia 61,704
Bālly (★ Calcutta) 147,735
Bālly (★ Calcutta) 54,859
Bālurghāt (★ 112,621) 104,646
Bānda 72,379
Bangalore (★ 2,950,000) 2,476,355
Bangaon 69,885
Bānkura 94,954
Bānsberia (★ Calcutta) 77,020
Bāpatla 55,347
Bārākpur (★ Calcutta) 115,253
Baranagar (★ Calcutta) 170,343
Bārāsat (★ Calcutta) 66,504
Bareilly (★ 449,425) 386,734
Barmer 55,554
Baroda (★ 744,881) 734,473
Bārsi 72,537
Bāruni 56,366
Basīrhāt 81,040
Basti 69,357
Batala (★ 101,966) 87,135
Beāwar 89,998
Begusarai (★ 68,305) 56,633
Behāla (South Suburban) (★ Calcutta) 378,765
Bela 49,932
Belgaum (★ 300,372) 274,430
Bellary 201,579
Berhampur 162,550
Bettiah 72,167
Bhadrakh 60,600
Bhadrāvati (★ 130,606) 53,551
Bhadrāvati New Town (★★ Bhadrāvati) 77,055
Bhadreswar (★ Calcutta) 58,858
Bhāgalpur 225,062
Bhandāra 56,025
Bharatpur 105,274
Bhathinda 124,453
Bhātpāra (★ Calcutta) 260,761
Bhaunagar (★ 308,642) 307,121
Bhilai (★ 490,214) 290,090
Bhīlwāra 122,625
Bhīmavaram 101,894
Bhind 74,515
Bhiwandi (★ Bombay) 115,298
Bhiwāni 101,277
Bhopāl 671,018
Bhubaneswar 219,211
Bhuj (★ 70,211) 69,693
Bhusāwal (★ 132,142) 123,133
Bīdar 78,856
Bihār 151,343
Bijāpur 147,313
Bijnor 56,713
Bīkaner (★ 287,712) 253,174
Bilāspur (★ 187,104) 147,218
Bīr 80,287
Bodhan 50,807
Bodināyakkanūr 59,168
Bokāro Steel City (★ 264,480) 224,099
Bombay (★ 9,950,000) .. 8,243,405
Botād 50,274
Brajrajnagar 54,033
Broach (★ 120,524) 110,070
Budaun 93,004
Budge Budge (★ Calcutta) 66,424
Bulandshahr 103,436
Bulsār (★ Bombay) 54,017
Burdwān 167,364
Burhānpur 140,896
• Calcutta (★ 11,100,000) 3,305,006
Calicut (★ 546,058) 394,447
Cambay 68,791
Cannanore (★ 157,797) 60,904
Chākdaha 59,308
Chakradharpur (★ 44,532) 29,272
Chālisgaon 59,342
Champdāni (★ Calcutta) 76,138
Chandannagar (★ Calcutta) 101,925
Chandausi 66,970
Chandīgarh (★ 422,841) 373,789
Chandrapur 115,777
Changanācheri 51,955
Channapatna 50,725
Chāpra 111,564
Chhatarpur 51,959
Chhindwāra 75,178
Chidambaram (★ 62,543) 55,920
Chikmagalūr 60,582
Chilakalurupet 61,645
Chīrāla 72,040
Chitradurga 74,580
Chittaranjan (★ 61,045) 50,748
Chittoor 86,230
Churu (★ 62,070) 61,811
Cochin (★ 685,836) 513,249
Coimbatore (★ 965,000) 704,514
Cooch Behār (★ 80,101) 62,127
Coonoor (★ 92,242) 44,750
Cuddalore 127,625
Cuddapah 103,125
Cuttack (★ 327,412) 269,950
Dabgram 76,402
Dāhod (★ 82,256) 55,256

C Census. E Official estimate. U Unofficial estimate.
• Largest city in country.
★ Population or designation of metropolitan area, including suburbs (see headnote).
▲ Population of an entire municipality, commune, or district, including rural area.

Dāltonganj 51,952
Damoh (★ 76,758) 75,573
Dānāpur (★ Patna) 58,684
Darbhanga 176,301
Darjiling 57,603
Datia 49,386
Dāvangere 196,621
Dehra Dūn (★ 293,010) 211,416
Dehri 90,409
Delhi (★ 7,200,000) 4,884,234
Delhi Cantonment (★ Delhi) 85,166
Deoband 51,270
Deoghar (★ 59,120) 52,904
Deolāli (★★ Nāsik) 77,666
Deolāli Cantonment (★ Nāsik) 57,745
Deoria 55,720
Dewās 83,465
Dhamtari 55,797
Dhānbād (★ 825,000) 120,221
Dharmapuri 51,223
Dharmavaram 50,969
Dhorāji (★ 77,716) 76,556
Dhrāngadhra 51,280
Dhule 210,759
Dibrugarh (1971 C) 80,348
Dindigul 164,103
Dombivli (★ Bombay) 103,222
Durg (★★ Bhilai) 114,637
Durgāpur 311,798
Elūru 168,154
English Bāzār 79,010
Erode (★ 275,999) 142,252
Etah 53,784
Etāwah 112,174
Faizābād (★ 143,167) 101,873
Farīdābad New Township (★ Delhi) 330,864
Farrukhābād (★ 160,796) 145,793
Fatehpur, Rājasthān state 51,084
Fatehpur, Uttar Pradesh state 84,831
Fīrozābād 202,338
Fīrozpur (★ 105,840) 61,162
Gadag 117,368
Gandhidham (★ 61,489) 61,415
Gandhinagar 62,443
Gangāwati 58,735
Garden Reach (★ Calcutta) 191,107
Gārulia (★ Calcutta) 57,061
Gauhāti (★ 200,377) (1971 C) 123,783
Gaya 247,075
Ghāziābād (★ 287,170) 271,730
Ghāzīpur 60,725
Giridih 65,444
Godhra (★ 86,228) 85,784
Gonda 70,847
Gondal (★ 66,818) 66,096
Gondia 100,423
Gorakhpur (★ 307,501) 290,814
Gudivāda 80,198
Gudiyāttam (★ 80,674) 75,044
Gulbarga 221,325
Guna (★ 64,659) 60,255
Guntakal 84,599
Guntūr 367,699
Gurgaon (★ 100,877) 89,115
Gwalior (★ 555,862) 539,015
Hābra (★ 129,610) 74,434
Hājīpur 62,520
Haldwāni 77,300
Hālisahar (★ Calcutta) 95,579
Hānsi 50,365
Hanumāngarh 60,071
Hāpur 102,837
Hardoi 67,259
Hardwār (★ 145,946) 114,180
Harihar 52,334
Hassan 71,534
Hāthras 92,962
Hazāribāgh 80,155
Hindupur 55,901
Hinganghāt 59,075
Hisār (★ 137,369) 131,309
Hoshiārpur 85,648
Hospet (★ 115,351) 90,572
Howrah (★ Calcutta) 744,429
Hubli-Dhārwār 527,108
Hugli-Chinsurah (★ Calcutta) 125,193
Hyderābād (★ 2,750,000) 2,187,262
Ichalkaranji 133,751
Imphāl 156,622
Indore (★ 850,000) 829,327
Itārsi (★ 69,619) 62,499
Jabalpur (★ 757,303) 614,162
Jabalpur Cantonment (★ Jabalpur) 61,026
Jādabpur (★ Calcutta) 251,968
Jagdalpur (★ 63,632) 51,286
Jagtiāl 53,213
Jaipur (★ 1,025,000) 977,165
Jālgaon 145,335
Jālna 122,276
Jalpaiguri 61,743
Jamālpur 78,356
Jammu (★ 223,361) 206,135
Jāmnagar (★ 317,362) 277,615
Jamshedpur (★ 669,580) 438,385
Jangoon 70,727
Jaridih (★ 101,946) 46,477
Jaunpur 105,140
Jetpur (★ 63,074) 62,806
Jeypore 53,981
Jhānsi (★ 284,141) 246,172
Jharia (★★ Dhānbād) 57,496
Jhārsuguda 54,859
Jīnd 56,748
Jodhpur 506,345
Jotacamund 78,277
Jullundur (★ 441,552) 408,186
Junāgadh (★ 120,416) 118,646
Kadaiyanallūr 60,306
Kadiri 52,774
Kaithal 58,385
Kākināda 226,409
Kālahasti 51,306
Kālol (★ Ahmadābād) 69,946
Kalyān (★ Bombay) 136,052
Kāmārhāti (★ Calcutta) 234,951
Kambam 50,340
Kāmthi (★ Nāgpur) 67,364
Kānchipuram (★ 145,254) 130,926
Kānchrāpāra (★ Calcutta) 88,798
Kānpur (★ 1,875,000) 1,481,789
Kānpur Cantonment (★ Kānpur) 90,311
Kapūrthala 50,300
Karād 54,364
Kāraikkudi (★ 100,141) 66,993
Karīmnagar 86,125
Karnāl 132,107
Karūr (★ 93,810) 72,692
Kāsganj 61,402
Kashīpur 51,773
Katihār (★ 122,005) 104,781
Kayankulam 61,327
Kerkend (★ Dhānbād) 75,186
Khadki Cantonment (★ Pune) 80,835
Khāmgaon 61,992
Khammam 98,757
Khandwa 114,725
Khanna 53,761
Kharagpur (★ 232,575) 150,475
Kharagpur Railway Settlement (★ Kharagpur) 82,100
Khargon 52,749
Khurja 67,119
Kishanganj 51,790
Kishangarh 62,032
Kolār 65,834
Kolār Gold Fields (★ 144,385) 77,679
Kolhāpur (★ 351,392) 340,625
Konnagar (★ Calcutta) 51,211
Korba 83,387
Kota 358,241
Kottagūdem 94,894
Kottayam 64,431
Kovilpatti 63,964
Krishnanagar 98,141
Kumbakonam (★ 141,794) 132,832
Kundla (★ 51,431) 49,740
Kurnool 206,362
Lakhīmpur 61,003
Lalitpur 55,756
Lātūr 111,986
Lucknow (★ 1,060,000) 895,721
Lucknow Cantonment (★ Lucknow) 59,614
Ludhiāna 607,052
Machilīpatnam (Bandar) 138,530
Madanapalle 54,938
Madgaon (Margao) (★ 64,858) 53,076
Madras (★ 4,475,000) 3,276,622
Madurai (★ 960,000) 820,891
Mahbūbnagar 87,503
Mahuva (★ 56,072) 53,625
Mainpuri 58,928
Mālegaon 245,883
Māler Kotla 65,756
Malkajgiri (★ Hyderābād) 65,776
Mandasor 77,603
Mandya 100,285
Mangalore (★ 306,078) 172,252
Mango (★ Jamshedpur) 67,284
Manjeri 53,959
Manmād 51,439
Mannārgudi 51,738
Mathura (★ 160,995) 147,493
Maunath Bhanjan 86,326
Māyūram 67,675
Meerut (★ 536,615) 417,395
Meerut Cantonment (★ Meerut) 94,210
Mehsāna (★ 73,024) 72,872
Melappālaiyam (★ Tirunelveli) 57,683
Mettuppālaiyam 59,537
Mhow (★ 76,037) 70,130
Midnapore 86,118
Miraj (★★ Sāngli) 105,455
Mirzāpur 127,787
Modinagar (★ 87,665) 78,243
Moga 80,272
Mokāma 51,047
Monghyr 129,260
Morādābād (★ 345,350) 330,051
Morena 69,864
Mormugao 69,684
Morvi 73,327
Motihāri (★ 63,212) 57,911
Muktsar 50,941
Murwāra (★ 123,017) 77,862
Muzaffarnagar 171,816
Muzaffarpur 190,416
Mysore (★ 479,081) 441,754
Nabadwip (★ 129,800) 109,108
Nadiād 142,689
Nāgappattinam (★ 90,650) 82,828
Nāgda 56,602
Nāgercoil 171,648
Nagīna 50,405
Nāgpur (★ 1,302,066) 1,219,461
Naihāti (★ Calcutta) 114,607
Najībābād 55,109
Nalgonda 62,458
Nānded 191,269
Nandurbār 65,394
Nandyāl 88,185
Nangi (★ Calcutta) 54,035
Narasaraopet 67,032
Nāsik (★ 429,034) 262,428
Navsāri (★ 129,266) 106,793
Nawābganj (★ 62,216) 51,518
Neemuch (★ 68,853) 65,860
Nellore 237,065
NEW DELHI (★★ Delhi) 273,036
Neyveli (★ 98,866) 88,000
Nizāmābād 183,061
North Bārākpur (★ Calcutta) 81,758
North Dum Dum (★ Calcutta) 96,418
Nowgong (1971 C) 56,537
Ongole 85,302
Orai 66,397
Outer Burnpur (★ Asansol) 86,803
Pālanpur 61,262
Pālayankottai (★★ Tirunelveli) 87,302
Pālghāt (★ 117,986) 111,245
Pāli 91,568
Pallavaram (★ Madras) 83,901
Palni (★ 68,389) 64,444
Pānchur (★ Calcutta) 51,223
Pandharpur 64,380
Pānihāti (★ Calcutta) 205,718
Pānīpat 137,927
Paramagudi 61,149
Parbhani 109,364
Pātan 79,196
Pathānkot 110,039
Patiāla (★ 206,254) 205,141
Patna (★ 1,025,000) 776,371
Pattukkottai 49,484
Phagwāra (★ 75,961) 72,499
Pīlibhīt 88,548
Pimpri-Chinchwad (★ Pune) 220,966
Pollāchi (★ 114,971) 82,354
Pondicherry (★ 251,420) 162,636
Ponmalai (★ Tiruchchirāppalli) 55,995
Ponnūru Nidubrolu 50,206
Porbandar (★ 133,307) 115,182
Port Blair 49,634
Proddatūr 107,070
Pudukkottai 87,952
Pune (Poona) (★ 1,775,000) 1,203,351
Pune Cantonment (★ Pune) 85,986
Puri 100,942
Purnea (★ 109,875) 91,144
Purūlia 73,904
Quilon (★ 167,598) 137,943
Rabkavi Banhatti 51,693
Rāe Bareli 89,697
Rāichūr 124,762
Raiganj (★ 66,705) 60,343
Raigarh (★ 69,791) 68,060
Raipur 338,245
Rājahmundry (★ 268,370) 203,358
Rājapālaiyam 101,640
Rajhara-Jharandalli 55,307
Rājkot 445,076
Rāj-Nāndgaon 86,367
Rājpura 58,645
Rāmpur 204,610
Rānāghāt (★ 83,744) 58,356
Rānchī (★ 502,771) 489,626
Rānībennur 58,118
Rānīganj (★ 119,101) 48,702
Ratlām (★ 155,578) 142,319
Raurkela (★ 322,610) 206,821
Raurkela Civil Township (★ Raurkela) 96,000
Rewa 100,641
Rewāri 51,562
Rishra (★ Calcutta) 81,001
Robertson Pet (★ Kolār Gold Fields) 61,099
Rohtak 166,767
Roorkee (★ 79,076) 61,851
Sāgar (★ 207,479) 160,392
Sahāranpur 295,355
Saharsa 57,580
Sahijpur Bogha (★ Ahmadābād) 65,327
Salem (★ 518,615) 361,394
Sambalpur (★ 162,214) 110,282
Sambhal 108,232
Sāngli (★ 268,988) 152,339
Sāntipur 82,980
Sardarnagar (★ Ahmadābād) 50,128
Sardārshahr (★ 56,388) 55,473
Sasarām 73,457
Sātāra 83,336
Satna (★ 96,667) 90,476
Saunda (★ 99,990) 70,780
Secunderābād Cantonment (★ Hyderābād) 135,994
Sehore 52,190
Seoni 54,017
Serampore (★ Calcutta) 127,304
Shāhjahānpur (★ 205,095) 185,396
Shāmli 51,850
Shillong (★ 174,703) 109,244
Shimoga 151,783
Shivpuri 75,738
Sholāpur (★ 514,860) 511,103
Shrirampur 55,491
Sidhpur (★ 52,706) 51,953
Sīkar 102,970
Silchar (1971 C) 52,596
Silīguri 154,378
Simla 70,604
Sindri (★★ Dhānbād) 70,645
Sirsa 89,068
Sītāpur 101,210
Sivakāsi (★ 83,072) 59,827
Siwān 51,284
Sonīpat 109,369
South Dum Dum (★ Calcutta) 230,266
Sri Gangānagar 123,692
Srīkākulam 68,145
Srīnagar (★ 606,002) 594,775
Srīrangam (★ Tiruchchirāppalli) 64,241
Srīvilliputtūr 61,458
Sujāngarh 55,546
Surat (★ 913,806) 776,583
Surendranagar (★ 130,602) 89,619
Tādepallegūdem 62,574
Tādpatri 53,920
Tāmbaram (★ Madras) 86,923
Tānda 54,474
Tanuku 53,618
Tellicherry (★ 98,704) 75,561
Tenāli 119,257
Tenkāsi 49,214
Thāna (★ Bombay) 309,897
Thānesar 49,052
Thanjāvūr 184,015
Theni-Allinagaram 53,018
Tindivanam 56,520
Tinsukia (1971 C) 54,911
Tiruchchirāppalli (★ 609,548) 362,045
Tiruchengodu 53,941
Tirunelveli (★ 323,344) 128,850
Tirupati 115,292
Tiruppattūr 52,422
Tiruppur (★ 215,859) 165,223
Tiruvannāmalai 89,462
Tiruvottiyūr (★ Madras) 134,014
Titāgarh (★ Calcutta) 104,534
Tonk 77,653
Trichūr (★ 170,122) 77,923
Trivandrum (★ 520,125) 483,086
Tumkūr 108,670
Tuticorin (★ 250,677) 192,949
Udaipur 232,588
Udamalpet 54,852
Udgīr 50,564
Ujjain (★ 282,203) 278,454
Ulhāsnagar (★ Bombay) 273,668
Unnāo 75,983
Upleta 54,907
Uttarpara-Kotrung (★ Calcutta) 79,598
Valparai 115,452
Vāniyambādi (★ 75,042) 59,107
Vārānasi (Benares) (★ 925,000) 708,647
Vellore (★ 274,041) 174,247
Verāval (★ 105,307) 85,048
Vidisha 65,521
Vijayawāda (★ 543,008) 454,577
Vikramasingapuram 49,319
Villupuram 77,091
Virudunagar 68,047
Vishākhapatnam (★ 603,630) 565,321
Vizianagaram 114,806
Warangal 335,150
Wardha 88,495
Yamunānagar (★ 160,424) 109,304
Yavatmāl 89,071
Yemmiganur 50,701

INDONESIA

1980 C 147,490,298

Cities and Towns

Ambon (▲ 207,702) 111,914
Balikpapan (▲ 279,852) 208,040
Banda Aceh (Kuturaja) 71,868
Bandung (★ 1,800,000) (1985 C) 1,633,000
Banjarmasin (1983 E) 424,000
Banyuwangi 90,378
Batang 49,328
Bekasi (★ Jakarta) 144,290
Binjai 71,444
Blitar (★ 100,000) 78,503
Bogor (★ 560,000) 246,946
Bojonegoro 57,483
Bukittinggi (▲ 70,691) 55,577
Cianjur 105,655
Cibinong 87,580
Cilacap 127,017
Cimahi (★ Bandung) (1971 C) 72,367
Ciparay 66,854
Cirebon (★ 275,000) 223,504
Denpasar 159,233
Depok (★ Jakarta) 126,693
Garut 145,624
Genteng 59,481
Gorontalo (▲ 97,610) 63,554
Gresik 86,418
• JAKARTA (★ 1,000,000) (1989 E) 9,200,000
Jambi (▲ 230,046) 155,761
Jayapura (Sukarnapura) 60,641
Jember 171,284
Jombang 58,800
Karawang 72,195
Kediri (▲ 221,830) 176,261
Kisaran 58,129
Klangenang 64,013
Klaten 117,560
Kudus 154,478
Kupang 84,587
Lumajang 58,495
Madiun (★ 180,000) 150,562
Magelang (★ 160,000) 123,358
Majalaya 87,474
Malang (1983 E) 547,000
Manado 217,091
Mataram 210,485
Medan (1985 E) 2,110,000
Mojokerto 68,849
Padang (▲ 657,000) (1983 E) 405,600
Padangsidempuan 56,984
Palangkaraya (▲ 60,447) 51,686
Palembang (1983 E) 874,000
Pangkalpinang 90,078
Parepare (▲ 86,360) 62,865
Pasuruan (★ 125,000) 95,864
Pati 50,159
Pekalongan (★ 260,000) 132,413
Pekanbaru 186,199
Pemalang 72,663
Pematangsiantar (★ 175,000) 150,296
Ponorogo 55,523
Pontianak (1983 E) 343,000
Pringsewu 56,115
Probolinggo 100,296
Purwakarta 61,995
Purwokerto 143,787
Salatiga 85,740
Samarinda (▲ 264,012) 182,473
Semarang (1983 E) 1,206,000
Serang 78,209
Sibolga 59,466
Sidoarjo 56,090
Singaraja 53,368
Singkawang 58,693
Situbondo 58,299
Sorong 52,041
Subang 52,041
Sukabumi (★ 225,000) 109,898
Surabaya (1985 E) 2,345,000
Surakarta (★ 575,000) (1983 E) 491,000
Taman 64,358
Tangerang 97,091
Tanjungkarang-Telukbetung (★ 375,000) 284,167
Tasikmalaya 192,267
Tebingtinggi (▲ 92,068) 69,569
Tegal (★ 340,000) 131,440
Tembilahan 52,140
Tulungagung 91,585
Ujungpandang (Makasar) (1983 E) 841,000
Yogyakarta (★ 510,000) (1983 E) 421,000

IRAN / Īrān

1986 C 49,445,010

Cities and Towns

Ābādān (1976 C) 296,081
Āghā Jārī (1982 E) 64,000
Ahar (1982 E) 52,000
Ahvāz 579,826
Āmol 118,242
Andīmeshk (1982 E) 53,000
Arāk 265,349
Ardabīl 281,973
Bābol 115,320
Bakhtarān (Kermānshāh) 560,514
Bandar-e 'Abbās 201,642

C Census. E Official estimate. U Unofficial estimate.
• Largest city in country.

★ Population or designation of metropolitan area, including suburbs (see headnote).
▲ Population of an entire municipality, commune, or district, including rural area.

Bandar-e Anzalī (Bandar-e Pahlavī) (1982 E) 83,000
Bandar-e Būshehr 120,787
Bandar-e Māh Shahr (1982 E) 88,000
Behbahān (1982 E) 84,000
Bīrjand (1982 E) 68,000
Bojnūrd (1982 E) 82,000
Borāzjān (1982 E) 53,000
Borūjerd 183,879
Dezfūl 151,420
Do Rūd (1982 E) 52,000
Emāmshahr (Shāhrūd) (1982 E) 68,000
Eşfahān (★ 1,175,000) 986,753
Eslāmābād (1982 E) 71,000
Eslāmshahr (★ Tehrān) 215,129
Fasā (1982 E) 67,000
Gonbad-e Qābūs (1982 E) 75,000
Gorgān 139,430
Hamadān 272,499
Īlām (1982 E) 75,000
Jahrom (1982 E) 68,000
Karaj (★ Tehrān) 275,100
Kāshān 138,599
Kāzerūn (1982 E) 63,000
Kermān 257,284
Khomeynīshahr (★ Eşfahān) 104,647
Khorramābād 208,592
Khorramshahr (1976 C) 146,709
Khvoy 115,343
Mahābād (1982 E) 63,000
Malāyer 103,640
Marāgheh 100,679
Marand (1982 E) 59,000
Marv Dasht (1982 E) 72,000
Mashhad 1,463,508
Masjed Soleymān 104,787
Mīāndoāb (1982 E) 52,000
Mīāneh (1982 E) 57,000
Najafābād 129,058
Neyshābūr 109,258
Orūmīyeh (Reẕā'īyeh) 300,746
Qā'emshahr 109,288
Qazvīn 248,591
Qom 543,139
Qomsheh (1982 E) 67,000
Qūchān (1982 E) 61,000
Rafsanjān (1982 E) 61,000
Rāmhormoz (1982 E) 53,000
Rasht 290,897
Sabzevār 129,103
Sanandaj 204,537
Saqqez (1982 E) 76,000
Sārī 141,020
Semnān (1982 E) 54,000
Shahr-e Kord (1982 E) 63,000
Shīrāz 848,289
Sīrjān (1982 E) 67,000
Tabrīz 971,482
• TEHRĀN (★ 7,500,000) 6,042,584
Torbat-e Ḩeydarīyeh (1982 E) 62,000
Varāmīn (1982 E) 51,000
Yazd 230,483
Zābol (1982 E) 58,000
Zāhedān 281,923
Zanjān 215,261
Zarrīn Shahr (1982 E) 69,000

IRAQ / Al 'Irāq

1985 E 15,584,987

Cities and Towns

Ad-Dīwānīyah (1970 E) 62,300
Al-'Amārah 131,758
Al-Başrah 616,700
Al-Ḩillah 215,249
Al-Kūt 73,022
Al-Mawşil 570,926
An-Najaf 242,603
An-Nāşirīyah 138,842
Ar-Ramādī 137,388
As-Samāwah 75,293
As-Sulaymānīyah 279,424
• BAGHDAD (1987 C) 3,841,268
Ba'qūbah 114,516
Irbīl 333,903
Karbalā' 184,574
Kirkūk (1970 E) 207,900

IRELAND / Éire

1986 C 3,540,643

Cities and Towns

Cork (★ 173,694) 133,271
• DUBLIN (BAILE ÁTHA CLIATH) (★ 1,140,000) 502,749
Dún Laoghaire (★ Dublin) 54,715
Galway 47,104
Limerick (★ 76,557) 56,279
Waterford (★ 41,054) 39,529

ISLE OF MAN

1986 C 64,282

Cities and Towns

• DOUGLAS (★ 28,500) 20,368

ISRAEL / Isrā'īl / Yisra'el

1989 E 4,386,000

Cities and Towns

Ashdod 74,700
Ashqelon 56,300
Bat Yam (★ Tel Aviv-Yafo) 133,100
Be'er Sheva (Beersheba) 113,200
Bene Beraq (★ Tel Aviv-Yafo) 109,400
Elat 24,700
Giv'atayim (★ Tel Aviv-Yafo) 45,600
Ḩefa (★ 435,000) 222,600
Herzliyya (★ Tel Aviv-Yafo) 71,600
Ḩolon (★ Tel Aviv-Yafo) 146,100
Kefar Sava (★ Tel Aviv-Yafo) 54,800
Lod (Lydda) (★ Tel Aviv-Yafo) 41,300
Nazerat (Nazareth) (★ 77,000) 50,600
Netanya (★ Tel Aviv-Yafo) 117,800
Petaḩ Tiqwa (★ Tel Aviv-Yafo) 133,600
Ra'anana (★ Tel Aviv-Yafo) 49,400
Ramat Gan (★ Tel Aviv-Yafo) 115,700
Reḩovot (★ Tel Aviv-Yafo) 72,500
Rishon leẔiyyon (★ Tel Aviv-Yafo) 123,800
• Tel Aviv-Yafo (★ 1,735,000) 317,800
YERUSHALAYIM (AL-QUDS) (JERUSALEM) (★ 530,000) 493,500

ISRAELI OCCUPIED TERRITORIES

1989 E 1,574,700

Cities and Towns

Al-Khalīl (Hebron) (1971 E) 43,000
Al-Quds (Jerusalem) (★ Yerushalayim) (1976 E) 90,000
Arīḩā (Jericho) (1967 C) 6,829
Bayt Laḩm (Bethlehem) (1971 E) 25,000
• Ghazzah (1967 C) 118,272
Khān Yūnis (1967 C) 52,997
Nābulus (1971 E) 64,000
Rafaḩ (1967 C) 49,812

ITALY / Italia

1987 E 57,290,519

Cities and Towns

Afragola (★ Napoli) 59,397
Alessandria (▲ 96,014) 76,100
Altamura 54,784
Ancona 104,409
Andria 88,348
Arezzo (▲ 91,681) 74,200
Asti (▲ 75,459) 63,600
Avellino 56,407
Aversa (★ Napoli) 57,827
Bari (★ 475,000) 362,524
Barletta 86,954
Benevento (▲ 65,661) 54,400
Bergamo (★ 345,000) 118,959
Biella 51,788
Bitonto 51,962
Bologna (★ 525,000) 432,406
Bolzano 101,515
Brescia 199,286
Brindisi 92,280
Busto Arsizio (★ Milano) 78,056
Cagliari (★ 305,000) 220,574
Caltanissetta 62,352
Carpi (▲ 60,614) 49,500
Carrara (★★ Massa) 69,229
Caserta 65,974
Casoria (★ Napoli) 54,100
Castellammare [di Stabia] (★ Napoli) 68,491
Catania (★ 550,000) 372,486
Catanzaro 102,558
Cava de'Tirreni (★ Salerno) 52,028
Cerignola 53,463
Cesena (▲ 90,012) 72,600
Chieti 55,827
Cinisello Balsamo (★ Milano) 78,917
Civitavecchia 50,806
Collegno (★ Torino) 49,334
Cologno Monzese (★ Milano) 52,554
Como (★ 165,000) 91,738
Cosenza (★ 150,000) 106,026
Cremona 76,979
Crotone (▲ 61,005) 53,600
Ercolano (★ Napoli) 62,783
Ferrara (▲ 143,950) 113,300
Firenze (★ 640,000) 425,835
Foggia 155,051
Forlì (▲ 110,482) 91,200
Gela 79,378
Genova (Genoa) (★ 805,000) 727,427
Giugliano in Campania (★ Napoli) 51,187
Grosseto (▲ 70,592) 56,400
La Spezia (★ 185,000) 108,937
Latina (▲ 98,479) 67,800
Lecce 100,981
Livorno 174,065
Lucca 88,024
Manfredonia 57,707
Mantova (▲ 56,817) 49,000
Marsala 80,468
Massa (★ 145,000) 66,872
Matera 52,819
Messina 268,896
Mestre (★ Venezia) 189,700
• Milano (Milan) (★ 3,750,000) 1,495,260
Modena 176,880
Molfetta 64,519
Moncalieri (★ Torino) 62,306
Monza (★ Milano) 122,064
Napoli (Naples) (★ 2,875,000) 1,204,211
Nicastro (▲ 67,562) 52,100
Novara 102,742
Padova (★ 270,000) 225,769
Palermo 723,732
Parma 175,842
Pavia 82,065
Perugia (▲ 146,713) 106,700
Pesaro (▲ 90,336) 78,700
Pescara 131,027
Piacenza 105,626
Pisa 104,384
Pistoia (▲ 90,689) 76,800
Pordenone 50,825
Portici (★ Napoli) 76,302
Potenza (▲ 67,114) 57,600
Pozzuoli (★ Napoli) 65,000
Prato (★ 215,000) 164,595
Quartu Sant'Elena 52,838
Ragusa 67,748
Ravenna (▲ 136,016) 86,500
Reggio di Calabria 178,821
Reggio nell'Emilia (▲ 130,086) 107,300
Rho (★ Milano) 50,876
Rimini (▲ 130,698) 114,600
Rivoli (★ Torino) 50,786
ROMA (ROME) (★ 3,175,000) 2,815,457
Salerno (★ 250,000) 154,848
San Giorgio a Cremano (★ Napoli) 63,656
San Remo 60,797
San Severo 55,239
Sassari 120,152
Savona (★ 112,000) 62,300
Scandicci (★ Firenze) 54,367
Sesto San Giovanni (★ Milano) 91,624
Siena 59,712
Siracusa 122,857
Taranto 244,997
Terni (▲ 111,157) 94,500
Torino (★ 1,550,000) 1,035,565
Torre Annunziata (★ Napoli) 57,508
Torre del Greco (★ Napoli) 105,066
Trapani (▲ 73,083) 63,000
Trento (▲ 100,202) 81,500
Treviso 85,083
Trieste (Triest) 239,031
Udine (★ 126,000) 100,211
Varese 88,353
Venezia (Venice) (★ 420,000) 88,700
Vercelli 51,008
Verona 259,151
Viareggio (▲ 59,146) 50,300
Vicenza 110,449
Vigevano 62,671
Vittoria 54,795

IVORY COAST / Côte d'Ivoire

1983 E 9,300,000

Cities and Towns

• ABIDJAN 1,950,000
Bouaké 275,000
Daloa 70,000
Korhogo 125,000
Man 55,000
YAMOUSSOUKRO 80,000

JAMAICA

1982 C 2,190,357

Cities and Towns

• KINGSTON (★ 770,000) (1987 E) 646,400
Montego Bay 70,265
Portmore (★ Kingston) 73,426
Spanish Town (★ Kingston) 89,097

JAPAN / Nihon

1985 C 121,048,923

Cities and Towns

Abiko (★ Tōkyō) 111,659
Ageo (★ Tōkyō) 178,587
Aizu-wakamatsu 118,140
Akashi (★ Ōsaka) 263,363
Akishima (★ Tōkyō) 97,543
Akita 296,400
Akō 52,374
Amagasaki (★ Ōsaka) 509,115
Anjō 133,059
Aomori 294,045
Arao (★ Ōmuta) 62,570
Asahikawa 363,631
Asaka (★ Tōkyō) 94,431
Ashikaga 167,656
Ashiya (★ Ōsaka) 87,127
Atami 49,374
Atsugi (★ Tōkyō) 175,600
Ayase (★ Tōkyō) 71,152
Beppu 134,775
Bisai (★ Nagoya) 56,234
Chiba (★ Tōkyō) 788,930
Chichibu 61,013
Chigasaki (★ Tōkyō) 185,030
Chikushino (★ Fukuoka) 63,242
Chiryū (★ Nagoya) 50,506
Chita (★ Nagoya) 70,013
Chitose 73,610
Chōfu (★ Tōkyō) 191,071
Chōshi 87,883
Daitō (★ Ōsaka) 122,441
Dazaifu (★ Fukuoka) 57,737
Ebetsu (★ Sapporo) 90,328
Ebina (★ Tōkyō) 93,159
Fuchū (★ Tōkyō) 201,972
Fuji (★ 370,000) 214,448
Fujieda (★ Shizuoka) 111,985
Fujiidera (★ Ōsaka) 65,252
Fujimi (★ Tōkyō) 85,697
Fujinomiya (★★ Fuji) 112,642
Fujisawa (★ Tōkyō) 328,387
Fuji-yoshida 54,796
Fukaya (▲ 89,121) 71,600
Fukuchiyama (▲ 65,995) 56,200
Fukui 250,261
Fukuoka (★ 1,750,000) 1,160,440
Fukushima 270,762
Fukuyama 360,261
Funabashi (★ Tōkyō) 506,966
Fussa (★ Tōkyō) 51,478
Gamagōri 85,580
Gifu 411,743
Ginowan 69,206
Gotemba 74,882
Gushikawa 51,351
Gyōda 79,359
Habikino (★ Ōsaka) 111,394
Hachinohe 241,430
Hachiōji (★ Tōkyō) 426,654
Hadano (★ Tōkyō) 141,803
Hagi 52,740
Hakodate 319,194
Hamada 51,071
Hamakita 77,228
Hamamatsu 514,118
Hanamaki (▲ 69,886) 54,500
Handa (★ Nagoya) 92,883
Hannō (★ Tōkyō) 66,550
Hashima 59,760
Hasuda (★ Tōkyō) 53,991
Hatogaya (★ Tōkyō) 55,424
Hatsukaichi (★ Hiroshima) 52,020
Hekinan 63,778
Higashihiroshima (★ Hiroshima) 84,717
Higashikurume (★ Tōkyō) 110,079
Higashimatsuyama 70,426
Higashimurayama (★ Tōkyō) 123,798
Higashiōsaka (★ Ōsaka) 522,805
Higashiyamato (★ Tōkyō) 69,881
Hikari (★ Tokuyama) 49,246
Hikone 94,204
Himeji (★ 660,000) 452,917
Himi (▲ 62,112) 52,300
Hino (★ Tōkyō) 156,031
Hirakata (★ Ōsaka) 382,257
Hiratsuka (★ Tōkyō) 229,990
Hirosaki (▲ 176,082) 134,800
Hiroshima (★ 1,575,000) 1,044,118
Hita (▲ 65,730) 57,900
Hitachi 206,074
Hōfu 118,067
Honjō 56,495
Hōya (★ Tōkyō) 91,568
Hyūga 59,163
Ibaraki (★ Ōsaka) 250,463
Ichihara (★ Tōkyō) 237,617
Ichikawa (★ Tōkyō) 397,822
Ichinomiya (★★ Nagoya) 257,388
Ichinoseki (▲ 60,941) 49,200
Iida (▲ 92,401) 65,000
Iizuka (★ 110,000) 81,868
Ikeda (★ Ōsaka) 101,683
Ikoma (★ Ōsaka) 86,293
Imabari 125,115
Imari (▲ 62,044) 50,700
Inagi (★ Tōkyō) 50,766
Inazawa (★ Nagoya) 94,479
Inuyama (★ Nagoya) 68,723
Iruma (★ Tōkyō) 118,603
Isahaya 88,376
Ise (Uji-yamada) 105,455
Isesaki 112,459
Ishinomaki 122,674
Itami (★ Ōsaka) 182,731
Itō 70,197
Iwaki (Taira) 350,569
Iwakuni 111,833
Iwamizawa 81,664
Iwata 80,810
Iwatsuki (★ Tōkyō) 100,903
Izumi (★ Ōsaka) 137,641
Izumi (★ Sendai) 124,216
Izumi-ōtsu (★ Ōsaka) 67,755
Izumi-sano (★ Ōsaka) 91,563
Izumo (▲ 80,749) 68,000
Jōyō (★ Ōsaka) 81,850
Kadoma (★ Ōsaka) 140,590
Kaga 68,630
Kagoshima 530,502
Kainan (★ Wakayama) 50,779
Kaizuka (★ Ōsaka) 79,591
Kakamigahara 124,464
Kakegawa (▲ 68,724) 55,600
Kakogawa (★ Ōsaka) 227,311
Kamagaya (★ Tōkyō) 85,705
Kamaishi 60,007
Kamakura (★ Tōkyō) 175,495
Kameoka 76,207
Kamifukuoka (★ Tōkyō) 57,638
Kanazawa 430,481
Kani (★ Nagoya) 69,630
Kanoya (▲ 76,029) 60,200
Kanuma (▲ 88,078) 73,200
Karatsu (▲ 78,744) 70,100
Kariya (★ Nagoya) 112,403
Kasai 52,107
Kasaoka (▲ 60,598) 53,500
Kashihara (★ Ōsaka) 112,888
Kashiwa (★ Tōkyō) 273,128
Kashiwara (★ Ōsaka) 73,252
Kashiwazaki (▲ 86,020) 73,350
Kasuga (★ Fukuoka) 75,555
Kasugai (★ Nagoya) 256,990
Kasukabe (★ Tōkyō) 171,890
Katano (★ Ōsaka) 64,205
Katsuta 102,763
Kawachi-nagano (★ Ōsaka) 91,313
Kawagoe (★ Tōkyō) 285,437
Kawaguchi (★ Tōkyō) 403,015
Kawanishi (★ Ōsaka) 136,376
Kawasaki (★ Tōkyō) 1,088,624
Kesennuma 68,137
Kimitsu (▲ 84,310) 71,900
Kiryū 131,267
Kisarazu 120,201
Kishiwada (★ Ōsaka) 185,731
Kitaibaraki 51,035
Kitakyūshū (★ 1,525,000) 1,056,402
Kitami 107,281
Kitamoto (★ Tōkyō) 58,114
Kiyose (★ Tōkyō) 65,066
Kōbe (★★ Ōsaka) 1,410,834
Kōchi 312,241
Kodaira (★ Tōkyō) 158,673
Kōfu 202,405
Koga (★ Tōkyō) 57,541
Koganei (★ Tōkyō) 104,642
Kokubunji (★ Tōkyō) 95,467
Komae (★ Tōkyō) 73,784
Komaki (★ Nagoya) 113,284
Komatsu 106,041
Kōnan (★ Nagoya) 92,049
Kōnosu (★ Tōkyō) 60,565
Kōriyama 301,673
Koshigaya (★ Tōkyō) 253,479
Kudamatsu (★★ Tokuyama) 54,445
Kuki (★ Tōkyō) 58,636
Kumagaya 143,496
Kumamoto 555,719
Kunitachi (★ Tōkyō) 64,881
Kurashiki 413,632
Kure (★★ Hiroshima) 226,488
Kurume 222,847
Kusatsu (★ Ōsaka) 87,542
Kushiro 214,541
Kuwana (★ Nagoya) 94,731
Kyōto (★★ Ōsaka) 1,479,218
Machida (★ Tōkyō) 321,188
Maebashi 277,319
Maizuru 98,775
Marugame 74,272
Matsubara (★ Ōsaka) 136,455
Matsudo (★ Tōkyō) 427,473
Matsue 140,005
Matsumoto 197,340
Matsusaka 116,886
Matsuyama 426,658
Mihara 85,975
Miki (★ Ōsaka) 74,527
Minō (★ Ōsaka) 114,770
Misato (★ Tōkyō) 107,964
Mishima (★★ Numazu) 99,600
Mitaka (★ Tōkyō) 166,252
Mito 228,985

C Census. E Official estimate. U Unofficial estimate.
• Largest city in country.
★ Population or designation of metropolitan area, including suburbs (see headnote).
▲ Population of an entire municipality, commune, or district, including rural area.

Miura (★ Tōkyō) 50,471
Miyako 61,654
Miyakonojō (▲ 132,098) 107,600
Miyazaki 279,114
Mobara 76,929
Moriguchi (★ Ōsaka) 159,400
Morioka 235,469
Moriyama 53,052
Mukō (★ Ōsaka) 52,216
Munakata 60,971
Muroran (★ 195,000) 136,208
Musashimurayama (★ Tōkyō) 60,930
Musashino (★ Tōkyō) 138,783
Mutsu 49,292
Nabari 56,474
Nagahama 55,531
Nagano 336,973
Nagaoka 183,756
Nagaokakyō (★ Ōsaka) 75,242
Nagareyama (★ Tōkyō) 124,682
Nagasaki 449,382
Nagoya (★ 4,800,000) 2,116,381
Naha 303,674
Nakama (★ Kitakyūshū) 50,294
Nakatsu 66,260
Nakatsugawa 53,277
Nanao 50,582
Nara (★ Ōsaka) 327,702
Narashino (★ Tōkyō) 136,365
Narita 77,181
Naruto 64,329
Naze 49,765
Neyagawa (★ Ōsaka) 258,228
Niigata 475,630
Niihama 132,184
Niitsu (▲ 63,846) 55,600
Niiza (★ Tōkyō) 129,287
Nishinomiya (★ Ōsaka) 421,267
Nishio 91,930
Nobeoka 136,381
Noboribetsu (★ Muroran) 58,370
Noda (★ Tōkyō) 105,937
Nōgata 64,479
Noshiro (▲ 59,170) 50,400
Numazu (★ 495,000) 210,490
Obihiro 162,932
Ōbu (★ Nagoya) 66,696
Ōdate (▲ 71,794) 60,900
Odawara 185,941
Ōgaki 145,910
Ōita 390,096
Okaya 61,747
Okayama 572,479
Okazaki 284,996
Okegawa (★ Tōkyō) 61,499
Okinawa 101,210
Ōme (★ Tōkyō) 110,828
Ōmi-hachiman (★ Ōsaka) 63,791
Ōmiya (★ Tōkyō) 373,022
Ōmura 69,472
Ōmuta (★ 225,000) 159,424
Ōnojō (★ Fukuoka) 69,435
Onomichi 100,640
Ōsaka (★ 16,450,000) 2,636,249
Ōta 133,670
Otaru (★★ Sapporo) 172,486
Ōtsu (★ Ōsaka) 234,551
Owariashi (★ Nagoya) 57,415
Oyama (▲ 134,242) 113,100
Sabae 61,452
Saeki 54,706
Saga 168,252
Sagamihara (★ Tōkyō) 482,778
Saijō 56,516
Sakado (★ Tōkyō) 87,586
Sakai (★ Ōsaka) 818,271
Sakaide 66,087
Sakata 101,392
Sakura (★ Tōkyō) 121,213
Sakurai 58,894
Sanjō 86,325
Sano 80,753
Sapporo (★ 1,900,000) 1,542,979
Sasebo 250,633
Satte 51,462
Sayama (★ Tōkyō) 144,366
Sayama (★ Ōsaka) 50,246
Seki 64,149
Sendai, Kagoshima pref. (▲ 71,444) 57,800
Sendai, Miyagi pref. (★ 1,175,000) 700,254
Sennan (★ Ōsaka) 60,059
Seto 124,623
Settsu (★ Ōsaka) 86,332
Shibata (▲ 77,219) 62,800
Shijōnawate (★ Ōsaka) 50,352
Shiki (★ Tōkyō) 58,935
Shimada (▲ 72,388) 63,200
Shimizu (★★ Shizuoka) 242,166
Shimodate (▲ 63,958) 52,400
Shimonoseki (★★ Kitakyūshū) 269,169
Shiogama (★ Sendai) 61,825
Shizuoka (★ 975,000) 468,362
Sōka (★ Tōkyō) 194,205
Suita (★ Ōsaka) 348,948
Suwa 52,329
Suzuka 164,936
Tachikawa (★ Tōkyō) 146,523
Tagajō (★ Sendai) 54,436
Tagawa 59,727
Tajimi (★ Nagoya) 84,829
Takada 130,659
Takaishi (★ Ōsaka) 66,974
Takamatsu 326,999
Takaoka (★ 220,000) 175,780
Takarazuka (★ Ōsaka) 194,273
Takasago (★ Ōsaka) 91,434
Takasaki 231,766
Takatsuki (★ Ōsaka) 348,784
Takayama 65,033
Takefu 69,148
Takikawa 52,004
Tama (★ Tōkyō) 122,135
Tamano 76,954
Tanabe (▲ 70,835) 59,800
Tanashi (★ Tōkyō) 71,331
Tatebayashi 75,141
Tenri 69,129
Tochigi 86,290
Toda (★ Tōkyō) 76,960
Tōkai (★ Nagoya) 95,278
Toki 65,308
Tokoname (★ Nagoya) 53,077
Tokorozawa (★ Tōkyō) 275,168
Tokushima 257,884
Tokuyama (★ 250,000) 112,638
• TŌKYŌ (★ 27,700,000) 8,354,615
Tomakomai 158,061
Tondabayashi (★ Ōsaka) 102,619
Toride (★ Tōkyō) 78,608
Tosu 55,791
Tottori 137,060
Toyama 314,111
Toyoake (★ Nagoya) 57,969
Toyohashi 322,142
Toyokawa 107,430
Toyonaka (★ Ōsaka) 413,213
Toyota 308,111
Tsu 150,690
Tsuchiura 120,175
Tsuruga 65,670
Tsuruoka 100,200
Tsushima (★ Nagoya) 58,735
Tsuyama 86,837
Ube (★ 230,000) 174,855
Ueda 116,178
Ueno (▲ 60,812) 51,800
Uji (★ Ōsaka) 165,411
Uozu 49,825
Urasoe 81,611
Urawa (★ Tōkyō) 377,235
Urayasu (★ Tōkyō) 93,756
Ushiku 51,926
Utsunomiya 405,375
Uwajima 71,381
Wakayama (★ 495,000) 401,352
Wakkanai 51,854
Wakō (★ Tōkyō) 55,212
Warabi (★ Tōkyō) 70,408
Yachiyo (★ Tōkyō) 142,184
Yaizu (★ Shizuoka) 108,558
Yamagata 245,158
Yamaguchi 124,213
Yamato (★ Tōkyō) 177,669
Yamato-kōriyama (★ Ōsaka) 89,624
Yamato-takada (★ Ōsaka) 65,223
Yao (★ Ōsaka) 276,394
Yashio (★ Tōkyō) 67,635
Yatsushiro (▲ 108,790) 88,700
Yawata (★ Ōsaka) 72,356
Yokkaichi 263,001
Yokohama (★★ Tōkyō) 2,992,926
Yokosuka (★ Tōkyō) 427,116
Yonago 131,792
Yonezawa 93,721
Yono (★ Tōkyō) 71,597
Yotsukaidō (★ Tōkyō) 67,008
Yukuhashi 65,527
Zama (★ Tōkyō) 100,000
Zushi (★ Tōkyō) 57,656

JERSEY

1986 C 80,212

Cities and Towns

• SAINT HELIER (★ 46,500) 27,083

JORDAN / Al-Urdun

1989 E 3,111,000

Cities and Towns

Al-Baq'ah (★ 'Ammān) 63,985
• 'AMMĀN (★ 1,450,000) 936,300
Ar-Ruṣayfah (★ 'Ammān) 72,580
As-Salṭ 47,585
Az-Zarqā' (★★ 'Ammān) 318,055
Irbid 167,785

KENYA

1990 E 24,870,000

Cities and Towns

Eldoret (1979 C) 50,503
Kisumu (1984 E) 167,100
Machakos (1983 E) 92,300
Meru (1979 C) 72,049
Mombasa 537,000
• NAIROBI 1,505,000
Nakuru (1984 E) 101,700

KIRIBATI

1988 E 68,207

Cities and Towns

BAIRIKI 2,230
• Bikenibeu 4,580

KOREA, NORTH / Chosŏn-minjujuŭi-inmīn-konghwaguk

1981 E 18,317,000

Cities and Towns

Ch'ŏngjin 490,000
Haeju (1983 E) 213,000
Hamhŭng (1970 E) 150,000
Hŭngnam (1976 E) 260,000
Kaesŏng 259,000
Kanggye (1967 E) 130,000
Kimch'aek (Sŏngjin) (1967 E) 265,000
Namp'o 241,000
• P'YŎNGYANG (★ 1,600,000) 1,283,000
Sinŭiju 305,000
Songnim (1983 C) 53,035
Wŏnsan 398,000

KOREA, SOUTH / Taehan-min'guk

1985 C 40,448,486

Cities and Towns

Andong 114,216
Anyang (★ Sŏul) 361,577
Bucheon (★ Sŏul) 456,292
Changwŏn (★ Masan) 173,508
Chech'on 102,274
Cheju 202,911
Chinhae 121,341
Chinju 227,309
Ch'ŏnan 170,196
Ch'ŏngju 350,256
Chŏnju 79,323
Chŏnju, Chŏlla Pukdo prov. 426,473
Ch'unch'ŏn 162,988
Ch'ungju 113,331
Ch'ungmu 87,459
Inch'ŏn (★★ Sŏul) (1989 E) 1,628,000
Iri 192,269
Kangnŭng 132,897
Kimch'ŏn 77,254
Kimhae 77,903
Kumi 142,094
Kŭmsŏng 58,897
Kunsan 185,649
Kwangju (1989 E) 1,165,000
Kwangmyŏng (★ Sŏul) 219,611
Kyŏngju 127,544
Masan (★ 625,000) 448,746
Mokp'o 236,085
Namwŏn 61,447
P'ohang 260,691
Pusan (★ 3,800,000) (1989 E) 3,773,000
P'yŏngt'aek (▲ 180,513) 63,400
Samch'ŏnp'o 62,466
Sangju (▲ 180,575) 28,300
Sŏgwipo 82,311
Sŏkch'o 69,501
Songjŏng (▲ 136,612) 35,300
Sŏngnam (★ Sŏul) 447,692
Songtan 66,357
• SŎUL (★ 15,850,000) (1989 E) 10,522,000
Sunch'ŏn (▲ 116,323) 121,958
Suwŏn (★ Sŏul) 430,752
T'aebaek 113,997
Taegu (1989 C) 2,207,000
Taejŏn (1989 E) 1,041,000
Tongduchŏn 68,633
Tonghae 91,691
Ŭijŏngbu (★ Sŏul) 162,700
Ulsan 551,014
Wŏnju 151,165
Yŏngch'ŏn 52,811
Yŏngju 84,742
Yŏsu 171,933

KUWAIT / Al-Kuwayt

1985 C 1,697,301

Cities and Towns

Al-Aḥmadī (★ 285,000) 26,899
Al-Farwānīyah (★ Al-Kuwayt) 68,701
Al-Fuḥayḥīl (★ Al-Aḥmadī) 50,081
Al-Jahrah (★ Al-Kuwayt) 111,222
• AL-KUWAYT (★ 1,375,000) 44,335
As-Sālimīyah (★ Al-Kuwayt) 153,359
Aṣ-Ṣulaybīyah (★ Al-Kuwayt) 51,314
Ḥawallī (★ Al-Kuwayt) 145,126
Qalīb ash-Shuyūkh (★ Al-Kuwayt) 114,771
South Khīṭān (★ Al-Kuwayt) 69,256
Subahiya (★ Al-Aḥmadī) 60,787

LAOS / Lao

1985 C 3,584,803

Cities and Towns

Savannakhet (1975 E) 53,000
Viangchan (Vientiane) 377,409

LEBANON / Lubnān

1982 1 2,637,000

Cities and Towns

• BAYRŪT (★ 1,675,000) 509,000
Ṣaydā 105,000
Ṭarābulus (Tripoli) 198,000

LESOTHO

1986 C 1,577,536

Cities and Towns

• MASERU 109,382

LIBERIA

1986 E 2,221,000

Cities and Towns

• MONROVIA 465,000

LIBYA / Lībiyā

1984 C 3,637,488

Cities and Towns

Banghāzī 435,886
Darnah 62,179
Misrātah 131,031
• ṬARĀBULUS (TRIPOLI) 990,697
Ṭubruq (Tobruk) 75,282
Zāwiyat al-Baydā' 67,120

LIECHTENSTEIN

1990 E 28,452

Cities and Towns

• VADUZ 4,874

LUXEMBOURG

1985 E 366,000

Cities and Towns

• LUXEMBOURG (★ 136,000) 76,130

MACAU

1987 E 429,000

Cities and Towns

• MACAU 429,000

MADAGASCAR / Madagasikara

1984 E 9,731,000

Cities and Towns

• ANTANANARIVO (1985 E) 663,000
Antsirabe (▲ 95,000) 50,100
Antsiranana 100,000
Fianarantsoa 130,000
Mahajanga 85,000
Toamasina 100,000
Toliara 55,000

MALAWI / Malaŵi

1987 C 7,982,607

Cities and Towns

• Blantyre 331,588
LILONGWE 233,973
Zomba 42,878

MALAYSIA

1980 C 13,136,109

Cities and Towns

Alor Setar 69,435
Batu Pahat 64,727
Butterworth (★★ George Town) 77,982
George Town (Pinang) (★ 495,000) 248,241
Ipoh 293,849
Johor Baharu (★ Singapore, Sing.) 246,395
Kelang 192,080
Keluang 50,315
Kota Baharu 167,872
Kota Kinabalu (Jesselton) 55,997
• KUALA LUMPUR (★ 1,475,000) 919,610
Kuala Terengganu 180,296
Kuantan 131,547
Kuching 72,555
Melaka 87,494
Miri 52,125
Muar (Bandar Maharani) 65,151
Petaling Jaya (★ Kuala Lumpur) 207,805
Sandakan 70,420
Seremban 132,911
Sibu 85,231
Taiping 146,000
Telok Anson 49,148

MALDIVES

1985 C 181,453

Cities and Towns

• MALE 46,334

MALI

1987 C 7,620,225

Cities and Towns

• BAMAKO 646,163
Gao 54,874
Mopti 73,979
Ségou 88,877
Sikasso 73,050
Tombouctou (Timbuktu) 31,925

MALTA

1989 E 349,014

Cities and Towns

• VALLETTA (★ 215,000) 9,210

MARSHALL ISLANDS

1980 C 30,873

Cities and Towns

• Jarej-Uliga-Delap 8,583

MARTINIQUE

1982 C 328,566

Cities and Towns

• FORT-DE-FRANCE (★ 116,017) 99,844

MAURITANIA / Mauritanie / Mūrītāniyā

1987 E 2,007,000

Cities and Towns

• NOUAKCHOTT 285,000

MAURITIUS

1987 E 1,008,864

Cities and Towns

Beau Bassin-Rose Hill (★ Port Louis) 93,125
Curepipe (★ Port Louis) 64,243
• PORT LOUIS (★ 420,000) 139,730
Quatre Bornes (★ Port Louis) 65,480
Vacoas-Phoenix (★ Port Louis) 55,667

MAYOTTE

1985 E 67,205

Cities and Towns

• DZAOUDZI (★ 6,979) 5,865

MEXICO / México

1980 C 67,395,826

Cities and Towns

Acapulco [de Juárez] 301,902
Aguascalientes 293,152
Atlixco 53,207
Campeche 128,434
Cancún 33,273
Celaya 141,675
Chihuahua 385,603
Chilpancingo [de los Bravo] 67,498
Ciudad Chetumal 56,709
Ciudad del Carmen 72,489
• CIUDAD DE MÉXICO (MEXICO CITY) (★ 14,100,000) 8,831,079
Ciudad de Valles 65,609
Ciudad Guzmán 60,938
Ciudad Juárez 544,496
Ciudad Madero (★ Tampico) 132,444
Ciudad Mante 70,647
Ciudad Obregón 165,572
Ciudad Victoria 140,161
Coatzacoalcos 127,170
Colima 86,044
Córdoba 99,972

C Census. E Official estimate. U Unofficial estimate.
• Largest city in country.
★ Population or designation of metropolitan area, including suburbs (see headnote).
▲ Population of an entire municipality, commune, or district, including rural area.

Cuernavaca 192,770
Culiacán 304,826
Delicias 65,504
Durango 257,915
Ecatepec (★ Ciudad de México) 741,821
Ensenada 120,483
Fresnillo 56,066
Garza García (★ Monterrey) 81,974
Gómez Palacio (★★ Torreón) 116,967
Guadalajara (★ 2,325,000) 1,626,152
Guadalupe (★ Monterrey) 370,524
Guaymas 54,826
Hermosillo 297,175
Hidalgo del Parral 75,590
Iguala 66,005
Irapuato 170,138
Jalapa Enríquez 204,594
La Paz 91,453
León [de los Aldamas] 593,002
Los Mochis 122,531
Matamoros 188,745
Mazatlán 199,830
Mérida 400,142
Mexicali (★ 365,000) 341,559
Minatitlán 106,765
Monclova 115,786
Monterrey (★ 2,015,000) 1,090,009
Morelia 297,544
Naucalpan de Juárez (★ Ciudad de México) 723,723
Navojoa 62,901
Nezahualcóyotl (★ Ciudad de México) .. 1,341,230
Nogales 65,603
Nuevo Laredo 201,731
Oaxaca [de Juárez] 154,223
Orizaba (★ 215,000) 114,848
Pachuca [de Soto] 110,351
Piedras Negras 67,455
Poza Rica de Hidalgo 166,799
Puebla [de Zaragoza] (★ 1,055,000) 835,759
Puerto Vallarta 38,645
Querétaro 215,976
Reynosa 194,693
Río Bravo 55,236
Salamanca 96,703
Saltillo 284,937
San Luis Potosí (★ 470,000) 362,371
San Luis Río Colorado 76,684
San Nicolás de los Garza (★ Monterrey) 280,696
Santa Catarina (★ Monterrey) 87,673
Soledad Díez Gutiérrez (★ San Luis Potosí) 49,173
Tampico (★ 435,000) 267,957
Tapachula 85,766
Tehuacán 79,547
Tepic 145,741
Tijuana 429,500
Tlalnepantla (★ Ciudad de México) 778,173
Tlaquepaque (★ Guadalajara) 133,500
Toluca [de Lerdo] 199,778
Torreón (★ 575,000) 328,086
Tulancingo 53,400
Tuxpan de Rodríguez Cano 56,037
Tuxtla Gutiérrez 131,096
Uruapan [del Progreso] 122,828
Veracruz [Llave] (★ 385,000) 284,822
Villahermosa 158,216
Zacatecas 80,088
Zamora de Hidalgo 86,998
Zapopan (★ Guadalajara) 345,390

MICRONESIA, FEDERATED STATES OF

1985 E 94,534

Cities and Towns

• KOLONIA 6,306

MONACO

1982 C 27,063

Cities and Towns

• MONACO (★ 87,000) 27,063

MONGOLIA / Mongol Ard Uls

1989 E 2,040,000

Cities and Towns

Darchan (1985 E) 69,800
• ULAANBAATAR 548,400

MONTSERRAT

1980 C 11,606

Cities and Towns

• PLYMOUTH 1,568

MOROCCO / Al-Magreb

1982 C 20,419,555

Cities and Towns

Agadir 110,479
Beni-Mellal 95,003
Berkane 60,490
• Casablanca (Dar-el-Beida) (★ 2,475,000) 2,139,204
El-Jadida (Mazagan) 81,455
Fès (★ 535,000) 448,823
Kenitra 188,194
Khemisset 58,925
Khouribga 127,181
Ksar-el-Kebir 73,541
Larache 63,893
Marrakech (★ 535,000) 439,728
Meknès (★ 375,000) 319,783
Mohammedia (Fedala) (★ Casablanca) 105,120
Nador 62,040
Oued-Zem 58,744
Oujda 260,082
RABAT (★ 980,000) 518,616
Safi 197,309
Salé (★★ Rabat) 289,391
Settat 65,203
Sidi Kacem 55,833
Sidi Slimane 50,457
Tanger (Tangier) (★ 370,000) 266,346
Taza 77,216
Tétouan 199,615

MOZAMBIQUE / Moçambique

1989 E 15,326,476

Cities and Towns

Beira 291,604
Chimoio (1986 E) 86,928
Inhambane (1986 E) 64,274
• MAPUTO 1,069,727
Nacala-Velha 101,615
Nampula 197,379
Pemba (1986 E) 50,215
Quelimane 78,520
Tete (1986 E) 56,178
Xai-Xai (1986 E) 51,620

NAMIBIA

1988 E 1,760,000

Cities and Towns

• WINDHOEK 114,500

NAURU / Naoero

1987 E 8,000

NEPAL / Nepāl

1981 C 15,022,839

Cities and Towns

Birātnagar 93,544
• KĀTHMĀNDAU (★ 320,000) 235,160

NETHERLANDS / Nederland

1989 E 14,880,000

Cities and Towns

Alkmaar (★ 121,000) (1987 E) 87,034
Almelo (1986 E) 62,421
Alphen aan den Rijn (1986 E) 55,812
Amersfoort (★ 130,158) (1986 E) 89,596
Amstelveen (★ Amsterdam) (1986 E) 68,090
• AMSTERDAM (★ 1,860,000) 696,500
Apeldoorn 147,300
Arnhem (★ 296,362) 129,000
Breda (★ 155,613) 121,400
Delft (★★ 's-Gravenhage) (1986 E) 87,440
Den Helder (1986 E) 63,231
Deventer (1986 E) 64,806
Dordrecht (★ 202,126) 108,300
Eindhoven (★ 379,377) 190,700
Enschede (★ 288,000) 145,200
Gouda (1986 E) 60,927
Groningen (★ 206,781) 167,800
Haarlem (★ Amsterdam) 149,200
Heerlen (★ 266,617) (1986 E) 93,871
Helmond (1987 E) 63,909
Hengelo (★★ Enschede) (1986 E) 76,694
Hilversum (★ Amsterdam) (1986 E) 86,125
Hoorn (1987 E) 53,788
IJmuiden (★ Amsterdam) (1986 E) 57,157
Kerkrade (★ Heerlen) (1986 E) 52,885
Leeuwarden (1986 E) 84,966
Leiden (★ 182,244) 109,200
Maastricht (★ 160,026) 116,400
Nieuwegein (★ Utrecht) (1987 E) 56,719
Nijmegen (★ 240,085) 145,400
Oss (1986 E) 50,343
Purmerend (★ Amsterdam) (1987 E) 52,257
Roosendaal (1986 E) 57,385
Rotterdam (★ 1,110,000) 576,300
Schiedam (★ Rotterdam) (1986 E) 69,078
'S-GRAVENHAGE (THE HAGUE) (★ 770,000) 443,900
's-Hertogenbosch (★ 189,067) (1986 E) 89,039
Spijkenisse (★ Rotterdam) (1987 E) 62,394
Tilburg (★ 224,934) 155,100
Utrecht (★ 518,779) 230,700
Venlo (★ 87,000) (1986 E) 63,475
Vlaardingen (★ Rotterdam) (1986 E) 75,536
Zaandam (★ Amsterdam) 129,600
Zeist (★ Utrecht) (1986 E) 59,743
Zoetermeer (★ 's-Gravenhage) (1987 E) 85,349
Zwolle (1986 E) 88,438

NETHERLANDS ANTILLES / Nederlandse Antillen

1990 E 189,687

Cities and Towns

• WILLEMSTAD (★ 130,000) (1981 C) 31,883

NEW CALEDONIA / Nouvelle-Calédonie

1989 C 164,173

Cities and Towns

• NOUMÉA (★ 88,000) 65,110

NEW ZEALAND

1986 C 3,307,084

Cities and Towns

• Auckland (★ 850,000) 149,046
Christchurch (★ 320,000) 168,200
Dunedin (★ 109,000) 76,964
Hamilton (★ 101,814) 94,511
Lower Hutt (★ Wellington) 63,862
Manukau (★ Auckland) 177,248
Napier (★ 107,060) 49,428
Palmerston North (★ 67,405) 60,503
Takapuna (★ Auckland) 69,419
Waitemata (★ Auckland) 96,365
WELLINGTON (★ 350,000) 137,495

NICARAGUA

1985 E 3,272,100

Cities and Towns

Chinandega 75,000
Granada (1981 E) 64,642
León 101,000
• MANAGUA 682,000
Masaya 75,000
Matagalpa 68,000

NIGER

1988 C 7,250,383

Cities and Towns

Agadez 50,164
Maradi 112,965
• NIAMEY 398,265
Tahoua 51,607
Zinder 120,892

NIGERIA

1987 E 101,907,000

Cities and Towns

Aba 239,800
Abakaliki 56,800
Abeokuta 341,300
Ado-Ekiti 287,000
Afikpo 65,790
Agege 83,810
Akure 129,600
Amaigbo 53,690
Apomu 49,570
Awka 88,800
Azare 50,020
Bauchi 68,840
Benin City 183,200
Bida 100,200
Calabar 139,800
Deba 110,600
Duku 52,880
Ede 245,200
Effon-Alaiye 122,300
Ejigbo 84,570
Emure-Ekiti 58,750
Enugu 252,500
Epe 80,560
Erin-Oshogbo 59,940
Eruwa 49,140
Fiditi 49,440
Gboko 49,390
Gbongan 53,990
Gombe 86,120
Gusau 126,200
Ibadan 1,144,000
Idah 50,550
Idanre 56,080
Ife 237,000
Ifon-Oshogbo 65,980
Igboho 85,230
Igbo-Ora 68,060
Igede-Ekiti 56,570
Ihiala 73,240
Ijebu-Igbo 78,680
Ijebu-Ode 124,900
Ijero-Ekiti 76,420
Ikare 112,500
Ikerre 195,400
Ikire 94,450
Ikirun 144,900
Ikole 71,860
Ikorodu 147,700
Ikot Ekpene 69,440
Ila 210,800
Ilawe-Ekiti 147,300
Ilesha 302,100
Ilobu 159,000
Ilorin 380,000
Inisa 95,630
Ipoti-Ekiti 53,220
Ise-Ekiti 82,580
Iseyin 173,500
Iwo 289,100
Jimeta 66,130
Jos 164,700
Kaduna 273,200
Kano 538,300
Katsina 165,000
Kaura Namoda 52,910
Keffi 57,790
Kishi 77,210
Kumo 118,200
Lafia 97,810
Lafiagi 57,580
• LAGOS (★ 3,800,000) .. 1,213,000
Lalupon 56,130
Lere 49,670
Maiduguri 255,100
Makurdi 98,350
Minna 109,300
Mubi 51,190
Mushin (★ Lagos) 266,100
Nguru 78,770
Offa 157,500
Ogbomosho 582,900
Oka 114,400
Oke-Mesi 55,040
Okwe 52,550
Olupona 65,720
Ondo 135,300
Onitsha 298,200
Opobo 64,620
Oron 62,260
Oshogbo 380,800
Owo 146,600
Oyan 50,930
Oyo 204,700
Pindiga 64,130
Port Harcourt 327,300
Potiskum 56,490
Sapele 111,200
Shagamu 93,610
Shaki 139,000
Shomolu (★ Lagos) 120,700
Sokoto 163,700
Ugep 81,910
Umuahia 52,550
Uyo 60,500
Warri 100,700
Zaria 302,800

NIUE

1986 C 2,531

Cities and Towns

• ALOFI 811

NORTHERN MARIANA ISLANDS

1980 C 16,780

Cities and Towns

• Chalan Kanoa 2,678

NORWAY / Norge

1987 E 4,190,000

Cities and Towns

Bærum (★ Oslo) (1985 E) 83,000
Bergen (★ 239,000) 209,320
Drammen (★ 73,000) (1985 E) 50,700
Fredrikstad (★ 52,000) (1983 E) 27,618
Hammerfest (1983 E) 7,208
Kristiansand (1985 E) 62,200
Narvik (1983 E) 19,080
• OSLO (★ 720,000) 452,415
Skien (★ 77,981) (1985 E) 46,700
Stavanger (★ 132,000) (1985 E) 94,200
Tromsø (1985 E) 47,800
Trondheim 135,010

OMAN / 'Umān

1981 E 919,000

Cities and Towns

• MASQAT (MUSCAT) 50,000
Ṣūr (1980 E) 30,000

PAKISTAN / Pākistān

1981 C 84,253,644

Cities and Towns

Ahmadpur East 56,979
Bahāwalnagar 74,533
Bahāwalpur (★ 180,263) 152,009
Chārsadda 62,530
Chīchāwatni 50,241
Chiniot 105,559
Chishtiān Mandi 61,959
Daska 55,555
Dera Ghāzi Khān 102,007
Dera Ismāīl Khān (★ 68,145) 64,358
Drigh Road Cantonment (★ Karāchi) 56,742
Faisalabad (Lyallpur) 1,104,209
Gojra 68,000
Gujrānwāla (★ 658,753) 600,993
Gujrānwāla Cantonment (★ Gujrānwāla) 57,760
Gujrāt 155,058
Hāfizābād 83,464
Hyderābād (★ 800,000) 702,539
ISLĀMĀBĀD (★★ Rāwalpindi) 204,364
Jacobābād 79,365
Jarānwāla 69,459
Jhang Maghiāna 195,558
Jhelum (★ 106,462) 92,646
Kamālia 61,107
Kāmoke 71,097
• Karāchi (★ 5,300,000) .. 4,901,627
Karāchi Cantonment (★ Karāchi) 181,981
Kasūr 155,523
Khairpur 61,447
Khānewāl 89,090
Khānpur 70,589
Khushāb 56,274
Kohāt (★ 77,604) 55,832
Lahore (★ 3,025,000) .. 2,707,215
Lahore Cantonment (★ Lahore) 245,474
Lārkāna 123,890
Leiah 51,482
Mandi Būrewāla 86,311
Mardān (★ 147,977) 141,842
Miānwāli 59,159
Mingāora 88,078
Mīrpur Khās 124,371
Multān (★ 732,070) 696,316
Muzaffargarh 53,000
Nawābshāh 102,139
Okāra (★ 153,483) 127,455
Pākpattan 69,820
Peshāwar (★ 566,248) 506,896
Peshāwar Cantonment (★ Peshāwar) 59,352
Quetta (★ 285,719) 244,842
Rahīmyār Khān (★ 132,635) 119,036
Rāwalpindi (★ 1,040,000) 457,091
Rāwalpindi Cantonment (★ Rāwalpindi) 337,752
Sādiqābād 63,935
Sāhīwal 150,954
Sargodha (★ 291,362) 231,895
Sargodha Cantonment (★ Sargodha) 59,467
Shekhūpura 141,168
Shikārpur 88,138
Siālkot (★ 302,009) 258,147
Sukkur 190,551
Tando Ādam 62,744
Turbat 52,337
Vihāri 53,799
Wāh 122,335
Wazīrābād 62,725

PALAU / Belau

1986 C 13,873

C Census. E Official estimate. U Unofficial estimate.
• Largest city in country.
★ Population or designation of metropolitan area, including suburbs (see headnote).
▲ Population of an entire municipality, commune, or district, including rural area.

Cities and Towns

• KOROR 8,629

PANAMA / Panamá

1990 C 2,315,047

Cities and Towns

Colón (★ 96,000) 54,469
David 65,635
• PANAMÁ (★ 770,000) 411,549
San Miguelito (★ Panamá) 242,529

PAPUA NEW GUINEA

1987 E 3,479,400

Cities and Towns

Lae 79,600
• PORT MORESBY 152,100
Rabaul (1980 C) 14,954

PARAGUAY

1985 E 3,279,000

Cities and Towns

• ASUNCIÓN (★ 700,000) 477,100
Fernando de la Mora (★ Asunción) 80,000
Lambaré (★ Asunción) 84,000
Puerto Presidente Stroessner 64,000
San Lorenzo (★ Asunción) (1982 C) 74,632

PERU / Perú

1981 C 17,031,221

Cities and Towns

Arequipa (★ 446,942) 108,023
Ayacucho (★ 69,533) 57,432
Breña (★ Lima) 112,398
Cajamarca 62,259
Callao (★★ Lima) 264,133
Cerro de Pasco (★ 66,373) 55,597
Chiclayo (★ 279,527) 213,095
Chimbote 223,341
Chorrillos (★ Lima) 141,881
Chosica 65,139
Cuzco (★ 184,550) 89,563
Huancayo (★ 164,954) 84,845
Huánuco 61,812
Ica 114,786
Iquitos 178,738
Jesús María (★ Lima) 83,179
Juliaca 87,651
La Victoria (★ Lima) 270,778
• LIMA (★ 4,608,010) 371,122
Lince (★ Lima) 80,456
Magdalena (★ Lima) 55,535
Miraflores (★ Lima) 103,453
Pisco 55,604
Piura (★ 207,934) 144,609
Pucallpa 112,263
Pueblo Libre (★ Lima) 83,985
Puno 67,397
Rímac (★ Lima) 184,484
San Isidro (★ Lima) 71,203
San Martín de Porras (★ Lima) 404,856
Santiago de Surco (★ Lima) 146,636
Sullana 89,037
Surquillo (★ Lima) 134,158
Tacna 97,173
Talara 57,351
Trujillo (★ 354,301) 202,469
Vitarte (★ Lima) 145,504

PHILIPPINES / Pilipinas

1990 C 60,477,000

Cities and Towns

Angeles 236,000
Antipolo (▲ 68,912) (1980 C) 54,117
Bacolod 364,000
Bacoor (★ Manila) (1980 C) 90,364
Baguio 183,000
Baliuag (1980 C) 70,555
Biñan (★ Manila) (1980 C) 83,684
Binangonan (1980 C) 80,980
Bocaue (1980 C) 49,693
Butuan (▲ 228,000) 99,000
Cabanatuan (▲ 173,000) 75,700
Cagayan de Oro (▲ 340,000) 255,000
Cainta (★ Manila) (1980 C) 59,025
Calamba (▲ 121,175) (1980 C) 72,359
Caloocan (★ Manila) 746,000
Carmona (★ Manila) (1980 C) 65,014
Cavite (★ 175,000) 92,000
Cebu (★ 720,000) 610,000
Cotabato 127,000
Dagupan 122,000
Davao (▲ 850,000) 569,300
Dumaguete 80,000
General Santos (Dadiangas) (▲ 250,000) 157,600
Guagua (1980 C) 72,609
Iloilo 311,000
Isabela (Basilan) (▲ 49,891) (1980 C) 11,491
Jolo (1980 C) 52,429
Lapu-Lapu (Opon) 146,000
Las Piñas (★ Manila) (1984 E) 190,364
Legaspi (▲ 121,000) 63,000
Lucena 151,000
Mabalacat (▲ 80,966) (1980 C) 54,988
Makati (★ Manila) (1984 E) 408,991
Malabon (★ Manila) (1984 E) 212,930
Malolos (1980 C) 95,699
Mandaluyong (★ Manila) (1984 E) 226,670
Mandaue (★ Cebu) 180,000
Mangaldan (1980 C) 50,434
• MANILA (★ 6,800,000) .. 1,587,000
Marawi 92,000
Marikina (★ Manila) (1984 E) 248,183
Meycauayan (★ Manila) (1980 C) 83,579
Muntinglupa (★ Manila) (1984 E) 172,421
Naga 115,000
Navotas (★ Manila) (1984 E) 146,899
Olongapo 192,000
Pagadian (▲ 107,000) 52,400
Parañaque (★ Manila) (1984 E) 252,791
Pasay (★ Manila) 354,000
Pasig (★ Manila) (1984 E) 318,853
Puerto Princesa (▲ 92,000) 52,000
Quezon City (★ Manila) .. 1,632,000
San Fernando (1980 C) 110,891
San Juan del Monte (★ Manila) (1984 E) 139,126
San Pablo (▲ 161,000) 83,900
San Pedro (1980 C) 74,556
Santa Cruz (1980 C) 60,620
Santa Rosa (★ Manila) (1980 C) 64,325
Tacloban 138,000
Tagbilaran 56,000
Tagig (★ Manila) (1984 E) 130,719
Taytay (★ Manila) (1980 C) 75,328
Valenzuela (★ Manila) (1984 E) 275,725
Zamboanga (▲ 444,000) 107,000

PITCAIRN

1988 C 59

Cities and Towns

• ADAMSTOWN 59

POLAND / Polska

1989 E 37,775,100

Cities and Towns

Będzin (★ Katowice) 77,300
Bełchatów 53,600
Biała Podlaska 50,900
Białystok 263,900
Bielsko-Biała 179,600
Bydgoszcz 377,900
Bytom (Beuthen) (★★ Katowice) 228,000
Chełm 63,300
Chorzów (★★ Katowice) 133,300
Częstochowa 254,600
Dąbrowa Górnicza (★ Katowice) 133,200
Elbląg (Elbing) 124,600
Ełk 49,600
Gdańsk (Danzig) (★ 909,000) 461,500
Gdynia (★★ Gdańsk) 250,200
Gliwice (Gleiwitz) (★★ Katowice) 222,500
Głogów 70,100
Gniezno 68,900
Gorzów Wielkopolski (Landsberg an der Warthe) 121,500
Grudziądz 99,900
Inowrocław 75,100
Jastrzębie-Zdrój 102,200
Jaworzno (★ Katowice) 97,400
Jelenia Góra (Hirschberg) 92,700
Kalisz 105,600
• Katowice (★ 2,778,000) 365,800
Kędzierzyn Kozle 71,600
Kielce 211,100
Konin 78,500
Koszalin (Köslin) 105,600
Kraków (★ 828,000) 743,700
Legionowo (★ Warszawa) 50,000
Legnica (Liegnitz) 102,800
Leszno 56,700
Łódź (★ 1,061,000) 851,500
Łomża 56,300
Lubin 78,800
Lublin (★ 389,000) 339,500
Mielec 58,600
Mysłowice (★ Katowice) 91,200
Nowy Sącz 75,100
Olsztyn (Allenstein) 158,800
Opole (Oppeln) 125,800
Ostrowiec Świętokrzyski 76,300
Ostrów Wielkopolski 71,200
Pabianice (★ Łódź) 74,400
Piekary Śląskie (★ Katowice) 68,200
Piła (Schneidemühl) (1988 E) 70,000
Piotrków Trybunalski 80,100
Płock 119,300
Poznań (★ 672,000) 586,500
Pruszków (★ Warszawa) 52,700
Przemyśl 67,300
Puławy 52,200
Racibórz (Ratibor) 61,700
Radom 223,600
Radomsko 49,700
Ruda Śląska (★ Katowice) 167,700
Rybnik 140,000
Rzeszów 148,600
Siedlce 69,200
Siemianowice Śląskie (★ Katowice) 79,200
Skarżysko-Kamienna 50,200
Słupsk (Stolp) 98,500
Sosnowiec (★★ Katowice) 258,700
Stalowa Wola 67,600
Starachowice 55,400
Stargard Szczeciński (Stargard in Pommern) 68,400
Suwałki 57,900
Świdnica (Schweidnitz) 61,800
Świętochłowice (★ Katowice) 58,700
Szczecin (Stettin) (★ 449,000) 409,500
Tarnów 119,100
Tarnowskie Góry (★ Katowice) 72,700
Tczew 58,400
Tomaszów Mazowiecki 69,200
Toruń 199,600
Tychy (★ Katowice) 187,600
Wałbrzych (Waldenburg) (★ 207,000) 141,400
WARSZAWA (★ 2,323,000) 1,651,200
Włocławek 119,500
Wodzisław Śląski 109,800
Wrocław (Breslau) 637,400
Zabrze (Hindenburg) (★★ Katowice) 201,400
Zamość 59,000
Zawiercie 55,700
Zgierz (★ Łódź) 58,500
Zielona Góra (Grünberg) 111,800
Żory 65,300

PORTUGAL

1981 C 9,833,014

Cities and Towns

Amadora (★ Lisboa) 95,518
Barreiro (★ Lisboa) 50,863
Braga 63,033
Coimbra 74,616
• LISBOA (LISBON) (★ 2,250,000) 807,167
Porto (★ 1,225,000) 327,368
Setúbal 77,885
Vila Nova de Gaia (★ Porto) 62,469

PUERTO RICO

1980 C 3,196,520

Cities and Towns

Aguadilla (★ 152,793) 22,039
Arecibo (★ 160,336) 48,779
Bayamón (★ San Juan) 185,087
Caguas (★ San Juan) 87,214
Carolina (★ San Juan) 147,835
Guaynabo (★ San Juan) 65,075
Mayagüez (★ 200,464) 82,968
Ponce (★ 232,551) 161,739
• SAN JUAN (★ 1,775,260) 424,600

QATAR / Qaṭar

1986 C 369,079

Cities and Towns

• AD-DAWḤAH (DOHA) (★ 310,000) 217,294
Ar-Rayyān (★ Ad-Dawḥah) 91,996

REUNION / Réunion

1982 C 515,814

Cities and Towns

• SAINT-DENIS (▲ 109,072) 84,400

ROMANIA / România

1986 E 22,823,479

Cities and Towns

Alba-Iulia 66,100
Alexandria 52,802
Arad 187,744
Bacău 179,877
Baia-Mare 139,704
Bîrlad 70,365
Bistrița 77,267
Botoșani 108,775
Brăila 235,620
Brașov 351,493
• BUCUREȘTI (BUCHAREST) (★ 2,275,000) 1,989,823
Buzău 136,080
Călărași 69,350
Cluj-Napoca 310,017
Constanța 327,676
Craiova 281,044
Deva 77,976
Drobeta-Turnu-Severin 99,366
Focșani 86,411
Galați 295,372
Gheorghe Gheorghiu-Dej 52,329
Giurgiu 68,002
Hunedoara 88,514
Iași 313,060
Lugoj 53,665
Medgidia 48,409
Mediaș 72,816
Oradea 213,846
Petroșani (★ 76,000) 49,131
Piatra-Neamț 109,393
Pitești 157,190
Ploiești (★ 310,000) 234,886
Reșița 105,914
Rîmnicu-Vîlcea 96,051
Roman 72,415
Satu Mare 130,082
Sfîntu-Gheorghe 67,587
Sibiu 177,511
Slatina 76,714
Suceava 96,317
Timișoara 325,272
Tîrgoviște 91,990
Tîrgu-Jiu 87,693
Tîrgu-Mureș 158,998
Tulcea 86,336
Turda 61,594
Vaslui 65,070
Zalău 57,283

RWANDA

1983 E 5,762,000

Cities and Towns

Butare 30,000
• KIGALI 181,600

SAINT HELENA

1987 C 5,644

Cities and Towns

• JAMESTOWN 1,413

SAINT KITTS AND NEVIS

1980 C 44,404

Cities and Towns

• BASSETERRE 14,725
Charlestown 1,771

SAINT LUCIA

1987 E 142,342

Cities and Towns

• CASTRIES 53,933

SAINT PIERRE AND MIQUELON / Saint-Pierre-et-Miquelon

1982 C 6,041

Cities and Towns

• SAINT-PIERRE 5,371

SAINT VINCENT AND THE GRENADINES

1987 E 112,589

Cities and Towns

• KINGSTOWN (★ 28,936) 19,028

SAN MARINO

1988 E 22,304

Cities and Towns

• SAN MARINO 2,777

SAO TOME AND PRINCIPE / São Tomé e Príncipe

1970 C 73,631

Cities and Towns

• SÃO TOMÉ 17,380

SAUDI ARABIA / Al-'Arabīyah as-Su'ūdīyah

1980 E 9,229,000

Cities and Towns

Abhā (1974 C) 30,150
Ad-Dammām 200,000
Al-Hufūf (1974 C) 101,271
Al-Khubar (1974 C) 48,817
Al-Madīnah (Medina) 290,000
Al-Mubarraz (1974 C) 54,325
AR-RIYĀḌ (RIYADH) .. 1,250,000
Aṭ-Ṭā'if 300,000
Buraydah (1974 C) 69,940
Ḥā'il (1974 C) 40,502
• Jiddah 1,300,000
Khamīs Mushayṭ (1974 C) 49,581
Makkah (Mecca) 550,000
Najrān (1974 C) 47,501
Tabūk (1974 C) 74,825

SENEGAL / Sénégal

1988 C 6,881,919

Cities and Towns

• DAKAR 1,447,642
Diourbel 77,548
Kaolack 152,007
Louga 52,763
Saint-Louis 160,689
Thiès 184,902
Ziguinchor 124,283

SEYCHELLES

1984 E 64,718

Cities and Towns

• VICTORIA 23,000

SIERRA LEONE

1985 C 3,515,812

Cities and Towns

Bo 59,768
• FREETOWN (★ 525,000) 469,776
Kenema 52,473
Koidu 82,474
Makeni 49,038

SINGAPORE

1989 E 2,685,400

Cities and Towns

• SINGAPORE (★ 3,025,000) 2,685,400

SOLOMON ISLANDS

1986 C 285,176

Cities and Towns

• HONIARA 30,413

SOMALIA / Somaliya

1984 E 5,423,000

Cities and Towns

Berbera 65,000
Hargeysa 70,000
Kismayu 70,000
Marka 60,000
• MUQDISHO 600,000

SOUTH AFRICA / Suid-Afrika

1985 C 23,385,645

Cities and Towns

Alberton (★ Johannesburg) 66,155
Alexandra (★ Johannesburg) 67,276
Atteridgeville (★ Pretoria) 73,439
Bellville (★ Cape Town) 68,915
Benoni (★ Johannesburg) 94,926
Bloemfontein (★ 235,000) 104,381

C Census. E Official estimate. U Unofficial estimate.
• Largest city in country.
★ Population or designation of metropolitan area, including suburbs (see headnote).
▲ Population of an entire municipality, commune, or district, including rural area.

Boksburg (★ Johannesburg) 110,832
Botshabelo (★ Bloemfontein) 95,625
Brakpan (★ Johannesburg) 46,416
CAPE TOWN (KAAPSTAD) (★ 1,790,000) 776,617
Carletonville (★ 120,499) 97,874
Daveyton (★ Johannesburg) 99,056
Diepmeadow (★ Johannesburg) 192,682
Durban (★ 1,550,000) 634,301
East London (Oos-Londen) (★ 320,000) 85,699
Edendale (★ Pietermaritzburg) 47,001
Elsies River (★ Cape Town)....................70,067
Empumalanga (★ Durban)...............47,938
Evaton (★ Vereeniging) 52,559
Galeshewe (★ Kimberley) 63,238
Germiston (★★ Johannesburg) 116,718
Grassy Park (★ Cape Town)....................50,193
Guguleto (★ Cape Town)....................63,893
• Johannesburg (★ 3,650,000) 632,369
Kagiso (★ Johannesburg) 50,647
Katlehong (★ Johannesburg) 137,745
Kayamnandi (★ Port Elizabeth) 220,548
Kempton Park (★ Johannesburg) 87,721
Kimberley (★ 145,000) 74,061
Klerksdorp (★ 205,000) 48,947
Kroonstad (★ 65,165) 22,886
Krugersdorp (★ Johannesburg) 73,767
Kwa Makuta (★ Durban)...............71,378
Kwa Mashu (★ Durban) 111,593
Kwanobuhle (★ Port Elizabeth) 52,376
Kwa-Thema (★ Johannesburg) 78,640
Ladysmith (★ 31,670) 25,102
Lekoa (Shapeville) (★ Vereeniging) 218,392
Madadeni (★ Newcastle).............65,832
Mamelodi (★ Pretoria) 127,033
Mangaung (★ Bloemfontein)..........79,851
Mosselbaai (★ 22,180) 20,404
Newcastle (★ 155,000) 34,931
Ntuzuma (★ Durban) 61,834
Nyanga (★ Cape Town) 148,882
Ozisweni (★ Newcastle) 51,934
Paarl (★★ Cape Town) 63,671
Parow (★ Cape Town) 60,294
Pietermaritzburg (★ 230,000).............133,809
Pinetown (★ Durban) 55,770
Port Elizabeth (★ 690,000).............272,844
Potchefstroom (★ 78,865)...............43,766
PRETORIA (★ 960,000) 443,059
Randburg (★ Johannesburg) 74,347
Randfontein (★ Johannesburg) 43,763
Roodepoort-Maraisburg (★ Johannesburg) 141,764
Sandton (★ Johannesburg) 86,089
Soshanguve (★ Pretoria) 68,598
Soweto (★ Johannesburg) 521,948
Springs (★ Johannesburg) 68,235
Tembisa (★ Johannesburg) 149,282
Uitenhage (★★ Port Elizabeth)...................54,987
Umlazi (★ Durban)..........194,933
Vanderbijlpark (★★ Vereeniging)..........59,865
Vereeniging (★ 525,000)..............60,584
Verwoerdburg (★ Pretoria) 49,891
Vosloosrus (★ Johannesburg) 52,061
Walvisbaai (Walvis Bay) (★ 16,607) 9,687
Welkom (★ 215,000) 54,488
Westonaria (★ Johannesburg).........46,523
Witbank (★ 77,171)..........41,784

SPAIN / España

1988 E 39,217,804

Cities and Towns

Albacete 125,997
Alcalá de Guadaira 50,935
Alcalá de Henares (★ Madrid) 150,021
Alcobendas (★ Madrid) 73,455
Alcorcón (★ Madrid) 139,796
Alcoy........................66,074
Algeciras 99,528
Alicante 261,051
Almería 157,644
Avilés (★ 131,000)...........87,811
Badajoz (▲ 122,407) 106,400
Badalona (★ Barcelona) 225,229
Baracaldo (★ Bilbao)........113,502
Barcelona (★ 4,040,000) 1,714,355
Bilbao (★ 985,000) 384,733
Burgos 160,561
Cáceres 71,598
Cádiz (★ 240,000)..........156,591
Cartagena (▲ 172,710) 70,000
Castelló de la Plana 131,809
Ciudad Real 56,300
Córdoba 302,301
Cornella (★ Barcelona) 86,866
Coslada (★ Madrid)..........68,765
Dos Hermanas (▲ 68,456) 60,600
Elche (▲ 180,256) 158,300
Elda.........................56,756
El Ferrol del Caudillo (★ 129,000) 86,503
El Puerto de Santa María (▲ 62,285) 49,900
Fuenlabrada (★ Madrid) 128,872
Getafe (★ Madrid) 135,367
Gijón 262,156
Granada...................263,334
Granollers (★ Barcelona) 49,045
Guadalajara 61,309
Hospitalet (★ Barcelona) 278,449
Huelva 137,826
Irún 54,886
Jaén 106,435
Jerez de la Frontera (▲ 183,007) 156,200
La Coruña.................248,862
La Línea 60,956
Las Palmas de Gran Canaria (▲ 366,347) 319,000
Leganés (★ Madrid) 168,403
León (★ 159,000) 136,558
Lérida (▲ 109,795) 91,500
Linares 58,622
Logroño 119,038
Lugo (▲ 78,795)............68,700
• MADRID (★ 4,650,000) ..3,102,846
Málaga 574,456
Manresa 65,607
Mataró 100,817
Mérida 52,368
Móstoles (★ Madrid)........181,648
Murcia (▲ 314,124) 149,800
Orense 106,042
Oviedo (▲ 190,073) 168,900
Palencia 76,692
Palma [de Mallorca] (▲ 314,608) 249,000
Pamplona 18,059
Parla (★ Madrid).............66,253
Portugalete (★ Bilbao) 57,813
Prat del Llobregat (★ Barcelona) 64,193
Puertollano 52,284
Reus 83,800
Sabadell (★ Barcelona) 189,489
Salamanca 159,342
San Baudilio de Llobregat (★ Barcelona) 77,502
San Fernando (★★ Cádiz).................81,975
San Sebastián (★ 285,000).............177,622
San Sebastián de los Reyes (★ Madrid) 51,653
Santa Coloma de Gramanet (★ Barcelona) 136,042
Santa Cruz de Tenerife 215,228
Santander (▲ 190,795) 166,800
Santiago de Compostela (▲ 88,110) 68,800
Santurce-Antiguo (★ Bilbao) 52,334
Segovia 54,402
Sevilla (★ 945,000) 663,132
Talavera de la Reina.........68,158
Tarragona (▲ 109,586) 63,500
Tarrasa (★ Barcelona) 161,410
Toledo 59,551
Torrejón de Ardoz (★ Madrid) 83,267
Torrente (★ València) 55,751
Valencia (★ 1,270,000) 743,933
Valladolid..................331,461
Vigo (▲ 271,128) 179,500
Vitoria (Gasteiz) 204,264
Zamora 62,047
Zaragoza 582,239

SPANISH NORTH AFRICA / Plazas de Soberanía en el Norte de África

1988 E 122,905

Cities and Towns

• Ceuta 67,188
Melilla 55,717

SRI LANKA

1986 E 16,117,000

Cities and Towns

Battaramulla (★ Colombo) (1981 C) 56,535
Batticaloa (1985 E) 47,000
• COLOMBO (★ 2,050,000) 683,000
Dehiwala-Mount Lavinia (★ Colombo) 191,000
Galle 109,000
Jaffna 143,000
Kalutara (1985 E)............47,000
Kandy 130,000
Kotikawatta (★ Colombo) (1981 C) 48,262
KOTTE (★ Colombo) 104,000
Maharagama (★ Colombo) (1981 C) 49,765
Matale (1985 E) 57,000
Matara (1985 E) 57,000
Moratuwa (★ Colombo) 138,000
Negombo (1985 E) 76,000
Ratnapura (1985 E) 51,000
Trincomalee (1985 E) 51,000

SUDAN / As-Sūdān

1983 C................ 20,564,364

Cities and Towns

Al-Fāshir (1973 C)...........51,932
• AL-KHARṬŪM (★ 1,450,000)...........476,218
Al-Kharṭūm Baḥrī (★ Al-Kharṭūm)...........341,146
Al-Qaḍārif (1973 C)..........66,465
Al-Ubayyiḍ 140,000
Atbarah 73,000
Būr Sūdān (Port Sudan) 206,727
Jūbā (1980 E) 116,000
Kassalā 143,000
Kūstī (1973 C)...............65,257
Nyala (1973 C) 59,852
Umm Durmān (Omdurman) (★★ Al-Kharṭūm) 526,287
Wad Madanī 141,000
Wāw (1980 E)..............116,000

SURINAME

1988 E.....................392,000

Cities and Towns

• PARAMARIBO (★ 296,000).............241,000

SWAZILAND

1986 C.....................712,131

Cities and Towns

LOBAMBA 0
Manzini (★ 30,000) 18,084
• MBABANE 38,290

SWEDEN / Sverige

1990 E..................8,527,036

Cities and Towns

Borås 101,231
Borlänge 46,424
Eskilstuna 89,460
Gävle (▲ 88,081) 67,500
Göteborg (★ 710,894) 431,840
Halmstad (▲ 79,362) 50,900
Helsingborg 108,359
Huddinge (★ Stockholm).............73,107
Järfälla (★ Stockholm) 56,386
Jönköping 110,860
Karlstad 76,120
Linköping 120,562
Luleå 67,903
Lund (★★ Malmö) 86,412
Malmö (★ 445,000).........232,908
Mölndal (★ Göteborg) 51,767
Nacka (★ Stockholm) 63,114
Norrköping 119,921
Örebro 120,353
Södertälje (★ Stockholm).............81,460
Sollentuna (★ Stockholm).............50,606
Solna (★ Stockholm).........51,427
• STOCKHOLM (★ 1,449,972) 672,187
Sundsvall (▲ 93,404) 50,600
Täby (★ Stockholm) 56,553
Trollhättan 50,602
Tumba (★ Stockholm) 68,255
Umeå (▲ 90,004)............58,700
Uppsala 164,754
Västerås 118,386
Växjö (▲ 68,849) 45,500

SWITZERLAND / Schweiz / Suisse / Svizzera

1990 E..................6,673,850

Cities and Towns

Arbon (★ 41,100)............12,284
Baden (★ 70,700) 14,545
Basel (Bâle) (★ 575,000) 169,587
BERN (BERNE) (★ 298,800) 134,393
Biel (Bienne) (★ 81,900) 52,023
Fribourg (Freiburg) (★ 56,800) 33,962
Genève (Geneva) (★ 460,000) 165,404
Lausanne (★ 259,900) 122,600
Locarno (★ 42,350)...........14,149
Lugano (★ 94,800) 26,055
Luzern (★ 159,500)..........59,115
Sankt Gallen (★ 125,000)...............73,191
Sankt Moritz (1987 E) 5,335
Solothurn (★ 56,800) 15,429
Thun (★ 77,200).............37,707
Winterthur (★ 107,400) 85,174
• Zürich (★ 860,000) 342,861

SYRIA / Sūrīyah

1988 E................ 11,338,000

Cities and Towns

Al-Ḥasakah (1981 C) 73,426
Al-Lādhiqīyah (Latakia) 249,000
Al-Qāmishlī 126,236
Ar-Raqqah 113,000
As-Suwaydā' 46,844
Dar'ā (1981 C) 49,534
Dārayyā 53,204
Dayr az-Zawr 112,000
• DIMASHQ (DAMASCUS) (★ 1,950,000) 1,326,000
Dūmā (★ Dimashq) 66,130
Ḥalab (Aleppo) (★ 1,275,000) 1,261,000
Ḥamāh 222,000
Ḥimṣ 447,000
Idlib (1981 C)...............51,682
Jaramānah (★ Dimashq).....96,681
Kābir aṣ Ṣaghīr 47,728
Madīnat ath Thawrah 58,151
Ṭarṭūs (1981 C) 52,589

TAIWAN / T'aiwan

1988 E................ 19,672,612

Cities and Towns

Changhua (▲ 206,603) 158,400
Chiai 254,875
Chilung.....................348,541
Chungho (★ T'aipei) 343,389
Chungli.....................247,639
Chutung....................104,797
Fangshan (★ Kaohsiung)...........276,259
Fengyüan (▲ 144,434) 115,300
Hsichih (★ T'aipei) (1980 C) 70,031
Hsinchu 309,899
Hsinchuang (★ T'aipei) 259,001
Hsintien (★ T'aipei) 205,094
Hualien 106,658
Ilan (▲ 81,751) (1980 C) 70,900
Kangshan (1980 C)...........78,049
Kaohsiung (★ 1,845,000)..........1,342,797
Lotung (1980 C) 57,925
Lukang (1980 C) 72,019
Miaoli (1980 C) 81,500
Nant'ou (1980 C)............84,038
P'ingchen (★ T'aipei) 134,925
P'ingtung (▲ 204,990) 167,600
Sanchung (★ T'aipei) 362,171
Shulin (★ T'aipei) (1980 C) 75,700
Tach'i (1980 C)..............67,209
T'aichung 715,107
T'ainan 656,927
• T'AIPEI (★ 6,130,000) ..2,637,100
T'aipeihsien (★ T'aipei) 506,220
T'aitung (▲ 109,358) 79,800
Taoyüan 220,255
T'oufen (1980 C) 66,536
T'uch'eng (★ T'aipei) 70,500
Yangmei (1980 C) 84,353
Yüanlin (▲ 116,936) 51,300
Yungho (★ T'aipei) 242,252
Yungkang (▲ 114,904) 59,600

TANZANIA

1984 E................ 21,062,000

Cities and Towns

Arusha 69,000
• DAR ES SALAAM 1,300,000
Dodoma.....................54,000
Iringa 67,000
Kigoma (1978 C) 50,044
Mbeya 93,000
Morogoro 72,000
Moshi 62,000
Mtwara (1978 C) 48,510
Mwanza (1978 C) 110,611
Tabora 87,000
Tanga 121,000
Ujiji (1967 C) 21,369
Zanzibar (1985 E) 133,000

THAILAND / Prathet Thai

1988 E................ 54,960,917

Cities and Towns

Chiang Mai 164,030
Hat Yai 138,046
Khon Kaen 131,340
• KRUNG THEP (BANGKOK) (★ 6,450,000) 5,716,779
Nakhon Ratchasima 204,982
Nakhon Sawan 105,220
Nakhon Si Thammarat 72,407
Nonthaburi (★ Krung Thep)..................218,354
Pattaya 56,402
Phitsanulok..................77,675
Phra Nakhon Si Ayutthaya 60,847
Samut Prakan (★ Krung Thep)...................73,327
Samut Sakhon 53,984
Saraburi 61,206
Songkhla 84,433
Ubon Ratchathani 100,374
Udon Thani..................81,202
Yala.........................67,383

TOGO

1981 C..................2,702,945

Cities and Towns

• LOMÉ (1984 E)............400,000
Sokodé 48,098

TOKELAU

1986 C........................1,690

TONGA

1986 C........................94,535

Cities and Towns

• NUKU'ALOFA 21,265

TRINIDAD AND TOBAGO

1990 C..................1,234,388

Cities and Towns

Arima 29,695
• PORT OF SPAIN (★ 370,000)..................50,878
San Fernando (★ 75,000) 30,092

TUNISIA / Tunis / Tunisie

1984 C..................6,975,450

Cities and Towns

Ariana (★ Tunis).............98,655
Bardo (★ Tunis) 65,669
Béja.........................46,708
Ben Arous (★ Tunis)..........52,105
Binzerte 94,509
Gabès 92,258
Gafsa 60,970
Hammam Lif (★ Tunis) 47,009
Houmt Essouk 92,269
Kairouan 72,254
Kasserine 47,606
La Goulette (★ Tunis) 61,609
Menzel Bourguiba 51,399
Nabeul (★ 75,000)...........39,531
Sfax (★ 310,000)...........231,911
Sousse (★ 160,000) 83,509
• TUNIS (★ 1,225,000) 596,654
Zarzis 49,063

TURKEY / Türkiye

1990 C................ 56,969,109

Cities and Towns

Adana......................931,555
Adapazarı 174,353
Adıyaman 101,306
Afyon 98,618
Ağrı 57,837
Akhisar......................74,002
Aksaray 92,038
Akşehir......................51,669
Amasya 55,602
ANKARA (★ 2,650,000) ..2,553,209
Antakya (Antioch) 124,443
Antalya 378,726

C Census. E Official estimate. U Unofficial estimate.
• Largest city in country.
★ Population or designation of metropolitan area, including suburbs (see headnote).
▲ Population of an entire municipality, commune, or district, including rural area.

Aydın 106,603
Bafra 66,209
Balıkesir 171,967
Bandırma 77,211
Batman 148,121
Bolu 60,600
Burdur 56,095
Bursa 838,323
Çanakkale 53,887
Ceyhan 85,000
Çorlu 77,025
Çorum 116,260
Denizli 203,130
Diyarbakır 375,767
Dörtyol 48,030
Düzce 62,606
Edirne 102,325
Elazığ 211,720
Elbistan 55,114
Ereğli, Konya prov. 74,332
Ereğli, Zonguldak prov. 63,776
Erzincan 90,799
Erzurum 241,344
Eskişehir 413,305
Gaziantep 627,584
Gebze (★ İstanbul) 156,594
Gemlik 50,212
Giresun 67,536
Gölcük 65,000
İçel (Mersin) 420,750
İnegöl 71,095
İskenderun 156,198
Isparta 111,706
• İstanbul (★ 7,550,000) 6,748,435
İzmir (★ 1,900,000) 1,762,849
İzmit 254,768
Kadirli 55,193
Kahramanmaraş 229,066
Karabük 104,869
Karaman 76,682
Kars 79,496
Kastamonu 52,363
Kayseri 416,276
Kilis 81,469
Kırıkhan 69,323
Kırıkkale 203,666
Kırşehir 74,546
Kızıltepe 60,445
Konya 509,208
Kozan 54,934
Kütahya 131,286
Lüleburgaz 51,978
Malatya 276,666
Manisa 158,283
Mardin 52,994
Nazilli 80,209
Nevşehir 52,514
Niğde 54,822
Nizip 58,259
Nusaybin 50,605
Ödemiş 511,110
Ordu 101,306
Osmaniye 122,315
Polatlı 61,026
Rize 51,586
Salihli 71,035
Samsun 301,412
Siirt 66,607
Silvan (Miyafarkin) 59,959
Sincan (★ Ankara) 92,262
Sivas 219,122
Siverek 63,366
Söke 50,598
Soma 50,165
Tarsus 191,333
Tatvan 52,404
Tekirdağ 80,207
Tokat 83,174
Trabzon 144,805
Tunceli 24,584
Turgutlu 73,734
Turhal 71,406
Urfa 278,516
Uşak 104,980
Van 153,525
Viranşehir 58,394
Yalova 72,874
Yarımca (1985 C) 48,420
Yozgat 51,360
Zonguldak (★ 220,000) 120,300

TURKS AND CAICOS ISLANDS

1990 C 12,350

Cities and Towns

• GRAND TURK 3,761

TUVALU

1979 C 7,349

Cities and Towns

• FUNAFUTI 2,191

UGANDA

1990 E 17,213,407

Cities and Towns

Entebbe (1980 C) 21,289
Jinja (1982 E) 55,000
• KAMPALA 1,008,707

UNION OF SOVIET SOCIALIST REPUBLICS / Sojuz Sovetskich Socialističeskich Respublik

1989 C 286,717,000

Cities and Towns

Abakan 154,000
Abovjan (1987 E) 53,000
Achtubinsk (1987 E) 53,000
Ačinsk 122,000
Akt'ubinsk 253,000
Alapajevsk (1987 E) 51,000
Aleksandrija 103,000
Aleksandrov (1987 E) 66,000
Aleksin (1987 E) 72,000
Ali-Bajramly (1987 E) 51,000
Alma-Ata (★ 1,190,000) 1,128,000
Almalyk 114,000
Al'metjevsk 129,000
Alytus (1987 E) 71,000
Amursk (1987 E) 54,000
Andižan 293,000
Angarsk 266,000
Angren 131,000
Antracit (★★ Krasnyj Luč) (1987 E) 70,000
Anžero-Sudžensk 108,000
Apatity (1987 E) 80,000
Archangel'sk 416,000
Arkalyk (1987 E) 71,000
Armavir 161,000
Arsenjev (1987 E) 67,000
Art'om (1987 E) 73,000
Art'omovsk (1987 E) 91,000
Arzamas 109,000
Asbest (1987 E) 83,000
Ašchabad 398,000
Astrachan' 509,000
Azov (1987 E) 81,000
Baku (★ 2,020,000) 1,150,000
Balakovo 198,000
Balašicha (★ Moskva) 136,000
Balašov (1987 E) 99,000
Balchaš (1987 E) 84,000
Baranoviči 159,000
Barnaul (★ 665,000) 602,000
Batajsk (★ Rostov-na-Donu) (1987 E) 98,000
Batumi 136,000
Bekabad (1987 E) 80,000
Belaja Cerkov' 197,000
Bel'cy 159,000
Belebej (1987 E) 51,000
Belgorod 300,000
Belgorod-Dnestrovskij (1987 E) 54,000
Belogorsk (1987 E) 71,000
Beloreck (1987 E) 75,000
Belovo (1987 E) 118,000
Bendery 130,000
Berd'ansk 132,000
Berdičev (1987 E) 89,000
Berdsk (★ Novosibirsk) (1987 E) 77,000
Berezniki 201,000
Ber'ozovskij (1987 E) 51,000
Bijsk 233,000
Birobidžan (1987 E) 82,000
Blagoveščensk 206,000
Bobrujsk 223,000
Bor (★ Gor'kij) (1987 E) 65,000
Borisoglebsk (1987 E) 69,000
Borisov 144,000
Boroviči (1987 E) 64,000
Br'anka (★ Stachanov) (1987 E) 65,000
Br'ansk 452,000
Bratsk 255,000
Brest 258,000
Brovary (★ Kijev) (1987 E) 73,000
Buchara 224,000
Bud'onnovsk (1987 E) 54,000
Bugul'ma (1987 E) 88,000
Buguruslan (1987 E) 53,000
Bujnaksk (1987 E) 53,000
Buzuluk (1987 E) 82,000
Čajkovskij (1987 E) 83,000
Čapajevsk (1987 E) 87,000
Čardžou 161,000
Čeboksary 420,000
Čechov (1987 E) 57,000
Čel'abinsk (★ 1,325,000) 1,143,000
Čelinograd 277,000
Čeremchovo (1987 E) 73,000
Čerepovec 310,000
Čerkassy 290,000
Čerkessk 113,000
Černigov 296,000
Černogorsk (1987 E) 80,000
Černovcy 257,000
Červonograd (1987 E) 71,000
Chabarovsk 601,000
Charcyzsk (★ Doneck) (1987 E) 69,000
Char'kov (★ 1,940,000) 1,611,000
Chasav'urt (1987 E) 74,000
Cherson 355,000
Chimki (★ Moskva) 133,000
Chmel'nickij 237,000
Chodžejli (1987 E) 55,000
Chodžent 160,000
Čholmsk (1987 E) 50,000
Čimkent 393,000
Čirčik (★ Taškent) 156,000
Čistopol' (1987 E) 65,000
Čita 366,000
Čusovoj (1987 E) 59,000
Daugavpils 127,000
Denau (1987 E) 53,000
Derbent (1987 E) 83,000
Dimitrov (★★ Krasnoarmejsk) (1987 E) 62,000
Dimitrovgrad 124,000
Dmitrov (1987 E) 64,000
Dneprodzeržinsk (★★ Dnepropetrovsk) 282,000
Dnepropetrovsk (★ 1,600,000) 1,179,000
Dolgoprudnyj (★ Moskva) (1987 E) 71,000
Domodedovo (★ Moskva) (1987 E) 51,000
Doneck (★ 2,200,000) 1,110,000
Drogobyč (1987 E) 76,000
Družkovka (★ Kramatorsk) (1987 E) 70,000
Dubna (1987 E) 64,000
Dušanbe 595,000
Džalal-Abad (1987 E) 74,000
Džambul 307,000
Džankoj (1987 E) 51,000
Dzeržinsk (★ Gor'kij) 285,000
Džezkazgan 109,000
Džizak 102,000
Ečmiadzin (★ Jerevan) (1987 E) 53,000
Ekibastuz 135,000
Elektrostal' 153,000
Elista (1987 E) 85,000
Engel's (★★ Saratov) 182,000
Fastov (1987 E) 55,000
Feodosija (1987 E) 83,000
Fergana 200,000
Fr'azino (★ Moskva) (1987 E) 52,000
Frunze 616,000
Gatčina (★ Leningrad) (1987 E) 81,000
Georgijevsk (1987 E) 62,000
Georgiu-Dež (1987 E) 54,000
Glazov 104,000
Gomel' 500,000
Gori (1987 E) 62,000
Gorlovka (★ 710,000) 337,000
Gorno-Altajsk (1979 C) 39,917
Grodno 270,000
Groznyj 401,000
Gubkin (1987 E) 75,000
Gukovo (1987 E) 72,000
Gulistan (1987 E) 51,000
Gurjev 149,000
Gus'-Chrustal'nyj (1987 E) 75,000
Iljičovsk (★ Odessa) (1987 E) 52,000
Inta (1987 E) 58,000
Irbit (1987 E) 53,000
Irkutsk 626,000
Išim (1987 E) 65,000
Išimbaj (1987 E) 67,000
Iskitim (1987 E) 69,000
Ivano-Frankovsk 214,000
Ivanovo 481,000
Ivantejevka (★ Moskva) (1987 E) 53,000
Iževsk 635,000
Izmail (1987 E) 90,000
Iz'um (1987 E) 63,000
Jakutsk 187,000
Jalta (1987 E) 89,000
Jangijul' (1987 E) 71,000
Jaroslavl' 633,000
Jefremov (1987 E) 58,000
Jegorjevsk (1987 E) 73,000
Jejsk (1987 E) 77,000
Jelec 120,000
Jelgava (1987 E) 72,000
Jenakijevo (★★ Gorlovka) 121,000
Jerevan (★ 1,315,000) 1,199,000
Jessentuki (1987 E) 84,000
Jevpatorija 108,000
Joškar-Ola 242,000
Jurga (1987 E) 92,000
Jūrmala (★ Rīga) (1987 E) 65,000
Južno-Sachalinsk 157,000
Kaliningrad (Königsberg) 401,000
Kaliningrad (★ Moskva) 160,000
Kaluga 312,000
Kaluš (1987 E) 67,000
Kamenec-Podol'skij 102,000
Kamensk-Šachtinskij (1987 E) 75,000
Kamensk-Ural'skij 209,000
Kamyšin 122,000
Kanaš (1987 E) 53,000
Kansk 110,000
Kara-Balta (1987 E) 55,000
Karaganda 614,000
Karši 156,000
Kaspijsk (1987 E) 61,000
Kattakurgan (1987 E) 63,000
Kaunas 423,000
Kazan' (★ 1,140,000) 1,094,000
Kemerovo 520,000
Kentau (1987 E) 60,000
Kerč' 174,000
Kijev (★ 2,900,000) 2,587,000
Kimry (1987 E) 61,000
Kinel' (1979 C) 40,873
Kinešma 105,000
Kiriši (1987 E) 51,000
Kirov 441,000
Kirovabad 278,000
Kirovakan (1987 E) 169,000
Kirovo-Čepeck (1987 E) 89,000
Kirovograd 269,000
Kisel'ovsk (★★ Prokopjevsk) 128,000
Kišin'ov 665,000
Kislovodsk 114,000
Kizel (1979 C) 40,157
Klaipėda (Memel) 204,000
Klimovsk (★ Moskva) (1987 E) 57,000
Klin (1987 E) 95,000
Klincy (1987 E) 72,000
Kohtla-Järve (1987 E) 78,000
Kokand 182,000
Kokčetav 137,000
Kol'čugino (1979 C) 43,686
Kolomna 162,000
Kolomyja (1987 E) 63,000
Kolpino (★ Leningrad) 142,000
Kommunarsk (★ Stachanov) 126,000
Komsomol'sk-na-Amure 315,000
Konotop (1987 E) 93,000
Konstantinovka 108,000
Kopejsk (★ Čel'abinsk) (1987 E) 99,000
Korkino (1981 E) 63,000
Korosten' (1987 E) 72,000
Korsakov (1979 C) 43,348
Kostroma 278,000
Kotlas (1987 E) 69,000
Kovel' (1987 E) 66,000
Kovrov 160,000
Kramatorsk (★ 465,000) 198,000
Krasnoarmejsk (★ 175,000) (1987 E) 70,000
Krasnodar 620,000
Krasnodon (1987 E) 52,000
Krasnogorsk (★ Moskva) (1987 E) 89,000
Krasnojarsk 912,000
Krasnokamensk (1987 E) 70,000
Krasnokamsk (1987 E) 58,000
Krasnoturjinsk (1987 E) 66,000
Krasnoufimsk (1979 C) 40,027
Krasnoural'sk (1979 C) 38,212
Krasnovodsk (1987 E) 59,000
Krasnyj Luč (★ 250,000) 113,000
Krasnyj Sulin (1979 C) 42,281
Kremenčug 236,000
Krivoj Rog 713,000
Kropotkin (1987 E) 73,000
Krymsk (1983 E) 50,000
Kstovo (★ Gor'kij) (1987 E) 64,000
Kujbyšev (1987 E) 51,000
Kul'ab (1987 E) 71,000
Kulebaki (1979 C) 48,302
Kumertau (1987 E) 62,000
Kungur (1987 E) 83,000
Kurgan 356,000
Kurgan-T'ube (1987 E) 55,000
Kursk 424,000
Kustanaj 224,000
Kušva (1979 C) 43,089
Kutaisi 235,000
Kuzneck (1987 E) 98,000
Kyzyl (1987 E) 80,000
Kzyl-Orda 153,000
Labinsk (1987 E) 58,000
Leninakan 120,000
Leningrad (St. Petersburg) (★ 5,825,000) 4,456,000
Leninogorsk, Tatarskaja A. S. S. R. (1987 E) 61,000
Leninogorsk, Vostočno-Kazachstanskaja oblast' (1987 E) 69,000
Leninsk-Kuzneckij 165,000
Lida (1987 E) 81,000
Liepāja 114,000
Lipeck 450,000
Lisičansk (★ 410,000) 127,000
Livny (1987 E) 51,000
Lobn'a (★ Moskva) (1987 E) 59,000
Lozovaja (1987 E) 68,000
L'ubercy (★ Moskva) 165,000
Lubny (1987 E) 58,000
Luck 198,000
Lugansk 497,000
L'vov 790,000
Lys'va (1987 E) 77,000
Lytkarino (★ Moskva) (1987 E) 51,000
Machačkala 315,000
Magadan 152,000
Magnitogorsk 440,000
Majkop 149,000
Makejevka (★★ Doneck) 430,000
Marganec (1987 E) 55,000
Margilan 125,000
Mariupol' (Ždanov) 517,000
Mary (1987 E) 89,000
Melitopol' 174,000
Meždurečensk 107,000
Miass 168,000
Michajlovka (1987 E) 58,000
Mičurinsk 109,000
Mineral'nyje Vody (1987 E) 75,000
Mingečaur (1987 E) 78,000
Minsk (★ 1,650,000) 1,589,000
Minusinsk (1987 E) 72,000
Mogil'ov 356,000
Molodečno (1987 E) 87,000
Mončegorsk (1987 E) 65,000
Moršansk (1987 E) 51,000
• MOSKVA (MOSCOW) (★ 13,100,000) 8,769,000
Mozyr' 101,000
Mukačevo (1987 E) 88,000
Murmansk 468,000
Murom 124,000
Mytišči (★ Moskva) 154,000
Naberežnyje Čelny 501,000
Nachičevan' (1987 E) 51,000
Nachodka 165,000
Nal'čik 235,000
Namangan 308,000
Naro-Fominsk (1987 E) 60,000
Narva (1987 E) 81,000
Navoi 107,000
Nazarovo (1987 E) 63,000
Nebit-Dag (1987 E) 85,000
Neftejugansk (1987 E) 86,000
Neftekamsk 107,000
Ner'ungri (1987 E) 68,000
Nevinnomyssk 121,000
Nežin (1987 E) 81,000
Nikolajev 503,000
Nikol'skij (1987 E) 64,000
Nikopol' 158,000
Nižnekamsk 191,000
Nižnevartovsk 242,000
Nižnij Novgorod (★ 2,025,000) 1,438,000
Nižnij Tagil 440,000
Noginsk 123,000
Nojabr'sk (1987 E) 77,000
Noril'sk 174,000
Novaja Kachovka (1987 E) 53,000
Novgorod 229,000
Novoaltajsk (★ Barnaul) (1987 E) 51,000
Novočeboksarsk 115,000
Novočerkassk 187,000
Novodvinsk (1987 E) 50,000
Novograd-Volynskij (1987 E) 52,000
Novokujbyševsk (★ Kujbyšev) 113,000
Novokuzneck 600,000
Novomoskovsk, Dnepropetrovsk oblast' (1987 E) 76,000
Novomoskovsk, Tula oblast' (★ 365,000) 146,000
Novopolock (1987 E) 90,000
Novorossijsk 186,000
Novošachtinsk 106,000
Novosibirsk (★ 1,600,000) 1,436,000
Novotroick 106,000
Novovolynsk (1987 E) 54,000
Novyj Urengoj (1987 E) 79,000
Nukus 169,000
Obninsk 100,000
Odessa (★ 1,185,000) 1,115,000
Odincovo (★ Moskva) 125,000
Okt'abr'skij 105,000
Omsk (★ 1,175,000) 1,148,000
Orechovo-Zujevo (★ 205,000) 137,000
Orenburg 547,000
Or'ol 337,000
Orša 123,000
Orsk 271,000
Oš 213,000
Osinniki (1987 E) 63,000
Panevėžys 126,000
Pärnu (1987 E) 53,000
Partizansk (1979 C) 45,628
P'atigorsk 129,000
Pavlodar 331,000
Pavlograd 131,000
Pavlovo (1987 E) 72,000
Pavlovskij Posad (1987 E) 71,000
Pečora (1987 E) 64,000
Penza 543,000
Perm' (★ 1,160,000) 1,091,000
Pervomajsk (1987 E) 79,000
Pervoural'sk 142,000
Petrodvorec (★ Leningrad) (1987 E) 77,000
Petropavlovsk 241,000
Petropavlovsk-Kamčatskij 269,000
Petrozavodsk 270,000
Pinsk 119,000
Podol'sk (★ Moskva) 210,000
Polevskoj (1987 E) 71,000
Polock (1987 E) 80,000
Poltava 315,000

C Census. E Official estimate. U Unofficial estimate.
• Largest city in country.
★ Population or designation of metropolitan area, including suburbs (see headnote).
▲ Population of an entire municipality, commune, or district, including rural area.

Poti (1977 E) 54,000
Priluki (1987 E) 73,000
Prochladnyj (1987 E) 53,000
Prokopjevsk (★ 410,000) 274,000
Prževal'sk (1987 E) 64,000
Pskov 204,000
Puškin (★ Leningrad) (1987 E) 97,000
Puškino (1987 E) 74,000
Ramenskoje (1987 E) 86,000
R'azan' 515,000
Razdan (1987 E) 56,000
Rečica (1987 E) 71,000
Reutov (★ Moskva) (1987 E) 68,000
Revda (1987 E) 66,000
Rīga (★ 1,005,000) 915,000
Romny (1987 E) 53,000
Roslavl' (1987 E) 61,000
Rossoš' (1987 E) 55,000
Rostov-na-Donu (★ 1,165,000) 1,020,000
Roven'ki (1987 E) 68,000
Rovno 228,000
Rubcovsk 172,000
Rubežnoje (★★ Lisičansk) (1987 E) 72,000
Rudnyj 124,000
Rustavi (★ Tbilisi) 159,000
Ruzajevka (1987 E) 53,000
Rybinsk 252,000
Rybnica (1987 E) 58,000
Ržev (1987 E) 70,000
Šachtinsk (1987 E) 62,000
Šacht'orsk (★★ Torez) (1987 E) 73,000
Šachty 224,000
Šadrinsk (1987 E) 87,000
Safonovo (1987 E) 56,000
Salavat 150,000
Sal'sk (1987 E) 62,000
Samara (★ 1,505,000) 1,257,000
Samarkand 366,000
Saran' (1987 E) 64,000
Saransk 312,000
Sarapul 111,000
Saratov (★ 1,155,000) 905,000
Ščelkovo (★ Moskva) 109,000
Ščokino (1987 E) 70,000
Ščučinsk (1987 E) 53,000
Šeki (Nucha) (1987 E) 54,000
Semipalatinsk 334,000
Serov 104,000
Serpuchov 144,000
Sevastopol' 356,000
Ševčenko 159,000
Severodoneck (★★ Lisičansk) 131,000
Severodvinsk 249,000
Severomorsk (1987 E) 55,000
Šiauliai 145,000
Simferopol' 344,000
Slav'ansk (★★ Kramatorsk) 135,000
Slav'ansk-Na-Kubani (1987 E) 57,000
Sluck (1987 E) 55,000
Smela (1987 E) 76,000
Smolensk 341,000
Snežnoje (★ Torez) (1987 E) 68,000
Soči 337,000
Sokol (1979 C) 45,424
Soligorsk (1987 E) 92,000
Solikamsk 110,000
Solncevo (★ Moskva) (1984 E) 62,000
Solnečnogorsk (★ Moskva) (1987 E) 53,000
Sosnovyj Bor (1987 E) 56,000
Šostka (1987 E) 87,000
Spassk-Dal'nij (1987 E) 60,000
Stachanov (★ 610,000) 112,000
Staryj Oskol 174,000
Stavropol' 318,000
Sterlitamak 248,000
Stryj (1987 E) 63,000
Stupino (1987 E) 73,000
Suchumi 121,000
Šuja (1987 E) 72,000
Sumgait (★ Baku) 231,000
Sumy 291,000
Surgut 248,000
Sverdlovsk, Sverdlovsk oblast' (★ 1,620,000) 1,367,000
Sverdlovsk, Vorosilovgrad oblast' (1987 E) 84,000
Svetlogorsk (1987 E) 68,000
Svetlovodsk (1987 E) 55,000
Svobodnyj (1987 E) 78,000
Syktyvkar 233,000
Syzran' 174,000
Taganrog 291,000
Taldy-Kurgan 119,000
Tallinn 482,000
Talnach (1987 E) 54,000
Tambov 305,000
Tartu 114,000
Tašauz 112,000
Taškent (★ 2,325,000) 2,073,000
Tbilisi (★ 1,460,000) 1,260,000
Temirtau 212,000
Termez (1987 E) 72,000
Ternopol' 205,000
Tichoreck (1987 E) 67,000
Tichvin (1987 E) 70,000
Tiraspol' 182,000
Tobol'sk (1987 E) 82,000
Tokmak (1987 E) 71,000
Toljatti 630,000
Tomsk 502,000
Torez (★ 290,000) (1987 E) 88,000
Toržok (1987 E) 51,000
Troick (1987 E) 91,000
Tuapse (1987 E) 64,000
Tujmazy (1987 E) 54,000
Tula (★ 640,000) 540,000
Tulun (1987 E) 56,000
T'umen' 477,000
Turkestan (1987 E) 77,000
Tver' 451,000
Tyndinskij (1987 E) 61,000
Uchta 111,000
Ufa (★ 1,100,000) 1,083,000
Uglič (1979 C) 39,872
Ulan-Ude 353,000
Uljanovsk 625,000
Uman' (1987 E) 89,000
Ural'sk 200,000
Urgenč 128,000
Usolje-Sibirskoje 107,000
Ussurijsk 162,000
Ust'-Ilimsk 109,000
Ust'-Kamenogorsk 324,000
Ust'-Kut (1987 E) 58,000
Užgorod 117,000
Uzlovaja (★ Novomoskovsk) (1987 E) 63,000
V'az'ma (1987 E) 57,000
Velikije Luki 114,000
Ventspils (1987 E) 52,000
Verchn'aja Salda (1987 E) 56,000
Vičuga (1987 E) 51,000
Vilnius 582,000
Vinnica 374,000
Vitebsk 350,000
Vladikavkaz 300,000
Vladimir 350,000
Vladivostok 648,000
Volchov (1987 E) 51,000
Volgodonsk 176,000
Volgograd (Stalingrad) (★ 1,360,000) 999,000
Vologda 283,000
Vol'sk (1987 E) 66,000
Volžsk (1987 E) 60,000
Volžskij (★ Volgograd) 269,000
Vorkuta 116,000
Voronež 887,000
Voskresensk (1987 E) 80,000
Votkinsk 103,000
Vyborg (1987 E) 81,000
Vyksa (1987 E) 60,000
Vyšnij Voločok (1987 E) 70,000
Zagorsk 115,000
Žanatas (1987 E) 53,000
Zaporožje 884,000
Zelenograd (★ Moskva) 158,000
Železnodorožnyj (★ Moskva) (1987 E) 90,000
Železnogorsk (1987 E) 81,000
Zel'onodol'sk (1987 E) 93,000
Žigulevsk (1977 E) 50,000
Zima (1987 E) 51,000
Žitomir 292,000
Zlatoust 208,000
Žlobin (1987 E) 52,000
Žodino (1987 E) 51,000
Žoltyje Vody (1987 E) 61,000
Žukovskij 101,000
Zyr'anovsk (1987 E) 55,000

UNITED ARAB EMIRATES / Al-Imārāt al-'Arabīyah al-Muttaḥidah

1980 C 980,000

Cities and Towns

ABŪ ZABY (ABU DHABI) 242,975
Al-'Ayn 101,663
Ash-Shāriqah 125,149
• Dubayy 265,702

UNITED KINGDOM

1981 C 55,678,079

UNITED KINGDOM: ENGLAND

1981 C 46,220,955

Cities and Towns

Aldershot (★ London) 53,665
Aylesbury 51,999
Barnsley 76,783
Barrow-in-Furness 50,174
Basildon (★ London) 94,800
Basingstoke 73,027
Bath 84,283
Bebington (★ Liverpool) 62,618
Bedford 75,632
Beeston and Stapleford (★ Nottingham) 64,785
Benfleet (★ London) 50,783
Birkenhead (★ Liverpool) 99,075
Birmingham (★ 2,675,000) 1,013,995
Blackburn (★ 221,900) 109,564
Blackpool (★ 280,000) 146,297
Bognor Regis 50,323
Bolton (★★ Manchester) 143,960
Bootle 70,860
Bournemouth (★ 315,000) 142,829
Bracknell (★ London) 52,257
Bradford (★★ Leeds) 293,336
Brentwood (★ London) 51,212
Brighton (★ 420,000) 134,581
Bristol (★ 630,000) 413,861
Burnley (★ 160,000) 76,365
Burton [upon Trent] 59,040
Bury (★ Manchester) 61,785
Bury Saint Edmunds 30,563
Cambridge 87,111
Cannock (★ Birmingham) 54,503
Canterbury 34,546
Carlisle 72,206
Carlton (★ Nottingham) 46,053
Chatham (★ London) 65,835
Cheadle and Gatley (★ Manchester) 59,478
Chelmsford (★ London) 91,109
Cheltenham 87,188
Cheshunt (★ London) 49,616
Chester 80,154
Chesterfield (★ 127,000) 73,352
Clacton-on-Sea 39,618
Colchester 87,476
Corby 48,704
Coventry (★ 645,000) 318,718
Crawley (★ London) 80,113
Crewe 59,097
Crosby (★ Liverpool) 54,103
Darlington 85,519
Dartford (★ London) 62,032
Derby (★ 275,000) 218,026
Dewsbury (★★ Leeds) 49,612
Doncaster 74,727
Dover 33,461
Dudley (★★ Birmingham) 186,513
Eastbourne 86,715
Eastleigh (★ Southampton) 58,585
Ellesmere Port (★ Liverpool) 65,829
Epsom and Ewell (★ London) 65,830
Exeter 88,235
Fareham / Portchester (★ Portsmouth) 55,563
Farnborough (★ London) 48,063
Felixstowe 24,207
Gateshead (★ Newcastle upon Tyne) 91,429
Gillingham (★ London) 92,531
Gloucester (★ 115,000) 106,526
Gosport (★ Portsmouth) 69,664
Gravesend (★ London) 53,450
Greasby / Moreton (★ Liverpool) 56,410
Great Yarmouth 54,777
Grimsby (★ 145,000) 91,532
Guildford (★ London) 61,509
Halesowen (★ Birmingham) 57,533
Halifax 76,675
Harlow (★ London) 79,150
Harrogate 63,637
Hartlepool (★★ Teesside) 91,749
Hastings 74,979
Havant (★ Portsmouth) 50,098
Hemel Hempstead (★ London) 80,110
Hereford 48,277
Hertford (★ London) 21,350
High Wycombe (▲ 156,800) 69,575
Hove (★ Brighton) 65,587
Huddersfield (▲ 377,400) 147,825
Huyton-with-Roby (★ Liverpool) 62,011
Ipswich 129,661
Keighley (★ Leeds) 49,188
Kidderminster 50,385
Kingston upon Hull (★ 350,000) 322,144
Kingswood (★ Bristol) 54,736
Kirkby (★ Liverpool) 52,825
Leeds (★ 1,540,000) 445,242
Leicester (★ 495,000) 324,394
Lincoln 79,980
Littlehampton 46,028
Liverpool (★ 1,525,000) 538,809
• LONDON (★ 11,100,000) 6,574,009
Loughborough 44,895
Lowestoft 59,430
Luton (★ 220,000) 163,209
Macclesfield 47,525
Maidenhead (★ London) 59,809
Maidstone 86,067
Manchester (★ 2,775,000) 437,612
Mansfield (★ 198,000) 71,325
Margate 53,137
Middleton (★ Manchester) 51,373
Milton Keynes 36,886
Newcastle-under-Lyme (★★ Stoke-on-Trent) 73,208
Newcastle upon Tyne (★ 1,300,000) 199,064
Northampton 154,172
Norwich (★ 230,000) 169,814
Nottingham (★ 655,000) 273,300
Nuneaton (★★ Coventry) 60,337
Oldbury / Smethwick (★ Birmingham) 153,268
Oldham (★★ Manchester) 107,095
Oxford (★ 230,000) 113,847
Penzance 18,501
Peterborough 113,404
Plymouth (★ 290,000) 238,583
Poole (★★ Bournemouth) 122,815
Portsmouth (★ 485,000) 174,218
Preston (★ 250,000) 166,675
Ramsgate 36,678
Reading (★ 200,000) 194,727
Redditch (★ Birmingham) 61,639
Rochdale (★★ Manchester) 97,292
Rotherham (★★ Sheffield) 122,374
Royal Leamington Spa (★★ Coventry) 56,552
Rugby 59,039
Runcorn (★ Liverpool) 63,995
Saint Albans (★ London) 76,709
Saint Helens 114,397
Sale (★ Manchester) 57,872
Salford (★ Manchester) 96,525
Scunthorpe 79,043
Sheffield (★ 710,000) 470,685
Shrewsbury 57,731
Slough (★ London) 106,341
Solihull (★ Birmingham) 93,940
Southampton (★ 415,000) 211,321
Southend-on-Sea (★ London) 155,720
Southport (★★ Liverpool) 88,596
South Shields (★★ Newcastle upon Tyne) 86,488
Stafford 60,915
Staines (★ London) 51,949
Stevenage 74,757
Stockport (★ Manchester) 135,489
Stoke-on-Trent (★ 440,000) 272,446
Stourbridge (★ Birmingham) 55,136
Stratford-upon-Avon 20,941
Stretford (★ Manchester) 47,522
Sunderland (★★ Newcastle upon Tyne) 195,064
Sutton Coldfield (★ Birmingham) 102,572
Swindon 127,348
Tamworth 63,260
Taunton 47,793
Teesside (★ 580,000) 245,215
Torquay (★ 112,400) 54,430
Tunbridge Wells 57,699
Wakefield (★★ Leeds) 74,764
Wallasey (★ Liverpool) 62,465
Walsall (★★ Birmingham) 177,923
Walton and Weybridge (★ London) 50,031
Warrington 81,366
Washington (★ Newcastle upon Tyne) 48,856
Waterlooville (★ Portsmouth) 57,296
Watford (★ London) 109,503
West Bromwich (★ Birmingham) 153,725
Weston-super-Mare 60,821
Widnes 55,973
Wigan (★★ Manchester) 88,725
Winchester 34,127
Windsor (★ London) 30,832
Woking (★ London) 92,667
Wolverhampton (★★ Birmingham) 263,501
Worcester 75,466
Worthing (★★ Brighton) 90,687
York (★ 145,000) 123,126

UNITED KINGDOM: NORTHERN IRELAND

1987 E 1,575,200

Cities and Towns

Antrim (1981 C) 22,342
Ballymena (1981 C) 28,166
Bangor (★ Belfast) 70,700
Belfast (★ 685,000) 303,800
Castlereagh (★ Belfast) 57,900
Londonderry (★ 97,200) 97,500
Lurgan (★ 63,000) (1981 C) 20,991
Newtownabbey (★ Belfast) 72,300

UNITED KINGDOM: SCOTLAND

1989 E 5,090,700

Cities and Towns

Aberdeen 210,700
Airdrie (★ Glasgow) (1981 C) 45,320
Ayr (★ 100,000) (1981 C) 48,493
Clydebank (★ Glasgow) (1981 C) 51,832
Coatbridge (1981 C) 50,831
Cumbernauld (★ Glasgow) 50,300
Dumfries (1981 C) 31,307
Dundee 172,540
Dunfermline (★ 125,817) (1981 C) 52,105
East Kilbride (★ Glasgow) 69,500
Edinburgh (★ 630,000) 433,200
Glasgow (★ 1,800,000) 695,630
Greenock (★ 101,000) (1981 C) 58,436
Hamilton (★ Glasgow) (1981 C) 51,666
Inverness (1981 C) 38,204
Irvine (★ 94,000) 55,900
Kilmarnock (★ 84,000) (1981 C) 51,799
Kirkcaldy (★ 148,171) (1981 C) 46,356
Paisley (★ Glasgow) (1981 C) 84,330
Perth (1981 C) 41,916
Saint Andrews (1981 C) 10,525
Stirling (★ 61,000) (1981 C) 36,640

UNITED KINGDOM: WALES

1981 C 2,790,462

Cities and Towns

Barry (★ Cardiff) 44,443
Caernarvon 9,271
Cardiff (★ 625,000) 262,313
Cwmbran (★ Newport) 44,592
Llanelli 45,336
Neath (★★ Swansea) 48,687
Newport (★ 310,000) 115,896
Pontypool (★★ Newport) 36,064
Port Talbot (★ 130,000) 40,078
Rhondda (★★ Cardiff) 70,980
Swansea (★ 275,000) 172,433
Wrexham 39,929

UNITED STATES

1990 C 248,709,873

UNITED STATES: ALABAMA

1990 C 4,040,587

Cities and Towns

Birmingham 265,968
Decatur 48,761
Dothan 53,589
Florence 36,426
Gadsden 42,523
Huntsville 159,789
Mobile 196,278
Montgomery 187,106
Tuscaloosa 77,759

UNITED STATES: ALASKA

1990 C 550,043

Cities and Towns

Anchorage 226,338
Fairbanks 30,843
Juneau 26,751
Sitka 8,588

UNITED STATES: ARIZONA

1990 C 3,665,228

Cities and Towns

Chandler 90,533
Flagstaff 45,857
Glendale 148,134
Mesa 288,091
Peoria 50,618
Phoenix 900,013
Scottsdale 130,069
Sun City 57,000
Tempe 141,865
Tucson 405,390
Yuma 54,923

C Census. E Official estimate. U Unofficial estimate.
• Largest city in country.
★ Population or designation of metropolitan area, including suburbs (see headnote).
▲ Population of an entire municipality, commune, or district, including rural area.

UNITED STATES: ARKANSAS

1990 C	2,350,725
Cities and Towns	
Fort Smith	72,798
Little Rock	175,795
North Little Rock	61,741
Pine Bluff	57,140

UNITED STATES: CALIFORNIA

1990 C	29,760,021
Cities and Towns	
Alameda	76,459
Alhambra	82,106
Anaheim	266,406
Antioch	62,195
Bakersfield	174,820
Baldwin Park	69,330
Bellflower	61,815
Berkeley	102,724
Beverly Hills	31,971
Buena Park	68,784
Burbank	93,643
Camarillo	52,303
Carlsbad	63,126
Carson	83,995
Cerritos	53,240
Chino	59,682
Chula Vista	135,163
Citrus Heights	107,439
Clovis	50,323
Compton	90,454
Concord	111,348
Corona	76,095
Costa Mesa	96,357
Cucamonga	101,409
Daly City	92,311
Diamond Bar	53,672
Downey	91,444
East Los Angeles	126,379
El Cajon	88,693
El Monte	106,209
Encinitas	55,386
Escondido	108,635
Fairfield	77,211
Fontana	87,535
Fountain Valley	53,691
Fremont	173,339
Fresno	354,202
Fullerton	114,144
Gardena	49,847
Garden Grove	143,050
Glendale	180,038
Hacienda Heights	52,354
Hawthorne	71,349
Hayward	111,498
Hesperia	50,418
Huntington Beach	181,519
Huntington Park	56,065
Inglewood	109,602
Irvine	110,330
La Habra	51,266
Lakewood	73,557
La Mesa	52,931
Lancaster	97,291
Livermore	56,741
Lodi	51,874
Long Beach	429,433
Los Angeles	3,485,398
Lynwood	61,945
Merced	56,216
Milpitas	50,686
Mission Viejo	72,820
Modesto	164,730
Montebello	59,564
Monterey Park	60,738
Moreno Valley	118,779
Mountain View	67,460
Napa	61,842
National City	54,249
Newport Beach	66,643
Norwalk	94,279
Oakland	372,242
Oceanside	128,398
Ontario	133,179
Orange	110,658
Oxnard	142,216
Palmdale	68,842
Palm Springs	40,181
Palo Alto	55,900
Pasadena	131,591
Pico Rivera	59,177
Pleasanton	50,553
Pomona	131,723
Redding	66,462
Redlands	60,394
Redondo Beach	60,167
Redwood City	66,072
Rialto	72,388
Richmond	87,425
Riverside	226,505
Rosemead	51,638
Sacramento	369,365
Salinas	108,777
San Bernardino	164,164
San Diego	1,110,549
San Francisco	723,959
San Jose	782,248
San Leandro	68,223
San Mateo	85,486
Santa Ana	293,742
Santa Barbara	85,571
Santa Clara	93,613
Santa Clarita	110,642
Santa Cruz	49,040
Santa Maria	61,284
Santa Monica	86,905
Santa Rosa	113,313
Santee	52,902
Simi Valley	100,217
South Gate	86,284
South San Francisco	54,312
Stockton	210,943
Sunnyvale	117,229
Thousand Oaks	104,352
Torrance	133,107
Tustin	50,689
Union City	53,762
Upland	63,374
Vacaville	71,479
Vallejo	109,199
Ventura (San Buenaventura)	92,575
Visalia	75,636
Vista	71,872
Walnut Creek	60,569
West Covina	96,086
Westminster	78,118
Whittier	77,671
Yorba Linda	52,422

UNITED STATES: COLORADO

1990 C	3,294,394
Cities and Towns	
Arvada	89,235
Aurora	222,103
Boulder	83,312
Colorado Springs	281,140
Denver	467,610
Fort Collins	87,758
Greeley	60,536
Lakewood	126,481
Longmont	51,555
Pueblo	98,640
Thornton	55,031
Westminster	74,625

UNITED STATES: CONNECTICUT

1990 C	3,287,116
Cities and Towns	
Bridgeport	141,686
Bristol	60,640
Danbury	65,585
East Hartford	50,452
Fairfield	52,400
Greenwich	58,000
Hamden	53,100
Hartford	139,739
Manchester	51,000
Meriden	59,479
Milford	48,168
New Britain	75,491
New Haven	130,474
Norwalk	78,331
Stamford	108,056
Stratford	50,400
Waterbury	108,961
West Hartford	59,100
West Haven	54,021

UNITED STATES: DELAWARE

1990 C	666,168
Cities and Towns	
Dover	27,630
Newark	25,098
Wilmington	71,529

UNITED STATES: DISTRICT OF COLUMBIA

1990 C	606,900
Cities and Towns	
WASHINGTON	606,900

UNITED STATES: FLORIDA

1990 C	12,937,926
Cities and Towns	
Boca Raton	61,492
Cape Coral	74,991
Carol City	52,800
City of Sunrise	64,407
Clearwater	98,784
Corol Springs	79,443
Daytona Beach	61,921
Delray Beach	47,181
Fort Lauderdale	149,377
Gainesville	84,770
Hialeah	188,004
Hollywood	121,697
Jacksonville	635,230
Kendall	53,100
Lakeland	70,576
Largo	65,674
Lauderhill	49,708
Melbourne	59,646
Miami	358,548
Miami Beach	92,639
North Miami	49,998
Orlando	164,693
Palm Bay	62,632
Pembroke Pines	65,452
Pensacola	58,165
Plantation	66,692
Pompano Beach	72,411
Port Saint Lucie	55,866
Saint Petersburg	238,629
Sarasota	50,961
Tallahassee	124,773
Tampa	280,015
West Palm Beach	67,643

UNITED STATES: GEORGIA

1990 C	6,478,216
Cities and Towns	
Albany	78,122
Athens	45,734
Atlanta	394,017
Columbus	178,681
Macon	106,612
Savannah	137,560

UNITED STATES: HAWAII

1990 C	1,108,229
Cities and Towns	
Hilo	37,808
Honolulu	365,272
Pearl City	30,993

UNITED STATES: IDAHO

1990 C	1,006,749
Cities and Towns	
Boise	125,738
Idaho Falls	43,929
Pocatello	46,080

UNITED STATES: ILLINOIS

1990 C	11,430,602
Cities and Towns	
Arlington Heights	75,460
Aurora	99,581
Bloomington	51,972
Champaign	63,502
Chicago	2,783,726
Cicero	67,436
Decatur	83,885
Des Plaines	53,223
Elgin	77,010
Evanston	73,233
Joliet	76,836
Mount Prospect	53,170
Naperville	85,351
Oak Lawn	56,182
Oak Park	53,648
Peoria	113,504
Rockford	139,426
Schaumburg	68,586
Skokie	59,432
Springfield	105,227
Waukegan	69,392
Wheaton	51,464

UNITED STATES: INDIANA

1990 C	5,544,159
Cities and Towns	
Anderson	59,459
Bloomington	60,633
Evansville	126,272
Fort Wayne	173,072
Gary	116,646
Hammond	84,236
Indianapolis	731,327
Kokomo	44,962
Lafayette	43,764
Michigan City	33,822
Muncie	71,035
South Bend	105,511
Terre Haute	57,483

UNITED STATES: IOWA

1990 C	2,776,755
Cities and Towns	
Ames	47,198
Cedar Rapids	108,751
Council Bluffs	54,315
Davenport	95,333
Des Moines	193,187
Dubuque	57,546
Iowa City	59,738
Sioux City	80,505
Waterloo	66,467

UNITED STATES: KANSAS

1990 C	2,477,574
Cities and Towns	
Kansas City	149,767
Lawrence	65,608
Olathe	63,352
Overland Park	111,790
Topeka	119,883
Wichita	304,011

UNITED STATES: KENTUCKY

1990 C	3,685,296
Cities and Towns	
Frankfort	25,968
Lexington	225,366
Louisville	269,063
Owensboro	53,549

UNITED STATES: LOUISIANA

1990 C	4,219,973
Cities and Towns	
Alexandria	49,188
Baton Rouge	219,531
Bossier City	52,721
Houma	96,982
Kenner	72,033
Lafayette	94,440
Lake Charles	70,580
Metairie	149,428
Monroe	54,909
New Orleans	496,938
Shreveport	198,525

UNITED STATES: MAINE

1990 C	1,227,928
Cities and Towns	
Augusta	21,325
Bangor	33,181
Lewiston	39,757
Portland	64,358

UNITED STATES: MARYLAND

1990 C	4,781,468
Cities and Towns	
Annapolis	33,187
Baltimore	736,014
Bethesda	62,936
Columbia	75,883
Dundalk	65,800
Rockville	44,835
Silver Spring	76,200
Towson	49,445
Wheaton	58,300

UNITED STATES: MASSACHUSETTS

1990 C	6,016,425
Cities and Towns	
Boston	574,283
Brockton	92,788
Brookline	54,718
Cambridge	95,802
Chicopee	56,632
Fall River	92,703
Framingham	64,989
Haverhill	51,418
Holyoke	43,704
Lawrence	70,207
Lowell	103,439
Lynn	81,245
Malden	53,884
Medford	57,407
New Bedford	99,922
Newton	82,585
Peabody	47,039
Pittsfield	48,622
Quincy	84,985
Salem	38,091
Somerville	76,210
Springfield	156,983
Taunton	49,832
Waltham	57,878
Weymouth	54,063
Worcester	169,759

UNITED STATES: MICHIGAN

1990 C	9,295,297
Cities and Towns	
Ann Arbor	109,592
Battle Creek	53,540
Clinton	85,866
Dearborn	89,286
Dearborn Heights	60,838
Detroit	1,027,974
East Lansing	50,677
Farmington Hills	74,652
Flint	140,761
Grand Rapids	189,126
Kalamazoo	80,277
Lansing	127,321
Livonia	100,850
Pontiac	71,166
Redford	54,387
Rochester Hills	61,766
Roseville	51,412
Royal Oak	65,410
Saginaw	69,512
Saint Clair Shores	68,107
Southfield	75,728
Sterling Heights	117,810
Taylor	70,811
Troy	72,884
Warren	144,864
Westland	84,724
Wyoming	63,891

UNITED STATES: MINNESOTA

1990 C	4,375,099
Cities and Towns	
Bloomington	86,335
Brooklyn Park	56,381
Burnsville	51,288
Coon Rapids	52,978
Duluth	85,493
Minneapolis	368,383
Minnetonka	48,370
Plymouth	50,889
Rochester	70,745
Saint Cloud	48,812
Saint Paul	272,235

UNITED STATES: MISSISSIPPI

1990 C	2,573,216
Cities and Towns	
Biloxi	46,319
Hattiesburg	41,882
Jackson	196,637

UNITED STATES: MISSOURI

1990 C	5,117,073
Cities and Towns	
Columbia	69,101
Florissant	51,206
Independence	112,301
Jefferson City	35,481
Kansas City	435,146
Saint Charles	54,555
Saint Joseph	71,852
Saint Louis	396,685
Springfield	140,494

UNITED STATES: MONTANA

1990 C	799,065
Cities and Towns	
Billings	81,151
Great Falls	55,097
Helena	24,569

UNITED STATES: NEBRASKA

1990 C	1,578,385
Cities and Towns	
Grand Island	39,386
Lincoln	191,972
Omaha	335,795

UNITED STATES: NEVADA

1990 C	1,201,833
Cities and Towns	
Carson City	40,443
Henderson	64,942
Las Vegas	258,295
Paradise	124,682
Reno	133,850
Sparks	53,367
Sunrise Manor	95,362

UNITED STATES: NEW HAMPSHIRE

1990 C	1,109,252
Cities and Towns	
Concord	36,006
Manchester	99,567
Nashua	79,662

UNITED STATES: NEW JERSEY

1990 C	7,730,188
Cities and Towns	
Atlantic City	37,986
Bayonne	61,444
Brick [Township]	64,800
Camden	87,492
Cherry Hill	69,319
Clifton	71,742
East Orange	73,552
Edison	88,680
Elizabeth	110,002
Irvington	59,774
Jersey City	228,537
Newark	275,221
Passaic	58,041
Paterson	140,891
Trenton	88,675
Union	50,024
Union City	58,012
Vineland	54,780
Woodbridge [Township] (1986 U)	95,100

UNITED STATES: NEW MEXICO

1990 C	1,515,069
Cities and Towns	
Albuquerque	384,736
Las Cruces	62,126
Roswell	44,654
Santa Fe	55,859

C Census. E Official estimate. U Unofficial estimate.
• Largest city in country.
★ Population or designation of metropolitan area, including suburbs (see headnote).
▲ Population of an entire municipality, commune, or district, including rural area.

UNITED STATES: NEW YORK

1990 C 17,990,455

Cities and Towns

Albany 101,082
Binghamton 53,008
Buffalo 328,123
Cheektowaga 84,387
Greece 64,600
Irondequoit 52,322
Levittown 53,286
Mount Vernon 67,153
New Rochelle 67,265
• New York 7,322,564
Niagara Falls 61,840
Rochester 231,636
Schenectady 65,566
Syracuse 163,860
Tonawanda 65,284
Troy 54,269
Utica 68,637
Yonkers 188,082

UNITED STATES: NORTH CAROLINA

1990 C 6,628,637

Cities and Towns

Asheville 61,607
Charlotte 395,934
Durham 136,611
Fayetteville 75,695
Gastonia 54,732
Greensboro 183,521
High Point 69,496
Raleigh 207,951
Rocky Mount 48,997
Wilmington 55,530
Winston-Salem 143,485

UNITED STATES: NORTH DAKOTA

1990 C 638,800

Cities and Towns

Bismarck 49,256
Fargo 74,111
Grand Forks 49,425

UNITED STATES: OHIO

1990 C 10,847,115

Cities and Towns

Akron 223,019
Canton 84,161
Cincinnati 364,040
Cleveland 505,616
Cleveland Heights 54,052
Columbus 632,910
Dayton 182,044
Elyria 56,746
Euclid 54,875
Hamilton 61,368
Kettering 60,569
Lakewood 59,718
Lorain 71,245
Mansfield 50,627
Parma 87,876
Springfield 70,487
Toledo 332,943
Warren 50,793
Youngstown 95,732

UNITED STATES: OKLAHOMA

1990 C 3,145,585

Cities and Towns

Broken Arrow 58,043
Edmond 52,315
Lawton 80,561
Midwest City 52,267
Norman 80,071
Oklahoma City 444,719
Tulsa 367,302

UNITED STATES: OREGON

1990 C 2,842,321

Cities and Towns

Beaverton 53,310
Eugene 112,669
Gresham 68,235
Portland 437,319
Salem 107,786

UNITED STATES: PENNSYLVANIA

1990 C 11,881,643

Cities and Towns

Abington Township 59,300
Allentown 105,090
Altoona 51,881
Bensalem 56,788
Bethlehem 71,428
Bristol 57,129
Erie 108,718
Harrisburg 52,376
Haverford Township 51,800
Lancaster 55,551
Lower Merion 58,003
Penn Hills 51,430
Philadelphia 1,585,577
Pittsburgh 369,879
Reading 78,380
Scranton 81,805
Upper Darby 86,100

UNITED STATES: RHODE ISLAND

1990 C 1,003,464

Cities and Towns

Cranston 76,060
East Providence 50,380
Pawtucket 72,644
Providence 160,728
Warwick 85,427

UNITED STATES: SOUTH CAROLINA

1990 C 3,486,703

Cities and Towns

Charleston 80,414
Columbia 98,052
Greenville 58,282
North Charleston 70,218

UNITED STATES: SOUTH DAKOTA

1990 C 696,004

Cities and Towns

Pierre 12,906
Rapid City 54,523
Sioux Falls 100,814

UNITED STATES: TENNESSEE

1990 C 4,877,185

Cities and Towns

Chattanooga 152,466
Clarksville 75,494
Jackson 48,949
Knoxville 165,121
Memphis 610,337
Nashville 487,969

UNITED STATES: TEXAS

1990 C 16,986,510

Cities and Towns

Abilene 106,654
Amarillo 157,615
Arlington 261,721
Austin 465,622
Baytown 63,850
Beaumont 114,323
Brownsville 98,962
Bryan 55,002
Carrollton 82,169
College Station 52,456
Corpus Christi 257,453
Dallas 1,006,877
Denton 66,270
El Paso 515,342
Fort Worth 447,619
Galveston 59,070
Garland 180,650
Grand Prairie 99,616
Houston 1,630,553
Irving 155,037
Killeen 63,535
Laredo 122,899
Longview 70,311
Lubbock 186,206
McAllen 84,021
Mesquite 101,484
Midland 89,443
Odessa 89,699
Pasadena 119,363
Plano 128,713
Port Arthur 58,724
Richardson 74,840
San Angelo 84,474
San Antonio 935,933
Temple 46,109
Tyler 75,450
Victoria 55,076
Waco 103,590
Wichita Falls 96,259

UNITED STATES: UTAH

1990 C 1,722,850

Cities and Towns

Ogden 63,909
Orem 67,561
Provo 86,835
Salt Lake City 159,936
Sandy 75,058
West Valley City 86,976

UNITED STATES: VERMONT

1990 C 562,758

Cities and Towns

Burlington 39,127
Montpelier 8,247
Rutland 18,230

UNITED STATES: VIRGINIA

1990 C 6,187,358

Cities and Towns

Alexandria 111,183
Arlington 170,936
Chesapeake 151,976
Danville 53,056
Hampton 133,793
Lynchburg 66,049
Newport News 170,045
Norfolk 261,229
Petersburg 38,386
Portsmouth 103,907
Richmond 203,056
Roanoke 96,397
Suffolk 52,141
Virginia Beach 393,069

UNITED STATES: WASHINGTON

1990 C 4,866,692

Cities and Towns

Bellevue 86,874
Bellingham 52,179
Everett 69,961
Lakewood Center 62,000
Olympia 33,840
Seattle 516,259
Spokane 177,196
Tacoma 176,664
Yakima 54,827

UNITED STATES: WEST VIRGINIA

1990 C 1,793,477

Cities and Towns

Charleston 57,287
Huntington 54,844
Parkersburg 33,862
Wheeling 34,882

UNITED STATES: WISCONSIN

1990 C 4,891,769

Cities and Towns

Appleton 65,695
Eau Claire 56,856
Green Bay 96,466
Janesville 52,133
Kenosha 80,352
La Crosse 51,003
Madison 191,262
Milwaukee 628,088
Oshkosh 55,006
Racine 84,298
Sheboygan 49,676
Waukesha 56,958
Wauwatosa 49,366
West Allis 63,221

UNITED STATES: WYOMING

1990 C 453,588

Cities and Towns

Casper 46,742
Cheyenne 50,008
Laramie 26,687

URUGUAY

1985 C 2,955,241

Cities and Towns

Las Piedras (★ Montevideo) 58,288
• MONTEVIDEO (★ 1,550,000) 1,251,647
Paysandú 76,191
Rivera 57,316
Salto 80,823

VANUATU

1989 C 142,419

Cities and Towns

• PORT VILA (★ 23,000) 18,905

VATICAN CITY / Città del Vaticano

1988 E 766

VENEZUELA

1981 C 14,516,735

Cities and Towns

Acarigua 91,662
Barcelona 156,461
Barinas 110,462
Barquisimeto 497,635
Baruta (★ Caracas) 200,063
Cabimas 140,435
Cagua 53,704
Calabozo 61,995
• CARACAS (★ 3,600,000) 1,816,901
Carora 58,694
Carúpano 64,579
Catia La Mar (★ Caracas) 87,916
Chacao (★ Caracas) 72,703
Ciudad Bolívar 182,941
Ciudad Guayana 314,497
Ciudad Ojeda (Lagunillas) 83,565
Coro 96,339
Cumaná 179,814
El Limón 65,122
El Tigre 73,595
Guacara 72,727
Guanare 64,025
Guarenas (★ Caracas) 101,742
La Victoria 70,828
Los Dos Caminos (★ Caracas) 63,346
Los Teques (★ Caracas) 112,857
Maiquetía (★ Caracas) 66,056
Maracaibo 890,643
Maracay 322,560
Maturín 154,976
Mérida 143,209
Petare (★ Caracas) 395,715
Porlamar 51,079
Pozuelos 80,342
Puerto Cabello 71,759
Puerto la Cruz 53,881
Punto Fijo 71,114
San Cristóbal 198,793
San Felipe 57,526
San Fernando de Apure 57,308
San Juan de los Morros 57,219
Turmero 111,186
Valencia 616,224
Valera 102,068
Valle de la Pascua 55,761

VIETNAM / Viet Nam

1979 C 52,741,766

Cities and Towns

Bac Giang 54,506
Bien Hoa 187,254
Buon Me Thuot 71,815
Ca Mau 67,484
Cam Pha 76,697
Cam Ranh (1973 E) 118,111
Can Tho 182,856
Da Lat 87,136
Da Nang 318,653
Hai Duong 54,579
Hai Phong (▲ 1,279,067) (1989 C) 456,000
HA NOI (★ 1,500,000) (1989 C) 1,089,000
Hoa Binh 51,187
Hon Gai 114,573
Hue 165,710
Long Xuyen 112,485
Minh Hai 72,517
My Tho 101,493
Nam Dinh 160,179
Nha Trang 172,663
Phan Thiet 75,241
Play Cu 58,088
Qui Nhon 127,211
Rach Gia 81,075
Sa Dec 73,104
Soc Trang 74,967
Thai Binh 79,566
Thai Nguyen 138,023
Thanh Hoa 72,646
• Thanh Pho Ho Chi Minh (Saigon) (★ 3,100,000) (1989 C) 3,169,000
Tuy Hoa 46,617
Viet Tri 72,108
Vinh 159,753
Vinh Long 71,505
Vung Tau 81,694

VIRGIN ISLANDS OF THE UNITED STATES

1980 C 96,569

Cities and Towns

• CHARLOTTE AMALIE (★ 32,000) 11,842

WALLIS AND FUTUNA / Wallis et Futuna

1983 E 12,408

Cities and Towns

• MATA-UTU 815

WESTERN SAHARA

1982 E 142,000

Cities and Towns

• EL AAIÚN 93,875

WESTERN SAMOA / Samoa i Sisifo

1981 C 156,349

Cities and Towns

• APIA 33,170

YEMEN / Al-Yaman

1990 1 15,267,000

Cities and Towns

'Adan (★ 318,000) (1984 E) 176,100
Al-Hudaydah (1986 C) 155,110
Al-Mukallā (1984 E) 58,000
• SAN'Ā' (1986 C) 427,150
Ta'izz (1986 C) 178,043

YUGOSLAVIA / Jugoslavija

1987 E 23,417,188

Cities and Towns

Banja Luka (▲ 193,890) 130,900
• BEOGRAD (★ 1,400,000) 1,130,000
Bitola (▲ 143,090) 76,200
Kragujevac (▲ 171,609) 94,800
Ljubljana (▲ 316,607) 233,200
Maribor (▲ 187,651) 107,400
Niš (▲ 240,219) 168,400
Novi Sad (▲ 266,772) 176,000
Osijek (▲ 162,490) 106,800
Pančevo (★ Beograd) 62,700
Priština (▲ 244,830) 125,400
Rijeka (▲ 199,282) 166,400
Sarajevo (▲ 479,688) 341,200
Skopje (▲ 547,214) 444,900
Split 191,074
Subotica (▲ 153,306) 100,500
Titograd (▲ 145,163) 82,500
Tuzla (▲ 129,967) 67,300
Zagreb 697,925
Zenica (▲ 144,869) 67,500
Zrenjanin (▲ 140,009) 65,400

ZAIRE / Zaïre

1984 C 29,671,407

Cities and Towns

Bandundu 63,189
Beni 73,319
Boma 88,556
Bukavu 171,064
Butembo 78,633
Gandajika 60,263
Gemena 62,641
Goma 76,745
Ilebo (Port-Francqui) 48,831
Isiro 78,871
Kabinda 81,752
Kalemie (Albertville) 70,694
Kananga (Luluabourg) 290,898
Kikwit 146,784
Kindu 68,044
• KINSHASA (LÉOPOLDVILLE) (1986 E) 3,000,000
Kisangani (Stanleyville) 282,650
Kolwezi 201,382
Likasi (Jadotville) 194,465
Lubumbashi (Élisabethville) 543,268
Manono 51,755
Matadi 144,742
Mbandaka (Coquilhatville) 125,263
Mbuji-Mayi (Bakwanga) 423,363
Mwene-Ditu 72,567
Tshikapa 105,484
Yangambi 53,726

ZAMBIA

1980 C 5,661,801

Cities and Towns

Chililabombwe (Bancroft) (★ 56,582) 25,900
Chingola 130,872
Kabwe (Broken Hill) 127,420
Kalulushi 53,383
Kitwe (★ 283,962) 207,500
Livingstone 61,296
Luanshya (★ 113,422) 61,600
• LUSAKA 535,830
Mufulira (★ 138,824) 77,100
Ndola 250,490

ZIMBABWE

1983 E 7,740,000

Cities and Towns

Bulawayo 429,000
Chitungwiza (★ Harare) 202,000
Gweru (1982 C) 78,940
• HARARE (★ 890,000) 681,000
Kwekwe (1982 C) 47,976
Mutare (1982 C) 75,358

C Census. E Official estimate. U Unofficial estimate.
• Largest city in country.
★ Population or designation of metropolitan area, including suburbs (see headnote).
▲ Population of an entire municipality, commune, or district, including rural area.

United States General Information

Geographical Facts

ELEVATION

The highest elevation in the United States is Mount McKinley, Alaska, 20,320 feet.

The lowest elevation in the United States is in Death Valley, California, 282 feet below sea level.

The average elevation of the United States is 2,500 feet.

EXTREMITIES

Direction	Location	Latitude	Longitude
North	Point Barrow, Ak.	71° 23'N.	156° 29'W.
South	Ka Lae (point) Hi.	18° 56'N.	155° 41'W.
East	West Quoddy Head, Me.	44° 49'N.	66° 57'W.
West	Cape Wrangell, Ak.	52° 55'N.	172° 27'E.

LENGTH OF BOUNDARIES

The total length of the Canadian boundary of the United States is 5,525 miles.

The total length of the Mexican boundary of the United States is 1,933 miles.

The total length of the Atlantic coastline of the United States is 2,069 miles.

The total length of the Pacific and Arctic coastline of the United States is 8,683 miles.

The total length of the Gulf of Mexico coastline of the United States is 1,631 miles.

The total length of all coastlines and land boundaries of the United States is 19,841 miles.

The total length of the tidal shoreline and land boundaries of the United States is 96,091 miles.

GEOGRAPHIC CENTERS

The geographic center of the United States (including Alaskaand Hawaii) is in Butte County, South Dakota at 44° 58'N., 103° 46'W.

The geographic center of North America is in North Dakota, a few miles west of Devils Lake, at 48° 10'N., 100° 10'W.

EXTREMES OF TEMPERATURE

The highest temperature ever recorded in the United States was 134° F., at Greenland Ranch, Death Valley, California, on July 10, 1913.

The lowest temperature ever recorded in the United States was -80° F., at Prospect Creek, Alaska, on January 23, 1971.

Historical Facts

TERRITORIAL ACQUISITIONS

Accession	Date	Area (sq. mi.)	Cost in Dollars
Original territory of the Thirteen States	1790	888,685	
Purchase of Louisiana Territory, from France	1803	827,192	$11,250,000
By treaty with Spain: Florida	1819	58,560	5,000,000
Other areas	1819	13,443	
Annexation of Texas	1845	390,144	
Oregon Territory, by treaty with Great Britain	1846	285,580	
Mexican Cession	1848	529,017	$15,000,000
Gadsden Purchase, from Mexico	1853	29,640	$10,000,000
Purchase of Alaska, from Russia	1867	586,412	7,200,000
Annexation of Hawaiian Islands	1898	6,450	
Puerto Rico, by treaty with Spain	1899	3,435	
Guam, by treaty with Spain	1899	212	
American Samoa, by treaty with Great Britain and Germany	1900	76	
Virgin Islands, by purchase from Denmark	1917	133	$25,000,000

Note: The Philippines, ceded by Spain in 1898 for $20,000,000 were a territorial possession of the United States from 1898 to 1946. On July 4, 1946 they became the independent Republic of the Philippines.

Note: The Canal Zone, ceded by Panama in 1903 for $10,000,000 was a territory of the United States from 1903 to 1979. As a result of treaties signed in 1977, sovereignty over the Canal Zone reverted to Panama in 1979.

WESTWARD MOVEMENT OF CENTER OF POPULATION

Year	U.S.Population Total at Census	Approximate Location
1790	3,929,214	23 miles east of Baltimore, Md.
1800	5,308,483	18 miles west of Baltimore, Md.
1810	7,239,881	40 miles northwest of Washington, D.C.
1820	9,638,453	16 miles east of Moorefield, W. Va.
1830	12,866,020	19 miles southwest of Moorefield, W. Va.
1840	17,069,453	16 miles south of Clarksburg, W. Va.
1850	23,191,876	23 miles southeast of Parkersburg, W. Va.
1860	31,443,321	20 miles southeast of Chillicothe, Ohio
1870	39,818,449	48 miles northeast of Cincinnati, Ohio
1880	50,155,783	8 miles southwest of Cincinnati, Ohio
1890	62,947,714	20 miles east of Columbus, Ind.
1900	75,994,575	6 miles southeast of Columbus, Ind.
1910	91,972,266	Bloomington, Ind.
1920	105,710,620	8 miles southeast of Spencer, Ind.
1930	122,775,046	3 miles northeast of Linton, Ind.
1940	131,669,275	2 miles southeast of Carlisle, Ind.
1950	150,697,361	8 miles northwest of Olney, Ill.
1960	179,323,175	6 miles northwest of Centralia, Ill.
1970	204,816,296	5 miles southeast of Mascoutah, Ill.
1980	226,549,010	1/4 mile west of DeSoto, Mo.

State Areas and Populations

STATE	Land Area square miles	Water Area* square miles	Total Area* square miles	Area Rank land area	1990 Population	1990 Population per square mile	1980 Population	1970 Population	1960 Population	Population Rank 1990	Population Rank 1980	Population Rank 1970
Alabama	50,766	938	51,704	28	4,062,608	80	3,894,046	3,444,354	3,266,740	22	22	21
Alaska	570,833	20,171	591,004	1	551,947	1.0	401,851	302,583	226,167	49	50	50
Arizona	113,510	492	114,002	6	3,677,985	32	2,716,756	1,775,399	1,302,161	24	29	33
Arkansas	52,082	1,109	53,191	27	2,362,239	45	2,286,357	1,923,322	1,786,272	33	33	32
California	156,297	2,407	158,704	3	29,839,250	191	23,667,372	19,971,069	15,717,204	1	1	1
Colorado	103,598	496	104,094	8	3,307,912	32	2,889,735	2,209,596	1,753,947	26	28	30
Connecticut	4,872	147	5,019	48	3,295,669	676	3,107,576	3,032,217	2,535,234	27	25	24
Delaware	1,933	112	2,045	49	668,696	346	594,317	548,104	446,292	.....	.....	.....
District of Columbia	63	6	69	.....	609,909	9,681	638,432	756,668	763,956	47	47	41
Florida	54,157	4,511	58,668	26	13,003,362	240	9,747,015	6,791,418	4,951,560	4	7	9
Georgia	58,060	854	58,914	21	6,508,419	112	5,462,982	4,587,930	3,943,116	11	13	15
Hawaii	6,427	46	6,473	47	1,115,274	174	964,691	769,913	632,772	40	39	40
Idaho	82,413	1,153	83,566	11	1,011,986	12	944,127	713,015	667,191	42	41	43
Illinois	55,646	2,226	57,872	24	11,466,682	206	11,427,414	11,110,285	10,081,158	6	5	5
Indiana	35,936	481	36,417	38	5,564,228	155	5,490,212	5,195,392	4,662,498	14	12	11
Iowa	55,965	310	56,275	23	2,787,424	50	2,913,808	2,825,368	2,757,537	30	27	25
Kansas	81,783	499	82,282	13	2,485,600	30	2,364,236	2,249,071	2,178,611	32	32	28
Kentucky	39,674	740	40,414	37	3,698,969	93	3,660,324	3,220,711	3,038,156	23	23	23
Louisiana	44,520	3,230	47,750	33	4,238,216	95	4,206,098	3,644,637	3,257,022	21	19	20
Maine	30,995	2,270	33,265	39	1,233,223	40	1,125,043	993,722	969,265	38	38	38
Maryland	9,838	623	10,461	42	4,798,622	488	4,216,933	3,923,897	3,100,689	19	18	18
Massachusetts	7,826	460	8,286	45	6,029,051	770	5,737,093	5,689,170	5,148,578	13	11	10
Michigan	56,959	40,148	97,107	22	9,328,784	164	9,262,044	8,881,826	7,823,194	8	8	7
Minnesota	79,548	7,066	86,614	14	4,387,029	55	4,075,970	3,806,103	3,413,864	20	21	19
Mississippi	47,234	457	47,691	31	2,586,443	55	2,520,698	2,216,994	2,178,141	31	31	29
Missouri	68,945	752	69,697	18	5,137,804	75	4,916,759	4,677,623	4,319,813	15	15	13
Montana	145,388	1,657	147,045	4	803,655	5.5	786,690	694,409	674,767	44	44	44
Nebraska	76,639	711	77,350	15	1,584,617	21	1,569,825	1,485,333	1,411,330	36	35	35
Nevada	109,895	667	110,562	7	1,206,152	11	800,508	488,738	285,278	39	43	47
New Hampshire	8,992	286	9,278	44	1,113,915	124	920,610	737,681	606,921	41	42	42
New Jersey	7,468	319	7,787	46	7,748,634	1,038	7,365,011	7,171,112	6,066,782	9	9	8
New Mexico	121,336	258	121,594	5	1,521,779	13	1,303,542	1,017,055	951,023	37	37	37
New York	47,379	5,358	52,737	30	18,044,505	381	17,558,165	18,241,391	16,782,304	2	2	2
North Carolina	48,843	3,826	52,669	29	6,657,630	136	5,880,415	5,084,411	4,556,155	10	10	12
North Dakota	69,299	1,403	70,702	17	641,364	9.3	652,717	617,792	632,446	46	46	46
Ohio	41,004	3,782	44,786	35	10,887,325	266	10,797,603	10,657,423	9,706,397	7	6	6
Oklahoma	68,656	1,301	69,957	19	3,157,604	46	3,025,487	2,559,463	2,328,284	28	26	27
Oregon	96,187	889	97,076	10	2,853,733	30	2,633,156	2,091,533	1,768,687	29	30	31
Pennsylvania	44,892	1,155	46,047	32	11,924,710	266	11,864,751	11,800,766	11,319,366	5	4	3
Rhode Island	1,054	158	1,212	50	1,005,984	954	947,154	949,723	859,488	43	40	39
South Carolina	30,207	909	31,116	40	3,505,707	116	3,120,730	2,590,713	2,382,594	25	24	26
South Dakota	75,956	1,164	77,120	16	699,999	9.2	690,768	666,257	680,514	45	45	45
Tennessee	41,154	989	42,143	34	4,896,641	119	4,591,023	3,926,018	3,567,089	17	17	17
Texas	262,015	4,790	266,805	2	17,059,805	65	14,225,288	11,198,655	9,579,677	3	3	4
Utah	82,076	2,826	84,902	12	1,727,784	21	1,461,037	1,059,273	890,627	35	36	36
Vermont	9,273	341	9,614	43	564,964	61	511,456	444,732	389,881	48	48	48
Virginia	39,700	1,063	40,763	36	6,216,568	157	5,346,797	4,651,448	3,966,949	12	14	14
Washington	66,512	1,627	68,139	20	4,887,941	73	4,132,353	3,413,244	2,853,214	18	20	22
West Virginia	24,124	112	24,236	41	1,801,625	75	1,950,186	1,744,237	1,860,421	34	34	34
Wisconsin	54,424	11,789	66,213	25	4,906,745	90	4,705,642	4,417,821	3,951,777	16	16	16
Wyoming	96,988	820	97,808	9	455,975	4.7	469,557	332,416	330,066	50	49	49
United States	3,539,341	139,967	3,679,245	.....	249,632,692	71	226,542,360	203,302,031	179,323,175	.....	.....	.....

*Includes United States area of the Great Lakes

United States Populations and Zip Codes

The following alphabetical list shows populations for all counties and over 15,000 selected cities and towns in the United States. ZIP codes are shown for all of the cities listed in the table. The state abbreviation following each name is that used by the United States Postal Service.

ZIP codes are listed for cities and towns after the state abbreviations. For each city with more than one ZIP code, the range of numbers assigned to the city is shown: For example, the ZIP code range for Chicago is 60601-99, and this indicates that the numbers between 60601 and 60699 are valid Chicago ZIP codes. ZIP codes are not listed for counties.

Populations for cities and towns appear as *italics* after the ZIP codes, and populations for counties appear after the state abbreviations. These populations are either 1990 census figures or, where census data are not available, estimates created by Rand McNally. City populations are for central cities, not metropolitan areas. For New England, 1990 census populations are given for incorporated cities. Estimates are used for unincorporated places that are not treated separately by the census. 'Town' (or 'township') populations are not included unless the town is considered to be primarily urban and contains only one commonly used placename.

Counties are identified by a square symbol (□).

Abbreviations for State Names

AK	Alaska	**IA**	Iowa	**MS**	Mississippi	**PA**	Pennsylvania
AL	Alabama	**ID**	Idaho	**MT**	Montana	**RI**	Rhode Island
AR	Arkansas	**IL**	Illinois	**NC**	North Carolina	**SC**	South Carolina
AZ	Arizona	**IN**	Indiana	**ND**	North Dakota	**SD**	South Dakota
CA	California	**KS**	Kansas	**NE**	Nebraska	**TN**	Tennessee
CO	Colorado	**KY**	Kentucky	**NH**	New Hampshire	**TX**	Texas
CT	Connecticut	**LA**	Louisiana	**NJ**	New Jersey	**UT**	Utah
DC	District of Columbia	**MA**	Massachusetts	**NM**	New Mexico	**VA**	Virginia
		MD	Maryland	**NV**	Nevada	**VT**	Vermont
DE	Delaware	**ME**	Maine	**NY**	New York	**WA**	Washington
FL	Florida	**MI**	Michigan	**OH**	Ohio	**WI**	Wisconsin
GA	Georgia	**MN**	Minnesota	**OK**	Oklahoma	**WV**	West Virginia
HI	Hawaii	**MO**	Missouri	**OR**	Oregon	**WY**	Wyoming

A

Abbeville, AL 36310 • *3,173*
Abbeville, LA 70510-11 • *11,187*
Abbeville, SC 29620 • *5,778*
Abbeville □, SC • *23,862*
Abbotsford, WI 54405 • *1,916*
Abbott Run Valley, RI 02864 • *1,050*
Aberdeen, ID 83210 • *1,406*
Aberdeen, MD 21001 • *13,087*
Aberdeen, MS 39730 • *6,837*
Aberdeen, NC 28315 • *2,700*
Aberdeen, OH 45101 • *1,329*
Aberdeen, SD 57401-02 • *24,927*
Aberdeen, WA 98520 • *16,565*
Abernathy, TX 79311 • *2,720*
Abilene, KS 67410 • *6,242*
Abilene, TX 79601-08 • *106,654*
Abingdon, IL 61410 • *3,597*
Abingdon, VA 24210 • *7,003*
Abington, MA 02351 • *13,817*
Abington [Township], PA 19001 • *59,084*
Abita Springs, LA 70420 • *1,296*
Absarokee, MT 59001 • *1,067*
Absecon, NJ 08201 • *7,298*
Academia, OH 43050 • *1,447*
Acadia □, LA • *55,882*
Accomack □, VA • *31,703*
Ackerman, MS 39735 • *1,573*
Ackley, IA 50601 • *1,696*
Acton, CA 93510 • *1,471*
Acton, MA 01720 • *2,300*
Acushnet, MA 02743 • *6,030*
Acworth, GA 30101 • *4,519*
Ada, MN 56510 • *1,708*
Ada, OH 45810 • *5,413*
Ada, OK 74820-21 • *15,820*
Ada □, ID • *205,775*
Adair □, IA • *8,409*
Adair □, KY • *15,360*
Adair □, MO • *24,577*
Adair □, OK • *18,421*
Adairsville, GA 30103 • *2,131*
Adams, CO 80022 • *2,200*
Adams, MA 01220 • *6,356*
Adams, NY 13605 • *1,753*
Adams, WI 53910 • *1,715*
Adams □, CO • *265,038*
Adams □, ID • *3,254*
Adams □, IL • *66,090*
Adams □, IN • *31,095*
Adams □, IA • *4,866*
Adams □, MS • *35,356*
Adams □, NE • *29,625*
Adams □, ND • *3,174*
Adams □, OH • *25,371*
Adams □, PA • *78,274*
Adams □, WA • *13,603*
Adams □, WI • *15,682*
Adams Center, NY 13606 • *1,675*
Adamstown, PA 19501 • *1,108*
Adamsville, AL 35005 • *4,161*
Adamsville, RI 02801 • *600*
Adamsville, TN 38310 • *1,745*
Addis, LA 70710 • *1,222*
Addison, CT 06033 • *2,460*
Addison, IL 60101 • *32,058*
Addison, NY 14801 • *1,842*
Addison, TX 75001 • *8,783*
Addison □, VT • *32,953*
Addyston, OH 45001 • *1,198*
Adel, GA 31620 • *5,093*
Adel, IA 50003 • *3,304*
Adelanto, CA 92301 • *8,517*
Adelphi, MD 20783 • *13,524*
Adobe Acres, NM 87105 • *2,400*
Adrian, MI 49221 • *22,097*
Adrian, MN 56110 • *1,141*
Adrian, MO 64720 • *1,582*
Advance, MO 63730 • *1,139*
Affton, MO 63123 • *21,106*
Afton, DE 19810 • *1,200*
Afton, MN 55001 • *2,645*
Afton, WY 83110 • *1,394*
Agawam, MA 01001 • *10,190*
Agoura Hills, CA 91301 • *20,390*
Ahoskie, NC 27910 • *4,391*
Aiea, HI 96701 • *8,906*
Aiken, SC 29801-03 • *19,872*
Aiken □, SC • *120,940*
Ainsworth, NE 69210 • *1,870*
Air Park West, NE 68524 • *3,100*
Aitkin, MN 56431 • *1,698*
Aitkin □, MN • *12,425*
Ajo, AZ 85321 • *2,919*
Akiachak, AK 99551 • *400*
Akron, CO 80720 • *1,599*
Akron, IA 51001 • *1,450*
Akron, NY 14001 • *2,906*
Akron, OH 44301-98 • *223,019*
Akron, PA 17501 • *3,869*
Alabaster, AL 35007 • *14,732*
Alachua, FL 32615 • *4,529*
Alachua □, FL • *181,596*
Alakanuk, AK 99554 • *544*
Alamance □, NC • *108,213*
Alameda, CA 94501 • *76,459*
Alameda, NM 87114 • *5,900*
Alameda □, CA • *1,279,182*
Alamo, CA 94507 • *12,277*
Alamo, NV 89001 • *400*
Alamo, TN 38001 • *2,426*
Alamo, TX 78516 • *8,210*
Alamogordo, NM 88310-11 • *27,596*
Alamo Heights, TX 78208 • *6,502*
Alamosa, CO 81101-02 • *7,579*
Alamosa □, CO • *13,617*
Alamosa East, CO 81101 • *1,389*
Albany, CA 94706 • *16,327*
Albany, GA 31701-07 • *78,122*
Albany, IN 47320 • *2,357*
Albany, KY 42602 • *2,062*
Albany, MN 56307 • *1,548*
Albany, MO 64402 • *1,958*
Albany, NY 12201-60 • *101,082*
Albany, OR 97321 • *29,462*
Albany, TX 76430 • *1,962*
Albany, WI 53502 • *1,140*
Albany □, NY • *292,594*
Albany □, WY • *30,797*
Albemarle, NC 28001-02 • *14,939*
Albemarle □, VA • *68,040*
Albert Lea, MN 56007 • *18,310*
Albertson, NY 11507 • *5,166*
Albertville, AL 35950 • *14,507*
Albertville, MN 55301 • *1,251*
Albia, IA 52531 • *3,870*
Albion, IL 62806 • *2,116*
Albion, IN 46701 • *1,823*
Albion, MI 49224 • *10,066*
Albion, NE 68620 • *1,916*
Albion, NY 14411 • *5,863*
Albion, PA 16401 • *1,575*
Albion, RI 02802 • *1,600*
Albuquerque, NM 87101-99 • *384,736*
Alburtis, PA 18011 • *1,415*
Alcester, SD 57001 • *843*
Alcoa, TN 37701 • *6,400*
Alcona □, MI • *10,145*
Alcorn □, MS • *31,722*
Alden, NY 14004 • *2,457*
Alderson, WV 24910 • *1,152*
Alderwood Manor, WA 98011 • *16,524*
Aledo, IL 61231 • *3,681*
Alexander □, IL • *10,626*
Alexander □, NC • *27,544*
Alexander City, AL 35010 • *14,917*
Alexandria, IN 46001 • *5,709*
Alexandria, KY 41001 • *5,592*
Alexandria, LA 71301-15 • *49,188*
Alexandria, MN 56308 • *7,838*
Alexandria, VA 22301-20 • *111,183*
Alexandria Bay, NY 13607 • *1,194*
Alfalfa □, OK • *6,416*
Alfred, NY 14802 • *4,559*
Alger □, MI • *8,972*
Algoma, WI 54201 • *3,353*
Algona, IA 50511 • *6,015*
Algona, WA 98001 • *1,694*
Algonac, MI 48001 • *4,551*
Algonquin, IL 60102 • *11,663*
Algood, TN 38501 • *2,399*
Alhambra, CA 91801-99 • *82,106*
Alice, TX 78332-33 • *19,788*
Aliceville, AL 35442 • *3,009*
Aliquippa, PA 15001 • *13,374*
Allamakee □, IA • *13,855*
Allegan, MI 49010 • *4,547*
Allegan □, MI • *90,509*
Allegany, NY 14706 • *1,980*
Allegany □, MD • *74,946*
Allegany □, NY • *50,470*
Alleghany □, NC • *9,590*
Alleghany □, VA • *13,176*
Allegheny □, PA • *1,336,449*
Allen, TX 75002 • *18,309*
Allen, TX 75002 • *18,309*
Allen □, IN • *300,836*
Allen □, KS • *14,638*
Allen □, KY • *14,628*
Allen □, LA • *21,226*
Allen □, OH • *109,755*
Allendale, NJ 07401 • *5,900*
Allendale, SC 29810 • *4,410*
Allendale □, SC • *11,722*
Allen Park, MI 48101 • *31,092*
Allenton, RI 02852 • *600*
Allentown, NJ 08501 • *1,828*
Allentown, PA 18101-95 • *105,090*
Alliance, NE 69301 • *9,765*
Alliance, OH 44601 • *23,376*
Allison, IA 50602 • *1,000*
Allison Park, PA 15101 • *5,600*
Allouez, WI 54301 • *14,431*
Alloway, NJ 08001 • *1,371*
Allyn, WA 98524 • *1,100*
Alma, AR 72921 • *2,959*
Alma, GA 31510 • *3,663*
Alma, MI 48801 • *9,034*
Alma, NE 68920 • *1,226*
Almont, MI 48003 • *2,354*
Aloha, OR 97006 • *34,284*
Alondra Park, CA 90249 • *12,215*
Alpena, MI 49707 • *11,354*
Alpena □, MI • *30,605*
Alpha, NJ 08865 • *2,530*
Alpharetta, GA 30201-02 • *13,002*
Alpine, CA 91901 • *9,695*
Alpine, NJ 07620 • *1,716*
Alpine, TX 79830-31 • *5,637*
Alpine, UT 84003 • *3,492*
Alpine □, CA • *1,113*
Alsip, IL 60658 • *18,227*
Alta, IA 51002 • *1,820*
Altadena, CA 91001-02 • *42,658*
Altamont, IL 62411 • *2,296*
Altamont, KS 67330 • *1,048*
Altamont, NY 12009 • *1,519*
Altamont, OR 97601 • *18,591*
Altamonte Springs, FL 32701 • *34,879*
Alta Sierra, CA 95949 • *5,709*
Altavista, VA 24517 • *3,686*
Alto, TX 75925 • *1,027*
Alton, IL 62002 • *32,905*
Alton, IA 51003 • *1,063*
Alton, NH 03809 • *975*
Alton Bay, NH 03810 • *1,000*
Altoona, FL 32702 • *1,300*
Altoona, IA 50009 • *7,191*
Altoona, PA 16601-03 • *51,881*
Altoona, WI 54720 • *5,889*
Alturas, CA 96101 • *3,231*
Altus, OK 73521-23 • *21,910*
Alva, FL 33920 • *1,200*
Alva, OK 73717 • *5,495*
Alvarado, TX 76009 • *2,918*
Alvin, TX 77511-12 • *19,220*
Amador □, CA • *30,039*
Amagansett, NY 11930 • *2,188*
Amana, IA 52203 • *540*
Amarillo, TX 79101-76 • *157,615*
Ambler, PA 19002 • *6,609*
Amboy, IL 61310 • *2,377*
Ambridge, PA 15003 • *8,133*
Amelia, LA 70340 • *2,447*
Amelia, OH 45102 • *1,837*
Amelia □, VA • *8,787*
Amenia, NY 12501 • *1,057*
American Canyon, CA 94589 • *7,706*
American Falls, ID 83211 • *3,757*
American Fork, UT 84003-04 • *15,696*
Americus, GA 31709 • *16,512*
Amery, WI 54001 • *2,657*
Ames, IA 50010 • *47,198*
Amesbury, MA 01913 • *12,109*
Amherst, MA 01002-04 • *17,824*
Amherst, NH 03031 • *850*
Amherst, NY 14226 • *45,600*
Amherst, OH 44001 • *10,332*
Amherst, VA 24521 • *1,060*
Amherst □, VA • *28,578*
Amherstdale, WV 25607 • *1,200*
Amite, LA 70422 • *4,236*
Amite □, MS • *13,328*
Amity, OR 97101 • *1,175*
Amityville, NY 11701 • *9,286*
Ammon, ID 83401 • *5,002*
Amory, MS 38821 • *7,093*
Amsterdam, NY 12010 • *20,714*
Anaconda, MT 59711 • *10,278*
Anacortes, WA 98221 • *11,451*
Anadarko, OK 73005 • *6,586*
Anaheim, CA 92801-25 • *266,406*
Anahola, HI 96703 • *1,181*
Anahuac, TX 77514 • *1,993*
Anamosa, IA 52205 • *5,100*
Anandale, LA 71301 • *2,000*
Anchorage, AK 99501-40 • *226,338*
Anchorage, KY 40223 • *2,082*
Andalusia, AL 36420 • *9,269*
Anderson, AK 99744 • *628*
Anderson, CA 96007 • *8,299*
Anderson, IN 46011-18 • *59,459*
Anderson, MO 64831 • *1,432*
Anderson, SC 29621-25 • *26,184*
Anderson □, KS • *7,803*
Anderson □, KY • *14,571*
Anderson □, SC • *145,196*
Anderson □, TN • *68,250*
Anderson □, TX • *48,024*
Andover, KS 67002 • *4,047*
Andover, MA 01810 • *8,242*
Andover, MN 55304 • *15,216*
Andover, NY 14806 • *1,125*
Andover, OH 44003 • *1,216*
Andrew □, MO • *14,632*
Andrews, IN 46702 • *1,118*
Andrews, NC 28901 • *2,551*
Andrews, SC 29510 • *3,050*
Andrews, TX 79714 • *10,678*
Andrews □, TX • *14,338*
Androscoggin □, ME • *105,259*
Angelina □, TX • *69,884*
Angels Camp, CA 95222 • *2,409*
Angier, NC 27501 • *2,235*
Angle Lake, WA 98188 • *5,000*
Angleton, TX 77515-16 • *17,140*
Angola, IN 46703 • *5,824*
Angola, NY 14006 • *2,231*
Angoon, AK 99820 • *638*
Aniak, AK 99557 • *540*
Anita, IA 50020 • *1,068*
Ankeny, IA 50021 • *18,482*
Anna, IL 62906 • *4,805*
Anna, OH 45302 • *1,164*
Annalee Heights, VA 22042 • *1,750*
Anna Maria, FL 34216 • *1,744*
Annandale, MN 55302 • *2,054*
Annandale, VA 22003 • *50,975*
Annapolis, MD 21401-05 • *33,187*
Ann Arbor, MI 48103-08 • *109,592*
Anne Arundel □, MD • *427,239*
Anniston, AL 36201-06 • *26,623*
Annville, PA 17003 • *4,294*
Anoka, MN 55303-04 • *17,192*
Anoka □, MN • *243,641*
Anson, TX 79501 • *2,644*
Anson □, NC • *23,474*
Ansonia, CT 06401 • *18,403*
Ansonia, OH 45303 • *1,279*
Ansted, WV 25812 • *1,643*
Antelope □, NE • *7,965*
Anthony, FL 32617 • *1,200*
Anthony, KS 67003 • *2,516*
Anthony, NM 88021 • *5,160*
Anthony, RI 02816 • *2,980*
Anthony, TX 88021 • *3,328*
Antigo, WI 54409 • *8,276*
Antioch, CA 94509 • *62,195*
Antioch, IL 60002 • *6,105*
Antlers, OK 74523 • *2,524*
Anton, TX 79313 • *1,212*
Antrim, NH 03440 • *1,325*
Antrim □, MI • *18,185*
Antwerp, OH 45813 • *1,677*
Apache, OK 73006 • *1,591*
Apache □, AZ • *61,591*
Apache Junction, AZ 85217-20 • *18,100*
Apalachicola, FL 32320 • *2,602*
Apalachin, NY 13732 • *1,208*
Apex, NC 27502 • *4,968*
Aplington, IA 50604 • *1,034*
Apollo, PA 15613 • *1,895*
Apollo Beach, FL 33572 • *6,025*
Apopka, FL 32703-04 • *13,512*
Appalachia, VA 24216 • *1,994*
Appanoose □, IA • *13,743*
Appleton, MN 56208 • *1,552*
Appleton, WI 54911-15 • *65,695*
Appleton City, MO 64724 • *1,280*
Apple Valley, CA 92307-08 • *46,079*
Apple Valley, MN 55124 • *34,598*
Applewood, CO 80401 • *11,069*
Appleyard, WA 98801 • *1,207*
Appling □, GA • *15,744*
Appomattox, VA 24522 • *1,707*
Appomattox □, VA • *12,298*
Aptos, CA 95003 • *9,061*
Aquia Harbour, VA 22554 • *6,308*
Arab, AL 35016 • *6,321*
Arabi, LA 70032 • *8,787*
Aransas □, TX • *17,892*
Aransas Pass, TX 78336 • *7,180*
Arapahoe, NE 68922 • *1,001*
Arapahoe □, CO • *391,511*
Arbuckle, CA 95912 • *1,912*
Arcade, CA 95821 • *47,900*
Arcade, NY 14009 • *2,081*
Arcadia, CA 91006-07 • *48,290*
Arcadia, FL 33821 • *6,488*
Arcadia, IN 46030 • *1,468*
Arcadia, LA 71001 • *3,079*
Arcadia, SC 29320 • *2,088*
Arcadia, WI 54612 • *2,166*
Arcanum, OH 45304 • *1,953*
Arcata, CA 95521 • *15,197*
Archbald, PA 18403 • *6,291*
Archbold, OH 43502 • *3,440*
Archdale, NC 27263 • *6,913*
Archer, FL 32618 • *1,372*
Archer □, TX • *7,973*
Archer City, TX 76351 • *1,748*
Archuleta □, CO • *5,345*
Arco, ID 83213 • *1,016*
Arcola, IL 61910 • *2,678*
Arden, CA 95825 • *62,900*
Arden Hills, MN 55112 • *9,199*
Ardmore, AL 35739 • *1,090*
Ardmore, IN 46628 • *2,250*
Ardmore, OK 73401-03 • *23,079*
Ardsley, NY 10502 • *4,272*
Arenac □, MI • *14,931*
Argos, IN 46501 • *1,642*
Arizona Sunsites, AZ 85625 • *1,100*
Arkadelphia, AR 71923 • *10,014*
Arkansas □, AR • *21,653*
Arkansas City, KS 67005 • *12,762*
Arkoma, OK 74901 • *2,393*
Arlington, GA 31713 • *1,513*
Arlington, MA 02174 • *44,630*
Arlington, MN 55307 • *1,886*
Arlington, NE 68002 • *1,178*
Arlington, NY 12603 • *11,948*
Arlington, OH 45814 • *1,267*
Arlington, SD 57212 • *908*
Arlington, TN 38002 • *1,541*
Arlington, TX 76010-18 • *261,721*
Arlington, VT 05250 • *1,311*
Arlington, VA 22201-19 • *170,936*
Arlington, WA 98223 • *4,037*
Arlington □, VA • *170,936*
Arlington Heights, IL 60004-07 • *75,460*
Arma, KS 66712 • *1,542*
Armada, MI 48005 • *1,548*
Armijo, NM 87105 • *14,600*
Armonk, NY 10504 • *2,745*
Armour, SD 57313 • *854*
Armstrong, IA 50514 • *1,025*
Armstrong □, PA • *73,478*
Armstrong □, TX • *2,021*
Arnaudville, LA 70512 • *1,444*
Arnold, MD 21012 • *20,261*
Arnold, MN 55803 • *1,500*
Arnold, MO 63010 • *18,828*
Arnold, PA 15068 • *6,113*
Arnold Mills, RI 02864 • *600*
Aroostook □, ME • *86,936*
Arroyo Grande, CA 93420-21 • *14,378*
Artesia, CA 90701-03 • *15,464*
Artesia, NM 88210-11 • *10,610*
Arthur, IL 61911 • *2,112*
Arthur □, NE • *462*
Arundel Village, MD 21225 • *3,370*
Arvada, CO 80001-06 • *89,235*
Arvin, CA 93203 • *9,286*
Asbury Park, NJ 07712 • *16,799*
Ascension □, LA • *58,214*
Ashaway, RI 02804 • *1,584*
Ashburn, GA 31714 • *4,827*
Ashburnham, MA 01430 • *1,300*
Ashdown, AR 71822 • *5,150*
Ashe □, NC • *22,209*
Asheboro, NC 27203 • *16,362*
Asherton, TX 78827 • *1,608*
Asheville, NC 28801-16 • *61,607*
Ashford, AL 36312 • *1,926*
Ash Grove, MO 65604 • *1,128*
Ashland, AL 36251 • *2,034*
Ashland, CA 94541 • *16,590*
Ashland, IL 62612 • *1,257*
Ashland, KS 67831 • *1,032*
Ashland, KY 41101-05 • *23,622*
Ashland, MA 01721 • *9,165*
Ashland, MO 65010 • *1,252*
Ashland, NE 68003 • *2,136*
Ashland, NH 03217 • *1,915*
Ashland, OH 44805 • *20,079*
Ashland, OR 97520 • *16,234*
Ashland, PA 17921 • *3,859*
Ashland, VA 23005 • *5,864*
Ashland, WI 54806 • *8,695*
Ashland □, OH • *47,507*
Ashland □, WI • *16,307*
Ashland City, TN 37015 • *2,552*
Ashley, ND 58413 • *1,052*
Ashley, OH 43003 • *1,059*
Ashley, PA 18706 • *3,291*
Ashley □, AR • *24,319*
Ashtabula, OH 44004 • *21,633*
Ashtabula □, OH • *99,821*
Ashton, ID 83420 • *1,114*
Ashton, IL 61006 • *1,042*
Ashton, MD 20861 • *1,800*
Ashton, RI 02864 • *820*
Ashville, AL 35953 • *1,494*
Ashville, OH 43103 • *2,254*
Ashwaubenon, WI 54304 • *16,376*
Asotin □, WA • *17,605*
Aspen, CO 81611-15 • *5,049*
Aspen Hill, MD 20906 • *45,494*
Aspermont, TX 79502 • *1,214*
Aspinwall, PA 15215 • *2,880*
Assinippi, MA 02339 • *1,400*
Assonet, MA 02702 • *1,200*
Assumption, IL 62510 • *1,244*
Assumption □, LA • *22,753*
Astoria, IL 61501 • *1,205*
Astoria, OR 97103 • *10,069*
Atascadero, CA 93422-23 • *23,138*
Atascosa □, TX • *30,533*
Atchison, KS 66002 • *10,656*
Atchison □, KS • *16,932*
Atchison □, MO • *7,457*
Atco, NJ 08004 • *2,020*
Athens, AL 35611 • *16,901*
Athens, GA 30601-13 • *45,734*
Athens, IL 62613 • *1,404*
Athens, NY 12015 • *1,708*
Athens, OH 45701 • *21,265*
Athens, PA 18810 • *3,468*
Athens, TN 37303 • *12,054*
Athens, TX 75751 • *10,967*
Athens □, OH • *59,549*
Atherton, CA 94027 • *7,163*
Athol, MA 01331 • *8,732*
Atkins, AR 72823 • *2,834*
Atkins, VA 24311 • *1,130*
Atkinson, NE 68713 • *1,380*
Atkinson □, GA • *613*
Atlanta, GA 30301-83 • *394,017*
Atlanta, IL 61723 • *1,616*
Atlanta, TX 75551 • *6,118*
Atlantic, IA 50022 • *7,432*
Atlantic □, NJ • *224,327*
Atlantic Beach, FL 32233 • *11,636*
Atlantic City, NJ 08401-06 • *37,986*
Atlantic Highlands, NJ 07716 • *4,629*
Atmore, AL 36502 • *8,046*
Atoka, OK 74525 • *3,298*
Atoka □, OK • *12,778*
Attala □, MS • *18,481*
Attalla, AL 35954 • *6,859*
Attica, IN 47918 • *3,457*
Attica, NY 14011 • *2,630*
Attleboro, MA 02703 • *38,383*
Atwater, CA 95301 • *22,282*
Atwater, MN 56209 • *1,053*
Atwood, IL 61913 • *1,253*
Atwood, KS 67730 • *1,388*
Atwood, TN 38220 • *1,066*
Auberry, CA 93602 • *1,866*
Auburn, AL 36830-49 • *33,830*
Auburn, CA 95603-04 • *10,592*

Auburn, GA 30203 • 3,139
Auburn, IL 62615 • 3,724
Auburn, IN 46706 • 9,379
Auburn, KY 42206 • 1,273
Auburn, ME 04210–12 • 24,309
Auburn, MA 01501 • 14,845
Auburn, MI 48611 • 1,855
Auburn, NE 68305 • 3,443
Auburn, NY 13021–24 • 31,258
Auburn, WA 98001–02 • 33,102
Auburndale, FL 33823 • 8,858
Auburn Heights, MI 48321 • 17,076
Audrain □, MO • 23,599
Audubon, IA 50025 • 2,524
Audubon, NJ 08106 • 9,205
Audubon, PA 19407 • 6,328
Audubon □, IA • 7,334
Auglaize □, OH • 44,585
August, CA 95201 • 6,376
Augusta, AR 72006 • 2,759
Augusta, GA 30901–19 • 44,639
Augusta, KS 67010 • 7,876
Augusta, KY 41002 • 1,336
Augusta, ME 04330–38 • 21,325
Augusta, WI 54722 • 1,510
Augusta □, VA • 54,677
Aulander, NC 27805 • 1,209
Ault, CO 80610 • 1,107
Aumsville, OR 97325 • 1,650
Aurora, CO 80010–19 • 222,103
Aurora, IL 60504–07 • 99,581
Aurora, IN 47001 • 3,825
Aurora, MN 55705 • 1,965
Aurora, MO 65605 • 6,459
Aurora, NE 68818 • 3,810
Aurora, OH 44202 • 9,192
Aurora □, SD • 3,135
Au Sable, MI 48750 • 1,542
Au Sable Forks, NY 12912 • 2,100
Austell, GA 30001 • 4,173
Austin, IN 47102 • 4,310
Austin, MN 55912 • 21,907
Austin, NV 89310 • 370
Austin, TX 78701–89 • 465,622
Austin □, TX • 19,832
Austintown, OH 44512 • 32,371
Autauga □, AL • 34,222
Ava, MO 65608 • 2,938
Avalon, CA 90704 • 2,918
Avalon, NJ 08202 • 1,809
Avalon, PA 15202 • 5,784
Avella, PA 15312 • 1,200
Avenal, CA 93204 • 9,770
Avenel, MD • 5,600
Avenel, NJ 07001 • 15,504
Aventura, FL 33180 • 14,914
Averill Park, NY 12018 • 1,656
Avery □, NC • 14,867
Avilla, IN 46710 • 1,366
Avis, PA 17721 • 1,506
Avoca, IA 51521 • 1,497
Avoca, NY 14809 • 1,033
Avoca, PA 18641 • 2,897
Avocado Heights, CA 91746 • 14,232
Avon, CT 06001 • 13,937
Avon, MA 02322 • 5,026
Avon, NY 14414 • 2,995
Avon, OH 44011 • 7,337
Avon by the Sea, NJ 07717 • 2,165
Avondale, AZ 85323 • 16,169
Avondale, LA 70094 • 5,813
Avondale, OH 45404 • 5,000
Avondale Estates, GA 30002 • 2,209
Avon Lake, OH 44012 • 15,066
Avonmore, PA 15618 • 1,089
Avon Park, FL 33825 • 8,042
Avoyelles □, LA • 39,159
Ayden, NC 28513 • 4,740
Ayer, MA 01432 • 2,889
Azalea Park, FL 32807 • 8,926
Azle, TX 76020 • 8,868
Aztec, NM 87410 • 5,479
Azusa, CA 91702 • 41,333

B

Babbitt, MN 55706 • 1,562
Babbitt, NV • 1,800
Babylon, NY 11702–04 • 12,249
Baca □, CO • 4,556
Bacliff, TX 77518 • 5,549
Bacon □, GA • 9,566
Bad Axe, MI 48413 • 3,484
Baden, PA 15005 • 5,074
Badin, NC 28009 • 1,481
Bagdad, AZ 86321 • 1,858
Bagdad, FL 32530 • 1,457
Baggs, WY 82321 • 272
Bagley, MN 56621 • 1,388
Bailey □, TX • 7,064
Baileys Crossroads, VA 22041 • 19,507
Bainbridge, GA 31717 • 10,712
Bainbridge, NY 13733 • 1,550
Baird, TX 79504 • 1,658
Bairdford, PA 15006 • 1,200
Baker, LA 70714 • 13,233
Baker, MT 59313 • 1,818
Baker, OR 97814 • 9,140
Baker □, FL • 18,486
Baker □, GA • 3,615
Baker □, OR • 15,317
Bakersfield, CA 93301–89 • 174,820
Balch Springs, TX 75180 • 17,406
Bald Knob, AR 72010 • 2,653
Baldwin, FL 32234 • 1,450
Baldwin, GA 30511 • 1,439
Baldwin, LA 70514 • 2,379
Baldwin, NY 11510 • 22,719
Baldwin, PA 15234 • 21,923
Baldwin, WI 54002 • 2,022
Baldwin □, AL • 98,280
Baldwin □, GA • 39,530
Baldwin City, KS 66006 • 2,961
Baldwin Park, CA 91706 • 69,330
Baldwinsville, NY 13027 • 6,591
Baldwinville, MA 01436 • 1,795
Baldwyn, MS 38824 • 3,204
Balfour, NC 28706 • 1,118
Ball, LA 71405 • 3,305
Ballard □, KY • 7,902
Ballardvale, MA 01810 • 1,270
Ballinger, TX 76821 • 3,975
Ballston Spa, NY 12020 • 4,937
Ballwin, MO 63011 • 21,816
Balmville, NY 12550 • 2,963
Baltic, CT 06330 • 2,000
Baltimore, MD 21201–99 • 736,014
Baltimore, OH 43105 • 2,971
Baltimore □, MD • 692,134
Baltimore Highlands, MD 21227 • 7,300
Bamberg, SC 29003 • 3,843
Bamberg □, SC • 16,902
Bandera □, TX • 10,562
Bandon, OR 97411 • 2,215
Bangor, ME 04401–02 • 33,181
Bangor, MI 49013 • 1,922
Bangor, PA 18013 • 5,383
Bangor, WI 54614 • 1,076
Bangor Township, MI 48706 • 17,494
Bangs, TX 76823 • 1,555
Banks □, GA • 10,308
Banner □, NE • 852
Banning, CA 92220 • 20,570
Bannock □, ID • 66,026
Baraboo, WI 53913 • 9,203
Baraga, MI 49908 • 1,231
Baraga □, MI • 7,954
Barataria, LA 70036 • 1,160
Barber □, KS • 5,874
Barberton, OH 44203 • 27,623
Barbour □, AL • 25,417
Barbour □, WV • 15,699
Barboursville, WV 25504 • 2,774
Barbourville, KY 40906 • 3,658
Bardstown, KY 40004 • 6,801
Bargersville, IN 46106 • 1,681
Bar Harbor, ME 04609 • 2,768
Barker Heights, NC 28739 • 1,137
Barling, AR 72923 • 4,078
Barnegat, NJ 08005 • 1,160
Barnes □, ND • 12,545
Barnesboro, PA 15714 • 2,530
Barnesville, GA 30204 • 4,747
Barnesville, MN 56514 • 2,066
Barnesville, OH 43713 • 4,326
Barnsdall, OK 74002 • 1,316
Barnstable, MA 02630 • 2,790
Barnstable □, MA • 186,605
Barnwell, SC 29812 • 5,255
Barnwell □, SC • 20,293
Barrackville, WV 26559 • 1,443
Barre, MA 01005 • 1,094
Barre, VT 05641 • 9,482
Barren □, KY • 34,001
Barrington, IL 60010–11 • 9,504
Barrington, NJ 08007 • 6,774
Barrington, RI 02806 • 15,849
Barron, WI 54812 • 2,986
Barron □, WI • 40,750
Barron Lake, MI 49120 • 1,600
Barrow, AK 99723 • 3,469
Barrow □, GA • 29,721
Barry, IL 62312 • 1,391
Barry □, MI • 50,057
Barry □, MO • 27,547
Barstow, CA 92310–12 • 21,472
Bartholomew □, IN • 63,657
Bartlesville, OK 74003–06 • 34,256
Bartlett, IL 60103 • 19,373
Bartlett, TN 38134 • 26,989
Bartlett, TX 76511 • 1,439
Barton, OH 43905 • 1,039
Barton, VT 05822 • 908
Barton □, KS • 29,382
Barton □, MO • 11,312
Bartonville, IL 61607 • 5,643
Bartow, FL 33830 • 14,716
Bartow □, GA • 55,911
Barview, OR 97420 • 1,402
Basalt, CO 81621 • 1,128
Basehor, KS 66007 • 1,591
Basile, LA 70515 • 1,808
Basin, WY 82410 • 1,180
Basking Ridge, NJ 07920 • 3,060
Bassett, VA 24055 • 1,579
Bass Lake, IN 46534 • 1,500
Bastrop, LA 71220–21 • 13,916
Bastrop, TX 78602 • 4,044
Bastrop □, TX • 38,263
Batavia, IL 60510 • 17,076
Batavia, NY 14020–21 • 16,310
Batavia, OH 45103 • 1,700
Bates □, MO • 15,025
Batesburg, SC 29006 • 4,082
Batesville, AR 72501–03 • 9,187
Batesville, IN 47006 • 4,720
Batesville, MS 38606 • 6,403
Bath, ME 04530 • 9,799
Bath, NY 14810 • 5,801
Bath, PA 18014 • 2,358
Bath, SC 29816 • 2,242
Bath □, KY • 9,692
Bath □, VA • 4,799
Baton Rouge, LA 70801–98 • 219,531
Battle Creek, MI 49015–17 • 53,540
Battle Ground, WA 98604 • 3,758
Battle Mountain, NV 89820 • 3,542
Baudette, MN 56623 • 1,146
Bawcomville, LA 71291 • 2,250
Baxley, GA 31513 • 3,841
Baxter, MN 56425 • 3,695
Baxter, TN 38544 • 1,289
Baxter □, AR • 31,186
Baxter Springs, KS 66713 • 4,351
Bay, AR 72411 • 1,660
Bay □, FL • 126,994
Bay □, MI • 111,723
Bayard, NE 69334 • 1,196
Bayard, NM 88023 • 2,598
Bayberry, NY 13088 • 6,710
Bay City, MI 48706–08 • 38,936
Bay City, OR 97107 • 1,027
Bay City, TX 77414 • 18,170
Bayfield, CO 81122 • 1,090
Bayfield □, WI • 14,008
Bay Head, NJ 08742 • 1,226
Baylor □, TX • 4,385
Bay Minette, AL 36507 • 7,168
Bayonet Point, FL 34667 • 21,860
Bayonne, NJ 07002 • 61,444
Bayou Cane, LA 70359 • 15,876
Bayou George, FL 32401 • 1,500
Bayou La Batre, AL 36509 • 2,456
Bay Pines, FL 33504 • 4,171
Bayport, MN 55003 • 3,200
Bayport, NY 11705 • 7,702
Bay Ridge, MD 21403 • 1,989
Bay Saint Louis, MS 39520–21 • 8,063
Bay Shore, NY 11706 • 21,279
Bayshore Gardens, FL 34207 • 17,062
Bayside, WI 53217 • 4,789
Bay Springs, MS 39422 • 1,729
Baytown, TX 77520–22 • 63,850
Bay Village, OH 44140 • 17,000
Bayville, NY 11709 • 7,193
Beach, IL 60085 • 9,513
Beach, ND 58621 • 1,205
Beach Haven, NJ 08008 • 1,475
Beachwood, NJ 08722 • 9,324
Beachwood, OH 44122 • 10,677
Beacon, NY 12508 • 13,243
Beacon Falls, CT 06403 • 1,285
Beacon Square, FL 34652 • 6,265
Beadle □, SD • 18,253
Bear, DE 19701 • 1,200
Bearden, AR 71720 • 1,021
Beardstown, IL 62618 • 5,270
Bear Lake □, ID • 6,084
Bear Town, MS 39648 • 1,277
Beatrice, NE 68310 • 12,354
Beatty, NV 89003 • 1,623
Beattyville, KY 41311 • 1,131
Beaufort, NC 28516 • 3,808
Beaufort, SC 29901–03 • 9,576
Beaufort □, NC • 42,283
Beaufort □, SC • 86,425
Beaumont, CA 92223 • 9,685
Beaumont, MS 39423 • 1,054
Beaumont, TX 77701–26 • 114,323
Beauregard □, LA • 30,083
Beaver, OK 73932 • 1,584
Beaver, PA 15009 • 5,028
Beaver, UT 84713 • 1,998
Beaver, WV 25813 • 1,244
Beaver □, OK • 6,023
Beaver □, PA • 186,093
Beaver □, UT • 4,765
Beavercreek, OH 45385 • 33,626
Beaverdale, PA 15921 • 1,000
Beaver Dam, KY 42320 • 2,904
Beaver Dam, WI 53916 • 14,196
Beaver Falls, PA 15010 • 10,687
Beaverhead □, MT • 8,424
Beaverton, MI 48612 • 1,150
Beaverton, OR 97005–07 • 53,310
Beckemeyer, IL 62219 • 1,070
Becker □, MN • 27,881
Beckham □, OK • 18,812
Beckley, WV 25801–02 • 18,296
Bedford, IN 47421 • 13,817
Bedford, IA 50833 • 1,528
Bedford, MA 01730 • 13,067
Bedford, NH 03102 • 1,400
Bedford, OH 44146 • 14,822
Bedford, PA 15522 • 3,137
Bedford, TX 76021–22 • 43,762
Bedford, VA 24523 • 6,073
Bedford □, PA • 47,919
Bedford □, TN • 30,411
Bedford □, VA • 45,656
Bedford Heights, OH 44146 • 12,131
Bedford Hills, NY 10507 • 3,140
Bee □, TX • 25,135
Beebe, AR 72012 • 4,455
Beecher, IL 60401 • 2,032
Beecher, MI 48458 • 14,465
Beech Grove, IN 46107 • 13,383
Beech Island, SC 29842 • 1,500
Bee Ridge, FL 34233 • 6,406
Beeville, TX 78102–04 • 13,547
Beggs, OK 74421 • 1,150
Bel Air, MD 21014 • 8,860
Bel Aire, KS 67220 • 3,695
Belchertown, MA 01007 • 2,339
Belcourt, ND 58316 • 2,458
Belding, MI 48809 • 5,969
Belen, NM 87002 • 6,547
Belfast, ME 04915 • 6,355
Belfast, NY 14711 • 1,100
Belfield, ND 58622 • 887
Belford, NJ 07718 • 6,300
Belgrade, MT 59714 • 3,411
Belhaven, NC 27810 • 2,269
Belington, WV 26250 • 1,850
Belknap □, NH • 49,216
Bell, CA 90201 • 34,365
Bell □, KY • 31,506
Bell □, TX • 191,088
Bellair, FL 32073 • 5,200
Bellaire, MI 49615 • 1,104
Bellaire, OH 43906 • 6,028
Bellaire, TX 77401–02 • 13,842
Bella Vista, AR 72712 • 9,083
Bellbrook, OH 45305 • 6,511
Belle, MO 65013 • 1,218
Belle, WV 25015 • 1,421
Belleair, FL 34616 • 3,968
Belle Chasse, LA 70037 • 8,512
Bellefontaine, OH 43311 • 12,142
Bellefontaine Neighbors, MO 63137 • 10,922
Bellefonte, DE 19809 • 1,243
Bellefonte, PA 16823 • 6,358
Belle Fourche, SD 57717 • 4,335
Belle Glade, FL 33430 • 16,177
Belle Isle, FL 32809 • 5,272
Belle Meade, TN 37205 • 2,839
Bellemoor, DE 19802 • 1,040
Belle Plaine, IA 52208 • 2,834
Belle Plaine, KS 67013 • 1,649
Belle Plaine, MN 56011 • 3,149
Belle Vernon, PA 15012 • 1,213
Belleview, FL 32506 • 8,000
Belleview, FL 32620 • 2,666
Belle View, VA 22307 • 3,500
Belleville, IL 62220–25 • 42,785
Belleville, KS 66935 • 2,517
Belleville, MI 48111–12 • 3,270
Belleville, NJ 07109 • 34,213
Belleville, PA 17004 • 1,589
Belleville, WI 53508 • 1,456
Bellevue, ID 83313 • 1,275
Bellevue, IA 52031 • 2,239
Bellevue, KY 41073 • 6,997
Bellevue, MI 49021 • 1,401
Bellevue, NE 68005 • 30,982
Bellevue, OH 44811 • 8,146
Bellevue, PA 15202 • 9,126
Bellevue, WA 98004–09 • 86,874
Bellflower, CA 90706–07 • 61,815
Bell Gardens, CA 90201 • 42,355
Bellingham, MA 02019 • 4,535
Bellingham, WA 98225–27 • 52,179
Bellmawr, NJ 08031 • 12,603
Bellmead, TX 76705 • 8,336
Bellmore, NY 11710 • 16,438
Bellows Falls, VT 05101 • 3,313
Bellport, NY 11713 • 2,572
Bells, TN 38006 • 1,643
Bellville, OH 44813 • 1,568
Bellville, TX 77418 • 3,378
Bellwood, IL 60104 • 20,241
Bellwood, PA 16617 • 1,976
Bellwood, VA 23234 • 6,178
Belmar, NJ 07719 • 5,877
Belmond, IA 50421 • 2,500
Belmont, CA 94002 • 24,127
Belmont, MA 02178 • 24,720
Belmont, MS 38827 • 1,554
Belmont, NY 14813 • 1,006
Belmont, NC 28012 • 8,434
Belmont □, OH • 71,074
Bel-Nor, MO 63133 • 2,935
Beloit, KS 67420 • 4,066
Beloit, OH 44609 • 1,037
Beloit, WI 53511–12 • 35,573
Beloit North, WI 53511 • 5,457
Belpre, OH 45714 • 6,796
Belt, MT 59412 • 571
Belton, MO 64012 • 18,150
Belton, SC 29627 • 4,646
Belton, TX 76513 • 12,476
Beltrami □, MN • 34,384
Beltsville, MD 20705 • 14,476
Belvedere, GA 30032 • 6,100
Belvedere, SC 29841 • 6,133
Belvedere Park, GA 30032 • 18,089
Belvidere, IL 61008 • 15,958
Belvidere, NJ 07823 • 2,669
Belzoni, MS 39038 • 2,536
Bement, IL 61813 • 1,668
Bemidji, MN 56601–19 • 11,245
Benavides, TX 78341 • 1,788
Benbrook, TX 76126 • 19,564
Bend, OR 97701–09 • 20,469
Benewah □, ID • 7,937
Ben Hill □, GA • 16,245
Benicia, CA 94510 • 24,437
Benkelman, NE 69021 • 1,193
Benld, IL 62009 • 1,604
Ben Lomond, CA 95005 • 7,884
Bennett, CO 80102 • 1,757
Bennett □, SD • 3,206
Bennettsville, SC 29512 • 9,345
Bennington, VT 05201 • 9,532
Bennington □, VT • 35,845
Bennion, UT 84118 • 9,575
Bensalem, PA 19020–21 • 52,368
Bensenville, IL 60106 • 17,767
Bensley, VA 23234 • 5,093
Benson, AZ 85602 • 3,824
Benson, MN 56215 • 3,235
Benson, NC 27504 • 2,810
Benson □, ND • 7,198
Bent □, CO • 5,048
Bentleyville, PA 15314 • 2,673
Benton, AR 72015 • 18,177
Benton, IL 62812 • 7,216
Benton, KY 42025 • 3,899
Benton, LA 71006 • 2,047
Benton □, AR • 97,499
Benton □, IN • 9,441
Benton □, IA • 22,429
Benton □, MN • 30,185
Benton □, MS • 8,046
Benton □, MO • 13,859
Benton □, OR • 70,811
Benton □, TN • 14,524
Benton □, WA • 112,560
Benton City, WA 99320 • 1,806
Benton Harbor, MI 49022–23 • 12,818
Benton Heights, MI 49022 • 5,465
Bentonville, AR 72712–14 • 11,257
Benwood, WV 26031 • 1,669
Benzie □, MI • 12,200
Beowawe, NV 89821 • 250
Berea, KY 40403 • 9,126
Berea, OH 44017 • 19,051
Berea, SC 29611 • 13,535
Beresford, SD 57004 • 1,849
Bergen, NY 14416 • 1,103
Bergen □, NJ • 825,380
Bergenfield, NJ 07621 • 24,458
Berkeley, CA 94701–10 • 102,724
Berkeley, IL 60163 • 5,137
Berkeley, MO 63134 • 12,450
Berkeley, RI 02864 • 830
Berkeley □, SC • 128,776
Berkeley □, WV • 59,253
Berkeley Heights, NJ 07922 • 11,980
Berkley, MI 48072 • 16,960
Berks □, PA • 336,523
Berkshire □, MA • 139,352
Berlin, CT 06037 • 1,040
Berlin, MD 21811 • 2,616
Berlin, NH 03570 • 11,824
Berlin, NJ 08009 • 5,672
Berlin, NY 12022 • 1,200
Berlin, PA 15530 • 2,064
Berlin, WI 54923 • 5,371
Bernalillo, NM 87004 • 5,960
Bernalillo □, NM • 480,577
Bernardsville, NJ 07924 • 6,597
Berne, IN 46711 • 3,559
Bernice, LA 71222 • 1,543
Bernie, MO 63822 • 1,847
Berrien □, GA • 14,153
Berrien □, MI • 161,378
Berrien Springs, MI 49103 • 1,927
Berry, AL 35546 • 1,218
Berryville, AR 72616 • 3,212
Berryville, VA 22611 • 3,097
Berthoud, CO 80513 • 2,990
Bertie □, NC • 20,388
Bertrand, MI 49120 • 5,500
Berwick, LA 70342 • 4,375
Berwick, ME 03901 • 2,378
Berwick, PA 18603 • 10,976
Berwyn, IL 60402 • 45,426
Berwyn, PA 19312 • 8,150
Bessemer, AL 35020–23 • 33,497
Bessemer, MI 49911 • 2,272
Bessemer, PA 16112 • 1,196
Bessemer City, NC 28016 • 4,698
Bethalto, IL 62010 • 9,507
Bethany, CT 06525 • 1,170
Bethany, IL 61914 • 1,369
Bethany, MO 64424 • 3,005
Bethany, OK 73008 • 20,075
Bethany, WV 26032 • 1,139
Bethany Beach, DE 19930 • 326
Bethel, AK 99559 • 4,674
Bethel, CT 06801 • 8,835
Bethel, ME 04217 • 1,225
Bethel, NC 27812 • 1,842
Bethel, OH 45106 • 2,407
Bethel, VT 05032 • 1,866
Bethel Acres, OK 74801 • 2,505
Bethel Park, PA 15102 • 33,823
Bethesda, MD 20813–17 • 62,936
Bethesda, OH 43719 • 1,161
Bethlehem, CT 06751 • 1,976
Bethlehem, PA 18015–18 • 71,428
Bethpage, NY 11714 • 15,761
Bettendorf, IA 52722 • 28,132
Beulah, ND 58523 • 3,363
Beverly, MA 01915 • 38,195
Beverly, NJ 08010 • 2,973
Beverly, OH 45715 • 1,444
Beverly Hills, CA 90209–13 • 31,971
Beverly Hills, FL 32665 • 6,163
Beverly Hills, MI 48009 • 10,610
Bexar □, TX • 1,185,394
Bexley, OH 43209 • 13,088
Bibb □, AL • 16,576
Bibb □, GA • 149,967
Bicknell, IN 47512 • 3,357
Biddeford, ME 04005 • 20,710
Bienville □, LA • 15,979
Big Bear City, CA 92314 • 3,500
Big Bend, WI 53103 • 1,299
Big Delta, AK 99737 • 400
Big Flats, NY 14814 • 2,658
Bigfork, MT 59911 • 1,080
Biggs, CA 95917 • 1,581
Big Horn □, MT • 11,337
Big Horn □, WY • 10,525
Big Lake, MN 55309 • 3,113
Big Lake, TX 76932 • 3,672
Big Pine, CA 93513 • 1,158
Big Piney, WY 83113 • 454
Big Rapids, MI 49307 • 12,603
Big Sandy, MT 59520 • 740
Big Sandy, TX 75755 • 1,185
Big Spring, TX 79720–21 • 23,093
Big Stone □, MN • 6,285
Big Stone Gap, VA 24219 • 4,748
Big Timber, MT 59011 • 1,557
Billerica, MA 01821–22 • 6,840
Billings, MT 59101–08 • 81,151
Billings □, ND • 1,108
Billings Heights, MT 59105 • 8,480
Biloxi, MS 39530–35 • 46,319
Biltmore Forest, NC 28803 • 1,327
Bingham, ME 04920 • 1,071
Bingham □, ID • 37,583
Binghamton, NY 13901–05 • 53,008
Birchwood City, MD 20745 • 4,870
Birchwood Park, DE 19711 • 2,250
Bird Island, MN 55310 • 1,326
Birdsboro, PA 19508 • 4,222
Birmingham, AL 35201–61 • 265,968
Birmingham, MI 48009–12 • 19,997
Bisbee, AZ 85603 • 6,288
Biscayne Gardens, FL 33168 • 13,000
Biscayne Park, FL 33161 • 3,068
Biscoe, NC 27209 • 1,484
Bishop, CA 93514–15 • 3,475
Bishop, TX 78343 • 3,337
Bishopville, SC 29010 • 3,560
Bismarck, MO 63624 • 1,579
Bismarck, ND 58501–07 • 49,256
Biwabik, MN 55708 • 1,097
Bixby, OK 74008 • 9,502
Black Canyon City, AZ 85324 • 1,811
Black Creek, WI 54106 • 1,152
Black Diamond, WA 98010 • 1,422
Black Earth, WI 53515 • 1,248
Blackfoot, ID 83221 • 9,646
Blackford □, IN • 14,067
Black Forest, CO 80908 • 8,143
Black Hawk, SD 57718 • 1,955
Black Hawk □, IA • 123,798
Black Jack, MO 63031 • 6,128
Black Lick, PA 15716 • 1,100
Blacklick Estates, OH 43227 • 10,080
Black Mountain, NC 28711 • 5,418
Black Point Beach Club, CT 06357 • 1,200
Black River, NY 13612 • 1,349
Black River Falls, WI 54615 • 3,490
Blacksburg, SC 29702 • 1,907
Blacksburg, VA 24060–63 • 34,590
Blackshear, GA 31516 • 3,263
Blackstone, MA 01504 • 4,460
Blackstone, VA 23824 • 3,497
Blackville, SC 29817 • 2,688
Blackwell, OK 74631 • 7,538
Blackwood, NJ 08012 • 5,120
Bladen □, NC • 28,663
Bladenboro, NC 28320 • 1,821
Bladensburg, MD 20710 • 8,064
Blades, DE 19973 • 834
Blaine, MN 55433 • 38,975
Blaine, TN 37709 • 1,326
Blaine, WA 98230 • 2,489
Blaine □, ID • 13,552
Blaine □, MT • 6,728
Blaine □, NE • 675
Blaine □, OK • 11,470
Blair, NE 68008 • 6,860
Blair, WI 54616 • 1,126
Blair □, PA • 130,542
Blairsville, PA 15717 • 3,595
Blakely, GA 31723 • 5,595
Blakely, PA 18447 • 7,222
Blanchard, LA 71009 • 1,175
Blanchard, OK 73010 • 1,922
Blanchester, OH 45107 • 4,206
Blanco, TX 78606 • 1,238
Blanco □, TX • 5,972
Bland □, VA • 6,514
Blanding, UT 84511 • 3,162
Blasdell, NY 14219 • 2,900

Blauvelt, NY 10913 • 4,470
Blawnox, PA 15238 • 1,626
Bleckley □, GA • 10,430
Bledsoe □, TN • 9,669
Blende, CO 81006 • 1,330
Blennerhassett, WV 26101 • 2,924
Blissfield, MI 49228 • 3,172
Block Island, RI 02807 • 620
Bloomer, WI 54724 • 3,085
Bloomfield, CT 06002 • 7,120
Bloomfield, IN 47424 • 2,592
Bloomfield, IA 52537 • 2,580
Bloomfield, MO 63825 • 1,800
Bloomfield, NE 68718 • 1,181
Bloomfield, NJ 07003 • 45,061
Bloomfield, NM 87413 • 5,214
Bloomfield Hills, MI 48302–04 • 4,288
Bloomfield Township, MI 48302 • 42,137
Bloomingdale, GA 31302 • 2,271
Bloomingdale, IL 60108 • 16,614
Bloomingdale, NJ 07403 • 7,530
Bloomingdale, TN 37660 • 10,953
Blooming Prairie, MN 55917 • 2,043
Bloomington, CA 92316 • 15,116
Bloomington, IL 61701–04 • 51,972
Bloomington, IN 47401–08 • 60,633
Bloomington, MN 55420 • 86,335
Bloomington, TX 77951 • 1,888
Bloomsburg, PA 17815 • 12,439
Blossburg, PA 16912 • 1,571
Blossom, TX 75416 • 1,440
Blount □, AL • 39,248
Blount □, TN • 85,969
Blountstown, FL 32424 • 2,404
Blountsville, AL 35031 • 1,527
Blountville, TN 37617 • 2,605
Blowing Rock, NC 28605 • 1,257
Blue Ash, OH 45242 • 11,860
Blue Diamond, NV 89004 • 420
Blue Earth, MN 56013 • 3,745
Blue Earth □, MN • 54,044
Bluefield, VA 24605 • 5,363
Bluefield, WV 24701 • 12,756
Blue Grass, IA 52726 • 1,214
Blue Hills, CT 06002 • 3,206
Blue Island, IL 60406 • 21,203
Blue Lake, CA 95525 • 1,235
Blue Mound, IL 62513 • 1,161
Blue Rapids, KS 66411 • 1,131
Blue Ridge, GA 30513 • 1,336
Blue Ridge, VA 24064 • 2,840
Blue Ridge Summit, PA 17214 • 1,800
Blue Springs, MO 64014–15 • 40,153
Bluewell, WV 24701 • 2,752
Bluff City, TN 37618 • 1,390
Bluffdale, UT 84065 • 2,152
Bluff Park, AL 35226 • 8,000
Bluffton, IN 46714 • 9,020
Bluffton, OH 45817 • 3,367
Blythe, CA 92225–26 • 8,428
Blytheville, AR 72315–19 • 22,906
Boalsburg, PA 16827 • 2,206
Boardman, OH 44512 • 38,596
Boardman, OR 97818 • 1,387
Boaz, AL 35957 • 6,928
Boca Grande, FL 33921 • 1,200
Boca Raton, FL 33431–34 • 61,492
Boerne, TX 78006 • 4,274
Bogalusa, LA 70427–29 • 14,280
Bogart, GA 30622 • 1,018
Bogata, TX 75417 • 1,421
Boger City, NC 28092 • 1,373
Bogota, NJ 07603 • 7,824
Bohemia, NY 11716 • 9,556
Boiling Springs, NC 28017 • 2,445
Boiling Springs, PA 17007 • 1,978
Boise, ID 83701–15 • 125,738
Boise □, ID • 3,509
Boise City, OK 73933 • 1,509
Bolingbrook, IL 60440 • 40,843
Bolivar, MO 65613 • 6,845
Bolivar, NY 14715 • 1,261
Bolivar, TN 38008 • 5,969
Bolivar □, MS • 41,875
Bollinger □, MO • 10,619
Bolton Landing, NY 12814 • 1,600
Bon Air, VA 23235 • 16,413
Bonaventure, FL 33317 • 6,000
Bond □, IL • 14,991
Bondsville, MA 01009 • 1,992
Bonduel, WI 54107 • 1,210
Bondurant, IA 50035 • 1,584
Bonham, TX 75418 • 6,686
Bon Homme □, SD • 7,089
Bonifay, FL 32425 • 2,612
Bonita, CA 91903 • 12,542
Bonita Springs, FL 33923 • 13,600
Bonneauville, PA 17325 • 1,282
Bonner □, ID • 26,622
Bonners Ferry, ID 83805 • 2,193
Bonner Springs, KS 66012 • 6,413
Bonne Terre, MO 63628 • 3,871
Bonneville □, ID • 72,207
Bonney Lake, WA 98390 • 7,494
Bonnie Doone, NC 28303 • 3,893
Bono, AR 72416 • 1,220
Booker, TX 79005 • 1,236
Boomer, WV 25031 • 1,051
Boone, IA 50036 • 12,392
Boone, NC 28607 • 12,915
Boone □, AR • 28,297
Boone □, IL • 30,806
Boone □, IN • 38,147
Boone □, IA • 25,186
Boone □, KY • 57,589
Boone □, MO • 112,379
Boone □, NE • 6,667
Boone □, WV • 25,870
Booneville, AR 72927 • 3,804
Booneville, MS 38829 • 7,955
Boonsboro, MD 21713 • 2,445
Boonton, NJ 07005 • 8,343
Boonville, CA 95415 • 1,000
Boonville, IN 47601 • 6,724
Boonville, MO 65233 • 7,095
Boonville, NY 13309 • 2,220
Boonville, NC 27011 • 1,009
Boothbay Harbor, ME 04538 • 1,267
Borden □, TX • 799
Bordentown, NJ 08505 • 4,341
Borger, TX 79007–08 • 15,675
Boron, CA 93516 • 2,101
Borrego Springs, CA 92004 • 2,244
Boscobel, WI 53805 • 2,706
Bosque □, TX • 15,125
Bossert Estates, NJ 08505 • 1,830
Bossier □, LA • 86,088
Bossier City, LA 71111–13 • 52,721
Boston, GA 31626 • 1,395
Boston, MA 02101–99 • 574,283
Boswell, PA 15531 • 1,485
Botetourt □, VA • 24,992
Bothell, WA 98011–12 • 12,345
Botkins, OH 45306 • 1,340
Bottineau, ND 58318 • 2,598
Bottineau □, ND • 8,011
Boulder, CO 80301–08 • 83,312
Boulder, MT 59632 • 1,316
Boulder □, CO • 225,339
Boulder City, NV 89005–06 • 12,567
Boulder Creek, CA 95006 • 6,725
Boulder Hill, IL 60538 • 8,894
Boulevard Heights, MD 20743 • 1,820
Boundary □, ID • 8,332
Bound Brook, NJ 08805 • 9,487
Bountiful, UT 84010–11 • 36,659
Bourbon, IN 46504 • 1,672
Bourbon, MO 65441 • 1,188
Bourbon □, KS • 14,966
Bourbon □, KY • 19,236
Bourbonnais, IL 60914 • 13,934
Bourg, LA 70343 • 2,073
Bourne, MA 02532 • 1,284
Boutte, LA 70039 • 1,200
Bovina, TX 79009 • 1,549
Bowdon, GA 30108 • 1,981
Bowie, MD 20715–21 • 37,589
Bowie, TX 76230 • 4,990
Bowie □, TX • 81,665
Bowling Green, FL 33834 • 1,836
Bowling Green, KY 42101–04 • 40,641
Bowling Green, MO 63334 • 2,976
Bowling Green, OH 43402 • 28,176
Bowman, ND 58623 • 1,741
Bowman, SC 29018 • 1,063
Bowman □, ND • 3,596
Box Butte □, NE • 13,130
Box Elder, SD 57719 • 2,680
Box Elder □, UT • 36,485
Boxford, MA 01921 • 2,072
Boyce, LA 71409 • 1,361
Boyd □, KY • 51,150
Boyd □, NE • 2,835
Boyertown, PA 19512 • 3,759
Boyes Hot Springs, CA 95416 • 5,973
Boyle □, KY • 25,641
Boyne City, MI 49712 • 3,478
Boynton Beach, FL 33435–37 • 46,194
Bozeman, MT 59715 • 22,660
Bracken □, KY • 7,766
Brackenridge, PA 15014 • 3,784
Brackettville, TX 78832 • 1,740
Braddock, PA 15104 • 4,682
Braddock Heights, MD 21714 • 4,778
Bradenton, FL 34201–10 • 43,779
Bradenville, PA 15620 • 1,100
Bradford, OH 45308 • 2,005
Bradford, PA 16701 • 9,625
Bradford, RI 02808 • 1,604
Bradford, TN 38316 • 1,154
Bradford, VT 05033 • 672
Bradford □, FL • 22,515
Bradford □, PA • 60,967
Bradfordwoods, PA 15015 • 1,329
Bradley, FL 33835 • 1,108
Bradley, IL 60915 • 10,792
Bradley, WV 25818 • 2,144
Bradley □, AR • 11,793
Bradley □, TN • 73,712
Bradley Beach, NJ 07720 • 4,475
Bradner, OH 43406 • 1,093
Brady, TX 76825 • 5,946
Braham, MN 55006 • 1,139
Braidwood, IL 60408 • 3,584
Brainerd, MN 56401 • 12,353
Braintree, MA 02184 • 33,836
Branch □, MI • 41,502
Branch Village, RI 02895 • 400
Branchville, SC 29432 • 1,107
Brandenburg, KY 40108 • 1,857
Brandon, FL 33510 • 57,985
Brandon, MS 39042–43 • 11,077
Brandon, SC 29611 • 2,170
Brandon, SD 57005 • 3,543
Brandon, VT 05733 • 1,902
Brandywine, MD 20613 • 1,406
Branford, CT 06405 • 27,603
Branford Hills, CT 06405 • 3,460
Branson, MO 65616 • 3,706
Brantley, AL 36009 • 1,015
Brantley □, GA • 11,077
Brant Rock, MA 02020 • 1,850
Bratenahl, OH 44108 • 1,356
Brattleboro, VT 05301–04 • 8,612
Brawley, CA 92227 • 18,923
Braxton □, WV • 12,998
Brazil, IN 47834 • 7,640
Brazoria, TX 77422 • 2,717
Brazoria □, TX • 191,707
Brazos □, TX • 121,862
Brea, CA 92621–22 • 32,873
Breathitt □, KY • 15,703
Breaux Bridge, LA 70517 • 6,515
Breckenridge, CO 80424 • 1,285
Breckenridge, MI 48615 • 1,301
Breckenridge, MN 56520 • 3,708
Breckenridge, TX 76024 • 5,665
Breckenridge Hills, MO 63114 • 5,404
Breckinridge □, KY • 16,312
Brecksville, OH 44141 • 11,818
Breese, IL 62230 • 3,567
Bremen, GA 30110 • 4,356
Bremen, IN 46506 • 4,725
Bremen, OH 43107 • 1,386
Bremer □, IA • 22,813
Bremerton, WA 98310–15 • 38,142
Bremond, TX 76629 • 1,110
Brenham, TX 77833–34 • 11,952
Brent, AL 35034 • 2,776
Brent, FL 32503 • 21,624
Brentwood, CA 94513 • 7,563
Brentwood, MD 20722 • 3,005
Brentwood, MO 63144 • 8,150
Brentwood, NY 11717 • 45,218
Brentwood, NY • 45,218
Brentwood, OH 45231 • 3,568
Brentwood, PA 15227 • 10,823
Brentwood, SC 29405 • 2,000
Brentwood, TN 37027 • 16,392
Brevard, NC 28712 • 5,388
Brevard □, FL • 398,978
Brewer, ME 04412 • 9,021
Brewster, MA 02631 • 1,818
Brewster, NY 10509 • 1,566
Brewster, OH 44613 • 2,307
Brewster, WA 98812 • 1,633
Brewster □, TX • 8,681
Brewton, AL 36426–27 • 5,885
Briarcliff Manor, NY 10510 • 7,070
Brick [Township], NJ 08723 • 55,473
Bridge City, LA 70094 • 8,327
Bridge City, TX 77611 • 8,034
Bridgehampton, NY 11932 • 1,997
Bridgeport, AL 35740 • 2,936
Bridgeport, CT 06601–50 • 141,686
Bridgeport, IL 62417 • 2,118
Bridgeport, MI 48722 • 8,569
Bridgeport, NE 69336 • 1,581
Bridgeport, OH 43912 • 2,318
Bridgeport, PA 19405 • 4,292
Bridgeport, TX 76026 • 3,581
Bridgeport, WA 98813 • 1,498
Bridgeport, WV 26330 • 6,739
Bridger, MT 59014 • 692
Bridgeton, MO 63044 • 17,779
Bridgeton, NJ 08302 • 18,942
Bridgetown, OH 45211 • 11,460
Bridgeview, IL 60455 • 14,402
Bridgeville, DE 19933 • 1,210
Bridgeville, PA 15017 • 5,445
Bridgewater, MA 02324 • 7,242
Bridgewater, NJ 08807 • 5,630
Bridgewater, VA 22812 • 3,918
Bridgman, MI 49106 • 2,140
Bridgton, ME 04009 • 2,195
Brielle, NJ 08730 • 4,406
Brigantine, NJ 08203 • 11,354
Brigham City, UT 84302 • 15,644
Brighton, AL 35020 • 4,518
Brighton, CO 80601 • 14,203
Brighton, IL 62012 • 2,270
Brighton, MI 48116 • 5,686
Brighton, NY 14610 • 34,455
Brilliant, OH 43913 • 1,672
Brillion, WI 54110 • 2,840
Brinkley, AR 72021 • 4,234
Briscoe □, TX • 1,971
Bristol, CT 06010–11 • 60,640
Bristol, IN 46507 • 1,133
Bristol, NH 03222 • 1,483
Bristol, RI 02809 • 21,625
Bristol, TN 37620–25 • 23,421
Bristol, VT 05443 • 1,801
Bristol, VA 24201–03 • 18,426
Bristol □, MA • 506,325
Bristol □, RI • 48,859
Bristol [Township], PA 19007 • 58,773
Bristow, OK 74010 • 4,062
Britt, IA 50423 • 2,133
Britton, SD 57430 • 1,394
Broadalbin, NY 12025 • 1,397
Broad Brook, CT 06016 • 1,280
Broadkill Beach, DE 19968 • 390
Broadus, MT 59317 • 572
Broadview, IL 60153 • 8,713
Broadview Heights, OH 44141 • 12,219
Broadview Park, FL 33314 • 6,109
Broadwater □, MT • 3,318
Broadway, VA 22815 • 1,209
Brockport, NY 14420 • 8,749
Brockton, MA 02401–05 • 92,788
Brockway, PA 15824 • 2,207
Brocton, NY 14716 • 1,387
Brodhead, KY 40409 • 1,140
Brodhead, WI 53520 • 3,165
Brodheadsville, PA 18322 • 1,500
Broken Arrow, OK 74011–14 • 58,043
Broken Bow, NE 68822 • 3,778
Broken Bow, OK 74728 • 3,961
Bronson, MI 49028 • 2,342
Bronx □, NY • 1,203,789
Bronxville, NY 10708 • 6,028
Brooke □, WV • 26,992
Brookfield, CT 06804 • 1,500
Brookfield, IL 60513 • 18,876
Brookfield, MA 01506 • 2,968
Brookfield, MO 64628 • 4,888
Brookfield, VA 22021 • 2,100
Brookfield, WI 53005 • 35,184
Brookfield Center, CT 06804 • 1,400
Brookhaven, MS 39601 • 10,243
Brookhaven, PA 19015 • 8,567
Brookhaven, WV 26505 • 3,836
Brookings, OR 97415 • 4,400
Brookings, SD 57006 • 16,270
Brookings □, SD • 25,207
Brooklawn, NJ 08030 • 1,805
Brookline, MA 02146 • 54,718
Brooklyn, CT 06234 • 1,400
Brooklyn, IN 46111 • 1,162
Brooklyn, IA 52211 • 1,439
Brooklyn, OH 44144 • 11,706
Brooklyn, SC 29720 • 1,850
Brooklyn Center, MN 55429 • 28,887
Brooklyn Park, MD 21225 • 10,987
Brooklyn Park, MN 55443 • 56,381
Brookneal, VA 24528 • 1,344
Brook Park, OH 44142 • 22,865
Brookport, IL 62910 • 1,070
Brooks, KY 40109 • 2,464
Brooks □, GA • 15,398
Brooks □, TX • 8,204
Brookshire, TX 77423 • 2,922
Brookside, AL 35036 • 1,365
Brookside, DE 19713 • 15,307
Brookston, IN 47923 • 1,804
Brooksville, FL 34601–14 • 7,440
Brooksville, MS 39739 • 1,098
Brookville, IN 47012 • 2,529
Brookville, NY 11545 • 3,716
Brookville, OH 45309 • 4,621
Brookville, PA 15825 • 4,184
Brookwood, NJ 08527 • 5,500
Broomall, PA 19008 • 10,930
Broome □, NY • 212,160
Broomfield, CO 80020–21 • 24,638
Broussard, LA 70518 • 3,213
Broward □, FL • 1,255,488
Browardale, FL 33311 • 6,257
Brown □, IL • 5,836
Brown □, IN • 14,080
Brown □, KS • 11,128
Brown □, MN • 26,984
Brown □, NE • 3,657
Brown □, OH • 34,966
Brown □, SD • 35,580
Brown □, TX • 34,371
Brown □, WI • 194,594
Brown City, MI 48416 • 1,244
Brown Deer, WI 53209 • 12,236
Brownfield, TX 79316 • 9,560
Brownfields, LA 70811 • 5,229
Browning, MT 59417 • 1,170
Brownsburg, IN 46112 • 7,628
Browns Mills, NJ 08015 • 11,429
Brownstown, IN 47220 • 2,872
Brownsville, FL 33142 • 15,607
Brownsville, OR 97327 • 1,281
Brownsville, PA 15417 • 3,164
Brownsville, TN 38012 • 10,019
Brownsville, TX 78520–26 • 98,962
Brownville, LA 71291 • 1,700
Brownville, NY 13615 • 1,138
Brownwood, TX 76803–04 • 18,387
Broxton, GA 31519 • 1,211
Broyhill Park, VA 22042 • 3,600
Bruce, MS 38915 • 2,127
Bruceton, TN 38317 • 1,586
Brule □, SD • 5,485
Brundidge, AL 36010 • 2,472
Brunswick, GA 31520–22 • 16,433
Brunswick, ME 04011 • 14,683
Brunswick, MD 21716 • 5,117
Brunswick, MO 65236 • 1,074
Brunswick, OH 44212 • 28,230
Brunswick □, NC • 50,985
Brunswick □, VA • 15,987
Brush, CO 80723 • 4,165
Brusly, LA 70719 • 1,824
Bryan, OH 43506 • 8,348
Bryan, TX 77801–06 • 55,002
Bryan □, GA • 15,438
Bryan □, OK • 32,089
Bryans Road, MD 20616 • 3,809
Bryant, AR 72022 • 5,269
Bryantville, MA 02327 • 1,800
Bryn Mawr, WA 98178 • 1,500
Bryson City, NC 28713 • 1,145
Buchanan, GA 30113 • 1,009
Buchanan, MI 49107 • 4,992
Buchanan, VA 24066 • 1,222
Buchanan □, IA • 20,844
Buchanan □, MO • 83,083
Buchanan □, VA • 31,333
Buckeye, AZ 85326 • 5,038
Buckeye Lake, OH 43008 • 2,986
Buckhannon, WV 26201 • 5,909
Buckingham □, VA • 12,873
Buckley, WA 98321 • 3,516
Bucknell Manor, VA 22307 • 2,300
Buckner, MO 64016 • 2,873
Bucks □, PA • 541,174
Bucksport, ME 04416 • 2,989
Bucksport, SC 29527 • 1,022
Bucyrus, OH 44820 • 13,496
Buda, TX 78610 • 1,795
Budd Lake 0L, NJ • 7,272
Buechel, KY 40218 • 7,081
Buena, NJ 08310 • 4,441
Buena Park, CA 90620–24 • 68,784
Buena Vista, CO 81211 • 1,752
Buena Vista, FL 34691 • 3,000
Buena Vista, GA 31803 • 1,472
Buena Vista, VA 24416 • 6,406
Buena Vista □, IA • 19,965
Buffalo, IA 52728 • 1,260
Buffalo, MN 55313 • 6,856
Buffalo, MO 65622 • 2,414
Buffalo, NY 14201–40 • 328,123
Buffalo, OK 73834 • 1,312
Buffalo, SC 29321 • 1,569
Buffalo, TX 75831 • 1,555
Buffalo, WY 82834 • 3,302
Buffalo □, NE • 37,447
Buffalo □, SD • 1,759
Buffalo □, WI • 13,584
Buffalo Center, IA 50424 • 1,081
Buffalo Grove, IL 60089 • 36,427
Buford, GA 30518 • 8,771
Buhl, ID 83316 • 3,516
Buhler, KS 67522 • 1,277
Buies Creek, NC 27506 • 2,085
Bullhead City, AZ 86430 • 21,951
Bullitt □, KY • 47,567
Bulloch □, GA • 43,125
Bullock □, AL • 11,042
Bull Shoals, AR 72619 • 1,534
Buna, TX 77612 • 1,900
Bunche Park, FL 33054 • 4,000
Buncombe □, NC • 174,821
Bunker Hill, IL 62014 • 1,722
Bunker Hill, OR 97420 • 1,242
Bunkerville, NV 89007 • 300
Bunkie, LA 71322 • 5,044
Bunnell, FL 32110 • 1,873
Buras, LA 70041 • 1,600
Burbank, CA 91501–10 • 93,643
Burbank, IL 60459 • 27,600
Burdickville, RI 02808 • 500
Bureau □, IL • 35,688
Burgaw, NC 28425 • 1,807
Burgettstown, PA 15021 • 1,634
Burgin, KY 40310 • 1,009
Burien, WA 98062 • 25,089
Burkburnett, TX 76354 • 10,145
Burke, SD 57523 • 756
Burke, VA 22015 • 57,734
Burke □, GA • 20,579
Burke □, NC • 75,744
Burke □, ND • 3,002
Burkesville, KY 42717 • 1,815
Burleigh □, ND • 60,131
Burleson, TX 76028 • 16,113
Burleson □, TX • 13,625
Burley, ID 83318 • 8,702
Burlingame, CA 94010–11 • 26,801
Burlingame, KS 66413 • 1,074
Burlington, CO 80807 • 2,941
Burlington, IA 52601 • 27,208
Burlington, KS 66839 • 2,735
Burlington, KY 41005 • 6,070
Burlington, MA 01803 • 23,302
Burlington, NJ 08016 • 9,835
Burlington, NC 27215–17 • 39,498
Burlington, ND 58722 • 995
Burlington, VT 05401–04 • 39,127
Burlington, WA 98233 • 4,349
Burlington, WI 53105 • 8,855
Burlington □, NJ • 395,066
Burnet, TX 78611 • 3,423
Burnet □, TX • 22,677
Burnett □, WI • 13,084
Burney, CA 96013 • 3,423
Burnham, PA 17009 • 2,197
Burns, OR 97720 • 2,913
Burns, TN 37029 • 1,127
Burns, WY 82053 • 254
Burns Flat, OK 73624 • 1,027
Burnsville, MN 55337 • 51,288
Burnsville, NC 28714 • 1,482
Burnt Hills, NY 12027 • 1,550
Burr Ridge, IL 60521 • 7,669
Burt □, NE • 7,868
Burton, MI 48509 • 27,617
Burton, OH 44021 • 1,349
Burton, SC 29902 • 6,917
Burtonsville, MD 20866 • 5,853
Burwell, NE 68823 • 1,278
Bushnell, FL 33513 • 1,998
Bushnell, IL 61422 • 3,288
Butler, AL 36904 • 1,872
Butler, GA 31006 • 1,673
Butler, IN 46721 • 2,601
Butler, MO 64730 • 4,099
Butler, NJ 07405 • 7,392
Butler, PA 16001–03 • 15,714
Butler, WI 53007 • 2,079
Butler □, AL • 21,892
Butler □, IA • 15,731
Butler □, KS • 50,580
Butler □, KY • 11,245
Butler □, MO • 38,765
Butler □, NE • 8,601
Butler □, OH • 291,479
Butler □, PA • 152,013
Butner, NC 27509 • 4,679
Butte, MT 59701–03 • 33,336
Butte □, CA • 182,120
Butte □, ID • 2,918
Butte □, SD • 7,914
Buttonwillow, CA 93206 • 1,301
Butts □, GA • 15,326
Buxton, NC 27920 • 1,300
Buzzards Bay, MA 02532 • 3,250
Byers, CO 80103 • 1,065
Byesville, OH 43723 • 2,435
Byfield, MA 01922 • 1,200
Bylas, AZ 85530 • 1,219
Byron, GA 31008 • 2,276
Byron, IL 61010 • 2,284
Byron, MN 55920 • 2,441
Byron, WY 82412 • 470

C

Cabarrus □, NC • 98,935
Cabell □, WV • 96,827
Cabin Creek, WV 25035 • 1,300
Cabin John, MD 20818 • 1,690
Cabool, MO 65689 • 2,006
Cabot, AR 72023 • 8,319
Cache, OK 73527 • 2,251
Cache □, UT • 70,183
Caddo □, LA • 248,253
Caddo □, OK • 29,550
Cadillac, MI 49601 • 10,104
Cadiz, KY 42211 • 2,148
Cadiz, OH 43907 • 3,439
Cadott, WI 54727 • 1,328
Cahaba Heights, AL 35243 • 4,778
Cahokia, IL 62206 • 17,550
Cairnbrook, PA 15924 • 1,081
Cairo, GA 31728 • 9,035
Cairo, IL 62914 • 4,846
Cairo, NY 12413 • 1,273
Calais, ME 04619 • 3,963
Calaveras □, CA • 31,998
Calavo Gardens, CA 91941 • 6,100
Calcasieu □, LA • 168,134
Calcutta, OH 43920 • 1,212
Caldwell, ID 83605–06 • 18,400
Caldwell, KS 67022 • 1,351
Caldwell, NJ 07006 • 7,549
Caldwell, OH 43724 • 1,786
Caldwell, TX 77836 • 3,181
Caldwell □, KY • 13,232
Caldwell □, LA • 9,810
Caldwell □, MO • 8,380
Caldwell □, NC • 70,709
Caldwell □, TX • 26,392
Caledonia, MN 55921 • 2,846
Caledonia, NY 14423 • 2,262
Caledonia □, VT • 27,846
Calera, AL 35040 • 2,136
Calera, OK 74730 • 1,536
Calexico, CA 92231–32 • 18,633
Calhoun, GA 30701 • 7,135
Calhoun □, AL • 116,034
Calhoun □, AR • 5,826
Calhoun □, FL • 11,011
Calhoun □, GA • 5,013
Calhoun □, IL • 5,322
Calhoun □, IA • 11,508
Calhoun □, MI • 135,982
Calhoun □, MS • 14,908
Calhoun □, SC • 12,753
Calhoun □, TX • 19,053
Calhoun □, WV • 7,885
Calhoun City, MS 38916 • 1,838
Calhoun Falls, SC 29628 • 2,328
Caliente, NV 89008 • 1,111
Califon, NJ 07830 • 1,073
California, MD 20619 • 7,626
California, MO 65018 • 3,465
California, PA 15419 • 5,748
Calipatria, CA 92233 • 2,690
Calistoga, CA 94515 • 4,468
Callahan □, TX • 11,859
Callaway, FL 32401 • 12,253
Callaway □, MO • 32,809
Calloway □, KY • 30,735
Calmar, IA 52132 • 1,026
Calumet □, WI • 34,291

Calumet City, IL 60409 • 37,840
Calumet Park, IL 60643 • 8,418
Calvert, TX 77837 • 1,536
Calvert □, MD • 51,372
Calvert City, KY 42029 • 2,531
Calverton, MD 20705 • 12,046
Calverton Park, MO 63136 • 1,404
Camanche, IA 52730 • 4,436
Camarillo, CA 93010–11 • 52,303
Camas, WA 98607 • 6,442
Camas □, ID • 727
Cambria, CA 93428 • 5,382
Cambria □, PA • 163,029
Cambrian Park, CA 95124 • 2,998
Cambridge, IL 61238 • 2,124
Cambridge, MD 21613 • 11,514
Cambridge, MA 02138 • 95,802
Cambridge, MN 55008 • 5,094
Cambridge, NE 69022 • 1,107
Cambridge, NY 12816 • 1,906
Cambridge, OH 43725 • 11,748
Cambridge City, IN 47327 • 2,091
Cambridge Springs, PA 16403 • 1,837
Camden, AL 36726 • 2,414
Camden, AR 71701 • 14,380
Camden, DE 19934 • 1,899
Camden, ME 04843 • 4,022
Camden, NJ 08101–10 • 87,492
Camden, NY 13316 • 2,552
Camden, OH 45311 • 2,210
Camden, SC 29020 • 6,696
Camden, TN 38320 • 3,643
Camden □, GA • 30,167
Camden □, MO • 27,495
Camden □, NJ • 502,824
Camden □, NC • 5,904
Camdenton, MO 65020 • 2,561
Camelot, WA 98002 • 4,900
Cameron, LA 70631 • 2,041
Cameron, MO 64429 • 4,831
Cameron, TX 76520 • 5,580
Cameron, WV 26033 • 1,177
Cameron, WI 54822 • 1,273
Cameron □, LA • 9,260
Cameron □, PA • 5,913
Cameron □, TX • 260,120
Cameron Park, CA 95682 • 11,897
Camilla, GA 31730 • 5,008
Camino, CA 95709 • 1,500
Camp □, TX • 9,904
Campbell, CA 95008–09 • 36,048
Campbell, FL 34746 • 3,884
Campbell, MO 63933 • 2,165
Campbell, OH 44405 • 10,038
Campbell □, KY • 83,866
Campbell □, SD • 1,965
Campbell □, TN • 35,079
Campbell □, VA • 47,572
Campbell □, WY • 29,370
Campbellsport, WI 53010 • 1,732
Campbellsville, KY 42718–19 • 9,577
Camp Hill, AL 36850 • 1,415
Camp Hill, PA 17011 • 7,831
Camp Point, IL 62320 • 1,230
Camp Springs, MD 20748 • 16,392
Camp Verde, AZ 86322 • 6,243
Canaan, CT 06018 • 1,194
Canadensis, PA 18325 • 1,200
Canadian, TX 79014 • 2,417
Canadian □, OK • 74,409
Canajoharie, NY 13317 • 2,278
Canal Fulton, OH 44614 • 4,157
Canal Winchester, OH 43110 • 2,617
Canandaigua, NY 14424–25 • 10,725
Canastota, NY 13032 • 4,673
Canby, MN 56220 • 1,826
Canby, OR 97013 • 8,983
Candler □, GA • 7,744
Candlewood Isle, CT 06812 • 1,100
Candlewood Shores, CT 06804 • 1,620
Cando, ND 58324 • 1,564
Caney, KS 67333 • 2,062
Canfield, OH 44406 • 5,409
Canisteo, NY 14823 • 2,421
Cannelton, IN 47520 • 1,786
Cannon □, TN • 10,467
Cannon Beach, OR 97110 • 1,221
Cannondale, CT 06897 • 1,500
Cannon Falls, MN 55009 • 3,232
Canon City, CO 81212 • 12,687
Canonsburg, PA 15317 • 9,200
Canterbury, DE 19943 • 500
Canton, CT 06019 • 1,563
Canton, GA 30114 • 4,817
Canton, IL 61520 • 13,922
Canton, MA 02021 • 18,182
Canton, MI 48187 • 57,047
Canton, MS 39046 • 10,062
Canton, MO 63435 • 2,623
Canton, NY 13617 • 6,379
Canton, NC 28716 • 3,790
Canton, OH 44701–99 • 84,161
Canton, PA 17724 • 1,966
Canton, SD 57013 • 2,787
Canton, TX 75103 • 2,949
Cantonment, FL 32533 • 3,200
Canutillo, TX 79835 • 4,500
Canyon, TX 79015 • 11,365
Canyon □, ID • 90,076
Canyon Lake, CA 92380 • 7,938
Canyon Lake, TX 78130 • 9,975
Canyonville, OR 97417 • 1,219
Capac, MI 48014 • 1,583
Cape Canaveral, FL 32920 • 8,014
Cape Charles, VA 23310 • 1,398
Cape Coral, FL 33904 • 74,991
Cape Elizabeth, ME 04107 • 8,854
Cape Girardeau, MO 63701–02 • 34,438
Cape Girardeau □, MO • 61,633
Cape May, NJ 08204 • 4,668
Cape May □, NJ • 95,089
Cape May Court House, NJ 08210 • 4,426
Cape Saint Claire, MD 21401 • 7,878
Capitola, CA 95010 • 10,171
Capitol Heights, MD 20743 • 3,633
Capitol View, SC 29209 • 10,456
Captain Cook, HI 96704 • 2,595
Captiva, FL 33924 • 1,200
Caraway, AR 72419 • 1,178
Carbon □, MT • 8,080
Carbon □, PA • 56,846
Carbon □, UT • 20,228
Carbon □, WY • 16,659
Carbondale, CO 81623 • 3,004
Carbondale, IL 62901–03 • 27,033
Carbondale, KS 66414 • 1,526
Carbondale, PA 18407 • 10,664
Carbon Hill, AL 35549 • 2,115
Cardington, OH 43315 • 1,770
Carencro, LA 70520 • 5,429
Carey, OH 43316 • 3,684
Caribou, ME 04736 • 9,415
Caribou □, ID • 6,963
Carle Place, NY 11514 • 5,107
Carleton, MI 48117 • 2,770
Carlin, NV 89822 • 2,220
Carlinville, IL 62626 • 5,416
Carlisle, AR 72024 • 2,253
Carlisle, IA 50047 • 3,241
Carlisle, KY 40311 • 1,639
Carlisle, OH 45005 • 4,872
Carlisle, PA 17013 • 18,419
Carlisle □, KY • 5,238
Carl Junction, MO 64834 • 4,123
Carlsbad, CA 92008–09 • 63,126
Carlsbad, NM 88220–21 • 24,952
Carlstadt, NJ 07072 • 5,510
Carlton, OR 97111 • 1,289
Carlton □, MN • 29,259
Carlyle, IL 62231 • 3,474
Carmel, CA 93921–23 • 4,239
Carmel, IN 46032 • 25,380
Carmel, NY 10512 • 3,395
Carmi, IL 62821 • 5,564
Carmichael, CA 95608–09 • 48,702
Carnation, WA 98014 • 1,243
Carnegie, OK 73015 • 1,593
Carnegie, PA 15106 • 9,278
Carney, MD 21234 • 25,578
Carneys Point, NJ 08069 • 7,686
Carnot, PA 15108 • 4,750
Caro, MI 48723 • 4,054
Carol City, FL 33055 • 53,331
Caroleen, NC 28019 • 1,100
Carolina Beach, NC 28428 • 3,630
Caroline □, MD • 27,035
Caroline □, VA • 19,217
Carol Stream, IL 60188 • 31,716
Carpentersville, IL 60110 • 23,049
Carpinteria, CA 93013–14 • 13,747
Carrabelle, FL 32322 • 1,200
Carrboro, NC 27510 • 11,553
Carrier Mills, IL 62917 • 1,991
Carrington, ND 58421 • 2,267
Carrizo Springs, TX 78834 • 5,745
Carrizozo, NM 88301 • 1,075
Carroll, IA 51401 • 9,579
Carroll □, AR • 18,654
Carroll □, GA • 71,422
Carroll □, IL • 16,805
Carroll □, IN • 18,809
Carroll □, IA • 21,423
Carroll □, KY • 9,292
Carroll □, MD • 123,372
Carroll □, MS • 9,237
Carroll □, MO • 10,748
Carroll □, NH • 35,410
Carroll □, OH • 26,521
Carroll □, TN • 27,514
Carroll □, VA • 26,594
Carrollton, AL 35447 • 1,170
Carrollton, GA 30117 • 16,029
Carrollton, IL 62016 • 2,507
Carrollton, KY 41008 • 3,715
Carrollton, MI 48724 • 6,521
Carrollton, MO 64633 • 4,406
Carrollton, OH 44615 • 3,042
Carrollton, TX 75006–08 • 82,169
Carrolltown, PA 15722 • 1,286
Carrollwood, FL 33618 • 11,400
Carson, CA 90749 • 83,995
Carson □, TX • 6,576
Carson City, MI 48811 • 1,158
Carson City, NV 89701–21 • 40,443
Carter □, KY • 24,340
Carter □, MO • 5,515
Carter □, MT • 1,503
Carter □, OK • 42,919
Carter □, TN • 51,505
Carteret, NJ 07008 • 19,025
Carteret □, NC • 52,556
Carter Lake, IA 51510 • 3,200
Cartersville, GA 30120 • 12,035
Carterville, IL 62918 • 3,630
Carterville, MO 64835 • 2,013
Carthage, IL 62321 • 2,657
Carthage, MS 39051 • 3,819
Carthage, MO 64836 • 10,747
Carthage, NY 13619 • 4,344
Carthage, TN 37030 • 2,386
Carthage, TX 75633 • 6,496
Caruthersville, MO 63830 • 7,389
Carver, MA 02330 • 1,500
Carver □, MN • 47,915
Carver Ranch Estates, FL 33023 • 5,600
Carville, LA 70721 • 1,108
Cary, IL 60013 • 10,043
Cary, NC 27511 • 43,858
Caryville, TN 37714 • 1,751
Casa de Oro, CA 92077 • 9,500
Casa Grande, AZ 85222 • 19,082
Casas Adobes, AZ 85704 • 12,155
Cascade, CO 80809 • 1,000
Cascade, ID 83611 • 877
Cascade, IA 52033 • 1,812
Cascade, MT 59421 • 729
Cascade □, MT • 77,691
Cascade Vista, WA 98058 • 7,800
Casey, IL 62420 • 2,914
Casey □, KY • 14,211
Cashion, AZ 85329 • 3,014
Cashmere, WA 98815 • 2,544
Casper, WY 82601–15 • 46,742
Caspian, MI 49915 • 1,031
Cass □, IL • 13,437
Cass □, IN • 38,413
Cass □, IA • 15,128
Cass □, MI • 49,477
Cass □, MN • 21,791
Cass □, MO • 63,808
Cass □, NE • 21,318
Cass □, ND • 102,874
Cass □, TX • 29,982
Cass City, MI 48726 • 2,276
Casselberry, FL 32707–08 • 18,911
Casselton, ND 58012 • 1,601
Cassia □, ID • 19,532
Cassopolis, MI 49031 • 1,822
Cassville, MO 65625 • 2,371
Cassville, WI 53806 • 1,144
Castanea, PA 17726 • 1,123
Castile, NY 14427 • 1,078
Castle Dale, UT 84513 • 1,704
Castle Hayne, NC 28429 • 1,182
Castle Hills, DE 19720 • 1,475
Castle Park, CA 92011 • 6,300
Castle Point, MO 63136 • 7,800
Castle Rock, CO 80104 • 8,708
Castle Rock, WA 98611 • 2,067
Castle Shannon, PA 15234 • 9,135
Castleton, VT 05735 • 600
Castleton on Hudson, NY 12033 • 1,491
Castlewood, VA 24224 • 2,110
Castro □, TX • 9,070
Castro Valley, CA 94546 • 48,619
Castroville, TX 78009 • 2,159
Caswell □, NC • 20,693
Catahoula □, LA • 11,065
Catalina Foothills, AZ 85718 • 1,470
Catasauqua, PA 18032 • 6,662
Cataumet, MA 02534 • 1,500
Catawba □, NC • 118,412
Catawissa, PA 17820 • 1,683
Cathedral City, CA 92234–35 • 30,085
Catlettsburg, KY 41129 • 2,231
Catlin, IL 61817 • 2,173
Catonsville, MD 21228 • 35,233
Catoosa, OK 74015 • 2,954
Catoosa □, GA • 42,464
Catron □, NM • 2,563
Catskill, NY 12414 • 4,690
Cattaraugus, NY 14719 • 1,100
Cattaraugus □, NY • 84,234
Cavalier, ND 58220 • 1,508
Cavalier □, ND • 6,064
Cave City, AR 72521 • 1,503
Cave City, KY 42127 • 1,953
Cave Creek, AZ 85331 • 2,925
Cave Junction, OR 97523 • 1,126
Cave Spring, VA 24018 • 24,053
Cavetown, MD 21720 • 1,533
Cayce, SC 29033 • 11,163
Cayuga, IN 47928 • 1,083
Cayuga □, NY • 82,313
Cayuga Heights, NY 14850 • 3,457
Cazenovia, NY 13035 • 3,007
Cecil □, MD • 71,347
Cedar □, IA • 17,381
Cedar □, MO • 12,093
Cedar □, NE • 10,131
Cedar Bluff, AL 35959 • 1,174
Cedar Bluff Two, TN 37722 • 2,000
Cedarburg, WI 53012 • 9,895
Cedar City, UT 84720–22 • 13,443
Cedar Crest, NM 87008 • 1,200
Cedaredge, CO 81413 • 1,380
Cedar Falls, IA 50613 • 34,298
Cedar Grove, NJ 07009 • 12,053
Cedar Grove, WV 25039 • 1,213
Cedar Grove, WI 53013 • 1,521
Cedar Hill, MO 63016 • 1,966
Cedar Hill, TX 75104 • 19,976
Cedar Hills, OR 97005 • 9,294
Cedarhurst, NY 11516 • 5,716
Cedar Lake, IN 46303 • 8,885
Cedar Rapids, IA 52401–10 • 108,751
Cedar Springs, MI 49319 • 2,600
Cedartown, GA 30125 • 7,978
Cedarville, NJ 08311 • 1,100
Cedarville, OH 45314 • 3,210
Celina, OH 45822 • 9,650
Celina, TN 38551 • 1,493
Celina, TX 75009 • 1,737
Celoron, NY 14720 • 1,232
Cementon, PA 18052 • 1,050
Center, CO 81125 • 1,963
Center, ND 58530 • 826
Center, TX 75935 • 4,950
Centerburg, OH 43011 • 1,323
Centereach, NY 11720 • 26,720
Center Line, MI 48015 • 9,026
Center Moriches, NY 11934 • 5,987
Center Point, AL 35215 • 22,657
Center Point, IA 52213 • 1,693
Centerville, IN 47330 • 2,398
Centerville, IA 52544 • 5,936
Centerville, MA 02632 • 9,190
Centerville, OH 45459 • 21,082
Centerville, PA 15417 • 3,842
Centerville, SD 57014 • 887
Centerville, TN 37033 • 3,616
Centerville, UT 84014 • 11,500
Central, NM 88026 • 1,835
Central, SC 29630 • 2,438
Central City, CO 80427 • 335
Central City, IL 62801 • 1,390
Central City, IA 52214 • 1,063
Central City, KY 42330 • 4,979
Central City, NE 68826 • 2,868
Central City, PA 15926 • 1,246
Central Falls, RI 02863 • 17,637
Central Heights, AZ 85501 • 1,500
Centralia, IL 62801 • 14,274
Centralia, MO 65240 • 3,414
Centralia, WA 98531 • 12,101
Central Islip, NY 11722 • 26,028
Central Park, WA 98520 • 2,669
Central Point, OR 97502 • 7,509
Central Square, NY 13036 • 1,671
Central Valley, CA 96019 • 4,340
Central Valley, NY 10917 • 1,929
Central Village, CT 06332 • 1,600
Centre, AL 35960 • 2,893
Centre □, PA • 123,786
Centre City, NJ 08051 • 2,070
Centre Hall, PA 16828 • 1,203
Centreville, AL 35042 • 2,508
Centreville, IL 62207 • 7,489
Centreville, MD 21617 • 2,097
Centreville, MI 49032 • 1,516
Centreville, MS 39631 • 1,771
Centreville, VA 22020 • 26,585
Century, FL 32535 • 1,989
Century Village, FL 33409 • 8,363
Ceredo, WV 25507 • 1,916
Ceres, CA 95307 • 26,314
Cerritos, CA 90703 • 53,240
Cerro Gordo, IL 61818 • 1,436
Cerro Gordo □, IA • 46,733
Chadbourn, NC 28431 • 2,005
Chadds Ford, PA 19317 • 1,200
Chadron, NE 69337 • 5,588
Chadwicks, NY 13319 • 2,000
Chaffee, MO 63740 • 3,059
Chaffee □, CO • 12,684
Chaffin, MA 01520 • 3,980
Chagrin Falls, OH 44022 • 4,146
Chalfonte, DE 19810 • 1,740
Challis, ID 83226 • 1,073
Chalmette, LA 70043–44 • 31,860
Chama, NM 87520 • 1,048
Chamberlain, SD 57325 • 2,347
Chambers □, AL • 36,876
Chambers □, TX • 20,088
Chambersburg, PA 17201 • 16,647
Chamblee, GA 30341 • 7,668
Champaign, IL 61820–21 • 63,502
Champaign □, IL • 173,025
Champaign □, OH • 36,019
Champion, OH 44481 • 5,270
Champlain, NY 12919 • 1,273
Champlin, MN 55316 • 16,849
Chandler, AZ 85224–27 • 90,533
Chandler, IN 47610 • 3,099
Chandler, OK 74834 • 2,596
Chandler, TX 75758 • 1,630
Chandler Heights, AZ 85227 • 1,000
Chanhassen, MN 55317 • 11,732
Channahon, IL 60410 • 4,266
Channel Lake, IL 60002 • 1,660
Channelview, TX 77530 • 25,564
Chantilly, VA 22021–22 • 29,337
Chanute, KS 66720 • 9,488
Chapel Hill, NC 27514–16 • 38,719
Chapel Square, VA 22003 • 2,400
Chapman, KS 67431 • 1,264
Chapmanville, WV 25508 • 1,110
Chappaqua, NY 10514 • 6,380
Chardon, OH 44024 • 4,446
Chariton, IA 50049 • 4,616
Chariton □, MO • 9,202
Charleroi, PA 15022 • 5,014
Charles □, MD • 101,154
Charles City, IA 50616 • 7,878
Charles City □, VA • 6,282
Charles Mix □, SD • 9,131
Charleston, AR 72933 • 2,128
Charleston, IL 61920 • 20,398
Charleston, MS 38921 • 2,328
Charleston, MO 63834 • 5,085
Charleston, SC 29401–22 • 80,414
Charleston, WV 25301–75 • 57,287
Charleston □, SC • 295,039
Charlestown, IN 47111 • 5,889
Charlestown, NH 03603 • 1,173
Charlestown, RI 02813 • 1,500
Charles Town, WV 25414 • 3,122
Charlevoix, MI 49720 • 3,116
Charlevoix □, MI • 21,468
Charlotte, MI 48813 • 8,083
Charlotte, NC 28201–41 • 395,934
Charlotte, TX 78011 • 1,475
Charlotte □, FL • 110,975
Charlotte □, VA • 11,688
Charlotte Hall, MD 20622 • 1,992
Charlotte Harbor, FL 33980 • 3,327
Charlottesville, VA 22901–08 • 40,341
Charlton □, GA • 8,496
Charlton City, MA 01508 • 1,400
Charter Oak, CA 91724 • 8,858
Chase □, KS • 3,021
Chase □, NE • 4,381
Chase City, VA 23924 • 2,442
Chaska, MN 55318 • 11,339
Chatfield, MN 55923 • 2,226
Chatham, IL 62629 • 6,074
Chatham, MA 02633 • 1,916
Chatham, NJ 07928 • 8,007
Chatham, NY 12037 • 1,920
Chatham, VA 24531 • 1,354
Chatham □, GA • 216,935
Chatham □, NC • 38,759
Chatom, AL 36518 • 1,094
Chatsworth, GA 30705 • 2,865
Chatsworth, IL 60921 • 1,186
Chattahoochee, FL 32324 • 4,382
Chattahoochee □, GA • 16,934
Chattanooga, TN 37401–22 • 152,466
Chattaroy, WV 25667 • 1,182
Chattooga □, GA • 22,242
Chautauqua □, KS • 4,407
Chautauqua □, NY • 141,895
Chauvin, LA 70344 • 3,375
Chaves □, NM • 57,849
Chazy, NY 12921 • 1,000
Cheatham □, TN • 27,140
Cheboygan, MI 49721 • 4,999
Cheboygan □, MI • 21,398
Checotah, OK 74426 • 3,290
Cheektowaga, NY 14225 • 84,387
Chehalis, WA 98532 • 6,527
Chelan, WA 98816 • 2,969
Chelan □, WA • 52,250
Chelmsford, MA 01824 • 32,388
Chelsea, MA 02150 • 28,710
Chelsea, MI 48118 • 3,772
Chelsea, OK 74016 • 1,620
Chelsea Estates, DE 19720 • 1,320
Cheltenham Township, PA 19012 • 35,509
Chemung □, NY • 95,195
Chenango □, NY • 51,768
Chenango Bridge, NY 13745 • 2,890
Cheney, KS 67025 • 1,560
Cheney, WA 99004 • 7,723
Cheneyville, LA 71325 • 1,005
Chenoa, IL 61726 • 1,732
Chenoweth, OR 97058 • 3,246
Chepachet, RI 02814 • 900
Cheraw, SC 29520 • 5,505
Cherokee, AL 35616 • 1,479
Cherokee, IA 51012 • 6,026
Cherokee, OK 73728 • 1,787
Cherokee □, AL • 19,543
Cherokee □, GA • 90,204
Cherokee □, IA • 14,098
Cherokee □, KS • 21,374
Cherokee □, NC • 20,170
Cherokee □, OK • 34,049
Cherokee □, SC • 44,506
Cherokee □, TX • 41,049
Cherokee Village, AR 72525 • 3,200
Cherry □, NE • 6,307
Cherry Hill, NJ 08002–03 • 69,319
Cherry Hills Village, CO 80110 • 5,245
Cherryland, CA 94541 • 11,088
Cherryvale, KS 67335 • 2,464
Cherry Valley, CA 92223 • 5,945
Cherry Valley, IL 61016 • 1,615
Cherry Valley, MA 01611 • 1,120
Cherryville, NC 28021 • 4,756
Chesaning, MI 48616 • 2,567
Chesapeake, OH 45619 • 1,073
Chesapeake, VA 23320–28 • 151,976
Chesapeake, WV 25315 • 1,896
Chesapeake Beach, MD 20732 • 2,403
Cheshire, CT 06410 • 25,684
Cheshire, MA 01225 • 1,100
Cheshire □, NH • 70,121
Chesilhurst, NJ 08089 • 1,526
Chesnee, SC 29323 • 1,280
Chester, CA 96020 • 2,082
Chester, CT 06412 • 1,563
Chester, IL 62233 • 8,194
Chester, MT 59522 • 942
Chester, NJ 07930 • 1,214
Chester, NY 10918 • 3,270
Chester, PA 19013–16 • 41,856
Chester, SC 29706 • 7,158
Chester, VT 05143 • 550
Chester, VA 23831 • 14,896
Chester, WV 26034 • 2,905
Chester □, PA • 376,396
Chester □, SC • 32,170
Chester □, TN • 12,819
Chester Depot, VT 05144 • 500
Chesterfield, IN 46017 • 2,730
Chesterfield, SC 29709 • 1,373
Chesterfield □, SC • 38,577
Chesterfield □, VA • 209,274
Chesterton, IN 46304 • 9,124
Chestertown, MD 21620 • 4,005
Chester Township, PA 19013 • 5,399
Chestnut Hill Estates, DE 19713 • 1,730
Chestnut Ridge, NY 10952 • 7,517
Cheswick, PA 15024 • 1,971
Cheswold, DE 19936 • 321
Chetek, WI 54728 • 1,953
Chetopa, KS 67336 • 1,357
Chevak, AK 99563 • 598
Cheverly, MD 20785 • 6,023
Cheviot, OH 45211 • 9,616
Chevy Chase, MD 20815 • 8,559
Chewelah, WA 99109 • 1,945
Cheyenne, WY 82001–09 • 50,008
Cheyenne □, CO • 2,397
Cheyenne □, KS • 3,243
Cheyenne □, NE • 9,494
Cheyenne Wells, CO 80810 • 1,128
Chicago, IL 60601–66 • 2,783,726
Chicago Heights, IL 60411 • 33,072
Chicago Ridge, IL 60415 • 13,643
Chickamauga, GA 30707 • 2,149
Chickasaw, AL 36611 • 6,649
Chickasaw □, IA • 13,295
Chickasaw □, MS • 18,085
Chickasha, OK 73018 • 14,988
Chico, CA 95926–28 • 40,079
Chicopee, MA 01013–22 • 56,632
Chicora, PA 16025 • 1,058
Chiefland, FL 32626 • 1,917
Childersburg, AL 35044 • 4,579
Childress, TX 79201 • 5,055
Childress □, TX • 5,953
Chilhowie, VA 24319 • 1,971
Chili Center, NY 14624 • 4,360
Chillicothe, IL 61523 • 5,959
Chillicothe, MO 64601 • 8,804
Chillicothe, OH 45601 • 21,923
Chillum, MD 20783 • 31,309
Chilton, WI 53014 • 3,240
Chilton □, AL • 32,458
Chimayo, NM 87522 • 2,789
China Grove, NC 28023 • 2,732
Chincoteague, VA 23336 • 3,572
Chinle, AZ 86503 • 5,059
Chino, CA 91708–10 • 59,682
Chinook, MT 59523 • 1,512
Chino Valley, AZ 86323 • 4,837
Chipley, FL 32428 • 3,866
Chippewa □, MI • 34,604
Chippewa □, MN • 13,228
Chippewa □, WI • 52,360
Chippewa Falls, WI 54729 • 12,727
Chisago □, MN • 30,521
Chisago City, MN 55013 • 2,009
Chisholm, ME 04239 • 1,653
Chisholm, MN 55719 • 5,290
Chittenango, NY 13037 • 4,734
Chittenden □, VT • 131,761
Choctaw, OK 73020 • 8,545
Choctaw □, AL • 16,018
Choctaw □, MS • 9,071
Choctaw □, OK • 15,302
Choteau, MT 59422 • 1,741
Chouteau, OK 74337 • 1,771
Chouteau □, MT • 5,452
Chowan □, NC • 13,506
Chowchilla, CA 93610 • 5,930
Chrisman, IL 61924 • 1,136
Christian □, IL • 34,418
Christian □, KY • 68,941
Christian □, MO • 32,644
Christiana, DE 19702 • 500
Christiana, PA 17509 • 1,045
Christiansburg, VA 24073 • 15,004
Christmas, FL 32709 • 1,200
Christopher, IL 62822 • 2,774
Chubbuck, ID 83202 • 7,791
Chugwater, WY 82210 • 192
Chula Vista, CA 91909–15 • 135,163
Church Hill, TN 37642 • 4,834
Churchill, OH 44505 • 7,700
Churchill □, NV • 17,938
Church Point, LA 70525 • 4,677
Churchville, NY 14428 • 1,731
Churubusco, IN 46723 • 1,781
Cibola □, NM • 23,794
Cicero, IL 60650 • 67,436
Cicero, IN 46034 • 3,268
Cimarron, KS 67835 • 1,626
Cimarron □, OK • 3,301
Cimarron Hills, CO 80906 • 11,160
Cincinnati, OH 45201–75 • 364,040
Cinnaminson, NJ 08077 • 14,583
Circle, MT 59215 • 805

Circle Pines, MN 55014 • 4,704
Circleville, OH 43113 • 11,666
Cisco, TX 76437 • 3,813
Citra, FL 32113 • 1,500
Citronelle, AL 36522 • 3,671
Citrus, CA 91702 • 9,481
Citrus □, FL • 93,515
Citrus Heights, CA 95610–11 • 107,439
City Of Sunrise, FL 33313 • 64,407
City View, SC 29611 • 1,490
Clackamas, OR 97015 • 2,578
Clackamas □, OR • 278,850
Claiborne, LA 71291 • 8,300
Claiborne □, LA • 17,405
Claiborne □, MS • 11,370
Claiborne □, TN • 26,137
Clair-Mel City, FL 33619 • 7,000
Clairton, PA 15025 • 9,656
Clallam □, WA • 56,464
Clanton, AL 35045 • 7,669
Clara City, MN 56222 • 1,307
Clare, MI 48617 • 3,021
Clare □, MI • 24,952
Claremont, CA 91711 • 32,503
Claremont, NH 03743 • 13,902
Claremore, OK 74017–18 • 13,280
Clarence, MO 63437 • 1,026
Clarendon, AR 72029 • 2,072
Clarendon, TX 79226 • 2,067
Clarendon □, SC • 28,450
Clarendon Hills, IL 60514 • 6,994
Claridge, PA 15623 • 1,200
Clarinda, IA 51632 • 5,104
Clarion, IA 50525 • 2,703
Clarion, PA 16214 • 6,457
Clarion □, PA • 41,699
Clark, NJ 07066 • 14,629
Clark, SD 57225 • 1,292
Clark □, AR • 21,437
Clark □, ID • 762
Clark □, IL • 15,921
Clark □, IN • 87,777
Clark □, KS • 2,418
Clark □, KY • 29,496
Clark □, MO • 7,547
Clark □, NV • 741,459
Clark □, OH • 147,548
Clark □, SD • 4,403
Clark □, WA • 238,053
Clark □, WI • 31,647
Clarkdale, AZ 86324 • 2,144
Clarke □, AL • 27,240
Clarke □, GA • 87,594
Clarke □, IA • 8,287
Clarke □, MS • 17,313
Clarke □, VA • 12,101
Clarkesville, GA 30523 • 1,151
Clarksburg, WV 26301–02 • 18,059
Clarksdale, MS 38614 • 19,717
Clarks Summit, PA 18411 • 5,433
Clarkston, GA 30021 • 5,385
Clarkston, MI 48346–48 • 1,005
Clarkston, WA 99403 • 6,753
Clarksville, AR 72830 • 5,833
Clarksville, DE 19970 • 500
Clarksville, IN 47129 • 19,833
Clarksville, IA 50619 • 1,382
Clarksville, TN 37040–43 • 75,494
Clarksville, TX 75426 • 4,311
Clarksville, VA 23927 • 1,243
Clarkton, MO 63837 • 1,113
Clatskanie, OR 97016 • 1,629
Clatsop □, OR • 33,301
Claude, TX 79019 • 1,199
Clawson, MI 48017 • 13,874
Claxton, GA 30417 • 2,464
Clay, KY 42404 • 1,173
Clay □, AL • 13,252
Clay □, AR • 18,107
Clay □, FL • 105,986
Clay □, GA • 3,364
Clay □, IL • 14,460
Clay □, IN • 24,705
Clay □, IA • 17,585
Clay □, KS • 9,158
Clay □, KY • 21,746
Clay □, MN • 50,422
Clay □, MS • 21,120
Clay □, MO • 153,411
Clay □, NE • 7,123
Clay □, NC • 7,155
Clay □, SD • 13,186
Clay □, TN • 7,238
Clay □, TX • 10,024
Clay □, WV • 9,983
Clay Center, KS 67432 • 4,613
Clay City, KY 40312 • 1,258
Claymont, DE 19702 • 9,800
Claypool, AZ 85532 • 1,942
Claysburg, PA 16625 • 1,399
Clayton, AL 36016 • 1,564
Clayton, DE 19938 • 1,163
Clayton, GA 30525 • 1,613
Clayton, MO 63105 • 13,874
Clayton, NJ 08312 • 6,155
Clayton, NM 88415 • 2,484
Clayton, NY 13624 • 2,160
Clayton, NC 27520 • 4,756
Clayton □, GA • 182,052
Clayton □, IA • 19,054
Clear Creek □, CO • 7,619
Clearfield, KY 40313 • 1,250
Clearfield, PA 16830 • 6,633
Clearfield, UT 84015 • 21,435
Clearfield □, PA • 78,097
Clearlake, CA 95422 • 11,804
Clear Lake, IA 50428 • 8,183
Clear Lake, SD 57226 • 1,247
Clearlake, WA 98235 • 1,100
Clear Lake Shores, TX 77565 • 1,096
Clearwater, FL 34615–30 • 98,784
Clearwater, KS 67026 • 1,875
Clearwater, SC 29822 • 4,731
Clearwater □, ID • 8,505
Clearwater □, MN • 8,309
Cleburne, TX 76031–33 • 22,205
Cleburne □, AL • 12,730
Cleburne □, AR • 19,411
Cle Elum, WA 98922 • 1,778
Cleland Heights, DE 19805 • 1,120
Clementon, NJ 08021 • 5,601
Clemmons, NC 27012 • 6,020
Clemson, SC 29631–33 • 11,096

Clendenin, WV 25045 • 1,203
Cleona, PA 17042 • 2,322
Clermont, FL 34711–12 • 6,910
Clermont □, OH • 150,187
Cleveland, GA 30528 • 1,653
Cleveland, MS 38732–33 • 15,384
Cleveland, OH 44101–99 • 505,616
Cleveland, OK 74020 • 3,156
Cleveland, TN 37311–12 • 30,354
Cleveland, TX 77327–28 • 7,124
Cleveland, WI 53015 • 1,398
Cleveland □, AR • 7,781
Cleveland □, NC • 84,714
Cleveland □, OK • 174,253
Cleveland Heights, OH 44118 • 54,052
Cleves, OH 45002 • 2,208
Clewiston, FL 33440 • 6,085
Cliffside Park, NJ 07010 • 20,393
Clifton, AZ 85533 • 2,840
Clifton, CO 81520 • 12,671
Clifton, IL 60927 • 1,347
Clifton, NJ 07011–15 • 71,742
Clifton, TX 76634 • 3,195
Clifton Forge, VA 24422 • 4,679
Clifton Heights, PA 19018 • 7,111
Clifton Knolls, NY 12065 • 5,636
Clifton Springs, NY 14432 • 2,175
Clinch □, GA • 6,160
Clint, TX 79836 • 1,035
Clinton, AR 72031 • 2,213
Clinton, CT 06413 • 3,439
Clinton, IL 61727 • 7,437
Clinton, IN 47842 • 5,040
Clinton, IA 52732–33 • 29,201
Clinton, KY 42031 • 1,547
Clinton, LA 70722 • 1,904
Clinton, ME 04927 • 1,485
Clinton, MD 20735 • 19,987
Clinton, MA 01510 • 7,943
Clinton, MI 49236 • 2,475
Clinton, MS 39056 • 21,847
Clinton, MO 64735 • 8,703
Clinton, NJ 08809 • 2,054
Clinton, NY 13323 • 2,238
Clinton, NC 28328 • 8,204
Clinton, OK 73601 • 9,298
Clinton, SC 29325 • 7,987
Clinton, TN 37716 • 8,972
Clinton, UT 84015 • 7,945
Clinton, WA 98236 • 2,000
Clinton, WI 53525 • 1,849
Clinton □, IL • 33,944
Clinton □, IN • 30,974
Clinton □, IA • 51,040
Clinton □, KY • 9,135
Clinton □, MI • 57,883
Clinton □, MO • 16,595
Clinton □, NY • 85,969
Clinton □, OH • 35,415
Clinton □, PA • 37,182
Clinton Township, MI 48043 • 85,866
Clintonville, WI 54929 • 4,351
Clintwood, VA 24228 • 1,542
Clio, AL 36017 • 1,365
Clio, MI 48420 • 2,629
Clive, IA 50322 • 7,462
Cloquet, MN 55720 • 10,885
Closter, NJ 07624 • 8,094
Cloud □, KS • 11,023
Clover, SC 29710 • 3,422
Cloverdale, CA 95425 • 4,924
Cloverdale, IN 46120 • 1,681
Cloverleaf, TX 77015 • 18,230
Cloverport, KY 40111 • 1,207
Clovis, CA 93612–13 • 50,323
Clovis, NM 88101–03 • 30,954
Clute, TX 77531 • 8,910
Clyde, NY 14433 • 2,409
Clyde, NC 28721 • 1,041
Clyde, OH 43410 • 5,776
Clyde, TX 79510 • 3,002
Clymer, PA 15728 • 1,499
Coachella, CA 92236 • 16,896
Coahoma, TX 79511 • 1,133
Coahoma □, MS • 31,665
Coal □, OK • 5,780
Coal City, IL 60416 • 3,907
Coal Fork, WV 25306 • 2,100
Coalgate, OK 74538 • 1,895
Coal Grove, OH 45638 • 2,251
Coalinga, CA 93210 • 8,212
Coalville, UT 84017 • 1,065
Coatesville, PA 19320 • 11,038
Coats, NC 27521 • 1,493
Cobb □, GA • 447,745
Cobden, IL 62920 • 1,090
Cobleskill, NY 12043 • 5,268
Cochise □, AZ • 97,624
Cochituate, MA 01778 • 6,046
Cochran, GA 31014 • 4,390
Cochran □, TX • 4,377
Cochranton, PA 16314 • 1,174
Cocke □, TN • 29,141
Cockeysville, MD 21030 • 18,668
Cockrell Hill, TX 75211 • 3,746
Cocoa, FL 32922–27 • 17,722
Cocoa Beach, FL 32931–32 • 12,123
Coconino □, AZ • 96,591
Coconut Creek, FL 33060 • 27,485
Codington □, SD • 22,698
Cody, WY 82414 • 7,897
Coeburn, VA 24230 • 2,165
Coeur d'Alene, ID 83814 • 24,563
Coffee □, AL • 40,240
Coffee □, GA • 29,592
Coffee □, TN • 40,339
Coffey □, KS • 8,404
Coffeyville, KS 67337 • 12,917
Cohasset, MA 02025 • 6,800
Cohoes, NY 12047 • 16,825
Cokato, MN 55321 • 2,180
Coke □, TX • 3,424
Cokeville, WY 83114 • 493
Colbert, OK 74733 • 1,043
Colbert □, AL • 51,666
Colby, KS 67701 • 5,396
Colby, WI 54421 • 1,532
Colchester, CT 06415 • 3,212
Colchester, IL 62326 • 1,645
Cold Bay, AK 99571 • 148
Cold Spring, KY 41076 • 2,880
Cold Spring, MN 56320 • 2,459
Cold Spring Harbor, NY 11724 • 4,789

Coldwater, MI 49036 • 9,607
Coldwater, MS 38618 • 1,502
Coldwater, OH 45828 • 4,335
Cole □, MO • 63,579
Colebrook, NH 03576 • 2,444
Cole Camp, MO 65325 • 1,054
Coleman, MI 48618 • 1,237
Coleman, TX 76834 • 5,410
Coleman □, TX • 9,710
Coleraine, MN 55722 • 1,041
Coles □, IL • 51,644
Colfax, CA 95713 • 1,306
Colfax, IA 50054 • 2,462
Colfax, LA 71417 • 1,696
Colfax, WA 99111 • 2,713
Colfax, WI 54730 • 1,110
Colfax □, NE • 9,139
Colfax □, NM • 12,925
College, AK 99701 • 11,249
Collegedale, TN 37315 • 5,048
College Park, GA 30337 • 20,457
College Park, MD 20740–41 • 21,927
College Place, WA 99324 • 6,308
College Station, AR 72053 • 3,800
College Station, TX 77840–45 • 52,456
Collegeville, PA 19426 • 4,227
Colleton □, SC • 34,377
Colleyville, TX 76034 • 12,724
Collier □, FL • 152,099
Collierville, TN 38017 • 14,427
Collin □, TX • 264,036
Collingdale, PA 19023 • 9,175
Collingswood, NJ 08108 • 15,289
Collingsworth □, TX • 3,573
Collins, MS 39428 • 2,541
Collins Park, DE 19720 • 2,100
Collinsville, AL 35961 • 1,429
Collinsville, CT 06022 • 2,591
Collinsville, IL 62234 • 22,446
Collinsville, OK 74021 • 3,612
Collinsville, VA 24078 • 7,280
Collinwood, TN 38450 • 1,014
Colmar Manor, MD 20722 • 1,249
Coloma, MI 49038 • 1,679
Colon, MI 49040 • 1,224
Colonia, NJ 07067 • 18,238
Colonial Beach, VA 22443 • 3,132
Colonial Heights, TN 37663 • 6,716
Colonial Heights, VA 23834 • 16,064
Colonial Park, PA 17109 • 13,777
Colonie, NY 12212 • 8,019
Colorado □, TX • 18,383
Colorado City, AZ 86021 • 2,426
Colorado City, CO 81019 • 1,149
Colorado City, TX 79512 • 4,749
Colorado Springs, CO 80901–99 • 281,140
Colquitt, GA 31737 • 1,991
Colquitt □, GA • 36,645
Colstrip, MT 59323 • 3,035
Colton, CA 92324 • 40,213
Columbia, CA 95310 • 1,799
Columbia, IL 62236 • 5,524
Columbia, KY 42728 • 3,845
Columbia, MD 21044–46 • 75,883
Columbia, MS 39429 • 6,815
Columbia, MO 65201–05 • 69,101
Columbia, PA 17512 • 10,701
Columbia, SC 29201–92 • 98,052
Columbia, TN 38401–02 • 28,583
Columbia □, AR • 25,691
Columbia □, FL • 42,613
Columbia □, GA • 66,031
Columbia □, NY • 62,982
Columbia □, OR • 37,557
Columbia □, PA • 63,202
Columbia □, WA • 4,024
Columbia □, WI • 45,088
Columbia City, IN 46725 • 5,706
Columbia City, OR 97018 • 1,003
Columbia Falls, MT 59912 • 2,942
Columbia Heights, MN 55421 • 18,910
Columbiana, AL 35051 • 2,968
Columbiana, OH 44408 • 4,961
Columbiana □, OH • 108,276
Columbine, CO 80123 • 23,969
Columbus, GA 31901–09 • 178,681
Columbus, IN 47201–03 • 31,802
Columbus, KS 66725 • 3,268
Columbus, MS 39701–05 • 23,799
Columbus, MT 59019 • 1,573
Columbus, NE 68601 • 19,480
Columbus, OH 43201–91 • 632,910
Columbus, TX 78934 • 3,367
Columbus, WI 53925 • 4,093
Columbus □, NC • 49,587
Columbus Grove, OH 45830 • 2,231
Columbus Junction, IA 52738 • 1,616
Colusa, CA 95932 • 4,934
Colusa □, CA • 16,275
Colver, PA 15927 • 1,024
Colville, WA 99114 • 4,360
Colwich, KS 67030 • 1,091
Comal □, TX • 51,832
Comanche, OK 73529 • 1,695
Comanche, TX 76442 • 4,087
Comanche □, KS • 2,313
Comanche □, OK • 111,486
Comanche □, TX • 13,381
Combee Settlement, FL 33801 • 5,463
Combined Locks, WI 54113 • 2,190
Comfort, TX 78013 • 1,477
Commack, NY 11725 • 36,124
Commerce, CA 90040 • 12,135
Commerce, GA 30529 • 4,108
Commerce, OK 74339 • 2,426
Commerce, TX 75428 • 6,825
Commerce City, CO 80022 • 16,466
Common Fence Point, RI 02871 • 860
Como, MS 38619 • 1,387
Compton, CA 90220–24 • 90,454
Comstock, MI 49041 • 5,600
Comstock Park, MI 49321 • 6,530
Concho □, TX • 3,044
Concord, CA 94518–24 • 111,348
Concord, MA 01742 • 4,680
Concord, MO 63128 • 19,859
Concord, NH 03301–03 • 36,006
Concord, NC 28025–27 • 27,347
Concord, TN 37901 • 3,420
Concordia, KS 66901 • 6,167
Concordia, MO 64020 • 2,160
Concordia □, LA • 20,828

Conecuh □, AL • 14,054
Conejos □, CO • 7,453
Conemaugh, PA 15909 • 1,470
Congers, NY 10920 • 8,003
Conklin, NY 13748 • 1,800
Conley, GA 30027 • 5,528
Conneaut, OH 44030 • 13,241
Connell, WA 99326 • 2,005
Connellsville, PA 15425 • 9,229
Connersville, IN 47331 • 15,550
Conover, NC 28613 • 5,465
Conrad, MT 59425 • 2,891
Conroe, TX 77301–05 • 27,610
Conshohocken, PA 19428 • 8,064
Constantia, NY 13044 • 1,140
Constantine, MI 49042 • 2,032
Continental, OH 45831 • 1,214
Contoocook, NH 03229 • 1,334
Contra Costa □, CA • 803,732
Converse, IN 46919 • 1,144
Converse, SC 29329 • 1,173
Converse, TX 78109 • 8,887
Converse □, WY • 11,128
Convoy, OH 45832 • 1,200
Conway, AR 72032 • 26,481
Conway, FL 32809 • 13,159
Conway, NH 03818 • 1,604
Conway, PA 15027 • 2,424
Conway, SC 29526–27 • 9,819
Conway □, AR • 19,151
Conway Springs, KS 67031 • 1,384
Conyers, GA 30207–08 • 7,380
Cook □, GA • 13,456
Cook □, IL • 5,105,067
Cook □, MN • 3,868
Cooke □, TX • 30,777
Cookeville, TN 38501–02 • 21,744
Coolidge, AZ 85228 • 6,927
Coon Rapids, IA 50058 • 1,266
Coon Rapids, MN 55433 • 52,978
Cooper, TX 75432 • 2,153
Cooper □, MO • 14,835
Cooper City, FL 33328 • 20,791
Cooper Road, LA 71107 • 11,050
Coopersburg, PA 18036 • 2,599
Cooperstown, NY 13326 • 2,180
Cooperstown, ND 58425 • 1,247
Coopersville, MI 49404 • 3,421
Coos □, NH • 34,828
Coos □, OR • 60,273
Coosa □, AL • 11,063
Coos Bay, OR 97420 • 15,076
Copake, NY 12516 • 1,200
Copiague, NY 11726 • 20,769
Copiah □, MS • 27,592
Coplay, PA 18037 • 3,267
Copperas Cove, TX 76522 • 24,079
Coquille, OR 97423 • 4,121
Coral Gables, FL 33134 • 40,091
Coral Hills, MD 20743 • 11,032
Coral Springs, FL 33065 • 79,443
Coral Terrace, FL 33157 • 23,255
Coralville, IA 52241 • 10,347
Coral Way Village, FL 33155 • 9,000
Coram, NY 11727 • 30,111
Coraopolis, PA 15108 • 6,747
Corbin, KY 40701–02 • 7,419
Corcoran, CA 93212 • 13,364
Corcoran, MN 55340 • 5,199
Cordaville, MA 01772 • 1,530
Cordele, GA 31015 • 10,321
Cordell, OK 73632 • 2,903
Cordova, AL 35550 • 2,623
Cordova, AK 99574 • 2,110
Cordova, NC 28330 • 1,200
Corinth, MS 38834 • 11,820
Corinth, NY 12822 • 2,760
Cornelia, GA 30531 • 3,219
Cornelius, NC 28031 • 2,581
Cornelius, OR 97113 • 6,148
Cornell, WI 54732 • 1,541
Corning, AR 72422 • 3,323
Corning, CA 96021 • 5,870
Corning, IA 50841 • 1,806
Corning, NY 14830 • 11,938
Cornville, AZ 86325 • 1,200
Cornwall, PA 17016 • 3,231
Cornwall on Hudson, NY 12520 • 3,093
Corona, CA 91718–20 • 76,095
Coronado, CA 92118 • 26,540
Coronado, CO 80229 • 6,890
Corpus Christi, TX 78401–82 • 257,453
Corrigan, TX 75939 • 1,764
Corriganville, MD 21524 • 1,020
Corry, PA 16407 • 7,216
Corsicana, TX 75110 • 22,911
Corson □, SD • 4,195
Corte Madera, CA 94925 • 8,272
Cortez, CO 81321 • 7,284
Cortez, FL 34215 • 4,509
Cortland, NY 13045 • 19,801
Cortland, OH 44410 • 5,666
Cortland □, NY • 48,963
Corunna, MI 48817 • 3,091
Corvallis, OR 97330–33 • 44,757
Corydon, IN 47112 • 2,661
Corydon, IA 50060 • 1,675
Coryell □, TX • 64,213
Coshocton, OH 43812 • 12,193
Coshocton □, OH • 35,427
Cosmopolis, WA 98537 • 1,372
Costa Mesa, CA 92626–28 • 96,357
Costilla □, CO • 3,190
Cottage Grove, MN 55016 • 22,935
Cottage Grove, OR 97424 • 7,402
Cottle □, TX • 2,247
Cottleville, MO 63338 • 2,936
Cotton □, OK • 6,651
Cottondale, AL 35453 • 1,960
Cotton Plant, AR 72036 • 1,150
Cottonport, LA 71327 • 2,600
Cotton Valley, LA 71018 • 1,130
Cottonwood, AL 36320 • 1,385
Cottonwood, AZ 86326 • 5,918
Cottonwood, CA 96022 • 1,747
Cottonwood, ID 83522 • 822
Cottonwood, UT 84121 • 11,554
Cottonwood □, MN • 12,694
Cottonwood Heights, UT 84121 • 28,766
Cotuit, MA 02635 • 1,750
Cotulla, TX 78014 • 3,694
Coudersport, PA 16915 • 2,854
Coulee Dam, WA 99116 • 1,087

Council, ID 83612 • 831
Council Bluffs, IA 51501–03 • 54,315
Council Grove, KS 66846 • 2,228
Country Club Hills, IL 60478 • 15,431
Country Homes, WA 99218 • 5,126
Countryside, IL 60525 • 5,716
Coupeville, WA 98239 • 1,377
Coushatta, LA 71019 • 1,845
Covedale, OH 45238 • 6,669
Covelo, CA 95428 • 1,057
Coventry, CT 06238 • 10,063
Coventry, DE 19720 • 1,165
Coventry, RI 02816 • 6,980
Covina, CA 91722–24 • 43,207
Covington, GA 30209 • 10,026
Covington, IN 47932 • 2,747
Covington, KY 41011–18 • 43,264
Covington, LA 70433–34 • 7,691
Covington, OH 45318 • 2,603
Covington, TN 38019 • 7,487
Covington, VA 24426 • 6,991
Covington □, AL • 36,478
Covington □, MS • 16,527
Cowan, TN 37318 • 1,738
Cowarts, AL 36321 • 1,400
Coweta, OK 74429 • 6,159
Coweta □, GA • 53,853
Cowley, WY 82420 • 477
Cowley □, KS • 36,915
Cowlitz □, WA • 82,119
Cowpens, SC 29330 • 2,176
Coxsackie, NY 12051 • 2,789
Cozad, NE 69130 • 3,823
Crab Orchard, WV 25827 • 2,919
Crabtree, PA 15624 • 1,000
Crafton, PA 15205 • 7,188
Craig, AK 99921 • 1,260
Craig, CO 81625–26 • 8,091
Craig □, OK • 14,104
Craig □, VA • 4,372
Craighead □, AR • 68,956
Craigsville, WV 26205 • 1,955
Cramerton, NC 28032 • 2,371
Cranbury, NJ 08512 • 1,255
Crandall, TX 75114 • 1,652
Crandon, WI 54520 • 1,958
Crane, AZ 85365 • 2,650
Crane, MO 65633 • 1,218
Crane, TX 79731 • 3,533
Crane □, TX • 4,652
Cranford, NJ 07016 • 22,624
Cranston, RI 02910 • 76,060
Craven □, NC • 81,613
Crawford, NE 69339 • 1,115
Crawford □, AR • 42,493
Crawford □, GA • 8,991
Crawford □, IL • 19,464
Crawford □, IN • 9,914
Crawford □, IA • 16,775
Crawford □, KS • 35,568
Crawford □, MI • 12,260
Crawford □, MO • 19,173
Crawford □, OH • 47,870
Crawford □, PA • 86,169
Crawford □, WI • 15,940
Crawfordsville, IN 47933 • 13,584
Crawfordville, FL 32327 • 1,110
Creedmoor, NC 27522 • 1,504
Creek □, OK • 60,915
Creighton, NE 68729 • 1,223
Creighton, PA 15030 • 1,658
Crenshaw □, AL • 13,635
Creola, AL 36525 • 1,896
Cresaptown, MD 21502 • 4,645
Crescent, OK 73028 • 1,236
Crescent City, CA 95531 • 4,380
Crescent City, FL 32112 • 1,859
Crescent Springs, KY 41016 • 2,179
Cresco, IA 52136 • 3,669
Cresskill, NJ 07626 • 7,558
Cresson, PA 16630 • 1,784
Cressona, PA 17929 • 1,694
Cresthaven, FL 33064 • 2,400
Crest Hill, IL 60435 • 10,643
Crestline, CA 92325 • 8,594
Crestline, OH 44827 • 4,934
Creston, IA 50801 • 7,911
Creston, OH 44217 • 1,848
Crestview, FL 32536 • 9,886
Crestview, HI 96797 • 1,000
Crestwood, IL 60445 • 10,823
Crestwood, KY 40014 • 1,435
Crestwood, MO 63126 • 11,234
Crestwood Village, NJ 08759 • 8,030
Creswell, OR 97426 • 2,431
Crete, IL 60417 • 6,773
Crete, NE 68333 • 4,841
Creve Coeur, IL 61611 • 5,938
Creve Coeur, MO 63141 • 12,304
Crewe, VA 23930 • 2,276
Cricket, NC 28659 • 2,015
Cridersville, OH 45806 • 1,885
Crisfield, MD 21817 • 2,880
Crisp □, GA • 20,011
Crittenden □, AR • 49,939
Crittenden □, KY • 9,196
Crocker, MO 65452 • 1,077
Crockett, CA 94525 • 3,228
Crockett, TX 75835 • 7,024
Crockett □, TN • 13,378
Crockett □, TX • 4,078
Crofton, MD 21114 • 12,781
Cromwell, CT 06416 • 1,100
Crook □, OR • 14,111
Crook □, WY • 5,294
Crookston, MN 56716 • 8,119
Crooksville, OH 43731 • 2,601
Crosby, MN 56441 • 2,073
Crosby, ND 58730 • 1,312
Crosby, TX 77532 • 1,811
Crosby □, TX • 7,304
Crosbyton, TX 79322 • 2,026
Cross □, AR • 19,225
Cross City, FL 32628 • 2,041
Crossett, AR 71635 • 6,282
Crosslake, MN 56442 • 1,132
Cross Lanes, WV 25313 • 10,878
Cross Plains, TN 37049 • 1,025
Cross Plains, TX 76443 • 1,063
Cross Plains, WI 53528 • 2,098
Crossville, AL 35962 • 1,350
Crossville, TN 38555 • 6,930
Croswell, MI 48422 • 2,174

Crothersville, IN 47229 • 1,687
Croton-on-Hudson, NY 10520 • 7,018
Crow Agency, MT 59022 • 1,446
Crowell, TX 79227 • 1,230
Crowley, LA 70526–27 • 13,983
Crowley, TX 76036 • 6,974
Crowley □, CO • 3,946
Crown Point, IN 46307 • 17,728
Crownpoint, NM 87313 • 2,108
Crow Wing □, MN • 44,249
Crozet, VA 22932 • 2,256
Crystal, MN 55428 • 23,788
Crystal Bay, NV 89402 • 1,200
Crystal Beach, FL 34681 • 1,450
Crystal City, MO 63019 • 4,088
Crystal City, TX 78839 • 8,263
Crystal Falls, MI 49920 • 1,922
Crystal Lake, CT 06029 • 1,200
Crystal Lake, FL 33803 • 5,300
Crystal Lake, IL 60014 • 24,512
Crystal Lawns, IL 60435 • 1,660
Crystal River, FL 32629 • 4,044
Crystal Springs, MS 39059 • 5,643
Cuba, IL 61427 • 1,440
Cuba, MO 65453 • 2,537
Cuba, NY 14727 • 1,690
Cuba City, WI 53807 • 2,024
Cucamonga, CA 91730 • 101,409
Cudahy, CA 90201 • 22,817
Cudahy, WI 53110 • 18,659
Cuero, TX 77954 • 6,700
Culberson □, TX • 3,407
Culbertson, MT 59218 • 796
Cullen, LA 71021 • 1,642
Cullman, AL 35055–56 • 13,367
Cullman □, AL • 67,613
Culloden, WV 25510 • 2,907
Cullowhee, NC 28723 • 1,200
Culpeper, VA 22701 • 8,581
Culpeper □, VA • 27,791
Culver, IN 46511 • 1,404
Culver City, CA 90230–33 • 38,793
Cumberland, KY 40823 • 3,112
Cumberland, MD 21501–05 • 23,706
Cumberland, WI 54829 • 2,163
Cumberland □, IL • 10,670
Cumberland □, KY • 6,784
Cumberland □, ME • 243,135
Cumberland □, NJ • 138,053
Cumberland □, NC • 274,566
Cumberland □, PA • 195,257
Cumberland □, TN • 34,736
Cumberland □, VA • 7,825
Cumberland Center, ME 04021 • 1,890
Cumberland Foreside, ME 04110 • 1,000
Cumberland Hill, RI 02864 • 6,379
Cuming □, NE • 10,117
Cumming, GA 30130 • 2,828
Cupertino, CA 95014–16 • 40,263
Currituck □, NC • 13,736
Curry □, NM • 42,207
Curry □, OR • 19,327
Curtisville, PA 15032 • 1,285
Curwensville, PA 16833 • 2,924
Cushing, OK 74023 • 7,218
Cusseta, GA 31805 • 1,107
Custer, SD 57730 • 1,741
Custer □, CO • 1,926
Custer □, ID • 4,133
Custer □, MT • 11,697
Custer □, NE • 12,270
Custer □, OK • 26,897
Custer □, SD • 6,179
Cut Bank, MT 59427 • 3,329
Cutchogue, NY 11935 • 1,730
Cuthbert, GA 31740 • 3,730
Cutler, FL 33157 • 16,201
Cutler Ridge, FL 33157 • 21,268
Cutlerville, MI 49508 • 11,228
Cut Off, LA 70345 • 5,325
Cuyahoga □, OH • 1,412,140
Cuyahoga Falls, OH 44221–24 • 48,950
Cynthiana, KY 41031 • 6,497
Cypress, CA 90630 • 42,655
Cypress Lake, FL 33919 • 10,491
Cypress Quarters, FL 34972 • 1,343
Cyril, OK 73029 • 1,072

D

Dacono, CO 80514 • 2,228
Dacula, GA 30211 • 2,217
Dade □, FL • 1,937,094
Dade □, GA • 13,147
Dade □, MO • 7,449
Dade City, FL 33525–26 • 5,633
Dadeville, AL 36853 • 3,276
Daggett □, UT • 690
Dagsboro, DE 19939 • 398
Dahlonega, GA 30533 • 3,086
Daingerfield, TX 75638 • 2,572
Dakota □, MN • 275,227
Dakota □, NE • 16,742
Dakota City, IA 50529 • 1,024
Dakota City, NE 68731 • 1,470
Dale, IN 47523 • 1,553
Dale □, AL • 49,633
Dale City, VA 22193 • 47,170
Daleville, AL 36322 • 5,117
Daleville, IN 47334 • 1,681
Dalhart, TX 79022 • 6,246
Dallam □, TX • 5,461
Dallas, GA 30132 • 2,810
Dallas, NC 28034 • 3,012
Dallas, OR 97338 • 9,422
Dallas, PA 18612 • 2,567
Dallas, TX 75201–99 • 1,006,877
Dallas □, AL • 48,130
Dallas □, AR • 9,614
Dallas □, IA • 29,755
Dallas □, MO • 12,646
Dallas □, TX • 1,852,810
Dallas Center, IA 50063 • 1,454
Dallas City, IL 62330 • 1,037
Dallastown, PA 17313 • 3,974
Dalton, GA 30720–22 • 21,761
Dalton, MA 01226–27 • 6,797
Dalton, OH 44618 • 1,377
Dalton, PA 18414 • 1,369
Dalton Gardens, ID 83814 • 1,951
Daly City, CA 94014–17 • 92,311
Damascus, MD 20872 • 9,817
Dana Point, CA 92629 • 31,896
Danbury, CT 06810–13 • 65,585
Danbury, TX 77534 • 1,447
Dandridge, TN 37725 • 1,540
Dane □, WI • 367,085
Dania, FL 33004 • 13,024
Daniels □, MT • 2,266
Danielson, CT 06239 • 4,441
Dannemora, NY 12929 • 4,005
Dansville, NY 14437 • 5,002
Dante, VA 24237 • 1,083
Danvers, MA 01923 • 24,174
Danville, AR 72833 • 1,585
Danville, CA 94526 • 31,306
Danville, IL 61832–34 • 33,828
Danville, IN 46122 • 4,345
Danville, KY 40422–23 • 12,420
Danville, OH 43014 • 1,001
Danville, PA 17821 • 5,165
Danville, VA 24540–43 • 53,056
Daphne, AL 36526 • 11,290
Darby, PA 19023 • 11,140
Darby Township, PA 19036 • 10,955
Dardanelle, AR 72834 • 3,722
Dare □, NC • 22,746
Darien, CT 06820 • 18,130
Darien, GA 31305 • 1,783
Darien, IL 60559 • 18,341
Darien, WI 53114 • 1,158
Darke □, OH • 53,619
Darley Woods, DE 19810 • 1,220
Darlington, SC 29532 • 7,311
Darlington, WI 53530 • 2,235
Darlington □, SC • 61,851
Darrington, WA 98241 • 1,042
Dartmouth Woods, DE 19810 • 1,970
Dassel, MN 55325 • 1,082
Dauphin □, PA • 237,813
Davenport, FL 33837 • 1,529
Davenport, IA 52801–09 • 95,333
Davenport, WA 99122 • 1,502
David City, NE 68632 • 2,522
Davidson, NC 28036 • 4,046
Davidson □, NC • 126,677
Davidson □, TN • 510,784
Davidsville, PA 15928 • 1,167
Davie, FL 33328 • 47,217
Davie □, NC • 27,859
Daviess □, IN • 27,533
Daviess □, KY • 87,189
Daviess □, MO • 7,865
Davis, CA 95616–17 • 46,209
Davis, OK 73030 • 2,543
Davis □, IA • 8,312
Davis □, UT • 187,941
Davison, MI 48423 • 5,693
Davison □, SD • 17,503
Davisville, RI 02852 • 500
Dawes □, NE • 9,021
Dawson, GA 31742 • 5,295
Dawson, MN 56232 • 1,626
Dawson □, GA • 9,429
Dawson □, MT • 9,505
Dawson □, NE • 19,940
Dawson □, TX • 14,349
Dawson Springs, KY 42408 • 3,129
Day □, SD • 6,978
Dayton, KY 41074 • 6,576
Dayton, MN 55327 • 4,443
Dayton, NV 89403 • 2,217
Dayton, NJ 08810 • 1,200
Dayton, OH 45401–90 • 182,044
Dayton, OR 97114 • 1,526
Dayton, TN 37321 • 5,671
Dayton, TX 77535 • 5,151
Dayton, WA 99328 • 2,468
Dayton, WY 82836 • 565
Daytona Beach, FL 32114–25 • 61,921
Dayville, CT 06241 • 1,500
Deadwood, SD 57732 • 1,830
Deaf Smith □, TX • 19,153
Deal, NJ 07723 • 1,179
Deale, MD 20751 • 4,151
Dearborn, MI 48120–26 • 89,286
Dearborn □, IN • 38,835
Dearborn Heights, MI 48127 • 60,838
De Baca □, NM • 2,252
De Bary, FL 32713 • 7,176
Decatur, AL 35601–03 • 48,761
Decatur, GA 30030–37 • 17,336
Decatur, IL 62521–26 • 83,885
Decatur, IN 46733 • 8,644
Decatur, MI 49045 • 1,760
Decatur, MS 39327 • 1,248
Decatur, TN 37322 • 1,361
Decatur, TX 76234 • 4,252
Decatur □, GA • 25,511
Decatur □, IN • 23,645
Decatur □, IA • 8,338
Decatur □, KS • 4,021
Decatur □, TN • 10,472
Decherd, TN 37324 • 2,196
Deckerville, MI 48427 • 1,015
Decorah, IA 52101 • 8,063
Dedham, MA 02026 • 23,782
Deep River, CT 06417 • 2,520
Deerfield, IL 60015 • 17,327
Deerfield, WI 53531 • 1,617
Deerfield Beach, FL 33441–43 • 46,325
Deer Lodge, MT 59722 • 3,378
Deer Lodge □, MT • 10,278
Deer Park, NY 11729 • 28,840
Deer Park, OH 45236 • 6,181
Deer Park, TX 77536 • 27,652
Deer Park, WA 99006 • 2,278
Defiance, OH 43512 • 16,768
Defiance □, OH • 39,350
De Forest, WI 53532 • 4,882
De Funiak Springs, FL 32433 • 5,120
De Graff, OH 43318 • 1,331
De Kalb, IL 60115 • 34,925
De Kalb, MS 39328 • 1,073
De Kalb, TX 75559 • 1,976
De Kalb □, AL • 54,651
De Kalb □, GA • 545,837
De Kalb □, IL • 77,932
De Kalb □, IN • 35,324
De Kalb □, MO • 9,967
De Kalb □, TN • 14,360
Delafield, WI 53018 • 5,347
Del Aire, CA 90250 • 8,040
Delanco, NJ 08075 • 3,316
De Land, FL 32720–24 • 16,491
Delano, CA 93215–16 • 22,762
Delano, MN 55328 • 2,709
Delavan, IL 61734 • 1,642
Delavan, WI 53115 • 6,073
Delavan Lake, WI 53115 • 2,177
Delaware, OH 43015 • 20,030
Delaware □, IN • 119,659
Delaware □, IA • 18,035
Delaware □, NY • 47,225
Delaware □, OH • 66,929
Delaware □, OK • 28,070
Delaware □, PA • 547,651
Delaware City, DE 19706 • 1,682
Delcambre, LA 70528 • 1,978
Del City, OK 73115 • 23,928
De Leon, TX 76444 • 2,190
De Leon Springs, FL 32130 • 1,481
Delevan, NY 14042 • 1,214
Delhi, LA 71232 • 3,169
Delhi, NY 13753 • 3,064
Delhi Hills, OH 45238 • 27,647
Dell Rapids, SD 57022 • 2,484
Dellwood, MO 63136 • 5,245
Del Mar, CA 92014 • 4,860
Delmar, DE 19940 • 962
Delmar, MD 21875 • 1,430
Delmar, NY 12054 • 8,360
Del Norte, CO 81132 • 1,674
Del Norte □, CA • 23,460
Del Park Manor, DE 19808 • 1,550
Delphi, IN 46923 • 2,531
Delphos, OH 45833 • 7,093
Delran, NJ 08075 • 14,811
Delray Beach, FL 33444–47 • 47,181
Del Rio, FL 33617 • 8,248
Del Rio, TX 78840–42 • 30,705
Delta, CO 81416 • 3,789
Delta, OH 43515 • 2,849
Delta, UT 84624 • 2,998
Delta □, CO • 20,980
Delta □, MI • 37,780
Delta □, TX • 4,857
Delta Junction, AK 99737 • 652
Deltaville, VA 23043 • 1,082
Deltona, FL 32725 • 50,828
Demarest, NJ 07627 • 4,800
Deming, NM 88030–31 • 10,970
Demopolis, AL 36732 • 7,512
Demorest, GA 30535 • 1,088
Demotte, IN 46310 • 2,482
Denham Springs, LA 70726–27 • 8,381
Denison, IA 51442 • 6,604
Denison, TX 75020–21 • 21,505
Denmark, SC 29042 • 3,762
Denmark, WI 54208 • 1,612
Dennis, MA 02638 • 2,500
Dennison, OH 44621 • 3,282
Dennis Port, MA 02639 • 2,775
Denny Terrace, SC 29203 • 1,885
Dent □, MO • 13,702
Denton, MD 21629 • 2,977
Denton, NC 27239 • 1,292
Denton, TX 76201–06 • 66,270
Denton □, TX • 273,525
Dentsville, SC 29204 • 11,839
Denver, CO 80201–95 • 467,610
Denver, IA 50622 • 1,600
Denver, PA 17517 • 2,861
Denver □, CO • 467,610
Denver City, TX 79323 • 5,145
Denville, NJ 07834 • 14,380
De Pere, WI 54115 • 16,569
Depew, NY 14043 • 17,673
Deposit, NY 13754 • 1,936
Depue, IL 61322 • 1,729
De Queen, AR 71832 • 4,633
De Quincy, LA 70633 • 3,474
Derby, CT 06418 • 12,199
Derby, KS 67037 • 14,699
Derby, NY 14047 • 1,200
Derby Line, VT 05830 • 855
De Ridder, LA 70634 • 9,868
Dermott, AR 71638 • 4,715
Derry, NH 03038 • 20,446
Derry, PA 15627 • 2,950
Derwood, MD 20855 • 1,500
Des Allemands, LA 70030 • 2,504
Des Arc, AR 72040 • 2,001
Deschutes □, OR • 74,958
Desert Hot Springs, CA 92240 • 11,668
Desha □, AR • 16,798
Deshler, OH 43516 • 1,876
Desloge, MO 63601 • 4,150
De Smet, SD 57231 • 1,172
Des Moines, IA 50301–95 • 193,187
Des Moines, WA 98188 • 17,283
Des Moines □, IA • 42,614
De Soto, IL 62924 • 1,500
De Soto, IA 50069 • 1,033
De Soto, KS 66018 • 2,291
De Soto, MO 63020 • 5,993
De Soto, TX 75115 • 30,544
De Soto □, FL • 23,865
De Soto □, LA • 25,346
De Soto □, MS • 67,910
Despard, WV 26301 • 1,018
Des Peres, MO 63131 • 8,395
Des Plaines, IL 60016–19 • 53,223
Destin, FL 32540–41 • 8,080
Destrehan, LA 70047 • 8,031
Detroit, MI 48201–44 • 1,027,974
Detroit Lakes, MN 56501–02 • 6,635
Deuel □, NE • 2,237
Deuel □, SD • 4,522
Devils Lake, ND 58301 • 7,782
Devine, TX 78016 • 3,928
Devola, OH 45750 • 2,736
Devon, PA 19333 • 6,620
Devonshire, DE 19810 • 2,120
Dewey, OK 74029 • 3,326
Dewey □, OK • 5,551
Dewey □, SD • 5,523
Dewey Beach, DE 19971 • 204
Deweyville, TX 77614 • 1,218
De Witt, AR 72042 • 3,553
De Witt, IA 52742 • 4,514
De Witt, MI 48820 • 3,964
De Witt, NY 13214 • 8,244
De Witt □, IL • 16,516
De Witt □, TX • 18,840
Dexter, ME 04930 • 2,650
Dexter, MI 48130 • 1,497
Dexter, MO 63841 • 7,559
Dexter, NY 13634 • 1,030
Diamond Bar, CA 91765 • 53,672
Diamond Hill, RI 02864 • 810
Diamond Lake, IL 60060 • 1,500
Diamond Springs, CA 95619 • 2,872
Diamondville, WY 83116 • 864
Diaz, AR 72043 • 1,363
D'Iberville, MS 39532 • 6,566
Diboll, TX 75941 • 4,341
Dickens □, TX • 2,571
Dickenson □, VA • 17,620
Dickey □, ND • 6,107
Dickinson, ND 58601–02 • 16,097
Dickinson, TX 77539 • 9,497
Dickinson □, IA • 14,909
Dickinson □, KS • 18,958
Dickinson □, MI • 26,831
Dickson, TN 37055 • 8,791
Dickson □, TN • 35,061
Dickson City, PA 18519 • 6,276
Dierks, AR 71833 • 1,263
Dighton, KS 67839 • 1,361
Dighton, MA 02715 • 1,100
Dillard, OR 97432 • 1,000
Dilley, TX 78017 • 2,632
Dillingham, AK 99576 • 2,017
Dillon, MT 59725 • 3,991
Dillon, SC 29536 • 6,829
Dillon □, SC • 29,114
Dillsboro, IN 47018 • 1,200
Dillsburg, PA 17019 • 1,925
Dilworth, MN 56529 • 2,562
Dimmit □, TX • 10,433
Dimmitt, TX 79027 • 4,408
Dimondale, MI 48821 • 1,247
Dingmans Ferry, PA 18328 • 1,200
Dinuba, CA 93618 • 12,743
Dinwiddie □, VA • 20,960
Dishman, WA 99213 • 9,671
District Heights-Forestville, MD 20747 • 6,704
District of Columbia 0T15, DC •
Divernon, IL 62530 • 1,178
Divide □, ND • 2,899
Dixfield, ME 04224 • 1,300
Dix Hills, NY 11746 • 25,849
Dixie □, FL • 10,585
Dixon, CA 95620 • 10,401
Dixon, IL 61021 • 15,144
Dixon, MO 65459 • 1,585
Dixon □, NE • 6,143
Dixonville, PA 15734 • 1,000
Dobbs Ferry, NY 10522 • 9,940
Dobson, NC 27017 • 1,195
Docena, AL 35060 • 1,000
Dock Junction, GA 31520 • 7,094
Doddridge □, WV • 6,994
Dodge □, GA • 17,607
Dodge □, MN • 15,731
Dodge □, NE • 34,500
Dodge □, WI • 76,559
Dodge Center, MN 55927 • 1,954
Dodge City, KS 67801 • 21,129
Dodge Park, MD 20785 • 4,842
Dodgeville, WI 53533 • 3,882
Dolgeville, NY 13329 • 2,452
Dolomite, AL 35061 • 2,590
Dolores □, CO • 1,504
Dolton, IL 60419 • 23,930
Dona Ana, NM 88032 • 950
Dona Ana □, NM • 135,510
Donaldsonville, LA 70346 • 7,949
Donalsonville, GA 31745 • 2,761
Doneraile, SC 29532 • 1,276
Doniphan, MO 63935 • 1,713
Doniphan □, KS • 8,134
Donley □, TX • 3,696
Donna, TX 78537 • 12,652
Donora, PA 15033 • 5,928
Dooly □, GA • 9,901
Door □, WI • 25,690
Dora, AL 35062 • 2,214
Doraville, GA 30340 • 7,626
Dorchester □, MD • 30,236
Dorchester □, SC • 83,060
Dormont, PA 15216 • 9,772
Dorothy Pond, MA 01527 • 1,670
Dorr, MI 49323 • 1,450
Dorset, VT 05251 • 550
Dorsey, MD 21227 • 1,186
Dothan, AL 36301–04 • 53,589
Double Springs, AL 35553 • 1,138
Dougherty □, GA • 96,311
Douglas, AZ 85607–08 • 12,822
Douglas, GA 31533 • 10,464
Douglas, MI 49406 • 1,040
Douglas, WY 82633 • 5,076
Douglas □, CO • 60,391
Douglas □, GA • 71,120
Douglas □, IL • 19,464
Douglas □, KS • 81,798
Douglas □, MN • 28,674
Douglas □, MO • 11,876
Douglas □, NE • 416,444
Douglas □, NV • 27,637
Douglas □, OR • 94,649
Douglas □, SD • 3,746
Douglas □, WA • 26,205
Douglas □, WI • 41,758
Douglass, KS 67039 • 1,722
Douglasville, GA 30133–35 • 11,635
Dousman, WI 53118 • 1,277
Dover, AR 72837 • 1,055
Dover, DE 19901–03 • 27,630
Dover, FL 33527 • 2,606
Dover, MA 02030 • 2,163
Dover, NH 03820 • 25,042
Dover, NJ 07801 • 15,115
Dover, OH 44622 • 11,329
Dover, PA 17315 • 1,884
Dover, TN 37058 • 1,341
Dover-Foxcroft, ME 04426 • 3,077
Dover Plains, NY 12522 • 1,847
Dowagiac, MI 49047 • 6,409
Downers Grove, IL 60515–17 • 46,858
Downey, CA 90239–42 • 91,444
Downingtown, PA 19335 • 7,749
Downs, KS 67437 • 1,119
Downsville, NY 13755 • 1,100
Doylestown, OH 44230 • 2,668
Doylestown, PA 18901 • 8,575
Dracut, MA 01826 • 25,594
Drain, OR 97435 • 1,011
Draper, UT 84020 • 7,257
Drayton, ND 58225 • 961
Drayton, SC 29333 • 1,443
Drayton Plains, MI 48330 • 18,000
Dreamland Villa, AZ 85205 • 3,400
Dresden, OH 43821 • 1,581
Dresden, TN 38225 • 2,488
Dresslerville, NV 89410 • 180
Drew, MS 38737 • 2,349
Drew □, AR • 17,369
Drexel, NC 28619 • 1,746
Drexel, OH 45427 • 5,143
Drexel Hill, PA 19026 • 29,744
Dripping Springs, TX 78620 • 1,033
Druid Hills, GA 30333 • 12,174
Drumright, OK 74030 • 2,799
Dryden, NY 13053 • 1,908
Dry Ridge, KY 41035 • 1,601
Duarte, CA 91010 • 20,688
Dublin, CA 94568 • 23,229
Dublin, GA 31021 • 16,312
Dublin, OH 43017 • 16,366
Dublin, PA 18917 • 1,985
Dublin, TX 76446 • 3,190
Dublin, VA 24084 • 2,012
Du Bois, PA 15801 • 8,286
Dubois, WY 82513 • 895
Dubois □, IN • 36,616
Duboistown, PA 17701 • 1,201
Dubuque, IA 52001–04 • 57,546
Dubuque □, IA • 86,403
Duchesne, UT 84021 • 1,308
Duchesne □, UT • 12,645
Dudley, MA 01570–71 • 3,700
Due West, SC 29639 • 1,220
Dukes □, MA • 11,639
Dulce, NM 87528 • 2,438
Duluth, GA 30136 • 9,029
Duluth, MN 55801–16 • 85,493
Dumas, AR 71639 • 5,520
Dumas, TX 79029 • 12,871
Dumfries, VA 22026 • 4,282
Dumont, NJ 07628 • 17,187
Dunaire, GA 30032 • 7,170
Dunbar, PA 15431 • 1,213
Dunbar, WV 25064 • 8,697
Duncan, OK 73533–34 • 21,732
Duncan, SC 29334 • 2,152
Duncan Falls, OH 43734 • 1,200
Duncannon, PA 17020 • 1,450
Duncansville, PA 16635 • 1,309
Duncanville, TX 75116 • 35,748
Dundalk, MD 21222 • 65,800
Dundee, FL 33838 • 2,335
Dundee, IL 60118 • 3,728
Dundee, MI 48131 • 2,664
Dundee, NY 14837 • 1,588
Dundee, OR 97115 • 1,663
Dundy □, NE • 2,582
Dunedin, FL 34697–98 • 34,012
Dunellen, NJ 08812 • 6,528
Dunkirk, IN 47336 • 2,739
Dunkirk, NY 14048 • 13,989
Dunklin □, MO • 33,112
Dunlap, IN 46514 • 5,705
Dunlap, IA 51529 • 1,251
Dunlap, TN 37327 • 3,731
Dunleith, DE 19801 • 2,600
Dunmore, PA 18512 • 15,403
Dunn, NC 28334–35 • 8,336
Dunn □, ND • 4,005
Dunn □, WI • 35,909
Dunnellon, FL 32630 • 1,624
Dunn Loring Woods, VA 22180 • 2,800
Dunseith, ND 58329 • 723
Dunsmuir, CA 96025 • 2,129
Dunwoody, GA 30338 • 26,302
Du Page □, IL • 781,666
Duplin □, NC • 39,995
Dupont, CO 80024 • 5,200
Dupont, PA 18641 • 2,984
Dupont Manor, DE 19901 • 1,059
Duquesne, PA 15110 • 8,525
Du Quoin, IL 62832 • 6,697
Durand, IL 61024 • 1,100
Durand, MI 48429 • 4,283
Durand, WI 54736 • 2,003
Durango, CO 81301–02 • 12,430
Durant, IA 52747 • 1,549
Durant, MS 39063 • 2,838
Durant, OK 74701–02 • 12,823
Durham, CA 95938 • 1,500
Durham, CT 06422 • 2,650
Durham, NH 03824 • 9,236
Durham, NC 27701–22 • 136,611
Durham □, NC • 181,835
Duryea, PA 18642 • 4,869
Duson, LA 70529 • 1,465
Dutchess □, NY • 259,462
Duval □, FL • 672,971
Duval □, TX • 12,918
Duxbury, MA 02331–32 • 1,637
Dwight, IL 60420 • 4,230
Dyer, IN 46311 • 10,923
Dyer, TN 38330 • 2,204
Dyer □, TN • 34,854
Dyersburg, TN 38024–25 • 16,317
Dyersville, IA 52040 • 3,703
Dysart, IA 52224 • 1,230

E

Eagan, MN 55121 • 47,409
Eagar, AZ 85925 • 4,025
Eagle, CO 81631 • 1,580
Eagle, ID 83616 • 3,327
Eagle, NE 68347 • 1,047
Eagle, WI 53119 • 1,182
Eagle □, CO • 21,928
Eagle Grove, IA 50533 • 3,671
Eagle Lake, MN 56024 • 1,703
Eagle Lake, TX 77434 • 3,551
Eagle Lake, WI 53139 • 1,000
Eagle Pass, TX 78852–53 • 20,651
Eagle Point, OR 97524 • 3,008
Eagle River, WI 54521 • 1,374
Eagleton Village, TN 37801 • 5,331
Earle, AR 72331 • 3,393
Earlham, IA 50072 • 1,157
Earlimart, CA 93219 • 5,881

Earlington, KY 42410 • 1,833
Earlville, IL 60518 • 1,435
Early □, GA • 11,854
Earth, TX 79031 • 1,228
Easley, SC 29640–42 • 15,195
East Alton, IL 62024 • 7,063
East Arlington, VT 05252 • 600
East Aurora, NY 14052 • 6,647
East Bangor, PA 18013 • 1,006
East Barre, VT 05649 • 700
East Baton Rouge □, LA • 380,105
East Berlin, PA 17316 • 1,175
East Bernard, TX 77435 • 1,544
East Bethel, MN 55005 • 8,050
East Billerica, MA 01821 • 3,830
East Brady, PA 16028 • 1,047
East Brewton, AL 36426 • 2,579
East Bridgewater, MA 02333 • 3,270
East Brookfield, MA 01515 • 1,396
East Brooklyn, CT 06239 • 1,481
East Brunswick, NJ 08816 • 43,548
East Carbon, UT 84520 • 1,270
East Carroll □, LA • 9,709
Eastchester, NY 10709 • 18,537
East Chicago, IN 46312 • 33,892
East Cleveland, OH 44112 • 33,096
East Compton, CA 90221 • 7,967
East Dennis, MA 02641 • 1,500
East Detroit, MI 48021 • 35,283
East Douglas, MA 01516 • 1,945
East Dubuque, IL 61025 • 1,914
East Falmouth, MA 02536 • 5,577
East Farmingdale, NY 11735 • 4,510
East Feliciana □, LA • 19,211
East Flat Rock, NC 28726 • 3,218
East Gaffney, SC 29340 • 3,278
Eastgate, WA 98007 • 4,434
East Glenville, NY 12302 • 6,518
East Granby, CT 06026 • 1,200
East Grand Forks, MN 56721 • 8,658
East Grand Rapids, MI 49506 • 10,807
East Greenville, PA 18041 • 3,117
East Greenwich, RI 02818 • 11,865
East Half Hollow Hills, NY 11746 • 7,010
Eastham, MA 02642 • 1,150
East Hampton, CT 06424 • 2,167
Easthampton, MA 01027 • 15,580
East Hampton, NY 11937 • 1,402
East Hanover, NJ • 9,926
East Hartford, CT 06128 • 50,452
East Haven, CT 06512 • 26,144
East Helena, MT 59635 • 1,538
East Hemet, CA 92343 • 17,611
East Hills, NY 11576 • 6,746
East Islip, NY 11730 • 14,325
East Jordan, MI 49727 • 2,240
Eastlake, OH 44094 • 21,161
East La Mirada, CA 90638 • 9,367
Eastland, TX 76448 • 3,690
Eastland □, TX • 18,488
East Lansing, MI 48823–26 • 50,677
East Las Vegas, NV 89112 • 11,087
East Liverpool, OH 43920 • 13,654
East Longmeadow, MA 01028 • 12,905
East Los Angeles, CA 90022 • 126,379
East Lyme, CT 06333 • 1,200
Eastman, GA 31023 • 5,153
East Marietta, GA 30062 • 11,900
East Marion, NY 11939 • 1,500
East Matunuck, RI 02879 • 500
East Meadow, NY 11554 • 36,609
East Middlebury, VT 05740 • 500
East Midvale, UT 84047 • 3,800
East Millinocket, ME 04430 • 2,075
East Moline, IL 61244 • 20,147
East Montpelier, VT 05651 • 600
East Naples, FL 33962 • 22,951
East Newark, NJ 07029 • 2,157
East Newnan, GA 30263 • 1,173
East Norriton, PA 19401 • 13,324
East Northport, NY 11731 • 20,411
Easton, MD 21601 • 9,372
Easton, PA 18042–44 • 26,276
East Orange, NJ 07017–19 • 73,552
East Orleans, MA 02643 • 1,850
Eastover, SC 29044 • 1,044
East Palatka, FL 32131 • 1,989
East Palestine, OH 44413 • 5,168
East Palo Alto, CA 94303 • 23,451
East Patchogue, NY 11772 • 20,195
East Pea Ridge, WV 25705 • 4,980
East Peoria, IL 61611 • 21,378
East Pepperell, MA 01463 • 2,296
East Petersburg, PA 17520 • 4,197
East Pittsburgh, PA 15112 • 2,160
Eastpoint, FL 32328 • 1,577
East Point, GA 30344 • 34,402
Eastport, ME 04631 • 1,965
Eastport, NY 11941 • 1,500
East Porterville, CA 93257 • 5,790
East Port Orchard, WA 98366 • 5,409
East Prairie, MO 63845 • 3,416
East Providence, RI 02914 • 50,380
East Quogue, NY 11942 • 4,372
East Richmond, CA 94805 • 5,100
East Ridge, TN 37412 • 21,101
East River, CT 06443 • 3,440
East Rochester, NY 14445 • 6,932
East Rockaway, NY 11518 • 10,152
East Rockingham, NC 28379 • 4,158
East Rutherford, NJ 07073 • 7,902
East Saint Louis, IL 62201–08 • 40,944
Eastsound, WA 98245 • 1,100
East Spencer, NC 28039 • 2,055
East Stroudsburg, PA 18301 • 8,781
East Tawas, MI 48730 • 2,887
East Templeton, MA 01438 • 1,300
East Troy, WI 53120 • 2,664
East Tustin, CA 92705 • 10,000
East Vestal, NY 13902 • 6,310
East View, WV 26301 • 1,222
East Walpole, MA 02032 • 3,760
East Wareham, MA 02538 • 1,500
East Washington, PA 15301 • 2,126
East Wenatchee, WA 98802 • 2,701
East Windsor, NJ 08520 • 15,000
Eastwood, MI 49001 • 6,340
Eastwood Hills, UT 84106 • 1,200
Eaton, CO 80615 • 1,959
Eaton, IN 47338 • 1,614
Eaton, OH 45320 • 7,396
Eaton □, MI • 92,879
Eaton Rapids, MI 48827 • 4,695
Eatonton, GA 31024 • 4,737
Eatontown, NJ 07724 • 13,800
Eatonville, WA 98328 • 1,374
Eau Claire, WI 54701–03 • 56,856
Eau Claire □, WI • 85,183
Ebensburg, PA 15931 • 3,872
Eccles, WV 25836 • 1,162
Echo Bay, NV 89040 • 120
Echols □, GA • 2,334
Eckhart Mines, MD 21528 • 1,333
Eclectic, AL 36024 • 1,087
Economy, PA 15005 • 9,519
Ecorse, MI 48229 • 12,180
Ector □, TX • 118,934
Edcouch, TX 78538 • 2,878
Eddy □, NM • 48,605
Eddy □, ND • 2,951
Eddystone, PA 19013 • 2,446
Eddyville, IA 52553 • 1,010
Eddyville, KY 42038 • 1,889
Eden, NY 14057 • 3,088
Eden, NC 27288 • 15,238
Eden, TX 76837 • 1,567
Eden Prairie, MN 55344 • 39,311
Edenton, NC 27932 • 5,268
Edgar, WI 54426 • 1,318
Edgar □, IL • 19,595
Edgartown, MA 02539 • 3,062
Edgecombe □, NC • 56,558
Edgefield, SC 29824 • 2,563
Edgefield □, SC • 18,375
Edgeley, ND 58433 • 680
Edgemere, MD 21221 • 9,226
Edgemont, SD 57735 • 906
Edgemoor, DE 19802 • 5,853
Edgerton, KS 66021 • 1,244
Edgerton, MN 56128 • 1,106
Edgerton, OH 43517 • 1,896
Edgerton, WI 53534 • 4,254
Edgerton, WY 82635 • 247
Edgewater, AL 35224 • 1,120
Edgewater, CO 80214 • 4,613
Edgewater, FL 32132 • 15,337
Edgewater, MD 21037 • 1,600
Edgewater, NJ 07020 • 5,001
Edgewater Park, NJ 08010 • 8,388
Edgewood, IN 46011 • 2,057
Edgewood, KY 41017 • 8,143
Edgewood, MD • 3,470
Edgewood, MD 21040 • 23,903
Edgewood, OH 44004 • 5,189
Edgewood, PA 15218 • 3,581
Edgewood, WA 98372 • 2,650
Edgeworth, PA 15143 • 1,670
Edina, MN 55410 • 46,070
Edina, MO 63537 • 1,283
Edinboro, PA 16412 • 7,736
Edinburg, TX 78539–40 • 29,885
Edinburgh, IN 46124 • 4,536
Edison, GA 31746 • 1,182
Edison, NJ 08817–20 • 88,680
Edmond, OK 73034 • 52,315
Edmonds, WA 98020 • 30,744
Edmondson Heights, MD 21207 • 4,750
Edmonson □, KY • 10,357
Edmonton, KY 42129 • 1,477
Edmore, MI 48829 • 1,126
Edmunds □, SD • 4,356
Edna, TX 77957 • 5,343
Edwards, MS 39066 • 1,279
Edwards □, IL • 7,440
Edwards □, KS • 3,787
Edwards □, TX • 2,266
Edwardsburg, MI 49112 • 1,142
Edwardsville, IL 62025 • 14,579
Edwardsville, KS 66113 • 3,979
Edwardsville, PA 18704 • 5,399
Effingham, IL 62401 • 11,851
Effingham □, GA • 25,687
Effingham □, IL • 31,704
Egg Harbor City, NJ 08215 • 4,583
Egypt, MA 02066 • 1,100
Egypt Lake, FL 33614 • 14,580
Ehrenberg, AZ 85334 • 1,500
Elba, AL 36323 • 4,011
Elbert □, CO • 9,646
Elbert □, GA • 18,949
Elberta, GA 31093 • 1,559
Elberton, GA 30635 • 5,682
Elbow Lake, MN 56531 • 1,186
Elburn, IL 60119 • 1,275
El Cajon, CA 92019–22 • 88,693
El Campo, TX 77437 • 10,511
El Centro, CA 92243–44 • 31,384
El Cerrito, CA 94530 • 22,869
Eldersburg, MD 21784 • 9,720
Eldon, IA 52554 • 1,070
Eldon, MO 65026 • 4,419
Eldora, IA 50627 • 3,038
El Dorado, AR 71730–31 • 23,146
Eldorado, IL 62930 • 4,536
El Dorado, KS 67042 • 11,504
Eldorado, TX 76936 • 2,019
El Dorado □, CA • 125,995
El Dorado Hills, CA 95630 • 6,395
El Dorado Springs, MO 64744 • 3,830
Eldridge, IA 52748 • 3,378
Eleanor, WV 25070 • 1,256
Electra, TX 76360 • 3,113
Eleele, HI 96705 • 1,489
El Encanto Heights, CA 93117 • 7,700
Elfers, FL 34680 • 12,356
Elgin, IL 60120–23 • 77,010
Elgin, ND 58533 • 765
Elgin, OR 97827 • 1,586
Elgin, TX 78621 • 4,846
Elida, OH 45807 • 1,486
Elizabeth, NJ 07201–08 • 110,002
Elizabeth City, NC 27906–09 • 14,292
Elizabethton, TN 37643–44 • 11,931
Elizabethtown, KY 42701–02 • 18,167
Elizabethtown, NC 28337 • 3,704
Elizabethtown, PA 17022 • 9,952
Elizabethville, PA 17023 • 1,467
Elk □, KS • 3,327
Elk □, PA • 34,878
Elkader, IA 52043 • 1,510
Elk City, OK 73644 • 10,428
Elk Grove, CA 95624 • 17,483
Elk Grove Village, IL 60009 • 33,429
Elkhart, IN 46514–17 • 43,627
Elkhart, KS 67950 • 2,318
Elkhart, TX 75839 • 1,076
Elkhart □, IN • 156,198
Elkhart Lake, WI 53020 • 1,019
Elkhorn, NE 68022 • 1,398
Elkhorn, WI 53121 • 5,337
Elkin, NC 28621 • 3,790
Elkins, WV 26241 • 7,420
Elkland, PA 16920 • 1,849
Elk Mountain, WY 82324 • 174
Elko, NV 89801–02 • 14,736
Elko □, NV • 33,530
Elk Point, SD 57025 • 1,423
Elk Rapids, MI 49629 • 1,626
Elkridge, MD 21227 • 12,953
Elk River, MN 55330 • 11,143
Elkton, KY 42220 • 1,789
Elkton, MD 21921–22 • 9,073
Elkton, VA 22827 • 1,935
Elkview, WV 25071 • 1,047
Ellaville, GA 31806 • 1,724
Ellendale, DE 19941 • 313
Ellendale, ND 58436 • 1,798
Ellensburg, WA 98926 • 12,361
Ellenton, FL 34222 • 2,573
Ellenville, NY 12428 • 4,243
Ellerbe, NC 28338 • 1,132
Ellerslie, MD 21529 • 1,500
Ellettsville, IN 47429 • 3,275
Ellicott City, MD 21043 • 41,396
Ellijay, GA 30540 • 1,178
Ellington, CT 06029 • 1,500
Ellinwood, KS 67526 • 2,329
Elliott □, KY • 6,455
Ellis, KS 67637 • 1,814
Ellis □, KS • 26,004
Ellis □, OK • 4,497
Ellis □, TX • 85,167
Ellisville, MS 39437 • 3,634
Ellisville, MO 63011 • 7,545
Ellport, PA 16117 • 1,243
Ellsworth, KS 67439 • 2,294
Ellsworth, ME 04605 • 5,975
Ellsworth, PA 15331 • 1,048
Ellsworth, WI 54011 • 2,706
Ellsworth □, KS • 6,586
Ellwood City, PA 16117 • 8,894
Elma, WA 98541 • 3,011
Elm City, NC 27822 • 1,624
Elmer, NJ 08318 • 1,571
Elm Grove, WI 53122 • 6,261
Elmhurst, IL 60126 • 42,029
Elmira, NY 14901–05 • 33,724
El Mirage, AZ 85335 • 5,001
Elmira Heights, NY 14903 • 4,359
Elmont, NY 11003 • 28,612
El Monte, CA 91731–34 • 106,209
Elmora, PA 15737 • 1,500
Elmore, OH 43416 • 1,334
Elmore □, AL • 49,210
Elmore □, ID • 21,205
Elmwood, IL 61529 • 1,841
Elmwood Park, IL 60635 • 23,206
Elmwood Park, NJ 07407 • 17,623
Elmwood Place, OH 45216 • 2,937
Eloise, FL 33880 • 1,408
Elon College, NC 27244 • 4,394
Eloy, AZ 85231 • 7,211
El Paso, IL 61738 • 2,499
El Paso, TX 79901–99 • 515,342
El Paso □, CO • 397,014
El Paso □, TX • 591,610
El Portal, FL 33138 • 2,457
El Reno, OK 73036 • 15,414
Elroy, WI 53929 • 1,533
Elsa, TX 78543 • 5,242
Elsberry, MO 63343 • 1,898
El Segundo, CA 90245 • 15,223
Elsmere, DE 19805 • 5,935
Elsmere, KY 41018 • 6,847
Elsmere, NY 12054 • 4,180
El Sobrante, CA 94803 • 9,852
Elton, LA 70532 • 1,277
El Toro, CA 92630 • 62,685
Elvins, MO 63601 • 1,391
Elwood, IN 46036 • 9,494
Elwood, KS 66024 • 1,079
Elwood, NJ 08217 • 1,400
Elwood, NY 11731 • 10,916
Ely, MN 55731 • 3,968
Ely, NV 89301 • 4,756
Elyria, OH 44035–39 • 56,746
Elysburg, PA 17824 • 1,890
Emanuel □, GA • 20,546
Emerson, GA 30137 • 1,201
Emerson, NJ 07630 • 6,930
Emery □, UT • 10,332
Eminence, KY 40019 • 2,055
Emmaus, PA 18049 • 11,157
Emmet □, IA • 11,569
Emmet □, MI • 25,040
Emmetsburg, IA 50536 • 3,940
Emmett, ID 83617 • 4,601
Emmitsburg, MD 21727 • 1,688
Emmonak, AK 99581 • 642
Emmons □, ND • 4,830
Empire, NV 89405 • 300
Emporia, KS 66801 • 25,512
Emporia, VA 23847 • 5,306
Emporium, PA 15834 • 2,513
Emsworth, PA 15202 • 2,892
Encampment, WY 82325 • 490
Encinitas, CA 92023–24 • 55,386
Enderlin, ND 58027 • 997
Endicott, NY 13760 • 13,531
Endwell, NY 13760 • 12,602
Enfield (Thompsonville), CT 06082–83 • 8,458
Enfield, NH 03748 • 1,560
Enfield, NC 27823 • 3,082
England, AR 72046 • 3,351
Engleside, VA 22309 • 24,058
Englewood, CO 80110–12 • 29,387
Englewood, FL 34223–24 • 15,025
Englewood, NJ 07631–32 • 24,850
Englewood, OH 45322 • 11,432
Englewood, TN 37329 • 1,611
Englewood Cliffs, NJ 07632 • 5,634
Englishtown, NJ 07726 • 1,268
Enid, OK 73701–06 • 45,309
Enka, NC 28728 • 5,567
Ennis, MT 59729 • 773
Ennis, TX 75119–20 • 13,883
Enoch, UT 84720 • 1,947
Enola, PA 17025 • 5,961
Enon, OH 45323 • 2,605
Enoree, SC 29335 • 1,107
Enosburg Falls, VT 05450 • 1,350
Ensley, FL 32504 • 16,362
Enterprise, AL 36330–31 • 20,123
Enterprise, OR 97828 • 1,905
Enterprise, WV 26568 • 1,058
Enumclaw, WA 98022 • 7,227
Ephraim, UT 84627 • 3,363
Ephrata, PA 17522 • 12,133
Ephrata, WA 98823 • 5,349
Epping, NH 03042 • 1,384
Epworth, IA 52045 • 1,297
Erath, LA 70533 • 2,428
Erath □, TX • 27,991
Erial, NJ 08081 • 2,500
Erick, OK 73645 • 1,083
Erie, CO 80516 • 1,258
Erie, IL 61250 • 1,572
Erie, KS 66733 • 1,276
Erie, PA 16501–65 • 108,718
Erie □, NY • 968,532
Erie □, OH • 76,779
Erie □, PA • 275,572
Erin, TN 37061 • 1,586
Erlanger, KY 41018 • 15,979
Erma, NJ 08204 • 2,045
Errol Heights, OR 97266 • 10,487
Erwin, NC 28339 • 4,061
Erwin, TN 37650 • 5,015
Escalon, CA 95320 • 4,437
Escambia □, AL • 35,518
Escambia □, FL • 262,798
Escanaba, MI 49829 • 13,659
Escatawpa, MS 39552 • 3,902
Escondido, CA 92025–27 • 108,635
Esmeralda □, NV • 1,344
Esmond, RI 02917 • 4,320
Espanola, NM 87532 • 8,389
Esparto, CA 95627 • 1,487
Esperance, WA 98043 • 11,236
Espy, PA 17815 • 1,430
Essex, CT 06426 • 2,500
Essex, MD 21221 • 40,872
Essex, MA 01929 • 1,507
Essex, VT 05451 • 800
Essex □, MA • 670,080
Essex □, NJ • 778,206
Essex □, NY • 37,152
Essex □, VT • 6,405
Essex □, VA • 8,689
Essex Fells, NJ 07021 • 2,363
Essex Junction, VT 05452–53 • 8,396
Essexville, MI 48732 • 4,088
Estacada, OR 97023 • 2,016
Estelle, LA 70072 • 14,091
Estell Manor, NJ 08319 • 1,404
Estes Park, CO 80517 • 3,184
Estherville, IA 51334 • 6,720
Estill, SC 29918 • 2,387
Estill □, KY • 14,614
Estill Springs, TN 37330 • 1,408
Etna, PA 15223 • 4,200
Etowah, TN 37331 • 3,815
Etowah □, AL • 99,840
Ettrick, VA 23803 • 5,290
Euclid, OH 44117 • 54,875
Eudora, AR 71640 • 3,155
Eudora, KS 66025 • 3,006
Eufaula, AL 36027 • 13,220
Eufaula, OK 74432 • 2,652
Eugene, OR 97401–05 • 112,669
Euless, TX 76039–40 • 38,149
Eunice, LA 70535 • 11,162
Eunice, NM 88231 • 2,676
Eupora, MS 39744 • 2,145
Eureka, CA 95501–02 • 27,025
Eureka, IL 61530 • 4,435
Eureka, KS 67045 • 2,974
Eureka, MO 63025 • 4,683
Eureka, MT 59917 • 1,043
Eureka, NV 89316 • 650
Eureka, SC 29706 • 1,738
Eureka, SD 57437 • 1,197
Eureka □, NV • 1,547
Eureka Springs, AR 72632 • 1,900
Eustis, FL 32726–27 • 12,967
Eutaw, AL 35462 • 2,281
Evangeline □, LA • 33,274
Evans, CO 80620 • 5,877
Evans, GA 30809 • 2,000
Evans □, GA • 8,724
Evans City, PA 16033 • 2,054
Evansdale, IA 50707 • 4,638
Evanston, IL 60201–04 • 73,233
Evanston, WY 82930–31 • 10,903
Evansville, IN 47701–37 • 126,272
Evansville, WI 53536 • 3,174
Evansville, WY 82636 • 1,403
Evart, MI 49631 • 1,744
Evarts, KY 40828 • 1,063
Eveleth, MN 55734 • 4,064
Everett, MA 02149 • 35,701
Everett, PA 15537 • 1,777
Everett, WA 98201–08 • 69,961
Evergreen, AL 36401 • 3,911
Evergreen, CO 80439 • 7,582
Evergreen Park, IL 60642 • 20,874
Everman, TX 76140 • 5,672
Everson, WA 98247 • 1,490
Ewa, HI 96706 • 3,780
Ewa Beach, HI 96706–07 • 14,315
Ewing Township, NJ 08618 • 34,185
Excelsior Springs, MO 64024 • 10,354
Exeter, CA 93221 • 7,276
Exeter, NH 03833 • 9,556
Exeter, PA 18643 • 5,691
Exmore, VA 23350 • 1,115
Experiment, GA 30223 • 3,762
Eyota, MN 55934 • 1,448

F

Fabens, TX 79838 • 5,599
Factoryville, PA 18419 • 1,310
Fairbank, IA 50629 • 1,018
Fairbanks, AK 99701 • 30,843
Fair Bluff, NC 28439 • 1,068
Fairborn, OH 45324 • 31,300
Fairburn, GA 30213 • 4,013
Fairbury, IL 61739 • 3,643
Fairbury, NE 68352 • 4,335
Fairchance, PA 15436 • 1,918
Fairdale, KY 40118 • 6,563
Fairfax, CA 94930 • 6,931
Fairfax, DE 19803 • 2,075
Fairfax, MN 55332 • 1,276
Fairfax, OK 74637 • 1,749
Fairfax, SC 29827 • 2,317
Fairfax, VA 22030–39 • 19,622
Fairfax □, VA • 818,584
Fairfield, AL 35064 • 12,200
Fairfield, CA 94533 • 77,211
Fairfield, CT 06430–32 • 53,418
Fairfield, IL 62837 • 5,439
Fairfield, IA 52556 • 9,768
Fairfield, ME 04937 • 2,794
Fairfield, NJ 07004 • 7,615
Fairfield, OH 45014 • 39,729
Fairfield, TX 75840 • 3,234
Fairfield □, CT • 827,645
Fairfield □, OH • 103,461
Fairfield □, SC • 22,295
Fairfield Bay, AR 72088 • 2,332
Fair Grove, NC 27360 • 1,500
Fairhaven, MA 02719 • 15,759
Fair Haven, NJ 07704 • 5,270
Fair Haven, VT 05743 • 2,432
Fairhope, AL 36532–33 • 8,485
Fair Lawn, NJ 07410 • 30,548
Fairlawn, OH 44313 • 5,779
Fairlawn, VA 24141 • 2,399
Fairlea, WV 24902 • 1,743
Fairless Hills, PA 19030 • 9,026
Fairmont, IL 60441 • 2,260
Fairmont, MN 56031 • 11,265
Fairmont, NC 28340 • 2,489
Fairmont, WV 26554–55 • 20,210
Fairmount, IN 46928 • 3,130
Fairmount, NY 13031 • 12,266
Fairmount Heights, MD 20743 • 1,238
Fair Oaks, CA 95628 • 26,867
Fair Oaks, GA 30060 • 6,996
Fairoaks, PA 15003 • 1,854
Fair Plain, MI 49022 • 8,051
Fairport, NY 14450 • 5,943
Fairport Harbor, OH 44077 • 2,978
Fairton, NJ 08320 • 1,359
Fairview, MT 59221 • 869
Fairview, NJ 07022 • 10,733
Fairview, OK 73737 • 2,936
Fairview, OR 97024 • 2,391
Fairview, PA 16415 • 1,988
Fairview, TN 37062 • 4,210
Fairview Heights, IL 62208 • 14,351
Fairview Park, IN 47842 • 1,446
Fairview Park, OH 44126 • 18,028
Fairview Shores, FL 32804 • 13,192
Fairway, KS 66205 • 4,173
Fairwood, WA 98058 • 2,000
Fairwood, WA 99218 • 5,807
Falconer, NY 14733 • 2,653
Falcon Heights, MN 55113 • 5,380
Falfurrias, TX 78355 • 5,788
Falkville, AL 35622 • 1,337
Fall Branch, TN 37656 • 1,203
Fallbrook, CA 92028 • 22,095
Fall City, WA 98024 • 1,582
Fall Creek, WI 54742 • 1,034
Fallon, NV 89406 • 6,438
Fallon □, MT • 3,103
Fall River, MA 02720–26 • 92,703
Fall River □, SD • 7,353
Falls □, TX • 17,712
Falls Church, VA 22040–46 • 9,578
Falls City, NE 68355 • 4,769
Falls Creek, PA 15840 • 1,087
Fallston, MD 21047 • 5,730
Falls Township, PA 19054 • 36,083
Falmouth, KY 41040 • 2,378
Falmouth, ME 04105 • 7,610
Falmouth, MA 02540 • 4,047
Falmouth, VA 22405 • 3,541
Fannin □, GA • 15,992
Fannin □, TX • 24,804
Fanwood, NJ 07023 • 7,115
Fargo, ND 58102–09 • 74,111
Faribault, MN 55021 • 17,085
Faribault □, MN • 16,937
Farley, IA 52046 • 1,354
Farmer City, IL 61842 • 2,114
Farmers Branch, TX 75234 • 24,250
Farmersburg, IN 47850 • 1,159
Farmersville, CA 93223 • 6,235
Farmerville, LA 71241 • 3,334
Farmingdale, ME 04345 • 2,070
Farmingdale, NJ 07727 • 1,462
Farmingdale, NY 11735 • 8,022
Farmington, AR 72730 • 1,322
Farmington, CT 06032 • 2,500
Farmington, IL 61531 • 2,535
Farmington, ME 04938 • 4,197
Farmington, MI 48335–36 • 10,132
Farmington, MN 55024 • 5,940
Farmington, MO 63640 • 11,598
Farmington, NH 03835 • 3,567
Farmington, NM 87401–02 • 33,997
Farmington, UT 84025 • 9,028
Farmington Hills, MI 48331–34 • 74,652
Farmingville, NY 11738 • 14,842
Farmland, IN 47340 • 1,412
Farmville, NC 27828 • 4,392
Farmville, VA 23901 • 6,046
Farragut, TN 37922 • 12,793
Farrell, PA 16121 • 6,841
Farwell, TX 79325 • 1,373
Faulk □, SD • 2,744
Faulkland Heights, DE 19808 • 1,300
Faulkner □, AR • 60,006
Faulkton, SD 57438 • 809
Fauquier □, VA • 48,741
Fayette, AL 35555 • 4,909
Fayette, IA 52142 • 1,317
Fayette, MS 39069 • 1,853
Fayette, MO 65248 • 2,888
Fayette, OH 43521 • 1,248
Fayette □, AL • 17,962
Fayette □, GA • 62,415
Fayette □, IL • 20,893
Fayette □, IN • 26,015
Fayette □, IA • 21,843
Fayette □, KY • 225,366
Fayette □, OH • 27,466
Fayette □, PA • 145,351

Fayette □, TN • *25,559*
Fayette □, TX • *20,095*
Fayette □, WV • *47,952*
Fayetteville, AR 72701–03 • *42,099*
Fayetteville, GA 30214 • *5,827*
Fayetteville, NC 28301–14 • *75,695*
Fayetteville, PA 17222 • *3,033*
Fayetteville, TN 37334 • *6,921*
Fayetteville, WV 25840 • *2,182*
Fayville, MA 01745 • *1,000*
Federal Heights, CO 80221 • *9,342*
Federalsburg, MD 21632 • *2,365*
Federal Way, WA 98003 • *67,554*
Feeding Hills, MA 01030 • *5,470*
Fellowship, NJ 08057 • *4,250*
Fellsmere, FL 32948 • *2,179*
Felton, CA 95041 • *5,350*
Felton, DE 19943 • *683*
Fennimore, WI 53809 • *2,378*
Fennville, MI 49408 • *1,023*
Fenton, MI 48430 • *8,444*
Fentress □, TN • *14,669*
Ferdinand, IN 47532 • *2,318*
Fergus □, MT • *12,083*
Fergus Falls, MN 56537–38 • *12,362*
Ferguson, MO 63135 • *22,286*
Fernandina Beach, FL 32034 • *8,765*
Fern Creek, KY 40291 • *16,406*
Ferndale, CA 95536 • *1,331*
Ferndale, MD 21061 • *16,355*
Ferndale, MI 48220 • *25,084*
Ferndale, PA 15905 • *2,020*
Ferndale, WA 98248 • *5,398*
Fernley, NV 89408 • *5,164*
Fern Park, FL 32730 • *8,294*
Fernway, PA 16063 • *9,072*
Ferriday, LA 71334 • *4,111*
Ferris, TX 75125 • *2,212*
Ferron, UT 84523 • *1,606*
Ferry □, WA • *6,295*
Ferry Farms, VA 22405 • *1,600*
Fessenden, ND 58438 • *655*
Festus, MO 63028 • *8,105*
Fieldale, VA 24089 • *1,018*
Fig Garden, CA 93704 • *9,000*
Filer, ID 83328 • *1,511*
Fillmore, CA 93015–16 • *11,992*
Fillmore, UT 84631 • *1,956*
Fillmore □, MN • *20,777*
Fillmore □, NE • *7,103*
Findlay, OH 45839–40 • *35,703*
Finley, TN 38030 • *1,014*
Finney □, KS • *33,070*
Fircrest, WA 98466 • *5,258*
Firebaugh, CA 93622 • *4,429*
Firestone, CO 80520 • *1,358*
Fisher, IL 61843 • *1,526*
Fisher □, TX • *4,842*
Fishers, IN 46038 • *7,508*
Fishkill, NY 12524 • *1,957*
Fiskdale, MA 01518 • *2,189*
Fitchburg, MA 01420 • *41,194*
Fitzgerald, GA 31750 • *8,612*
Five Points, NM 87105 • *4,200*
Flagler □, FL • *28,701*
Flagler Beach, FL 32136 • *3,820*
Flagstaff, AZ 86001–16 • *45,857*
Flanders, NJ 07836 • *3,040*
Flandreau, SD 57028 • *2,311*
Flathead □, MT • *59,218*
Flatonia, TX 78941 • *1,295*
Flat River, MO 63601 • *4,823*
Flat Rock, MI 48134 • *7,290*
Flat Rock, NC 28731 • *1,200*
Flatwoods, KY 41139 • *7,799*
Fleetwood, PA 19522 • *3,478*
Fleming □, KY • *12,292*
Flemingsburg, KY 41041 • *3,071*
Flemington, NJ 08822 • *4,047*
Flemington, PA 17745 • *1,321*
Fletcher, NC 28732 • *2,787*
Fletcher, OK 73541 • *1,002*
Flint, MI 48501–32 • *140,761*
Flint City, AL 35601 • *1,033*
Flippin, AR 72634 • *1,006*
Flomaton, AL 36441 • *1,811*
Flora, IL 62839 • *5,054*
Flora, IN 46929 • *2,179*
Flora, MS 39071 • *1,482*
Floraia, AL 36442 • *2,075*
Floral City, FL 32636 • *2,609*
Floral Park, NY 11001–05 • *15,947*
Florence, AL 35630–33 • *36,426*
Florence, AZ 85232 • *7,510*
Florence, CA 90001 • *43,900*
Florence, CO 81226 • *2,990*
Florence, KY 41042 • *18,624*
Florence, MS 39073 • *1,831*
Florence, NJ 08518 • *4,203*
Florence, OR 97439 • *5,162*
Florence, SC 29501–06 • *29,813*
Florence □, SC • *114,344*
Florence □, WI • *4,590*
Floresville, TX 78114 • *5,247*
Florham Park, NJ 07932 • *8,521*
Florida, NY 10921 • *2,497*
Florida City, FL 33034 • *5,806*
Florida Ridge, FL 32960 • *12,218*
Florin, CA 95828 • *24,330*
Florissant, MO 63031–34 • *51,206*
Flossmoor, IL 60422 • *8,651*
Flower Hill, NY 11050 • *4,490*
Flowery Branch, GA 30542 • *1,251*
Flowood, MS 39208 • *2,860*
Floyd □, GA • *81,251*
Floyd □, IN • *64,404*
Floyd □, IA • *17,058*
Floyd □, KY • *43,586*
Floyd □, TX • *8,497*
Floyd □, VA • *12,005*
Floydada, TX 79235 • *3,896*
Flushing, MI 48433 • *8,542*
Flushing, OH 43977 • *1,042*
Fluvanna □, VA • *12,429*
Foard □, TX • *1,794*
Folcroft, PA 19032 • *7,506*
Foley, AL 36535–36 • *4,937*
Foley, MN 56329 • *1,854*
Folkston, GA 31537 • *2,285*
Follansbee, WV 26037 • *3,339*
Folly Beach, SC 29439 • *1,398*
Folsom, CA 95630 • *29,802*
Folsom, NJ 08037 • *2,181*

Fonda, NY 12068 • *1,007*
Fond du Lac, WI 54935–36 • *37,757*
Fond du Lac □, WI • *90,083*
Fontana, CA 92334–36 • *87,535*
Fontana, WI 53125 • *1,635*
Foothill Farms, CA 95841 • *17,135*
Ford □, IL • *14,275*
Ford □, KS • *27,463*
Ford City, CA 93268 • *3,781*
Ford City, PA 16226 • *3,413*
Ford Heights, IL 60411 • *4,259*
Fords, NJ 08863 • *14,392*
Fords Prairie, WA 98531 • *2,480*
Fordyce, AR 71742 • *4,729*
Foreman, AR 71836 • *1,267*
Forest, MS 39074 • *5,060*
Forest, OH 45843 • *1,594*
Forest □, PA • *4,802*
Forest □, WI • *8,776*
Forest Acres, SC 29206 • *7,197*
Forest City, IA 50436 • *4,430*
Forest City, NC 28043 • *7,475*
Forest City, PA 18421 • *1,846*
Forestdale, AL 35214 • *10,395*
Forestdale, RI 02824 • *530*
Forest Dale, VT 05745 • *350*
Forest Grove, OR 97116 • *13,559*
Forest Hill, TX 76119 • *11,482*
Forest Hills, PA 15221 • *7,335*
Forest Knolls, CA 94933 • *2,000*
Forest Lake, MN 55025 • *5,833*
Forest Park, GA 30050–51 • *16,925*
Forest Park, IL 60130 • *14,918*
Forest Park, LA 71291 • *1,400*
Forest Park, OH 45240 • *18,609*
Forked River, NJ 08731 • *1,950*
Forks, WA 98331 • *2,862*
Forney, TX 75126 • *4,070*
Forrest, IL 61741 • *1,124*
Forrest □, MS • *68,314*
Forrest City, AR 72335 • *13,364*
Forreston, IL 61030 • *1,361*
Forsyth, GA 31029 • *4,268*
Forsyth, IL 62535 • *1,275*
Forsyth, MO 65653 • *1,175*
Forsyth, MT 59327 • *2,178*
Forsyth □, GA • *44,083*
Forsyth □, NC • *265,878*
Fort Ashby, WV 26719 • *1,288*
Fort Atkinson, WI 53538 • *10,227*
Fort Bend □, TX • *225,421*
Fort Benton, MT 59442 • *1,660*
Fort Bragg, CA 95437 • *6,078*
Fort Branch, IN 47648 • *2,447*
Fort Collins, CO 80521–26 • *87,758*
Fort Covington, NY 12937 • *1,200*
Fort Davis, TX 79734 • *1,100*
Fort Defiance, AZ 86504 • *4,489*
Fort Deposit, AL 36032 • *1,240*
Fort Dodge, IA 50501 • *25,894*
Fort Edward, NY 12828 • *3,561*
Fort Fairfield, ME 04742 • *1,729*
Fort Gaines, GA 31751 • *1,248*
Fort Gibson, OK 74434 • *3,359*
Fort Hall, ID 83203 • *2,681*
Fort Kent, ME 04743 • *2,123*
Fort Laramie, WY 82212 • *243*
Fort Lauderdale, FL 33301–51 • *149,377*
Fort Lee, NJ 07024 • *31,997*
Fort Loramie, OH 45845 • *1,042*
Fort Loudon, PA 17224 • *1,200*
Fort Lupton, CO 80621 • *5,159*
Fort Madison, IA 52627 • *11,618*
Fort McKinley, OH 45426 • *9,740*
Fort Meade, FL 33841 • *4,976*
Fort Mill, SC 29715 • *4,930*
Fort Mitchell, KY 41017 • *7,438*
Fort Morgan, CO 80701 • *9,068*
Fort Myers, FL 33901–19 • *45,206*
Fort Myers Beach, FL 33931–32 • *9,284*
Fort Myers Shores, FL 33905 • *5,460*
Fort Oglethorpe, GA 30742 • *5,880*
Fort Payne, AL 35967 • *11,838*
Fort Pierce, FL 34945–54 • *36,830*
Fort Pierre, SD 57532 • *1,854*
Fort Plain, NY 13339 • *2,416*
Fort Recovery, OH 45846 • *1,313*
Fort Scott, KS 66701 • *8,362*
Fort Shawnee, OH 45806 • *4,128*
Fort Smith, AR 72901–17 • *72,798*
Fort Stockton, TX 79735 • *8,524*
Fort Sumner, NM 88119 • *1,269*
Fort Thomas, KY 41075 • *16,032*
Fortuna, CA 95540 • *8,788*
Fort Valley, GA 31030 • *8,198*
Fortville, IN 46040 • *2,690*
Fort Walton Beach, FL 32547–48 • *21,471*
Fort Washington Forest, MD 20744 • *1,010*
Fort Wayne, IN 46801–99 • *173,072*
Fort Wingate, NM 87316 • *950*
Fort Worth, TX 76101–85 • *447,619*
Fort Wright, KY 41011 • *6,570*
Forty Fort, PA 18704 • *5,049*
Fort Yukon, AK 99740 • *580*
Fosston, MN 56542 • *1,529*
Foster □, ND • *3,983*
Foster City, CA 94404 • *28,176*
Foster Village, HI 96818 • *3,700*
Fostoria, OH 44830 • *14,983*
Fountain, CO 80817 • *9,984*
Fountain □, IN • *17,808*
Fountain Hill, PA 18015 • *4,637*
Fountain Inn, SC 29644 • *4,388*
Fountain Place, LA • *9,200*
Fountain Valley, CA 92708 • *53,691*
Four Corners, OR 97301 • *12,156*
Four Oaks, NC 27524 • *1,308*
Fowler, CA 93625 • *3,208*
Fowler, CO 81039 • *1,154*
Fowler, IN 47944 • *2,333*
Fowlerville, MI 48836 • *2,648*
Foxboro, MA 02035 • *5,706*
Fox Chapel, PA 15238 • *5,319*
Fox Lake, IL 60020 • *7,478*
Fox Lake, WI 53933 • *1,269*
Fox Point, WI 53217 • *7,238*
Fox River Grove, IL 60021 • *3,551*
Frackville, PA 17931 • *4,700*
Framingham, MA 01701 • *64,994*
Franconia, VA 22310 • *19,882*
Frankenmuth, MI 48734 • *4,408*
Frankford, DE 19945 • *591*
Frankfort, IL 60423 • *7,180*

Frankfort, IN 46041 • *14,754*
Frankfort, KY 40601–22 • *25,968*
Frankfort, MI 49635 • *1,546*
Frankfort, NY 13340 • *2,693*
Frankfort, OH 45628 • *1,065*
Franklin, IN 46131 • *12,907*
Franklin, KY 42134–35 • *7,607*
Franklin, LA 70538 • *9,004*
Franklin, MA 02038 • *9,965*
Franklin, NE 68939 • *1,112*
Franklin, NH 03235 • *8,304*
Franklin, NJ 07416 • *4,977*
Franklin, NC 28734 • *2,873*
Franklin, OH 45005 • *11,026*
Franklin, PA 16323 • *7,329*
Franklin, TN 37064–65 • *20,098*
Franklin, TX 77856 • *1,336*
Franklin, VA 23851 • *7,864*
Franklin, WI 53132 • *21,855*
Franklin □, AL • *27,814*
Franklin □, AR • *14,897*
Franklin □, FL • *8,967*
Franklin □, GA • *16,650*
Franklin □, ID • *9,232*
Franklin □, IL • *40,319*
Franklin □, IN • *19,580*
Franklin □, IA • *11,364*
Franklin □, KS • *21,994*
Franklin □, KY • *43,781*
Franklin □, LA • *22,387*
Franklin □, ME • *29,008*
Franklin □, MA • *70,092*
Franklin □, MS • *8,377*
Franklin □, MO • *80,603*
Franklin □, NE • *3,938*
Franklin □, NY • *46,540*
Franklin □, NC • *36,414*
Franklin □, OH • *961,437*
Franklin □, PA • *121,082*
Franklin □, TN • *34,725*
Franklin □, TX • *7,802*
Franklin □, VT • *39,980*
Franklin □, VA • *39,549*
Franklin □, WA • *37,473*
Franklin Lakes, NJ 07417 • *9,873*
Franklin Park, IL 60131 • *18,485*
Franklin Park, PA 15143 • *10,109*
Franklin Square, NY 11010 • *28,205*
Franklinton, LA 70438 • *4,007*
Franklinton, NC 27525 • *1,615*
Franklinville, NJ 08322 • *1,020*
Franklinville, NY 14737 • *1,739*
Frankston, TX 75763 • *1,127*
Frankton, IN 46044 • *1,736*
Fraser, MI 48026 • *13,899*
Frazee, MN 56544 • *1,176*
Frazeysburg, OH 43822 • *1,165*
Frazier Park, CA 93225 • *2,201*
Frederic, WI 54837 • *1,124*
Frederica, DE 19946 • *761*
Frederick, MD 21701–02 • *40,148*
Frederick, OK 73542 • *5,221*
Frederick □, MD • *150,208*
Frederick □, VA • *45,723*
Fredericksburg, IA 50630 • *1,011*
Fredericksburg, TX 78624 • *6,934*
Fredericksburg, VA 22401–08 • *19,027*
Fredericktown, MO 63645 • *3,950*
Fredericktown, OH 43019 • *2,443*
Fredericktown, PA 15333 • *1,052*
Fredonia, AZ 86022 • *1,207*
Fredonia, KS 66736 • *2,599*
Fredonia, NY 14063 • *10,436*
Fredonia, WI 53021 • *1,558*
Freeborn □, MN • *33,060*
Freeburg, IL 62243 • *3,115*
Freedom, CA 95019 • *8,361*
Freedom, PA 15042 • *1,897*
Freedom, WY 83120 • *450*
Freehold, NJ 07728 • *10,742*
Freeland, MI 48623 • *1,421*
Freeland, PA 18224 • *3,909*
Freeman, SD 57029 • *1,293*
Freemansburg, PA 18017 • *1,946*
Freeport, IL 61032 • *25,840*
Freeport, ME 04032 • *1,829*
Freeport, NY 11520 • *39,894*
Freeport, PA 16229 • *1,983*
Freeport, TX 77541 • *11,389*
Freer, TX 78357 • *3,271*
Freestone □, TX • *15,818*
Fremont, CA 94536–39 • *173,339*
Fremont, IN 46737 • *1,407*
Fremont, MI 49412 • *3,875*
Fremont, NE 68025 • *23,680*
Fremont, NC 27830 • *1,710*
Fremont, OH 43420 • *17,648*
Fremont □, CO • *32,273*
Fremont □, ID • *10,937*
Fremont □, IA • *8,226*
Fremont □, WY • *33,662*
French Island, WI 54601 • *4,478*
French Lick, IN 47432 • *2,087*
Frenchtown, NJ 08825 • *1,528*
Fresno, CA 93701–94 • *354,202*
Fresno □, CA • *667,490*
Frewsburg, NY 14738 • *1,817*
Friars Point, MS 38631 • *1,334*
Friday Harbor, WA 98250 • *1,492*
Fridley, MN 55432 • *28,335*
Friend, NE 68359 • *1,111*
Friendship, NY 14739 • *1,423*
Friendswood, TX 77546 • *22,814*
Frio □, TX • *13,472*
Friona, TX 79035 • *3,688*
Frisco, CO 80443 • *1,601*
Frisco City, AL 36445 • *1,581*
Fritch, TX 79036 • *2,335*
Frontenac, KS 66762 • *2,588*
Frontier □, NE • *3,101*
Front Royal, VA 22630 • *11,880*
Frostburg, MD 21532 • *8,075*
Frostproof, FL 33843 • *2,808*
Fruita, CO 81521 • *4,045*
Fruit Heights, UT 84037 • *3,900*
Fruitland, ID 83619 • *2,400*
Fruitland, MD 21826 • *3,511*
Fruitland Park, FL 34731 • *2,754*
Fruitport, MI 49415 • *1,090*
Fruitvale, CO 81504 • *1,070*
Fruitvale, WA 98902 • *4,125*
Fruitville, FL 34232 • *9,808*
Fryeburg, ME 04037 • *1,580*

Fulda, MN 56131 • *1,212*
Fullerton, CA 92631–35 • *114,144*
Fullerton, NE 68638 • *1,452*
Fulton, IL 61252 • *3,698*
Fulton, KY 42041 • *3,078*
Fulton, MS 38843 • *3,387*
Fulton, MO 65251 • *10,033*
Fulton, NY 13069 • *12,929*
Fulton □, AR • *10,037*
Fulton □, GA • *648,951*
Fulton □, IL • *38,080*
Fulton □, IN • *18,840*
Fulton □, KY • *8,271*
Fulton □, NY • *54,191*
Fulton □, OH • *38,498*
Fulton □, PA • *13,837*
Fultondale, AL 35068 • *6,400*
Funkstown, MD 21734 • *1,136*
Fuquay-Varina, NC 27526 • *4,562*
Furnas □, NE • *5,553*
Fyffe, AL 35971 • *1,094*

G

Gabbs, NV 89409 • *667*
Gadsden, AL 35901–05 • *42,523*
Gadsden □, FL • *41,105*
Gaffney, SC 29340–42 • *13,145*
Gage □, NE • *22,794*
Gages Lake, IL 60030 • *8,349*
Gahanna, OH 43230 • *27,791*
Gaines □, TX • *14,123*
Gainesboro, TN 38562 • *1,002*
Gainesville, FL 32601–14 • *84,770*
Gainesville, GA 30501–07 • *17,885*
Gainesville, TX 76240 • *14,256*
Gaithersburg, MD 20877–79 • *39,542*
Galax, VA 24333 • *6,670*
Galena, AK 99741 • *833*
Galena, IL 61036 • *3,647*
Galena, KS 66739 • *3,308*
Galesburg, IL 61401–02 • *33,530*
Galesburg, MI 49053 • *1,863*
Gales Ferry, CT 06335 • *1,191*
Galesville, WI 54630 • *1,278*
Galeton, PA 16922 • *1,370*
Galeville, NY 13088 • *4,695*
Galion, OH 44833 • *11,859*
Gallatin, MO 64640 • *1,864*
Gallatin, TN 37066 • *18,794*
Gallatin □, IL • *6,909*
Gallatin □, KY • *5,393*
Gallatin □, MT • *50,463*
Gallia □, OH • *30,954*
Galliano, LA 70354 • *4,294*
Gallipolis, OH 45631 • *4,831*
Gallitzin, PA 16641 • *2,003*
Gallup, NM 87301–05 • *19,154*
Galt, CA 95632 • *8,889*
Galva, IL 61434 • *2,742*
Galveston, IN 46932 • *1,609*
Galveston, TX 77550–54 • *59,070*
Galveston □, TX • *217,399*
Gambell, AK 99742 • *525*
Gambier, OH 43022 • *2,073*
Gambrills, MD 21054 • *1,200*
Ganado, AZ 86505 • *3,400*
Ganado, TX 77962 • *1,701*
Gang Mills, NY 14870 • *2,738*
Gantt, SC 29605 • *13,891*
Gap, PA 17527 • *1,200*
Garberville, CA 95440 • *1,200*
Garden □, NE • *2,460*
Gardena, CA 90247–49 • *49,847*
Garden City, GA 31408 • *7,410*
Garden City, ID 83704 • *6,369*
Garden City, KS 67846 • *24,097*
Garden City, MI 48135–36 • *31,846*
Garden City, MO 64747 • *1,225*
Garden City, NY 11530 • *21,686*
Garden City Park, NY 11040 • *7,437*
Gardendale, AL 35071 • *9,251*
Garden Grove, CA 92640–45 • *143,050*
Garden Home, OR 97223 • *5,500*
Gardiner, ME 04345 • *6,746*
Gardner, IL 60424 • *1,237*
Gardner, KS 66030 • *3,191*
Gardner, MA 01440 • *20,125*
Gardnerville, NV 89410 • *2,177*
Gardnerville Ranchos, NV 89410 • *7,455*
Garfield, NJ 07026 • *26,727*
Garfield □, CO • *29,974*
Garfield □, MT • *1,589*
Garfield □, NE • *2,141*
Garfield □, OK • *56,735*
Garfield □, UT • *3,980*
Garfield □, WA • *2,248*
Garfield Heights, OH 44125 • *31,739*
Garfield Park, DE 19720 • *1,415*
Garland, TX 75040–48 • *180,650*
Garland, UT 84312 • *1,637*
Garland □, AR • *73,397*
Garner, IA 50438 • *2,916*
Garner, NC 27529 • *14,967*
Garnett, KS 66032 • *3,210*
Garrard □, KY • *11,579*
Garretson, SD 57030 • *924*
Garrett, IN 46738 • *5,349*
Garrett □, MD • *28,138*
Garrettsville, OH 44231 • *2,014*
Garrison, MD 21055 • *5,045*
Garrison, ND 58540 • *1,530*
Garvin □, OK • *26,605*
Garwood, NJ 07027 • *4,227*
Gary, IN 46401–11 • *116,646*
Gary, WV 24836 • *1,355*
Garysburg, NC 27831 • *1,057*
Garyville, LA 70051 • *3,181*
Garza □, TX • *5,143*
Gas City, IN 46933 • *6,296*
Gasconade □, MO • *14,006*
Gasport, NY 14067 • *1,336*
Gassville, AR 72635 • *1,167*
Gaston, NC 27832 • *1,003*
Gaston □, NC • *175,093*
Gastonia, NC 28051–56 • *54,732*
Gate City, VA 24251 • *2,214*
Gates, NY 14624 • *30,000*
Gates □, NC • *9,305*
Gatesville, TX 76528 • *11,492*
Gatlinburg, TN 37738 • *3,417*

Gautier, MS 39553 • *10,088*
Gaylord, MI 49735 • *3,256*
Gaylord, MN 55334 • *1,935*
Gearhart, OR 97138 • *1,027*
Geary, OK 73040 • *1,347*
Geary □, KS • *30,453*
Geauga □, OH • *81,129*
Geistown, PA 15904 • *2,749*
Gem □, ID • *11,844*
Genesee, ID 83832 • *725*
Genesee, MI 48437 • *1,400*
Genesee □, MI • *430,459*
Genesee □, NY • *60,060*
Geneseo, IL 61254 • *5,990*
Geneseo, NY 14454 • *7,187*
Geneva, AL 36340 • *4,681*
Geneva, IL 60134 • *12,617*
Geneva, IN 46740 • *1,280*
Geneva, NE 68361 • *2,310*
Geneva, NY 14456 • *14,143*
Geneva, OH 44041 • *6,597*
Geneva □, AL • *23,647*
Geneva-on-the-Lake, OH 44041 • *1,626*
Genoa, IL 60135 • *3,083*
Genoa, NE 68640 • *1,082*
Genoa, NV 89411 • *190*
Genoa, OH 43430 • *2,262*
Genoa City, WI 53128 • *1,277*
Gentry, AR 72734 • *1,726*
Gentry □, MO • *6,848*
George, IA 51237 • *1,066*
George □, MS • *16,673*
Georgetown, CA 95634 • *2,000*
Georgetown, CT 06829 • *1,694*
Georgetown, DE 19947 • *3,732*
Georgetown, IL 61846 • *3,678*
Georgetown, IN 47122 • *2,092*
Georgetown, KY 40324 • *11,414*
Georgetown, MA 01833 • *2,100*
Georgetown, OH 45121 • *3,627*
Georgetown, SC 29440–42 • *9,517*
Georgetown, TX 78626–28 • *14,842*
Georgetown □, SC • *46,302*
George West, TX 78022 • *2,586*
Georgiana, AL 36033 • *1,933*
Gering, NE 69341 • *7,946*
Gerlach, NV 89412 • *200*
Germantown, IL 62245 • *1,167*
Germantown, MD 20874 • *41,145*
Germantown, OH 45327 • *4,916*
Germantown, TN 38138 • *32,893*
Germantown, WI 53022 • *13,658*
Gettysburg, PA 17325 • *7,025*
Gettysburg, SD 57442 • *1,510*
Giants Neck, CT 06357 • *1,200*
Gibbon, NE 68840 • *1,525*
Gibbstown, NJ 08027 • *5,404*
Gibsland, LA 71028 • *1,224*
Gibson □, IN • *31,913*
Gibson □, TN • *46,315*
Gibsonburg, OH 43431 • *2,579*
Gibson City, IL 60936 • *3,396*
Gibsonia, FL 33805 • *5,168*
Gibsonia, PA 15044 • *3,500*
Gibsonton, FL 33534 • *7,706*
Gibsonville, NC 27249 • *3,441*
Giddings, TX 78942 • *4,093*
Gideon, MO 63848 • *1,104*
Gifford, FL 32960 • *6,278*
Gig Harbor, WA 98335 • *3,236*
Gila □, AZ • *40,216*
Gila Bend, AZ 85337 • *1,747*
Gilbert, AZ 85234 • *29,188*
Gilbert, MN 55741 • *1,934*
Gilbert, OR 97266 • *4,000*
Gilbertsville, PA 19525 • *3,994*
Gilbertville, MA 01031 • *1,029*
Gilchrist □, FL • *9,667*
Gilcrest, CO 80623 • *1,084*
Giles □, TN • *25,741*
Giles □, VA • *16,366*
Gilford Park, NJ 08753 • *8,668*
Gillespie, IL 62033 • *3,645*
Gillespie □, TX • *17,204*
Gillett, WI 54124 • *1,303*
Gillette, WY 82716–17 • *17,635*
Gilliam □, OR • *1,717*
Gilman, IL 60938 • *1,816*
Gilman, VT 05904 • *500*
Gilmer, TX 75644 • *4,822*
Gilmer □, GA • *13,368*
Gilmer □, WV • *7,669*
Gilpin □, CO • *3,070*
Gilroy, CA 95020–21 • *31,487*
Girard, IL 62640 • *2,164*
Girard, KS 66743 • *2,794*
Girard, OH 44420 • *11,304*
Girard, PA 16417 • *2,879*
Girardville, PA 17935 • *1,889*
Glacier □, MT • *12,121*
Glades □, FL • *7,591*
Glade Spring, VA 24340 • *1,435*
Gladeview, FL 33138 • *15,637*
Gladewater, TX 75647 • *6,027*
Gladstone, MI 49837 • *4,565*
Gladstone, MO 64118 • *26,243*
Gladstone, NJ 07934 • *2,111*
Gladstone, OR 97027 • *10,152*
Gladwin, MI 48624 • *2,682*
Gladwin □, MI • *21,896*
Glasco, NY 12432 • *1,538*
Glascock □, GA • *2,357*
Glasford, IL 61533 • *1,115*
Glasgow, KY 42141–42 • *12,351*
Glasgow, MO 65254 • *1,295*
Glasgow, MT 59230 • *3,572*
Glasgow, VA 24555 • *1,140*
Glasgow Village, MO 63137 • *5,199*
Glassboro, NJ 08028 • *15,614*
Glasscock □, TX • *1,447*
Glassport, PA 15045 • *5,582*
Glastonbury, CT 06033 • *7,082*
Gleason, TN 38229 • *1,402*
Glen Allen, VA 23060 • *9,010*
Glen Avon, CA • *12,663*
Glenbrook, NV 89413 • *400*
Glen Burnie, MD 21061 • *37,305*
Glen Burnie Park, MD 21061 • *3,260*
Glen Carbon, IL 62034 • *7,731*
Glencoe, AL 35905 • *4,670*
Glencoe, IL 60022 • *8,499*
Glencoe, MN 55336 • *4,648*
Glen Cove, NY 11542 • *24,149*

Glendale, AZ 85301–12 • *148,134*
Glendale, CA 91201–14 • *180,038*
Glendale, CO 80222 • *2,453*
Glendale, MS 39401 • *1,329*
Glendale, MO 63122 • *5,945*
Glendale, OH 45246 • *2,445*
Glendale, RI 02826 • *700*
Glendale, SC 29346 • *1,049*
Glen Dale, WV 26038 • *1,612*
Glendale, WI 53209 • *14,088*
Glendale Heights, IL 60139 • *27,973*
Glendive, MT 59330 • *4,802*
Glendo, WY 82213 • *195*
Glendola, NJ 07719 • *2,340*
Glendora, CA 91740 • *47,828*
Glendora, NJ 08029 • *5,201*
Glen Ellyn, IL 60137–38 • *24,944*
Glen Gardner, NJ 08826 • *1,665*
Glenham, NY 12527 • *2,832*
Glen Head, NY 11545 • *6,870*
Glen Lyon, PA 18617 • *2,082*
Glenmora, LA 71433 • *1,686*
Glenn □, CA • *24,798*
Glennallen, AK 99588 • *451*
Glenn Dale, MD 20769 • *9,689*
Glenns Ferry, ID 83623 • *1,304*
Glennville, GA 30427 • *3,676*
Glenolden, PA 19036 • *7,260*
Glenpool, OK 74033 • *6,688*
Glen Raven, NC 27215 • *2,616*
Glen Ridge, NJ 07028 • *7,076*
Glen Rock, NJ 07452 • *10,883*
Glen Rock, PA 17327 • *1,688*
Glenrock, WY 82637 • *2,153*
Glen Rose, TX 76043 • *1,949*
Glens Falls, NY 12801 • *15,023*
Glenside, PA 19038 • *8,704*
Glen Ullin, ND 58631 • *927*
Glenview, IL 60025 • *37,093*
Glenville, WV 26351 • *1,923*
Glenwood, AR 71943 • *1,354*
Glenwood, IL 60425 • *9,289*
Glenwood, IA 51534 • *4,571*
Glenwood, MN 56334 • *2,573*
Glenwood, VA 24541 • *2,276*
Glenwood City, WI 54013 • *1,026*
Glenwood Farms, VA 23223 • *3,200*
Glenwood Hills, GA 30032 • *5,240*
Glenwood Springs, CO 81601–02 • *6,561*
Glidden, IA 51443 • *1,099*
Globe, AZ 85501–02 • *6,062*
Gloster, MS 39638 • *1,323*
Gloucester, MA 01930–31 • *28,716*
Gloucester, VA 23061 • *1,200*
Gloucester □, NJ • *230,082*
Gloucester □, VA • *30,131*
Gloucester City, NJ 08030 • *12,649*
Gloucester Point, VA 23062 • *8,509*
Glouster, OH 45732 • *2,001*
Gloversville, NY 12078 • *16,656*
Gloverville, SC 29828 • *2,753*
Glynn □, GA • *62,496*
Gnadenhutten, OH 44629 • *1,226*
Goddard, KS 67052 • *1,804*
Godfrey, IL 62035 • *5,436*
Goffstown, NH 03045 • *2,700*
Gogebic □, MI • *18,052*
Golconda, NV 89414 • *200*
Gold Bar, WA 98251 • *1,078*
Gold Beach, OR 97444 • *1,546*
Golden, CO 80401–03 • *13,116*
Goldendale, WA 98620 • *3,319*
Golden Gate, FL 33999 • *14,148*
Golden Glades, FL 33055 • *25,474*
Golden Meadow, LA 70357 • *2,049*
Golden Valley, MN 55427 • *20,971*
Golden Valley □, MT • *912*
Golden Valley □, ND • *2,108*
Goldfield, NV 89013 • *600*
Goldsboro, NC 27530–34 • *40,709*
Goldthwaite, TX 76844 • *1,658*
Goleta, CA 93117 • *28,600*
Golf Manor, OH 45237 • *4,154*
Goliad, TX 77963 • *1,946*
Goliad □, TX • *5,980*
Gonzales, CA 93926 • *4,660*
Gonzales, LA 70737 • *7,003*
Gonzales, TX 78629 • *6,527*
Gonzales □, TX • *17,205*
Gonzalez, FL 32560 • *7,669*
Goochland □, VA • *14,163*
Goodhue □, MN • *40,690*
Gooding, ID 83330 • *2,820*
Gooding □, ID • *11,633*
Goodland, FL 33933 • *1,000*
Goodland, IN 47948 • *1,033*
Goodland, KS 67735 • *4,983*
Goodlettsville, TN 37072 • *11,219*
Goodman, MS 39079 • *1,256*
Goodman, MO 64843 • *1,094*
Goodsprings, NV 89019 • *150*
Goodview, MN 55987 • *2,878*
Goodwater, AL 35072 • *1,840*
Goodwell, OK 73939 • *1,065*
Goodyear, AZ 85338 • *6,258*
Goose Creek, SC 29445 • *24,692*
Gordo, AL 35466 • *1,918*
Gordon, GA 31031 • *2,468*
Gordon, NE 69343 • *1,803*
Gordon □, GA • *35,072*
Gordonsville, VA 22942 • *1,351*
Gorham, ME 04038 • *3,618*
Gorham, NH 03581 • *1,910*
Gorman, TX 76454 • *1,290*
Goshen, IN 46526 • *23,797*
Goshen, NY 10924 • *5,255*
Goshen, OH 45122 • *1,400*
Goshen □, WY • *12,373*
Gosnell, AR 72319 • *3,783*
Gosper □, NE • *1,928*
Gothenburg, NE 69138 • *3,232*
Gould, AR 71643 • *1,470*
Goulding, FL 32503 • *4,159*
Goulds, FL 33170 • *7,284*
Gouverneur, NY 13642 • *4,604*
Gove □, KS • *3,231*
Gowanda, NY 14070 • *2,901*
Gower, MO 64454 • *1,249*
Gowrie, IA 50543 • *1,028*
Grace, ID 83241 • *973*
Graceville, FL 32440 • *2,675*
Gracewood, GA 30812 • *1,000*
Grady □, GA • *20,279*
Grady □, OK • *41,747*
Grafton, MA 01519 • *1,520*
Grafton, ND 58237 • *4,840*
Grafton, OH 44044 • *3,344*
Grafton, WV 26354 • *5,524*
Grafton, WI 53024 • *9,340*
Grafton □, NH • *74,929*
Graham, CA 90002 • *10,600*
Graham, NC 27253 • *10,426*
Graham, TX 76046 • *8,986*
Graham □, AZ • *26,554*
Graham □, KS • *3,543*
Graham □, NC • *7,196*
Grainger □, TN • *17,095*
Grain Valley, MO 64029 • *1,898*
Grambling, LA 71245 • *5,484*
Gramercy, LA 70052 • *2,412*
Granbury, TX 76048–49 • *4,045*
Granby, CT 06035 • *9,369*
Granby, MA 01033 • *1,327*
Granby, MO 64844 • *1,945*
Grand □, CO • *7,966*
Grand □, UT • *6,620*
Grand Bay, AL 36541 • *3,383*
Grand Blanc, MI 48439 • *7,760*
Grand Caillou, LA 70360 • *1,400*
Grand Canyon, AZ 86023 • *1,499*
Grand Coteau, LA 70541 • *1,118*
Grandfield, OK 73546 • *1,224*
Grand Forks, ND 58201–06 • *49,425*
Grand Forks □, ND • *70,683*
Grand Haven, MI 49417 • *11,951*
Grand Island, NE 68801–03 • *39,386*
Grand Isle, LA 70358 • *1,455*
Grand Isle □, VT • *5,318*
Grand Junction, CO 81501–06 • *29,034*
Grand Ledge, MI 48837 • *7,579*
Grand Marais, MN 55604 • *1,171*
Grand Prairie, TX 75050–54 • *99,616*
Grand Rapids, MI 49501–99 • *189,126*
Grand Rapids, MN 55744 • *7,976*
Grand Saline, TX 75140 • *2,630*
Grand Terrace, CA 92324 • *10,946*
Grand Traverse □, MI • *64,273*
Grandview, MO 64030 • *24,967*
Grandview, WA 98930 • *7,169*
Grandview Heights, OH 43212 • *7,010*
Grandville, MI 49418 • *15,624*
Granger, IN 46530 • *20,241*
Granger, TX 76530 • *1,190*
Granger, WA 98932 • *2,053*
Grangeville, ID 83530 • *3,226*
Granite, OK 73547 • *1,844*
Granite □, MT • *2,548*
Granite City, IL 62040 • *32,862*
Granite Falls, MN 56241 • *3,083*
Granite Falls, NC 28630 • *3,253*
Granite Falls, WA 98252 • *1,060*
Granite Quarry, NC 28072 • *1,646*
Graniteville, MA 01886 • *1,010*
Graniteville, SC 29829 • *1,158*
Graniteville, VT 05654 • *500*
Grant, NE 69140 • *1,239*
Grant □, AR • *13,948*
Grant □, IN • *74,169*
Grant □, KS • *7,159*
Grant □, KY • *15,737*
Grant □, LA • *17,526*
Grant □, MN • *6,246*
Grant □, NE • *769*
Grant □, NM • *27,676*
Grant □, ND • *3,549*
Grant □, OK • *5,689*
Grant □, OR • *7,853*
Grant □, SD • *8,372*
Grant □, WA • *54,758*
Grant □, WV • *10,428*
Grant □, WI • *49,264*
Grant Park, IL 60940 • *1,024*
Grants, NM 87020 • *8,626*
Grantsburg, WI 54840 • *1,144*
Grants Pass, OR 97526–27 • *17,488*
Grantsville, UT 84029 • *4,500*
Grantville, GA 30220 • *1,180*
Granville, IL 61326 • *1,407*
Granville, NY 12832 • *2,646*
Granville, OH 43023 • *4,353*
Granville □, NC • *38,345*
Grapeland, TX 75844 • *1,450*
Grapevine, TX 76051 • *29,202*
Grasonville, MD 21638 • *2,439*
Grass Lake, IL 60002 • *2,191*
Grass Valley, CA 95945 • *9,048*
Gratiot □, MI • *38,982*
Graves □, KY • *33,550*
Gravette, AR 72736 • *1,412*
Gray, GA 31032 • *2,189*
Gray, LA 70359 • *1,500*
Gray □, KS • *5,396*
Gray □, TX • *23,967*
Grayling, MI 49738 • *1,944*
Graylyn Crest, DE 19810 • *4,380*
Grays Harbor □, WA • *64,175*
Grayslake, IL 60030 • *7,388*
Grayson, KY 41143 • *3,510*
Grayson □, KY • *21,050*
Grayson □, TX • *95,021*
Grayson □, VA • *16,278*
Graysville, AL 35073 • *2,241*
Graysville, TN 37338 • *1,301*
Grayville, IL 62844 • *2,043*
Great Barrington, MA 01230 • *2,810*
Great Bend, KS 67530 • *15,427*
Great Falls, MT 59401–06 • *55,097*
Great Falls, SC 29055 • *2,307*
Great Falls, VA 22066 • *6,945*
Great Neck, NY 11020–27 • *8,745*
Great Neck Estates, NY 11021 • *2,790*
Greece, NY 14626 • *15,632*
Greece, NY • *15,632*
Greeley, CO 80631–34 • *60,536*
Greeley □, KS • *1,774*
Greeley □, NE • *3,006*
Green, OR 97470 • *5,076*
Green □, KY • *10,371*
Green □, WI • *30,339*
Greenacres, CA 93308 • *7,379*
Green Acres, DE 19803 • *1,140*
Greenacres, WA 99016 • *4,250*
Greenacres City, FL 33463 • *18,683*
Green Bay, WI 54301–24 • *96,466*
Greenbelt, MD 20770 • *21,096*
Greenbriar, VA 22033 • *6,200*
Greenbrier, AR 72058 • *2,130*
Green Brier, TN 37073 • *2,873*
Greenbrier □, WV • *34,693*
Green Brook, NJ 08812 • *2,380*
Greencastle, IN 46135 • *8,984*
Greencastle, PA 17225 • *3,600*
Green Cove Springs, FL 32043 • *4,497*
Greendale, IN 47025 • *3,881*
Greendale, WI 53129 • *15,128*
Greene, IA 50636 • *1,142*
Greene, NY 13778 • *1,812*
Greene □, AL • *10,153*
Greene □, AR • *31,804*
Greene □, GA • *11,793*
Greene □, IL • *15,317*
Greene □, IN • *30,410*
Greene □, IA • *10,045*
Greene □, MS • *10,220*
Greene □, MO • *207,949*
Greene □, NY • *44,739*
Greene □, NC • *15,384*
Greene □, OH • *136,731*
Greene □, PA • *39,550*
Greene □, TN • *55,853*
Greene □, VA • *10,297*
Greeneville, TN 37743–44 • *13,532*
Greenfield, CA 93927 • *7,464*
Greenfield, IL 62044 • *1,162*
Greenfield, IN 46140 • *11,657*
Greenfield, IA 50849 • *2,074*
Greenfield, MA 01301–02 • *14,016*
Greenfield, MO 65661 • *1,416*
Greenfield, OH 45123 • *5,172*
Greenfield, TN 38230 • *2,105*
Greenfield, WI 53220 • *33,403*
Greenfield Plaza, IA 50315 • *2,200*
Green Forest, AR 72638 • *2,050*
Green Harbor, MA 02041 • *1,900*
Greenhills, OH 45218 • *4,393*
Green Island, NY 12183 • *2,490*
Green Lake, WI 54941 • *1,064*
Green Lake □, WI • *18,651*
Greenlawn, NY 11740 • *13,208*
Greenlee □, AZ • *8,008*
Greenock, PA 15047 • *2,500*
Greenport, NY 11944 • *2,070*
Green River, WY 82935 • *12,711*
Green Rock, IL 61241 • *2,615*
Greensboro, AL 36744 • *3,047*
Greensboro, GA 30642 • *2,860*
Greensboro, MD 21639 • *1,441*
Greensboro, NC 27401–95 • *183,521*
Greensburg, IN 47240 • *9,286*
Greensburg, KS 67054 • *1,792*
Greensburg, KY 42743 • *1,990*
Greensburg, PA 15601 • *16,318*
Green Springs, OH 44836 • *1,446*
Greensville □, VA • *8,853*
Greentown, IN 46936 • *2,172*
Green Tree, PA 15220 • *4,905*
Greenup, IL 62428 • *1,616*
Greenup, KY 41144 • *1,158*
Greenup □, KY • *36,742*
Green Valley, AZ 85614 • *13,231*
Green Valley, MD 21771 • *9,424*
Greenview, SC 29203 • *5,515*
Greenville, AL 36037 • *7,492*
Greenville, CA 95947 • *1,396*
Greenville, DE 19807 • *800*
Greenville, GA 30222 • *1,167*
Greenville, IL 62246 • *4,806*
Greenville, KY 42345 • *4,689*
Greenville, ME 04441 • *1,601*
Greenville, MI 48838 • *8,101*
Greenville, MS 38701–04 • *45,226*
Greenville, NH 03048 • *1,135*
Greenville, NY 10583 • *9,528*
Greenville, NC 27834–36 • *44,972*
Greenville, OH 45331 • *12,863*
Greenville, PA 16125 • *6,734*
Greenville, RI 02828 • *8,303*
Greenville, SC 29601–16 • *58,282*
Greenville, TX 75401–03 • *23,071*
Greenville □, SC • *320,167*
Greenwich, CT 06830–36 • *58,441*
Greenwich, NY 12834 • *1,961*
Greenwich, OH 44837 • *1,442*
Greenwood, AR 72936 • *3,984*
Greenwood, DE 19950 • *578*
Greenwood, IN 46142 • *26,265*
Greenwood, LA 71033 • *2,092*
Greenwood, MS 38930 • *18,906*
Greenwood, MO 64034 • *1,505*
Greenwood, PA 16601 • *1,650*
Greenwood, SC 29646–49 • *20,807*
Greenwood □, KS • *7,847*
Greenwood □, SC • *59,567*
Greenwood Lake, NY 10925 • *3,208*
Greenwood Village, CO 80111 • *7,589*
Greer, SC 29650–52 • *10,322*
Greer □, OK • *6,559*
Gregg □, TX • *104,948*
Gregory, SD 57533 • *1,384*
Gregory □, SD • *5,359*
Greilickville, MI 49684 • *1,060*
Grenada, MS 38901 • *10,864*
Grenada □, MS • *21,555*
Gresham, OR 97030 • *68,235*
Gresham Park, GA 30316 • *9,000*
Gretna, FL 32332 • *1,981*
Gretna, LA 70053–54 • *17,208*
Gretna, NE 68028 • *2,249*
Gretna, VA 24557 • *1,339*
Greybull, WY 82426 • *1,789*
Gridley, CA 95948 • *4,631*
Gridley, IL 61744 • *1,304*
Griffin, GA 30223–24 • *21,347*
Griffith, IN 46319 • *17,916*
Grifton, NC 28530 • *2,393*
Griggs □, ND • *3,303*
Griggsville, IL 62340 • *1,218*
Grimes, IA 50111 • *2,653*
Grimes □, TX • *18,828*
Grindall Creek, VA 23234 • *1,710*
Grinnell, IA 50112 • *8,902*
Griswold, IA 51535 • *1,049*
Groesbeck, OH 45239 • *6,684*
Groesbeck, TX 76642 • *3,185*
Grosse Ile, MI 48138 • *9,781*
Grosse Pointe, MI 48236 • *5,681*
Grosse Pointe Farms, MI 48236 • *10,092*
Grosse Pointe Park, MI 48230 • *12,857*
Grosse Pointe Woods, MI 48225 • *17,715*
Grossmont, CA 91941 • *2,600*
Groton, CT 06340 • *9,837*
Groton, MA 01450 • *1,044*
Groton, NY 13073 • *2,398*
Groton, SD 57445 • *1,196*
Grottoes, VA 24441 • *1,455*
Grove, OK 74344 • *4,020*
Grove City, FL 34224 • *2,374*
Grove City, OH 43123 • *19,661*
Grove City, PA 16127 • *8,240*
Grove Hill, AL 36451 • *1,551*
Groveland, FL 34736 • *2,300*
Groveland, MA 01834 • *3,780*
Groveport, OH 43125 • *2,948*
Grover City, CA 93433 • *11,656*
Groves, TX 77619 • *16,513*
Groveton, NH 03582 • *1,255*
Groveton, TX 75845 • *1,071*
Groveton, VA 22303 • *19,997*
Groveton Gardens, VA 22303 • *2,600*
Grovetown, GA 30813 • *3,596*
Groveville, NJ 08620 • *2,900*
Gruetli-Laager, TN 37339 • *1,810*
Grulla, TX 78548 • *1,335*
Grundy, VA 24614 • *1,305*
Grundy □, IL • *32,337*
Grundy □, IA • *12,029*
Grundy □, MO • *10,536*
Grundy □, TN • *13,362*
Grundy Center, IA 50638 • *2,491*
Gruver, TX 79040 • *1,172*
Guadalupe, AZ 85283 • *5,458*
Guadalupe, CA 93434 • *5,479*
Guadalupe □, NM • *4,156*
Guadalupe □, TX • *64,873*
Guernsey, WY 82214 • *1,155*
Guernsey □, OH • *39,024*
Gueydan, LA 70542 • *1,611*
Guilford, CT 06437 • *2,588*
Guilford, ME 04443 • *1,082*
Guilford □, NC • *347,420*
Guin, AL 35563 • *2,464*
Gulf □, FL • *11,504*
Gulf Breeze, FL 32561 • *5,530*
Gulf Gate Estates, FL 34231 • *11,622*
Gulfport, FL 33707 • *11,727*
Gulfport, MS 39501–07 • *40,775*
Gulf Shores, AL 36542 • *3,261*
Gumboro, DE 19945 • *200*
Gunnison, CO 81230 • *4,636*
Gunnison, UT 84634 • *1,298*
Gunnison □, CO • *10,273*
Guntersville, AL 35976 • *7,038*
Gurdon, AR 71743 • *2,199*
Gurley, AL 35748 • *1,007*
Gurnee, IL 60031 • *13,701*
Gustine, CA 95322 • *3,931*
Guthrie, KY 42234 • *1,504*
Guthrie, OK 73044 • *10,518*
Guthrie □, IA • *10,935*
Guthrie Center, IA 50115 • *1,614*
Guttenberg, IA 52052 • *2,257*
Guttenberg, NJ 07093 • *8,268*
Guymon, OK 73942 • *7,803*
Gwinhurst, DE 19809 • *1,340*
Gwinn, MI 49841 • *2,370*
Gwinner, ND 58040 • *585*
Gwinnett □, GA • *352,910*
Gypsum, CO 81637 • *1,750*

H

Haakon □, SD • *2,624*
Habersham □, GA • *27,621*
Hacienda Heights, CA 91745 • *52,354*
Hackensack, NJ 07601–08 • *37,049*
Hackettstown, NJ 07840 • *8,120*
Hackleburg, AL 35564 • *1,161*
Haddam, CT 06438 • *1,200*
Haddonfield, NJ 08033 • *11,628*
Haddon Heights, NJ 08035 • *7,860*
Hadlock, WA 98339 • *1,752*
Hagerman, NM 88232 • *961*
Hagerstown, IN 47346 • *1,835*
Hagerstown, MD 21740 • *35,445*
Hahira, GA 31632 • *1,353*
Hahnville, LA 70057 • *2,599*
Hailey, ID 83333 • *3,687*
Haines, AK 99827 • *1,238*
Haines City, FL 33844 • *11,683*
Hainesport, NJ 08036 • *1,250*
Halawa Heights, HI 96701 • *7,000*
Hale □, AL • *15,498*
Hale □, TX • *34,671*
Hale Center, TX 79041 • *2,067*
Haledon, NJ 07508 • *6,951*
Haleiwa, HI 96712 • *2,442*
Hales Corners, WI 53130 • *7,623*
Halethorpe, MD 21227 • *19,750*
Haleyville, AL 35565 • *4,452*
Half Hollow Hills, NY 11746 • *5,110*
Half Moon, NC 28540 • *6,306*
Half Moon Bay, CA 94019 • *8,886*
Halfway, MD 21740 • *8,873*
Halifax □, NC • *55,516*
Halifax □, VA • *29,033*
Haliimaile, HI 96768 • *841*
Hall □, GA • *95,428*
Hall □, NE • *48,925*
Hall □, TX • *3,905*
Hallandale, FL 33009 • *30,996*
Hallettsville, TX 77964 • *2,718*
Hallie, WI 54729 • *1,300*
Hallock, MN 56728 • *1,304*
Hallowell, ME 04347 • *2,534*
Halls, TN 37918 • *6,450*
Halls, TN 38040 • *2,431*
Halls Crossroads, TN 37918 • *1,900*
Hallstead, PA 18822 • *1,274*
Hallsville, TX 75650 • *2,288*
Halstead, KS 67056 • *2,015*
Haltom City, TX 76117 • *32,856*
Hamblen □, TN • *50,480*
Hamburg, AR 71646 • *3,098*
Hamburg, IA 51640 • *1,248*
Hamburg, NJ 07419 • *2,566*
Hamburg, NY 14075 • *10,442*
Hamburg, PA 19526 • *3,987*
Hamden, CT 06514 • *52,434*
Hamel, MN 55340 • *3,096*
Hamilton, AL 35570 • *5,787*
Hamilton, IL 62341 • *3,281*
Hamilton, MA 01936 • *1,000*
Hamilton, MI 49419 • *1,000*
Hamilton, MO 64644 • *1,737*
Hamilton, MT 59840 • *2,737*
Hamilton, NY 13346 • *3,790*
Hamilton, OH 45011–18 • *61,368*
Hamilton, TX 76531 • *2,937*
Hamilton □, FL • *10,930*
Hamilton □, IL • *8,499*
Hamilton □, IN • *108,936*
Hamilton □, IA • *16,071*
Hamilton □, KS • *2,388*
Hamilton □, NE • *8,862*
Hamilton □, NY • *5,279*
Hamilton □, OH • *866,228*
Hamilton □, TN • *285,536*
Hamilton □, TX • *7,733*
Hamilton City, CA 95951 • *1,811*
Hamilton Square, NJ 08690 • *10,970*
Ham Lake, MN 55304 • *8,924*
Hamlet, NC 28345 • *6,196*
Hamlin, TX 79520 • *2,791*
Hamlin, WV 25523 • *1,030*
Hamlin □, SD • *4,974*
Hammond, IN 46320–27 • *84,236*
Hammond, LA 70401–04 • *15,871*
Hammond, WI 54015 • *1,097*
Hammonton, NJ 08037 • *12,208*
Hampden, ME 04444 • *3,895*
Hampden □, MA • *456,310*
Hampden Highlands, ME 04444 • *1,540*
Hampshire, IL 60140 • *1,843*
Hampshire □, MA • *146,568*
Hampshire □, WV • *16,498*
Hampstead, MD 21074 • *2,608*
Hampton, AR 71744 • *1,562*
Hampton, GA 30228 • *2,694*
Hampton, IA 50441 • *4,133*
Hampton, NH 03842 • *7,989*
Hampton, NJ 08827 • *1,515*
Hampton, SC 29924 • *2,997*
Hampton, TN 37658 • *2,236*
Hampton, VA 23651–70 • *133,793*
Hampton □, SC • *18,191*
Hampton Bays, NY 11946 • *7,893*
Hamtramck, MI 48212 • *18,372*
Hana, HI 96713 • *683*
Hanahan, SC 29406 • *13,176*
Hanamaulu, HI 96715 • *3,611*
Hanapepe, HI 96716 • *1,395*
Hanceville, AL 35077 • *2,246*
Hancock, MD 21750 • *1,926*
Hancock, MI 49930 • *4,547*
Hancock, NY 13783 • *1,330*
Hancock □, GA • *8,908*
Hancock □, IL • *21,373*
Hancock □, IN • *45,527*
Hancock □, IA • *12,638*
Hancock □, KY • *7,864*
Hancock □, ME • *46,948*
Hancock □, MS • *31,760*
Hancock □, OH • *65,536*
Hancock □, TN • *6,739*
Hancock □, WV • *35,233*
Hand □, SD • *4,272*
Hanford, CA 93230–32 • *30,897*
Hankinson, ND 58041 • *1,038*
Hanna, WY 82327 • *1,076*
Hanna City, IL 61536 • *1,205*
Hannibal, MO 63401 • *18,004*
Hanover, IN 47243 • *3,610*
Hanover, MA 02339 • *2,500*
Hanover, NH 03755 • *6,538*
Hanover, PA 17331 • *14,399*
Hanover □, VA • *63,306*
Hanover Center, MA 02339 • *1,000*
Hanover Park, IL 60103 • *32,895*
Hanover Township, NJ 07981 • *11,538*
Hansen, ID 83334 • *848*
Hansford □, TX • *5,848*
Hanson, MA 02341 • *2,188*
Hanson □, SD • *2,994*
Hapeville, GA 30354 • *5,483*
Happy Valley, OR 97236 • *1,519*
Harahan, LA 70123 • *9,927*
Haralson □, GA • *21,966*
Harbeson, DE 19951 • *500*
Harbor, OR 97415 • *2,143*
Harbor Beach, MI 48441 • *2,089*
Harborcreek, PA 16421 • *1,500*
Harbor Springs, MI 49740 • *1,540*
Hardee □, FL • *19,499*
Hardeeville, SC 29927 • *1,583*
Hardeman □, TN • *23,377*
Hardeman □, TX • *5,283*
Hardin, IL 62047 • *1,071*
Hardin, MT 59034 • *2,940*
Hardin □, IL • *5,189*
Hardin □, IA • *19,094*
Hardin □, KY • *89,240*
Hardin □, OH • *31,111*
Hardin □, TN • *22,633*
Hardin □, TX • *41,320*
Harding □, NM • *987*
Harding □, SD • *1,669*
Hardinsburg, KY 40143 • *1,906*
Hardwick, GA 31034 • *8,800*
Hardwick, VT 05843 • *1,400*
Hardy □, WV • *10,977*
Harford □, MD • *182,132*
Hargill, TX 78549 • *1,030*
Harker Heights, TX 76543 • *12,841*
Harkers Island, NC 28531 • *1,759*
Harlan, IN 46743 • *1,200*
Harlan, IA 51537 • *5,148*
Harlan, KY 40831 • *2,686*
Harlan □, KY • *36,574*
Harlan □, NE • *3,810*
Harlem, FL 33440 • *2,826*
Harlem, GA 30814 • *2,199*
Harlem, MT 59526 • *882*
Harleysville, PA 19438 • *7,405*
Harlingen, TX 78550–52 • *48,735*
Harlowton, MT 59036 • *1,049*
Harmon □, OK • *3,793*
Harmony, MN 55939 • *1,081*
Harmony, PA 16037 • *1,054*
Harmony, RI 02829 • *820*
Harnett □, NC • *67,822*
Harney □, OR • *7,060*
Harper, KS 67058 • *1,735*
Harper □, KS • *7,124*

Harper □, OK • 4,063
Harpers Ferry, WV 25425 • 308
Harper Woods, MI 48225 • 14,903
Harrah, OK 73045 • 4,206
Harriman, TN 37748 • 7,119
Harrington, DE 19952 • 2,311
Harrington Park, NJ 07640 • 4,623
Harris, RI 02816 • 1,050
Harris □, GA • 17,788
Harris □, TX • 2,818,199
Harrisburg, AR 72432 • 1,943
Harrisburg, IL 62946 • 9,289
Harrisburg, OR 97446 • 1,939
Harrisburg, PA 17101–13 • 52,376
Harris Hill, NY 14221 • 4,577
Harrison, AR 72601–02 • 9,922
Harrison, MI 48625 • 1,835
Harrison, NJ 07029 • 13,425
Harrison, NY 10528 • 23,308
Harrison, OH 45030 • 7,518
Harrison, TN 37341 • 7,191
Harrison □, IN • 29,890
Harrison □, IA • 14,730
Harrison □, KY • 16,248
Harrison □, MS • 165,365
Harrison □, MO • 8,469
Harrison □, OH • 16,085
Harrison □, TX • 57,483
Harrison □, WV • 69,371
Harrisonburg, VA 22801 • 30,707
Harrison Township, MI 48045 • 24,685
Harrisonville, MO 64701 • 7,683
Harristown, IL 62537 • 1,319
Harrisville, RI 02830 • 1,654
Harrisville, UT 84404 • 3,004
Harrisville, WV 26362 • 1,839
Harrodsburg, KY 40330 • 7,335
Hart, MI 49420 • 1,942
Hart, TX 79043 • 1,221
Hart □, GA • 19,712
Hart □, KY • 14,890
Hartford, AL 36344 • 2,448
Hartford, CT 06101–99 • 139,739
Hartford, IL 62048 • 1,676
Hartford, KY 42347 • 2,532
Hartford, MI 49057 • 2,341
Hartford, SD 57033 • 1,262
Hartford, VT 05047 • 500
Hartford, WI 53027 • 8,188
Hartford □, CT • 851,783
Hartford City, IN 47348 • 6,960
Hartington, NE 68739 • 1,583
Hartland, ME 04943 • 1,038
Hartland, WI 53029 • 6,906
Hartley, IA 51346 • 1,632
Hartley □, TX • 3,634
Hartsdale, NY 10530 • 9,587
Hartselle, AL 35640 • 10,795
Hartshorne, OK 74547 • 2,120
Hartsville, SC 29550 • 8,372
Hartsville, TN 37074 • 2,188
Hartville, OH 44632 • 2,031
Hartwell, GA 30643 • 4,555
Harvard, IL 60033 • 5,975
Harvard, MA 01451 • 1,200
Harvey, IL 60426 • 29,771
Harvey, LA 70058 • 21,222
Harvey, MI 49855 • 1,377
Harvey, ND 58341 • 2,263
Harvey □, KS • 31,028
Harwich, MA 02645 • 4,399
Harwich Port, MA 02646 • 2,300
Harwinton, CT 06791 • 5,228
Harwood Heights, IL 60656 • 7,680
Hasbrouck Heights, NJ 07604 • 11,488
Haskell, AR 72015 • 1,342
Haskell, OK 74436 • 2,143
Haskell, TX 79521 • 3,362
Haskell □, KS • 3,886
Haskell □, OK • 10,940
Haskell □, TX • 6,820
Haslett, MI 48840 • 10,230
Hastings, MI 49058 • 6,549
Hastings, MN 55033 • 15,445
Hastings, NE 68901–02 • 22,837
Hastings, PA 16646 • 1,431
Hastings-on-Hudson, NY 10706 • 8,000
Hatboro, PA 19040 • 7,382
Hatch, NM 87937 • 1,136
Hatfield, MA 01038 • 1,234
Hatfield, PA 19440 • 2,650
Hatteras, NC 27943 • 1,000
Hattiesburg, MS 39401–07 • 41,882
Hatton, ND 58240 • 800
Haubstadt, IN 47639 • 1,455
Haughton, LA 71037 • 1,664
Hauppauge, NY 11788 • 19,750
Hauula, HI 96717 • 3,479
Havana, FL 32333 • 1,654
Havana, IL 62644 • 3,610
Havelock, NC 28532 • 20,268
Haven, KS 67543 • 1,198
Haverford [Township], PA 19083 • 52,371
Haverhill, MA 01830–35 • 51,418
Haverstraw, NY 10927 • 9,438
Havre, MT 59501 • 10,201
Havre de Grace, MD 21078 • 8,952
Havre North, MT 59501 • 1,110
Hawaii □, HI • 120,317
Hawaiian Gardens, CA 90716 • 13,639
Hawarden, IA 51023 • 2,439
Hawi, HI 96719 • 924
Hawkins □, TN • 44,565
Hawkinsville, GA 31036 • 3,527
Hawley, MN 56549 • 1,655
Hawley, PA 18428 • 1,244
Haworth, NJ 07641 • 3,384
Haw River, NC 27258 • 1,855
Hawthorne, CA 90250–51 • 71,349
Hawthorne, FL 32640 • 1,305
Hawthorne, NV 89415–16 • 4,162
Hawthorne, NJ 07506 • 17,084
Hawthorne, NY 10532 • 4,764
Hayden, CO 81639 • 1,444
Hayden, ID 83835 • 3,744
Hayes □, NE • 1,222
Hayesville, OR 97303 • 14,318
Hayfield, MN 55940 • 1,283
Hayfield, VA 22310 • 2,300
Hayfork, CA 96041 • 2,605
Haynesville, LA 71038 • 2,854
Hays, KS 67601 • 17,767
Hays □, TX • 65,614
Haysville, KS 67060 • 8,364
Hayti, MO 63851 • 3,280
Hayward, CA 94540–46 • 111,498
Hayward, WI 54843 • 1,897
Hayward Addition, SD 57106 • 1,000
Haywood □, NC • 46,942
Haywood □, TN • 19,437
Hazard, KY 41701 • 5,416
Hazardville, CT 06082 • 5,179
Hazel Crest, IL 60429 • 13,334
Hazel Dell, WA 98660 • 15,386
Hazel Green, AL 35750 • 2,208
Hazel Green, WI 53811 • 1,171
Hazel Park, MI 48030 • 20,051
Hazelwood, MO 63042–45 • 15,324
Hazelwood, NC 28738 • 1,678
Hazen, AR 72064 • 1,668
Hazen, ND 58545 • 2,818
Hazlehurst, GA 31539 • 4,202
Hazlehurst, MS 39083 • 4,221
Hazlet, NJ 07730 • 23,013
Hazleton, PA 18201 • 24,730
Headland, AL 36345 • 3,266
Healdsburg, CA 95448 • 9,469
Healdton, OK 73438 • 2,872
Healy, AK 99743 • 487
Heard □, GA • 8,628
Hearne, TX 77859 • 5,132
Heath, OH 43056 • 7,231
Heavener, OK 74937 • 2,601
Hebbronville, TX 78361 • 4,465
Heber City, UT 84032 • 4,782
Heber Springs, AR 72543 • 5,628
Hebron, IN 46341 • 3,183
Hebron, KY 41048 • 1,200
Hebron, NE 68370 • 1,765
Hebron, ND 58638 • 888
Hebron, OH 43025 • 2,076
Hector, MN 55342 • 1,145
Heeia, HI 96744 • 5,010
Heflin, AL 36264 • 2,906
Hegins, PA 17938 • 1,200
Helena, AL 35080 • 3,918
Helena, AR 72342 • 7,491
Helena, GA 31037 • 1,256
Helena, MT 59601–26 • 24,569
Helena, OK 73741 • 1,043
Hellam, PA 17406 • 1,375
Hellertown, PA 18055 • 5,662
Helmetta, NJ 08828 • 1,211
Helotes, TX 78023 • 1,535
Helper, UT 84526 • 2,148
Hemet, CA 92343–44 • 36,094
Hemlock, MI 48626 • 1,601
Hemphill, TX 75948 • 1,182
Hemphill □, TX • 3,720
Hempstead, NY 11550–54 • 49,453
Hempstead, TX 77445 • 3,551
Hempstead □, AR • 21,621
Henagar, AL 35978 • 1,934
Henderson, KY 42420 • 25,945
Henderson, LA 70517 • 1,543
Henderson, NV 89015–16 • 64,942
Henderson, NC 27536 • 15,655
Henderson, TN 38340 • 4,760
Henderson, TX 75652–53 • 11,139
Henderson □, IL • 8,096
Henderson □, KY • 43,044
Henderson □, NC • 69,285
Henderson □, TN • 21,844
Henderson □, TX • 58,543
Henderson's Point, MS 39571 • 1,114
Hendersonville, NC 28739 • 7,284
Hendersonville, TN 37075 • 32,188
Hendricks □, IN • 75,717
Hendry □, FL • 25,773
Hennepin □, MN • 1,032,431
Hennessey, OK 73742 • 1,902
Henniker, NH 03242 • 1,693
Henrico □, VA • 217,881
Henrietta, NY 14467 • 1,200
Henrietta, NC 28076 • 1,412
Henrietta, TX 76365 • 2,896
Henry, IL 61537 • 2,591
Henry □, AL • 15,374
Henry □, GA • 58,741
Henry □, IL • 51,159
Henry □, IN • 48,139
Henry □, IA • 19,226
Henry □, KY • 12,823
Henry □, MO • 20,044
Henry □, OH • 29,108
Henry □, TN • 27,888
Henry □, VA • 56,942
Henryetta, OK 74437 • 5,872
Henryville, IN 47126 • 1,132
Hephzibah, GA 30815 • 2,466
Heppner, OR 97836 • 1,412
Herculaneum, MO 63048 • 2,263
Hercules, CA 94547 • 16,829
Hereford, TX 79045 • 14,745
Herington, KS 67449 • 2,685
Heritage Village, CT 06488 • 9,700
Herkimer, NY 13350 • 7,945
Herkimer □, NY • 65,797
Hermann, MO 65041 • 2,754
Hermantown, MN 55811 • 6,761
Herminie, PA 15637 • 2,000
Hermiston, OR 97838 • 10,040
Hermitage, PA 16148 • 15,300
Hermosa Beach, CA 90254 • 18,219
Hernando, FL 32642 • 2,103
Hernando, MS 38632 • 3,125
Hernando □, FL • 101,115
Herndon, VA 22070–71 • 16,139
Herrin, IL 62948 • 10,857
Herscher, IL 60941 • 1,278
Hershey, PA 17033 • 11,860
Hertford, NC 27944 • 2,105
Hertford □, NC • 22,523
Hesperia, CA 92345 • 50,418
Hesston, KS 67062 • 3,012
Hettinger, ND 58639 • 1,574
Hettinger □, ND • 3,445
Hewitt, TX 76643 • 8,983
Hewlett, NY 11557 • 6,620
Heyburn, ID 83336 • 2,714
Heyworth, IL 61745 • 1,627
Hialeah, FL 33010–16 • 188,004
Hiawatha, IA 52233 • 4,986
Hiawatha, KS 66434 • 3,603
Hibbing, MN 55746–47 • 18,046
Hickman, KY 42050 • 2,689
Hickman, NE 68372 • 1,081
Hickman □, KY • 5,566
Hickman □, TN • 16,754
Hickory, NC 28601–03 • 28,301
Hickory □, MO • 7,335
Hickory Hills, IL 60457 • 13,021
Hicksville, NY 11801–05 • 40,174
Hicksville, OH 43526 • 3,664
Hico, TX 76457 • 1,342
Hidalgo, TX 78557 • 3,292
Hidalgo □, NM • 5,958
Hidalgo □, TX • 383,545
Higganum, CT 06441 • 1,692
Higginsville, MO 64037 • 4,693
High Bridge, NJ 08829 • 3,886
Highland, CA 92346 • 34,439
Highland, IL 62249 • 7,525
Highland, IN 46322 • 23,696
Highland, MI 48356–57 • 750
Highland, NY 12528 • 4,492
Highland □, OH • 35,728
Highland □, VA • 2,635
Highland Falls, NY 10928 • 3,937
Highland Heights, OH 44124 • 6,249
Highland Lakes, NJ 07422 • 4,550
Highland Park, IL 60035 • 30,575
Highland Park, MI 48203 • 20,121
Highland Park, NJ 08904 • 13,279
Highland Park, TX 75205 • 8,739
Highlands, NJ 07732 • 4,849
Highlands, TX 77562 • 6,632
Highlands □, FL • 68,432
Highland Springs, VA 23075 • 13,823
Highmore, SD 57345 • 835
High Point, NC 27260–65 • 69,496
High Ridge, MO 63049 • 2,380
High Spire, PA 17034 • 2,668
High Springs, FL 32643 • 3,144
Hightstown, NJ 08520 • 5,126
Highview, KY 40228 • 14,814
Highwood, IL 60040 • 5,331
Hilbert, WI 54129 • 1,211
Hildale, UT 84784 • 1,325
Hill □, MT • 17,654
Hill □, TX • 27,146
Hill City, KS 67642 • 1,835
Hillcrest, NY 10977 • 6,447
Hillcrest Center, CA 93306 • 26,900
Hillcrest Heights, MD 20748 • 17,136
Hilliard, FL 32046 • 1,751
Hilliard, OH 43026 • 11,796
Hillsboro, IL 62049 • 4,400
Hillsboro, KS 67063 • 2,704
Hillsboro, MO 63050 • 1,625
Hillsboro, NH 03244 • 1,826
Hillsboro, ND 58045 • 1,488
Hillsboro, OH 45133 • 6,235
Hillsboro, OR 97123–24 • 37,520
Hillsboro, TX 76645 • 7,072
Hillsboro, WI 54634 • 1,288
Hillsborough, CA 94010 • 10,667
Hillsborough, NC 27278 • 4,263
Hillsborough □, FL • 834,054
Hillsborough □, NH • 336,073
Hillsdale, MI 49242 • 8,170
Hillsdale, NJ 07642 • 9,750
Hillsdale □, MI • 43,431
Hillside, IL 60162 • 7,672
Hillside, NJ 07205 • 21,044
Hillside Heights, DE 19711 • 1,500
Hillsville, VA 24343 • 2,008
Hillview, KY 40229 • 6,119
Hilo, HI 96720–21 • 37,808
Hilton, NY 14468 • 5,216
Hilton Head Island, SC 29928 • 23,694
Hinckley, IL 60520 • 1,682
Hinds □, MS • 254,441
Hines, OR 97738 • 1,452
Hinesville, GA 31313 • 21,603
Hingham, MA 02043 • 5,454
Hinsdale, IL 60521–22 • 16,029
Hinsdale, NH 03451 • 1,718
Hinsdale □, CO • 467
Hinton, OK 73047 • 1,233
Hinton, WV 25951 • 3,433
Hiram, GA 30141 • 1,389
Hiram, OH 44234 • 1,330
Hitchcock, TX 77563 • 5,868
Hitchcock □, NE • 3,750
Hitchcock Lake, CT 06716 • 1,640
Hobart, IN 46342 • 21,822
Hobart, OK 73651 • 4,305
Hobbs, NM 88240–41 • 29,115
Hobe Sound, FL 33455 • 11,507
Hoboken, NJ 07030 • 33,397
Hockessin, DE 19707 • 2,430
Hocking □, OH • 25,533
Hockley □, TX • 24,199
Hodgeman □, KS • 2,177
Hodgenville, KY 42748 • 2,721
Hoffman Estates, IL 60194–95 • 46,561
Hogansville, GA 30230 • 2,976
Hohenwald, TN 38462 • 3,760
Ho-Ho-Kus, NJ 07423 • 3,935
Hoisington, KS 67544 • 3,182
Hoke □, NC • 22,856
Hokes Bluff, AL 35903 • 3,739
Holbrook, AZ 86025–29 • 4,686
Holbrook, MA 02343 • 11,041
Holbrook, NY 11741 • 25,273
Holcomb, KS 67851 • 1,400
Holden, MA 01520 • 4,040
Holden, MO 64040 • 2,389
Holden, WV 25625 • 1,246
Holden Heights, FL 32805 • 4,387
Holdenville, OK 74848 • 4,792
Holdrege, NE 68949 • 5,671
Holgate, OH 43527 • 1,290
Holiday, FL 34690 • 19,360
Holiday City at Berkeley, NJ 08757 • 5,750
Holladay, UT 84117 • 22,189
Holland, MI 49422–24 • 30,745
Holland, NY 14080 • 1,288
Holland, OH 43528 • 1,210
Holland, PA 18966 • 5,250
Holland, TX 76534 • 1,118
Hollandale, MS 38748 • 3,576
Holley, NY 14470 • 1,890
Holliday, TX 76366 • 1,475
Hollidaysburg, PA 16648 • 5,624
Hollins, VA 24019 • 13,305
Hollis, OK 73550 • 2,584
Hollister, CA 95023–24 • 19,212
Hollister, MO 65672 • 2,628
Holliston, MA 01746 • 12,622
Holly, MI 48442 • 5,595
Holly Hill, FL 32117 • 11,141
Holly Hill, SC 29059 • 1,478
Holly Springs, GA 30142 • 2,406
Holly Springs, MS 38634–35 • 7,261
Hollywood, FL 33019–29 • 121,697
Hollywood, SC 29449 • 2,094
Holmen, WI 54636 • 3,220
Holmes □, FL • 15,778
Holmes □, MS • 21,604
Holmes □, OH • 32,849
Holstein, IA 51025 • 1,449
Holt, AL 35404 • 4,125
Holt, MI 48842 • 11,744
Holt □, MO • 6,034
Holt □, NE • 12,599
Holton, KS 66436 • 3,196
Holtsville, NY 11742 • 14,972
Holtville, CA 92250 • 4,820
Holualoa, HI 96725 • 3,834
Holyoke, CO 80734 • 1,931
Holyoke, MA 01040–41 • 43,704
Homedale, ID 83628 • 1,963
Home Gardens, CA 91720 • 7,780
Homeland Park, SC 29621 • 6,569
Home Place, IN 46240 • 1,300
Homer, AK 99603 • 3,660
Homer, IL 61849 • 1,264
Homer, LA 71040 • 4,152
Homer, MI 49245 • 1,758
Homer, NY 13077 • 3,476
Homer City, PA 15748 • 1,809
Homerville, GA 31634 • 2,560
Homestead, FL 33030–35 • 26,866
Homestead, PA 15120 • 4,179
Hometown, IL 60456 • 4,769
Homewood, AL 35209 • 22,922
Homewood, IL 60430 • 19,278
Homewood, OH 45015 • 2,550
Hominy, OK 74035 • 2,342
Homosassa, FL 32646 • 2,113
Hondo, TX 78861 • 6,018
Honea Path, SC 29654 • 3,841
Honeoye Falls, NY 14472 • 2,340
Honesdale, PA 18431 • 4,972
Honey Brook, PA 19344 • 1,184
Honey Grove, TX 75446 • 1,681
Honeypot Glen, CT 06410 • 1,200
Honeyville, UT 84314 • 1,112
Honokaa, HI 96727 • 2,186
Honolulu, HI 96801–50 • 365,272
Honolulu □, HI • 836,231
Honomu, HI 96728 • 532
Hood □, TX • 28,981
Hood River, OR 97031 • 4,632
Hood River □, OR • 16,903
Hoodsport, WA 98548 • 1,100
Hooker, OK 73945 • 1,551
Hooker □, NE • 793
Hooksett, NH 03106 • 2,573
Hoonah, AK 99829 • 795
Hooper Bay, AK 99604 • 845
Hoopeston, IL 60942 • 5,871
Hoosick Falls, NY 12090 • 3,490
Hoover, AL 35216 • 39,788
Hooverson Heights, WV 26037 • 3,056
Hopatcong, NJ 07843 • 15,586
Hope, AR 71801 • 9,643
Hope, IN 47246 • 2,171
Hope, RI 02831 • 270
Hopedale, MA 01747 • 3,961
Hope Mills, NC 28348 • 8,184
Hope Valley, RI 02832 • 1,446
Hopewell, NJ 08525 • 1,968
Hopewell, VA 23860 • 23,101
Hopewell Junction, NY 12533 • 1,786
Hopkins, MN 55343–47 • 16,534
Hopkins, SC 29061 • 1,600
Hopkins □, KY • 46,126
Hopkins □, TX • 28,833
Hopkinsville, KY 42240–41 • 29,809
Hopkinton, MA 01748 • 2,305
Hopkinton, RI 02833 • 550
Hopwood, PA 15445 • 2,021
Hoquiam, WA 98550 • 8,972
Horicon, WI 53032 • 3,873
Hornell, NY 14843 • 9,877
Horn Lake, MS 38637 • 9,069
Horry □, SC • 144,053
Horse Cave, KY 42749 • 2,284
Horseheads, NY 14844–45 • 6,802
Horsham, PA 19044 • 15,051
Horton, KS 66439 • 1,885
Hortonville, WI 54944 • 2,029
Hot Spring □, AR • 26,115
Hot Springs, SD 57747 • 4,325
Hot Springs □, WY • 4,809
Hot Springs National Park, AR 71901–14 • 32,462
Hot Springs Village, AR 71901 • 6,361
Houghton, MI 49931 • 7,498
Houghton, NY 14744 • 1,740
Houghton □, MI • 35,446
Houghton Lake, MI 48629 • 3,353
Houghton Lake Heights, MI 48630 • 2,449
Houlton, ME 04730 • 5,627
Houma, LA 70360–64 • 96,982
Housatonic, MA 01236 • 1,184
Houston, DE 19954 • 487
Houston, MN 55943 • 1,013
Houston, MS 38851 • 3,903
Houston, MO 65483 • 2,118
Houston, PA 15342 • 1,445
Houston, TX 77001–99 • 1,630,553
Houston □, AL • 81,331
Houston □, GA • 89,208
Houston □, MN • 18,497
Houston □, TN • 7,018
Houston □, TX • 21,375
Houtzdale, PA 16651 • 1,204
Howard, SD 57349 • 1,156
Howard, WI 54303 • 9,874
Howard □, AR • 13,569
Howard □, IN • 80,827
Howard □, IA • 9,809
Howard □, MD • 187,328
Howard □, MO • 9,631
Howard □, NE • 6,055
Howard □, TX • 32,343
Howard City, MI 49329 • 1,351
Howard Lake, MN 55349 • 1,343
Howards Grove-Millersville, WI 53083 • 2,329
Howell, MI 48843–44 • 8,184
Howell □, MO • 31,447
Howland, ME 04448 • 1,304
Howland, OH 44484 • 6,732
Hoxie, AR 72433 • 2,676
Hoxie, KS 67740 • 1,342
Hoyt Lakes, MN 55750 • 2,348
Huachuca City, AZ 85616 • 1,782
Hubbard, OH 44425 • 8,248
Hubbard, OR 97032 • 1,881
Hubbard, TX 76648 • 1,589
Hubbard □, MN • 14,939
Hubbell, MI 49934 • 1,174
Huber Heights, OH 45424 • 38,696
Huber Ridge, OH 43081 • 5,255
Huber South, OH 45439 • 4,800
Hudson, FL 34667 • 7,344
Hudson, IL 61748 • 1,006
Hudson, IA 50643 • 2,037
Hudson, MA 01749 • 14,267
Hudson, MI 49247 • 2,580
Hudson, NH 03051 • 7,626
Hudson, NY 12534 • 8,034
Hudson, NC 28638 • 2,819
Hudson, OH 44236 • 5,159
Hudson, WI 54016 • 6,378
Hudson, WY 82515 • 392
Hudson □, NJ • 553,099
Hudson Falls, NY 12839 • 7,651
Hudson Lake, IN 46552 • 1,347
Hudsonville, MI 49426 • 6,170
Hudspeth □, TX • 2,915
Huerfano □, CO • 6,009
Hueytown, AL 35023 • 15,280
Huffakers, NV 89501 • 150
Hughes, AR 72348 • 1,810
Hughes □, OK • 13,023
Hughes □, SD • 14,817
Hughesville, MD 20637 • 1,319
Hughesville, PA 17737 • 2,049
Hugo, MN 55038 • 4,417
Hugo, OK 74743 • 5,978
Hugoton, KS 67951 • 3,179
Hulett, WY 82720 • 429
Hull, IA 51239 • 1,724
Hull, MA 02045 • 10,466
Humansville, MO 65674 • 1,084
Humble, TX 77338–39 • 12,060
Humboldt, IA 50548 • 4,438
Humboldt, KS 66748 • 2,178
Humboldt, NE 68376 • 1,003
Humboldt, TN 38343 • 9,651
Humboldt □, CA • 119,118
Humboldt □, IA • 10,756
Humboldt □, NV • 12,844
Hummels Wharf, PA 17831 • 1,069
Humphreys □, MS • 12,134
Humphreys □, TN • 15,795
Hunt □, TX • 64,343
Hunterdon □, NJ • 107,776
Huntertown, IN 46748 • 1,330
Huntingburg, IN 47542 • 5,242
Huntingdon, PA 16652 • 6,843
Huntingdon, TN 38344 • 4,180
Huntingdon □, PA • 44,164
Huntington, IN 46750 • 16,389
Huntington, MA 01050 • 1,200
Huntington, NY 11743 • 18,243
Huntington, TX 75949 • 1,794
Huntington, UT 84528 • 1,875
Huntington, VA 22303 • 7,489
Huntington, WV 25701–79 • 54,844
Huntington □, IN • 35,427
Huntington Bay, NY 11743 • 1,521
Huntington Beach, CA 92646–49 • 181,519
Huntington Park, CA 90255 • 56,065
Huntington Station, NY 11746 • 28,247
Huntington Woods, MI 48070 • 6,419
Huntley, IL 60142 • 2,453
Huntsville, AL 35801–24 • 159,789
Huntsville, AR 72740 • 1,605
Huntsville, MO 65259 • 1,567
Huntsville, TX 77340–44 • 27,925
Hurley, NM 88043 • 1,534
Hurley, NY 12443 • 4,644
Hurley, WI 54534 • 1,782
Hurlock, MD 21643 • 1,706
Huron, OH 44839 • 7,030
Huron, SD 57350 • 12,448
Huron □, MI • 34,951
Huron □, OH • 56,240
Hurricane, UT 84737 • 3,915
Hurricane, WV 25526 • 4,461
Hurst, TX 76053–54 • 33,574
Hurt, VA 24563 • 1,294
Hutchins, TX 75141 • 2,719
Hutchinson, KS 67501–05 • 39,308
Hutchinson, MN 55350 • 11,523
Hutchinson □, SD • 8,262
Hutchinson □, TX • 25,689
Huxley, IA 50124 • 2,047
Hyannis, MA 02601 • 14,120
Hyannis Port, MA 02647 • 1,100
Hyattsville, MD 20780–89 • 13,864
Hybla Valley, VA 22306 • 15,491
Hydaburg, AK 99922 • 384
Hyde, PA 16843 • 1,643
Hyde □, NC • 5,411
Hyde □, SD • 1,696
Hyde Park, NY 12538 • 2,550
Hyde Park, UT 84318 • 2,190
Hydeville, VT 05750 • 450
Hyndman, PA 15545 • 1,019
Hyrum, UT 84319 • 4,829

I

Iberia □, LA • 68,297
Iberville □, LA • 31,049
Ida, MI 48140 • 1,000
Ida □, IA • 8,365
Idabel, OK 74745 • 6,957
Ida Grove, IA 51445 • 2,357
Idaho □, ID • 13,783
Idaho Falls, ID 83401–15 • 43,929
Idaho Springs, CO 80452 • 1,834
Idalou, TX 79329 • 2,074
Ilion, NY 13357 • 8,888

Illmo, MO 63780 • 1,368
Imlay, NV 89418 • 250
Imlay City, MI 48444 • 2,921
Immokalee, FL 33934 • 14,120
Imperial, CA 92251 • 4,113
Imperial, NE 69033 • 2,007
Imperial, PA 15126 • 3,200
Imperial □, CA • 109,303
Imperial Beach, CA 91932–33 • 26,512
Incline Village, NV 89450 • 4,500
Independence, CA 93526 • 1,000
Independence, IA 50644 • 5,972
Independence, KS 67301 • 9,942
Independence, KY 41051 • 10,444
Independence, LA 70443 • 1,632
Independence, MO 64050–58 • 112,301
Independence, OH 44131 • 6,500
Independence, OR 97351 • 4,425
Independence, WI 54747 • 1,041
Independence □, AR • 31,192
Indiana, PA 15701 • 15,174
Indiana □, PA • 89,994
Indianapolis, IN 46201–90 • 731,327
Indian Harbour Beach, FL 32937 • 6,933
Indian Head, MD 20640 • 3,531
Indian Heights, IN 46902 • 3,669
Indian Hills, CO 80454 • 2,000
Indian Neck, CT 06405 • 2,430
Indianola, IA 50125 • 11,340
Indianola, MS 38751 • 11,809
Indian Ridge Estates, AZ 85715 • 1,260
Indian River □, FL • 90,208
Indian Rocks Beach, FL 34635 • 3,963
Indian Springs, NV 89018 • 1,164
Indiantown, FL 34956 • 4,794
Indian Trail, NC 28079 • 1,942
Indio, CA 92201–02 • 36,793
Ingalls Park, IL 60431 • 2,730
Ingham □, MI • 281,912
Ingleside, TX 78362 • 5,696
Inglewood, CA 90301–12 • 109,602
Inglewood, TX 98011 • 6,500
Ingram, PA 15205 • 3,901
Inkom, ID 83245 • 769
Inkster, MI 48141 • 30,772
Inman, KS 67546 • 1,035
Inman, SC 29349 • 1,742
Inniswold, LA 70809 • 1,100
Inola, OK 74036 • 1,444
Institute, WV 25112 • 1,400
Interlachen, FL 32148 • 1,160
International Falls, MN 56649 • 8,325
Inver Grove Heights, MN 55076–77 • 22,477
Inverness, CA 94937 • 1,422
Inverness, FL 32650–52 • 5,797
Inverness, IL 60067 • 6,503
Inverness, MS 38753 • 1,174
Inwood, FL 33880 • 6,824
Inwood, NY 11696 • 7,767
Inwood, WV 25428 • 1,360
Inyo □, CA • 18,281
Iola, KS 66749 • 6,351
Iola, WI 54945 • 1,125
Iona, ID 83427 • 1,049
Ione, CA 95640 • 6,516
Ionia, MI 48846 • 5,935
Ionia □, MI • 57,024
Iosco □, MI • 30,209
Iota, LA 70543 • 1,256
Iowa, LA 70647 • 2,588
Iowa □, IA • 14,630
Iowa □, WI • 20,150
Iowa City, IA 52240–46 • 59,738
Iowa Falls, IA 50126 • 5,424
Iowa Park, TX 76367 • 6,072
Ipswich, MA 01938 • 4,132
Ipswich, SD 57451 • 965
Iraan, TX 79744 • 1,322
Iredell □, NC • 92,931
Irion □, TX • 1,629
Irmo, SC 29063 • 11,280
Iron □, MI • 13,175
Iron □, MO • 10,726
Iron □, UT • 20,789
Iron □, WI • 6,153
Irondale, AL 35210 • 9,454
Irondequoit, NY 14617 • 52,322
Ironia, NJ 07845 • 1,110
Iron Mountain, MI 49801 • 8,525
Iron River, MI 49935 • 2,095
Ironton, MO 63650 • 1,539
Ironton, OH 45638 • 12,751
Ironwood, MI 49938 • 6,849
Iroquois □, IL • 30,787
Irvine, CA 92713–20 • 110,330
Irvine, KY 40336 • 2,836
Irving, TX 75060–63 • 155,037
Irvington, KY 40146 • 1,180
Irvington, NJ 07111 • 59,774
Irvington, NY 10533 • 6,348
Irwin, PA 15642 • 4,604
Irwin □, GA • 8,649
Isabella □, MI • 54,624
Isanti, MN 55040 • 1,228
Isanti □, MN • 25,921
Iselin, NJ 08830 • 16,141
Ishpeming, MI 49849 • 7,200
Islamorada, FL 33036 • 1,220
Island □, WA • 60,195
Island Heights, NJ 08732 • 1,470
Island Park, NY 11558 • 4,860
Island Park, RI 02871 • 1,240
Island Pond, VT 05846 • 1,222
Isla Vista, CA 93117 • 20,395
Isle of Palms, SC 29451 • 3,680
Isle of Wight □, VA • 25,053
Isleta, NM 87022 • 1,703
Islington, MA 02090 • 4,920
Islip, NY 11751 • 18,924
Islip Terrace, NY 11752 • 5,530
Issaquah, WA 98027 • 7,786
Issaquena □, MS • 1,909
Italy, TX 76651 • 1,699
Itasca, IL 60143 • 6,947
Itasca, TX 76055 • 1,523
Itasca □, MN • 40,863
Itawamba □, MS • 20,017
Ithaca, MI 48847 • 3,009
Ithaca, NY 14850–52 • 29,541
Itta Bena, MS 38941 • 2,377
Iuka, MS 38852 • 3,122
Iva, SC 29655 • 1,174
Ives Estates, FL 33162 • 13,531
Ivins, UT 84738 • 1,630
Ivoryton, CT 06442 • 2,200
Izard □, AR • 11,364

J

Jacinto City, TX 77029 • 9,343
Jack □, TX • 6,981
Jackpot, NV 89825 • 570
Jacksboro, TN 37757 • 1,568
Jacksboro, TX 76056 • 3,350
Jackson, AL 36545 • 5,819
Jackson, CA 95642 • 3,545
Jackson, GA 30233 • 4,076
Jackson, KY 41339 • 2,466
Jackson, LA 70748 • 3,891
Jackson, MI 49201–04 • 37,446
Jackson, MN 56143 • 3,559
Jackson, MS 39201–98 • 196,637
Jackson, MO 63755 • 9,256
Jackson, OH 45640 • 6,144
Jackson, SC 29831 • 1,681
Jackson, TN 38301–08 • 48,949
Jackson, WI 53037 • 2,486
Jackson, WY 83001–02 • 4,472
Jackson □, AL • 47,796
Jackson □, AR • 18,944
Jackson □, CO • 1,605
Jackson □, FL • 41,375
Jackson □, GA • 30,005
Jackson □, IL • 61,067
Jackson □, IN • 37,730
Jackson □, IA • 19,950
Jackson □, KS • 11,525
Jackson □, KY • 11,955
Jackson □, LA • 15,705
Jackson □, MI • 149,756
Jackson □, MN • 11,677
Jackson □, MS • 115,243
Jackson □, MO • 633,232
Jackson □, NC • 26,846
Jackson □, OH • 30,230
Jackson □, OK • 28,764
Jackson □, OR • 146,389
Jackson □, SD • 2,811
Jackson □, TN • 9,297
Jackson □, TX • 13,039
Jackson □, WV • 25,938
Jackson □, WI • 16,588
Jackson Center, OH 45334 • 1,398
Jacksonville, AL 36265 • 10,283
Jacksonville, AR 72076 • 29,101
Jacksonville, FL 32201–98 • 635,230
Jacksonville, IL 62650–51 • 19,324
Jacksonville, NC 28540–46 • 30,013
Jacksonville, OR 97530 • 1,896
Jacksonville, TX 75766 • 12,765
Jacksonville Beach, FL 32250 • 17,839
Jaffrey, NH 03452 • 2,558
Jal, NM 88252 • 2,156
Jamesburg, NJ 08831 • 5,294
James City, NC 28560 • 4,279
James City □, VA • 34,859
James Island, SC 29412 • 24,124
Jamestown, CA 95327 • 2,178
Jamestown, KY 42629 • 1,641
Jamestown, NY 14701–02 • 34,681
Jamestown, NC 27282 • 2,600
Jamestown, ND 58401–02 • 15,571
Jamestown, OH 45335 • 1,794
Jamestown, RI 02835 • 2,156
Jamestown, TN 38556 • 1,862
James Town, WY 82935 • 280
Janesville, CA 96114 • 1,200
Janesville, MN 56048 • 1,969
Janesville, WI 53545–47 • 52,133
Jarrettsville, MD 21084 • 2,148
Jasmine Estates, FL 34668 • 17,136
Jasonville, IN 47438 • 2,200
Jasper, AL 35501–02 • 13,553
Jasper, FL 32052 • 2,099
Jasper, GA 30143 • 1,772
Jasper, IN 47546–47 • 10,030
Jasper, TN 37347 • 2,780
Jasper, TX 75951 • 6,959
Jasper □, GA • 8,453
Jasper □, IL • 10,609
Jasper □, IN • 24,960
Jasper □, IA • 34,795
Jasper □, MS • 17,114
Jasper □, MO • 90,465
Jasper □, SC • 15,487
Jasper □, TX • 31,102
Jay, OK 74346 • 2,220
Jay □, IN • 21,512
Jean, NV 89019 • 150
Jeanerette, LA 70544 • 6,205
Jeannette, PA 15644 • 11,221
Jeff Davis □, GA • 12,032
Jeff Davis □, TX • 1,946
Jefferson, GA 30549 • 2,763
Jefferson, IA 50129 • 4,292
Jefferson, LA 70121 • 14,521
Jefferson, NC 28640 • 1,300
Jefferson, OH 44047 • 3,331
Jefferson, OR 97352 • 1,805
Jefferson, PA 15025 • 9,533
Jefferson, TX 75657 • 2,199
Jefferson, WI 53549 • 6,078
Jefferson □, AL • 651,525
Jefferson □, AR • 85,487
Jefferson □, CO • 438,430
Jefferson □, FL • 11,296
Jefferson □, GA • 17,408
Jefferson □, ID • 16,543
Jefferson □, IL • 37,020
Jefferson □, IN • 29,797
Jefferson □, IA • 16,310
Jefferson □, KS • 15,905
Jefferson □, KY • 664,937
Jefferson □, LA • 448,306
Jefferson □, MS • 8,653
Jefferson □, MO • 171,380
Jefferson □, MT • 7,939
Jefferson □, NE • 8,759
Jefferson □, NY • 110,943
Jefferson □, OH • 80,298
Jefferson □, OK • 7,010
Jefferson □, OR • 13,676
Jefferson □, PA • 46,083
Jefferson □, TN • 33,016
Jefferson □, TX • 239,397
Jefferson □, WA • 20,146
Jefferson □, WV • 35,926
Jefferson □, WI • 67,783
Jefferson City, MO 65101–10 • 35,481
Jefferson City, TN 37760 • 5,494
Jefferson Davis □, LA • 30,722
Jefferson Davis □, MS • 14,051
Jefferson Farms, DE 19720 • 3,130
Jefferson Manor, VA 22303 • 2,300
Jeffersontown, KY 40299 • 23,221
Jefferson Valley, NY 10535 • 6,420
Jefferson Village, VA 22042 • 2,500
Jeffersonville, GA 31044 • 1,545
Jeffersonville, IN 47129–31 • 21,841
Jeffersonville, KY 40337 • 1,854
Jeffersonville, OH 43128 • 1,281
Jeffrey City, WY 82310 • 1,882
Jellico, TN 37762 • 2,447
Jemez Pueblo, NM 87024 • 1,301
Jemison, AL 35085 • 1,898
Jena, LA 71342 • 2,626
Jenison, MI 49428–29 • 17,882
Jenkins, KY 41537 • 2,751
Jenkins □, GA • 8,247
Jenkintown, PA 19046 • 4,574
Jenks, OK 74037 • 7,493
Jennings, LA 70546 • 11,305
Jennings, MO 63136 • 15,905
Jennings □, IN • 23,661
Jennings Lodge, OR 97222 • 11,480
Jensen Beach, FL 34957–58 • 9,884
Jerauld □, SD • 2,425
Jericho, NY 11753 • 13,141
Jericho, VT 05465 • 1,300
Jermyn, PA 18433 • 2,263
Jerome, ID 83338 • 6,529
Jerome, PA 15937 • 1,074
Jerome □, ID • 15,138
Jersey □, IL • 20,539
Jersey City, NJ 07301–11 • 228,537
Jersey Shore, PA 17740 • 4,353
Jerseyville, IL 62052 • 7,382
Jessamine □, KY • 30,508
Jessup, MD 20794 • 6,537
Jessup, PA 18434 • 4,605
Jesup, GA 31545 • 8,958
Jesup, IA 50648 • 2,121
Jewell, IA 50130 • 1,106
Jewell □, KS • 4,251
Jewett City, CT 06351 • 3,349
Jim Hogg □, TX • 5,109
Jim Thorpe, PA 18229 • 5,048
Jim Wells □, TX • 37,679
Joanna, SC 29351 • 1,735
Jo Daviess □, IL • 21,821
John Day, OR 97845 • 1,836
Johnson, KS 67855 • 1,348
Johnson, VT 05656 • 1,470
Johnson □, AR • 18,221
Johnson □, GA • 8,329
Johnson □, IL • 11,347
Johnson □, IN • 88,109
Johnson □, IA • 96,119
Johnson □, KS • 355,054
Johnson □, KY • 23,248
Johnson □, MO • 42,514
Johnson □, NE • 4,673
Johnson □, TN • 13,766
Johnson □, TX • 97,165
Johnson □, WY • 6,145
Johnsonburg, PA 15845 • 3,350
Johnson City, NY 13790 • 16,890
Johnson City, TN 37601–15 • 49,381
Johnson Creek, WI 53038 • 1,259
Johnsonville, SC 29555 • 1,415
Johnston, IA 50131 • 4,702
Johnston, RI 02919 • 26,542
Johnston, SC 29832 • 2,688
Johnston □, NC • 81,306
Johnston □, OK • 10,032
Johnston City, IL 62951 • 3,706
Johnstown, CO 80534 • 1,579
Johnstown, NY 12095 • 9,058
Johnstown, OH 43031 • 3,237
Johnstown, PA 15901–09 • 28,134
Joliet, IL 60431–36 • 76,836
Jones, OK 73049 • 2,424
Jones □, GA • 20,739
Jones □, IA • 19,444
Jones □, MS • 62,031
Jones □, NC • 9,414
Jones □, SD • 1,324
Jones □, TX • 16,490
Jonesboro, AR 72401–03 • 46,535
Jonesboro, GA 30236–37 • 3,635
Jonesboro, IL 62952 • 1,728
Jonesboro, IN 46938 • 2,073
Jonesboro, LA 71251 • 4,305
Jonesborough, TN 37659 • 3,091
Jones Creek, TX 77541 • 2,160
Jonesport, ME 04649 • 1,525
Jonestown, MS 38639 • 1,467
Jonesville, LA 71343 • 2,720
Jonesville, MI 49250 • 2,283
Jonesville, NC 28642 • 1,549
Jonesville, SC 29353 • 1,205
Joplin, MO 64801–04 • 40,961
Joppatowne, MD 21085 • 11,084
Jordan, MN 55352 • 2,909
Jordan, NY 13080 • 1,325
Joseph, OR 97846 • 1,073
Josephine □, OR • 62,649
Joshua, TX 76058 • 3,828
Joshua Tree, CA 92252 • 3,898
Jourdanton, TX 78026 • 3,220
Juab □, UT • 5,817
Juanita, WA 98033 • 10,500
Judith Basin □, MT • 2,282
Judsonia, AR 72081 • 1,915
Julesburg, CO 80737 • 1,295
Julian, CA 92036 • 1,284
Junction, TX 76849 • 2,654
Junction City, KS 66441 • 20,604
Junction City, KY 40440 • 1,983
Junction City, OR 97448 • 3,670
Juneau, AK 99801–03 • 26,751
Juneau, WI 53039 • 2,157
Juneau □, WI • 21,650
Juniata □, PA • 20,625
Jupiter, FL 33458 • 24,986
Justice, IL 60458 • 11,137
Justin, TX 76247 • 1,234

K

Kaaawa, HI 96730 • 1,138
Kadoka, SD 57543 • 736
Kahaluu, HI 96725 • 380
Kahaluu, HI 96744 • 3,068
Kahoka, MO 63445 • 2,195
Kahuku, HI 96731 • 2,063
Kahului, HI 96732–33 • 16,889
Kailua, HI 96734 • 36,818
Kailua Kona, HI 96739–40 • 9,126
Kake, AK 99830 • 700
Kalaheo, HI 96741 • 3,592
Kalama, WA 98625 • 1,210
Kalamazoo, MI 49001–09 • 80,277
Kalamazoo □, MI • 223,411
Kalawao □, HI • 130
Kalispell, MT 59901 • 11,917
Kalkaska, MI 49646 • 1,952
Kalkaska □, MI • 13,497
Kalona, IA 52247 • 1,942
Kamas, UT 84036 • 1,061
Kamiah, ID 83536 • 1,157
Kamuela (Waimea), HI 96743 • 5,972
Kanab, UT 84741 • 3,289
Kanabec □, MN • 12,802
Kanawha □, WV • 207,619
Kandiyohi □, MN • 38,761
Kane, PA 16735 • 4,590
Kane □, IL • 317,471
Kane □, UT • 5,169
Kaneohe, HI 96744 • 35,448
Kankakee, IL 60901 • 27,575
Kankakee □, IL • 96,255
Kannapolis, NC 28081–83 • 29,696
Kansas City, KS 66101–19 • 149,767
Kansas City, MO 64101–99 • 435,146
Kapaa, HI 96746 • 8,149
Kapaau, HI 96755 • 1,083
Kaplan, LA 70548 • 4,535
Karnes □, TX • 12,455
Karnes City, TX 78118 • 2,916
Karns, TN 37921 • 1,458
Kasson, MN 55944 • 3,514
Kathleen, FL 33849 • 2,743
Katy, TX 77449–50 • 8,005
Kauai □, HI • 51,177
Kaufman, TX 75142 • 5,238
Kaufman □, TX • 52,220
Kaukauna, WI 54130 • 11,982
Kaumakani, HI 96747 • 803
Kaunakakai, HI 96748 • 2,658
Kay □, OK • 48,056
Kaycee, WY 82639 • 256
Kayenta, AZ 86033 • 4,372
Kaysville, UT 84037 • 13,961
Keaau, HI 96749 • 1,584
Kealakekua, HI 96750 • 1,453
Kealia, HI 96751 • 700
Keansburg, NJ 07734 • 11,069
Kearney, MO 64060 • 1,790
Kearney, NE 68847–48 • 24,396
Kearney □, NE • 6,629
Kearns, UT 84118 • 28,374
Kearny, AZ 85237 • 2,262
Kearny, NJ 07031–32 • 34,874
Kearny □, KS • 4,027
Keego Harbor, MI 48320 • 2,932
Keene, NH 03431 • 22,430
Keene, TX 76059 • 3,944
Keeseville, NY 12944 • 1,854
Keewatin, MN 55753 • 1,118
Keith □, NE • 8,584
Keizer, OR 97303 • 21,884
Kekaha, HI 96752 • 3,506
Keller, TX 76248 • 13,683
Kellogg, ID 83837 • 2,591
Kelseyville, CA 95451 • 2,861
Kelso, WA 98626 • 11,820
Kemmerer, WY 83101 • 3,020
Kemp, TX 75143 • 1,184
Kemper □, MS • 10,356
Kenai, AK 99611 • 6,327
Kenbridge, VA 23944 • 1,264
Ken Caryl, CO 80123 • 24,391
Kendall, FL 33156 • 87,271
Kendall □, IL • 39,413
Kendall □, TX • 14,589
Kendall Park, NJ 08824 • 7,127
Kendallville, IN 46755 • 7,773
Kenedy, TX 78119 • 3,763
Kenedy □, TX • 460
Kenilworth, IL 60043 • 2,402
Kenilworth, NJ 07033 • 7,574
Kenly, NC 27542 • 1,549
Kenmare, ND 58746 • 1,214
Kenmore, NY 14217 • 17,180
Kenmore, WA 98028 • 8,917
Kennebec □, ME • 115,904
Kennebunk, ME 04043 • 4,206
Kennebunkport, ME 04046 • 1,100
Kennedy Heights, LA 70094 • 2,000
Kennedy Township, PA 15108 • 7,152
Kenner, LA 70062–65 • 72,033
Kennesaw, GA 30144 • 8,936
Kennett, MO 63857 • 10,941
Kennett Square, PA 19348 • 5,218
Kennewick, WA 99336–37 • 42,155
Kennydale, WA 98056 • 2,000
Kenosha, WI 53140–44 • 80,352
Kenosha □, WI • 128,181
Kenova, WV 25530 • 3,748
Ken Rock, IL 61109 • 3,300
Kensett, AR 72082 • 1,741
Kensington, CA 94707 • 4,974
Kensington, CT 06037 • 8,306
Kensington, MD 20895 • 1,713
Kent, OH 44240 • 28,835
Kent, WA 98031–32 • 37,960
Kent □, DE • 110,993
Kent □, MD • 17,842
Kent □, MI • 500,631
Kent □, RI • 161,135
Kent □, TX • 1,010
Kentfield, CA 94904 • 6,030
Kentland, IN 47951 • 1,798
Kenton, DE 19955 • 232
Kenton, OH 43326 • 8,356
Kenton, TN 38233 • 1,366
Kenton □, KY • 142,031
Kentwood, LA 70444 • 2,468
Kentwood, MI 49508 • 37,826
Kenvil, NJ 07847 • 3,050
Kenwood, OH 45236 • 7,469
Kenyon, MN 55946 • 1,552
Kenyon, RI 02836 • 400
Keokea, HI 96790 • 900
Keokuk, IA 52632 • 12,451
Keokuk □, IA • 11,624
Keosauqua, IA 52565 • 1,020
Keota, IA 52248 • 1,000
Kerens, TX 75144 • 1,702
Kerhonkson, NY 12446 • 1,629
Kermit, TX 79745 • 6,875
Kern □, CA • 543,477
Kernersville, NC 27284–85 • 10,836
Kernville, CA 93238 • 1,656
Kerr □, TX • 36,304
Kerrville, TX 78028–29 • 17,384
Kershaw, SC 29067 • 1,814
Kershaw □, SC • 43,599
Ketchikan, AK 99901 • 8,263
Ketchum, ID 83340 • 2,523
Kettering, MD 20772 • 9,901
Kettering, OH 45429 • 60,569
Kettle Falls, WA 99141 • 1,272
Kewanee, IL 61443 • 12,969
Kewaskum, WI 53040 • 2,515
Kewaunee, WI 54216 • 2,750
Kewaunee □, WI • 18,878
Keweenaw □, MI • 1,701
Keya Paha □, NE • 1,029
Key Biscayne, FL 33149 • 8,854
Key Largo, FL 33037 • 11,336
Keyport, NJ 07735 • 7,586
Keyser, WV 26726 • 5,870
Keystone Heights, FL 32656 • 1,315
Key West, FL 33040–41 • 24,832
Kiana, AK 99749 • 385
Kidder □, ND • 3,332
Kiel, WI 53042 • 2,910
Kihei, HI 96753 • 11,107
Kilauea, HI 96754 • 1,685
Kilgore, TX 75662–63 • 11,066
Killdeer, ND 58640 • 722
Killeen, TX 76540–47 • 63,535
Killen, AL 35645 • 1,047
Kilmarnock, VA 22482 • 1,109
Kimball, NE 69145 • 2,574
Kimball □, NE • 4,108
Kimberly, AL 35091 • 1,096
Kimberly, ID 83341 • 2,367
Kimberly, WI 54136 • 5,406
Kimble □, TX • 4,122
Kincaid, IL 62540 • 1,353
Kinder, LA 70648 • 2,246
Kinderhook, NY 12106 • 1,293
King, NC 27021 • 4,059
King □, TX • 354
King □, WA • 1,507,319
King and Queen □, VA • 6,289
King City, CA 93930 • 7,634
King Cove, AK 99612 • 451
Kingfisher, OK 73750 • 4,095
Kingfisher □, OK • 13,212
King George □, VA • 13,527
Kingman, AZ 86401–02 • 12,722
Kingman, KS 67068 • 3,196
Kingman □, KS • 8,292
King of Prussia, PA 19406 • 18,406
Kings, MS 39180 • 1,165
Kings □, CA • 101,469
Kings □, NY • 2,300,664
King Salmon, AK 99613 • 696
Kingsburg, CA 93631 • 7,205
Kingsbury □, SD • 5,925
Kingsford, MI 49801 • 5,480
Kingsgate, WA 98011 • 14,259
Kingsland, GA 31548 • 4,699
Kingsland, TX 78639 • 2,725
Kingsley, IA 51028 • 1,129
Kings Mountain, NC 28086 • 8,763
Kings Park, NY 11754 • 17,773
Kings Park, VA 22151 • 6,000
Kings Park West, VA 22032 • 6,000
Kings Point, FL 33484 • 12,422
Kings Point, NY 11024 • 4,843
Kingsport, TN 37660–65 • 36,365
Kingston, ID 83839 • 1,000
Kingston, MA 02364 • 4,774
Kingston, NJ 08528 • 1,200
Kingston, NY 12401 • 23,095
Kingston, OH 45644 • 1,153
Kingston, OK 73439 • 1,237
Kingston, PA 18704 • 14,507
Kingston, RI 02881 • 6,504
Kingston, TN 37763 • 4,552
Kingston Springs, TN 37082 • 1,529
Kingstown, MD 21620 • 1,660
Kingstree, SC 29556 • 3,858
Kingsville, MD 21087 • 3,550
Kingsville (North Kingsville), OH 44048 • 1,243
Kingsville, TX 78363–64 • 25,276
King William □, VA • 10,913
Kingwood, TX 77339 • 37,397
Kingwood, WV 26537 • 3,243
Kinloch, MO 63140 • 2,702
Kinnelon, NJ 07405 • 8,470
Kinney □, TX • 3,119
Kinsey, AL 36301 • 1,679
Kinsley, KS 67547 • 1,875
Kinston, NC 28501–03 • 25,295
Kiowa, KS 67070 • 1,160
Kiowa □, CO • 1,688
Kiowa □, KS • 3,660
Kiowa □, OK • 11,347
Kipnuk, AK 99614 • 470
Kirby, TX 78219 • 8,326
Kirbyville, TX 75956 • 1,871
Kirkland, IL 60146 • 1,011
Kirkland, WA 98033–34 • 40,052
Kirksville, MO 63501 • 17,152
Kirkwood, DE 19708 • 350
Kirkwood, MO 63122 • 27,291
Kirtland, NM 87417 • 3,552
Kirtland, OH 44094 • 5,881
Kissimmee, FL 34741–46 • 30,050
Kit Carson □, CO • 7,140
Kitsap □, WA • 189,731
Kittanning, PA 16201 • 5,120
Kittery, ME 03904 • 5,151

Kittery Point, ME 03905 • *1,093*
Kittitas □, WA • *26,725*
Kittson □, MN • *5,767*
Kitty Hawk, NC 27949 • *1,937*
Klamath □, OR • *57,702*
Klamath Falls, OR 97601–03 • *17,737*
Klawock, AK 99925 • *722*
Kleberg □, TX • *30,274*
Klein, TX 77379 • *12,000*
Klickitat □, WA • *16,616*
Knightdale, NC 27545 • *1,884*
Knights Landing, CA 95645 • *1,000*
Knightstown, IN 46148 • *2,048*
Knob Noster, MO 65336 • *2,261*
Knott □, KY • *17,906*
Knox, IN 46534 • *3,705*
Knox, PA 16232 • *1,182*
Knox □, IL • *56,393*
Knox □, IN • *39,884*
Knox □, KY • *29,676*
Knox □, ME • *36,310*
Knox □, MO • *4,482*
Knox □, NE • *9,534*
Knox □, OH • *47,473*
Knox □, TN • *335,749*
Knox □, TX • *4,837*
Knox City, TX 79529 • *1,440*
Knoxville, IL 61448 • *3,243*
Knoxville, IA 50138 • *8,232*
Knoxville, TN 37901–50 • *165,121*
Kodiak, AK 99615 • *6,365*
Kohler, WI 53044 • *1,817*
Kokomo, IN 46901–04 • *44,962*
Koloa, HI 96756 • *1,791*
Konawa, OK 74849 • *1,508*
Koochiching □, MN • *16,299*
Koontz Lake, IN 46574 • *1,615*
Kootenai □, ID • *69,795*
Koppel, PA 16136 • *1,024*
Kosciusko, MS 39090 • *6,986*
Kosciusko □, IN • *65,294*
Kossuth □, IA • *18,591*
Kotlik, AK 99620 • *461*
Kotzebue, AK 99752 • *2,751*
Kountze, TX 77625 • *2,056*
Kouts, IN 46347 • *1,603*
Krebs, OK 74554 • *1,955*
Kremmling, CO 80459 • *1,166*
Krotz Springs, LA 70750 • *1,285*
Kula, HI 96790 • *1,300*
Kulpmont, PA 17834 • *3,233*
Kuna, ID 83634 • *1,955*
Kurtistown, HI 96760 • *910*
Kutztown, PA 19530 • *4,704*
Kwethluk, AK 99621 • *558*
Kwigillingok, AK 99622 • *278*
Kyle, TX 78640 • *2,225*

L

Labadieville, LA 70372 • *1,821*
La Barge, WY 83123 • *493*
La Belle, FL 33935 • *2,703*
Labette □, KS • *23,693*
La Canada Flintridge, CA 91011 • *19,378*
Lac du Flambeau, WI 54538 • *1,180*
La Center, KY 42056 • *1,040*
Lacey, WA 98503 • *19,279*
Lackawanna, NY 14218 • *20,585*
Lackawanna □, PA • *219,039*
Laclede □, MO • *27,158*
Lacombe, LA 70445 • *6,523*
Lacon, IL 61540 • *1,986*
Laconia, NH 03246–47 • *15,743*
Lacoochee, FL 33537 • *2,072*
Lac qui Parle □, MN • *8,924*
La Crescent, MN 55947 • *4,311*
La Crescenta, CA 91214 • *12,500*
La Crosse, KS 67548 • *1,427*
La Crosse, WI 54601–03 • *51,003*
La Crosse □, WI • *97,904*
La Cygne, KS 66040 • *1,066*
Ladd, IL 61329 • *1,283*
Ladera Heights, CA 90045 • *6,316*
Ladoga, IN 47954 • *1,124*
Ladson, SC 29456 • *13,540*
Ladue, MO 63124 • *8,847*
Lady Lake, FL 32159 • *8,071*
Ladysmith, WI 54848 • *3,938*
Lafayette, AL 36862 • *3,151*
Lafayette, CA 94549 • *23,501*
Lafayette, CO 80026 • *14,548*
Lafayette, GA 30728 • *6,313*
Lafayette, IN 47901–06 • *43,764*
Lafayette, LA 70501–09 • *94,440*
Lafayette, NC 28304 • *3,200*
Lafayette, OR 97127 • *1,292*
La Fayette, RI 02852 • *640*
Lafayette, TN 37083 • *3,641*
Lafayette □, AR • *9,643*
Lafayette □, FL • *5,578*
Lafayette □, LA • *164,762*
Lafayette □, MS • *31,826*
Lafayette □, MO • *31,107*
Lafayette □, WI • *16,076*
Lafayette Southwest, LA • *5,500*
La Feria, TX 78559 • *4,360*
Lafitte, LA 70067 • *1,507*
La Follette, TN 37766 • *7,192*
Lafourche □, LA • *85,860*
La Grande, OR 97850 • *11,766*
La Grange, GA 30240–41 • *25,597*
La Grange, IL 60525 • *15,362*
Lagrange, IN 46761 • *2,382*
La Grange, KY 40031 • *3,853*
La Grange, MO 63448 • *1,102*
La Grange, NC 28551 • *2,805*
Lagrange, OH 44050 • *1,199*
La Grange, TX 78945 • *3,951*
Lagrange □, IN • *29,477*
La Grange Highlands, IL 60525 • *3,660*
La Grange Park, IL 60525 • *12,861*
Laguna Beach, CA 92651–54 • *23,170*
Laguna Hills, CA 92653 • *46,731*
Laguna Niguel, CA 92677 • *44,400*
La Habra, CA 90631–33 • *51,266*
Lahaina, HI 96761 • *9,073*
La Harpe, IL 61450 • *1,407*
Laie, HI 96762 • *5,577*
Laingsburg, MI 48848 • *1,148*
La Junta, CO 81050 • *7,637*

Lake □, CA • *50,631*
Lake □, CO • *6,007*
Lake □, FL • *152,104*
Lake □, IL • *516,418*
Lake □, IN • *475,594*
Lake □, MI • *8,583*
Lake □, MN • *10,415*
Lake □, MT • *21,041*
Lake □, OH • *215,499*
Lake □, OR • *7,186*
Lake □, SD • *10,550*
Lake □, TN • *7,129*
Lake Alfred, FL 33850 • *3,622*
Lake Andes, SD 57356 • *846*
Lake Arrowhead, CA 92317 • *6,539*
Lake Arthur, LA 70549 • *3,194*
Lake Barcroft, VA 22041 • *8,686*
Lake Bluff, IL 60044 • *5,513*
Lake Butler, FL 32054 • *2,116*
Lake Carmel, NY 10512 • *8,489*
Lake Charles, LA 70601–29 • *70,580*
Lake City, AR 72437 • *1,833*
Lake City, FL 32055–56 • *10,005*
Lake City, IA 51449 • *1,841*
Lake City, MN 55041 • *4,391*
Lake City, PA 16423 • *2,519*
Lake City, SC 29560 • *7,153*
Lake City, TN 37769 • *2,166*
Lake Crystal, MN 56055 • *2,084*
Lake Delta, NY 13440 • *1,980*
Lake Delton, WI 53940 • *1,470*
Lake Elmo, MN 55042 • *5,903*
Lake Elsinore, CA 92330–31 • *18,285*
Lake Erie Beach, NY 14006 • *4,509*
Lakefield, MN 56150 • *1,679*
Lake Forest, FL 33023 • *5,400*
Lake Forest, IL 60045 • *17,836*
Lake Geneva, WI 53147 • *5,979*
Lake Grove, NY 11755 • *9,612*
Lake Hamilton, AR 71913 • *1,331*
Lake Havasu City, AZ 86403–05 • *24,363*
Lake Helen, FL 32744 • *2,344*
Lakehurst, NJ 08733 • *3,078*
Lake in the Hills, IL 60102 • *5,866*
Lake Jackson, TX 77566 • *22,776*
Lake Katrine, NY 12449 • *1,998*
Lakeland, FL 33801–13 • *70,576*
Lakeland, GA 31635 • *2,467*
Lakeland Highlands, FL 33801 • *9,972*
Lakeland Village, CA 92330 • *5,159*
Lake Linden, MI 49945 • *1,203*
Lake Lorraine, FL 32569 • *6,779*
Lake Luzerne, NY 12846 • *1,160*
Lake Magdalene, FL 33612 • *15,973*
Lake Mary, FL 32746 • *5,929*
Lake Mills, IA 50450 • *2,143*
Lake Mills, WI 53551 • *4,143*
Lakemore, OH 44250 • *2,684*
Lake Odessa, MI 48849 • *2,256*
Lake Of The Woods □, MN • *4,076*
Lake Orion, MI 48360–62 • *3,057*
Lake Oswego, OR 97034–35 • *30,576*
Lake Park, FL 33403 • *6,704*
Lake Placid, FL 33852 • *1,158*
Lake Placid, NY 12946 • *2,485*
Lakeport, CA 95453 • *4,390*
Lake Preston, SD 57249 • *663*
Lake Providence, LA 71254 • *5,380*
Lake Ridge, VA 22192 • *23,862*
Lake Ronkonkoma, NY 11779 • *18,997*
Lake Shore, MD 21122 • *13,269*
Lakeside, CA 92040 • *39,412*
Lakeside, CT 06488 • *1,200*
Lakeside, FL 32073 • *29,137*
Lakeside, OR 97449 • *1,437*
Lakeside, VA 23228 • *12,081*
Lakeside Park, KY 41017 • *3,131*
Lakeside-Pinetop, AZ 85935 • *2,422*
Lake Station, IN 46405 • *13,899*
Lake Stevens, WA 98258 • *3,380*
Lake Telemark, NJ 07866 • *1,121*
Lakeview, GA 30741 • *5,237*
Lake View, IA 51450 • *1,303*
Lakeview, MI 48850 • *1,108*
Lake View, NY 14085 • *1,460*
Lakeview, NY 11552 • *5,476*
Lakeview, OH 43331 • *1,056*
Lakeview, OR 97630 • *2,526*
Lake Villa, IL 60046 • *2,857*
Lake Village, AR 71653 • *2,791*
Lakeville, CT 06039 • *1,800*
Lakeville, MA 02346 • *1,948*
Lakeville, MN 55044 • *24,854*
Lakeville, NY 14480 • *1,000*
Lake Wales, FL 33853 • *9,670*
Lake Wissota, WI 54729 • *2,175*
Lakewood, CA 90711–16 • *73,557*
Lakewood, CO 80215 • *126,481*
Lakewood, IL 60014 • *1,609*
Lakewood, IA 50211 • *1,950*
Lakewood, NJ 08701 • *26,095*
Lakewood, NY 14750 • *3,564*
Lakewood, OH 44107 • *59,718*
Lakewood, WA 98259 • *58,412*
Lakewood Center, WA 98499 • *58,412*
Lakewood Park, FL 34951 • *7,211*
Lake Worth, FL 33460–67 • *28,564*
Lake Zurich, IL 60047 • *14,947*
Lakin, KS 67860 • *2,060*
Lakota, ND 58344 • *898*
La Luz, NM 88337 • *1,625*
Lamar, CO 81052 • *8,343*
Lamar, MO 64759 • *4,168*
Lamar, PA 16848 • *1,200*
Lamar, SC 29069 • *1,125*
Lamar □, AL • *15,715*
Lamar □, GA • *13,038*
Lamar □, MS • *30,424*
Lamar □, TX • *43,949*
La Marque, TX 77568 • *14,120*
Lamb □, TX • *15,072*
Lambert, MS 38643 • *1,131*
Lambertville, MI 48144 • *7,860*
Lambertville, NJ 08530 • *3,927*
La Mesa, CA 91941–44 • *52,931*
La Mesa, NM 88044 • *900*
Lamesa, TX 79331 • *10,809*
La Mirada, CA 90637–38 • *40,452*
Lamoille, NV 89828 • *110*
Lamoille □, VT • *19,735*
Lamoni, IA 50140 • *2,319*
Lamont, CA 93241 • *11,517*
La Moure, ND 58458 • *970*

La Moure □, ND • *5,383*
Lampasas, TX 76550 • *6,382*
Lampasas □, TX • *13,521*
Lanai City, HI 96763 • *2,400*
Lanark, IL 61046 • *1,382*
Lancashire, DE 19810 • *1,175*
Lancaster, CA 93534–39 • *97,291*
Lancaster, KY 40444 • *3,421*
Lancaster, NH 03584 • *1,859*
Lancaster, NY 14086 • *11,940*
Lancaster, OH 43130 • *34,507*
Lancaster, PA 17601–05 • *55,551*
Lancaster, SC 29720–21 • *8,914*
Lancaster, TX 75146 • *22,117*
Lancaster, WI 53813 • *4,192*
Lancaster □, NE • *213,641*
Lancaster □, PA • *422,822*
Lancaster □, SC • *54,516*
Lancaster □, VA • *10,896*
Lancaster Village, DE 19805 • *1,100*
Landen, OH 45040 • *9,263*
Lander, WY 82520 • *7,023*
Lander □, NV • *6,266*
Landess, IN 46944 • *1,500*
Landis, NC 28088 • *2,333*
Land O' Lakes, FL 34639 • *7,892*
Landover, MD 20784 • *5,052*
Landrum, SC 29356 • *2,347*
Lane □, KS • *2,375*
Lane □, OR • *282,912*
Lanesboro, MA 01237 • *1,000*
Lanett, AL 36863 • *8,985*
Langdon, ND 58249 • *2,241*
Langeloth, PA 15054 • *1,112*
Langhorne, PA 19047 • *1,361*
Langlade □, WI • *19,505*
Langley, SC 29834 • *1,714*
Langley Park, MD 20783 • *17,474*
Langston, OK 73050 • *1,471*
Lanham, MD 20706 • *5,000*
Lanier □, GA • *5,531*
Lansdale, PA 19446 • *16,362*
Lansdowne, MD 21227 • *9,430*
Lansdowne, PA 19050 • *11,712*
L'Anse, MI 49946 • *2,151*
Lansford, PA 18232 • *4,583*
Lansing, IL 60438 • *28,086*
Lansing, IA 52151 • *1,007*
Lansing, KS 66043 • *7,120*
Lansing, MI 48901–33 • *127,321*
Lantana, FL 33462 • *8,392*
La Palma, CA 90623 • *15,392*
La Paz □, AZ • *13,844*
Lapeer, MI 48446 • *7,759*
Lapeer □, MI • *74,768*
Lapel, IN 46051 • *1,742*
La Place, LA 70068–69 • *24,194*
La Plata, MD 20646 • *5,841*
La Plata, MO 63549 • *1,401*
La Plata □, CO • *32,284*
Laporte, CO 80535 • *1,300*
La Porte, IN 46350 • *21,507*
La Porte, TX 77571–72 • *27,910*
La Porte □, IN • *107,066*
La Porte City, IA 50651 • *2,128*
La Pryor, TX 78872 • *1,343*
La Puente, CA 91744–49 • *36,955*
Lapwai, ID 83540 • *932*
Laramie, WY 82063–71 • *26,687*
Laramie □, WY • *73,142*
Larchmont, NY 10538 • *6,181*
Larchmont North, NY 10538 • *11,240*
Laredo, TX 78040–44 • *122,899*
Largo, FL 34640–49 • *65,674*
Larimer □, CO • *186,136*
Larimore, ND 58251 • *1,464*
La Riviera, CA 95826 • *10,986*
Larkspur, CA 94939 • *11,070*
Larksville, PA 18704 • *4,700*
Larned, KS 67550 • *4,490*
Larose, LA 70373 • *5,772*
Larue □, KY • *11,679*
La Salle, CO 80645 • *1,783*
La Salle, IL 61301 • *9,717*
La Salle □, IL • *106,913*
La Salle □, LA • *13,662*
La Salle □, TX • *5,254*
Las Animas, CO 81054 • *2,481*
Las Animas □, CO • *13,765*
Las Cruces, NM 88001–08 • *62,126*
Lassen □, CA • *27,598*
Las Vegas, NV 89101–99 • *258,295*
Las Vegas, NM 87701 • *14,753*
Latah □, ID • *30,617*
Lathrop, MO 64465 • *1,794*
Lathrop Wells, NV 89020 • *350*
Latimer □, OK • *10,333*
Laton, CA 93242 • *1,415*
Latrobe, PA 15650 • *9,265*
Latta, SC 29565 • *1,565*
Lauderdale □, AL • *79,661*
Lauderdale □, MS • *75,555*
Lauderdale □, TN • *23,491*
Lauderdale Lakes, FL 33313 • *27,341*
Lauderhill, FL 33313 • *49,708*
Laughlin, NV 89028–29 • *140*
Laughlintown, PA 15655 • *1,000*
Laurel, DE 19956 • *3,226*
Laurel, FL 34272 • *8,245*
Laurel, MD 20707–09 • *19,438*
Laurel, MS 39440–42 • *18,827*
Laurel, MT 59044 • *5,686*
Laurel, VA 23060 • *13,011*
Laurel □, KY • *43,438*
Laurel Bay, SC 29902 • *4,972*
Laureldale, PA 19605 • *3,726*
Laurel Hill, NC 28351 • *2,314*
Laurence Harbor, NJ 08879 • *6,361*
Laurens, IA 50554 • *1,550*
Laurens, SC 29360 • *9,694*
Laurens □, GA • *39,988*
Laurens □, SC • *58,092*
Laurinburg, NC 28352–53 • *11,643*
Laurium, MI 49913 • *2,268*
Lavaca, AR 72941 • *1,253*
Lavaca □, TX • *18,690*
La Vale, MD 21502 • *5,000*
Lavallette, NJ 08735 • *2,299*
La Vergne, TN 37086 • *7,499*
La Verkin, UT 84745 • *1,771*
La Verne, CA 91750 • *30,897*
Laverne, OK 73848 • *1,269*
La Vista, GA 30329 • *4,900*

La Vista, NE 68128 • *9,840*
Lavonia, GA 30553 • *1,840*
Lawai, HI 96765 • *1,787*
Lawndale, CA 90260–61 • *27,331*
Lawnside, NJ 08045 • *2,841*
Lawrence, IN 46226 • *26,763*
Lawrence, KS 66044–46 • *65,608*
Lawrence, MA 01840–45 • *70,207*
Lawrence, NY 11559 • *6,513*
Lawrence □, AL • *31,513*
Lawrence □, AR • *17,457*
Lawrence □, IL • *15,972*
Lawrence □, IN • *42,836*
Lawrence □, KY • *13,998*
Lawrence □, MS • *12,458*
Lawrence □, MO • *30,236*
Lawrence □, OH • *61,834*
Lawrence □, PA • *96,246*
Lawrence □, TN • *35,303*
Lawrenceburg, IN 47025 • *4,375*
Lawrenceburg, KY 40342 • *5,911*
Lawrenceburg, TN 38464 • *10,412*
Lawrence Park, PA 16511 • *4,310*
Lawrenceville, GA 30243–46 • *16,848*
Lawrenceville, IL 62439 • *4,897*
Lawrenceville, NJ 08648 • *6,446*
Lawrenceville, VA 23868 • *1,486*
Lawson, MO 64062 • *1,876*
Lawsonia, MD 21817 • *1,326*
Lawtell, LA 70550 • *1,014*
Lawton, MI 49065 • *1,685*
Lawton, OK 73501–07 • *80,561*
Layton, UT 84040–41 • *41,784*
Laytonville, CA 95454 • *1,133*
Lea □, NM • *55,765*
Leachville, AR 72438 • *1,743*
Lead, SD 57754 • *3,632*
Leadville, CO 80461 • *2,629*
Leadwood, MO 63653 • *1,247*
League City, TX 77573–74 • *30,159*
Leake □, MS • *18,436*
Leakesville, MS 39451 • *1,129*
Lealman, FL 33714 • *21,748*
Leavenworth, KS 66048 • *38,495*
Leavenworth, WA 98826 • *1,692*
Leavenworth □, KS • *64,371*
Leavittsburg, OH 44430 • *2,220*
Leawood, KS 66206 • *19,693*
Lebanon, DE 19901 • *130*
Lebanon, IL 62254 • *3,688*
Lebanon, IN 46052 • *12,059*
Lebanon, KY 40033 • *5,695*
Lebanon, MO 65536 • *9,983*
Lebanon, NH 03766 • *12,183*
Lebanon, NJ 08833 • *1,036*
Lebanon, OH 45036 • *10,453*
Lebanon, OR 97355 • *10,950*
Lebanon, PA 17042 • *24,800*
Lebanon, TN 37087–88 • *15,208*
Lebanon, VA 24266 • *3,386*
Lebanon □, PA • *113,744*
Lebanon Junction, KY 40150 • *1,741*
Le Center, MN 56057 • *2,006*
Le Claire, IA 52753 • *2,734*
Lecompte, LA 71346 • *1,592*
Lee, MA 01238 • *2,020*
Lee □, AL • *87,146*
Lee □, AR • *13,053*
Lee □, FL • *335,113*
Lee □, GA • *16,250*
Lee □, IL • *34,392*
Lee □, IA • *38,687*
Lee □, KY • *7,422*
Lee □, MS • *65,581*
Lee □, NC • *41,374*
Lee □, SC • *18,437*
Lee □, TX • *12,854*
Lee □, VA • *24,496*
Leechburg, PA 15656 • *2,504*
Leedom Estates, DE 19720 • *1,100*
Leeds, AL 35094 • *9,946*
Leelanau □, MI • *16,527*
Lee Park, PA 18702 • *3,800*
Leesburg, FL 34748–49 • *14,903*
Leesburg, GA 31763 • *1,452*
Leesburg, OH 45135 • *1,063*
Leesburg, VA 22075 • *16,202*
Lees Summit, MO 64063–64 • *46,418*
Leesville, LA 71446 • *7,638*
Leesville, SC 29070 • *2,025*
Leetonia, OH 44431 • *2,070*
Leetsdale, PA 15056 • *1,387*
Leflore □, MS • *37,341*
Le Flore □, OK • *43,270*
Le Grand, CA 95333 • *1,205*
Lehi, UT 84043 • *8,475*
Lehigh □, PA • *291,130*
Lehigh Acres, FL 33936 • *13,611*
Lehighton, PA 18235 • *5,914*
Leicester, MA 01524 • *3,200*
Leipsic, DE 19901 • *236*
Leipsic, OH 45856 • *2,203*
Leisure City, FL 33033 • *19,379*
Leitchfield, KY 42754–55 • *4,965*
Leland, MS 38756 • *6,366*
Le Mars, IA 51031 • *8,454*
Lemay, MO 63125 • *18,005*
Lemhi □, ID • *6,899*
Lemmon, SD 57638 • *1,614*
Lemmon Valley, NV 89501 • *4,100*
Lemon Grove, CA 91945–46 • *23,984*
Lemont, IL 60439 • *7,348*
Lemont, PA 16851 • *2,613*
Lemoore, CA 93245 • *13,622*
Lena, IL 61048 • *2,605*
Lenawee □, MI • *91,476*
Lenexa, KS 66215 • *34,034*
Lennox, CA 90304 • *22,757*
Lennox, SD 57039 • *1,767*
Lenoir, NC 28645 • *14,192*
Lenoir □, NC • *57,274*
Lenoir City, TN 37771 • *6,147*
Lenox, IA 50851 • *1,303*
Lenox, MA 01240 • *1,687*
Leo, IN 46765 • *1,200*
Leominster, MA 01453 • *38,145*
Leon, IA 50144 • *2,047*
Leon □, FL • *192,493*
Leon □, TX • *12,665*
Leonard, TX 75452 • *1,744*
Leonardo, NJ 07737 • *3,720*
Leonardtown, MD 20650 • *1,475*
Leonia, NJ 07605 • *8,365*

Leon Valley, TX 78238 • *9,581*
Leoti, KS 67861 • *1,738*
Lepanto, AR 72354 • *2,033*
Le Roy, IL 61752 • *2,777*
Le Roy, NY 14482 • *4,974*
Leslie, MI 49251 • *1,872*
Leslie, SC 29730 • *1,102*
Leslie □, KY • *13,642*
Lester Prairie, MN 55354 • *1,180*
Le Sueur, MN 56058 • *3,714*
Le Sueur □, MN • *23,239*
Letcher □, KY • *27,000*
Levelland, TX 79336–38 • *13,986*
Levittown, NY 11756 • *53,286*
Levittown, PA 19058 • *55,362*
Levy □, FL • *25,923*
Lewes, DE 19958 • *2,295*
Lewis □, ID • *3,516*
Lewis □, KY • *13,029*
Lewis □, MO • *10,233*
Lewis □, NY • *26,796*
Lewis □, TN • *9,247*
Lewis □, WA • *59,358*
Lewis □, WV • *17,223*
Lewis and Clark □, MT • *47,495*
Lewisburg, OH 45338 • *1,584*
Lewisburg, PA 17837 • *5,785*
Lewisburg, TN 37091 • *9,879*
Lewisburg, WV 24901 • *3,598*
Lewisport, KY 42351 • *1,778*
Lewiston, ID 83501 • *28,082*
Lewiston, ME 04240–43 • *39,757*
Lewiston, MN 55952 • *1,298*
Lewiston, NY 14092 • *3,048*
Lewiston, UT 84320 • *1,532*
Lewistown, IL 61542 • *2,572*
Lewistown, MT 59457 • *6,051*
Lewistown, PA 17044 • *9,341*
Lewisville, AR 71845 • *1,424*
Lewisville, TX 75067 • *46,521*
Lexington, IL 61753 • *1,809*
Lexington, KY 40501–96 • *225,366*
Lexington, MA 02173 • *28,974*
Lexington, MS 39095 • *2,227*
Lexington, MO 64067 • *4,860*
Lexington, NE 68850 • *6,601*
Lexington, NC 27292–93 • *16,581*
Lexington, OH 44904 • *4,124*
Lexington, OK 73051 • *1,776*
Lexington, SC 29071–73 • *3,289*
Lexington, TN 38351 • *5,810*
Lexington, VA 24450 • *6,959*
Lexington □, SC • *167,611*
Lexington Park, MD 20653 • *9,943*
Libby, MT 59923 • *2,532*
Liberal, KS 67901–05 • *16,573*
Liberty, IN 47353 • *2,051*
Liberty, KY 42539 • *1,937*
Liberty, MO 64068 • *20,459*
Liberty, NY 12754 • *4,128*
Liberty, NC 27298 • *2,047*
Liberty, SC 29657 • *3,228*
Liberty, TX 77575 • *7,733*
Liberty □, FL • *5,569*
Liberty □, GA • *52,745*
Liberty □, MT • *2,295*
Liberty □, TX • *52,726*
Liberty Acres, CA 90250 • *4,700*
Liberty Center, OH 43532 • *1,084*
Liberty Lake, WA 99019 • *2,015*
Libertyville, IL 60048 • *19,174*
Licking, MO 65542 • *1,328*
Licking □, OH • *128,300*
Lidgerwood, ND 58053 • *799*
Lighthouse Point, FL 33064 • *10,378*
Ligonier, IN 46767 • *3,443*
Ligonier, PA 15658 • *1,638*
Lihue, HI 96766 • *5,536*
Lilbourn, MO 63862 • *1,378*
Lilburn, GA 30247 • *9,301*
Lillington, NC 27546 • *2,048*
Lilly, PA 15938 • *1,162*
Lima, NY 14485 • *2,165*
Lima, OH 45801–09 • *45,549*
Limestone, ME 04750–51 • *1,245*
Limestone □, AL • *54,135*
Limestone □, TX • *20,946*
Limon, CO 80828 • *1,831*
Lincoln, AL 35096 • *2,941*
Lincoln, AR 72744 • *1,460*
Lincoln, CA 95648 • *7,248*
Lincoln, DE 19960 • *500*
Lincoln, IL 62656 • *15,418*
Lincoln, KS 67455 • *1,381*
Lincoln, ME 04457 • *3,399*
Lincoln, MA 01773 • *2,860*
Lincoln, NE 68501–72 • *191,972*
Lincoln □, AR • *13,690*
Lincoln □, CO • *4,529*
Lincoln □, GA • *7,442*
Lincoln □, ID • *3,308*
Lincoln □, KS • *3,653*
Lincoln □, KY • *20,045*
Lincoln □, LA • *41,745*
Lincoln □, ME • *30,357*
Lincoln □, MN • *6,890*
Lincoln □, MS • *30,278*
Lincoln □, MO • *28,892*
Lincoln □, MT • *17,481*
Lincoln □, NE • *32,508*
Lincoln □, NV • *3,775*
Lincoln □, NM • *12,219*
Lincoln □, NC • *50,319*
Lincoln □, OK • *29,216*
Lincoln □, OR • *38,889*
Lincoln □, SD • *15,427*
Lincoln □, TN • *28,157*
Lincoln □, WA • *8,864*
Lincoln □, WV • *21,382*
Lincoln □, WI • *26,993*
Lincoln □, WY • *12,625*
Lincoln Acres, CA 91947 • *1,800*
Lincoln City, OR 97367 • *5,892*
Lincoln Heights, OH 45215 • *4,805*
Lincoln Park, CO 81212 • *3,728*
Lincoln Park, GA 30286 • *1,755*
Lincoln Park, MI 48146 • *41,832*
Lincoln Park, NJ 07035 • *10,978*
Lincolnshire, IL 60069 • *4,931*
Lincolnton, GA 30817 • *1,476*
Lincolnton, NC 28092 • *6,847*
Lincoln Village, CA 95207 • *4,236*
Lincoln Village, OH 43228 • *9,958*

Lincolnwood, IL 60645 • *11,365*
Lincroft, NJ 07738 • *4,740*
Linda, CA 95901 • *13,033*
Lindale, GA 30147 • *4,187*
Lindale, TX 75771 • *2,428*
Linden, AL 36748 • *2,548*
Linden, MI 48451 • *2,415*
Linden, NJ 07036 • *36,701*
Linden, TN 37096 • *1,099*
Linden, TX 75563 • *2,375*
Lindenhurst, IL 60046 • *8,038*
Lindenhurst, NY 11757 • *26,879*
Lindenwold, NJ 08021 • *18,734*
Lindgren Acres, FL 33177 • *22,290*
Lindon, UT 84042 • *3,818*
Lindsay, CA 93247 • *8,338*
Lindsay, OK 73052 • *2,947*
Lindsborg, KS 67456 • *3,076*
Lindstrom, MN 55045 • *2,461*
Linesville, PA 16424 • *1,166*
Lineville, AL 36266 • *2,394*
Lingle, WY 82223 • *473*
Linglestown, PA 17112 • *3,700*
Linn, MO 65051 • *1,148*
Linn □, IA • *168,767*
Linn □, KS • *8,254*
Linn □, MO • *13,885*
Linn □, OR • *91,227*
Lino Lakes, MN 55014 • *8,807*
Linthicum Heights, MD • *2,950*
Linthicum Heights, MD 21090 • *7,547*
Linton, IN 47441 • *5,814*
Linton, ND 58552 • *1,410*
Linwood, NJ 08221 • *6,866*
Lipscomb, AL 35020 • *2,892*
Lipscomb □, TX • *3,143*
Lisbon, IA 52253 • *1,452*
Lisbon, ME 04250 • *1,240*
Lisbon, NH 03585 • *1,246*
Lisbon, ND 58054 • *2,177*
Lisbon, OH 44432 • *3,037*
Lisbon Falls, ME 04252 • *4,674*
Lisle, IL 60532 • *19,512*
Litchfield, CT 06759 • *1,378*
Litchfield, IL 62056 • *6,883*
Litchfield, MI 49252 • *1,317*
Litchfield, MN 55355 • *6,041*
Litchfield □, CT • *174,092*
Litchfield Park, AZ 85340 • *3,303*
Lithia Springs, GA 30057 • *11,403*
Lithonia, GA 30058 • *2,448*
Lititz, PA 17543 • *8,280*
Little Canada, MN 55110 • *8,971*
Little Chute, WI 54140 • *9,207*
Little Compton, RI 02837 • *500*
Little Creek, DE 19961 • *167*
Little Falls, MN 56345 • *7,232*
Little Falls, NJ 07424 • *11,294*
Little Falls, NY 13365 • *5,829*
Little Ferry, NJ 07643 • *9,989*
Littlefield, TX 79339 • *6,489*
Little River □, AR • *13,966*
Little Rock, AR 72201–31 • *175,795*
Little Silver, NJ 07739 • *5,721*
Littlestown, PA 17340 • *2,974*
Littleton, CO 80120–27 • *33,685*
Littleton, MA 01460 • *2,867*
Littleton, NH 03561 • *4,633*
Little Valley, NY 14755 • *1,188*
Live Oak, CA 95062 • *15,212*
Live Oak, CA 95953 • *4,320*
Live Oak, FL 32060 • *6,332*
Live Oak, TX 78233 • *10,023*
Live Oak □, TX • *9,556*
Live Oak Manor, LA 70094 • *2,150*
Livermore, CA 94550 • *56,741*
Livermore, KY 42352 • *1,534*
Livermore Falls, ME 04254 • *1,935*
Livingston, AL 35470 • *3,530*
Livingston, CA 95334 • *7,317*
Livingston, MT 59047 • *6,701*
Livingston, NJ 07039 • *26,609*
Livingston, TN 38570 • *3,809*
Livingston, TX 77351 • *5,019*
Livingston □, IL • *39,301*
Livingston □, KY • *9,062*
Livingston □, LA • *70,526*
Livingston □, MI • *115,645*
Livingston □, MO • *14,592*
Livingston □, NY • *62,372*
Livingston Manor, NY 12758 • *1,482*
Livonia, MI 48150–54 • *100,850*
Livonia, NY 14487 • *1,434*
Llangollen Estates, DE 19720 • *1,070*
Llano, TX 78643 • *2,962*
Llano □, TX • *11,631*
Lloyd Harbor, NY 11743 • *3,343*
Lochearn, MD 21207 • *25,240*
Loch Lomond, VA 22110 • *3,292*
Lockhart, FL 32810 • *11,636*
Lockhart, TX 78644 • *9,205*
Lock Haven, PA 17745 • *9,230*
Lockland, OH 45215 • *4,357*
Lockney, TX 79241 • *2,207*
Lockport, IL 60441 • *9,401*
Lockport, LA 70374 • *2,503*
Lockport, NY 14094 • *24,426*
Lockwood, MO 65682 • *1,041*
Lockwood, MT 59101 • *3,967*
Locust, NC 28097 • *1,940*
Locust Grove, GA 30248 • *1,681*
Locust Grove, OK 74352 • *1,326*
Lodi, CA 95240–42 • *51,874*
Lodi, NJ 07644 • *22,355*
Lodi, OH 44254 • *3,042*
Lodi, WI 53555 • *2,093*
Logan, IA 51546 • *1,401*
Logan, OH 43138 • *6,725*
Logan, UT 84321 • *32,762*
Logan, WV 25601 • *2,206*
Logan □, AR • *20,557*
Logan □, CO • *17,567*
Logan □, IL • *30,798*
Logan □, KS • *3,081*
Logan □, KY • *24,416*
Logan □, NE • *878*
Logan □, ND • *2,847*
Logan □, OH • *42,310*
Logan □, OK • *29,011*
Logan □, WV • *43,032*
Logandale, NV 89021 • *500*
Logansport, IN 46947 • *16,812*
Logansport, LA 71049 • *1,390*
Loganville, GA 30249 • *3,180*
Lolo, MT 59847 • *2,746*
Loma Linda, CA 92354 • *17,400*
Lombard, IL 60148 • *39,408*
Lomira, WI 53048 • *1,542*
Lomita, CA 90717 • *19,382*
Lompoc, CA 93436 • *37,649*
Lonaconing, MD 21539 • *1,122*
London, KY 40741 • *5,757*
London, OH 43140 • *7,807*
Londonderry, NH 03053 • *10,114*
Londontown, MD 21037 • *6,992*
Lone Grove, OK 73443 • *4,114*
Lone Pine, CA 93545 • *1,818*
Long □, GA • *6,202*
Long Beach, CA 90801–88 • *429,433*
Long Beach, IN 46360 • *2,044*
Long Beach, MS 39560 • *15,804*
Long Beach, NY 11561 • *33,510*
Long Beach, WA 98631 • *1,236*
Longboat Key, FL 34228 • *5,937*
Long Branch, NJ 07740 • *28,658*
Long Lake, IL 60041 • *2,888*
Longmeadow, MA 01106 • *15,467*
Longmont, CO 80501–02 • *51,555*
Longport, NJ 08403 • *1,224*
Long Prairie, MN 56347 • *2,786*
Long Valley, NJ 07853 • *1,744*
Long View, NC 28601 • *3,229*
Longview, TX 75601–15 • *70,311*
Longview, WA 98632 • *31,499*
Longwood, FL 32750 • *13,316*
Lonoke, AR 72086 • *4,022*
Lonoke □, AR • *39,268*
Lonsdale, MN 55046 • *1,252*
Lonsdale, RI 02865 • *3,850*
Loogootee, IN 47553 • *2,884*
Lookout Mountain, TN 37350 • *1,901*
Lorain, OH 44052–55 • *71,245*
Lorain □, OH • *271,126*
Lordsburg, NM 88045 • *2,951*
Lorenzo, TX 79343 • *1,208*
Loretto, PA 15940 • *1,072*
Loretto, TN 38469 • *1,515*
Loris, SC 29569 • *2,067*
Lorton, VA 22079 • *15,385*
Los Alamitos, CA 90720–21 • *11,676*
Los Alamos, NM 87544 • *11,455*
Los Alamos □, NM • *18,115*
Los Altos, CA 94022–24 • *26,303*
Los Altos Hills, CA 94022 • *7,514*
Los Angeles, CA 90001–99 • *3,485,398*
Los Angeles □, CA • *8,863,164*
Los Banos, CA 93635 • *14,519*
Los Fresnos, TX 78566 • *2,473*
Los Gatos, CA 95030–32 • *27,357*
Los Lunas, NM 87031 • *6,013*
Los Molinos, CA 96055 • *1,709*
Los Nietos, CA 90606 • *7,100*
Los Osos, CA 93402 • *8,000*
Los Padillas, NM 87105 • *2,400*
Los Ranchos de Albuquerque, NM 87107 • *3,955*
Los Serranos, CA 91709 • *7,099*
Lost Hills, CA 93249 • *1,212*
Loudon, TN 37774 • *4,026*
Loudon □, TN • *31,255*
Loudonville, NY 12211 • *10,822*
Loudonville, OH 44842 • *2,915*
Loudoun □, VA • *86,129*
Louisa, KY 41230 • *1,990*
Louisa, VA 23093 • *1,088*
Louisa □, IA • *11,592*
Louisa □, VA • *20,325*
Louisburg, KS 66053 • *1,964*
Louisburg, NC 27549 • *3,037*
Louisiana, MO 63353 • *3,967*
Louisville, CO 80027 • *12,361*
Louisville, GA 30434 • *2,429*
Louisville, IL 62858 • *1,098*
Louisville, KY 40201–99 • *269,063*
Louisville, MS 39339 • *7,169*
Louisville, OH 44641 • *8,087*
Loup □, NE • *683*
Loup City, NE 68853 • *1,104*
Love □, OK • *8,157*
Loveland, CO 80537–39 • *37,352*
Loveland, OH 45140 • *9,990*
Loveland Park, OH 45140 • *1,357*
Lovell, WY 82431 • *2,131*
Lovelock, NV 89419 • *2,069*
Loves Park, IL 61111 • *15,462*
Loving, NM 88256 • *1,243*
Loving □, TX • *107*
Lovington, IL 61937 • *1,143*
Lovington, NM 88260 • *9,322*
Lowell, AR 72745 • *1,224*
Lowell, IN 46356 • *6,430*
Lowell, MA 01850–54 • *103,439*
Lowell, MI 49331 • *3,983*
Lowell, NC 28098 • *2,704*
Lowellville, OH 44436 • *1,349*
Lower Burrell, PA 15068 • *12,251*
Lower Merion Township, PA 19003 • *59,629*
Lower Paia, HI 96779 • *1,500*
Lowndes □, AL • *12,658*
Lowndes □, GA • *75,981*
Lowndes □, MS • *59,308*
Lowville, NY 13367 • *3,632*
Loxley, AL 36551 • *1,161*
Loyal, WI 54446 • *1,244*
Loyall, KY 40854 • *1,100*
Lubbock, TX 79401–99 • *186,206*
Lubbock □, TX • *222,636*
Lucas □, IA • *9,070*
Lucas □, OH • *462,361*
Lucasville, OH 45648 • *1,575*
Luce □, MI • *5,763*
Lucedale, MS 39452 • *2,592*
Lucerne, CA 95458 • *2,011*
Lucernemines, PA 15754 • *1,074*
Lucerne Valley, CA 92356 • *1,300*
Luck, WI 54853 • *1,022*
Ludington, MI 49431 • *8,507*
Ludlow, KY 41016 • *4,736*
Ludlow, MA 01056 • *18,150*
Ludlow, VT 05149 • *1,123*
Ludowici, GA 31316 • *1,291*
Lufkin, TX 75901–03 • *30,206*
Lugoff, SC 29078 • *3,211*
Lula, GA 30554 • *1,018*
Luling, LA 70070 • *2,803*
Luling, TX 78648 • *4,661*
Lumber City, GA 31549 • *1,429*
Lumberport, WV 26386 • *1,014*
Lumberton, MS 39455 • *2,121*
Lumberton, NC 28358–59 • *18,601*
Lumpkin, GA 31815 • *1,250*
Lumpkin □, GA • *14,573*
Luna □, NM • *18,110*
Luna Pier, MI 48157 • *1,507*
Lund, NV 89317 • *330*
Lunenburg, MA 01462 • *1,694*
Lunenburg □, VA • *11,419*
Luray, VA 22835 • *4,587*
Lusk, WY 82225 • *1,504*
Lutcher, LA 70071 • *3,907*
Luther, OK 73054 • *1,560*
Lutherville-Timonium, MD 21093 • *16,442*
Lutz, FL 33549 • *10,552*
Luverne, AL 36049 • *2,555*
Luverne, MN 56156 • *4,382*
Luxemburg, WI 54217 • *1,151*
Luxora, AR 72358 • *1,338*
Luzerne, PA 18709 • *3,206*
Luzerne □, PA • *328,149*
Lycoming □, PA • *118,710*
Lyford, TX 78569 • *1,674*
Lykens, PA 17048 • *1,986*
Lyman, SC 29365 • *2,271*
Lyman, WY 82937 • *1,896*
Lyman □, SD • *3,638*
Lynbrook, NY 11563 • *19,208*
Lynch, KY 40855 • *1,166*
Lynchburg, OH 45142 • *1,212*
Lynchburg, TN 37352 • *4,721*
Lynchburg, VA 24501–06 • *66,049*
Lyncourt, NY 13208 • *4,516*
Lynden, WA 98264 • *5,709*
Lyndhurst, NJ 07071 • *18,262*
Lyndhurst, OH 44124 • *15,982*
Lyndon, KY 40222 • *8,037*
Lyndonville, VT 05851 • *1,255*
Lyndora, PA 16045 • *3,000*
Lynn, IN 47355 • *1,183*
Lynn, MA 01901–08 • *81,245*
Lynn □, TX • *6,758*
Lynne Acres, MD 21207 • *5,910*
Lynnfield, MA 01940 • *11,274*
Lynn Garden, TN 37665 • *7,213*
Lynn Garden, TN 37665 • *3,950*
Lynn Haven, FL 32444 • *9,298*
Lynnwood, WA 98036–37 • *28,695*
Lynwood, CA 90262 • *61,945*
Lyon □, IA • *11,952*
Lyon □, KS • *34,732*
Lyon □, KY • *6,624*
Lyon □, MN • *24,789*
Lyon □, NV • *20,001*
Lyon Mountain, NY 12952 • *1,000*
Lyons, CO 80540 • *1,227*
Lyons, GA 30436 • *4,502*
Lyons, IL 60534 • *9,828*
Lyons, KS 67554 • *3,688*
Lyons, NE 68038 • *1,144*
Lyons, NY 14489 • *4,280*
Lytle, TX 78052 • *2,255*

M

Mabank, TX 75147 • *1,739*
Mableton, GA 30059 • *25,725*
Mabscott, WV 25871 • *1,543*
Mabton, WA 98935 • *1,482*
MacClenny, FL 32063 • *3,966*
Macedon, NY 14502 • *1,400*
Macedonia, OH 44056 • *7,509*
Machesney Park, IL 61111 • *19,033*
Machias, ME 04654 • *1,773*
Mackinac □, MI • *10,674*
Mackinaw, IL 61755 • *1,331*
Mackinaw City, MI 49701 • *875*
Macomb, IL 61455 • *19,952*
Macomb □, MI • *717,400*
Macon, GA 31201–95 • *106,612*
Macon, IL 62544 • *1,282*
Macon, MS 39341 • *2,256*
Macon, MO 63552 • *5,571*
Macon □, AL • *24,928*
Macon □, GA • *13,114*
Macon □, IL • *117,206*
Macon □, MO • *15,345*
Macon □, NC • *23,499*
Macon □, TN • *15,906*
Macoupin □, IL • *47,679*
Macungie, PA 18062 • *2,597*
Madawaska, ME 04756 • *3,653*
Madeira, OH 45243 • *9,141*
Madelia, MN 56062 • *2,237*
Madera, CA 93637–39 • *29,281*
Madera □, CA • *88,090*
Madill, OK 73446 • *3,069*
Madison, AL 35758 • *14,904*
Madison, AR 72359 • *1,263*
Madison, CT 06443 • *2,139*
Madison, FL 32340 • *3,345*
Madison, GA 30650 • *3,483*
Madison, IL 62060 • *4,629*
Madison, IN 47250 • *12,006*
Madison, ME 04950 • *2,956*
Madison, MN 56256 • *1,951*
Madison, MS 39110 • *7,471*
Madison, NE 68748 • *2,135*
Madison, NJ 07940 • *15,850*
Madison, NC 27025 • *2,371*
Madison, OH 44057 • *2,477*
Madison, SD 57042 • *6,257*
Madison, WV 25130 • *3,051*
Madison, WI 53701–19 • *191,262*
Madison □, AL • *238,912*
Madison □, AR • *11,618*
Madison □, FL • *16,569*
Madison □, GA • *21,050*
Madison □, ID • *23,674*
Madison □, IL • *249,238*
Madison □, IN • *130,669*
Madison □, IA • *12,483*
Madison □, KY • *57,508*
Madison □, LA • *12,463*
Madison □, MS • *53,794*
Madison □, MO • *11,127*
Madison □, MT • *5,989*
Madison □, NE • *32,655*
Madison □, NY • *69,120*
Madison □, NC • *16,953*
Madison □, OH • *37,068*
Madison □, TN • *77,982*
Madison □, TX • *10,931*
Madison □, VA • *11,949*
Madison Heights, MI 48071 • *32,196*
Madison Heights, VA 24572 • *11,700*
Madisonville, KY 42431 • *16,200*
Madisonville, TN 37354 • *3,033*
Madisonville, TX 77864 • *3,569*
Madras, OR 97741 • *3,443*
Madrid, IA 50156 • *2,395*
Maeser, UT 84078 • *2,598*
Magalia, CA 95954 • *8,987*
Magdalena, NM 87825 • *861*
Magee, MS 39111 • *3,607*
Magna, UT 84044 • *17,829*
Magnolia, AR 71753 • *11,151*
Magnolia, MS 39652 • *2,245*
Magnolia, NJ 08049 • *4,861*
Magoffin □, KY • *13,077*
Mahanoy City, PA 17948 • *5,209*
Mahaska □, IA • *21,522*
Mahnomen, MN 56557 • *1,154*
Mahnomen □, MN • *5,044*
Mahomet, IL 61853 • *3,103*
Mahoning □, OH • *264,806*
Mahopac, NY 10541 • *7,755*
Mahwah, NJ 07430 • *7,500*
Maiden, NC 28650 • *2,574*
Maili, HI 96792 • *6,059*
Maine, NY 13802 • *1,110*
Maitland, FL 32751 • *9,110*
Maize, KS 67101 • *1,520*
Major □, OK • *8,055*
Makaha, HI 96792 • *7,990*
Makakilo City, HI 96706 • *9,828*
Makawao, HI 96768 • *5,405*
Makaweli, HI 96769 • *700*
Malabar, FL 32950 • *1,977*
Malad City, ID 83252 • *1,946*
Malaga, NJ 08328 • *2,140*
Malakoff, TX 75148 • *2,038*
Malden, MA 02148 • *53,884*
Malden, MO 63863 • *5,123*
Malheur □, OR • *26,038*
Malibu, CA 90264–65 • *10,000*
Malone, NY 12953 • *6,777*
Malta, MT 59538 • *2,340*
Malvern, AR 72104 • *9,256*
Malvern, IA 51551 • *1,210*
Malvern, OH 44644 • *1,112*
Malvern, PA 19355 • *2,944*
Malverne, NY 11565 • *9,054*
Mamaroneck, NY 10543 • *17,325*
Mammoth, AZ 85618 • *1,845*
Mammoth Lakes, CA 93546 • *4,785*
Mammoth Spring, AR 72554 • *1,097*
Mamou, LA 70554 • *3,483*
Manahawkin, NJ 08050 • *1,594*
Manasquan, NJ 08736 • *5,369*
Manassas, VA 22110–11 • *27,957*
Manassas Park, VA 22111 • *6,734*
Manatee □, FL • *211,707*
Manawa, WI 54949 • *1,169*
Mancelona, MI 49659 • *1,370*
Manchaug, MA 01526 • *1,000*
Manchester, CT 06040 • *51,618*
Manchester, GA 31816 • *4,104*
Manchester, IA 52057 • *5,137*
Manchester, KY 40962 • *1,634*
Manchester, MD 21102 • *2,810*
Manchester, MA 01944 • *5,424*
Manchester, MI 48158 • *1,753*
Manchester, MO 63011 • *6,542*
Manchester, NH 03101–10 • *99,567*
Manchester, NY 14504 • *1,598*
Manchester, OH 45144 • *2,223*
Manchester, PA 17345 • *1,830*
Manchester, TN 37355 • *7,709*
Manchester, VT 05254 • *561*
Manchester Center, VT 05255 • *1,574*
Mandan, ND 58554 • *15,177*
Mandeville, LA 70448 • *7,083*
Mangum, OK 73554 • *3,344*
Manhasset, NY 11030 • *7,718*
Manhattan, KS 66502 • *37,712*
Manhattan, MT 59741 • *1,034*
Manhattan Beach, CA 90266 • *32,063*
Manheim, PA 17545 • *5,011*
Manila, AR 72442 • *2,635*
Manistee, MI 49660 • *6,734*
Manistee □, MI • *21,265*
Manistique, MI 49854 • *3,456*
Manito, IL 61546 • *1,711*
Manitou Springs, CO 80829 • *4,535*
Manitowoc, WI 54220–21 • *32,520*
Manitowoc □, WI • *80,421*
Mankato, KS 66956 • *1,037*
Mankato, MN 56001–03 • *31,477*
Manlius, NY 13104 • *4,764*
Manly, IA 50456 • *1,349*
Mannford, OK 74044 • *1,826*
Manning, IA 51455 • *1,484*
Manning, SC 29102 • *4,428*
Mannington, WV 26582 • *2,184*
Manokotak, AK 99628 • *385*
Manomet, MA 02345 • *1,500*
Manor, TX 78653 • *1,041*
Manorhaven, NY 11050 • *5,672*
Mansfield, AR 72944 • *1,018*
Mansfield, LA 71052 • *5,389*
Mansfield, MA 02048 • *7,170*
Mansfield, MO 65704 • *1,429*
Mansfield, OH 44901–07 • *50,627*
Mansfield, PA 16933 • *3,538*
Mansfield, TX 76063 • *15,607*
Mansfield Center, CT 06250 • *1,043*
Manson, IA 50563 • *1,844*
Mansura, LA 71350 • *1,601*
Manteca, CA 95336 • *40,773*
Manteno, IL 60950 • *3,488*
Manti, UT 84642 • *2,268*
Manton, MI 49663 • *1,161*
Mantua, NJ 08051 • *1,350*
Mantua, OH 44255 • *1,178*
Mantua Hills, VA 22031 • *1,600*
Manvel, TX 77578 • *3,733*
Manville, NJ 08835 • *10,567*
Manville, RI 02838 • *3,030*
Many, LA 71449 • *3,112*
Many Farms, AZ 86538 • *1,294*
Maple Bluff, WI 53704 • *1,352*
Maple Grove, MN 55369 • *38,736*
Maple Heights, OH 44137 • *27,089*
Maple Lake, MN 55358 • *1,394*
Maple Plain, MN 55359 • *2,005*
Maple Shade, NJ 08052 • *19,211*
Mapleton, IA 51034 • *1,294*
Mapleton, MN 56065 • *1,526*
Mapleton, UT 84663 • *3,572*
Maple Valley, WA 98038 • *1,211*
Mapleville, RI 02839 • *1,300*
Maplewood, MN 55109 • *30,954*
Maplewood, MO 63143 • *9,962*
Maplewood, NJ 07040 • *21,756*
Maquoketa, IA 52060 • *6,111*
Marana, AZ 85653 • *2,187*
Marathon, FL 33050 • *8,857*
Marathon, NY 13803 • *1,107*
Marathon, WI 54448 • *1,606*
Marathon □, WI • *115,400*
Marble Falls, TX 78654 • *4,007*
Marblehead, MA 01945 • *19,971*
Marble Hill, MO 63764 • *1,447*
Marbleton, WY 83113 • *634*
Marbury, MD 20658 • *1,244*
Marceline, MO 64658 • *2,645*
Marcellus, MI 49067 • *1,193*
Marco, FL 33937 • *9,493*
Marcus, IA 51035 • *1,171*
Marcus Hook, PA 19061 • *2,546*
Marengo, IL 60152 • *4,768*
Marengo, IA 52301 • *2,270*
Marengo □, AL • *23,084*
Marfa, TX 79843 • *2,424*
Margate, FL 33063 • *42,985*
Margate, MD 21060 • *1,900*
Margate City, NJ 08402 • *8,431*
Marianna, AR 72360 • *5,910*
Marianna, FL 32446 • *6,292*
Maricopa, AZ 85239 • *1,600*
Maricopa, CA 93252 • *1,193*
Maricopa □, AZ • *2,122,101*
Mariemont, OH 45227 • *3,118*
Marienville, PA 16239 • *1,400*
Maries □, MO • *7,976*
Marietta, GA 30060–68 • *44,129*
Marietta, OH 45750 • *15,026*
Marietta, OK 73448 • *2,306*
Marin □, CA • *230,096*
Marina, CA 93933 • *26,436*
Marina del Rey, CA 90292 • *7,431*
Marine City, MI 48039 • *4,556*
Marinette, WI 54143 • *11,843*
Marinette □, WI • *40,548*
Maringouin, LA 70757 • *1,149*
Marion, AL 36756 • *4,211*
Marion, AR 72364 • *4,391*
Marion, IL 62959 • *14,545*
Marion, IN 46952–53 • *32,618*
Marion, IA 52302 • *20,403*
Marion, KS 66861 • *1,906*
Marion, KY 42064 • *3,320*
Marion, MA 02738 • *1,426*
Marion, MS 39342 • *1,359*
Marion, NY 14505 • *1,080*
Marion, NC 28752 • *4,765*
Marion, OH 43301–02 • *34,075*
Marion, PA 17235 • *1,000*
Marion, SC 29571 • *7,658*
Marion, SD 57043 • *831*
Marion, VA 24354 • *6,630*
Marion, WI 54950 • *1,242*
Marion □, AL • *29,830*
Marion □, AR • *12,001*
Marion □, FL • *194,833*
Marion □, GA • *5,590*
Marion □, IL • *41,561*
Marion □, IN • *797,159*
Marion □, IA • *30,001*
Marion □, KS • *12,888*
Marion □, KY • *16,499*
Marion □, MS • *25,544*
Marion □, MO • *27,682*
Marion □, OH • *64,274*
Marion □, OR • *228,483*
Marion □, SC • *33,899*
Marion □, TN • *24,860*
Marion □, TX • *9,984*
Marion □, WV • *57,249*
Marionville, MO 65705 • *1,920*
Mariposa, CA 95338 • *1,152*
Mariposa □, CA • *14,302*
Marissa, IL 62257 • *2,375*
Marked Tree, AR 72365 • *3,100*
Markesan, WI 53946 • *1,496*
Markham, IL 60426 • *13,136*
Markham, TX 77456 • *1,206*
Markle, IN 46770 • *1,208*
Marks, MS 38646 • *1,758*
Marksville, LA 71351 • *5,526*
Marlboro, NY 12542 • *2,200*
Marlboro □, SC • *29,361*
Marlborough, CT 06447 • *5,535*
Marlborough, MA 01752 • *31,813*
Marlborough, NH 03455 • *1,211*
Marlene Village, OR 97005 • *1,500*
Marlette, MI 48453 • *1,924*
Marley, MD 21060 • *7,100*
Marlin, TX 76661 • *6,386*
Marlinton, WV 24954 • *1,148*
Marlow, OK 73055 • *4,416*
Marlow Heights, MD 20748 • *5,885*
Marlton, NJ 08053 • *10,228*
Marmaduke, AR 72443 • *1,164*
Marmet, WV 25315 • *1,879*
Maroa, IL 61756 • *1,602*
Marquette, MI 49855 • *21,977*
Marquette □, MI • *70,887*
Marquette □, WI • *12,321*
Marquette Heights, IL 61554 • *3,077*
Marrero, LA 70072–73 • *36,671*
Mars, PA 16046 • *1,713*
Marseilles, IL 61341 • *4,811*
Marshall, AR 72650 • *1,318*
Marshall, IL 62441 • *3,555*
Marshall, MI 49068 • *6,891*
Marshall, MN 56258 • *12,023*
Marshall, MO 65340 • *12,711*
Marshall, TX 75670–71 • *23,682*
Marshall, WI 53559 • *2,329*
Marshall □, AL • *70,832*
Marshall □, IL • *12,846*
Marshall □, IN • *42,182*

Marshall □, IA • 38,276
Marshall □, KS • 11,705
Marshall □, KY • 27,205
Marshall □, MN • 10,993
Marshall □, MS • 30,361
Marshall □, OK • 10,829
Marshall □, SD • 4,844
Marshall □, TN • 21,539
Marshall □, WV • 37,356
Marshallton, DE 19808 • 1,765
Marshalltown, IA 50158 • 25,178
Marshallville, GA 31057 • 1,457
Marshfield, MA 02050 • 4,002
Marshfield, MO 65706 • 4,374
Marshfield, WI 54449 • 19,291
Marshfield Hills, MA 02051 • 2,201
Mars Hill, ME 04758 • 1,500
Mars Hill, NC 28754 • 1,611
Marshville, NC 28103 • 2,020
Marsing, ID 83639 • 798
Marstons Mills, MA 02648 • 8,017
Mart, TX 76664 • 2,004
Martha Lake, WA 98012 • 10,155
Martin, SD 57551 • 1,151
Martin, TN 38237 • 8,600
Martin □, FL • 100,900
Martin □, IN • 10,369
Martin □, KY • 12,526
Martin □, MN • 22,914
Martin □, NC • 25,078
Martin □, TX • 4,956
Martinez, CA 94553 • 31,808
Martinez, GA 30907 • 33,731
Martinsburg, PA 16662 • 2,119
Martinsburg, WV 25401 • 14,073
Martins Ferry, OH 43935 • 7,990
Martinsville, IL 62442 • 1,161
Martinsville, IN 46151 • 11,677
Martinsville, VA 24112–15 • 16,162
Marvell, AR 72366 • 1,545
Maryland City, MD 20724 • 6,813
Maryland Heights, MO 63043 • 25,407
Marysville, CA 95901 • 12,324
Marysville, KS 66508 • 3,359
Marysville, MI 48040 • 8,515
Marysville, OH 43040 • 9,656
Marysville, PA 17053 • 2,425
Marysville, WA 98270 • 10,328
Maryville, MO 64468 • 10,663
Maryville, TN 37801–04 • 19,208
Mascot, TN 37806 • 2,138
Mascoutah, IL 62258 • 5,511
Mason, MI 48854 • 6,768
Mason, NV 89447 • 400
Mason, OH 45040 • 11,452
Mason, TX 76856 • 2,041
Mason, WV 25260 • 1,053
Mason □, IL • 16,269
Mason □, KY • 16,666
Mason □, MI • 25,537
Mason □, TX • 3,423
Mason □, WA • 38,341
Mason □, WV • 25,178
Masonboro, NC 28403 • 7,010
Mason City, IL 62664 • 2,323
Mason City, IA 50401 • 29,040
Masontown, PA 15461 • 3,759
Massac □, IL • 14,752
Massapequa, NY 11758 • 22,018
Massapequa Park, NY 11762 • 18,044
Massena, NY 13662 • 11,719
Massillon, OH 44646–48 • 31,007
Mastic, NY 11950 • 13,778
Mastic Beach, NY 11951 • 10,293
Masury, OH 44438 • 1,836
Matagorda □, TX • 36,928
Matamoras, PA 18336 • 1,934
Matawan, NJ 07747 • 9,270
Mather, PA 15346 • 1,300
Mathews □, VA • 8,348
Mathis, TX 78368 • 5,423
Matoaca, VA 23803 • 1,967
Mattapoisett, MA 02739 • 2,949
Matteson, IL 60443 • 11,378
Matthews, NC 28105–06 • 13,651
Mattituck, NY 11952 • 3,902
Mattoon, IL 61938 • 18,441
Mattydale, NY 13211 • 6,418
Matunuck, RI 02879 • 550
Maud, OK 74854 • 1,204
Maugansville, MD 21767 • 1,707
Maui □, HI • 100,374
Mauldin, SC 29662 • 11,587
Maumee, OH 43537 • 15,561
Maunaloa, HI 96770 • 405
Maunawili, HI 96734 • 4,847
Maury □, TN • 54,812
Mauston, WI 53948 • 3,439
Maverick □, TX • 36,378
Maxton, NC 28364 • 2,373
Maxwell Acres, WV 26041 • 1,000
Mayer, AZ 86333 • 1,800
Mayes □, OK • 33,366
Mayfield, KY 42066 • 9,935
Mayfield, PA 18433 • 1,890
Mayfield Heights, OH 44124 • 19,847
Mayflower, AR 72106 • 1,415
Mayflower Village, CA 91016 • 4,978
Maynard, MA 01754 • 10,325
Maynardville, TN 37807 • 1,298
Mayo, MD 21106 • 2,537
Mayodan, NC 27027 • 2,471
Mays Landing, NJ 08330 • 2,090
Maysville, KY 41056 • 7,169
Maysville, MO 64469 • 1,176
Maysville, OK 73057 • 1,203
Mayville, MI 48744 • 1,010
Mayville, NY 14757 • 1,636
Mayville, ND 58257 • 2,092
Mayville, WI 53050 • 4,374
Maywood, CA 90270 • 27,850
Maywood, IL 60153–54 • 27,139
Maywood, NJ 07607 • 9,473
Mazomanie, WI 53560 • 1,377
McAdoo, PA 18237 • 2,459
McAlester, OK 74501–02 • 16,370
McAllen, TX 78501–04 • 84,021
McAlmont, AR 72117 • 1,800
McAlpine, MD 21043 • 2,230
McArthur, OH 45651 • 1,541
McCall, ID 83638 • 2,005
McCamey, TX 79752 • 2,493
McCandless, PA 15237 • 28,781
McCaysville, GA 30555 • 1,065
McClain □, OK • 22,795
McCleary, WA 98557 • 1,235
McCloud, CA 96057 • 1,555
McClure, PA 17841 • 1,070
McColl, SC 29570 • 2,685
McComb, MS 39648 • 11,591
McComb, OH 45858 • 1,544
McCone □, MT • 2,276
McConnellsburg, PA 17233 • 1,106
McConnelsville, OH 43756 • 1,804
McCook, NE 69001 • 8,112
McCook □, SD • 5,688
McCormick, SC 29835 • 1,659
McCormick □, SC • 8,868
McCracken □, KY • 62,879
McCreary □, KY • 15,603
McCrory, AR 72101 • 1,971
McCulloch □, TX • 8,778
McCurtain □, OK • 33,433
McDermitt, NV 89421 • 373
McDonald □, MO • 16,938
McDonough, GA 30253 • 2,929
McDonough □, IL • 35,244
McDowell □, NC • 35,681
McDowell □, WV • 35,233
McDuffie □, GA • 20,119
McEwen, TN 37101 • 1,442
McFarland, CA 93250 • 7,005
McFarland, WI 53558 • 5,232
McGehee, AR 71654 • 4,997
McGill, NV 89318 • 1,258
McGrath, AK 99627 • 528
McGraw, NY 13101 • 1,074
McGregor, TX 76657 • 4,683
McHenry, IL 60050–51 • 16,177
McHenry □, IL • 183,241
McHenry □, ND • 6,528
McIntosh □, GA • 8,634
McIntosh □, ND • 4,021
McIntosh □, OK • 16,779
McKean □, PA • 47,131
McKee City, NJ 08232 • 1,200
McKeesport, PA 15130–35 • 26,016
McKees Rocks, PA 15136 • 7,691
McKenzie, TN 38201 • 5,168
McKenzie □, ND • 6,383
McKinley □, NM • 60,686
McKinleyville, CA 95521 • 10,749
McKinney, TX 75069–70 • 21,283
McLaughlin, SD 57642 • 780
McLean, VA 22101 • 38,168
McLean □, IL • 129,180
McLean □, KY • 9,628
McLean □, ND • 10,457
McLeansboro, IL 62859 • 2,677
McLennan □, TX • 189,123
McLeod □, MN • 32,030
McLoud, OK 74851 • 2,493
McMechen, WV 26040 • 2,130
McMinn □, TN • 42,383
McMinnville, OR 97128 • 17,894
McMinnville, TN 37110 • 11,194
McMullen □, TX • 817
McNairy □, TN • 22,422
McPherson, KS 67460 • 12,422
McPherson □, KS • 27,268
McPherson □, NE • 546
McPherson □, SD • 3,228
McQueeney, TX 78123 • 2,063
McRae, GA 31055 • 3,007
McRoberts, KY 41835 • 1,101
McSherrystown, PA 17344 • 2,769
Mead, WA 99021 • 2,150
Meade, KS 67864 • 1,526
Meade □, KS • 4,247
Meade □, KY • 24,170
Meade □, SD • 21,878
Meadowbrook, FL 32808 • 5,200
Meadowood, DE 19711 • 2,100
Meadville, PA 16335 • 14,318
Meagher □, MT • 1,819
Mebane, NC 27302 • 4,754
Mecca, CA 92254 • 1,966
Mechanic Falls, ME 04256 • 2,388
Mechanicsburg, OH 43044 • 1,803
Mechanicsburg, PA 17055 • 9,452
Mechanicsville, IA 52306 • 1,012
Mechanicsville, VA 23111 • 22,027
Mechanicville, NY 12118 • 5,249
Mecklenburg □, NC • 511,433
Mecklenburg □, VA • 29,241
Mecosta □, MI • 37,308
Medfield, MA 02052 • 5,985
Medford, MA 02155 • 57,407
Medford, NJ 08055 • 1,800
Medford, NY 11763 • 21,274
Medford, OK 73759 • 1,172
Medford, OR 97501–04 • 46,951
Medford, WI 54451 • 4,283
Medford Lakes, NJ 08055 • 4,462
Media, PA 19063–65 • 5,957
Mediapolis, IA 52637 • 1,637
Medical Lake, WA 99022 • 3,664
Medicine Bow, WY 82329 • 389
Medicine Lodge, KS 67104 • 2,453
Medina, NY 14103 • 6,686
Medina, OH 44256 • 19,231
Medina, WA 98039 • 2,981
Medina □, OH • 122,354
Medina □, TX • 27,312
Medway, MA 02053 • 3,890
Meeker, CO 81641 • 2,098
Meeker, OK 74855 • 1,003
Meeker □, MN • 20,846
Meeteetse, WY 82433 • 368
Mehlville, MO 63129 • 27,557
Meigs, GA 31765 • 1,120
Meigs □, OH • 22,987
Meigs □, TN • 8,033
Meiners Oaks, CA 93023 • 3,329
Melbourne, AR 72556 • 1,562
Melbourne, FL 32901–10 • 59,646
Melbourne Beach, FL 32951 • 3,021
Melcher, IA 50163 • 1,302
Mellette □, SD • 2,137
Melrose, FL 32666 • 1,700
Melrose, MA 02176 • 28,150
Melrose, MN 56352 • 2,561
Melrose Park, FL 33312 • 6,477
Melrose Park, IL 60160–63 • 20,859
Melville, LA 71353 • 1,562
Melville, NY 11747 • 12,586
Melvindale, MI 48122 • 11,216
Memphis, FL 34221 • 6,760
Memphis, MI 48041 • 1,221
Memphis, MO 63555 • 2,094
Memphis, TN 38101–87 • 610,337
Memphis, TX 79245 • 2,465
Mena, AR 71953 • 5,475
Menahga, MN 56464 • 1,076
Menands, NY 12204 • 4,333
Menard, TX 76859 • 1,606
Menard □, IL • 11,164
Menard □, TX • 2,252
Menasha, WI 54952 • 14,711
Mendenhall, MS 39114 • 2,463
Mendham, NJ 07945 • 4,890
Mendocino, CA 95460 • 1,008
Mendocino □, CA • 80,345
Mendota, CA 93640 • 6,821
Mendota, IL 61342 • 7,018
Mendota Heights, MN 55118 • 9,431
Menifee □, KY • 5,092
Menlo Park, CA 94025–28 • 28,040
Menno, SD 57045 • 768
Menominee, MI 49858 • 9,398
Menominee □, MI • 24,920
Menominee □, WI • 3,890
Menomonee Falls, WI 53051–52 • 26,840
Menomonie, WI 54751 • 13,547
Mentor, OH 44060–61 • 47,358
Mentor-on-the-Lake, OH 44060 • 8,271
Mequon, WI 53092 • 18,885
Meraux, LA 70075 • 8,000
Merced, CA 95339–44 • 56,216
Merced □, CA • 178,403
Mercedes, TX 78570 • 12,694
Mercer, PA 16137 • 2,444
Mercer, WI 54547 • 1,300
Mercer □, IL • 17,290
Mercer □, KY • 19,148
Mercer □, MO • 3,723
Mercer □, NJ • 325,824
Mercer □, ND • 9,808
Mercer □, OH • 39,443
Mercer □, PA • 121,003
Mercer □, WV • 64,980
Mercer Island, WA 98040 • 20,816
Mercersburg, PA 17236 • 1,640
Mercerville, NJ 08619 • 15,600
Merchantville, NJ 08109 • 4,095
Meredith, NH 03253 • 1,654
Meredosia, IL 62665 • 1,134
Meriden, CT 06450 • 59,479
Meridian, ID 83642 • 9,596
Meridian, MS 39301–09 • 41,036
Meridian, PA 16001 • 3,473
Meridian, TX 76665 • 1,390
Meridian Hills, IN 46260 • 1,728
Meridianville, AL 35759 • 2,852
Meriwether □, GA • 22,411
Merkel, TX 79536 • 2,469
Merriam, KS 66203 • 11,821
Merrick, NY 11566 • 23,042
Merrick □, NE • 8,042
Merrifield, VA 22031 • 8,399
Merrill, WI 54452 • 9,860
Merrillville, IN 46410 • 27,257
Merrimac, MA 01860 • 2,050
Merrimack, NH 03054 • 1,300
Merrimack □, NH • 120,005
Merritt Island, FL 32952–54 • 32,886
Merryville, LA 70653 • 1,235
Merton, WI 53056 • 1,199
Mesa, AZ 85201–16 • 288,091
Mesa □, CO • 93,145
Mescalero, NM 88340 • 1,159
Mesilla, NM 88046 • 1,975
Mesquite, NV 89024 • 1,871
Mesquite, TX 75149–50 • 101,484
Metairie, LA 70001–11 • 149,428
Metamora, IL 61548 • 2,520
Metcalfe, MS 38760 • 1,092
Metcalfe □, KY • 8,963
Methuen, MA 01844 • 39,990
Metlakatla, AK 99926 • 1,407
Metropolis, IL 62960 • 6,734
Metter, GA 30439 • 3,707
Metuchen, NJ 08840 • 12,804
Metzger, OR 97223 • 3,149
Mexia, TX 76667 • 6,933
Mexico, ME 04257 • 2,302
Mexico, MO 65265 • 11,290
Mexico, NY 13114 • 1,555
Meyersdale, PA 15552 • 2,518
Miami, AZ 85539 • 2,018
Miami, FL 33101–99 • 358,548
Miami, OK 74354–55 • 13,142
Miami □, IN • 36,897
Miami □, KS • 23,466
Miami □, OH • 93,182
Miami Beach, FL 33139 • 92,639
Miami Lakes, FL 33014 • 12,750
Miamisburg, OH 45342–43 • 17,834
Miami Shores, FL 33138 • 10,084
Miami Springs, FL 33166 • 13,268
Micco, FL 32958 • 8,757
Michigan Center, MI 49254 • 4,863
Michigan City, IN 46360 • 33,822
Middleboro (Middleborough Center), MA
02346 • 6,837
Middleburg, FL 32068 • 6,223
Middleburg, PA 17842 • 1,422
Middleburgh, NY 12122 • 1,436
Middleburg Heights, OH 44130 • 14,702
Middlebury, CT 06762 • 4,140
Middlebury, IN 46540 • 2,004
Middlebury, VT 05753 • 6,007
Middlefield, CT 06455 • 1,200
Middlefield, OH 44062 • 1,898
Middle Island, NY 11953 • 7,848
Middleport, NY 14105 • 1,876
Middleport, OH 45760 • 2,725
Middle River, MD 21220 • 24,616
Middlesboro, KY 40965 • 11,328
Middlesex, NJ 08846 • 13,055
Middlesex □, CT • 143,196
Middlesex □, MA • 1,398,468
Middlesex □, NJ • 671,780
Middlesex □, VA • 8,653
Middleton, ID 83644 • 1,851
Middleton, MA 01949 • 4,135
Middleton, WI 53562 • 13,289
Middletown, CA 95461 • 2,000
Middletown, CT 06457 • 42,762
Middletown, DE 19709 • 3,834
Middletown, IN 47356 • 2,333
Middletown, KY 40243 • 5,016
Middletown, MD 21769 • 1,834
Middletown, NJ 07718 • 62,298
Middletown, NY 10940 • 24,160
Middletown, OH 45042–44 • 46,022
Middletown, PA 17057 • 9,254
Middletown, RI 02840 • 3,350
Middletown, VA 22645 • 1,061
Middletown Township, PA 19037 • 6,866
Middleville, MI 49333 • 1,966
Midfield, AL 35228 • 5,559
Midland, MI 48640–42 • 38,053
Midland, PA 15059 • 3,321
Midland, TX 79701–12 • 89,443
Midland □, MI • 75,651
Midland □, TX • 106,611
Midland City, AL 36350 • 1,819
Midland Park, KS 67216 • 1,200
Midland Park, NJ 07432 • 7,047
Midland Park, SC 29405 • 1,300
Midlothian, IL 60445 • 14,372
Midlothian, TX 76065 • 5,141
Midvale, UT 84047 • 11,886
Midway, DE 19971 • 500
Midway, KY 40347 • 1,290
Midway, OR 97233 • 19,000
Midway, PA 15060 • 1,043
Midway, UT 84049 • 1,554
Midwest, WY 82643 • 495
Midwest City, OK 73110 • 52,267
Mifflin □, PA • 46,197
Mifflinburg, PA 17844 • 3,480
Mifflinville, PA 18631 • 1,329
Milaca, MN 56353 • 2,182
Milam □, TX • 22,946
Milan, GA 31060 • 1,056
Milan, IL 61264 • 5,831
Milan, IN 47031 • 1,529
Milan, MI 48160 • 4,040
Milan, MO 63556 • 1,767
Milan, NM 87021 • 1,911
Milan, OH 44846 • 1,464
Milan, TN 38358 • 7,512
Milbank, SD 57252 • 3,879
Milesburg, PA 16853 • 1,144
Miles City, MT 59301 • 8,461
Milford, CT 06460 • 48,168
Milford, DE 19963 • 6,040
Milford, IL 60953 • 1,512
Milford, IN 46542 • 1,388
Milford, IA 51351 • 2,170
Milford, ME 04461 • 2,228
Milford, MA 01757 • 23,339
Milford, MI 48380–82 • 5,511
Milford, NE 68405 • 1,886
Milford, NH 03055 • 8,015
Milford, NJ 08848 • 1,273
Milford, OH 45150 • 5,660
Milford, PA 18337 • 1,064
Milford, UT 84751 • 1,107
Mililani Town, HI 96789 • 29,359
Millard □, UT • 11,333
Millbrae, CA 94030 • 20,412
Millbrook, AL 36054 • 6,050
Millbrook, NY 12545 • 1,339
Millburn, NJ 07041 • 18,630
Millbury, MA 01527 • 4,940
Millbury, OH 43447 • 1,081
Mill City, OR 97360 • 1,555
Millcreek, UT 84109 • 32,230
Millcreek Township, PA 16505 • 46,100
Milledgeville, GA 31061 • 17,727
Milledgeville, IL 61051 • 1,076
Mille Lacs □, MN • 18,670
Millen, GA 30442 • 3,808
Miller, SD 57362 • 1,678
Miller □, AR • 38,467
Miller □, GA • 6,280
Miller □, MO • 20,700
Miller Place, NY 11764 • 9,315
Millersburg, OH 44654 • 3,051
Millersburg, PA 17061 • 2,729
Millers Falls, MA 01349 • 1,084
Millersport, OH 43046 • 1,010
Millersville, PA 17551 • 8,099
Mill Hall, PA 17751 • 1,702
Milliken, CO 80543 • 1,605
Millington, MI 48746 • 1,114
Millington, TN 38053 • 17,866
Millinocket, ME 04462 • 6,922
Millis, MA 02054 • 3,777
Millport, AL 35576 • 1,203
Mills, WY 82644 • 1,574
Mills □, IA • 13,202
Mills □, TX • 4,531
Millsboro, DE 19966 • 1,643
Millstadt, IL 62260 • 2,566
Milltown, NJ 08850 • 6,968
Millvale, PA 15209 • 4,341
Mill Valley, CA 94941–42 • 13,038
Millville, MA 01529 • 1,693
Millville, NJ 08332 • 25,992
Millville, UT 84326 • 1,202
Millwood, WA 99212 • 1,559
Milnor, ND 58060 • 651
Milo, ME 04463 • 2,129
Milpitas, CA 95035–36 • 50,686
Milroy, PA 17063 • 1,456
Milstead, GA 30207 • 1,500
Milton, DE 19968 • 1,417
Milton, FL 32570–71 • 7,216
Milton, MA 02186 • 25,725
Milton, NH 03851 • 1,000
Milton, NY 12547 • 1,140
Milton, PA 17847 • 6,746
Milton, VT 05468 • 1,578
Milton, WA 98354 • 4,995
Milton, WV 25541 • 2,242
Milton, WI 53563 • 4,434
Milton-Freewater, OR 97862 • 5,533
Milwaukee, WI 53201–95 • 628,088
Milwaukee □, WI • 959,275
Milwaukie, OR 97222 • 18,692
Mimosa Park, LA 70070 • 4,516
Mims, FL 32754 • 9,412
Mina, NV 89422 • 400
Minco, OK 73059 • 1,411
Minden, LA 71055 • 13,661
Minden, NE 68959 • 2,749
Minden, NV 89423 • 1,441
Mine Hill, NJ 07801 • 3,250
Mineola, NY 11501 • 18,994
Mineola, TX 75773 • 4,321
Miner, MO 63801 • 1,218
Miner □, SD • 3,272
Mineral □, CO • 558
Mineral □, MT • 3,315
Mineral □, NV • 6,475
Mineral □, WV • 26,697
Mineral Point, WI 53565 • 2,428
Mineral Springs, AR 71851 • 1,004
Mineral Wells, TX 76067 • 14,870
Minersville, PA 17954 • 4,877
Minerva, OH 44657 • 4,318
Minetto, NY 13115 • 1,252
Mineville, NY 12956 • 1,000
Mingo □, WV • 33,739
Mingo Junction, OH 43938 • 4,297
Minidoka □, ID • 19,361
Minier, IL 61759 • 1,155
Minneapolis, KS 67467 • 1,983
Minneapolis, MN 55401–80 • 368,383
Minnehaha □, SD • 123,809
Minneota, MN 56264 • 1,417
Minnetonka, MN 55345 • 48,370
Minocqua, WI 54548 • 1,280
Minonk, IL 61760 • 1,982
Minooka, IL 60447 • 2,561
Minot, ND 58701–02 • 34,544
Minquadale, DE 19720 • 790
Minster, OH 45865 • 2,650
Mint Hill, NC 28212 • 11,567
Minturn, CO 81645 • 1,066
Mio, MI 48647 • 1,500
Mira Loma, CA 91752 • 15,786
Miramar, FL 33023 • 40,663
Misenheimer, NC 28109 • 1,000
Mishawaka, IN 46544–46 • 42,608
Mishicot, WI 54228 • 1,296
Missaukee □, MI • 12,147
Mission, KS 66205 • 9,504
Mission, TX 78572 • 28,653
Mission Hills, KS 66205 • 3,446
Mission Viejo, CA 92691 • 72,820
Mississippi □, AR • 57,525
Mississippi □, MO • 14,442
Mississippi State, MS 39762 • 12,400
Missoula, MT 59801–07 • 42,918
Missoula □, MT • 78,687
Missouri City, TX 77459 • 36,176
Missouri Valley, IA 51555 • 2,888
Mitchell, IL 62040 • 1,320
Mitchell, IN 47446 • 4,669
Mitchell, NE 69357 • 1,743
Mitchell, SD 57301 • 13,798
Mitchell □, GA • 20,275
Mitchell □, IA • 10,928
Mitchell □, KS • 7,203
Mitchell □, NC • 14,433
Mitchell □, TX • 8,016
Mitchellville, IA 50169 • 1,670
Mizpah, NJ 08342 • 1,000
Moab, UT 84532 • 3,971
Moberly, MO 65270 • 12,839
Mobile, AL 36601–95 • 196,278
Mobile □, AL • 378,643
Mobridge, SD 57601 • 3,768
Mocanaqua, PA 18655 • 1,100
Mocksville, NC 27028 • 3,399
Modesto, CA 95350–56 • 164,730
Modoc □, CA • 9,678
Moenkopi, AZ 86045 • 1,200
Moffat □, CO • 11,357
Mogadore, OH 44260 • 4,008
Mohall, ND 58761 • 931
Mohave □, AZ • 93,497
Mohawk, NY 13407 • 2,986
Mohnton, PA 19540 • 2,484
Mojave, CA 93501–02 • 3,763
Mokena, IL 60448 • 6,128
Molalla, OR 97038 • 3,651
Moline, IL 61265 • 43,202
Molino, FL 32577 • 1,207
Momence, IL 60954 • 2,968
Monaca, PA 15061 • 6,739
Monahans, TX 79756 • 8,101
Monarch Mills, SC 29379 • 2,214
Moncks Corner, SC 29461 • 5,607
Mondovi, WI 54755 • 2,491
Monee, IL 60449 • 1,044
Monessen, PA 15062 • 9,901
Monett, MO 65708 • 6,529
Monette, AR 72447 • 1,115
Monfort Heights, OH 45239 • 9,745
Moniteau □, MO • 12,298
Monmouth, IL 61462 • 9,489
Monmouth, OR 97361 • 6,288
Monmouth □, NJ • 553,124
Monmouth Beach, NJ 07750 • 3,303
Monmouth Junction, NJ 08852 • 1,570
Mono □, CA • 9,956
Monon, IN 47959 • 1,585
Monona, IA 52159 • 1,520
Monona, WI 53716 • 8,637
Monona □, IA • 10,034
Monongah, WV 26554 • 1,018
Monongahela, PA 15063 • 4,928
Monongalia □, WV • 75,509
Monroe, GA 30655 • 9,759
Monroe, IA 50170 • 1,739
Monroe, LA 71201–13 • 54,909
Monroe, MI 48161 • 22,902
Monroe, NY 10950 • 6,672
Monroe, NC 28110–12 • 16,127
Monroe, OH 45050 • 4,490
Monroe, UT 84754 • 1,472
Monroe, WA 98272 • 4,278
Monroe, WI 53566 • 10,241
Monroe □, AL • 23,968
Monroe □, AR • 11,333
Monroe □, FL • 78,024
Monroe □, GA • 17,113
Monroe □, IL • 22,422
Monroe □, IN • 108,978
Monroe □, IA • 8,114
Monroe □, KY • 11,401
Monroe □, MI • 133,600
Monroe □, MS • 36,582
Monroe □, MO • 9,104
Monroe □, NY • 713,968
Monroe □, OH • 15,497
Monroe □, PA • 95,709
Monroe □, TN • 30,541
Monroe □, WV • 12,406

Monroe □, WI • 36,633
Monroe Center, CT 06468 • 7,900
Monroe City, MO 63456 • 2,701
Monroe Park, DE 19807 • 1,000
Monroeville, AL 36460–61 • 6,993
Monroeville, IN 46773 • 1,232
Monroeville, OH 44847 • 1,381
Monroeville, PA 15146 • 29,169
Monrovia, CA 91016 • 35,761
Monsey, NY 10952 • 13,986
Monson, MA 01057 • 2,101
Montague, CA 96064 • 1,415
Montague, MI 49437 • 2,276
Montague □, TX • 17,274
Mont Alto, PA 17237 • 1,395
Montauk, NY 11954 • 3,001
Mont Belvieu, TX 77580 • 1,323
Montcalm □, MI • 53,059
Montchanin, DE 19710 • 500
Montclair, CA 91763 • 28,434
Montclair, NJ 07042–44 • 37,729
Mont Clare, PA 19453 • 1,800
Monteagle, TN 37356 • 1,138
Montebello, CA 90640 • 59,564
Montecito, CA 93108 • 9,300
Montello, NV 89830 • 200
Montello, WI 53949 • 1,329
Monterey, CA 93940 • 31,954
Monterey, TN 38574 • 2,559
Monterey □, CA • 355,660
Monterey Park, CA 91754 • 60,738
Montesano, WA 98563 • 3,064
Montevallo, AL 35115 • 4,239
Montevideo, MN 56265 • 5,499
Monte Vista, CO 81144 • 4,324
Montezuma, GA 31063 • 4,506
Montezuma, IN 47862 • 1,134
Montezuma, IA 50171 • 1,651
Montezuma □, CO • 18,672
Montgomery, AL 36101–99 • 187,106
Montgomery, IL 60538 • 4,267
Montgomery, MN 56069 • 2,399
Montgomery, NY 12549 • 2,696
Montgomery, OH 45242 • 9,753
Montgomery, PA 17752 • 1,631
Montgomery, WV 25136 • 2,449
Montgomery □, AL • 209,085
Montgomery □, AR • 7,841
Montgomery □, GA • 7,163
Montgomery □, IL • 30,728
Montgomery □, IN • 34,436
Montgomery □, IA • 12,076
Montgomery □, KS • 38,816
Montgomery □, KY • 19,561
Montgomery □, MD • 757,027
Montgomery □, MS • 12,388
Montgomery □, MO • 11,355
Montgomery □, NY • 51,981
Montgomery □, NC • 23,346
Montgomery □, OH • 573,809
Montgomery □, PA • 678,111
Montgomery □, TN • 100,498
Montgomery □, TX • 182,201
Montgomery □, VA • 73,913
Montgomery City, MO 63361 • 2,281
Montgomery Village, MD 20879 • 32,315
Monticello, AR 71655 • 8,116
Monticello, FL 32344 • 2,573
Monticello, GA 31064 • 2,289
Monticello, IL 61856 • 4,549
Monticello, IN 47960 • 5,237
Monticello, IA 52310 • 3,522
Monticello, KY 42633 • 5,357
Monticello, MN 55362 • 4,941
Monticello, MS 39654 • 1,755
Monticello, NY 12701 • 6,597
Monticello, UT 84535 • 1,806
Monticello, WI 53570 • 1,140
Montmorency □, MI • 8,936
Montour □, PA • 17,735
Montour Falls, NY 14865 • 1,845
Montoursville, PA 17754 • 4,983
Montpelier, ID 83254 • 2,656
Montpelier, IN 47359 • 1,880
Montpelier, OH 43543 • 4,299
Montpelier, VT 05601–02 • 8,247
Montrose, AL 36559 • 1,400
Montrose, CO 81401–02 • 8,854
Montrose, MI 48457 • 1,811
Montrose, PA 18801 • 1,982
Montrose, VA 23231 • 6,405
Montrose □, CO • 24,423
Montvale, NJ 07645 • 6,946
Montville, CT 06353 • 16,673
Montville, NJ 07045 • 2,600
Monument, CO 80132 • 1,020
Monument Beach, MA 02553 • 1,800
Monument Heights, VA 23226 • 2,500
Moodus, CT 06469 • 1,170
Moody, TX 76557 • 1,329
Moody □, SD • 6,507
Moonachie, NJ 07074 • 2,817
Moorcroft, WY 82721 • 768
Moore, OK 73160 • 40,318
Moore □, NC • 59,013
Moore □, TN • 4,721
Moore □, TX • 17,865
Moorefield, WV 26836 • 2,148
Moore Haven, FL 33471 • 1,432
Mooreland, OK 73852 • 1,157
Moorestown, NJ 08057 • 16,500
Mooresville, IN 46158 • 5,541
Mooresville, NC 28115 • 9,317
Moorhead, MN 56560–61 • 32,295
Moorhead, MS 38761 • 2,417
Moorpark, CA 93020–21 • 25,494
Moose Lake, MN 55767 • 1,206
Moosic, PA 18507 • 5,339
Moosup, CT 06354 • 3,289
Mora, MN 55051 • 2,905
Mora, NM 87732 • 1,200
Mora □, NM • 4,264
Moraga, CA 94556 • 15,852
Moraine, OH 45439 • 5,989
Moravia, NY 13118 • 1,559
Morehead, KY 40351 • 8,357
Morehead City, NC 28557 • 6,046
Morehouse, MO 63868 • 1,068
Morehouse □, LA • 31,938
Morenci, AZ 85540 • 1,799
Morenci, MI 49256 • 2,342
Moreno Valley, CA 92387–88 • 118,779
Morgan, UT 84050 • 2,023
Morgan □, AL • 100,043
Morgan □, CO • 21,939
Morgan □, GA • 12,883
Morgan □, IL • 36,397
Morgan □, IN • 55,920
Morgan □, KY • 11,648
Morgan □, MO • 15,574
Morgan □, OH • 14,194
Morgan □, TN • 17,300
Morgan □, UT • 5,528
Morgan □, WV • 12,128
Morgan City, LA 70380–81 • 14,531
Morganfield, KY 42437 • 3,776
Morgan Hill, CA 95037–38 • 23,928
Morganton, NC 28655 • 15,085
Morgantown, KY 42261 • 2,284
Morgantown, MS 39120 • 3,288
Morgantown, WV 26502–07 • 25,879
Moriarty, NM 87035 • 1,399
Morningdale, MA 01505 • 1,130
Morocco, IN 47963 • 1,044
Moroni, UT 84646 • 1,115
Morrill □, NE • 5,423
Morrilton, AR 72110 • 6,551
Morris, AL 35116 • 1,136
Morris, IL 60450 • 10,270
Morris, MN 56267 • 5,613
Morris, OK 74445 • 1,216
Morris □, KS • 6,198
Morris □, NJ • 421,353
Morris □, TX • 13,200
Morrison, IL 61270 • 4,363
Morrison □, MN • 29,604
Morrison City, TN 37660 • 2,032
Morrisonville, IL 62546 • 1,113
Morrisonville, NY 12962 • 1,742
Morris Plains, NJ 07950 • 5,219
Morristown, NJ 07960–63 • 16,189
Morristown, TN 37813–16 • 21,385
Morrisville, NY 13408 • 2,732
Morrisville, PA 19067 • 9,765
Morrisville, VT 05661 • 1,984
Morro Bay, CA 93442–43 • 9,664
Morrow, GA 30260 • 5,168
Morrow, OH 45152 • 1,206
Morrow □, OH • 27,749
Morrow □, OR • 7,625
Morton, IL 61550 • 13,799
Morton, MS 39117 • 3,212
Morton, TX 79346 • 2,597
Morton, WA 98356 • 1,130
Morton □, KS • 3,480
Morton □, ND • 23,700
Morton Grove, IL 60053 • 22,408
Moscow, ID 83843 • 18,519
Moscow, PA 18444 • 1,527
Moses Lake, WA 98837 • 11,235
Mosheim, TN 37818 • 1,451
Mosinee, WI 54455 • 3,820
Moss Bluff, LA 70611 • 8,039
Moss Point, MS 39563 • 17,837
Motley □, TX • 1,532
Mott, ND 58646 • 1,019
Moulton, AL 35650 • 3,248
Moultrie, GA 31768 • 14,865
Moultrie □, IL • 13,930
Mound, MN 55364 • 9,634
Mound Bayou, MS 38762 • 2,222
Mound City, MO 64470 • 1,273
Moundridge, KS 67107 • 1,531
Mounds, IL 62964 • 1,407
Mounds View, MN 55432 • 12,541
Moundsville, WV 26041 • 10,753
Moundville, AL 35474 • 1,348
Mountainair, NM 87036 • 926
Mountain Brook, AL 35223 • 19,810
Mountain City, NV 89831 • 110
Mountain City, TN 37683 • 2,169
Mountain Grove, MO 65711 • 4,182
Mountain Home, AR 72653 • 9,027
Mountain Home, ID 83647 • 7,913
Mountain Iron, MN 55768 • 3,362
Mountain Lake, MN 56159 • 1,906
Mountain Lake Park, MD 21550 • 1,938
Mountain Lakes, NJ 07046 • 3,847
Mountain Park, GA 30087 • 11,025
Mountainside, NJ 07092 • 6,657
Mountain View, AR 72560 • 2,439
Mountain View, CA 94039–43 • 67,460
Mountain View, CO 80521 • 2,100
Mountain View, MO 65548 • 2,036
Mountain View, NM 87105 • 2,300
Mountain View, OK 73062 • 1,086
Mountain View, WY 82604 • 1,200
Mountain View, WY 82939 • 1,189
Mountain Village, AK 99632 • 674
Mount Airy, MD 21771 • 3,730
Mount Airy, NC 27030 • 7,156
Mount Angel, OR 97362 • 2,778
Mount Arlington, NJ 07856 • 3,630
Mount Ayr, IA 50854 • 1,796
Mount Carmel, IL 62863 • 8,287
Mount Carmel, PA 17851 • 7,196
Mount Carroll, IL 61053 • 1,726
Mount Clemens, MI 48043–46 • 18,405
Mount Dora, FL 32757 • 7,196
Mount Ephraim, NJ 08059 • 4,517
Mount Freedom, NJ 07970 • 1,920
Mount Gay, WV 25637 • 1,200
Mount Gilead, NC 27306 • 1,336
Mount Gilead, OH 43338 • 2,846
Mount Healthy, OH 45231 • 7,580
Mount Holly, NJ 08060 • 10,639
Mount Holly, NC 28120 • 7,710
Mount Holly Springs, PA 17065 • 1,925
Mount Hope, WV 25880 • 1,573
Mount Horeb, WI 53572 • 4,182
Mount Jackson, VA 22842 • 1,583
Mount Jewett, PA 16740 • 1,029
Mount Joy, PA 17552 • 6,398
Mount Juliet, TN 37122 • 5,389
Mount Kisco, NY 10549 • 9,108
Mountlake Terrace, WA 98043 • 19,320
Mount Lebanon, PA 15228 • 33,362
Mount Morris, IL 61054 • 2,919
Mount Morris, MI 48458 • 3,292
Mount Morris, NY 14510 • 3,102
Mount Olive, AL 35117 • 2,270
Mount Olive, IL 62069 • 2,126
Mount Olive, NC 28365 • 4,582
Mount Olympus, UT 84117 • 7,413
Mount Orab, OH 45154 • 1,929
Mount Penn, PA 19606 • 2,883
Mount Pleasant, IA 52641 • 8,027
Mount Pleasant, MI 48858–59 • 23,285
Mount Pleasant, NC 28124 • 1,027
Mount Pleasant, PA 15666 • 4,787
Mount Pleasant, SC 29464–65 • 30,108
Mount Pleasant, TN 38474 • 4,278
Mount Pleasant, TX 75455 • 12,291
Mount Pleasant, UT 84647 • 2,092
Mount Pocono, PA 18344 • 1,795
Mount Prospect, IL 60056 • 53,170
Mount Pulaski, IL 62548 • 1,610
Mountrail □, ND • 7,021
Mount Rainier, MD 20712 • 7,954
Mount Savage, MD 21545 • 1,640
Mount Shasta, CA 96067 • 3,460
Mount Sinai, NY 11766 • 8,023
Mount Sterling, IL 62353 • 1,922
Mount Sterling, KY 40353 • 5,362
Mount Sterling, OH 43143 • 1,647
Mount Union, PA 17066 • 2,878
Mount Vernon, GA 30445 • 1,914
Mount Vernon, IL 62864 • 16,988
Mount Vernon, IN 47620 • 7,217
Mount Vernon, IA 52314 • 3,657
Mount Vernon, KY 40456 • 2,654
Mount Vernon, MO 65712 • 3,726
Mount Vernon, NY 10550–53 • 67,153
Mount Vernon, OH 43050 • 14,550
Mount Vernon, TX 75457 • 2,219
Mount Vernon, WA 98273 • 17,647
Mount View, RI 02852 • 610
Mount Washington, KY 40047 • 5,226
Mount Wolf, PA 17347 • 1,365
Mount Zion, IL 62549 • 4,522
Moville, IA 51039 • 1,306
Moweaqua, IL 62550 • 1,785
Mower □, MN • 37,385
Moyock, NC 27958 • 1,400
Muenster, TX 76252 • 1,387
Muhlenberg □, KY • 31,318
Mukilteo, WA 98275 • 7,007
Mukwonago, WI 53149 • 4,457
Mulberry, AR 72947 • 1,448
Mulberry, FL 33860 • 2,988
Mulberry, IN 46058 • 1,262
Mulberry, NC 28659 • 2,339
Muldraugh, KY 40155 • 1,376
Muldrow, OK 74948 • 2,889
Muleshoe, TX 79347 • 4,571
Mullan, ID 83846 • 821
Mullens, WV 25882 • 2,006
Mullica Hill, NJ 08062 • 1,117
Mullins, SC 29574 • 5,910
Multnomah □, OR • 583,887
Mulvane, KS 67110 • 4,674
Muncie, IN 47302–08 • 71,035
Muncy, PA 17756 • 2,702
Munday, TX 76371 • 1,600
Mundelein, IL 60060 • 21,215
Munford, TN 38058 • 2,326
Munfordville, KY 42765 • 1,556
Munhall, PA 15120 • 13,158
Munising, MI 49862 • 2,783
Munster, IN 46321 • 19,949
Murfreesboro, AR 71958 • 1,542
Murfreesboro, NC 27855 • 2,580
Murfreesboro, TN 37129–33 • 44,922
Murphy, MO 63026 • 9,342
Murphy, NC 28906 • 1,575
Murphys, CA 95247 • 1,517
Murphysboro, IL 62966 • 9,176
Murray, KY 42071 • 14,439
Murray, UT 84107 • 31,282
Murray □, GA • 26,147
Murray □, MN • 9,660
Murray □, OK • 12,042
Murrells Inlet, SC 29576 • 3,334
Murrysville, PA 15668 • 17,240
Muscatine, IA 52761 • 22,881
Muscatine □, IA • 39,907
Muscle Shoals, AL 35661 • 9,611
Muscoda, WI 53573 • 1,287
Muscogee □, GA • 179,278
Muscoy, CA 92405 • 7,541
Muse, PA 15350 • 1,250
Muskego, WI 53150 • 16,813
Muskegon, MI 49440–45 • 40,283
Muskegon □, MI • 158,983
Muskegon Heights, MI 49444 • 13,176
Muskingum □, OH • 82,068
Muskogee, OK 74401–03 • 37,708
Muskogee □, OK • 68,078
Musselshell □, MT • 4,106
Mustang, OK 73064 • 10,434
Myerstown, PA 17067 • 3,236
Myrtle Beach, SC 29577–78 • 24,848
Myrtle Grove, FL 32506 • 17,402
Myrtle Point, OR 97458 • 2,712
Mystic, CT 06355 • 2,618
Mystic Island, NJ 08087 • 7,400

N

Naalehu, HI 96772 • 1,027
Naamans Gardens, DE 19810 • 1,500
Nabnasset, MA 01886 • 3,600
Nacogdoches, TX 75961–63 • 30,872
Nacogdoches □, TX • 54,753
Nags Head, NC 27959 • 1,838
Nahant, MA 01908 • 3,828
Nahunta, GA 31553 • 1,049
Nampa, ID 83651–53 • 28,365
Nanakuli, HI 96792 • 9,575
Nance □, NE • 4,275
Nanticoke, PA 18634 • 12,267
Nantucket, MA 02554 • 3,069
Nantucket □, MA • 6,012
Nanty Glo, PA 15943 • 3,190
Nanuet, NY 10954 • 14,065
Napa, CA 94558–59 • 61,842
Napa □, CA • 110,765
Napanoch, NY 12458 • 1,068
Naperville, IL 60540 • 85,351
Naples, FL 33939–42 • 19,505
Naples, NY 14512 • 1,237
Naples, TX 75568 • 1,508
Naples, UT 84078 • 1,334
Naples Park, FL 33963 • 8,002
Napoleon, ND 58561 • 930
Napoleon, OH 43545 • 8,884
Nappanee, IN 46550 • 5,510
Naranja, FL 33032 • 5,790
Narberth, PA 19072 • 4,278
Narragansett, RI 02882 • 3,721
Narrows, VA 24124 • 2,082
Naselle, WA 98638 • 1,000
Nash, TX 75569 • 2,162
Nash □, NC • 76,677
Nashua, IA 50658 • 1,476
Nashua, NH 03060–63 • 79,662
Nashville, AR 71852 • 4,639
Nashville, GA 31639 • 4,782
Nashville, IL 62263 • 3,202
Nashville, MI 49073 • 1,654
Nashville, NC 27856 • 3,617
Nashville, TN 37201–35 • 487,969
Nashwauk, MN 55769 • 1,026
Nassau, NY 12123 • 1,254
Nassau □, FL • 43,941
Nassau □, NY • 1,287,348
Nassau Shores, NY 11758 • 5,110
Natalia, TX 78059 • 1,216
Natchez, MS 39120–22 • 19,460
Natchitoches, LA 71457–58 • 16,609
Natchitoches □, LA • 36,689
Natick, MA 01760 • 30,100
National City, CA 91950–51 • 54,249
National Park, NJ 08063 • 3,413
Natrona □, WY • 61,226
Natrona Heights, PA 15065 • 12,200
Naugatuck, CT 06770 • 30,625
Nautilus Park, CT 06340 • 6,500
Nauvoo, IL 62354 • 1,108
Navajo □, AZ • 77,658
Navarre, OH 44662 • 1,635
Navarro □, TX • 39,926
Navasota, TX 77868–69 • 6,296
Navesink, NJ 07752 • 1,420
Nazareth, PA 18064 • 5,713
Neah Bay, WA 98357 • 1,300
Nebraska City, NE 68410 • 6,547
Nederland, CO 80466 • 1,099
Nederland, TX 77627 • 16,192
Nedrow, NY 13120 • 2,980
Needham, MA 02192 • 27,557
Needles, CA 92363 • 5,191
Needville, TX 77461 • 2,199
Neenah, WI 54956–57 • 23,219
Neffs, OH 43940 • 1,213
Negaunee, MI 49866 • 4,741
Neillsville, WI 54456 • 2,680
Nekoosa, WI 54457 • 2,557
Neligh, NE 68756 • 1,742
Nelson □, KY • 29,710
Nelson □, ND • 4,410
Nelson □, VA • 12,778
Nelsonville, OH 45764 • 4,563
Nemacolin, PA 15351 • 1,097
Nemaha □, KS • 10,446
Nemaha □, NE • 7,980
Nenana, AK 99760 • 393
Neodesha, KS 66757 • 2,837
Neoga, IL 62447 • 1,678
Neosho, MO 64850 • 9,254
Neosho □, KS • 17,035
Nephi, UT 84648 • 3,515
Neptune, NJ 07753 • 28,366
Neptune Beach, FL 32233 • 6,816
Neptune City, NJ 07753 • 4,997
Nesconset, NY 11767 • 10,712
Nescopeck, PA 18635 • 1,651
Neshoba □, MS • 24,800
Nesquehoning, PA 18240 • 3,364
Ness □, KS • 4,033
Ness City, KS 67560 • 1,724
Netcong, NJ 07857 • 3,311
Nether Providence Township, PA 19013 • 13,229
Nettleton, MS 38858 • 2,462
Nevada, IA 50201 • 6,009
Nevada, MO 64772 • 8,597
Nevada □, AR • 10,101
Nevada □, CA • 78,510
Nevada City, CA 95959 • 2,855
New Albany, IN 47150–51 • 36,322
New Albany, MS 38652 • 6,775
New Albany, OH 43054 • 1,621
Newark, AR 72562 • 1,159
Newark, CA 94560 • 37,861
Newark, DE 19711–15 • 25,098
Newark, NJ 07101–75 • 275,221
Newark, NY 14513 • 9,849
Newark, OH 43055–58 • 44,389
Newark Valley, NY 13811 • 1,082
New Athens, IL 62264 • 2,010
Newaygo, MI 49337 • 1,336
Newaygo □, MI • 38,202
New Baden, IL 62265 • 2,602
New Baltimore, MI 48047 • 5,798
New Bedford, MA 02740–48 • 99,922
Newberg, OR 97132 • 13,086
New Berlin, NY 13411 • 1,220
New Berlin, WI 53151 • 33,592
New Bern, NC 28560–64 • 17,363
Newbern, TN 38059 • 2,515
Newberry, FL 32669 • 1,644
Newberry, MI 49868 • 1,873
Newberry, SC 29108 • 10,542
Newberry □, SC • 33,172
New Bethlehem, PA 16242 • 1,151
New Bloomfield, PA 17068 • 1,092
New Boston, MI 48164 • 1,200
New Boston, OH 45662 • 2,717
New Boston, TX 75570 • 5,057
New Braunfels, TX 78130–33 • 27,334
New Bremen, OH 45869 • 2,558
New Brighton, MN 55112 • 22,207
New Brighton, PA 15066 • 6,854
New Britain, CT 06050–53 • 75,491
New Brockton, AL 36351 • 1,184
New Brunswick, NJ 08901–06 • 41,711
New Buffalo, MI 49117 • 2,317
Newburg, KY 40218 • 21,647
Newburgh, IN 47629–30 • 2,880
Newburgh, NY 12550–53 • 26,454
Newburgh Heights, OH 44105 • 2,310
Newburyport, MA 01950–52 • 16,317
New Canaan, CT 06840 • 17,864
New Carlisle, IN 46552 • 1,446
New Carlisle, OH 45344 • 6,049
New Carrollton, MD 20784 • 12,002
New Cassel, NY 11590 • 10,257
New Castle, AL 35119 • 1,100
New Castle, DE 19720 • 4,837
New Castle, IN 47362 • 17,753
Newcastle, OK 73065 • 4,214
New Castle, PA 16101–08 • 28,334
Newcastle, WY 82701 • 3,003
New Castle □, DE • 441,946
New City, NY 10956 • 33,673
Newcomerstown, OH 43832 • 4,012
New Concord, OH 43762 • 2,086
New Cumberland, PA 17070 • 7,665
New Cumberland, WV 26047 • 1,363
New Egypt, NJ 08533 • 2,327
Newell, IA 50568 • 1,089
Newell, WV 26050 • 1,724
New Ellenton, SC 29809 • 2,515
Newellton, LA 71357 • 1,576
New England, ND 58647 • 663
New Fairfield, CT 06812 • 4,600
Newfane, NY 14108 • 3,001
Newfield, NJ 08344 • 1,592
New Franklin, MO 65274 • 1,107
New Freedom, PA 17349 • 2,920
New Glarus, WI 53574 • 1,899
New Hampton, IA 50659 • 3,660
New Hanover □, NC • 120,284
New Hartford, CT 06057 • 1,269
New Haven, CT 06501–36 • 130,474
New Haven, IN 46774 • 9,320
New Haven, MI 48048 • 2,331
New Haven, MO 63068 • 1,757
New Haven, WV 25265 • 1,632
New Haven □, CT • 804,219
New Holland, GA 30501 • 1,200
New Holland, PA 17557 • 4,484
New Holstein, WI 53061 • 3,342
New Hope, AL 35760 • 2,248
New Hope, MN 55428 • 21,853
New Hope, NC 27604 • 5,694
New Hope, PA 18938 • 1,400
New Hyde Park, NY 11040 • 9,728
New Iberia, LA 70560–62 • 31,828
Newington, CT 06131 • 29,208
Newington, VA 22122 • 17,965
New Johnsonville, TN 37134 • 1,643
New Kensington, PA 15068 • 15,894
New Kent □, VA • 10,445
Newkirk, OK 74647 • 2,168
New Lenox, IL 60451 • 9,627
New Lexington, OH 43764 • 5,117
New Lisbon, WI 53950 • 1,491
Newllano, LA 71461 • 2,660
New London, CT 06320 • 28,540
New London, IA 52645 • 1,922
New London, NH 03257 • 3,180
New London, OH 44851 • 2,642
New London, WI 54961 • 6,658
New London □, CT • 254,957
New Madrid, MO 63869 • 3,350
New Madrid □, MO • 20,928
Newman, CA 95360 • 4,151
Newmanstown, PA 17073 • 1,410
Newmarket, NH 03857 • 4,917
New Market, TN 37820 • 1,086
New Market, VA 22844 • 1,435
New Martinsville, WV 26155 • 6,705
New Matamoras, OH 45767 • 1,002
New Miami, OH 45011 • 2,555
New Milford, CT 06776 • 5,775
New Milford, NJ 07646 • 15,990
Newnan, GA 30263–65 • 12,497
New Orleans, LA 70101–95 • 496,938
New Oxford, PA 17350 • 1,617
New Paltz, NY 12561 • 5,463
New Paris, IN 46553 • 1,007
New Paris, OH 45347 • 1,801
New Philadelphia, OH 44663 • 15,698
New Philadelphia, PA 17959 • 1,283
New Plymouth, ID 83655 • 1,313
Newport, AR 72112 • 7,459
Newport, DE 19804 • 1,240
Newport, KY 41071–76 • 18,871
Newport, ME 04953 • 1,843
Newport, MI 48166 • 1,100
Newport, MN 55055 • 3,720
Newport, NH 03773 • 3,772
Newport, NC 28570 • 2,516
Newport, OR 97365 • 8,437
Newport, PA 17074 • 1,568
Newport, RI 02840 • 28,227
Newport, TN 37821 • 7,123
Newport, VT 05855 • 4,434
Newport, WA 99156 • 1,691
Newport □, RI • 87,194
Newport Beach, CA 92657–63 • 66,643
Newport East, RI 02840 • 11,080
Newport Hills, WA 98002 • 14,736
Newport News, VA 23601–09 • 170,045
New Port Richey, FL 34652–56 • 14,044
New Prague, MN 56071 • 3,569
New Preston, CT 06777 • 1,217
New Providence, NJ 07974 • 11,439
New Richland, MN 56072 • 1,237
New Richmond, OH 45157 • 2,408
New Richmond, WI 54017 • 5,106
New River Station, NC 28542 • 9,732
New Roads, LA 70760 • 5,303
New Rochelle, NY 10801–05 • 67,265
New Rockford, ND 58356 • 1,604
New Salem, ND 58563 • 909
New Sarpy, LA 70078 • 2,946
New Sharon, IA 50207 • 1,136
New Smyrna Beach, FL 32168–70 • 16,543
New Tazewell, TN 37825 • 1,864
Newton, AL 36352 • 1,580
Newton, IL 62448 • 3,154
Newton, IA 50208 • 14,789
Newton, KS 67114 • 16,700
Newton, MA 02158 • 82,585
Newton, MS 39345 • 3,701
Newton, NJ 07860 • 7,521
Newton, NC 28658 • 9,304
Newton, TX 75966 • 1,885
Newton □, AR • 7,666
Newton □, GA • 41,808
Newton □, IN • 13,551
Newton □, MS • 20,291
Newton □, MO • 44,445
Newton □, TX • 13,569
Newton Falls, OH 44444 • 4,866
Newtown, CT 06470 • 1,800
New Town, ND 58763 • 1,388
Newtown, OH 45244 • 1,589
Newtown Square, PA 19073 • 11,366

New Ulm, MN 56073 • 13,132
Newville, PA 17241 • 1,349
New Washington, OH 44854 • 1,057
New Washoe City, NV 89701 • 2,875
New Waterford, OH 44445 • 1,278
New Whiteland, IN 46184 • 4,097
New Wilmington, PA 16142 • 2,706
New Windsor, NY 12553 • 8,898
New York, NY 10001–99 • 7,322,564
New York □, NY • 1,487,536
Nez Perce □, ID • 33,754
Niagara, WI 54151 • 1,999
Niagara □, NY • 220,756
Niagara Falls, NY 14301–05 • 61,840
Niantic, CT 06357 • 3,048
Nibley, UT 84321 • 1,167
Niceville, FL 32578 • 10,507
Nicholas □, KY • 6,725
Nicholas □, WV • 26,775
Nicholasville, KY 40356 • 13,603
Nicholls, GA 31554 • 1,003
Nichols Hills, OK 73116 • 4,020
Nickerson, KS 67561 • 1,137
Nicollet □, MN • 28,076
Nicoma Park, OK 73066 • 2,353
Nikishka, AK 99635 • 1,109
Niland, CA 92257 • 1,183
Niles, IL 60648 • 28,284
Niles, MI 49120 • 12,458
Niles, OH 44446 • 21,128
Ninety Six, SC 29666 • 2,099
Ninilchik, AK 99639 • 456
Niobrara □, WY • 2,499
Nipomo, CA 93444 • 7,109
Niskayuna, NY 12309 • 4,942
Nisswa, MN 56468 • 1,391
Nitro, WV 25143 • 6,851
Niwot, CO 80544 • 2,666
Nixa, MO 65714 • 4,707
Nixon, NV 89424 • 150
Nixon, TX 78140 • 1,995
Noank, CT 06340 • 1,406
Noble, OK 73068 • 4,710
Noble □, IN • 37,877
Noble □, OH • 11,336
Noble □, OK • 11,045
Nobles □, MN • 20,098
Noblesville, IN 46060 • 17,655
Nocatee, FL 33864 • 1,300
Nocona, TX 76255 • 2,870
Nodaway □, MO • 21,709
Noel, MO 64854 • 1,169
Nogales, AZ 85621 • 19,489
Nokomis, FL 34274–75 • 3,448
Nokomis, IL 62075 • 2,534
Nolan □, TX • 16,594
Nome, AK 99762 • 3,500
Noorvik, AK 99763 • 531
Nora Springs, IA 50458 • 1,505
Norco, CA 91760 • 23,302
Norco, LA 70079 • 3,385
Norcross, GA 30071 • 5,947
Norfolk, CT 06058 • 1,500
Norfolk, NE 68701 • 21,476
Norfolk, NY 13667 • 1,412
Norfolk, VA 23501–93 • 261,229
Norfolk □, MA • 616,087
Norland, FL 33169 • 22,109
Normal, IL 61761 • 40,023
Norman, OK 73069–72 • 80,071
Norman □, MN • 7,975
Normandy, MO 63121 • 4,480
Norridge, IL 60656 • 14,459
Norridgewock, ME 04957 • 1,496
Norris, TN 37828 • 1,303
Norris City, IL 62869 • 1,341
Norristown, PA 19401–09 • 30,749
North Adams, MA 01247 • 16,797
North Albany, OR 97321 • 4,325
North Amherst, MA 01059 • 6,239
North Amityville, NY 11701 • 13,849
Northampton, MA 01060–61 • 29,289
Northampton, PA 18067 • 8,717
Northampton □, NC • 20,798
Northampton □, PA • 247,105
Northampton □, VA • 13,061
North Andover, MA 01845 • 20,129
North Andrews Gardens, FL 33308 • 9,002
North Apollo, PA 15673 • 1,391
North Arlington, NJ 07032 • 13,790
North Atlanta, GA 30319 • 27,812
North Attleboro, MA 02760–63 • 16,178
North Auburn, CA 95603 • 10,301
North Augusta, SC 29841 • 15,351
North Aurora, IL 60542 • 5,940
North Babylon, NY 11703 • 18,081
North Baltimore, OH 45872 • 3,139
North Bay Shore, NY 11706 • 12,799
North Beach, MD 20714 • 1,173
North Bellmore, NY 11710 • 19,707
North Bellport, NY 11713 • 8,182
North Belmont, NC 28012 • 10,762
North Bend, NE 68649 • 1,249
North Bend, OR 97459 • 9,614
North Bend, WA 98045 • 2,578
North Bennington, VT 05257 • 1,520
North Bergen, NJ 07047 • 48,414
North Berwick, ME 03906 • 1,568
North Billerica, MA 01862 • 5,400
Northborough, MA 01532 • 5,761
North Braddock, PA 15104 • 7,036
North Branch, MI 48461 • 1,023
North Branch, MN 55056 • 1,867
North Branch, NJ 08876 • 2,620
North Branford, CT 06471 • 6,600
Northbridge, MA 01534 • 3,570
Northbrook, IL 60062 • 32,308
Northbrook, OH 45231 • 11,471
North Brookfield, MA 01535 • 2,635
North Brunswick, NJ 08902 • 31,287
North Brunswick Township, NJ 08902 • 31,287
North Caldwell, NJ 07006 • 5,832
North Canton, OH 44720 • 14,748
North Cape May, NJ 08204 • 3,574
North Charleston, SC 29406 • 70,218
North Chicago, IL 60064 • 34,978
North City, WA 98155 • 8,200
North Cohasset, MA 02025 • 1,045
North College Hill, OH 45239 • 11,002
North Collins, NY 14111 • 1,335
North Conway, NH 03860 • 2,032
North Corbin, KY 40701 • 1,601
North Crossett, AR 71635 • 3,358
North Dartmouth, MA 02747 • 8,080
North Decatur, GA 30033 • 13,936
North Dighton, MA 02764 • 1,174
North Druid Hills, GA 30033 • 14,170
North Eagle Butte, SD 57625 • 1,423
North East, MD 21901 • 1,913
North East, PA 16428 • 4,617
North Eastham, MA 02651 • 1,570
Northeast Henrietta, NY 14534 • 10,650
North Easton, MA 02356 • 4,420
North Fair Oaks, CA 94025 • 13,912
North Falmouth, MA 02556 • 3,150
Northfield, IL 60093 • 4,635
Northfield, MA 01360 • 1,322
Northfield, MN 55057 • 14,684
Northfield, NH 03276 • 1,375
Northfield, NJ 08225 • 7,305
Northfield, OH 44067 • 3,624
Northfield, VT 05663 • 1,889
Northfield Falls, VT 05664 • 600
North Fond du Lac, WI 54935 • 4,292
Northford, CT 06472 • 3,180
North Fort Myers, FL 33903 • 30,027
Northglenn, CO 80233 • 27,195
North Grafton, MA 01536 • 3,050
North Great River, NY 11722 • 3,964
North Grosvenordale, CT 06255 • 1,705
North Gulfport, MS 39501 • 4,966
North Haledon, NJ 07508 • 7,987
North Hampton, NH 03862 • 1,000
North Haven, CT 06473 • 22,249
North Highlands, CA 95660 • 42,105
North Hill, WA 98166 • 5,706
North Houston, TX 77086 • 12,800
North Hudson, WI 54016 • 3,101
North Industry, OH 44707 • 3,250
North Judson, IN 46366 • 1,582
North Kansas City, MO 64116 • 4,130
North Kingstown, RI 02852–54 • 2,750
North Kingsville, OH 44068 • 2,672
North La Junta, CO 81050 • 1,076
Northlake, IL 60164 • 12,505
North Las Vegas, NV 89030–31 • 47,707
North Lauderdale, FL 33068 • 26,506
North Lewisburg, OH 43060 • 1,160
North Liberty, IN 46554 • 1,366
North Liberty, IA 52317 • 2,926
North Lindenhurst, NY 11757 • 10,563
North Little Rock, AR 72114–20 • 61,741
North Logan, UT 84321 • 3,768
North Madison, OH 44057 • 8,699
North Manchester, IN 46962 • 6,383
North Mankato, MN 56001 • 10,164
North Massapequa, NY 11758 • 19,365
North Merrick, NY 11566 • 12,113
North Merrydale, LA 70812 • 4,000
North Miami, FL 33161 • 49,998
North Miami Beach, FL 33162 • 35,359
North Muskegon, MI 49445 • 3,919
North Myrtle Beach, SC 29582 • 8,636
North Naples, FL 33963 • 13,422
North New Hyde Park, NY 11040 • 14,359
North Ogden, UT 84404 • 11,668
North Olmsted, OH 44070 • 34,204
North Oxford, MA 01537 • 1,250
North Palm Beach, FL 33408 • 11,343
North Park, IL 61111 • 15,806
North Patchogue, NY 11772 • 7,374
North Pembroke, MA 02358 • 2,485
North Plainfield, NJ 07060 • 18,820
North Platte, NE 69101–03 • 22,605
Northport, AL 35476 • 17,366
North Port, FL 34287 • 11,973
Northport, NY 11768 • 7,572
North Prairie, WI 53153 • 1,322
North Providence, RI 02911 • 32,090
North Reading, MA 01864 • 11,455
North Richland Hills, TX 76118 • 45,895
Northridge, OH 45502 • 5,939
Northridge, OH 45414 • 9,448
North Ridgeville, OH 44039 • 21,564
North Riverside, IL 60546 • 6,005
North Royalton, OH 44133 • 23,197
North Salt Lake, UT 84054 • 6,474
North Sarasota, FL 34234 • 6,702
North Scituate, MA 02060 • 4,891
North Sioux City, SD 57049 • 2,019
North Springfield, OR 97477 • 5,451
North Springfield, VT 05150 • 750
North Springfield, VA 22151 • 8,996
North Star, DE 19711 • 1,030
North St. Paul, MN 55109 • 12,376
North Sudbury, MA 01776 • 2,630
North Syracuse, NY 13212 • 7,363
North Tarrytown, NY 10591 • 8,152
North Terre Haute, IN 47805 • 2,000
North Tewksbury, MA 01876 • 1,030
North Tonawanda, NY 14120 • 34,989
North Troy, VT 05859 • 723
North Tunica, MS 38676 • 1,314
Northumberland, PA 17857 • 3,860
Northumberland □, PA • 96,771
Northumberland □, VA • 10,524
North Uxbridge, MA 01538 • 1,500
Northvale, NJ 07647 • 4,563
North Valley Stream, NY 11580 • 14,574
North Vernon, IN 47265 • 5,311
North Versailles, PA 15137 • 12,302
Northview, MI 49505 • 13,712
Northview, OH 45322 • 10,337
Northville, MI 48167 • 6,226
Northville, NY 12134 • 1,180
North Wales, PA 19454 • 3,802
North Wantagh, NY 11793 • 12,276
North Warren, PA 16365 • 1,232
North Wildwood, NJ 08260 • 5,017
North Wilkesboro, NC 28659 • 3,384
North Windham, ME 04062 • 4,077
Northwood, IA 50459 • 1,940
Northwood, ND 58267 • 1,166
Northwood, OH 43619 • 5,506
Northwoods, MO 63121 • 5,106
North York, PA 17404 • 1,689
Norton, KS 67654 • 3,017
Norton, MA 02766 • 1,899
Norton, OH 44203 • 11,477
Norton, VA 24273 • 4,247
Norton □, KS • 5,947
Norton Shores, MI 49441 • 21,755
Nortonville, KY 42442 • 1,209
Norwalk, CA 90650–52 • 94,279
Norwalk, CT 06850–56 • 78,331
Norwalk, IA 50211 • 5,726
Norwalk, OH 44857 • 14,731
Norway, ME 04268 • 3,023
Norway, MI 49870 • 2,910
Norwell, MA 02061 • 1,200
Norwich, CT 06360 • 37,391
Norwich, NY 13815 • 7,613
Norwich, VT 05055 • 1,000
Norwood, MA 02062 • 28,700
Norwood, MN 55368 • 1,351
Norwood, NJ 07648 • 4,858
Norwood, NY 13668 • 1,841
Norwood, NC 28128 • 1,617
Norwood, OH 45212 • 23,674
Norwood, PA 19074 • 6,162
Norwoodville, IA 50317 • 1,200
Nottoway □, VA • 14,993
Novato, CA 94947–49 • 47,585
Novi, MI 48374–77 • 32,998
Nowata, OK 74048 • 3,896
Nowata □, OK • 9,992
Noxubee □, MS • 12,604
Nuckolls □, NE • 5,786
Nueces □, TX • 291,145
Nulato, AK 99765 • 359
Nunda, NY 14517 • 1,347
Nutley, NJ 07110 • 27,099
Nutter Fort, WV 26301 • 1,819
Nutting Lake, MA 01865 • 3,180
Nyack, NY 10960 • 6,558
Nye □, NV • 17,781
Nyssa, OR 97913 • 2,629

O

Oak Bluffs, MA 02557 • 1,124
Oak Brook, IL 60521 • 9,178
Oak Creek, WI 53154 • 19,513
Oakdale, CA 95361 • 11,961
Oakdale, GA 30080 • 1,080
Oakdale, LA 71463 • 6,832
Oakdale, MN 55128 • 18,374
Oakdale, NY 11769 • 7,875
Oakdale, PA 15071 • 1,752
Oakes, ND 58474 • 1,775
Oakfield, NY 14125 • 1,818
Oakfield, WI 53065 • 1,003
Oak Forest, IL 60452 • 26,203
Oak Grove, KY 42262 • 2,863
Oak Grove, LA 71263 • 2,126
Oak Grove, OR 97267 • 12,576
Oak Grove, SC 29073 • 7,173
Oak Harbor, OH 43449 • 2,637
Oak Harbor, WA 98277 • 17,176
Oak Hill, MI 49660 • 1,000
Oak Hill, OH 45656 • 1,831
Oak Hill, WV 25901 • 6,812
Oakhurst, OK 74050 • 2,200
Oakland, CA 94601–62 • 372,242
Oakland, IA 51560 • 1,496
Oakland, ME 04963 • 3,510
Oakland, MD 21550 • 2,078
Oakland, NE 68045 • 1,279
Oakland, NJ 07436 • 11,997
Oakland, RI 02830 • 600
Oakland □, MI • 1,083,592
Oakland City, IN 47660 • 2,810
Oakland Park, FL 33334 • 26,326
Oak Lawn, IL 60453–59 • 56,182
Oaklawn, KS 67216 • 4,200
Oakley, CA 94561 • 18,374
Oakley, KS 67748 • 2,045
Oaklyn, NJ 08107 • 4,430
Oakmont, PA 15139 • 6,961
Oak Orchard, DE 19966 • 350
Oak Park, CA 91301 • 5,000
Oak Park, IL 60301–05 • 53,648
Oak Park, MI 48237 • 30,462
Oak Ridge, FL 32809 • 15,388
Oakridge, OR 97463 • 3,063
Oak Ridge, TN 37830 • 27,310
Oakton, VA 22124 • 24,610
Oak Valley, NJ 08090 • 5,400
Oakville, CT 06779 • 8,741
Oakville, MO 63129 • 31,750
Oakwood, GA 30566 • 1,464
Oakwood, IL 61858 • 1,533
Oakwood, OH 45419 • 3,392
Oberlin, KS 67749 • 2,197
Oberlin, LA 70655 • 1,808
Oberlin, OH 44074 • 8,191
Obetz, OH 43207 • 3,167
Obion, TN 38240 • 1,241
Obion □, TN • 31,717
Oblong, IL 62449 • 1,616
O'Brien □, IA • 15,444
Ocala, FL 32670–78 • 42,045
Ocean □, NJ • 433,203
Oceana, WV 24870 • 1,791
Oceana □, MI • 22,454
Ocean Bluff, MA 02065 • 2,500
Ocean City, FL 32548 • 5,422
Ocean City, MD 21842 • 5,146
Ocean City, NJ 08226 • 15,512
Ocean Gate, NJ 08740 • 2,078
Ocean Grove, MA 02777 • 4,560
Oceano, CA 93445 • 6,169
Ocean Park, WA 98640 • 1,650
Ocean Port, NJ 07757 • 6,146
Oceanside, CA 92054–56 • 128,398
Oceanside, NY 11572 • 32,423
Ocean Springs, MS 39564–65 • 14,658
Ocean [Township], NJ 07712 • 23,570
Ocean View, DE 19970 • 606
Oceanville, NJ 08231 • 1,000
Ochiltree □, TX • 9,128
Ocilla, GA 31774 • 3,182
Ocoee, FL 34761 • 12,778
Oconee □, GA • 17,618
Oconee □, SC • 57,494
Oconomowoc, WI 53066 • 10,993
Oconto, WI 54153 • 4,474
Oconto □, WI • 30,226
Oconto Falls, WI 54154 • 2,584
Odebolt, IA 51458 • 1,158
Odell, IL 60460 • 1,030
Odem, TX 78370 • 2,366
Odenton, MD 21113 • 12,833
Odessa, DE 19730 • 303
Odessa, MO 64076 • 3,695
Odessa, TX 79760–68 • 89,699
Odin, IL 62870 • 1,150
Odon, IN 47562 • 1,475
O'Donnell, TX 79351 • 1,102
Oelwein, IA 50662 • 6,493
O'Fallon, IL 62269 • 16,073
O'Fallon, MO 63366 • 18,698
Ogallala, NE 69153 • 5,095
Ogden, IA 50212 • 1,909
Ogden, KS 66517 • 1,494
Ogden, UT 84401–14 • 63,909
Ogdensburg, NJ 07439 • 2,722
Ogdensburg, NY 13669 • 13,521
Ogemaw □, MI • 18,681
Ogle □, IL • 45,957
Oglesby, IL 61348 • 3,619
Oglethorpe, GA 31068 • 1,302
Oglethorpe □, GA • 9,763
Ogunquit, ME 03907 • 1,492
Ohatchee, AL 36271 • 1,042
Ohio □, IN • 5,315
Ohio □, KY • 21,105
Ohio □, WV • 50,871
Ohioville, PA 15059 • 3,865
Oil City, LA 71061 • 1,282
Oil City, PA 16301 • 11,949
Oildale, CA 93308 • 26,553
Oilton, OK 74052 • 1,060
Ojai, CA 93023–24 • 7,613
Okaloosa □, FL • 143,776
Okanogan, WA 98840 • 2,370
Okanogan □, WA • 33,350
Okarche, OK 73762 • 1,160
Okauchee, WI 53069 • 2,300
Okauchee Lake, WI 53058 • 3,819
Okawville, IL 62271 • 1,274
Okeechobee, FL 34972–74 • 4,943
Okeechobee □, FL • 29,627
Okeene, OK 73763 • 1,343
Okemah, OK 74859 • 3,085
Okemos, MI 48864 • 20,216
Okfuskee □, OK • 11,551
Oklahoma □, OK • 599,611
Oklahoma City, OK 73101–80 • 444,719
Oklawaha, FL 32179 • 1,200
Okmulgee, OK 74447 • 13,441
Okmulgee □, OK • 36,490
Okolona, KY 40219 • 18,902
Okolona, MS 38860 • 3,267
Oktibbeha □, MS • 38,375
Ola, AR 72853 • 1,090
Olathe, CO 81425 • 1,263
Olathe, KS 66061–62 • 63,352
Olcott, NY 14126 • 1,432
Old Bethpage, NY 11804 • 5,610
Old Bridge, NJ 08857 • 22,151
Old Forge, NY 13420 • 1,061
Old Forge, PA 18518 • 8,834
Oldham □, KY • 33,263
Oldham □, TX • 2,278
Old Harbor, AK 99643 • 284
Old Orchard Beach, ME 04064 • 7,789
Old Saybrook, CT 06475 • 1,820
Oldsmar, FL 34677 • 8,361
Old Tappan, NJ 07675 • 4,254
Old Town, ME 04468 • 8,317
Olean, NY 14760 • 16,946
Olive Branch, MS 38654 • 3,567
Olive Hill, KY 41164 • 1,809
Olivehurst, CA 95961 • 9,738
Oliver, PA 15472 • 3,271
Oliver □, ND • 2,381
Oliver Springs, TN 37840 • 3,433
Olivet, MI 49076 • 1,604
Olivette, MO 63132 • 7,573
Olivia, MN 56277 • 2,623
Olla, LA 71465 • 1,410
Olmito, TX 78575 • 1,400
Olmos Park, TX 78212 • 2,161
Olmsted □, MN • 106,470
Olmsted Falls, OH 44138 • 6,741
Olney, IL 62450 • 8,664
Olney, MD 20832 • 23,019
Olney, TX 76374 • 3,519
Olton, TX 79064 • 2,116
Olympia, WA 98501–07 • 33,840
Olympia Heights, FL 33175 • 36,900
Olyphant, PA 18447 • 5,222
Omaha, NE 68101–72 • 335,795
Omak, WA 98841 • 4,117
Omro, WI 54963 • 2,836
Onalaska, WI 54650 • 11,284
Onancock, VA 23417 • 1,434
Onarga, IL 60955 • 1,281
Onawa, IA 51040 • 2,936
Onaway, MI 49765 • 1,039
Oneco, FL 34264 • 6,417
Oneida, NY 13421 • 10,850
Oneida, OH 45042 • 1,650
Oneida, TN 37841 • 3,502
Oneida □, ID • 3,492
Oneida □, NY • 250,836
Oneida □, WI • 31,679
O'Neill, NE 68763 • 3,852
Oneonta, AL 35121 • 4,844
Oneonta, NY 13820 • 13,954
Onida, SD 57564 • 761
Onondaga □, NY • 468,973
Onset, MA 02558 • 1,461
Onslow □, NC • 149,838
Ontario, CA 91761–62 • 133,179
Ontario, OH 44862 • 4,026
Ontario, OR 97914 • 9,392
Ontario □, NY • 95,101
Ontonagon, MI 49953 • 2,040
Ontonagon □, MI • 8,854
Oolitic, IN 47451 • 1,424
Ooltewah, TN 37363 • 1,200
Oostburg, WI 53070 • 1,931
Opal Cliffs, CA 95062 • 5,940
Opa-Locka, FL 33054–56 • 15,283
Opelika, AL 36801–03 • 22,122
Opelousas, LA 70570–71 • 18,151
Opp, AL 36467 • 6,985
Opportunity, WA 99206 • 22,326
Oquawka, IL 61469 • 1,442
Oracle, AZ 85623 • 3,043
Oradell, NJ 07649 • 8,024
Oran, MO 63771 • 1,164
Orange, CA 92664–69 • 110,658
Orange, CT 06477 • 12,830
Orange, MA 01364 • 3,791
Orange, NJ 07050–52 • 29,925
Orange, TX 77630–31 • 19,381
Orange, VA 22960 • 2,582
Orange □, CA • 2,410,556
Orange □, FL • 677,491
Orange □, IN • 18,409
Orange □, NY • 307,647
Orange □, NC • 93,851
Orange □, TX • 80,509
Orange □, VT • 26,149
Orange □, VA • 21,421
Orange Beach, AL 36561 • 2,253
Orangeburg, SC 29115–16 • 13,739
Orangeburg □, SC • 84,803
Orange City, FL 32763 • 5,347
Orange City, IA 51041 • 4,940
Orange Grove, MS 39503 • 15,676
Orange Grove, TX 78372 • 1,175
Orange Lake, FL 32681 • 1,000
Orange Park, FL 32073 • 9,488
Orangevale, CA 95662 • 26,266
Orangeville, UT 84537 • 1,459
Orchard City, CO 81410 • 2,218
Orchard Homes, MT 59801 • 10,317
Orchard Mesa, CO 81501 • 5,977
Orchard Park, NY 14127 • 3,280
Orchards, WA 98662 • 8,828
Orchard Valley, WY 82007 • 3,321
Orcutt, CA 93455 • 1,500
Ord, NE 68862 • 2,481
Ordway, CO 81063 • 1,025
Oregon, IL 61061 • 3,891
Oregon, OH 43616 • 18,334
Oregon, WI 53575 • 4,519
Oregon □, MO • 9,470
Oregon City, OR 97045 • 14,698
Orem, UT 84057–59 • 67,561
Orfordville, WI 53576 • 1,219
Orient, NY 11957 • 1,000
Orinda, CA 94563 • 16,642
Orion, IL 61273 • 1,821
Oriskany, NY 13424 • 1,450
Orland, CA 95963 • 5,052
Orlando, FL 32801–72 • 164,693
Orland Park, IL 60462 • 35,720
Orleans, IN 47452 • 2,083
Orleans, IN 47452 • 2,161
Orleans, MA 02653 • 1,699
Orleans, VT 05860 • 806
Orleans □, LA • 496,938
Orleans □, NY • 41,846
Orleans □, VT • 24,053
Orlovista, FL 32811 • 5,990
Ormond Beach, FL 32174–76 • 29,721
Ormond By The Sea, FL 32174 • 8,157
Orofino, ID 83544 • 2,868
Orono, ME 04473 • 9,789
Orono, MN 55323 • 7,285
Orosi, CA 93647 • 5,486
Oroville, CA 95965–66 • 11,960
Oroville, WA 98844 • 1,505
Orrville, OH 44667 • 7,712
Orting, WA 98360 • 2,106
Ortonville, MI 48462 • 1,252
Ortonville, MN 56278 • 2,205
Orwell, OH 44076 • 1,258
Orwigsburg, PA 17961 • 2,780
Osage, IA 50461 • 3,439
Osage, WY 82723 • 350
Osage □, KS • 15,248
Osage □, MO • 12,018
Osage □, OK • 41,645
Osage Beach, MO 65065 • 2,599
Osage City, KS 66523 • 2,689
Osakis, MN 56360 • 1,256
Osawatomie, KS 66064 • 4,590
Osborne, KS 67473 • 1,778
Osborne □, KS • 4,867
Osburn, ID 83849 • 1,579
Osceola, AR 72370 • 8,930
Osceola, IN 46561 • 1,999
Osceola, IA 50213 • 4,164
Osceola, WI 54020 • 2,075
Osceola □, FL • 107,728
Osceola □, IA • 7,267
Osceola □, MI • 20,146
Osceola Mills, PA 16666 • 1,310
Oscoda, MI 48750 • 1,061
Oscoda □, MI • 7,842
Osgood, IN 47037 • 1,688
Oshkosh, WI 54901–04 • 55,006
Oskaloosa, IA 52577 • 10,632
Oskaloosa, KS 66066 • 1,074
Osprey, FL 34229 • 2,597
Osseo, MN 55369 • 2,704
Osseo, WI 54758 • 1,551
Ossian, IN 46777 • 2,428
Ossining, NY 10562 • 22,582
Osterville, MA 02655 • 2,911
Oswego, IL 60543 • 3,876
Oswego, KS 67356 • 1,870
Oswego, NY 13126 • 19,195
Oswego □, NY • 121,771
Otay, CA 92010 • 6,400
Oteen, NC 28805 • 1,400
Otego, NY 13825 • 1,068
Otero □, CO • 20,185
Otero □, NM • 51,928
Othello, WA 99327 • 4,638
Otis Orchards, WA 99027 • 3,200
Otoe □, NE • 14,252
Otsego, MI 49078 • 3,937
Otsego □, MI • 17,957
Otsego □, NY • 60,517
Ottawa, IL 61350 • 17,451
Ottawa, KS 66067 • 10,667
Ottawa, OH 45875 • 3,999
Ottawa □, KS • 5,634
Ottawa □, MI • 187,768
Ottawa □, OH • 40,029
Ottawa □, OK • 30,561
Ottawa Hills, OH 43606 • 4,543
Otterbein, IN 47970 • 1,291
Otter Tail □, MN • 50,714
Ottumwa, IA 52501 • 24,488
Ouachita □, AR • 30,574
Ouachita □, LA • 142,191
Ouray, CO 81427 • 644
Ouray □, CO • 2,295
Outagamie □, WI • 140,510
Overland, MO 63114 • 17,987
Overland Park, KS 66204 • 111,790
Overlea, MD 21206 • 12,137
Overlook, OH 45431 • 6,000
Overton, NV 89040 • 1,111

Overton, TX 75684 • 2,105
Overton □, TN • 17,636
Ovid, MI 48866 • 1,442
Owasso, OK 74055 • 11,151
Owatonna, MN 55060 • 19,386
Owego, NY 13827 • 4,442
Owen □, IN • 17,281
Owen □, KY • 9,035
Owensboro, KY 42301–03 • 53,549
Owensville, IN 47665 • 1,053
Owensville, MO 65066 • 2,325
Owensville, OH 45160 • 1,019
Owenton, KY 40359 • 1,306
Owings Mills, MD 21117 • 9,474
Owingsville, KY 40360 • 1,491
Owosso, MI 48867 • 16,322
Owsley □, KY • 5,036
Owyhee, NV 89832 • 908
Owyhee □, ID • 8,392
Oxford, AL 36203 • 9,362
Oxford, CT 06483 • 1,600
Oxford, GA 30267 • 1,945
Oxford, IN 47971 • 1,273
Oxford, KS 67119 • 1,143
Oxford, MA 01540 • 5,969
Oxford, MI 48370–71 • 2,929
Oxford, MS 38655 • 9,984
Oxford, NJ 07863 • 1,767
Oxford, NY 13830 • 1,738
Oxford, NC 27565 • 7,913
Oxford, OH 45056 • 18,937
Oxford, PA 19363 • 3,769
Oxford □, ME • 52,602
Oxnard, CA 93030–35 • 142,216
Oxon Hill, MD 20745 • 36,267
Oyster Bay, NY 11771 • 6,687
Ozark, AL 36360–61 • 12,922
Ozark, AR 72949 • 3,330
Ozark, MO 65721 • 4,243
Ozark □, MO • 8,598
Ozaukee □, WI • 72,831
Ozona, FL 34660 • 1,500
Ozona, TX 76943 • 3,181

P

Paauilo, HI 96776 • 620
Pace, FL 32571 • 6,277
Pacific, MO 63069 • 4,350
Pacific, WA 98047 • 4,622
Pacific □, WA • 18,882
Pacifica, CA 94044 • 37,670
Pacific Beach, WA 98571 • 1,200
Pacific City, OR 97135 • 1,500
Pacific Grove, CA 93950 • 16,117
Pacific Palisades, HI 96782 • 10,000
Packwood, WA 98361 • 1,010
Pacolet, SC 29372 • 1,736
Paddock Lake, WI 53168 • 2,662
Paden City, WV 26159 • 2,862
Paducah, KY 42001–03 • 27,256
Paducah, TX 79248 • 1,788
Page, AZ 86040 • 6,598
Page □, IA • 16,870
Page □, VA • 21,690
Pageland, SC 29728 • 2,666
Page Manor, OH 45431 • 9,300
Pagosa Springs, CO 81147 • 1,207
Pahala, HI 96777 • 1,520
Pahoa, HI 96778 • 1,027
Pahokee, FL 33476 • 6,822
Pahrump, NV 89041 • 7,424
Paia, HI 96779 • 2,091
Paincourtville, LA 70391 • 1,550
Painesville, OH 44077 • 15,699
Painted Post, NY 14870 • 1,950
Paintsville, KY 41240 • 4,354
Pajarito, NM 87105 • 1,400
Palacios, TX 77465 • 4,418
Palatine, IL 60067 • 39,253
Palatka, FL 32177 • 10,201
Palestine, IL 62451 • 1,619
Palestine, TX 75801–02 • 18,042
Palisade, CO 81526 • 1,871
Palisades Park, NJ 07650 • 14,536
Palm Bay, FL 32905 • 62,632
Palm Beach, FL 33480 • 9,814
Palm Beach □, FL • 863,518
Palm Beach Gardens, FL 33410 • 22,965
Palm Coast, FL 32135 • 14,287
Palmdale, CA 93550–51 • 68,842
Palm Desert, CA 92260–61 • 23,252
Palmer, AK 99645 • 2,866
Palmer, MA 01069 • 4,069
Palmer, MS 39401 • 2,765
Palmer, TX 75152 • 1,659
Palmer Lake, CO 80133 • 1,480
Palmer Park, MD 20785 • 7,019
Palmerton, PA 18071 • 5,394
Palmetto, FL 34220–21 • 9,268
Palmetto, GA 30268 • 2,612
Palmetto Estates, FL 33157 • 12,293
Palm Harbor, FL 34682–85 • 50,256
Palm Springs, CA 92262–64 • 40,181
Palm Springs, FL 33460 • 9,763
Palm Springs North, FL 33015 • 5,300
Palm Valley, FL 32082 • 9,960
Palmyra, MO 63461 • 3,371
Palmyra, NJ 08065 • 7,056
Palmyra, NY 14522 • 3,566
Palmyra, PA 17078 • 6,910
Palmyra, WI 53156 • 1,539
Palo Alto, CA 94301–09 • 55,900
Palo Alto □, IA • 10,669
Palo Pinto □, TX • 25,055
Palos Heights, IL 60463 • 11,478
Palos Hills, IL 60465 • 17,803
Palos Park, IL 60464 • 4,199
Palos Verdes Estates, CA 90274 • 13,512
Pamlico □, NC • 11,372
Pampa, TX 79065–66 • 19,959
Pamplico, SC 29583 • 1,314
Pana, IL 62557 • 5,796
Panaca, NV 89042 • 700
Panama, OK 74951 • 1,528
Panama City, FL 32401–13 • 34,378
Panama City Beach, FL 32407–08 • 4,051
Pandora, OH 45877 • 1,009
Panguitch, UT 84759 • 1,444
Panhandle, TX 79068 • 2,353
Panola □, MS • 29,996
Panola □, TX • 22,035
Panora, IA 50216 • 1,100
Panthersville, GA 30032 • 9,874
Paola, KS 66071 • 4,698
Paoli, IN 47454 • 3,542
Paoli, PA 19301 • 5,603
Paonia, CO 81428 • 1,403
Papaikou, HI 96781 • 1,634
Papillion, NE 68046 • 10,372
Paradise, CA 95969 • 25,408
Paradise, NV 89109 • 124,682
Paradise Hills, NM 87114 • 5,513
Paradise Valley, AZ 85253 • 11,671
Paradise Valley, NV 89426 • 150
Paragould, AR 72450–51 • 18,540
Paramount, CA 90723 • 47,669
Paramount, MD 21740 • 1,878
Paramus, NJ 07652–53 • 25,067
Parchment, MI 49004 • 1,958
Pardeeville, WI 53954 • 1,630
Paris, AR 72855 • 3,674
Paris, IL 61944 • 8,987
Paris, KY 40361–62 • 8,730
Paris, MO 65275 • 1,486
Paris, TN 38242 • 9,332
Paris, TX 75460–61 • 24,699
Park □, CO • 7,174
Park □, MT • 14,562
Park □, WY • 23,178
Park City, KS 67219 • 5,050
Park City, UT 84060 • 4,468
Parke □, IN • 15,410
Parker, AZ 85344 • 2,897
Parker, CO 80134 • 5,450
Parker, FL 32401 • 4,598
Parker, SD 57053 • 984
Parker □, TX • 64,785
Parker City, IN 47368 • 1,323
Parkersburg, IA 50665 • 1,804
Parkersburg, WV 26101–06 • 33,862
Parkesburg, PA 19365 • 2,981
Park Falls, WI 54552 • 3,104
Park Forest, IL 60466 • 24,656
Park Hills, KY 41015 • 3,321
Parkin, AR 72373 • 1,847
Parkland, WA 98444 • 20,882
Park Layne, OH 45344 • 4,895
Park Rapids, MN 56470 • 2,863
Park Ridge, IL 60068 • 36,175
Park Ridge, NJ 07656 • 8,102
Park River, ND 58270 • 1,725
Parkrose, OR 97230 • 21,108
Parkston, SD 57366 • 1,572
Parkville, MD 21234 • 31,617
Parkville, MO 64152 • 2,402
Parkwater, WA 99211 • 4,300
Parkway, CA 95823 • 12,000
Parkwood, NC 27713 • 4,123
Parkwood, WA 98366 • 6,853
Parlier, CA 93648 • 7,938
Parma, ID 83660 • 1,597
Parma, OH 44129 • 87,876
Parma Heights, OH 44130 • 21,448
Parmer □, TX • 9,863
Parole, MD 21401 • 10,054
Parowan, UT 84761 • 1,873
Parrish, AL 35580 • 1,433
Parshall, ND 58770 • 943
Parsons, KS 67357 • 11,924
Parsons, TN 38363 • 2,033
Parsons, WV 26287 • 1,453
Pasadena, CA 91101–09 • 131,591
Pasadena, MD 21122 • 10,012
Pasadena, TX 77501–08 • 119,363
Pascagoula, MS 39567–68 • 25,899
Pasco, WA 99301–02 • 20,337
Pasco □, FL • 281,131
Pascoag, RI 02859 • 5,011
Paso Robles, CA 93446–47 • 18,583
Pasquotank □, NC • 31,298
Passaic, NJ 07055 • 58,041
Passaic □, NJ • 453,060
Pass Christian, MS 39571 • 5,557
Pataskala, OH 43062 • 3,046
Patchogue, NY 11772 • 11,060
Paterson, NJ 07501–44 • 140,891
Patrick □, VA • 17,473
Patten, ME 04765 • 1,256
Patterson, LA 70392 • 4,736
Patterson, NY 12563 • 1,200
Patton, PA 16668 • 2,206
Paul, ID 83347 • 901
Paulding, OH 45879 • 2,605
Paulding □, GA • 41,611
Paulding □, OH • 20,488
Paullina, IA 51046 • 1,124
Paulsboro, NJ 08066 • 6,577
Pauls Valley, OK 73075 • 6,150
Pawcatuck, CT 06379 • 5,289
Paw Creek, NC 28130 • 1,700
Pawhuska, OK 74056 • 3,825
Pawling, NY 12564 • 1,974
Pawnee, IL 62558 • 2,384
Pawnee, OK 74058 • 2,197
Pawnee □, KS • 7,555
Pawnee □, NE • 3,317
Pawnee □, OK • 15,575
Pawnee City, NE 68420 • 1,008
Paw Paw, MI 49079 • 3,169
Pawtucket, RI 02860–65 • 72,644
Paxton, IL 60957 • 4,289
Paxton, MA 01612 • 1,550
Payette, ID 83661 • 5,592
Payette □, ID • 16,434
Payne, OH 45880 • 1,244
Payne □, OK • 61,507
Paynesville, MN 56362 • 2,275
Payson, AZ 85541 • 8,377
Payson, IL 62360 • 1,114
Payson, UT 84651 • 9,510
Peabody, KS 66866 • 1,349
Peabody, MA 01960–61 • 47,039
Peace Dale, RI 02883 • 3,100
Peach □, GA • 21,189
Peach Orchard, GA 30906 • 13,800
Peachtree City, GA 30269 • 19,027
Pea Ridge, AR 72751 • 1,620
Pearisburg, VA 24134 • 2,064
Pearl, MS 39208 • 19,588
Pearland, TX 77581 • 18,697
Pearl City, HI 96782 • 30,993
Pearl River, LA 70452 • 1,507
Pearl River, NY 10965 • 15,314
Pearl River □, MS • 38,714
Pearsall, TX 78061 • 6,924
Pearson, GA 31642 • 1,714
Pecatonica, IL 61063 • 1,760
Pecos, NM 87552 • 1,012
Pecos, TX 79772 • 12,069
Pecos □, TX • 14,675
Peculiar, MO 64078 • 1,777
Pedricktown, NJ 08067 • 1,500
Peebles, OH 45660 • 1,782
Peekskill, NY 10566 • 19,536
Pegram, TN 37143 • 1,371
Pekin, IL 61554–55 • 32,254
Pekin, IN 47165 • 1,095
Pelahatchie, MS 39145 • 1,553
Pelham, AL 35124 • 9,765
Pelham, GA 31779 • 3,869
Pelham, NY 10803 • 6,413
Pelham Manor, NY 10803 • 5,443
Pelican Rapids, MN 56572 • 1,886
Pella, IA 50219 • 9,270
Pell City, AL 35125 • 8,118
Pell Lake, WI 53157 • 2,018
Pemberton, NJ 08068 • 1,367
Pemberville, OH 43450 • 1,279
Pembina □, ND • 9,238
Pembroke, GA 31321 • 1,503
Pembroke, MA 02359 • 2,000
Pembroke, NC 28372 • 2,241
Pembroke, VA 24136 • 1,064
Pembroke Park, FL 33009 • 4,933
Pembroke Pines, FL 33024 • 65,452
Pemiscot □, MO • 21,921
Pen Argyl, PA 18072 • 3,492
Penbrook, PA 17103 • 2,791
Pender, NE 68047 • 1,208
Pender □, NC • 28,855
Pendleton, IN 46064 • 2,309
Pendleton, OR 97801 • 15,126
Pendleton, SC 29670 • 3,314
Pendleton □, KY • 12,036
Pendleton □, WV • 8,054
Pendley Hills, GA 30032 • 5,400
Pend Oreille □, WA • 8,915
Penfield, NY 14526 • 6,260
Penn Acres, DE 19720 • 2,430
Penn Hills, PA 15235 • 51,430
Pennington, NJ 08534 • 2,537
Pennington □, MN • 13,306
Pennington □, SD • 81,343
Pennington Gap, VA 24277 • 1,922
Pennsauken, NJ 08110 • 34,733
Pennsboro, WV 26415 • 1,282
Pennsburg, PA 18073 • 2,460
Penns Grove, NJ 08069 • 5,228
Pennsville, NJ 08070 • 12,218
Penn Yan, NY 14527 • 5,248
Penobscot □, ME • 146,601
Pensacola, FL 32501–26 • 58,165
Pentwater, MI 49449 • 1,050
Peoria, AZ 85345 • 50,618
Peoria, IL 61601–56 • 113,504
Peoria □, IL • 182,827
Peoria Heights, IL 61614 • 6,930
Peotone, IL 60468 • 2,947
Pepeekeo, HI 96783 • 1,813
Pepin □, WI • 7,107
Pepperell, MA 01463 • 2,350
Pepper Pike, OH 44124 • 6,185
Pequannock, NJ 07440 • 12,844
Perdido, AL 36562 • 1,200
Perham, MN 56573 • 2,075
Perkasie, PA 18944 • 7,878
Perkins, OK 74059 • 1,925
Perkins □, NE • 3,367
Perkins □, SD • 3,932
Perquimans □, NC • 10,447
Perrine, FL 33157 • 15,576
Perris, CA 92370 • 21,460
Perry, FL 32347 • 7,151
Perry, GA 31069 • 9,452
Perry, IA 50220 • 6,652
Perry, MI 48872 • 2,163
Perry, NY 14530 • 4,219
Perry, OH 44081 • 1,012
Perry, OK 73077 • 4,978
Perry, UT 84302 • 1,211
Perry □, AL • 12,759
Perry □, AR • 7,969
Perry □, IL • 21,412
Perry □, IN • 19,107
Perry □, KY • 30,283
Perry □, MS • 10,865
Perry □, MO • 16,648
Perry □, OH • 31,557
Perry □, PA • 41,172
Perry □, TN • 6,612
Perry Hall, MD 21128 • 22,723
Perry Heights, OH 44646 • 9,055
Perryman, MD 21130 • 2,160
Perrysburg, OH 43551–52 • 12,551
Perryton, TX 79070 • 7,607
Perryville, AR 72126 • 1,141
Perryville, MD 21903 • 2,456
Perryville, MO 63775 • 6,933
Pershing □, NV • 4,336
Person □, NC • 30,180
Perth Amboy, NJ 08861–63 • 41,967
Peru, IL 61354 • 9,302
Peru, IN 46970 • 12,843
Peru, NE 68421 • 1,110
Peru, NY 12972 • 1,565
Peshtigo, WI 54157 • 3,154
Petal, MS 39465 • 7,883
Petaluma, CA 94952–55 • 43,184
Peterborough, NH 03458 • 2,685
Petersburg, AK 99833 • 3,207
Petersburg, IL 62675 • 2,261
Petersburg, IN 47567 • 2,449
Petersburg, MI 49270 • 1,201
Petersburg, TX 79250 • 1,292
Petersburg, VA 23801–05 • 38,386
Petersburg, WV 26847 • 2,360
Petersville, AL 35633 • 1,730
Petoskey, MI 49770 • 6,056
Petroleum □, MT • 519
Petros, TN 37845 • 1,286
Pettis □, MO • 35,437
Pevely, MO 63070 • 2,831
Pewaukee, WI 53072 • 4,941
Pewee Valley, KY 40056 • 1,283
Pharr, TX 78577 • 32,921
Phelps, KY 41553 • 1,120
Phelps, NY 14532 • 1,978
Phelps □, MO • 35,248
Phelps □, NE • 9,715
Phenix City, AL 36867–69 • 25,312
Philadelphia, MS 39350 • 6,758
Philadelphia, NY 13673 • 1,478
Philadelphia, PA 19101–96 • 1,585,577
Philadelphia □, PA • 1,585,577
Phil Campbell, AL 35581 • 1,317
Philip, SD 57567 • 1,077
Philippi, WV 26416 • 3,132
Philipsburg, MT 59858 • 925
Philipsburg, PA 16866 • 3,048
Phillips, TX 79007 • 1,729
Phillips, WI 54555 • 1,592
Phillips □, AR • 28,838
Phillips □, CO • 4,189
Phillips □, KS • 6,590
Phillips □, MT • 5,163
Phillipsburg, KS 67661 • 2,828
Phillipsburg, NJ 08865 • 15,757
Philmont, NY 12565 • 1,623
Philo, IL 61864 • 1,028
Philomath, OR 97370 • 2,983
Phoenix, AZ 85001–82 • 983,403
Phoenix, IL 60426 • 2,217
Phoenix, NY 13135 • 2,435
Phoenix, OR 97535 • 3,239
Phoenixville, PA 19460 • 15,066
Piatt □, IL • 15,548
Picayune, MS 39466 • 10,633
Picher, OK 74360 • 1,714
Pickaway □, OH • 48,255
Pickens, MS 39146 • 1,285
Pickens, SC 29671 • 3,042
Pickens □, AL • 20,699
Pickens □, GA • 14,432
Pickens □, SC • 93,894
Pickerington, OH 43147 • 5,668
Pickett □, TN • 4,548
Pico Rivera, CA 90660–61 • 59,177
Piedmont, AL 36272 • 5,288
Piedmont, CA 94611 • 10,602
Piedmont, MO 63957 • 2,166
Piedmont, OK 73078 • 2,522
Piedmont, SC 29673 • 4,143
Piedmont, WV 26750 • 1,094
Pierce, ID 83546 • 746
Pierce, NE 68767 • 1,615
Pierce □, GA • 13,328
Pierce □, NE • 7,827
Pierce □, ND • 5,052
Pierce □, WA • 586,203
Pierce □, WI • 32,765
Pierce City, MO 65723 • 1,382
Pierceton, IN 46562 • 1,030
Pierre, SD 57501 • 12,906
Pierre Part, LA 70339 • 3,053
Pierson, FL 32180 • 2,988
Pierz, MN 56364 • 1,014
Pigeon, MI 48755 • 1,207
Pigeon Cove, MA 01966 • 1,660
Pigeon Forge, TN 37863 • 3,027
Piggott, AR 72454 • 3,777
Pike □, AL • 27,595
Pike □, AR • 10,086
Pike □, GA • 10,224
Pike □, IL • 17,577
Pike □, IN • 12,509
Pike □, KY • 72,583
Pike □, MS • 36,882
Pike □, MO • 15,969
Pike □, OH • 24,249
Pike □, PA • 27,966
Pike Lake, MN 55811 • 1,004
Pikesville, MD 21208 • 24,815
Piketon, OH 45661 • 1,717
Pikeville, KY 41501–02 • 6,324
Pikeville, TN 37367 • 1,771
Pilot Mountain, NC 27041 • 1,181
Pilot Point, TX 76258 • 2,538
Pilot Rock, OR 97868 • 1,478
Pilot Station, AK 99650 • 463
Pima, AZ 85543 • 1,725
Pima □, AZ • 666,880
Pimmit Hills, VA 22043 • 6,019
Pinal □, AZ • 116,379
Pinardville, NH 03045 • 4,654
Pinckney, MI 48169 • 1,603
Pinckneyville, IL 62274 • 3,372
Pinconning, MI 48650 • 1,291
Pine □, MN • 21,264
Pine Bluff, AR 71601–13 • 57,140
Pine Bluffs, WY 82082 • 1,054
Pine Bridge, CT 06403 • 1,160
Pine Bush, NY 12566 • 1,445
Pine Castle, FL 32809 • 8,276
Pine City, MN 55063 • 2,613
Pinedale, WY 82941 • 1,181
Pine Grove, PA 17963 • 2,118
Pine Grove Mills, PA 16868 • 1,129
Pine Hill, NJ 08021 • 9,854
Pine Hills, FL 32808 • 35,322
Pinehurst, MA 01866 • 6,614
Pinehurst, NJ 08201 • 1,850
Pinehurst, NC 28374 • 5,103
Pine Island, MN 55963 • 2,125
Pine Island, NY 10969 • 1,200
Pine Knot, KY 42635 • 1,549
Pine Lawn, MO 63120 • 5,092
Pine Level, NC 27568 • 1,217
Pinellas □, FL • 851,659
Pinellas Park, FL 34664–66 • 43,426
Pine Plains, NY 12567 • 1,312
Pine Ridge, SD 57770 • 2,596
Pinetops, NC 27864 • 1,514
Pine Valley, CA 91962 • 1,297
Pineville, KY 40977 • 2,198
Pineville, LA 71360–61 • 12,251
Pineville, NC 28134 • 2,970
Pinewald, NJ 08721 • 1,700
Pinewood, FL 33168 • 15,518
Pinewood Park, FL 33168 • 8,300
Piney Point, MD 20674 • 1,200
Piney View, WV 25906 • 1,085
Pinole, CA 94564 • 17,460
Pinson, AL 35126 • 1,430
Pioche, NV 89043 • 830
Pioneer, OH 43554 • 1,287
Pipestone, MN 56164 • 4,554
Pipestone □, MN • 10,491
Piqua, OH 45356 • 20,612
Pirtleville, AZ 85626 • 1,364
Piscataquis □, ME • 18,653
Piscataway, NJ 08854–55 • 42,223
Pisgah, OH 45069 • 15,660
Pisgah Forest, NC 28768 • 1,899
Pismo Beach, CA 93448–49 • 7,669
Pitcairn, PA 15140 • 4,087
Pitkin □, CO • 12,661
Pitman, NJ 08071 • 9,365
Pitt □, NC • 107,924
Pittsboro, NC 27312 • 1,436
Pittsburg, CA 94565 • 47,564
Pittsburg, KS 66762 • 17,775
Pittsburg, TX 75686 • 4,007
Pittsburg □, OK • 40,581
Pittsburgh, PA 15201–90 • 369,879
Pittsfield, IL 62363 • 4,231
Pittsfield, ME 04967 • 3,222
Pittsfield, MA 01201–03 • 48,622
Pittsfield, NH 03263 • 1,717
Pittsford, VT 05763 • 650
Pittston, PA 18640–44 • 9,389
Pittsylvania □, VA • 55,655
Piute □, UT • 1,277
Pixley, CA 93256 • 2,457
Placentia, CA 92670 • 41,259
Placer □, CA • 172,796
Placerville, CA 95667 • 8,355
Plain City, OH 43064 • 2,278
Plain City, UT 84404 • 2,722
Plain Dealing, LA 71064 • 1,074
Plainedge, NY 11714 • 8,739
Plainfield, CT 06374 • 2,856
Plainfield, IL 60544 • 4,557
Plainfield, IN 46168 • 10,433
Plainfield, NJ 07059–63 • 46,567
Plainfield, VT 05667 • 600
Plainfield Heights, MI 49505 • 5,000
Plains, MT 59859 • 992
Plains, PA 18705 • 4,694
Plains, TX 79355 • 1,422
Plainsboro, NJ 08536 • 1,560
Plainview, MN 55964 • 2,768
Plainview, NE 68769 • 1,333
Plainview, NY 11803 • 26,207
Plainview, TX 79072–73 • 21,700
Plainville, CT 06062 • 17,392
Plainville, KS 67663 • 2,173
Plainville, MA 02762 • 5,857
Plainwell, MI 49080 • 4,057
Plaistow, NH 03865 • 1,850
Plano, IL 60545 • 5,104
Plano, TX 75074–75 • 128,713
Plantation, FL 33317 • 66,692
Plant City, FL 33564–67 • 22,754
Plantersville, MS 38862 • 1,046
Plantsite, AZ 85540 • 1,500
Plantsville, CT 06479 • 7,050
Plaquemine, LA 70764–65 • 7,186
Plaquemines □, LA • 25,575
Platte, SD 57369 • 1,311
Platte □, MO • 57,867
Platte □, NE • 29,820
Platte □, WY • 8,145
Platte City, MO 64079 • 2,947
Platteville, CO 80651 • 1,515
Platteville, WI 53818 • 9,708
Plattsburg, MO 64477 • 2,248
Plattsburgh, NY 12901 • 21,255
Plattsmouth, NE 68048 • 6,412
Pleasant Gap, PA 16823 • 1,699
Pleasant Garden, NC 27313 • 2,228
Pleasant Grove, AL 35127 • 8,458
Pleasant Grove, UT 84062 • 13,476
Pleasant Hill, CA 94523 • 31,585
Pleasant Hill, IL 62366 • 1,030
Pleasant Hill, IA 50301 • 3,671
Pleasant Hill, MO 64080 • 3,827
Pleasant Hill, OH 45359 • 1,066
Pleasant Hills, PA 15236 • 8,884
Pleasanton, CA 94566 • 50,553
Pleasanton, KS 66075 • 1,231
Pleasanton, TX 78064 • 7,678
Pleasant Prairie, WI 53158 • 11,961
Pleasants □, WV • 7,546
Pleasant Valley, MO 64068 • 2,731
Pleasant Valley, NY 12569 • 1,688
Pleasant View, CO 80401 • 3,460
Pleasant View, UT 84404 • 3,603
Pleasantville, IA 50225 • 1,536
Pleasantville, NJ 08232 • 16,027
Pleasantville, NY 10570–72 • 6,592
Pleasure Beach, CT 06385 • 1,356
Pleasure Ridge Park, KY 40258 • 25,131
Plentywood, MT 59254 • 2,136
Plover, WI 54467 • 8,176
Plum, PA 15239 • 25,609
Plumas □, CA • 19,739
Plumsteadville, PA 18949 • 1,200
Plymouth, CT 06782 • 1,070
Plymouth, FL 32768 • 2,700
Plymouth, IN 46563 • 8,303
Plymouth, MA 02360–61 • 7,258
Plymouth, MI 48170 • 9,560
Plymouth, MN 55441 • 50,889
Plymouth, NH 03264 • 3,967
Plymouth, NC 27962 • 4,328
Plymouth, OH 44865 • 1,942
Plymouth, PA 18651 • 7,134
Plymouth, WI 53073 • 6,769
Plymouth □, IA • 23,388
Plymouth □, MA • 435,276
Plymouth Township, PA 19401 • 17,168
Poca, WV 25159 • 1,124
Pocahontas, AR 72455 • 6,151
Pocahontas, IA 50574 • 2,085
Pocahontas □, IA • 9,525
Pocahontas □, WV • 9,008
Pocasset, MA 02559 • 2,200
Pocatalico, WV 25320 • 2,450
Pocatello, ID 83201–06 • 46,080
Pocola, OK 74902 • 3,664
Pocomoke City, MD 21851 • 3,922
Poinsett □, AR • 24,664
Point Clear, AL 36564 • 2,125
Pointe Coupee □, LA • 22,540
Point Hope, AK 99766 • 639
Point Marion, PA 15474 • 1,344
Point Pleasant, NJ 08742 • 18,177
Point Pleasant, WV 25550 • 4,996
Point Pleasant Beach, NJ 08742 • 5,112
Poipu, HI 96756 • 975
Polk, PA 16342 • 1,267
Polk □, AR • 17,347

Polk □, FL • *405,382*
Polk □, GA • *33,815*
Polk □, IA • *327,140*
Polk □, MN • *32,498*
Polk □, MO • *21,826*
Polk □, NE • *5,675*
Polk □, NC • *14,416*
Polk □, OR • *49,541*
Polk □, TN • *13,643*
Polk □, TX • *30,687*
Polk □, WI • *34,773*
Polk City, FL 33868 • *1,439*
Polk City, IA 50226 • *1,908*
Polo, IL 61064 • *2,514*
Polson, MT 59860 • *3,283*
Pomeroy, OH 45769 • *2,259*
Pomeroy, WA 99347 • *1,393*
Pomona, CA 91765–69 • *131,723*
Pomona, NJ 08240 • *2,624*
Pompano Beach, FL 33060–69 • *72,411*
Pompano Beach Highlands, FL 33060 • *17,915*
Pompton Lakes, NJ 07442 • *10,539*
Ponca City, OK 74601–04 • *26,359*
Ponchatoula, LA 70454 • *5,425*
Pondera □, MT • *6,433*
Ponte Vedra Beach, FL 32082 • *1,700*
Pontiac, IL 61764 • *11,428*
Pontiac, MI 48340–43 • *71,166*
Pontotoc, MS 38863 • *4,570*
Pontotoc □, MS • *22,237*
Pontotoc □, OK • *34,119*
Pooler, GA 31322 • *4,453*
Poolesville, MD 20837 • *3,796*
Pope □, AR • *45,883*
Pope □, IL • *4,373*
Pope □, MN • *10,745*
Poplar, MT 59255 • *881*
Poplar Bluff, MO 63901 • *16,996*
Poplarville, MS 39470 • *2,561*
Poquonock Bridge, CT 06340 • *2,770*
Poquoson, VA 23662 • *11,005*
Portage, IN 46368 • *29,060*
Portage, MI 49081 • *41,042*
Portage, PA 15946 • *3,105*
Portage, WI 53901 • *8,640*
Portage □, OH • *142,585*
Portage □, WI • *61,405*
Portage Lakes, OH 44319 • *13,373*
Portageville, MO 63873 • *3,401*
Portales, NM 88130 • *10,690*
Port Allegany, PA 16743 • *2,391*
Port Allen, LA 70767 • *6,277*
Port Angeles, WA 98362 • *17,710*
Port Aransas, TX 78373 • *2,233*
Port Arthur, TX 77640–43 • *58,724*
Port Barre, LA 70577 • *2,144*
Port Bolivar, TX 77650 • *1,600*
Port Byron, IL 61275 • *1,002*
Port Byron, NY 13140 • *1,359*
Port Carbon, PA 17965 • *2,134*
Port Charlotte, FL 33952 • *41,535*
Port Chester, NY 10573 • *24,728*
Port Clinton, OH 43452 • *7,106*
Port Dickinson, NY 13901 • *1,785*
Port Edwards, WI 54469 • *1,848*
Porter, IN 46304 • *3,118*
Porter, TX 77365 • *7,000*
Porter □, IN • *128,932*
Porterdale, GA 30270 • *1,278*
Porterville, CA 93257–58 • *29,563*
Port Ewen, NY 12466 • *3,444*
Port Gibson, MS 39150 • *1,810*
Port Henry, NY 12974 • *1,263*
Port Hueneme, CA 93041–44 • *20,319*
Port Huron, MI 48060–61 • *33,694*
Port Isabel, TX 78578 • *4,467*
Port Jefferson, NY 11777 • *7,455*
Port Jefferson Station, NY 11776 • *7,232*
Port Jervis, NY 12771 • *9,060*
Portland, CT 06480 • *5,645*
Portland, IN 47371 • *6,483*
Portland, ME 04101–12 • *64,358*
Portland, MI 48875 • *3,889*
Portland, OR 97201–99 • *437,319*
Portland, TN 37148 • *5,165*
Portland, TX 78374 • *12,224*
Port Lavaca, TX 77979 • *10,886*
Port Monmouth, NJ 07758 • *3,800*
Port Neches, TX 77651 • *12,974*
Port Norris, NJ 08349 • *1,701*
Port O'Connor, TX 77982 • *1,031*
Portola, CA 96122 • *2,193*
Port Orange, FL 32127 • *35,317*
Port Orchard, WA 98366 • *4,984*
Port Orford, OR 97465 • *1,025*
Port Penn, DE 19731 • *300*
Port Richey, FL 34667–74 • *2,523*
Port Royal, SC 29935 • *2,985*
Port Saint Joe, FL 32456 • *4,044*
Port Saint Lucie, FL 34952 • *55,866*
Port Salerno, FL 34992 • *7,786*
Portsmouth, NH 03801–02 • *25,925*
Portsmouth, OH 45662 • *22,676*
Portsmouth, RI 02871 • *3,540*
Portsmouth, VA 23701–09 • *103,907*
Port St. John, FL 32922 • *8,933*
Port Sulphur, LA 70083 • *3,523*
Port Townsend, WA 98368 • *7,001*
Portville, NY 14770 • *1,040*
Port Vue, PA 15133 • *4,641*
Port Washington, NY 11050 • *15,387*
Port Washington, WI 53074 • *9,338*
Port Wentworth, GA 31407 • *4,012*
Posen, IL 60469 • *4,226*
Posey □, IN • *25,968*
Poseyville, IN 47633 • *1,089*
Post, TX 79356 • *3,768*
Post Falls, ID 83854 • *7,349*
Postville, IA 52162 • *1,472*
Poteau, OK 74953 • *7,210*
Poteet, TX 78065 • *3,206*
Poth, TX 78147 • *1,642*
Potlatch, ID 83855 • *790*
Potomac, MD 20851 • *45,634*
Potomac Heights, MD 20640 • *1,524*
Potomac Park, MD 21502 • *1,800*
Potosi, MO 63664 • *2,683*
Potsdam, NY 13676 • *10,251*
Pottawatomie □, KS • *16,128*
Pottawatomie □, OK • *58,760*
Pottawattamie □, IA • *82,628*
Potter □, PA • *16,717*
Potter □, SD • *3,190*
Potter □, TX • *97,874*
Potter Valley, CA 95469 • *1,500*
Pottstown, PA 19464 • *21,831*
Pottsville, PA 17901 • *16,603*
Poughkeepsie, NY 12601–03 • *28,844*
Poulsbo, WA 98370 • *4,848*
Poultney, VT 05764 • *1,731*
Poway, CA 92064 • *43,516*
Powder River □, MT • *2,090*
Powder Springs, GA 30073 • *6,893*
Powell, OH 43065 • *2,154*
Powell, TN 37849 • *7,534*
Powell, WY 82435 • *5,292*
Powell □, KY • *11,686*
Powell □, MT • *6,620*
Powellhurst, OR 97236 • *28,756*
Powellton, WV 25161 • *1,905*
Power □, ID • *7,086*
Poweshiek □, IA • *19,033*
Powhatan □, VA • *15,328*
Powhatan Point, OH 43942 • *1,807*
Poydras, LA 70085 • *4,029*
Poynette, WI 53955 • *1,662*
Prague, OK 74864 • *2,308*
Prairie □, AR • *9,518*
Prairie □, MT • *1,383*
Prairie City, IA 50228 • *1,360*
Prairie City, OR 97869 • *1,117*
Prairie du Chien, WI 53821 • *5,659*
Prairie du Sac, WI 53578 • *2,380*
Prairie Grove, AR 72753 • *1,761*
Prairie View, TX 77446 • *4,004*
Prairie Village, KS 66208 • *23,186*
Pratt, KS 67124 • *6,687*
Pratt □, KS • *9,702*
Prattville, AL 36066–67 • *19,587*
Preble □, OH • *40,113*
Premont, TX 78375 • *2,914*
Prentiss, MS 39474 • *1,487*
Prentiss □, MS • *23,278*
Prescott, AZ 86301–14 • *26,455*
Prescott, AR 71857 • *3,673*
Prescott, WI 54021 • *3,243*
Presho, SD 57568 • *654*
Presidio, TX 79845 • *3,072*
Presidio □, TX • *6,637*
Presque Isle, ME 04769 • *10,550*
Presque Isle □, MI • *13,743*
Preston, ID 83263 • *3,710*
Preston, IA 52069 • *1,025*
Preston, MN 55965 • *1,530*
Preston □, WV • *29,037*
Prestonsburg, KY 41653 • *3,558*
Price, UT 84501 • *8,712*
Price □, WI • *15,600*
Prichard, AL 36610 • *34,311*
Priest River, ID 83856 • *1,560*
Primrose, RI 02895 • *500*
Prince Edward □, VA • *17,320*
Prince Frederick, MD 20678 • *1,885*
Prince George □, VA • *27,394*
Prince Georges □, MD • *729,268*
Princes Lakes, IN 46164 • *1,055*
Princess Anne, MD 21853 • *1,666*
Princeton, FL 33032 • *7,073*
Princeton, IL 61356 • *7,197*
Princeton, IN 47670 • *8,127*
Princeton, KY 42445 • *6,940*
Princeton, MN 55371 • *3,719*
Princeton, MO 64673 • *1,021*
Princeton, NJ 08540–43 • *12,016*
Princeton, NC 27569 • *1,181*
Princeton, WV 24740 • *7,043*
Princeton, WI 54968 • *1,458*
Princeton Junction, NJ 08550 • *2,362*
Princeville, IL 61559 • *1,421*
Princeville, NC 27886 • *1,652*
Prince William □, VA • *215,686*
Prineville, OR 97754 • *5,355*
Prior Lake, MN 55372 • *11,482*
Proctor, MN 55810 • *2,974*
Proctor, VT 05765 • *1,979*
Proctorsville, VT 05153 • *480*
Prophetstown, IL 61277 • *1,749*
Prospect, CT 06712 • *6,807*
Prospect, KY 40059 • *2,788*
Prospect, OH 43342 • *1,148*
Prospect, OR 97536 • *1,200*
Prospect, PA 16052 • *1,122*
Prospect Heights, IL 60070 • *15,239*
Prospect Park, NJ 07508 • *5,053*
Prospect Park, PA 19076 • *6,764*
Prosperity, SC 29127 • *1,116*
Prosperity, WV 25909 • *1,322*
Prosser, WA 99350 • *4,476*
Providence, KY 42450 • *4,123*
Providence, RI 02901–40 • *160,728*
Providence, UT 84332 • *3,344*
Providence □, RI • *596,270*
Provincetown, MA 02657 • *3,374*
Provo, UT 84601–06 • *86,835*
Prowers □, CO • *13,347*
Prudenville, MI 48651 • *1,100*
Prudhoe Bay, AK 99734 • *47*
Pryor, OK 74361–62 • *8,327*
Pueblo, CO 81001–19 • *98,640*
Pueblo □, CO • *123,051*
Puhi, HI 96766 • *1,210*
Pukalani, HI 96788 • *5,879*
Pulaski, NY 13142 • *2,525*
Pulaski, TN 38478 • *7,895*
Pulaski, VA 24301 • *9,985*
Pulaski, WI 54162 • *2,200*
Pulaski □, AR • *349,660*
Pulaski □, GA • *8,108*
Pulaski □, IL • *7,523*
Pulaski □, IN • *12,643*
Pulaski □, KY • *49,489*
Pulaski □, MO • *41,307*
Pulaski □, VA • *34,496*
Pullman, WA 99163–65 • *23,478*
Pumphrey, MD 21227 • *5,483*
Punta Gorda, FL 33948–55 • *10,747*
Punxsutawney, PA 15767 • *6,782*
Purcell, OK 73080 • *4,784*
Purcellville, VA 22132 • *1,744*
Purvis, MS 39475 • *2,140*
Pushmataha □, OK • *10,997*
Putnam, CT 06260 • *6,835*
Putnam □, FL • *65,070*
Putnam □, GA • *14,137*
Putnam □, IL • *5,730*
Putnam □, IN • *30,315*
Putnam □, MO • *5,079*
Putnam □, NY • *83,941*
Putnam □, OH • *33,819*
Putnam □, TN • *51,373*
Putnam □, WV • *42,835*
Putney, VT 05346 • *1,100*
Puyallup, WA 98371–74 • *23,875*

Q

Quail Oaks, VA 23234 • *1,500*
Quaker Hill, CT 06375 • *2,052*
Quakertown, PA 18951 • *8,982*
Quanah, TX 79252 • *3,413*
Quarryville, PA 17566 • *1,642*
Quartz Hill, CA 93536 • *9,626*
Quartzsite, AZ 85346 • *1,876*
Quay □, NM • *10,823*
Quechee, VT 05059 • *550*
Queen Annes □, MD • *33,953*
Queen City, TX 75572 • *1,748*
Queen Creek, AZ 85242 • *2,667*
Queens □, NY • *1,951,598*
Queensborough, WA 98021 • *4,850*
Questa, NM 87556 • *1,707*
Quidnessett, RI 02852 • *3,300*
Quidnick, RI 02816 • *2,300*
Quilcene, WA 98376 • *1,200*
Quincy, CA 95971 • *2,700*
Quincy, FL 32351 • *7,444*
Quincy, IL 62301–06 • *39,681*
Quincy, MA 02169 • *84,985*
Quincy, MI 49082 • *1,680*
Quincy, WA 98848 • *3,738*
Quinebaug, CT 06262 • *1,031*
Quinhagak, AK 99655 • *501*
Quinlan, TX 75474 • *1,360*
Quinton, OK 74561 • *1,133*
Quitman, GA 31643 • *5,292*
Quitman, MS 39355 • *2,736*
Quitman, TX 75783 • *1,684*
Quitman □, GA • *2,209*
Quitman □, MS • *10,490*
Quonochontaug, RI 02813 • *1,500*

R

Rabun □, GA • *11,648*
Raceland, KY 41169 • *2,256*
Raceland, LA 70394 • *5,564*
Racine, WI 53401–08 • *84,298*
Racine □, WI • *175,034*
Radcliff, KY 40159–60 • *19,772*
Radford, VA 24141–43 • *15,940*
Radnor Township, PA 19087 • *28,705*
Raeford, NC 28376 • *3,469*
Ragland, AL 35131 • *1,807*
Rahway, NJ 07065–67 • *25,325*
Rainbow City, AL 35901 • *7,673*
Rainelle, WV 25962 • *1,681*
Rainier, OR 97048 • *1,674*
Rains □, TX • *6,715*
Rainsville, AL 35986 • *3,875*
Raleigh, MS 39153 • *1,291*
Raleigh, NC 27601–61 • *207,951*
Raleigh □, WV • *76,819*
Raleigh Hills, OR 97225 • *6,066*
Ralls, TX 79357 • *2,172*
Ralls □, MO • *8,476*
Ralston, NE 68127 • *6,236*
Rambleton Acres, DE 19720 • *1,700*
Ramblewood, NJ 08054 • *6,181*
Ramona, CA 92065 • *13,040*
Ramsay, MI 49959 • *1,075*
Ramseur, NC 27316 • *1,186*
Ramsey, MN 55303 • *12,408*
Ramsey, NJ 07446 • *13,228*
Ramsey □, MN • *485,765*
Ramsey □, ND • *12,681*
Ranchester, WY 82839 • *676*
Rancho Cordova, CA 95670 • *48,731*
Rancho Mirage, CA 92270 • *9,778*
Rancho Palos Verdes, CA 90274 • *41,659*
Rancho Rinconado, CA 95014 • *4,206*
Ranchos de Taos, NM 87557 • *1,779*
Rancocas Woods, NJ 08060 • *1,250*
Rand, WV 25306 • *2,400*
Randall □, TX • *89,673*
Randallstown, MD 21133 • *26,277*
Randleman, NC 27317 • *2,612*
Randolph, ME 04345 • *1,949*
Randolph, MA 02368 • *30,093*
Randolph, NY 14772 • *1,298*
Randolph, VT 05060 • *2,200*
Randolph, WI 53956 • *1,729*
Randolph □, AL • *19,881*
Randolph □, AR • *16,558*
Randolph □, GA • *8,023*
Randolph □, IL • *34,583*
Randolph □, IN • *27,148*
Randolph □, MO • *24,370*
Randolph □, NC • *106,546*
Randolph □, WV • *27,803*
Randolph Hills, MD 20852 • *4,180*
Random Lake, WI 53075 • *1,439*
Rangely, CO 81648 • *2,278*
Ranger, TX 76470 • *2,803*
Rankin, PA 15104 • *2,503*
Rankin, TX 79778 • *1,011*
Rankin □, MS • *87,161*
Ransom □, ND • *5,921*
Ransomville, NY 14131 • *1,542*
Ranson, WV 25438 • *2,890*
Rantoul, IL 61866 • *17,212*
Raoul, GA 30510 • *1,400*
Rapid City, SD 57701–09 • *54,523*
Rapides □, LA • *131,556*
Rapid Valley, SD 57701 • *5,968*
Rappahannock □, VA • *6,622*
Raritan, NJ 08869 • *5,798*
Rathdrum, ID 83858 • *2,000*
Raton, NM 87740 • *7,372*
Ravalli □, MT • *25,010*
Raven, VA 24639 • *2,640*
Ravena, NY 12143 • *3,547*
Ravenel, SC 29470 • *2,165*
Ravenna, NE 68869 • *1,317*
Ravenna, OH 44266 • *12,069*
Ravenswood, WV 26164 • *4,189*
Rawlins, WY 82301 • *9,380*
Rawlins □, KS • *3,404*
Ray, ND 58849 • *603*
Ray □, MO • *21,971*
Raymond, MS 39154 • *2,275*
Raymond, NH 03077 • *2,516*
Raymond, WA 98577 • *2,901*
Raymondville, TX 78580 • *8,880*
Raymore, MO 64083 • *5,592*
Rayne, LA 70578 • *8,502*
Raynham, MA 02767 • *3,709*
Raynham Center, MA 02768 • *3,709*
Raytown, MO 64133 • *30,601*
Rayville, LA 71269 • *4,411*
Reading, MA 01867 • *22,539*
Reading, MI 49274 • *1,127*
Reading, OH 45215 • *12,038*
Reading, PA 19601–12 • *78,380*
Reagan □, TX • *4,514*
Real □, TX • *2,412*
Reamstown, PA 17567 • *2,649*
Rector, AR 72461 • *2,268*
Red Bank, NJ 07701–04 • *10,636*
Red Bank, SC 29073 • *6,112*
Red Bank, TN 37415 • *12,322*
Red Bay, AL 35582 • *3,451*
Redbird, OH 44057 • *1,600*
Red Bluff, CA 96080 • *12,363*
Red Bud, IL 62278 • *2,918*
Red Cloud, NE 68970 • *1,204*
Redding, CA 96001–03 • *66,462*
Redding, CT 06875 • *1,000*
Redfield, AR 72132 • *1,082*
Redfield, SD 57469 • *2,770*
Redford, MI 48239 • *54,387*
Redgranite, WI 54970 • *1,009*
Red Hook, NY 12571 • *1,794*
Redkey, IN 47373 • *1,383*
Red Lake □, MN • *4,525*
Red Lake Falls, MN 56750 • *1,481*
Redlands, CA 92373–75 • *60,394*
Red Lion, PA 17356 • *6,130*
Red Lodge, MT 59068 • *1,958*
Redmond, OR 97756 • *7,163*
Redmond, WA 98052–53 • *35,800*
Red Oak, GA 30272 • *2,800*
Red Oak, IA 51566 • *6,264*
Red Oak, TX 75154 • *3,124*
Red Oaks, LA 70815 • *1,600*
Red Oaks Mill, NY 12603 • *4,906*
Redondo Beach, CA 90277–78 • *60,167*
Red River □, LA • *9,387*
Red River □, TX • *14,317*
Red Springs, NC 28377 • *3,799*
Red Willow □, NE • *11,705*
Red Wing, MN 55066 • *15,134*
Redwood, UT 84119 • *1,850*
Redwood □, MN • *17,254*
Redwood City, CA 94061–65 • *66,072*
Redwood Falls, MN 56283 • *4,859*
Redwood Valley, CA 95470 • *1,300*
Reed City, MI 49677 • *2,379*
Reedley, CA 93654 • *15,791*
Reedsburg, WI 53959 • *5,834*
Reedsport, OR 97467 • *4,796*
Reedsville, PA 17084 • *1,030*
Reedsville, WI 54230 • *1,182*
Reedurban, OH 44710 • *6,650*
Reese, MI 48757 • *1,414*
Reeves □, TX • *15,852*
Reform, AL 35481 • *2,105*
Refugio, TX 78377 • *3,158*
Refugio □, TX • *7,976*
Rehoboth Beach, DE 19971 • *1,234*
Reidland, KY 42001 • *4,054*
Reidsville, GA 30453 • *2,469*
Reidsville, NC 27320–23 • *12,183*
Reinbeck, IA 50669 • *1,605*
Reisterstown, MD 21136 • *19,314*
Reliance, WY 82943 • *500*
Remington, IN 47977 • *1,247*
Remsen, IA 51050 • *1,513*
Reno, NV 89501–70 • *133,850*
Reno □, KS • *62,389*
Renovo, PA 17764 • *1,526*
Rensselaer, IN 47978 • *5,045*
Rensselaer, NY 12144 • *8,255*
Rensselaer □, NY • *154,429*
Renton, WA 98055–59 • *41,688*
Renville, MN 56284 • *1,315*
Renville □, MN • *17,673*
Renville □, ND • *3,160*
Republic, MI 49879 • *1,100*
Republic, MO 65738 • *6,292*
Republic, PA 15475 • *1,400*
Republic □, KS • *6,482*
Reserve, LA 70084 • *8,847*
Reston, VA 22090 • *48,556*
Revere, MA 02151 • *42,786*
Rexburg, ID 83440 • *14,302*
Reynolds, GA 31076 • *1,166*
Reynolds □, MO • *6,661*
Reynoldsburg, OH 43068 • *25,748*
Reynoldsville, PA 15851 • *2,818*
Rhea □, TN • *24,344*
Rhinebeck, NY 12572 • *2,725*
Rhinelander, WI 54501 • *7,427*
Rialto, CA 92376–77 • *72,388*
Rice □, KS • *10,610*
Rice □, MN • *49,183*
Rice Lake, WI 54868 • *7,998*
Rich □, UT • *1,725*
Richardson, TX 75080–83 • *74,840*
Richardson □, NE • *9,937*
Richardson Park, DE 19804 • *1,100*
Richardton, ND 58652 • *625*
Richboro, PA 18954 • *5,332*
Richfield, MN 55423 • *35,710*
Richfield, UT 84701 • *5,593*
Richfield Springs, NY 13439 • *1,565*
Richford, VT 05476 • *1,425*
Rich Hill, MO 64779 • *1,317*
Richland, GA 31825 • *1,668*
Richland, MO 65556 • *2,029*
Richland, WA 99352 • *32,315*
Richland □, IL • *16,545*
Richland □, LA • *20,629*
Richland □, MT • *10,716*
Richland □, ND • *18,148*
Richland □, OH • *126,137*
Richland □, SC • *285,720*
Richland □, WI • *17,521*
Richland Center, WI 53581 • *5,018*
Richland Hills, TX 76118 • *7,978*
Richlands, VA 24641 • *4,456*
Richlandtown, PA 18955 • *1,195*
Richmond, CA 94801–08 • *87,425*
Richmond, IL 60071 • *1,016*
Richmond, IN 47374–75 • *38,705*
Richmond, KY 40475–76 • *21,155*
Richmond, ME 04357 • *1,775*
Richmond, MI 48062 • *4,141*
Richmond, MO 64085 • *5,738*
Richmond, TX 77469 • *9,801*
Richmond, UT 84333 • *1,955*
Richmond, VT 05477 • *650*
Richmond, VA 23201–94 • *203,056*
Richmond □, GA • *189,719*
Richmond □, NY • *378,977*
Richmond □, NC • *44,518*
Richmond □, VA • *7,273*
Richmond Beach, WA 98160 • *5,000*
Richmond Heights, FL 33156 • *8,583*
Richmond Heights, MO 63117 • *10,448*
Richmond Heights, OH 44143 • *9,611*
Richmond Highlands, WA 98133 • *26,037*
Richmond Hill, GA 31324 • *2,934*
Rich Square, NC 27869 • *1,058*
Richton, MS 39476 • *1,034*
Richton Park, IL 60471 • *10,523*
Richwood, OH 43344 • *2,186*
Richwood, WV 26261 • *2,808*
Riddle, OR 97469 • *1,143*
Ridge, NY 11961 • *11,734*
Ridgecrest, CA 93555 • *27,725*
Ridgecrest, WA 98155 • *5,500*
Ridgefield, CT 06877 • *6,363*
Ridgefield, NJ 07657 • *9,996*
Ridgefield, WA 98642 • *1,297*
Ridgefield Park, NJ 07660 • *12,454*
Ridgeland, MS 39157–58 • *11,714*
Ridgeland, SC 29936 • *1,071*
Ridgely, MD 21660 • *1,034*
Ridgely, TN 38080 • *1,775*
Ridgetop, TN 37152 • *1,132*
Ridgeville, SC 29472 • *1,625*
Ridgewood, NJ 07450–52 • *24,152*
Ridgway, IL 62979 • *1,103*
Ridgway, PA 15853 • *4,793*
Ridley Park, PA 19078 • *7,592*
Ridley Township, PA 19018 • *33,771*
Rifle, CO 81650 • *4,636*
Rigby, ID 83442 • *2,681*
Riley □, KS • *67,139*
Rimersburg, PA 16248 • *1,053*
Rincon, GA 31326 • *2,697*
Ringgold, GA 30736 • *1,675*
Ringgold, LA 71068 • *1,856*
Ringgold □, IA • *5,420*
Ringling, OK 73456 • *1,250*
Ringwood, NJ 07456 • *12,623*
Rio, FL 34957 • *1,054*
Rio Arriba □, NM • *34,365*
Rio Blanco □, CO • *5,972*
Rio Dell, CA 95562 • *3,012*
Rio Del Mar, CA 95003 • *8,919*
Rio Grande, NJ 08242 • *2,505*
Rio Grande □, CO • *10,770*
Rio Grande City, TX 78582 • *9,891*
Rio Hondo, TX 78583 • *1,793*
Rio Linda, CA 95673 • *9,481*
Rio Rancho, NM 87124 • *32,505*
Rio Vista, CA 94571 • *3,316*
Ripley, MS 38663 • *5,371*
Ripley, NY 14775 • *1,189*
Ripley, OH 45167 • *1,816*
Ripley, TN 38063 • *6,188*
Ripley, WV 25271 • *3,023*
Ripley □, IN • *24,616*
Ripley □, MO • *12,303*
Ripon, WI 54971 • *7,241*
Rising Sun, DE 19934 • *540*
Rising Sun, IN 47040 • *2,311*
Rising Sun, MD 21911 • *1,263*
Rison, AR 71665 • *1,258*
Ritchie □, WV • *10,233*
Rittman, OH 44270 • *6,147*
Ritzville, WA 99169 • *1,725*
Riverbank, CA 95367 • *8,547*
Riverdale, CA 93656 • *1,980*
Riverdale, GA 30274 • *9,359*
Riverdale, IL 60627 • *13,671*
Riverdale, MD 20737–38 • *5,185*
Riverdale, NJ 07457 • *2,370*
Riverdale, UT 84405 • *6,419*
River Edge, NJ 07661 • *10,603*
River Falls, WI 54022 • *10,610*
River Forest, IL 60305 • *11,669*
River Grove, IL 60171 • *9,961*
Riverhead, NY 11901 • *8,814*
River Heights, UT 84321 • *1,274*
River Hills, WI 53217 • *1,612*
River Oaks, TX 76114 • *6,580*
River Pines, MA 01821 • *3,620*
River Ridge, LA 70123 • *14,800*
River Road, OR 97404 • *9,443*
River Rouge, MI 48218 • *11,314*
Riverside, AL 35135 • *1,004*
Riverside, CA 92501–19 • *226,505*
Riverside, IL 60546 • *8,774*
Riverside, NJ 08075 • *7,974*
Riverside, PA 17868 • *1,991*
Riverside □, CA • *1,170,413*
Riverton, IL 62561 • *2,638*
Riverton, NJ 08077 • *2,775*
Riverton, UT 84065 • *11,261*
Riverton, VT 05663 • *150*
Riverton, WY 82501 • *9,202*
Riverton Heights, WA 98188 • *14,182*
River Vale, NJ 07675 • *9,410*
Riverview, FL 33569 • *6,478*
Riverview, MI 48192 • *13,894*
Rivesville, WV 26588 • *1,064*
Riviera Beach, FL 33404 • *27,639*
Riviera Beach, MD 21122 • *11,376*
Roane □, TN • *47,227*
Roane □, WV • *15,120*
Roan Mountain, TN 37687 • *1,220*
Roanoke, AL 36274 • *6,362*
Roanoke, IL 61561 • *1,910*
Roanoke, IN 46783 • *1,018*
Roanoke, TX 76262 • *1,616*
Roanoke, VA 24001–38 • *96,397*
Roanoke □, VA • *79,332*
Roanoke Rapids, NC 27870 • *15,722*
Roaring Spring, PA 16673 • *2,615*

Robbins, IL 60472 • 7,498
Robbinsdale, MN 55422 • 14,396
Robersonville, NC 27871 • 1,940
Robert Lee, TX 76945 • 1,276
Roberts, WI 54023 • 1,043
Roberts □, SD • 9,914
Roberts □, TX • 1,025
Robertsdale, AL 36567 • 2,401
Robertson □, KY • 2,124
Robertson □, TN • 41,494
Robertson □, TX • 15,511
Robertsville, NJ 07746 • 9,841
Robeson □, NC • 105,179
Robinson, IL 62454 • 6,740
Robinson, TX 76706 • 7,111
Robstown, TX 78380 • 12,849
Rochdale, MA 01542 • 1,105
Rochelle, GA 31079 • 1,510
Rochelle, IL 61068 • 8,769
Rochelle Park, NJ 07662 • 5,587
Rochester, IL 62563 • 2,676
Rochester, IN 46975 • 5,969
Rochester, MI 48306–09 • 7,130
Rochester, MN 55901–06 • 70,745
Rochester, NH 03867–68 • 26,630
Rochester, NY 14601–92 • 231,636
Rochester, PA 15074 • 4,156
Rochester, VT 05767 • 500
Rochester, WA 98579 • 1,150
Rochester Hills, MI 48309 • 61,766
Rock □, MN • 9,806
Rock □, NE • 2,019
Rock □, WI • 139,510
Rockaway, NJ 07866 • 6,243
Rockbridge □, VA • 18,350
Rockcastle □, KY • 14,803
Rock Creek, MN 55067 • 1,040
Rock Creek 0M, OR • 8,282
Rockdale, IL 60436 • 1,709
Rockdale, MD 21207 • 5,885
Rockdale, TX 76567 • 5,235
Rockdale □, GA • 54,091
Rock Falls, IL 61071 • 9,654
Rockford, IL 61101–32 • 139,426
Rockford, MI 49341 • 3,750
Rockford, MN 55373 • 2,665
Rockford, OH 45882 • 1,119
Rock Hall, MD 21661 • 1,584
Rock Hill, MO 63124 • 5,217
Rock Hill, SC 29730–32 • 41,643
Rockingham, NC 28379 • 9,399
Rockingham □, NH • 245,845
Rockingham □, NC • 86,064
Rockingham □, VA • 57,482
Rock Island, IL 61201–04 • 40,552
Rock Island □, IL • 148,723
Rockland, ME 04841 • 7,972
Rockland, MA 02370 • 15,695
Rockland □, NY • 265,475
Rockledge, FL 32955–56 • 16,023
Rockledge, PA 19111 • 2,679
Rocklin, CA 95677 • 19,033
Rockmart, GA 30153 • 3,356
Rockport, IN 47635 • 2,315
Rockport, ME 04856 • 1,100
Rockport, MA 01966 • 4,690
Rock Port, MO 64482 • 1,438
Rockport, TX 78382 • 4,753
Rock Rapids, IA 51246 • 2,601
Rock River, WY 82083 • 190
Rocksprings, TX 78880 • 1,339
Rock Springs, WY 82901–02 • 19,050
Rockton, IL 61072 • 2,928
Rock Valley, IA 51247 • 2,540
Rockville, IN 47872 • 2,706
Rockville, MD 20847–59 • 44,835
Rockville Centre, NY 11570–71 • 24,727
Rockwall, TX 75087 • 10,486
Rockwall □, TX • 25,604
Rockwell, IA 50469 • 1,008
Rockwell, NC 28138 • 1,598
Rockwell City, IA 50579 • 1,981
Rockwell Park, NC 28213 • 2,600
Rockwood, MI 48173 • 3,141
Rockwood, OR 97233 • 11,000
Rockwood, PA 15557 • 1,014
Rockwood, TN 37854 • 5,348
Rocky Creek, FL 33615 • 7,800
Rocky Ford, CO 81067 • 4,162
Rocky Hill, CT 06067 • 14,559
Rocky Mount, NC 27801–04 • 48,997
Rocky Mount, VA 24151 • 4,098
Rocky Point, NY 11778 • 8,596
Rocky River, OH 44116 • 20,410
Rodeo, CA 94572 • 7,589
Roderfield, WV 24881 • 1,200
Rodney Village, DE 19901 • 1,745
Roebling, NJ 08554 • 2,415
Roebuck, SC 29376 • 1,966
Roeland Park, KS 66203 • 7,706
Roessleville, NY 12205 • 10,753
Roger Mills □, OK • 4,147
Rogers, AR 72756–57 • 24,692
Rogers, TX 76569 • 1,131
Rogers □, OK • 55,170
Rogers City, MI 49779 • 3,642
Rogersville, AL 35652 • 1,125
Rogersville, TN 37857 • 4,149
Rogue River, OR 97537 • 1,759
Rohnert Park, CA 94927–28 • 36,326
Roland, IA 50236 • 1,035
Roland, OK 74954 • 2,481
Rolette □, ND • 12,772
Rolla, MO 65401 • 14,090
Rolla, ND 58367 • 1,286
Rolling Fork, MS 39159 • 2,444
Rolling Hills Estates, CA 90274 • 7,789
Rolling Meadows, IL 60008 • 22,591
Rollinsford, NH 03869 • 2,645
Roma, TX 78584 • 8,059
Rome, GA 30161–65 • 30,326
Rome, IL 61562 • 1,902
Rome, NY 13440 • 44,350
Rome City, IN 46784 • 1,138
Romeo, MI 48065 • 3,520
Romeoville, IL 60441 • 14,074
Romney, WV 26757 • 1,966
Romulus, MI 48174 • 22,897
Ronan, MT 59864 • 1,547
Ronceverte, WV 24970 • 1,754
Ronkonkoma, NY 11779 • 20,391
Roodhouse, IL 62082 • 2,139
Rooks □, KS • 6,039
Roosevelt, NY 11575 • 15,030
Roosevelt, UT 84066 • 3,915
Roosevelt □, MT • 10,999
Roosevelt □, NM • 16,702
Roosevelt Park, MI 49441 • 3,885
Rosamond, CA 93560 • 7,430
Roscoe, IL 61073 • 2,079
Roscoe, TX 79545 • 1,446
Roscommon □, MI • 19,776
Roseau, MN 56751 • 2,396
Roseau □, MN • 15,026
Roseboro, NC 28382 • 1,441
Rosebud, TX 76570 • 1,638
Rosebud □, MT • 10,505
Roseburg, OR 97470 • 17,032
Rosedale, MD 21237 • 18,703
Rosedale, MS 38769 • 2,595
Rose Hill, KS 67133 • 2,399
Rose Hill, NC 28458 • 1,287
Rose Hill, VA 22310 • 12,675
Roseland, CA 95407 • 8,779
Roseland, FL 32957 • 1,379
Roseland, LA 70456 • 1,093
Roseland, NJ 07068 • 4,847
Roseland, OH 44906 • 3,000
Roselle, IL 60172 • 20,819
Roselle, NJ 07203 • 20,314
Roselle Park, NJ 07204 • 12,805
Rosemead, CA 91770 • 51,638
Rosemont, CA 95826 • 22,851
Rosemount, MN 55068 • 8,622
Rosenberg, TX 77471 • 20,183
Rosepine, LA 70659 • 1,135
Roseto, PA 18013 • 1,555
Roseville, CA 95678 • 44,685
Roseville, IL 61473 • 1,151
Roseville, MI 48066 • 51,412
Roseville, MN 55113 • 33,485
Roseville, OH 43777 • 1,847
Rosewood Heights, IL 62024 • 4,821
Rosiclare, IL 62982 • 1,378
Roslyn Heights, NY 11577 • 6,405
Ross, OH 45061 • 2,124
Ross □, OH • 69,330
Rossford, OH 43460 • 5,861
Rossmoor, CA 90720 • 9,893
Ross Township, PA 15237 • 33,482
Rossville, GA 30741–42 • 3,601
Rossville, IL 60963 • 1,334
Rossville, IN 46065 • 1,175
Rossville, KS 66533 • 1,052
Roswell, GA 30075–77 • 47,923
Roswell, NM 88201–02 • 44,654
Rotan, TX 79546 • 1,913
Rothschild, WI 54474 • 3,310
Rothsville, PA 17543 • 2,097
Rotterdam, NY 12303 • 21,228
Roulette, PA 16746 • 1,500
Round Lake, IL 60073 • 3,550
Round Lake Beach, IL 60073 • 16,434
Round Mountain, NV 89045 • 210
Round Rock, TX 78664 • 30,923
Roundup, MT 59072 • 1,808
Rouses Point, NY 12979 • 2,377
Routt □, CO • 14,088
Rouzerville, PA 17250 • 1,188
Rowan □, KY • 20,353
Rowan □, NC • 110,605
Rowland, NC 28383 • 1,139
Rowland Heights, CA 91748 • 32,700
Rowlett, TX 75088 • 23,260
Rowley, MA 01969 • 1,144
Roxboro, NC 27573 • 7,332
Roy, UT 84067 • 24,603
Royal Oak, MI 48067–73 • 65,410
Royal Pines, NC 28704 • 1,600
Royalton, IL 62983 • 1,191
Royersford, PA 19468 • 4,458
Royse City, TX 75089 • 2,206
Royston, GA 30662 • 2,758
Rubidoux, CA 92509 • 24,367
Rugby, ND 58368 • 2,909
Ruidoso, NM 88345 • 4,600
Ruidoso Downs, NM 88346 • 920
Ruleville, MS 38771 • 3,245
Rumford, ME 04276 • 5,419
Rumson, NJ 07760 • 6,701
Runge, TX 78151 • 1,139
Runnels □, TX • 11,294
Runnemede, NJ 08078 • 9,042
Rupert, ID 83350 • 5,455
Rupert, WV 25984 • 1,104
Rural Hall, NC 27045 • 1,652
Rush □, IN • 18,129
Rush □, KS • 3,842
Rush City, MN 55069 • 1,497
Rushford, MN 55971 • 1,485
Rushmere, VA 23430 • 1,064
Rush Springs, OK 73082 • 1,229
Rushville, IL 62681 • 3,229
Rushville, IN 46173 • 5,533
Rushville, NE 69360 • 1,127
Rusk, TX 75785 • 4,366
Rusk □, TX • 43,735
Rusk □, WI • 15,079
Ruskin, FL 33570–73 • 6,046
Russell, KS 67665 • 4,781
Russell, KY 41169 • 4,014
Russell, PA 16345 • 1,000
Russell □, AL • 46,860
Russell □, KS • 7,835
Russell □, KY • 14,716
Russell □, VA • 28,667
Russell Springs, KY 42642 • 2,363
Russellville, AL 35653 • 7,812
Russellville, AR 72801 • 21,260
Russellville, KY 42276 • 7,454
Russellville, OR 97216 • 6,500
Russellville, TN 37860 • 1,069
Ruston, LA 71270–73 • 20,027
Ruth, NV 89319 • 550
Rutherford, NJ 07070–75 • 17,790
Rutherford, TN 38369 • 1,303
Rutherford □, NC • 56,918
Rutherford □, TN • 118,570
Rutherfordton, NC 28139 • 3,617
Rutland, MA 01543 • 2,145
Rutland, VT 05701–02 • 18,230
Rutland □, VT • 62,142
Rye, NH 03870 • 835
Rye, NY 10580 • 14,936
Rye Brook, NY 10573 • 7,765

S

Sabattus, ME 04280 • 3,696
Sabetha, KS 66534 • 2,341
Sabina, OH 45169 • 2,662
Sabinal, TX 78881 • 1,584
Sabine □, LA • 22,646
Sabine □, TX • 9,586
Sac □, IA • 12,324
Sacaton, AZ 85221 • 1,452
Sac City, IA 50583 • 2,492
Sachse, TX 75040 • 5,346
Sackets Harbor, NY 13685 • 1,313
Saco, ME 04072 • 15,181
Sacramento, CA 95801–66 • 369,365
Sacramento □, CA • 1,041,219
Saddle Brook, NJ 07662 • 13,296
Saddle River, NJ 07458 • 2,950
Saegertown, PA 16433 • 1,066
Safety Harbor, FL 34695 • 15,124
Safford, AZ 85546 • 7,359
Sagadahoc □, ME • 33,535
Sagamore, MA 02561 • 2,589
Sagamore Hills, OH 44067 • 4,700
Sag Harbor, NY 11963 • 2,134
Saginaw, MI 48601–08 • 69,512
Saginaw, TX 76179 • 8,551
Saginaw □, MI • 211,946
Saguache □, CO • 4,619
Saint Albans, VT 05478 • 7,339
Saint Albans, WV 25177 • 11,194
Saint Andrews, SC 29407 • 9,908
Saint Andrews, SC 29210 • 25,692
Saint Ann, MO 63074 • 14,489
Saint Anne, IL 60964 • 1,153
Saint Ansgar, IA 50472 • 1,063
Saint Anthony, ID 83445 • 3,010
Saint Anthony, MN 55418 • 7,727
Saint Augustine, FL 32084–86 • 11,692
Saint Bernard, OH 45217 • 5,344
Saint Bernard □, LA • 66,631
Saint Charles, IL 60174–75 • 22,501
Saint Charles, MD 20601 • 28,717
Saint Charles, MI 48655 • 2,144
Saint Charles, MN 55972 • 2,642
Saint Charles, MO 63301–03 • 54,555
Saint Charles □, LA • 42,437
Saint Charles □, MO • 212,907
Saint Charles Mesa, CO 81006 • 7,050
Saint Clair, MI 48079 • 5,116
Saint Clair, MO 63077 • 3,917
Saint Clair, PA 17970 • 3,524
Saint Clair □, AL • 50,009
Saint Clair □, IL • 262,852
Saint Clair □, MI • 145,607
Saint Clair □, MO • 8,457
Saint Clair Shores, MI 48080–82 • 68,107
Saint Clairsville, OH 43950 • 5,162
Saint Cloud, FL 34769–73 • 12,453
Saint Cloud, MN 56301–04 • 48,812
Saint Croix □, WI • 50,251
Saint Croix Falls, WI 54024 • 1,640
Saint David, AZ 85630 • 1,500
Saint Elmo, IL 62458 • 1,473
Saint Francis, KS 67756 • 1,495
Saint Francis, MN 55070 • 2,538
Saint Francis, SD 57572 • 815
Saint Francis, WI 53207 • 9,245
Saint Francis □, AR • 28,497
Saint Francisville, LA 70775 • 1,700
Saint Francois □, MO • 48,904
Sainte Genevieve, MO 63670 • 4,411
Sainte Genevieve □, MO • 16,037
Saint George, SC 29477 • 2,077
Saint George, UT 84770–71 • 28,502
Saint Georges, DE 19733 • 500
Saint Helena, CA 94574 • 4,990
Saint Helena □, LA • 9,874
Saint Helens, OR 97051 • 7,535
Saint Henry, OH 45883 • 1,907
Saint Ignace, MI 49781 • 2,568
Saint Ignatius, MT 59865 • 778
Saint James, MN 56081 • 4,364
Saint James, MO 65559 • 3,256
Saint James, NY 11780 • 12,703
Saint James □, LA • 20,879
Saint James City, FL 33956 • 1,094
Saint Jo, TX 76265 • 1,048
Saint John, IN 46373 • 4,921
Saint John, KS 67576 • 1,357
Saint Johns, AZ 85936 • 3,294
Saint Johns, MI 48879 • 7,284
Saint Johns, MO 63114 • 7,466
Saint Johns □, FL • 83,829
Saint Johnsbury, VT 05819 • 6,424
Saint Johnsville, NY 13452 • 1,825
Saint John the Baptist □, LA • 39,996
Saint Joseph, IL 61873 • 2,052
Saint Joseph, LA 71366 • 1,517
Saint Joseph, MI 49085 • 9,214
Saint Joseph, MN 56374 • 3,294
Saint Joseph, MO 64501–08 • 71,852
Saint Joseph □, IN • 247,052
Saint Joseph □, MI • 58,913
Saint Landry □, LA • 80,331
Saint Lawrence □, NY • 111,974
Saint Leo, FL 33574 • 1,009
Saint Louis, MI 48880 • 3,828
Saint Louis, MO 63101–88 • 396,685
Saint Louis □, MN • 198,213
Saint Louis □, MO • 993,529
Saint Louis Park, MN 55426 • 43,787
Saint Lucie □, FL • 150,171
Saint Maries, ID 83861 • 2,442
Saint Martin □, LA • 43,978
Saint Martinville, LA 70582 • 7,137
Saint Mary □, LA • 58,086
Saint Marys, AK 99658 • 441
Saint Marys, GA 31558 • 8,187
Saint Marys, IN 46556 • 1,800
Saint Marys, KS 66536 • 1,791
Saint Marys, OH 45885 • 8,441
Saint Marys, PA 15857 • 5,511
Saint Marys, WV 26170 • 2,148
Saint Marys □, MD • 75,974
Saint Marys City, MD 20686 • 3,200
Saint Matthews, KY 40207 • 15,800
Saint Matthews, SC 29135 • 2,345
Saint Michael, MN 55376 • 2,506
Saint Michaels, MD 21663 • 1,301
Saint Paris, OH 43072 • 1,842
Saint Paul, AK 99660 • 763
Saint Paul, IN 47272 • 1,032
Saint Paul, MN 55101–89 • 272,235
Saint Paul, MO 63366 • 1,192
Saint Paul, NE 68873 • 2,009
Saint Paul, VA 24283 • 1,007
Saint Paul Park, MN 55071 • 4,965
Saint Pauls, NC 28384 • 1,992
Saint Peter, MN 56082 • 9,421
Saint Peters, MO 63376 • 45,779
Saint Petersburg, FL 33701–84 • 238,629
Saint Petersburg Beach, FL 33706 • 9,200
Saint Rose, LA 70087 • 2,800
Saint Simons Island, GA 31522 • 12,026
Saint Stephen, SC 29479 • 1,697
Saint Stephens, NC 28601 • 8,734
Saint Tammany □, LA • 144,508
Salamanca, NY 14779 • 6,566
Sale Creek, TN 37373 • 1,050
Salem, AR 72576 • 1,474
Salem, IL 62881 • 7,470
Salem, IN 47167 • 5,619
Salem, MA 01970–71 • 38,091
Salem, MO 65560 • 4,486
Salem, NH 03079 • 12,000
Salem, NJ 08079 • 6,883
Salem, OH 44460 • 12,233
Salem, OR 97301–14 • 107,786
Salem, SD 57058 • 1,289
Salem, UT 84653 • 2,284
Salem, VA 24153 • 23,756
Salem, WV 26426 • 2,063
Salem, WI 53168 • 1,020
Salem □, NJ • 65,294
Salida, CO 81201 • 4,737
Salina, KS 67401–02 • 42,303
Salina, OK 74365 • 1,153
Salina, UT 84654 • 1,943
Salinas, CA 93901–15 • 108,777
Saline, MI 48176 • 6,660
Saline □, AR • 64,183
Saline □, IL • 26,551
Saline □, KS • 49,301
Saline □, MO • 23,523
Saline □, NE • 12,715
Salineville, OH 43945 • 1,474
Salisbury, CT 06068 • 1,600
Salisbury, MD 21801–03 • 20,592
Salisbury, MA 01952 • 3,729
Salisbury, MO 65281 • 1,881
Salisbury, NC 28144–46 • 23,087
Sallisaw, OK 74955 • 7,122
Salmon, ID 83467 • 2,941
Salmon Creek, WA 98665 • 11,989
Saltillo, MS 38866 • 1,782
Salt Lake □, UT • 725,956
Salt Lake City, UT 84101–90 • 159,936
Salt Springs, FL 32113 • 1,500
Saltville, VA 24370 • 2,300
Saltwater, WA 98188 • 2,200
Saluda, SC 29138 • 2,798
Saluda □, SC • 16,357
Salyersville, KY 41465 • 1,917
Samoset, FL 34208 • 3,119
Sampson □, NC • 47,297
Samson, AL 36477 • 2,190
Samtown, LA 71301 • 3,500
San Andreas, CA 95249 • 2,115
San Angelo, TX 76901–06 • 84,474
San Anselmo, CA 94960 • 11,743
San Antonio, TX 78201–99 • 935,933
Sanatoga, PA 19464 • 5,534
San Augustine, TX 75972 • 2,337
San Augustine □, TX • 7,999
San Benito, TX 78586 • 20,125
San Benito □, CA • 36,697
San Bernardino, CA 92401–27 • 164,164
San Bernardino □, CA • 1,418,380
Sanborn, IA 51248 • 1,345
Sanborn □, SD • 2,833
San Bruno, CA 94066 • 38,961
San Carlos, AZ 85550 • 2,918
San Carlos, CA 94070 • 26,167
San Carlos Park, FL 33912 • 11,785
San Clemente, CA 92672–74 • 41,100
Sandalfoot Cove, FL 33433 • 14,214
Sanders □, MT • 8,669
Sanderson, TX 79848 • 1,128
Sandersville, GA 31082 • 6,290
Sand Hill, MA 02066 • 1,800
Sandia, NM 87047 • 6,742
San Diego, CA 92101–99 • 1,110,549
San Diego, TX 78384 • 4,983
San Diego □, CA • 2,498,016
San Dimas, CA 91773 • 32,397
Sandoval, IL 62882 • 1,535
Sandoval □, NM • 63,319
Sand Point, AK 99661 • 878
Sandpoint, ID 83862–65 • 5,203
Sand Springs, OK 74063 • 15,346
Sandston, VA 23150 • 3,630
Sandstone, MN 55072 • 2,057
Sandusky, MI 48471 • 2,403
Sandusky, OH 44870–71 • 29,764
Sandusky □, OH • 61,963
Sandwich, IL 60548 • 5,567
Sandwich, MA 02563 • 2,998
Sandy, OR 97055 • 4,152
Sandy, UT 84070 • 75,058
Sandy Hook, CT 06482 • 1,100
Sandy Springs, GA 30328 • 67,842
Sandy Springs, SC 29677 • 1,200
San Felipe Pueblo, NM 87001 • 1,557
San Fernando, CA 91340–46 • 22,580
Sanford, FL 32771–73 • 32,387
Sanford, ME 04073 • 10,296
Sanford, NC 27330–31 • 14,475
San Francisco, CA 94101–88 • 723,959
San Francisco □, CA • 723,959
Sangamon □, IL • 178,386
Sanger, CA 93657 • 16,839
Sanger, TX 76266 • 3,508
Sanibel, FL 33957 • 5,468
Sanilac □, MI • 39,928
San Jacinto, CA 92383 • 16,210
San Jacinto □, TX • 16,372
San Joaquin □, CA • 480,628
San Jose, CA 95101–96 • 782,248
San Juan, TX 78589 • 10,815
San Juan □, CO • 745
San Juan □, NM • 91,605
San Juan □, UT • 12,621
San Juan □, WA • 10,035
San Juan Capistrano, CA 92690–93 • 26,183
San Leandro, CA 94577–79 • 68,223
San Lorenzo, CA 94580 • 19,987
San Luis, AZ 85634 • 4,212
San Luis Obispo, CA 93401–12 • 41,958
San Luis Obispo □, CA • 217,162
San Manuel, AZ 85631 • 4,009
San Marcos, CA 92069 • 38,974
San Marcos, TX 78666–67 • 28,743
San Marino, CA 91108 • 12,959
San Mateo, CA 94401–04 • 85,486
San Mateo □, CA • 649,623
San Miguel □, CO • 3,653
San Miguel □, NM • 25,743
San Pablo, CA 94806 • 25,158
San Patricio □, TX • 58,749
Sanpete □, UT • 16,259
San Rafael, CA 94901–15 • 48,404
San Ramon, CA 94583 • 35,303
San Remo, NY 11754 • 7,770
San Saba, TX 76877 • 2,626
San Saba □, TX • 5,401
Sans Souci, SC 29609 • 7,612
Santa Ana, CA 92701–08 • 293,742
Santa Anna, TX 76878 • 1,249
Santa Barbara, CA 93101–90 • 85,571
Santa Barbara □, CA • 369,608
Santa Clara, CA 95050–56 • 93,613
Santa Clara, OR 97404 • 12,834
Santa Clara, UT 84765 • 2,322
Santa Clara □, CA • 1,497,577
Santa Cruz, CA 95060–67 • 49,040
Santa Cruz, NM 87567 • 975
Santa Cruz □, AZ • 29,676
Santa Cruz □, CA • 229,734
Santa Fe, NM 87501–06 • 55,859
Santa Fe, TX 77510 • 8,429
Santa Fe □, NM • 98,928
Santa Fe Springs, CA 90670–71 • 15,520
Santa Margarita, CA 93453 • 1,200
Santa Maria, CA 93454–56 • 61,284
Santa Monica, CA 90401–11 • 86,905
Santa Paula, CA 93060–61 • 25,062
Santaquin, UT 84655 • 2,386
Santa Rosa, CA 95401–09 • 113,313
Santa Rosa, NM 88435 • 2,263
Santa Rosa □, FL • 81,608
Santa Venetia, CA 94901 • 6,000
Santa Ynez, CA 93460 • 4,200
Santee, CA 92071 • 52,902
Santo Domingo Pueblo, NM 87052 • 2,866
San Ygnacio, TX 78067 • 1,000
Sappington, MO 63126 • 10,917
Sapulpa, OK 74066–67 • 18,074
Saraland, AL 36571 • 11,751
Saranac, MI 48881 • 1,461
Saranac Lake, NY 12983 • 5,377
Sarasota, FL 34230–43 • 50,961
Sarasota □, FL • 277,776
Sarasota Springs, FL 34232 • 16,088
Saratoga, CA 95070–71 • 28,061
Saratoga, TX 77585 • 1,200
Saratoga, WY 82331 • 1,969
Saratoga □, NY • 181,276
Saratoga Springs, NY 12866 • 25,001
Sarcoxie, MO 64862 • 1,330
Sardis, GA 30456 • 1,116
Sardis, MS 38666 • 2,128
Sargent □, ND • 4,549
Sarpy □, NE • 102,583
Sartell, MN 56377 • 5,393
Satanta, KS 67870 • 1,073
Satellite Beach, FL 32937 • 9,889
Satsuma, AL 36572 • 5,194
Saugerties, NY 12477 • 3,915
Saugus, MA 01906 • 25,549
Sauk □, WI • 46,975
Sauk Centre, MN 56378 • 3,581
Sauk City, WI 53583 • 3,019
Sauk Rapids, MN 56379 • 7,825
Sauk Village, IL 60411 • 9,926
Saukville, WI 53080 • 3,695
Sault Sainte Marie, MI 49783 • 14,689
Saunders □, NE • 18,285
Saunderstown, RI 02874 • 400
Sausalito, CA 94965–66 • 7,152
Savage, MD 20763 • 2,850
Savage, MN 55378 • 9,906
Savanna, IL 61074 • 3,819
Savannah, GA 31401–20 • 137,560
Savannah, MO 64485 • 4,352
Savannah, TN 38372 • 6,547
Savoonga, AK 99769 • 519
Savoy, IL 61874 • 2,674
Sawyer □, WI • 14,181
Saxonburg, PA 16056 • 1,345
Saxtons River, VT 05154 • 541
Saybrook Manor, CT 06475 • 1,073
Saydel, IA 50313 • 3,500
Saylesville, RI 02865 • 3,510
Saylorsburg, PA 18353 • 1,500
Sayre, OK 73662 • 2,881
Sayre, PA 18840 • 5,791
Sayreville, NJ 08872 • 34,986
Sayville, NY 11782 • 16,550
Scalp Level, PA 15963 • 1,158
Scappoose, OR 97056 • 3,529
Scarborough, ME 04074 • 2,586
Scarsdale, NY 10583 • 16,987
Schaumburg, IL 60192–94 • 68,586
Schenectady, NY 12301–09 • 65,566
Schenectady □, NY • 149,285
Schererville, IN 46375 • 19,926
Schertz, TX 78154 • 10,555
Schiller Park, IL 60176 • 11,189
Schleicher □, TX • 2,990
Schley □, GA • 3,588
Schofield, WI 54476 • 2,415
Schoharie, NY 12157 • 1,045
Schoharie □, NY • 31,859
Schoolcraft, MI 49087 • 1,517
Schoolcraft □, MI • 8,302
Schroon Lake, NY 12870 • 1,100
Schulenburg, TX 78956 • 2,455
Schurz, NV 89427 • 617
Schuyler, NE 68661 • 4,052
Schuyler □, IL • 7,498
Schuyler □, MO • 4,236
Schuyler □, NY • 18,662
Schuylerville, NY 12871 • 1,364
Schuylkill □, PA • 152,585

Schuylkill Haven, PA 17972 • 5,610
Scioto □, OH • 80,327
Scituate, MA 02066 • 5,180
Scobey, MT 59263 • 1,154
Scotch Plains, NJ 07076 • 21,160
Scotchtown, NY 10940 • 8,765
Scotia, CA 95565 • 1,200
Scotia, NY 12302 • 7,359
Scotland, SD 57059 • 968
Scotland □, MO • 4,822
Scotland □, NC • 33,754
Scotland Neck, NC 27874 • 2,575
Scotlandville, LA 70807 • 15,113
Scott, LA 70583 • 4,912
Scott □, AR • 10,205
Scott □, IL • 5,644
Scott □, IN • 20,991
Scott □, IA • 150,979
Scott □, KS • 5,289
Scott □, KY • 23,867
Scott □, MN • 57,846
Scott □, MS • 24,137
Scott □, MO • 39,376
Scott □, TN • 18,358
Scott □, VA • 23,204
Scott City, KS 67871 • 3,785
Scott City, MO 63780 • 4,292
Scottdale, GA 30079 • 8,636
Scottdale, PA 15683 • 5,184
Scott Lake, FL 33055 • 14,588
Scottsbluff, NE 69361–63 • 13,711
Scotts Bluff □, NE • 36,025
Scottsboro, AL 35768 • 13,786
Scottsburg, IN 47170 • 5,334
Scottsdale, AZ 85250–71 • 130,069
Scotts Valley, CA 95066–67 • 8,615
Scottsville, KY 42164 • 4,278
Scottsville, NY 14546 • 1,912
Scott Township, PA 15106 • 17,118
Scottville, MI 49454 • 1,287
Scranton, PA 18501–19 • 81,805
Screven □, GA • 13,842
Scurry □, TX • 18,634
Seabreeze, DE 19971 • 350
Sea Bright, NJ 07760 • 1,693
Seabrook, MD 20706 • 7,660
Seabrook, NJ 08302 • 1,457
Seabrook, TX 77586 • 6,685
Sea Cliff, NY 11579 • 5,054
Seadrift, TX 77983 • 1,277
Seaford, DE 19973 • 5,689
Seaford, NY 11783 • 15,597
Seaford, VA 23696 • 2,340
Seagate, NC 28403 • 5,444
Sea Girt, NJ 08750 • 2,099
Seagoville, TX 75159 • 8,969
Seagraves, TX 79359 • 2,398
Sea Isle City, NJ 08243 • 2,692
Seal Beach, CA 90740 • 25,098
Sealy, TX 77474 • 4,541
Seaman, OH 45679 • 1,013
Searchlight, NV 89029 • 430
Searcy, AR 72143 • 15,180
Searcy □, AR • 7,841
Searsport, ME 04974 • 1,151
Seaside, CA 93955 • 38,901
Seaside, OR 97138 • 5,359
Seaside Heights, NJ 08751 • 2,366
Seaside Park, NJ 08752 • 1,871
Seat Pleasant, MD 20743 • 5,359
Seattle, WA 98101–99 • 516,259
Sebastian, FL 32958 • 10,205
Sebastian □, AR • 99,590
Sebewaing, MI 48759 • 1,923
Sebree, KY 42455 • 1,510
Sebring, FL 33870–72 • 8,900
Sebring, OH 44672 • 4,848
Secaucus, NJ 07094 • 14,061
Security, CO 80911 • 6,660
Sedalia, MO 65301–02 • 19,800
Sedan, KS 67361 • 1,306
Sedgwick, KS 67135 • 1,438
Sedgwick □, CO • 2,690
Sedgwick □, KS • 403,662
Sedona, AZ 86336 • 7,720
Sedro Woolley, WA 98284 • 6,031
Seekonk, MA 02771 • 12,269
Seeley, CA 92273 • 1,228
Seelyville, IN 47878 • 1,090
Seguin, TX 78155–56 • 18,853
Seiling, OK 73663 • 1,031
Selah, WA 98942 • 5,113
Selawik, AK 99770 • 596
Selby, SD 57472 • 707
Selbyville, DE 19975 • 1,335
Selden, NY 11784 • 20,608
Seldovia, AK 99663 • 316
Selinsgrove, PA 17870 • 5,384
Sellersburg, IN 47172 • 5,745
Sellersville, PA 18960 • 4,479
Sells, AZ 85634 • 2,750
Selma, AL 36701–02 • 23,755
Selma, CA 93662 • 14,757
Selma, NC 27576 • 4,600
Selmer, TN 38375 • 3,838
Seminole, OK 74868 • 7,071
Seminole, TX 79360 • 6,342
Seminole □, FL • 287,529
Seminole □, GA • 9,010
Seminole □, OK • 25,412
Seminole Park, FL 34647 • 8,000
Semmes, AL 36575 • 2,250
Senath, MO 63876 • 1,622
Senatobia, MS 38668 • 4,772
Seneca, IL 61360 • 1,878
Seneca, KS 66538 • 2,027
Seneca, MO 64865 • 1,885
Seneca, PA 16346 • 1,300
Seneca, SC 29678–79 • 7,726
Seneca □, NY • 33,683
Seneca □, OH • 59,733
Seneca Falls, NY 13148 • 7,370
Sequatchie □, TN • 8,863
Sequim, WA 98382 • 3,616
Sequoyah □, OK • 33,828
Sergeant Bluff, IA 51054 • 2,772
Sesser, IL 62884 • 2,087
Seven Hills, OH 44131 • 12,339
Seven Oaks, SC 29210 • 15,722
Severn, MD 21144 • 24,499
Severna Park, MD 21146 • 25,879
Sevier □, AR • 13,637
Sevier □, TN • 51,043
Sevier □, UT • 15,431
Sevierville, TN 37862 • 7,178
Seville, OH 44273 • 1,810
Sewanee, TN 37375 • 2,128
Seward, AK 99664 • 2,699
Seward, NE 68434 • 5,634
Seward □, KS • 18,743
Seward □, NE • 15,450
Sewell, NJ 08080 • 1,870
Sewickley, PA 15143 • 4,134
Seymour, CT 06483 • 14,288
Seymour, IN 47274 • 15,576
Seymour, MO 65746 • 1,636
Seymour, TN 37865 • 7,026
Seymour, TX 76380 • 3,185
Seymour, WI 54165 • 2,782
Seymourville, LA 70764 • 2,891
Shackelford □, TX • 3,316
Shady Cove, OR 97539 • 1,351
Shady Side, MD 20764 • 4,107
Shadyside, OH 43947 • 3,934
Shady Spring, WV 25918 • 1,929
Shafter, CA 93263 • 8,409
Shaftsbury, VT 05262 • 700
Shaker Heights, OH 44120 • 30,831
Shakopee, MN 55379 • 11,739
Shaler Township, PA 15116 • 30,533
Shallowater, TX 79363 • 1,708
Shamokin, PA 17872 • 9,184
Shamokin Dam, PA 17876 • 1,690
Shamrock, TX 79079 • 2,286
Shannock, RI 02875 • 950
Shannon, GA 30172 • 1,703
Shannon, MS 38868 • 1,419
Shannon □, MO • 7,613
Shannon □, SD • 9,902
Shannontown, SC 29150 • 7,900
Sharkey □, MS • 7,066
Sharon, MA 02067 • 5,893
Sharon, PA 16146 • 17,493
Sharon, TN 38255 • 1,047
Sharon, WI 53585 • 1,250
Sharon Hill, PA 19079 • 5,771
Sharonville, OH 45241 • 13,153
Sharp □, AR • 14,109
Sharpes, FL 32922 • 3,348
Sharpley, DE 19803 • 1,250
Sharpsburg, MD 21782 • 659
Sharpsburg, NC 27878 • 1,536
Sharpsburg, PA 15215 • 3,781
Sharpsville, PA 16150 • 4,729
Shasta □, CA • 147,036
Shattuck, OK 73858 • 1,454
Shaw, MS 38773 • 2,349
Shawano, WI 54166 • 7,598
Shawano □, WI • 37,157
Shawnee, KS 66203 • 37,993
Shawnee, OK 74801–02 • 26,017
Shawnee □, KS • 160,976
Shawneetown, IL 62984 • 1,575
Sheboygan, WI 53081–83 • 49,676
Sheboygan □, WI • 103,877
Sheboygan Falls, WI 53085 • 5,823
Sheffield, AL 35660–62 • 10,380
Sheffield, IA 50475 • 1,174
Sheffield, MA 01257 • 1,100
Sheffield, PA 16347 • 1,294
Sheffield Lake, OH 44054 • 9,825
Shelbina, MO 63468 • 2,172
Shelburn, IN 47879 • 1,147
Shelburne Falls, MA 01370 • 1,996
Shelby, MI 49455 • 48,655
Shelby, MS 38774 • 2,806
Shelby, MT 59474 • 2,763
Shelby, NC 28150–51 • 14,669
Shelby, OH 44875 • 9,564
Shelby □, AL • 99,358
Shelby □, IL • 22,261
Shelby □, IN • 40,307
Shelby □, IA • 13,230
Shelby □, KY • 24,824
Shelby □, MO • 6,942
Shelby □, OH • 44,915
Shelby □, TN • 826,330
Shelby □, TX • 22,034
Shelbyville, IL 62565 • 4,943
Shelbyville, IN 46176 • 15,336
Shelbyville, KY 40065 • 6,238
Shelbyville, TN 37160 • 14,049
Sheldon, IL 60966 • 1,109
Sheldon, IA 51201 • 4,937
Sheldon, TX 77028 • 1,653
Shelley, ID 83274 • 3,536
Shell Lake, WI 54871 • 1,161
Shellman, GA 31786 • 1,162
Shell Rock, IA 50670 • 1,385
Shelter Island, NY 11964 • 1,193
Shelton, CT 06484 • 35,418
Shelton, WA 98584 • 7,241
Shenandoah, IA 51601 • 5,572
Shenandoah, PA 17976 • 6,221
Shenandoah, VA 22849 • 2,213
Shenandoah □, VA • 31,636
Shepherd, MI 48883 • 1,413
Shepherd, TX 77371 • 1,812
Shepherdstown, WV 25443 • 1,287
Shepherdsville, KY 40165 • 4,805
Sherborn, MA 01770 • 1,490
Sherburn, MN 56171 • 1,105
Sherburne, NY 13460 • 1,531
Sherburne □, MN • 41,945
Sheridan, AR 72150 • 3,098
Sheridan, CO 80110 • 4,976
Sheridan, IL 60551 • 1,288
Sheridan, IN 46069 • 2,046
Sheridan, OR 97378 • 3,979
Sheridan, WY 82801 • 13,900
Sheridan □, KS • 3,043
Sheridan □, MT • 4,732
Sheridan □, NE • 6,750
Sheridan □, ND • 2,148
Sheridan □, WY • 23,562
Sheridan Beach, WA 98155 • 6,518
Sherman, TX 75090–91 • 31,601
Sherman □, KS • 6,926
Sherman □, NE • 3,718
Sherman □, OR • 1,918
Sherman □, TX • 2,858
Sherrelwood, CO 80221 • 16,636
Sherrill, NY 13461 • 2,864
Sherwood, AR 72116 • 18,893
Sherwood, OR 97140 • 3,093
Sherwood Manor, CT 06082 • 6,357
Sherwood Park, DE 19808 • 2,000
Shiawassee □, MI • 69,770
Shickshinny, PA 18655 • 1,108
Shillington, PA 19607 • 5,062
Shiloh, OH 44878 • 11,607
Shiloh, PA 17404 • 8,245
Shiner, TX 77984 • 2,074
Shinglehouse, PA 16748 • 1,243
Shinnston, WV 26431 • 2,543
Ship Bottom, NJ 08008 • 1,352
Shippensburg, PA 17257 • 5,331
Shiprock, NM 87420 • 7,687
Shirley, MA 01464 • 1,559
Shirley, NY 11967 • 22,936
Shishmaref, AK 99772 • 456
Shively, KY 40216 • 15,535
Shoemakersville, PA 19555 • 1,443
Shore Acres, MA 02066 • 1,200
Shores Acres, RI 02852 • 410
Shoreview, MN 55112 • 24,587
Shorewood, IL 60435 • 6,264
Shorewood, MN 55331 • 5,917
Shorewood, WI 53211 • 14,116
Shorewood Hills, WI 53705 • 1,680
Short Beach, CT 06405 • 2,500
Shortsville, NY 14548 • 1,485
Shoshone, ID 83352 • 1,249
Shoshone □, ID • 13,931
Shoshoni, WY 82649 • 497
Show Low, AZ 85901 • 5,019
Shreve, OH 44676 • 1,584
Shreveport, LA 71101–10 • 198,525
Shrewsbury, MA 01545 • 23,400
Shrewsbury, MO 63119 • 6,416
Shrewsbury, NJ 07702 • 3,096
Shrewsbury, PA 17361 • 2,672
Shullsburg, WI 53586 • 1,236
Shungnak, AK 99773 • 223
Sibley, IA 51249 • 2,815
Sibley □, MN • 14,366
Sicklerville, NJ 08081 • 1,750
Sidney, IL 61877 • 1,027
Sidney, IA 51652 • 1,253
Sidney, MT 59270 • 5,217
Sidney, NE 69162 • 5,959
Sidney, NY 13838 • 4,720
Sidney, OH 45365 • 18,710
Siegle, LA 71291 • 1,600
Sierra □, CA • 3,318
Sierra □, NM • 9,912
Sierra Madre, CA 91024 • 10,762
Sierra Vista, AZ 85635–36 • 32,983
Siesta Key, FL 34242 • 7,772
Signal Hill, CA 90806 • 8,371
Signal Mountain, TN 37377 • 7,034
Sigourney, IA 52591 • 2,111
Sikeston, MO 63801 • 17,641
Siler City, NC 27344 • 4,808
Siloam Springs, AR 72761 • 8,151
Silsbee, TX 77656 • 6,368
Silt, CO 81652 • 1,095
Silver Bay, MN 55614 • 1,894
Silver Bow □, MT • 33,941
Silver City, NV 89428 • 100
Silver City, NM 88061–62 • 10,683
Silver Creek, NY 14136 • 2,927
Silverdale, WA 98383 • 7,660
Silver Grove, KY 41085 • 1,102
Silver Hill, MD 20746 • 1,580
Silver Lake, KS 66539 • 1,390
Silver Lake, MA 01887 • 2,900
Silver Lake, WI 53170 • 1,801
Silverpeak, NV 89047 • 190
Silver Spring, MD 20901–12 • 76,046
Silver Springs, FL 32688 • 1,082
Silver Springs, NV 89429 • 2,253
Silver Springs Shores, FL 32672 • 6,421
Silverton, NJ 08753 • 9,175
Silverton, OH 45236 • 5,859
Silverton, OR 97381 • 5,635
Silview, DE 19804 • 1,500
Silvis, IL 61282 • 6,926
Simi Valley, CA 93062–65 • 100,217
Simmesport, LA 71369 • 2,092
Simpson, PA 18407 • 1,670
Simpson □, KY • 15,145
Simpson □, MS • 23,953
Simpsonville, SC 29681 • 11,708
Simsbury, CT 06070 • 5,577
Sinclair, WY 82334 • 500
Sinton, TX 78387 • 5,549
Sioux □, IA • 29,903
Sioux □, NE • 1,549
Sioux □, ND • 3,761
Sioux Center, IA 51250 • 5,074
Sioux City, IA 51101–11 • 80,505
Sioux Falls, SD 57101–18 • 100,814
Siskiyou □, CA • 43,531
Sisseton, SD 57262 • 2,181
Sistersville, WV 26175 • 1,797
Sitka, AK 99835 • 8,588
Skagit □, WA • 79,555
Skagway, AK 99840 • 692
Skamania □, WA • 8,289
Skaneateles, NY 13152 • 2,724
Skiatook, OK 74070 • 4,910
Skokie, IL 60076–77 • 59,432
Skowhegan, ME 04976 • 6,990
Sky Lake, FL 32809 • 6,202
Skyland, NV 89448 • 660
Skyland, NC 28776 • 1,100
Skyway, WA 98178 • 8,500
Slackwoods, NJ 08638 • 8,100
Slater, IA 50244 • 1,268
Slater, MO 65349 • 2,186
Slater, SC 29683 • 1,000
Slatersville, RI 02876 • 2,330
Slatington, PA 18080 • 4,678
Slaton, TX 79364 • 6,078
Slayton, MN 56172 • 2,147
Sleepy Eye, MN 56085 • 3,694
Slickville, PA 15684 • 1,178
Slidell, LA 70458–61 • 24,124
Slinger, WI 53086 • 2,340
Slippery Rock, PA 16057 • 3,008
Sloan, NY 14225 • 3,830
Sloatsburg, NY 10974 • 3,035
Slocomb, AL 36375 • 1,906
Slope □, ND • 907
Smackover, AR 71762 • 2,232
Smethport, PA 16749 • 1,734
Smith □, KS • 5,078
Smith □, MS • 14,798
Smith □, TN • 14,143
Smith □, TX • 151,309
Smith Center, KS 66967 • 2,016
Smithers, WV 25186 • 1,162
Smithfield, NC 27577 • 7,540
Smithfield, PA 15478 • 1,000
Smithfield, UT 84335 • 5,566
Smithfield, VA 23430 • 4,686
Smith River, CA 95567 • 1,000
Smiths, AL 36877 • 1,700
Smithsburg, MD 21783 • 1,221
Smithton, IL 62285 • 1,587
Smithtown, NY 11787 • 25,638
Smithville, MO 64089 • 2,525
Smithville, OH 44677 • 1,354
Smithville, TN 37166 • 3,791
Smithville, TX 78957 • 3,196
Smyrna, DE 19977 • 5,231
Smyrna, GA 30080–82 • 30,981
Smyrna, TN 37167 • 13,647
Smyth □, VA • 32,370
Sneads, FL 32460 • 1,746
Sneedville, TN 37869 • 1,446
Snellville, GA 30278 • 12,084
Snohomish, WA 98290 • 6,499
Snohomish □, WA • 465,642
Snoqualmie, WA 98065 • 1,546
Snowflake, AZ 85937 • 3,679
Snow Hill, MD 21863 • 2,217
Snow Hill, NC 28580 • 1,378
Snyder, OK 73566 • 1,619
Snyder, TX 79549 • 12,195
Snyder □, PA • 36,680
Soap Lake, WA 98851 • 1,149
Socastee, SC 29577 • 10,426
Social Circle, GA 30279 • 2,755
Socorro, NM 87801 • 8,159
Socorro □, NM • 14,764
Soda Springs, ID 83276 • 3,111
Soddy-Daisy, TN 37379 • 8,240
Sodus, NY 14551 • 1,904
Sodus Point, NY 14555 • 1,190
Solana, FL 33950 • 1,128
Solana Beach, CA 92075 • 12,962
Solano □, CA • 340,421
Soldotna, AK 99669 • 3,482
Soledad, CA 93960 • 7,146
Solomons, MD 20688 • 1,500
Solon, IA 52333 • 1,050
Solon, OH 44139 • 18,548
Solvay, NY 13209 • 6,717
Somerdale, NJ 08083 • 5,440
Somers, CT 06071 • 9,108
Somerset, KY 42501–02 • 10,733
Somerset, MA 02725 • 17,655
Somerset, NJ 08873–75 • 22,070
Somerset, OH 43783 • 1,390
Somerset, PA 15501 • 6,454
Somerset, TX 78069 • 1,144
Somerset, WI 54025 • 1,065
Somerset □, ME • 49,767
Somerset □, MD • 23,440
Somerset □, NJ • 240,279
Somerset □, PA • 78,218
Somers Point, NJ 08244 • 11,216
Somersville, CT 06072 • 1,200
Somersworth, NH 03878 • 11,249
Somerton, AZ 85350 • 5,282
Somervell □, TX • 5,360
Somerville, MA 02143 • 76,210
Somerville, NJ 08876–77 • 11,632
Somerville, TN 38068 • 2,047
Somerville, TX 77879 • 1,542
Somonauk, IL 60552 • 1,263
Sonoma, CA 95476 • 8,121
Sonoma □, CA • 388,222
Sonora, CA 95370 • 4,153
Sonora, TX 76950 • 2,751
Soperton, GA 30457 • 2,797
Sophia, WV 25921 • 1,182
Soquel, CA 95073 • 9,188
Sorrento, LA 70778 • 1,119
Souderton, PA 18964 • 5,957
Sound Beach, NY 11789 • 9,102
South Acton, MA 01720 • 3,220
South Amboy, NJ 08879 • 7,863
South Amherst, MA 01002 • 5,053
South Amherst, OH 44001 • 1,765
Southampton, NY 11968–69 • 3,980
Southampton □, VA • 17,550
South Ashburnham, MA 01466 • 1,110
Southaven, MS 38671 • 17,949
South Barre, VT 05670 • 1,314
South Bay, FL 33493 • 3,558
South Belmar, NJ 07719 • 1,482
South Beloit, IL 61080 • 4,072
South Bend, IN 46601–80 • 105,511
South Bend, WA 98586 • 1,551
South Berwick, ME 03908 • 5,877
Southborough, MA 01772 • 1,450
South Boston, VA 24592 • 6,997
South Bound Brook, NJ 08880 • 4,185
South Bradenton, FL 34205 • 20,398
Southbridge, MA 01550 • 13,631
South Broadway, WA 98902 • 2,735
South Burlington, VT 05403 • 12,809
Southbury, CT 06488 • 3,000
South Charleston, OH 45368 • 1,626
South Charleston, WV 25303 • 13,645
South Chicago Heights, IL 60411 • 3,597
South Congaree, SC 29169 • 2,406
South Connellsville, PA 15425 • 2,204
South Dartmouth, MA 02748 • 9,850
South Daytona, FL 32121 • 12,482
South Decatur, GA 30034 • 19,350
South Deerfield, MA 01373 • 1,906
South Dennis, MA 02660 • 2,500
South Duxbury, MA 02332 • 3,017
South Easton, MA 02375 • 1,530
South Elgin, IL 60177 • 7,474
South El Monte, CA 91733 • 20,850
Southern Pines, NC 28387–88 • 9,129
South Euclid, OH 44121 • 23,866
South Fallsburg, NY 12779 • 2,115
South Farmingdale, NY 11735 • 15,377
Southfield, MI 48034 • 75,728
South Fork, PA 15956 • 1,197
South Fulton, TN 38257 • 2,688
South Gastonia, NC 28052 • 5,487
South Gate, CA 90280 • 86,284
Southgate, FL 34239 • 7,324
Southgate, KY 41071 • 3,266
South Gate, MD 21061 • 27,564
Southgate, MI 48195 • 30,771
South Glastonbury, CT 06073 • 1,570
Southglenn, CO 80122 • 43,087
South Glens Falls, NY 12801 • 3,506
South Grafton, MA 01560 • 2,610
South Hackensack, NJ 07606 • 2,229
South Hadley, MA 01075 • 5,340
South Hadley Falls, MA 01075 • 5,100
South Hamilton, MA 01982 • 2,720
South Haven, IN 46383 • 6,112
South Haven, MI 49090 • 5,563
South Hill, NY 14850 • 5,423
South Hill, VA 23970 • 4,217
South Hingham, MA 02043 • 4,080
South Holland, IL 60473 • 22,105
South Hooksett, NH 03106 • 3,638
South Hopkinton, RI 02813 • 900
South Houston, TX 77587 • 14,207
South Huntington, NY 11746 • 9,624
South Hutchinson, KS 67505 • 2,444
Southington, CT 06489 • 38,518
South International Falls, MN 56679 • 2,806
South Jacksonville, IL 62650 • 3,187
South Jordan, UT 84065 • 12,220
South Lake Tahoe, CA 95702 • 21,586
South Lancaster, MA 01561 • 1,772
South Laramie, WY 82070 • 1,500
South Laurel, MD 20708 • 18,591
South Lebanon, OH 45065 • 2,696
South Lockport, NY 14094 • 7,112
South Lyon, MI 48178 • 5,857
South Miami, FL 33143 • 10,404
South Miami Heights, FL 33157 • 30,030
South Milwaukee, WI 53172 • 20,958
South Nyack, NY 10960 • 3,352
South Ogden, UT 84403 • 12,105
Southold, NY 11971 • 5,192
South Orange, NJ 07079 • 16,390
South Paris, ME 04281 • 2,320
South Pasadena, CA 91030 • 23,936
South Patrick Shores, FL 32937 • 10,249
South Pekin, IL 61564 • 1,184
South Pittsburg, TN 37380 • 3,295
South Plainfield, NJ 07080 • 20,489
Southport, FL 32409 • 1,992
Southport, IN 46227 • 1,969
Southport, NY 14904 • 7,753
Southport, NC 28461 • 2,369
South Portland, ME 04106 • 23,163
South River, NJ 08882 • 13,692
South Royalton, VT 05068 • 700
South Saint Paul, MN 55075–77 • 20,197
South Salt Lake, UT 84115 • 10,129
South San Francisco, CA 94080–83 • 54,312
South San Gabriel, CA 91770 • 7,700
South San Jose Hills, CA 91744 • 17,814
South Sarasota, FL 34239 • 5,298
South Setauket, NY 11733 • 5,990
Southside, AL 35901 • 5,580
Southside Place, TX 77005 • 1,392
South Sioux City, NE 68776 • 9,677
South Stony Brook, NY 11790 • 6,120
South Streator, IL 61364 • 2,334
South Sumter, SC 29150 • 4,371
South Toms River, NJ 08757 • 3,869
South Torrington, WY 82240 • 300
South Tucson, AZ 85713 • 5,093
South Valley Stream, NY 11581 • 5,328
South Venice, FL 34293 • 11,951
South Walpole, MA 02071 • 1,300
South Waverly, PA 14892 • 1,049
South Wellfleet, MA 02663 • 2,300
South Westbury, NY 11590 • 9,732
Southwest Harbor, ME 04679 • 1,952
South Whitley, IN 46787 • 1,482
South Whittier, CA 90605 • 51,100
Southwick, MA 01077 • 1,170
South Williamsport, PA 17701 • 6,496
South Windham, CT 06266 • 1,644
South Windham, ME 04082 • 1,350
South Windsor, CT 06074 • 10,800
Southwood, CO 80120 • 2,050
Southwood Acres, CT 06082 • 8,963
South Woodstock, CT 06267 • 1,112
South Yarmouth, MA 02664 • 10,358
South Yuba City, CA 95991 • 8,816
South Zanesville, OH 43701 • 1,969
Spalding □, GA • 54,457
Spanaway, WA 98387 • 15,001
Spangler, PA 15775 • 2,068
Spanish Fork, UT 84660 • 11,272
Spanish Fort, AL 36527 • 3,732
Spanish Lake, MO 63138 • 20,322
Sparks, GA 31647 • 1,205
Sparks, NV 89431–36 • 53,367
Sparr, FL 32192 • 1,100
Sparta, GA 31087 • 1,710
Sparta, IL 62286 • 4,853
Sparta, MI 49345 • 3,968
Sparta (Lake Mohawk), NJ 07871 • 8,930
Sparta, NC 28675 • 1,957
Sparta, TN 38583 • 4,681
Sparta, WI 54656 • 7,788
Spartanburg, SC 29301–18 • 43,467
Spartanburg □, SC • 226,800
Spearfish, SD 57783 • 6,966
Spearman, TX 79081 • 3,197
Speedway, IN 46224 • 13,092
Spencer, IN 47460 • 2,609
Spencer, IA 51301 • 11,066
Spencer, MA 01562 • 6,306
Spencer, NC 28159 • 3,219
Spencer, TN 38585 • 1,125
Spencer, WV 25276 • 2,279
Spencer, WI 54479 • 1,757
Spencer □, IN • 19,490
Spencer □, KY • 6,801
Spencerport, NY 14559 • 3,606
Spencerville, MD 20868 • 1,780
Spencerville, OH 45887 • 2,288
Spicer, MN 56288 • 1,020
Spindale, NC 28160 • 4,040
Spink □, SD • 7,981
Spirit Lake, ID 83869 • 790
Spirit Lake, IA 51360 • 3,871
Spiro, OK 74959 • 2,146
Spokane, WA 99201–28 • 177,196
Spokane □, WA • 361,364
Spooner, WI 54801 • 2,464
Spotswood, NJ 08884 • 7,983
Spotsylvania □, VA • 57,403
Sprague, WV 25926 • 2,090

Spring, TX 77373 • 33,111
Spring Arbor, MI 49283 • 2,010
Springboro, OH 45066 • 6,590
Spring City, PA 19475 • 3,433
Spring City, TN 37381 • 2,199
Spring Creek 0M, NV • 5,866
Springdale, AR 72764-66 • 29,941
Springdale, OH 45246 • 10,621
Springdale, PA 15144 • 3,992
Springdale, SC 29169 • 3,226
Springer, NM 87747 • 1,262
Springerville, AZ 85938 • 1,802
Springfield, CO 81073 • 1,475
Springfield, FL 32401 • 8,715
Springfield, GA 31329 • 1,415
Springfield, IL 62701-94 • 105,227
Springfield, KY 40069 • 2,875
Springfield, MA 01101-05 • 156,983
Springfield, MI 49015 • 5,582
Springfield, MN 56087 • 2,173
Springfield, MO 65801-99 • 140,494
Springfield, NE 68059 • 1,426
Springfield, NJ 07081 • 13,240
Springfield, OH 45501-06 • 70,487
Springfield, OR 97477-78 • 44,683
Springfield, PA 19064 • 24,160
Springfield, SD 57062 • 834
Springfield, TN 37172 • 11,227
Springfield, VT 05156 • 4,207
Springfield, VA 22150 • 23,706
Spring Garden, PA 17403 • 11,127
Spring Green, WI 53588 • 1,283
Spring Grove, IL 60081 • 1,066
Spring Grove, MN 55974 • 1,153
Spring Grove, PA 17362 • 1,863
Spring Hill, FL 34606 • 31,117
Spring Hill, KS 66083 • 2,191
Springhill, LA 71075 • 5,668
Spring Hill, TN 37174 • 1,464
Spring Hope, NC 27882 • 1,221
Spring Lake, MI 49456 • 2,537
Spring Lake, NJ 07762 • 3,499
Spring Lake, NC 28390 • 7,524
Spring Lake Heights, NJ 07762 • 5,341
Spring Lake Park, MN 55432 • 6,532
Springvale, ME 04083 • 3,542
Spring Valley, IL 61362 • 5,246
Spring Valley, MN 55975 • 2,461
Spring Valley, NY 10977 • 21,802
Spring Valley, WI 54767 • 1,051
Springville, AL 35146 • 1,910
Springville, IA 52336 • 1,068
Springville, NY 14141 • 4,310
Springville, UT 84663-64 • 13,950
Spruce Pine, NC 28777 • 2,010
Spur, TX 79370 • 1,300
Staatsburg, NY 12580 • 1,100
Stafford, KS 67578 • 1,344
Stafford □, KS • 5,365
Stafford □, VA • 61,236
Stafford Springs, CT 06076 • 4,100
Stambaugh, MI 49964 • 1,281
Stamford, CT 06901-12 • 108,056
Stamford, NY 12167 • 1,211
Stamford, TX 79553 • 3,817
Stamford, VT 05352 • 400
Stamps, AR 71860 • 2,478
Stanaford, WV 25927 • 1,706
Stanberry, MO 64489 • 1,310
Standish, MI 48658 • 1,377
Stanfield, AZ 85272 • 1,700
Stanfield, OR 97875 • 1,568
Stanford, CA 94305 • 18,097
Stanford, KY 40484 • 2,686
Stanhope, NJ 07874 • 3,393
Stanislaus □, CA • 370,522
Stanley, NC 28164 • 2,823
Stanley, ND 58784 • 1,371
Stanley, VA 22851 • 1,186
Stanley, WI 54768 • 2,011
Stanley □, SD • 2,453
Stanleytown, VA 24168 • 1,563
Stanleyville, NC 27045 • 4,779
Stanly □, NC • 51,765
Stanton, CA 90680 • 30,491
Stanton, KY 40380 • 2,795
Stanton, MI 48888 • 1,504
Stanton, NE 68779 • 1,549
Stanton, TX 79782 • 2,576
Stanton □, KS • 2,333
Stanton □, NE • 6,244
Stanwood, WA 98292 • 1,961
Staples, MN 56479 • 2,754
Stapleton, AL 36578 • 1,300
Starbuck, MN 56381 • 1,143
Star City, AR 71667 • 2,138
Star City, WV 26505 • 1,251
Stargo, AZ 85540 • 1,038
Stark □, IL • 6,534
Stark □, ND • 22,832
Stark □, OH • 367,585
Starke, FL 32091 • 5,226
Starke □, IN • 22,747
Starkville, MS 39759 • 18,458
Starr □, TX • 40,518
Startex, SC 29377 • 1,162
State Center, IA 50247 • 1,248
State College, PA 16801-05 • 38,923
Stateline, NV 89449 • 1,379
State Line, PA 17263 • 1,253
Statesboro, GA 30458 • 15,854
Statesville, NC 28677 • 17,567
Statham, GA 30666 • 1,360
Staunton, IL 62088 • 4,806
Staunton, VA 24401 • 24,461
Stayton, OR 97383 • 5,011
Steamboat, NV 89511 • 450
Steamboat Springs, CO 80487 • 6,695
Stearns, KY 42647 • 1,550
Stearns □, MN • 118,791
Stebbins, AK 99671 • 400
Steele, AL 35987 • 1,046
Steele, MO 63877 • 2,395
Steele, ND 58482 • 762
Steele □, MN • 30,729
Steele □, ND • 2,420
Steeleville, IL 62288 • 2,059
Steelton, PA 17113 • 5,152
Steelville, MO 65565 • 1,465
Steger, IL 60475 • 8,584
Steilacoom, WA 98388 • 5,728
Stephens, AR 71764 • 1,137
Stephens □, GA • 23,257
Stephens □, OK • 42,299
Stephens □, TX • 9,010
Stephens City, VA 22655 • 1,186
Stephenson □, IL • 48,052
Stephenville, TX 76401 • 13,502
Sterling, AK 99672 • 3,802
Sterling, CO 80751 • 10,362
Sterling, IL 61081 • 15,132
Sterling, KS 67579 • 2,115
Sterling, MA 01564 • 1,250
Sterling, VA 22170 • 20,512
Sterling □, TX • 1,438
Sterling City, TX 76951 • 1,096
Sterling Heights, MI 48310-14 • 117,810
Sterlington, LA 71280 • 1,140
Steuben □, IN • 27,446
Steuben □, NY • 99,088
Steubenville, OH 43952 • 22,125
Stevens □, KS • 5,048
Stevens □, MN • 10,634
Stevens □, WA • 30,948
Stevenson, AL 35772 • 2,046
Stevenson, WA 98648 • 1,147
Stevens Point, WI 54481 • 23,006
Stevensville, MI 49127 • 1,230
Stevensville, MT 59870 • 1,221
Stewart □, GA • 5,654
Stewart □, TN • 9,479
Stewartstown, PA 17363 • 1,308
Stewartville, MN 55976 • 4,520
Stickney, IL 60402 • 5,678
Stigler, OK 74462 • 2,574
Stillwater, MN 55082-83 • 13,882
Stillwater, NY 12170 • 1,531
Stillwater, OK 74074-76 • 36,676
Stillwater □, MT • 6,536
Stilwell, OK 74960 • 2,663
Stinnett, TX 79083 • 2,166
Stirling, NJ 07980 • 1,800
Stockbridge, GA 30281 • 3,359
Stockbridge, MA 01262 • 2,408
Stockbridge, MI 49285 • 1,202
Stockdale, TX 78160 • 1,268
Stockholm, NJ 07460 • 1,200
Stockton, CA 95201-19 • 210,943
Stockton, IL 61085 • 1,871
Stockton, KS 67669 • 1,507
Stockton, MO 65785 • 1,579
Stoddard □, MO • 28,895
Stokes □, NC • 37,223
Stokesdale, NC 27357 • 2,134
Stollings, WV 25646 • 1,200
Stone □, AR • 9,775
Stone □, MS • 10,750
Stone □, MO • 19,078
Stoneboro, PA 16153 • 1,091
Stoneham, MA 02180 • 22,203
Stone Harbor, NJ 08247 • 1,025
Stone Mountain, GA 30083 • 6,494
Stoneville, NC 27048 • 1,109
Stonewall, LA 71078 • 1,266
Stonewall, MS 39363 • 1,148
Stonewall □, TX • 2,013
Stonewood, WV 26301 • 1,996
Stonington, CT 06378 • 1,100
Stonington, IL 62567 • 1,006
Stony Brook, NY 11790 • 13,726
Stony Point, NY 10980 • 10,587
Stony Point, NC 28678 • 1,286
Storey □, NV • 2,526
Storm Lake, IA 50588 • 8,769
Storrs, CT 06268 • 12,198
Story, WY 82842 • 700
Story □, IA • 74,252
Story City, IA 50248 • 2,959
Stottville, NY 12172 • 1,369
Stoughton, MA 02072 • 26,777
Stoughton, WI 53589 • 8,786
Stow, MA 01775 • 1,200
Stow, OH 44224 • 27,702
Stowe, PA 19464 • 3,598
Stowe, VT 05672 • 450
Stowe Township, PA 15136 • 7,681
Strabane, PA 15363 • 1,200
Strafford, MO 65757 • 1,166
Strafford □, NH • 104,233
Strasburg, CO 80136 • 1,005
Strasburg, OH 44680 • 1,995
Strasburg, PA 17579 • 2,568
Strasburg, VA 22657 • 3,762
Stratford, CT 06497 • 49,389
Stratford, DE 19720 • 1,950
Stratford, NJ 08084 • 7,614
Stratford, OK 74872 • 1,404
Stratford, TX 79084 • 1,781
Stratford, WI 54484 • 1,515
Stratford Landing, VA 22308 • 2,800
Strathmore, CA 93267 • 2,353
Strathmore, NJ 07747 • 7,060
Strawberry Point, IA 52076 • 1,357
Streamwood, IL 60103 • 30,987
Streator, IL 61364 • 14,121
Streetsboro, OH 44241 • 9,932
Stromsburg, NE 68666 • 1,241
Strongsville, OH 44136 • 35,308
Stroud, OK 74079 • 2,666
Stroudsburg, PA 18360 • 5,312
Struthers, OH 44471 • 12,284
Stryker, OH 43557 • 1,468
Stuart, FL 34994-97 • 11,936
Stuart, IA 50250 • 1,522
Stuarts Draft, VA 24477 • 5,087
Sturbridge, MA 01566 • 2,093
Sturgeon Bay, WI 54235 • 9,176
Sturgis, KY 42459 • 2,184
Sturgis, MI 49091 • 10,130
Sturgis, SD 57785 • 5,330
Sturtevant, WI 53177 • 3,803
Stutsman □, ND • 22,241
Stuttgart, AR 72160 • 10,420
Sublette, KS 67877 • 1,378
Sublette □, WY • 4,843
Sublimity, OR 97385 • 1,491
Succasunna, NJ 07876 • 7,750
Sudbury, MA 01776 • 1,860
Sudbury Center, MA 01776 • 2,590
Sudley, VA 22110 • 7,321
Suffern, NY 10901 • 11,055
Suffield, CT 06078 • 1,353
Suffolk, VA 23432-38 • 52,141
Suffolk □, MA • 663,906
Suffolk □, NY • 1,321,864
Sugar City, ID 83448 • 1,275
Sugar Creek, MO 64054 • 3,982
Sugarcreek, PA 16323 • 5,532
Sugar Grove, VA 24375 • 1,027
Sugar Hill, GA 30518 • 4,557
Sugar Land, TX 77478-79 • 24,529
Sugarland Run, VA 22170 • 9,357
Sugar Loaf, VA 24018 • 2,000
Sugar Notch, PA 18706 • 1,044
Suisun City, CA 94585 • 22,686
Suitland, MD 20746 • 35,400
Sulligent, AL 35586 • 1,886
Sullivan, IL 61951 • 4,354
Sullivan, IN 47882 • 4,663
Sullivan, MO 63080 • 5,661
Sullivan □, IN • 18,993
Sullivan □, MO • 6,326
Sullivan □, NH • 38,592
Sullivan □, NY • 69,277
Sullivan □, PA • 6,104
Sullivan □, TN • 143,596
Sullivans Island, SC 29482 • 1,623
Sully □, SD • 1,589
Sulphur, LA 70663-64 • 20,125
Sulphur, OK 73086 • 4,824
Sulphur Springs, TX 75482 • 14,062
Sultan, WA 98294 • 2,236
Sumiton, AL 35148 • 2,604
Summerfield, NC 27358 • 2,051
Summers □, WV • 14,204
Summersville, WV 26651 • 2,906
Summerville, GA 30747 • 5,025
Summerville, SC 29483-85 • 22,519
Summit, IL 60501 • 9,971
Summit, MS 39666 • 1,566
Summit, NJ 07901 • 19,757
Summit, TN 37363 • 8,307
Summit □, CO • 12,881
Summit □, OH • 514,990
Summit □, UT • 15,518
Summit Hill, PA 18250 • 3,332
Sumner, IL 62466 • 1,083
Sumner, IA 50674 • 2,078
Sumner, WA 98390 • 6,281
Sumner □, KS • 25,841
Sumner □, TN • 103,281
Sumter, SC 29150-54 • 41,943
Sumter □, AL • 16,174
Sumter □, FL • 31,577
Sumter □, GA • 30,228
Sumter □, SC • 102,637
Sunbury, OH 43074 • 2,046
Sunbury, PA 17801 • 11,591
Sun City, AZ 85351 • 38,126
Sun City, CA 92381 • 14,930
Sun City Center, FL 33573 • 8,326
Suncook, NH 03275 • 5,214
Sundance, WY 82729 • 1,139
Sundown, TX 79372 • 1,759
Sunflower □, MS • 32,867
Sunland Park, NM 88063 • 8,179
Sunny Isles, FL 33160 • 11,772
Sunnyside, CA 93727 • 5,000
Sunnyside, WA 98944 • 11,238
Sunnyvale, CA 94086-89 • 117,229
Sun Prairie, WI 53590 • 15,333
Sunray, TX 79086 • 1,729
Sunrise Manor, NV 89110 • 95,362
Sunset, FL 33143 • 15,810
Sunset, LA 70584 • 2,201
Sunset, UT 84015 • 5,128
Sunset Beach, HI 96712 • 800
Sun Valley, ID 83353-54 • 938
Sun Valley, NV 89433 • 11,391
Superior, AZ 85273 • 3,468
Superior, MT 59872 • 881
Superior, NE 68978 • 2,397
Superior, WI 54880 • 27,134
Superior, WY 82945 • 273
Suquamish, WA 98392 • 3,105
Surf City, NJ 08008 • 1,375
Surfside, FL 33154 • 4,108
Surfside Beach, SC 29575 • 3,845
Surgoinsville, TN 37873 • 1,499
Surprise, AZ 85374 • 7,122
Surrey, ND 58785 • 856
Surry □, NC • 61,704
Surry □, VA • 6,145
Susanville, CA 96130 • 7,279
Susquehanna, PA 18847 • 1,760
Susquehanna □, PA • 40,380
Sussex, NJ 07461 • 2,201
Sussex, WI 53089 • 5,039
Sussex □, DE • 113,229
Sussex □, NJ • 130,943
Sussex □, VA • 10,248
Sutherland, NE 69165 • 1,032
Sutherlin, OR 97479 • 5,020
Sutter □, CA • 64,415
Sutter Creek, CA 95685 • 1,835
Sutton, NE 68979 • 1,353
Sutton □, TX • 4,135
Suwanee, GA 30174 • 2,412
Suwannee □, FL • 26,780
Swain □, NC • 11,268
Swainsboro, GA 30401 • 7,361
Swampscott, MA 01907 • 13,650
Swannanoa, NC 28778 • 3,538
Swansboro, NC 28584 • 1,165
Swansea, IL 62221 • 8,201
Swanton, OH 43558 • 3,557
Swanton, VT 05488 • 2,360
Swanwyck Estates, DE 19720 • 1,320
Swarthmore, PA 19081 • 6,157
Swartz Creek, MI 48473 • 4,851
Swatara Township, PA 17111 • 19,700
Swayzee, IN 46986 • 1,059
Swedesboro, NJ 08085 • 2,024
Sweeny, TX 77480 • 3,297
Sweet Grass □, MT • 3,154
Sweet Home, OR 97386 • 6,850
Sweet Springs, MO 65351 • 1,595
Sweetwater, FL 33152 • 13,909
Sweetwater, TN 37874 • 5,066
Sweetwater, TX 79556 • 11,967
Sweetwater □, WY • 38,823
Sweetwater Creek, FL 33614 • 18,000
Swift □, MN • 10,724
Swisher □, TX • 8,133
Swissvale, PA 15218 • 10,637
Switzer, WV 25647 • 1,004
Switzerland, FL 32043 • 2,400
Switzerland □, IN • 7,738
Swoyerville, PA • 5,630
Sycamore, AL 35149 • 1,250
Sycamore, IL 60178 • 9,708
Sykesville, MD 21784 • 2,303
Sykesville, PA 15865 • 1,387
Sylacauga, AL 35150 • 12,520
Sylva, NC 28779 • 1,809
Sylvan Beach, NY 13157 • 1,119
Sylvania, GA 30467 • 2,871
Sylvania, OH 43560 • 17,301
Sylvan Lake, MI 48320 • 1,884
Sylvester, GA 31791 • 5,702
Syosset, NY 11791 • 18,967
Syracuse, IN 46567 • 2,729
Syracuse, KS 67878 • 1,606
Syracuse, NE 68446 • 1,646
Syracuse, NY 13201-90 • 163,860
Syracuse, UT 84075 • 4,658

T

Tabor City, NC 28463 • 2,330
Tacoma, WA 98401-99 • 176,664
Taft, CA 93268 • 5,902
Taft, TX 78390 • 3,222
Tahlequah, OK 74464-65 • 10,398
Tahoe City, CA 95730 • 1,300
Tahoka, TX 79373 • 2,868
Takoma Park, MD 20912 • 16,700
Talbot □, GA • 6,524
Talbot □, MD • 30,549
Talbotton, GA 31827 • 1,046
Talent, OR 97540 • 3,274
Taliaferro □, GA • 1,915
Talihina, OK 74571 • 1,297
Talladega, AL 35160 • 18,175
Talladega □, AL • 74,107
Tallahassee, FL 32301-17 • 124,773
Tallahatchie □, MS • 15,210
Tallapoosa, GA 30176 • 2,805
Tallapoosa □, AL • 38,826
Tallassee, AL 36078 • 5,112
Talleyville, DE 19803 • 6,346
Tallmadge, OH 44278 • 14,870
Tallulah, LA 71282-84 • 8,526
Tama, IA 52339 • 2,697
Tama □, IA • 17,419
Tamalpais Valley, CA 94941 • 5,000
Tamaqua, PA 18252 • 7,943
Tamarac, FL 33321 • 44,822
Tamiami, FL 33165 • 33,845
Tampa, FL 33601-97 • 280,015
Tanana, AK 99777 • 345
Taney □, MO • 25,561
Taneytown, MD 21787 • 3,695
Tangipahoa □, LA • 85,709
Taos, NM 87571 • 4,065
Taos □, NM • 23,118
Taos Pueblo, NM 87571 • 1,030
Tappahannock, VA 22560 • 1,550
Tappan, NY 10983 • 6,867
Tara Hills, CA 94564 • 6,000
Tarboro, NC 27886 • 11,037
Tarentum, PA 15084 • 5,674
Tariffville, CT 06081 • 1,477
Tarkio, MO 64491 • 2,243
Tarpey, CA 93727 • 4,045
Tarpon Springs, FL 34688-91 • 17,906
Tarrant, AL 35217 • 8,046
Tarrant □, TX • 1,170,103
Tarrytown, NY 10591 • 10,739
Tate, GA 30177 • 1,000
Tate □, MS • 21,432
Tattnall □, GA • 17,722
Taunton, MA 02780 • 49,832
Tavares, FL 32778 • 7,383
Tavernier, FL 33070 • 2,433
Tawas City, MI 48763-64 • 2,009
Taylor, AZ 85939 • 2,418
Taylor, MI 48180 • 70,811
Taylor, PA 18517 • 6,941
Taylor, TX 76574 • 11,472
Taylor □, FL • 17,111
Taylor □, GA • 7,642
Taylor □, IA • 7,114
Taylor □, KY • 21,146
Taylor □, TX • 119,655
Taylor □, WV • 15,144
Taylor □, WI • 18,901
Taylor Mill, KY 41015 • 5,530
Taylors, SC 29687 • 19,619
Taylorsville, IN 47280 • 1,044
Taylorsville, MS 39168 • 1,412
Taylorsville, NC 28681 • 1,566
Taylorville, IL 62568 • 11,133
Tazewell, TN 37879 • 2,150
Tazewell, VA 24651 • 4,176
Tazewell □, IL • 123,692
Tazewell □, VA • 45,960
Tchula, MS 39169 • 2,186
Teague, TX 75860 • 3,268
Teaneck, NJ 07666 • 37,825
Teaticket, MA 02536 • 2,600
Tecumseh, MI 49286 • 7,462
Tecumseh, NE 68450 • 1,702
Tecumseh, OK 74873 • 5,750
Tehachapi, CA 93561 • 5,791
Tehama □, CA • 49,625
Tekamah, NE 68061 • 1,852
Telfair □, GA • 11,000
Telford, PA 18969 • 4,238
Tell City, IN 47586 • 8,088
Teller □, CO • 12,468
Telluride, CO 81435 • 1,309
Temecula, CA 92390 • 27,099
Tempe, AZ 85280-85 • 141,865
Temperance, MI 48182 • 6,542
Temple, GA 30179 • 1,870
Temple, OK 73568 • 1,223
Temple, PA 19560 • 1,491
Temple, TX 76501-05 • 46,109
Temple City, CA 91780 • 31,100
Temple Terrace, FL 33617 • 16,444
Templeton, MA 01468 • 1,000
Tenafly, NJ 07670 • 13,326
Tenaha, TX 75974 • 1,072
Tenino, WA 98589 • 1,292
Tennessee Ridge, TN 37178 • 1,271
Tennille, GA 31089 • 1,552
Tensas □, LA • 7,103
Ten Sleep, WY 82442 • 311
Terra Alta, WV 26764 • 1,713
Terrebonne □, LA • 96,982
Terre Haute, IN 47801-08 • 57,483
Terre Hill, PA 17581 • 1,282
Terrell, TX 75160 • 12,490
Terrell □, GA • 10,653
Terrell □, TX • 1,410
Terrell Hills, TX 78209 • 4,592
Terry, MT 59349 • 659
Terry □, TX • 13,218
Terrytown, LA 70053 • 23,787
Terryville, CT 06786 • 5,426
Terryville, NY 11776 • 7,380
Tesuque, NM 87574 • 1,490
Teton □, ID • 3,439
Teton □, MT • 6,271
Teton □, WY • 11,172
Teton Village, WY 83025 • 250
Teutopolis, IL 62467 • 1,417
Tewksbury, MA 01876 • 10,540
Texarkana, AR 75502 • 22,631
Texarkana, TX 75501-05 • 31,656
Texas □, MO • 21,476
Texas □, OK • 16,419
Texas City, TX 77590-92 • 40,822
Texico, NM 88135 • 966
Thatcher, AZ 85552 • 3,763
Thayer, MO 65791 • 1,996
Thayer □, NE • 6,635
Thayne, WY 83127 • 267
The Colony, TX 75056 • 22,113
The Dalles, OR 97058 • 11,060
Theodore, AL 36582 • 6,509
The Plains, OH 45780 • 2,644
Thermalito, CA 95965 • 5,646
Thermopolis, WY 82443 • 3,247
The Village, OK 73120 • 10,353
The Village of Indian Hill, OH 45243 • 5,383
The Woodlands, TX 77380 • 29,205
Thibodaux, LA 70301-02 • 14,035
Thief River Falls, MN 56701 • 8,010
Thiensville, WI 53092 • 3,301
Thomas, OK 73669 • 1,246
Thomas □, GA • 38,986
Thomas □, KS • 8,258
Thomas □, NE • 851
Thomasboro, IL 61878 • 1,250
Thomaston, CT 06787 • 3,590
Thomaston, GA 30286 • 9,127
Thomaston, ME 04861 • 2,445
Thomasville, AL 36784 • 4,301
Thomasville, GA 31792 • 17,457
Thomasville, NC 27360-61 • 15,915
Thompson, ND 58278 • 930
Thompson Falls, MT 59873 • 1,319
Thomson, GA 30824 • 6,862
Thonotosassa, FL 33592 • 1,500
Thoreau, NM 87323 • 1,099
Thorndale, TX 76577 • 1,092
Thorndike, MA 01079 • 1,100
Thornton, CO 80229 • 55,031
Thorntown, IN 46071 • 1,506
Thornwood, NY 10594 • 7,025
Thorofare, NJ 08086 • 1,800
Thorp, WI 54771 • 1,657
Thorsby, AL 35171 • 1,465
Thousand Oaks, CA 91359-62 • 104,352
Three Forks, MT 59752 • 1,203
Three Oaks, MI 49128 • 1,786
Three Rivers, MA 01080 • 3,006
Three Rivers, MI 49093 • 7,413
Three Rivers, TX 78071 • 1,889
Throckmorton, TX 76083 • 1,036
Throckmorton □, TX • 1,880
Throop, PA 18512 • 4,070
Thunderbolt, GA 31404 • 2,786
Thurmont, MD 21788 • 3,398
Thurston □, NE • 6,936
Thurston □, WA • 161,238
Tiburon, CA 94920 • 7,532
Tice, FL 33905 • 3,971
Ticonderoga, NY 12883 • 2,770
Tierra Amarilla, NM 87575 • 900
Tiffin, OH 44883 • 18,604
Tift □, GA • 34,998
Tifton, GA 31793-94 • 14,215
Tigard, OR 97223 • 29,344
Tillamook, OR 97141 • 4,001
Tillamook □, OR • 21,570
Tillman □, OK • 10,384
Tillmans Corner, AL 36619 • 17,988
Tillson, NY 12486 • 1,688
Tilton, IL 61833 • 2,729
Tilton, NH 03276 • 1,380
Tiltonsville, OH 43963 • 1,517
Timberlake, VA 24502 • 10,314
Timberville, VA 22853 • 1,596
Timmonsville, SC 29161 • 2,182
Timpson, TX 75975 • 1,029
Tinley Park, IL 60477 • 37,121
Tinton Falls, NJ 07724 • 12,361
Tioga, LA 71477 • 1,200
Tioga, ND 58852 • 1,278
Tioga □, NY • 52,337
Tioga □, PA • 41,126
Tippah □, MS • 19,523
Tipp City, OH 45371 • 6,027
Tippecanoe □, IN • 130,598
Tipton, CA 93272 • 1,383
Tipton, IN 46072 • 4,751
Tipton, IA 52772 • 2,998
Tipton, MO 65081 • 2,026
Tipton, OK 73570 • 1,043
Tipton □, IN • 16,119
Tipton □, TN • 37,568
Tiptonville, TN 38079 • 2,149
Tishomingo, OK 73460 • 3,116
Tishomingo □, MS • 17,683
Titus □, TX • 24,009
Titusville, FL 32780-83 • 39,394
Titusville, PA 16354 • 6,434
Tiverton, RI 02878 • 7,259
Tivoli, NY 12583 • 1,035
Toast, NC 27049 • 2,125
Tobyhanna, PA 18466 • 1,200
Toccoa, GA 30577 • 8,266
Todd □, KY • 10,940
Todd □, MN • 23,363
Todd □, SD • 8,352
Todd Estates, DE 19713 • 2,000
Togiak, AK 99678 • 613
Tohatchi, NM 87325 • 661
Tok, AK 99780 • 935
Toledo, IL 62468 • 1,199

Toledo, IA 52342 • *2,380*
Toledo, OH 43601–99 • *332,943*
Toledo, OR 97391 • *3,174*
Tolland, CT 06084 • *1,200*
Tolland □, CT • *128,699*
Tolleson, AZ 85353 • *4,434*
Tolono, IL 61880 • *2,605*
Toluca, IL 61369 • *1,315*
Tomah, WI 54660 • *7,570*
Tomahawk, WI 54487 • *3,328*
Tomball, TX 77375 • *6,370*
Tombstone, AZ 85638 • *1,220*
Tom Green □, TX • *98,458*
Tompkins □, NY • *94,097*
Tompkinsville, KY 42167 • *2,861*
Toms River, NJ 08753–57 • *7,524*
Tonawanda, NY 14150–51 • *17,284*
Tonawanda, NY 14223 • *65,284*
Tonganoxie, KS 66086 • *2,347*
Tonkawa, OK 74653 • *3,127*
Tonopah, NV 89049 • *3,616*
Tooele, UT 84074 • *13,887*
Tooele □, UT • *26,601*
Toole □, MT • *5,046*
Toombs □, GA • *24,072*
Topeka, KS 66601–99 • *119,883*
Toppenish, WA 98948 • *7,419*
Topsfield, MA 01983 • *2,711*
Topsham, ME 04086 • *6,147*
Topton, PA 19562 • *1,987*
Toronto, OH 43964 • *6,127*
Torrance, CA 90501–10 • *133,107*
Torrance □, NM • *10,285*
Torrington, CT 06790 • *33,687*
Torrington, WY 82240 • *5,651*
Totowa, NJ 07512 • *10,177*
Touisset, MA 02777 • *1,520*
Toulon, IL 61483 • *1,328*
Towaco, NJ 07082 • *1,020*
Towanda, KS 67144 • *1,289*
Towanda, PA 18848 • *3,242*
Tower City, PA 17980 • *1,518*
Town and Country, WA 99210 • *4,921*
Town Creek, AL 35672 • *1,379*
Towner, ND 58788 • *669*
Towner □, ND • *3,627*
Town 'n Country, FL 33615 • *60,946*
Towns □, GA • *6,754*
Townsend, DE 19734 • *322*
Townsend, MA 01469 • *1,164*
Townsend, MT 59644 • *1,635*
Towson, MD 21204 • *49,445*
Tracy, CA 95376–78 • *33,558*
Tracy, MN 56175 • *2,059*
Tracy City, TN 37387 • *1,556*
Tracyton, WA 98393 • *2,621*
Traer, IA 50675 • *1,552*
Trafford, PA 15085 • *3,345*
Trail Creek, IN 46360 • *2,463*
Traill □, ND • *8,752*
Transylvania □, NC • *25,520*
Travelers Rest, SC 29690 • *3,069*
Traverse □, MN • *4,463*
Traverse City, MI 49684 • *15,155*
Travis □, TX • *576,407*
Treasure □, MT • *874*
Treasure Island, FL 33706 • *7,266*
Trego □, KS • *3,694*
Tremont, IL 61568 • *2,088*
Tremont, PA 17981 • *1,814*
Tremonton, UT 84337 • *4,264*
Trempealeau, WI 54661 • *1,039*
Trempealeau □, WI • *25,263*
Trenton, FL 32693 • *1,287*
Trenton, GA 30752 • *1,994*
Trenton, IL 62293 • *2,481*
Trenton, MI 48183 • *20,586*
Trenton, MO 64683 • *6,129*
Trenton, NJ 08601–91 • *88,675*
Trenton, OH 45067 • *6,189*
Trenton, TN 38382 • *4,836*
Tresckow, PA 18254 • *1,033*
Treutlen □, GA • *5,994*
Trevorton, PA 17881 • *2,058*
Triangle, VA 22172 • *4,740*
Tri City, OR 97457 • *3,585*
Trigg □, KY • *10,361*
Tri Lakes, IN 46725 • *3,299*
Trimble □, KY • *6,090*
Trinidad, CO 81082 • *8,580*
Trinidad, TX 75163 • *1,056*
Trinity, AL 35673 • *1,380*
Trinity, NC 27370 • *5,469*
Trinity, TX 75862 • *2,648*
Trinity □, CA • *13,063*
Trinity □, TX • *11,445*
Trion, GA 30753 • *1,661*
Tripoli, IA 50676 • *1,188*
Tripp □, SD • *6,924*
Triumph, LA 70041 • *1,200*
Trona, CA 93562 • *1,400*
Trooper, PA 19401 • *5,137*
Trotwood, OH 45426 • *8,816*
Troup □, GA • *55,536*
Trousdale □, TN • *5,920*
Troutdale, OR 97060 • *7,852*
Troutman, NC 28166 • *1,493*
Troy, AL 36081 • *13,051*
Troy, ID 83871 • *699*
Troy, IL 62294 • *6,046*
Troy, KS 66087 • *1,073*
Troy, MI 48083–84 • *72,884*
Troy, MO 63379 • *3,811*
Troy, MT 59935 • *953*
Troy, NH 03465 • *2,097*
Troy, NY 12180–83 • *54,269*
Troy, NC 27371 • *3,404*
Troy, OH 45373 • *19,478*
Troy, PA 16947 • *1,262*
Troy, TN 38260 • *1,047*
Truckee, CA 95734 • *3,484*
Truman, MN 56088 • *1,292*
Trumann, AR 72472 • *6,304*
Trumansburg, NY 14886 • *1,611*
Trumbull, CT 06611 • *32,000*
Trumbull □, OH • *227,813*
Trussville, AL 35173 • *8,266*
Truth or Consequences (Hot Springs), NM 87901 • *6,221*
Tryon, NC 28782 • *1,680*
Tualatin, OR 97062 • *15,013*
Tuba City, AZ 86045 • *7,323*
Tuckahoe, NY 10707 • *6,302*
Tucker, GA 30084 • *25,781*
Tucker □, WV • *7,728*
Tuckerman, AR 72473 • *2,020*
Tuckerton, NJ 08087 • *3,048*
Tucson, AZ 85701–51 • *405,390*
Tucumcari, NM 88401 • *6,831*
Tukwila, WA 98188 • *11,874*
Tulare, CA 93274–75 • *33,249*
Tulare □, CA • *311,921*
Tularosa, NM 88352 • *2,615*
Tulelake, CA 96134 • *1,010*
Tulia, TX 79088 • *4,699*
Tullahoma, TN 37388 • *16,761*
Tulsa, OK 74101–94 • *367,302*
Tulsa □, OK • *503,341*
Tumwater, WA 98502 • *9,976*
Tunica, MS 38676 • *1,175*
Tunica □, MS • *8,164*
Tunkhannock, PA 18657 • *2,251*
Tununak, AK 99681 • *316*
Tuolumne, CA 95379 • *1,686*
Tuolumne □, CA • *48,456*
Tupelo, MS 38801–03 • *30,685*
Tupper Lake, NY 12986 • *4,087*
Turley, OK 74156 • *2,930*
Turlock, CA 95380–81 • *42,198*
Turner, OR 97392 • *1,281*
Turner □, GA • *8,703*
Turner □, SD • *8,576*
Turners Falls, MA 01376 • *4,731*
Turtle Creek, PA 15145 • *6,556*
Turtle Lake, ND 58575 • *681*
Tuscaloosa, AL 35401–06 • *77,759*
Tuscaloosa □, AL • *150,522*
Tuscarawas □, OH • *84,090*
Tuscola, IL 61953 • *4,155*
Tuscola □, MI • *55,498*
Tuscumbia, AL 35674 • *8,413*
Tuskegee, AL 36083 • *12,257*
Tustin, CA 92680–81 • *50,689*
Tuttle, OK 73089 • *2,807*
Tutwiler, MS 38963 • *1,391*
Tuxedo Park, DE 19804 • *1,300*
Twentynine Palms, CA 92277–78 • *11,821*
Twiggs □, GA • *9,806*
Twin City, GA 30471 • *1,466*
Twin Falls, ID 83301–03 • *27,591*
Twin Falls □, ID • *53,580*
Twin Knolls, AZ 85207 • *5,210*
Twin Lakes, CA 95060 • *5,379*
Twin Lakes, WI 53181 • *3,989*
Twin Rivers, NJ 08520 • *7,715*
Twinsburg, OH 44087 • *9,606*
Two Harbors, MN 55616 • *3,651*
Two Rivers, WI 54241 • *13,030*
Tybee Island, GA 31328 • *2,842*
Tyler, MN 56178 • *1,257*
Tyler, TX 75701–13 • *75,450*
Tyler □, TX • *16,646*
Tyler □, WV • *9,796*
Tyler Heights, WV 25312 • *4,070*
Tylertown, MS 39667 • *1,938*
Tyndall, SD 57066 • *1,201*
Tyrone, NM 88065 • *950*
Tyrone, PA 16686 • *5,743*
Tyrrell □, NC • *3,856*
Tysons Corner, VA 22102 • *13,124*

U

Ucon, ID 83454 • *895*
Uhrichsville, OH 44683 • *5,604*
Uinta □, WY • *18,705*
Uintah □, UT • *22,211*
Ukiah, CA 95482 • *14,599*
Uleta, FL 33162 • *10,000*
Ulster □, NY • *165,304*
Ulysses, KS 67880 • *5,474*
Umatilla, FL 32784 • *2,350*
Umatilla, OR 97882 • *3,046*
Umatilla □, OR • *59,249*
Unadilla, GA 31091 • *1,620*
Unadilla, NY 13849 • *1,265*
Unalakleet, AK 99684 • *714*
Unalaska, AK 99685 • *3,089*
Uncasville, CT 06382 • *1,597*
Underwood, AL 35630 • *1,950*
Underwood, ND 58576 • *976*
Unicoi □, TN • *16,549*
Union, KY 41091 • *1,001*
Union, MS 39365 • *1,875*
Union, MO 63084 • *5,909*
Union, NJ 07083 • *50,024*
Union, OH 45322 • *5,501*
Union, OR 97883 • *1,847*
Union, SC 29379 • *9,836*
Union, UT 84047 • *13,684*
Union □, AR • *46,719*
Union □, FL • *10,252*
Union □, GA • *11,993*
Union □, IL • *17,619*
Union □, IN • *6,976*
Union □, IA • *12,750*
Union □, KY • *16,557*
Union □, LA • *20,690*
Union □, MS • *22,085*
Union □, NJ • *493,819*
Union □, NM • *4,124*
Union □, NC • *84,211*
Union □, OH • *31,969*
Union □, OR • *23,598*
Union □, PA • *36,176*
Union □, SC • *30,337*
Union □, SD • *10,189*
Union □, TN • *13,694*
Union Beach, NJ 07735 • *6,156*
Union City, CA 94587 • *53,762*
Union City, GA 30291 • *8,375*
Union City, IN 47390 • *3,612*
Union City, MI 49094 • *1,767*
Union City, NJ 07087 • *58,012*
Union City, OH 45390 • *1,984*
Union City, OK 73090 • *1,000*
Union City, PA 16438 • *3,537*
Union City, TN 38261 • *10,513*
Uniondale, NY 11553 • *20,328*
Union Gap, WA 98903 • *3,120*
Union Grove, WI 53182 • *3,669*
Union Lake, MI 48386–87 • *8,500*
Union Park, FL 32817 • *6,890*
Union Pier, MI 49129 • *1,039*
Union Point, GA 30669 • *1,753*
Union Springs, AL 36089 • *3,975*
Union Springs, NY 13160 • *1,142*
Uniontown, AL 36786 • *1,730*
Uniontown, KY 42461 • *1,008*
Uniontown, OH 44685 • *1,500*
Uniontown, PA 15401 • *12,034*
Union Village, RI 02895 • *2,150*
Unionville, CT 06085 • *3,500*
Unionville, MO 63565 • *1,989*
Universal City, TX 78148 • *13,057*
University City, MO 63130 • *40,087*
University Gardens, NY 11020 • *4,600*
University Heights, IA 52240 • *1,042*
University Heights, OH 44118 • *14,790*
University Park, IL 60466 • *6,204*
University Park, NM 88003 • *4,520*
University Park, TX 75205 • *22,259*
University Place, WA 98465 • *27,701*
Upland, CA 91785–86 • *63,374*
Upland, IN 46989 • *3,295*
Upper Arlington, OH 43221 • *34,128*
Upper Darby, PA 19082–83 • *84,054*
Upper Dublin Township, PA 19002 • *22,348*
Upper Greenwood Lake, NJ 07421 • *2,734*
Upper Merion Township, PA 19406 • *26,138*
Upper Moreland Township, PA 19090 • *25,874*
Upper Providence Township, PA 19063 • *9,727*
Upper Saddle River, NJ 07458 • *7,198*
Upper Saint Clair, PA 15241 • *19,692*
Upper Sandusky, OH 43351 • *5,906*
Upshur □, TX • *31,370*
Upshur □, WV • *22,867*
Upson □, GA • *26,300*
Upton, MA 01568 • *1,500*
Upton, WY 82730 • *980*
Upton □, TX • *4,447*
Urbana, IL 61801 • *36,344*
Urbana, OH 43078 • *11,353*
Urbandale, IA 50322 • *23,500*
Usquepaug, RI 02892 • *400*
Utah □, UT • *263,590*
Utica, MI 48315–18 • *5,081*
Utica, MS 39175 • *1,033*
Utica, NY 13501–05 • *68,637*
Utica, OH 43080 • *1,997*
Uvalde, TX 78801–02 • *14,729*
Uvalde □, TX • *23,340*
Uxbridge, MA 01569 • *3,340*

V

Vacaville, CA 95687–88 • *71,479*
Vacherie, LA 70090 • *2,169*
Vadnais Heights, MN 55110 • *11,041*
Vail, CO 81657–58 • *3,659*
Valatie, NY 12184 • *1,487*
Valdese, NC 28690 • *3,914*
Valdez, AK 99686 • *4,068*
Valdosta, GA 31601–04 • *39,806*
Vale, OR 97918 • *1,491*
Valencia, AZ 85326 • *1,200*
Valencia □, NM • *45,235*
Valencia Heights, SC 29205 • *4,122*
Valentine, NE 69201 • *2,826*
Valhalla, NY 10595 • *6,200*
Valinda, CA 91744 • *18,735*
Vallejo, CA 94589–92 • *109,199*
Valle Vista, CA 92343 • *8,751*
Valley, AL 36854 • *8,173*
Valley, NE 68064 • *1,775*
Valley □, ID • *6,109*
Valley □, MT • *8,239*
Valley □, NE • *5,169*
Valley Center, KS 67147 • *3,624*
Valley City, ND 58072 • *7,163*
Valley Cottage, NY 10989 • *9,007*
Valley Falls, KS 66088 • *1,253*
Valley Falls, RI 02864 • *11,175*
Valley Forge, PA 19481–82 • *1,500*
Valley Mills, TX 76689 • *1,085*
Valley Park, MO 63088 • *4,165*
Valley Ridge, WA 98188 • *6,500*
Valley Springs, SD 57068 • *739*
Valley Station, KY 40272 • *22,840*
Valley Stream, NY 11580–82 • *33,946*
Valley View, PA 17983 • *1,749*
Valparaiso, FL 32580 • *4,672*
Valparaiso, IN 46383–84 • *24,414*
Val Verda, UT 84010 • *3,712*
Val Verde □, TX • *38,721*
Van, TX 75790 • *1,854*
Van Alstyne, TX 75095 • *2,090*
Van Buren, AR 72956 • *14,979*
Van Buren, ME 04785 • *2,759*
Van Buren □, AR • *14,008*
Van Buren □, IA • *7,676*
Van Buren □, MI • *70,060*
Van Buren □, TN • *4,846*
Vance □, NC • *38,892*
Vanceburg, KY 41179 • *1,713*
Vancleave, MS 39564 • *3,214*
Vancouver, WA 98660–68 • *46,380*
Vandalia, IL 62471 • *6,114*
Vandalia, MO 63382 • *2,683*
Vandalia, OH 45377 • *13,882*
Vandenberg Village, CA 93436 • *5,871*
Vander, NC 28301 • *1,179*
Vanderburgh □, IN • *165,058*
Vandergrift, PA 15690 • *5,904*
Van Horn, TX 79855 • *2,930*
Van Lear, KY 41265 • *1,050*
Vansant, VA 24656 • *1,187*
Van Vleck, TX 77482 • *1,534*
Van Wert, OH 45891 • *10,891*
Van Wert □, OH • *30,464*
Van Zandt □, TX • *37,944*
Varina, VA 23231 • *2,500*
Varnville, SC 29944 • *1,970*
Vassar, MI 48768 • *2,559*
Vaughn, MT 59487 • *2,270*
Veazie, ME 04401 • *1,610*
Veedersburg, IN 47987 • *2,192*
Velda Rose Estates, AZ 85205 • *2,330*
Velva, ND 58790 • *968*
Venango □, PA • *59,381*
Veneta, OR 97487 • *2,519*
Venice, FL 34292–93 • *16,922*
Venice, IL 62090 • *3,571*
Venice Gardens, FL 34293 • *7,701*
Ventnor City, NJ 08406 • *11,005*
Ventura (San Buenaventura), CA 93001–07 • *92,575*
Ventura □, CA • *669,016*
Veradale, WA 99037 • *7,836*
Verda, KY 40828 • *1,133*
Verdi, NV 89439 • *1,140*
Vergennes, VT 05491 • *2,578*
Vermilion, OH 44089 • *11,127*
Vermilion □, IL • *88,257*
Vermilion □, LA • *50,055*
Vermillion, SD 57069 • *10,034*
Vermillion □, IN • *16,773*
Vernal, UT 84078–79 • *6,644*
Vernon, AL 35592 • *2,247*
Vernon, CT 06066 • *30,200*
Vernon, TX 76384 • *12,001*
Vernon □, LA • *61,961*
Vernon □, MO • *19,041*
Vernon □, WI • *25,617*
Vernon Hills, IL 60061 • *15,319*
Vernonia, OR 97064 • *1,808*
Vero Beach, FL 32960–68 • *17,350*
Verona, MS 38879 • *2,893*
Verona, NJ 07044 • *13,597*
Verona, PA 15147 • *3,260*
Verona, WI 53593 • *5,374*
Versailles, IN 47042 • *1,791*
Versailles, KY 40383 • *7,269*
Versailles, MO 65084 • *2,365*
Versailles, OH 45380 • *2,351*
Vestal, NY 13850–51 • *5,530*
Vestavia Hills, AL 35216 • *19,749*
Vevay, IN 47043 • *1,393*
Vian, OK 74962 • *1,414*
Vicksburg, MI 49097 • *2,216*
Vicksburg, MS 39180–82 • *20,908*
Victor, NY 14564 • *2,308*
Victoria, KS 67671 • *1,157*
Victoria, TX 77901–05 • *55,076*
Victoria, VA 23974 • *1,830*
Victoria □, TX • *74,361*
Victorville, CA 92392–93 • *40,674*
Vidalia, GA 30474 • *11,078*
Vidalia, LA 71373 • *4,953*
Vidor, TX 77662 • *10,935*
Vienna, GA 31092 • *2,708*
Vienna, IL 62995 • *1,446*
Vienna, VA 22180–83 • *14,852*
Vienna, WV 26105 • *10,862*
View Park, CA 90043 • *5,900*
Vigo □, IN • *106,107*
Vilas □, WI • *17,707*
Villa Grove, IL 61956 • *2,734*
Villa Hills, KY 41016 • *7,739*
Villa Park, CA 92667 • *6,299*
Villa Park, IL 60181 • *22,253*
Villa Rica, GA 30180 • *6,542*
Villas, NJ 08251 • *8,136*
Ville Platte, LA 70586 • *9,037*
Villisca, IA 50864 • *1,332*
Vilonia, AR 72173 • *1,133*
Vincennes, IN 47591 • *19,859*
Vincent, AL 35178 • *1,767*
Vine Grove, KY 40175 • *3,586*
Vineland, NJ 08360 • *54,780*
Vineyard Haven, MA 02568 • *1,762*
Vinita, OK 74301 • *5,804*
Vinton, IA 52349 • *5,103*
Vinton, LA 70668 • *3,154*
Vinton, VA 24179 • *7,665*
Vinton □, OH • *11,098*
Viola, NY 10952 • *4,504*
Violet, LA 70092 • *8,574*
Virden, IL 62690 • *3,635*
Virginia, IL 62691 • *1,767*
Virginia, MN 55792 • *9,410*
Virginia Beach, VA 23450–67 • *393,069*
Virginia City, NV 89440 • *920*
Viroqua, WI 54665 • *3,922*
Visalia, CA 93277–79 • *75,636*
Vista, CA 92083–84 • *71,872*
Vivian, LA 71082 • *4,156*
Volcano, HI 96785 • *1,516*
Volga, SD 57071 • *1,263*
Volusia □, FL • *370,712*

W

Wabash, IN 46992 • *12,127*
Wabash □, IL • *13,111*
Wabash □, IN • *35,069*
Wabasha, MN 55981 • *2,384*
Wabasha □, MN • *19,744*
Wabasso, FL 32970 • *1,145*
Wabaunsee □, KS • *6,603*
Waco, TX 76701–16 • *103,590*
Waconia, MN 55387 • *3,498*
Wade Hampton, SC 29607 • *20,014*
Wadena, MN 56482 • *4,131*
Wadena □, MN • *13,154*
Wadesboro, NC 28170 • *3,645*
Wading River, NY 11792 • *5,317*
Wadley, GA 30477 • *2,473*
Wadsworth, IL 60083 • *1,826*
Wadsworth, NV 89442 • *640*
Wadsworth, OH 44281 • *15,718*
Wagner, SD 57380 • *1,462*
Wagoner, OK 74467 • *6,894*
Wagoner □, OK • *47,883*
Wahiawa, HI 96786 • *17,386*
Wahkiakum □, WA • *3,327*
Wahoo, NE 68066 • *3,681*
Wahpeton, ND 58074–75 • *8,751*
Waialua, HI 96791 • *3,943*
Waianae, HI 96792 • *8,758*
Waikapu, HI 96793 • *729*
Wailua, HI 96746 • *2,018*
Wailuku, HI 96793 • *10,688*
Waimanalo, HI 96795 • *3,508*
Waimea, HI 96712 • *600*
Waimea, HI 96796 • *5,972*
Wainwright, AK 99782 • *492*
Waipahu, HI 96797 • *31,435*
Waipio Acres, HI 96786 • *5,304*
Waite Park, MN 56387 • *5,020*
Wakarusa, IN 46573 • *1,667*
Wake □, NC • *423,380*
Wa Keeney, KS 67672 • *2,161*
Wakefield, MA 01880 • *24,825*
Wakefield, MI 49968 • *2,318*
Wakefield, NE 68784 • *1,082*
Wakefield, RI 02879–83 • *3,450*
Wakefield, VA 23888 • *1,070*
Wake Forest, NC 27587–88 • *5,769*
Wakulla □, FL • *14,202*
Walbridge, OH 43465 • *2,736*
Walcott, IA 52773 • *1,356*
Walden, NY 12586 • *5,836*
Waldo, AR 71770 • *1,495*
Waldo, FL 32694 • *1,017*
Waldo □, ME • *33,018*
Waldoboro, ME 04572 • *1,420*
Waldport, OR 97394 • *1,595*
Waldron, AR 72958 • *3,024*
Waldwick, NJ 07463 • *9,757*
Walhalla, ND 58282 • *1,131*
Walhalla, SC 29691 • *3,755*
Walker, LA 70785 • *3,727*
Walker, MI 49504 • *17,279*
Walker □, AL • *67,670*
Walker □, GA • *58,340*
Walker □, TX • *50,917*
Walkersville, MD 21793 • *4,145*
Walkerton, IN 46574 • *2,061*
Walkertown, NC 27051 • *1,200*
Walkerville, MT 59701 • *605*
Wall, SD 57790 • *834*
Wallace, ID 83873 • *1,010*
Wallace, NC 28466 • *2,939*
Wallace □, KS • *1,821*
Walla Walla, WA 99362 • *26,478*
Walla Walla □, WA • *48,439*
Walled Lake, MI 48390 • *6,278*
Wallen, IN 46806 • *1,000*
Waller, TX 77484 • *1,493*
Waller □, TX • *23,390*
Wallingford, CT 06492 • *17,827*
Wallingford, VT 05773 • *1,148*
Wallington, NJ 07057 • *10,828*
Wallis, TX 77485 • *1,001*
Wallkill, NY 12589 • *2,125*
Wallowa □, OR • *6,911*
Walnut, CA 91789 • *29,105*
Walnut, IL 61376 • *1,463*
Walnut Cove, NC 27052 • *1,088*
Walnut Creek, CA 94593–98 • *60,569*
Walnut Park, CA 90255 • *14,722*
Walnutport, PA 18088 • *2,055*
Walnut Ridge, AR 72476 • *4,388*
Walpole, MA 02081 • *5,495*
Walsenburg, CO 81089 • *3,300*
Walsh □, ND • *13,840*
Walterboro, SC 29488 • *5,492*
Walters, OK 73572 • *2,519*
Walthall □, MS • *14,352*
Waltham, MA 02154 • *57,878*
Walthourville, GA 31333 • *2,024*
Walton, IN 46994 • *1,053*
Walton, KY 41094 • *2,034*
Walton, NY 13856 • *3,326*
Walton □, FL • *27,760*
Walton □, GA • *38,586*
Walworth, WI 53184 • *1,614*
Walworth □, SD • *6,087*
Walworth □, WI • *75,000*
Wamac, IL 62801 • *1,501*
Wamego, KS 66547 • *3,706*
Wamesit, MA 01876 • *2,700*
Wamsutter, WY 82336 • *240*
Wanaque, NJ 07465 • *9,711*
Wanchese, NC 27981 • *1,380*
Wando Woods, SC 29405 • *5,253*
Wantagh, NY 11793 • *18,567*
Wapakoneta, OH 45895 • *9,214*
Wapato, WA 98951 • *3,795*
Wapello, IA 52653 • *2,013*
Wapello □, IA • *35,687*
Wappingers Falls, NY 12590 • *4,605*
War, WV 24892 • *1,081*
Ward, AR 72176 • *1,269*
Ward □, ND • *57,921*
Ward □, TX • *13,115*
Warden, WA 98857 • *1,639*
Ware, MA 01082 • *6,533*
Ware □, GA • *35,471*
Wareham, MA 02571 • *2,607*
Warehouse Point, CT 06088 • *1,880*
Ware Shoals, SC 29692 • *2,497*
Waretown, NJ 08758 • *1,283*
Warminster, PA 18974 • *35,463*
Warner, OK 74469 • *1,479*
Warner Robins, GA 31088 • *43,726*
Warr Acres, OK 73132 • *9,288*
Warren, AR 71671 • *6,455*
Warren, IL 61087 • *1,550*
Warren, IN 46792 • *1,185*
Warren, MA 01083 • *1,516*
Warren, MI 48089–93 • *144,864*
Warren, MN 56762 • *1,813*
Warren, OH 44481–85 • *50,793*
Warren, PA 16365 • *11,122*
Warren, RI 02885 • *11,385*
Warren, VT 05674 • *350*
Warren □, GA • *6,078*
Warren □, IL • *19,181*
Warren □, IN • *8,176*
Warren □, IA • *36,033*
Warren □, KY • *76,673*
Warren □, MS • *47,880*
Warren □, MO • *19,534*
Warren □, NJ • *91,607*
Warren □, NY • *59,209*
Warren □, NC • *17,265*
Warren □, OH • *113,909*
Warren □, PA • *45,050*
Warren □, TN • *32,992*
Warren □, VA • *26,142*
Warren Park, IN 46219 • *1,763*
Warrensburg, IL 62573 • *1,274*
Warrensburg, MO 64093 • *15,244*
Warrensburg, NY 12885 • *3,204*
Warrensville Heights, OH 44122 • *15,745*
Warrenton, GA 30828 • *2,056*
Warrenton, MO 63383 • *3,564*
Warrenton, OR 97146 • *2,681*
Warrenton, VA 22186 • *4,830*
Warrenville, IL 60555 • *11,333*
Warrenville, SC 29851 • *1,029*
Warrick □, IN • *44,920*
Warrington, FL 32507 • *16,040*
Warrington, PA 18976 • *6,980*

Warrior, AL 35180 • *3,280*
Warroad, MN 56763 • *1,679*
Warsaw, IL 62379 • *1,882*
Warsaw, IN 46580–81 • *10,968*
Warsaw, KY 41095 • *1,202*
Warsaw, MO 65355 • *1,696*
Warsaw, NY 14569 • *3,830*
Warsaw, NC 28398 • *2,859*
Warwick, NY 10990 • *5,984*
Warwick, RI 02886–89 • *85,427*
Wasatch □, UT • *10,089*
Wasco, CA 93280 • *12,412*
Wasco □, OR • *21,683*
Waseca, MN 56093 • *8,385*
Waseca □, MN • *18,079*
Washakie □, WY • *8,388*
Washburn, IL 61570 • *1,075*
Washburn, IA 50706 • *1,400*
Washburn, ME 04786 • *1,880*
Washburn, ND 58577 • *1,506*
Washburn, WI 54891 • *2,285*
Washburn □, WI • *13,772*
Washington, DC 20001–99 • *606,900*
Washington, GA 30673 • *4,279*
Washington, IL 61571 • *10,099*
Washington, IN 47501 • *10,838*
Washington, IA 52353 • *7,074*
Washington, KS 66968 • *1,304*
Washington, LA 70589 • *1,253*
Washington, MO 63090 • *10,704*
Washington, NJ 07882 • *6,474*
Washington, NC 27889 • *9,075*
Washington, PA 15301 • *15,864*
Washington, UT 84780 • *4,198*
Washington □, AL • *16,694*
Washington □, AR • *113,409*
Washington □, CO • *4,812*
Washington □, FL • *16,919*
Washington □, GA • *19,112*
Washington □, ID • *8,550*
Washington □, IL • *14,965*
Washington □, IN • *23,717*
Washington □, IA • *19,612*
Washington □, KS • *7,073*
Washington □, KY • *10,441*
Washington □, LA • *43,185*
Washington □, ME • *35,308*
Washington □, MD • *121,393*
Washington □, MN • *145,896*
Washington □, MS • *67,935*
Washington □, MO • *20,380*
Washington □, NE • *16,607*
Washington □, NY • *59,330*
Washington □, NC • *13,997*
Washington □, OH • *62,254*
Washington □, OK • *48,066*
Washington □, OR • *311,554*
Washington □, PA • *204,584*
Washington □, RI • *110,006*
Washington □, TN • *92,315*
Washington □, TX • *26,154*
Washington □, UT • *48,560*
Washington □, VT • *54,928*
Washington □, VA • *45,887*
Washington □, WI • *95,328*
Washington Court House, OH 43160 • *12,983*
Washington Park, FL 33314 • *6,930*
Washington Park, IL 62204 • *7,431*
Washington Terrace, UT 84403 • *8,189*
Washington Township, NJ 07675 • *9,245*
Washita □, OK • *11,441*
Washoe □, NV • *254,667*
Washoe City, NV 89701 • *400*
Washougal, WA 98671 • *4,764*
Washtenaw □, MI • *282,937*
Wasilla, AK 99687 • *4,028*
Waskom, TX 75692 • *1,812*
Watauga, TX 76148 • *20,009*
Watauga □, NC • *36,952*
Watchung, NJ 07060 • *5,110*
Waterbury, CT 06701–26 • *108,961*
Waterbury, VT 05676 • *1,702*
Waterbury Center, VT 05677 • *500*
Waterford, CT 06385 • *17,930*
Waterford, MI 48327–29 • *66,692*
Waterford, NY 12188 • *2,370*
Waterford, PA 16441 • *1,492*
Waterford, WI 53185 • *2,431*
Waterford Works, NJ 08089 • *1,200*
Waterloo, IL 62298 • *5,072*
Waterloo, IN 46793 • *2,040*
Waterloo, IA 50701–07 • *66,467*
Waterloo, NY 13165 • *5,116*
Waterloo, WI 53594 • *2,712*
Waterman, IL 60556 • *1,074*
Waterproof, LA 71375 • *1,080*
Watertown, CT 06795 • *20,456*
Watertown, FL 32055 • *3,340*
Watertown, MA 02172 • *33,284*
Watertown, NY 13601–03 • *29,429*
Watertown, SD 57201 • *17,592*
Watertown, TN 37184 • *1,250*
Watertown, WI 53094 • *19,142*
Water Valley, MS 38965 • *3,610*
Waterville, ME 04901–03 • *17,173*
Waterville, MN 56096 • *1,771*
Waterville, NY 13480 • *1,664*
Waterville, OH 43566 • *4,517*
Watervliet, MI 49098 • *1,867*
Watervliet, NY 12189 • *11,061*
Watford City, ND 58854 • *1,784*
Wathena, KS 66090 • *1,160*
Watkins Glen, NY 14891 • *2,207*
Watkinsville, GA 30677 • *1,600*
Watonga, OK 73772 • *3,408*
Watonwan □, MN • *11,682*
Watseka, IL 60970 • *5,424*
Watsontown, PA 17777 • *2,310*
Watsonville, CA 95076–77 • *31,099*
Wattsville, SC 29360 • *1,324*
Wauchula, FL 33873 • *3,253*
Wauconda, IL 60084 • *6,294*
Waukee, IA 50263 • *2,512*
Waukegan, IL 60085–87 • *69,392*
Waukesha, WI 53186–88 • *56,958*
Waukesha □, WI • *304,715*
Waukomis, OK 73773 • *1,322*
Waukon, IA 52172 • *4,019*
Waunakee, WI 53597 • *5,897*
Waupaca, WI 54981 • *4,957*
Waupaca □, WI • *46,104*
Waupun, WI 53963 • *8,207*

Wauregan, CT 06387 • *1,200*
Waurika, OK 73573 • *2,088*
Wausau, WI 54401–02 • *37,060*
Wauseon, OH 43567 • *6,322*
Waushara □, WI • *19,385*
Wautoma, WI 54982 • *1,784*
Wauwatosa, WI 53213 • *49,366*
Waveland, MS 39576 • *5,369*
Waverly, IL 62692 • *1,402*
Waverly, IA 50677 • *8,539*
Waverly, MI 48917 • *15,614*
Waverly, NE 68462 • *1,869*
Waverly, NY 14892 • *4,787*
Waverly, OH 45690 • *4,477*
Waverly, TN 37185 • *3,925*
Waverly, VA 23890 • *2,223*
Waxahachie, TX 75165 • *18,168*
Waxhaw, NC 28173 • *1,294*
Waycross, GA 31501 • *16,410*
Wayland, MA 01778 • *2,550*
Wayland, MI 49348 • *2,751*
Wayland, NY 14572 • *1,976*
Waylyn, SC 29405 • *2,400*
Waymart, PA 18472 • *1,337*
Wayne, MI 48184–88 • *19,899*
Wayne, NE 68787 • *5,142*
Wayne, NJ 07470–74 • *47,025*
Wayne, WV 25570 • *1,128*
Wayne □, GA • *22,356*
Wayne □, IL • *17,241*
Wayne □, IN • *71,951*
Wayne □, IA • *7,067*
Wayne □, KY • *17,468*
Wayne □, MI • *2,111,687*
Wayne □, MS • *19,517*
Wayne □, MO • *11,543*
Wayne □, NE • *9,364*
Wayne □, NY • *89,123*
Wayne □, NC • *104,666*
Wayne □, OH • *101,461*
Wayne □, PA • *39,944*
Wayne □, TN • *13,935*
Wayne □, UT • *2,177*
Wayne □, WV • *41,636*
Wayne City, IL 62895 • *1,099*
Waynesboro, GA 30830 • *5,701*
Waynesboro, MS 39367 • *5,143*
Waynesboro, PA 17268 • *9,578*
Waynesboro, TN 38485 • *1,824*
Waynesboro, VA 22980 • *18,549*
Waynesburg, OH 44688 • *1,068*
Waynesburg, PA 15370 • *4,270*
Waynesville, MO 65583 • *3,207*
Waynesville, NC 28786 • *6,758*
Waynesville, OH 45068 • *1,949*
Waynewood, VA 22308 • *5,000*
Wayzata, MN 55391 • *3,806*
Weakley □, TN • *31,972*
Weatherford, OK 73096 • *10,124*
Weatherford, TX 76086–87 • *14,804*
Weatherly, PA 18255 • *2,640*
Weatogue, CT 06089 • *2,521*
Weaver, AL 36277 • *2,715*
Weaverville, CA 96093 • *3,370*
Weaverville, NC 28787 • *2,107*
Webb, AL 36376 • *1,039*
Webb □, TX • *133,239*
Webb City, MO 64870 • *7,449*
Webberville, MI 48892 • *1,698*
Weber □, UT • *158,330*
Weber City, VA 24251 • *1,377*
Webster, MA 01570 • *11,849*
Webster, NY 14580 • *5,464*
Webster, PA 15087 • *1,000*
Webster, SD 57274 • *2,017*
Webster □, GA • *2,263*
Webster □, IA • *40,342*
Webster □, KY • *13,955*
Webster □, LA • *41,989*
Webster □, MS • *10,222*
Webster □, MO • *23,753*
Webster □, NE • *4,279*
Webster □, WV • *10,729*
Webster City, IA 50595 • *7,894*
Webster Groves, MO 63119 • *22,987*
Websterville, VT 05678 • *600*
Wedgewood, MO 63031 • *6,700*
Weed, CA 96094 • *3,062*
Weed Heights, NV 89447 • *230*
Weedsport, NY 13166 • *1,996*
Weehawken, NJ 07087 • *12,385*
Weeping Water, NE 68463 • *1,008*
Weigelstown, PA 17315 • *8,665*
Weimar, TX 78962 • *2,052*
Weippe, ID 83553 • *532*
Weirsdale, FL 32195 • *1,500*
Weirton, WV 26062 • *22,124*
Weiser, ID 83672 • *4,571*
Wekiva Springs, FL 32750 • *23,026*
Welch, WV 24801 • *3,028*
Welcome, SC 29611 • *6,560*
Weld □, CO • *131,821*
Weldon, NC 27890 • *1,392*
Weleetka, OK 74880 • *1,112*
Wellesley, MA 02181 • *26,615*
Wellfleet, MA 02667 • *1,200*
Wellford, SC 29385 • *2,511*
Wellington, CO 80549 • *1,340*
Wellington, FL 33414 • *20,670*
Wellington, KS 67152 • *8,411*
Wellington, NV 89444 • *280*
Wellington, OH 44090 • *4,140*
Wellington, TX 79095 • *2,456*
Wellington, UT 84542 • *1,632*
Wellman, IA 52356 • *1,085*
Wells, ME 04090 • *1,200*
Wells, MI 49894 • *1,150*
Wells, MN 56097 • *2,465*
Wells, NV 89835 • *1,256*
Wells □, IN • *25,948*
Wells □, ND • *5,864*
Wellsboro, PA 16901 • *3,430*
Wellsburg, WV 26070 • *3,385*
Wellston, OH 45692 • *6,049*
Wellsville, KS 66092 • *1,563*
Wellsville, MO 63384 • *1,430*
Wellsville, NY 14895 • *5,241*
Wellsville, OH 43968 • *4,532*
Wellsville, UT 84339 • *2,206*
Wellton, AZ 85356 • *1,066*
Welsh, LA 70591 • *3,299*
Wenatchee, WA 98801–07 • *21,756*
Wendell, ID 83355 • *1,963*

Wendell, NC 27591 • *2,822*
Wendover, UT 84083 • *1,127*
Wenham, MA 01984 • *3,897*
Wenonah, NJ 08090 • *2,331*
Wentzville, MO 63385 • *5,088*
Weslaco, TX 78596 • *21,877*
Wesleyville, PA 16510 • *3,655*
Wessington Springs, SD 57382 • *1,083*
Wesson, MS 39191 • *1,510*
West, TX 76691 • *2,515*
West Acton, MA 01720 • *5,230*
West Alexandria, OH 45381 • *1,460*
West Allis, WI 53214 • *63,221*
West Andover, MA 01810 • *1,970*
West Athens, CA 90247 • *8,859*
West Babylon, NY 11704 • *42,410*
West Barnstable, MA 02668 • *1,000*
West Baton Rouge □, LA • *19,419*
West Bay Shore, NY 11706 • *4,907*
West Bend, WI 53095 • *23,916*
West Berlin, NJ 08091 • *2,970*
West Billerica, MA 01862 • *1,920*
West Blocton, AL 35184 • *1,468*
Westborough, MA 01581 • *3,917*
West Bountiful, UT 84087 • *4,477*
West Boylston, MA 01583 • *3,130*
West Bradenton, FL 34205 • *4,528*
West Branch, IA 52358 • *1,908*
West Branch, MI 48661 • *1,914*
West Bridgewater, MA 02379 • *2,140*
Westbrook, CT 06498 • *2,060*
Westbrook, ME 04092 • *16,121*
West Brookfield, MA 01585 • *1,419*
West Burlington, IA 52655 • *3,083*
Westbury, NY 11590 • *13,060*
Westby, WI 54667 • *1,866*
West Caldwell, NJ 07004 • *10,422*
West Cape May, NJ 08204 • *1,026*
West Carroll □, LA • *12,093*
West Carrollton, OH 45449 • *14,403*
West Carson, CA 90502 • *20,143*
West Carthage, NY 13619 • *2,166*
West Chatham, MA 02669 • *1,504*
Westchester, FL 33136 • *29,883*
Westchester, IL 60153 • *17,301*
West Chester, PA 19380–82 • *18,041*
Westchester □, NY • *874,866*
West Chicago, IL 60185–86 • *14,796*
West Columbia, SC 29169–72 • *10,588*
West Columbia, TX 77486 • *4,372*
West Compton, CA 90220 • *5,451*
West Concord, MA 01742 • *5,761*
West Concord, NC 28027 • *5,859*
West Covina, CA 91790–93 • *96,086*
West Crossett, AR 71635 • *2,019*
West Dennis, MA 02670 • *2,307*
West Des Moines, IA 50265 • *31,702*
West Elmira, NY 14905 • *5,218*
Westerly, RI 02891 • *16,477*
Westernport, MD 21562 • *2,454*
Western Springs, IL 60558 • *11,984*
Westerville, OH 43081–82 • *30,269*
West Fairview, PA 17025 • *1,403*
West Falmouth, MA 02574 • *1,600*
West Fargo, ND 58078 • *12,287*
West Feliciana □, LA • *12,915*
Westfield, IN 46074 • *3,304*
Westfield, MA 01085–86 • *38,372*
Westfield, NJ 07090–92 • *28,870*
Westfield, NY 14787 • *3,451*
Westfield, PA 16950 • *1,119*
Westfield, WI 53964 • *1,125*
Westford, MA 01886 • *1,200*
West Fork, AR 72774 • *1,607*
West Frankfort, IL 62896 • *8,526*
West Freehold, NJ 07728 • *11,166*
Westgate, FL 33401 • *2,100*
West Gate, VA 22110 • *6,565*
West Gate of Lomond, VA 22110 • *5,400*
West Glens Falls, NY 12801 • *5,964*
West Goshen, PA 19380 • *8,948*
West Grove, PA 19390 • *2,128*
Westham, VA 23229 • *3,200*
West Hanover, MA 02339 • *1,700*
West Hartford, CT 06127 • *60,110*
West Haven, CT 06516 • *54,021*
West Haven, OR 97225 • *3,400*
West Haverstraw, NY 10993 • *9,183*
West Hazleton, PA 18201 • *4,136*
West Helena, AR 72390 • *9,695*
West Hempstead, NY 11552 • *17,689*
West Hollywood, CA 90069 • *36,118*
Westhope, ND 58793 • *578*
West Hyannisport, MA 02672 • *1,200*
West Islip, NY 11795 • *28,419*
West Jefferson, NC 28694 • *1,002*
West Jefferson, OH 43162 • *4,504*
West Jordan, UT 84084 • *42,892*
West Kingston, RI 02892 • *1,150*
West Lafayette, IN 47906–07 • *25,907*
West Lafayette, OH 43845 • *2,129*
Westlake, LA 70669 • *5,007*
Westlake, OH 44145 • *27,018*
Westlake Village, CA 91361 • *7,455*
Westland, MI 48185 • *84,724*
West Lawn, PA 19609 • *1,606*
West Liberty, IA 52776 • *2,935*
West Liberty, KY 41472 • *1,887*
West Liberty, OH 43357 • *1,613*
West Liberty, WV 26074 • *1,434*
West Linn, OR 97068 • *16,367*
West Long Branch, NJ 07764 • *7,690*
West Marion, NC 28752 • *1,291*
West Medway, MA 02053 • *1,940*
West Melbourne, FL 32901 • *8,399*
West Memphis, AR 72301 • *28,259*
Westmere, NY 12203 • *6,750*
West Miami, FL 33174 • *5,727*
West Mifflin, PA 15122–23 • *23,644*
West Milford, NJ 07480 • *25,430*
West Milton, OH 45383 • *4,348*
West Milwaukee, WI 53214 • *3,973*
Westminster, CA 92683–84 • *78,118*
Westminster, CO 80030–31 • *74,625*
Westminster, MD 21157 • *13,068*
Westminster, SC 29693 • *3,120*
West Modesto, CA 95351 • *6,135*
West Monroe, LA 71291–94 • *14,096*
Westmont, CA 90044 • *31,100*
Westmont, IL 60559 • *21,228*
Westmont, NJ 08108 • *5,630*
Westmont, PA 15905 • *5,789*
Westmoreland, TN 37186 • *1,726*

Westmoreland □, PA • *370,321*
Westmoreland □, VA • *15,480*
Westmorland, CA 92281 • *1,380*
West Mystic, CT 06388 • *3,595*
West Newton, PA 15089 • *3,152*
West New York, NJ 07093 • *38,125*
West Norriton, PA 19401 • *15,209*
West Nyack, NY 10960 • *3,437*
Weston, CT 06883 • *1,370*
Weston, MA 02193 • *11,169*
Weston, MO 64098 • *1,528*
Weston, OH 43569 • *1,716*
Weston, WV 26452 • *4,994*
Weston, WI 54476 • *9,714*
Weston □, WY • *6,518*
West Orange, NJ 07052 • *39,103*
Westover, WV 26505 • *4,201*
West Palm Beach, FL 33401–20 • *67,643*
West Pasco, WA 99301 • *7,312*
West Paterson, NJ 07424 • *10,982*
West Pawlet, VT 05775 • *350*
West Pensacola, FL 32505 • *22,107*
West Peoria, IL 61604 • *5,314*
West Pittsburg, CA 94565 • *17,453*
West Pittsburg, PA 16160 • *1,133*
West Pittston, PA 18643 • *5,590*
West Plains, MO 65775 • *8,913*
West Point, CA 95255 • *1,500*
West Point, GA 31833 • *3,571*
West Point, IA 52656 • *1,079*
West Point, KY 40177 • *1,216*
West Point, MS 39773 • *8,489*
West Point, NE 68788 • *3,250*
West Point, NY 10996–97 • *8,024*
West Point, UT 84015 • *4,258*
West Point, VA 23181 • *2,938*
Westport, CT 06880–83 • *24,407*
Westport, IN 47283 • *1,478*
Westport, WA 98595 • *1,892*
West Portsmouth, OH 45662 • *3,551*
West Puente Valley, CA 91744 • *20,254*
West Reading, PA 19611 • *4,142*
West Rutland, VT 05777 • *2,246*
West Sacramento, CA 95691 • *28,898*
West Saint Paul, MN 55118 • *19,248*
West Salem, IL 62476 • *1,042*
West Salem, OH 44287 • *1,534*
West Salem, WI 54669 • *3,611*
West Sayville, NY 11796 • *4,680*
West Seneca, NY 14224 • *47,866*
West Simsbury, CT 06092 • *2,149*
West Slope, OR 97225 • *7,959*
West Springfield, MA 01089–90 • *27,537*
West Springfield, VA 22152 • *28,126*
West Swanzey, NH 03469 • *1,055*
West Terre Haute, IN 47885 • *2,495*
West Union, IA 52175 • *2,490*
West Union, OH 45693 • *3,096*
West Unity, OH 43570 • *1,677*
West University Place, TX 77005 • *12,920*
West Upton, MA 01587 • *1,300*
Westvale, NY 13219 • *5,952*
West Valley City, UT 84120 • *86,976*
Westview, FL 33168 • *9,668*
West View, PA 15229 • *7,734*
Westville, IL 61883 • *3,387*
Westville, IN 46391 • *5,255*
Westville, NJ 08093 • *4,573*
Westville, OK 74965 • *1,374*
West Wareham, MA 02576 • *2,059*
West Warren, MA 01092 • *1,200*
West Warwick, RI 02893 • *29,268*
West Webster, NY 14580 • *8,690*
Westwego, LA 70094–96 • *11,218*
West Whittier, CA 90606 • *13,800*
West Willow, MI 48198 • *4,300*
Westwood, CA 96137 • *2,017*
Westwood, KS 66205 • *1,772*
Westwood, KY 41101 • *5,300*
Westwood, MD 20090 • *6,500*
Westwood, MI 49007 • *8,957*
Westwood, NJ 07675 • *10,446*
Westwood Lakes, FL 33165 • *11,522*
West Wyoming, PA 18644 • *3,117*
West Yarmouth, MA 02673 • *5,409*
West Yellowstone, MT 59758 • *913*
West York, PA 17404 • *4,283*
Wethersfield, CT 06129 • *25,651*
Wetumka, OK 74883 • *1,427*
Wetumpka, AL 36092 • *4,670*
Wetzel □, WV • *19,258*
Wewahitchka, FL 32465 • *1,779*
Wewoka, OK 74884 • *4,050*
Wexford □, MI • *26,360*
Weyauwega, WI 54983 • *1,665*
Weymouth, MA 02188 • *54,063*
Whalom, MA 01420 • *1,340*
Wharton, NJ 07885 • *5,405*
Wharton, TX 77488 • *9,011*
Wharton □, TX • *39,955*
Whatcom □, WA • *127,780*
Wheatland, CA 95692 • *1,631*
Wheatland, WY 82201 • *3,271*
Wheatland □, MT • *2,246*
Wheaton, IL 60187–89 • *51,464*
Wheaton, MD 20902 • *58,300*
Wheaton, MN 56296 • *1,615*
Wheat Ridge, CO 80033–34 • *29,419*
Wheeler, TX 79096 • *1,393*
Wheeler □, GA • *4,903*
Wheeler □, NE • *948*
Wheeler □, OR • *1,396*
Wheeler □, TX • *5,879*
Wheelersburg, OH 45694 • *5,113*
Wheeling, IL 60090 • *29,911*
Wheeling, WV 26003 • *34,882*
Whitacres, CT 06082 • *2,410*
White □, AR • *54,676*
White □, GA • *13,006*
White □, IL • *16,522*
White □, IN • *23,265*
White □, TN • *20,090*
White Bear Lake, MN 55110 • *24,704*
White Bluff, TN 37187 • *1,988*
White Castle, LA 70788 • *2,102*
White Center, WA 98126 • *15,700*
White City, OR 97503 • *5,891*
White City, UT 84070 • *6,506*
White Cloud, MI 49349 • *1,147*
White Deer, TX 79097 • *1,125*
Whitefield, NH 03598 • *1,041*
Whitefish, MT 59937 • *4,368*
Whitefish Bay, WI 53217 • *14,272*

White Hall, AR 71602 • *3,849*
White Hall, IL 62092 • *2,814*
Whitehall, MI 49461 • *3,027*
Whitehall, MT 59759 • *1,067*
Whitehall, NY 12887 • *3,071*
Whitehall, OH 43213 • *20,572*
Whitehall, PA 15227 • *14,451*
Whitehall, WI 54773 • *1,494*
White Haven, PA 18661 • *1,132*
White Horse, NJ 08610 • *9,397*
White Horse Beach, MA 02381 • *1,200*
Whitehouse, OH 43571 • *2,528*
White House, TN 37188 • *2,987*
White House Station, NJ 08889 • *1,400*
White Island Shores, MA 02538 • *2,000*
White Meadow Lake, NJ 07866 • *8,002*
White Oak, MD 20901 • *18,671*
White Oak, OH 45239 • *12,430*
White Oak, PA 15131 • *8,761*
White Pigeon, MI 49099 • *1,458*
White Pine, MI 49971 • *1,142*
White Pine, TN 37890 • *1,771*
White Pine □, NV • *9,264*
White Plains, MD 20695 • *3,560*
White Plains, NY 10601–07 • *48,718*
Whiteriver, AZ 85941 • *3,775*
White River Junction, VT 05001 • *2,521*
White Rock, NM 87544 • *6,192*
White Salmon, WA 98672 • *1,861*
Whitesboro, NY 13492 • *4,195*
Whitesboro, TX 76273 • *3,209*
Whitesburg, KY 41858 • *1,636*
White Settlement, TX 76108 • *15,472*
Whiteside □, IL • *60,186*
White Sulphur Springs, MT 59645 • *963*
White Sulphur Springs, WV 24986 • *2,779*
Whiteville, NC 28472 • *5,078*
Whiteville, TN 38075 • *1,050*
Whitewater, WI 53190 • *12,636*
Whitewood, SD 57793 • *891*
Whitewright, TX 75491 • *1,713*
Whitfield □, GA • *72,462*
Whitfield Estates, FL 34243 • *3,152*
Whiting, IN 46394 • *5,155*
Whiting, WI 54481 • *1,838*
Whitinsville, MA 01588 • *5,639*
Whitley □, IN • *27,651*
Whitley □, KY • *33,326*
Whitley City, KY 42653 • *1,133*
Whitman, MA 02382 • *13,534*
Whitman, WV 25652 • *1,651*
Whitman □, WA • *38,775*
Whitman Square, NJ 08012 • *3,490*
Whitmire, SC 29178 • *1,702*
Whitmore Lake, MI 48189 • *3,251*
Whitmore Village, HI 96786 • *3,373*
Whitney, SC 29303 • *4,052*
Whitney, TX 76692 • *1,626*
Whitney Point, NY 13862 • *1,054*
Whittier, AK 99693 • *243*
Whittier, CA 90601–12 • *77,671*
Whitwell, TN 37397 • *1,622*
Wibaux, MT 59353 • *628*
Wibaux □, MT • *1,191*
Wichita, KS 67201–78 • *304,011*
Wichita □, KS • *2,758*
Wichita □, TX • *122,378*
Wichita Falls, TX 76301–11 • *96,259*
Wickenburg, AZ 85358 • *4,515*
Wickliffe, OH 44092 • *14,558*
Wickliffe, OH 44515 • *7,240*
Wicomico □, MD • *74,339*
Wiconisco, PA 17097 • *1,321*
Widefield, CO 80911 • *12,112*
Wiggins, MS 39577 • *3,185*
Wilbarger □, TX • *15,121*
Wilber, NE 68465 • *1,527*
Wilberforce, OH 45384 • *2,639*
Wilbraham, MA 01095 • *3,352*
Wilburton, OK 74578 • *3,092*
Wilcox, PA 15870 • *1,000*
Wilcox □, AL • *13,568*
Wilcox □, GA • *7,008*
Wilder, ID 83676 • *1,232*
Wilder, VT 05088 • *1,576*
Wildorado, TX 79098 • *2,000*
Wildwood, FL 34785 • *3,421*
Wildwood, IL 60030 • *2,034*
Wildwood, NJ 08260 • *4,484*
Wildwood Crest, NJ 08260 • *3,631*
Wilkes □, GA • *10,597*
Wilkes □, NC • *59,393*
Wilkes-Barre, PA 18701–73 • *47,523*
Wilkesboro, NC 28697 • *2,573*
Wilkin □, MN • *7,516*
Wilkinsburg, PA 15221 • *21,080*
Wilkinson □, GA • *10,228*
Wilkinson □, MS • *9,678*
Wilkins Township, PA 15145 • *7,487*
Will □, IL • *357,313*
Willacoochee, GA 31650 • *1,205*
Willacy □, TX • *17,705*
Willamina, OR 97396 • *1,717*
Willard, MO 65781 • *2,177*
Willard, NY 14588 • *1,339*
Willard, OH 44890 • *6,210*
Willard, UT 84340 • *1,298*
Willcox, AZ 85643 • *3,122*
Williams, AZ 86046 • *2,532*
Williams, CA 95987 • *2,297*
Williams □, ND • *21,129*
Williams □, OH • *36,956*
Williams Bay, WI 53191 • *2,108*
Williamsburg, IA 52361 • *2,174*
Williamsburg, KY 40769 • *5,493*
Williamsburg, MA 01096 • *1,200*
Williamsburg, OH 45176 • *2,322*
Williamsburg, PA 16693 • *1,456*
Williamsburg, VA 23185–88 • *11,530*
Williamsburg □, SC • *36,815*
Williamson, NY 14589 • *1,768*
Williamson, WV 25661 • *4,154*
Williamson □, IL • *57,733*
Williamson □, TN • *81,021*
Williamson □, TX • *139,551*
Williamsport, IN 47993 • *1,798*
Williamsport, MD 21795 • *2,103*
Williamsport, PA 17701–03 • *31,933*
Williamston, MI 48895 • *2,922*
Williamston, NC 27892 • *5,503*
Williamston, SC 29697 • *3,876*
Williamstown, KY 41097 • *3,023*
Williamstown, MA 01267 • *4,791*

Williamstown, NJ 08094 • *10,891*
Williamstown, PA 17098 • *1,509*
Williamstown, VT 05679 • *650*
Williamstown, WV 26187 • *2,774*
Williamsville, IL 62693 • *1,140*
Williamsville, NY 14221 • *5,583*
Willimantic, CT 06226 • *14,746*
Willingboro, NJ 08046 • *36,291*
Willis, TX 77378 • *2,764*
Williston, FL 32696 • *2,179*
Williston, ND 58801–02 • *13,131*
Williston, SC 29853 • *3,099*
Williston Park, NY 11596 • *7,516*
Willits, CA 95490 • *5,027*
Willmar, MN 56201 • *17,531*
Willoughby, OH 44094–95 • *20,510*
Willoughby Hills, OH 44092 • *8,427*
Willow Brook, CA 90222 • *32,772*
Willowbrook, IL 60521 • *8,598*
Willow Grove, PA 19090 • *16,325*
Willowick, OH 44094 • *15,269*
Willow Run, DE 19805 • *1,600*
Willow Run, MI 48198 • *7,200*
Willows, CA 95988 • *5,988*
Willow Springs, IL 60480 • *4,509*
Willow Springs, MO 65793 • *2,038*
Willston, VA 22044 • *2,000*
Wilmerding, PA 15148 • *2,222*
Wilmette, IL 60091 • *26,690*
Wilmington, DE 19801–99 • *71,529*
Wilmington, IL 60481 • *4,743*
Wilmington, MA 01887 • *17,654*
Wilmington, NC 28401–12 • *55,530*
Wilmington, OH 45177 • *11,199*
Wilmington, VT 05363 • *550*
Wilmington Island, GA 31410 • *11,230*
Wilmington Manor, DE 19720 • *8,568*
Wilmington Manor Gardens, DE 19720 • *1,500*
Wilmore, KY 40390 • *4,215*
Wilmot, AR 71676 • *1,047*
Wilson, AR 72395 • *1,068*
Wilson, NY 14172 • *1,307*
Wilson, NC 27893–95 • *36,930*
Wilson, OK 73463 • *1,639*
Wilson, PA 18042 • *7,830*
Wilson, WY 83014 • *500*
Wilson □, KS • *10,289*
Wilson □, NC • *66,061*
Wilson □, TN • *67,675*
Wilson □, TX • *22,650*
Wilsonville, AL 35186 • *1,185*
Wilsonville, OR 97070 • *7,106*
Wilton, CT 06897 • *7,200*
Wilton, IA 52778 • *2,577*
Wilton, ME 04294 • *2,453*
Wilton, NH 03086 • *1,165*
Wilton, ND 58579 • *728*
Wilton Manors, FL 33334 • *11,804*
Wimauma, FL 33598 • *2,932*
Winamac, IN 46996 • *2,262*
Winchendon, MA 01475 • *4,316*
Winchester, IL 62694 • *1,769*
Winchester, IN 47394 • *5,095*
Winchester, KY 40391–92 • *15,799*
Winchester, MA 01890 • *20,267*
Winchester, NV 89101 • *23,365*
Winchester, NH 03470 • *1,735*
Winchester, TN 37398 • *6,305*
Winchester, VA 22601 • *21,947*
Windber, PA 15963 • *4,756*
Windcrest, TX 78239 • *5,331*
Winder, GA 30680 • *7,373*
Windgap, PA 18091 • *2,741*
Windham, CT 06280 • *1,100*
Windham, OH 44288 • *2,943*
Windham □, CT • *102,525*
Windham □, VT • *41,588*
Wind Lake, WI 53185 • *3,000*
Windom, MN 56101 • *4,283*
Window Rock, AZ 86515 • *3,306*
Wind Point, WI 53402 • *1,941*
Windsor, CO 80550 • *5,062*
Windsor, CT 06095 • *27,817*
Windsor, IL 61957 • *1,143*
Windsor, MO 65360 • *3,044*
Windsor, NC 27983 • *2,056*
Windsor, PA 17366 • *1,355*
Windsor, VT 05089 • *3,478*
Windsor, VA 23487 • *1,025*
Windsor □, VT • *54,055*
Windsor Heights, IA 50311 • *5,190*
Windsor Hills, CA 90052 • *6,200*
Windsor Locks, CT 06096 • *12,358*
Windy Hill, SC 29506 • *1,622*
Windy Hills, DE 19711 • *1,130*
Winfield, AL 35594 • *3,689*
Winfield, IA 52659 • *1,051*
Winfield, KS 67156 • *11,931*
Winfield, NJ 07036 • *1,785*
Winfield, WV 25213 • *1,164*
Wingate, NC 28174 • *2,821*
Wink, TX 79789 • *1,189*
Winkler □, TX • *8,626*
Winlock, WA 98596 • *1,027*
Winn □, LA • *16,269*
Winnebago, IL 61088 • *1,840*
Winnebago, MN 56098 • *1,565*
Winnebago, WI 54985 • *1,433*
Winnebago □, IL • *252,913*
Winnebago □, IA • *12,122*
Winnebago □, WI • *140,320*
Winneconne, WI 54986 • *2,059*
Winnemucca, NV 89445 • *6,134*
Winner, SD 57580 • *3,354*
Winneshiek □, IA • *20,847*
Winnetka, IL 60093 • *12,174*
Winnfield, LA 71483 • *6,138*
Winnsboro, LA 71295 • *5,755*
Winnsboro, SC 29180 • *3,475*
Winnsboro, TX 75494 • *2,904*
Winnsboro Mills, SC 29180 • *2,275*
Winona, MN 55987 • *25,399*
Winona, MS 38967 • *5,705*
Winona, MO 65588 • *1,081*
Winona □, MN • *47,828*
Winona Lake, IN 46590 • *4,053*
Winooski, VT 05404 • *6,649*
Winslow, AZ 86047 • *8,190*
Winslow, ME 04901 • *5,436*
Winsted, CT 06098 • *8,254*
Winsted, MN 55395 • *1,581*
Winston, FL 33801 • *9,118*
Winston, OR 97496 • *3,773*
Winston □, AL • *22,053*
Winston □, MS • *19,433*
Winston-Salem, NC 27101–27 • *143,485*
Winter Garden, FL 34787 • *9,745*
Winter Haven, FL 33880–84 • *24,725*
Winter Park, FL 32789–90 • *22,242*
Winter Park, NC 28403 • *4,504*
Winterport, ME 04496 • *1,274*
Winters, CA 95694 • *4,639*
Winters, TX 79567 • *2,905*
Winterset, IA 50273 • *4,196*
Winter Springs, FL 32708 • *22,151*
Wintersville, OH 43952 • *4,102*
Winterville, NC 28590 • *2,816*
Winthrop, ME 04364 • *2,819*
Winthrop, MA 02152 • *18,127*
Winthrop, MN 55396 • *1,279*
Winthrop Harbor, IL 60096 • *6,240*
Winton, CA 95388 • *7,559*
Wirt □, WV • *5,192*
Wiscasset, ME 04578 • *1,350*
Wisconsin Dells, WI 53965 • *2,393*
Wisconsin Rapids, WI 54494–95 • *18,245*
Wise, VA 24293 • *3,193*
Wise □, TX • *34,679*
Wise □, VA • *39,573*
Wishek, ND 58495 • *1,171*
Wisner, LA 71378 • *1,153*
Wisner, NE 68791 • *1,253*
Withamsville, OH 45245 • *5,000*
Witherbee, NY 12998 • *1,000*
Wittenberg, WI 54499 • *1,145*
Wixom, MI 48393 • *8,550*
Woburn, MA 01801 • *35,943*
Wolcott, CT 06716 • *6,070*
Wolcott, NY 14590 • *1,544*
Wolfe □, KY • *6,503*
Wolfeboro, NH 03894 • *2,783*
Wolfe City, TX 75496 • *1,505*
Wolf Lake, MI 49442 • *4,110*
Wolf Point, MT 59201 • *2,880*
Wolf Trap, VA 22182 • *13,133*
Womelsdorf, PA 19567 • *2,270*
Wonder Lake, IL 60097 • *6,664*
Wood □, OH • *113,269*
Wood □, TX • *29,380*
Wood □, WV • *86,915*
Wood □, WI • *73,605*
Woodbine, GA 31569 • *1,212*
Woodbine, IA 51579 • *1,500*
Woodbine, NJ 08270 • *2,678*
Woodbourne, NY 12788 • *1,155*
Woodbourne, OH 45459 • *6,000*
Woodbridge, CT 06525 • *7,924*
Woodbridge, NJ 07095 • *17,434*
Woodbridge, VA 22191–94 • *26,401*
Woodbridge [Township], NJ 07095 • *17,434*
Woodburn, IN 46797 • *1,321*
Woodburn, OR 97071 • *13,404*
Woodbury, CT 06798 • *1,212*
Woodbury, GA 30293 • *1,429*
Woodbury, MN 55125 • *20,075*
Woodbury, NJ 08096 • *10,904*
Woodbury, NY 11797 • *8,008*
Woodbury, TN 37190 • *2,287*
Woodbury □, IA • *98,276*
Woodcliff Lake, NJ 07675 • *5,303*
Wood Dale, IL 60191 • *12,425*
Woodfield, SC 29206 • *8,862*
Woodford □, IL • *32,653*
Woodford □, KY • *19,955*
Woodhaven, MI 48183 • *11,631*
Woodlake, CA 93286 • *5,678*
Woodland, CA 95695 • *39,802*
Woodland, ME 04694 • *1,287*
Woodland, WA 98674 • *2,500*
Woodland Park, CO 80863 • *4,610*
Woodlawn, KY 42001 • *1,600*
Woodlawn, MD 21207 • *5,329*
Woodlawn, MD 20784 • *5,329*
Woodlawn, OH 45215 • *2,674*
Woodlawn, VA 24381 • *1,689*
Woodlynne, NJ 08107 • *2,547*
Woodmere, NY 11598 • *15,578*
Woodmont, CT 06460 • *1,770*
Woodmoor, MD 21207 • *8,630*
Woodridge, IL 60517 • *26,256*
Wood-Ridge, NJ 07075 • *7,506*
Wood River, IL 62095 • *11,490*
Wood River, NE 68883 • *1,156*
Woodruff, SC 29388 • *4,365*
Woodruff, WI 54568 • *1,500*
Woodruff □, AR • *9,520*
Woods □, OK • *9,103*
Woodsboro, TX 78393 • *1,731*
Woods Cross, UT 84087 • *5,384*
Woodsfield, OH 43793 • *2,832*
Woods Hole, MA 02543 • *1,080*
Woodside, CA 94062 • *5,035*
Woodson □, KS • *4,116*
Woodstock, GA 30188 • *4,361*
Woodstock, IL 60098 • *14,353*
Woodstock, NY 12498 • *1,870*
Woodstock, VT 05091 • *1,037*
Woodstock, VA 22664 • *3,182*
Woodstown, NJ 08098 • *3,154*
Woodsville, NH 03785 • *1,122*
Woodville, FL 32362 • *2,760*
Woodville, MS 39669 • *1,393*
Woodville, OH 43469 • *1,953*
Woodville, TX 75979 • *2,636*
Woodward, IA 50276 • *1,197*
Woodward, OK 73801–02 • *12,340*
Woodward □, OK • *18,976*
Woodway, TX 76710 • *8,695*
Woonsocket, RI 02895 • *43,877*
Woonsocket, SD 57385 • *766*
Wooster, OH 44691 • *22,191*
Worcester, MA 01601–15 • *169,759*
Worcester □, MD • *35,028*
Worcester □, MA • *709,705*
Worland, WY 82401 • *5,742*
Worth, IL 60482 • *11,208*
Worth □, GA • *19,745*
Worth □, IA • *7,991*
Worth □, MO • *2,440*
Wortham, TX 76693 • *1,020*
Worthington, IN 47471 • *1,473*
Worthington, KY 41183 • *1,751*
Worthington, MN 56187 • *9,977*
Worthington, OH 43085 • *14,869*
Wrangell, AK 99929 • *2,479*
Wray, CO 80758 • *1,998*
Wrens, GA 30833 • *2,414*
Wrentham, MA 02093 • *2,110*
Wright, FL 32548 • *18,945*
Wright □, IA • *14,269*
Wright □, MN • *68,710*
Wright □, MO • *16,758*
Wright City, MO 63390 • *1,250*
Wrightstown, NJ 08562 • *3,843*
Wrightstown, WI 54180 • *1,262*
Wrightsville, AR 72183 • *1,062*
Wrightsville, GA 31096 • *2,331*
Wrightsville, PA 17368 • *2,396*
Wrightsville Beach, NC 28480 • *2,937*
Wrightwood, CA 92397 • *3,308*
Wurtsboro, NY 12790 • *1,048*
Wyandanch, NY 11798 • *8,950*
Wyandot □, OH • *22,254*
Wyandotte, MI 48192 • *30,938*
Wyandotte □, KS • *161,993*
Wyanet, IL 61379 • *1,017*
Wyckoff, NJ 07481 • *15,372*
Wymore, NE 68466 • *1,611*
Wynne, AR 72396–97 • *8,187*
Wynnewood, OK 73098 • *2,451*
Wyoming, DE 19934 • *977*
Wyoming, IL 61491 • *1,462*
Wyoming, MI 49509 • *63,891*
Wyoming, MN 55092 • *2,142*
Wyoming, OH 45215 • *8,128*
Wyoming, PA 18644 • *3,255*
Wyoming □, NY • *42,507*
Wyoming □, PA • *28,076*
Wyoming □, WV • *28,990*
Wyomissing, PA 19610 • *7,332*
Wythe □, VA • *25,466*
Wytheville, VA 24382 • *8,038*

X

Xenia, OH 45385 • *24,664*

Y

Yadkin □, NC • *30,488*
Yadkinville, NC 27055 • *2,525*
Yakima, WA 98901–09 • *54,827*
Yakima □, WA • *188,823*
Yakutat, AK 99689 • *534*
Yale, MI 48097 • *1,977*
Yale, OK 74085 • *1,392*
Yalobusha □, MS • *12,033*
Yamhill □, OR • *65,551*
Yancey □, NC • *15,419*
Yanceyville, NC 27379 • *1,973*
Yankton, SD 57078 • *12,703*
Yankton □, SD • *19,252*
Yaphank, NY 11980 • *5,000*
Yardley, PA 19067 • *2,288*
Yardville, NJ 08620 • *6,190*
Yarmouth, ME 04096 • *3,338*
Yarmouth, MA 02675 • *1,200*
Yarnell, AZ 85362 • *1,500*
Yates □, NY • *22,810*
Yates Center, KS 66783 • *1,815*
Yavapai □, AZ • *107,714*
Yazoo □, MS • *25,506*
Yazoo City, MS 39194 • *12,427*
Yeadon, PA 19050 • *11,980*
Yeagertown, PA 17099 • *1,150*
Yell □, AR • *17,759*
Yellow Medicine □, MN • *11,684*
Yellow Springs, OH 45387 • *3,973*
Yellowstone □, MT • *113,419*
Yellowstone National Park, WY 82190 • *400*
Yellowstone National Park □, MT • *52*
Yellville, AR 72687 • *1,181*
Yelm, WA 98597 • *1,337*
Yerington, NV 89447 • *2,367*
Yermo, CA 92398 • *1,092*
Yoakum, TX 77995 • *5,611*
Yoakum □, TX • *8,786*
Yolo □, CA • *141,092*
Yonkers, NY 10701–10 • *188,082*
Yorba Linda, CA 92686 • *52,422*
York, AL 36925 • *3,160*
York, ME 03909 • *3,130*
York, NE 68467 • *7,884*
York, PA 17401–07 • *42,192*
York, SC 29745 • *6,709*
York □, ME • *164,587*
York □, NE • *14,428*
York □, PA • *339,574*
York □, SC • *131,497*
York □, VA • *42,422*
Yorketown, NJ 07726 • *6,313*
York Harbor, ME 03911 • *2,555*
Yorklyn, DE 19736 • *600*
Yorkshire, NY 14173 • *1,340*
Yorktown, IN 47396 • *4,106*
Yorktown, NY 10598 • *5,270*
Yorktown, TX 78164 • *2,207*
Yorktown, VA 23690–93 • *270*
Yorktown Heights, NY 10598 • *7,690*
Yorktown Manor, RI 02852 • *2,520*
Yorkville, IL 60560 • *3,925*
Yorkville, NY 13495 • *2,972*
Yorkville, OH 43971 • *1,246*
Yosemite National Park, CA 95389 • *1,073*
Young □, TX • *18,126*
Youngstown, NY 14174 • *2,075*
Youngstown, OH 44501–15 • *95,732*
Youngsville, LA 70592 • *1,195*
Youngsville, PA 16371 • *1,775*
Youngtown, AZ 85363 • *2,542*
Youngwood, PA 15697 • *3,372*
Ypsilanti, MI 48197–98 • *24,846*
Yreka, CA 96097 • *6,948*
Yuba □, CA • *58,228*
Yuba City, CA 95991–92 • *27,437*
Yucaipa, CA 92399 • *20,000*
Yucca Valley, CA 92284–86 • *13,701*
Yukon, OK 73099 • *20,935*
Yulee, FL 32097 • *6,915*
Yuma, AZ 85364–69 • *54,923*
Yuma, CO 80759 • *2,719*
Yuma □, AZ • *106,895*
Yuma □, CO • *8,954*

Z

Zachary, LA 70791 • *9,036*
Zanesville, OH 43701–02 • *26,778*
Zapata, TX 78076 • *7,119*
Zapata □, TX • *9,279*
Zavala □, TX • *12,162*
Zebulon, GA 30295 • *1,035*
Zebulon, NC 27597 • *3,173*
Zeeland, MI 49464 • *5,417*
Zeigler, IL 62999 • *1,746*
Zelienople, PA 16063 • *4,158*
Zenith, WA 98188 • *1,100*
Zephyr Cove, NV 89448 • *1,700*
Zephyrhills, FL 33539–44 • *8,220*
Ziebach □, SD • *2,220*
Zillah, WA 98953 • *1,911*
Zilwaukee, MI 48604 • *1,850*
Zimmerman, MN 55398 • *1,350*
Zion, IL 60099 • *19,775*
Zionsville, IN 46077 • *5,281*
Zolfo Springs, FL 33890 • *1,219*
Zumbrota, MN 55992 • *2,312*
Zuni (Zuni Pueblo), NM 87327 • *5,857*
Zwolle, LA 71486 • *1,779*